Council of
Michigan
Foundations

Serving grantmakers. Advancing giving.

FOUNDATION
CENTER
Knowledge to build on.

THE
MICHIGAN
FOUNDATION
DIRECTORY

Courtesy of Michigan
Nonprofit Association's
Michigan NOW! Program

Council of Michigan Foundations
Foundation Center

Available from:

COUNCIL OF MICHIGAN FOUNDATIONS
P.O. Box 599
Grand Haven, MI 49417
616/842-7080
info@cmif.org

ISBN 1-891445-15-4
ISBN-13 978-1-891445-15-6

Printed and Bound in the United States of America

TABLE OF CONTENTS

FOREWORD

The Council of Michigan Foundations (CMF) and the Foundation Center (FC) in New York are pleased to present the 15th edition of *The Michigan Foundation Directory*. The *Directory* continues to be the number one resource on organized philanthropy in Michigan for the grantseeking community in Michigan. We are pleased to share that philanthropy continues to grow with 265 new foundations created in Michigan since the 14th edition two years ago.

CMF is a regional association of Michigan foundations and corporations that make grants for charitable purposes. Members include family, independent, community, corporate and public foundations, as well as companies with philanthropic giving programs. Our mission is to strengthen, promote and increase philanthropy in Michigan.

The Foundation Center's mission is to strengthen the nonprofit sector by advancing knowledge about U.S. philanthropy. Established in 1956, the Foundation Center is the nation's leading authority on philanthropy, connecting nonprofits and the grantmakers supporting them to tools they can use and information they can trust. The Center maintains the most comprehensive database on U.S. grantmakers and their grants.

We thank all those that make *The Michigan Foundation Directory* such a valuable research tool and to the nonprofit community—grantmakers and grantseekers—for their collaborative energy. We are fortunate to have generous people and organizations that believe and contribute to the Michigan economy and the well-being of its citizens.

Robert S. Collier
President

INTRODUCTION

THE 2006 EDITION

This fifteenth edition of *The Michigan Foundation Directory* contains descriptive entries for 2,583 organizations located in Michigan that meet the Foundation Center's definition of a foundation, corporate giving program or grantmaking public charity. The tables and information provided in this introduction reflect statistics based solely on the 2,251 *private and community foundations* located within Michigan. To complete the picture of Michigan funding, entries for an additional 295 out-of-state grantmakers, with stated funding interests in Michigan are included.

WHAT IS A FOUNDATION?

The Foundation Center defines a foundation as a nongovernmental, nonprofit 501(c)(3) organization with its own funds (from a single source, either an individual, family, corporation, or the community at large) and program managed by its own trustees and directors, that was established to maintain or aid educational, social, charitable, religious, or other activities serving the common welfare, primarily by making grants to other nonprofit organizations.

TYPES OF GRANTMAKERS

Grantmakers included in this volume fall into one of six categories:

Independent Foundation: A fund or endowment designated by the Internal Revenue Service as a private foundation under the law, the primary function of which is the making of grants. The assets of most independent foundations are derived from the gift of an individual or family. Some function under the direction of family members and are known as "family foundations." Depending on their range of giving, independent foundations may also be known as "general purpose" or "special purpose" foundations.

Company-Sponsored Foundation: A private foundation under the tax code that derives its funds from a profit-making company or corporation but is independently constituted, the purpose of which is to make grants, usually on a broad basis although not without regard for the business interests of the corporation. Company-sponsored foundations are legally distinct from contributions programs administered within the corporation directly from corporate funds.

Operating Foundation: A fund or endowment designated under the tax code by the Internal Revenue Service as a private operating foundation, the primary purpose of which is to operate research, social welfare, or other programs determined by its governing body or charter.

Community Foundation: In its general charitable purposes, a community foundation is much like a private foundation; its funds, however, are derived from many donors rather than a single source, as is usually the case with private foundations. Further, community foundations are classified under the tax code as public charities (see below) also known as public foundations and are therefore subject to different rules and regulations than those which govern private foundations.

Corporate Giving Program: Corporate giving programs make grants directly through the company. The grant making apparatus exists within the corporation and is administered by corporate personnel.

Public Charity: Public, grantmaking charities, also known as public foundations, redistribute funds that have been raised primarily from the public-at-large. In most instances, the funds are raised through a fund-raising campaign or endowed gifts as in the case of community foundations.

SOURCES OF INFORMATION

To identify organizations for inclusion in this directory, Foundation Center staff monitors IRS information returns for private foundations and public charities (Forms 990 and 990-PF), journal and newspaper articles, press releases and news services concerned with foundation activities, and grantmaker publications such as newsletters and annual reports. Entries are prepared from the most recent information available; the largest and mid-sized foundations were mailed copies of their entries for verification.

A breakdown of the 2,251 Michigan private and community foundations in this volume by fiscal year-end date reveals the following: 13 foundations (less than 1 percent) with 2006 fiscal data; 1,471 foundations (65.4 percent) with 2005 fiscal data; 660 foundations (29.3 percent) with 2004 fiscal data; 68 foundations (3 percent) with 2003 fiscal data; and 9 foundations (less than 1 percent) with 2002 fiscal data. There are 30 foundations (1.3 percent) with no fiscal data. Thus, 2006, 2005, and 2004 fiscal information is reported for 97.7 percent of the private and community foundations listed. Even when more recent financial information was not available, grantmaker addresses, program information, and application procedures reflect the latest updates received through September 2006.

The following 216 grantmakers (198 in Michigan, 18 out of state) voluntarily provided the Foundation Center with information about their grantmaking activities within the past year either by letter, by responding to a questionnaire, or electronically through the Foundation Center's Foundation Directory Online Updater (fconline.fdncenter.org/gmupdate/login.jsp):

MICHIGAN GRANTMAKERS PROVIDING INFORMATION

City	Grantmaker Name	City	Grantmaker Name
Ada	Alticor Inc. Corporate Giving Program	Detroit	Benson and Edith Ford Fund
Albion	Albion Community Foundation	Detroit	Eleanor and Edsel Ford Fund
Allegan	Allegan County Community Foundation	Detroit	Walter and Josephine Ford Fund
Almont	Four County Community Foundation	Detroit	William and Martha Ford Fund
Alpena	Community Foundation for Northeast Michigan	Detroit	Edsel B. Ford II Fund
Alpena	First Federal Community Foundation	Detroit	The Henry Ford II Fund
Alpena	Iosco County Community Foundation	Detroit	General Motors Foundation, Inc.
Alpena	North Central Michigan Community Foundation	Detroit	The Gilmour Fund
Alpena	Straits Area Community Foundation	Detroit	GM Corporate Giving Program
Ann Arbor	Bonisteel Foundation	Detroit	Hudson-Webber Foundation
Ann Arbor	Borders Group, Inc. Corporate Giving Program	Detroit	Ernest and Rosemarie Kanzler Foundation
Ann Arbor	David A. Brandon Foundation	Detroit	Robert Kutz Foundation
Ann Arbor	The Cresswell Family Foundation, Inc.	Detroit	McGregor Fund
Ann Arbor	Earhart Foundation	Detroit	Metro Health Foundation
Ann Arbor	James A. and Faith Knight Foundation	Detroit	National Healthcare Scholars Foundation
Ann Arbor	Sigurd & Jarmila Rislov Foundation	Detroit	Herbert and Elsa Ponting Foundation
Ann Arbor	Jean M. R. Smith Foundation	Detroit	Whitney Fund
Ann Arbor	The Helmut Stern Foundation	Detroit	Matilda R. Wilson Fund
Baldwin	Lake County Community Foundation	Detroit	Coleman A. Young Foundation
Battle Creek	Battle Creek Community Foundation	East Jordan	Charlevoix County Community Foundation
Battle Creek	Guido A. & Elizabeth H. Binda Foundation	Elk Rapids	The Herrington-Fitch Family Foundation, Inc.
Battle Creek	W. K. Kellogg Foundation	Farmington Hills	American Dysautonomia Institute
Battle Creek	Patricia A. & William E. LaMothe Foundation	Farmington Hills	Amerisure Mutual Insurance Company Contributions Program
Battle Creek	The Miller Foundation		
Battle Creek	Southwest Michigan Rehab Foundation	Flint	Community Foundation of Greater Flint
Big Rapids	Mecosta County Community Foundation	Flint	Charles Stewart Mott Foundation
Birmingham	Birmingham-Bloomfield Symphony Orchestra	Flint	James A. Welch Foundation
Bloomfield Hills	The Holley Foundation	Franklin	Milton M. Ratner Foundation
Bloomfield Hills	A. Alfred Taubman Foundation	Fraser	Triford Foundation
Bloomfield Hills	The Taubman Foundation	Fremont	Fremont Area Community Foundation
Bloomfield Hills	Vlasic Foundation	Fremont	The Gerber Foundation
Bloomfield Hills	Samuel L. Westerman Foundation	Galesburg	Galesburg-Augusta Education Foundation
Bloomfield Hills	The White Foundation	Grand Haven	JSJ Foundation
Bloomfield Hills	Young Foundation	Grand Rapids	The Batts Foundation
Brighton	Sage Foundation	Grand Rapids	Hugh Michael Beahan Foundation
Byron Center	Byron Center Fine Arts Foundation	Grand Rapids	The Blodgett Foundation
Cadillac	Huckle Family Fund	Grand Rapids	M. E. Davenport Foundation
Caro	Tuscola County Community Foundation	Grand Rapids	Daniel and Pamella DeVos Foundation
Clinton Township	Jane and Frank Warchol Foundation	Grand Rapids	Dick & Betsy DeVos Foundation
Dearborn	Ford Motor Company Contributions Program	Grand Rapids	Douglas & Maria DeVos Foundation
Dearborn	Ford Motor Company Fund	Grand Rapids	The Richard and Helen DeVos Foundation
Detroit	The Anderson Fund	Grand Rapids	The Dogwood Foundation
Detroit	Comerica Bank Corporate Giving Program	Grand Rapids	Dole Family Foundation
Detroit	Community Foundation for Southeastern Michigan	Grand Rapids	Dyer-Ives Foundation
Detroit	DTE Energy Foundation	Grand Rapids	Gerald R. Ford Foundation
Detroit	Ethel and James Flinn Foundation	Grand Rapids	Frey Foundation
Detroit	William & Lisa Ford Foundation	Grand Rapids	Grand Rapids Community Foundation
		Grand Rapids	Grand Rapids Label Foundation

City	Grantmaker Name	City	Grantmaker Name
Grand Rapids	Ferris Greeney Family Foundation	Marquette	Louis G. Kaufman Endowment Fund
Grand Rapids	Ionia County Community Foundation	Menominee	M & M Area Community Foundation
Grand Rapids	Jewish Federation of Grand Rapids	Midland	Allen Foundation, Inc.
Grand Rapids	Keller Foundation	Midland	The Dow Chemical Company Foundation
Grand Rapids	Lowell Area Community Fund	Midland	The Rollin M. Gerstacker Foundation
Grand Rapids	Peak Street Foundation	Midland	Howard & Ivah Hoffmeyer Charitable Trust
Grand Rapids	Southeast Ottawa Community Foundation	Midland	Midland Area Community Foundation
Grand Rapids	Sparta Community Foundation	Midland	Elsa U. Pardee Foundation
Grand Rapids	Spectrum Health Foundation	Milford	The Hilda E. Bretzlaff Foundation, Inc.
Grand Rapids	Steelcase Foundation	Monroe	Community Foundation of Monroe County
Grand Rapids	Jerry L. & Marcia D. Tubergen Foundation	Monroe	La-Z-Boy Foundation
Grand Rapids	Jay and Betty Van Andel Foundation	Northport	Leelanau Township Community Foundation, Inc.
Grand Rapids	Robert & Cheri Vanderweide Foundation	Novi	Americana Foundation
Grand Rapids	Wege Foundation	Novi	Novi Educational Foundation
Grand Rapids	Word Investments, Inc.	Orchard Lake	Tuktawa Foundation
Grand Rapids	Wyoming Community Foundation	Owosso	Shiawassee Community Foundation
Greenville	Stanley and Blanche Ash Foundation	Petoskey	Petoskey-Harbor Springs Area Community Foundation
Greenville	Greenville Area Community Foundation		
Gregory	Michigan Friends of Education	Plymouth	Thompson Foundation
Grosse Pointe	Buffalo Bills Youth Foundation, Inc.	Port Huron	James C. Acheson Foundation
Grosse Pointe	RJK Foundation	Port Huron	Community Foundation of St. Clair County
Grosse Pointe Farms	Elizabeth, Allan and Warren Shelden Fund	Rochester	The W. B. McCardell Family Foundation
Grosse Pointe Farms	Young Woman's Home Association	Romeo	L & L Educational Foundation
Harbor Springs	Baiardi Family Foundation, Inc.	Roscommon	Roscommon County Community Foundation
Harper Woods	The Irwin Foundation	Saginaw	Charles F. and Adeline L. Barth Charitable Foundation
Hastings	Barry Community Foundation		
Hillsdale	Hillsdale County Community Foundation	Saginaw	Harvey Randall Wickes Foundation
Holland	The Community Foundation of the Holland/Zeeland Area	Saginaw	Wickson-Link Memorial Foundation
		Sandusky	Sanilac County Community Foundation
Holland	Haworth Inc. Corporate Giving Program	Southfield	The Alix Foundation
Holland	Springview Foundation	Southfield	ArtServe Michigan
Houghton	Keweenaw Community Foundation	Southfield	Asthma & Allergy Foundation of America - Michigan Chapter
Ithaca	Gratiot County Community Foundation		
Jackson	The Jackson County Community Foundation	Southfield	Mandell L. and Madeleine H. Berman Foundation
Jackson	Bill & Vi Sigmund Foundation	Southfield	DENSO International America, Inc. Corporate Giving Program
Kalamazoo	Arcus Foundation		
Kalamazoo	The Burdick-Thorne Foundation	Southfield	DENSO North America Foundation
Kalamazoo	The H. P. and Genevieve Connable Fund	Southfield	The Rodney Fund
Kalamazoo	Irving S. Gilmore Foundation	Southfield	Southfield Community Foundation
Kalamazoo	Ronald F. Kinney Foundation, Inc.	Southgate	Colina Foundation
Kalamazoo	Donald and Ann Parfet Family Foundation	St. Clair Shores	Dryer Family Foundation
Kalamazoo	Preston S. Parish Foundation	St. Joseph	Berrien Community Foundation, Inc.
Kalamazoo	The Power Foundation	St. Joseph	Frederick S. Upton Foundation
Lake City	Missaukee County Community Foundation	Taylor	Masco Corporation Contributions Program
Lansing	Talbert & Leota Abrams Foundation	Taylor	Masco Corporation Foundation
Lansing	Capital Region Community Foundation	Tecumseh	Lenawee Community Foundation
Lansing	Great Lakes Fishery Trust	Tecumseh	Elizabeth Ruthruff Wilson Foundation
Lansing	Michigan Dental Association Relief Fund	Three Rivers	Three Rivers Area Community Foundation
Lansing	Michigan Humanities Council	Traverse City	The Les and Anne Biederman Foundation, Inc.
Lapeer	Lapeer County Community Foundation	Traverse City	Rotary Charities of Traverse City
Livonia	Livonia Community Foundation, Inc.	Troy	Delphi Corporation Contributions Program
Livonia	Michigan Women's Foundation	Troy	Delphi Foundation, Inc.
Mackinac Island	Mackinac Island Community Foundation	Troy	James and Lynelle Holden Fund
Manistee	Manistee County Community Foundation	Vicksburg	Vicksburg Foundation
		Waterford	Waterford Foundation for Public Education

OUT-OF-STATE GRANTMAKERS PROVIDING INFORMATION

State	City	Grantmaker Name
AZ	Tucson	Jasam Foundation Fund B
FL	Fort Lauderdale	The Lou Church Educational Foundation, Inc.
FL	Winter Park	Edyth Bush Charitable Foundation, Inc.
IL	Chicago	The Northern Trust Company Charitable Trust
IL	Chicago	The Seabury Foundation
IN	Indianapolis	Walther Cancer Institute and Foundation, Inc.
IN	Muncie	Edmund F. and Virginia B. Ball Foundation, Inc.
MN	Wayzata	TCF Foundation
NY	New York	The Ford Foundation
NY	New York	The F. B. Heron Foundation
OH	Bowling	Green Sky Foundation
OH	Cleveland	The Cleveland-Cliffs Foundation
OH	Cleveland	National City Corporation Contributions Program
OH	Maumee	Anderson Foundation
PA	Swarthmore	The Pryor Foundation
WI	Green Bay	Green Bay Packers, Inc. Corporate Giving Program
WI	Madison	Bradshaw-Knight Foundation, Inc.
WI	Milwaukee	C. S. and Marion F. McIntyre Foundation

LARGE AND SMALL FOUNDATIONS

In all, private and community foundations in Michigan hold over $24 billion in assets and make annual contributions of over $1.4 billion (Table 2). Most of these assets and funds are managed by a small portion of the 2,251 Michigan foundations described in this volume (Table 1). Although they represent less than 12 percent of the private and community foundations located in Michigan, the 266 largest foundations—defined as holding assets of $5 million or more—account for $22.8 billion or over 94 percent of the assets held and $1.2 billion or nearly 88 percent of the total giving reported. In contrast, the 1,529 smallest foundations—defined as having assets under $1 million—account for only $376 million or 1.6 percent of the assets held and less than $90 million or 6.4 percent of the grants awarded, even though they comprise 68 percent of the private and community foundations in Michigan.

Tables 3, 4, and 5 illustrate an analysis of independent, company-sponsored, and community foundations respectively. Although the tables are sorted by assets, they also indicate foundation name, city of location, fiscal date, expenditures, and total giving.

Table 3 represents the top 50 independent foundations by assets, while tables 4 and 5, the tables for the top 31 company-sponsored and 55 community foundations respectively, list only those foundations with assets over $1 million.

GEOGRAPHIC DISTRIBUTION OF FOUNDATIONS BY COUNTY

Table 6 shows the distribution of Michigan private and community foundations by county with corresponding aggregate fiscal data. While 73 of Michigan's 83 counties are represented in *The Michigan Foundation Directory* (all except Alcona, Arenac, Claire, Crawford, Keweenaw, Luce, Montmorency, Ogemaw, Ontonagon, and Presque Isle counties), the distribution of foundations across the state is uneven. Oakland County has the most foundations (604), followed by Wayne County (333) and Kent County (294). In contrast, 11 counties have one foundation each and 46 have fewer than ten.

Many of the foundations located in Michigan are national in scope and do not generally focus on or limit their funding to local organizations. At the same time, 1,648 of the 2,251 (73.2 percent) Michigan private and community foundations listed in this volume are considered local funders. Grantseekers should take careful note of any geographic limitation statements in order to gain a clear picture of funding patterns in their own area.

In comparing the size and grantmaking activities of Michigan foundations in urban versus towns and rural areas (Figure 1), there is a noticeable disparity. Michigan foundations in urban/metropolitan areas account for over 89 percent of all foundations in Michigan, hold over 96 percent of the overall Michigan foundation assets, and distribute over 97 percent of all Michigan foundation grants.

ANALYSIS OF FOUNDATION GRANTS BY SUBJECT

A breakdown of the grants by Michigan foundations in the top 10 major subject areas (Table 7) reflects a broad scope of giving interests. More than 65 percent of the total dollar amount awarded fell into three broad categories: education ($200.1 million or 23.9 percent); public affairs/society benefit ($185.4 million or 22.2 percent); and human services ($159 million or 19 percent). Grants by out-of-state foundations (Table 8) show the additional foundation dollars that flow into Michigan. The four largest areas of giving, which make up 80 percent of total giving by out-of-state foundations to Michigan nonprofits, are education ($29.5 million or 34.2 percent); public affairs/society benefit ($20.2 million or 23.4 percent); health ($9.8 million or 11.4 percent); and human services ($9.5 million or 10.9 percent).

SELECTED GRANTS

To illustrate a grantmaker's giving pattern, selected grants to recipient organizations have been provided with the listings in the Descriptive Directory wherever possible. Up to ten grants have been included for grantmakers with annual giving of at least $80,000. Grants to individuals are not listed. Of the 2,251 entries for the private and community foundations in Michigan listed in this volume, 239 (11 percent) include lists of selected grants. In all, 2,252 grants are included, totaling close to $400 million in support to organizations. These grants may serve to illustrate fields of interest and geographic preferences. In general, however, the selected grants represent large awards and may not reveal the full spectrum of programs and giving interests of a foundation. The complete descriptive entry should always be examined carefully to determine a foundation's current funding emphasis. Where available, the "average" grant amount noted in the fiscal information section also should be consulted to ascertain the typical range of grants awarded.

We are pleased to share examples, in the pages immediately following this introduction, of grants awarded in Michigan, with recipient and dollar amount by major subject categories, to provide you another view of grantmaking in Michigan.

HOW GRANTS ARE CLASSIFIED

The Foundation Center's grants classification system arranges 26 Major Field Areas according to 10 basic divisions. This system has been used to categorize the information provided in Tables 7 and 8 of where foundation money is allocated in Michigan.

The classification system can be applied to many practical purposes, including:

♦ Grantmakers can compare their patterns of giving with that of their peers.

♦ Grantmakers can advise grantseekers about finding appropriate funding sources.

- The data can enrich public discussion about the use of community resources, as it will be possible to compare funding patterns with perceived needs and priorities.

- The findings can assist those who regulate foundations to better understand the beneficial impact grantmakers have in their region. It will put into perspective any unrealistic expectations about philanthropy filling gaps in government funding.

- The data offers a comparable basis for use in tracking grantmaking trends and becomes an invaluable planning and assessment tool.

The following descriptive text defines the 10 basic divisions of grants classification.

Arts & Humanities
arts & culture
historical societies & related historical activities
media & communications
museums
performing arts
visual arts

Education
adult/continuing education
elementary & secondary
graduate/professional schools
higher education
libraries
scholarships
student services & organizations
vocational/technical schools

Environment
animal protection & welfare
botanical/horticultural activities & gardens
environmental beautification & open spaces, including community
beautification programs
conservation & protection
environmental education & outdoor survival
humane societies
natural resources
wildlife preservation & protection
pollution abatement & control
veterinary services
zoos & aquariums

Health Care
diseases/disorder/medical disciplines
general & rehabilitative
mental health, crisis intervention
medical records

Human Services
employment/jobs
food/nutrition/agriculture
housing/shelter
multipurpose human service organizations
public protection: crime/courts/legal services
public safety/disaster preparedness & relief
recreation, leisure, sports, athletics
youth development

International
exchange programs
foreign policy research & analysis
international development
international human rights
international relief services
peace & security

Public Affairs/Society Benefit
civil rights, social action, advocacy
community improvement/capacity building
consumer rights/education
economic development
government & public administration
military/veterans' organizations
philanthropy, voluntarism & grantmaking foundations
public policy research
public transportation systems
public utilities
science research institutes/services
social science research institutes/services

Religion
Buddhism
Christian churches, missionary societies
Confucianism
Islamic temples, mosques & related agencies
Jewish synagogues & related agencies
other specific religions

Mutual Benefit
cemeteries & burial services
fraternal beneficiary societies
insurance providers & services
pension & retirement funds

Unclassifiable
unknown

SAMPLE GRANTS LIST

Subject	Foundation Name	Recipient Name	Recipient City	Amount	Grant Year	Descriptive Text
Arts, Culture & Humanities	Charles Stewart Mott Foundation	Genesee Area Focus Council	Flint	$ 75,000	2005	For operating support for work of Red Ink Studios which transforms underused buildings in Flint into free studio space for artists thereby providing artistic and economic revitalization of the downtown area
	JSJ Foundation	West Shore Symphony Orchestra	Muskegon	4,000	2005	For operating support
	Keller Foundation	Grand Rapids Ballet Company	Grand Rapids	10,250	2005	For general support
	Richard & Jane Manoogian Foundation	Jewish Ensemble Theater	West Bloomfield	12,500	2005	For operating support
	Three Rivers Area Community Foundation	Carnegie Center Council for the Arts	Three Rivers	2,500	2005	For equipment
Education	DENSO North America Foundation	Lawrence Technological University	Southfield	45,000	2005	For building improvement
	Grand Rapids Community Foundation	15 Pearls and a Promise	Byron Center	35,000	2005	To pilot one-on-one reading instruction to impact reading comprehension by end of third grade
	Metro Health Foundation	Macomb Community College Foundation	Warren	8,000	2005	To provide scholarships for students in MCC nursing program who successfully complete at least 12 credit hours of study in nursing curriculum each term, maintain a 3.0 GPA, and demonstrate financial need with preference given to minority students
	Nartel Family Foundation	Mott Community College	Flint	20,000	2005	For general support
	The Rollin M. Gerstacker Foundation	Pere Marquette District Library	Clare	50,000	2005	
Environment/ Animals	Charlevoix County Community Foundation	Conservation Resource Alliance	Traverse City	6,000	2005	For general support
	George R. and Elise M. Fink Foundation	Grosse Pointe Animal Adoption Society	Grosse Pointe Farms	15,000	2005	For general operating support
	Grand Rapids Label Foundation	Land Conservancy of West Michigan	Grand Rapids	2,125	2005	For general support
	W. K. Kellogg Foundation	Michigan State University	East Lansing	5,900,000	2005	To establish sustainable land-use network for Michigan, to bring about lasting change in land-use policy, practice, and outcomes by fostering needed partnerships, producing credible, timely, and relevant information, educating state residents, and empowering communities
Health	Alden and Vada Dow Family Foundations	Mercy Hospital	Grayling	50,000	2005	For general support
	Comerica Foundation	Mercy General Health Partners	Muskegon	3,300	2005	For general support
	Community Foundation of Greater Flint	American Red Cross-Lapeer Chapter	Flint	35,000	2005	For Emergency Dental Program to assist low-income, uninsured or underinsured individuals, 18 or older, residing in Genesee County, in accessing emergency dental services including fillings crowns, partials and preventive care
	Hudson-Webber Foundation	Detroit Medical Center	Detroit	97,000	2005	For Neighborhood Framework Plan
	The Skillman Foundation	Childrens Charter of the Courts of Michigan	Lansing	160,000	2005	To improve substance abuse assessment and referral skills of home visitors through comprehensive skills training

SAMPLE GRANTS LIST (continued)

Subject	Foundation Name	Recipient Name	Recipient City	Amount	Grant Year	Descriptive Text
Human Services	Battle Creek Community Foundation	Community Action Agency of South Central Michigan	Battle Creek	$ 19,786	2005	For Latino After-School Program
	Clannad Foundation	HAVEN (Help Against Violent Encounters Now)	Pontiac	5,000	2005	For general support
	Consumers Energy Foundation	American Red Cross	Jackson	21,301	2005	For challenge grant for relief efforts for Hurricane Katrina
	McGregor Fund	Alternatives for Girls	Detroit	150,000	2005	For Emergency Shelter/Transition to Independent Living and Street Outreach programs for young women, including challenge to expand shelter capacity by encouraging new donors and larger gifts from current donors
International/ Foreign Affairs	The Kresge Foundation	University of Pretoria	Pretoria	496,373	2005	For challenge grant toward implementation of strategic development plan as part of KF Special Initiative in South Africa
	W. K. Kellogg Foundation	International Center for Tropical Agriculture	Cali	293,500	2005	To strengthen rural entrepreneurial development in Andean Region Comprehensive Clusters in Bolivia and Peru through cross-country learning alliance focused on institution building and use of information technology
Public/Society Benefit	Dyer-Ives Foundation	Steepletown Neighborhood Services	Grand Rapids	5,000	2005	For staff position
	Kalamazoo Community Foundation	Neighborhood Housing Services of Kalamazoo	Kalamazoo	15,000	2005	To provide leadership training through nationally recognized curriculum, Community Builders program
	La-Z-Boy Foundation	Village of Carleton	Carleton	5,000	2005	For playscape
	The Gerber Foundation	Wayne State University	Detroit	304,200	2005	For evaluation of harmful effects of fatty acid supplementation on cognitive development
Religion	Arcus Foundation	Ministry with Community	Kalamazoo	25,000	2005	For general support
	Jennings Memorial Foundation	Lamb of God Church	Montrose	4,000	2005	For operating support
	Richard & Jane Manoogian Foundation	Sainte Anne de Michilimackinac Parish	Mackinac Island	15,000	2005	For operating support

SURVEY OF MICHIGAN
FOUNDATION PHILANTHROPY

TABLE 1. ANALYSIS OF MICHIGAN GRANTMAKING FOUNDATIONS BY ASSET CATEGORY (All dollar figures expressed in thousands)

Asset Category	Number of Foundations	%	Assets	%	Gifts Received	%	Expenditures	%	Total Giving	%
$100 million and over	31	1.4	$18,340,820	75.7	$ 539,107	50.5	$ 956,953	59.4	$ 882,150	62.9
$50 to $100 million	21	0.9	1,451,429	6.0	98,032	9.2	140,772	8.7	119,877	8.6
$25 to $50 million	30	1.3	1,041,357	4.3	132,980	12.5	89,18	5.5	63,358	4.5
$10 to $25 million	80	3.6	1,273,324	5.3	82,609	7.7	114,245	7.1	91,496	6.5
$5 to $10 million	104	4.6	730,344	3.0	44,958	4.2	104,148	6.5	72,429	5.2
$1 to $5 million	456	20.3	1,017,000	4.2	81,656	7.7	100,386	6.2	83,025	5.9
Under $1 million	1,529	67.9	376,117	1.6	88,019	8.2	105,331	6.5	89,685	6.4
Total	**2,251**	**100.0**	**$24,230,392**	**100.0**	**$ 1,067,361**	**100.0**	**$ 1,611,016**	**100.**b	**$ 1,402,019**	**100.0**

Note: Figures may not add up due to rounding.

TABLE 2. AGGREGATE FISCAL DATA OF MICHIGAN GRANTMAKING FOUNDATIONS BY FOUNDATION TYPE (All dollar figures expressed in thousands)

Asset Category	Number of Foundations	%	Assets	%	Gifts Received	%	Expenditures	%	Total Giving	%
Independent	1,889	83.9	$20,415,745	84.3	$ 594,347	55.7	$1,201,533	74.6	$1,077,458	76.9
Company-Sponsored	86	3.8	935,851	3.9	284,843	26.7	187,481	11.6	218,033	15.6
Community	96	4.3	1,977,215	8.2	151,451	14.2	134,540	8.4	97,410	6.9
Operating	180	8.0	901,581	3.7	36,719	3.4	87,462	5.4	9,118	0.7
Total	**2,251**	**100.0**	**$24,230,392**	**100.0**	**$1,067,361**	**100.0**	**$1,611,016**	**100.0**	**$1,402,019**	**100.0**

Note: Figures may not add up due to rounding.

TABLE 3. Top 50 Michigan Independent Foundations By Assets

Foundation Name	City	Fiscal Date	Assets	Expenditures	Total Giving
W. K. Kellogg Foundation	Battle Creek	8/31/2005	$ 7,298,383,532	$291,302,569	$219,862,847
The Kresge Foundation	Troy	12/31/2004	2,752,257,750	37,171,023	97,714,540
Charles Stewart Mott Foundation	Flint	12/31/2005	2,480,562,766	137,952,616	113,334,381
The Herbert H. and Grace A. Dow Foundation	Midland	12/31/2004	548,526,968	23,230,223	19,050,685
The Skillman Foundation	Detroit	12/31/2004	507,839,550	28,321,026	21,588,613
Richard & Jane Manoogian Foundation	Taylor	6/30/2005	228,638,216	10,319,837	8,334,005
Ruth Mott Foundation	Flint	12/31/2004	212,620,490	9,238,493	5,875,517
Irving S. Gilmore Foundation	Kalamazoo	12/31/2005	212,065,300	11,353,748	10,000,390
The Rollin M. Gerstacker Foundation	Midland	12/31/2005	210,230,699	11,554,220	11,116,969
Herrick Foundation	Detroit	9/30/2005	178,431,140	10,321,013	9,167,959
McGregor Fund	Detroit	6/30/2005	172,095,146	11,229,395	8,773,181
Manoogian Simone Foundation	Taylor	12/31/2005	169,166,081	8,308,856	8,194,600
Wege Foundation	Grand Rapids	12/31/2004	161,051,374	17,490,860	16,098,666
The Ave Maria Foundation	Ann Arbor	12/31/2004	155,512,954	95,955,753	91,925,690
Hudson-Webber Foundation	Detroit	12/31/2005	150,376,115	8,608,489	7,299,369
Jay and Betty Van Andel Foundation	Grand Rapids	12/31/2004	137,756,955	20,930,979	18,294,313
Frey Foundation	Grand Rapids	12/31/2005	131,802,000	5,726,000	4,847,000
The Carls Foundation	Detroit	12/31/2005	117,703,559	6,099,742	4,937,070
Elsa U. Pardee Foundation	Midland	12/31/2005	106,019,850	5,449,762	5,100,135
Alex and Marie Manoogian Foundation	Taylor	12/31/2005	96,323,619	1,394,474	261,815
The Gerber Foundation	Fremont	12/31/2005	82,646,107	5,141,405	4,277,576
Orville D. & Ruth A. Merillat Foundation	Adrian	2/28/2005	82,292,161	6,187,154	5,508,132
The Richard and Helen DeVos Foundation	Grand Rapids	12/31/2004	80,290,190	36,983,711	34,548,985
The Meijer Foundation	Grand Rapids	9/30/2004	78,473,710	8,766,407	8,350,502
John E. Fetzer Memorial Trust Fund	Vicksburg	6/30/2005	75,803,696	3,675,421	3,000,000
Arcus Foundation	Kalamazoo	12/31/2005	72,827,720	18,328,731	16,657,143
The Harry A. and Margaret D. Towsley Foundation	Midland	12/31/2005	69,709,596	3,130,534	2,808,843
Earhart Foundation	Ann Arbor	12/31/2005	61,971,515	12,735,116	11,441,524
The Charles J. Strosacker Foundation	Midland	12/31/2005	61,186,503	2,973,950	2,741,450
The Harding Foundation	Flint	6/30/2005	59,823,077	2,657,016	2,086,753
Thompson Foundation	Plymouth	12/31/2004	59,643,368	3,130,561	2,694,647
The Isabel Foundation	Flint	6/30/2005	59,112,952	2,948,087	2,665,580
Sage Foundation	Brighton	12/31/2004	57,068,154	3,236,665	2,659,000
Heritage Mark Foundation	East Lansing	9/30/2005	55,360,390	8,080,706	7,681,917
DeRoy Testamentary Foundation	Southfield	12/31/2005	50,962,525	2,966,903	2,274,637
The Duffy Foundation	Ann Arbor	12/31/2005	45,090,284	3,690,981	3,552,500
Harvey Randall Wickes Foundation	Saginaw	12/31/2005	43,166,791	2,072,590	1,750,003
Matilda R. Wilson Fund	Detroit	12/31/2004	42,694,094	2,497,823	2,057,700
John C. Lasko Foundation	Belleville	12/31/2005	42,264,033	1,972,967	1,836,875
The Samuel and Jean Frankel Jewish Heritage Foundation	Troy	12/31/2004	41,959,950	11,438	0
Elizabeth, Allan and Warren Shelden Fund	Grosse Pointe Farms	12/31/2005	38,878,888	2,175,254	2,075,500
Dorothy U. Dalton Foundation, Inc.	Kalamazoo	12/31/2004	38,574,100	2,234,074	2,077,442
Frederick S. Upton Foundation	St. Joseph	12/31/2005	37,985,021	1,907,268	1,593,377
The Morey Foundation	Winn	12/31/2005	37,432,216	854,067	422,564
Benson and Edith Ford Fund	Detroit	12/31/2005	34,280,463	1,976,757	1,815,000
Samuel & Jean Frankel Foundation	Bloomfield Hills	12/31/2004	33,882,371	579,550	537,231
The Miller Foundation	Battle Creek	12/31/2005	32,755,296	1,703,280	932,630
The Henry Ford II Fund	Detroit	12/31/2005	30,804,263	2,226,055	2,100,000
Thompson Educational Foundation	Plymouth	12/31/2003	30,621,639	226,701	152,000
The Cold Heading Foundation	Warren	12/31/2005	29,265,309	1,658,673	1,227,450
Total: 50			**$17,594,190,446**	**$898,688,923**	**$813,304,706**

TABLE 4.   Top 31 Michigan Company-Sponsored Foundations By Assets

Foundation Name	City	Fiscal Date	Assets	Expenditures	Total Giving
General Motors Foundation, Inc.	Detroit	12/31/2004	$255,698,530	$ 35,642,725	$ 34,416,411
The Dow Chemical Company Foundation	Midland	12/31/2005	115,244,709	15,955,345	15,953,729
Steelcase Foundation	Grand Rapids	11/30/2005	113,151,982	7,930,027	7,337,772
Ford Motor Company Fund	Dearborn	12/31/2004	107,283,149	40,236,667	77,916,903
Kellogg Company 25-Year Employees Fund, Inc.	Battle Creek	12/31/2004	61,365,510	1,267,200	1,105,899
Blue Cross and Blue Shield of Michigan Foundation	Detroit	12/31/2004	60,069,406	3,224,278	2,218,038
DaimlerChrysler Corporation Fund	Auburn Hills	12/31/2005	37,859,586	27,102,579	25,954,013
Citizens First Foundation, Inc.	Port Huron	12/31/2004	23,163,631	1,048,810	1,023,740
DTE Energy Foundation	Detroit	12/31/2004	22,311,575	6,641,424	6,409,972
La-Z-Boy Foundation	Monroe	12/31/2005	22,078,876	1,278,780	1,179,350
Delphi Foundation, Inc.	Troy	12/31/2004	17,728,304	1,034,308	777,608
Dow Corning Foundation	Midland	12/31/2004	17,446,131	1,721,245	1,612,006
Kellogg's Corporate Citizenship Fund	Battle Creek	12/31/2004	14,881,783	4,277,240	3,959,388
Masco Corporation Foundation	Taylor	12/31/2005	8,204,339	5,687,612	5,596,950
DENSO North America Foundation	Southfield	12/31/2005	7,570,508	374,612	373,500
Comerica Foundation	Detroit	12/31/2004	5,456,570	7,692,490	7,687,140
Edward F. Redies Foundation, Inc.	Saline	12/31/2004	5,154,561	271,846	232,000
HFF Foundation	West Bloomfield	12/31/2005	3,588,700	450,584	448,686
Consumers Energy Foundation	Jackson	12/31/2004	2,520,448	587,945	587,925
The Batts Foundation	Grand Rapids	12/31/2005	2,331,949	123,492	96,000
Wolverine World Wide Foundation	Rockford	12/31/2004	2,263,581	650,792	636,790
Collins & Aikman Foundation	Troy	12/31/2004	2,250,978	188,432	183,127
Zatkoff Family Foundation	Farmington Hills	12/31/2005	2,163,215	106,133	103,933
The Visteon Fund	Belleville	12/31/2004	2,009,718	1,335,572	1,328,918
Isabella Bank and Trust Foundation	Mount Pleasant	12/31/2004	1,744,450	164,659	158,155
MEEMIC Foundation for the Future of Education	Auburn Hills	12/31/2005	1,718,302	73,406	47,705
Volkswagen of America Foundation	Auburn Hills	12/31/2005	1,596,719	562,500	562,500
The Alro Steel Foundation	Jackson	12/31/2005	1,306,358	157,681	150,903
Fabiano Foundation	Mount Pleasant	12/31/2005	1,230,146	126,810	124,500
General Motors Cancer Research Foundation, Inc.	Detroit	12/31/2004	1,151,133	2,926,130	1,962,000
Dearborn Cable Communications Fund	Dearborn Heights	12/31/2005	1,039,986	75,376	42,894
Total: 31			**$921,584,833**	**$168,916,700**	**$200,188,455**

TABLE 5. Top 55 Michigan Community Foundations By Assets

Foundation Name	City	Fiscal Date	Assets	Expenditures	Total Giving
Community Foundation for Southeastern Michigan	Detroit	12/31/2005	$ 454,103,157	$ 33,870,694	$ 27,473,684
Kalamazoo Community Foundation	Kalamazoo	12/31/2005	265,355,347	17,903,599	14,156,832
Fremont Area Community Foundation	Fremont	12/31/2005	194,738,922	11,557,038	9,386,427
Grand Rapids Community Foundation	Grand Rapids	6/30/2005	194,189,277	10,829,473	7,824,644
Community Foundation of Greater Flint	Flint	12/31/2005	117,794,673	7,753,362	5,369,711
Community Foundation for Muskegon County	Muskegon	12/31/2004	88,320,829	4,879,031	2,726,558
Battle Creek Community Foundation	Battle Creek	3/31/2005	82,360,581	5,203,743	2,700,511
Midland Area Community Foundation	Midland	12/31/2005	55,817,605	3,861,367	1,467,133
Capital Region Community Foundation	Lansing	12/31/2004	49,361,717	2,484,522	1,905,979
Ann Arbor Area Community Foundation	Ann Arbor	12/31/2005	40,146,458	2,143,548	1,229,398
Grand Haven Area Community Foundation, Inc.	Grand Haven	3/31/2004	37,641,101	2,763,806	2,385,118
Saginaw Community Foundation	Saginaw	12/31/2005	33,429,153	1,934,559	680,194
Community Foundation of St. Clair County	Port Huron	12/31/2004	27,914,951	1,617,994	1,095,716
Bay Area Community Foundation	Bay City	12/31/2005	27,868,887	1,753,645	1,253,218
Grand Traverse Regional Community Foundation	Traverse City	12/31/2005	24,244,902	1,868,231	1,472,738
Community Foundation for Northeast Michigan	Alpena	9/30/2005	22,968,969	999,172	716,392
The Community Foundation of the Holland/Zeeland Area	Holland	12/31/2004	22,308,089	2,916,521	2,579,111
The Jackson County Community Foundation	Jackson	12/31/2005	18,768,103	1,470,533	913,909
Charlevoix County Community Foundation	East Jordan	12/31/2005	18,113,170	1,384,316	1,051,556
Berrien Community Foundation, Inc.	St. Joseph	12/31/2005	17,419,418	876,810	599,889
Greenville Area Community Foundation	Greenville	12/31/2005	11,579,845	595,874	379,573
Allegan County Community Foundation	Allegan	12/31/2005	11,351,519	547,758	261,026
Petoskey-Harbor Springs Area Community Foundation	Petoskey	3/31/2005	10,166,572	745,296	441,144
Sturgis Area Community Foundation	Sturgis	3/31/2005	9,848,117	596,844	410,045
Four County Community Foundation	Almont	12/31/2005	9,563,324	492,273	329,983
Marshall Community Foundation	Marshall	9/30/2005	8,600,689	308,340	204,378
Community Foundation of the Upper Peninsula	Escanaba	12/31/2004	8,356,884	1,192,119	886,119
Barry Community Foundation	Hastings	6/30/2005	8,257,821	598,870	427,253
Hillsdale County Community Foundation	Hillsdale	9/30/2004	8,103,365	463,436	217,080
Marquette Community Foundation	Marquette	12/31/2004	7,055,237	369,682	206,806
Lapeer County Community Foundation	Lapeer	12/31/2005	6,487,314	176,989	59,194
Lenawee Community Foundation	Tecumseh	9/30/2005	5,557,456	628,358	458,989
Roscommon County Community Foundation	Roscommon	12/31/2005	5,437,067	219,935	116,722
Cadillac Area Community Foundation	Cadillac	12/31/2005	5,395,867	196,964	60,582
Michigan Gateway Community Foundation	Buchanan	3/31/2005	4,761,078	362,838	135,554
Dickinson Area Community Foundation	Iron Mountain	4/30/2005	4,755,081	201,528	107,142
Mount Pleasant Area Community Foundation	Mount Pleasant	12/31/2004	4,572,440	232,395	74,450
Gratiot County Community Foundation	Ithaca	9/30/2005	4,480,738	156,957	78,449
Mackinac Island Community Foundation	Mackinac Island	12/31/2004	4,426,241	278,944	96,599
M & M Area Community Foundation	Menominee	12/31/2004	4,085,254	267,278	85,783
Branch County Community Foundation	Coldwater	9/30/2005	4,057,246	2,912,569	2,728,581
Tuscola County Community Foundation	Caro	12/31/2004	4,029,874	191,693	102,817
Albion Community Foundation	Albion	12/31/2004	3,997,866	323,362	216,385
Community Foundation of Monroe County	Monroe	3/31/2005	3,799,971	412,713	173,463
Shiawassee Community Foundation	Owosso	9/30/2005	3,136,526	190,398	105,123
Sanilac County Community Foundation	Sandusky	12/31/2005	2,993,521	161,022	129,953
Keweenaw Community Foundation	Houghton	3/31/2005	2,463,492	96,265	28,086
Leelanau Township Community Foundation, Inc.	Northport	12/31/2004	2,251,363	156,777	78,320
Greater Frankenmuth Area Community Foundation	Frankenmuth	12/31/2004	2,133,048	300,421	276,140
Southfield Community Foundation	Southfield	6/30/2004	1,802,367	170,500	30,247
Canton Community Foundation	Canton	6/30/2005	1,760,767	318,480	87,878
Otsego County Community Foundation	Gaylord	12/31/2004	1,752,898	172,731	88,992
Three Rivers Area Community Foundation	Three Rivers	12/31/2004	1,413,862	75,526	44,142
Huron County Community Foundation	Bad Axe	12/31/2004	1,146,580	136,032	47,568
Manistee County Community Foundation	Manistee	12/31/2005	1,145,466	123,328	72,189
Total: 55			**$1,973,592,065**	**$132,446,459**	**$96,235,473**

Table 6.   Fiscal Data of Michigan Foundations by County

County	Number of Foundations	Assets	Gifts Received	Expenditures	Total Giving
Alger	1	$ 0	$ 0	$ 0	$ 0
Allegan	9	16,300,815	1,265,870	1,678,582	1,333,663
Alpena	7	47,467,915	5,626,617	2,644,464	1,625,297
Antrim	4	4,512,931	138,853	380,514	189,707
Baraga	1	772,764	92,308	79,086	20,900
Barry	8	53,475,218	2,470,613	3,110,018	572,831
Bay	13	39,055,278	2,546,390	2,610,896	2,030,755
Benzie	3	27,644,134	347,873	1,483,612	1,400,666
Berrien	28	95,236,557	10,873,920	15,235,145	13,255,116
Branch	15	14,050,171	2,717,756	3,786,167	3,191,746
Calhoun	24	7,545,305,280	228,462,769	307,405,500	231,335,062
Cass	10	131,262,990	481,772	6,721,894	730,420
Charlevoix	6	32,131,584	2,436,615	3,145,637	2,692,533
Cheboygan	4	5,928,942	92,324	229,568	26,000
Chippewa	2	1,749,298	0	94,901	72,455
Clinton	3	612,117	38,654	62,553	39,800
Delta	6	14,599,236	1,160,202	1,497,327	1,156,343
Dickinson	7	5,433,537	79,624	263,437	166,767
Eaton	11	2,389,438	127,543	471,252	333,495
Emmet	13	22,524,724	1,947,759	2,358,701	1,862,141
Genesee	111	3,135,166,913	11,454,631	178,004,451	138,007,803
Gladwin	1	68,152	40,020	43,625	43,438
Gogebic	1	254,700	125	18,816	14,000
Grand Traverse	32	80,287,974	19,339,773	6,116,791	4,594,185
Gratiot	8	7,929,163	2,598,584	1,170,178	1,057,301
Hillsdale	3	8,205,217	574,017	481,479	234,067
Houghton	3	2,925,400	83,873	130,598	56,803
Huron	6	2,656,698	93,626	236,660	121,258
Ingham	41	227,965,586	21,653,550	30,668,006	20,019,407
Ionia	3	1,758,942	506,375	490,057	52,000
Iosco	2	1,600,335	303,425	95,933	73,106
Iron	3	743,398	0	72,988	42,271
Isabella	6	45,009,531	1,337,569	1,380,182	779,769
Jackson	37	76,053,166	3,091,604	5,908,865	4,616,687
Kalamazoo	66	1,201,373,005	88,478,014	86,969,423	58,406,913
Kalkaska	1	204,175	116,559	14,655	0
Kent	294	1,321,859,932	63,520,549	155,468,575	137,233,545
Lake	1	0	0	0	0
Lapeer	4	16,076,317	328,116	693,769	412,965
Leelanau	9	3,925,701	185,915	361,432	257,752
Lenawee	25	119,584,521	1,849,725	9,505,119	8,318,843
Livingston	15	64,553,330	254,152	3,714,363	2,909,865
Mackinac	1	4,426,241	296,124	278,944	96,599
Macomb	78	166,965,551	10,535,915	13,120,596	11,317,675
Manistee	7	6,957,824	906,759	393,052	280,031
Marquette	12	17,094,121	565,103	889,578	648,835
Mason	3	2,563,103	162,257	117,608	105,300
Mecosta	2	86,382	0	4,498	4,050
Menominee	2	5,941,318	212,974	316,689	85,783
Midland	27	1,229,612,204	132,257,701	70,902,968	61,729,571
Missaukee	2	578,537	0	27,210	24,905
Monroe	17	74,339,866	668,541	6,831,196	6,153,941
Montcalm	5	18,642,585	1,183,544	915,733	635,366
Muskegon	11	109,919,663	3,499,419	5,551,452	3,202,379
Newaygo	9	282,356,231	3,223,975	17,267,388	13,848,829
Oakland	604	3,664,085,075	164,562,724	159,626,434	206,713,829
Oceana	1	0	0	0	0
Osceola	2	153,941	6,338	7,420	7,383
Oscoda	1	1,392,625	0	138,038	53,402
Otsego	3	2,222,437	92,169	201,666	115,007
Ottawa	74	179,697,642	14,002,323	27,381,045	25,191,270
Roscommon	3	11,834,602	176,511	392,200	254,722
Saginaw	54	140,665,965	7,234,738	8,887,969	6,512,278
Saint Clair	20	71,596,264	4,070,465	4,048,418	3,263,633
Saint Joseph	10	16,021,464	769,606	929,676	673,275
Sanilac	3	4,913,026	745,711	238,632	198,453
Schoolcraft	1	0	0	0	0
Shiawassee	7	16,264,139	295,877	938,876	738,161
Tuscola	5	5,030,532	219,908	237,487	147,252
Van Buren	4	931,060	114,500	149,559	137,875
Washtenaw	102	448,144,053	65,217,424	133,999,332	118,061,803
Wayne	333	3,363,904,139	179,278,835	322,220,049	302,469,420
Wexford	1	5,395,867	343,586	196,964	60,582
Total	**2,251**	**$24,230,391,542**	**$1,067,360,691**	**$1,611,015,896**	**$1,402,019,284**

TABLE 7. Grant Distribution in Major Subject Categories by Michigan Foundations, circa 2004

Subject	Amount	%	No.	%
Arts, Culture & Humanities	$ 95,836,451	11.5	659	12.0
Education	200,055,394	23.9	1,155	21.0
Environment/Animals	69,818,934	8.4	369	6.7
Health	90,504,586	10.8	539	9.8
Human Services	159,049,584	19.0	1,164	21.1
International/Foreign Affairs	15,811,064	1.9	83	1.5
Public Affairs/Society Benefit	185,381,209	22.2	1,346	24.4
Religion	14,935,191	1.8	192	3.5
Mutual/Membership Benefit	4,083,000	0.5	2	0.0
Nonclassifiable Entities	195,000	0.0	3	0.1
Total	**$835,670,413**	**100.0**	**5,512**	**100.0**

Source: The Foundation Center, 2006. The Foundation Center's grants sample database (circa 2004) includes grants of $10,000 or more awarded to organizations by a sample of 1,172 larger foundations. For community foundations, only discretionary and donor-advised grants are included. Grants to individuals are not included. Grants included for the 45 Michigan foundations in the sample accounted for approximately two thirds of total giving reported by all Michigan foundations in 2004.

TABLE 8. Grant Distribution in Major Subject Categories by Out-of-State Foundations to Michigan Nonprofit Organizations, circa 2004

Subject	Amount	%	No.	%
Arts, Culture & Humanities	$ 8,450,426	9.8	78	8.8
Education	29,523,989	34.2	212	23.8
Environment/Animals	6,152,302	7.1	48	5.4
Health	9,815,524	11.4	89	10.0
Human Services	9,456,394	10.9	188	21.1
International/Foreign Affairs	225,093	0.3	9	1.0
Public Affairs/Society Benefit	20,200,021	23.4	231	26.0
Religion	2,625,486	3.0	35	3.9
Mutual/Membership Benefit	0	0.0	0	0.0
Nonclassifiable Entities	0	0.0	0	0.0
Total	**$86,449,235**	**100.0**	**890**	**100.0**

Source: The Foundation Center, 2006.The Foundation Center's grants sample database (circa 2004) includes grants of $10,000 or more awarded to organizations by a sample of 1,172 larger foundations. For community foundations, only discretionary and donor-advised grants are included. Grants to individuals are not included. Grants made by the 209 out-of-state foundations included in the sample accounted for approximately one fifth of total grant dollars awarded to Michigan nonprofit organizations in 2004.

FIGURE 1. Share of Foundation Number, Assets, and Giving by Urban vs. Town and Rural Michigan Foundations*

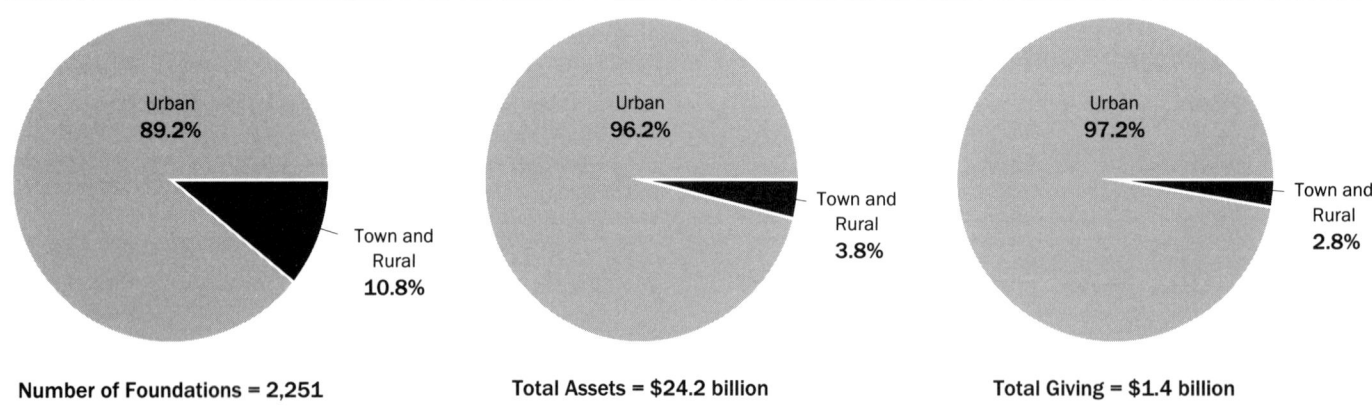

Number of Foundations = 2,251   Total Assets = $24.2 billion   Total Giving = $1.4 billion

*Urban corresponds to "metropolitan areas" defined by the U.S. Office of Management and Budget (OMB) as of December 2005. Towns and rural locations include all places outside OMB-defined metropolitan areas.

DOING YOUR HOMEWORK: HOW TO RESEARCH A GRANTMAKER

Doing your homework will assure that your proposal will be sent to foundations or corporations that make grants to your type of organization, in the geographic area in which you function and for your field of interest. Foundations and corporations reject many of the proposals they receive because the proposals do not fit their guidelines. Be clear about your goals, the needs to be met by your project, the amount of money necessary to achieve objectives and the availability of funds from other sources—especially local support.

If you represent a small organization or a new organization looking for funding for a project limited to the local community, first seek local funding through your own local constituency, community support and neighborhood business donations. Starting with community fund-raising efforts now may help secure funding for a larger, more important project in the future.

Foundation or corporate funding is not for everyone. A great deal of time, frustration and disappointment will be saved if you assess the appropriateness of foundation/corporate funding in advance.

1. CHECK THESE SITES ON THE INTERNET

- Go to foundationcenter.org to learn about the Foundation Center's *Guide to Grantseeking on the Web* and link to Foundation Finder. For the most comprehensive and current data, turn to the *Foundation Directory Online* for all currently active U.S. grantmakers, over 80,000. It provides links to foundation 990 or 990-PF tax returns, facts on over 500,000 grants and indexes to guide searches. Preview this fundraising tool at fconline.fdncenter.org

- GuideStar: www.guidestar.org for a copy of a foundation 990 or 990-PF form, the annual filing required by the IRS.

- The Grantsmanship Center: www.tgci.com for training and resources on fundraising

- Internet NonProfit Center: www.nonprofits.org/

- The Chronicle of Philanthropy: philanthropy.com

- The Dorothy A. Johnson Center for Philanthropy & Nonprofit Leadership: www.gvsu.edu/jcp

- State and federal grant information can be found at www.michigan.gov and www.grants.gov

- www.groundspring.org: an online fundraising resource.

2. USE *THE MICHIGAN FOUNDATION DIRECTORY*

Because almost all funding is local, start with foundations in Michigan. Most public libraries and each of the Cooperating Collections listed in the next section have copies, or contact the Council of Michigan Foundations at www.cmif.org to purchase a copy of *The Michigan Foundation Directory*, 2006—available in print and on CD-ROM. Use the "Subject Index" and the "Geographic Index" to begin establishing a list. Using the main entries, note each foundation's and corporation's purposes and limitations to rule out those that are inappropriate. If the foundation or corporation publishes an annual report, see if it is available in the Cooperating Collection or online.

For further information on the grant records of Michigan foundations, consult the annual tax returns (Form 990-PF for private, Form 990 for community foundations) filed with the Internal Revenue Service that include a complete list of grants for the year indicated. Foundation Center Cooperating Collections in Michigan have these returns on CD-ROM for all Michigan foundations. Many foundations include their return on their web site. You can also view the 990s and 990-PFs at foundationcenter.org or www.guidestar.org.

3. VISIT A FOUNDATION CENTER COOPERATING COLLECTION

The Foundation Center in New York (foundationcenter.org) has established a network of free funding information centers in libraries, community foundations and nonprofit centers in Michigan. We encourage you to visit one. Each of these centers has the same basic collection of information on state and national foundations (including 990-PF forms for Michigan private foundations) and corporate giving programs, along with supplementary materials (books, periodicals, annual reports, newsletters and press clippings) on grantsmanship, fund-raising and philanthropy. Please telephone individual sites for more information about their holdings and hours.

Alpena County Library
211 N. First Street
Alpena 49707
989.356.6188

**University of Michigan—Ann
Arbor**
Graduate Library
Reference Services Dept.
209 Hatcher North
Ann Arbor 48109-1205
734.763.1539

Willard Public Library
Nonprofit & Funding Resource
Collections
7 West Van Buren Street
Battle Creek 49017
269.968.8166

Purdy/Kresge Library
134 Purdy/Kresge Library
Wayne State University
Detroit 48202
313.577.6424

**Michigan State University
Libraries**
Main Library Funding Center
100 Library
East Lansing 48824-1049
517.432.6123

Farmington Community Library
32737 West 12 Mile Road
Farmington Hills 48334
248.553.0300

Flint Public Library
1026 E. Kearsley Street
Flint 48502-1994
810.232.7111

Grand Rapids Public Library
Reference Department
111 Library Street, NE
Grand Rapids 49503-3268
616.988.5400

**Michigan Technological
University**
Corporate Services
ATDC Building, Suite 200
1402 E. Sharon Avenue
Houghton 49931-1295
906.487.2228

Peter White Public Library
217 N. Front Street
Marquette, MI 49855
906.226.4311

Petoskey Public Library
500 E. Mitchell Street
Petoskey 49770
231.758.3100

**Public Libraries of
Saginaw-Hoyt Public Library**
505 Janes Avenue
Saginaw 48607
989.755.0904

**West Shore Community College
Library**
3000 North Stiles Road
Scottville 49454-0277
231.845.6211

Traverse Area District Library
610 Woodmere Avenue
Traverse City 49686
231.932.8500

THE COOPERATING COLLECTIONS' NATIONAL DIRECTORIES OF GRANTS TO ORGANIZATIONS

Check to see if the national directories contain any additional information on the Michigan foundations or corporations on your list. They can also be used to determine which non-Michigan foundations might give to Michigan organizations. (These non-Michigan grantmakers are included in *The Michigan Foundation Directory*, as well.)

Grant Guides serve as a beginning step to approach your study through 12 subject fields of grantmaking. Descriptions of actual grants of $10,000 or more to nonprofit organizations reflect the current interests of the listed foundations. Restrictions on their grantmaking may also appear. Recipients of grants are indexed.

For comprehensive information about the largest foundations, refer to *The Foundation 1000*. Although it includes only the largest foundations, they account for about 60 percent of all foundation grant dollars. In addition to analysis of grants, it contains in-depth information about foundations: trustees and staff, fiscal data, history, publications, policies and application procedures.

The Foundation Directory describes 10,000 of the top foundations, including corporate foundations, by total giving. These largest foundations also award 92 percent of all U.S. grant dollars. This directory contains a statistical breakdown of the foundation community by geography, assets and grants.

The Foundation Directory, Part 2 includes the next 10,000 largest foundations, those with grant programs between

$90,000-$250,000+. Complete coverage is provided on 10,000 foundations.

The Foundation Center's *National Directory of Corporate Giving*, 12th Edition, published in 2006, includes complete corporate giving profiles on more than 3,700 companies.

Begin your list of potential funding sources with those whose recent grants indicate a possible interest in your project, that are located or award grants in your geographic area and that have made grants in dollar amounts comparable to the amount you are seeking.

NATIONAL DIRECTORIES OF GRANTS TO INDIVIDUALS

About 6,200 foundations that conduct ongoing grant programs for individuals are included in *Foundation Grants to Individuals*, 15th edition. (This publication is also available online.) Research can be done by subject, type of support, geography, company-related grants and specific educational institutions. General welfare and medical assistance are included, as well as scholarships, loans, prizes and travel grants. Program limitations are also described.

4. COMMUNICATE DIRECTLY WITH THE FOUNDATION OR CORPORATION

Call those that are staffed or write to request an annual report or guidelines. Always check their web site.

ADVICE FROM A FOUNDATION PROGRAM OFFICER

THE PROPOSAL PROCESS

The business of foundations is to give away money to qualified organizations for the purposes approved by the foundations' board of trustees. To carry out their charitable mission, foundations need good ideas—good projects effectively presented in written proposals from nonprofit organizations. Foundations need nonprofits' problem-solving skills and ability as much as nonprofits need foundation financial support.

The process through which foundations award grants varies greatly. *The Michigan Foundation Directory* reveals the great diversity of programming interests and priorities among foundations. However, the basics of the proposal process are the same whether for community foundations, corporate foundations or independent foundations. Understanding both sides of the process, i.e. how the nonprofit requests funds and what the foundation's perspective is, will improve your proposal and the likelihood of foundation support. It will also help you realistically assess your chances and make decisions about whether or not to apply for a grant.

The proposal process has four essential phases:
1) Pre-Proposal Preparation, 2) The Proposal, 3) The Grant Decision, and 4) The Grant's Execution. Think through all four phases relative to your idea before writing and submitting the proposal.

PRE-PROPOSAL PREPARATION

Grants are made to qualified tax-exempt organizations under Federal (not state) law, since foundation taxes and potential penalties are assessed by the Federal government. "Tax-exempt" refers to Section 501(c)(3) of the Internal Revenue Code and to its classification that an organization is not a private foundation as defined under Section 509(a). Evidence of tax exemption may be requested with the proposal. Make sure it is current information and that the name on the Treasury Department's letter is the same as that on your organization's letterhead.

Foundations are permitted to make grants to individuals or to non-501(c)(3) organizations to carry out charitable activities. However, few foundations do so since the Internal Revenue Service requires them to exercise special "expenditure responsibility" over such grants. The few foundations that do make grants directly to individuals usually have special programs for this purpose.

Foundations scrutinize all indicators that help determine whether an organization is stable, has a strong board of directors, has adequate finances and related oversight, and, perhaps most importantly, has the capacity to successfully operate the proposed program. Therefore, the proposal writer must know the nonprofit organization well and be able to succinctly summarize its history, operations, mission and sources of revenue.

Define the purpose of your funding request before researching foundations. Without a clear purpose, it is much more difficult to assess the likelihood of a particular foundation's interest. A foundation looks at the grant's purpose as well as the organization requesting the funds to determine whether a proposal fits within its funding guidelines and priorities. A foundation's program and geographic areas are usually published in its annual report and/or printed guidelines.

Make sure your proposal's purpose fits the foundation both programmatically and geographically. Learn what grants the foundation made in the past, which are listed in its annual report or Form 990-PF. This form is available at Foundation Center Cooperating Collections, on many foundation web sites and at foundationcenter.org or www.guidestar.org. But there is no guarantee that similar grants will be made in the future.

The Michigan Foundation Directory is a great place to begin foundation research, but try going directly to the foundation for a copy of its latest annual report or guidelines. Guidelines are subject to change. Follow the guidelines or the request may be denied on a technicality or not considered at all. If your program or organization doesn't fit the foundation's stated interests, it is a waste of time to send a proposal. Some foundations will respond to a letter of inquiry or discuss it at a meeting or over the phone.

Tailor your proposal to fit each foundation on your list. "Tailor" means knowing to whom to address the request at the foundation, understanding required information about the foundation's areas of interest, and then focusing your proposal to meet the foundation's funding priorities. In some cases, a foundation might completely fund your program. However, in many cases, you may want to ask different foundations to support different aspects or components of your program. Some are more willing to provide grants for furniture or computer equipment. Others emphasize support for construction and renovation of facilities. Still others limit their support to actual delivery of specific human services.

Start with foundations close to home. These will be more concerned with local organizations and problems than large foundations with national programs. Generally, the latter are looking for programs with national significance and solutions to problems that can be applied elsewhere. And local foundations generally have made a much larger investment in your community over time than national foundations.

Remember that foundation people exchange information about proposals and grantees, just as you exchange information about potential grantors with other nonprofits. Although it may be appropriate to directly contact trustees of family foundations and foundations which serve as extensions of the donor's personal philanthropy, it is not appropriate with staffed foundations. Trying to influence trustees can even have an adverse effect on your proposal. Professional staffs are employed to communicate with potential grantees. They will help you as much as they can.

THE PROPOSAL

There are many books and articles about how to write proposals that can be helpful. Some foundations have specific formats to follow. Some do not. More than 100 Michigan grantmakers use the Council of Michigan Foundations' *Common Grant Application Form* that can be found at the end of this section and on the web at www.cmif.org. Proposals can be elaborate or simply written in letter format. In any event, brief (5-7 pages), tightly written proposals are preferred. But be sure to include all the information requested in a foundation's guidelines. If something is not applicable, say so and why not.

Follow the outline of the required information as contained in the guidelines. Do not include an administrative charge for items already accounted for in the budget. Avoid jargon, and define terms. Assume the foundation is not familiar with your organization. Include a brief history, since most foundations will not take the time to learn more about it.

Proposals not only ask for a grant, but they build the case for awarding one to your organization. State why the organization is qualified to conduct the program, what long-lasting results will come of it, how the grant funds will be spent, the organization's past successes with similar efforts and the expertise of the staff. Be sure to document any claims made; superlatives are ineffective. Avoid emotional language or stories that do not enhance a proposal.

Emphasize how the grant program's performance will be evaluated. Evaluation should be planned from the beginning with specific data collection and analysis outlined in the proposal. Make sure the organization can complete the grant's program and also document its outcomes. You may also use the Council of Michigan Foundations' *Common Report Form* found at the end of this section and on the web at www.cmif.org.

Foundations do not want to support a program over a long period nor do they want grantees to become dependent upon their funding. Foundations want to know how the program or purpose will be funded when the grant concludes. "Increased fund raising" is insufficient; list specific sources of future revenue or those likely to give to sustain the program.

THE GRANT DECISION

Many more proposals are denied than funded by any foundation. However, some grant requests may be deferred for a future decision. Some grants are awarded for a lesser amount than originally requested.

Letters of denial may not state specifically why a proposal was denied. However, it is rarely because there was something "wrong" with the proposal that if fixed would then result in a grant. Usually proposals are declined because: a) the foundation's grant budget was insufficient, b) the program or purpose wasn't a priority or c) the organization did not demonstrate the capacity to carry out the proposal.

The letter confirming the award will include the foundation's conditions and expectations. Prompt acknowledgement and thanks on receipt of the grant letter is the right thing to do. The Executive Director or an officer of the organization may be asked to complete a grant contract confirming its tax-exempt status, the purpose for which the money will be used, and that the organization will refrain from activities that jeopardize its tax-exempt status. If the agreement is not adhered to, the foundation could ask for the grant's return. Many foundations also reserve the right to audit your financial records on a project.

THE GRANT'S EXECUTION

During the period of the grant, your organization is responsible for ensuring that every effort is made to conduct the program as outlined in the proposal. However, changes may be necessary. If so, contact the foundation and let them know of changes. They will appreciate knowing earlier rather than later. The foundation is interested in the program's progress. Send periodic reports every six months with copies of any publicity about the program, particularly if it mentions the foundation.

An accounting that confirms expenditure of the grant funds is due to the foundation at the close of the grant period. Share future plans for the program and how the organization plans to build upon progress made during the grant. Let the foundation know if other organizations are interested in your program.

CONCLUSION

The proposal process and the grant decision are not mysterious. Each foundation does its best to serve its community within the framework of its mission and funding guidelines. By doing your research, you will understand what foundations look for in terms of form and content. However, the original, creative idea of the proposal is still up to you. Foundation grant decisions are made in many different ways but never in a vacuum. Your proposal competes in a "marketplace of ideas." The proposal will ultimately succeed or fail on its own merits.

TYPICAL QUESTIONS A FOUNDATION MIGHT ASK ABOUT A GRANT APPLICATION

A foundation staff member or trustee may ask any combination of the following questions when considering a grant request. Consider how your proposal provides the answers. Does the application include:

- verification of 501(c)(3) non-profit charitable tax status?

- how the project addresses the Foundation's current priorities?

- making a case for the need?

- if the project duplicates or overlaps other existing programs?

- evidence of collaboration with other nonprofits?

- new and innovative activities or request general operating support for an ongoing effort?

- measurable outcomes and provision for project evaluation?

- a one or multiple year budget?

- other potential and actual sources of support?

- information on the role of the executive director and other managers of the project?

- a listing of the board of directors with their organization affiliation?

- the current year's board-approved operating budget?

- the most recent audit?

COMMON GRANT APPLICATION FORM

The following form was composed by a committee of private, corporate and community foundations, all members of the Council of Michigan Foundations, and chaired by Ann Tabor of the Grand Haven Area Community Foundation. The idea of the "common form" is to eliminate the grantseeker's burden of creating multiple versions of a request in order to meet differing information requirements of grantmakers. It also offers funders more consistent information for evaluating a pool of requests.

Keep in mind that every grantmaker has different guidelines and priorities, as well as different deadlines and timetables, and any funder that has agreed to accept this form may request additional information. If the foundation does not have an application form or use the Common Grant Application Form, this Form can still serve as an excellent guide to writing a proposal. Although forms and styles may vary, this Form includes all the basics required for a complete proposal.

Common Grant Application

Cover Sheet

Date of Application: _____

Legal name of organization applying:_____
(Should be same as on IRS determination letter and as supplied on IRS Form 990.)

Year Founded: _____   Current Operating Budget: $_____

Executive Director: _____Phone number_____
(include Area Code)

Contact person/title/phone number
(if different from executive director):   _____
_____

Address *(principal/administrative office):* _____

City/State/Zip: _____

Fax Number: _____ E-mail Address:_____

List any previous support from this funder in the last five years: _____
_____
_____

Project Name: _____

Purpose of Grant *(one sentence):* _____
_____
_____
_____

Dates of the Project: _____ Amount Requested: $_____

Total Project Cost: $_____

Geographic Area Served: _____

_____   _____
Signature, Chairperson, Board of Directors   *Date*
_____
Typed Name and Title

_____   _____
Signature, Executive Director   *Date*
_____
Typed Name and Title

9/02

Common Grant Application Format

Please provide the following information in this order. Use these headings, subheadings and numbers provided in your own word processing format, thus leaving flexibility for length of response.

A. *Narrative*

1. Executive Summary
- Begin with a half-page executive summary. Briefly explain why your agency is requesting this grant, what outcomes you hope to achieve, and how you will spend the funds if the grant is made.

2. Purpose of Grant
- Statement of needs/problems to be addressed; description of target population and how they will benefit.
- Description of project goals, measurable objectives, action plans, and statements as to whether this is a new or ongoing part of the sponsoring organization.
- Timetable for implementation.
- List of other partners in the project and their roles.
- List of similar existing projects or agencies, if any, and explanation of how your agency or proposal differs and what effort will be made to work cooperatively.
- Description of the active involvement of constituents in defining problems to be addressed, making policy, and planning the program.
- Description of the qualifications of key staff and volunteers that will ensure the success of the program. List of specific staff training needs for this project.
- Long-term strategies for funding this project at end of grant period.

3. Evaluation
- Plans for evaluation, including how success will be defined and measured.
- Description of how evaluation results will be used and/or disseminated and, if appropriate, how the project will be replicated.
- Description of the active involvement of constituents in evaluating the program.

4. Budget Narrative/Justification
- Grant budget; use the **Grant Budget Format** that follows, if appropriate.
- A plan (on a separate sheet) that shows how each budget item relates to the project and how the budgeted amount was calculated.
- List of amounts requested from other foundations, corporations and other funding sources to which this proposal has been submitted.
- List of priority items in the proposed grant budget, in the event that we are unable to meet your full request.

5. Organization Information
- Brief summary of organization's history.
- Brief statement of organization's mission and goals.
- Description of current programs, activities and accomplishments.
- Organizational chart, including board, staff and volunteer involvement.

B. *Attachments*

1. **A copy of the current IRS determination letter** (indicating 501(c)(3) tax-exempt status)
2. **List of Board of Directors with affiliations**
3. **Finances**
   - Organization's current annual operating budget, including expenses and revenue.
   - Most recent annual financial statement (independently audited, if available; if not available, attach IRS Form 990).
4. **Letters of support** (should verify project need and collaboration with other organizations)—*Optional*
5. **Annual report** (if available)

COMMON GRANT BUDGET FORMAT

Grant Budget Format

Listed below are standard budget items. Please provide the project budget in this format and in this order.

A. Organizational fiscal year:_____

B. Time period this budget covers:_____

C. For a CAPITAL request, substitute your format for listing expenses. These will likely include: architectural fees, land/building purchase, construction costs, and campaign expenses.

D. **Expenses:** include a ***description and the total amount*** for each of the following budget categories, in this order:

		Amount requested from this organization	*Total project expenses*
1.	Salaries	$_____	$_____
2.	Payroll Taxes	$_____	$_____
3.	Fringe Benefits	$_____	$_____
4.	Consultants and Professional Fees	$_____	$_____
5.	Insurance	$_____	$_____
6.	Travel	$_____	$_____
7.	Equipment	$_____	$_____
8.	Supplies	$_____	$_____
9.	Printing and Copying	$_____	$_____
10.	Telephone and Fax	$_____	$_____
11.	Postage and Delivery	$_____	$_____
12.	Rent	$_____	$_____
13.	Utilities	$_____	$_____
14.	Maintenance	$_____	$_____
15.	Evaluation	$_____	$_____
16.	Marketing	$_____	$_____
17.	Other *(specify)*	$_____	$_____
	Total amount requested **$**_____		*Total project expenses* **$**_____

D. **Revenue:** include a ***description and the total amount*** for each of the following budget categories, in this order; please indicate which sources of revenue are committed and which are pending.

	Committed	*Pending*
1. Grants/Contracts/Contributions		
Local Government	$_____	$_____
State Government	$_____	$_____
Federal Government	$_____	$_____
Foundations *(itemize)*	$_____	$_____
Corporations *(itemize)*	$_____	$_____
Individuals	$_____	$_____
Other *(specify)*	$_____	$_____
2. Earned Income		
Events	$_____	$_____
Publications and Products	$_____	$_____
3. Membership Income	$_____	$_____
4. In-kind Support	$_____	$_____
5. Other *(specify)*	$_____	$_____
Total revenue **$**_____		**$**_____

9/02

COMMON REPORT FORM

COMMON REPORT FORM FORMAT
Cover Sheet

The purpose of the Common Report Form is to help grantees save time in reporting to you and to help grantmakers simplify the process of gathering standard grant evaluation information.

Date of Report: _____

Legal name of organization applying:_____
(Should be same as on IRS determination letter and as supplied on IRS Form 990.)

Executive Director: _____Phone number_____

Contact person/title/phone number
(if different from executive director): _____

_____

Address *(principal/administrative office):* _____

City/State/Zip: _____

Fax Number: _____E-mail Address:_____

Project/Program Name:_____

Purpose of Grant *(one sentence)*:_____
_____
_____

Dates of the Project:_____ Amount of Grant Awarded: $_____

Have there been any changes to your organization's IRS 501(c)(3) not-for-profit status since your request for this grant? *(yes or no):*_____If yes, please explain:_____
_____

Dates covered by this report: from_____to_____.

Check one: ____ This is an interim report   ____ This is a final report

_____   _____
Signature, Executive Director   *Date*

_____
Typed Name and Title

COMMON REPORT FORM FORMAT
Narrative & Financials

I.   *Narrative* — Two to five pages.

    A.   Results
        1.   List the original goals and objectives of the grant, and tell how they were met during this reporting period. Describe current status on meeting any special terms of this grant (e.g. challenges, contingencies, etc.).
        2.   If possible, explain results in outcome-based terms. For example, what difference did this grant make in your community and for the population you are serving?
        3.   Variance from original project plans often occurs. In what ways did the actual project vary from your initial plans? Describe how and why.
        4.   Describe any unanticipated benefits or challenges encountered with this project.
        5.   Describe how collaborative/cooperative efforts with individuals and organizations involved in planning, implementing, funding and/or evaluating this project/grant affected outcomes.

    B.   Lessons Learned
        1.   What are the most important outcomes and lessons learned from this project?
        2.   What recommendations would you make to the Foundation or to other project directors working in this area?
        3.   If you were to undertake this project again, would you do anything differently? If yes, please explain.
        4.   Other lessons?

    C.   Future Plans
        1.   What is your vision of this project over the next three years? Include plans and rationale for ongoing funding, expansion, replication or termination.

    D.   Public Relations
        1.   Provide a "human interest" story that helps explain the success of the project.
        2.   Attach any printed material relating to the funded project: press or news items, brochures, letters of support, photographs, etc.

II.   *Financials*

    A.   Using the budget from the original application, provide detailed expenses and income for the project for this period. Provide narrative on any variances from the original projected budget.

    B.   Include a complete, detailed accounting of how the specific grant dollars from this grant were spent.

HOW TO USE *THE MICHIGAN FOUNDATION DIRECTORY*

ARRANGEMENT

The descriptive directory of *The Michigan Foundation Directory* is arranged in five sections: independent foundations, corporate funders, community foundations, public charities, and operating foundations. Within each grantmaker type section, the entries of both Michigan funders and out-of-state funders are arranged alphabetically by grantmaker name. Each entry is assigned a sequence number, and references in the indexes refer to these entry numbers.

WHAT'S IN AN ENTRY?

There are 37 basic data elements that could be included in a *Michigan Foundation Directory* entry. The content of entries varies widely due to differences in the grantmaker type, size and nature of grantmaker programs and the availability of information from grantmakers. Specific data elements that could be included are:

1. The full legal **name of the grantmaker.**

2. Other names associated with the grantmaker, such as **former name, also known as,** and **doing business as.**

3. The **street address, city, and zip code** of the grantmaker's principal office.

4. The **telephone number** of the grantmaker.

5. The name and title of the **contact person** at the grantmakers.

6. Any **additional address** (such as a separate application address) supplied by the grantmaker. Additional telephone or fax numbers as well as e-mail and/or URL addresses also may be listed here.

7. **Establishment data,** including the legal form (usually a trust or corporation) and the year and state in which the grantmaker was established.

8. The **donor(s)** or principal contributor(s) to the grantmaker, including individuals, families, and corporations. If a donor is deceased, the symbol ‡ follows the name.

9. **Grantmaker type:** community, company-sponsored, independent, or operating foundation; corporate giving program; or public charity.

10. The **year-end date** of the grantmaker's accounting period for which financial data is supplied.

11. **Revenue:** the total amount of contributions and support received by a public charity, including investment income, program service revenue, net profits from sale of assets, etc.

12. **Assets:** the total value of the grantmaker's investments at the end of the accounting period. In a few instances, grantmakers that act as "pass-throughs" for annual corporate or individual gifts report zero assets.

13. **Asset type:** generally, assets are reported at market value (M) or ledger value (L).

14. **Gifts received:** the total amount of new capital received by the grantmaker in the year of record.

15. **Expenditures:** total disbursements of the grantmaker, including overhead expenses (salaries; investment, legal, and other professional fees; interest; rent; etc.) and federal excise taxes, as well as the total amount paid for grants, scholarships, and matching gifts.

16. **Total giving:** Gifts, contributions, grants paid; total amount for all grants and contributions during the year. This amount generally excludes loans and the costs of foundation-operated programs, but includes all other forms of support such as grants, scholarships, and employee matching gifts.

17. **Program services expenses:** includes all expenses by public charities that are directly involved in carrying out charitable activities, including total grants paid.

18. The total amount of **qualifying distributions** made by the grantmaker in the year of record. This figure includes all grants paid, qualifying administrative expenses, loans and program-related investments, set-asides, and amounts paid to acquire assets used directly in carrying out charitable purposes.

19. The dollar value and number of **grants paid** during the year, with the largest grant paid **(high)** and smallest grant paid **(low)**. When supplied by the grantmaker, the average range of grant payments is also indicated. Grant figures generally do not include commitments for future payment or amounts spent for grants to individuals, employee matching gifts, loans, or grantmaker-administered programs.

20. The total dollar value of **set-asides** made by the grantmaker during the year. Although set-asides count as qualifying distributions toward the foundation's annual payout requirement, they are distinct from any amounts listed as grants paid.

21. The total amount and number of **grants made directly to or on behalf of individuals,** including scholarships, fellowships, awards, and medical payments. When supplied by the grantmaker, high, low, and average range are also indicated.

22. The dollar amount and number of **employee matching gifts** awarded, generally by company-sponsored grantmakers.

23. The total dollars expended for **programs administered by the grantmaker** and the number of grantmaker-administered programs. These programs can include museums or other institutions supported exclusively by the grantmaker, research programs administered by the grantmaker, etc.

24. The dollar amount and number of **loans/program-related investments** made to nonprofit organizations by the grantmaker. These can include emergency loans to help nonprofits that are waiting for grants or other income payments, etc. When supplied by the grantmaker, high, low, and average range are also indicated.

25. The number of **loans to individuals** and the total amount loaned. When supplied by the grantmaker, high, low, and average range are also indicated.

26. The monetary value and number of **in-kind gifts.**

27. The **purpose and activities,** in general terms, of the grantmaker. This statement reflects funding interests as expressed by the grantmaker or, if no grantmaker statement is available, an analysis of the actual grants awarded by the grantmaker during the most recent period for which public records exist. Many grantmakers leave statements of purpose intentionally broad, indicating only the major program areas within which they fund. More specific areas of interest can often be found in the "Fields of Interest" section of the entry.

28. The **fields of interest** reflected in the grantmaker's giving program. The terminology used in this section conforms to the Foundation Center's Grants Classification System (GCS). The terms also provide access to grantmaker entries through the Subject Index at the back of the volume.

29. The **international giving interests** of the grantmaker.

30. The **types of support** (such as endowment funds, support for building/renovation, equipment, fellowships, etc.) offered by the grantmaker. Definitions of the terms used to describe the forms of support available are provided at the beginning of the Type of Support Index at the back of this volume.

31. Any stated **limitations** on the grantmaker's giving program, including geographic preferences, restrictions by subject focus or type of recipient, or specific types of support the grantmaker cannot provide. It is noted here if a grantmaker does not accept unsolicited applications.

32. **Publications** or other printed materials distributed by the grantmaker that describe its activities and giving program. These can include annual or multi-year reports, newsletters, corporate giving reports, informational brochures, grant lists, etc.

33. **Application information,** including the preferred form of application, the number of copies of proposals requested, application deadlines, frequency and dates of board meetings, and the general amount of time the grantmaker requires to notify applicants of the board's decision. Some grantmakers have indicated that their funds are currently committed to ongoing projects.

34. The names and titles of **officers, principal administrators, trustees, directors,** and members of other governing bodies. An asterisk following the individual's name indicates an officer who is also a trustee or director.

35. The number of professional and support **staff** employed by the grantmaker, and an indication of part-time or full-time status of these employees, as reported by the grantmaker.

36. **EIN:** the Employer Identification Number assigned to a foundation or public charity by the Internal Revenue Service for tax purposes. This number can be useful when ordering copies of the grantmaker's annual information return, Form 990-PF for foundations and Form 990 for public charities.

37. A list of **selected grants,** generally for those foundations with annual giving of at least $80,000. Up to ten grants reported during a given fiscal year may be provided. Grants to individuals are not included.

INDEXES

Five indexes to the descriptive entries are provided at the back of the book to assist grantseekers and other users of *The Michigan Foundation Directory:*

1. The **Index to Donors, Officers, Trustees** is an alphabetical list of individual and corporate donors, officers, and members of governing boards whose names appear in *The Michigan Foundation Directory* entries. Many grantseekers find this index helpful in determining whether current or prospective members of their own governing boards, alumni of their schools, or current contributors are affiliated with any grantmakers.

2. The **Type of Support Index** provides access to grantmaker entries by the specific types of support the grantmaker awards. A glossary of the forms of support listed appears at the beginning of the index. Under each type of support term, entry numbers are listed by state location and abbreviated name of the grantmaker. Grantmakers that award grants on a national, regional, or international basis are indicated in bold type.

3. The **Subject Index** provides access to the giving interests of grantmakers based on the "Fields of Interest" sections of their entries. The terminology in the index conforms to the Foundation Center's Grants Classification System (GCS). A complete alphabetical list of the subject headings in the current edition is provided at the beginning of the index as well as "see also" references to related subject areas included in this volume. Under each subject term, entry numbers are listed by state location and abbreviated name of the grantmaker. As in the Type of Support Index, grantmakers that award grants on a national, regional, or international basis are indicated in bold type.

4. The **Grantmaker Name Index** is an alphabetical list of all grantmakers appearing in this edition of *The Michigan Foundation Directory.* Former, also known as, and doing business as names of grantmakers appear with "see" references to the appropriate entry numbers.

5. The **Geographic Index** references grantmaker entries by the state and city in which the grantmaker maintains its principal offices. Grantmakers that award grants on a national, regional, or international basis are indicated in bold type. The remaining grantmakers generally limit their giving to the county or city in which they are located.

DESCRIPTIVE DIRECTORY

INDEPENDENT FOUNDATIONS

1

41 Washington St. Foundation
41 Washington St., Ste. 315
Grand Haven, MI 49417-1378
Contact: James P. Hovinga, Dir.

Established in 2003 in MI.
Donor: The James P. and Debra K. Hovinga Charitable Foundation.
Grantmaker type: Independent foundation.
Financial data (yr. ended 12/31/05): Assets, $1,022,121 (M); gifts received, $150,000; expenditures, $292,096; total giving, $281,700; qualifying distributions, $281,700; giving activities include $281,700 for 13 grants (high: $200,500; low: $500).
Fields of interest: Higher education, college; Christian agencies & churches.
Limitations: Giving primarily in Grand Rapids and Holland, MI.
Application information: Application form not required.
  Deadline(s): None
Officer: Sue Boschma, Pres. and Treas.
Directors: Debra K. Hovinga; James P. Hovinga.
EIN: 611438980

2

The Abbarah Foundation
26300 Telegraph Rd., 2nd Fl.
Southfield, MI 48034

Established in 1994.
Grantmaker type: Independent foundation.
Financial data (yr. ended 12/31/05): Assets, $196,641 (M); expenditures, $13,523; total giving, $7,469; qualifying distributions, $7,469; giving activities include $7,469 for grants.
Fields of interest: Higher education; Speech/hearing centers.
Type of support: General/operating support.
Officer: Thabet Abbarah, Pres.
EIN: 383134949

3

The Caitlin Conley Abbatt Foundation
39900 Willis Rd.
Belleville, MI 48111

Established in 1990 in MI.
Grantmaker type: Independent foundation.
Financial data (yr. ended 12/31/04): Assets, $16,375 (M); expenditures, $731; total giving, $0; qualifying distributions, $0.
Limitations: Applications not accepted. Giving limited to MI. No grants to individuals.
Application information: Contributes only to pre-selected organizations.
Officers and Directors:* Maureen A. O'Connor,* Chair. and Treas.; William G. Abbatt,* Pres. and Secy.
EIN: 382919107

4

Frances H. Abbott Memorial Foundation
c/o Fifth Third Bank
P.O. Box 3636
Grand Rapids, MI 49501-3636
Application address: c/o Gwendolyn Harris, Riverside-Brookfield High School, 1st Ave. and Ridgewood Rd., Riverside, IL 60546

Grantmaker type: Independent foundation.
Financial data (yr. ended 12/31/05): Assets, $46,765 (M); expenditures, $9,215; total giving, $5,100; qualifying distributions, $5,100; giving activities include $5,100 for grants to individuals.
Purpose and activities: Scholarship awards to graduating seniors of Riverside-Brookfield High School, IL.
Type of support: Scholarships—to individuals.
Limitations: Giving limited to residents of Riverside, IL.
Application information:
  Initial approach: Letter
  Deadline(s): 1st Tuesday in May
Trustee: Fifth Third Bank.
EIN: 366672535

5

Abdole Foundation
P.O. Box 87
Sandusky, MI 48471

Established in 2004 in MI.
Donors: Asthma, Allergy & Sinus Center; Mutee H. Abdole, M.D.
Grantmaker type: Independent foundation.
Financial data (yr. ended 12/31/05): Assets, $136,739 (M); gifts received, $20,000; expenditures, $8,508; total giving, $4,500; qualifying distributions, $4,500; giving activities include $4,500 for grants.
Limitations: Applications not accepted. No grants to individuals.
Application information: Contributes only to pre-selected organizations.
Officer and Directors:* Mutee H. Abdole, M.D.*, Pres.; Mohamad H. Abdole Jaber.
EIN: 383691874

6

Edward and Marie Abele Memorial Fund
c/o Citizens Bank
328 S. Saginaw St., M/C 00272
Flint, MI 48502
Application address: c/o Abele Loan Comm., 5800 Weiss St., Saginaw, MI 48603, tel.: (989) 799-7910

Established in MI.
Grantmaker type: Independent foundation.
Financial data (yr. ended 7/31/04): Assets, $371,210 (M); expenditures, $7,683; total giving, $0; qualifying distributions, $13,454; giving activities include $6,600 for 4 loans to individuals.
Purpose and activities: Educational loans for practicing Catholics in Saginaw County, MI.

Fields of interest: Roman Catholic agencies & churches.
Type of support: Student loans—to individuals.
Limitations: Giving limited to Saginaw County, MI.
Application information: Application form required.
  Deadline(s): May 5
Trustee: Citizens Bank.
EIN: 386356628

7

Hawa and Aki Abiragi Foundation
66 Belle Meade St.
Grosse Pointe Shores, MI 48236-1553

Established in 2000 in MI.
Donors: Ronald A. Simon; Theresa Simon.
Grantmaker type: Independent foundation.
Financial data (yr. ended 12/31/05): Assets, $28,938 (M); gifts received, $17,400; expenditures, $12,720; total giving, $12,700; qualifying distributions, $12,700; giving activities include $12,700 for grants.
Fields of interest: Theological school/education; Roman Catholic agencies & churches.
International interests: Lebanon.
Limitations: Giving primarily in Lebanon.
Officers and Directors:* Victor Abiragi, Chair.; Antoine Abiragi, Pres.; Roger Abiragi,* V.P.; Ronald A. Simon,* Secy.; Theresa Simon,* Treas.; Charbel Abi-Ragi; Archbishop Youssef Bechara.
EIN: 383508827

8

Talbert & Leota Abrams Foundation
P.O. Box 27337
Lansing, MI 48909-7337
Contact: Joe C. Foster, Jr., Secy.

Established in 1960 in MI.
Donors: Leota Abrams†; Talbert Abrams†.
Grantmaker type: Independent foundation.
Financial data (yr. ended 12/31/05): Assets, $9,924,766 (M); expenditures, $569,091; total giving, $326,500; qualifying distributions, $442,417; giving activities include $326,500 for 10 grants (high: $144,000; low: $2,000).
Purpose and activities: Support primarily for a library and an educational science program; giving also for universities and colleges and community funds.
Fields of interest: Higher education; Adult education—literacy, basic skills & GED; Libraries/library science; Education, reading; Federated giving programs.
Type of support: Program development; Scholarship funds; Research.
Limitations: Giving primarily in central MI. No support for churches for sectarian use, or for athletic activities. No grants to individuals, or for operating or traveling expenses; no loans.
Publications: Annual report.
Application information: Application form not required.
  Initial approach: 2-page letter

Copies of proposal: 1
Deadline(s): May 31 for next calendar year
Board meeting date(s): June
Officers and Directors:* Barbara J. Brown,* Pres.;
Kyle C. Abbott,* Exec. V.P.; Joe C. Foster, Jr.,*
Secy.; Craig C. Brown,* Treas.; Shane A. Patzer;
Tiffany L. Patzer.
Number of staff: 5 part-time professional.
EIN: 386082194

9
Abu-Akeel Foundation
c/o Melamed, Dailey & Akeel, P.C.
26611 Woodward Ave.
Huntington Woods, MI 48070-1332
Contact: Hadi Abu-Akeel, Board Member

Established in 2000 in MI.
Grantmaker type: Independent foundation.
Financial data (yr. ended 12/31/05): Assets,
$21,549 (M); expenditures, $2,600; total giving,
$2,600; qualifying distributions, $2,600; giving
activities include $2,600 for grants.
Board Members: Hadi Abu-Akeel; Nezar Akeel;
Shereef H. Akeel.
EIN: 383470704

10
James C. Acheson Foundation
c/o Donna Niester
600 Fort St., Ste. 101
Port Huron, MI 48060

Established in 1999 in MI.
Donor: James C. Acheson.
Grantmaker type: Independent foundation.
Financial data (yr. ended 12/31/04): Assets,
$16,482,673 (M); gifts received, $10,000;
expenditures, $998,774; total giving, $864,844;
qualifying distributions, $899,635; giving activities
include $864,844 for 13 grants (high: $660,000;
low: $450).
Purpose and activities: Support for the arts, health,
the environment, human services, and community
development.
Fields of interest: Museums; Environment; Health
care; Mental health/crisis services; Human
services; American Red Cross; Community
development; Federated giving programs.
Limitations: Applications not accepted. Giving
primarily in MI. No grants to individuals.
Application information: Contributes only to
pre-selected organizations.
Officers: James C. Acheson, Pres.; Douglas R.
Austin, Secy.-Treas.; Donna M. Niester, Mgr.
EIN: 383463509

11
John W. J. Ackermans Foundation
c/o Comerica Bank
P.O. Box 75000, M/C 3302
Detroit, MI 48275

Grantmaker type: Independent foundation.
Financial data (yr. ended 12/31/05): Assets,
$459,429 (M); expenditures, $21,047; total giving,
$15,000; qualifying distributions, $15,000; giving
activities include $15,000 for grants.
Purpose and activities: Support only for
Academisch Zienkenhuis Maastricht.

Fields of interest: Hospitals (general).
International interests: Netherlands.
Limitations: Applications not accepted. Giving
limited to the Netherlands. No grants to individuals.
Application information: Contributes only to a
pre-selected organization.
Trustee: Comerica Bank.
EIN: 386359181

12
Barry A. Adelman Family Foundation
c/o Barry A. Adelman
48 Hampton Rd.
Scarsdale, NY 10583

Established in 2001 in NY.
Donor: Barry A. Adelman.
Grantmaker type: Independent foundation.
Financial data (yr. ended 9/30/04): Assets,
$337,027 (M); gifts received, $20,095;
expenditures, $104,140; total giving, $102,935;
qualifying distributions, $103,538; giving activities
include $102,935 for 1 grant.
Fields of interest: Higher education, university.
Type of support: Scholarship funds.
Limitations: Applications not accepted. Giving
primarily in Ann Arbor, MI. No grants to individuals.
Application information: Contributes only to
pre-selected organizations.
Officers: Barry A. Adelman, Pres. and Treas.; Robin
Adelman, V.P. and Secy.; Lauren B. Adelman, V.P.;
Todd M. Adelman, V.P.
EIN: 134199594

13
Adopt an Orca, Inc.
c/o Thomas Newhof
6550 Old Darby Trail N.E.
Ada, MI 49301

Established in 2001 in MI.
Donors: Jeff Demain; Thomas Newhof; Garretta
Newhof.
Grantmaker type: Independent foundation.
Financial data (yr. ended 12/31/05): Assets, $133
(M); gifts received, $56,120; expenditures,
$56,326; total giving, $55,470; qualifying
distributions, $55,470; giving activities include
$55,470 for grants.
Fields of interest: Environment; Animals/wildlife,
preservation/protection.
Type of support: Research.
Officers: Thomas Newhof, Pres.; Peter Friedes,
Secy.-Treas.
Directors: Susan Friedes; Garretta Newhof.
EIN: 383562103

14
Adray Foundation, Inc.
3001 W. Big Beaver Rd., Ste. 704
Troy, MI 48084 (248) 643-6500
Contact: Joseph M. McGlynn, Dir.

Established in 1983.
Grantmaker type: Independent foundation.
Financial data (yr. ended 12/31/05): Assets,
$753,503 (M); expenditures, $45,347; total giving,
$37,650; qualifying distributions, $37,650; giving
activities include $37,650 for grants.

Purpose and activities: Giving for support for
athletics with an emphasis on hockey leagues.
Fields of interest: Athletics/sports, winter sports.
Type of support: General/operating support;
Equipment; Endowments.
Limitations: Giving limited to MI.
Application information: Application form not
required.
Initial approach: Proposal
Deadline(s): None
Directors: Deborah Adray; Louise Adray; Joseph M.
McGlynn.
EIN: 382435251

15
Dr. Uttam Chand Advani and Smt Narain Advani Charitable Trust
6815 Sunrise Ct. S.E.
Grand Rapids, MI 49546-6644
Contact: Rajir Advani, Tr.

Established in 1996.
Donor: Ram Advani†.
Grantmaker type: Independent foundation.
Financial data (yr. ended 12/31/03): Assets,
$22,667; expenditures, $166; total giving, $0;
qualifying distributions, $0.
Application information: Application form not
required.
Deadline(s): None
Trustees: Meena Advani; Rajir Advani.
EIN: 383301349

16
Africa Christian Ministries, Inc.
P.O. Box 461
Keego Harbor, MI 48320

Established in 1993 in MI.
Grantmaker type: Independent foundation.
Financial data (yr. ended 6/30/05): Assets,
$5,848 (M); gifts received, $137,048;
expenditures, $139,124; total giving, $104,195;
qualifying distributions, $104,195; giving activities
include $104,195 for grants.
Purpose and activities: Support only through the
Africa Christian Ministries, Inc. its giving for ministry
camps in South Africa; also scholarship awards
though its seminary for students who are African
citizens and who plan to work in their home
countries.
Fields of interest: Christian agencies & churches.
International interests: South Africa; Southern
Africa.
Type of support: Building/renovation; Scholarship
funds.
Limitations: Applications not accepted. Giving
limited to South Africa. No grants to individuals.
Application information: Contributes only to a
pre-selected organization.
Officers: Robert Tice, Pres.; Walter Davis, V.P.; Sally
Galloway, Secy.; Edward Goodman, Treas.; Rev.
Isaia Mafu, Mgr.
Directors: Gail Bryan; Jeanette Faber; Stanley
Hoffman, M.D.; Jerome McAffe; C. Murrill-Brumfield;
Sharon Tice.
EIN: 382719112

17
Randolph J. & Judith A. Agley Foundation
400 Talon Ctr.
Detroit, MI 48207-5035

Established in 1984.
Donors: Randolph J. Agley; Talon, Inc.
Grantmaker type: Independent foundation.
Financial data (yr. ended 12/31/04): Assets, $36,351 (M); gifts received, $76,145; expenditures, $125,542; total giving, $125,300; qualifying distributions, $125,299; giving activities include $125,300 for 16 grants (high: $33,000; low: $125).
Fields of interest: Arts; Education; Cancer.
Type of support: General/operating support.
Limitations: Applications not accepted. Giving primarily in MI. No support for government groups, churches for sectarian use, or political organizations. No grants to individuals, or for operating expenses, athletic activities, or traveling expenses; no loans.
Publications: Annual report.
Application information: Contributes only to pre-selected organizations.
Officers: Randolph J. Agley, Pres.; Judith A. Agley, V.P.; Wayne C. Inman, Secy.
EIN: 382519168

18
John F. Aho Foundation
47736 Edinburgh Dr.
Plymouth, MI 48170

Established in 1998 in MI.
Grantmaker type: Independent foundation.
Financial data (yr. ended 12/31/03): Assets, $9,880 (M); gifts received, $31,465; expenditures, $32,624; total giving, $5,700; qualifying distributions, $5,700; giving activities include $5,700 for grants.
Purpose and activities: Support only for Children's Leukemia Foundation, Southfield, Michigan.
Limitations: Applications not accepted. Giving limited to Southfield, MI. No grants to individuals.
Application information: Contributes only to a pre-selected organization.
Officer: George G. Aho, Chair.
EIN: 383397505

19
The Aikens Family Foundation
2690 Crooks Rd., Ste. 400
Troy, MI 48084

Established in 1999 in MI.
Grantmaker type: Independent foundation.
Financial data (yr. ended 11/30/04): Assets, $949,149 (M); expenditures, $286,517; total giving, $274,042; qualifying distributions, $274,970; giving activities include $274,042 for 15 grants (high: $150,000; low: $250).
Fields of interest: Education; Health care; Christian agencies & churches.
Limitations: Applications not accepted. Giving on a national basis. No grants to individuals.
Application information: Contributes only to pre-selected organizations.

Officers and Directors:* Robert B. Aikens,* Pres.; Kimberly Aikens Levanovich, Secy.; Ann S. Aikens,* Treas.
EIN: 383475628

20
The Akers Foundation
c/o Paul W. Carter
One Towne Sq., Ste. 600
Southfield, MI 48076

Established in 1958 in OH.
Donor: Phyllis M. Akers.
Grantmaker type: Independent foundation.
Financial data (yr. ended 12/31/05): Assets, $1,312,661 (M); expenditures, $82,735; total giving, $74,836; qualifying distributions, $74,836; giving activities include $74,836 for 57 grants (high: $15,000; low: $18).
Fields of interest: Higher education; Health organizations; Human services; Jewish federated giving programs; Jewish agencies & temples.
Type of support: General/operating support.
Limitations: Applications not accepted. Giving primarily in MI and OH. No grants to individuals.
Application information: Contributes only to pre-selected organizations.
Officers and Trustees:* James Akers,* Pres.; Joel Levine, Secy.; Joan Binkow.
EIN: 346549129

21
Forrest H. Akers Trust
c/o Roger Wilkinson
2142 Pawnee Cir.
Okemos, MI 48864

Grantmaker type: Independent foundation.
Financial data (yr. ended 12/31/05): Assets, $8,092,700 (M); expenditures, $427,056; total giving, $395,338; qualifying distributions, $395,338; giving activities include $395,338 for grants.
Purpose and activities: Support only to Michigan State University, East Lansing, MI.
Fields of interest: Higher education, university.
Type of support: General/operating support.
Limitations: Applications not accepted. Giving limited to East Lansing, MI. No grants to individuals.
Application information: Contributes only to a pre-selected organization.
Trustees: Brian Breslin; Nancy E. Craig; Stephen J. Terry; Roger Wilkinson.
EIN: 386066391

22
The Akl Foundation
c/o Ahmed M. Aki, M.D.
26300 Telegraph Rd., 2nd Fl.
Southfield, MI 48034

Established in 1999 in MI.
Donor: Ahmed M. Akl, M.D.
Grantmaker type: Independent foundation.
Financial data (yr. ended 12/31/05): Assets, $945,862 (M); gifts received, $184,800; expenditures, $42,991; total giving, $40,000; qualifying distributions, $40,000; giving activities include $40,000 for grants.
Fields of interest: Islam.

Type of support: General/operating support.
Officer: Ahmed M. Akl, M.D., Pres.
EIN: 383436622

23
The Al-Ameri Foundation
26300 Telegraph Rd., 2nd Fl.
Southfield, MI 48034-2436

Established in 1994 in MI.
Grantmaker type: Independent foundation.
Financial data (yr. ended 12/31/04): Assets, $308,924 (M); gifts received, $135,000; expenditures, $79,800; total giving, $79,800; qualifying distributions, $79,800; giving activities include $79,800 for grants (high: $44,000).
Fields of interest: Human services.
Type of support: General/operating support.
Officer: Mohammed W. Al-Ameri, Pres.
EIN: 383134935

24
Al-Azem Foundation
26300 Telegraph Rd., 2nd Fl.
Southfield, MI 48034

Established in 1999.
Grantmaker type: Independent foundation.
Financial data (yr. ended 12/31/05): Assets, $1,266,038 (M); gifts received, $331,500; expenditures, $83,425; total giving, $78,906; qualifying distributions, $78,906; giving activities include $78,906 for grants.
Officer: Imad Al-Azam, M.D., Pres.
EIN: 383440690

25
The Al-Hadidi Foundation
26300 Telegraph Rd., 2nd Fl.
Southfield, MI 48034

Established in 1995 in MI.
Grantmaker type: Independent foundation.
Financial data (yr. ended 12/31/04): Assets, $294,863 (M); gifts received, $100,000; expenditures, $7,700; total giving, $6,250; qualifying distributions, $6,250; giving activities include $6,250 for grants.
Fields of interest: Higher education.
Type of support: General/operating support.
Limitations: Giving primarily in DE.
Officer: Samir Al-Hadidi, Pres.
EIN: 383245436

26
The Al-Harastani Foundation
26300 Telegraph Rd., 2nd Fl.
Southfield, MI 48034

Established in 2003.
Grantmaker type: Independent foundation.
Financial data (yr. ended 12/31/05): Assets, $232,890 (M); gifts received, $100,000; expenditures, $36,662; total giving, $35,500; qualifying distributions, $35,500; giving activities include $35,500 for grants.
Officer: Mohhammad Al-Harastani, Pres.
EIN: 383689101

27
Alabaster Fund
125 Park St. Ste. 450
Traverse City, MI 49684
Contact: Ms. Leslie M. Falconer, V.P.
E-mail: leslie@falconergroup.com

Established in 2003 in MI.
Donor: Erik J. Falconer.
Grantmaker type: Independent foundation.
Financial data (yr. ended 12/31/04): Assets,
$1,079,460 (M); expenditures, $57,832; total
giving, $45,000; qualifying distributions, $44,956;
giving activities include $45,000 for 3 grants (high:
$20,000; low: $10,000).
Purpose and activities: The foundation is dedicated
to healing and strengthening families in
northwestern Michigan by awarding grants to
programs and agencies that provide support
services, educational programs, training, and/or
counseling to families.
Fields of interest: Family services.
Limitations: Giving limited to northwestern MI for
the benefit of the citizens of the greater Traverse Bay
Area and the surrounding areas. No grants to
individuals, or for annual campaigns or
endowments; generally no grants for multi-year
funding.
Application information: The foundation prefers to
support proposals for new initiatives, special
projects, or expansion of current programs. Only 1
application may be submitted in any 12-month
period.
   Initial approach: Applicants are encouraged to
      discuss their proposals with foundation staff
      by telephone or in person prior to formal
      submission
   Deadline(s): Mar. 1 and Sept. 1
Officers and Trustees: Erik J. Falconer,* Pres. and
Secy.-Treas.; Leslie M. Falconer,* V.P.
EIN: 200126213

28
Alacin Foundation
c/o Riverwood LLC
1000 John R Rd., Ste. 250
Troy, MI 48083-4317

Established in 1999 in MI.
Donors: Albert Schornberg; Cindy Schornberg.
Grantmaker type: Independent foundation.
Financial data (yr. ended 12/31/04): Assets,
$828,482 (M); expenditures, $43,087; total giving,
$39,332; qualifying distributions, $39,332; giving
activities include $39,332 for grants.
Fields of interest: Health care, infants.
Type of support: General/operating support.
Limitations: Applications not accepted. Giving
primarily in Charlottesville, VA. No grants to
individuals.
Application information: Contributes only to
pre-selected organizations.
Officers and Directors: Albert Schornberg,* Chair.
and Treas.; Cindy Schornberg,* Vice-Chair. and
Secy.
EIN: 383492408

29
The Aletheia Foundation
P.O. Box 127
Belmont, MI 49306

Established in 2004 in MI.
Grantmaker type: Independent foundation.
Financial data (yr. ended 12/31/05): Assets, $23
(M); expenditures, $2; total giving, $0; qualifying
distributions, $2.
Officers: Robert Wynalda, Pres. and Treas.; Connie
Wynalda, V.P. and Secy.
Director: Robert Wynalda III.
EIN: 201861132

30
Alexandrowski Family Foundation, Inc.
7633 Quackenbush Rd.
Reading, MI 49274 (517) 283-3723
Contact: Muriel F. Alexandrowski, Pres.

Established in MI.
Donor: Muriel Alexandrowski.
Grantmaker type: Independent foundation.
Financial data (yr. ended 12/31/04): Assets,
$29,071 (M); expenditures, $10,540; total giving,
$10,540; qualifying distributions, $10,540; giving
activities include $10,540 for grants.
Fields of interest: Education; Foundations
(community).
Type of support: Scholarship funds.
Limitations: Giving primarily in Hillsdale, MI.
Application information:
   Initial approach: Letter with college transcripts
   Deadline(s): None
Officers: Muriel F. Alexandrowski, Pres.; Joseph A.
Alexandrowski, V.P.
EIN: 383443665

31
The Alix Foundation
(formerly Jay & Maryanne Alix Foundation)
c/o Jean A. Wiley
2000 Town Ctr., Ste. 2400
Southfield, MI 48075
E-mail: jwiley@alixpartners.com

Established in 1994 in MI.
Donors: Jay Alix; Maryanne Alix†.
Grantmaker type: Independent foundation.
Financial data (yr. ended 12/31/04): Assets,
$1,059,559 (M); gifts received, $1,140,603;
expenditures, $1,348,591; total giving,
$1,344,782; qualifying distributions, $1,347,080;
giving activities include $1,344,782 for 23 grants
(high: $110,000; low: $250).
Purpose and activities: Giving primarily for health
care, with an emphasis on cancer; funding also for
education and human services.
Fields of interest: Elementary/secondary
education; Higher education; Health care; Cancer;
Human services; Jewish agencies & temples.
Limitations: Applications not accepted. Giving
primarily in MI. No grants to individuals.
Application information: Contributes only to
pre-selected organizations.
Officer: Jay Alix, Pres. and Secy.-Treas.
EIN: 383171122
Selected grants: The following grants were reported
in 2003.
$76,500 to Lighthouse P.A.T.H., Pontiac, MI. For
   general support.
$50,000 to Common Ground, Royal Oak, MI. For
   general support.
$50,000 to Henry Ford Health System, Detroit, MI.

$33,334 to Heinz C. Prechter Bipolar Research
   Fund, Southgate, MI.
$25,000 to Teikyo Post University, Waterbury, CT.
$25,000 to William J. Clinton Presidential
   Foundation, Little Rock, AR.
$20,000 to Edison Institute, Dearborn, MI.
$20,000 to Interfaith Hospitality Network of Greater
   Grand Rapids, Grand Rapids, MI.
$15,167 to Detroit Country Day School, Beverly
   Hills, MI.
$10,000 to Michigan State University, East Lansing,
   MI.

32
The Aljabban Foundation
26300 Telegraph Rd., 2nd Fl.
Southfield, MI 48034

Grantmaker type: Independent foundation.
Financial data (yr. ended 12/31/05): Assets,
$4,528 (M); gifts received, $50,000; expenditures,
$48,239; total giving, $47,120; qualifying
distributions, $47,120; giving activities include
$47,120 for grants.
Fields of interest: Higher education, college; Islam.
Type of support: General/operating support.
Officer: Mohamad Aljabban, Pres.
EIN: 383485589

33
The Norman and Esther Allan Foundation
(formerly N.E.A. Foundation)
27777 Franklin Rd., Ste. 2500
Southfield, MI 48034-8214

Donors: Norman Allan; Nettie Cohen.
Grantmaker type: Independent foundation.
Financial data (yr. ended 10/31/05): Assets,
$1,172,187 (M); gifts received, $75,000;
expenditures, $28,931; total giving, $13,093;
qualifying distributions, $13,093; giving activities
include $13,093 for 1 grant.
Fields of interest: Jewish agencies & temples.
Limitations: Applications not accepted. Giving
primarily in MI. No grants to individuals.
Application information: Contributes only to
pre-selected organizations.
Officers and Trustees: Ira J. Jaffe,* Pres. and
Treas.; Joel S. Golden,* Secy.; Lawrence Allan;
Arthur A. Weiss.
EIN: 386089688

34
Alldredge Family Foundation
P.O. Box 489
Glen Arbor, MI 49636

Established in 1997 in IL.
Donors: Barbara A. Alldredge; William T. Alldredge.
Grantmaker type: Independent foundation.
Financial data (yr. ended 12/31/05): Assets,
$154,676 (M); gifts received, $22,800;
expenditures, $29,161; total giving, $28,975;
qualifying distributions, $28,975; giving activities
include $28,975 for grants.
Fields of interest: Performing arts; Arts;
Environment; Human services; Christian agencies &
churches.
Type of support: Building/renovation; Capital
campaigns; General/operating support.

Limitations: Applications not accepted. Giving primarily in Rockford, IL, and MI. No grants to individuals.
Application information: Contributes only to pre-selected organizations.
Trustees: Barbara A. Alldredge; William C. Alldredge; William T. Alldredge; Anne E. Butt.
EIN: 391891063

35
Allen Edwin Friendship Foundation
2186 E. Centre St.
Portage, MI   49002-4420

Established in MI.
Donors: Jim Sanderson; Scott Sanderson.
Grantmaker type: Independent foundation.
Financial data (yr. ended 12/31/04): Assets, $21,499 (M); gifts received, $24,746; expenditures, $92,706; total giving, $90,886; qualifying distributions, $92,571; giving activities include $90,886 for grants.
Fields of interest: Education; Housing/shelter; Recreation.
Limitations: Giving primarily in Kalamazoo, MI. No grants to individuals.
Application information: Application form required.
   Initial approach: Contact foundation for information
   Deadline(s): Jan. 1 and Apr. 1
   Final notification: Feb. 28 and May 31
Officers: Greg Dehaan, Pres.; Barry Root, Secy.; Trenton Hayward, Treas.
Directors: James Boll; Gary Brown; Kathleen Stryker Clark; Brent Hepp; Carol Kenaga.
EIN: 383498880

36
Lecester and Mattie Allen Family Foundation
3000 Town Ctr., Ste. 2450
Southfield, MI   48075-1163

Established in 2004 in MI.
Grantmaker type: Independent foundation.
Financial data (yr. ended 12/31/04): Assets, $100,003 (M); gifts received, $100,000; expenditures, $12; total giving, $0; qualifying distributions, $0.
Limitations: Applications not accepted. No grants to individuals.
Application information: Contributes only to pre-selected organizations.
Officers: Lecester L. Allen, Pres.; Jerrold M. Bigelman, V.P.; Mattie L. Allen, Secy.-Treas.
EIN: 202005066

37
Allen Foundation, Inc.
P.O. Box 1606
Midland, MI   48641-1606
Contact: Dale Baum, Secy.
FAX: (989) 832-8842; URL: http://www.allenfoundation.org/

Established in 1975 in MI.
Grantmaker type: Independent foundation.
Financial data (yr. ended 12/31/05): Assets, $12,283,170 (M); expenditures, $412,450; total giving, $337,641; qualifying distributions,

$349,763; giving activities include $337,641 for 7 grants (high: $79,828; low: $15,190).
Purpose and activities: The foundation focuses on projects that benefit nutritional programs in the areas of education, training and research. A lower priority is given to proposals that help solve immediate or emergency hunger and malnutrition problems.
Fields of interest: Higher education; Hospitals (general); Nutrition.
Limitations: Giving on a national basis. No grants to individuals.
Publications: Application guidelines; Annual report; Grants list.
Application information: Application forms and latest information available on foundation Web site. All applications are to be submitted online. Application form not required.
   Initial approach: See Web site
   Deadline(s): Dec. 31
   Board meeting date(s): Annually
   Final notification: June
Officers and Trustees:* Gail E. Lanphear,* Chair.; Mark Ostahowski, M.D.*, Pres.; William Lauderbach,* V.P., Finance; Dale Baum,* Secy.; William James Allen; Laurie Bouwman; Leslie Hildebrandt, Ph.D.; Ann F. Jay; Pat Oriel, Ph.D.
Number of staff: 1 part-time support.
EIN: 510152562

38
William & Louise Allen Scholarship Trust
P.O. Box 3636
Grand Rapids, MI   49501-3636
Application address: c/o Fifth Third Bank, Trust Dept., 3101 W. 95th St., Evergreen Park, IL 60805

Established in 2002 in IN.
Donor: Georgia Louise Allen†.
Grantmaker type: Independent foundation.
Financial data (yr. ended 12/31/05): Assets, $718,601 (M); expenditures, $45,751; total giving, $35,000; qualifying distributions, $35,000; giving activities include $35,000 for grants.
Type of support: Scholarships—to individuals.
Application information: Application form required.
   Initial approach: Letter
   Deadline(s): Mar. 15
Trustee: Fifth Third Bank.
EIN: 266010234

39
Margaret Acheson Allesee and Robert A. Allesee Foundation
6560 Red Maple Ln.
Bloomfield Hills, MI   48301

Established in 1997 in MI.
Donor: Margaret Acheson Allesee.
Grantmaker type: Independent foundation.
Financial data (yr. ended 12/31/05): Assets, $39,655 (M); gifts received, $249,540; expenditures, $229,130; total giving, $229,079; qualifying distributions, $229,130; giving activities include $229,079 for 128 grants (high: $74,050; low: $10).
Fields of interest: Museums; Performing arts; Arts; Elementary/secondary education; Higher education, university; Education; Health organizations, association; Youth development; Human services.

Limitations: Applications not accepted. Giving primarily in MI. No grants to individuals.
Application information: Contributes only to pre-selected organizations.
Officer: Margaret Acheson Allesee, Pres.
EIN: 383379630

40
Alliance for Gifted Children
2200 Fuller Ct., Ste. 1101B
Ann Arbor, MI   48105
Contact: David Klimek Ph.D., Pres.

Established in 2001 in MI.
Donor: Nagy Family Foundation.
Grantmaker type: Independent foundation.
Financial data (yr. ended 12/31/05): Assets, $19,598 (M); gifts received, $50,250; expenditures, $32,448; total giving, $31,501; qualifying distributions, $31,501; giving activities include $31,501 for grants.
Purpose and activities: Provides ongoing psychological therapy for children, including parent and teacher consultations.
Fields of interest: Mental health, counseling/support groups; Children/youth.
Limitations: Giving primarily in Ann Arbor, MI.
Application information: Application form required.
   Deadline(s): None
Officer: David Klimek, Ph.D., Pres.
Directors: James Gleason, J.D.; Kathy S. Nagy; Rebecca Patrias, M.D.; Timothy Wadhams.
EIN: 383555369

41
The Alnour Foundation
26300 Telegraph Rd., 2nd Fl.
Southfield, MI   48034

Established in 2000 in MI.
Grantmaker type: Independent foundation.
Financial data (yr. ended 12/31/05): Assets, $798,951 (M); gifts received, $151,000; expenditures, $45,482; total giving, $43,800; qualifying distributions, $43,800; giving activities include $43,800 for 2 grants (high: $36,800; low: $7,000).
Purpose and activities: Giving for local Islamic centers.
Fields of interest: Community development, neighborhood development; Islam.
Limitations: Giving primarily in MI.
Officer: Jamal Hammoud, M.D., Pres.
EIN: 382502540

42
Alon and Shari Friendship Foundation, Inc.
3000 Pontiac Trail
Commerce Township, MI   48390
(248) 863-3000
Contact: Alon Kaufman, Pres.

Established in 1999 in MI.
Donors: Alon Kaufman; Shari Kaufman.
Grantmaker type: Independent foundation.
Financial data (yr. ended 12/31/04): Assets, $1,141,642 (L); gifts received, $350,000; expenditures, $114,338; total giving, $113,718; qualifying distributions, $113,718; giving activities

include $113,718 for 21 grants (high: $34,000; low: $50).
Purpose and activities: Giving primarily to Jewish agencies, temples, schools, and federated giving programs.
Fields of interest: Education; Parkinson's disease; Human services; Children/youth, services; Jewish federated giving programs; Jewish agencies & temples.
Limitations: Giving primarily in MI.
Application information:
  Initial approach: Letter
  Deadline(s): None
Officers and Directors:* Alon Kaufman,* Pres.; Shari Kaufman,* Secy.-Treas.
EIN: 383504283

43
E. Bryce & Harriet Alpern Foundation
4716 Overton Cove
Bloomfield Hills, MI 48302

Donors: E. Bryce Alpern; Harriet Alpern.
Grantmaker type: Independent foundation.
Financial data (yr. ended 10/31/05): Assets, $664,255 (M); expenditures, $7,962; total giving, $4,600; qualifying distributions, $4,600; giving activities include $4,600 for grants.
Fields of interest: Performing arts, orchestra (symphony); Education; Hospitals (general); Human services; Jewish agencies & temples; General charitable giving.
Limitations: Applications not accepted. No grants to individuals.
Application information: Contributes only to pre-selected organizations.
Trustees: E. Bryce Alpern; Harriet Alpern.
EIN: 237441861

44
Robert & Marjorie Alpern Foundation
36800 Woodward Ave., Ste. 112
Bloomfield Hills, MI 48304-0916

Established in 1968.
Donors: Marjorie Alpern; Robert Alpern.
Grantmaker type: Independent foundation.
Financial data (yr. ended 10/31/04): Assets, $1,127,149 (M); gifts received, $70,375; expenditures, $97,753; total giving, $81,179; qualifying distributions, $92,753; giving activities include $81,179 for grants.
Fields of interest: Arts; Education; Human services; Jewish agencies & temples.
Limitations: Applications not accepted. Giving primarily in MI. No grants to individuals.
Application information: Contributes only to pre-selected organizations.
Trustees: Marjorie Alpern; Robert Alpern; Nancy Levin.
EIN: 386161747

45
Ida and Benjamin Alpert Foundation
34119 W. 12 Mile Rd., Ste. 355
Farmington Hills, MI 48331

Donor: Myron Alpert.
Grantmaker type: Independent foundation.

Financial data (yr. ended 12/31/05): Assets, $767,400 (M); gifts received, $40,464; expenditures, $40,800; total giving, $40,000; qualifying distributions, $40,000; giving activities include $40,000 for grants.
Purpose and activities: Giving for education.
Fields of interest: Higher education.
Type of support: Scholarship funds.
Limitations: Applications not accepted. Giving limited to MI. No grants to individuals.
Application information: Contributes only to pre-selected organizations.
Officers and Directors:* Myron Alpert,* Pres.; Doris Alpert,* V.P.; David M. Caplan,* Secy.; Sanford Mandell,* Treas.; Elaine Stern.
EIN: 386143935

46
Ambrosiani Foundation
4253 W. Herbison Rd.
Dewitt, MI 48820
Contact: Sherrill Ambrosiani Kovach, Tr.

Established in 1992 in WV.
Donors: F. Peter Ambrosiani; Irene P. Ambrosiani.
Grantmaker type: Independent foundation.
Financial data (yr. ended 12/31/05): Assets, $595,130 (M); expenditures, $33,195; total giving, $31,725; qualifying distributions, $31,725; giving activities include $31,725 for grants.
Purpose and activities: Giving primarily for education and Catholic charities.
Fields of interest: Higher education, college; Hospitals (general); Cancer research; Salvation Army; Roman Catholic agencies & churches.
Limitations: Giving on a national basis. No grants to individuals.
Application information:
  Deadline(s): None
Trustees: David Kovach; Sherrill Ambrosiani Kovach.
EIN: 550668197

47
Americana Foundation
28115 Meadowbrook Rd.
Novi, MI 48377-3128   (248) 347-3863
Contact: Marlene J. Fluharty, Exec. Dir.
FAX: (248) 347-3349; E-mail: fluhart5@msu.edu

Established in 1978 in MI.
Donors: Adolph H. Meyer†; Ida M. Meyer†.
Grantmaker type: Independent foundation.
Financial data (yr. ended 12/31/05): Assets, $20,764,640 (M); expenditures, $1,220,393; total giving, $762,510; qualifying distributions, $1,081,694; giving activities include $762,510 for 36 grants (high: $67,500; low: $250).
Purpose and activities: Support for education and advocacy programs that address issues of conserving agriculture and natural resources, and the preservation of the American heritage.
Fields of interest: Museums (history); Historic preservation/historical societies; Environment; Agriculture.
Type of support: General/operating support; Building/renovation; Program development; Conferences/seminars; Publication; Internship funds; Technical assistance; Matching/challenge support.

Limitations: Giving primarily in MI. No support for private foundations or for political purposes. No grants to individuals, or for fundraising events, tables, or scholarships.
Publications: Annual report (including application guidelines); Grants list; Informational brochure (including application guidelines).
Application information: Application form not required.
  Initial approach: Letter or telephone
  Copies of proposal: 1
  Deadline(s): Middle of Jan., Apr., July, and Oct.
  Board meeting date(s): Quarterly
  Final notification: 3 months
Officers and Trustees:* Robert Janson,* Pres.; Jonathan Thomas,* V.P.; Thomas F. Ranger,* Treas.; Marlene J. Fluharty, Exec. Dir.; Norman Brown; Kathryn Eckert; Kate Harper; Gary Rentrop.
Number of staff: 1 full-time professional; 1 part-time support.
EIN: 382269431
Selected grants: The following grants were reported in 2004.
$66,570 to Michigan State University, East Lansing, MI. For restoration needed at Tollgate Farm.
$50,000 to Metropolitan Museum of Art, New York, NY. For exhibition of colonial cabinetmaker, John Townsend.
$35,000 to Michigan Environmental Council, Lansing, MI. To unify grassroots action for land preservation.
$33,900 to Michigan Society of Planning Officials, Rochester, MI. To educate planners and elected officials in farmland preservation.
$30,000 to Mackinac Associates, Mackinaw City, MI. For restoration of historic lighthouse barn.
$30,000 to Michigan Land Use Institute, Beulah, MI. To inform citizens and encourage governor to view sprawl as high priority.
$30,000 to Museum of Fine Arts, Houston, Houston, TX. For internship for Bayou Bend.
$25,000 to Michigan Lighthouse Fund, Dewitt, MI. To offer stewards training and assistance.
$23,400 to Michigan Technological University, Houghton, MI. For development of county land-use plan.
$20,000 to Keweenaw Land Trust, Houghton, MI. For project specialist for land protection projects.
$15,000 to Pewabic Pottery, Detroit, MI. To catalogue and conserve archived materials.
$1,200 to Michigan Barn Preservation Network, Mount Pleasant, MI. To upgrade current Barn Preservation Display.

48
Amy Foundation
c/o The Amy Writing Awards
P.O. Box 16091
Lansing, MI 48901-6091

Established in 1976.
Donors: Walter J. Russell†; Phyllis M. Russell.
Grantmaker type: Independent foundation.
Financial data (yr. ended 12/31/05): Assets, $284,121 (M); gifts received, $110,355; expenditures, $138,692; total giving, $93,342; qualifying distributions, $138,692; giving activities include $56,592 for 19 grants (high: $22,700; low: $200), and $36,750 for 39 grants to individuals (high: $10,000; low: $50).
Purpose and activities: Sponsors the Amy Writing Awards program for communicating biblical truth to

a secular audience; support also for Christian organizations.
Fields of interest: Christian agencies & churches.
Limitations: Applications not accepted. Giving on a national basis. No grants to individuals.
Publications: Informational brochure; Newsletter.
Application information: Contributes only to pre-selected organizations.
Officers: Phyllis M. Russell, V.P.; Dale G. Walter, Secy.-Treas.
Number of staff: 2 full-time professional; 1 full-time support.
EIN: 237044543

49
The Anchor Foundation
3141 N. Lake Shore Dr.
Holland, MI   49424

Established in 1997 in MI.
Donors: Elizabeth I. Huizenga; Herman Kanis; Suzanne Kanis.
Grantmaker type: Independent foundation.
Financial data (yr. ended 12/31/04): Assets, $0 (M); expenditures, $382,349; total giving, $277,500; qualifying distributions, $277,500; giving activities include $277,500 for 10 grants (high: $50,000; low: $10,000).
Purpose and activities: Giving primarily to Christian organizations and family services.
Fields of interest: Theological school/education; Family services; Christian agencies & churches.
Limitations: Applications not accepted. Giving on a national basis, with some emphasis on MI. No grants to individuals.
Application information: Contributes only to pre-selected organizations.
Officers and Directors: Suzanne Kanis,* Pres.; Herman Kanis,* Mgr.; Michael J. Kanis; Sally J. Nimmo; April L. Smith.
EIN: 383353871
Selected grants: The following grants were reported in 2003.
$50,000 to Focus on the Family, Colorado Springs, CO. For general support.
$30,000 to Westminster Theological Seminary, Glenside, PA. For general support.
$25,000 to Bible League, Chicago, IL. For general support.
$25,000 to Geneva Camp and Retreat Center, Holland, MI. For general support.
$25,000 to Mission 21 India, Grand Rapids, MI. For general support.
$25,000 to Northwestern College, Orange City, IA. For general support.
$20,000 to Words of Hope, Grand Rapids, MI. For general support.
$15,000 to English Language Institute in China, San Dimas, CA. For general support.
$15,000 to Hope College, Holland, MI. For general support.
$10,000 to Holland Rescue Mission, Holland, MI. For school math software.

50
Frank N. Andersen Foundation
P.O. Box 225
Bridgeport, MI   48722-0225   (989) 777-2361
Contact: Gerald Barber, V.P.

Established in 1955 in MI.

Donor: Frank N. Andersen†.
Grantmaker type: Independent foundation.
Financial data (yr. ended 12/31/05): Assets, $10,788,972 (M); expenditures, $893,028; total giving, $809,169; qualifying distributions, $809,169; giving activities include $809,169 for 32 grants (high: $200,000; low: $1,000).
Purpose and activities: Emphasis on human services and higher education; support also for arts and humanities.
Fields of interest: Performing arts; Historic preservation/historical societies; Higher education; Education; Food services; Human services.
Type of support: Capital campaigns; Building/renovation; Equipment; Scholarship funds.
Limitations: Giving limited to Saginaw and Bay counties, MI. No grants to individuals.
Application information: Application form required.
  Initial approach: Letter requesting application form
  Deadline(s): None
  Board meeting date(s): Quarterly
Officers and Trustees: William McNally,* Pres.; Gerald Barber,* V.P.; R. Ronald Zeros,* Secy.-Treas.; John Gilmour; Arnold L. Johnson; Barbara Lincoln; Paul Wendler.
Number of staff: 2 part-time professional.
EIN: 386062616

51
Andrew F. & Mary H. Anderson Charitable Foundation
1140 Rosemary Ln.
Essexville, MI   48732

Established in 2003 in MI.
Donor: Mary H. Anderson.
Grantmaker type: Independent foundation.
Financial data (yr. ended 12/31/04): Assets, $413,588 (M); expenditures, $5,000; total giving, $4,500; qualifying distributions, $4,915; giving activities include $4,000 for 3 grants, and $500 for 1 grant to an individual.
Purpose and activities: Support primarily for a community foundation. Scholarship awards for students of Delta Community College must be residents of Bay County, MI. Recipients from Northwood University have no geographic limitations.
Fields of interest: Community development; Foundations (community).
Type of support: Scholarships—to individuals.
Limitations: Giving primarily in MI.
Application information: Scholarship recipients selected from Delta Community College or Northwood University. Application form required.
  Deadline(s): Jan. 31
Officers: Mary H. Anderson, Pres.; Ashley Anderson, V.P.
Director: Lori Appold.
EIN: 200464768

52
Anderson Foundation
480 W. Dussel Dr.
P.O. Box 119
Maumee, OH   43537-0119
Application address: c/o Ms. Fredi Heywood, 608 Madison Ave., Ste. 1540, Toledo, OH 43604, tel.: (419) 243-1706

Trust established in 1949 in OH.
Donor: Partners in The Andersons, Inc.
Grantmaker type: Independent foundation.
Financial data (yr. ended 12/31/04): Assets, $4,633,464 (M); gifts received, $455,500; expenditures, $484,450; total giving, $450,858; qualifying distributions, $460,365; giving activities include $450,858 for 122 grants (high: $83,333; low: $50).
Purpose and activities: Grants primarily for community funds, higher and secondary education, and cultural programs; support also for social service and youth agencies, civic and community efforts, educational and research associations, and religion.
Fields of interest: Arts; Education, association; Secondary school/education; Higher education; Education; Agriculture; Human services; Children/youth, services; Community development; Federated giving programs; Government/public administration; Religion.
Type of support: General/operating support; Annual campaigns; Capital campaigns; Building/renovation; Emergency funds; Program development; Conferences/seminars; Publication; Seed money; Scholarship funds; Research; Matching/challenge support.
Limitations: Giving primarily in the greater Toledo, OH, area, including Maumee and Columbus. Giving also to organizations located within the areas of the Anderson plants in the following cities: Champaign, IL, Delphi and Dunkirk, IN, and Albion, Potterville, Webberville, and White Pigeon, MI. No support for private foundations, public high schools or elementary schools. No grants to individuals, or for endowment funds, travel, or building or operating funds for churches or elementary schools.
Publications: Application guidelines.
Application information: Application form not required.
  Initial approach: Proposal not exceeding 5 pages
  Copies of proposal: 1
  Deadline(s): 3 weeks before board meetings
  Board meeting date(s): Mar., June, Sept., and Dec., usually the 3rd Mon. of the month
  Final notification: Generally 3 months; depends on completeness of proposal
Officer and Trustees: Thomas H. Anderson,* Chair.; Charles W. Anderson; Jeffrey W. Anderson; Matthew C. Anderson; Richard M. Anderson; Richard P. Anderson; Dale W. Fallat; John P. Kraus.
EIN: 346528868

53
Anderson Foundation
5158 Lakeshore Rd.
Fort Gratiot, MI   48059-3115

Established in 1996.
Grantmaker type: Independent foundation.
Financial data (yr. ended 12/31/05): Assets, $0 (M); gifts received, $10,350; expenditures, $13,649; total giving, $13,011; qualifying distributions, $13,011; giving activities include $13,011 for grants.
Limitations: Applications not accepted. Giving primarily in Port Huron, MI. No grants to individuals.
Application information: Contributes only to pre-selected organizations.
Officer: Richard T. Anderson, Pres.
EIN: 383294782

54
Olson L. Anderson and Catherine Bastow Anderson Scholarship Trust
c/o National City Bank
2322 Tittabawassee Rd.
Saginaw, MI 48604-9476
Application address: c/o Central Michigan Univ., Financial Aid Office, 204 Warriner Hall, Mount Pleasant, MI 48858, tel.: (989) 775-3674

Established in 1987 MI.
Grantmaker type: Independent foundation.
Financial data (yr. ended 12/31/05): Assets, $1,250,799 (M); expenditures, $73,777; total giving, $58,019; qualifying distributions, $58,019; giving activities include $58,019 for grants to individuals.
Purpose and activities: Awards scholarships only to full-time undergraduates at Central Michigan University, with a preference for students from Bay County.
Type of support: Scholarships—to individuals.
Limitations: Giving primarily to residents of Bay County, MI.
Application information: Application form required.
  Initial approach: Letter for initial applicants; Financial Aid Form for continuing students
  Deadline(s): May 15
Trustee: National City Bank.
EIN: 386345071

55
Harold R. Anderson, Bernard R. MacNeil and Marie Anderson MacNeil Trust
(formerly Marie MacNeil Trust)
c/o Citizens Bank, Wealth Mgmt.
101 N. Washington Ave., Ste. 332021
Saginaw, MI 48607

Grantmaker type: Independent foundation.
Financial data (yr. ended 4/30/03): Assets, $386,697 (M); expenditures, $25,017; total giving, $19,512; qualifying distributions, $20,057; giving activities include $19,512 for grants.
Purpose and activities: Support only for Mason County Dept. of Social Service, Oceana County Dept. of Social Service, and West Shore Community College, MI.
Fields of interest: Higher education; Human services.
Limitations: Applications not accepted. Giving limited to Hart, Ludington, and Scottville, MI. No grants to individuals.
Application information: Contributes only to 3 pre-selected organizations.
Trustee: Citizens Bank.
EIN: 526158958

56
The Andrah Foundation
c/o Edward H. Koster
117 N. 1st St., Ste. 111
Ann Arbor, MI 48104

Established in 1996 in MI.
Donors: Thomas Knoll; Ruth Knoll.
Grantmaker type: Independent foundation.
Financial data (yr. ended 12/31/04): Assets, $0 (M); expenditures, $378,770; total giving, $348,487; qualifying distributions, $348,487; giving activities include $348,487 for 13 grants (high: $289,637; low: $500).
Purpose and activities: Support primarily for a school.
Fields of interest: Elementary/secondary education.
Limitations: Applications not accepted. Giving primarily in Ann Arbor, MI. No grants to individuals.
Application information: Contributes only to pre-selected organizations.
Officers: Thomas Knoll, Pres. and Treas.; Ruth Knoll, Secy.
EIN: 383267840

57
The Rhoda Burke Andrews Foundation
567 Purdy St.
Birmingham, MI 48009-1736 (248) 642-0910
Contact: Edward F. Andrews, Jr., Pres.

Established in 1992 in MI.
Donor: Edward F. Andrews, Jr.
Grantmaker type: Independent foundation.
Financial data (yr. ended 12/31/05): Assets, $748,585 (M); gifts received, $25,000; expenditures, $51,079; total giving, $50,500; qualifying distributions, $50,500; giving activities include $50,500 for grants.
Limitations: Giving primarily in southeastern MI. No grants to individuals.
Application information:
  Initial approach: Proposal
  Deadline(s): None
  Final notification: 2 months
Officers: Edward F. Andrews, Jr., Pres. and Treas.; Colleen M. Andrews, V.P. and Secy.
EIN: 383017759

58
Angel Foundation
13919 S. W. Bayshore Dr., Rm. G-01
Traverse City, MI 49684

Established in 2004 in MI.
Donors: His Foundation; Rock Foundation.
Grantmaker type: Independent foundation.
Financial data (yr. ended 12/31/05): Assets, $22,691 (M); gifts received, $75,820; expenditures, $63,694; total giving, $32,236; qualifying distributions, $53,396; giving activities include $32,236 for grants.
Fields of interest: Protestant agencies & churches.
Limitations: Applications not accepted. Giving primarily in Traverse City, MI. No grants to individuals.
Application information: Contributes only to pre-selected organizations.
Officers and Directors:* Stan Holzhauer,* Chair.; Peter Semeyn,* Vice-Chair.; Karin Cooney, Exec. Dir.; Wayne Mueller; Kirstin Nielson; Edwin Thome; Carey Waldie.
EIN: 201000748

59
Stephen Ross Angel Private Charitable Foundation
c/o Russellene Angel
4826 Country Woods Ln.
Greensboro, NC 27410-1814 (336) 292-2227

Established in 1997 in NC.
Donor: B. Ross Angel.
Grantmaker type: Independent foundation.
Financial data (yr. ended 4/30/05): Assets, $785,851 (M); expenditures, $0; total giving, $0; qualifying distributions, $0.
Purpose and activities: Giving for higher education.
Fields of interest: Higher education.
Limitations: Giving primarily in MI and NC.
Application information:
  Initial approach: Letter and resume
  Deadline(s): Annually
Officers: B. Ross Angel, Chair.; Richard C. Forman, Secy.-Treas.
EIN: 562013753

60
The Animal Rescue League
4799 Barber Rd.
Metamora, MI 48455

Established in 1996 in CT.
Donors: Barbara S. Brack; Reginald K. Brack.
Grantmaker type: Independent foundation.
Financial data (yr. ended 12/31/04): Assets, $3,177 (M); gifts received, $18,893; expenditures, $15,987; total giving, $15,788; qualifying distributions, $15,987; giving activities include $15,788 for grants.
Fields of interest: Animal welfare.
Type of support: General/operating support.
Limitations: Applications not accepted. Giving primarily in St. Marten, West Indies. No grants to individuals.
Application information: Contributes only to pre-selected organizations.
Trustee: Audrey L. Waldron.
EIN: 066434286

61
The Anne Family Foundation
5155 Norko Dr.
Flint, MI 48507

Established in 2002 in MI.
Donor: Suresh Anne.
Grantmaker type: Independent foundation.
Financial data (yr. ended 12/31/05): Assets, $9,958 (M); gifts received, $51,771; expenditures, $43,569; total giving, $34,700; qualifying distributions, $41,114; giving activities include $34,700 for grants.
Limitations: Applications not accepted. No grants to individuals.
Application information: Contributes only to pre-selected organizations.
Officers: Suresh Anne, Pres. and Treas.; Aruna Anne, V.P. and Secy.
EIN: 364503970

62
Ted Annis Foundation
2997 Devonshire Rd.
Ann Arbor, MI 48104
Contact: Ted C. Annis, Chair.

Established in 1997 in MI.
Donor: Ted C. Annis.
Grantmaker type: Independent foundation.

Financial data (yr. ended 12/31/04): Assets, $368,577 (M); gifts received, $127,500; expenditures, $53,582; total giving, $31,523; qualifying distributions, $48,401; giving activities include $31,523 for grants.
Fields of interest: Higher education; Hospitals (general); Health care; Health organizations; Human services; Economic development; Community development.
International interests: Peru.
Type of support: General/operating support; Building/renovation; Equipment; Endowments; Scholarship funds.
Limitations: Giving primarily in MI, with emphasis on Ann Arbor; some giving also in San Pedro, Peru.
Application information: Application form not required.
  Initial approach: Proposal
  Deadline(s): None
Officer and Trustees:* Ted C. Annis,* Chair. and Pres.; Ann Annis; Susan Kornfield.
EIN: 383346207

63
Charles Anthony Foundation
8080 Wilderness Trail, N.E.
Ada, MI   49301   (616) 676-1164
Contact: Matthew J. Heynen, Pres.

Established in 1996 in MI.
Donors: Matthew J. Heynen; Sarah L. Heynen.
Grantmaker type: Independent foundation.
Financial data (yr. ended 12/31/04): Assets, $1,884 (M); gifts received, $4,000; expenditures, $4,410; total giving, $4,000; qualifying distributions, $4,000; giving activities include $4,000 for 2 grants (high: $3,000; low: $1,000).
Limitations: Giving in the U.S.
Officers and Directors:* Matthew J. Heynen,* Pres.; Sara L. Heynen,* Secy.
EIN: 383089441

64
The Antique Orphanage (Doll & Bear Museum)
212 Stockbridge Ave.
Kalamazoo, MI   49001

Established in 1995 in MI.
Donors: Frank Newman; Sandra Newman.
Grantmaker type: Independent foundation.
Financial data (yr. ended 12/31/04): Assets, $175,336 (M); gifts received, $2,000; expenditures, $8,226; total giving, $1,500; qualifying distributions, $2,523; giving activities include $1,500 for grants.
Limitations: Applications not accepted. Giving primarily in MI. No grants to individuals.
Application information: Contributes only to pre-selected organizations.
Officers and Directors:* Sandra Newman,* Pres.; Dorothy Meninga,* Secy.; Patricia Buckert, Treas.; James Bridenstine.
EIN: 383247285

65
The Gebran S. & Suzanne P. Anton Foundation
79 Macomb Pl.
Mount Clemens, MI   48043

Established in 1996 in MI.
Donor: Gebran S. Anton.
Grantmaker type: Independent foundation.
Financial data (yr. ended 12/31/04): Assets, $568,665 (M); gifts received, $153,520; expenditures, $168,469; total giving, $151,993; qualifying distributions, $158,629; giving activities include $151,993 for 61 grants (high: $25,000; low: $100).
Purpose and activities: Giving primarily for health, education, and religion.
Fields of interest: Education; Health care; Human services; Christian agencies & churches.
Type of support: General/operating support.
Limitations: Applications not accepted. Giving primarily in MI. No grants to individuals.
Application information: Contributes only to pre-selected organizations.
Directors: Anne-Marie Z. Anton; Gebran S. Anton; Suzanne P. Anton; Denise A. David; Lori S. Huling; Cathy M. Miserendino.
EIN: 383249913
Selected grants: The following grants were reported in 2004.
$25,000 to Mount Clemens General Hospital, Mount Clemens, MI.
$5,000 to YMCA, Macomb Family, Mount Clemens, MI.
$1,000 to Cranbrook Schools, Bloomfield Hills, MI.
$1,000 to De La Salle Collegiate High School, Warren, MI. For capital campaign.
$1,000 to Grosse Pointe Academy, Grosse Pointe, MI.
$1,000 to Mayo Foundation, Rochester, MN. For Alzheimers and ALS research.
$500 to Hospice of Michigan, Detroit, MI. For Caring Circle.
$500 to Make-A-Wish Foundation of Michigan, Lansing, MI.
$500 to Wayne State University, Detroit, MI.
$350 to Services for Older Citizens, Grosse Pointe Woods, MI.

66
The Aparche Foundation
1001 Coach Light Dr. S.E.
Byron Center, MI   49315

Established in 1999 in MI.
Donor: Frederick P. Spica.
Grantmaker type: Independent foundation.
Financial data (yr. ended 12/31/04): Assets, $1,056,114 (M); gifts received, $1,825; expenditures, $76,567; total giving, $54,675; qualifying distributions, $68,121; giving activities include $54,675 for 10 grants (high: $13,000; low: $50).
Fields of interest: Christian agencies & churches.
Limitations: Applications not accepted. Giving primarily in MI. No grants to individuals.
Application information: Contributes only to pre-selected organizations.
Officers and Directors:* Julaine M. Spica,* Pres.; Tammy L. Hedke,* V.P.; Christina M. Halblaub,* Secy.; Joseph P. Spica,* Treas.; Frederick P. Spica.
EIN: 383518799
Selected grants: The following grants were reported in 2003.
$85,000 to International Steward, Grand Rapids, MI.
$10,000 to Mars Hill Bible Church, Wyoming, MI.
$5,325 to Grace Youth Camp of Michigan, Mears, MI.

$4,000 to Cornerstone University, Grand Rapids, MI.
$3,500 to Kentwood Community Church, Kentwood, MI.
$1,000 to Pioneers Balks.
$233 to Pregnancy Resource Center, Grand Rapids, MI.
$95 to That the World May Know Ministries, Holland, MI.

67
The Eugene Applebaum Family Foundation
39400 Woodward Ave., Ste. 100
Bloomfield Hills, MI   48304
Contact: Pamela Applebaum Wyett, Treas.

Donors: Pamela Applebaum Wyett; Eugene Applebaum Charitable Lead Trust; Lisa S. Applebaum.
Grantmaker type: Independent foundation.
Financial data (yr. ended 11/30/05): Assets, $10,308,373 (M); gifts received, $9,417,791; expenditures, $4,026,120; total giving, $3,925,218; qualifying distributions, $3,960,670; giving activities include $3,925,218 for 134 grants (high: $1,533,333; low: $20; average: $5,000–$250,000).
Purpose and activities: Giving primarily to Jewish organizations, including federated giving programs; support also for education, the arts, and health care.
Fields of interest: Arts; Elementary/secondary education; Higher education; Education; Health care; Jewish federated giving programs; Jewish agencies & temples.
Limitations: Giving primarily in MI, and New York, NY; some funding nationally.
Application information:
  Deadline(s): None
Officers: Eugene Applebaum, Pres.; Marcia Applebaum, V.P.; Lisa Applebaum Haddad, Secy.; Pamela Applebaum Wyett, Treas.
EIN: 382782955

68
Theophil & Amanda Aprill Family Foundation, Inc.
4777 W. Liberty Rd.
Ann Arbor, MI   48103

Established in 1969.
Grantmaker type: Independent foundation.
Financial data (yr. ended 12/31/05): Assets, $1,073,633 (M); expenditures, $56,170; total giving, $54,038; qualifying distributions, $54,038; giving activities include $54,038 for grants.
Purpose and activities: Giving to human services and Christian agencies.
Fields of interest: Human services; Christian agencies & churches.
Limitations: Applications not accepted. Giving primarily in Ann Arbor, MI. No grants to individuals.
Application information: Contributes only to pre-selected organizations.
Officers: Theophil Aprill, Jr., Pres.; Virginia A. Burr, V.P.; Johanna C. Johnson, Secy.-Treas.
Trustees: Brian T. Aprill; Ruth P. Aprill; William C. Burr; Kathleen L. Weber.
EIN: 383002691

69

The Arctica and Abbey Foundation
3703 Blackberry Ln.
Kalamazoo, MI 49008-3333

Established in 2003 in MI.
Donors: Che-Shen C. Tomich; Paul K. Tomich.
Grantmaker type: Independent foundation.
Financial data (yr. ended 12/31/05): Assets, $401,645 (M); gifts received, $8,000; expenditures, $28,362; total giving, $23,000; qualifying distributions, $23,000; giving activities include $23,000 for grants.
Officers: Che-Shen C. Tomich, Pres.; Paul K. Tomich, Secy.-Treas.
EIN: 200396535

70

Arcus Foundation
(formerly Jon L. Stryker Foundation)
402 E. Michigan Ave.
Kalamazoo, MI 49007 (269) 373-4373
Contact: Daniel Schwartz, Board Member
E-mail: contact@arcusfoundation.org; New York address: 119 W. 24th St., 9th Fl., New York, NY 10011, tel.: (212) 488-3000; URL: http://www.arcusfoundation.org

Established in 1997 in MI.
Donor: Jon L. Stryker.
Grantmaker type: Independent foundation.
Financial data (yr. ended 12/31/05): Assets, $72,827,720 (M); gifts received, $61,880,962; expenditures, $18,328,731; total giving, $16,657,143; qualifying distributions, $17,852,484; giving activities include $16,657,143 for 89 grants (high: $5,151,456; low: $25; average: $10,000–$500,000).
Purpose and activities: Support for programs that fight prejudice and discrimination and protect and defend human and civil rights for the gay, lesbian, bisexual and transgender community. Giving also for Great Apes Sanctuary and Conservation.
Fields of interest: Animals/wildlife, endangered species; Animals/wildlife, sanctuaries; Animals/wildlife, special services; Civil rights, gays/lesbians; Civil rights; LGBTQ.
Type of support: General/operating support; Continuing support; Annual campaigns; Capital campaigns; Building/renovation; Endowments; Program development; Conferences/seminars; Publication; Curriculum development; Technical assistance; Consulting services; Program evaluation; Program-related investments/loans; Employee matching gifts; Matching/challenge support.
Limitations: Giving on a national basis, with emphasis on Kalamazoo, MI for some programs. No grants to individuals, of for religious or political activities, medical research or film/video production.
Publications: Annual report (including application guidelines); Newsletter.
Application information: For funding applications only use the foundation's Michigan address. Formal proposal accepted by invitation only following letter of inquiry process. See foundation Web site for complete formal proposal requirements. Application form not required.
   Initial approach: Letter, no more than 2 pages
   Copies of proposal: 4
   Deadline(s): Apr. 1 and Sept. 1 for letter of inquiry; May 1 and Oct. 1 for invited proposals

Board meeting date(s): June and Dec.
   Final notification: Within three weeks for letter of inquiry
Officers: Jon L. Stryker, Pres.; Jeff Arnstein, C.F.O.; Urvashi Vaid, Exec. Dir.
Board Member: Daniel Schwartz.
Number of staff: 12 full-time professional; 10 part-time professional.
EIN: 383332791
Selected grants: The following grants were reported in 2004.
$14,750,000 to Fauna and Flora International, Cambridge, England. 2 grants: $9,000,000 (For general support), $5,750,000 (For general support).
$8,098,387 to Center for Captive Chimpanzee Care, Fort Pierce, FL. 3 grants: $1,234,273 (For general support), $4,433,600 (For general support), $2,430,514 (For general support).
$2,500,000 to Center for Great Apes, Wauchula, FL. For general support.
$850,000 to National Gay and Lesbian Task Force (NGLTF), DC. 2 grants: $425,000 each (For general support).
$350,000 to Gay and Lesbian Alliance Against Defamation (GLAAD), Los Angeles, CA. For general support.
$334,000 to Gay, Lesbian and Straight Education Network (GLSEN), New York, NY. For general support.

71

Richard and Mary Arden Foundation Trust
c/o Comerica Bank
P.O. Box 75000 M/C 3302
Detroit, MI 48275-3302
Contact: Joseph Powers
Application address: c/o UBS Paine Webber, P.O. Box 7350, Portland, ME 04112-7350

Established in 2002 in NY.
Donors: Richard Arden; Mary Arden.
Grantmaker type: Independent foundation.
Financial data (yr. ended 11/30/05): Assets, $103,451 (M); expenditures, $4,803; total giving, $1,600; qualifying distributions, $1,600; giving activities include $1,600 for grants.
Purpose and activities: Awards scholarships to journalism students.
Fields of interest: Media, journalism/publishing.
Type of support: Scholarships—to individuals.
Application information: Application form required.
   Deadline(s): Dec. 31
Trustees: Mary Arden; Richard Arden; Comerica Bank.
EIN: 550807783

72

The Aries Foundation, Inc.
1150 Puritan Ave.
Birmingham, MI 48009-1060

Established in 1986 in MI.
Donor: William C. Halbert.
Grantmaker type: Independent foundation.
Financial data (yr. ended 12/31/04): Assets, $1,784 (M); expenditures, $210; total giving, $150; qualifying distributions, $150; giving activities include $150 for grants.
Limitations: Applications not accepted. Giving primarily in MI. No grants to individuals.

Application information: Contributes only to pre-selected organizations.
Officer: William C. Halbert, Pres.
EIN: 382661885

73

Arman Foundation
12900 Hall Rd., Ste. 500
Sterling Heights, MI 48313-1153

Established in 1998 in MI.
Donor: Vincent C. Secontine.
Grantmaker type: Independent foundation.
Financial data (yr. ended 12/31/05): Assets, $148,786 (M); expenditures, $10,658; total giving, $10,500; qualifying distributions, $10,500; giving activities include $10,500 for grants.
Limitations: Applications not accepted. Giving primarily in Birmingham, MI. No grants to individuals.
Application information: Contributes only to pre-selected organizations.
Officers and Directors:* Robert W. Appleford,* Pres.; Vincent C. Secontine,* Secy.; Anthony P. Frabotta,* Treas.; Douglas A. Colwell; Robert Lovell.
EIN: 383430120

74

The Arman Foundation
26300 Telegraph Rd., 2nd Fl.
Southfield, MI 48034

Established in 2002 in MI.
Grantmaker type: Independent foundation.
Financial data (yr. ended 12/31/04): Assets, $306,162 (M); gifts received, $400,000; expenditures, $289,945; total giving, $289,355; qualifying distributions, $289,355; giving activities include $289,355 for 11+ grants (high: $235,200).
Fields of interest: Human services.
Officer: Mohammed Arman, Pres.
EIN: 300069735

75

The Arnold Family Foundation
3390 Clover Dr.
Saline, MI 48176

Established in 2000 in MI.
Donor: Barbara J. Arnold Trust.
Grantmaker type: Independent foundation.
Financial data (yr. ended 12/31/05): Assets, $7,821 (M); gifts received, $2,000; expenditures, $1,115; total giving, $500; qualifying distributions, $500; giving activities include $500 for grants.
Limitations: Applications not accepted. Giving primarily in MI. No grants to individuals.
Application information: Contributes only to pre-selected organizations.
Officers: Charles B. Arnold, Pres.; Barbara J. Arnold, Secy.-Treas.
EIN: 383538451

76

Stanley and Blanche Ash Foundation
P.O. Box 310
Greenville, MI 48838-0310
Contact: Blanche E. Ash, Pres.

Established in 1991 in MI as successor to Stanley & Blanche Ash Foundation.
Donors: Blanche E. Ash; Stanley P. Ash†; Greenville Tool and Die Co.
Grantmaker type: Independent foundation.
Financial data (yr. ended 12/31/05): Assets, $6,486,577 (M); expenditures, $272,472; total giving, $238,217; qualifying distributions, $238,217; giving activities include $109,945 for 47 grants (high: $40,000; low: $45), and $128,272 for 134 grants to individuals (high: $2,250; low: $350).
Purpose and activities: Scholarship funds restricted to students in the Montcalm County, MI, area who show financial need and have satisfactory grades.
Fields of interest: Higher education; Education; Health organizations, association; Christian agencies & churches.
Type of support: Scholarship funds; Research; Scholarships—to individuals.
Limitations: Giving limited to the western MI area.
Application information: Accepts Standard Scholarship Form used by the college of the applicant's choice. Application form required.
  Deadline(s): None
  Board meeting date(s): Quarterly
Officer and Directors:* Blanche E. Ash,* Pres.; Jennifer K. Ash.
Number of staff: None.
EIN: 382966745

77
Michael M. and Rose Assarian Family Foundation

(formerly Michael M. Assarian Foundation)
23775 Northwestern Hwy.
Southfield, MI 48075-3336

Established in 1980 in MI.
Donors: Michael M. Assarian†; Rose Assarian.
Grantmaker type: Independent foundation.
Financial data (yr. ended 12/31/04): Assets, $1,292,988 (M); gifts received, $50,403; expenditures, $17,211; total giving, $7,889; qualifying distributions, $7,889; giving activities include $7,889 for grants.
Fields of interest: Protestant agencies & churches.
Limitations: Applications not accepted. Giving primarily in MI. No grants to individuals.
Application information: Contributes only to pre-selected organizations.
Officers: Rose Assarian, Pres.; Gary S. Assarian, V.P.; Michael T. Assarian, V.P.; Marianne Sneideraitis, V.P.; Eugene Driker, Secy.; S. Sam Tootalian, Treas.
EIN: 382183587

78
Raymond V. Attanasio Charitable Trust

c/o Comerica Bank
P.O. Box 75000, M/C 8280
Detroit, MI 48275-8280
Contact: Rev. Joseph Szulwach, Dir.
Application address: 109 Laurence Pkwy., Laurence Harbor, NJ 08879

Established in 2000 in NJ.
Donor: Raymond V. Attanasio.
Grantmaker type: Independent foundation.
Financial data (yr. ended 6/30/05): Assets, $931,123 (M); expenditures, $122,882; total giving, $103,500; qualifying distributions,

$104,499; giving activities include $103,500 for grants.
Fields of interest: Religion.
Application information:
  Initial approach: Letter
  Deadline(s): None
Director: Rev. Joseph Szulwach.
Trustee: Comerica Bank.
EIN: 226855593

79
The Ethel Atterberry Foundation

225 Merton Rd., Ste. 410
Detroit, MI 48203

Established in 2004 in MI.
Donors: Ethel Atterberry; Michelle Puryear.
Grantmaker type: Independent foundation.
Financial data (yr. ended 12/31/05): Assets, $5,124 (M); gifts received, $1,425; expenditures, $1,379; total giving, $1,072; qualifying distributions, $1,072; giving activities include $1,072 for grants.
Limitations: Giving primarily in MI.
Trustees: Ethel Atterberry; Michelle Puryear.
EIN: 201257742

80
Attwood Foundation

42005 North Dr.
Canton, MI 48188

Established in 1953 in MI.
Grantmaker type: Independent foundation.
Financial data (yr. ended 12/31/04): Assets, $1,207,629 (M); expenditures, $57,865; total giving, $55,000; qualifying distributions, $55,000; giving activities include $55,000 for grants.
Fields of interest: Secondary school/education; Higher education; Human services; Salvation Army; Protestant agencies & churches.
Type of support: General/operating support; Scholarship funds.
Limitations: Applications not accepted. Giving primarily in MI. No grants to individuals.
Application information: Contributes only to pre-selected organizations.
Officers: Warren Attwood, Pres. and Treas.; Leonard Downes, V.P.; Marian Attwood Downes, Secy.
Director: Eleanor Fair Attwood.
EIN: 386082584

81
AtWater Foundation

3031 W. Grand Blvd., Ste. 415
Detroit, MI 48202
Contact: Vivian L. Carpenter, Pres.

Established in 1997 in MI.
Grantmaker type: Independent foundation.
Financial data (yr. ended 12/31/04): Assets, $20,734 (M); gifts received, $30,000; expenditures, $19,800; total giving, $18,300; qualifying distributions, $18,300; giving activities include $18,300 for 11 grants (high: $5,000; low: $500).
Purpose and activities: Giving primarily for youth services and community development in Detroit, MI.

Fields of interest: Arts; Elementary/secondary education; Youth, services; Christian agencies & churches.
Type of support: Curriculum development.
Limitations: Giving limited to Detroit, MI. No grants to individuals, or for operating expenses.
Publications: Financial statement.
Application information: Application form not required.
  Copies of proposal: 1
Officer and Trustee:* Vivian L. Carpenter,* Pres.
EIN: 383219694

82
Auto Material Corporation

(also known as Leslie H. & Edith C. Green Family Foundation Trust)
c/o Comerica Bank, Trust Tax Div.
P.O. Box 75000
Detroit, MI 48275

Established in MI.
Grantmaker type: Independent foundation.
Financial data (yr. ended 12/31/05): Assets, $164,510 (M); expenditures, $3,571; total giving, $0; qualifying distributions, $0.
Limitations: Giving limited to MI. No grants to individuals.
Application information:
  Initial approach: Letter
  Deadline(s): July 31
Trustee: Comerica Bank.
EIN: 386043565

83
The Ave Maria Foundation

(formerly The Mater Christi Foundation)
1 Ave Maria Dr.
P.O. Box 373
Ann Arbor, MI 48106-0373 (734) 930-3150
URL: http://www.avemariafoundation.org

Established in 1983 in MI.
Donors: Domino's Pizza, Inc.; Thomas S. Monaghan; Elaine McInerney; Martin McInerney; Albert Schaller; Marilyn Schaller; Kimberly Gates; James Gates; Dennis Ardi; William McIntyre.
Grantmaker type: Independent foundation.
Financial data (yr. ended 12/31/04): Assets, $155,512,954 (M); gifts received, $53,389,111; expenditures, $95,955,753; total giving, $91,925,690; qualifying distributions, $91,925,690; giving activities include $91,925,690 for 21 grants (high: $73,084,645; low: $1,121; average: $30,000–$1,345,610), and $835 for 1 foundation-administered program.
Purpose and activities: Giving primarily for religion, education, and social services.
Fields of interest: Education; Human services; Roman Catholic agencies & churches; Religion.
Type of support: Program development.
Limitations: Applications not accepted. Giving primarily in MI. No grants to individuals.
Application information: Unsolicited applications not considered.
  Board meeting date(s): Annually
Officers and Director:* Thomas S. Monaghan,* Pres.; Jeff Randolph, Secy.; Paul Roney, Treas.
Number of staff: 1 part-time professional.
EIN: 382514364

Selected grants: The following grants were reported in 2004.

$73,084,645 to Ave Maria University, Naples, FL. For construction and start-up support.

$8,247,895 to Ave Maria School of Law, Ann Arbor, MI. For general support.

$4,550,120 to Ave Maria College, Ypsilanti, MI. For general support.

$1,373,784 to Spiritus Sanctus Academy, Ann Arbor, MI. 2 grants: $1,345,610 (For general support), $28,174 (For general support).

$250,103 to Saint Marys College, Orchard Lake, MI. For general support.

$55,450 to National Association of Private Catholic Independent Schools (NAPCIS), Sacramento, CA. For general support.

$37,004 to Father Gabriel Richard High School, Ann Arbor, MI. For general support.

$30,000 to Catholic Schools Textbook Project, Ventura, CA. For general support.

$24,700 to Shepherd Montessori Center, Ann Arbor, MI.

84
Baese Family Foundation, Inc.
8944 One Putt Pl.
Port St. Lucie, FL   34986

Established in 1995 in FL.
Donor: Richard L. Baese.
Grantmaker type: Independent foundation.
Financial data (yr. ended 12/31/04): Assets, $1 (M); gifts received, $90; expenditures, $511; total giving, $0; qualifying distributions, $0.
Purpose and activities: Scholarship awards to graduating high school students in MI.
Fields of interest: Scholarships/financial aid.
Type of support: Scholarships—to individuals.
Limitations: Applications not accepted. Giving primarily to residents of MI.
Application information: Unsolicited request for funds not accepted.
Officer and Directors:* Richard L. Baese,* Mgr.; James L. Baese; Mary Lou Hanold.
EIN: 650600086

85
The Bahadur Family Foundation
3222 Middlebelt Rd.
West Bloomfield, MI   48323-1938

Established in 2000 in MI.
Donors: B.N. Bahadur; Rani Bahadur.
Grantmaker type: Independent foundation.
Financial data (yr. ended 12/31/04): Assets, $0 (M); expenditures, $213,434; total giving, $205,000; qualifying distributions, $211,846; giving activities include $205,000 for 3 grants (high: $175,000; low: $5,000).
Fields of interest: Higher education; Housing/shelter.
International interests: India.
Limitations: Applications not accepted. Giving in the U.S. and India. No grants to individuals.
Application information: Contributes only to pre-selected organizations.
Officers: B.N. Bahadur, Pres.; Nikhil Bahadur, Secy.; Rani Bahadur, Treas.
EIN: 383573929

86
Baiardi Family Foundation, Inc.
2328 Pinecrest St.
Harbor Springs, MI   49740-9261
(231) 526-8395
Contact: Chris A. Baiardi, Pres.
FAX: (231) 526-7966;
E-mail: info@baiardifoundation.org; Additional E-mail: grants@baiardifoundation.org; URL: http://www.baiardifoundation.org

Established in 1999.
Donors: Chris A. Baiardi; Cindy J. Baiardi; Angelo Baiardi‡.
Grantmaker type: Independent foundation.
Financial data (yr. ended 12/31/04): Assets, $5,165,695 (M); gifts received, $3,221; expenditures, $278,314; total giving, $262,415; qualifying distributions, $261,195; giving activities include $262,415 for 41 grants (high: $27,500; low: $475).
Fields of interest: Education; Hospitals (general); Health organizations; Human services; Federated giving programs.
Limitations: Giving primarily in MI, with concentrations in the Detroit metropolitan area community and in northwest lower Michigan, specifically Emmet County.
Application information: See foundation Web site for application guidelines.
   Initial approach: Letter
Officers and Directors:* Chris A. Baiardi,* Pres.; Kristen L. Baiardi,* V.P.; Suzanne M. Baiardi,* V.P.; Cindy J. Baiardi,* Secy.-Treas.
EIN: 383430867

87
The Howard Baker Foundation
4057 Pioneer Dr., Ste. 500
Walled Lake, MI   48390
Application address: c/o Michele Baker, Exec. Dir., P.O. Box 441453, Detroit, MI 48244, tel.: (313) 587-6207,
E-mail: mbaker@howardbakerfoundation.org;
URL: http://www.howardbakerfoundation.org

Established in 1992 in MI.
Donor: Howard Baker Trust.
Grantmaker type: Independent foundation.
Financial data (yr. ended 9/30/04): Assets, $3,929,350 (M); expenditures, $652,347; total giving, $536,311; qualifying distributions, $534,855; giving activities include $536,311 for 7 grants (high: $306,311; low: $5,000).
Purpose and activities: Giving primarily for human services, as well as to a fund that has been established to provide assistance to residents of Detroit, MI, in financing their education at Wayne State University, and to encourage continued progress towards a degree.
Fields of interest: Higher education, university; Human services.
Type of support: General/operating support; Scholarship funds.
Limitations: Giving primarily in Detroit, and southeastern MI. No grants to individuals.
Application information: See foundation Web site for scholarship guidelines.
   Initial approach: Proposal
Officers: Charlie J. Williams, Pres.; Ronald F. Michaels, V.P.; Dennis Gabrian, Secy.; O'Neal O'Wright, Treas.; Michelle L. Baker, Exec. Dir.

Directors: Paul J. Gampka; John J. Howe.
EIN: 383083465

88
Robert and Jane Baker Foundation
9535 Amber Cir.
Kalamazoo, MI   49009

Established in 1998 in MI.
Grantmaker type: Independent foundation.
Financial data (yr. ended 12/31/04): Assets, $158,130 (M); expenditures, $12,892; total giving, $10,350; qualifying distributions, $11,594; giving activities include $10,350 for grants.
Fields of interest: Protestant agencies & churches.
Type of support: General/operating support.
Limitations: Applications not accepted. Giving primarily in MI, with emphasis on Kalamazoo. No grants to individuals.
Application information: Contributes only to pre-selected organizations.
Officers: Robert S. Baker, Pres.; Jane Baker, V.P.
EIN: 383439074

89
Balaji Foundation, Inc.
4370 Fashion Sq. Blvd.
Saginaw, MI   48603

Donors: Bangalore S. Prabhaker; Indira Prabhaker.
Grantmaker type: Independent foundation.
Financial data (yr. ended 12/31/04): Assets, $364,142 (M); expenditures, $42,548; total giving, $30,000; qualifying distributions, $30,000; giving activities include $30,000 for grants.
Purpose and activities: Giving for an affiliated foundation in India.
Fields of interest: Foundations (private independent).
International interests: India.
Limitations: Applications not accepted. Giving limited to Bangalore, India. No grants to individuals.
Application information: Contributes only to pre-selected organizations.
Officers: Bangalore S. Prabhaker, Pres.; Indira Prabhaker, V.P.
EIN: 382893231

90
Baldwin Foundation
P.O. Box 3636
Grand Rapids, MI   49501-3636
Application address: c/o Daniel Oumedian, 111 Lyon St. N.W., Grand Rapids, MI 49503, tel.: (616) 653-5418

Trust established in 1964 in MI.
Donor: Members of the Baldwin family.
Grantmaker type: Independent foundation.
Financial data (yr. ended 11/30/05): Assets, $3,713,985 (M); expenditures, $215,427; total giving, $206,450; qualifying distributions, $206,808; giving activities include $206,450 for 21 grants (high: $35,000; low: $2,500).
Fields of interest: Arts; Higher education; Hospitals (general); Human services; Children/youth, services; Christian agencies & churches.
Type of support: Annual campaigns; Capital campaigns; Building/renovation; Equipment; Professorships; Fellowships.

Limitations: Giving primarily in western MI. No grants to individuals.
Application information: Application form not required.
Deadline(s): None
Board meeting date(s): July or Aug.
Officers: Dana Baldwin II, Pres.; Lee Mulnix III, V.P.; Daniel Oumedian, Secy.-Treas.
Trustee: Fifth Third Bank.
EIN: 386085641
Selected grants: The following grants were reported in 2004.
$25,000 to Kent Intermediate School District, Grand Rapids, MI. For Bright Beginnings program.
$20,000 to Dwelling Place of Grand Rapids, Grand Rapids, MI. For capital campaign.
$20,000 to Grand Rapids Art Museum, Grand Rapids, MI. For capital campaign.
$20,000 to Public Museum of Grand Rapids, Grand Rapids, MI. For advancement program.
$10,000 to Michigan State University, East Lansing, MI. For scholarships.
$10,000 to University of Michigan, Ann Arbor, MI. For Science in the City program.
$5,400 to North American Choral Company, Grand Rapids, MI. For computer equipment.
$5,000 to Charlevoix Public Library, Charlevoix, MI. For building fund.
$5,000 to Grand Rapids Ballet Company, Grand Rapids, MI. For capital campaign.
$5,000 to Saint Andrews School, Grand Rapids, MI. For capital campaign.

91
James & Shirley Balk Foundation
1230 Monroe Ave. N.W.
Grand Rapids, MI 49505-4620
Contact: James H. Balk II, Tr.

Established in 1984 in MI.
Donors: James H. Balk II; Shirley Balk.
Grantmaker type: Independent foundation.
Financial data (yr. ended 12/31/05): Assets, $4,936,428 (M); gifts received, $15,000; expenditures, $148,042; total giving, $145,761; qualifying distributions, $145,761; giving activities include $145,761 for 28 grants (high: $39,625; low: $150).
Purpose and activities: Giving primarily for Christian education; support also for the arts, churches, human services, and botanical gardens.
Fields of interest: Arts; Higher education; Education; Botanical gardens; Human services; Federated giving programs; Christian agencies & churches.
Type of support: General/operating support.
Limitations: Giving primarily in Grand Rapids, MI. No grants to individuals.
Application information:
Initial approach: Letter on organization's letterhead
Deadline(s): None
Trustees: James H. Balk; James H. Balk II; Martin Balk; Shirley Balk; Steven Balk.
EIN: 382556356

92
Edmund F. and Virginia B. Ball Foundation, Inc.
P.O. Box 1408
Muncie, IN 47308-1408
Contact: Kris Gross

Established in 1994 in IN.
Donors: Edmund F. Ball‡; Virginia B. Ball‡.
Grantmaker type: Independent foundation.
Financial data (yr. ended 9/30/05): Assets, $27,300,514 (M); expenditures, $1,020,053; total giving, $869,087; qualifying distributions, $869,330; giving activities include $869,087 for 7 grants (high: $350,000; low: $250).
Fields of interest: Arts; Education; Recreation; Children/youth, services.
Limitations: Giving primarily in MI and IN. No grants to individuals.
Application information:
Initial approach: Proposal
Deadline(s): None
Officers and Directors:* Frank E. Ball,* Pres.; Robert B. Ball,* V.P.; Douglas J. Foy,* Secy.-Treas.; Douglas A. Bakken.
EIN: 351911169
Selected grants: The following grants were reported in 2003.
$240,000 to Ball State University, Muncie, IN. For Muncie Center for the Arts.
$235,000 to Minnetrista Cultural Foundation, Muncie, IN. 2 grants: $200,000 (For catalyst sculpture), $35,000 (For publications fund).
$100,000 to Interlochen Center for the Arts, Interlochen, MI.
$35,000 to Asheville School, Asheville, NC. For endowed chair for archives.
$25,000 to Muncie Center for the Arts, Muncie, IN. For Interlochen scholarship.
$15,000 to Indiana Humanities Council, Indianapolis, IN.
$10,000 to Johns Hopkins University, Wilmer Ophthalmological Institute, Baltimore, MD. For Directors Discovery Fund.
$10,000 to Unitarian Universalist Church, Muncie, IN.
$1,000 to Ball Memorial Hospital Foundation, Muncie, IN.

93
Joseph C. Bancroft Educational & Charitable Foundation
c/o Trustmark National Bank
P.O. Box 291
Jackson, MS 39205-0291
Application address: c/o Gerald M. Abdalla, P.O. Box 826, McComb, MS 39648, tel.: (601) 684-6121

Established in 1978.
Donor: Joseph C. Bancroft.
Grantmaker type: Independent foundation.
Financial data (yr. ended 6/30/04): Assets, $1,597,307 (M); expenditures, $73,378; total giving, $53,220; qualifying distributions, $71,079; giving activities include $53,220 for grants.
Purpose and activities: Giving primarily for a camp and youth organizations. The foundation will also consider grants and loans to students in AL, AR, FL, GA, LA, MI, MS, and NC; and grants to needy immigrants who express desire to become U.S. citizens and live in the above-mentioned states.

Fields of interest: Education; Recreation, camps; Children/youth, services.
Type of support: General/operating support; Grants to individuals; Student loans—to individuals.
Limitations: Giving limited to residents in AL, AR, FL, GA, LA, MI, MS, and NC.
Application information: Application form required.
Initial approach: Letter or telephone
Deadline(s): None
Officers and Trustees:* Robert M. Bird, Pres.; Gerald M. Abdalla, Jr.,* Secy.-Treas.; Tom A. Abdalla; Trustmark National Bank.
EIN: 640602590

94
Steven G. Bandstra Foundation
5000 Hakes Dr., Ste. 600
Norton Shores, MI 49441-5567

Established in 2000 in MI.
Donor: Steven G. Bandstra.
Grantmaker type: Independent foundation.
Financial data (yr. ended 12/31/05): Assets, $620,577 (M); gifts received, $50,000; expenditures, $43,294; total giving, $40,500; qualifying distributions, $40,520; giving activities include $40,500 for grants.
Fields of interest: Education; Foundations (community); Christian agencies & churches.
Type of support: General/operating support.
Limitations: Applications not accepted. Giving primarily in MI. No grants to individuals.
Application information: Contributes only to pre-selected organizations.
Officer: Steven G. Bandstra, Pres. and Secy.-Treas.
EIN: 383580356

95
Banfield, Inc.
P.O. Box 786
Ironwood, MI 49938-4786

Established in 1992 in MI.
Donor: Irene R. Banfield.
Grantmaker type: Independent foundation.
Financial data (yr. ended 6/30/05): Assets, $254,700 (M); gifts received, $125; expenditures, $18,816; total giving, $14,000; qualifying distributions, $14,000; giving activities include $14,000 for grants.
Limitations: Applications not accepted. Giving primarily in Ironwood, MI. No grants to individuals.
Application information: Contributes only to pre-selected organizations.
Officers and Directors:* Lillian M. Anderson, Pres.; Mildred E. Heikkila, V.P.; William Carroll,* Secy.; Eero J. Haukkala, Treas.; Carl Kinnunen; Lila E. Nurmi.
EIN: 383054903

96
The Bar-Levav Family Foundation
29600 Northwestern Hwy., Ste. 100
Southfield, MI 48034

Established in 1995 in MI.
Grantmaker type: Independent foundation.
Financial data (yr. ended 12/31/03): Assets, $2,870,552 (M); gifts received, $30,125; expenditures, $132,339; total giving, $129,986;

qualifying distributions, $131,850; giving activities include $129,986 for 28+ grants (high: $19,300).
Fields of interest: Higher education; Education; Jewish federated giving programs; Jewish agencies & temples.
Type of support: General/operating support.
Limitations: Giving primarily in Detroit, MI. No grants to individuals.
Officers: Leora Bar-Levav, Pres.; Pamela Torraco, Secy.; Doron Bar-Levav, Treas.; Ilana Bar-Levav, Treas.
EIN: 383257742
Selected grants: The following grants were reported in 2003.
$19,300 to United Jewish Foundation, Bloomfield Hills, MI.
$18,000 to Jewish Charitable Trust.
$13,700 to Jewish National Fund, Southfield, MI.
$11,500 to Kol Shalom Community for Humanistic Judaism, Beaverton, OR.
$11,300 to Hillel Day School of Metropolitan Detroit, Farmington Hills, MI.
$7,350 to Jewish Federation, MI.
$5,360 to Zionist Organization of America, MI.
$5,000 to World Jewish Congress American Section, New York, NY.
$2,500 to Wittenberg University, Springfield, OH. For general support.
$1,000 to University of Texas, Austin, TX.

97
Barber Foundation
4635 N. Breton Ct. S.E.
Kentwood, MI 49508

Established in 1991 in MI.
Donor: Gerald L. Barber.
Grantmaker type: Independent foundation.
Financial data (yr. ended 12/31/05): Assets, $1,480,514 (M); gifts received, $40,000; expenditures, $38,317; total giving, $35,000; qualifying distributions, $35,000; giving activities include $35,000 for 5 grants (high: $26,000; low: $1,000).
Fields of interest: Higher education, college; Human services; Roman Catholic agencies & churches.
Limitations: Applications not accepted. Giving primarily in MI, with emphasis on Grand Rapids. No grants to individuals.
Application information: Contributes only to pre-selected organizations.
Officer: Gerald L. Barber, Pres.
EIN: 382964580

98
Theodore and Mina Bargman Foundation
c/o Lawrence S. Jackier
121 W. Long Lake Rd., 2nd Fl.
Bloomfield Hills, MI 48304-2719

Incorporated in 1954 in MI.
Donor: Mina Bargman†.
Grantmaker type: Independent foundation.
Financial data (yr. ended 12/31/04): Assets, $1,663,880 (M); expenditures, $327,193; total giving, $213,139; qualifying distributions, $278,554; giving activities include $213,139 for 46 grants (high: $50,000; low: $150).
Purpose and activities: Emphasis on Jewish welfare funds, higher education in Israel, and temple support.

Fields of interest: Higher education; Hospitals (specialty); Human services; Jewish federated giving programs; Jewish agencies & temples.
International interests: Israel.
Type of support: General/operating support; Continuing support; Annual campaigns; Building/renovation.
Limitations: Applications not accepted. Giving primarily in MI. No grants to individuals, or for endowment funds, scholarships, fellowships, or matching gifts; no loans.
Application information: Contributes only to pre-selected organizations.
Officers and Trustees:* Lawrence S. Jackier,* Pres.; Bruce Mayhew,* V.P.; Dale Rands,* V.P.; Mark Schlussel,* Secy.
EIN: 386087158
Selected grants: The following grants were reported in 2004.
$54,321 to Jewish Federation of Metropolitan Detroit, Bloomfield Hills, MI. 2 grants: $10,000, $44,321
$50,000 to Childrens Hospital of Michigan, Detroit, MI.
$15,000 to American Society for Technion-Israel Institute of Technology, Southfield, MI. For leadership development program.
$12,500 to Jewish Academy of Metropolitan Detroit, West Bloomfield, MI.
$10,000 to Jewish Vocational Service and Community Workshop, Southfield, MI. For endowment campaign.
$6,250 to Jewish Hospice and Chaplaincy Network, Bloomfield, MI.
$4,000 to Holocaust Memorial Center, Farmington Hills, MI.
$2,500 to Miracle League of Michigan, Birmingham, MI.
$2,500 to Yeshivath Beth Yehudah, Southfield, MI.

99
Anthony David Barlow Memorial Trust Foundation
32300 Northwestern Hwy., Ste. 250
Farmington Hills, MI 48334

Established in 1995.
Grantmaker type: Independent foundation.
Financial data (yr. ended 12/31/04): Assets, $0 (L); gifts received, $1,000; expenditures, $1,000; total giving, $1,000; qualifying distributions, $1,000; giving activities include $1,000 for grants.
Trustees: Beverly Barlow; Jeffrey D. Spilman.
EIN: 386657539

100
The J. Spencer Barnes Memorial Foundation
109 Logan St. S.W.
Grand Rapids, MI 49503 (616) 949-4854
Contact: Robert C. Woodhouse, Jr., Pres.

Established in 1999 in MI.
Donor: John P. Williams.
Grantmaker type: Independent foundation.
Financial data (yr. ended 6/30/05): Assets, $112,043 (M); gifts received, $626; expenditures, $13,166; total giving, $9,150; qualifying distributions, $9,150; giving activities include $9,150 for grants.
Limitations: Giving primarily in MI.

Application information:
Initial approach: Proposal
Deadline(s): None
Officers and Directors:* Robert C. Woodhouse, Jr.,* Pres.; Stevens Wharton-Bickley,* V.P.; Scott Dwyer,* Secy.; Sam Massie III,* Treas.; John Rahilly; Stuart Shockley.
EIN: 383499166

101
G. & A. Barnett Scholarship Trust
c/o Century Bank and Trust
100 W. Chicago St.
Coldwater, MI 49036

Established in 2004 in MI.
Donor: Aileen Barnett Charitable Trust.
Grantmaker type: Independent foundation.
Financial data (yr. ended 12/31/05): Assets, $372,438 (M); expenditures, $22,841; total giving, $18,000; qualifying distributions, $18,000; giving activities include $18,000 for grants.
Fields of interest: Higher education.
Type of support: Scholarship funds.
Limitations: Applications not accepted. No grants to individuals.
Application information: Contributes only to pre-selected organizations.
Trustee: Century Bank and Trust.
EIN: 367432274

102
A. Barnett Trust f/b/o Branch County District Library
c/o Century Bank and Trust
100 W. Chicago St.
Coldwater, MI 49036

Established in 2004 in MI.
Donor: Aileen Barnett Charitable Trust.
Grantmaker type: Independent foundation.
Financial data (yr. ended 12/31/05): Assets, $275,358 (M); expenditures, $16,845; total giving, $12,866; qualifying distributions, $12,866; giving activities include $12,866 for grants.
Purpose and activities: Support only for the Branch County District Library, Coldwater, MI.
Fields of interest: Libraries (public).
Type of support: General/operating support.
Limitations: Applications not accepted. Giving limited to Coldwater, MI. No grants to individuals.
Application information: Contributes only to a pre-selected organization.
Trustee: Century Bank and Trust.
EIN: 386824537

103
A. Barnett Trust f/b/o First United Methodist Church
c/o Century Bank and Trust
100 W. Chicago St.
Coldwater, MI 49036

Established in 2004 in MI.
Donor: Aileen Barnett Charitable Trust.
Grantmaker type: Independent foundation.
Financial data (yr. ended 12/31/05): Assets, $275,117 (M); expenditures, $17,085; total giving, $12,807; qualifying distributions, $12,807; giving activities include $12,807 for grants.

Purpose and activities: Support only for the United Methodist Church.
Fields of interest: Protestant agencies & churches.
Limitations: Applications not accepted. No grants to individuals.
Application information: Contributes only to a pre-selected organization.
Trustee: Century Bank and Trust.
EIN: 367432338

104
A. Barnett Trust f/b/o Salvation Army
c/o Century Bank and Trust
100 W. Chicago St.
Coldwater, MI 49036

Established in 2004 in MI.
Donor: Aileen Barnett Charitable Trust.
Grantmaker type: Independent foundation.
Financial data (yr. ended 12/31/05): Assets, $275,200 (M); expenditures, $17,081; total giving, $12,803; qualifying distributions, $12,803; giving activities include $12,803 for grants.
Purpose and activities: Support only for the Salvation Army, Coldwater.
Fields of interest: Salvation Army.
Type of support: General/operating support.
Limitations: Applications not accepted. Giving limited to Coldwater, MI. No grants to individuals.
Application information: Contributes only to a pre-selected organization.
Trustee: Century Bank and Trust.
EIN: 386824535

105
A. Barnett Trust f/b/o Tibbets Theatre
c/o Century Bank and Trust
100 W. Chicago St.
Coldwater, MI 49036

Established in 2004 in MI.
Donor: Aileen Barnett Charitable Trust.
Grantmaker type: Independent foundation.
Financial data (yr. ended 12/31/05): Assets, $275,264 (M); expenditures, $16,938; total giving, $12,965; qualifying distributions, $12,965; giving activities include $12,965 for grants.
Purpose and activities: Support only for the Tibbets Theatre, Coldwater.
Fields of interest: Performing arts.
Type of support: General/operating support.
Limitations: Applications not accepted. Giving limited to Coldwater, MI. No grants to individuals.
Application information: Contributes only to a pre-selected organization.
Trustee: Century Bank and Trust.
EIN: 386824511

106
Shelley & Terry Barr Foundation
29600 Northwestern Hwy., Ste. 102
Southfield, MI 48034

Established in MI.
Donor: Terry A. Barr.
Grantmaker type: Independent foundation.
Financial data (yr. ended 12/31/04): Assets, $69,374 (M); gifts received, $8,000; expenditures, $8,000; total giving, $8,000; qualifying

distributions, $8,000; giving activities include $8,000 for grants to individuals.
Purpose and activities: Scholarship awards to graduates of Grand Rapids Central High School, Grand Rapids, MI and Rogers High School, Wyoming, MI.
Type of support: Scholarships—to individuals.
Limitations: Giving limited to residents of Grand Rapids and Wyoming, MI.
Application information: Application form required.
 Deadline(s): None
Officers: Terry A. Barr, Pres. and Treas.; Shelly E. Barr, V.P.; Mary C. Kravutske, Secy.
EIN: 382258156

107
The Harold and Roberta Barron Charitable Foundation
180 E. Pearson St.
Chicago, IL 60611

Established in 1993 in IL.
Donors: Harold Barron; Roberta Barron.
Grantmaker type: Independent foundation.
Financial data (yr. ended 12/31/05): Assets, $150,028 (M); gifts received, $62,609; expenditures, $22,918; total giving, $22,000; qualifying distributions, $22,000; giving activities include $22,000 for grants.
Fields of interest: Education; Health care; Jewish federated giving programs; Jewish agencies & temples.
Type of support: General/operating support.
Limitations: Applications not accepted. Giving on a national basis, with emphasis on Chicago, IL, MI, NY, and PA. No grants to individuals.
Application information: Contributes only to pre-selected organizations.
Officers: Harold Barron, Pres.; Roberta Barron, V.P.
Directors: Jean L. Barron; Lawrence I. Barron.
EIN: 363925736

108
Nora Lee & Guy Barron Foundation
5970 Wing Lake Rd.
Bloomfield Hills, MI 48301

Established in 1980 in MI.
Donors: Guy L. Barron; Nora Lee Barron.
Grantmaker type: Independent foundation.
Financial data (yr. ended 11/30/04): Assets, $3,200,826 (M); expenditures, $124,656; total giving, $102,490; qualifying distributions, $105,908; giving activities include $102,490 for 32 grants (high: $27,000; low: $500).
Purpose and activities: Funding primarily for Jewish federated giving programs and Jewish agencies and temples.
Fields of interest: Arts; Higher education; Human services; Jewish federated giving programs; Jewish agencies & temples.
Limitations: Applications not accepted. Giving primarily in the greater Detroit, MI, area. No grants to individuals.
Application information: Contributes only to pre-selected organizations.
Trustees: Guy L. Barron; Nora Lee Barron.
EIN: 382346776
Selected grants: The following grants were reported in 2003.

$130,000 to Jewish Federation of Metropolitan Detroit, Bloomfield Hills, MI. For general support.
$10,000 to Child Abuse and Neglect Council of Oakland County, Pontiac, MI. For general support.
$10,000 to Desert Community Foundation, Palm Desert, CA. For general support.
$10,000 to JARC, Farmington Hills, MI. For general support.
$8,400 to Skowhegan School of Painting and Sculpture, New York, NY. For general support.
$4,000 to Beaumont Foundation, Southfield, MI. For general support.
$3,500 to Detroit Institute of Arts, Detroit, MI. For general support.
$2,500 to Detroit Symphony Orchestra, Detroit, MI. For general support.
$2,000 to Oakland University, Meadow Brook Theatre, Rochester, MI. For general support.
$2,000 to Sarcoma Foundation of America, Damascus, MD. For general support.

109
The Barstow Foundation
c/o Chemical Bank & Trust Co.
235 E. Main St.
Midland, MI 48640
Contact: Bruce M. Groom, Secy., Chemical Bank & Trust Co.

Trust established in 1967 in MI.
Donors: Florence K. Barstow†; Ruth M. Dixon.
Grantmaker type: Independent foundation.
Financial data (yr. ended 12/31/05): Assets, $7,369,867 (M); expenditures, $180,320; total giving, $147,500; qualifying distributions, $147,500; giving activities include $147,500 for 6 grants (high: $32,500; low: $16,250).
Fields of interest: Environment; Boys & girls clubs; Human services; Children/youth, services; Foundations (community).
Type of support: General/operating support; Annual campaigns; Equipment; Endowments; Emergency funds; Program development; Seed money; Technical assistance; Matching/challenge support.
Limitations: Giving primarily in AZ and NY; some funding nationally, particularly in Midland, MI. No grants to individuals, or for research, continuing support, deficit financing, scholarships, or fellowships; no loans.
Application information: Application form not required.
 Initial approach: Letter
 Copies of proposal: 2
 Deadline(s): July 31
 Board meeting date(s): Nov.
 Final notification: After annual meeting
Officers and Trustees:* David O. Barstow,* Co-Chair.; William R. Dixon,* Co-Chair.; Bruce M. Groom,* Secy.; John C. Barstow; Richard G. Barstow; Robert G. Barstow; Robert O. Barstow; Ruth M. Dixon.
EIN: 386151026

110
Charles F. and Adeline L. Barth Charitable Foundation
3023 Davenport St.
P.O. Box 3275
Saginaw, MI 48605
Contact: Lloyd J. Yeo, Treas.

Established in 1989 in MI.
Donor: Adeline L. Barth†.
Grantmaker type: Independent foundation.
Financial data (yr. ended 12/31/05): Assets, $1,121,352 (M); expenditures, $88,893; total giving, $65,737; qualifying distributions, $65,737; giving activities include $65,737 for 23 grants (high: $8,500; low: $900).
Purpose and activities: Giving primarily for the arts, higher education and human services.
Fields of interest: Arts; Higher education; Hospitals (general); Human services; Federated giving programs.
Type of support: General/operating support; Capital campaigns; Building/renovation; Program development; Matching/challenge support.
Limitations: Giving primarily in Saginaw, MI.
Application information: Application form not required.
  Initial approach: Letter
  Copies of proposal: 3
  Deadline(s): None
  Board meeting date(s): Semiannually
Officers: Jane Barth, Pres.; Susan Langhorne, V.P.; Lloyd J. Yeo, Treas.
Trustees: Richard Stringer; Judy Weldy.
Number of staff: 1 part-time professional.
EIN: 386556893
Selected grants: The following grants were reported in 2003.
$16,000 to Saginaw Art Museum, Saginaw, MI. For general support.
$11,000 to Saginaw Valley Zoological Society, Saginaw, MI. For general support.
$8,500 to Pit and Balcony, Saginaw, MI. For general support.
$7,500 to Underground Railroad, Saginaw, MI. For general support.
$6,667 to Mid-Michigan Childrens Museum, Saginaw, MI. For general support.
$6,200 to American Heart Association, Dallas, TX. For general support.
$5,000 to Boys and Girls Club of Saginaw County, Saginaw, MI. For general support.
$5,000 to United Way of Saginaw County, Saginaw, MI. For general support.
$3,900 to HealthSource Saginaw, Saginaw, MI. For general support.
$3,500 to Saginaw Symphony, Saginaw, MI. For general support.

111
Bartsch Memorial Trust
(formerly Ruth Bartsch Memorial Bank Trust)
c/o JPMorgan Services Inc.
P.O. Box 6089
Newark, DE   19714-6089
Application address: c/o Peggy Swarzman, V.P., JPMorgan Chase Bank, 345 Park Ave., 4th Fl., New York NY 10154; tel.: (212) 464-2342

Established in 1983 in NY.
Donor: Ruth Bartsch†.
Grantmaker type: Independent foundation.
Financial data (yr. ended 11/30/05): Assets, $9,543,782 (M); expenditures, $521,306; total giving, $420,000; qualifying distributions, $451,681; giving activities include $420,000 for 8 grants (high: $168,000; low: $21,000).
Fields of interest: Secondary school/education; Hospitals (general); Health organizations, association; Human services.

Limitations: Giving on a national basis, with emphasis on CT, FL, IL, and MI. No grants to individuals.
Application information: Application form not required.
  Initial approach: Letter
  Deadline(s): None
Trustees: Vincent William Richards, Jr.; JPMorgan Chase Bank, N.A.
EIN: 133188775

112
Bash Family Foundation, Inc.
2110 21st Ave. S.
Escanaba, MI   49829

Established in 1993 in MI.
Donors: Theodore L. Bash; Joycelyn A. Bash.
Grantmaker type: Independent foundation.
Financial data (yr. ended 12/31/05): Assets, $516,885 (M); expenditures, $18,791; total giving, $13,900; qualifying distributions, $13,900; giving activities include $13,900 for 6 grants (high: $10,000; low: $400).
Fields of interest: Education; Children/youth, services.
Limitations: Applications not accepted. Giving in the U.S., primarily in MI. No grants to individuals.
Application information: Contributes only to pre-selected organizations.
Officers: Joycelyn A. Bash, Pres. and Treas.; James D. Bash, V.P.; Theodore A. Bash, Secy.
EIN: 383083909

113
Basha Foundation
26300 Telegraph Rd., 2nd Fl.
Southfield, MI   48034

Established in 2002.
Grantmaker type: Independent foundation.
Financial data (yr. ended 12/31/05): Assets, $14,621 (M); gifts received, $20,500; expenditures, $71,329; total giving, $69,433; qualifying distributions, $69,433; giving activities include $69,433 for grants.
Officer: Ismael M. Basha, Pres.
EIN: 364507978

114
Barry Bashur Foundation
3072 Newport Ct.
Troy, MI   48084   (248) 649-0174
Contact: Margaret Barry Bashur, Pres.

Established in 2004 in MI.
Donors: John Bashur; Margaret Barry Bashur.
Grantmaker type: Independent foundation.
Financial data (yr. ended 12/31/05): Assets, $13,708 (M); gifts received, $10,000; expenditures, $8,775; total giving, $8,775; qualifying distributions, $8,775; giving activities include $8,775 for grants.
Fields of interest: Animal welfare; Medical research.
Limitations: Giving primarily in MI.
Application information:
  Initial approach: Letter
  Deadline(s): Varies
Officers: Margaret Barry Bashur, Pres.; John Bashur, V.P.

Director: John Grenke.
EIN: 201149345

115
Mary Friedman Baske Family Foundation, Inc.
2876 Dozer Dr.
St. Joseph, MI   49085
Contact: Mary Friedman Baske, Dir.

Established in 1999 in FL and MI.
Grantmaker type: Independent foundation.
Financial data (yr. ended 12/31/05): Assets, $880,791 (M); expenditures, $51,772; total giving, $45,755; qualifying distributions, $45,755; giving activities include $45,755 for grants.
Purpose and activities: Giving to a children's museum; funding also for human services.
Fields of interest: Museums (children's); Higher education; Human services; Children/youth, services.
Type of support: General/operating support; Building/renovation.
Limitations: Giving primarily in MI, especially St. Joseph; some funding nationally.
Application information: Application form not required.
  Deadline(s): None
Directors: Douglas Baske; Mary Friedman Baske; Elizabeth Friedman O'Connor.
EIN: 582462400

116
The Bates Foundation
40700 Woodward Ave., Ste. A
Bloomfield Hills, MI   48304   (248) 642-5770

Established in 1997 in MI.
Donors: Gwendolyn H. Bates; Martha J. Bates.
Grantmaker type: Independent foundation.
Financial data (yr. ended 12/31/04): Assets, $65,967 (M); expenditures, $5,865; total giving, $5,800; qualifying distributions, $5,800; giving activities include $5,800 for grants.
Fields of interest: Human services.
Type of support: General/operating support.
Limitations: Giving primarily in MI. No grants to individuals.
Application information:
  Initial approach: Letter
  Deadline(s): None
Officers: Gwendolyn H. Bates, Pres.; Martha J. Bates, V.P.; James H. LoPrete, Secy.
EIN: 383278032

117
Royal M. Bates Trust
c/o Comerica Bank
P.O. Box 75000
Detroit, MI   48275-3302

Grantmaker type: Independent foundation.
Financial data (yr. ended 7/31/05): Assets, $98,226 (M); expenditures, $9,381; total giving, $5,000; qualifying distributions, $5,000; giving activities include $5,000 for grants.
Limitations: Applications not accepted. No grants to individuals.
Application information: Contributes only to pre-selected organizations.

Trustee: Comerica Bank.
EIN: 386550717

118
Bath Family Foundation
764 Satterlee Rd.
Bloomfield Hills, MI 48304-3148
Contact: Clifford O. Bath, Jr., Pres.

Established in 1999 in MI.
Donors: Clifford O. Bath, Jr.; Isabel J. Bath.
Grantmaker type: Independent foundation.
Financial data (yr. ended 12/31/05): Assets,
$389,689 (M); gifts received, $620; expenditures,
$53,120; total giving, $52,500; qualifying
distributions, $52,500; giving activities include
$52,500 for grants.
Purpose and activities: Giving primarily to
Methodist churches and a theological seminary.
Fields of interest: Theological school/education;
Education; Human services; Community
development; Protestant agencies & churches.
Type of support: Annual campaigns; Capital
campaigns.
Limitations: Giving primarily in the north central
U.S., with some emphasis on MI. No grants to
individuals.
Application information: Application form not
required.
  Initial approach: Letter
  Copies of proposal: 1
  Deadline(s): None
  Board meeting date(s): Spring and fall
Officers: Clifford O. Bath, Jr., Pres.; Isabel J. Bath,
V.P.; Susan J. Thomasson, Secy.; Marianne B.
Conner, Treas.
EIN: 383497199

119
Battle Foundation, Inc.
c/o Comerica Bank
P.O. Box 75000 M/C 3302
Detroit, MI 48275-3302
Contact: Robert Edwards
Application address: 131 N. Church St., 4th Fl.,
Rocky Mount, NC 27802, tel.: (252) 454-4016

Established in NC.
Grantmaker type: Independent foundation.
Financial data (yr. ended 11/30/04): Assets,
$596,259 (M); expenditures, $7,474; total giving,
$1,000; qualifying distributions, $1,000; giving
activities include $1,000 for grants.
Fields of interest: Arts; Libraries (public); Health
care.
Limitations: Giving primarily in eastern NC. No
grants to individuals.
Application information:
  Initial approach: Proposal
  Deadline(s): None
  Final notification: Within 3 months
Officers and Trustees:* Thomas R. Battle,* Pres.;
Robert R. Keller,* Secy.-Treas.; Charlotte T. Battle;
Craig L. Battle; Charlotte R. Robbins.
EIN: 566060618

120
Peggy Bauervic Foundation
(formerly Bauervic-Carroll Foundation)
3 Bluffwood Dr.
South Haven, MI 49090 (616) 639-8931
Contact: Peggy L. Maitland, Pres.

Established in 1984 in MI.
Grantmaker type: Independent foundation.
Financial data (yr. ended 12/31/04): Assets,
$477,065 (M); expenditures, $4,621; total giving,
$0; qualifying distributions, $80.
Purpose and activities: Giving primarily for health
associations and research.
Fields of interest: Arts; Education; Biomedicine;
Medical research, institute; Human services.
Limitations: Giving primarily in MI. No grants to
individuals.
Application information: Application form required.
  Initial approach: Letter
  Copies of proposal: 1
  Deadline(s): Oct. 1
Officers and Directors:* Peggy L. Maitland,* Pres.
and Secy.; Jane Carroll, V.P.; Stuart Maitland,*
Treas.; Lynne M. Carroll; Steve Peffer.
Number of staff: 1 full-time professional.
EIN: 382494383

121
Charles M. Bauervic Foundation, Inc.
2155 Butterfield Dr., Ste. 305A
Troy, MI 48084
Application address: c/o Exec. Dir., 10260 E. Hilltop
Rd., Suttons Bay, MI 49682

Incorporated in 1967 in MI.
Donor: Charles M. Bauervic‡.
Grantmaker type: Independent foundation.
Financial data (yr. ended 12/31/05): Assets,
$4,354,778 (M); expenditures, $277,100; total
giving, $150,000; qualifying distributions,
$219,427; giving activities include $150,000 for 32
grants (high: $15,000; low: $500).
Fields of interest: Arts; Elementary/secondary
education; Higher education; Health organizations;
Nutrition.
Type of support: Building/renovation; Equipment;
Program development.
Limitations: Giving primarily in MI. No support for
organizations lacking 501(c)(3) status. No grants to
individuals, or for scholarship funds, operating
expenses, fund drives, or building campaigns.
Publications: Application guidelines.
Application information: Application form required.
  Initial approach: Letter
  Copies of proposal: 2
  Deadline(s): Apr. 30
  Board meeting date(s): June
  Final notification: June 30
Officers: Patricia A. Leonard, Pres. and Secy.;
Beverly D. Sewell, V.P.; Theodore Leonard, Treas.
Directors: John C. Leonard; Kathryn R. Leonard;
Timothy J. Leonard.
Number of staff: 1 part-time support.
EIN: 386146352
Selected grants: The following grants were reported
in 2004.
$15,000 to Institute in Basic Life Principles, Oak
   Brook, IL. To expand Nashville Medical Facility.
$15,000 to Southwest College of Naturopathic
   Medicine and Health Science, Tempe, AZ. For
   anatomy lab improvement and class studies
   enrichment.

$10,000 to Ave Maria School of Law, Ann Arbor, MI.
   For satellite downlink equipment.
$10,000 to Educational Center for Life, Troy, MI. For
   computer and educational materials.
$10,000 to Hillsdale College, Hillsdale, MI. For
   teacher seminar on free enterprise.
$5,000 to Everest Academy, Clarkston, MI. For
   Riggs Language Arts Program.
$3,000 to Traverse Symphony Orchestra, Traverse
   City, MI. For Music in the Schools Program.
$1,000 to City Opera House Heritage Association,
   Traverse City, MI. For restoration of historic
   center.
$1,000 to Rose Hill Center, Holly, MI. For digital
   projector.
$1,000 to Saint Anne School, Linwood, MI. For
   Catholic Writing Program.

122
Bauervic-Paisley Foundation
c/o Board of Directors
501 E. Mullett Lake Rd.
Indian River, MI 49749 (231) 238-7817

Established in 1984 in MI.
Grantmaker type: Independent foundation.
Financial data (yr. ended 12/31/05): Assets,
$1,186,078 (M); expenditures, $104,100; total
giving, $10,000; qualifying distributions, $10,000;
giving activities include $10,000 for grants.
Purpose and activities: Giving primarily for
education, health care, and human services.
Fields of interest: Higher education; Hospitals
(general); Housing/shelter; Youth development;
Human services; Residential/custodial care,
hospices.
Type of support: General/operating support;
Building/renovation; Equipment; Program
development.
Limitations: Giving primarily in MI. No grants to
individuals.
Application information: Application form required.
  Deadline(s): Oct. 1
Officers and Directors:* Beverly Paisley,* Pres.;
Martha Paisley,* V.P.; Bonnie Paisley, Secy.; Peter
Paisley, Treas.; Charles Paisley; Peter Paisley, Jr.
EIN: 382494390

123
The Baum Family Foundation
660 W. Indian Hills Dr.
Hastings, MI 49058-9480

Established in 1998 in MI.
Donors: Larry R. Baum; A. Earlene Baum.
Grantmaker type: Independent foundation.
Financial data (yr. ended 6/30/05): Assets,
$420,176 (M); gifts received, $1,000;
expenditures, $19,600; total giving, $19,600;
qualifying distributions, $19,600; giving activities
include $19,600 for grants.
Purpose and activities: Giving primarily to a
Protestant church and for human services.
Fields of interest: Human services; YM/YWCAs &
YM/YWHAs; Protestant agencies & churches.
Limitations: Applications not accepted. Giving
primarily in Hastings, MI. No grants to individuals.
Application information: Contributes only to
pre-selected organizations.

Officers and Directors:* Larry R. Baum,* Pres.; David L. Baum,* V.P.; A. Earlene Baum,* Secy.; Arthur E. Albin, Treas.
EIN: 383443737

124
Fitch H. Beach Charitable Foundation
c/o National City Bank of the Midwest
P.O. Box 94651
Cleveland, OH 44101-4651

Established in 1994 in MI.
Grantmaker type: Independent foundation.
Financial data (yr. ended 12/31/05): Assets, $2,607,798 (M); expenditures, $154,953; total giving, $124,060; qualifying distributions, $124,060; giving activities include $124,060 for grants.
Purpose and activities: Giving limited to the American Lung Association, Oak Park, the American Red Cross, Mid-Michigan Chapter, Lansing, the Hayes-Green-Beach Hospital, Charlotte, and Starr Commonwealth Schools, Albion.
Fields of interest: Education; Hospitals (general); Lung diseases; American Red Cross.
Limitations: Applications not accepted. Giving limited to Albion, Charlotte, Lansing, and Oak Park, MI. No grants to individuals.
Application information: Contributes only to 4 pre-selected organizations.
Trustee: National City Bank of the Midwest.
EIN: 383162304

125
Bernard H. Beal Scholarship Foundation
c/o National City Bank
2322 Tittabawassee Rd.
Saginaw, MI 48604
Application address: c/o Millington High School, 8780 Dean Dr., Millington, MI 48746, tel.: (989) 871-5220

Established in 1998 in MI.
Grantmaker type: Independent foundation.
Financial data (yr. ended 12/31/05): Assets, $596,219 (M); expenditures, $32,912; total giving, $27,750; qualifying distributions, $27,750; giving activities include $27,750 for grants to individuals.
Purpose and activities: Provides scholarships to graduates of Millington High School, MI.
Type of support: Scholarships—to individuals.
Limitations: Giving limited to Millington, MI.
Application information: Application form required.
Deadline(s): Jan. 31
Trustee: National City Bank.
EIN: 383381079

126
Joseph & Mari Beals Family Foundation
16824 Kercheval Pl., Ste. 202
Grosse Pointe, MI 48230 (313) 886-8700

Established in 1999 in MI.
Donor: Joseph M. Beals.
Grantmaker type: Independent foundation.
Financial data (yr. ended 7/31/05): Assets, $1 (M); expenditures, $1,000; total giving, $1,000; qualifying distributions, $1,000; giving activities include $1,000 for grants.
Fields of interest: Christian agencies & churches.

Type of support: General/operating support.
Officer: Joseph M. Beals, Mgr.
EIN: 383478253

127
H. H. Beaman Fund
c/o Citizens Bank Wealth Mgmt., N.A.
328 S. Saginaw St., M/C 002072
Flint, MI 48502 (866) 308-7878
Contact: Marge Weidman, Trust Off., Citizens Bank Wealth Mgmt.

Established in IA.
Grantmaker type: Independent foundation.
Financial data (yr. ended 6/30/05): Assets, $54,323 (M); expenditures, $1,980; total giving, $500; qualifying distributions, $1,810; giving activities include $500 for 1 grant to an individual.
Purpose and activities: Giving to organizations that aid the needy women and children of Marshalltown, IA.
Fields of interest: Children/youth, services; Women, centers/services; Women.
Limitations: Giving limited to Marshalltown, IA. No grants to individuals.
Application information:
Initial approach: Letter
Deadline(s): None
Trustee: Citizens Bank.
EIN: 237182175

128
Robert F. Beard Charitable Foundation
3720 Woodland Dr.
Highland, MI 48356 (248) 887-4191
Contact: Robert F. Beard, Pres.

Established in 1994 in MI.
Donor: Robert F. Beard.
Grantmaker type: Independent foundation.
Financial data (yr. ended 12/31/04): Assets, $9,009 (M); expenditures, $500; total giving, $500; qualifying distributions, $500; giving activities include $500 for grants.
Fields of interest: Salvation Army.
Type of support: General/operating support.
Limitations: Giving limited to southeastern MI. No grants to individuals.
Application information:
Initial approach: Letter
Deadline(s): Dec. 31
Officers and Directors:* Robert F. Beard,* Pres.; Richard W. Beard,* Secy.-Treas.
EIN: 383168934

129
Joseph E. Beauchamp Charitable Trust
c/o JPMorgan Chase Bank, N.A.
P.O. Box 1308
Milwaukee, WI 53201
Contact: Michael Barry, Mgr.
Application address: c/o JPMorgan Chase Bank, N.A., Endowment and Foundation Div., 611 Woodward Ave., Detroit, MI 48226, tel.: (313) 225-1249; E-mail: michael_barry@em.fcnbd.com

Established in 1976 in MI.
Grantmaker type: Independent foundation.
Financial data (yr. ended 12/31/05): Assets, $328,836 (M); expenditures, $14,644; total giving,

$9,000; qualifying distributions, $9,000; giving activities include $9,000 for grants.
Purpose and activities: Giving to religious, charitable, scientific, literary, or educational purposes, or for the prevention of cruelty to children or animals.
Fields of interest: Education; Animals/wildlife; Crime/violence prevention, child abuse; Religion.
Type of support: General/operating support; Continuing support; Annual campaigns; Equipment; Program development.
Limitations: Giving limited to MI. No grants to individuals.
Application information: Application form not required.
Initial approach: Letter or telephone
Deadline(s): None
Officer: Michael Barry, Mgr.
Trustee: JPMorgan Chase Bank, N.A.
EIN: 382119454

130
Nicholas & Nota Becharas Foundation
14501 Hamilton Ave.
Highland Park, MI 48203 (313) 259-7777

Established in MI.
Grantmaker type: Independent foundation.
Financial data (yr. ended 12/31/04): Assets, $10,588 (M); expenditures, $6,436; total giving, $1,500; qualifying distributions, $3,968; giving activities include $1,500 for grants.
Fields of interest: Education.
Limitations: Applications not accepted. Giving limited to Troy, MI.
Application information: Contributes only to pre-selected organizations.
Officer and Trustee:* Nicholas D. Becharas,* Pres. and Secy.-Treas.
EIN: 382140271

131
William F. and Patricia A. Beck Family Foundation
111 Michigan Ave.
P.O. Box 1147
Frankfort, MI 49635

Established in 1998 in MI.
Donor: William F. Beck.
Grantmaker type: Independent foundation.
Financial data (yr. ended 12/31/05): Assets, $728,326 (M); gifts received, $183,497; expenditures, $46,096; total giving, $42,075; qualifying distributions, $43,790; giving activities include $42,075 for grants.
Fields of interest: Education; Christian agencies & churches.
Type of support: General/operating support.
Application information: Application form not required.
Deadline(s): None
Trustees: Patricia A. Beck; William F. Beck.
EIN: 367236926

132
The Julius H. and Barbara B. Beers Family Foundation
102 E. Front St.
Traverse City, MI 49684

Established in 1998 in MI.
Donors: Julius Beers; Barbara Beers.
Grantmaker type: Independent foundation.
Financial data (yr. ended 12/31/05): Assets, $1,977,843 (M); expenditures, $111,092; total giving, $96,833; qualifying distributions, $102,158; giving activities include $96,833 for grants.
Fields of interest: Higher education, university; Environment; Health care; Human services; Family services; Women, centers/services; Foundations (community); Federated giving programs; Protestant agencies & churches.
Limitations: Applications not accepted. Giving primarily in Traverse City, MI. No grants to individuals.
Application information: Contributes only to pre-selected organizations.
Officer and Director:* Barbara Beers,* Pres.
EIN: 383417343

133
John & Nesbeth Bees School Foundation
c/o Citizens Bank Wealth Mgmt., N.A.
328 S. Saginaw St., M/C 002072
Flint, MI 48502
Application address: c/o Helen James, Citizens Bank Wealth Mgmt., N.A., 101 N. Washington Ave., Saginaw, MI 48607, tel.: (989) 776-7368

Established in 1997 in MI.
Grantmaker type: Independent foundation.
Financial data (yr. ended 12/31/05): Assets, $657,528 (M); expenditures, $41,105; total giving, $28,220; qualifying distributions, $28,220; giving activities include $28,220 for grants to individuals.
Type of support: Scholarships—to individuals.
Limitations: Giving limited to residents of Saginaw County, MI.
Application information: Application form required.
   Deadline(s): May 1
Trustee: Citizens Bank.
EIN: 386601371

134
Florence and Minnie Behl Trust f/b/o Alma College
c/o Hibernia National Bank
P.O. Box 61540
New Orleans, LA 70161

Established in 1989 in LA.
Donors: Florence Behl‡; Minnie Behl‡.
Grantmaker type: Independent foundation.
Financial data (yr. ended 12/31/04): Assets, $362,616 (M); expenditures, $21,832; total giving, $16,397; qualifying distributions, $16,397; giving activities include $16,397 for grants.
Purpose and activities: Support only for Alma College, MI.
Fields of interest: Higher education.
Type of support: General/operating support.
Limitations: Applications not accepted. Giving limited to Alma, MI. No grants to individuals.
Application information: Contributes only to a pre-selected organization specified in the trust instrument.
Trustees: George Griffing; Hibernia National Bank.
EIN: 726099159

135
Florence and Minnie Behl Trust f/b/o Westminister Presbyterian Church
c/o Hibernia National Bank
P.O. Box 61540
New Orleans, LA 70161

Established in 1989 in LA.
Donors: Florence Behl‡; Minnie Behl‡.
Grantmaker type: Independent foundation.
Financial data (yr. ended 12/31/03): Assets, $513,000 (M); expenditures, $39,974; total giving, $33,709; qualifying distributions, $34,016; giving activities include $33,709 for grants.
Purpose and activities: Support only for Westminster Presbyterian Church, Grand Rapids, MI.
Fields of interest: Protestant agencies & churches.
Limitations: Applications not accepted. Giving limited to Grand Rapids, MI. No grants to individuals.
Application information: Contributes only to a pre-selected organization specified in the governing instrument.
Trustees: George Griffing; Hibernia National Bank.
EIN: 726099157

136
Larry L. Behrenwald Foundation
c/o Larry L. Behrenwald
8800 Darby Rd.
Clarksville, MI 48815-9711

Donors: Larry L. Behrenwald; Kay Behrenwald.
Grantmaker type: Independent foundation.
Financial data (yr. ended 4/30/05): Assets, $10,049 (M); gifts received, $10,000; expenditures, $690; total giving, $0; qualifying distributions, $0.
Purpose and activities: Giving to Christian ministries.
Fields of interest: Christian agencies & churches.
Limitations: Applications not accepted. No grants to individuals.
Application information: Contributes only to pre-selected organizations.
Officer: Larry L. Behrenwald, Pres.
Director: Kay Behrenwald.
EIN: 382326961

137
The Gloria Wille Bell and Carlos R. Bell Charitable Trust
P.O. Box 397
Richmond, VA 23218-0397
Application addresses: c/o Univ. of MI, College of Engineering Scholarship Office, 1221 Beal Ave., Ann Arbor, MI 48109-2102, FAX: (734) 647-7126, E-mail: coe.scholarships@umich.edu; c/o Univ. of MI, College of Literature, Science and the Arts, Undergraduate Recruitment and Scholarship Office, 1045 Haven Hall, 505 S. State St., Ann Arbor, MI 48109-1045, FAX: (734) 615-0588, E-mail: lsascholarship@umich.edu

Established in 2002 in VA.
Donor: Carlos R. Bell‡.
Grantmaker type: Independent foundation.
Financial data (yr. ended 6/30/05): Assets, $5,469,203 (M); gifts received, $711; expenditures, $326,888; total giving, $250,000; qualifying distributions, $289,438; giving activities

include $250,000 for 5 grants to individuals (high: $80,000; low: $30,000).
Purpose and activities: Funds scholarship awards to first year students attending the University of Michigan, Ann Arbor, entering the College of Engineering or the College of Literature, Science, and the Arts, who are enrolled in an undergraduate degree program in the sciences and who meet specific geographic criteria.
Fields of interest: Engineering school/education; Scholarships/financial aid.
Type of support: Scholarship funds.
Limitations: Giving limited to benefit University of MI students at Ann Arbor.
Application information: Individual scholarship recipients selected by University of Michigan Selection Committee. Application form required.
   Initial approach: Completed application form
   Deadline(s): Mar. 1
Trustee: John B. O'Grady.
EIN: 546500526

138
Frances and John Bell Family Foundation
c/o John D. Bell
39312 Woodward Ave., Ste. 100
Bloomfield, MI 48304-5007

Established in 2003 in MI.
Donors: John D. Bell; Frances G. Bell.
Grantmaker type: Independent foundation.
Financial data (yr. ended 12/31/04): Assets, $100,000 (M); gifts received, $102,710; expenditures, $2,710; total giving, $0; qualifying distributions, $0.
Limitations: Applications not accepted. No grants to individuals.
Application information: Contributes only to pre-selected organizations.
Officers: John D. Bell, Pres. and Treas.; Frances G. Bell, V.P. and Secy.
EIN: 900059582

139
Bell Trust
P.O. Box 110
Tecumseh, MI 49286-0110

Established in 1987 in MI.
Donors: Robert F. Bell; Muriel L. Bell.
Grantmaker type: Independent foundation.
Financial data (yr. ended 12/31/04): Assets, $19,648 (M); expenditures, $5,837; total giving, $5,600; qualifying distributions, $5,838; giving activities include $5,600 for grants.
Fields of interest: Performing arts; Higher education; Education; Health care; Youth development; Federated giving programs.
Limitations: Applications not accepted. Giving primarily in MI, with emphasis on Adrian. No grants to individuals.
Application information: Contributes only to pre-selected organizations.
Trustees: Muriel L. Bell; Robert F. Bell.
EIN: 382704083

140
Don & Iva Bellinger Scholarship Fund
c/o Citizens Bank Wealth Mgmt., N.A.
328 S. Saginaw St., M/C 002072
Flint, MI 48502 (989) 776-7368
Application address: c/o Helen M. James, Citizens
Bank Wealth Mgmt., N.A., 101 N. Washington Ave.,
Saginaw, MI 48607, tel.: (989) 776-7368

Established in 1993 in MI.
Donor: Iva Bellinger†.
Grantmaker type: Independent foundation.
Financial data (yr. ended 12/31/05): Assets,
$1,057,794 (M); expenditures, $67,104; total
giving, $45,700; qualifying distributions, $45,700;
giving activities include $45,700 for grants.
Purpose and activities: Scholarships to students
admitted to or already enrolled in a nursing program.
Fields of interest: Nursing care.
Type of support: Scholarships—to individuals.
Limitations: Giving limited to MI.
Application information: Application form required.
   Deadline(s): Jan. 31
Trustee: Citizens Bank.
EIN: 386615679

141
Samuel L. Bemis Scholarship Fund
c/o Fifth Third Bank
P.O. Box 3636
Grand Rapids, MI 49501-3636

Established in 1995 in IL.
Grantmaker type: Independent foundation.
Financial data (yr. ended 12/31/05): Assets,
$1,320,433 (M); expenditures, $92,730; total
giving, $71,543; qualifying distributions, $71,543;
giving activities include $71,543 for grants.
Purpose and activities: Scholarship awards limited
to graduating female seniors of Brattleboro Union
High School, VT; giving also to Union High School.
Fields of interest: Secondary school/education.
Type of support: Scholarships—to individuals.
Limitations: Giving limited to residents of
Brattleboro, VT.
Application information:
   Initial approach: Format provided by school
   Deadline(s): May 10
Trustee: Fifth Third Bank.
EIN: 367112890

142
Betzer Benson Charitable Trust
c/o Fifth Third Bank
P.O. Box 3636
Grand Rapids, MI 49501

Established in 1997 in IL.
Grantmaker type: Independent foundation.
Financial data (yr. ended 12/31/05): Assets,
$421,803 (M); expenditures, $13,900; total giving,
$9,600; qualifying distributions, $9,600; giving
activities include $9,600 for grants.
Fields of interest: Christian agencies & churches.
Limitations: Applications not accepted. Giving
limited to Chicago, IL, and Boston, MA. No grants to
individuals.
Application information: Contributes only to 2
pre-selected organizations.
Trustee: Fifth Third Bank.
EIN: 367057883

143
Alvin M. Bentley Foundation
P.O. Box 1516
Owosso, MI 48867-6516 (989) 723-7464
Contact: Ann Marie Bentley, V.P.

Incorporated in 1961 in MI.
Donors: Alvin M. Bentley†; Arvella D. Bentley†.
Grantmaker type: Independent foundation.
Financial data (yr. ended 12/31/05): Assets,
$2,670,127 (M); expenditures, $216,293; total
giving, $186,250; qualifying distributions,
$186,250; giving activities include $186,250 for 10
grants (high: $108,750; low: $500).
Purpose and activities: Giving primarily for higher
education.
Fields of interest: Higher education; Human
services.
Type of support: Scholarship funds.
Limitations: Giving primarily in MI. No grants to
individuals, or for building or endowment funds, or
matching gifts.
Publications: Informational brochure.
Application information: Application form not
required.
   Initial approach: Letter
   Deadline(s): Mar. 1
Officers: Paul Brown, Pres.; Ann Marie Bentley, V.P.;
Marianne Manderfield, Secy.; Richard A. Batchelor,
Treas.
Trustees: Denise Bannan; Alvin M. Bentley IV;
Susan Bentley; Mary Alice Campbell; Constance E.
Cook; Ruth Gordon Hastie; George W. Hoddy; David
McDowell.
Number of staff: 1 part-time support.
EIN: 386076280
Selected grants: The following grants were reported
in 2004.
$108,750 to University of Michigan, Ann Arbor, MI.
   For scholarships.
$70,000 to Albion College, Albion, MI. For
   scholarships.
$1,000 to American Red Cross. For operating
   support.
$1,000 to Boy Scouts of America, Tall Pine Council,
   Flint, MI. For operating support.
$1,000 to Girl Scouts of the U.S.A., Fair Winds
   Council, Flint, MI. For operating support.
$500 to Respite. For operating support.
$500 to Saint Vincent de Paul Society, Flint, MI. For
   operating support.
$500 to Salvation Army of Owosso, Owosso, MI. For
   operating support.
$500 to YMCA of Shiawassee, Owosso, MI. For
   operating support.

144
**The Stanley L. and Phyllis Berger Family
Foundation**
17117 W. Nine Mile Rd., Ste. 1100
Southfield, MI 48075

Established in 2001 in MI.
Donors: Debbie Berger; Karen Berger; Michael
Berger; Phyllis Berger; Stanley L. Berger; Steven
Berger.
Grantmaker type: Independent foundation.
Financial data (yr. ended 12/31/04): Assets,
$198,611 (M); gifts received, $172,286;
expenditures, $168,725; total giving, $108,970;
qualifying distributions, $108,970; giving activities
include $108,970 for 22 grants (high: $31,000;
low: $50).

Fields of interest: Education; Human services;
Federated giving programs; Jewish agencies &
temples.
Limitations: Applications not accepted. Giving
primarily in MI. No grants to individuals.
Application information: Contributes only to
pre-selected organizations.
Officers: Stanley L. Berger, Pres. and Treas.; Phyllis
Berger, V.P.; Michael Berger, Secy.
Directors: Steven Berger; Laurie Bounds.
EIN: 383614706

145
Mary Maybury Berkery Memorial Trust
c/o Comerica Bank
P.O. Box 75000
Detroit, MI 48275-3302 (313) 222-3797
Application address: c/o Michelle Sica, 101 N. Main
St., Ste. 100, Ann Arbor, MI 48104, tel.: (734)
930-2413

Established in 1998 in MI.
Donor: Berkery Trust.
Grantmaker type: Independent foundation.
Financial data (yr. ended 8/31/05): Assets,
$331,380 (M); expenditures, $15,762; total giving,
$11,000; qualifying distributions, $11,000; giving
activities include $11,000 for grants.
Purpose and activities: Giving restricted to Roman
Catholic colleges and universities for scholarships
to women; some giving to organizations assisting
the needy.
Fields of interest: Roman Catholic agencies &
churches; Women; Economically disadvantaged.
Type of support: Scholarship funds.
Limitations: Giving limited to MI. No grants to
individuals.
Application information: Application form not
required.
   Initial approach: Letter
   Deadline(s): None
Trustee: Comerica Bank.
EIN: 386719148

146
Alfred Berkowitz Foundation
c/o David M. Levine
30445 Northwestern Hwy., Ste. 140
Farmington Hills, MI 48334

Donors: J. Berkowitz†; A. Berkowitz†.
Grantmaker type: Independent foundation.
Financial data (yr. ended 12/31/04): Assets,
$1,222,737 (M); expenditures, $253,915; total
giving, $160,000; qualifying distributions,
$209,258; giving activities include $160,000 for 7
grants (high: $50,000; low: $3,500).
Purpose and activities: Giving primarily to
educational institutions, hospitals, and human
services.
Fields of interest: Higher education; Hospitals
(general); Human services; Jewish agencies &
temples.
Limitations: Applications not accepted. Giving on a
national basis. No grants to individuals.
Application information: Contributes only to
pre-selected organizations.
Trustee: David M. Levine.
EIN: 386585623

147
Hy and Greta Berkowitz Foundation
c/o Grant Committee
1600 Beard Dr. S.E.
Grand Rapids, MI 49546

Established in 1969 in MI.
Donors: Rogers Department Store; Hyman Berkowitz; Greta Berkowitz.
Grantmaker type: Independent foundation.
Financial data (yr. ended 12/31/04): Assets, $1,324,889 (M); gifts received, $41,235; expenditures, $55,869; total giving, $54,086; qualifying distributions, $54,086; giving activities include $54,086 for 8 grants (high: $50,000; low: $84).
Fields of interest: Higher education; Medical research; Children/youth, services; International development.
Limitations: Giving primarily in Colorado Springs, CO, Grand Rapids, MI and Middleton, OH. No grants to individuals.
Application information:
Initial approach: Letter
Deadline(s): None
Officers: Shirley B. Hurwitz, Pres. and Secy.; Luanne B. Thodey, V.P. and Treas.
EIN: 381907981

148
The Marvin Berlin Foundation
c/o Kathie Ling
400 W. Maple Rd., Ste. 200
Birmingham, MI 48009

Established in 1986 in MI.
Donors: Marvin Berlin‡; Alice Berlin.
Grantmaker type: Independent foundation.
Financial data (yr. ended 12/31/04): Assets, $34,550 (M); gifts received, $249,760; expenditures, $221,605; total giving, $221,575; qualifying distributions, $221,601; giving activities include $221,575 for 41 grants (high: $109,741; low: $15).
Fields of interest: Jewish agencies & temples.
Limitations: Applications not accepted. Giving primarily in Southfield, MI. No grants to individuals.
Application information: Contributes only to pre-selected organizations.
Officers: Alice Berlin, Pres.; William E. Berlin, Treas.
EIN: 382731819

149
Mandell L. and Madeleine H. Berman Foundation
(formerly Madeleine and Mandell L. Berman Foundation)
c/o Sarai Brachman Shoup
29100 Northwestern Hwy., Ste. 370
Southfield, MI 48034

Established in 1994 in MI.
Grantmaker type: Independent foundation.
Financial data (yr. ended 12/31/04): Assets, $12,387,014 (M); gifts received, $1,467,250; expenditures, $971,808; total giving, $596,829; qualifying distributions, $638,453; giving activities include $596,829 for grants.
Fields of interest: Arts; Animal welfare; Jewish agencies & temples; Disabilities, people with.
International interests: Israel.

Limitations: Applications not accepted. Giving on a national and international basis, and in the Detroit, MI, area. No grants to individuals.
Application information: Contributes only to pre-selected organizations.
Trustee: Mandell L. Berman.
Number of staff: 2 part-time professional.
EIN: 386644875
Selected grants: The following grants were reported in 2003.
$214,000 to Allied Jewish Campaign, Detroit, MI. For unrestricted support.
$100,000 to American Jewish Joint Distribution Committee, New York, NY. For unrestricted support.
$50,000 to Jewish Womens Foundation of Metropolitan Detroit, Bloomfield Hills, MI. For unrestricted support.
$25,000 to Brandeis University, Waltham, MA. For unrestricted support.
$25,000 to Detroit Institute of Arts, Detroit, MI. For unrestricted support.
$15,000 to Detroit Symphony Orchestra, Detroit, MI. For unrestricted support.
$10,000 to Camp Tamarack Association, Canada. For unrestricted support.
$10,000 to Oakland Family Services, Pontiac, MI. For unrestricted support.
$5,500 to Wayne State University, Detroit, MI. For unrestricted support.
$5,000 to Michigan State University, East Lansing, MI. For unrestricted support.

150
Edward & June Bernstein Foundation
588 Brookside
Birmingham, MI 48009

Established in MI.
Donors: Yale Bernstein; Martin Bernstein.
Grantmaker type: Independent foundation.
Financial data (yr. ended 6/30/05): Assets, $225,783 (M); expenditures, $11,166; total giving, $9,650; qualifying distributions, $10,383; giving activities include $9,650 for grants.
Fields of interest: Human services; Jewish federated giving programs; Jewish agencies & temples.
Type of support: General/operating support.
Limitations: Applications not accepted. Giving primarily in MI. No grants to individuals.
Application information: Contributes only to pre-selected organizations.
Officers: Yale Bernstein, Pres.; Martin Bernstein, V.P.
EIN: 386087510

151
Berrien-Cass-Van Buren Foundation, Inc.
499 W. Main St.
Benton Harbor, MI 49022 (800) 533-5800
Contact: Patricia Holden, Interim Exec. Dir.

Grantmaker type: Independent foundation.
Financial data (yr. ended 6/30/05): Assets, $7,907 (M); expenditures, $905; total giving, $0; qualifying distributions, $0.
Fields of interest: Children/youth.
Limitations: Giving limited to residents of Berrien, Cass, and Van Buren counties, MI.
Application information:

Initial approach: Letter
Deadline(s): None
Officers and Trustees:* John Tapper, Sr.,* Chair.; Arnie Redjicker,* Vice-Chair.; Patricia Holden, Interim Exec. Dir.; James Sayer; Harold Schuitmaker.
EIN: 382534692

152
The Berry Foundation
3505 Stanton Ct.
Ann Arbor, MI 48105-3032

Established in 1997 in OH.
Donor: Philip C. Berry.
Grantmaker type: Independent foundation.
Financial data (yr. ended 12/31/05): Assets, $24,584 (M); gifts received, $14,775; expenditures, $11,518; total giving, $11,500; qualifying distributions, $11,500; giving activities include $11,500 for grants.
Limitations: Giving primarily in MI; giving also in NC. No grants to individuals.
Trustees: Philip C. Berry; Philip K. Berry; Kathleen B. Irvin.
EIN: 311538611

153
John W. and Margaret G. Bertsch Charitable Foundation
525 Buena Vista
Spring Lake, MI 49456
Contact: Margaret G. Bertsch, Pres.

Established in MI.
Donor: John W. Bertsch.
Grantmaker type: Independent foundation.
Financial data (yr. ended 12/31/05): Assets, $221,864 (M); expenditures, $8,622; total giving, $7,500; qualifying distributions, $7,500; giving activities include $7,500 for grants.
Limitations: Giving primarily in Grand Rapids, MI. No grants to individuals.
Application information:
Initial approach: Letter
Deadline(s): None
Officers: Margaret G. Bertsch, Pres.; J.R. Bertsch, Secy.-Treas.
EIN: 382772589

154
Beson Family Foundation
143 Cady Ctr., Ste. 356
Northville, MI 48167

Established in 1999 in MI.
Donor: Robert J. Beson Charitable Annuity Lead Trust.
Grantmaker type: Independent foundation.
Financial data (yr. ended 12/31/05): Assets, $2,000,895 (M); gifts received, $285,000; expenditures, $196,802; total giving, $193,331; qualifying distributions, $194,993; giving activities include $193,331 for 11 grants (high: $56,331; low: $500).
Fields of interest: Higher education; Cancer; Health organizations; Medical research; Human services; Residential/custodial care, hospices.
Type of support: General/operating support.

Limitations: Applications not accepted. Giving primarily in MI. No grants to individuals.
Application information: Contributes only to pre-selected organizations.
Officers and Directors:* Elizabeth Beson,* Pres.; Alan Ferrara,* Secy.; Gary Dabkowski,* Treas.; Jim Beson; Kevin Beson; Stephen Beson; Terry Marrs.
EIN: 383308555

155
Besser Foundation
123 N. 2nd Ave., Ste. 3
Alpena, MI 49707-2801 (989) 354-4722
Contact: J. Richard Wilson, Pres.
FAX: (989) 354-8099; E-mail: bessfdtn@freeway.net

Incorporated in 1944 in MI.
Donors: J.H. Besser‡; Besser Co.
Grantmaker type: Independent foundation.
Financial data (yr. ended 12/31/04): Assets, $17,289,894 (M); expenditures, $1,028,176; total giving, $874,908; qualifying distributions, $952,110; giving activities include $874,908 for 46 grants (high: $220,000; low: $600; average: $300–$448,353).
Purpose and activities: Grants primarily to local schools and colleges and health and social service agencies; giving also to Africare for projects in underdeveloped nations in Africa. In addition, the foundation partially supports the Jesse Besser Museum, a local historical and art museum.
Fields of interest: Museums; Arts; Education; Human services; Children/youth, services.
Type of support: General/operating support; Continuing support; Capital campaigns; Building/renovation; Matching/challenge support.
Limitations: Giving limited to the Alpena, MI, area. No support for video projects. No grants to individuals, or for endowment funds, meeting or conference expenses, travel, or research.
Publications: Annual report (including application guidelines).
Application information: Applications sent via fax accepted. Application form not required.
  Initial approach: Letter of introduction
  Copies of proposal: 1
  Deadline(s): End of 1st month in each calendar quarter
  Board meeting date(s): Quarterly beginning in Mar.
Officers and Trustees:* J. Richard Wilson,* Pres. and Treas.; James C. Park,* V.P.; Patricia Gardner,* Secy.; Gary Dawley; Carl E. Reitz; Harold A. Ruemenapp.
Number of staff: 2 part-time support.
EIN: 386071938

156
Betmar Charitable Foundation, Inc.
4868 Fairway Ridge S.
West Bloomfield, MI 48323 (248) 855-0606
Contact: Allan Jacobs, Pres.

Established in 1999 in MI.
Donor: Howard Bayer.
Grantmaker type: Independent foundation.
Financial data (yr. ended 12/31/05): Assets, $1,766,900 (M); gifts received, $309,294; expenditures, $169,757; total giving, $96,003; qualifying distributions, $96,003; giving activities include $96,003 for 73 grants (high: $10,500; low: $100).

Fields of interest: Education; Health organizations, association; Human services; Jewish federated giving programs; Jewish agencies & temples.
Limitations: Giving primarily in MI, with some giving in IL and MA. No grants to individuals.
Application information: Application form not required.
  Initial approach: Letter
  Deadline(s): None
Officers and Directors:* Allan Jacobs,* Pres. and Secy.; Douglas Shiffman,* V.P. and Treas.; Goldie Jacobs.
EIN: 383515213

157
Tony Betten Family Foundation
3839 Plainfield Ave. N.E.
Grand Rapids, MI 49525

Established in 2000 in MI.
Donors: Anthony J. Betten; Tony Betten & Son's Ford, Inc.
Grantmaker type: Independent foundation.
Financial data (yr. ended 12/31/05): Assets, $103,831 (M); gifts received, $34,354; expenditures, $36,813; total giving, $35,753; qualifying distributions, $35,753; giving activities include $35,753 for grants.
Limitations: Applications not accepted. Giving primarily in Grand Rapids, MI. No grants to individuals.
Application information: Unsolicited requests for funds not accepted.
Officers: Jerome Betten, Pres. and Treas.; Dennis Betten, Secy.
Director: Anthony J. Betten.
EIN: 383555251

158
Marion & Marlene Betten Foundation
(formerly The Betten Auto Family Foundation)
440 28th St. S.E.
Grand Rapids, MI 49508

Established in 1988 in MI.
Donors: Marion Betten; Marlene Betten.
Grantmaker type: Independent foundation.
Financial data (yr. ended 12/31/05): Assets, $2,155,764 (M); gifts received, $279,892; expenditures, $73,872; total giving, $53,571; qualifying distributions, $58,071; giving activities include $53,571 for 19 grants (high: $29,121; low: $100).
Purpose and activities: Giving primarily to Christian organizations.
Fields of interest: Education; Health organizations; Human services; Christian agencies & churches.
Limitations: Applications not accepted. Giving primarily in Grand Rapids, MI. No grants to individuals.
Application information: Contributes only to pre-selected organizations.
Officers: Marion Betten, Pres.; Marlene Betten, V.P.; Laura Lamer, Secy.; Alice Scholten, Treas.
Directors: Gregory Betten; Rodney Betten.
EIN: 382848189

159
The Betty and Bob Foundation, Inc.
(formerly Pleasant Lake Park, Inc.)
901 Wilshire Dr., Ste. 400
Troy, MI 48084

Established in 1997 in MI; funded in 1999.
Donor: James Merritt.
Grantmaker type: Independent foundation.
Financial data (yr. ended 12/31/05): Assets, $1,317,952 (M); expenditures, $57,220; total giving, $53,672; qualifying distributions, $53,672; giving activities include $53,672 for grants.
Purpose and activities: Giving primarily for projects that promote religious teachings and Christian fellowship.
Fields of interest: Human services; Christian agencies & churches.
Type of support: General/operating support.
Limitations: Applications not accepted. Giving on a national basis. No grants to individuals.
Application information: Contributes only to pre-selected organizations.
Officers: Robert J. Foster, Pres.; Mary E. Foster, V.P.; John P. McCulloch, Secy.
EIN: 383353832

160
Herbert and Barbara Beyer Foundation, Inc.
999 Stratford Pl.
Bloomfield Hills, MI 48304

Established in 1998 in MI.
Donors: Herbert Beyer; Barbara Beyer.
Grantmaker type: Independent foundation.
Financial data (yr. ended 12/31/05): Assets, $38,511 (M); expenditures, $2,828; total giving, $2,190; qualifying distributions, $2,190; giving activities include $2,190 for grants.
Limitations: Applications not accepted. No grants to individuals.
Application information: Contributes only to pre-selected organizations.
Officers: Barbara Beyer, Pres.
Director: Mark Beyer.
EIN: 383398996

161
Beyler-Volpert Senior Citizen's Trust
c/o Fifth Third Bank
P.O. Box 3636, 111 Lyon St. N.W.
Grand Rapids, MI 49501

Grantmaker type: Independent foundation.
Financial data (yr. ended 6/30/04): Assets, $115,992 (M); expenditures, $5,513; total giving, $4,400; qualifying distributions, $4,400; giving activities include $4,400 for grants.
Purpose and activities: Support only for Marshall County Council on Aging, IN.
Fields of interest: Residential/custodial care, senior continuing care; Aging.
Type of support: General/operating support.
Limitations: Applications not accepted. Giving limited to Marshall County, IN. No grants to individuals.
Application information: Contributes only to a pre-selected organization.
Officers: Ron Liechty, Mgr.; Clem Miller, Jr., Mgr.; Jean Miller, Mgr.; Jackie Wright, Mgr.

Trustee: Fifth Third Bank.
EIN: 351780133

162
BFK Foundation
c/o Stephen Kaplan
1213 S. Forest Ave.
Ann Arbor, MI   48104-3922

Established in MD.
Donors: Beatrice Kaplan; Rubin H. Kaplan.
Grantmaker type: Independent foundation.
Financial data (yr. ended 12/31/05): Assets,
$301,626 (M); expenditures, $52,354; total giving,
$50,000; qualifying distributions, $52,250; giving
activities include $50,000 for 17 grants (high:
$4,000; low: $2,000).
Purpose and activities: Giving primarily for
environmental protection and to Jewish
organizations.
Fields of interest: Environment, natural resources;
Human services; Jewish agencies & temples.
Type of support: General/operating support.
Limitations: Applications not accepted. Giving
primarily in CA, Washington, DC, OH, NY, and VA. No
grants to individuals.
Application information: Contributes only to
pre-selected organizations.
Directors: Abram W. Kaplan; Rachel Kaplan;
Stephen Kaplan.
EIN: 522069703
Selected grants: The following grants were reported
in 2004.
$20,000 to American Farmland Trust, DC.
$20,000 to Ohio Environmental Council, Columbus,
   OH.
$17,000 to American Jewish World Service, New
   York, NY.
$10,000 to Trust for Public Land, San Francisco, CA.
$9,000 to New Israel Fund, DC.
$5,000 to Environmental Defense, New York, NY.
$5,000 to FINCA International, DC.
$5,000 to Global Greengrants Fund, Boulder, CO.
$5,000 to Heifer Project International, Little Rock,
   AR.
$5,000 to Jewish Social Service Agency of
   Metropolitan Washington, Rockville, MD.

163
Bhargava Foundation
26275 Northpointe Dr.
Farmington Hills, MI   48331

Established in 2001 in MI.
Donor: Rai Bhargava.
Grantmaker type: Independent foundation.
Financial data (yr. ended 12/31/04): Assets,
$310,748 (M); gifts received, $12,000;
expenditures, $20,469; total giving, $20,194;
qualifying distributions, $20,194; giving activities
include $20,194 for grants.
Limitations: Applications not accepted. No grants to
individuals.
Application information: Contributes only to
pre-selected organizations.
Officers and Directors:* Rai Bhargava,* Pres.;
Vanita Bhargava,* Secy.
EIN: 383628004

164
Erma E. Biedermann Trust
c/o Comerica Bank
P.O. Box 75000, Trust Tax, Mail Code 3302
Detroit, MI   48275

Established in 1983 in MI.
Grantmaker type: Independent foundation.
Financial data (yr. ended 11/30/04): Assets,
$561,072 (M); expenditures, $75,155; total giving,
$61,474; qualifying distributions, $61,474; giving
activities include $61,474 for grants.
Purpose and activities: Support only for the Jackson
Community Foundation, for its student loan
program.
Fields of interest: Foundations (community).
Limitations: Applications not accepted. Giving
limited to Jackson, MI. No grants to individuals.
Application information: Contributes only to a
pre-selected organization.
Trustee: Comerica Bank.
EIN: 386453506

165
Gustave and Hilda Bierlein Charitable
Foundation, Inc.
c/o National City Bank
171 Monroe Ave. N.W., KC17-63
Grand Rapids, MI   49503-2634

Established in 1987 in MI.
Grantmaker type: Independent foundation.
Financial data (yr. ended 12/31/05): Assets,
$742,504 (M); expenditures, $39,977; total giving,
$34,500; qualifying distributions, $34,500; giving
activities include $34,500 for grants.
Purpose and activities: Giving primarily for Lutheran
organizations, including schools, churches, and
social services organizations.
Fields of interest: Higher education; Human
services; Protestant agencies & churches.
Limitations: Applications not accepted. Giving
primarily in MI. No grants to individuals.
Application information: Contributes only to
pre-selected organizations.
Trustee: National City Bank.
EIN: 382803975

166
Duane & Dorothy Bierlein Family
Foundation
c/o Andrews Hooper & Pavlik
516 S. Main St.
Frankenmuth, MI   48734
Contact: H. Duane Bierlein, Pres.
Application address: 444 Mary Ln., Frankenmuth, MI
48734

Established in 2001 in MI.
Donors: Duane Bierlein; Dorothy P. Bierlein.
Grantmaker type: Independent foundation.
Financial data (yr. ended 12/31/05): Assets,
$272,338 (M); gifts received, $42,000;
expenditures, $15,181; total giving, $9,666;
qualifying distributions, $9,666; giving activities
include $9,666 for grants.
Application information:
   Initial approach: Letter
   Deadline(s): None

Officers: H. Duane Bierlein, Pres.; Dorothy P.
Bierlein, V.P.; Randall D. Bierlein, Secy.; Robert A.
Loesel, Treas.
Director: Barbara Harvey.
EIN: 383637097

167
Guido A. & Elizabeth H. Binda Foundation
1415 Heritage Twr.
Battle Creek, MI   49017
Contact: Elizabeth H. Binda, Pres.

Established in 1977 in MI.
Donor: Guido A. Binda†.
Grantmaker type: Independent foundation.
Financial data (yr. ended 6/30/05): Assets,
$15,362,290 (M); expenditures, $956,772; total
giving, $766,545; qualifying distributions,
$792,221; giving activities include $766,545 for 75
grants (high: $100,000; low: $100).
Purpose and activities: Giving primarily for
education; support also for health care, community
development, and human services.
Fields of interest: Visual arts, architecture; Arts;
Elementary school/education; Secondary school/
education; Higher education; Adult education—
literacy, basic skills & GED; Scholarships/financial
aid; Education, reading; Education; Environment;
Health care; Substance abuse, services; Human
services; Community development; Minorities;
Economically disadvantaged.
Type of support: Program development; Seed
money; Curriculum development; Scholarship funds.
Limitations: Giving limited to Battle Creek and
southwestern MI. No grants to individuals, or for
endowments or capital campaigns.
Publications: Application guidelines; Informational
brochure (including application guidelines).
Application information: Application form required.
   Initial approach: Letter or telephone
   Copies of proposal: 11
   Deadline(s): Dec. 1 to May 1
   Board meeting date(s): Jan. and June
   Final notification: 10 days
Officers and Trustees:* Elizabeth H. Binda,* Pres.
and Secy.; Richard Tsoumas,* V.P.; E. James
Swan,* Treas.; Robert Binda; LaVerne H. Boss;
Norman Brown; Chris T. Christ; John Hosking; Joel
Orosz; Cindy S. Ruble.
Number of staff: 1 part-time support.
EIN: 382184423

168
Bingham Family Foundation
P.O. Box 290
St. Clair Shores, MI   48080-0290

Established in 1999 in MI.
Donors: Richard Bingham; Susan Beaufait
Bingham.
Grantmaker type: Independent foundation.
Financial data (yr. ended 12/31/05): Assets,
$432,366 (M); expenditures, $23,031; total giving,
$20,000; qualifying distributions, $20,000; giving
activities include $20,000 for grants.
Limitations: Applications not accepted. Giving on a
national basis, with some emphasis on MI.
Trustees: Richard Bingham; Susan Beaufait
Bingham; Michael Murray.
EIN: 383507412

169
Bird Foundation
13400 S. Horrell Rd.
Fenton, MI 48430

Established in 2004 in MI.
Donor: William Bird.
Grantmaker type: Independent foundation.
Financial data (yr. ended 12/31/04): Assets,
$103,824 (M); gifts received, $100,000;
expenditures, $5,113; total giving, $5,113;
qualifying distributions, $5,113; giving activities
include $5,113 for 3 grants (high: $3,888; low:
$225).
Limitations: Applications not accepted. No grants to
individuals.
Application information: Contributes only to
pre-selected organizations.
Officer: William Bird, Jr., Pres.
EIN: 201819569

170
Birtwistle Family Foundation
(formerly Donald B. Birtwistle Foundation)
300 S. Rath Ave., Apt. 25
Ludington, MI 49431 (616) 843-2501
Contact: Donald B. Birtwistle, Pres.

Established in 1987 in MI.
Donor: Donald B. Birtwistle.
Grantmaker type: Independent foundation.
Financial data (yr. ended 12/31/04): Assets,
$1,769,533 (M); gifts received, $159,490;
expenditures, $90,208; total giving, $86,550;
qualifying distributions, $89,590; giving activities
include $70,550 for 9 grants, and $16,000 for 4
grants to individuals.
Purpose and activities: Giving primarily for
education, including scholarships to graduates of
the Ludington, MI, area school district. Giving also
to community development and human services.
Applicants must be in their senior year of college for
scholarships.
Fields of interest: Education; Human services;
Community development; Foundations (community);
Jewish federated giving programs.
Type of support: General/operating support;
Scholarships—to individuals.
Limitations: Giving limited to MI, primarily in the
Ludington area.
Application information: Application form required.
Deadline(s): Apr. 1 for applicants who are in their
senior year of high school
Officers: Donald B. Birtwistle, Pres. and Treas.;
Joclyn Birtwistle, V.P. and Secy.
EIN: 382787567

171
Bishai Family Foundation
105 Lakeshore Dr.
Grosse Pointe Farms, MI 48236

Established in 2002 in MI.
Donors: Yousef B. Bishai, M.D.; Turid Eileen Bishai.
Grantmaker type: Independent foundation.
Financial data (yr. ended 12/31/04): Assets,
$87,115 (M); gifts received, $30,000;
expenditures, $16,076; total giving, $12,250;
qualifying distributions, $12,250; giving activities
include $12,250 for grants.

Limitations: Applications not accepted. No grants to
individuals.
Application information: Contributes only to
pre-selected organizations.
Officers and Directors:* Yousef B. Bishai, M.D.*,
Pres.; Turid Eileen Bishai,* V.P. and Treas.; Robert
Bishai, Secy.
EIN: 481291534

172
A. G. Bishop Charitable Trust
c/o JPMorgan Chase Bank, N.A.
P.O. Box 1308
Milwaukee, WI 53201
Application address: c/o JPMorgan Chase Bank,
N.A., 111 E. Court St., Ste. 100, Flint MI, 48502,
tel.: (810) 237-3836

Trust established in 1944 in MI.
Donor: Arthur Giles Bishop†.
Grantmaker type: Independent foundation.
Financial data (yr. ended 12/31/04): Assets,
$11,847,747 (M); expenditures, $585,631; total
giving, $491,083; qualifying distributions,
$516,189; giving activities include $491,083 for 42
grants (high: $100,000; low: $1,500).
Purpose and activities: Giving primarily for health
care, education, the arts, and to youth and social
services.
Fields of interest: Arts; Higher education; Hospitals
(general); Health care; Human services; YM/YWCAs
& YM/YWHAs; Children/youth, services; Federated
giving programs.
Type of support: General/operating support;
Continuing support; Annual campaigns; Building/
renovation; Equipment; Land acquisition; Debt
reduction; Emergency funds; Seed money;
Research.
Limitations: Giving limited to the Flint and Genesee
County, MI, community. No grants to individuals, or
for endowment funds, scholarships, fellowships, or
matching gifts; no loans.
Publications: Application guidelines.
Application information: Application form not
required.
Initial approach: Letter
Copies of proposal: 3
Deadline(s): None
Board meeting date(s): 2 to 3 times per year
Final notification: 6 months
Trustees: Robert J. Bellairs, Jr.; Elizabeth B.
Wentworth; JPMorgan Chase Bank, N.A.
EIN: 386040693

173
**The Joseph J. and Deanna I. Bittker
Foundation**
200 E. Long Lake Rd., Ste. 175
Bloomfield Hills, MI 48304
Contact: Joseph J. Bittker, Pres.

Established in 1987 in MI.
Donors: Joseph J. Bittker; Deanna I. Bittker.
Grantmaker type: Independent foundation.
Financial data (yr. ended 12/31/05): Assets,
$47,969 (M); expenditures, $35,350; total giving,
$25,660; qualifying distributions, $25,660; giving
activities include $25,660 for grants.
Fields of interest: Higher education; Cancer
research; Children, adoption; General charitable
giving.

Type of support: General/operating support.
Limitations: Giving primarily in MI. No grants to
individuals.
Officers: Joseph J. Bittker, Pres.; Deanna I. Bittker,
Secy.
EIN: 382745504

174
The Phillip L. Bittker Foundation
6960 Orchard Lake Rd., Ste. 303
West Bloomfield, MI 48322

Established in 1986 in MI.
Donor: Phillip L. Bittker.
Grantmaker type: Independent foundation.
Financial data (yr. ended 12/31/04): Assets,
$3,094 (M); gifts received, $31,325; expenditures,
$30,986; total giving, $29,417; qualifying
distributions, $29,799; giving activities include
$29,417 for grants.
Fields of interest: Health care; Human services;
Jewish agencies & temples.
Limitations: Applications not accepted. Giving
primarily in MI. No grants to individuals.
Application information: Contributes only to
pre-selected organizations.
Officers: Phillip L. Bittker, Pres.; Ernest J. Weiner,
Secy.; Allan M. Bittker, Treas.
EIN: 382708652

175
Bizer Charitable Trust
1938 Long Lake Shore Dr.
Bloomfield Hills, MI 48302

Established in MI.
Grantmaker type: Independent foundation.
Financial data (yr. ended 12/31/04): Assets,
$35,331 (M); expenditures, $4,288; total giving,
$3,682; qualifying distributions, $3,682; giving
activities include $3,682 for grants.
Fields of interest: Jewish agencies & temples.
Limitations: Applications not accepted. Giving
primarily in MI. No grants to individuals.
Application information: Contributes only to
pre-selected organizations.
Trustees: Lawrence S. Bizer, M.D.; Judith S.
Stillman.
EIN: 386087554

176
BJB Charitable Trust
6115-28th St. S.E.
Grand Rapids, MI 49546
Contact: Daniel J. Kamphuis, Tr.
Application address: 8513 Keiser Rd., Alto, MI
49302, tel.: (616) 942-9166

Established in 1995 in MI.
Donors: Daniel J. Kamphuis; Rhonda Kamphuis.
Grantmaker type: Independent foundation.
Financial data (yr. ended 12/31/04): Assets,
$227,649 (M); gifts received, $107,500;
expenditures, $37,600; total giving, $36,700;
qualifying distributions, $36,700; giving activities
include $36,700 for 4 grants (high: $34,200; low:
$500).
Fields of interest: Christian agencies & churches.
Limitations: Giving primarily in MI.

Application information: Application form not required.
Deadline(s): None
Trustees: William Hitchcock; Daniel J. Kamphuis.
EIN: 383266496

177
Willard C. and Pauline H. Blackney Memorial Scholarship Fund
c/o Paul J. Blackney
3131 Slaton Dr. N.W., Ste. 35
Atlanta, GA 30305

Established in 1991 in IL.
Donor: Paul J. Blackney.
Grantmaker type: Independent foundation.
Financial data (yr. ended 5/31/05): Assets, $257,588 (M); gifts received, $137,300; expenditures, $40,567; total giving, $36,000; qualifying distributions, $36,000; giving activities include $36,000 for grants.
Fields of interest: Arts education; Elementary/secondary education; Higher education.
Limitations: Applications not accepted. Giving primarily in Atlanta, GA, and Port Huron, MI. No grants to individuals.
Application information: Contributes only to pre-selected organizations.
Trustees: Christina Blackney; Paul J. Blackney.
EIN: 363779819

178
The Edwin and Helen Blake Memorial Foundation
P.O. Box 2458
Midland, MI 48641-2458

Established in 2001 in MI.
Donor: Friends of Grace A. Dom Memorial Library.
Grantmaker type: Independent foundation.
Financial data (yr. ended 5/31/05): Assets, $228,875 (M); expenditures, $110,837; total giving, $104,750; qualifying distributions, $104,750; giving activities include $104,750 for grants.
Fields of interest: Education, reading.
Type of support: General/operating support.
Limitations: Giving limited to the Midland County and surrounding areas, MI. No grants to individuals.
Application information:
Initial approach: Letter
Deadline(s): None
Officers: Janis Bond, Pres.; Patti Klein, V.P.; Marilyn Gay, Secy.; Kim White, Treas.
EIN: 383644120

179
Dorothy Blakely Foundation
100 S. Jackson St., Ste. 206
Jackson, MI 49201 (517) 787-5600
Contact: Charles H. Aymond, Secy.

Donor: Dorothy M. Blakely.
Grantmaker type: Independent foundation.
Financial data (yr. ended 11/30/04): Assets, $2,790,198 (M); expenditures, $196,204; total giving, $160,000; qualifying distributions, $160,000; giving activities include $160,000 for 14 grants (high: $55,000; low: $2,000).
Fields of interest: Museums; Arts; Human services.

Limitations: Giving primarily in the Jackson, MI, area. No grants to individuals.
Application information:
Initial approach: Letter
Deadline(s): Nov. 1
Officers: Douglas Burdick, Pres.; Charles H. Aymond, Secy.
Director: James A. Hildreth.
EIN: 616055236

180
Blaske-Hill Foundation
25001 Battle Creek Hwy.
Bellevue, MI 49021-9603
Contact: E. Robert Blaske, Secy.-Treas.

Established in MI.
Donors: Patricia MacLeod; Members of the Blaske Family.
Grantmaker type: Independent foundation.
Financial data (yr. ended 2/28/05): Assets, $395,733 (M); expenditures, $27,307; total giving, $26,000; qualifying distributions, $25,892; giving activities include $26,000 for 13 grants to individuals.
Purpose and activities: Scholarship awards to graduates of Battle Creek Central, Battle Creek St. Philip, and Niles high schools, MI.
Type of support: Scholarships—to individuals.
Limitations: Giving limited to Battle Creek and Niles, MI.
Application information: Application form required.
Initial approach: Letter
Deadline(s): Mar. 15
Officers: Patricia MacLeod, Pres.; Thomas H. Blaske, V.P.; E. Robert Blaske, Secy.-Treas.
EIN: 382525817

181
Leland F. Blatt Family Foundation
20416 Harper Ave.
Harper Woods, MI 48225

Established in 2000 in MI.
Donors: Elaine E. Blatt; John A. Blatt; Leland D. Blatt; Cheryl A. Saunders.
Grantmaker type: Independent foundation.
Financial data (yr. ended 12/31/04): Assets, $42,927 (M); gifts received, $208,020; expenditures, $209,400; total giving, $206,600; qualifying distributions, $206,600; giving activities include $206,600 for 34 grants (high: $100,000; low: $100).
Fields of interest: Arts; Higher education, university; Hospitals (general); Health organizations, association; Human services; Children/youth, services.
Limitations: Applications not accepted. No grants to individuals.
Application information: Contributes only to pre-selected organizations.
Officers: Elaine E. Blatt, Pres.; Cheryl A. Saunders, V.P.; Leland D. Blatt, Secy.; John A. Blatt, Treas.
EIN: 383553310

182
Ruth Miles Bleasdale & J. Laurence Bleasdale Family Foundation
101 N. Washington Ave.
Saginaw, MI 48607

Established in 1985 in MI.
Grantmaker type: Independent foundation.
Financial data (yr. ended 6/30/05): Assets, $120,773 (M); expenditures, $34,234; total giving, $30,000; qualifying distributions, $30,000; giving activities include $30,000 for grants.
Limitations: Applications not accepted. Giving primarily in Saginaw, MI. No grants to individuals.
Application information: Contributes only to pre-selected organizations.
Officers: Hugo E. Braun, Jr., Pres.; Dale L. Sielaff, V.P.; Michael T. Tribble, Treas.
EIN: 382578327

183
Blissfield American Legion Trust
c/o Comerica Bank
P.O. Box 75000, MC 8280
Detroit, MI 48275-8280

Established in 2001 in MI.
Grantmaker type: Independent foundation.
Financial data (yr. ended 12/31/05): Assets, $389,447 (M); expenditures, $5,758; total giving, $0; qualifying distributions, $0.
Purpose and activities: Support only for the Blissfield American Legion, MI.
Fields of interest: Military/veterans' organizations.
Type of support: Building/renovation.
Limitations: Applications not accepted. Giving limited to Blissfield, MI. No grants to individuals.
Application information: Contributes only to a pre-selected organization.
Trustee: Comerica Bank.
EIN: 386314373

184
The Blodgett Foundation
2740 Littlefield Dr. N.E.
Grand Rapids, MI 49506-1231
Contact: Vicki Patton

Established in 1994 in MI.
Donor: Edith I. Blodgett.
Grantmaker type: Independent foundation.
Financial data (yr. ended 12/31/05): Assets, $1,848,621 (M); expenditures, $336,625; total giving, $308,800; qualifying distributions, $313,478; giving activities include $308,800 for 34 grants (high: $55,000; low: $500).
Purpose and activities: Giving primarily for the arts, higher education, and human services.
Fields of interest: Arts; Higher education; Human services; Children/youth, services; Aging, centers/services.
Type of support: Building/renovation; Equipment; Program development; Curriculum development; Consulting services; Program evaluation; Matching/challenge support.
Limitations: Giving primarily in the west MI area. No support for religious groups or affiliations. No grants to individuals.
Publications: Application guidelines.
Application information: Application form required.
Initial approach: Letter
Copies of proposal: 1
Deadline(s): None
Board meeting date(s): Spring and fall
Officer: Edith I. Blodgett, Pres.
Trustee: Wendy Greeney.

Number of staff: 1 part-time support.
EIN: 383202330
Selected grants: The following grants were reported in 2004.
$50,000 to Ryerson Library Foundation, Grand Rapids, MI. For general support.
$25,000 to Clark Retirement Community, Grand Rapids, MI. For general support.
$15,000 to Community Counseling and Personal Growth Ministry, Grand Rapids, MI. For general support.
$10,000 to Grand Rapids Symphony, Grand Rapids, MI. For general support.
$10,000 to Guardian Angel Homes, Grand Rapids, MI. For general support.
$5,000 to Grand Rapids Civic Theater, Grand Rapids, MI. For general support.
$3,000 to Opera Grand Rapids, Grand Rapids, MI. For general support.
$2,000 to Community Circle Theater, Grand Rapids, MI. For general support.
$1,000 to Arts Council of Greater Grand Rapids, Grand Rapids, MI. For general support.
$1,000 to Grand Rapids Childrens Museum, Grand Rapids, MI. For general support.

185
Herbert & Betty Bloom Foundation
4212 Ramsgate Ln.
Bloomfield Hills, MI 48302-1635

Established in MI.
Grantmaker type: Independent foundation.
Financial data (yr. ended 12/31/04): Assets, $324,854 (M); expenditures, $23,763; total giving, $22,782; qualifying distributions, $23,397; giving activities include $22,782 for grants.
Fields of interest: Jewish agencies & temples.
Limitations: Applications not accepted. Giving primarily in MI. No grants to individuals.
Application information: Contributes only to pre-selected organizations.
Officers: Stephen Bloom, Pres.; Linda Weissman, Secy.; Michael Bloom, Treas.
EIN: 386087211

186
Louis C. Blumberg Foundation
121 W. Long Lake Rd., 2nd Fl.
Bloomfield Hills, MI 48304-2719

Established in 1958 in MI.
Donor: Louis C. Blumberg‡.
Grantmaker type: Independent foundation.
Financial data (yr. ended 3/31/05): Assets, $1,993,900 (M); expenditures, $121,831; total giving, $72,700; qualifying distributions, $72,700; giving activities include $72,700 for grants.
Purpose and activities: Giving for Jewish organizations.
Fields of interest: Higher education, university; Hospitals (general); Jewish federated giving programs; Jewish agencies & temples.
Limitations: Applications not accepted. Giving primarily in MI. No grants to individuals.
Application information: Contributes only to pre-selected organizations.
Officers and Trustees:* Graham Landau,* Pres.; Arlene Landau,* V.P.; Lawrence S. Jackier,* Secy.
EIN: 386089255

187
Wallace and June Blume Charitable Foundation
4666 Leighton Lakes Dr.
Wayland, MI 49348

Established in 2004 in MI.
Donors: Wallace Blume; June Blume.
Grantmaker type: Independent foundation.
Financial data (yr. ended 9/30/05): Assets, $19,826 (M); expenditures, $14,470; total giving, $4,471; qualifying distributions, $4,471; giving activities include $4,471 for grants.
Purpose and activities: Support for a ministry.
Fields of interest: Christian agencies & churches.
Type of support: Building/renovation.
Limitations: Applications not accepted. Giving primarily in Tulsa, OK. No grants to individuals.
Application information: Contributes only to pre-selected organizations.
Officers: Wallace Blume, Pres. and Treas.; June Blume, V.P. and Secy.
Directors: Jonathan Blume; Neal Glaeser; Rick Renner.
EIN: 200499831

188
Harold & Penny B. Blumenstein Foundation Corporation
32400 Telegraph Rd., Ste. 202
Bingham Farms, MI 48025

Established in 1986 in MI.
Donors: Harold Blumenstein; Penny B. Blumenstein.
Grantmaker type: Independent foundation.
Financial data (yr. ended 12/31/05): Assets, $5,328,393 (M); gifts received, $1,100,000; expenditures, $1,446,248; total giving, $1,429,247; qualifying distributions, $1,429,247; giving activities include $1,429,247 for 110 grants (high: $225,000; low: $18).
Purpose and activities: Giving primarily for Jewish agencies and federated giving programs.
Fields of interest: Arts; Education; Health organizations, association; Jewish federated giving programs; Jewish agencies & temples.
Limitations: Applications not accepted. Giving primarily in MI. No grants to individuals.
Application information: Contributes only to pre-selected organizations.
Officers: Harold Blumenstein, Pres.; Penny B. Blumenstein, V.P. and Secy.; Richard C. Blumenstein, V.P.; Lauren A. Cohen, V.P.; Randall S. Blumenstein, Treas.
EIN: 382710389

189
Blystone Foundation
13515 Ballantyne Corp. Pl.
Charlotte, NC 28277

Established in 1997 in MI.
Donor: John B. Blystone.
Grantmaker type: Independent foundation.
Financial data (yr. ended 12/31/05): Assets, $7,738 (M); gifts received, $2,516; expenditures, $6,150; total giving, $5,300; qualifying distributions, $5,300; giving activities include $5,300 for grants.

Purpose and activities: Support primarily for a Roman Catholic education foundation.
Fields of interest: Education; Medical research, institute; Roman Catholic federated giving programs; Roman Catholic agencies & churches.
Limitations: Applications not accepted. Giving primarily in South Bend, IN, and NC; some giving also in Muskegon, MI. No grants to individuals.
Application information: Contributes only to pre-selected organizations.
Officers and Directors:* John B. Blystone,* Pres. and Treas.; Julie A. Blystone,* Secy.; Christopher J. Kearney; James M. Sheridan.
EIN: 383381956

190
Brooks F. and Pamela A. Bock Foundation
5764 Bloomfield Glens Rd.
West Bloomfield, MI 48322

Established in 1998 in MI.
Donor: Brooks F. Bock.
Grantmaker type: Independent foundation.
Financial data (yr. ended 12/31/05): Assets, $45,911 (M); expenditures, $2,846; total giving, $2,195; qualifying distributions, $2,195; giving activities include $2,195 for grants.
Limitations: Applications not accepted. No grants to individuals.
Application information: Contributes only to pre-selected organizations.
Officers: Pamela A. Bock, Pres. and Treas.; Brooks F. Bock, Secy.
EIN: 383400746

191
Boersma Charitable Foundation
319 Walnut Ct.
Holland, MI 49423

Established in 1988 in MI.
Donors: Max D. Boersma‡; Constance M. Boersma.
Grantmaker type: Independent foundation.
Financial data (yr. ended 12/31/05): Assets, $981,883 (M); expenditures, $275,000; total giving, $275,000; qualifying distributions, $275,000; giving activities include $275,000 for 2 grants (high: $150,000; low: $125,000).
Purpose and activities: Giving primarily for community development and higher education.
Fields of interest: Higher education; Community development; Protestant agencies & churches.
Type of support: General/operating support.
Limitations: Applications not accepted. Giving primarily in MI. No grants to individuals.
Application information: Contributes only to pre-selected organizations.
Trustee: Constance M. Boersma.
EIN: 382798716

192
John A. & Marlene L. Boll Foundation
100 Maple Park Blvd., Ste. 118
St. Clair Shores, MI 48081
Contact: Kristine Boll Mestdagh, Dir.

Established in 1986 in MI.
Donors: John A. Boll; Marlene L. Boll.
Grantmaker type: Independent foundation.

Financial data (yr. ended 12/31/04): Assets, $18,498,845 (M); expenditures, $1,727,777; total giving, $1,466,165; qualifying distributions, $1,466,165; giving activities include $1,466,165 for 132 grants (high: $200,000; low: $30).
Purpose and activities: Giving educational scholarships to institutions with curriculum based, in part, on Judeo-Christian traditions.
Fields of interest: Arts; Higher education; Scholarships/financial aid; Health care; Human services; Christian agencies & churches.
Type of support: General/operating support.
Limitations: Giving primarily in MI. No grants to individuals.
Application information: Letters of recommendation for scholarship candidates are required for further review. Application form not required.
  Deadline(s): None
Directors: John A. Boll; Marlene L. Boll; Kristine B. Mestdagh.
EIN: 382708121

193
Bonisteel Foundation
P.O. Box 7348
Ann Arbor, MI   48107-7348
Contact: Edmund J. Sikorski, Jr., Asst. Secy.

Established in 1972 in MI.
Donors: Roscoe O. Bonisteel, Sr.‡; Lillian Bonisteel‡.
Grantmaker type: Independent foundation.
Financial data (yr. ended 12/31/05): Assets, $3,079,859 (M); expenditures, $232,791; total giving, $191,245; qualifying distributions, $191,245; giving activities include $191,245 for 6 grants (high: $125,000; low: $170).
Purpose and activities: Giving primarily for higher education and arts centers.
Fields of interest: Arts; Higher education.
Type of support: General/operating support; Capital campaigns; Building/renovation; Equipment.
Limitations: Giving primarily in Washtenaw County, MI. No support for political organizations. No grants to individuals.
Application information: Application form not required.
  Initial approach: Letter
  Copies of proposal: 5
  Deadline(s): Oct. 15
  Board meeting date(s): Dec. 15
  Final notification: Dec. 31
Officer and Trustees:* Jean B. Knecht,* Pres. and Secy.; Mary C. Byl; Betty B. Johnson.
Number of staff: None.
EIN: 237155774
Selected grants: The following grants were reported in 2004.
$100,000 to Interlochen Arts Academy, Interlochen, MI. For building fund.
$5,000 to Boy Scouts of America, Great Sauk Trail Council, Ann Arbor, MI. For building fund.
$5,000 to Child Care Network Washtenaw Regional 4C, Ann Arbor, MI. For equipment upgrade.
$3,966 to Father Gabriel Richard High School, Ann Arbor, MI. For building fund.
$600 to University of Michigan, Ann Arbor, MI. For operating support.
$250 to Eastern Michigan University, Ypsilanti, MI. For operating support.

194
Margaret Bonn Scholarship Trust
c/o Citizens Bank Wealth Mgmt., N.A.
328 S. Saginaw St., M/C 002072
Flint, MI   48502
Application address: c/o Michael Kresl, 1601 S. Webster Ave., Green Bay, WI 54301, tel.: (920) 436-1605

Established in WI.
Grantmaker type: Independent foundation.
Financial data (yr. ended 12/31/05): Assets, $15,128 (M); expenditures, $792; total giving, $350; qualifying distributions, $350; giving activities include $350 for grants to individuals.
Purpose and activities: Scholarships are awarded to seniors of Bloomington Senior High School who are graduating with at least a B average and who have demonstrated good moral character.
Type of support: Scholarships—to individuals.
Limitations: Giving limited to Bloomington, WI.
Application information: Application form required.
  Initial approach: Letter or telephone
  Deadline(s): End of school year
Trustee: Citizens Bank.
EIN: 391446095

195
The Bonner Foundation
507 N. Barnard St.
Howell, MI   48843   (517) 540-1873
Contact: Ben V. Bonner, Pres.

Established in MI.
Donors: Asa W. Bonner, Sr.‡; A.T. & G. Co., Inc.; M.S. Fetcher Co.
Grantmaker type: Independent foundation.
Financial data (yr. ended 12/31/04): Assets, $706,445 (M); expenditures, $41,332; total giving, $36,000; qualifying distributions, $41,117; giving activities include $36,000 for grants.
Fields of interest: Higher education; Protestant agencies & churches.
Type of support: General/operating support; Scholarship funds.
Limitations: Giving primarily in AR and MI.
Application information:
  Initial approach: Letter or proposal
  Deadline(s): Sept. 30
Officer: Ben V. Bonner, Pres.
EIN: 386068648

196
Joseph Sloan Bonsall and Mary Ann Bonsall Foundation
16845 Kercheval, Ste. 5
Grosse Pointe, MI   48230
Contact: Joseph Sloan Bonsall, Pres.

Established in 1997 in MI.
Grantmaker type: Independent foundation.
Financial data (yr. ended 12/31/05): Assets, $74,962 (M); gifts received, $651; expenditures, $2,681; total giving, $2,000; qualifying distributions, $2,000; giving activities include $2,000 for grants.
Fields of interest: Arts; Elementary/secondary education; Education, reading; Animal welfare.
Type of support: General/operating support.
Limitations: Giving primarily in Hendersonville and Nashville, TN. No grants to individuals.

Application information: Application form not required.
  Deadline(s): None
Officers and Trustees:* Joseph Sloan Bonsall,* Pres.; S. Gary Spicer,* Secy.; Mary Ann Bonsall,* Treas.
EIN: 383377889

197
Bordelove Family Foundation
6186 Pickwood Dr.
West Bloomfield, MI   48322-2221

Established in MI.
Donor: Manuel O. Bordelove.
Grantmaker type: Independent foundation.
Financial data (yr. ended 12/31/05): Assets, $1 (M); gifts received, $46,500; expenditures, $46,500; total giving, $46,500; qualifying distributions, $46,500; giving activities include $46,500 for grants.
Fields of interest: Cancer research.
Limitations: Applications not accepted. No grants to individuals.
Application information: Contributes only to pre-selected organizations.
Directors: Manuel O. Bordelove; Mark S. Bordelove; Shelley Bordelove; Terri Friedman.
EIN: 383541128

198
Tom and Sarah Borman Foundation
719 Maple Hill Ln.
Birmingham, MI   48009-1675
Application address: c/o Johanna R. Borman, 555 S. Old Woodward, Ste. 608, Birmingham, MI 48009

Established about 1958 in MI.
Donors: Paul D. Borman; Sarah Borman; Tom Borman.
Grantmaker type: Independent foundation.
Financial data (yr. ended 11/30/05): Assets, $2,544,925 (M); gifts received, $50,316; expenditures, $120,376; total giving, $112,162; qualifying distributions, $118,702; giving activities include $112,162 for 5 grants (high: $100,000; low: $500).
Fields of interest: Human services; Jewish federated giving programs.
Limitations: Giving primarily in MI. No grants to individuals.
Application information: Application form not required.
  Deadline(s): None
Officers: Paul D. Borman, Pres.; Johanna R. Borman, V.P.
EIN: 386058645

199
The Borman's, Inc. Fund
(formerly The Borman Fund)
P.O. Box 250520
Franklin, MI   48025   (248) 203-9333
Contact: Paul Borman, Pres.

Established in 1955 in MI.
Donors: Borman's, Inc.; The Great Atlantic & Pacific Tea Co., Inc.; Paul Borman; Marlene Borman.
Grantmaker type: Independent foundation.

Financial data (yr. ended 12/31/04): Assets, $120,365 (M); gifts received, $5,141; expenditures, $33,940; total giving, $31,850; qualifying distributions, $33,850; giving activities include $31,850 for grants.
Purpose and activities: Giving primarily for Jewish welfare and social services; support also for the arts, education, and job training.
Fields of interest: Arts; Education; Employment; Human services; Community development; Jewish federated giving programs.
International interests: Israel.
Type of support: Annual campaigns; Capital campaigns.
Limitations: Giving primarily in southeastern MI. No grants to individuals.
Publications: Application guidelines.
Application information: Application form not required.
   Initial approach: Letter
   Copies of proposal: 1
   Deadline(s): None
Officers: Paul Borman, Pres.; Marlene Borman, V.P.; Gilbert Borman, Secy.-Treas.
Number of staff: 1 part-time support.
EIN: 386069267

200
Bornman Educational Trust
c/o Comerica Bank
P.O. Box 75000, MC 9413
Detroit, MI   48275-9413

Established in 1996 in MI.
Grantmaker type: Independent foundation.
Financial data (yr. ended 12/31/05): Assets, $318,478 (M); gifts received, $8,048; expenditures, $22,356; total giving, $18,053; qualifying distributions, $18,053; giving activities include $18,053 for grants.
Purpose and activities: Support only for Hillsdale College, Liberty University, and Regent University.
Limitations: Applications not accepted. Giving limited to MI and VA. No grants to individuals.
Application information: Contributes only to 3 pre-selected organizations.
Trustee: Comerica Bank.
EIN: 386592814

201
Frederick D. Bornman Trust for Conservative Causes
c/o Comerica Bank
P.O. Box 75000
Detroit, MI   48275-9413

Grantmaker type: Independent foundation.
Financial data (yr. ended 12/31/05): Assets, $615,187 (M); gifts received, $16,097; expenditures, $51,740; total giving, $43,806; qualifying distributions, $43,806; giving activities include $43,806 for grants.
Limitations: Applications not accepted. Giving limited to Washington, DC, IL, IN, MI, MO, NJ, and VA. No grants to individuals.
Application information: Contributes only to 11 pre-selected organizations.
Trustee: Comerica Bank.
EIN: 386592813

202
Borovoy Family Foundation
c/o Mathew Borovoy
6529 Pleasant Lake Ct.
West Bloomfield, MI   48322

Established in 1995 in MI.
Donor: Mathew Borovoy.
Grantmaker type: Independent foundation.
Financial data (yr. ended 12/31/04): Assets, $22,829 (M); gifts received, $21,063; expenditures, $35,363; total giving, $34,376; qualifying distributions, $34,376; giving activities include $34,376 for grants.
Fields of interest: Theology; Higher education; Education; Environment, natural resources; Cancer; Arthritis; Multiple sclerosis; Diabetes; American Red Cross; Jewish agencies & temples.
Type of support: General/operating support.
Limitations: Giving primarily in MI.
Application information:
   Initial approach: Letter
   Deadline(s): None
Officer: Joyce Borovoy, Secy.
Directors: Marc A. Borovoy; Cynthia R. Diskin; Debra L. Garemk.
EIN: 383227208

203
Borwell Charitable Foundation
c/o Naomi T. Borwell
1040 N. Lake Shore Dr.
Chicago, IL   60611

Established in 1981 in IL.
Donors: Naomi T. Borwell; Robert C. Borwell, Sr.; Mrs. Robert C. Borwell, Sr.
Grantmaker type: Independent foundation.
Financial data (yr. ended 10/31/05): Assets, $96,860 (M); gifts received, $827,943; expenditures, $1,112,889; total giving, $1,096,300; qualifying distributions, $1,100,571; giving activities include $1,096,300 for 34 grants (high: $220,000; low: $100).
Purpose and activities: Giving primarily for arts and culture, including a music education program for disadvantaged youth; funding also for hospitals and health associations, social services, and to Episcopal and Presbyterian churches.
Fields of interest: Arts education; Performing arts, orchestra (symphony); Arts; Environment, land resources; Health organizations, association; Human services; Urban/community development; Protestant agencies & churches.
Limitations: Applications not accepted. Giving primarily in IL, with emphasis on Chicago; some giving also in MI. No grants to individuals.
Application information: Contributes only to pre-selected organizations.
Officers and Directors:* Naomi T. Borwell,* Pres.; Robert C. Borwell, Jr.,* V.P.; Herbert T. Knight,* V.P.; Elsie B. Revenaugh,* V.P.; Gail Carpenter Van Goethem,* Secy.-Treas.
EIN: 363155489

204
The Lawrence D. Bos, Sr. and E. Dolores Bos Foundation
5396 Michigan St. N.E.
Ada, MI   49301

Established in 1998 in MI.
Donors: Lawrence D. Bos, Sr.; E. Dolores Bos.
Grantmaker type: Independent foundation.
Financial data (yr. ended 12/31/04): Assets, $11,506 (M); gifts received, $7,875; expenditures, $7,447; total giving, $6,500; qualifying distributions, $6,870; giving activities include $6,500 for grants.
Fields of interest: Performing arts, orchestra (symphony).
Limitations: Applications not accepted. Giving primarily in MI. No grants to individuals.
Application information: Contributes only to pre-selected organizations.
Officers: Lawrence D. Bos, Sr., Pres. and Treas.; E. Dolores Bos, V.P. and Secy.
Directors: Lawrence D. Bos, Jr.; Mary Ellen Spring.
EIN: 383393300

205
Katherine M. Bosch Foundation
227 W. Monroe St.
Chicago, IL   60606-4016

Donor: James A. Ruppe.
Grantmaker type: Independent foundation.
Financial data (yr. ended 12/31/04): Assets, $313,481 (M); expenditures, $15,758; total giving, $14,678; qualifying distributions, $14,678; giving activities include $14,678 for grants.
Purpose and activities: Support only for Portage Health Systems, Michigan Tech Scholarship Fund, Keweenaw Memorial Health Center, Bay Cliff Health Corp., and Houghton County Medical Care, MI.
Limitations: Applications not accepted. Giving limited to MI. No grants to individuals.
Application information: Contributes only to 5 pre-selected organizations.
Officers: Philip E. Ruppe, Pres.; James A. Ruppe, Secy.-Treas.
EIN: 366210899

206
Arthur & Doris Boschan Family Fund
30100 Telegraph Rd., Ste. 354
Bingham Farms, MI   48025

Donors: Arthur Boschan; Doris Boschan; James Boschan.
Grantmaker type: Independent foundation.
Financial data (yr. ended 3/31/05): Assets, $301,211 (M); expenditures, $15,123; total giving, $13,600; qualifying distributions, $13,600; giving activities include $13,600 for grants.
Limitations: Applications not accepted. Giving primarily in Bloomfield Hills, MI. No grants to individuals.
Application information: Contributes only to pre-selected organizations.
Officers: Doris Boschan, Pres.; James Boschan, V.P.; Suzanne Boschan, Secy.-Treas.
EIN: 381775596

207
Arthur J. Bott, Sr. Foundation
7507 Red Osier Dr. S.W.
Byron Center, MI   49315

Established in MI.
Donor: Arthur J. Bott, Sr.

Grantmaker type: Independent foundation.
Financial data (yr. ended 12/31/04): Assets, $182,028 (M); expenditures, $25,439; total giving, $21,900; qualifying distributions, $22,975; giving activities include $21,900 for grants.
Limitations: Applications not accepted. Giving primarily in Grand Rapids, MI. No grants to individuals.
Application information: Contributes only to pre-selected organizations.
Officers: Arthur J. Bott, Sr., Pres.; Judith A. Bott, Secy.; Arthur J. Bott, Jr., Treas.
EIN: 383024290

208
Henry Bouma, Jr. and Carolyn L. Bouma Foundation
2749 Beechtree Dr. S.W.
Byron Center, MI   49315-9475

Established in 1993 in MI.
Donors: Henry Bouma, Jr.; Carolyn L. Bouma.
Grantmaker type: Independent foundation.
Financial data (yr. ended 12/31/05): Assets, $778 (M); gifts received, $1,050; expenditures, $103,390; total giving, $101,615; qualifying distributions, $101,615; giving activities include $101,615 for 14 grants (high: $20,000; low: $1,000).
Purpose and activities: Giving primarily for Christian churches, ministries, and schools.
Fields of interest: Elementary/secondary education; Higher education; Human services; Youth, services; Christian agencies & churches.
Limitations: Giving primarily in Grand Rapids, MI. No grants to individuals.
Trustees: Carolyn L. Bouma; Henry Bouma, Jr.
EIN: 383106861
Selected grants: The following grants were reported in 2004.
$36,000 to Heritage Christian Reformed Church, Byron Center, MI. For annual support.
$25,000 to Bethany Christian Services, Grand Rapids, MI. For annual support.
$12,500 to Christian Reformed World Missions, Grand Rapids, MI. For annual support.
$12,200 to Reformed Bible College, Grand Rapids, MI. For annual support.
$6,000 to Davenport University, Grand Rapids, MI. For annual support.
$5,000 to Calvin Theological Seminary, Grand Rapids, MI. For annual support.
$5,000 to Christian Reformed Home Missions, Grand Rapids, MI. For annual support.
$5,000 to Guiding Light Mission, Grand Rapids, MI. For annual support.
$5,000 to South Christian High School, Grand Rapids, MI. For annual support.
$1,000 to Gerald R. Ford Foundation, Grand Rapids, MI. For annual support.

209
John Bouma, Sr. and Sharon K. Bouma Foundation
2915 Lakeshore Dr.
Holland, MI   49424-6023

Established in 1993 in MI.
Donors: John Bouma, Sr.; Sharon K. Bouma.
Grantmaker type: Independent foundation.

Financial data (yr. ended 12/31/05): Assets, $33,702 (M); gifts received, $155,568; expenditures, $128,880; total giving, $127,500; qualifying distributions, $128,125; giving activities include $127,500 for 53 grants (high: $40,000; low: $250).
Purpose and activities: Giving for Christian churches, ministries, and schools.
Fields of interest: Education; Youth development; Human services; Christian agencies & churches.
Limitations: Applications not accepted. Giving primarily in MI. No grants to individuals.
Application information: Contributes only to pre-selected organizations.
Trustees: John Bouma, Sr.; Sharon K. Bouma.
EIN: 383106862

210
Boutell Memorial Fund
(formerly Arnold and Gertrude Boutell Memorial Fund)
c/o Citizens Bank Wealth Mgmt., N.A.
328 S. Saginaw St., M/C 002072
Flint, MI   48502
Application address: c/o Helen James, Citizens Bank Wealth Mgmt., N.A., 101 N. Washington Ave., Saginaw, MI 48607, tel.: (989) 776-7368

Established in 1961 in MI.
Donors: Arnold Boutell†; Gertrude Boutell†.
Grantmaker type: Independent foundation.
Financial data (yr. ended 3/31/06): Assets, $12,414,223 (M); expenditures, $690,605; total giving, $560,164; qualifying distributions, $575,701; giving activities include $560,164 for 26 grants (high: $100,000; low: $1,000).
Purpose and activities: Giving primarily for children, youth and social services, and for community development.
Fields of interest: Performing arts; Health care; Human services; Children/youth, services; Community development; Foundations (community).
Type of support: Equipment; Program development.
Limitations: Giving limited to Saginaw County, MI. No grants to individuals, or for endowment funds.
Application information: Application form required.
Initial approach: Letter
Copies of proposal: 1
Deadline(s): None
Board meeting date(s): 3rd Wed. of Mar., June, Sept., and Dec.
Trustee: Citizens Bank.
EIN: 386040492

211
The Bouwer Foundation
2819 Cotswold Ln. S.E.
East Grand Rapids, MI   49506-2023

Established in 1994 in MI.
Donors: John Bouwer; Marian Bouwer.
Grantmaker type: Independent foundation.
Financial data (yr. ended 12/31/05): Assets, $65,503 (M); expenditures, $27,879; total giving, $26,500; qualifying distributions, $26,500; giving activities include $26,500 for grants.
Fields of interest: Higher education; Botanical gardens; Christian agencies & churches.
Limitations: Applications not accepted. Giving primarily in Grand Rapids, MI. No grants to individuals.

Application information: Contributes only to pre-selected organizations.
Officers: John Bouwer, Pres.; Marian Bouwer, V.P.; Kathryn Bouwer, Secy.; Thomas Bouwer, Treas.
EIN: 383148915

212
The William B. Bowie Foundation
c/o William H. Bowie
99 Monroe Ave., Ste. 1100
Grand Rapids, MI   49503-2639

Established in 1993 in MI.
Grantmaker type: Independent foundation.
Financial data (yr. ended 12/31/05): Assets, $576,715 (M); expenditures, $34,621; total giving, $31,000; qualifying distributions, $31,000; giving activities include $31,000 for grants.
Fields of interest: Performing arts, opera; Recreation, camps; Human services; Protestant agencies & churches.
Limitations: Applications not accepted. Giving primarily in Grand Rapids, MI. No grants to individuals.
Application information: Contributes only to pre-selected organizations.
Officers: Jack M. Bowie, Pres.; William H. Bowie, Secy.; Janice J. Bowie, Treas.
EIN: 383121370

213
The Boyd Foundation
1200 Fero Rd.
Lowell, MI   49331

Grantmaker type: Independent foundation.
Financial data (yr. ended 12/31/05): Assets, $189,680 (M); expenditures, $12,997; total giving, $10,250; qualifying distributions, $10,250; giving activities include $10,250 for grants.
Limitations: Applications not accepted. Giving primarily in San Francisco, CA. No grants to individuals.
Application information: Contributes only to pre-selected organizations.
Officer: Katharine B. Dernocoeur, Pres.; Lawrence G. Robinson, Sr., Treas.
EIN: 383104434

214
Charles & Jessie Brackett Memorial Fund
c/o Comerica Bank
49 W. Michigan Ave.
Battle Creek, MI   49017-3603

Established in MI.
Grantmaker type: Independent foundation.
Financial data (yr. ended 12/31/05): Assets, $59,224 (M); expenditures, $7,691; total giving, $3,200; qualifying distributions, $3,200; giving activities include $3,200 for 4 grants to individuals (high: $800; low: $800).
Purpose and activities: Scholarship awards to graduates of Battle Creek Central High School, MI, pursuing a degree in the fields of medicine, law, engineering, or home economics.
Type of support: Scholarships—to individuals.
Limitations: Giving limited to residents of Battle Creek, MI.

Application information: Contact Comerica Bank for details. Application form required.
Deadline(s): Nov. 15
Trustee: Comerica Bank.
EIN: 386053232

215
Bradshaw-Knight Foundation, Inc.
(formerly Cavaliere Foundation, Inc.)
712 Harrison St.
Madison, WI 53711
Contact: James A. Knight, Pres.
E-mail: bkfd@mac.com; URL: http://www.bkfnd.org

Established in 1999 in WI.
Donor: James A. Knight, Sr.†.
Grantmaker type: Independent foundation.
Financial data (yr. ended 12/31/04): Assets, $5,883,367 (M); expenditures, $521,004; total giving, $404,500; qualifying distributions, $453,554; giving activities include $404,500 for 19 grants (high: $73,000; low: $500).
Purpose and activities: Giving primarily for environmental education, environmental justice, ecological restoration, and religious approaches to environmental problems.
Fields of interest: Environment, ethics; Environment, natural resources; Environment.
Type of support: Emergency funds; Curriculum development; General/operating support; Equipment; Program development; Conferences/seminars; Seed money; Research.
Limitations: Giving primarily in the West Slope of CO, and the Upper Midwest Region of IA, IL, MI and WI. No grants to individuals.
Publications: Grants list; Program policy statement.
Application information: Application form required.
Initial approach: Letter or E-mail
Copies of proposal: 7
Deadline(s): Sept. 15
Board meeting date(s): Oct. 15
Final notification: 2 months
Officers and Directors:* James A. Knight,* Pres.; Renee Miller Knight, Exec. Dir.; Kathe Conn; Mike Heck; Ed Marston; Warren Porter; Vern Visick.
Number of staff: 1 part-time professional.
EIN: 391960035

216
Bradstrum Charitable Trust
(formerly Gladys Bradstrum Charitable Trust)
c/o Fifth Third Bank
P.O. Box 3636
Grand Rapids, MI 49501-3636

Established in 1996 in MI.
Grantmaker type: Independent foundation.
Financial data (yr. cndcd 3/31/05): Assets, $1,356,247 (M); expenditures, $80,640; total giving, $69,002; qualifying distributions, $69,002; giving activities include $69,002 for grants.
Purpose and activities: Support only for the Adrian College and Albion College, MI.
Fields of interest: Higher education.
Type of support: General/operating support.
Limitations: Applications not accepted. Giving limited to Adrian and Albion, MI. No grants to individuals.
Application information: Contributes only to 2 pre-selected organizations.

Trustee: Fifth Third Bank.
EIN: 383189696

217
David A. Brandon Foundation
660 Barton Shore Dr.
Ann Arbor, MI 48105

Established in 1987 in MI.
Donor: David A. Brandon.
Grantmaker type: Independent foundation.
Financial data (yr. ended 12/31/05): Assets, $2,128,167 (M); gifts received, $162,906; expenditures, $295,360; total giving, $293,560; qualifying distributions, $293,560; giving activities include $293,560 for 51 grants (high: $100,000; low: $250).
Fields of interest: Performing arts, orchestra (symphony); Arts; Elementary/secondary education; Higher education; Scholarships/financial aid; Hospitals (general); Health organizations; Human services; Protestant agencies & churches.
Limitations: Applications not accepted. Giving primarily in MI. No grants to individuals.
Application information: Contributes only to pre-selected organizations.
Officers: David A. Brandon, Pres. and Treas.; Jan A. Brandon, Secy.
Directors: Chris Brandon; Nick Brandon; Arthur Fediuk.
EIN: 382750356
Selected grants: The following grants were reported in 2004.
$25,150 to Michigans Thanksgiving Parade Foundation, Detroit, MI. For general support.
$22,609 to Mott Childrens Health Center, Flint, MI. For general support.
$10,000 to Cornerstone Schools, Detroit, MI. For general support.
$6,250 to Saint Joseph Mercy Hospital, Ann Arbor, MI. For general support.
$5,120 to University of Michigan, Ann Arbor, MI. For general support.
$5,000 to Purple Rose Theater Company, Chelsea, MI. For general support.
$3,000 to HelpSource, Ann Arbor, MI. For general support.
$2,500 to Motor City Lyric Opera, Detroit, MI. For general support.
$1,000 to Ann Arbor Symphony Orchestra, Ann Arbor, MI. For general support.
$1,000 to Washtenaw Housing Alliance, Ann Arbor, MI. For general support.

218
Rose Braude Foundation
c/o Comerica Bank
P.O. Box 75000
Detroit, MI 48275

Established in 1996 in MI.
Grantmaker type: Independent foundation.
Financial data (yr. ended 4/30/05): Assets, $2,193,984 (M); expenditures, $116,644; total giving, $71,098; qualifying distributions, $71,098; giving activities include $71,098 for grants.
Purpose and activities: Support only for the Jewish Home for the Aged, MI, and Hadassah, NY.
Fields of interest: Housing/shelter, aging; Jewish agencies & temples.
Type of support: Continuing support.

Limitations: Applications not accepted. Giving limited to MI and NY. No grants to individuals.
Application information: Contributes only to 2 pre-selected organizations.
Trustee: Comerica Bank.
EIN: 386664680

219
The Brauer Foundation
300 N. 5th Ave., Ste. 200
Ann Arbor, MI 48104-1410
Contact: Carl A. Brauer, Jr., Pres.

Established around 1978 in MI.
Donor: Carl A. Brauer, Jr.
Grantmaker type: Independent foundation.
Financial data (yr. ended 3/31/05): Assets, $1,444,157 (M); expenditures, $100,830; total giving, $97,500; qualifying distributions, $97,500; giving activities include $97,500 for grants.
Purpose and activities: Giving for organizations whose philosophy and/or purpose is consistent with the teachings of Jesus Christ.
Fields of interest: Elementary/secondary education; Higher education; Human services; Christian agencies & churches.
Type of support: General/operating support; Continuing support; Annual campaigns; Capital campaigns; Building/renovation; Endowments.
Limitations: Giving primarily in MI. No support for advocacy, athletic, political or veterans organizations, the United Way, or state and local government agencies. No grants to individuals, or for special events.
Application information: Application form not required.
Deadline(s): None
Officers and Trustees:* Carl A. Brauer, Jr.,* Pres.; Carol D. Schmidt,* V.P.; Isabelle M. Brauer,* Secy.-Treas.; Janet E. Ash; Richard D. Brauer.
EIN: 382156710

220
Viola E. Bray Charitable Trust
c/o JPMorgan Chase Bank, N.A.
P.O. Box 1308
Milwaukee, WI 53201
Application address: c/o Carol J. Scholten-Elcoate, 320 Howard St., Petoskey, MI 49770, tel.: (231) 348-6281

Established in 1961 in MI.
Donor: Viola E. Bray†.
Grantmaker type: Independent foundation.
Financial data (yr. ended 9/30/05): Assets, $3,406,952 (M); expenditures, $201,793; total giving, $163,520; qualifying distributions, $177,091; giving activities include $163,520 for 18 grants (high: $63,865; low: $875).
Purpose and activities: Giving primarily for women's services.
Fields of interest: Museums (art); Reproductive health, family planning; American Red Cross; YM/YWCAs & YM/YWHAs; Children/youth, services; Women, centers/services.
Type of support: Continuing support; Annual campaigns; Building/renovation; Equipment; Emergency funds; Seed money; Matching/challenge support.

Limitations: Giving limited to the Flint, MI, area. No grants to individuals, or for research, scholarships, or fellowships; no loans.
Publications: Application guidelines; Program policy statement.
Application information: Application form not required.
  Initial approach: 1-page proposal
  Copies of proposal: 6
  Deadline(s): Aug. 31
  Board meeting date(s): Sept.
  Final notification: 3 months
Trustees: James Johnson; Molly Bray McCormick; Sally Richards Ricker; William L. Ricker; JPMorgan Chase Bank, N.A.
EIN: 386039741
Selected grants: The following grants were reported in 2005.
  $63,865 to Flint Institute of Arts, Flint, MI. For general support of the Bray Gallery.
  $10,780 to Every Womans Place, Muskegon, MI. For general support.
  $10,000 to American Red Cross. For Hurricane Disaster Relief Fund.
  $10,000 to Flint Cultural Center Corporation, Flint, MI. For underserved youth project.
  $10,000 to Kentucky Fish and Wildlife Education and Resource Foundation, Frankfort, KY. For national Archery In Schools program.
  $7,500 to Junior Achievement, Greater Genesee Valley, Flint, MI. For program support.
  $5,800 to Flint Institute of Music, Flint, MI. For general support of Troubadour program.
  $5,800 to Ted Nugents Kamp for Kids, Brighton, MI. For general support.
  $5,800 to Womens Resource Center of Northern Michigan, Petoskey, MI. For capital support.
  $5,000 to Arts Council of White Lake, Montague, MI. For general support of summer concert series.

221
Jonathan D. Brege Memorial Foundation
c/o JPMorgan Chase Bank, N.A.
P.O. Box 1308
Milwaukee, WI 53201-1308
Application address: c/o Donald R. Brege, 5224 Byron Rd., Corunna, MI 48817

Established in MI.
Donor: Donald R. Brege.
Grantmaker type: Independent foundation.
Financial data (yr. ended 9/30/04): Assets, $454,010 (M); gifts received, $10,000; expenditures, $38,902; total giving, $33,500; qualifying distributions, $35,474; giving activities include $33,500 for grants.
Purpose and activities: Scholarship primarily to graduating students from Onaway High School and New Lothrop High School, MI.
Type of support: Scholarships—to individuals.
Limitations: Giving limited to MI.
Application information: Application form required.
  Initial approach: Letter
  Deadline(s): None
Trustee: JPMorgan Chase Bank, N.A.
EIN: 386477703

222
Benjamin and Marion Bregi Foundation
500 Woodward Ave., Ste. 2500
Detroit, MI 48226

Established in 1999 in MI.
Donor: Marion Bregi.
Grantmaker type: Independent foundation.
Financial data (yr. ended 12/31/05): Assets, $296,506 (M); gifts received, $55,148; expenditures, $21,598; total giving, $15,500; qualifying distributions, $15,500; giving activities include $15,500 for grants.
Purpose and activities: Giving primarily to Lutheran agencies and churches, and for education.
Fields of interest: Higher education; Human services; Protestant agencies & churches.
Type of support: General/operating support; Annual campaigns.
Limitations: Applications not accepted. Giving primarily in MI. No grants to individuals.
Application information: Contributes only to pre-selected organizations.
Officers: Marion Bregi, Chair.; Nancy Bregi Warren, Pres.; James Bregi, V.P.; Curtis J. DeRoo, Secy.
EIN: 383507162

223
The John H. Brems Foundation
c/o David Hempstead
100 Renaissance Ctr., 34th Fl.
Detroit, MI 48243

Established in 2002 in MI.
Donor: John Brems Purcell High School Irrevocable Charitable Trust.
Grantmaker type: Independent foundation.
Financial data (yr. ended 12/31/05): Assets, $1,072,480 (M); expenditures, $66,219; total giving, $54,000; qualifying distributions, $54,000; giving activities include $54,000 for grants.
Purpose and activities: Support only for Purcell Marian High School, Cincinnati, OH.
Fields of interest: Secondary school/education; Roman Catholic agencies & churches.
Type of support: General/operating support.
Limitations: Applications not accepted. Giving limited to Cincinnati, OH. No grants to individuals.
Application information: Contributes only to a pre-selected organization.
Officers and Directors:* Marian Brems,* Pres.; David Hempstead,* Secy.-Treas.
EIN: 352184579

224
The Brennan Family Charitable Trust
123 Noren Rd.
Iron River, MI 49935
Contact: Margaret M. Brennan, Tr.

Established in 1995 in OH.
Grantmaker type: Independent foundation.
Financial data (yr. ended 12/31/05): Assets, $206,548 (M); expenditures, $20,162; total giving, $14,810; qualifying distributions, $14,810; giving activities include $14,810 for grants.
Limitations: Giving primarily in Iron River, MI. No grants to individuals.
Application information:
  Initial approach: Proposal
  Deadline(s): Jan., Apr., July, Oct.
Trustees: James R. Brennan; Margaret M. Brennan.
EIN: 341813450

225
C. William Brenske Scholarship Fund
c/o Citizens Bank Wealth Mgmt., N.A.
328 S. Saginaw St., M/C 002072
Flint, MI 48502
Application address: c/o Helen James, Citizens Bank, N.A. Wealth Mgmt., 101 N. Washington Ave., Saginaw, MI 48607, tel.: (989) 776-7368

Grantmaker type: Independent foundation.
Financial data (yr. ended 12/31/05): Assets, $144,957 (M); expenditures, $10,459; total giving, $6,400; qualifying distributions, $6,400; giving activities include $6,400 for grants to individuals.
Purpose and activities: Scholarships only to residents of Saginaw County, MI, attending Nouvel Catholic Central High School.
Type of support: Scholarships—to individuals.
Limitations: Giving limited to residents of Saginaw County, MI.
Application information: Application form required.
  Deadline(s): May 1
Trustee: Citizens Bank.
EIN: 386568888

226
Anthony Stephen & Elizabeth E. Brenske Student Loan Fund
c/o Citizens Bank Wealth Mgmt., N.A.
328 S. Saginaw St., M/C 002072
Flint, MI 48502
Application address: c/o Helen James, Citizens Bank Wealth Mgmt., N.A., 101 N. Washington Ave., Saginaw, MI 48607, tel.: (989) 776-7368

Established in MI.
Grantmaker type: Independent foundation.
Financial data (yr. ended 12/31/05): Assets, $221,585 (M); expenditures, $4,783; total giving, $0; qualifying distributions, $0.
Purpose and activities: Loans only to residents of Saginaw County attending a Michigan college or university.
Type of support: Student loans—to individuals.
Limitations: Giving limited to residents of Saginaw County, MI.
Application information: Application form required.
  Deadline(s): May 1
Trustee: Citizens Bank.
EIN: 386568889

227
The Frank and Ethel Bresto Family Foundation
53873 Lynnham Ln.
Shelby Township, MI 48316

Established in 2001 in MI.
Donor: Ethel Bresto.
Grantmaker type: Independent foundation.
Financial data (yr. ended 12/31/05): Assets, $611,640 (M); gifts received, $558,385; expenditures, $32,199; total giving, $30,750; qualifying distributions, $30,750; giving activities include $30,750 for grants.
Limitations: Applications not accepted. Giving primarily in MI. No grants to individuals.
Application information: Contributes only to pre-selected organizations.
Officers: Joan M. Chura, Pres.; Robert A. Chura, Secy.-Treas.

Trustees: Lori A. Brunell; Kelly Chura-Singh; Jeanine McCloskey.
EIN: 383632669

228
The Hilda E. Bretzlaff Foundation, Inc.
1550 N. Milford Rd.
Milford, MI   48381
Contact: Janelle M. Radtke, V.P.
E-mail: jradtke@hebf.org; Additional E-mail:
klindbeck@hebf.org; URL: http://www.hebf.org

Established in 1994 in MI.
Donor: Hilda E. Bretzlaff‡.
Grantmaker type: Independent foundation.
Financial data (yr. ended 12/31/05): Assets,
$26,212,343 (M); gifts received, $100;
expenditures, $1,311,838; total giving, $767,678;
qualifying distributions, $1,049,203; giving
activities include $685,540 for 39 grants (high:
$50,000; low: $2,500), and $82,138 for grants to
individuals (high: $3,750; low: $200).
Purpose and activities: The foundation provides
educational grants to assist students in attending
educational institutions in the United States or
England that promote high educational, moral, and
conservative ideals.
Fields of interest: Scholarships/financial aid.
Type of support: Scholarship funds.
Limitations: Applications not accepted. Giving
primarily for the benefit of U.S. citizens or individuals
in the process of becoming U.S. citizens. Some
giving also in England. No support for schools that
are not conservative. No grants to individuals
directly.
Application information: Funds administered
through educational institutions. Applicants must
have and maintain a minimum of 2.0 GPA. The
foundation's mission statement indicates that all
applicants must be financially needy, moral,
conservative, and a credit to America.
  Board meeting date(s): Bimonthly
Officers: Gerald W. Radtke, Pres.; Susan J. Vogt,
V.P. and Secy.; Janelle M. Radtke, V.P.; Kathleen M.
Lindbeck, Mgr.
Number of staff: 4 part-time professional.
EIN: 382619845

229
Jewell Brewer Trust
(formerly Brewer Trust Fund for Deserving Students)
c/o Standard Federal Bank N.A.
135 S. LaSalle St., Ste. 2060
Chicago, IL   60603
Application address: c/o The American Legion Dept.
of Michigan, 212 N. Verlinden, Lansing, MI 48915,
tel.: (517) 371-4720

Established in MI.
Grantmaker type: Independent foundation.
Financial data (yr. ended 8/31/05): Assets,
$70,206 (M); expenditures, $6,478; total giving,
$2,500; qualifying distributions, $2,500; giving
activities include $2,500 for grants to individuals.
Purpose and activities: Scholarship awards to
residents of MI who are the legal offspring of
honorably discharged veterans.
Fields of interest: Education.
Type of support: Scholarships—to individuals.
Limitations: Giving limited to residents of MI.

Application information: Application form required.
  Deadline(s): May 15
Trustee: Standard Federal Bank N.A.
EIN: 386461214

230
The Briarwood Farm Foundation
136 E. Michigan Ave., Ste. 1201
Kalamazoo, MI   49007-3936   (269) 382-5800
Contact: James C. Melvin, Secy.

Established in 1995 in MI.
Donors: Paul H. Todd, Jr.; Ruth N. Todd; George N.
Todd; Elizabeth R. Todd.
Grantmaker type: Independent foundation.
Financial data (yr. ended 12/31/05): Assets,
$1,098,199 (M); gifts received, $49,318;
expenditures, $62,883; total giving, $45,000;
qualifying distributions, $45,000; giving activities
include $45,000 for grants.
Fields of interest: Higher education; Environment,
natural resources.
Limitations: Applications not accepted. Giving
primarily in Kalamazoo, MI. No grants to individuals.
Application information: Contributes only to
pre-selected organizations.
Officers: Paul H. Todd, Jr., Pres.; George N. Todd,
V.P.; James C. Melvin, Secy.; James S. Hilboldt,
Treas.
Trustees: Clare K. Todd; Elizabeth R. Todd.
EIN: 383265310

231
John C. Brier Trust
c/o National City Bank
P.O. Box 94651
Cleveland, OH   44101-4651

Grantmaker type: Independent foundation.
Financial data (yr. ended 12/31/02): Assets,
$173,630 (M); expenditures, $7,285; total giving,
$4,528; qualifying distributions, $5,729; giving
activities include $4,528 for grants.
Fields of interest: Higher education.
Type of support: General/operating support.
Limitations: Applications not accepted. Giving
primarily in MI. No grants to individuals.
Application information: Contributes only to
pre-selected organizations.
Trustee: National City Bank.
EIN: 386345036

232
Brinkerhoff-Sample Family Foundation
1011 Lincoln Ave.
Ann Arbor, MI   48104

Established in 2004 in MI.
Donors: William F. Brinkerhoff; Kathleen Sample.
Grantmaker type: Independent foundation.
Financial data (yr. ended 12/31/05): Assets,
$205,429 (M); expenditures, $22,045; total giving,
$17,850; qualifying distributions, $20,870; giving
activities include $17,850 for 15 grants.
Fields of interest: Protestant agencies & churches.
Type of support: General/operating support.
Limitations: Applications not accepted. Giving
primarily in MI. No grants to individuals.

Officers: William F. Brinkerhoff, Pres.; Kathleen
Sample, Secy.-Treas.
EIN: 201389996

233
Robert L. Brintnall Family Foundation
1086 Brunn Ave.
St. Joseph, MI   49085-2817   (269) 983-4891
Contact: Robert L. Brintnall, Pres.

Established in 1986 in IL.
Donor: Robert L. Brintnall.
Grantmaker type: Independent foundation.
Financial data (yr. ended 12/31/05): Assets,
$65,218 (M); gifts received, $23,848;
expenditures, $11,387; total giving, $9,350;
qualifying distributions, $9,350; giving activities
include $9,350 for grants.
Limitations: Giving on a national basis, with some
emphasis on the Midwest. No grants to individuals.
Application information:
  Initial approach: Proposal
  Deadline(s): None
Officers and Directors:* Robert L. Brintnall,* Pres.
and Treas.; Helen W. Brintnall,* Secy.; James W.
Brintnall.
EIN: 363488562

234
Broadleaf Foundation
111 Lyon St. N.W., Ste. 900
Grand Rapids, MI   49503-2487

Established in 1998 in MI.
Donor: Jonathan M. Wege.
Grantmaker type: Independent foundation.
Financial data (yr. ended 12/31/05): Assets,
$2,234 (M); expenditures, $15,735; total giving,
$10,000; qualifying distributions, $10,000; giving
activities include $10,000 for grants.
Fields of interest: Arts; Environment, natural
resources; Nursing home/convalescent facility.
Type of support: General/operating support.
Limitations: Applications not accepted. Giving
primarily in MI. No grants to individuals.
Application information: Contributes only to
pre-selected organizations.
Officers: Jonathan M. Wege, Pres.; Anna C. Wege,
V.P.; Jeffrey B. Power, Secy.-Treas.
EIN: 383419873

235
Herman and Dina Brodsky Family
Charitable Foundation
26711 Woodward Ave., Ste. 307
Huntington Woods, MI   48070-1369

Established in 1987 in MI.
Donor: Herman Brodsky.
Grantmaker type: Independent foundation.
Financial data (yr. ended 12/31/04): Assets,
$1,315,514 (M); gifts received, $50,000;
expenditures, $87,988; total giving, $79,954;
qualifying distributions, $79,954; giving activities
include $79,954 for grants.
Fields of interest: Education; Jewish federated
giving programs; Jewish agencies & temples.
Limitations: Applications not accepted. Giving
primarily in MI. No grants to individuals.

Application information: Contributes only to pre-selected organizations.
Officers: Jeffrey Brodsky, Pres.; Dina Brodsky, Secy.
EIN: 382712626

236
The Brodsky Family Foundation
6150 Highland Rd.
Waterford, MI   48327

Established in 1999 in MI.
Donor: Pearl Brodsky.
Grantmaker type: Independent foundation.
Financial data (yr. ended 7/31/05): Assets, $97,824 (M); expenditures, $14,270; total giving, $12,539; qualifying distributions, $12,539; giving activities include $12,539 for grants.
Limitations: Applications not accepted. No grants to individuals.
Application information: Contributes only to pre-selected organizations.
Officers: Pearl Brodsky, Pres.; Bernard Brodsky, V.P. and Treas.; Gordon I. Ginsberg, Secy.
EIN: 383504677

237
Wallace and Irene Bronner Family Charitable Foundation
P.O. Box 264
Frankenmuth, MI   48734

Established in 1989 in MI.
Donor: Wallace and Irene Bronner Family Trust.
Grantmaker type: Independent foundation.
Financial data (yr. ended 12/31/05): Assets, $3,709,977 (M); gifts received, $345,500; expenditures, $157,580; total giving, $154,336; qualifying distributions, $154,336; giving activities include $154,336 for 242 grants (high: $15,000; low: $50).
Purpose and activities: Giving primarily to Christian churches and organizations; funding also for education, health and human services.
Fields of interest: Higher education; Health organizations, association; Cancer; Youth development; Human services; Religious federated giving programs; Christian agencies & churches.
Type of support: General/operating support; Scholarship funds.
Limitations: Giving primarily in MI, with emphasis on Frankenmuth and Saginaw. No loans or program-related investments.
Application information:
Initial approach: Letter
Deadline(s): None
Officer: Wallace J. Bronner, Pres.
Trustee: Irene R. Bronner.
EIN: 382834541

238
Carol Young Brooke Foundation
22425 Ventura Blvd., Ste. 144
Woodland Hills, CA   91364-1524

Established in 1998 in CA.
Donor: Carol Young Brooke.
Grantmaker type: Independent foundation.
Financial data (yr. ended 12/31/05): Assets, $2,576,234 (M); expenditures, $524,126; total giving, $100,000; qualifying distributions,

$100,000; giving activities include $100,000 for grants.
Purpose and activities: Grants primarily to promote the arts and education.
Fields of interest: Arts education; Arts; Higher education, college; Higher education, university; Hospitals (general).
Limitations: Applications not accepted. Giving primarily in CA; some giving also in MI. No grants to individuals.
Application information: Contributes only to pre-selected organizations.
Officers and Directors:* Michael P. Chmura,* Pres.; Hon. Edward M. Ross,* V.P. and Secy.; Carol Young Brooke.
EIN: 954692391

239
William & Katherine Brooks Charitable Foundation
1057 E. Juliah Ave.
Flint, MI   48505

Established in 2002 in MI.
Grantmaker type: Independent foundation.
Financial data (yr. ended 12/31/04): Assets, $53,875 (M); gifts received, $50,700; expenditures, $2,000; total giving, $2,000; qualifying distributions, $2,000; giving activities include $2,000 for grants.
Fields of interest: Christian agencies & churches.
Type of support: General/operating support.
Limitations: Applications not accepted. No grants to individuals.
Application information: Contributes only to pre-selected organizations.
Officer and Trustees:* Katherine Brooks,* Secy.; William Brooks.
EIN: 141857965

240
The Victor and Sonnie Brooks Foundation
4286 Chimney Point Dr.
Bloomfield Hills, MI   48302   (248) 626-9642
Contact: Victor L. Brooks, Pres.

Established in 1997 in MI.
Donor: Victor L. Brooks.
Grantmaker type: Independent foundation.
Financial data (yr. ended 12/31/04): Assets, $41,378 (M); expenditures, $3,214; total giving, $1,200; qualifying distributions, $1,200; giving activities include $1,200 for grants.
Fields of interest: Protestant agencies & churches.
Limitations: Applications not accepted. Giving primarily in MI. No grants to individuals.
Application information: Contributes only to pre-selected organizations.
Officers: Victor L. Brooks, Pres.; Florence S. Brooks, Secy.
Directors: David E. Brooks; Susan M. Brooks.
EIN: 383323835

241
Broomfield Charitable Foundation
9910 E. Bexhill Dr.
Kensington, MD   20895   (301) 942-4882
Contact: William S. Broomfield, Pres.

Established in 1993 in MI.

Grantmaker type: Independent foundation.
Financial data (yr. ended 11/30/05): Assets, $880,579 (M); expenditures, $48,014; total giving, $35,600; qualifying distributions, $35,600; giving activities include $35,600 for grants.
Fields of interest: Hospitals (general); Health organizations, association; Human services.
Type of support: General/operating support.
Limitations: Giving primarily in MI; some giving also in the greater metropolitan Washington, DC, area, including VA and MD. No grants to individuals.
Application information:
Initial approach: Proposal
Deadline(s): None
Officers: William S. Broomfield, Pres.; Jane Broomfield, V.P. and Secy.-Treas.
Directors: Nancy Broomfield Aiken; Barbara Broomfield Shaffer.
Trustee: JPMorgan Chase Bank, N.A.
EIN: 383083449

242
Gregory & Helayne Brown Charitable Foundation
3716 White Trillium Dr. E.
Saginaw, MI   48603
Contact: Gregory S. Brown, Pres.

Established in 2000 in MI.
Donor: Gregory S. Brown.
Grantmaker type: Independent foundation.
Financial data (yr. ended 12/31/05): Assets, $238,771 (M); expenditures, $18,477; total giving, $15,000; qualifying distributions, $15,000; giving activities include $15,000 for grants.
Application information:
Initial approach: Letter
Deadline(s): None
Officers: Gregory S. Brown, Pres. and Treas.; Helayne Brown, V.P. and Secy.
EIN: 383507502

243
Peter D. and Dorothy S. Brown Charitable Trust
3631 Wabeek Lake Dr. W.
Bloomfield Hills, MI   48302-1273

Established in 1987 in FL.
Donors: Peter D. Brown; Dorothy S. Brown; A. Bart Lewis; Susan Lewis.
Grantmaker type: Independent foundation.
Financial data (yr. ended 12/31/05): Assets, $10,394,020 (M); expenditures, $723,333; total giving, $592,350; qualifying distributions, $601,100; giving activities include $592,350 for 6 grants (high: $250,000; low: $550).
Fields of interest: Jewish federated giving programs; Jewish agencies & temples.
Limitations: Applications not accepted. Giving primarily in MI; some funding also in FL. No grants to individuals.
Application information: Contributes only to pre-selected organizations.
Trustees: Dorothy S. Brown; A. Bart Lewis.
EIN: 386517224

244
The Sid & Esther Brown Family Foundation
4565 Chamberlain Dr.
East China, MI 48054

Established in 2000 in MI.
Donors: Robert S. Brown; Esther A. Brown.
Grantmaker type: Independent foundation.
Financial data (yr. ended 12/31/05): Assets, $418,279 (M); expenditures, $28,471; total giving, $20,430; qualifying distributions, $20,430; giving activities include $20,430 for grants.
Purpose and activities: Giving primarily for the township of East China, Michigan.
Fields of interest: Community development.
Limitations: Applications not accepted. Giving primarily in East China, MI. No grants to individuals.
Application information: Contributes only to pre-selected organizations.
Officers and Directors:* Robert S. Brown II,* Pres.; Robert S. Brown III,* V.P.; Mollie E. Beaver,* Secy.; Julie A. Witherspoon,* Treas.; Esther A. Brown.
EIN: 912092923

245
The John and Rosemary Brown Family Foundation
490 W. South St.
Kalamazoo, MI 49007

Established in 1997 in MI.
Donors: John W. Brown; Rosemary K. Brown.
Grantmaker type: Independent foundation.
Financial data (yr. ended 12/31/05): Assets, $13,635,285 (M); gifts received, $1,598,450; expenditures, $842,900; total giving, $840,500; qualifying distributions, $841,475; giving activities include $840,500 for 40 grants (high: $400,000; low: $500).
Purpose and activities: Giving primarily for higher education, economic development, and Christian churches; funding also for health associations, the arts, and children, youth, and social services.
Fields of interest: Arts; Higher education; Education; Health organizations, association; Medical research, institute; Human services; Children/youth, services; Economic development; Community development; Federated giving programs; Christian agencies & churches.
Limitations: Applications not accepted. Giving primarily in MI, with emphasis on Kalamazoo. No grants to individuals.
Application information: Contributes only to pre-selected organizations.
Trustees: John W. Brown; Rosemary K. Brown.
EIN: 586343478

246
The Brown Family Foundation, Ltd
840 W. Long Lake Rd., Ste. 200
Troy, MI 48098

Established in 2002 in MI.
Donors: Robert N. Brown; Claire P. Brown.
Grantmaker type: Independent foundation.
Financial data (yr. ended 12/31/04): Assets, $573,749 (M); gifts received, $40,000; expenditures, $5,709; total giving, $2,000; qualifying distributions, $5,694; giving activities include $2,000 for grants.

Limitations: Applications not accepted. No grants to individuals.
Application information: Contributes only to pre-selected organizations.
Officers: Claire P. Brown, Pres.; David M. Thoms, V.P.; Robert N. Brown, Secy.-Treas.
EIN: 113653776

247
Edalene and Ed Brown Family Foundation, Ltd.
840 W. Long Lake Rd., Ste. 200
Troy, MI 48098   (248) 267-4342
Contact: David M. Thomas, Pres.
FAX: (248) 879-2001; E-mail: thoms@millercanfield.com

Established in 2002 in MI.
Grantmaker type: Independent foundation.
Financial data (yr. ended 12/31/04): Assets, $308,617 (M); gifts received, $307,121; expenditures, $0; total giving, $0; qualifying distributions, $0.
Limitations: Applications not accepted.
Application information: Contributes only to pre-selected organizations.
Officer: David M. Thoms, Pres.
EIN: 364493141

248
Richard H. Brown Foundation
6293 Cannon Highlands Dr. N.E.
Belmont, MI 49306
Contact: Richard H. Brown, Pres.

Established in 1995 in MI.
Donors: Richard H. Brown; Geraldine C. Brown.
Grantmaker type: Independent foundation.
Financial data (yr. ended 12/31/04): Assets, $2,495,958 (M); expenditures, $162,697; total giving, $130,000; qualifying distributions, $152,491; giving activities include $130,000 for 3 + grants (high: $102,000).
Purpose and activities: Giving primarily for a Methodist church and a state university.
Fields of interest: Higher education, university; Protestant agencies & churches.
Limitations: Giving primarily in MI and Vergennes, VT.
Application information: Application form not required.
    Deadline(s): None
Officers and Directors:* Richard H. Brown,* Pres. and Treas.; Charles L. Brown,* Secy.; Nancy Brown.
EIN: 383267368

249
Richard M. & Sharon R. Brown Foundation, Inc.
1200 Ardmoor Dr.
Bloomfield Hills, MI 48301-2158

Donor: Richard M. Brown.
Grantmaker type: Independent foundation.
Financial data (yr. ended 7/31/05): Assets, $0 (L); gifts received, $54,000; expenditures, $78,080; total giving, $77,105; qualifying distributions, $77,075; giving activities include $77,105 for 42 grants (high: $48,000; low: $25).

Purpose and activities: Giving primarily to Jewish organizations; support also for medical research, welfare, and education.
Fields of interest: Education; Medical research; Human services; Jewish federated giving programs; Jewish agencies & temples.
Limitations: Giving primarily in MI. No grants to individuals.
Application information:
    Initial approach: Letter
    Deadline(s): None
Officers: Richard M. Brown, Pres.; Sharon R. Brown, Secy.-Treas.
EIN: 382266194

250
Robert W. & Lynn H. Browne Foundation
(formerly Browne Foundation)
333 Trust Bldg.
40 Pearl St. N.W.
Grand Rapids, MI 49503-3028   (616) 459-2009
Contact: Robert W. Browne, Pres.

Established around 1983.
Donors: Robert W. Browne; Lynn H. Browne.
Grantmaker type: Independent foundation.
Financial data (yr. ended 12/31/05): Assets, $2,575,457 (M); expenditures, $3,173; total giving, $0; qualifying distributions, $0.
Fields of interest: Higher education.
Limitations: Giving primarily in MI.
Application information:
    Initial approach: Letter
    Deadline(s): None
Officers and Directors:* Robert W. Browne,* Pres.; James R. Browne,* V.P.; Charles M. Bloom, Secy.-Treas.; James N. Deboer.
EIN: 382452645
Selected grants: The following grants were reported in 2004.
$350,000 to University of Michigan, Kellogg Eye Center, Ann Arbor, MI.

251
The Bruce Family Charitable Foundation
c/o The Northern Trust Co.
50 S. LaSalle St.
Chicago, IL 60675

Established in 1997 in IN.
Donor: Barbara P. Bruce.
Grantmaker type: Independent foundation.
Financial data (yr. ended 12/31/05): Assets, $370,866 (M); expenditures, $21,705; total giving, $17,000; qualifying distributions, $17,000; giving activities include $17,000 for grants.
Limitations: Applications not accepted. Giving primarily in IN and MI. No grants to individuals.
Application information: Contributes only to pre-selected organizations.
Trustee: The Northern Trust Co.
EIN: 352015314

252
Brucker Charitable Foundation
P.O. Box 324
Mountain Home, TX 78058-0324

Established in 2003 in MI.
Grantmaker type: Independent foundation.

Financial data (yr. ended 12/31/04): Assets, $46,073 (M); gifts received, $42,255; expenditures, $36,870; total giving, $8,802; qualifying distributions, $8,802; giving activities include $8,802 for grants.
Fields of interest: Christian agencies & churches; General charitable giving.
Type of support: General/operating support.
Limitations: Applications not accepted. Giving primarily in MI, with some emphasis on Clinton Township. No grants to individuals.
Application information: Contributes only to pre-selected organizations.
Officer and Trustees: * Brenda Brucker,* Secy.; Emil Brucker.
EIN: 912166944

253
Charles F. and Edith E. Brunkow Memorial Trust
c/o B.J. Humphreys
4800 Fashion Sq. Blvd., Ste. 410A
Saginaw, MI 48604

Established in MI.
Donor: Edith Brunkow‡.
Grantmaker type: Independent foundation.
Financial data (yr. ended 12/31/04): Assets, $439,981 (M); expenditures, $26,766; total giving, $20,253; qualifying distributions, $20,253; giving activities include $20,253 for grants.
Purpose and activities: Support only for the St. John Lutheran Church, the American Cancer Society, Lansing, and Buena Vista Township School and Covenant Healthcare Fund, Saginaw, MI.
Fields of interest: Elementary/secondary education; Health care, research; Hospitals (general); Health organizations, association; Protestant agencies & churches.
Type of support: General/operating support.
Limitations: Applications not accepted. Giving limited to Lansing and Saginaw, MI. No grants to individuals.
Application information: Contributes only to 4 pre-selected organizations.
Trustee: B.J. Humphreys.
EIN: 386492107

254
Brust Family Foundation
3905 Preserve Dr.
Dexter, MI 48130

Established in 2000.
Donors: Eric Brust; Cheryl Brust.
Grantmaker type: Independent foundation.
Financial data (yr. ended 12/31/05): Assets, $20,303 (M); gifts received, $80,000; expenditures, $74,500; total giving, $74,500; qualifying distributions, $74,500; giving activities include $74,500 for grants.
Limitations: Applications not accepted. No grants to individuals.
Application information: Contributes only to pre-selected organizations.
Officers: Cheryl Brust, Pres.; Eric Brust, V.P.
EIN: 383553367

255
Bryan Foundation
751 Kolinske Rd.
Petoskey, MI 49770
Contact: Garth Bryan, Dir.
Application address: 1107 W. Division St., Boyne City, MI 49712

Grantmaker type: Independent foundation.
Financial data (yr. ended 12/31/05): Assets, $258,652 (M); expenditures, $20,672; total giving, $14,940; qualifying distributions, $14,940; giving activities include $14,940 for grants.
Fields of interest: Education, public education; Christian agencies & churches.
Type of support: General/operating support.
Limitations: Giving primarily in MI. No grants to individuals.
Application information:
  Initial approach: Letter
  Deadline(s): None
  Final notification: Within 60 days
Officers: Mark Bryan, Pres.; Janet Bryan, Secy.; Garth Bryan, C.F.O.
Directors: Jeffrey Bradford; Julie Bradford; Janet Milos; Wayne Milos.
EIN: 382292185

256
Laura Schaeffer Bucknell College Scholarship Trust
c/o Citizens Bank Wealth Mgmt., N.A.
328 S. Saginaw St., M/C 002072
Flint, MI 48502
Application address: c/o Sturgis Public Schools, Attn.: High School Gudiance Dept., 216 Vinewood, Sturgis, MI 49091, tel.: (269) 659-1500

Grantmaker type: Independent foundation.
Financial data (yr. ended 12/31/05): Assets, $39,767 (M); expenditures, $4,912; total giving, $3,550; qualifying distributions, $4,409; giving activities include $3,550 for 1 grant to an individual.
Purpose and activities: Scholarship awards to graduates of Sturgis High School, MI.
Fields of interest: Higher education.
Type of support: Scholarships—to individuals.
Limitations: Giving limited to residents of Sturgis, MI.
Application information: Application form required.
  Deadline(s): Apr. 30
Trustee: Citizens Bank, N.A.
EIN: 316502430

257
The Buer-Den Foundation
21751 Wildwood St.
Dearborn, MI 48128

Established in 1986 in MI.
Donors: Cyril J. Buersmeyer; June L. Buersmeyer.
Grantmaker type: Independent foundation.
Financial data (yr. ended 12/31/05): Assets, $389,870 (M); expenditures, $22,938; total giving, $22,500; qualifying distributions, $22,500; giving activities include $22,500 for grants.
Purpose and activities: Giving primarily for Catholic charitable and school organizations.
Fields of interest: Roman Catholic agencies & churches.

Limitations: Applications not accepted. Giving primarily in the Detroit, MI, area. No grants to individuals.
Application information: Contributes only to pre-selected organizations.
Officers and Trustees: * Cyril J. Buersmeyer,* Pres. and Treas.; June L. Buersmeyer,* V.P. and Secy.
EIN: 382703710

258
The Bugas Fund
P.O. Box 1882
Jackson, MI 49204-1882

Established in 1956 in MI.
Grantmaker type: Independent foundation.
Financial data (yr. ended 11/30/05): Assets, $1,857,785 (M); expenditures, $273,323; total giving, $223,000; qualifying distributions, $244,533; giving activities include $223,000 for 16 grants (high: $100,000; low: $1,000).
Fields of interest: Higher education; Hospitals (general); Health care; Cancer; Alzheimer's disease; Diabetes; Human services; Salvation Army.
Limitations: Applications not accepted. Giving primarily in MI. No grants to individuals.
Application information: Contributes only to pre-selected organizations.
  Board meeting date(s): Early Nov.
Officers: Patricia Bugas Harris, Pres.; John S. Bugas, Jr., V.P.; Catherine A. Nowak, Secy.; George E. Veach, Treas.
Director: John R. Fowler.
EIN: 386067261
Selected grants: The following grants were reported in 2004.
$50,000 to University of Michigan, Ann Arbor, MI. For Charles G. Harris Neurological Research Fund.
$25,000 to Community Respite Center, Jackson, MI.
$25,000 to Memorial Sloan-Kettering Cancer Center, New York, NY.
$15,000 to Mott Childrens Health Center, Flint, MI.
$10,000 to Saint Joseph Mercy Health System, Ann Arbor, MI.
$3,000 to Chelsea Community Hospital, Chelsea, MI.
$3,000 to Jackson Interfaith Shelter, Jackson, MI.
$3,000 to Lily Missions Center, Jackson, MI.
$2,500 to Shelter Association of Washtenaw County, Ann Arbor, MI.
$2,500 to Silver Maples of Chelsea, Chelsea, MI.

259
Buhr Foundation
401 E. Stadium Blvd.
Ann Arbor, MI 48104

Established in 1953 in MI.
Donor: Buhr Machine Tool Co.
Grantmaker type: Independent foundation.
Financial data (yr. ended 12/31/05): Assets, $4,182,485 (M); expenditures, $203,646; total giving, $183,783; qualifying distributions, $198,543; giving activities include $183,783 for 27 grants (high: $40,000; low: $1,000).
Fields of interest: Higher education; Adult/continuing education; Education; Hospitals (general); Human services; American Red Cross;

Children/youth, services; Aging, centers/services; Christian agencies & churches.
Type of support: Capital campaigns; Building/ renovation.
Limitations: Applications not accepted. Giving limited to the Ann Arbor, MI, area. No grants to individuals, or for operating funds.
Application information: Contributes only to pre-selected organizations.
Officers and Trustees:* Martha B. Grimes,* Pres.; Richard J. Buhr,* Secy.; James D. Buhr,* Treas.; Phillip J. Bowen; Thomas A. Buhr; C. Wendell Dunbar.
EIN: 386072288
Selected grants: The following grants were reported in 2003.
$44,700 to University of Michigan, Ann Arbor, MI. For program support.
$27,350 to Ann Arbor Area Community Foundation, Ann Arbor, MI. For program support.
$9,500 to Peace Neighborhood Center, Ann Arbor, MI. For program support.
$5,000 to Greenhills School, Ann Arbor, MI. For program support.
$5,000 to McKinley Foundation, Ann Arbor, MI. For program support.
$5,000 to Michigan Theater Foundation, Ann Arbor, MI. For program support.
$4,700 to American Red Cross, Ann Arbor, MI. For program support.
$3,000 to Youth Empowerment Project, Ann Arbor, MI. For program support.
$2,000 to Saint Joseph Mercy Hospital, Ann Arbor, MI. For program support.
$1,000 to Arbor Hospice, Ann Arbor, MI. For program support.

260
A. Dale Buist Family Foundation
4994 W. River Dr. N.E.
Comstock Park, MI 49321

Established in 1994 in MI.
Donors: A. Dale Buist; Mary K. Buist; D & R Leasing, LLC.
Grantmaker type: Independent foundation.
Financial data (yr. ended 3/31/05): Assets, $287,530 (M); gifts received, $20,000; expenditures, $12,626; total giving, $11,000; qualifying distributions, $11,000; giving activities include $11,000 for grants.
Limitations: Applications not accepted. No grants to individuals.
Application information: Contributes only to pre-selected organizations.
Officers: Mary K. Buist, Pres.; Betsy Gaastra, Secy.; Robert D. Buist, Treas.
EIN: 383211000

261
The Bunker Foundation
(formerly The Susan Ingemanson McNealy Foundation)
P.O. Box 223609
Carmel, CA 93922-3609

Established in 1994 in CA.
Donors: Scott McNealy; Susan McNealy; Susan Ingemanson.
Grantmaker type: Independent foundation.

Financial data (yr. ended 11/30/04): Assets, $13,444,435 (M); expenditures, $615,438; total giving, $613,000; qualifying distributions, $615,438; giving activities include $613,000 for 27 grants (high: $200,000; low: $500).
Purpose and activities: Giving primarily for education, and health and social services.
Fields of interest: Arts; Education; Hospitals (general); Health organizations, association; Human services; Protestant agencies & churches.
Limitations: Applications not accepted. Giving primarily in CA; giving also in CO, MA, and MI. No grants to individuals.
Application information: Contributes only to pre-selected organizations.
Officer and Directors:* Susan Ingemanson,* Pres.; Paul Ingemanson.
EIN: 943215751
Selected grants: The following grants were reported in 2003.
$350,000 to Lucile Packard Foundation for Childrens Health, Palo Alto, CA. For general support.
$210,000 to Portola Valley Schools Foundation, Portola Valley, CA. For general support.
$200,000 to Kettering University, Flint, MI. For general support.
$100,000 to Media and Technology Charter High School (MATCH), Boston, MA. For general support.
$100,000 to University of California, San Francisco, CA. For general support.
$50,000 to Child Advocates of Santa Clara and San Mateo Counties, Milpitas, CA. For general support.
$50,000 to Cities in Schools, Ravenswood, East Palo Alto, CA. For general support.
$50,000 to Stanford University, School of Medicine, Stanford, CA. For general support.
$40,000 to Childrens Health Council, Palo Alto, CA. For general support.
$35,000 to Valley Presbyterian Church, Portola Valley, CA. For general support.

262
Burch Family Foundation
29 Lumberman Way
Saginaw, MI 48603
Contact: Wilbur Burch, Dir.

Established in 1997 in MI.
Donor: Wilbur Burch.
Grantmaker type: Independent foundation.
Financial data (yr. ended 12/31/04): Assets, $347,400 (M); gifts received, $25,209; expenditures, $33,951; total giving, $17,669; qualifying distributions, $25,574; giving activities include $17,669 for grants.
Fields of interest: Higher education.
Limitations: Giving primarily in KS.
Application information: Application form not required.
Initial approach: Letter
Deadline(s): None
Directors: Michael Burch; Wilbur Burch; Anita Tribble.
EIN: 383373898

263
The Burdick-Thorne Foundation
136 E. Michigan Ave., Ste. 1201
Kalamazoo, MI 49007-3936
Contact: David S. Kruis, Treas.

Established in 1990 in MI.
Donors: James M. Thorne†; Mary B. Thorne†.
Grantmaker type: Independent foundation.
Financial data (yr. ended 12/31/05): Assets, $10,585,747 (M); gifts received, $7,281; expenditures, $553,407; total giving, $439,000; qualifying distributions, $518,578; giving activities include $439,000 for 49 grants (high: $80,000; low: $1,000).
Purpose and activities: Giving for higher education, the arts, social services, and natural resource preservation and enhancement.
Fields of interest: Arts councils; Performing arts; Performing arts, music; Higher education; Environment, natural resources; Human services.
Type of support: General/operating support; Continuing support; Annual campaigns; Capital campaigns; Building/renovation.
Limitations: Applications not accepted. Giving limited to Kalamazoo, MI. No grants to individuals.
Application information: Contributes only to pre-selected organizations.
Board meeting date(s): Varies
Officers and Trustees:* James S. Hilboldt,* Pres.; James C. Melvin,* V.P.; Loyal A. Eldridge III,* Secy.; David S. Kruis, Treas.; Andrea M. Thorne; Betsy V. Thorne.
EIN: 382904527
Selected grants: The following grants were reported in 2003.
$70,000 to Kalamazoo College, Kalamazoo, MI. For recital hall.
$22,000 to Arts Council of Greater Kalamazoo, Kalamazoo, MI. For general operating support.
$11,500 to Fontana Chamber Arts, Kalamazoo, MI. For general operating support.
$5,000 to Birmingham-Bloomfield Symphony Orchestra, Birmingham, MI. For general operating support.
$5,000 to Michigan Youth Arts Festival, Midland, MI. For general operating support.
$3,000 to Salvation Army of Kalamazoo, Kalamazoo, MI. For general operating support.
$3,000 to YMCA of Kalamazoo, Kalamazoo, MI. For general operating support.
$2,000 to Crescendo Academy of Music, Kalamazoo, MI. For scholarships.
$2,000 to Kalamazoo Junior Symphony, Kalamazoo, MI. For scholarships.
$1,000 to New Vic Theatricals, Kalamazoo, MI. For general operating support.

264
Leo Burnett Foundation, Inc.
35 W. Wacker Dr.
Chicago, IL 60601

Grantmaker type: Independent foundation.
Financial data (yr. ended 12/31/04): Assets, $505,531 (M); expenditures, $29,897; total giving, $28,000; qualifying distributions, $28,000; giving activities include $28,000 for grants.
Purpose and activities: Support for the University of Michigan.
Fields of interest: Higher education, university.
Type of support: Program development; Scholarship funds.

Limitations: Applications not accepted. Giving limited to MI. No grants to individuals.
Application information: Contributes only to a pre-selected organization.
Officers and Directors:* Linda S. Wolf,* Pres.; Kristin L. Anderson, Secy. and Mgr.; Gregory J. Vichick, Treas. and Mgr.; Cheryl Berman; Christian Kimball.
EIN: 362605413

265
Daniel R. Burnham Memorial Foundation
c/o Dennis Petri, Follmer Rudzewicz Advs.
12900 Hall Rd., Ste. 500
Sterling Heights, MI 48313-1153

Established in 2000 in MI.
Donors: Alice M. Burnham; David Burnham; Donald F. Burnham.
Grantmaker type: Independent foundation.
Financial data (yr. ended 6/30/05): Assets, $128,599 (M); gifts received, $20,129; expenditures, $18,329; total giving, $12,100; qualifying distributions, $12,100; giving activities include $12,100 for grants.
Limitations: Applications not accepted. No grants to individuals.
Application information: Contributes only to pre-selected organizations.
Officers: Donald F. Burnham, Pres. and Treas.; Alice M. Burnham, V.P. and Secy.
Directors: Dennis J. Petri; David Stone.
EIN: 383554595

266
Edward J. Burns Athletic Trust f/b/o Children of St. Anselm Parish
17650 W. Outer Dr.
Dearborn Heights, MI 48127-2569

Established in 1997.
Donor: Edward J. Burns Trust.
Grantmaker type: Independent foundation.
Financial data (yr. ended 6/30/03): Assets, $161,844 (M); expenditures, $8,905; total giving, $8,638; qualifying distributions, $8,824; giving activities include $8,638 for grants.
Fields of interest: Elementary/secondary education; Roman Catholic agencies & churches.
Type of support: General/operating support.
Limitations: Applications not accepted. Giving limited to Dearborn Heights, MI. No grants to individuals.
Application information: Contributes only to a pre-selected organization.
Trustee: Rev. Msgr. James A. Moloney.
EIN: 386704674

267
Burns Foundation, Inc.
c/o ION, Inc.
P.O. Box 370
Petoskey, MI 49770-0370

Grantmaker type: Independent foundation.
Financial data (yr. ended 12/31/04): Assets, $735,356 (M); expenditures, $33,362; total giving, $25,000; qualifying distributions, $25,000; giving activities include $25,000 for grants.

Fields of interest: Higher education; Libraries (public); Education; Health care.
Type of support: General/operating support.
Limitations: Applications not accepted. Giving primarily in Petoskey, MI. No grants to individuals.
Application information: Contributes only to pre-selected organizations.
Officers: Dean D. Burns, Pres.; Edward H. Fenlon, V.P.; George Spanos, Secy.-Treas.
Directors: Anne Behan; Shirley Burns.
EIN: 386034469

268
Dean Burrier Scholarship Fund, Inc.
26399 York Rd.
Huntington Woods, MI 48070-1312

Established in 1988 in MI.
Donor: Little Caesar Enterprises, Inc.
Grantmaker type: Independent foundation.
Financial data (yr. ended 12/31/03): Assets, $23,330 (M); expenditures, $0; total giving, $0; qualifying distributions, $0.
Type of support: Scholarships—to individuals.
Limitations: Applications not accepted. Giving limited to Southfield, MI, residents.
Directors: Rodney T. Burrier; Susan K. Burrier; Mark D. Sherbow; Susan S. Sherbow.
EIN: 386529633

269
Burroughs Memorial Trust
c/o Citizens Bank Wealth Mgmt., N.A.
328 S. Saginaw St., M/C 002072
Flint, MI 48502

Established in 1966 in MI.
Grantmaker type: Independent foundation.
Financial data (yr. ended 12/31/05): Assets, $1,556,313 (M); expenditures, $102,391; total giving, $81,010; qualifying distributions, $81,010; giving activities include $81,010 for grants.
Purpose and activities: Giving primarily for human services, federated giving programs, and general charitable giving.
Fields of interest: Animal welfare; Human services; Children/youth, services; Federated giving programs; General charitable giving.
Type of support: Continuing support; Annual campaigns; Capital campaigns; Building/renovation; Endowments; Program development.
Limitations: Applications not accepted. Giving limited to Genesee County, MI. No grants to individuals.
Application information: Contributes only to pre-selected organizations.
Trustees: George H. Burroughs; Jonathan E. Burroughs II; Samuel S. Stewart III; Citizens Bank.
EIN: 386041206

270
Burt Foundation
c/o Erik H. Serr, Miller Canfield
101 N. Main St., 7th Fl.
Ann Arbor, MI 48104

Established in 1996 in MI.
Donor: Andrea L. Holmes.
Grantmaker type: Independent foundation.

Financial data (yr. ended 12/31/05): Assets, $4,784,260 (M); gifts received, $182,517; expenditures, $605,651; total giving, $580,000; qualifying distributions, $580,000; giving activities include $580,000 for 20 grants (high: $250,000; low: $5,000).
Purpose and activities: Giving primarily for animal welfare; funding also for health care, human services and the environment.
Fields of interest: Environment; Animal welfare; Animals/wildlife, preservation/protection; Animals/wildlife, sanctuaries; Health care; Human services; Aging, centers/services.
Limitations: Applications not accepted. Giving primarily in MI. No grants to individuals.
Application information: Contributes only to pre-selected organizations.
Officer: Andrea L. Holmes, Pres. and Treas.
EIN: 383309907

271
Flora M. Burt Foundation
20412 Jerusalem Rd.
Chelsea, MI 48118

Established in 1999 in MI.
Grantmaker type: Independent foundation.
Financial data (yr. ended 12/31/05): Assets, $279,895 (M); gifts received, $202,567; expenditures, $7,903; total giving, $0; qualifying distributions, $0.
Limitations: Applications not accepted. No grants to individuals.
Application information: Contributes only to pre-selected organizations.
Officers and Directors:* Flora M. Burt,* Pres.; Risa L. Richards,* Secy.; Jean Burke,* Treas.
EIN: 383505282

272
Busby Memorial Educational Fund
c/o Comerica Bank
P.O. Box 75000, MC 9413
Detroit, MI 48275-9413

Established around 1995 in MI.
Grantmaker type: Independent foundation.
Financial data (yr. ended 12/31/05): Assets, $1,998,475 (M); expenditures, $75,265; total giving, $50,000; qualifying distributions, $52,792; giving activities include $50,000 for grants.
Fields of interest: Arts; Higher education.
Limitations: Applications not accepted. Giving primarily in MI. No grants to individuals.
Application information: Contributes only to pre-selected organizations.
Trustees: John M. Chase, Jr.; Comerica Bank.
EIN: 382683345

273
Busch Family Foundation
148 S. Industrial Dr.
Saline, MI 48176
Application address: c/o Clinton High School, Attn.: Tim Wilson, Principal, 341 E. Michigan Ave., Clinton, MI 49236

Donor: Timothy R. Busch.
Grantmaker type: Independent foundation.

Financial data (yr. ended 12/31/05): Assets, $102,178 (M); expenditures, $33,507; total giving, $23,500; qualifying distributions, $23,500; giving activities include $23,500 for grants.
Purpose and activities: Scholarship awards to graduates of Clinton High School, MI; giving also to Catholic churches and organizations.
Fields of interest: Higher education; Roman Catholic agencies & churches.
Type of support: General/operating support; Scholarships—to individuals.
Limitations: Giving limited to residents of the Clinton, MI, area for scholarships, and to CA and NY for other grants.
Application information: Application form required for scholarships.
   Deadline(s): None
Trustees: Stephan L. Busch; Timothy R. Busch.
EIN: 382671217

274
Edyth Bush Charitable Foundation, Inc.
199 E. Welbourne Ave.
P.O. Box 1967
Winter Park, FL   32790-1967   (407) 647-4322
Contact: David A. Odahowski, C.E.O.
FAX: (407) 647-7716;
E-mail: dhessler@edythbush.org; Deborah Hessler direct tel.: x17; Additional tel.: (888) 647-4322;
URL: http://www.edythbush.org

Originally incorporated in 1966 in MN; reincorporated in 1973 in FL.
Donor: Edyth Bassler Bush†.
Grantmaker type: Independent foundation.
Financial data (yr. ended 8/31/05): Assets, $78,748,750 (M); expenditures, $3,877,618; total giving, $2,178,953; qualifying distributions, $2,178,953; giving activities include $2,121,366 for 92 grants (high: $750,000; low: $100), $57,587 for employee matching gifts, and $87,790 for foundation-administered programs.
Purpose and activities: Support for charitable, educational, and health service organizations, with emphasis on human services, the elderly, youth services, the handicapped, and nationally recognized quality arts or cultural programs. Provides limited number of program-related investment loans for construction, land purchase, emergency or similar purposes to organizations otherwise qualified to receive grants. Active programs directly managed and/or financed for management/volunteer development of nonprofits.
Fields of interest: Arts education; Arts; Education; Health care; Crime/violence prevention, domestic violence; Human services; Children/youth, services; Aging, centers/services; Nonprofit management; Philanthropy/voluntarism, association; Aging; Disabilities, people with; Women; Economically disadvantaged; Homeless.
Type of support: Management development/ capacity building; Capital campaigns; Building/ renovation; Equipment; Land acquisition; Emergency funds; Program development; Technical assistance; Consulting services; Program-related investments/loans; Employee matching gifts; Matching/challenge support.
Limitations: Giving primarily within Orange, Seminole, and Osceola counties, FL. No support for alcohol or drug abuse prevention/treatment projects or organizations, religious facilities or functions, primarily (50 percent or more) tax-supported institutions, advocacy organizations, foreign

organizations, or, generally, for cultural programs. No grants to individuals, or for scholarships or individual research projects, endowments, fellowships, travel, routine operating expenses, annual campaigns, or deficit financing.
Publications: Application guidelines; Financial statement; Grants list; Informational brochure; Program policy statement.
Application information: See Policy Statement and call foundation office before applying. Application guidelines available upon request. Application form not required.
   Initial approach: Telephone
   Copies of proposal: 2
   Deadline(s): None
   Board meeting date(s): Quarterly
   Final notification: 3 weeks after board meetings
Officers and Directors:* Mary Gretchen Belloff,* Vice-Chair.; David A. Odahowski,* C.E.O. and Pres.; Michael R. Cross, V.P., Fin. and C.I.O.; Deborah J. Hessler, Corp. Secy. and Prog. Off.; Mary Ellen Hutcheson, Treas. and C.F.O.; Matthew Certo; Gerald F. Hilbrich; Herbert W. Holm; John S. Lord; Joan Ruffier.
Number of staff: 3 full-time professional; 3 full-time support.
EIN: 237318041
Selected grants: The following grants were reported in 2004.
$330,913 to Rollins College, Winter Park, FL. For Philanthropy and Non-profit Leadership Center.
$120,000 to Ounce of Prevention Fund of Florida, Tallahassee, FL. For Jump Start Program.
$98,160 to American Red Cross, Winter Park, FL. To expand fundraising infrastructure.
$95,740 to Community Service Center of South Orange County, Orlando, FL. For Development Department.
$85,404 to Civic Theater of Central Florida, Orlando, FL. For Edyth Bush Theater renovation.
$66,386 to Shepherds Hope, Orlando, FL. For Development Director.
$66,200 to Second Harvest Food Bank of Central Florida, Orlando, FL. For capacity building.
$63,295 to Justice and Peace Office, Apopka, FL. For Development Director.
$60,700 to Coalition for the Homeless of Central Florida, Orlando, FL. To implement Development Office.
$50,430 to Federation of Congregations United to Serve (FOCUS), Orlando, FL. For Executive Assistant and office equipment.

275
M. W. Buster Charitable Trust
c/o Bank of America, N.A.
P.O. Box 1802
Providence, RI   02901-1802

Established in 1992 in MD.
Donor: Melvin Buster†.
Grantmaker type: Independent foundation.
Financial data (yr. ended 8/31/05): Assets, $1,358,831 (M); expenditures, $63,662; total giving, $50,368; qualifying distributions, $50,368; giving activities include $50,368 for grants.
Purpose and activities: Support only for Hillsdale College, MI and Liberty University, Lynchburg, VA.
Type of support: Scholarship funds.
Limitations: Applications not accepted. Giving limited to Hillsdale, MI and Lynchburg, VA. No grants to individuals.

Application information: Contributes only to 2 pre-selected organizations.
Trustee: Bank of America, N.A.
EIN: 546325354

276
John William Butler Foundation, Inc.
29600 Southfield Rd.
Southfield, MI   48076

Established in MI.
Donor: Butler Properties.
Grantmaker type: Independent foundation.
Financial data (yr. ended 12/31/04): Assets, $179,703 (M); expenditures, $37,774; total giving, $35,230; qualifying distributions, $35,230; giving activities include $35,230 for grants.
Fields of interest: Protestant agencies & churches.
Limitations: Applications not accepted. Giving primarily in MI. No grants to individuals.
Application information: Contributes only to pre-selected organizations.
Officers and Directors:* John William Butler, Sr.,* Pres.; John William Butler, Jr.,* V.P.; Keith D. Butler, Treas.
EIN: 382293252

277
George F. Butts Foundation
c/o Edward J. Phillips
901 Wilshire Dr., Ste. 400
Troy, MI   48084

Established in 1999 in MI.
Donor: George F. Butts.
Grantmaker type: Independent foundation.
Financial data (yr. ended 12/31/05): Assets, $54,686 (M); expenditures, $14,717; total giving, $13,400; qualifying distributions, $13,400; giving activities include $13,400 for grants.
Fields of interest: Theological school/education; Health care; Down syndrome; Medical research; Christian agencies & churches.
Limitations: Applications not accepted. Giving in the U.S., primarily in FL. No grants to individuals.
Application information: Contributes only to pre-selected organizations.
Officer: George F. Butts, Pres.
EIN: 383487909

278
Byrne Family Foundation
P.O. Box 306
Rockford, MI   49341

Established in 2000 in MI.
Donors: Norman Byrne; Rosemary Byrne.
Grantmaker type: Independent foundation.
Financial data (yr. ended 12/31/05): Assets, $65,945 (M); gifts received, $12,000; expenditures, $8,000; total giving, $8,000; qualifying distributions, $8,000; giving activities include $8,000 for grants.
Limitations: Applications not accepted. No grants to individuals.
Application information: Contributes only to pre-selected organizations.
Officers: Norman Byrne, Pres.; Rosemary Byrne, Secy.-Treas.
EIN: 383574869

279
Mary Ida Cady Trust
c/o Citizens Bank
328 S. Saginaw St.
Flint, MI   48502-2401

Established in MI.
Grantmaker type: Independent foundation.
Financial data (yr. ended 12/31/05): Assets, $297,795 (M); expenditures, $15,201; total giving, $8,563; qualifying distributions, $10,366; giving activities include $8,563 for 1 grant.
Purpose and activities: Support only for the Michigan Historical Museum, Lansing, MI.
Fields of interest: Museums (history).
Type of support: General/operating support.
Limitations: Applications not accepted. Giving limited to Lansing, MI. No grants to individuals.
Application information: Contributes only to a pre-selected organization.
Trustees: Albert Aldrich; Philip J. Curtis; Citizens Bank.
EIN: 386054013

280
Caesar Puff Foundation
c/o Comerica Bank
P.O. Box 75000, MC 3302
Detroit, MI   48275
Contact: Beverly Suchenek

Established in 2000 in PA.
Donor: Virginia A. Campana.
Grantmaker type: Independent foundation.
Financial data (yr. ended 3/31/05): Assets, $262,096 (M); expenditures, $304,772; total giving, $292,833; qualifying distributions, $293,284; giving activities include $292,833 for grants.
Fields of interest: Higher education; Libraries/library science; Animals/wildlife; Christian agencies & churches.
Limitations: Giving primarily in PA. No grants to individuals.
Application information: Application form not required.
  Deadline(s): None
Trustees: Virginia A. Campana; Comerica Bank.
EIN: 226866488

281
The Cairn Foundation
320 N. Main St., Ste. 300
Ann Arbor, MI   48104

Established in 2002 in MI.
Donor: David D. Marvin II.
Grantmaker type: Independent foundation.
Financial data (yr. ended 12/31/04): Assets, $979,206 (M); expenditures, $75,708; total giving, $72,000; qualifying distributions, $72,000; giving activities include $72,000 for grants.
Fields of interest: Higher education.
Limitations: Applications not accepted. Giving primarily in MI. No grants to individuals.
Application information: Contributes only to pre-selected organizations.
Officers and Trustees:* Pearson M. Macek,* Pres and Secy.; Robert C. Macek,* V.P. and Treas.
EIN: 161639339

282
Will & Jeanne Caldwell Foundation
2733 Glenbrooke Ct.
Bloomfield Hills, MI   48302-0966

Established in 1985 in MI.
Donor: Will M. Caldwell.
Grantmaker type: Independent foundation.
Financial data (yr. ended 12/31/04): Assets, $574,104 (M); gifts received, $85,320; expenditures, $36,620; total giving, $36,300; qualifying distributions, $36,406; giving activities include $36,300 for grants.
Purpose and activities: Giving primarily to the United Way, as well as for higher education, health, and human services.
Fields of interest: Higher education; Hospitals (general); Health organizations, association; Cancer research; Children/youth, services; Human services; Federated giving programs.
Limitations: Applications not accepted. Giving primarily in MI. No grants to individuals.
Application information: Contributes only to pre-selected organizations.
Officers: Will M. Caldwell, Pres.; Jeanne B. Caldwell, Secy.-Treas.
Director: Elizabeth Caldwell.
EIN: 382640832

283
Calling God's Tower Ministries, Inc.
15 Cardinal Dr.
Coldwater, MI   49036-1017

Established in MI.
Donor: Floyd Eby.
Grantmaker type: Independent foundation.
Financial data (yr. ended 12/31/04): Assets, $606,767 (M); expenditures, $77,580; total giving, $19,618; qualifying distributions, $32,441; giving activities include $19,618 for grants.
Fields of interest: Christian agencies & churches.
Limitations: Applications not accepted. Giving on a national basis. No grants to individuals.
Application information: Contributes only to pre-selected organizations.
Officers: Robert L. Goodwin, Pres.; Sonet J. Goodwin, 1st V.P.; Phyliss Eby, 2nd V.P.; Patricia Eby, Secy.-Treas.
EIN: 382155228

284
The Cameron Foundation
710 Suffield Ave.
Birmingham, MI   48009-1258
Contact: James C. Cameron, Treas.

Established in 2004 in MI.
Grantmaker type: Independent foundation.
Financial data (yr. ended 12/31/05): Assets, $114,613 (M); gifts received, $127,840; expenditures, $6,459; total giving, $6,250; qualifying distributions, $6,250; giving activities include $6,250 for grants.
Application information: Application form available on foundation Web site. Application form required.
  Initial approach: Letter
  Deadline(s): Varies

Officers: Marjorie B. Gell, Pres.; Bruce P. Cameron, V.P.; Scott R. Cameron, Secy.; James C. Cameron, Treas.
EIN: 201628724

285
Samuel Higby Camp Foundation
c/o Comerica Bank, Trust Dept.
245 W. Michigan Ave.
Jackson, MI   49201-2265
Application address: c/o Maclay Gwinn, 951 Thorntree Blvd., Jackson, MI 49203

Established in 1951 in MI.
Donor: Donna Ruth Camp‡.
Grantmaker type: Independent foundation.
Financial data (yr. ended 12/31/04): Assets, $1,751,502 (M); expenditures, $117,513; total giving, $93,300; qualifying distributions, $93,300; giving activities include $93,300 for grants.
Purpose and activities: Giving primarily for education, including higher and business education, community development, and cultural programs.
Fields of interest: Arts; Higher education; Business school/education; Medical school/education; Libraries/library science; Education; Animal welfare; Recreation; Children/youth, services; Residential/custodial care, hospices; Community development; Biological sciences; Government/public administration.
Type of support: General/operating support; Annual campaigns; Capital campaigns; Debt reduction; Curriculum development.
Limitations: Giving primarily in south central MI, with emphasis on Jackson.
Application information: Application form not required.
  Initial approach: Letter or proposal
  Copies of proposal: 1
  Deadline(s): Aug. 15
  Board meeting date(s): As needed
  Final notification: Oct. or Nov.
Officers: Walter R. Boris, Chair. and Pres.; Maclay D. Gwinn, Vice-Chair.; Linda S. Sekerke, Secy.; Frederick Davies, Treas.
EIN: 381643281

286
Camp Rotary Foundation
3023 Davenport Ave.
Saginaw, MI   48602

Established in MI.
Grantmaker type: Independent foundation.
Financial data (yr. ended 12/31/05): Assets, $894,940 (M); expenditures, $25,095; total giving, $18,300; qualifying distributions, $23,509; giving activities include $18,300 for grants, and $4,772 for foundation-administered programs.
Purpose and activities: Support only for the Boy Scouts of America, Lake Huron Council, Michigan.
Fields of interest: Boy scouts.
Type of support: General/operating support.
Limitations: Applications not accepted. Giving limited to the Lake Huron area of northeast lower MI. No grants to individuals.
Application information: Contributes only to a pre-selected organization.
Officers: Carl Hubinger, Pres.; Peter Bender, Treas.
Director: Charles Shelley.
EIN: 386087987

287
Kenneth H. Campbell Foundation for Neurological Research
c/o Fifth Third Bank
P.O. Box 3636
Grand Rapids, MI 49501-3636
Application address: c/o Dan Oumedian, 111 Lyon St. N.W., Grand Rapids, MI 49503, tel.: (888) 218-7878

Grantmaker type: Independent foundation.
Financial data (yr. ended 12/31/05): Assets, $1,139,595 (M); expenditures, $62,900; total giving, $50,500; qualifying distributions, $50,500; giving activities include $50,500 for grants.
Purpose and activities: Grants for neurological research.
Fields of interest: Neuroscience; Neuroscience research.
Type of support: Research.
Limitations: Giving primarily in MI.
Application information:
   Initial approach: Letter
   Deadline(s): None
Officers: John Butzer, Pres.; Barbara Kramer, V.P.; James R. Dice, Secy.-Treas.
Directors: Charles Bennett; Thomas Jones; David Van Dyke; James Van Putten.
Trustee: Fifth Third Bank.
EIN: 386049653

288
The Campbell Fund
427 N. Main St.
Ann Arbor, MI 48105

Established in 1997 in MI.
Donor: Brian P. Campbell.
Grantmaker type: Independent foundation.
Financial data (yr. ended 12/31/05): Assets, $5,508,411 (M); gifts received, $395,000; expenditures, $270,619; total giving, $268,600; qualifying distributions, $269,532; giving activities include $268,600 for 2 grants (high: $265,000; low: $3,600).
Purpose and activities: Giving primarily for fire and rescue associations and fire departments, and medical education.
Type of support: General/operating support.
Limitations: Applications not accepted. Giving primarily in MI. No grants to individuals.
Application information: Contributes only to pre-selected organizations.
Officers and Directors: * Brian P. Campbell,* Pres.; Mary L. Campbell,* Secy.-Treas.; Elizabeth L. Campbell.
EIN: 383334874

289
Canaan Foundation
13919 S. West Bay Shore Dr., Ste. G-1
Traverse City, MI 49684 (231) 946-8772
Contact: Dale M. Nielson, Tr.

Established in 1999 in MI.
Grantmaker type: Independent foundation.
Financial data (yr. ended 12/31/04): Assets, $6,197,689 (M); gifts received, $5,996,389; expenditures, $75,142; total giving, $59,200; qualifying distributions, $59,200; giving activities include $59,200 for grants.

Fields of interest: Health organizations, association; Housing/shelter; Human services; Residential/custodial care, hospices; Women, centers/services.
Type of support: General/operating support.
Limitations: Giving limited to MI, primarily in Traverse City.
Application information:
   Initial approach: Letter
   Deadline(s): None
Trustee: Dale M. Nielson.
EIN: 383444062

290
The Carls Foundation
333 W. Fort St., Ste. 1940
Detroit, MI 48226 (313) 965-0990
Contact: Elizabeth A. Stieg, Exec. Dir.
FAX: (313) 965-0547; URL: http://www.carlsfdn.org

Established in 1961 in MI.
Donor: William Carls‡.
Grantmaker type: Independent foundation.
Financial data (yr. ended 12/31/05): Assets, $117,703,559 (M); expenditures, $6,099,742; total giving, $4,937,070; qualifying distributions, $5,590,203; giving activities include $4,937,070 for 66 grants (high: $1,000,000; low: $1,164; average: $10,000–$100,000).
Purpose and activities: The principal purpose and mission of the foundation is: 1) Children's Welfare including: health care facilities and programs, with special emphasis on the prevention and treatment of hearing impairment, and recreational, educational, and welfare programs especially for children who are disadvantaged for economic and/or health reasons; and 2) Preservation of natural areas, open space and historic buildings and areas having special natural beauty or significance in maintaining America's heritage and historic ideals, through assistance to land trusts and land conservancies and directly related environmental educational programs.
Fields of interest: Historic preservation/historical societies; Education; Environment, natural resources; Hospitals (general); Speech/hearing centers; Health care; Recreation; Children/youth, services.
Type of support: Capital campaigns; Seed money.
Limitations: Giving primarily in MI. No grants to individuals, or for publications, film, research, endowments, fellowships, travel, conferences, special event sponsorships, playground or athletic facilities, or seminars; no educational loans.
Publications: Annual report.
Application information: Letter of inquiry is not required and phone calls are welcome. Use of the CMF Common Grant Application Form is optional and acceptable. Application form not required.
   Initial approach: Proposal
   Copies of proposal: 1
   Deadline(s): Mar. 1, July 1, and Nov. 1
   Board meeting date(s): Jan., May, and Sept.
   Final notification: Notification letter sent to all applicants
Officers and Trustees: * Arthur B. Derisley,* Pres. and Treas.; Harold E. Stieg,* V.P. and Secy.; Elizabeth A. Stieg, Exec. Dir.; Henry Fleischer; Teresa R. Krieger.
Advisory Board: Brian A. Derisley; Homer E. Nye; Rev. Delayne H. Pauling; Robert A. Sajdak; Edward C. Stieg.

Number of staff: 1 full-time professional; 1 part-time professional; 1 full-time support.
EIN: 386099935
Selected grants: The following grants were reported in 2003.
$1,500,000 to Beaumont Foundation, Southfield, MI. For Pediatric Medical Center of the new South Hospital at the Royal Oak Campus.
$1,200,000 to YMCA of Metropolitan Detroit, Detroit, MI. For capital campaign to construct full-service facility for Huron Valley YMCA.
$250,000 to Grand Traverse Regional Land Conservancy, Traverse City, MI. For land acquisition, purchase of development rights and establishment of a revolving fund for future purchases.
$200,000 to Barbara Ann Karmanos Cancer Institute, Detroit, MI. For minorities with cancer and other bone diseases requiring bone marrow transplants.
$175,000 to Arthritis Foundation, Michigan Chapter, Troy, MI. For initiative to educate families about juvenile arthritis.
$150,000 to Covenant House Michigan, Detroit, MI. For renovations to areas to be used by outreach and residential programs.
$100,000 to Detroit Medical Center, Detroit, MI. For Pediatric Mobile Team providing health care services.
$100,000 to Neighborhood Centers, Detroit, MI. For renovations and expansion to facility providing outreach programs in Southwest Detroit.
$100,000 to Providence Hospital, Southfield, MI. For construction and furnishing of Northwest Detroit Health Center.
$75,000 to Judson Center, Royal Oak, MI. For renovation and construction of residential homes for abused and neglected children.

291
Dwight Carlson Foundation, Inc.
25 Southwick Ct.
Ann Arbor, MI 48105

Established in 1997 in MI.
Donor: Dwight D. Carlson.
Grantmaker type: Independent foundation.
Financial data (yr. ended 12/31/04): Assets, $59,126 (M); expenditures, $13,401; total giving, $12,500; qualifying distributions, $12,500; giving activities include $12,500 for grants.
Fields of interest: Mental health, addictions; Community development.
Limitations: Applications not accepted. Giving primarily in Ann Arbor, MI. No grants to individuals.
Application information: Contributes only to pre-selected organizations.
Officers: Denise L. Fuller, Pres.; Mark Fuller, V.P. and Secy.-Treas.
Director: Dwight D. Carlson.
EIN: 383385919

292
The Carlson Foundation
18877 W. Ten Mile Rd., Ste. 210
Southfield, MI 48075

Established in MI.
Grantmaker type: Independent foundation.
Financial data (yr. ended 12/31/05): Assets, $1 (M); expenditures, $1,218; total giving, $1,174;

qualifying distributions, $1,174; giving activities include $1,174 for grants.
Fields of interest: Human services; Foundations (public).
Type of support: General/operating support.
Limitations: Applications not accepted. No grants to individuals.
Application information: Contributes only to pre-selected organizations.
Officers: Glen A. Carlson, Jr., Pres.; Harry E. Carlson, Treas.
EIN: 386086336

293
Norman & Ardis Carpenter Scholarship Trust
c/o Bank One Trust Co., N.A.
P.O. Box 1308
Milwaukee, WI 53201
Application address: c/o Jeff Pettinga, 7517 Noffke Dr., Caledonia, MI 49316, tel.: (616) 891-9961

Established in 2004 in MI.
Donor: Ardis Carpenter†.
Grantmaker type: Independent foundation.
Financial data (yr. ended 7/31/05): Assets, $200,402 (M); gifts received, $195,625; expenditures, $2,635; total giving, $0; qualifying distributions, $659.
Purpose and activities: Scholarship awards to graduating seniors who are members of Caledonia Christian Reformed Church, MI.
Fields of interest: Higher education.
Type of support: Scholarships—to individuals.
Limitations: Giving primarily to residents of Caledonia, MI.
Application information: Application form required.
 Deadline(s): None
Trustee: Bank One Trust Co., N.A.
EIN: 203485260

294
Cascadia Foundation
136 E. Michigan Ave., Ste. 1201
Kalamazoo, MI 49007-3936 (269) 382-5800
Contact: James C. Melvin, Secy.

Established in 2001 in MI.
Donors: Catherine B. Levi; Shaul Levi; Boaz Levi; Aaron Levi; Ethan Levi.
Grantmaker type: Independent foundation.
Financial data (yr. ended 12/31/05): Assets, $1,082,210 (M); gifts received, $224,631; expenditures, $41,844; total giving, $28,000; qualifying distributions, $28,000; giving activities include $28,000 for grants.
Limitations: Giving in the U.S., with emphasis on OR. No grants to individuals.
Officers and Directors: Shaul Levi,* Pres.; Catherine B. Levi,* V.P.; James C. Melvin,* Secy.; James S. Hilboldt,* Treas.; Aaron Levi.
EIN: 300006469

295
Thomas and Jane Cassel Charitable Foundation
1573 Ashford Ln.
Birmingham, MI 48009

Established in 2003 in MI.

Donors: Thomas R. Cassel; Jane K. Cassel.
Grantmaker type: Independent foundation.
Financial data (yr. ended 12/31/05): Assets, $241,187 (M); gifts received, $10,230; expenditures, $35,000; total giving, $35,000; qualifying distributions, $35,000; giving activities include $35,000 for 1 grant.
Fields of interest: Transportation.
Limitations: Applications not accepted. Giving primarily in IN. No grants to individuals.
Application information: Contributes only to pre-selected organizations.
Trustees: Jane K. Cassel; Thomas R. Cassel.
EIN: 206084643

296
Scott and Laura Cassel Family Foundation
3635 Lombardi Ct.
Bloomfield Hills, MI 48301

Established in 2003 in MI.
Donors: Laura B. Cassel; Scott T. Cassel.
Grantmaker type: Independent foundation.
Financial data (yr. ended 12/31/05): Assets, $133,346 (M); gifts received, $26,088; expenditures, $81,641; total giving, $81,520; qualifying distributions, $81,520; giving activities include $81,520 for 8 grants (high: $62,500; low: $500).
Fields of interest: Recreation, camps; Transportation; Christian agencies & churches.
Limitations: Applications not accepted. Giving primarily on a national basis, with some emphasis in IN. No grants to individuals.
Application information: Contributes only to pre-selected organizations.
Trustees: Laura B. Cassel; Scott T. Cassel.
EIN: 562422292

297
James C. Cassie, Jr. Foundation
629 Byron Ct.
Rochester Hills, MI 48307

Established in MI.
Grantmaker type: Independent foundation.
Financial data (yr. ended 12/31/04): Assets, $500 (M); expenditures, $0; total giving, $0; qualifying distributions, $0.
Officer and Director: James C. Cassie, Jr., Pres.
EIN: 352195948

298
Castaing Family Foundation
6394 Muirfield Ct.
Bloomfield Hills, MI 48301

Established in 1998 in MI.
Donor: Francois J. Castaing.
Grantmaker type: Independent foundation.
Financial data (yr. ended 12/31/04): Assets, $1,318,721 (M); expenditures, $108,082; total giving, $93,300; qualifying distributions, $94,200; giving activities include $93,300 for 7 grants (high: $38,750; low: $250).
Purpose and activities: Giving primarily for the arts.
Fields of interest: Arts, association; Museums (science/technology); Performing arts, orchestra (symphony); Arts; Human services.

Limitations: Applications not accepted. Giving primarily in Detroit, MI. No grants to individuals.
Application information: Contributes only to pre-selected organizations.
Officers: Eva J. Wirthlin, Pres.; Maria M. Castaing, Secy.-Treas.
Trustees: Brigitte M. Castaing; Francois J. Castaing; Laura M. Castaing; Marta M. Castaing.
EIN: 383443775

299
C. Glen and Barbara A. Catt Foundation
P.O. Box 304
Petoskey, MI 49770
Contact: Thomas J. Webb, Secy.-Treas.

Established in 1995 in MI.
Donors: C. Glenn Catt; Barbara A. Catt.
Grantmaker type: Independent foundation.
Financial data (yr. ended 6/30/05): Assets, $431,106 (M); expenditures, $24,219; total giving, $21,560; qualifying distributions, $21,560; giving activities include $21,560 for grants.
Fields of interest: Hospitals (general).
Limitations: Giving primarily in Gaylord, MI. No grants to individuals.
Application information:
 Initial approach: Letter
 Deadline(s): None
Officers: Barbara A. Catt, Pres.; Russell H. VanGilder, V.P.; Thomas J. Webb, Secy.-Treas.
EIN: 383249470

300
James F. Causley, Jr. Family Foundation
c/o James F. Causley, Jr.
37910 Seaway Ct.
Harrison Township, MI 48045-6201

Established in 2000 in MI.
Donor: James F. Causley, Jr.
Grantmaker type: Independent foundation.
Financial data (yr. ended 12/31/05): Assets, $847 (M); gifts received, $76,000; expenditures, $76,795; total giving, $74,790; qualifying distributions, $76,795; giving activities include $74,790 for 16 grants (high: $32,000; low: $100).
Fields of interest: Education; Disasters, Hurricane Katrina; Roman Catholic agencies & churches.
Type of support: General/operating support.
Limitations: Applications not accepted. Giving primarily in MI. No grants to individuals.
Application information: Contributes only to pre-selected organizations.
Officers: James F. Causley, Jr., Pres.; H. Rollin Allen, Secy.; James A. Weis, Treas.
Director: Hunter Wendt.
EIN: 383534503

301
Bernard J. & Camille Cebelak Foundation
1840 Oak Industrial Dr. N.E.
Grand Rapids, MI 49505

Established in 1986 in MI.
Donors: Bernard J. Cebelak†; Camille L. Cebelak; Kent Manufacturing Co.
Grantmaker type: Independent foundation.
Financial data (yr. ended 12/31/05): Assets, $3,773,982 (M); expenditures, $69,632; total

giving, $47,500; qualifying distributions, $48,553; giving activities include $47,500 for 1 grant.
Purpose and activities: Giving primarily for education and for Christian and Roman Catholic organizations and agencies.
Fields of interest: Secondary school/education; Education; Medical research, institute; Christian agencies & churches; Roman Catholic agencies & churches.
Limitations: Applications not accepted. Giving primarily in Grand Rapids, MI. No grants to individuals.
Application information: Contributes only to pre-selected organizations.
Officers and Directors:* Camille L. Cebelak,* Pres.; Sr. Patrice Konwinski,* V.P.; Joseph M. Sweeny,* V.P.; Suzanne Singel,* Secy.; Michael J. Muraski,* Treas.
EIN: 382641979
Selected grants: The following grants were reported in 2004.
$45,000 to Help Pregnancy Crisis Aid, Grand Rapids, MI.
$10,000 to Saint Vincent and Sarah Fisher Center, Farmington Hills, MI.
$5,000 to Acton Institute for the Study of Religion and Liberty, Grand Rapids, MI.
$5,000 to Diocese of Grand Rapids, Grand Rapids, MI.
$5,000 to Guardian Angel Homes, Grand Rapids, MI.
$5,000 to Saint Anselm Catholic Church, Chicago, IL.
$5,000 to Saint Johns Home, Grand Rapids, MI.
$3,000 to Franciscan Life Process Child Development Center, Lowell, MI.
$2,000 to HAVEN (Help Against Violent Encounters Now), Pontiac, MI.
$1,000 to School Sisters of Notre Dame, Milwaukee, WI.

302
Joseph B. Cejka and Florence V. Cejka Foundation, Inc.
c/o Barbara Littleton
2900 Orchard Pl.
Orchard Lake, MI 48324-2356

Established in 1995 in NJ.
Donor: Florence V. Cejka†.
Grantmaker type: Independent foundation.
Financial data (yr. ended 9/30/05): Assets, $3,092,102 (M); gifts received, $898,738; expenditures, $135,276; total giving, $114,500; qualifying distributions, $119,023; giving activities include $114,500 for 8 grants (high: $30,000; low: $500).
Fields of interest: Elementary/secondary education; Higher education; Education.
Type of support: Fellowships; Program development; Scholarship funds; General/operating support.
Limitations: Applications not accepted. Giving in the U.S., primarily in MI and NJ. No grants to individuals.
Application information: Contributes only to pre-selected organizations.
Manager: Barbara C. Littleton.
EIN: 223338313

303
Celani Charitable Foundation, Inc
2600 Turtle Lake Dr.
Bloomfield Hills, MI 48302

Established in 2000 in MI.
Donor: Thomas Celani.
Grantmaker type: Independent foundation.
Financial data (yr. ended 12/31/04): Assets, $129,604 (M); gifts received, $97,210; expenditures, $75,500; total giving, $75,500; qualifying distributions, $75,500; giving activities include $75,500 for 5 grants (high: $50,000; low: $500).
Fields of interest: Performing arts; Higher education.
Limitations: Applications not accepted. Giving in MI, primarily in Detroit. No grants to individuals.
Application information: Contributes only to pre-selected organizations.
Officer and Director:* Thomas Celani,* Pres. and Secy.-Treas.
EIN: 383544723

304
Ceres Foundation
P.O. Box 8203
Northfield, IL 60093

Established in 1991 in IL.
Donors: Burton W. Hales; Daniel B. Hales; Marion J. Hales; Hales Charitable Fund, Inc.
Grantmaker type: Independent foundation.
Financial data (yr. ended 12/31/03): Assets, $6,342,529 (M); expenditures, $331,726; total giving, $300,250; qualifying distributions, $302,107; giving activities include $300,250 for 63 grants (high: $51,000; low: $250).
Purpose and activities: Giving primarily for the arts, education, conservation, health, human services, and community foundations.
Fields of interest: Arts; Education; Hospitals (general); Health organizations, association; Human services; Children/youth, services; Foundations (community); Federated giving programs.
Limitations: Applications not accepted. Giving primarily in IL with emphasis on Chicago, and MI; some funding nationally. No grants to individuals.
Application information: Contributes only to pre-selected organizations.
Officers and Directors:* Burton W. Hales, Jr.,* Pres.; Daniel R.J. Hales,* V.P.; Daniel B. Hales,* Secy.; Florence H. Testa,* Treas.
EIN: 363735653
Selected grants: The following grants were reported in 2003.
$51,000 to Chicago Commons Association, Chicago, IL.
$10,000 to Art Institute of Chicago, Chicago, IL.
$5,000 to Latin School of Chicago, Chicago, IL.
$5,000 to Mercy Home for Boys and Girls, Chicago, IL.
$5,000 to Rush-Presbyterian-Saint Lukes Medical Center, Chicago, IL.
$2,000 to Fabretto Childrens Foundation, Evanston, IL.
$2,000 to Hillsdale College, Hillsdale, MI.
$1,000 to Yellow Dog Watershed Preserve, Big Bay, MI.
$500 to Next Theater Company, Evanston, IL.
$500 to Teen Living Programs, Chicago, IL.

305
The Chamberlain Foundation
1680 Crooks Rd.
Troy, MI 48084 (248) 540-7200
Contact: Calvin M. Chamberlain, Pres.

Established in 1988 in MI.
Donor: Calvin M. Chamberlain.
Grantmaker type: Independent foundation.
Financial data (yr. ended 5/31/05): Assets, $101,504 (M); expenditures, $10,832; total giving, $9,925; qualifying distributions, $9,925; giving activities include $9,925 for grants.
Fields of interest: Education; Youth development; Protestant agencies & churches.
Type of support: General/operating support; Scholarship funds.
Limitations: Giving primarily in MI.
Application information:
  Initial approach: Letter
  Deadline(s): None
Officers and Directors:* Calvin M. Chamberlain,* Pres.; Janet R. Chamberlain,* Secy.
EIN: 382837915

306
Gerald W. Chamberlin Foundation, Inc.
21 Kercheval Ave., Ste. 270
Grosse Pointe Farms, MI 48236

Incorporated in 1955 in MI.
Donors: Gerald W. Chamberlin†; Myrtle F. Chamberlin†; Donald F. Chamberlin, Sr.; Joanne M. Chamberlin; Chamberlin Products.
Grantmaker type: Independent foundation.
Financial data (yr. ended 12/31/03): Assets, $680,287 (M); expenditures, $5,131; total giving, $0; qualifying distributions, $0.
Fields of interest: Education; Recreation, camps; Youth development; Christian agencies & churches.
Type of support: General/operating support.
Limitations: Applications not accepted. Giving on a national basis, with emphasis on MI. No grants to individuals.
Application information: Contributes only to pre-selected organizations.
Officers: Donald F. Chamberlin, Sr., Pres. and Treas.; John W. Butler, V.P.; Joy Robbins, Secy.
Trustees: Donald F. Chamberlin, Jr.; Jeri Ann Traub.
EIN: 386055730

307
The Chandler Family Foundation
37000 Woodward Ave., Ste. 200
Bloomfield Hills, MI 48304-0924

Established in 2000 in MI.
Donors: Maurice Chandler; Doris Chandler.
Grantmaker type: Independent foundation.
Financial data (yr. ended 12/31/04): Assets, $503,486 (M); gifts received, $102,492; expenditures, $20,442; total giving, $18,303; qualifying distributions, $18,303; giving activities include $18,303 for grants.
Purpose and activities: Giving primarily to a yeshiva.
Fields of interest: Elementary/secondary education; Jewish agencies & temples.
Limitations: Applications not accepted. Giving primarily in MI. No grants to individuals.
Application information: Contributes only to pre-selected organizations.

Officers: Maurice Chandler, Pres. and Treas.; Dorris Chandler, V.P. and Secy.
Directors: Debra Chandler; Paul Chandler; Evelyn Rosen.
EIN: 383563300

308
Chang Foundation
807 Asa Gray Dr., Ste. 401
Ann Arbor, MI 48105-2566
Contact: Cheng-Yang Chang M.D., Dir.

Established in 1987 in MI.
Donors: Cheng-Yang Chang, M.D.; Shirley Chang.
Grantmaker type: Independent foundation.
Financial data (yr. ended 9/30/05): Assets, $246,392 (M); gifts received, $5,000; expenditures, $12,405; total giving, $11,400; qualifying distributions, $11,400; giving activities include $11,400 for grants.
Purpose and activities: Scholarship awards through pre-selected universities to students who have exhibited a potential and the talent to excel in the field of Chinese traditional art in Taiwan.
Type of support: Scholarship funds.
Limitations: Giving primarily in Taiwan.
Application information: Recipients are recommended by their respective department heads.
  Initial approach: Essay, resume and transcript of college grades
  Deadline(s): Varies
Directors: Cheng-Yang Chang, M.D.; Shirley Chang.
EIN: 382796315

309
Chapman Scholarship Trust
c/o Fifth Third Bank
P.O. Box 3636
Grand Rapids, MI 49501-3636

Grantmaker type: Independent foundation.
Financial data (yr. ended 12/31/05): Assets, $139,971 (M); expenditures, $2,709; total giving, $0; qualifying distributions, $0.
Purpose and activities: Scholarships to full time undergraduate students at Western Michigan University.
Fields of interest: Higher education.
Type of support: Scholarship funds.
Limitations: Applications not accepted. Giving limited to Kalamazoo, MI.
Application information: Unsolicited requests for funds not accepted.
Trustee: Fifth Third Bank.
EIN: 386088631

310
Lawrence S. Charfoos Charitable Foundation
5510 Woodward Ave.
Detroit, MI 48202
Contact: Alan A. May, Secy.
Application address: 3000 Town Ctr., Southfield, MI 48075, tel.: (248) 358-3800

Grantmaker type: Independent foundation.
Financial data (yr. ended 10/31/04): Assets, $13,456 (M); gifts received, $2,000; expenditures, $3,394; total giving, $2,571; qualifying

distributions, $2,561; giving activities include $2,571 for 2 grants to individuals.
Purpose and activities: Scholarship awards to students living in Detroit, MI, or the surrounding area, and enrolled in an accredited state school.
Type of support: Scholarships—to individuals.
Limitations: Giving primarily in Detroit, MI.
Application information: Application form required.
  Initial approach: Letter
  Deadline(s): May 31
Officers: Lawrence S. Charfoos, Pres.; Alan A. May, Secy.
EIN: 237328773

311
Charis Foundation II
11373 Willow Wood Ln.
Plymouth, MI 48170

Established in 2005 in MI.
Donor: Kevin R. Ruark.
Grantmaker type: Independent foundation.
Financial data (yr. ended 6/30/05): Assets, $79,850 (M); gifts received, $79,850; expenditures, $0; total giving, $0; qualifying distributions, $0.
Limitations: Applications not accepted. No grants to individuals.
Application information: Contributes only to pre-selected organizations.
Officers and Directors:* Kevin R. Ruark,* Pres.; Janice L. Ruark,* Secy.-Treas.
EIN: 201901084

312
Allen and Franka Charlupski Foundation
6230 Orchard Lake Rd., Ste. 100
West Bloomfield, MI 48322-2393
Contact: Moniek Milberger, Mgr.

Established in 1972 in MI.
Donors: Helen Charlupski; Allen Charlupski; Franka Charlupski.
Grantmaker type: Independent foundation.
Financial data (yr. ended 9/30/04): Assets, $992,064 (M); gifts received, $703,379; expenditures, $31,134; total giving, $25,919; qualifying distributions, $25,919; giving activities include $25,919 for grants.
Purpose and activities: Giving primarily for educational and religious institutions.
Fields of interest: Arts; Education; Hospitals (general); Human services; Jewish federated giving programs; Jewish agencies & temples.
Type of support: General/operating support.
Limitations: Giving primarily in MI. No grants to individuals.
Application information: Application form not required.
  Initial approach: Letter or proposal
  Deadline(s): None
Officers: Allen Charlupski, Pres.; Helen Charlupski, V.P.; Franka Charlupski, Secy.-Treas.; Moniek Milberger, Mgr.
Director: Lawrence Charlupski.
EIN: 237191093

313
Alfred W. Chase Foundation
2915 W. Main St.
Kalamazoo, MI 49006-2953

Established in 1991 in MI.
Grantmaker type: Independent foundation.
Financial data (yr. ended 12/31/04): Assets, $1,279,784 (M); expenditures, $81,693; total giving, $68,500; qualifying distributions, $75,004; giving activities include $68,500 for grants.
Fields of interest: American Red Cross.
Limitations: Applications not accepted. Giving primarily in MI. No grants to individuals.
Application information: Contributes only to pre-selected organizations.
Officer: Roger G. Kidston, Pres.
EIN: 383003328

314
The Hattie & Floyd Chatmon Scholarship Fund, Inc.
3266 Winchester Rd.
West Bloomfield, MI 48322-2420

Established in 2004 in MI.
Grantmaker type: Independent foundation.
Financial data (yr. ended 6/30/05): Assets, $54,404 (M); gifts received, $607; expenditures, $7,311; total giving, $3,000; qualifying distributions, $3,000; giving activities include $3,000 for grants.
Officers: Norman Garland, Pres.; Zachari Lawrsile, V.P.; Emily Marlasa, Treas.; James L. Williams, Secy.
EIN: 200141005

315
Stanley W. Cheff Foundation
7901 Alaska Ave.
Caledonia, MI 49316

Established in 2002 in MI.
Donor: Stanley W. Cheff, Jr.
Grantmaker type: Independent foundation.
Financial data (yr. ended 12/31/05): Assets, $62,453 (M); gifts received, $20,000; expenditures, $6,023; total giving, $6,023; qualifying distributions, $6,023; giving activities include $6,023 for grants.
Limitations: Applications not accepted. Giving primarily in MI. No grants to individuals.
Application information: Contributes only to pre-selected organizations.
Officer: Stanley W. Cheff, Jr., Pres.
Director: David L. Smith.
EIN: 061677039

316
Chelsea Kiwanis Club Foundation
P.O. Box 61
Chelsea, MI 48118

Grantmaker type: Independent foundation.
Financial data (yr. ended 9/30/05): Assets, $20,892 (M); gifts received, $3,095; expenditures, $1,500; total giving, $1,500; qualifying distributions, $1,500; giving activities include $1,500 for grants.
Application information:

Initial approach: Letter
Deadline(s): None
Officers: David Schaible, Pres.; Sam Vogel, V.P.; Ray Kemner, Secy.
EIN: 383044995

317
Edward Cherney Irrevocable Charitable Living Trust dated 12/26/86
4784 Walnut Lake Rd.
Bloomfield Hills, MI   48301-1329

Established in 1986 in MI.
Grantmaker type: Independent foundation.
Financial data (yr. ended 12/31/05): Assets, $75,451 (M); gifts received, $251; expenditures, $11,058; total giving, $10,500; qualifying distributions, $10,500; giving activities include $10,500 for grants.
Fields of interest: Human services; Christian agencies & churches.
Type of support: General/operating support.
Limitations: Applications not accepted. Giving primarily in Detroit, MI. No grants to individuals.
Application information: Contributes only to pre-selected organizations.
Trustee: John M. Sirhal.
EIN: 386510710

318
Lila Cherri Foundation
551 Ridgedale Ave.
Birmingham, MI   48009

Established in 1995 in MI.
Donor: Lila Cherri.
Grantmaker type: Independent foundation.
Financial data (yr. ended 12/31/05): Assets, $179,892 (M); gifts received, $73,387; expenditures, $17,605; total giving, $17,500; qualifying distributions, $17,500; giving activities include $17,500 for grants.
Limitations: Applications not accepted. Giving on a national basis, with some emphasis on MI. No grants to individuals.
Application information: Contributes only to pre-selected organizations.
Officer: Lila Cherri, Pres.
EIN: 383178229

319
Chormann Family Foundation
c/o Merrill Lynch Trust Co.
P.O. Box 1525, MSC 06-03
Pennington, NJ   08534-1525

Established in 1998 in MI.
Donor: Richard F. Chormann.
Grantmaker type: Independent foundation.
Financial data (yr. ended 7/31/05): Assets, $2,673,860 (M); gifts received, $345,676; expenditures, $275,496; total giving, $241,667; qualifying distributions, $243,175; giving activities include $241,667 for 2 grants (high: $216,667; low: $25,000).
Fields of interest: Higher education, university.
Type of support: General/operating support.
Limitations: Applications not accepted. Giving primarily in MI. No grants to individuals.

Application information: Contributes only to pre-selected organizations.
Officers: Gregory Chormann, Jr., Pres.; James Chormann, V.P. and Treas.; Cynthia Hann, V.P.
Trustee: Merrill Lynch Trust Co.
EIN: 383439226

320
Chortkiv Foundation, Inc.
2109 Clinton View Cir.
Rochester Hills, MI   48309-2984

Established in 2002 in MI.
Donor: Joseph & Rostyslava Jachnycky Trust.
Grantmaker type: Independent foundation.
Financial data (yr. ended 12/31/05): Assets, $32,103 (M); expenditures, $10,201; total giving, $10,000; qualifying distributions, $10,000; giving activities include $10,000 for grants.
Fields of interest: Historical activities.
Limitations: Applications not accepted. Giving primarily in MI and NY. No grants to individuals.
Application information: Contributes only to pre-selected organizations.
Officers: Lubomyr M. Jachnycky, Pres.; Lydia Kachan Jachnycky, V.P. and Treas.; Christine Diachenko, Secy.
Directors: Ihor Diachenko.
EIN: 383630582

321
Christian Advancement, Inc.
850 Stephenson Hwy., Ste. 410
Troy, MI   48083
Contact: Henry E. Mistele, Pres.

Established in MI.
Donor: Harold E. Mistele.
Grantmaker type: Independent foundation.
Financial data (yr. ended 12/31/03): Assets, $23,517 (M); gifts received, $3,000; expenditures, $1,173; total giving, $600; qualifying distributions, $1,143; giving activities include $600 for grants.
Fields of interest: Christian agencies & churches.
Type of support: General/operating support.
Application information:
Initial approach: Letter
Deadline(s): None
Officers: Henry E. Mistele, Pres.; Harold E. Mistele, V.P.; Elisabeth M. Mistele, Secy.-Treas.
EIN: 386089267

322
Christian Evangelical Foundation
618 Kenmoor Ave. S.E., Rm. 120
Grand Rapids, MI   49546

Established in 1987 in IL.
Donors: John C. Huizenga; Elizabeth I. Huizenga Foundation.
Grantmaker type: Independent foundation.
Financial data (yr. ended 12/31/04): Assets, $2,972,480 (M); gifts received, $13,230; expenditures, $1,236,543; total giving, $1,206,850; qualifying distributions, $1,206,850; giving activities include $1,206,850 for 49 grants (high: $250,000; low: $100).
Purpose and activities: Giving primarily to Christian organizations and for Christian education.

Fields of interest: Higher education; Education; Human services; Children, services; Family services; Christian agencies & churches.
Type of support: General/operating support.
Limitations: Applications not accepted. Giving on a national basis with emphasis on MI. No grants to individuals.
Application information: Contributes only to pre-selected organizations. Unsolicited requests for funds not accepted.
Officers: John C. Huizenga, Pres. and Mgr.; John Grant, Secy.; Laura B. Huizenga, Treas.
EIN: 363501198
Selected grants: The following grants were reported in 2003.
$250,000 to Haggai Institute for Advanced Leadership Training, Atlanta, GA. For general support.
$102,000 to Geneva Camp and Retreat Center, Holland, MI. For general support.
$63,740 to Campus Crusade for Christ, Dallas, TX. For general support.
$40,000 to Young Life in Grand Rapids, Grand Rapids, MI. For general support.
$25,000 to Calvin College, Grand Rapids, MI. For general support.
$25,000 to Inner City Impact, Chicago, IL. For general support.
$25,000 to Kids Hope USA, Holland, MI. For general support.
$21,000 to Potters House, Grand Rapids, MI. For general support.
$15,000 to Open Doors International, Santa Ana, CA. For general support.
$15,000 to Pine Rest Foundation, Grand Rapids, MI. For general support.

323
Christian Foundation
(formerly Christian Heritage Communication Foundation)
c/o Lee Tucker
P.O. Box 27577
Lansing, MI   48909

Established in 1975 in MI.
Donor: Douglas A. Reniger.
Grantmaker type: Independent foundation.
Financial data (yr. ended 6/30/04): Assets, $1,019,072 (M); gifts received, $50,256; expenditures, $48,425; total giving, $47,775; qualifying distributions, $47,775; giving activities include $47,775 for 30 grants (high: $25,000; low: $25).
Fields of interest: Christian agencies & churches.
Limitations: Applications not accepted. No grants to individuals.
Application information: Contributes only to pre-selected organizations.
Officers: Douglas A. Reniger, Pres.; Jerilyn J. Reniger, V.P. and Secy.; Susan Southwood, Treas.
EIN: 237450037

324
Christian Missionary Scholarship Foundation
3441 W. Sahara Ave., Ste. B7
Las Vegas, NV   89102

Established in MI.

Donors: Stanley Van Reken; Randall S. Van Reken; Capital Ventures of NV.
Grantmaker type: Independent foundation.
Financial data (yr. ended 12/31/04): Assets, $6,703,939 (M); gifts received, $31,575; expenditures, $398,031; total giving, $353,167; qualifying distributions, $384,367; giving activities include $353,167 for 8 grants (high: $213,575; low: $1,000).
Purpose and activities: Scholarship awards paid directly to college or university for children of missionaries families of specific Christian organizations.
Fields of interest: Theological school/education; Christian agencies & churches.
Type of support: Scholarship funds.
Limitations: Applications not accepted. Giving primarily in MI and IL; some giving on a national basis and in Dublin, Ireland. No grants to individuals.
Application information: Unsolicited request for funds not accepted.
Officers: Stanley R. Van Reken, Pres.; Randall Van Reken, Treas.
Directors: Tom Dykstra; Jerry Morren; Kurt Vangenveren.
EIN: 363553749

325
The Christopher Foundation
5089 Shady Creek Dr.
Troy, MI 48085-3200
Contact: Carroll J. Christopher, Pres.

Established in 2002 in MI.
Donor: Carroll J. Christopher.
Grantmaker type: Independent foundation.
Financial data (yr. ended 12/31/05): Assets, $120,595 (M); gifts received, $1,589; expenditures, $4,210; total giving, $2,064; qualifying distributions, $2,064; giving activities include $2,064 for grants.
Limitations: Giving primarily in MI. No grants to individuals.
Application information: Application form not required.
Deadline(s): None
Officers and Director:* Carroll J. Christopher,* Pres.; Kimberly A. Christopher, Secy.-Treas.
EIN: 371422862

326
The Lou Church Educational Foundation, Inc.
c/o Robert D. Helmholdt
1700 N.E. 26th St.
Fort Lauderdale, FL 33305 (954) 563-5861
FAX: (954) 563-3651;
E-mail: DrRDHelmholdt@aol.com

Established in 1986 in FL.
Grantmaker type: Independent foundation.
Financial data (yr. ended 12/31/04): Assets, $2,508,595 (M); expenditures, $171,814; total giving, $106,000; qualifying distributions, $106,000; giving activities include $106,000 for 6 grants (high: $23,000; low: $10,000).
Purpose and activities: Support for private educational institutions.
Fields of interest: Education.

Type of support: Scholarship funds; Fellowships; Endowments; Continuing support.
Limitations: Applications not accepted. Giving primarily in AL, FL, MI, NY and PA. No support for public entities. No grants to individuals.
Application information: Contributes only to pre-selected organizations.
Board meeting date(s): Semiannually
Officers and Directors:* Robert D. Helmholdt,* Pres.; Jack Drury,* V.P.; Arthur L. Bigelow,* Secy.-Treas.; D. Allen Johnson; C. Edward Meehan.
Number of staff: 1 full-time professional.
EIN: 592761512
Selected grants: The following grants were reported in 2004.
$23,000 to Westminster Academy, Fort Lauderdale, FL.
$20,000 to Junior Achievement of South Florida, Pompano Beach, FL.
$17,667 to Christ Church School, Fort Lauderdale, FL.
$17,667 to Hillsdale College, Hillsdale, MI.
$17,666 to Grove City College, Grove City, PA.
$10,000 to Cardinal Gibbons High School, Fort Lauderdale, FL.

327
The Cimmarrusti/Gray Family Foundation
(formerly Timmis Family Foundation No. 2)
21 Kercheval Ave., Ste. 265
Grosse Pointe Farms, MI 48236

Established in 1994 in MI.
Donor: Michael T. Timmis.
Grantmaker type: Independent foundation.
Financial data (yr. ended 12/31/05): Assets, $1 (M); gifts received, $150; expenditures, $150; total giving, $0; qualifying distributions, $0.
Fields of interest: Christian agencies & churches.
Limitations: Applications not accepted. No grants to individuals.
Application information: Contributes only to pre-selected organizations.
Trustees: Anthony B. Cimmarusti; Bryce D. Gray.
EIN: 383208089

328
The Cipa Foundation
P.O. Box 70451
Rochester Hills, MI 48307 (248) 299-0745
Contact: Chris A. Wilson, Pres.

Established in 1999 in MI.
Donors: Bernard J. Cipa; Scott Cipa; Drew M. Cipa; Bernard D. Cipa.
Grantmaker type: Independent foundation.
Financial data (yr. ended 12/31/04): Assets, $828,916 (M); expenditures, $74,078; total giving, $51,410; qualifying distributions, $72,698; giving activities include $51,410 for grants.
Fields of interest: Education; Diabetes research; Human services; Christian agencies & churches.
Type of support: Program development; Research.
Limitations: Giving primarily in MI.
Application information: Application form not required.
Deadline(s): Varies
Officers: Chris A. Wilson, Pres.; Lisa Cipa, V.P.; Bernard J. Cipa, Secy.-Treas.

Directors: Bernard D. Cipa; Drew M. Cipa; Eleanor R. Cipa; Scott Cipa.
EIN: 383506568

329
Clannad Foundation
40700 Woodward Ave., Ste. A
Bloomfield Hills, MI 48304

Established in 1994 in MI.
Donors: Jeanne H. Graham; Ralph A. Graham.
Grantmaker type: Independent foundation.
Financial data (yr. ended 10/31/05): Assets, $2,458,792 (M); expenditures, $139,856; total giving, $115,600; qualifying distributions, $115,600; giving activities include $115,600 for 36 grants (high: $15,000; low: $1,000).
Purpose and activities: Giving primarily for the environment and youth services.
Fields of interest: Visual arts, architecture; Humanities; Environment, natural resources; Food services; Human services; Children/youth, services; Human services, emergency aid; Economically disadvantaged.
Type of support: General/operating support; Continuing support; Annual campaigns; Equipment; Land acquisition; Emergency funds.
Limitations: Giving primarily in MI and NC. No grants to individuals.
Publications: Informational brochure.
Application information: Application form not required.
Initial approach: Letter
Copies of proposal: 1
Deadline(s): None
Officers: Jeanne H. Graham, Pres. and Treas.; Ralph A. Graham, Exec. V.P.; David Laughlin, V.P.; James H. LoPrete, Secy.; Annie West Graham, Recording Secy.
Director: William Graham.
Number of staff: 2 part-time support.
EIN: 383209484
Selected grants: The following grants were reported in 2003.
$18,000 to Michigan Land Use Institute, Beulah, MI.
$9,000 to Michigan Architectural Foundation, Detroit, MI.
$6,000 to Pisgah Legal Services, Asheville, NC.
$5,000 to Domestic Violence Shelter and Services, Wilmington, NC.
$5,000 to Wilmington Interfaith Hospitality Network, Wilmington, NC.
$4,000 to Cranbrook Educational Community, Bloomfield Hills, MI. For Horizons-Upward Bound program.
$4,000 to Daisys in Recovery, Holly, MI.
$4,000 to Greater Lansing Non-Profit Housing Corporation, Lansing, MI.
$3,000 to HAVEN (Help Against Violent Encounters Now), Pontiac, MI.
$3,000 to Oakland Land Conservancy, Rochester, MI.

330
Charles I. and Emma J. Clapp Scholarship Fund
c/o National City Bank
108 E. Michigan Ave., No. K-B01-2A
Kalamazoo, MI 49007-3966
Application address: c/o National City Bank,
Attn: Jim Yankoviak, Trust Off., 110 E. Allegan St.,
Otsego, MI 49078

Established in MI.
Grantmaker type: Independent foundation.
Financial data (yr. ended 12/31/04): Assets,
$284,405 (M); expenditures, $5,850; total giving,
$0; qualifying distributions, $0; giving activities
include $6,000 for loans to individuals.
Purpose and activities: Loans to non-smoking,
non-drinking female students and non-drinking male
students.
Fields of interest: Higher education.
Type of support: Student loans—to individuals.
Application information: Application form required.
  Deadline(s): None
Trustee: National City Bank.
EIN: 386041673

331
Robert & Lottie Clark Charitable Trust
c/o Northern Michigan Bank & Trust Co.
1502 W. Washington St.
Marquette, MI 49855

Established in 2001 in MI.
Donor: Lottie R. Clark.
Grantmaker type: Independent foundation.
Financial data (yr. ended 12/31/05): Assets,
$503,049 (M); gifts received, $614; expenditures,
$30,624; total giving, $24,800; qualifying
distributions, $24,800; giving activities include
$24,800 for grants.
Fields of interest: Education; Environment;
Foundations (community); Protestant agencies &
churches.
Limitations: Applications not accepted. Giving
primarily in Marquette and East Lansing, MI. No
grants to individuals.
Application information: Contributes only to
pre-selected organizations.
Trustee: Northern Michigan Bank & Trust Co.
EIN: 386777836

332
Clark Fund
606 Tanview Dr.
Oxford, MI 48371-4763

Established in MI.
Donor: Walter W. Clark†.
Grantmaker type: Independent foundation.
Financial data (yr. ended 12/31/05): Assets,
$343,003 (M); expenditures, $23,740; total giving,
$17,400; qualifying distributions, $17,400; giving
activities include $17,400 for grants.
Fields of interest: Youth development; Human
services.
Type of support: General/operating support.
Limitations: Applications not accepted. Giving
primarily in MI. No grants to individuals.
Application information: Contributes only to
pre-selected organizations.

Officers: Colette Chadwick, Pres.; Donald J.
Chadwick, V.P. and Treas.; Elise Kargol, Secy.
EIN: 386115484

333
Sonja Clason Charitable Trust
c/o Citizens Bank Wealth Mgmt., N.A.
328 S. Saginaw St., M/C 002072
Flint, MI 48502

Established in 2002 in MI.
Donor: Sonja Clason†.
Grantmaker type: Independent foundation.
Financial data (yr. ended 10/31/05): Assets,
$463,263 (M); expenditures, $26,450; total giving,
$20,073; qualifying distributions, $20,073; giving
activities include $20,073 for grants.
Fields of interest: Animal welfare.
Type of support: General/operating support.
Limitations: Applications not accepted. Giving
limited to MI. No grants to individuals.
Application information: Contributes only to
pre-selected organizations.
Trustee: Citizens Bank.
EIN: 300147944

334
Thomas H. and Nancy J. Claus Charitable Foundation
1553 Woodlawn Ave. S.E.
East Grand Rapids, MI 49506-4910

Established in 2000 in MI.
Donors: Thomas H. Claus; Nancy J. Claus.
Grantmaker type: Independent foundation.
Financial data (yr. ended 12/31/05): Assets,
$530,273 (M); expenditures, $34,831; total giving,
$34,259; qualifying distributions, $34,259; giving
activities include $34,259 for grants.
Fields of interest: Higher education; Human
services; Christian agencies & churches.
Type of support: General/operating support.
Limitations: Applications not accepted. Giving
primarily in Grand Rapids, MI. No grants to
individuals.
Application information: Contributes only to
pre-selected organizations.
Officers and Directors:* Nancy J. Claus,* Pres.;
Thomas H. Claus,* Secy.-Treas.
EIN: 383570800

335
Clearbrook Charitable Foundation, Inc.
2901 28th St. S.W.
Grandville, MI 49418-1164

Established in 1991 in MI.
Donors: Harvey J. Koning; Robert J. Sandling; Grand
Oldsmobile Center, Inc.; Wittenbach Sales &
Service.
Grantmaker type: Independent foundation.
Financial data (yr. ended 12/31/05): Assets,
$33,689 (M); gifts received, $172,116;
expenditures, $216,428; total giving, $216,400;
qualifying distributions, $216,400; giving activities
include $216,400 for 43 grants (high: $91,900).
Purpose and activities: Giving primarily to Christian
educational institutions and churches.
Fields of interest: Higher education; Education;
Human services; Christian agencies & churches.

Type of support: General/operating support.
Limitations: Applications not accepted. Giving
primarily in MI. No grants to individuals.
Application information: Contributes only to
pre-selected organizations.
Officers and Directors:* Harvey J. Koning,* Pres.;
Jack Bos, V.P.; Spencer Galloway,* Secy.-Treas.;
Harvey Koning III.
EIN: 383024306
Selected grants: The following grants were reported
in 2003.
$104,000 to Reformed Bible College, Grand Rapids,
  MI. For operating support.
$80,000 to Seymour Christian Reformed Church,
  Grand Rapids, MI. 2 grants: $64,200 (For
  operating support), $15,800 (For operating
  support).
$55,000 to Calvin Theological Seminary, Grand
  Rapids, MI. For operating support.
$14,000 to Trinity International University, Trinity
  Evangelical Divinity School, Deerfield, IL. For
  operating support.
$11,500 to ArtWorks, Grand Rapids, MI. For
  operating support.
$6,000 to Calvin College, Grand Rapids, MI. For
  operating support.
$5,100 to Navigators, The, Colorado Springs, CO.
  For operating support.
$4,000 to InterVarsity Christian Fellowship/USA,
  Grand Rapids, MI. For operating support.
$3,000 to Potters House, Grand Rapids, MI. For
  operating support.

336
The Cline Foundation
1629 Haslett Rd., PMB 220
Haslett, MI 48840 (517) 347-4676
Contact: James F. Carr, Pres.

Established in 1953.
Grantmaker type: Independent foundation.
Financial data (yr. ended 7/31/04): Assets,
$1,377,753 (M); expenditures, $91,337; total
giving, $83,910; qualifying distributions, $86,763;
giving activities include $83,910 for grants.
Purpose and activities: Giving for the arts, health,
recreation, education, and the prevention of cruelty
to children.
Fields of interest: Higher education; Hospitals
(general); Protestant agencies & churches.
Limitations: Giving primarily in MI. No grants to
individuals.
Application information:
  Initial approach: Letter
  Deadline(s): None
Officers: James F. Carr, Jr., Pres.; Diane S. Carr,
V.P.; Daniel B. Solomon, Secy.
EIN: 386077480

337
Clinton Rotary Scholarship Foundation
13081 Bartlett Hwy.
Clinton, MI 49236
Contact: James M. Rolland, Pres.
Application address: P.O. Box 692, 109 W. Church
St., Clinton, MI 49236

Grantmaker type: Independent foundation.
Financial data (yr. ended 6/30/05): Assets,
$116,764 (M); gifts received, $8,075;
expenditures, $7,255; total giving, $7,200;

qualifying distributions, $7,200; giving activities include $7,200 for 4 grants to individuals.
Purpose and activities: Scholarship awards only to graduates of Clinton High School, MI.
Type of support: Scholarships—to individuals.
Limitations: Giving limited to Clinton, MI.
Application information: Application form required.
Deadline(s): None
Officers: James M. Rolland, Pres.; Alan E. Beatty, V.P.; William Zimmerman, Secy.; Bernam G. Fraley, Treas.
Trustee: Howard Osterling.
EIN: 386150118

338
Clinton Township-Yasu City Cultural Exchange Board, Inc.
40700 Romeo Plank Rd.
Clinton Township, MI 48038-2952

Established in 2004 in MI.
Grantmaker type: Independent foundation.
Financial data (yr. ended 12/31/05): Assets, $5,520 (M); gifts received, $100; expenditures, $23,201; total giving, $0; qualifying distributions, $0.
Officers: Mike Lopez, Pres.; Brian Forest, V.P.; Ray Rickert, Secy.; Mary Ann Hosey, Treas.
EIN: 383117126

339
John H. Clupper Scholarship Trust
c/o Fifth Third Bank
P.O. Box 3636
Grand Rapids, MI 49501-3636
Contact: Susan J. Rice, Chair.
Application address: c/o Clupper Scholarship Comm., Dowagiac High School, Dowagiac, MI 49047, tel.: (269) 424-5092

Established in MI.
Grantmaker type: Independent foundation.
Financial data (yr. ended 12/31/04): Assets, $20,730 (M); expenditures, $1,904; total giving, $1,000; qualifying distributions, $1,250; giving activities include $1,000 for 1 grant to an individual.
Purpose and activities: Scholarship awards only to graduates of Dowagiac High School, MI.
Type of support: Scholarships—to individuals.
Limitations: Giving limited to the Dowagiac, MI, area.
Application information: Recipients must be graduates of Dowagiac High School.
Deadline(s): None
Scholarship Committee: Robert Follett; G. Bruce Laing; David Mohar; Susan J. Rice; Bruce Springsteen; John Steimle; Paul Wicks.
Trustee: Fifth Third Bank.
EIN: 386080386

340
Edgar G. Cochrane M.D. and Agnes L. Cochrane Foundation
1575 Lakeview Ave.
Sylvan Lake, MI 48320-1642
Contact: Gaylen Curtis, Dir.

Established in 2001 in MI.
Donor: Agnes L. Cochrane Trust.
Grantmaker type: Independent foundation.

Financial data (yr. ended 12/31/05): Assets, $1,320,936 (M); expenditures, $71,325; total giving, $62,250; qualifying distributions, $62,250; giving activities include $62,250 for grants.
Fields of interest: Medical school/education; Cancer; Human services, mind/body enrichment; Christian agencies & churches.
Type of support: General/operating support; Research.
Limitations: Giving on a national basis, with emphasis on MI.
Application information: Application form not required.
Deadline(s): None
Director: Gaylen Curtis.
EIN: 383616370

341
Jerry Cohen Foundation
3040 Chickering Ln.
Bloomfield Hills, MI 48302

Established in 1998 in MI.
Donor: Jerry Cohen.
Grantmaker type: Independent foundation.
Financial data (yr. ended 12/31/04): Assets, $39,039 (M); expenditures, $31,477; total giving, $27,600; qualifying distributions, $27,600; giving activities include $27,600 for grants.
Fields of interest: Education; Public affairs; Jewish agencies & temples.
Type of support: General/operating support.
Limitations: Applications not accepted. Giving on a national basis. No grants to individuals.
Application information: Contributes only to pre-selected organizations.
Officers: Jerry Cohen, Chair.; Harland E. Cohen, Exec. Dir.
EIN: 383359054

342
The Cold Heading Foundation
(formerly DeSeranno Educational Foundation, Inc.)
c/o Edward Miller
21777 Hoover Rd.
Warren, MI 48089

Established in 1968 in MI.
Donors: Cold Heading Co.; Ajax Metal Processing, Inc.; Beachlawn Mortgage Co.
Grantmaker type: Independent foundation.
Financial data (yr. ended 12/31/05): Assets, $29,265,309 (M); expenditures, $1,658,673; total giving, $1,227,450; qualifying distributions, $1,385,705; giving activities include $1,227,450 for 41+ grants (high: $550,000).
Purpose and activities: Giving primarily for education, as well as for health associations, and to Roman Catholic churches and organizations.
Fields of interest: Higher education; Health care; Health organizations, association; Foundations (private grantmaking); Roman Catholic agencies & churches.
Type of support: General/operating support.
Limitations: Applications not accepted. Giving primarily in MI.
Application information: Unsolicited requests for funds not accepted.
Officers: Derek Stevens, Pres.; Elizabeth Stevens, V.P. and Secy.; Gregory Stevens, Treas.
Trustee: Aline DeSerrano.

Number of staff: 3 part-time support.
EIN: 237005737

343
Cole Family Foundation
4569 Canterwood Dr.
Ada, MI 49301

Established in 2004 in MI.
Donor: Universal Forest Products, Inc.
Grantmaker type: Independent foundation.
Financial data (yr. ended 12/31/05): Assets, $10,209; expenditures, $8,691; total giving, $8,431; qualifying distributions, $8,431; giving activities include $8,431 for grants.
Limitations: Applications not accepted. Giving primarily in Grand Rapids, MI. No grants to individuals.
Application information: Contributes only to pre-selected organizations.
Officer: Michael R. Cole, Pres.
EIN: 300246444

344
Jack, Evelyn, and Richard Cole Family Foundation
37000 Grand River Ave.
Farmington Hills, MI 48335

Established in 2001 in MI.
Donor: Richard K. Cole.
Grantmaker type: Independent foundation.
Financial data (yr. ended 12/31/05): Assets, $836,426 (M); expenditures, $59,211; total giving, $44,000; qualifying distributions, $44,000; giving activities include $44,000 for grants.
Limitations: Applications not accepted. No grants to individuals.
Application information: Contributes only to pre-selected organizations.
Officers and Trustees:* Richard K. Cole,* Pres.; Herbert Goldstein,* V.P. and Treas.; Georgette Sheehan,* Secy.
EIN: 383614797

345
Bradford Cole Trust
c/o Comerica Bank
P.O. Box 75000, MC 3302
Detroit, MI 48275

Established in 1996 in FL.
Grantmaker type: Independent foundation.
Financial data (yr. ended 12/31/05): Assets, $127,501 (M); expenditures, $5,974; total giving, $3,000; qualifying distributions, $3,700; giving activities include $3,000 for 1 grant to an individual.
Purpose and activities: Scholarship awards to 1 male and 1 female graduate from high schools in Carver, MA who have been accepted to a four-year institution of higher learning, have been a resident of Carver, MA for at least five years prior to receiving the scholarship and require financial assistance to continue their education.
Fields of interest: Higher education.
Type of support: Scholarships—to individuals.
Limitations: Applications not accepted. Giving limited to residents of Carver, MA.
Application information: Recipients selected by committee independent of the trust.

Trustee: Comerica Bank.
EIN: 596829423

346
Cole-Belin Education Foundation
(formerly Marlin Cole and Connie Belin Charitable Foundation)
4222 Forest Ave.
Des Moines, IA 50311-2541

Established in 1985 in IA.
Grantmaker type: Independent foundation.
Financial data (yr. ended 12/31/04): Assets, $4,009,824 (M); expenditures, $268,391; total giving, $202,000; qualifying distributions, $200,056; giving activities include $202,000 for 3 grants (high: $192,000; low: $5,000).
Purpose and activities: Giving primarily for educational institutions and programs.
Fields of interest: Education, gifted students; Higher education; Education.
Type of support: General/operating support; Scholarship funds.
Limitations: Applications not accepted. Giving primarily in IA, and Ann Arbor, MI. No grants to individuals.
Application information: Contributes only to pre-selected organizations.
Officers: Laurie Belin, Pres.; Thomas Richard Belin, V.P.; James M. Belin, Secy.-Treas.
Director: Joy Elizabeth Belin.
EIN: 421263748
Selected grants: The following grants were reported in 2004.
$192,000 to University of Iowa Foundation, Iowa City, IA.
$5,000 to Civic Music Association of Des Moines, Des Moines, IA.
$5,000 to Roosevelt Elementary, Des Moines, IA.

347
Colina Foundation
1 Heritage Pl., Ste. 220
Southgate, MI 48195   (734) 283-8847
Contact: John Colina, Pres.
FAX: (734) 283-3725; E-mail (for John Colina): johnc36034@aol.com

Established in 1992 in MI.
Donors: John Colina; Nancy Colina.
Grantmaker type: Independent foundation.
Financial data (yr. ended 12/31/05): Assets, $2,582,594 (M); gifts received, $62,000; expenditures, $178,939; total giving, $139,573; qualifying distributions, $170,010; giving activities include $139,573 for 37 grants (high: $10,000; low: $100).
Purpose and activities: Giving primarily for programs assisting children ages 18 and under that are school-connected and/or community-based.
Fields of interest: Education, early childhood education; Youth development, services; Children/youth, services; Family services, parent education.
Type of support: Program development; Conferences/seminars; Seed money; Matching/challenge support.
Limitations: Giving limited to southern Wayne County, MI, and areas where trustees reside.
Publications: Application guidelines; Annual report; Annual report (including application guidelines); Grants list.

Application information: Application form required.
Initial approach: Letter
Copies of proposal: 1
Deadline(s): 30 days prior to board meeting
Board meeting date(s): Monthly
Final notification: Within 60 days
Officers: John Colina, Pres.; Nancy Colina, Secy.-Treas.
Trustees: Lori Colina-Lee; JoMarie Goerge; Michael Goerge; Simon Lee.
Number of staff: None.
EIN: 383082610
Selected grants: The following grants were reported in 2003.
$10,000 to Downriver Council for the Arts, Taylor, MI. For Detroit Mosaic Theater and Trenton Theater.
$10,000 to Everybody Ready, Trenton, MI. For parent newsletters.
$10,000 to Guidance Center, Southgate, MI. For parents' newsletters.
$10,000 to Ingham Intermediate School District, Mason, MI. For media campaign, Be Their Hero.
$10,000 to Oakwood Healthcare System Foundation, Dearborn, MI. For car seat program at South Shore Hospital.
$5,000 to Childrens Outreach, River Rouge, MI.
$2,000 to Centennial High School, Fort Collins, CO. For roads scholar community service project to Chile.
$2,000 to Tri-City Community Development Corporation, Detroit, MI. For River Rouge Youth Program.
$1,700 to Childrens Resource Network, New Boston, MI. For childcare conference.
$1,000 to Planned Parenthood of the Rocky Mountains, Denver, CO.

348
Coller Foundation
35 S. Elk St.
Sandusky, MI 48471
Contact: John Paterson, Pres.
Application address: P.O. Box 311, Sandusky, MI 48471, tel.: (810) 648-2414

Established around 1989.
Grantmaker type: Independent foundation.
Financial data (yr. ended 12/31/05): Assets, $1,782,766 (M); expenditures, $69,102; total giving, $64,000; qualifying distributions, $64,000; giving activities include $64,000 for grants to individuals.
Purpose and activities: Scholarships awarded to graduates of high schools of Sanilac and Tuscola counties, MI.
Type of support: Scholarships—to individuals.
Limitations: Giving limited to residents of Sanilac and Tuscola counties, MI.
Application information: Application form required.
Deadline(s): Mar. 1
Officers: John Paterson, Pres.; Gerald Hicks, Secy.
Directors: Allen Jones; Kenneth Michlash; Donald Teeple.
EIN: 382832816

349
Julius V. & Alice G. Combs Foundation
200 Riverfront Park, Apt. 17-K
Detroit, MI 48226-4525

Established in 1997 in MI.
Grantmaker type: Independent foundation.
Financial data (yr. ended 12/31/04): Assets, $0 (M); gifts received, $51,765; expenditures, $48,357; total giving, $47,354; qualifying distributions, $47,288; giving activities include $47,354 for 63 grants (high: $16,500; low: $50).
Fields of interest: Performing arts; Higher education.
Type of support: Capital campaigns; General/operating support; Scholarship funds.
Limitations: Applications not accepted. Giving primarily in Detroit, MI. No support for political organizations. No grants to individuals.
Publications: Financial statement.
Application information: Contributes only to pre-selected organizations.
Officers: Julius V. Combs, Pres. and Treas.; Alice G. Combs, V.P. and Secy.
EIN: 383352692

350
Robert & Sara S. Comloquoy Charitable Foundation
c/o Wachovia Bank, N.A.
100 N. Main St., 13th Fl.
Winston Salem, NC 27150

Established in PA.
Grantmaker type: Independent foundation.
Financial data (yr. ended 12/31/04): Assets, $10,083,394 (M); expenditures, $484,910; total giving, $466,628; qualifying distributions, $466,628; giving activities include $466,628 for 46 grants (high: $29,164; low: $2,601).
Purpose and activities: Support primarily for education, hospitals, human services, and Protestant churches.
Fields of interest: Elementary/secondary education; Higher education; Hospitals (general); Health organizations; Youth development; Human services; Protestant agencies & churches.
Type of support: General/operating support.
Limitations: Applications not accepted. Giving primarily in PA, with emphasis on Reading, Philadelphia, Pottsville, and St. Davids; some giving also in Boyne City, MI. No grants to individuals.
Application information: Contributes only to pre-selected organizations.
Trustees: Philip C. Herr II; Wachovia Bank, N.A.
EIN: 236604053

351
Community Christian Ministries
P.O. Box 282
Grandville, MI 49468-0282   (616) 247-7845

Established in 2002 in MI.
Grantmaker type: Independent foundation.
Financial data (yr. ended 12/31/04): Assets, $728,190 (M); expenditures, $29,647; total giving, $24,000; qualifying distributions, $24,000; giving activities include $24,000 for 9 grants (high: $5,000; low: $1,000).
Purpose and activities: Giving to provide aid to the poor and needy in the greater Grand Rapids, MI, area.
Fields of interest: Human services; Economically disadvantaged.
Limitations: Giving limited to the greater Grand Rapids, MI, area.

Application information:
Initial approach: Letter
Deadline(s): None
Officers: Herm Scholten, Pres.; Jim Holkeboer, Secy.; Jan Vander Weide, Treas.
Directors: Jim Brock; Mike DeVries; Marv Mingerink; Cheryl Nielsen; Jan Van Manen; Tom Waalkes.
EIN: 381381272

352
Community Financial Scholarship Fund
(formerly Community Federal Credit Union Scholarship Fund)
500 S. Harvey St.
P.O. Box 8050
Plymouth, MI 48170-8050
E-mail: scholarships@cfcu.org; URL: http://www.cfcu.org/youth_scholarship.php

Established in 1998 in MI.
Donors: Doreen A. Lawton; Community Federal Credit Union.
Grantmaker type: Independent foundation.
Financial data (yr. ended 12/31/05): Assets, $52,242 (M); gifts received, $13,145; expenditures, $11,289; total giving, $10,000; qualifying distributions, $10,000; giving activities include $10,000 for grants to individuals.
Purpose and activities: Scholarships are granted to outstanding credit union members who demonstrated high honors in school while contributing to their community. Scholarships limited to applicants with a Community Financial account, who are living or working within Community Financial's charter area including the communities of Plymouth, Canton, Northville and Novi and the counties of Alpena, Otsego and Montmorency in northern Michigan.
Type of support: Scholarships—to individuals.
Limitations: Giving limited to individuals living or working within Community Financial's charter area including the communities of Plymouth, Canton, Northville and Novi and the counties of Alpena, Otsego and Montmorency in northern MI.
Application information: Application form required.
Deadline(s): Mar. 4
Officers: Roger Ballard, Chair.; Bill Lawton, Secy.; Dan Herriman, Treas.
Directors: Margaret Dunning; Doreen A. Lawton.
EIN: 382786953

353
The H. P. and Genevieve Connable Fund
136 E. Michigan Ave., Ste. 1201
Kalamazoo, MI 49007-3936
Contact: David S. Kruis, Treas.

Established in 1987 in MI.
Donors: H.P. Connable†; Genevieve W. Connable†.
Grantmaker type: Independent foundation.
Financial data (yr. ended 12/31/05): Assets, $4,394,261 (M); expenditures, $220,140; total giving, $164,000; qualifying distributions, $198,016; giving activities include $164,000 for 40 grants (high: $30,000; low: $1,000).
Purpose and activities: Giving to higher education, the arts, social services, and natural resource preservation and enhancement.
Fields of interest: Arts; Higher education; Environment, natural resources; Health organizations, association; Human services.

Limitations: Applications not accepted. Giving primarily in Kalamazoo, MI. No grants to individuals.
Application information: Unsolicited requests for funds not accepted.
Officers and Trustees:* James S. Hilboldt,* Pres.; James C. Melvin,* V.P.; Loyal A. Eldridge III,* Secy.; David S. Kruis,* Treas.
EIN: 382710894
Selected grants: The following grants were reported in 2004.
$30,000 to Kalamazoo College, Kalamazoo, MI. For Light Fine Arts renovation.
$15,000 to Big Brothers/Big Sisters of Greater Kalamazoo, Kalamazoo, MI. For general operating support.
$10,000 to Family and Childrens Services, Kalamazoo, MI. For general operating support.
$10,000 to Kalamazoo Valley Community College Foundation, Kalamazoo, MI. For Center for New Media.
$5,000 to Arts Council of Greater Kalamazoo, Kalamazoo, MI. For general operating support.
$5,000 to Kalamazoo Community in Schools Foundation, Kalamazoo, MI. For general operating support.
$5,000 to United Way, Greater Kalamazoo, Kalamazoo, MI. For general operating support.
$3,000 to Bach Festival Society of Kalamazoo, Kalamazoo, MI. For general operating support.
$3,000 to Boy Scouts of America, Southwest Michigan Council, Kalamazoo, MI. For general operating support.
$3,000 to Girl Scouts of the U.S.A., Glowing Embers Council, Kalamazoo, MI. For general operating support.

354
The Conrad-Johnston Foundation
c/o Barrett & Assoc.
130 Kercheval, Ste. 130
Grosse Pointe Farms, MI 48236

Donors: James D. Johnston; Margaret M. Johnston.
Grantmaker type: Independent foundation.
Financial data (yr. ended 11/30/05): Assets, $283,029 (M); gifts received, $31,845; expenditures, $9,250; total giving, $9,250; qualifying distributions, $9,250; giving activities include $9,250 for grants.
Fields of interest: Museums; Children/youth, services; Roman Catholic agencies & churches.
Type of support: General/operating support.
Limitations: Applications not accepted. Giving primarily in Washington, DC. No grants to individuals.
Application information: Contributes only to pre-selected organizations.
Trustees: James D. Johnston; Margaret M. Johnston; Frederick R. Keydel.
EIN: 382623282

355
Nadalynn Conway Charitable Trust
4080G Miller Rd.
Flint, MI 48507-1242 (810) 733-5140
Contact: Dale E. McClelland, Tr.

Established in 1996 in MI.
Grantmaker type: Independent foundation.
Financial data (yr. ended 12/31/04): Assets, $1,100,628 (M); expenditures, $74,144; total

giving, $35,465; qualifying distributions, $35,465; giving activities include $35,465 for grants.
Purpose and activities: Grant awards are given for the care and/or preservation of animals.
Fields of interest: Animals/wildlife, preservation/protection; Animals/wildlife.
Type of support: General/operating support.
Limitations: Giving on a national basis.
Application information:
Initial approach: Letter
Deadline(s): None
Trustee: Dale E. McClelland.
EIN: 386609288

356
Conway Family Foundation
5000 Meandering Creek Dr., N.E.
Belmont, MI 49306

Established in 2000 in MI.
Donors: Joseph G. Conway†; Stephen M. Conway.
Grantmaker type: Independent foundation.
Financial data (yr. ended 12/31/05): Assets, $829,040 (M); expenditures, $43,796; total giving, $41,000; qualifying distributions, $41,000; giving activities include $41,000 for grants.
Fields of interest: Health organizations; Crime/violence prevention, domestic violence; Children/youth, services; Women.
Limitations: Applications not accepted. Giving primarily in MI. No grants to individuals.
Application information: Contributes only to pre-selected organizations.
Officers: Susan O. "Sue" Conway, Pres.; Stephen M. Conway, Secy.-Treas.
EIN: 383529723

357
Cook Charitable Foundation
618 Kenmoor Ave. S.E., Ste. 100
Grand Rapids, MI 49546
Contact: Peter C. Cook, Pres.

Established in 1987.
Donors: Peter C. Cook; Emajean Cook; Peter C. Cook Trust.
Grantmaker type: Independent foundation.
Financial data (yr. ended 12/31/04): Assets, $5,104,660 (M); gifts received, $32,500; expenditures, $1,884,899; total giving, $1,805,293; qualifying distributions, $1,805,293; giving activities include $1,805,293 for 59 grants (high: $410,000; low: $201).
Purpose and activities: Giving primarily for education and religious organizations. Some support also for human service organizations, health associations, and arts and cultural organizations.
Fields of interest: Arts; Health organizations, association; Human services; Human services, mind/body enrichment; Christian agencies & churches.
Type of support: General/operating support.
Limitations: Applications not accepted. Giving limited to the Grand Rapids, MI, area. No grants to individuals.
Application information: Contributes only to pre-selected organizations.
Officers and Directors:* Peter C. Cook,* Pres.; Robert D. Brower,* Secy.; Carrie L. Boer; Thomas H. Claus; Thomas M. Cook.
EIN: 382752251

358
Cook Family Foundation
P.O. Box 278
Owosso, MI 48867-0578 (989) 725-1621
Contact: Bruce L. Cook, Pres.
FAX: (989) 725-3138;
E-mail: tom_cook@chartermi.net

Established in 1979 in MI.
Donors: Donald O. Cook‡; Florence-Etta Cook‡; Donald O. Cook Charitable Trust; Wolverine Sign Works.
Grantmaker type: Independent foundation.
Financial data (yr. ended 12/31/04): Assets, $9,927,242 (L); gifts received, $942; expenditures, $502,668; total giving, $439,751; qualifying distributions, $488,882; giving activities include $439,751 for 27 grants (high: $100,000; low: $50).
Purpose and activities: Giving primarily for education and youth programs.
Fields of interest: Historic preservation/historical societies; Higher education; Environmental education; Children/youth, services.
Type of support: General/operating support; Annual campaigns; Capital campaigns; Building/renovation; Program development; Internship funds; Scholarship funds.
Limitations: Applications not accepted. Giving limited to MI. No grants to individuals.
Publications: Annual report; Informational brochure.
Application information: Contributes only to pre-selected organizations.
   Board meeting date(s): Quarterly
Officers: Bruce L. Cook, Pres.; Laurie Caszatt Cook, V.P.; Thomas B. Cook, Secy.-Treas.
Trustees: Jacqueline P. Cook; Paul C. Cook; Anna E. Owens.
Number of staff: 1 part-time professional.
EIN: 382283809

359
Brenton & Susan Cook Foundation
864 S. Heathwood Dr.
Marco Island, FL 34145

Established in 1999 in MI.
Donors: Brenton P. Cook; Susan L. Cook.
Grantmaker type: Independent foundation.
Financial data (yr. ended 12/31/05): Assets, $378,524 (M); gifts received, $50,000; expenditures, $7,338; total giving, $3,000; qualifying distributions, $3,000; giving activities include $3,000 for grants.
Fields of interest: Libraries (public); Animal welfare.
Limitations: Applications not accepted. Giving primarily in Battle Creek, MI; some giving also in OH. No grants to individuals.
Application information: Contributes only to pre-selected organizations.
Officers: Brenton P. Cook, Pres. and Treas.; Susan L. Cook, Secy.
EIN: 383476657

360
Joanne Cross Coon Foundation
3 Locust Ln.
Lansing, MI 48911-1153
Contact: Joanne L. Coon, Pres.

Grantmaker type: Independent foundation.

Financial data (yr. ended 9/30/05): Assets, $429,767 (M); expenditures, $29,319; total giving, $29,100; qualifying distributions, $29,100; giving activities include $29,100 for grants.
Purpose and activities: Giving primarily to Seventh Day Adventists organizations and activities.
Fields of interest: Christian agencies & churches.
Type of support: General/operating support.
Limitations: Giving limited to MI, with emphasis on the greater Lansing area. No grants to individuals.
Application information:
   Initial approach: Letter
   Deadline(s): None
Officers: Joanne L. Coon, Pres.; Max A. Coon, V.P.; Patricia A. Markoff, Secy.; Jeff A. Coon, Treas.
Director: David Markoff.
EIN: 382359335

361
Cooper Foundation
240 Marblehead Rd.
Bloomfield Hills, MI 48304

Established in 1986 in MI.
Donors: Susan E. Cooper; David Cooper.
Grantmaker type: Independent foundation.
Financial data (yr. ended 11/30/05): Assets, $345,519 (M); gifts received, $87,947; expenditures, $184,232; total giving, $174,642; qualifying distributions, $174,642; giving activities include $174,642 for 16 grants (high: $79,567; low: $75).
Fields of interest: Education; Eye diseases; Human services; Family services.
Type of support: General/operating support.
Limitations: Applications not accepted. Giving limited to MI. No grants to individuals.
Application information: Contributes only to pre-selected organizations.
Officers: Susan E. Cooper, Pres.; David Cooper, Secy.-Treas.
EIN: 382728525

362
Allan B. Copley Charitable Foundation
711 Cedar Ln.
Jackson, MI 49203

Established in 2003 in MI.
Donor: Allan B. Copley.
Grantmaker type: Independent foundation.
Financial data (yr. ended 12/31/05): Assets, $334,079 (M); gifts received, $90,000; expenditures, $19,134; total giving, $14,000; qualifying distributions, $14,000; giving activities include $14,000 for grants.
Limitations: Applications not accepted. No grants to individuals.
Application information: Contributes only to pre-selected organizations.
Trustees: Eileen L. Idziak; Kathleen M. O'Connell.
EIN: 611458325

363
Corinthian Developments, Inc.
1725 Caniff St.
Hamtramck, MI 48212

Established in MI.

Donors: Comerica Bank; Standard Federal Bank N.A.; Charter One Bank; Charter One Foundation.
Grantmaker type: Independent foundation.
Financial data (yr. ended 12/31/05): Assets, $86,666 (M); gifts received, $20,000; expenditures, $56,961; total giving, $0; qualifying distributions, $0.
Officers: Rev. Joseph R. Jordan, Pres.; Charles Mathews, V.P.; Bonnie J. Fussello, Secy.; Alease Alexander, Treas.; Esmeralda Copeland, Exec. Dir.
Board Members: Rose Edwards; Aspachia Fisher; Darryl Latimer; Lillie Mae Smith; Barbara Washington Bass.
EIN: 382856673

364
Corr Family Foundation
c/o Jean Corr Haas
2801 S.E. 29th St.
Ocala, FL 34471

Established in 1998 in FL.
Donor: Jean A. Corr.
Grantmaker type: Independent foundation.
Financial data (yr. ended 12/31/05): Assets, $232,088 (M); expenditures, $45,614; total giving, $27,413; qualifying distributions, $27,413; giving activities include $27,413 for grants.
Fields of interest: Higher education, university.
Type of support: General/operating support.
Limitations: Giving primarily in FL; some giving also in MI. No grants to individuals.
Trustee: Jean Corr Haas.
EIN: 597116855

365
Max and Lucille Cortright Marshall Education Foundation
203 E. Michigan Ave.
Marshall, MI 49068

Established in 2004 in MI.
Donors: Max Cortright; Lucille Cortright.
Grantmaker type: Independent foundation.
Financial data (yr. ended 12/31/05): Assets, $429,524 (M); expenditures, $38,546; total giving, $38,000; qualifying distributions, $38,000; giving activities include $38,000 for grants.
Purpose and activities: Support only for the Marshal Public Schools, MI.
Fields of interest: Education, public education.
Type of support: General/operating support.
Limitations: Applications not accepted. Giving limited to Marshall, MI. No grants to individuals.
Application information: Contributes only to a pre-selected organization.
Officers: Timothy Cortright, Pres.; Wendy Ford, V.P.; Ronald J. DeGraw, Secy.-Treas.
EIN: 201289656

366
Evelyn Cossin Trust
c/o Bank of America, N.A., Private Clients Group
P.O. Box 1802
Providence, RI 02901-1802

Grantmaker type: Independent foundation.
Financial data (yr. ended 12/31/04): Assets, $212,586 (M); expenditures, $10,761; total giving,

$7,530; qualifying distributions, $9,342; giving activities include $7,530 for grants.

Purpose and activities: Support only for the City of Cedar Springs, MI, the Town of Cedar Springs, MN, Silent Unity, Unity Village, MO, Foundation for Christian Living, Pawling, NY, Chicago Theological Seminary, IL, and West Lebanon Cemetery, IN.

Fields of interest: Theological school/education; Government/public administration; Christian agencies & churches.

Type of support: General/operating support.

Limitations: Applications not accepted. Giving limited to Chicago, IL, Lebanon, IN, Cedar Springs, MI, Cedar Springs, MN, Unity Village, MO, and Pawling, NY. No grants to individuals.

Application information: Contributes only to 6 pre-selected organizations.

Trustee: Bank of America, N.A.

EIN: 046462976

367
Virginia A. Cott & Richard S. Cott Charitable Trust

3957 Blue Water Rd.
Traverse City, MI 49686
Contact: Ann Carolus, Tr.

Established in 1990 in IL.
Donor: Virginia A. Cott.
Grantmaker type: Independent foundation.
Financial data (yr. ended 12/31/05): Assets, $209,054 (M); expenditures, $3,363; total giving, $2,500; qualifying distributions, $2,500; giving activities include $2,500 for grants.
Fields of interest: Protestant agencies & churches.
Limitations: Giving primarily in Peoria, IL. No grants to individuals.
Application information: Application form not required.
  Deadline(s): None
Trustee: Ann Carolus.
EIN: 371270577

368
William Courtney Family Foundation

c/o Comerica Bank
P.O. Box 7500 M/C 8280
Detroit, MI 48275-8280   (313) 222-5257
Contact: Paula Gralewski

Established in 1999 in OH.
Donor: William F. Courtney†.
Grantmaker type: Independent foundation.
Financial data (yr. ended 12/31/05): Assets, $2,044,670 (M); expenditures, $128,414; total giving, $77,200; qualifying distributions, $77,200; giving activities include $77,200 for grants.
Fields of interest: Arts; Education; Christian agencies & churches.
Limitations: Giving primarily in CA. No grants to individuals.
Application information:
  Initial approach: Letter
  Deadline(s): None
Advisory Committee: Christopher Courtney; Frank Courtney.
Trustee: Comerica Bank.
EIN: 341905199

369
Cowan Slavin Foundation

(formerly The Lillian L. and Harry A. Cowan Foundation Corporation)
24 School St.
Newton, MA 02458-1518
Contact: Marjorie Slavin Bovee, Pres.
Application address: 7881 Dell Rd., Saline, MI 48176

Incorporated in 1962 in MA.
Donor: Harry A. Cowan†.
Grantmaker type: Independent foundation.
Financial data (yr. ended 4/30/04): Assets, $4,393,109 (M); expenditures, $218,417; total giving, $179,370; qualifying distributions, $205,789; giving activities include $179,370 for 27 grants (high: $10,000; low: $1,000).
Purpose and activities: Giving primarily to charitable organizations whose budgets are under $1 million and which aid disadvantaged children, teens, the elderly, the physically challenged, and the homeless.
Fields of interest: Education, special; AIDS; Legal services; Food services; Recreation, camps; Children/youth, services; Family services; Homeless, human services; Aging; Disabilities, people with; AIDS, people with; Economically disadvantaged; Homeless.
Type of support: General/operating support; Continuing support; Equipment; Program development; Seed money; Matching/challenge support.
Limitations: Giving primarily in Boston, MA, Ann Arbor, MI, and New York, NY. No support for national umbrella agencies. No grants to individuals, or for capital or annual campaigns, or building funds.
Application information: Application form not required.
  Initial approach: Proposal
  Copies of proposal: 1
  Deadline(s): Mar. 15 and Aug. 1
  Board meeting date(s): Apr. and Sept.
Officers and Trustees:* David Bovee,* Chair.; Marjorie Slavin Bovee,* Pres. and Exec. Dir.; Andrea Weinstein,* V.P.; Matthew Hersom, Clerk.
Director: Emily Weinstein.
Number of staff: 1 part-time professional; 1 part-time support.
EIN: 046130077
Selected grants: The following grants were reported in 2003.
$10,000 to Bread and Jams, Cambridge, MA. For general support.
$10,000 to Crossroads of Michigan, Detroit, MI. For children and teen programs.
$10,000 to Hope Clinic, Ypsilanti, MI. For educational programs.
$10,000 to Interfaith Hospitality Network of Washtenaw County, Ann Arbor, MI. For general support.
$10,000 to Ozone House, Ann Arbor, MI.
$10,000 to Solution at Work, Cambridge, MA. For programs for elderly.
$10,000 to Youth Forum Maine, Tenants Harbor, ME.
$9,952 to Peace Neighborhood Center, Ann Arbor, MI.
$8,500 to Friends in Deed Washtenaw Area Social Ministries Network, Ypsilanti, MI. For emergency hotline.
$7,500 to Lady Liberty Educational Alliance, New York, NY. For general operating support.

370
Coyne Foundation

3926 Oakland Dr.
Bloomfield Hills, MI 48301

Established in 1991 in MI.
Donors: Gerald J. Coyne; Catherine A. Coyne.
Grantmaker type: Independent foundation.
Financial data (yr. ended 12/31/05): Assets, $47,781 (M); gifts received, $50,000; expenditures, $17,170; total giving, $17,000; qualifying distributions, $17,000; giving activities include $17,000 for grants.
Fields of interest: Human services; Homeless, human services; Roman Catholic agencies & churches.
Limitations: Applications not accepted. Giving primarily in MI. No grants to individuals.
Application information: Contributes only to pre-selected organizations.
Officer: Gerald J. Coyne, Pres.
EIN: 382961009

371
Peter J. & Constance M. Cracchiolo Foundation

24055 Jefferson Ave., Ste. 200
St. Clair Shores, MI 48080-1514

Established in 1984 in MI.
Donors: Peter J. Cracchiolo; Constance M. Cracchiolo.
Grantmaker type: Independent foundation.
Financial data (yr. ended 6/30/05): Assets, $11,300,795 (M); gifts received, $214,980; expenditures, $512,180; total giving, $435,102; qualifying distributions, $454,343; giving activities include $435,102 for 43 grants (high: $86,150; low: $100).
Purpose and activities: Giving primarily to Roman Catholic agencies and churches.
Fields of interest: Education; Hospitals (general); Health organizations, association; Human services; Roman Catholic agencies & churches.
Type of support: General/operating support.
Limitations: Applications not accepted. Giving primarily in MI. No grants to individuals.
Application information: Contributes only to pre-selected organizations.
Officers: Peter J. Cracchiolo, Pres.; Constance M. Cracchiolo, Secy.; Peter T. Cracchiolo, Treas.
EIN: 382561770
Selected grants: The following grants were reported in 2003.
$100,000 to Our Lady Star of the Sea Parish, Grosse Pointe, MI. For building fund.
$86,150 to Solanus Casey Center, Detroit, MI. For operating support.
$75,000 to Saint John Health Foundation, Madison Heights, MI. For operating support.
$33,000 to Pope John Paul II Cultural Foundation, Detroit, MI. For operating support.
$29,759 to Detroit Institute of Arts, Detroit, MI. For operating support.
$25,000 to Archdiocese of Detroit, Detroit, MI. For operating support.
$24,000 to Genesis Foundation, Detroit, MI. For operating support.
$14,000 to Most Holy Trinity School, Detroit, MI. For operating support.
$4,000 to Holy Cross Childrens Services, Clinton, MI. For operating support.

$2,500 to Oakwood Healthcare System Foundation, Dearborn, MI. For operating support.

372
Raymond M. & Jane E. Cracchiolo Foundation
24055 Jefferson Ave., Ste. 200
St. Clair Shores, MI 48080-1514
Contact: Raymond M. Cracchiolo, Pres.

Established in 1984 in MI.
Donors: Raymond M. Cracchiolo; Jane E. Cracchiolo.
Grantmaker type: Independent foundation.
Financial data (yr. ended 6/30/05): Assets, $4,945,634 (M); gifts received, $1,100,030; expenditures, $162,646; total giving, $133,375; qualifying distributions, $144,001; giving activities include $133,375 for 20 grants (high: $25,000; low: $250).
Purpose and activities: Giving primarily for youth and child welfare; support also for religious organizations.
Fields of interest: Human services; Children/youth, services; Roman Catholic agencies & churches.
Type of support: General/operating support.
Limitations: Applications not accepted. Giving limited to MI. No grants to individuals.
Application information: Contributes only to pre-selected organizations.
Officers: Raymond M. Cracchiolo, Pres.; Janice G. Ducsay, Secy.; Jane E. Cracchiolo, Treas.
Directors: Heidi Cracchiolo Bell; Natalie Ceniza; David Cracchiolo; Christi Cracchiolo Small.
EIN: 382556359

373
Thomas and Carol Cracchiolo Foundation
24055 Jefferson Ave., Ste. 200
St. Clair Shores, MI 48080-1514

Established in 1984 in MI.
Donors: Carol A. Cracchiolo; Thomas A. Cracchiolo.
Grantmaker type: Independent foundation.
Financial data (yr. ended 6/30/05): Assets, $10,315,749 (M); gifts received, $342,000; expenditures, $478,345; total giving, $420,260; qualifying distributions, $445,924; giving activities include $420,260 for 45 grants (high: $82,000; low: $25).
Purpose and activities: Giving primarily for health and human services, and to Roman Catholic agencies and churches.
Fields of interest: Education; Hospitals (general); Health organizations, association; Children/youth, services; Roman Catholic agencies & churches.
Type of support: General/operating support.
Limitations: Applications not accepted. Giving primarily in MI. No grants to individuals.
Application information: Contributes only to pre-selected organizations.
Officers and Directors:* Thomas A. Cracchiolo,* Pres.; Carol A. Cracchiolo,* V.P.; Ann M. Caraway,* Secy.; Lisa A. Peracchio,* Treas.; Bernadette Cracchiolo Hanauske; Carol N. Laub.
EIN: 382543263
Selected grants: The following grants were reported in 2005.
$82,000 to Holy Cross Childrens Services, Clinton, MI. For operating support.

$75,200 to Saint John Health Foundation, Madison Heights, MI. For operating support.
$50,800 to Solanus Casey Center, Detroit, MI. For capital campaign.
$35,333 to Pope John Paul II Cultural Foundation, Detroit, MI. For operating support.
$26,500 to Our Lady Star of the Sea Parish, Grosse Pointe, MI. 2 grants: $11,500 (For operating support), $15,000 (For operating support).
$20,000 to Saint Cecilia School, Detroit, MI. For operating support.
$12,000 to Camp Sancta Maria Trust, Gaylord, MI. For operating support.
$12,000 to Most Holy Trinity School, Detroit, MI. For operating support.
$4,000 to Cornerstone Schools Association, Detroit, MI. For operating support.

374
Wilson H. Craig, Jr. Foundation
c/o Citizens Bank Wealth Mgmt., N.A.
311 Woodworth Ave.
Alma, MI 48801-1826

Established in 1996 in MI.
Donor: Wilson H. Craig, Jr.
Grantmaker type: Independent foundation.
Financial data (yr. ended 12/31/04): Assets, $454,025 (M); expenditures, $35,894; total giving, $28,123; qualifying distributions, $28,123; giving activities include $28,123 for grants.
Limitations: Applications not accepted. Giving limited to MI. No grants to individuals.
Application information: Contributes only to pre-selected organizations.
Trustees: James Brinkert; Larry M. Dillon; Tina Travis; Paul Vandelester; Richard Werner.
EIN: 383269646

375
Crain Family Foundation
1155 Gratiot Ave.
Detroit, MI 48207-2913

Established in 2001 in MI.
Donor: Keith E. Crain.
Grantmaker type: Independent foundation.
Financial data (yr. ended 12/31/05): Assets, $1,664,337 (M); expenditures, $106,650; total giving, $85,000; qualifying distributions, $85,000; giving activities include $85,000 for grants.
Limitations: Applications not accepted. No grants to individuals.
Application information: Contributes only to pre-selected organizations.
Officers: Alexandra T. Crain, Pres.; Christopher T. Crain, Secy.; Keith E. Crain, Treas.
EIN: 383618818

376
Matilda & Harold Crane Foundation
c/o Standard Federal Bank N.A., Wealth Mgmt.
135 S. LaSalle St., Ste. 2060
Chicago, IL 60603

Established in 1989 in MI.
Donor: Matilda M. Crane.
Grantmaker type: Independent foundation.
Financial data (yr. ended 12/31/04): Assets, $718,235 (M); expenditures, $56,300; total giving,

$47,000; qualifying distributions, $47,000; giving activities include $47,000 for grants.
Fields of interest: Education; Human services; Community development.
Type of support: General/operating support; Continuing support; Scholarship funds.
Limitations: Applications not accepted. Giving primarily in Grand Rapids, MI. No grants to individuals.
Application information: Contributes only to pre-selected organizations.
Board meeting date(s): May
Officers: Matilda M. Crane, Pres.; Aldonna H. Kammeraad, V.P.; John Martin, Secy.; Donald J. Swierenga, Treas.
Advisory Committee: Terri Disselkoen; Franklin H. Kammeraad.
Trustee: Standard Federal Bank N.A.
EIN: 382903301

377
Crawford Family Foundation
3000 Immokalee
Naples, FL 34110

Established in 1998 in MI.
Donor: Richard S. Crawford.
Grantmaker type: Independent foundation.
Financial data (yr. ended 12/31/04): Assets, $237,089 (M); gifts received, $430; expenditures, $17,592; total giving, $3,600; qualifying distributions, $17,592; giving activities include $3,600 for grants.
Fields of interest: Education; Federated giving programs; Religion, association.
Limitations: Applications not accepted. Giving primarily in Detroit, MI. No grants to individuals.
Application information: Contributes only to pre-selected organizations.
Officers and Directors:* Richard S. Crawford,* Pres.; Ira J. Jaffe,* Secy.; Elizabeth Crawford,* Treas.
EIN: 383444302

378
The Cresswell Family Foundation, Inc.
1968 Boulder Dr.
Ann Arbor, MI 48104-4164
Contact: Ronald M. Cresswell, Dir.

Established in 1999 in MI.
Donor: Ronald M. Cresswell.
Grantmaker type: Independent foundation.
Financial data (yr. ended 12/31/05): Assets, $1,534,173 (M); gifts received, $124,178; expenditures, $243,329; total giving, $231,000; qualifying distributions, $231,000; giving activities include $231,000 for 17 grants (high: $150,000; low: $500).
Purpose and activities: Giving primarily for education, health, and human services.
Fields of interest: Higher education; Health care; American Red Cross; Human services.
Limitations: Giving on a national basis. No support for private foundations. No grants to individuals.
Publications: Grants list.
Application information: Application form not required.
Initial approach: Letter
Copies of proposal: 1
Deadline(s): None

Board meeting date(s): Annually
Final notification: 1 month
Directors: Susan Mary Brice; Eleanor Lynn Costin; Margaret B. Cresswell; Ronald M. Cresswell; Sheena Livingstone Cresswell; Jennifer Margaret Petrie; Katherine Ann Tisserand.
Number of staff: None.
EIN: 383483412
Selected grants: The following grants were reported in 2004.
$150,500 to University of Michigan, Ann Arbor, MI. 2 grants: $500 (For scholarships), $150,000 to College of Pharmacy (For fellowship in medicinal chemistry).
$10,000 to University of Strathclyde, Glasgow, Scotland. For annual support.
$7,000 to Saint Joseph Mercy Hospital, Ann Arbor, MI. For annual support.
$7,000 to University of Michigan Health System, Cancer Center, Ann Arbor, MI. For annual support.
$5,000 to Womens Community Clinic, San Francisco, CA. For general support.
$2,000 to Oak Grove School, Ojai, CA. For school garden project.
$1,000 to Autism Society of Michigan, Lansing, MI. For general support.

379
CRN Foundation
1900 E. 9th St., Rm. 3200
Cleveland, OH 44114-3485

Established in 2004 in OH.
Grantmaker type: Independent foundation.
Financial data (yr. ended 12/31/04): Assets, $1,354,691 (M); gifts received, $2,223,500; expenditures, $880,000; total giving, $850,000; qualifying distributions, $850,000; giving activities include $850,000 for 3 grants (high: $500,000; low: $100,000).
Fields of interest: Higher education; Family services.
Limitations: Applications not accepted. Giving primarily in OH and MI. No grants to individuals.
Application information: Contributes only to pre-selected organizations.
Officers and Trustees:* Richard Neu,* Pres.; Cheryl Neu,* Secy.; Troy Decello,* Treas.
EIN: 201413635

380
The Cromarty Foundation, Inc.
500 Woodward Ave., Ste. 2500
Detroit, MI 48226

Established in 2000 in MI.
Donor: Inverness Counsel, Inc.
Grantmaker type: Independent foundation.
Financial data (yr. ended 12/31/04): Assets, $167,426 (M); gifts received, $50,000; expenditures, $10,742; total giving, $5,800; qualifying distributions, $8,247; giving activities include $5,800 for grants.
Limitations: Applications not accepted. Giving primarily in NY. No grants to individuals.
Application information: Contributes only to pre-selected organizations.

Officers: Mary L.C. Flood, Pres.; Elizabeth D. Mooney, V.P.; Mark J. Stasa, Secy.; Roberty B. Deans III, Treas.
EIN: 383565496

381
Cronin Foundation
203 E. Michigan Ave.
Marshall, MI 49068 (269) 781-9851
Contact: Ronald J. DeGraw, Secy.-Treas.

Established in 1990 in MI.
Donors: Elizabeth Cronin†; Mary Virginia Cronin†.
Grantmaker type: Independent foundation.
Financial data (yr. ended 12/31/05): Assets, $12,447,945 (M); gifts received, $562,791; expenditures, $320,220; total giving, $311,217; qualifying distributions, $311,217; giving activities include $311,217 for 12 grants (high: $100,000; low: $900).
Purpose and activities: Giving primarily for educational, social, economic, civic, and cultural needs of the community contained within the Marshall, MI, school district.
Fields of interest: Education; Environment; Hospitals (general); Medical care, rehabilitation; Recreation, parks/playgrounds; Athletics/sports, soccer; Youth development, centers/clubs; Human services; Community development.
Type of support: Building/renovation; Equipment; Program development.
Limitations: Giving limited to Calhoun County, MI. No grants to individuals.
Application information: Letter or telephone for guidelines.
Initial approach: Proposal
Deadline(s): Mar. 1, June 1, Sept. 1, and Dec. 1
Board meeting date(s): Following application deadlines and as needed
Final notification: Following board meeting
Officers and Directors:* Helen L. Hensick,* Pres.; Monica Anderson,* V.P.; Ronald J. DeGraw,* Secy.-Treas.; Duane Cowgill; Joyce K. Phillips.
Number of staff: 1 part-time professional.
EIN: 382908362

382
The Carl and Lee Croskey Foundation, Inc.
c/o Carl Croskey, Pres.
180 Country Club Dr.
Grosse Pointe Farms, MI 48236-2902

Established in 2001 in MI.
Donor: Carl Croskey.
Grantmaker type: Independent foundation.
Financial data (yr. ended 11/30/05): Assets, $458,548 (M); expenditures, $67,518; total giving, $50,650; qualifying distributions, $50,650; giving activities include $50,650 for 6 grants (high: $24,000; low: $100).
Fields of interest: Secondary school/education; Women, centers/services; Christian agencies & churches; Roman Catholic agencies & churches.
Type of support: General/operating support.
Limitations: Applications not accepted. Giving primarily in MI; some giving also in IL. No grants to individuals.
Application information: Contributes only to pre-selected organizations.

Officers and Directors:* Carl Croskey,* Chair., Pres. and Treas.; Lee Croskey,* V.P. and Secy.
EIN: 300002523

383
The Crowther Foundation
8253 New Haven Way
Canton, MI 48187

Donors: H. Richard Crowther; Nancy A. Crowther.
Grantmaker type: Independent foundation.
Financial data (yr. ended 12/31/04): Assets, $838,043 (M); gifts received, $35,000; expenditures, $57,516; total giving, $53,500; qualifying distributions, $57,516; giving activities include $53,500 for 8 grants (high: $10,000; low: $1,000).
Purpose and activities: Giving for youth activities, including clubs, counseling, and athletic programs.
Fields of interest: Athletics/sports, training; Boys & girls clubs; Youth development.
Limitations: Applications not accepted. Giving limited to PA, with emphasis on Reading. No grants to individuals.
Application information: Contributes only to pre-selected organizations.
Officers: H. Richard Crowther, Pres.; Nancy H. Crowther, V.P.; Brian V. Howe, Secy.; Timothy Richard Crowther, Treas.
EIN: 383353260

384
CSO, Inc.
c/o G. Robert Reichenbach
3155 Big Beaver Rd., Ste. 207
Troy, MI 48084

Established in 1999 in MI.
Grantmaker type: Independent foundation.
Financial data (yr. ended 12/31/05): Assets, $597,048 (M); expenditures, $28,374; total giving, $27,370; qualifying distributions, $28,374; giving activities include $27,370 for grants.
Limitations: Applications not accepted. Giving primarily in MI. No grants to individuals.
Application information: Contributes only to pre-selected organizations.
Officers: G. Robert Reichenbach, Pres.; Hemmat Toma, V.P.
EIN: 383433075

385
William Alexander Fleet Culver American Legion Scholarship Trust
c/o Fifth Third Bank
P.O. Box 3636
Grand Rapids, MI 49503
Application addresses: c/o Brenda Sheldon, 701 N. School St., Culver, IN 46511, tel.: (219) 842-3391, c/o John Babcock, Culver Educational Foundation, Culver, IN 4651, tel.: (219) 842-7000

Established in AL.
Grantmaker type: Independent foundation.
Financial data (yr. ended 12/31/05): Assets, $7,904 (M); expenditures, $2,050; total giving, $0; qualifying distributions, $0.
Purpose and activities: Scholarship awards limited to students of Culver Community School Corp., IN.
Fields of interest: Higher education, college.

Type of support: Scholarships—to individuals.
Limitations: Giving limited to Culver, IN.
Application information: Application form required.
 Deadline(s): Apr. 15
Trustee: Fifth Third Bank.
EIN: 351844698

386
The Cummings Fund
c/o Hendon & Slate
P.O. Box 9
Fremont, MI 49412
Application address: c/o Michael Kunzler, Exec. Dir.,
2907 Belknap Ave., N.E., Grand Rapids, MI 49505,
tel: (616) 447-2077, FAX: (616) 447-0385,
E-mail: MLKunzler@cummingsfund.org; URL: http://
www.cummingsfund.org

Established in 1963 in MI.
Donors: Harrington M. Cummings; Gay C.
Cummings.
Grantmaker type: Independent foundation.
Financial data (yr. ended 12/31/05): Assets,
$2,794,299 (M); gifts received, $13,300;
expenditures, $143,372; total giving, $90,300;
qualifying distributions, $90,300; giving activities
include $90,300 for grants.
Purpose and activities: The fund is dedicated to
promoting individual responsibility,
self-improvement, and civic duty through strategic
investments in private charity. Its work supports
entrepreneurial solutions to social problems,
eliminating dependence on governmental programs
by actively aiding groups with measurable and
sustainable long-term gains for individuals in need.
Fields of interest: Performing arts, theater;
Housing/shelter, rehabilitation; Human services;
Youth, services.
Type of support: Grants to individuals; Seed money;
Capital campaigns; General/operating support.
Limitations: Giving in the U.S., with some emphasis
on MI, TX, and CO.
Application information: See fund's Web site for
application guidelines.
 Initial approach: Completed applications should
  be issued as a plain-text email (no
  attachments). Applications may also be filled
  out and faxed or mailed
 Deadline(s): None, grant applications are
  reviewed on a continuing basis
 Final notification: Grant awards made at year end
Officers: Mimi F. Cummings, Pres.; Samuel M.
Cummings, Treas.
Directors: Andrew M. Cummings; Gay C. Cummings;
Liss Flaherty.
EIN: 386079631

387
The Louis Cunningham Scholarship Foundation
21411 Civic Center Dr., Ste. 206
Southfield, MI 48076   (248) 263-7630
Contact: Louis E. Cunningham, Treas.

Established in 1997 in MI.
Grantmaker type: Independent foundation.
Financial data (yr. ended 12/31/04): Assets,
$144,489 (M); gifts received, $20; expenditures,
$11,577; total giving, $11,500; qualifying
distributions, $11,500; giving activities include
$11,500 for grants to individuals.

Type of support: Scholarships—to individuals.
Limitations: Giving primarily in MI.
Application information: Application form required.
 Deadline(s): Varies
Officers: Kenneth A. McKanders, Pres.; Walter
Watkins, V.P.; Louis E. Cunningham, Treas.
EIN: 383197360

388
William G. Currie Foundation
2801 E. Beltline N.E.
Grand Rapids, MI 49505

Established in 1985 in MI.
Donors: William G. Currie; Universal Forest
Products, Inc.
Grantmaker type: Independent foundation.
Financial data (yr. ended 12/31/05): Assets,
$1,672,784 (M); gifts received, $74,000;
expenditures, $267,809; total giving, $247,588;
qualifying distributions, $247,588; giving activities
include $247,588 for 91 grants (high: $100,000;
low: $15).
Fields of interest: Education; Children/youth,
services; Human services; Religion.
Limitations: Applications not accepted. Giving
primarily in Grand Rapids, MI. No grants to
individuals.
Application information: Contributes only to
pre-selected organizations.
Officers and Director:* William G. Currie,* Pres.;
Matthew J. Missad, Secy.-Treas.
EIN: 382641091
Selected grants: The following grants were reported
in 2004.
$100,000 to Magi, The, Grand Rapids, MI.
$3,300 to Michigan State University, East Lansing,
 MI.
$1,000 to Grand Rapids Youth Commonwealth,
 Grand Rapids, MI.
$1,000 to Hope Network Foundation, Grand Rapids,
 MI.
$925 to Forest Hills Educational Foundation, Grand
 Rapids, MI.
$500 to Education Freedom Fund, Grand Rapids,
 MI.
$500 to YMCA of Greater Grand Rapids, Grand
 Rapids, MI.
$500 to YWCA of Grand Rapids, Grand Rapids, MI.
$400 to Grand Rapids Symphony, Grand Rapids, MI.
$250 to Grand Rapids Community Foundation,
 Grand Rapids, MI.

389
Robbie Curtis Charitable Foundation
P.O. Box 766
Jackson, MI 49204-0766

Established in 2003 in MI.
Donors: Philip J. Curtis; Denise R. Curtis.
Grantmaker type: Independent foundation.
Financial data (yr. ended 12/31/05): Assets,
$86,860 (M); gifts received, $14,100;
expenditures, $2,544; total giving, $2,500;
qualifying distributions, $2,500; giving activities
include $2,500 for grants.
Limitations: Applications not accepted. No grants to
individuals.
Application information: Contributes only to
pre-selected organizations.

Trustees: Denise R. Curtis; Philip J. Curtis.
EIN: 300201166

390
Glenn D. Curtis Edmore Trust
c/o JPMorgan Chase Bank, N.A.
P.O. Box 1308
Milwaukee, WI 53201

Established in MI.
Donor: Glenn D. Curtis Family Trust.
Grantmaker type: Independent foundation.
Financial data (yr. ended 5/31/05): Assets,
$2,676,148 (M); expenditures, $282,921; total
giving, $265,650; qualifying distributions,
$270,507; giving activities include $265,650 for
grants.
Purpose and activities: Support only for the Village
of Edmore, MI.
Fields of interest: Community development.
Type of support: General/operating support.
Limitations: Applications not accepted. Giving
limited to Edmore, MI. No grants to individuals.
Application information: Contributes only to a
pre-selected organization.
Trustee: JPMorgan Chase Bank, N.A.
EIN: 386173942

391
The Cecelia B. and Kenneth B. Cutler Foundation
10 Westway
Bronxville, NY 10708

Established in 1986 in NY.
Donors: Cecelia B. Cutler; Kenneth B. Cutler.
Grantmaker type: Independent foundation.
Financial data (yr. ended 11/30/05): Assets,
$319,780 (M); expenditures, $11,315; total giving,
$10,202; qualifying distributions, $10,202; giving
activities include $10,202 for grants.
Fields of interest: Higher education.
Limitations: Applications not accepted. Giving
primarily in NY and PA; some giving also in MI. No
grants to individuals.
Application information: Contributes only to
pre-selected organizations.
Trustees: Cecelia B. Cutler; Kenneth B. Cutler.
EIN: 133316060

392
The Robert and Elizabeth Cutler Foundation
590 N. Glenwood Ave.
North Muskegon, MI 49445-2440

Established in 1986 in MI.
Grantmaker type: Independent foundation.
Financial data (yr. ended 12/31/05): Assets,
$280,307 (M); expenditures, $16,979; total giving,
$15,480; qualifying distributions, $15,480; giving
activities include $15,480 for grants.
Fields of interest: Christian agencies & churches.
Limitations: Applications not accepted. Giving
primarily in the Muskegon, MI, area. No grants to
individuals.
Application information: Contributes only to
pre-selected organizations.
Officers: Robert J. Cutler,* Pres.; Elizabeth M.
Cutler,* Secy.-Treas.

Director: Robert Jefferson Cutler.
EIN: 382709484

393
The Allen B. Cutting Foundation
c/o Planning Alternatives
838 W. Long Lake Rd., Rm. 100
Bloomfield Hills, MI 48302

Established in 1996 in MI.
Donors: Joan L. Cutting; Margaret Cutting Manuel; Rebecca Cutting Broderick; Amy E. Cutting.
Grantmaker type: Independent foundation.
Financial data (yr. ended 12/31/04): Assets, $6,683,009 (M); expenditures, $220,031; total giving, $200,000; qualifying distributions, $200,000; giving activities include $200,000 for 2 grants (high: $100,000; low: $100,000).
Purpose and activities: Giving primarily to a Roman Catholic school and for family services.
Fields of interest: Elementary/secondary education; Family services, domestic violence.
Limitations: Applications not accepted. Giving primarily in Dallas, TX. No grants to individuals.
Application information: Contributes only to pre-selected organizations.
Officers: Joan L. Cutting, Pres.; Margaret Cutting Manuel, V.P. and Secy.; Rebecca Cutting Broderick, V.P. and Treas.; Amy E. Cutting, V.P.
EIN: 383319000

394
Mary Czado Catholic Education Fund
2112 Cawdor Ct.
Lansing, MI 48917 (517) 321-0440
Contact: Deborah J. Zale, Pres.

Established in 2002 in MI.
Grantmaker type: Independent foundation.
Financial data (yr. ended 12/31/04): Assets, $249,717 (M); expenditures, $42,938; total giving, $0; qualifying distributions, $0.
Purpose and activities: Scholarship awards to Christian students for higher education.
Fields of interest: Higher education; Christian agencies & churches.
Type of support: Scholarships—to individuals.
Application information: Application form required.
Deadline(s): None
Officers: Deborah J. Zale, Pres.; Jeanne Larvick, V.P.; Sheila M. Harper, Secy.-Treas.
EIN: 383269233

395
D.U. Memorial Foundation
2608 Traver Rd.
Ann Arbor, MI 48105-1297 (734) 663-3877
Contact: John Markiewicz, Pres.
Additional application address: c/o Will McGarrity, 1331 Hill St., Ann Arbor, MI 48104

Grantmaker type: Independent foundation.
Financial data (yr. ended 12/31/04): Assets, $14,956 (M); expenditures, $2,799; total giving, $2,000; qualifying distributions, $2,700; giving activities include $2,000 for 4 grants to individuals (high: $500; low: $500).
Purpose and activities: Scholarships only to students attending the University of Michigan.
Type of support: Scholarships—to individuals.

Limitations: Giving limited to students attending the University of Michigan, Ann Arbor.
Application information:
Initial approach: Letter
Deadline(s): May 31
Officer: John Markiewicz, Pres.
EIN: 386157774

396
Paul & Marjorie Dabney Foundation
16726 Country Knoll Dr.
Northville, MI 48167

Established in 1997 in MI.
Donor: Marjorie E. Dabney.
Grantmaker type: Independent foundation.
Financial data (yr. ended 12/31/05): Assets, $22,919 (M); gifts received, $3,000; expenditures, $2,387; total giving, $2,140; qualifying distributions, $2,140; giving activities include $2,140 for grants.
Limitations: Applications not accepted. Giving primarily in MI. No grants to individuals.
Application information: Contributes only to pre-selected organizations.
Officers: Marjorie E. Dabney, Pres.; Dennis Gabel, V.P.; Eugene M. Paulsen, Secy.-Treas.
EIN: 383308229

397
Robert & Jeanine Dagenais Foundation
1505 N. Lincoln Rd.
Escanaba, MI 49829 (906) 786-6834
Contact: Robert A. Dagenais, Pres.

Established in 1994 in MI.
Donor: Robert A. Dagenais.
Grantmaker type: Independent foundation.
Financial data (yr. ended 12/31/05): Assets, $867,298 (M); gifts received, $157,969; expenditures, $27,965; total giving, $26,983; qualifying distributions, $26,983; giving activities include $26,983 for grants.
Fields of interest: Hospitals (general); Heart & circulatory diseases; YM/YWCAs & YM/YWHAs; Family services; Federated giving programs.
Type of support: General/operating support; Building/renovation; Equipment; Program development; Scholarship funds.
Limitations: Giving primarily in the upper peninsula of MI. No grants to individuals.
Application information: Accepts CMF Common Grant Application Form. Application form required.
Deadline(s): None
Final notification: Within 60 days
Officers: Robert A. Dagenais, Pres.; Jeanine K. Dagenais, Secy.-Treas.
Trustees: Matthew A. Dagenais; Paul R. Dagenais; Timothy R. Dagenais.
EIN: 383195426

398
Dorothy U. Dalton Foundation, Inc.
c/o Greenleaf Trust
100 W. Michigan Ave., Ste. 100
Kalamazoo, MI 49007 (269) 388-9800
Contact: Ronald N. Kilgore, Secy.-Treas.

Incorporated in 1978 in MI as successor to Dorothy U. Dalton Foundation Trust.

Donor: Dorothy U. Dalton†.
Grantmaker type: Independent foundation.
Financial data (yr. ended 12/31/04): Assets, $38,574,100 (M); expenditures, $2,234,074; total giving, $2,077,442; qualifying distributions, $2,141,197; giving activities include $2,077,442 for 80 grants (high: $250,000; low: $1,000; average: $1,000–$15,000).
Purpose and activities: Emphasis on higher education, mental health, social service and youth agencies, and cultural programs.
Fields of interest: Performing arts; Performing arts, theater; Performing arts, music; Arts; Environment; Hospitals (general); Mental health/crisis services; Housing/shelter, development; Recreation, parks/playgrounds; Human services; Youth, services; Community development.
Type of support: General/operating support; Continuing support; Capital campaigns; Building/renovation; Equipment; Land acquisition; Debt reduction; Emergency funds; Program development; Seed money; Research; Matching/challenge support.
Limitations: Giving primarily in Kalamazoo County, MI. No support for religious organizations. No grants to individuals, or for annual campaigns, scholarships, fellowships, publications, or conferences; no loans.
Application information: Application form required.
Initial approach: Proposal
Copies of proposal: 5
Deadline(s): Submit proposal preferably in Apr. and Oct.
Board meeting date(s): May and Nov.
Final notification: 30 days after board meetings
Officers and Directors:* Suzanne D. Parish,* Pres.; Howard Kalleward,* V.P.; Ronald N. Kilgore,* Secy.-Treas.; Thompson Bennett.
EIN: 382240062

399
Opal Dancey Memorial Foundation
c/o Plante Moran Trust
27400 Northwestern Hwy.
Southfield, MI 48037
Contact: Sandra K. Campbell
Application address: c/o Betty D. Godard, Chair., 2637 Revere Rd., Akron, OH 44313;
E-mail: bethinbath@juno.com

Established in 1976 in MI.
Donor: Russell V. Dancey†.
Grantmaker type: Independent foundation.
Financial data (yr. ended 10/31/05): Assets, $2,228,919 (M); expenditures, $119,028; total giving, $105,000; qualifying distributions, $106,313; giving activities include $105,000 for 13 grants (high: $36,000; low: $3,000).
Fields of interest: Theological school/education.
Type of support: Scholarship funds.
Limitations: Giving primarily in the Great Lakes region, with emphasis on IL and OH.
Application information: Application form required.
Initial approach: Request application
Deadline(s): June 15
Board meeting date(s): July
Final notification: Aug. 15
Officers and Trustees:* Betty V. Godard,* Chair.; Susan Dudas,* Secy; Timothy F. Godard,* Treas.; David Dudas; Kathy Godard; Rev. Alice D. Murphy; Rev. Don Richards.
EIN: 386361282

400
Jack Danieleski Scholarship Fund
4688 Locust Rd.
Saginaw, MI 48604
Contact: John J. Danieleski, Jr., Tr.

Grantmaker type: Independent foundation.
Financial data (yr. ended 12/31/05): Assets, $32,186 (M); expenditures, $7,637; total giving, $3,000; qualifying distributions, $4,637; giving activities include $3,000 for 4 grants to individuals (high: $1,000; low: $500).
Purpose and activities: Scholarship awards for graduates of the Roscommon County High School, MI.
Fields of interest: Higher education.
Type of support: Scholarships—to individuals.
Limitations: Giving limited to residents of Roscommon, MI.
Application information: High school transcript, writing sample.
  Initial approach: Letter
  Deadline(s): May 21
Trustees: John J. Danieleski, Jr.; Roman Pacella; Robert Ranusch; Edward Rzycki.
EIN: 912166703

401
The Daoud Foundation
16010 19 Mile Rd., Ste. 102
Clinton Township, MI 48038-1141

Established in 1986 in MI.
Donor: Tarik S. Daoud.
Grantmaker type: Independent foundation.
Financial data (yr. ended 12/31/05): Assets, $247,996 (M); expenditures, $173,150; total giving, $172,000; qualifying distributions, $172,000; giving activities include $172,000 for 18 grants (high: $20,000; low: $2,500).
Fields of interest: Higher education; Health care; Human services; Roman Catholic agencies & churches.
Type of support: General/operating support; Capital campaigns; Building/renovation; Equipment; Scholarship funds.
Limitations: Applications not accepted. Giving primarily in Detroit, MI. No grants to individuals.
Application information: Contributes only to pre-selected organizations.
Trustees: Helen C. Daoud; Tarik S. Daoud; Michael J. Lazzara.
EIN: 382709932

402
Carolyn Darch Ministries, Inc.
154 E. Lovell Dr.
Troy, MI 48098-1573

Grantmaker type: Independent foundation.
Financial data (yr. ended 12/31/05): Assets, $836 (M); gifts received, $12,376; expenditures, $12,944; total giving, $0; qualifying distributions, $0.
Limitations: Applications not accepted. Giving primarily in MI. No grants to individuals.
Application information: Contributes only to pre-selected organizations.
Officers and Directors:* Carolyn Darch,* Pres.; Dennis Darch,* Secy.-Treas.
EIN: 383130189

403
The Dart Foundation
(formerly Solid Waste Management Foundation)
500 Hogsback Rd.
Mason, MI 48854-9547
Contact: James D. Lammers, V.P.

Established in 1989 in MI.
Donor: W.A. Dart Foundation.
Grantmaker type: Independent foundation.
Financial data (yr. ended 10/31/05): Assets, $3,838,086 (M); gifts received, $5,323,000; expenditures, $4,125,041; total giving, $3,859,666; qualifying distributions, $4,124,641; giving activities include $3,859,666 for 111 grants (high: $800,000; low: $250; average: $1,000–$100,000), and $250,355 for 4 foundation-administered programs.
Fields of interest: Performing arts, theater; Higher education; Education; Hospitals (general); Health organizations, association; Alzheimer's disease research; Boys & girls clubs; Human services; YM/YWCAs & YM/YWHAs; Children/youth, services; Federated giving programs; Engineering/technology; Public affairs.
Type of support: General/operating support; Continuing support; Building/renovation; Program development; Conferences/seminars; Publication; Curriculum development; Research; Matching/challenge support.
Limitations: Giving primarily in Sarasota, FL and central MI. No grants to individuals.
Application information: Application form not required.
  Initial approach: Letter
  Copies of proposal: 2
  Deadline(s): None
Officers and Directors:* William A. Dart,* Pres. and Secy.; Claire T. Dart,* V.P. and Treas.; Kenneth B. Dart,* V.P.; Robert C. Dart,* V.P.; James D. Lammers, V.P.
EIN: 382849841
Selected grants: The following grants were reported in 2004.
$550,000 to University of Washington, Seattle, WA. 3 grants: $100,000 (To endow a professorship), $200,000 to Dart Center for Journalism and Trauma, $250,000 to Dart Center for Journalism and Trauma.
$150,000 to Highfields, Onondaga, MI. For capital improvements.
$100,000 to Boys and Girls Club of Sarasota County, Sarasota, FL. For capital campaign.
$100,000 to Capital Region Community Foundation, Lansing, MI. For H.O.P.E. Scholarship program.
$100,000 to Education Foundation for Sarasota County, Sarasota, FL. For mobile science lab project and Academic Olympics.
$100,000 to YMCA, Sarasota Family, Sarasota, FL. To build three new residences at Renaissance Ranch.
$50,000 to American Cave Conservation Association, Horse Cave, KY. For American Cave and Karsi Center.
$50,000 to Hospice of Lansing, Lansing, MI. For construction of Hospice Residence.

404
M. E. Davenport Foundation
415 E. Fulton St., Warren Hall, Main Fl.
Grand Rapids, MI 49503 (616) 732-1098
Contact: Margaret E. Moceri, Chair. and C.E.O

FAX: (616) 732-1147;
E-mail: pmoceri@davenport.edu; URL: http://www.medavenport.org

Established in 1986 in MI.
Donors: Robert W. and Margaret D. Sneden Foundation; Margaret Moceri; Gregory Moceri; Kathleen Sneden; Mary Sneden Sullivan; Watson Pierce; Elsie Pierce; Barbara DeMoor.
Grantmaker type: Independent foundation.
Financial data (yr. ended 9/30/05): Assets, $14,135,534 (M); gifts received, $1,358; expenditures, $913,649; total giving, $664,979; qualifying distributions, $765,621; giving activities include $664,979 for 12 grants (high: $533,979; low: $1,000).
Purpose and activities: Support primarily for private institutions of higher education, and specific social and community needs, usually related to business education, training, employment, and community stability, such as housing.
Fields of interest: Higher education; Employment, training; Youth development, business.
Type of support: Building/renovation; Capital campaigns; Program development; Seed money; Curriculum development.
Limitations: Giving primarily in western lower MI. No support for religious or political agendas. No grants to individuals, debt retirement, and taxable organizations or activities.
Publications: Application guidelines; Annual report; Financial statement; Grants list; Occasional report.
Application information: Application form required.
  Initial approach: Letter
  Copies of proposal: 1
  Deadline(s): None
  Board meeting date(s): Triannually
  Final notification: 30-45 days
Officers and Trustees:* Margaret E. Moceri,* Chair. and C.E.O.; Gregory C. Moceri, V.P.; Mary P. Sullivan, Secy.; Kathleen M. Sneden; Marcia A. Sneden.
Number of staff: 2 full-time professional.
EIN: 382646809

405
Robert J. Daverman Foundation
c/o The Northern Trust Co.
P.O. Box 803878
Chicago, IL 60680

Established in IL.
Donors: Robert J. Daverman‡; Edward H. Daverman.
Grantmaker type: Independent foundation.
Financial data (yr. ended 12/31/05): Assets, $2,366,908 (M); expenditures, $108,798; total giving, $83,000; qualifying distributions, $83,000; giving activities include $83,000 for grants.
Fields of interest: Arts; Education; Health care; Community development; Religion.
Limitations: Applications not accepted. Giving primarily in Grand Rapids, MI. No grants to individuals.
Application information: Contributes only to pre-selected organizations.
Trustee: James Daverman; Robert W. Daverman; Carl Dufandach; The Northern Trust Co.
EIN: 386073572

406
William Davidson Foundation
2300 Harmon Rd.
Auburn Hills, MI 48326-1714

Established in 2005 in MI.
Donor: William M. Davidson.
Grantmaker type: Independent foundation.
Financial data (yr. ended 12/31/05): Assets, $100,134 (M); gifts received, $100,000; expenditures, $0; total giving, $0; qualifying distributions, $0.
Limitations: Applications not accepted. No grants to individuals.
Application information: Contributes only to pre-selected organizations.
Officers and Directors: * William M. Davidson,* Chair.; Jonathan Aaron,* Pres.; Rose Calcaterra,* Secy.-Treas.; Ethan Davidson; Karen Davidson.
EIN: 203899187

407
Isaac and Dora Davis Family Reunion, Inc.
713 Ferry St.
P.O. Box 874
Niles, MI 49120-0874

Established in 2003 in MI.
Donor: Nann Davis.
Grantmaker type: Independent foundation.
Financial data (yr. ended 12/31/04): Assets, $81,638 (M); gifts received, $2,477; expenditures, $2,732; total giving, $500; qualifying distributions, $500; giving activities include $500 for grants to individuals.
Type of support: Scholarships—to individuals.
Officer and Director: * Evelyn Davis-Fleming,* Chair.
EIN: 582597339

408
The John R. & M. Margrite Davis Foundation
40700 Woodward Ave., Ste. A
Bloomfield Hills, MI 48304
Contact: Raymond C. Cunningham, Jr., Pres.
Application address: c/o Raymond C. Cunningham, Jr., 85 Plantation Dr., Sea Pines Plantation, Hilton Head, SC 29928

Established in 1955 in MI.
Donors: John R. Davis†; M. Margrite Davis.
Grantmaker type: Independent foundation.
Financial data (yr. ended 12/31/04): Assets, $9,363,502 (M); expenditures, $232,837; total giving, $198,600; qualifying distributions, $201,823; giving activities include $198,600 for 35 grants (high: $30,000; low: $100).
Fields of interest: Higher education; Hospitals (general); Medical research, institute; Human services; Children/youth, services.
Type of support: Continuing support; Annual campaigns; Capital campaigns; Building/renovation; Research.
Limitations: Giving primarily in MI and SC. No grants to individuals.
Application information:
  Initial approach: Letter
  Copies of proposal: 1
  Deadline(s): None
  Board meeting date(s): Dec.

Officers and Trustees: * Raymond C. Cunningham, Jr., Pres. and Treas.; Deborah Sue Cunningham,* Secy.; Debra Cunningham; John E. Grenke; James H. LoPrete.
EIN: 386058593

409
Jean M. Davis Trust
c/o Elmira Sundell
3390 Hazelton Ave.
Rochester Hills, MI 48307-4922

Grantmaker type: Independent foundation.
Financial data (yr. ended 12/31/05): Assets, $67,331 (M); expenditures, $24,718; total giving, $21,000; qualifying distributions, $21,000; giving activities include $21,000 for grants.
Purpose and activities: Scholarships for veterinary students attending Michigan State University, Ohio State University, or Purdue University.
Fields of interest: Veterinary medicine.
Type of support: Scholarships—to individuals.
Limitations: Applications not accepted. Giving primarily in MI; some giving also in IN and OH.
Application information: Unsolicited requests for funds not accepted.
Trustees: Franklin M. Carmona; Grace H. Harold; David R. Smith; Albert Sundell; Elmira Sundell.
EIN: 596828711

410
John and Jeanine Dawson Foundation
7400 E. McCormick Pkwy., Ste. B200
Scottsdale, AZ 85258

Established in 2000 in AZ.
Donor: John Dawson.
Grantmaker type: Independent foundation.
Financial data (yr. ended 12/31/05): Assets, $711,339 (M); expenditures, $272,720; total giving, $270,059; qualifying distributions, $271,495; giving activities include $270,059 for 9 grants (high: $100,000; low: $500).
Fields of interest: Arts; Education; Health organizations, association; Community development.
Limitations: Applications not accepted. Giving primarily in AZ, with some giving in Washington, DC and MI. No grants to individuals.
Application information: Contributes only to pre-selected organizations.
Officers: John Dawson, Pres.; Jeanine Dawson, V.P.; Kirk Mathers, Secy.-Treas.
EIN: 861011524
Selected grants: The following grants were reported in 2004.
$100,400 to Heritage Foundation, DC.
$50,000 to Cato Institute, DC.
$25,000 to American Heart Association, Tempe, AZ.
$25,000 to Center for First Principles, DC.
$25,000 to Goldwater Institute, Phoenix, AZ.
$1,200 to Beta Theta Pi Foundation, Oxford, OH. For Beta Leadership Fund.
$1,000 to Fund for American Studies, DC.

411
Joseph C. Day Foundation
P.O. Box 957
Bloomfield Hills, MI 48303-0957
Contact: Joseph C. Day, Tr.

Established in 2000 in MI.
Donor: Joseph C. Day.
Grantmaker type: Independent foundation.
Financial data (yr. ended 12/31/05): Assets, $1,402,186 (M); expenditures, $104,289; total giving, $95,600; qualifying distributions, $98,600; giving activities include $95,600 for grants.
Fields of interest: Education; Health care; Children/youth, services; Community development.
Limitations: Giving on a national basis, with some emphasis on CT, MA, and MI. No grants to individuals.
Application information:
  Initial approach: Letter
  Deadline(s): Dec. 31
Officer and Trustees: * Erin Day Healer,* Mgr.; Joseph C. Day; Shannon Day Drumm; Marri Fairbanks.
EIN: 383543776

412
Daystar Foundation
7188 Thornapple River Dr. S.E.
Caledonia, MI 49316 (616) 554-9557
Contact: Douglas J. Bouma, Pres.

Established in 1999 in MI.
Donors: Douglas J. Bouma; Sherri L. Bouma.
Grantmaker type: Independent foundation.
Financial data (yr. ended 12/31/05): Assets, $1,399 (M); expenditures, $10,580; total giving, $10,000; qualifying distributions, $10,000; giving activities include $10,000 for grants.
Fields of interest: Religion.
Limitations: Giving primarily in MI.
Application information:
  Initial approach: Letter
  Deadline(s): None
Officers: Douglas J. Bouma, Pres.; Sherri L. Bouma, Secy.-Treas.
EIN: 383486245

413
The de Irala Foundation
4922 Quincy Ct.
Saline, MI 48176-8727

Established in 1999 in MI.
Donors: Mikel de Irala; Barbara de Irala.
Grantmaker type: Independent foundation.
Financial data (yr. ended 12/31/05): Assets, $977 (M); gifts received, $5,000; expenditures, $7,000; total giving, $6,000; qualifying distributions, $6,000; giving activities include $6,000 for grants.
Limitations: Applications not accepted. No grants to individuals.
Application information: Contributes only to pre-selected organizations.
Officers: Mikel de Irala, Pres.; Barbara de Irala, V.P.; K. de Irala, Secy.
EIN: 383478204

414
The Dean Family Foundation
5208 Sunset Dr.
Midland, MI 48640-2536

Established in 2001 in MI.
Donors: Dale T. Dean; Judith T. Dean.
Grantmaker type: Independent foundation.

Financial data (yr. ended 12/31/05): Assets, $138,314 (M); expenditures, $7,385; total giving, $6,800; qualifying distributions, $6,800; giving activities include $6,800 for grants.
Limitations: Applications not accepted. No grants to individuals.
Application information: Contributes only to pre-selected organizations.
Officers and Trustees:* Dale T. Dean,* Pres.; Heather Dahley,* V.P.; Jennifer Rose,* Secy.; Judith T. Dean,* Treas.; Brian Dahley; Chris Rose.
EIN: 383631938

415
Debower Foundation Charitable Trust
P.O. Box 479
Muskegon, MI 49443
Contact: Charles E. Silky, Jr., Tr.
Application address: P.O. Box 1242, Muskegon, MI 49443-1242, tel.: (616) 726-4853

Grantmaker type: Independent foundation.
Financial data (yr. ended 12/31/04): Assets, $62,972 (M); expenditures, $11,496; total giving, $3,953; qualifying distributions, $7,615; giving activities include $3,953 for grants.
Fields of interest: Higher education.
Type of support: Scholarship funds.
Limitations: Giving primarily in MI. No grants to individuals.
Application information: Application form required.
  Deadline(s): None
Trustees: Cathy Houseman; Christine O'Connell; Charles E. Silky, Jr.
EIN: 386475514

416
The DeBruyn Foundation
c/o The Huntington National Bank
101 E. Main Ave.
Zeeland, MI 49464-1757
Contact: Robert D. DeBruyn, Tr.
Application address: c/o DeBruyn Produce Co., P.O. Box 76, Zeeland, MI 49464, tel.: (616) 772-2436

Established in 1961 in MI.
Donor: Robert D. DeBruyn.
Grantmaker type: Independent foundation.
Financial data (yr. ended 12/31/04): Assets, $275,757 (M); gifts received, $5,600; expenditures, $20,328; total giving, $16,100; qualifying distributions, $18,212; giving activities include $16,100 for grants.
Fields of interest: Secondary school/education; Higher education; Health care; Human services; International development; Christian agencies & churches.
Limitations: Giving primarily in Grand Rapids, MI. No grants to individuals.
Application information:
  Initial approach: Letter
  Deadline(s): None
Trustees: Robert D. DeBruyn; Linda Pynnonen; The Huntington National Bank.
EIN: 386056545

417
George S. and Helen G. Deffenbaugh Foundation
5842 E. Millerway Rd.
Bloomfield Hills, MI 48301
Application address: c/o Joellyn D. Kuhn, 30100 Telegraph Rd., Ste. 337, Bingham Farms, MI 4805-5807

Established in 1991 in MI.
Grantmaker type: Independent foundation.
Financial data (yr. ended 12/31/04): Assets, $4,932,828 (M); expenditures, $207,679; total giving, $191,576; qualifying distributions, $190,536; giving activities include $191,576 for 14 grants (high: $75,000; low: $500).
Fields of interest: Performing arts; Hospitals (general); Human services; Christian agencies & churches.
Type of support: Scholarship funds; General/operating support; Building/renovation.
Limitations: Giving primarily in MI.
Application information: Application form not required.
  Initial approach: Letter
  Copies of proposal: 1
  Deadline(s): Dec. 31
  Board meeting date(s): Quarterly
Officer: Joellyn D. Kuhn, Pres. and Secy.-Treas.
Number of staff: 3 part-time professional.
EIN: 383117862
Selected grants: The following grants were reported in 2004.
$75,000 to Detroit Rotary Foundation, Detroit, MI. For Outside Historic Lighting Project.
$48,591 to Furniture Bank of Oakland County, Pontiac, MI. 2 grants: $28,591 (To purchase truck), $20,000 (For furniture pick up program).
$37,500 to Brighton Hospital, Brighton, MI. To build serenity garden.
$5,000 to North Oakland SCAMP Funding Corporation, Clarkston, MI. For summer camps scholarships.
$5,000 to Special Olympics Michigan, Mount Pleasant, MI. For state winter games.
$3,000 to Saint Andrews by the Lake Episcopal Church, Harrisville, MI.
$2,500 to Scarab Club, Detroit, MI. For school music programs.
$600 to Grace Christian Church, Warren, MI. For church mission trip to California.
$500 to Boy Scouts of America, Clinton Valley Council, Pontiac, MI. For camp scholarships.

418
Defoe Family Foundation
3050 Hathaway Dr. S.E.
Grand Rapids, MI 49506
Contact: James B. Defoe, Pres.

Established in 1999 in MI.
Donor: James B. Defoe.
Grantmaker type: Independent foundation.
Financial data (yr. ended 12/31/05): Assets, $244,533 (M); gifts received, $22,779; expenditures, $3,604; total giving, $0; qualifying distributions, $0.
Fields of interest: Protestant agencies & churches.
Limitations: Applications not accepted. Giving primarily in Grand Rapids, MI. No grants to individuals.
Application information: Contributes only to pre-selected organizations.

Officers: James B. Defoe, Pres. and Treas.; Susanne R. Defoe, V.P. and Secy.
EIN: 383505281

419
Degroot Family Foundation
5530 N. Coloma Rd.
P.O. Box 934
Coloma, MI 49038

Established in 2002 in MI.
Donor: Louise Degroot.
Grantmaker type: Independent foundation.
Financial data (yr. ended 12/31/05): Assets, $1,133,344 (M); expenditures, $333,234; total giving, $320,000; qualifying distributions, $323,643; giving activities include $320,000 for 6 grants (high: $100,000; low: $10,000).
Purpose and activities: Giving for cancer research and aid to disenfranchised women and children.
Fields of interest: Pediatrics; Cancer research; Housing/shelter, homeless; Children/youth, services.
Limitations: Applications not accepted. Giving on a national basis. No grants to individuals.
Application information: Contributes only to pre-selected organizations.
Officers: Louise Degroot, Chair.; Shirley Leith, Pres.; Eric Brown, Secy.
EIN: 061654753

420
The Laura Deibel and Tim Allen Foundation
30600 Northwestern Hwy., Ste. 245
Farmington Hills, MI 48334

Established in 1999 in MI.
Donor: Timothy Dick.
Grantmaker type: Independent foundation.
Financial data (yr. ended 12/31/04): Assets, $2,801 (M); expenditures, $0; total giving, $0; qualifying distributions, $0.
Purpose and activities: Giving primarily to museums and for human services.
Fields of interest: Media/communications; Museums; Education; Cancer; Food services; Salvation Army; Homeless.
Limitations: Giving primarily in CA; giving also in MI.
Officers: Laura Deibel, Pres. and Secy.; Timothy Dick, V.P. and Treas.
EIN: 383446053

421
The Dejard P. Foundation, Inc.
911 E. Myrtle Ave.
Flint, MI 48505

Established in 2001 in MI.
Donor: A.J. Porter.
Grantmaker type: Independent foundation.
Financial data (yr. ended 6/30/05): Assets, $127,007 (M); gifts received, $64,188; expenditures, $11,166; total giving, $7,770; qualifying distributions, $7,770; giving activities include $7,770 for grants.
Limitations: Applications not accepted. No grants to individuals.
Application information: Contributes only to pre-selected organizations.

Directors: Arthur J. Pointer; Demark Pointer; Lillian Joan Pointer; P.J. Pointer.
EIN: 383623353

422
DeKorne Family Foundation
c/o Jack M. DeKorne
1825 Meadowfield Dr. N.E.
Grand Rapids, MI 49505-4802

Established in 1994.
Donors: Jack M. DeKorne; Betsy DeKorne.
Grantmaker type: Independent foundation.
Financial data (yr. ended 12/31/05): Assets, $178,023 (M); gifts received, $10,000; expenditures, $9,177; total giving, $9,000; qualifying distributions, $9,000; giving activities include $9,000 for grants.
Fields of interest: International relief; Christian agencies & churches.
International interests: India.
Type of support: Building/renovation.
Limitations: Applications not accepted. Giving on a national basis, primarily for the benefit of India. No grants to individuals.
Application information: Contributes only to pre-selected organizations.
Officers: Jack M. DeKorne, Pres.; Betsy DeKorne, V.P.
Directors: Jack E. DeKorne; Jane E. DeKorne; Joan E. Ranney.
EIN: 383210772

423
The Mignon Sherwood Delano Foundation
c/o Dietrich, Smith, Howard & VanderRoest
P.O. Box 50646
Kalamazoo, MI 49005 (269) 344-9236
Contact: Philip W. Dietrich, Dir.

Incorporated in 1985 in MI.
Donor: Mignon Sherwood Delano†.
Grantmaker type: Independent foundation.
Financial data (yr. ended 12/31/04): Assets, $4,356,794 (M); expenditures, $210,494; total giving, $173,470; qualifying distributions, $196,405; giving activities include $173,470 for 26 grants (high: $25,000; low: $1,400).
Fields of interest: Arts; Libraries (public); Reproductive health, family planning; Health care; Health organizations; Human services; Youth, services; Child development, services; Community development.
Type of support: General/operating support; Continuing support; Building/renovation; Equipment; Program development; Curriculum development.
Limitations: Giving limited to southwestern MI, with emphasis on Allegan County. No grants to individuals.
Application information: Application form required.
Copies of proposal: 3
Deadline(s): Second Tue. in Sept.
Officers: Bernard Riker, Pres.; Ellen Altamore, V.P.; G. Philip Dietrich, Secy.; Julie Sosnowski, Treas.
Directors: Rebecca Burnett; Philip W. Dietrich.
Trustee: National City Bank.
EIN: 382557743
Selected grants: The following grants were reported in 2004.

$18,000 to Allegan County Crisis Response Services, Allegan, MI. For operating support.
$16,095 to Allegan Area Arts Council, Allegan, MI. For program support.
$10,000 to Four-H Clubs of Allegan County, Allegan, MI. For program support.
$10,000 to Gildas Club Grand Rapids, Grand Rapids, MI. For program support.
$8,570 to Family Planning Association of Allegan County, Allegan, MI. For operating support.
$7,055 to Sylvias Place, Allegan, MI. For equipment.
$7,000 to Association for the Blind and Visually Impaired, Grand Rapids, MI. For operating support.
$5,000 to Center for Women in Transition, Holland, MI. For operating support.
$5,000 to Kairos Dwelling, Kalamazoo, MI. For operating support.
$2,200 to Kalamazoo Symphony Orchestra, Kalamazoo, MI. For program support.

424
Delta Foundation
c/o Michael O'Brien, Tr.
1249 Waukegan Rd.
Glenview, IL 60025-3077

Established in 1994 in IL.
Donor: Jean F. Deal.
Grantmaker type: Independent foundation.
Financial data (yr. ended 5/31/05): Assets, $4,700,245 (M); expenditures, $295,230; total giving, $204,999; qualifying distributions, $294,208; giving activities include $204,999 for 27 grants (high: $18,500; low: $833).
Fields of interest: Higher education; Education; Arthritis research; Recreation; Human services; YM/YWCAs & YM/YWHAs; Children, services; Community development; Christian agencies & churches.
Limitations: Applications not accepted. Giving primarily in IL and MI. No grants to individuals.
Application information: Contributes only to pre-selected organizations.
Trustees: Harmon B. Deal III; Jean F. Deal; Michael O'Brien; Nancy D. Walch.
EIN: 363917119
Selected grants: The following grants were reported in 2004.
$19,500 to Illinois College, Jacksonville, IL.
$19,500 to MacMurray College, Jacksonville, IL.
$15,638 to Evanston Northwestern Healthcare, Evanston, IL. For arthritis and rheumatology research.
$10,000 to YMCA, Sherwood Eddy Memorial, Jacksonville, IL. For general operating support.
$7,500 to Greater Saginaw Amateur Hockey Association, Saginaw, MI. For improvements to and new equipment for Saginaw Bay Ice Arena.
$5,000 to Saginaw Community Foundation, Saginaw, MI. For Thomas Township Parks Endowment.
$5,000 to West Shore Community College Foundation, Scottville, MI.
$2,000 to YMCA of Saginaw, Saginaw, MI. For Invest in Youth campaign.
$1,638 to Morgan-Scott Volunteer Health Clinic, Jacksonville, IL.
$1,000 to United Way, Prairieland, Jacksonville, IL.

425
Delta Theta Phi Metropolitan Detroit Alumni Senate Foundation
6905 Telegraph Rd., No. 125
Bloomfield Hills, MI 48301 (248) 644-7222
Contact: Edgar W. Pugh, Jr., Pres.

Established in 1998 in MI.
Grantmaker type: Independent foundation.
Financial data (yr. ended 12/31/05): Assets, $20,887 (M); gifts received, $1,050; expenditures, $1,082; total giving, $1,050; qualifying distributions, $1,050; giving activities include $1,050 for grants.
Purpose and activities: Scholarship awards to members in good standing of Delta Theta Phi Law Fraternity attending Detroit College of Law, Wayne State University, or the University of Detroit Law School.
Fields of interest: Higher education; Higher education, college.
Type of support: Scholarship funds.
Limitations: Applications not accepted. Giving limited to MI. No grants to individuals.
Application information: Unsolicited requests for funds not accepted.
Officers and Directors:* Edgar W. Pugh, Jr.,* Pres.; Movses J. Shrikian,* Secy.; H. Rollin Allen,* Treas.; Nancy Aishie A. Abraham; Samuel Paul Huth; Harold W. Oehmke.
EIN: 383417689

426
The Demashkieh Foundation
26300 Telegraph Rd., 2nd Fl.
Southfield, MI 48034

Established in 2003.
Grantmaker type: Independent foundation.
Financial data (yr. ended 12/31/05): Assets, $24,162 (M); gifts received, $5,000; expenditures, $25,785; total giving, $25,170; qualifying distributions, $25,170; giving activities include $25,170 for grants.
Officer: Fadi Demashkieh, Pres.
EIN: 371461108

427
The Dennard Foundation
14510 Faust Ave.
Detroit, MI 48223

Established in 2004 in MI.
Grantmaker type: Independent foundation.
Financial data (yr. ended 12/31/04): Assets, $800 (M); gifts received, $800; expenditures, $0; total giving, $0; qualifying distributions, $0.
Limitations: Applications not accepted. No grants to individuals.
Application information: Contributes only to pre-selected organizations.
Officers and Trustees:* Kevin J. Dennard,* Exec. Dir.; Valerie S. Dennard,* Secy.
EIN: 200381149

428
The Denniston Family Foundation
134 Green Bay Rd., Ste. 301
Winnetka, IL 60093

Grantmaker type: Independent foundation.
Financial data (yr. ended 12/31/05): Assets, $4,396 (M); expenditures, $600; total giving, $500; qualifying distributions, $500; giving activities include $500 for grants.
Fields of interest: Higher education.
Type of support: General/operating support.
Limitations: Giving primarily in IL and MI.
Trustees: James R. Denniston; John L. Denniston; Dorothy D. Moran.
EIN: 363486553

429

The John O. Deradoorian & Margaret C. Deradoorian Family Foundation

c/o Margaret C. Deradoorian
3974 Hillsdale Dr.
Auburn Hills, MI 48326-4303

Established in 1995 in MI.
Donor: Margaret C. Deradoorian.
Grantmaker type: Independent foundation.
Financial data (yr. ended 12/31/05): Assets, $4,467 (M); gifts received, $9,710; expenditures, $6,423; total giving, $5,000; qualifying distributions, $5,000; giving activities include $5,000 for grants.
Fields of interest: Christian agencies & churches.
Limitations: Applications not accepted. Giving primarily in MI. No grants to individuals.
Application information: Contributes only to pre-selected organizations.
Officers: Margaret C. Deradoorian, Pres.; David J. Deradoorian, Secy.
Directors: Daniel J. Deradoorian; John R. Deradoorian; Lori J. Deradoorian.
EIN: 383245499

430

DeRoy Testamentary Foundation

26999 Central Park Blvd., Ste. 160N
Southfield, MI 48076 (248) 827-0920
Contact: Julie A. Rodecker Holly, V.P. and Prog. Off.
FAX: (248) 827-0922; E-mail: deroyfdtn@aol.com

Established in 1979 in MI.
Donor: Helen L. DeRoy‡.
Grantmaker type: Independent foundation.
Financial data (yr. ended 12/31/05): Assets, $50,962,525 (M); expenditures, $2,966,903; total giving, $2,274,637; qualifying distributions, $2,560,810; giving activities include $2,274,637 for 127 grants (high: $700,000; low: $1,000).
Purpose and activities: Giving primarily for the arts, education, human services, and health care.
Fields of interest: Arts education; Arts; Higher education; Education; Hospitals (general); Human services; Children/youth, services; Jewish federated giving programs; Jewish agencies & temples.
Type of support: Program development.
Limitations: Giving primarily in MI. No grants to individuals.
Application information:
  Deadline(s): None
  Board meeting date(s): Monthly
Officers and Trustees:* Arthur Rodecker,* Pres.; Julie A.Rodecker Holly,* V.P. and Prog. Off.; Gregg D. Watkins,* Secy.; Sarah W. Keidan, Treas.
EIN: 382208833

Selected grants: The following grants were reported in 2003.
$100,000 to Detroit Science Center, Detroit, MI.
$100,000 to Detroit Zoological Society, Royal Oak, MI.
$100,000 to National Jewish Medical and Research Center, Denver, CO.
$97,000 to Oakland Family Services, Pontiac, MI.
$75,000 to Huron Valley-Sinai Hospital, Commerce Township, MI.
$70,000 to Hospice of Michigan, Detroit, MI.
$50,000 to Alzheimers Association, Southfield, MI.
$50,000 to YMCA of Metropolitan Detroit, Detroit, MI.
$35,000 to Childrens Museum Friends, Detroit, MI.
$30,000 to Detroit Symphony Orchestra, Detroit, MI.

431

Detroit Armory Corporation

1943 Common Rd.
Warren, MI 48092-2164
Contact: Edward L. Cox, Jr., Secy.-Treas.

Established in 1882 in MI.
Grantmaker type: Independent foundation.
Financial data (yr. ended 11/30/05): Assets, $1,206,285 (M); expenditures, $66,433; total giving, $37,500; qualifying distributions, $37,500; giving activities include $37,500 for grants.
Fields of interest: Hospitals (general); Health organizations, association; Heart & circulatory diseases; Heart & circulatory research; Human services.
Type of support: General/operating support; Continuing support; Equipment; Publication; In-kind gifts; Matching/challenge support.
Limitations: Giving limited to MI, with emphasis on the metropolitan Detroit area. No grants to individuals or for scholarships; no loans.
Publications: Annual report; Biennial report (including application guidelines); Informational brochure.
Application information: Application form not required.
  Initial approach: Letter
  Copies of proposal: 2
  Deadline(s): None
  Board meeting date(s): As required
Officers and Directors:* Lonnie G. VanNoy,* Pres.; Stanley J. Wilk,* V.P.; Edward L. Cox, Jr.,* Secy.-Treas.; George A. Bronson; James F. Clark; Sylvin J. Gaynor; William R. Hardtke; Walter G. Hinckfoot, Jr.; Ruth A. Newman; Joseph G. Saad; Clarence E. Weinand.
Number of staff: 1 part-time professional.
EIN: 386066969

432

Detroit Chapter of the International Order of the King's Daughters & Sons

24901 Northwestern Hwy., Ste. 316
Southfield, MI 48075-2209

Established in 1994 in MI.
Donor: Evelyn G. Stephens‡.
Grantmaker type: Independent foundation.
Financial data (yr. ended 12/31/04): Assets, $1,857,034 (M); expenditures, $84,793; total giving, $61,600; qualifying distributions, $61,600;

---

giving activities include $61,600 for 12 grants (high: $10,000; low: $1,000).
Purpose and activities: Giving primarily for religion and human services.
Fields of interest: Health care; Human services; Salvation Army; Christian agencies & churches.
Limitations: Applications not accepted. Giving primarily in MI, with emphasis on Southfield and Detroit. No grants to individuals.
Application information: Contributes only to pre-selected organizations.
Officers: Helen Jefferson, Pres.; Rhoda Johnson, 1st V.P.; Olga Brocklehurst, 2nd V.P.; Marilyn Churchill, Recording Secy.; Betty Gordon, Corresponding Secy.; Sandra Baker, Treas.
EIN: 381358202

433

Detroit Golf Club Caddie Scholarship Foundation

201 W. Big Beaver Rd., Ste. 1020
Troy, MI 48084

Established in 2002 in MI.
Donor: Members of the Detroit Golf Club.
Grantmaker type: Independent foundation.
Financial data (yr. ended 12/31/04): Assets, $111,045 (M); gifts received, $62,855; expenditures, $16,858; total giving, $14,000; qualifying distributions, $14,000; giving activities include $14,000 for 7 grants to individuals (high: $2,000; low: $2,000).
Purpose and activities: The foundation awards scholarships toward college tuition to caddies at the Detroit Golf Club.
Type of support: Scholarships—to individuals.
Limitations: Giving primarily to residents of MI.
Application information: Scholarship candidates should begin the application process in May of their junior year of high school.
Officers: Randall Gillary, Pres.; Nancy Flynn, V.P.; William Mitchell III, Secy.; Leonard Winzer, Treas.
EIN: 300023878

434

Detroit Industrial School

21420 Greater Mack Ave.
St. Clair Shores, MI 48080-2353
Application address: c/o Projects Chair., 349 Notre Dame St., Grosse Pointe Park, MI 48230-1520

Established in MI.
Grantmaker type: Independent foundation.
Financial data (yr. ended 10/31/05): Assets, $1,485,610 (M); gifts received, $966; expenditures, $80,266; total giving, $74,775; qualifying distributions, $74,775; giving activities include $74,775 for grants.
Purpose and activities: Giving for children and youth services.
Fields of interest: Human services; American Red Cross; Youth, services.
Limitations: Giving limited to southeastern MI.
Application information: Request application form. Application form required.
  Deadline(s): Mar. 1 and Aug. 1
Officers: Marianne Endicott, Pres.; Marylou Wood, V.P.; Joanne Grierson, Recording Secy.; Lucinda Prost, Corresponding Secy.; Carol Lytle, Treas.
EIN: 381360534

435
Detroit Track and Field Old Timers
c/o Thomas W. Sledge
4221 Leslie St.
Detroit, MI   48238

Established in 2002 in MI.
Grantmaker type: Independent foundation.
Financial data (yr. ended 12/31/05): Assets, $3,609 (M); gifts received, $1,000; expenditures, $2,946; total giving, $1,015; qualifying distributions, $1,015; giving activities include $1,015 for grants.
Limitations: Giving primarily in Detroit, MI.
Officers: Allen Tellis, Pres.; John Telford, V.P.; Richard Ford, Secy.; Thomas W. Sledge, Treas.
EIN: 383397918

436
The Richard C. Devereaux Foundation
39533 Woodward Ave., Ste. 200
Bloomfield Hills, MI   48304

Donors: Mrs. Richard C. Devereaux; S.W. Smith; Adelyn Devereaux Trust.
Grantmaker type: Independent foundation.
Financial data (yr. ended 8/31/05): Assets, $6,930,655 (M); gifts received, $84,721; expenditures, $919,146; total giving, $852,500; qualifying distributions, $885,332; giving activities include $852,500 for 19 grants (high: $100,000; low: $10,000).
Purpose and activities: Giving primarily for education, health organizations, particularly for cancer research, and wildlife preservation; funding also for human services and for a public television station.
Fields of interest: Media, television; Higher education; Animals/wildlife, preservation/protection; Health organizations; Cancer research; Human services.
Type of support: General/operating support.
Limitations: Applications not accepted. Giving primarily in Washington, DC, IL, MI, and VA. No grants to individuals.
Application information: Contributes only to pre-selected organizations.
Officers: Leslie C. Devereaux, Pres. and Treas.; Sidney W. Smith, Jr., V.P.; Curtis J. Mann, Secy.
EIN: 382638858
Selected grants: The following grants were reported in 2003.
$100,000 to Barbara Ann Karmanos Cancer Institute, Detroit, MI. For operating support.
$90,000 to Paralyzed Veterans of America, DC. For operating support.
$60,000 to Cancer Research and Prevention Foundation, Alexandria, VA. For operating support.
$50,000 to Alzheimers Association, Chicago, IL. For operating support.
$40,000 to World Wildlife Fund, DC. For general support.
$37,500 to Nature Conservancy, Baltimore, MD. For operating support.
$35,000 to African Wildlife Foundation, DC. For operating support.
$15,000 to National Geographic Society, DC. For operating support.
$10,000 to Detroit Educational Television Foundation-W T V S Channel 56, Detroit, MI. For operating support.

$10,000 to Hospice of Michigan, Detroit, MI. For operating support.

437
The DeVlieg Foundation
(formerly The Charles DeVlieg Foundation)
500 Woodward Ave., Ste. 2500
Detroit, MI   48226
Contact: Curtis J. DeRoo, Secy.-Treas.

Incorporated in 1961 in MI.
Donors: Charles B. DeVlieg†; Charles R. DeVlieg†; Kathryn S. DeVlieg†; DeVlieg Machine Co.
Grantmaker type: Independent foundation.
Financial data (yr. ended 12/31/04): Assets, $9,175,426 (M); gifts received, $4,000; expenditures, $614,350; total giving, $368,500; qualifying distributions, $475,338; giving activities include $368,500 for 25 grants (high: $87,000; low: $1,000).
Purpose and activities: Support largely for higher and other education, including grants to a university for fellowships and a scholarship program for engineering, wildlife education, youth agencies, the arts, environmental organizations, and science and technology.
Fields of interest: Arts; Higher education; Engineering school/education; Environment, natural resources; Environment; Youth, services; Engineering/technology; Engineering; Science.
Type of support: General/operating support; Professorships; Scholarship funds.
Limitations: Giving primarily in ID, southeastern MI, and WA. No grants to individuals, or for endowment funds; no loans.
Publications: Annual report (including application guidelines).
Application information: Application form required.
Initial approach: Letter
Copies of proposal: 2
Deadline(s): None
Board meeting date(s): Semiannually
Officers and Directors:* Janet DeVlieg Pope,* Pres.; Curtis J. DeRoo,* Secy.-Treas.; Julia DeVlieg; Richard A. Jerue; Gary Stetler; Gerald Stetler.
Number of staff: 1 part-time professional.
EIN: 386075696
Selected grants: The following grants were reported in 2003.
$130,000 to University of Idaho, Moscow, ID. 2 grants: $35,000 to College of Engineering, $95,000 to College of Natural Resources
$30,000 to Michigan Colleges Foundation, Southfield, MI. For general support.
$20,000 to Michigan State University, College of Engineering, East Lansing, MI.
$20,000 to Michigan Technological University, Houghton, MI.
$20,000 to Oakland University, Department of Engineering, Rochester, MI.
$20,000 to Wayne State University, College of Engineering, Detroit, MI.
$17,000 to Kettle Falls School District, Kettle Falls, WA. For general support.
$10,000 to Chief Joseph Foundation, Lapwai, ID. For general support.
$10,000 to Michigan Wildlife Habitat Foundation, Lansing, MI.

438
Daniel and Pamella DeVos Foundation
P.O. Box 230257
Grand Rapids, MI   49523-0257   (616) 643-4700
Contact: Ginny Vander Hart, Exec. Dir.
FAX: (616) 774-0116; E-mail: virginiav@rdvcorp.com

Established in 1992 in MI.
Donor: The Richard and Helen DeVos Foundation.
Grantmaker type: Independent foundation.
Financial data (yr. ended 12/31/04): Assets, $730,939 (M); expenditures, $773,193; total giving, $703,589; qualifying distributions, $752,631; giving activities include $703,589 for 67 grants (high: $209,980; low: $200).
Purpose and activities: Giving for museums, performing arts centers, arts and culture, education, human services and Christian agencies.
Fields of interest: Museums; Performing arts centers; Arts; Libraries/library science; Education; Human services; Children/youth, services; Christian agencies & churches.
Type of support: General/operating support; Continuing support; Annual campaigns; Capital campaigns; Building/renovation; Program development; Seed money; Matching/challenge support.
Limitations: Giving primarily in Grand Rapids, MI. No grants to individuals.
Publications: Informational brochure (including application guidelines).
Application information: Application form not required.
Initial approach: Letter
Copies of proposal: 1
Deadline(s): None
Final notification: 3 to 5 months
Officers: Daniel G. DeVos, Pres.; Pamella DeVos, V.P.; Jerry L. Tubergen, Secy.-Treas.
EIN: 383035976

439
Dick & Betsy DeVos Foundation
P.O. Box 230257
Grand Rapids, MI   49523-0257   (616) 643-4700
Contact: Ginny Vander Hart, Exec. Dir.; Sue Volkers, Fdn. Admin.
FAX (for Ginny Vander Hart): (616) 774-0116; E-mail (for Ginny Vander Hart): virginiav@rdvcorp.com

Established in 1989 in MI.
Donors: Dick DeVos; Betsy DeVos; Prince Foundation.
Grantmaker type: Independent foundation.
Financial data (yr. ended 12/31/04): Assets, $27,126,765 (M); gifts received, $14,005,615; expenditures, $3,549,065; total giving, $3,239,999; qualifying distributions, $3,366,407; giving activities include $3,239,999 for 133 grants (high: $453,349; low: $250; average: $1,000–$25,000).
Purpose and activities: The foundation seeks to create a legacy of caring and stewardship through its support of projects that build a strong community. To demonstrate this commitment, the foundation concentrates its funding in support of various initiatives that promote a healthier community, with a focus on the arts, health and children's causes.
Fields of interest: Arts; Education; Children/youth, services; Family services; Public policy, research; Christian agencies & churches.

Type of support: General/operating support; Continuing support; Annual campaigns; Capital campaigns.
Limitations: Giving primarily in west MI. No grants to individuals.
Publications: Application guidelines.
Application information: Application form not required.
Initial approach: Letter
Copies of proposal: 1
Deadline(s): 2 weeks prior to review
Board meeting date(s): Quarterly
Final notification: 4 to 5 months
Officers and Directors: * Jerry L. Tubergen,* C.O.O., V.P. and Secy.; Richard M. DeVos, Jr.,* Pres.; Elisabeth DeVos,* V.P.; Robert H. Schierbeek, Treas.; Ginny Vander Hart, Exec. Dir. and Fdn. Dir.
EIN: 382902412
Selected grants: The following grants were reported in 2004.
$453,349 to Flannel, Grand Rapids, MI. For general support.
$303,000 to Education Freedom Fund, Grand Rapids, MI. For general support.
$150,000 to Institute for Marriage and Public Policy (iMAPP), DC. For general support.
$100,000 to Blodgett Butterworth Health Care Foundation, Grand Rapids, MI. For general support.
$30,000 to Act One, Los Angeles, CA. For general support.
$25,000 to CURE International, Harrisburg, PA. For general support.
$10,000 to English Language Institute in China, San Dimas, CA. For general support.
$10,000 to Snow Bible Church, Kent City, MI. For general support.
$5,000 to Grand Rapids Christian High School, Grand Rapids, MI.
$5,000 to Van Andel Institute, Grand Rapids, MI.

440
Douglas & Maria DeVos Foundation
P.O. Box 230257
Grand Rapids, MI   49523-0257   (616) 643-4700
Contact: Ginny Vander Hart, Exec. Dir.
FAX: (616) 774-0116; E-mail: virginiav@rdvcorp.com

Established in 1992 in MI.
Donors: Douglas DeVos; Maria DeVos.
Grantmaker type: Independent foundation.
Financial data (yr. ended 12/31/04): Assets, $16,703,303 (M); gifts received, $14,500,000; expenditures, $1,650,558; total giving, $1,574,291; qualifying distributions, $1,621,249; giving activities include $1,574,291 for grants.
Purpose and activities: The foundation hopes to build a legacy of caring and stewardship that combines the heart and skill of philanthropy in order to improve the quality of people's lives and build a stronger community. Its focus is on organizations, projects, or programs that demonstrate Christian charity to meet both the spiritual and physical needs of people. Its primary commitment is to the support of the Grand Rapids, MI, community with goals of strengthening the bond of families, rebuilding strong neighborhoods, and providing opportunity for disadvantaged youth.
Fields of interest: Health care; Human services; Family services; Christian agencies & churches.
Type of support: General/operating support; Continuing support; Annual campaigns; Capital

campaigns; Building/renovation; Program development; Matching/challenge support.
Limitations: Giving primarily in west MI.
Publications: Application guidelines.
Application information: Application form not required.
Initial approach: Letter
Copies of proposal: 1
Deadline(s): 2 weeks prior to review
Board meeting date(s): Quarterly
Final notification: Within 3 to 5 months
Officers: Douglas DeVos, Pres.; Maria DeVos, V.P.; Jerry L. Tubergen, Secy.-Treas.
EIN: 383035972

441
The Richard and Helen DeVos Foundation
P.O. Box 230257
Grand Rapids, MI   49523-0257   (616) 643-4700
Contact: Ginny Vander Hart, Exec. Dir.

Incorporated in 1969 in MI.
Donors: Richard M. DeVos; Helen J. DeVos; Alticor Inc.
Grantmaker type: Independent foundation.
Financial data (yr. ended 12/31/04): Assets, $80,290,190 (M); gifts received, $4,066,394; expenditures, $36,983,711; total giving, $34,548,985; qualifying distributions, $36,175,698; giving activities include $34,548,985 for 176 grants (high: $3,600,000; low: $500; average: $5,000–$50,000), and $806,662 for 1 foundation-administered program.
Purpose and activities: The foundation primarily supports the work of religious agencies, churches, and schools in ministry, outreach, and education. Its secondary focus includes social outreach, the arts, public policy, and health care. The foundation focuses its funding in the areas of western Michigan and central Florida.
Fields of interest: Arts; Health care; Social sciences; Public policy, research; Religion.
Type of support: General/operating support; Continuing support; Annual campaigns; Capital campaigns; Building/renovation; Program development; Seed money; Matching/challenge support.
Limitations: Giving primarily in central FL and western MI. No grants to individuals.
Publications: Application guidelines.
Application information: Application form not required.
Initial approach: Letter
Copies of proposal: 1
Deadline(s): 2 weeks prior to review
Board meeting date(s): Every 3 months
Final notification: 4 to 5 months
Officers: Helen J. DeVos, Pres.; Jerry L. Tubergen, V.P. and Secy.; Robert H. Schierbeek, Treas.; Ginny Vander Hart, Exec. Dir.
EIN: 237066873
Selected grants: The following grants were reported in 2004.
$3,000,000 to National Constitution Center, Philadelphia, PA. For general support.
$2,500,000 to Gospel Communications International, Muskegon, MI. For general support.
$2,005,000 to DeVos Childrens Hospital Foundation, Grand Rapids, MI. For general support.
$1,510,000 to Coral Ridge Presbyterian Church, Fort Lauderdale, FL. For general support.

$1,250,000 to Grand Rapids Symphony, Grand Rapids, MI. For general support.
$1,000,000 to Prison Fellowship Ministries, Lansdowne, VA. For general support.
$600,000 to Heritage Foundation, DC. For general support.
$500,000 to Focus on the Family, Colorado Springs, CO. For general support.
$500,000 to George Washingtons Mount Vernon Estate and Gardens, Mount Vernon, VA. For general support.
$500,000 to Haggai Institute for Advanced Leadership Training, Atlanta, GA. For general support.

442
James H. and Judith L. DeVries Charitable Foundation
1535-44th St. S.W., Ste. 400
Wyoming, MI   49509   (616) 742-1602
Contact: James H. DeVries, Pres.
Application address: P.O. Box 141583, Grand Rapids, MI 49514-1583

Established in 1988 in MI.
Donors: James H. DeVries; Judith L. DeVries; DLP, Inc.
Grantmaker type: Independent foundation.
Financial data (yr. ended 12/31/05): Assets, $64 (M); expenditures, $574; total giving, $0; qualifying distributions, $574.
Purpose and activities: Giving primarily for religious organizations.
Fields of interest: Arts; Higher education; Crime/law enforcement; Human services; Civil rights; Christian agencies & churches; Protestant agencies & churches.
International interests: India.
Type of support: General/operating support; Seed money.
Limitations: Giving primarily in MI. No grants to individuals.
Application information: Application form not required.
Initial approach: Letter or telephone
Deadline(s): None
Board meeting date(s): Semiannually
Officers: James H. DeVries, Pres. and Treas.; Judith L. DeVries, Secy.
EIN: 382805125

443
Eileen and Brian G. DeVries Family Foundation
444 Michigan St. N.E.
Grand Rapids, MI   49503

Established in 1993 in MI.
Donors: Eileen DeVries; Brian G. DeVries.
Grantmaker type: Independent foundation.
Financial data (yr. ended 12/31/04): Assets, $155,943 (M); gifts received, $111,445; expenditures, $95,404; total giving, $93,985; qualifying distributions, $93,985; giving activities include $93,985 for 18 grants (high: $35,000; low: $25).
Fields of interest: Museums; Higher education; Hospitals (general); Youth development; Federated giving programs; Protestant agencies & churches.
Type of support: Program development; General/operating support.

Limitations: Applications not accepted. Giving primarily in Grand Rapids, MI. No grants to individuals.
Application information: Contributes only to pre-selected organizations.
Officers and Directors:* Eileen DeVries,* Pres. and Treas.; Brian G. DeVries,* V.P. and Secy.
EIN: 383180271

444
Milo & Abby DeVries Foundation
8750 76th St.
Alto, MI 49302

Established in 1998 in MI.
Donors: Milo DeVries; Abby DeVries.
Grantmaker type: Independent foundation.
Financial data (yr. ended 6/30/05): Assets, $7,065 (M); gifts received, $45,000; expenditures, $70,135; total giving, $67,795; qualifying distributions, $67,795; giving activities include $67,795 for grants.
Fields of interest: Performing arts, orchestra (symphony); Education; Human services; Children/ youth, services; Christian agencies & churches.
Limitations: Applications not accepted. No grants to individuals.
Application information: Contributes only to pre-selected organizations.
Officers: Milo DeVries, Pres.; Abby DeVries, V.P.; Larry Vanderwal, Secy.; Ron Sakowski, Treas.
Directors: David DeVries; Abby Whiteford; Cynthia Wolff.
EIN: 383427252

445
Howard Dewey Educational Trust
c/o Fifth Third Bank, Trust Dept.
P.O. Box 3636
Grand Rapids, MI 49501-3636

Grantmaker type: Independent foundation.
Financial data (yr. ended 12/31/05): Assets, $83,467 (M); expenditures, $2,021; total giving, $0; qualifying distributions, $265.
Purpose and activities: Support only for Aurora University, East Aurora High School, and West Aurora High School, IL.
Fields of interest: Higher education; Higher education, university.
Type of support: General/operating support; Scholarship funds.
Limitations: Applications not accepted. Giving limited to Aurora, IL. No grants to individuals.
Application information: Contributes only to 3 pre-selected organizations.
Trustee: Fifth Third Bank.
EIN: 366449286

446
DeWitt Families Conduit Foundation
280 N. River Ave., Ste. B
Holland, MI 49424

Established in 1987 in MI.
Donors: Brian DeWitt; Lisa DeWitt; Dawn Brinks; Kurt Brinks; Deb Koop; J.P. Koop; Donald DeWitt; Minnie DeWitt; Gary D. DeWitt; Joyce DeWitt; Julia M. Morrison; Kathy Muyskens; Chris Muyskens; Keith DeWitt; Mary E. DeWitt; Kelly DeWitt; Kristin

DeWitt; Kerri Sue Smits; James Smits; Lisa Vanderkolk; Jon Vanderkolk; Marilyn Norman; Thomas Norman; Marvin G. DeWitt; Jerene L. DeWitt; Merle DeWitt; Sheri DeWitt; Shirley Dedoes; William DeWitt, Jr.; Mary DeWitt; and members of the DeWitt family.
Grantmaker type: Independent foundation.
Financial data (yr. ended 12/31/05): Assets, $15,513 (M); gifts received, $1,057,416; expenditures, $1,053,733; total giving, $1,036,898; qualifying distributions, $1,041,040; giving activities include $1,036,898 for 131 grants (high: $114,919; low: $100).
Purpose and activities: Giving for Christian churches, religious missionary organizations, and educational institutions.
Fields of interest: Elementary/secondary education; Higher education; Theological school/ education; Education; Youth, services; Family services; Christian agencies & churches.
Limitations: Applications not accepted. Giving on a national basis, with some emphasis on MI. No grants to individuals.
Application information: Contributes only to pre-selected organizations.
Officers and Trustees:* Marvin G. DeWitt,* Pres.; Gary D. DeWitt,* V.P.; William G. DeWitt,* V.P.; William J. DeWitt,* Secy.-Treas.
EIN: 382761226
Selected grants: The following grants were reported in 2003.
$287,340 to Western Theological Seminary, Holland, MI. For annual support.
$260,730 to Hope College, Holland, MI. For annual support.
$228,900 to Geneva Camp and Retreat Center, Holland, MI. For annual support.
$192,650 to Community Reformed Church, Holland, MI. For annual support.
$132,800 to Focus on the Family, Colorado Springs, CO. For annual support.
$104,397 to Ottawa Reformed Church, West Olive, MI. For annual support.
$64,000 to Lakeshore Pregnancy Center, Holland, MI. For annual support.
$45,000 to Northwestern College, Orange City, IA. For annual support.
$20,000 to Eastmanville United Reformed Church, Coopersville, MI. For annual support.
$15,000 to Campus Crusade for Christ, Lebanon, OH. For annual support.

447
Marvin G. and Jerene L. DeWitt Family Foundation
c/o Marvin G. DeWitt
RR 1, P.O. Box 9903
Zeeland, MI 49464-9801 (616) 895-6651

Established in 1997 in MI.
Grantmaker type: Independent foundation.
Financial data (yr. ended 12/31/05): Assets, $18,100 (M); expenditures, $1,395; total giving, $0; qualifying distributions, $0.
Limitations: Applications not accepted. Giving primarily in Zeeland, MI. No grants to individuals.
Application information: Contributes only to pre-selected organizations.
Officers: Marvin G. DeWitt, Pres. and Treas.; Jerene L. DeWitt, V.P. and Secy.
EIN: 383336470

448
Jack and Mary DeWitt Family Foundation
205 Norwood Dr.
Holland, MI 49424-2730

Established in 1992 in MI.
Donors: Jack L. DeWitt; Jacqueline Curtis; Linda E. Berghorst; Laurie S. Wierda.
Grantmaker type: Independent foundation.
Financial data (yr. ended 12/31/05): Assets, $254,825 (M); gifts received, $267,349; expenditures, $302,677; total giving, $297,000; qualifying distributions, $299,917; giving activities include $297,000 for 59 grants (high: $21,000; low: $500).
Purpose and activities: Support primarily for Christian churches and organizations.
Fields of interest: Higher education; Graduate/ professional education; Human services; Family services; Christian agencies & churches.
Type of support: Annual campaigns.
Limitations: Applications not accepted. Giving primarily in MI. No grants to individuals.
Application information: Contributes only to pre-selected organizations.
Officers: Jack L. DeWitt, Pres. and Treas.; Mary E. DeWitt, V.P. and Secy.
EIN: 383080740
Selected grants: The following grants were reported in 2005.
$21,000 to Young Life, Colorado Springs, CO. For annual support.
$20,000 to Youth for Christ, Holland, MI. For annual support.
$15,500 to Focus on the Family, Colorado Springs, CO. For annual support.
$15,500 to Winning at Home, Holland, MI. For annual support.
$11,000 to Good Samaritan Ministries, Holland, MI. For annual support.
$11,000 to Van Houten Ministries, Holland, MI. For annual support.
$10,000 to Gun Lake Community Church, Wayland, MI. For annual support.
$10,000 to Holland Rescue Mission, Holland, MI. For annual support.
$9,500 to Camp Geneva, Holland, MI. For annual support.
$8,500 to Dave Draveckys Outreach of Hope, Colorado Springs, CO. For annual support.

449
Louis M. Dexter Memorial Foundation, Inc.
1514 Wildwood Ln.
Naples, FL 34105-3207 (239) 649-6627
Contact: Kirk Munroe, Tr.

Established in 1998 in MI.
Grantmaker type: Independent foundation.
Financial data (yr. ended 12/31/05): Assets, $894,698 (M); expenditures, $45,709; total giving, $43,300; qualifying distributions, $43,300; giving activities include $43,300 for grants.
Purpose and activities: Giving primarily for higher education and human services.
Fields of interest: Performing arts; Higher education; Human services; Christian agencies & churches.
Type of support: General/operating support.
Limitations: Giving primarily in MI, with emphasis on Grand Rapids.
Application information:

Initial approach: Letter
  Deadline(s): None
Officer: Janice Jacobson, Secy.
Trustees: Andrea Darling; Kirk Munroe; Marjorie R. Wege.
EIN: 383383892

450
The DHL Private Charitable Foundation
(formerly The DHL Charitable Foundation)
3025 Exmoor Rd.
Ann Arbor, MI 48104

Established in 1994 in CO.
Donor: David H. Lord.
Grantmaker type: Independent foundation.
Financial data (yr. ended 7/31/05): Assets, $616,189 (M); expenditures, $89,840; total giving, $79,569; qualifying distributions, $79,569; giving activities include $79,569 for grants.
Fields of interest: Human services.
Limitations: Applications not accepted. Giving primarily in FL. No grants to individuals.
Application information: Contributes only to pre-selected organizations.
Officer and Trustees:* Charles Lord,* Pres.; Richard Lord; Edith Lord-Wolff.
EIN: 841299114

451
Dickinson County War Veterans Scholarship Association
P.O. Box 370
Iron Mountain, MI 49801-0370
Contact: Johana Ostwald, Pres.
Application address: c/o Dickinson-Iron Intermediate School, 1074 Pyle Dr., Kingsford, MI 49802, tel.: (906) 774-2690

Established in MI.
Grantmaker type: Independent foundation.
Financial data (yr. ended 12/31/05): Assets, $24,647 (M); expenditures, $1,217; total giving, $1,200; qualifying distributions, $1,200; giving activities include $1,200 for grants to individuals.
Purpose and activities: Scholarship awards to veterans or children of veterans who are graduates of Dickinson County high schools, MI.
Type of support: Scholarships—to individuals.
Limitations: Giving limited to residents of Dickinson County, MI.
Application information: Application form required.
  Deadline(s): Varies
Officers: Johana Ostwald, Pres.; Denny Chartier, Secy.; Dan A. Peterson, Treas.
Trustee: Chris Ninomiya.
EIN: 237265519

452
Gino and Luciana DiClemente Foundation
5135 Iron Gate
Bloomfield Hills, MI 48304-3737

Established in 1997 in MI.
Donor: Gino DiClemente.
Grantmaker type: Independent foundation.
Financial data (yr. ended 12/31/05): Assets, $810,630 (M); gifts received, $33,797; expenditures, $37,040; total giving, $35,945;

qualifying distributions, $35,945; giving activities include $35,945 for grants.
Fields of interest: Higher education; Education; Christian agencies & churches.
Type of support: General/operating support.
Limitations: Applications not accepted. Giving primarily in MI. No grants to individuals.
Application information: Contributes only to pre-selected organizations.
Officer and Directors:* Gino DiClemente,* Pres. and Secy.-Treas.; Gino M. DiClemente; John F. DiClemente; Luciana DiClemente; Perry G. DiClemente; Steven L. DiClemente.
EIN: 383440485

453
Lucile K. Diebel Charitable Trust
c/o National City Bank
P.O. Box 94651
Cleveland, OH 44101-4651

Established in 1993 in MI.
Grantmaker type: Independent foundation.
Financial data (yr. ended 12/31/04): Assets, $1,024,778 (M); expenditures, $45,284; total giving, $40,000; qualifying distributions, $42,655; giving activities include $40,000 for grants.
Purpose and activities: Support only for the Alden Methodist Church, Kewadin United Methodist Church, Salvation Army, Saginaw, St. Lukes Methodist Church, Essexville, MI and American Bible Society, NY.
Fields of interest: YM/YWCAs & YM/YWHAs; Protestant agencies & churches.
Limitations: Applications not accepted. Giving limited to MI and NY. No grants to individuals.
Application information: Contributes only to 5 pre-selected organizations.
Trustee: National City Bank.
EIN: 386542792

454
Diebolt Foundation
43850 Plymouth Oaks Blvd.
Plymouth, MI 48170

Established in 1998 in MI.
Donor: Michael C. Diebolt.
Grantmaker type: Independent foundation.
Financial data (yr. ended 12/31/04): Assets, $9,117,330 (M); gifts received, $2,000,000; expenditures, $456,013; total giving, $200,000; qualifying distributions, $200,000; giving activities include $200,000 for grants.
Purpose and activities: Support only for the University of Michigan, Ann Arbor, MI.
Fields of interest: Higher education, university; Medical research.
Type of support: General/operating support.
Limitations: Applications not accepted. Giving limited to Ann Arbor, MI. No grants to individuals.
Application information: Contributes only to a pre-selected organization.
Officers: Michael C. Diebolt, Pres.; Linda J. Diebolt, Secy.-Treas.
EIN: 383444677

455
The Angelo & Margaret DiPonio Foundation
14800 Farmington Rd., Ste. 102
Livonia, MI 48154
Contact: Ralph H. Houghton, Jr., Dir.

Established in 1987 in MI.
Donor: Margaret E. DiPonio.
Grantmaker type: Independent foundation.
Financial data (yr. ended 10/31/05): Assets, $3,722,610 (M); expenditures, $622,383; total giving, $593,125; qualifying distributions, $593,125; giving activities include $593,125 for 9 grants (high: $500,000; low: $125).
Purpose and activities: Giving primarily for higher education, medical research, organizations providing medical assistance or treatment, and organizations providing assistance for persons temporarily out of work or homeless.
Fields of interest: Cancer; Human services; Family services; Family services, domestic violence; Christian agencies & churches.
Type of support: Building/renovation.
Limitations: Giving limited to MI. No grants to individuals.
Application information: Telephone inquiries will not be accepted.
  Initial approach: Proposal
  Deadline(s): None
Directors: Charles E. Bietler; Margaret E. DiPonio; Ralph H. Houghton, Jr.
EIN: 382828486

456
Randy & Terri Disselkoen Foundation
6959 Wildermere N.E.
Rockford, MI 49341 (616) 874-8283

Established in 1999 in MI.
Donors: Randy Disselkoen; Terri Disselkoen.
Grantmaker type: Independent foundation.
Financial data (yr. ended 12/31/04): Assets, $94,503 (M); expenditures, $15,070; total giving, $15,000; qualifying distributions, $15,000; giving activities include $15,000 for grants.
Fields of interest: Christian agencies & churches.
Limitations: Applications not accepted. Giving primarily in MI. No grants to individuals.
Application information: Contributes only to pre-selected organizations.
Directors: Randy Disselkoen; Terri Disselkoen.
EIN: 383505708

457
Dixie Foundation
c/o Roger L. Duval, C.P.A.
27313 Southfield Rd.
Lathrup Village, MI 48076-3408

Donor: Bobby G. Stevenson.
Grantmaker type: Independent foundation.
Financial data (yr. ended 4/30/05): Assets, $5,176 (M); gifts received, $28; expenditures, $528; total giving, $500; qualifying distributions, $500; giving activities include $500 for grants.
Limitations: Giving primarily in Denver, CO.
Officers: Melinda D. Fiore, Pres.; Bobby G. Stevenson, V.P. and Treas.; Delaine Stevenson, V.P.; Roger L. Duval, Secy.
EIN: 841463859

458
DJD Foundation
1062 N. Meadow Dr. S.W.
P.O. Box 1032
Byron Center, MI 49315 (616) 261-2679
Contact: Gordon Brinks, C.P.A.

Established in 2000 in MI.
Donors: David A. Daane; L. Jean Daane.
Grantmaker type: Independent foundation.
Financial data (yr. ended 12/31/05): Assets,
$982,715 (M); gifts received, $20,000;
expenditures, $50,860; total giving, $50,500;
qualifying distributions, $50,500; giving activities
include $50,500 for grants.
Fields of interest: Christian agencies & churches.
Limitations: Giving primarily in Grand Rapids, MI. No
grants to individuals.
Application information:
  Initial approach: Letter
  Deadline(s): None
Officers: L. Jean Daane, Pres.; David A. Daane, V.P.
and Treas.; Jana Baker, Secy.
EIN: 383553476

459
The Doan Family Foundation
(formerly The Herbert & Junia Doan Foundation)
3801 Valley Dr.
P.O. Box 169
Midland, MI 48641-2765 (989) 631-2471
Contact: Junia Doan, V.P.

Established in 1964 in MI.
Donor: Herbert D. Doan†.
Grantmaker type: Independent foundation.
Financial data (yr. ended 12/31/05): Assets,
$2,352,392 (M); expenditures, $117,045; total
giving, $108,350; qualifying distributions,
$109,442; giving activities include $108,350 for 17
grants (high: $23,000; low: $500).
Fields of interest: Arts; Higher education, university;
Federated giving programs; Chemistry; Engineering/
technology; Science.
Type of support: General/operating support;
Continuing support; Annual campaigns.
Limitations: Giving primarily in Midland, MI. No
grants to individuals.
Application information: Application form not
required.
  Initial approach: Letter
  Deadline(s): May 1
Officers and Trustees:* Junia Doan, V.P. and Secy.;
Jeffrey Doan,* V.P.; Michael Doan,* V.P.
Number of staff: 1 part-time support.
EIN: 386078714

460
The Herbert and Junia Doan Foundation
3801 Valley Dr.
Midland, MI 48640 (989) 631-2471
Contact: Junia Doan, V.P.

Established in 2003 in MI.
Donor: The Doan Family Foundation.
Grantmaker type: Independent foundation.
Financial data (yr. ended 12/31/05): Assets,
$2,359,864 (M); expenditures, $119,518; total
giving, $111,000; qualifying distributions,
$111,000; giving activities include $111,000 for
grants.

Purpose and activities: Giving primarily for a center
for the arts; giving also for education, youth, and
Jewish agencies and temples.
Fields of interest: Arts; Education; Youth
development; Human services; Jewish agencies &
temples.
Type of support: General/operating support.
Limitations: Giving primarily in Midland, MI.
Application information:
  Initial approach: Letter
  Deadline(s): May 1
Officer: Junia Doan, V.P. and Secy.
EIN: 200048522

461
The Umakant S. and Shreedevi U. Doctor Family Charitable Trust
6635 Wyndham Dr.
Kalamazoo, MI 49009

Established in 1997 in MI.
Donors: Umakant S. Doctor; Shreedevi U. Doctor.
Grantmaker type: Independent foundation.
Financial data (yr. ended 12/31/04): Assets,
$772,765 (M); expenditures, $30,830; total giving,
$26,000; qualifying distributions, $27,775; giving
activities include $26,000 for grants.
Fields of interest: Federated giving programs;
Protestant agencies & churches.
Type of support: General/operating support.
Limitations: Applications not accepted. Giving
primarily in MI. No grants to individuals.
Application information: Contributes only to
pre-selected organizations.
Trustees: Shreedevi U. Doctor; Umakant S. Doctor.
EIN: 367225642

462
Doezema Charitable Trust
40 Pearl St. N.W., Ste. 300
Grand Rapids, MI 49503-3091

Donors: Charles W. Doezema; Geraldine Doezema.
Grantmaker type: Independent foundation.
Financial data (yr. ended 12/31/05): Assets,
$45,783 (M); expenditures, $6,387; total giving,
$5,300; qualifying distributions, $5,300; giving
activities include $5,300 for grants.
Limitations: Applications not accepted. Giving
primarily in MI. No grants to individuals.
Application information: Contributes only to
pre-selected organizations.
Officer: Geraldine Doezema, Mgr.
EIN: 382297595

463
The Dogwood Foundation
c/o Susan Meyers, Warner, Norcross & Judd
111 Lyon St. N.W., Ste. 900
Grand Rapids, MI 49503

Established in 1994 in FL.
Donors: Dorothy Scott Merrill†; Dorothy Scott Merrill
Charitable Lead Unitrust.
Grantmaker type: Independent foundation.
Financial data (yr. ended 12/31/04): Assets,
$14,694,113 (M); gifts received, $398,728;
expenditures, $889,161; total giving, $784,568;
qualifying distributions, $857,012; giving activities

include $784,568 for 15 grants (high: $479,159;
low: $2,500).
Purpose and activities: Giving primarily for
community foundations, education, particularly a
military academy, the arts, and human services.
Fields of interest: Museums (specialized);
Performing arts, theater; Historic preservation/
historical societies; Arts; Libraries/library science;
Education; Crime/violence prevention, domestic
violence; Human services; Foundations
(community).
Limitations: Applications not accepted. Giving on a
national basis, with emphasis on FL, MI, TX, and the
Midwest. No grants to individuals.
Application information: Contributes only to
pre-selected organizations.
Trustees: Kyle Merrill Converse; John H. Martin;
Danielle Merrill; Frank G. Merrill; Holly S. Merrill.
EIN: 650499552

464
Dole Family Foundation
1536 Eastlawn Rd. S.E.
Grand Rapids, MI 49506-4110

Established in 2000 in MI.
Donors: Stanley F. Dole; Elizabeth G. Dole.
Grantmaker type: Independent foundation.
Financial data (yr. ended 12/31/04): Assets,
$548,706 (M); gifts received, $5,924;
expenditures, $77,052; total giving, $76,050;
qualifying distributions, $76,050; giving activities
include $76,050 for grants.
Purpose and activities: Giving only to organizations
which the foundation has had prior relationship.
Fields of interest: Environment; Reproductive
health, family planning.
Type of support: General/operating support;
Continuing support; Capital campaigns.
Limitations: Applications not accepted. No grants to
individuals.
Application information: Contributes only to
pre-selected organizations.
Officers: Stanley F. Dole, Pres. and Treas.; Elizabeth
G. Dole, V.P. and Secy.
EIN: 383519399

465
Doll-Loesel Foundation
4344 Maplewoods W.
Saginaw, MI 48603

Established in 1994 in MI.
Donors: George F. Loesel; Susan D. Loesel.
Grantmaker type: Independent foundation.
Financial data (yr. ended 12/31/05): Assets,
$761,453 (M); gifts received, $66,000;
expenditures, $232,962; total giving, $227,490;
qualifying distributions, $227,490; giving activities
include $227,490 for 16 grants (high: $105,000;
low: $2,000).
Purpose and activities: Provides food services for
human services groups; support also for education
and the arts.
Fields of interest: Arts; Education; Food services;
Youth development; Human services; Neighborhood
centers.
Type of support: Continuing support; Equipment.
Limitations: Applications not accepted. No grants to
individuals.

Application information: Contributes only to pre-selected organizations; unsolicited requests for funds not accepted.
Board meeting date(s): Nov.
Directors: George F. Loesel; Susan D. Loesel.
EIN: 383212771
Selected grants: The following grants were reported in 2004.
$112,500 to Saginaw Art Museum, Saginaw, MI.
$20,000 to Salvation Army of Saginaw, Saginaw, MI.
$10,000 to East Side Soup Kitchen, Saginaw, MI.
$6,000 to Neighborhood House, Saginaw, MI.
$5,000 to Hidden Harvest, Saginaw, MI.
$4,000 to Teen Challenge of Saginaw, Saginaw, MI.
$2,000 to Delta College, University Center, MI.
$2,000 to Restoration Community Outreach, Saginaw, MI.
$1,500 to Saginaw Bay Orchestra, Saginaw, MI.
$1,000 to Saginaw Choral Society, Saginaw, MI.

466
Patricia A. and Richard M. Donahey Foundation, Inc.
500 Woodward Ave., Ste. 2500
Detroit, MI 48226

Donors: Richard M. Donahey; Patricia A. Donahey.
Grantmaker type: Independent foundation.
Financial data (yr. ended 12/31/04): Assets, $153,710 (M); gifts received, $2,500; expenditures, $69,253; total giving, $54,010; qualifying distributions, $54,010; giving activities include $54,010 for grants.
Fields of interest: Cancer research; Human services; Protestant agencies & churches.
Type of support: General/operating support.
Limitations: Applications not accepted. Giving primarily in MI. No grants to individuals.
Application information: Contributes only to pre-selected organizations.
Officers: Richard M. Donahey, Pres.; Patricia A. Donahey, V.P.; E. Peter Drolet, Secy.; Linda Susan Paris, Treas.
EIN: 383496123

467
Mildred Mary Donlin Charitable Corporation
2850 Dixie Hwy.
Waterford, MI 48328   (248) 674-2291
Contact: Peter J. Donlin, Exec. Dir.

Grantmaker type: Independent foundation.
Financial data (yr. ended 12/31/04): Assets, $39,851 (M); gifts received, $1,000; expenditures, $620; total giving, $575; qualifying distributions, $575; giving activities include $575 for grants.
Fields of interest: Arts; Education; Aging, centers/services; Religion.
Type of support: General/operating support.
Application information:
Initial approach: Letter
Deadline(s): None
Officer: Peter J. Donlin, Exec. Dir.
Trustee: Kathleen Donlin.
EIN: 383082159

468
The Door to Door Medical Supply Foundation
333 Park St.
Troy, MI 48083
Contact: Howard B. Goldman, Pres.
Application address: 3500 West Maple Rd., Stes. A&B, Bloomfield, MI 48301, tel.: (248) 433-0375

Established in 2003 in MI.
Donor: Howard B. Goldman.
Grantmaker type: Independent foundation.
Financial data (yr. ended 12/31/04): Assets, $49,298 (M); expenditures, $1,280; total giving, $1,280; qualifying distributions, $1,274; giving activities include $1,280 for grants.
Application information:
Initial approach: Letter
Deadline(s): Varies
Officer: Howard B. Goldman, Pres.
EIN: 300182028

469
The Doornink Foundation
c/o Jeffrey B. Power, Warner, Norcross & Judd LLP
111 Lyon St. N.W., Ste. 900
Grand Rapids, MI 49503-2487

Established in 1997 in MI.
Donor: Mary Welch Corl.
Grantmaker type: Independent foundation.
Financial data (yr. ended 12/31/05): Assets, $13,912,524 (M); gifts received, $100,000; expenditures, $630,993; total giving, $594,000; qualifying distributions, $598,110; giving activities include $594,000 for 12 grants (high: $250,000; low: $1,500).
Fields of interest: Museums (art); Arts; Education; Mental health, counseling/support groups; Human services; Children/youth, services; Federated giving programs.
Type of support: General/operating support; Capital campaigns; Program development.
Limitations: Applications not accepted. Giving primarily in Grand Rapids, MI.
Application information: Unsolicited requests for funds not accepted.
Officers and Trustees:* Mary W. Corl,* Pres.; Robert W. Corl, Jr.,* V.P.; Jeffrey B. Power,* Secy.-Treas.; James M. Corl; Jeanne L. Corl; Kelli R. Corl; Robert W. Corl III.
EIN: 383386701
Selected grants: The following grants were reported in 2003.
$300,000 to East Grand Rapids, City of, East Grand Rapids, MI. For public works project.
$100,000 to United Way, Heart of West Michigan, Grand Rapids, MI. For general support.
$16,000 to Indian Trails Camp, Grand Rapids, MI. For market analysis.
$10,000 to Grand Rapids Ballet Company, Grand Rapids, MI. For expansion of ballet corps.
$10,000 to North Hills Classical Academy, Grand Rapids, MI. For general support.
$1,500 to Emma Willard School, Troy, NY. For general support.
$1,000 to ArtWorks, Grand Rapids, MI. For general support.

470
The Doran Foundation
1 Prestwick Ct.
Dearborn, MI 48120

Established in 1994 in MI.
Donor: Wayne S. Doran.
Grantmaker type: Independent foundation.
Financial data (yr. ended 11/30/05): Assets, $950,117 (M); gifts received, $100,575; expenditures, $210,777; total giving, $200,708; qualifying distributions, $200,708; giving activities include $200,708 for 11 grants (high: $176,825; low: $1,000).
Purpose and activities: Support primarily for college scholarship funds.
Fields of interest: Higher education; Scholarships/financial aid.
Type of support: Scholarship funds.
Limitations: Giving primarily in AZ and MI. No grants to individuals.
Application information:
Initial approach: Letter
Deadline(s): None
Officers: Wayne S. Doran, Pres.; Maureen K. Doran, Secy.; Robert Bacon, Treas.
EIN: 383211447
Selected grants: The following grants were reported in 2004.
$91,892 to Arizona State University Foundation, Tempe, AZ. For scholarships.
$12,677 to Eastern Michigan University, Ypsilanti, MI. For scholarships.
$6,000 to Banana Newsbagel Institute. For general support.
$5,000 to Arthritis Foundation. For general support.
$2,500 to First Tee of Michigan Foundation, Huntington Woods, MI. For general support.
$600 to Macomb Community College, Warren, MI. For scholarships.
$500 to Boy Scouts of America, Detroit Area Council, Detroit, MI. For general support.
$500 to HomeBase Youth Services, Phoenix, AZ. For general support.

471
Henry S. & Mala Dorfman Foundation
838 W. Long Lake, Ste. 205
Bloomfield Hills, MI 48302
Contact: Joel Dorfman, V.P.

Established in 1972 in MI.
Donors: Henry Dorfman‡; Mala Dorfman.
Grantmaker type: Independent foundation.
Financial data (yr. ended 9/30/05): Assets, $432,149 (M); gifts received, $100,000; expenditures, $49,595; total giving, $49,150; qualifying distributions, $49,150; giving activities include $49,150 for grants.
Purpose and activities: Giving primarily for the arts and education.
Fields of interest: Performing arts, dance; Performing arts, theater; Elementary/secondary education; Scholarships/financial aid; Hospitals (general); Jewish agencies & temples.
Type of support: General/operating support.
Limitations: Giving on a national basis. No grants to individuals.
Application information:
Initial approach: Letter
Deadline(s): None

Officers: Mala Dorfman, Chair. and C.E.O.; Carolyn Dorfman, Pres.; Joel Dorfman, V.P. and Treas.; Gayle Dorfman, Secy.
EIN: 237191091
Selected grants: The following grants were reported in 2003.
$87,910 to Jewish Federation of Metropolitan Detroit, Bloomfield Hills, MI.
$50,000 to American ORT Federation, Detroit, MI.
$37,500 to Jewish Ensemble Theater, West Bloomfield, MI.
$25,000 to Carolyn Dorfman Dance Company, Union, NJ.
$25,000 to Congregation Shaarey Zedek, Southfield, MI.
$15,100 to Aventura Turnberry Jewish Center Beth Jacob, Miami, FL.
$2,250 to Hillel Day School of Metropolitan Detroit, Farmington Hills, MI.
$1,100 to Friends of the Israel Defense Forces, New York, NY.
$1,000 to Jewish Federation of Greater Miami, Miami, FL.
$600 to Yad Ezra, Oak Park, MI.

472
Dorrell Farms Foundation
300 Ferndale Ave.
Birmingham, MI 48009

Established in 2000 in MI.
Donor: Ileane Thal.
Grantmaker type: Independent foundation.
Financial data (yr. ended 12/31/05): Assets, $125,023 (M); gifts received, $44,543; expenditures, $8,748; total giving, $8,291; qualifying distributions, $8,291; giving activities include $8,291 for grants.
Limitations: Applications not accepted. Giving primarily in MI and PA. No grants to individuals.
Application information: Contributes only to pre-selected organizations.
Officers: Bruce E. Thal, Pres.; Denise Thal, V.P.; Robert Thal, V.P.; Susan Thal, V.P.; Ileane Thal, Secy.-Treas.
EIN: 383563292

473
Albert Dorris Charitable Trust
(formerly Albert W. Dorris Trust)
c/o Citizens Bank, N.A.
100 E. Michigan Ave.
Jackson, MI 49201

Grantmaker type: Independent foundation.
Financial data (yr. ended 12/31/05): Assets, $68,740 (M); expenditures, $3,111; total giving, $1,630; qualifying distributions, $1,630; giving activities include $1,630 for 1 grant.
Purpose and activities: Support only for the Presbyterian Church of Homer, MI.
Fields of interest: Protestant agencies & churches.
Type of support: General/operating support.
Limitations: Applications not accepted. Giving limited to Homer, MI. No grants to individuals.
Application information: Contributes only to a pre-selected organization.
Trustee: Citizens Bank, N.A.
EIN: 386187670

474
Doshi Family Foundation
1607 E. Big Beaver Rd., Ste. 200
Troy, MI 48083

Established in 2003 in MI.
Donor: Shailesh N. Doshi.
Grantmaker type: Independent foundation.
Financial data (yr. ended 12/31/04): Assets, $4,500 (M); expenditures, $5,500; total giving, $5,500; qualifying distributions, $5,500; giving activities include $5,500 for grants.
Limitations: Applications not accepted. No grants to individuals.
Application information: Contributes only to pre-selected organizations.
Trustees: Rekha N. Doshi; Shailesh N. Doshi.
EIN: 200533828

475
Howard R. and Margaret Bellows Doud Scholarship Foundation
(also known as Doud Scholarship Foundation)
4055 Wyatt Rd.
Traverse City, MI 49684

Established in 1991 in MI.
Donors: Howard R. Doud; Margaret Bellows Doud.
Grantmaker type: Independent foundation.
Financial data (yr. ended 12/31/04): Assets, $38,993 (M); expenditures, $3,995; total giving, $2,880; qualifying distributions, $2,880; giving activities include $2,880 for grants.
Fields of interest: General charitable giving.
Type of support: General/operating support; Scholarship funds.
Limitations: Applications not accepted. Giving on a national basis, with some emphasis on CA and PA.
Application information: Contributes only to pre-selected organizations.
Trustee: Monika L. Lovewell.
EIN: 386569667

476
Doulos Foundation, Inc.
(formerly Beverly A. Kane Foundation, Inc.)
322 N. Old Woodward Ave.
Birmingham, MI 48009

Established in 1986 in MI.
Donor: Beverly A. Kane.
Grantmaker type: Independent foundation.
Financial data (yr. ended 11/30/05): Assets, $847,166 (M); expenditures, $65,880; total giving, $47,200; qualifying distributions, $47,200; giving activities include $47,200 for grants.
Fields of interest: Protestant agencies & churches; General charitable giving.
Limitations: Applications not accepted. Giving primarily in MI. No grants to individuals.
Application information: Contributes only to pre-selected organizations.
Officers and Directors:* C. Thomas Toppin,* Secy.; Beverly A. Davis,* Mgr.; Terry Altman.
EIN: 382705143

477
Herbert H. and Barbara C. Dow Foundation
P.O. Box 393
Frankfort, MI 49635-0393

Incorporated in 1957 in MI.
Donors: Herbert H. Dow‡; Barbara C. Dow‡; Dow 2005 Charitable Annuity Trust.
Grantmaker type: Independent foundation.
Financial data (yr. ended 12/31/05): Assets, $23,262,552 (M); gifts received, $164,376; expenditures, $1,234,299; total giving, $1,164,691; qualifying distributions, $1,171,417; giving activities include $1,164,691 for 35 grants (high: $101,441; low: $1,000).
Purpose and activities: Support primarily for the arts, higher education, the environment, neuroscience and other medical research, and Christian ministries and organizations.
Fields of interest: Museums (art); Arts; Higher education; Environment, natural resources; Hospitals (specialty); Nursing care; Health care; Cancer research; Alzheimer's disease research; Neuroscience research; Medical research; Human services; Children/youth, services; Family services; Christian agencies & churches.
Type of support: General/operating support; Continuing support; Capital campaigns; Building/renovation; Endowments; Program development; Scholarship funds; Research.
Limitations: Applications not accepted. Giving primarily in AZ, MI, OH and TX; some giving nationally. No grants to individuals.
Application information: Contributes only to pre-selected organizations.
Board meeting date(s): Annually
Officers and Trustees:* Willard H. Dow II,* Pres.; Dana D. Schuler,* Secy.; Pamela G. Dow,* Treas.
EIN: 386058513
Selected grants: The following grants were reported in 2003.
$75,000 to Focus on the Family, Colorado Springs, CO. For general operating support.
$65,000 to Habitat for Humanity, Dallas Area, Dallas, TX. For general operating support.
$50,000 to Grand Traverse Regional Land Conservancy, Traverse City, MI. For coastal campaign.
$50,000 to Hillsdale College, Hillsdale, MI. For campus speakers program.
$50,000 to National Coalition for the Protection of Children and Families, Cincinnati, OH. For general operating support.
$50,000 to Phoenix Art Museum, Phoenix, AZ. For general operating support.
$50,000 to Scottsdale Healthcare Foundation, Scottsdale, AZ. For Virginia G. Piper Cancer Center.
$40,000 to Barrow Neurological Foundation, Phoenix, AZ. For Alzheimer's research.
$35,000 to Paul Oliver Memorial Hospital Foundation, Frankfort, MI. For campaign for advanced life support.
$25,000 to Baylor Health Care System Foundation, Dallas, TX. For Psoriasis research.

478
The Herbert H. and Grace A. Dow Foundation
1018 W. Main St.
Midland, MI 48640-4292 (989) 631-3699
Contact: Margaret Ann Riecker, Pres.
FAX: (989) 631-0675;
E-mail: info@hhdowfoundation.org; URL: http://www.hhdowfoundation.org

Trust established in 1936 in MI.
Donor: Grace A. Dow‡.

Grantmaker type: Independent foundation.
Financial data (yr. ended 12/31/04): Assets, $548,526,968 (M); expenditures, $23,230,223; total giving, $19,050,685; qualifying distributions, $23,570,047; giving activities include $19,050,685 for 229 grants (high: $1,500,000; low: $1,000; average: $212–$500,000), and $1,270,657 for foundation-administered programs.
Purpose and activities: Support for religious, charitable, scientific, literacy, or educational purposes for the public benefaction of the inhabitants of the city of Midland and of the people of the state of Michigan. Grants largely for education, particularly higher education, community and social services, civic improvement, conservation, scientific research, church support (only in Midland County, MI), and cultural programs; maintains Dow Gardens, a public horticultural garden.
Fields of interest: Arts; Higher education; Libraries/library science; Education; Environment, natural resources; Human services; Community development; Engineering/technology; Science.
Type of support: General/operating support; Building/renovation; Equipment; Endowments; Program development; Seed money; Research; Matching/challenge support.
Limitations: Giving limited to MI, with emphasis on Midland County. No support for political organizations or sectarian religious organizations or programs, other than churches in Midland County. No grants to individuals, or for travel or conferences; no loans.
Publications: Annual report (including application guidelines); Financial statement; Grants list.
Application information: Application form not required.
   Initial approach: Proposal
   Copies of proposal: 1
   Deadline(s): None
   Board meeting date(s): Bimonthly
   Final notification: 2 months
Officers and Trustees:* Margaret Ann Riecker,* Pres.; Michael Lloyd Dow,* V.P.; Margaret E. Thompson,* Secy.; Macauley Whiting, Jr.,* Treas.; Jenee Velasquez, Exec. Dir.; Julie Carol Arbury; Diane Dow Hullet; Andrew N. Liveris; Bonnie B. Matheson; Terence F. Moore; Ruth B. Wheeler; Helen Dow Whiting.
EIN: 381437485
Selected grants: The following grants were reported in 2004.
$1,500,000 to Nature Conservancy, Lansing, MI. For land purchase.
$1,002,502 to Hope College, Holland, MI. For science facility.
$998,312 to Midland County Historical Society, Midland, MI. 2 grants: $502,681 (For historical museum), $495,631 (For historical museum).
$996,409 to Central Michigan University, Mount Pleasant, MI. For operating support.
$625,000 to FACE - Truth and Clarity on Alcohol, Clare, MI. For operating support.
$578,178 to Little Forks Conservancy, Midland, MI. For operating support.
$498,973 to Saginaw Valley State University, University Center, MI. For Regional Education Center.
$495,631 to Midland Center for the Arts, Midland, MI. For operating support.
$487,496 to Education and Training Connection, Midland, MI. For facility renovation.

479
Alden & Vada Dow Fund
315 Post St.
Midland, MI   48640-2658
Contact: Craig McDonald, Grants Coord.

Established in 1960 in MI.
Donors: Alden Dow‡; Vada Dow‡; Vada B. Dow Charitable Unitrust.
Grantmaker type: Independent foundation.
Financial data (yr. ended 12/31/05): Assets, $9,709,190 (M); gifts received, $500,000; expenditures, $730,525; total giving, $482,415; qualifying distributions, $558,975; giving activities include $482,415 for 28 grants (high: $50,000; low: $2,500).
Purpose and activities: Giving primarily for social services, particularly children, youth, family and community; some giving also for the arts, and education.
Fields of interest: Performing arts, theater; Performing arts, music; Arts; Elementary/secondary education; Education; Environment; Zoos/zoological societies; Health care; Food services, congregate meals; Recreation, fairs/festivals; Athletics/sports, baseball; Recreation; Human services; American Red Cross; Children/youth, services; Youth, services; Family services; Women, centers/services.
Type of support: General/operating support; Continuing support; Annual campaigns; Capital campaigns; Equipment; Endowments; Conferences/seminars.
Limitations: Applications not accepted. Giving primarily in MI. No grants to individuals.
Application information: Contributes only to pre-selected organizations.
   Board meeting date(s): Feb. 15 and Sept. 15
Officers and Trustees:* Michael Lloyd Dow,* Pres.; Steven Carras,* Secy.; Lloyd Mills,* Treas.; Barbara D. Carras; Diane Hullet; Chris Mills.
Number of staff: 1 part-time professional.
EIN: 386058512

480
The Drake Quinn Family Foundation
c/o Marilyn J.Q. Drake
7178 Aqua Fria Ct. S.E.
Grand Rapids, MI   49546

Established in 1992.
Donors: John K. Drake; Marilyn J.Q. Drake; Rosalie A. Drake‡.
Grantmaker type: Independent foundation.
Financial data (yr. ended 12/31/04): Assets, $3,697,481 (M); gifts received, $3,993; expenditures, $193,345; total giving, $163,210; qualifying distributions, $170,613; giving activities include $163,210 for 26 grants (high: $100,000; low: $100).
Purpose and activities: Giving primarily for cultural institutes with emphasis on the general needs of local organizations in the Grand Rapids, MI, area.
Fields of interest: Arts; Housing/shelter; Human services; Roman Catholic agencies & churches.
Type of support: General/operating support; Continuing support; Capital campaigns; Building/renovation; Endowments; Emergency funds.
Limitations: Applications not accepted. Giving primarily in Grand Rapids, MI.
Application information: Unsolicited requests for funds not accepted.
   Board meeting date(s): Varies

Officers and Trustees:* Marilyn J.Q. Drake,* Pres.; John K. Drake,* V.P.; Leann L. Rowland, Secy.-Treas.; Joanne Q.D. Cooke; Rosemarie J. Drake; Kathleen E.D. Sanders.
EIN: 383068965
Selected grants: The following grants were reported in 2003.
$100,000 to Grand Rapids Art Museum, Grand Rapids, MI. For endowment.
$25,000 to Aquinas College, Grand Rapids, MI. For annual campaign.
$10,000 to Lake County Community Foundation, Baldwin, MI. For program support.
$3,000 to Saint Anns Catholic Church, Baldwin, MI. For food pantry.
$2,500 to Roosevelt University, Chicago, IL. For general support.
$1,000 to Grand Rapids Community Foundation, Grand Rapids, MI. For AIDS Project.
$1,000 to Mary Free Bed Hospital and Rehabilitation Center, Grand Rapids, MI. For general support.
$1,000 to Saint Marys College, Notre Dame, IN. For general support.
$1,000 to Salvation Army of Grand Rapids, Grand Rapids, MI. For general support.
$1,000 to Van Andel Institute, Grand Rapids, MI. For Hope on the Hill.

481
Drew & Mike Charitable Private Foundation
c/o Comerica Bank
P.O. Box 75000
Detroit, MI   48275-3302
Application address: c/o Kimberly Hill, 101 N. Main St., Ann Arbor, MI 48104, tel.: (734) 930-2405

Established in 2002 in MI.
Donors: Lynn Marie Temby; D&M Productions.
Grantmaker type: Independent foundation.
Financial data (yr. ended 12/31/05): Assets, $127,550 (M); gifts received, $25,050; expenditures, $14,294; total giving, $12,000; qualifying distributions, $12,500; giving activities include $12,000 for grants.
Purpose and activities: Financial assistance to families of members of law enforcement or local armed forces from the seven counties in southeast Michigan.
Type of support: Grants to individuals.
Limitations: Giving in the seven counties of southeast MI.
Application information:
   Initial approach: Letter
   Deadline(s): None
Trustee: Comerica Bank.
EIN: 436874093

482
Drew Family Foundation
P.O. Box 639
Suttons Bay, MI   49682-0639   (231) 271-4127
Contact: Gary P. Drew, Pres.

Established in 1998 in MI.
Donors: Gary Drew; Sandra Drew.
Grantmaker type: Independent foundation.
Financial data (yr. ended 12/31/05): Assets, $179,810 (M); expenditures, $22,075; total giving,

$20,800; qualifying distributions, $20,800; giving activities include $20,800 for grants.
Limitations: Giving on a national basis, with some emphasis on MI. No support for organizations lacking 501(c)(3) status. No grants to individuals.
Application information:
Initial approach: Letter
Deadline(s): None
Officers and Directors:* Gary Drew,* Pres. and Treas.; Sandra Drew,* V.P. and Secy.
EIN: 383417301

483
Dryden Family Foundation
2560 Dease Lake Rd.
Hale, MI 48739-8812

Established in 2000 in MI.
Donors: Richard G. Dryden; Janet M. Dryden.
Grantmaker type: Independent foundation.
Financial data (yr. ended 12/31/05): Assets, $1,060,022 (M); gifts received, $300,000; expenditures, $52,474; total giving, $45,606; qualifying distributions, $45,606; giving activities include $45,606 for grants.
Fields of interest: Education; Animal welfare; Human services; Christian agencies & churches.
Type of support: General/operating support.
Limitations: Applications not accepted. Giving on a national basis, with some emphasis on FL and MI. No grants to individuals.
Application information: Contributes only to pre-selected organizations.
Officers: Richard G. Dryden, Pres.; Janet M. Dryden, Secy.
Directors: Daniel A. Dryden; Jill M. Ihrke; Susan E. Roberts; Jay D. Rogers; Julie B. Welker.
EIN: 383527211

484
Dryer Family Foundation
19503 E. 8 Mile Rd.
St. Clair Shores, MI 48080-1643
(586) 775-3100
Contact: Jon B. Gandelot, Tr.
FAX: (586) 775-3250; E-mail: jbg@gandelot.com

Grantmaker type: Independent foundation.
Financial data (yr. ended 12/31/05): Assets, $550,000 (M); total giving, $27,500; giving activities include $27,500 for grants.
Purpose and activities: Provides funding for youth and for diseases of the eye.
Fields of interest: Eye diseases; Youth.
Limitations: Applications not accepted. Giving primarily in the metropolitan Detroit, MI, area.

485
DSL Foundation
P.O. Box 20339
Ferndale, MI 48220

Established in MI.
Donor: Charles L. Levin.
Grantmaker type: Independent foundation.
Financial data (yr. ended 11/30/04): Assets, $91,751 (M); expenditures, $13,795; total giving, $12,358; qualifying distributions, $13,709; giving activities include $12,358 for grants.

Fields of interest: Health organizations; Jewish agencies & temples.
Limitations: Applications not accepted. Giving primarily in Detroit, MI. No grants to individuals.
Application information: Contributes only to pre-selected organizations.
Officers and Trustees:* Charles L. Levin,* Pres.; Arthur D. Levin,* V.P.; Amy Regan,* Secy.
EIN: 382527474

486
DSLT Foundation
(formerly The Diamond Crystal Foundation)
c/o Fifth Third Bank
P.O. Box 630858
Cincinnati, OH 45263
Contact: Frederick S. Moore, Tr.
Application address: 1362 N. River Rd., St. Clair, MI 48079

Established in 1955 in MI.
Grantmaker type: Independent foundation.
Financial data (yr. ended 12/31/04): Assets, $957,176 (M); expenditures, $54,033; total giving, $47,300; qualifying distributions, $46,282; giving activities include $47,300 for grants.
Purpose and activities: Giving primarily for health and social services.
Fields of interest: Education; Health organizations, association; Human services; Community development; Federated giving programs.
Limitations: Giving in MI, primarily in St. Clair and Port Huron. No grants to individuals.
Publications: Annual report.
Application information:
Initial approach: Letter
Deadline(s): None
Trustees: Hugh McMorran; Franklin H. Moore, Jr.; Frederick S. Moore.
EIN: 386055060

487
Ruth Dubois Scholarship Fund
c/o Fifth Third Bank
P.O. Box 630858
Cincinnati, OH 45263

Established in 1995 in MI.
Donor: Ruth Dubois‡.
Grantmaker type: Independent foundation.
Financial data (yr. ended 12/31/05): Assets, $590,228 (M); expenditures, $5,832; total giving, $0; qualifying distributions, $0.
Purpose and activities: Support only for Ludington Area Public Schools, Ludington, MI.
Fields of interest: Elementary/secondary education.
Type of support: Scholarship funds.
Limitations: Applications not accepted. Giving limited to Ludington, MI. No grants to individuals.
Application information: Contributes only to a pre-selected organization.
Trustee: Fifth Third Bank.
EIN: 386664958

488
Doris J. & Donald L. Duchene Foundation
c/o Comerica Bank
P.O. Box 75000, M/C 3302
Detroit, MI 48275
Contact: Gary Spicer, Secy.
Application address: 16845 Kercheval, Ste. 5, Grosse Pointe, MI 48230, tel.: (313) 884-9700

Established in 1997 in MI.
Donor: Doris Duchene.
Grantmaker type: Independent foundation.
Financial data (yr. ended 12/31/05): Assets, $718,963 (M); expenditures, $53,354; total giving, $43,000; qualifying distributions, $43,000; giving activities include $43,000 for grants.
Purpose and activities: Giving primarily for education.
Fields of interest: Elementary/secondary education; Higher education; Roman Catholic agencies & churches.
Limitations: Giving primarily in Detroit, MI.
Application information: Application form not required.
Deadline(s): None
Officers: Donald L. Duchene, Sr., Pres.; Gary Spicer, Secy.; David Wind, Treas.
EIN: 383312705

489
The Robert J. Duffey Foundation
206 W. Noble Ave.
Monroe, MI 48162

Established in 1999 in MI.
Grantmaker type: Independent foundation.
Financial data (yr. ended 12/31/04): Assets, $428,392 (M); expenditures, $112,876; total giving, $111,805; qualifying distributions, $111,663; giving activities include $111,805 for 21 grants (high: $55,750; low: $25).
Fields of interest: Arts; Education; Roman Catholic agencies & churches.
Limitations: Giving primarily in MI.
Board Members: Terry Carlton; Colleen Duffey; John K. Duffey; Robert Duffey II.
EIN: 383472631

490
The Duffy Foundation
c/o Miller Canfield, Attn.: Erik H. Serr
101 N. Main St., 7th Fl.
Ann Arbor, MI 48104

Established in 1989 in MI.
Donors: Howard S. Holmes; Andrea L. Holmes; Mary B. Holmes.
Grantmaker type: Independent foundation.
Financial data (yr. ended 12/31/05): Assets, $45,090,284 (M); expenditures, $3,690,981; total giving, $3,552,500; qualifying distributions, $3,552,500; giving activities include $3,552,500 for 52 grants (high: $1,500,000; low: $2,500).
Purpose and activities: Giving primarily to a hospital; giving also to animal protection organizations, environmental conservation, human services, and services for the elderly.
Fields of interest: Arts; Environment, natural resources; Animal welfare; Animals/wildlife, special services; Hospitals (general); Crime/violence prevention, domestic violence; Food services; YM/

YWCAs & YM/YWHAs; Children/youth, services; Aging.
Limitations: Applications not accepted. Giving primarily in MI, with emphasis on Ann Arbor and Washtenaw County. No grants to individuals.
Application information: Contributes only to pre-selected organizations.
Officers and Directors:* Andrea L. Holmes,* Pres. and Treas.; Christine M. Holmes,* V.P.; Kathryn W. Holmes,* V.P.
EIN: 382908719

491
Hubert and Marie Duffy Memorial Trust
120 S. Berkshire Rd.
Bloomfield Hills, MI 48302-0410

Established in 1991 in MI.
Donor: Marie Duffy‡.
Grantmaker type: Independent foundation.
Financial data (yr. ended 9/30/05): Assets, $642,069 (M); expenditures, $43,896; total giving, $40,000; qualifying distributions, $40,000; giving activities include $40,000 for grants.
Fields of interest: Roman Catholic agencies & churches.
Limitations: Applications not accepted. No grants to individuals.
Application information: Contributes only to pre-selected organizations.
Trustee: Gerald R. Gase.
EIN: 386559353

492
Dul Foundation, Inc.
5600 Curtis Rd.
Plymouth, MI 48170

Established in 1997 in MI.
Grantmaker type: Independent foundation.
Financial data (yr. ended 12/31/04): Assets, $704,998 (M); expenditures, $32,234; total giving, $30,500; qualifying distributions, $30,571; giving activities include $30,500 for grants.
Fields of interest: Philanthropy/voluntarism.
Limitations: Applications not accepted. Giving primarily in Hudson, OH. No grants to individuals.
Application information: Contributes only to pre-selected organizations.
Officers: Kathleen D. Aznavorian, Pres.
Directors: John A. Gallina; Philip T. Tobin.
EIN: 383340073

493
Evangeline L. Dumesnil Trust
c/o National City Bank of MI/IL
P.O. Box 94651
Cleveland, OH 44101-4651

Established in 1983 in MI.
Donor: Evangeline L. Dumesnil‡.
Grantmaker type: Independent foundation.
Financial data (yr. ended 12/31/05): Assets, $5,835,971 (M); expenditures, $229,594; total giving, $187,498; qualifying distributions, $187,498; giving activities include $187,498 for grants.
Purpose and activities: Giving limited to music scholarships at the University of Michigan and Wayne State University.

Fields of interest: Performing arts, music.
Type of support: Scholarship funds.
Limitations: Applications not accepted. Giving limited to Ann Arbor and Detroit, MI. No grants to individuals.
Application information: Contributes only to 2 pre-selected organizations.
Trustee: Myron Alpert.
EIN: 386473007

494
Dunagan Family Foundation
6660 Delmonico Dr., Ste. D
Colorado Springs, CO 80919-1856

Established in 1997 in MI.
Donor: Rick Dunagan.
Grantmaker type: Independent foundation.
Financial data (yr. ended 12/31/04): Assets, $19,845 (M); gifts received, $36,992; expenditures, $70,693; total giving, $70,395; qualifying distributions, $70,395; giving activities include $70,395 for grants.
Fields of interest: Christian agencies & churches.
Limitations: Applications not accepted. Giving primarily in IL and MI. No grants to individuals.
Application information: Contributes only to pre-selected organizations.
Directors: Judy A. Dunagan; Rick Dunagan.
EIN: 421475698

495
The Dunn-Mason Foundation
26233 Dundalk Ln.
Farmington Hills, MI 48334

Established in 2002 in MI.
Donor: Wendell Mason.
Grantmaker type: Independent foundation.
Financial data (yr. ended 12/31/02): Assets, $0 (M); gifts received, $21,600; expenditures, $22,171; total giving, $8,068; qualifying distributions, $0; giving activities include $8,068 for grants.
Limitations: Applications not accepted. No grants to individuals.
Application information: Contributes only to pre-selected organizations.
Trustees: Mary F. Dunn-Mason; Kamaria Mason; Wendell Mason.
EIN: 141837385

496
Margaret Dunning Foundation
994 Penniman Ave.
Plymouth, MI 48170-1624   (734) 453-7566
Contact: Margaret Dunning, Pres.

Established in 1997 in MI.
Donors: Margaret Dunning; Irene Walldorf.
Grantmaker type: Independent foundation.
Financial data (yr. ended 12/31/05): Assets, $327,691 (M); expenditures, $15,482; total giving, $7,496; qualifying distributions, $7,496; giving activities include $7,496 for grants.
Fields of interest: Historic preservation/historical societies.
Limitations: Giving primarily in Plymouth, MI.
Application information:

Initial approach: Proposal
Deadline(s): None
Officers: Margaret Dunning, Pres.; Robert M. Stulberg, V.P. and Secy.
Trustees: Phillip M. Appel; Robert Appel; Betty Barbour; Lloyd Leach; Lois Stulberg.
EIN: 383352930

497
Dunnings Foundation, Inc.
530 S. Pine St.
Lansing, MI 48933

Grantmaker type: Independent foundation.
Financial data (yr. ended 9/30/05): Assets, $250,344 (M); expenditures, $17,204; total giving, $13,445; qualifying distributions, $13,445; giving activities include $13,445 for grants.
Officers: Stuart J. Dunnings, Jr., Pres. and Secy.-Treas.
Director: Susan Dunnings.
EIN: 382709388

498
Duzyj Charitable Foundation
26657 Haverhill Dr.
Warren, MI 48091

Grantmaker type: Independent foundation.
Financial data (yr. ended 11/30/05): Assets, $169,026 (M); gifts received, $8,500; expenditures, $8,520; total giving, $8,500; qualifying distributions, $8,500; giving activities include $8,500 for grants.
Fields of interest: Education.
Type of support: General/operating support.
Limitations: Applications not accepted. No grants to individuals.
Application information: Contributes only to pre-selected organizations.
Officer: Jaroslaw Duzyj, Pres.
Directors: Warren J. Decook; Robert B. Frederick.
EIN: 383215252

499
Dyer-Ives Foundation
Waters Bldg.
161 Ottawa Ave. N.W., Ste. 501-H
Grand Rapids, MI 49503   (616) 452-4502
Contact: Linda B. Patterson, Exec. Dir.
FAX: (616) 454-8545; E-mail: dyer_ives@msn.com; Additional E-mail: linda@dyer-ives.org; URL: http://www.dyer-ives.org

Established in 1961 in MI.
Donor: John R. Hunting.
Grantmaker type: Independent foundation.
Financial data (yr. ended 8/31/05): Assets, $7,305,920 (M); expenditures, $481,913; total giving, $300,684; qualifying distributions, $415,725; giving activities include $300,684 for 39 grants (high: $24,000; low: $220), and $66,577 for 2 foundation-administered programs.
Purpose and activities: Acts primarily as a catalyst and stimulator for small innovative projects that encourage a sense of community in educational, social, environmental or cultural fields.
Fields of interest: Humanities; Arts; Education; Environment; Employment; Housing/shelter; Youth development, services; Human services;

Community development, neighborhood development.

Type of support: Program development; Publication; Seed money; Curriculum development; Technical assistance; Consulting services.

Limitations: Giving limited to the central city of Grand Rapids, MI. No grants to individuals, or for building or endowment funds, operating budgets, or scholarship funds.

Publications: Biennial report (including application guidelines); Financial statement; Grants list; Informational brochure (including application guidelines); Multi-year report.

Application information: Application form not required.

Initial approach: Telephone and proposal
Copies of proposal: 1
Deadline(s): None
Board meeting date(s): Monthly
Final notification: After board meetings

Officers: John R. Hunting, Chair.; John D. Hibbard, Jr., Vice-Chair.; Bradford Mathis, Pres.; Jose L. Rayna, V.P.; R. Malcolm Cumming, Secy.; Susan Cobb, Treas.; Linda B. Patterson, Exec. Dir.

Directors: George A. Bayard; Jocelyn Dettloff; Paul Haan; Debra K. Muller; David Schroeder; Mary Banghart Therrien; Carol L. Townsend.

Number of staff: 2 part-time professional.

EIN: 386049657

Selected grants: The following grants were reported in 2003.

$20,000 to Michigan Organizing Project, Kalamazoo, MI.

$15,000 to Lighthouse Communities, Grand Rapids, MI. For townhomes.

$13,000 to Roosevelt Park Neighborhood Association, Grand Rapids, MI. For Grandville Avenue Infrastructure Survey.

$11,600 to United Way, Heart of West Michigan, Grand Rapids, MI. To establish Web site.

$10,000 to Grand Rapids Community College Foundation, Grand Rapids, MI. For Neighborhood Planning Project.

$7,000 to Dwelling Place of Grand Rapids, Grand Rapids, MI.

$6,736 to City Vision, Grand Rapids, MI. For computer equipment and training.

$6,000 to Creston Neighborhood Association, Grand Rapids, MI.

$5,000 to Aquinas College, Grand Rapids, MI. For Get the Lead Out Project.

$4,000 to Comprehensive Therapy Center, Grand Rapids, MI. For promotional video.

500
Robert T. and Marthene Vandyke Dykstra Charitable Foundation
P.O. Box 902
Wyoming, MI   49509

Established in 1988 in MI.

Donors: Robert T. Dykstra; Marthene Van Dyke Dykstra; Thomas Dykstra; Deborah Dykstra.

Grantmaker type: Independent foundation.

Financial data (yr. ended 12/31/04): Assets, $330,755 (M); expenditures, $55,245; total giving, $52,345; qualifying distributions, $54,520; giving activities include $52,345 for grants.

Purpose and activities: Giving for religious organizations.

Fields of interest: Higher education, college; Christian agencies & churches.

Limitations: Applications not accepted. Giving on a national basis, with some emphasis on MI. No grants to individuals.

Application information: Contributes only to pre-selected organizations.

Trustee: Thomas Dykstra.

EIN: 382843644

501
Dykstra Foundation
1173 W. Glengarry Cir.
Bloomfield Hills, MI   48301   (248) 644-8264
Contact: Betty Steele, Pres.

Grantmaker type: Independent foundation.

Financial data (yr. ended 12/31/05): Assets, $539,314 (M); expenditures, $26,729; total giving, $25,000; qualifying distributions, $25,000; giving activities include $25,000 for grants.

Fields of interest: Hospitals (general).

Limitations: Giving in the U.S., with emphasis on Detroit, MI. No grants to individuals.

Application information: Application form not required.

Deadline(s): None

Officers: Betty Steele, Pres.; Marion Hawkins, V.P.; John O. Steele, Secy.-Treas.

EIN: 386066092

502
E-B Foundation
32606 Pine Ridge Dr.
Warren, MI   48093-1000

Established in 2001 in MI.

Donor: Earl-Beth Foundation.

Grantmaker type: Independent foundation.

Financial data (yr. ended 12/31/05): Assets, $2,294,163 (M); expenditures, $148,479; total giving, $109,925; qualifying distributions, $123,937; giving activities include $109,925 for 27 grants (high: $25,000; low: $250).

Fields of interest: Education; Human services; Children/youth, services.

Limitations: Applications not accepted. Giving primarily in IL, MI, and NY. No grants to individuals.

Application information: Contributes only to pre-selected organizations.

Officers and Directors:* Mark Holley,* Pres.; Guadalupe M. Holley,* V.P.; Helen M. Fowler,* Secy.-Treas.

EIN: 383577561

503
E.D.P. Foundation
5940 Tahoe Dr. S.E.
Grand Rapids, MI   49546-7121

Established in 1996 in MI.

Donors: Daniel B. Pfeiffer; Eugene K. Pfeiffer.

Grantmaker type: Independent foundation.

Financial data (yr. ended 6/30/05): Assets, $26,705 (M); gifts received, $50,000; expenditures, $46,477; total giving, $46,477; qualifying distributions, $46,477; giving activities include $46,477 for grants.

Limitations: Applications not accepted. Giving primarily in Grand Rapids, MI. No grants to individuals.

Application information: Contributes only to pre-selected organizations.

Officers and Directors:* Daniel B. Pfeiffer,* Pres.; Ronald Sytsma,* V.P.; Timothy P. Miller,* Secy.-Treas.

EIN: 383323377

504
The Eagle Family Foundation
c/o Campbell & Assocs.
462 Stevens Ave., No. 103
Solana Beach, CA   92075

Established in 1999 in IN.

Donors: Juanita K. Eagle; Michael L. Eagle; Eagle Charitable Lead Unitrust.

Grantmaker type: Independent foundation.

Financial data (yr. ended 12/31/04): Assets, $52,598 (M); gifts received, $36,539; expenditures, $138,005; total giving, $137,167; qualifying distributions, $136,436; giving activities include $137,167 for 5 grants (high: $100,000; low: $2,500).

Fields of interest: Museums (art); Higher education; Children/youth, services.

Limitations: Applications not accepted. Giving primarily in IN and MI; giving also in NM. No grants to individuals.

Application information: Contributes only to pre-selected organizations.

Trustees: Juanita L. Eagle; Michael L. Eagle.

EIN: 356664755

505
Eagle Foundation
235 Central Ave.
Holland, MI   49423-3128

Established in 1989 in MI.

Donors: Craig Wierda; Emilie D. Wierda; Prince Holding Corp.

Grantmaker type: Independent foundation.

Financial data (yr. ended 6/30/05): Assets, $3,218 (M); expenditures, $10,040; total giving, $10,100; qualifying distributions, $10,100; giving activities include $10,100 for grants.

Fields of interest: Higher education; Family services.

Type of support: General/operating support.

Limitations: Applications not accepted. Giving primarily in CO and MI. No grants to individuals.

Application information: Contributes only to pre-selected organizations.

Officers: Emilie D. Wierda, Pres.; Robert Haveman, Secy.; Craig Wierda, Treas.

EIN: 382902414

506
Earhart Foundation
2200 Green Rd., Ste. H
Ann Arbor, MI   48105
Contact: Ingrid A. Gregg, Pres.

Incorporated in 1929 in MI.

Donor: Harry Boyd Earhart‡.

Grantmaker type: Independent foundation.

Financial data (yr. ended 12/31/05): Assets, $61,971,515 (M); expenditures, $12,735,116; total giving, $11,441,524; qualifying distributions, $12,423,221; giving activities include $7,671,934 for 306 grants (high: $1,722,048; low: $400; average: $5,000–$50,000), and $3,769,590 for 304 grants to individuals (high: $41,800; low: $375; average: $6,700–$25,000).

Purpose and activities: H.B. Earhart Fellowships for graduate study awarded through a special nominating process for which direct applications will not be accepted; research fellowships for individual projects in economics, history, philosophy, international affairs, and political science awarded upon direct application to faculty members; grants also to educational and research organizations legally qualified for private foundation support.

Fields of interest: History/archaeology; Philosophy/ethics; Graduate/professional education; Economics; Political science; International studies.

Type of support: Conferences/seminars; Publication; Curriculum development; Fellowships; Research; Grants to individuals; Scholarships—to individuals.

Publications: Annual report (including application guidelines).

Application information: Direct applications from candidates or uninvited sponsors for H.B. Earhart Fellowships (for graduate study) are not accepted. Application form not required.

Initial approach: Letter
Copies of proposal: 1
Deadline(s): Proposal should be submitted at least 120 days before beginning of project work period
Board meeting date(s): Monthly except in Aug.

Officers and Trustees:* Dennis L. Bark,* Chair.; John H. Moore,* Vice-Chair.; Ingrid A. Gregg,* Pres.; Montgomery B. Brown, Secy. and Dir., Progs.; Kathleen B. Mason, Treas.; Peter B. Clark, Tr. Emeritus; Paul W. McCracken, Tr. Emeritus; Richard A. Ware, Tr. Emeritus; Thomas J. Bray; Kimberly O. Dennis; Earl I. Heenan III; Ann K. Irish; David B. Kennedy; Robert L. Queller.

Number of staff: 2 full-time professional; 3 full-time support.

EIN: 386008273

Selected grants: The following grants were reported in 2004.

$75,000 to Intercollegiate Studies Institute, Wilmington, DE. For fellowships.

$60,000 to Social Philosophy and Policy Foundation, Bowling Green, OH. For visiting scholars in fields of history and philosophy.

$55,100 to Jamestown Foundation, DC. For publication of Terrorism Focus.

$50,000 to Citizens Research Council of Michigan, Livonia, MI. For project, Facilitating Michigan Local Government Response to Financial Pressures.

$33,841 to University of Chicago, Law School, Chicago, IL. For visiting fellowship in Law, Economics and Government.

$27,273 to Mississippi State University, Center for International Security and Strategic Studies, Mississippi State, MS. For International Cooperation in War Against Terror in Asia-Pacific Region.

$25,000 to Philadelphia Society, Chicago, IL. For travel by graduate students and/or junior faculty to attend National Meeting in Chicago, Illinois and Regional Meeting in Philadelphia, Pennsylvania.

$15,000 to Sarah Lawrence College, Bronxville, NY. For Benardete Archive for graduate student's assistance in organizing and archival of Seth Benardete Papers housed in Raymond Fogelman Library of New School University.

$13,925 to Tufts University, Fletcher School of Law and Diplomacy, Medford, MA. For graduate fellowship in International Security Studies.

$13,000 to Westminster Theological Seminary, Department of Church History, Glenside, PA. For graduate fellowship in Religion.

507
Eva Earle Charitable Trust
c/o Citizens Bank Wealth Mgmt., N.A.
328 S. Saginaw St., M/C 002072
Flint, MI 48507

Grantmaker type: Independent foundation.

Financial data (yr. ended 12/31/05): Assets, $209,730 (M); expenditures, $17,143; total giving, $13,599; qualifying distributions, $13,599; giving activities include $13,599 for grants.

Purpose and activities: Support only for Hartley Memorial Library and Thomas Township Library, MI.

Fields of interest: Libraries/library science.

Limitations: Applications not accepted. Giving limited to MI. No grants to individuals.

Application information: Contributes only to 2 pre-selected organizations.

Trustee: Citizens Bank.

EIN: 386246574

508
C. K. Eddy Family Memorial Fund
c/o Citizens Bank Wealth Mgmt., N.A.
328 S. Saginaw St., M/C 002072
Flint, MI 48502
Application address: Helen James, Trust Off., c/o Citizens Bank Wealth Mgmt., N.A., 101 N. Washington Ave., Saginaw, MI 48007, tel.: (989) 776-7368

Trust established in 1925 in MI.

Donor: Arthur D. Eddy†.

Grantmaker type: Independent foundation.

Financial data (yr. ended 6/30/05): Assets, $16,004,061 (M); expenditures, $918,201; total giving, $703,191; qualifying distributions, $1,091,984; giving activities include $703,191 for 27 grants (high: $101,000; low: $2,025), and $225,200 for 64 loans to individuals (high: $4,000; low: $1,000).

Purpose and activities: Giving primarily for student loans and community programs.

Fields of interest: Museums (children's); Education; Boys & girls clubs; Human services; Children/youth, services; Federated giving programs.

Type of support: Equipment; Program development; Student loans—to individuals.

Limitations: Giving limited to Saginaw County, MI, with some emphasis on the city of Saginaw.

Publications: Application guidelines.

Application information: Application form required.
Deadline(s): None for grants; May 1 for student loans
Board meeting date(s): 3rd Wed. of Mar., June, Sept., and Dec.

Trustee: Citizens Bank.

EIN: 386040506

509
Edelweiss Foundation
32606 Pine Ridge Dr.
Warren, MI 48093

Established in 2000 in MI.

Donor: Earl-Beth Foundation.

Grantmaker type: Independent foundation.

Financial data (yr. ended 12/31/05): Assets, $2,109,770 (M); expenditures, $116,955; total giving, $78,700; qualifying distributions, $78,700; giving activities include $78,700 for 12 grants (high: $50,000; low: $200).

Fields of interest: Museums; Elementary/secondary education.

Limitations: Applications not accepted. Giving primarily in MI. No grants to individuals.

Application information: Contributes only to pre-selected organizations.

Officers: Janie Holley Fleckenstein, Pres. and Secy.; John A. Fleckenstein, Treas.

EIN: 383576636

510
John and Penny Edison Family Foundation
161 Ottawa Ave. N.W., Ste. 511
Grand Rapids, MI 49503

Grantmaker type: Independent foundation.

Financial data (yr. ended 12/31/05): Assets, $176,538 (M); gifts received, $150,759; expenditures, $9,021; total giving, $8,500; qualifying distributions, $8,500; giving activities include $8,500 for grants.

Limitations: Applications not accepted. No grants to individuals.

Application information: Contributes only to pre-selected organizations.

Directors: Hennetta B. Edison; Jeffrey S. Edison; John S. Edison; Lewis S. Edison; Paul M. Edison.

EIN: 383648319

511
Ruth Edrington Charitable Foundation
c/o Comerica Bank
P.O. Box 75000, M/C 3302
Detroit, MI 48275-3302

Established in 2003 in MI.

Donor: Ruth Edrington Charitable Remainder Trust.

Grantmaker type: Independent foundation.

Financial data (yr. ended 10/31/05): Assets, $723,110 (M); gifts received, $511,148; expenditures, $45,654; total giving, $29,847; qualifying distributions, $29,847; giving activities include $29,847 for grants.

Limitations: Applications not accepted. No grants to individuals.

Application information: Contributes only to pre-selected organizations.

Trustee: Comerica Bank.

EIN: 043792853

512
Eddie K. & Mary D. Edwards Foundation
19025 Wildemere St.
Detroit, MI 48221-2293

Established in 2002 in MI.

Grantmaker type: Independent foundation.

Financial data (yr. ended 12/31/03): Assets, $23,523 (M); gifts received, $23,275; expenditures, $0; total giving, $0; qualifying distributions, $0.

Trustees: Eddie K. Edwards; Mary D. Edwards.
EIN: 050524614

513
William J. and Julia M. Edwards Foundation
3023 Davenport Ave.
Saginaw, MI 48602-3652
Contact: William J. Edwards, Pres.

Grantmaker type: Independent foundation.
Financial data (yr. ended 4/30/05): Assets,
$904,500 (M); expenditures, $46,200; total giving,
$44,000; qualifying distributions, $44,000; giving
activities include $44,000 for grants.
Fields of interest: Higher education, college; Higher
education, university; Health organizations,
association; Human services; Christian agencies &
churches.
Limitations: Giving primarily in FL, with some giving
in IL and MI.
Application information:
Initial approach: Letter
Deadline(s): None
Officers: William J. Edwards, Pres.; Julia M.
Edwards, V.P.; Julia B. Edwards, Secy.
Directors: Stacey Riley Baker; Lance C. Edwards;
Anne E. Riley; Bruce A. Riley; Bruce P. Riley; Linda
E. Riley.
EIN: 382529635

514
The Effendi Foundation
26300 Telegraph Rd., 2nd Fl.
Southfield, MI 48034

Established in 2003.
Grantmaker type: Independent foundation.
Financial data (yr. ended 12/31/05): Assets,
$197,686 (M); gifts received, $75,000;
expenditures, $18,555; total giving, $17,850;
qualifying distributions, $17,850; giving activities
include $17,850 for grants.
Officer: Abdul R. Effendi, Pres.
EIN: 200504669

515
The Egger Private Foundation, Inc.
14243 Balmoral Rd.
Riverview, MI 48192

Established in 1997 in FL; funded in 1998.
Donor: Jewell Egger.
Grantmaker type: Independent foundation.
Financial data (yr. ended 12/31/05): Assets,
$81,709 (M); expenditures, $6,586; total giving,
$5,000; qualifying distributions, $5,000; giving
activities include $5,000 for grants.
Fields of interest: Protestant agencies & churches.
Type of support: General/operating support.
Limitations: Applications not accepted. Giving
primarily in FL. No grants to individuals.
Application information: Contributes only to
pre-selected organizations.
Officers: Jewell Egger, Pres.; Kenneth L. Egger, Jr.,
V.P.; Kimberly I. Egger, V.P.; Kenneth L. Egger,
Secy.-Treas.
EIN: 650746709

516
Arnulf F. Ehmer Foundation
P.O. Box 766
Jackson, MI 49204-0766

Established in 2000 in MI.
Grantmaker type: Independent foundation.
Financial data (yr. ended 12/31/05): Assets,
$48,649 (M); expenditures, $6,600; total giving,
$5,000; qualifying distributions, $5,000; giving
activities include $5,000 for grants.
Fields of interest: Roman Catholic agencies &
churches.
Limitations: Applications not accepted. Giving
primarily in MI and MO. No grants to individuals.
Application information: Contributes only to
pre-selected organizations.
Trustee: Philip J. Curtis.
EIN: 383573622

517
Pat & Herb Eldean Family Foundation
1 Eldean Dr.
Macatawa, MI 49434-0006

Established in 2003 in MI.
Donors: Herb Eldean; Pat Eldean.
Grantmaker type: Independent foundation.
Financial data (yr. ended 12/31/05): Assets,
$171,149 (M); gifts received, $62,022;
expenditures, $6,670; total giving, $6,500;
qualifying distributions, $6,500; giving activities
include $6,500 for grants.
Limitations: Applications not accepted. No grants to
individuals.
Application information: Contributes only to
pre-selected organizations.
Officers: Herb Eldean, Pres.; Pat Eldean, V.P.
EIN: 412026050

518
Phillip G. Ellias Scholarship Foundation
2727 Rutledge St.
Trenton, MI 48183-2563

Established in 1993.
Grantmaker type: Independent foundation.
Financial data (yr. ended 12/31/04): Assets,
$22,944 (M); gifts received, $731; expenditures,
$3,032; total giving, $3,000; qualifying
distributions, $3,000; giving activities include
$3,000 for grants.
Fields of interest: Education.
Type of support: Scholarship funds.
Limitations: Applications not accepted. Giving
primarily in Trenton, MI.
Application information: Contributes only to
pre-selected organizations.
Officers: Ellen Charnes, Pres.; Howard Ellias, Secy.;
Margaret Charnes, Treas.
EIN: 383143094

519
The Elson Family Charitable Trust
c/o Donald Croy
2281 Kirk Rd.
Fairview, MI 48621 (989) 848-5651

Established in 1995 in OH.
Grantmaker type: Independent foundation.
Financial data (yr. ended 12/31/04): Assets,
$1,392,625 (M); expenditures, $138,038; total
giving, $53,402; qualifying distributions, $67,661;
giving activities include $53,402 for grants.
Purpose and activities: Giving primarily for youth
development and services.
Fields of interest: Recreation; YM/YWCAs & YM/
YWHAs.
Type of support: General/operating support.
Limitations: Applications not accepted. Giving
primarily in OH. No grants to individuals.
Application information: Contributes only to
pre-selected organizations.
Trustee: Donald Croy.
EIN: 346855820

520
Alvin and Marty Elzinga Foundation
c/o Steven C. Elzinga
125 Meadow Green Ct.
Caledonia, MI 49316

Established in 2003 in MI.
Donors: Alvin B. Elzinga; Marty Elzinga.
Grantmaker type: Independent foundation.
Financial data (yr. ended 12/31/04): Assets,
$60,739 (M); gifts received, $5,000; expenditures,
$7,423; total giving, $6,675; qualifying
distributions, $6,675; giving activities include
$6,675 for grants.
Limitations: Applications not accepted. No grants to
individuals.
Application information: Contributes only to
pre-selected organizations.
Officers: Alvin B. Elzinga, Pres. and Treas.; Marty
Elzinga, V.P. and Secy.
Director: Steven Elzinga.
EIN: 100274373

521
Emergency Medicine Education and Research Foundation
2384 Heronwood Dr.
Bloomfield Hills, MI 48302

Established in 1991 in MI.
Donors: Mrs. Thomas J. Petinga, Jr.; Thomas J.
Petinga, Jr.
Grantmaker type: Independent foundation.
Financial data (yr. ended 12/31/05): Assets,
$44,290 (M); gifts received, $1,500; expenditures,
$4,013; total giving, $3,500; qualifying
distributions, $3,500; giving activities include
$3,500 for grants.
Fields of interest: Medical care, in-patient care;
Health care, EMS.
Limitations: Applications not accepted. Giving
primarily in Bloomfield, MI. No grants to individuals.
Application information: Contributes only to
pre-selected organizations.
Officers: Thomas J. Petinga, Jr., Pres. and Treas.;
Christina Petinga, Secy.
EIN: 383019607

522
David & Edith Emerman Foundation, Inc.
31155 Northwestern Hwy., Ste. 250
Farmington Hills, MI 48334

Grantmaker type: Independent foundation.

Financial data (yr. ended 12/31/05): Assets, $144,689 (M); expenditures, $11,630; total giving, $9,865; qualifying distributions, $9,865; giving activities include $9,865 for grants.
Purpose and activities: Giving primarily for Jewish federated giving programs, education, health and human services.
Fields of interest: Education; Health care; Human services; Jewish federated giving programs.
Limitations: Applications not accepted. Giving primarily in Detroit, MI. No grants to individuals.
Application information: Contributes only to pre-selected organizations.
Officers: Denise Schmerin, Pres.; David Schmerin, V.P.
EIN: 386086967

523
En Gedi Foundation

P.O. Box 2172
Grand Rapids, MI 49501   (616) 530-7000
Contact: Daniel A. Gordon, Pres.

Established in 2000 in MI.
Donors: Daniel A. Gordon; Marguerite B. Gordon.
Grantmaker type: Independent foundation.
Financial data (yr. ended 12/31/05): Assets, $444,496 (M); gifts received, $75,000; expenditures, $13,255; total giving, $12,000; qualifying distributions, $12,000; giving activities include $12,000 for grants.
Application information:
  Initial approach: Letter
  Deadline(s): None
Officers: Daniel A. Gordon, Pres.; Marguerite B. Gordon, Secy.-Treas.
EIN: 383569279

524
Enberg Family Charitable Foundation

11601 Wilshire Blvd.
Los Angeles, CA 90025

Established in 1997 in CA.
Donors: Richard A. Enberg; Barbara Enberg.
Grantmaker type: Independent foundation.
Financial data (yr. ended 4/30/05): Assets, $521,626 (M); expenditures, $22,751; total giving, $22,000; qualifying distributions, $22,000; giving activities include $22,000 for grants.
Fields of interest: Higher education; Education.
Limitations: Applications not accepted. Giving primarily in CA and IN; some giving also in MI. No grants to individuals.
Application information: Contributes only to pre-selected organizations.
Trustees: Barbara Enberg; Richard A. Enberg.
EIN: 957027924

525
Marjory and Donald Epstein Family Charitable Foundation

16055 W. 12 Mile Rd.
Southfield, MI 48076   (248) 557-1600
Contact: Marjory Epstein, Dir.

Established in 1997 in MI.
Donor: Vesco Oil Corporation.
Grantmaker type: Independent foundation.

Financial data (yr. ended 12/31/05): Assets, $206,925 (M); gifts received, $31,000; expenditures, $8,164; total giving, $8,164; qualifying distributions, $8,164; giving activities include $8,164 for grants.
Fields of interest: Jewish agencies & temples.
Limitations: Giving primarily in MI; some giving also in New York, NY. No grants to individuals.
Application information: Application form not required.
  Deadline(s): None
Directors: Donald R. Epstein; Lillian J. Epstein; Marjory Epstein.
EIN: 383350806

526
Erb Foundation

800 N. Old Woodward Ave., Ste. 201
Birmingham, MI 48009-3802

Established in 1963.
Donors: Fred A. Erb; D.I.Y. Home Warehouse, Inc.
Grantmaker type: Independent foundation.
Financial data (yr. ended 12/31/04): Assets, $2,886,421 (M); expenditures, $907,425; total giving, $906,579; qualifying distributions, $906,825; giving activities include $110,258 for 89 grants (high: $25,000; low: $35), and $796,321 for 3 in-kind gifts.
Purpose and activities: Giving primarily to a zoological society, a sympohony, and for human and children's services.
Fields of interest: Performing arts, orchestra (symphony); Arts; Zoos/zoological societies; Human services; Children/youth, services; Federated giving programs; Government/public administration; Christian agencies & churches.
Type of support: General/operating support.
Limitations: Applications not accepted. Giving primarily in MI, with emphasis on Detroit. No grants to individuals.
Application information: Contributes only to pre-selected organizations.
Officers: Fred A. Erb, Pres.; Ira J. Jaffe, Secy.; John M. Erb, Treas.
EIN: 386083275

527
The Joseph & Linda Erlich Foundation

26172 Meadow Dr.
Franklin, MI 48025

Established in 1998 in MI.
Donors: Joseph E. Erlich; Linda Erlich.
Grantmaker type: Independent foundation.
Financial data (yr. ended 12/31/04): Assets, $75,410 (M); expenditures, $5,842; total giving, $5,288; qualifying distributions, $5,424; giving activities include $5,288 for grants.
Application information: Application form not required.
  Deadline(s): None
Directors: Joseph E. Erlich; Linda Erlich.
EIN: 383416469

528
J. F. Ervin Foundation

P.O. Box 1168
Ann Arbor, MI 48106-1168   (734) 769-4600
Contact: John Pearson, Pres. and Secy.

Established in 1953 in MI.
Donor: J.F. Ervin†.
Grantmaker type: Independent foundation.
Financial data (yr. ended 12/31/05): Assets, $2,945,242 (M); expenditures, $160,360; total giving, $158,500; qualifying distributions, $158,553; giving activities include $158,500 for 37 grants (high: $10,000; low: $1,000).
Purpose and activities: To assist in local needs; primary areas of interest include child welfare and development, delinquency, the elderly, and health services.
Fields of interest: Humanities; Arts; Child development, education; Hospitals (general); Health care; Substance abuse, services; Crime/violence prevention, youth; Children/youth, services; Child development, services; Aging, centers/services; Homeless, human services; Aging; Homeless.
Type of support: General/operating support; Continuing support; Annual campaigns; Emergency funds; Program development.
Limitations: Giving limited to Ann Arbor and Adrian, MI. No grants to individuals, or for scholarships; no loans.
Publications: Annual report (including application guidelines).
Application information: Application form not required.
  Initial approach: Proposal in letter form
  Copies of proposal: 1
  Deadline(s): None
Officers and Trustees:* John E. Pearson,* Pres. and Secy; James T. Pearson,* V.P.; Heidi Pearson,* Treas.; Susan R. Pearson.
Number of staff: 2 part-time support.
EIN: 386053755
Selected grants: The following grants were reported in 2003.
$10,000 to Salvation Army of Ann Arbor, Ann Arbor, MI.
$6,000 to Lenawee County Education Foundation, Adrian, MI.
$5,000 to American Red Cross, Adrian, MI.
$5,000 to Boys and Girls Club of Lenawee, Adrian, MI.
$4,000 to Ann Arbor Symphony Orchestra, Ann Arbor, MI.
$4,000 to Young Adults Health Center, Ypsilanti, MI.
$3,000 to Peace Neighborhood Center, Ann Arbor, MI.
$2,500 to Catholic Social Services of Lenawee County, Adrian, MI.
$2,000 to Ann Arbor Hands-On Museum, Ann Arbor, MI.
$1,000 to YMCA, Ann Arbor, Ann Arbor, MI.

529
The Rudolf & Ruth Eschbach Family Foundation

25101 Groesbeck Hwy.
Warren, MI 48089-1970

Established in 1997 in MI.
Donors: Reinhard Eschbach; Lisa Eschbach; Roland Eschbach.
Grantmaker type: Independent foundation.
Financial data (yr. ended 12/31/05): Assets, $117,241 (M); gifts received, $4,000; expenditures, $15,993; total giving, $15,000; qualifying distributions, $15,000; giving activities include $15,000 for grants.
Fields of interest: Performing arts, opera.
Limitations: Giving primarily in MI.

Application information:
Initial approach: Letter
Deadline(s): None
Officers: Ruth Eschbach, Pres.; Dietmar Eschbach, V.P.; Reinhard Eschbach, V.P.; Anita Hobbs, Secy.; Monica Eschbach, Treas.
EIN: 383310055

530
The Esperance Family Foundation
c/o Foundation Source
501 Silverside Rd., Ste. 123
Wilmington, DE   19809

Donors: Roger S. Newton; Coco Newton.
Grantmaker type: Independent foundation.
Financial data (yr. ended 12/31/04): Assets, $10,470,693 (M); gifts received, $9,729,000; expenditures, $313,568; total giving, $110,000; qualifying distributions, $131,289; giving activities include $110,000 for 2 grants (high: $75,000; low: $35,000).
Fields of interest: Performing arts, music; Performing arts, education; YM/YWCAs & YM/YWHAs.
Limitations: Applications not accepted. Giving primarily in CT and MI. No grants to individuals.
Application information: Contributes only to pre-selected organizations.
Officers and Directors:* Roger S. Newton, Pres.; Alex Newton,* V.P.; Coco Newton,* V.P.; Keri Newton, V.P.; Russell Newton,* V.P.
EIN: 200494459

531
Eliesabeth Esser Charitable Trust
c/o Comerica Bank, Trust Dept.
101 N. Main St., Ste. 100
Ann Arbor, MI   48104

Established in FL.
Grantmaker type: Independent foundation.
Financial data (yr. ended 10/31/05): Assets, $506,655 (M); expenditures, $34,144; total giving, $25,878; qualifying distributions, $25,878; giving activities include $25,878 for grants.
Fields of interest: Salvation Army.
Type of support: General/operating support.
Limitations: Applications not accepted. Giving primarily in FL. No grants to individuals.
Application information: Contributes only to pre-selected organizations.
Trustee: Comerica Bank.
EIN: 596551153

532
Elliott M. & Constance L. Estes Foundation
5434 E. Lincoln Dr., Ste. 44
Paradise Valley, AZ   85253

Established around 1982.
Grantmaker type: Independent foundation.
Financial data (yr. ended 12/31/05): Assets, $503,228 (M); expenditures, $114,487; total giving, $106,000; qualifying distributions, $106,000; giving activities include $106,000 for 26 grants (high: $36,000; low: $1,000).

Fields of interest: Arts; Higher education; Environment, natural resources; Hospitals (general); Human services; Christian agencies & churches.
Limitations: Applications not accepted. Giving primarily in AZ; giving also in MI. No grants to individuals.
Application information: Contributes only to pre-selected organizations.
Officers and Trustees:* Constance L. Estes,* Pres. and Treas.; Sidney W. Smith, Jr.,* Secy.; Curtis J. Mann.
EIN: 382319855
Selected grants: The following grants were reported in 2004.
$36,000 to Saint Joseph Mercy Oakland, Pontiac, MI. For general operating support.
$5,000 to Scottsdale Healthcare Foundation, Scottsdale, AZ. For general operating support.
$2,000 to Phoenix Symphony Association, Phoenix, AZ. For general operating support.
$1,000 to Alzheimers Disease and Related Disorders Association, Detroit, MI. For general operating support.
$1,000 to American Diabetes Association, Phoenix, AZ. For general operating support.
$1,000 to Heard Museum, Phoenix, AZ. For general operating support.
$1,000 to Pets on Wheels, Scottsdale, AZ. For general operating support.
$1,000 to Saint Marys Food Bank, Phoenix, AZ. For general operating support.
$1,000 to Salvation Army of Phoenix, Phoenix, AZ. For general operating support.
$1,000 to United Ways of Arizona, Phoenix, AZ. For general operating support.

533
Charles Robert Evenson Foundation
c/o Fredric Sytsma
P.O. Box 352
Bridgewater Pl.
Grand Rapids, MI   49501-0352
Application address: c/o James D. Wright, 200 Ottawa Ave. N.W., Grand Rapids, MI 48503, tel.: (616) 771-7780

Established in MI.
Grantmaker type: Independent foundation.
Financial data (yr. ended 10/31/05): Assets, $272,155 (M); expenditures, $17,879; total giving, $13,500; qualifying distributions, $13,500; giving activities include $13,500 for grants.
Fields of interest: Museums; Performing arts; Environment, natural resources.
Limitations: Giving limited to Grand Rapids, MI. No grants to individuals.
Application information:
Initial approach: Letter
Deadline(s): None
Officers: Robert Evenson, Jr., V.P.; Joan Newberry, V.P.
Trustee: JPMorgan Chase Bank, N.A.
EIN: 386085626

534
Ever Young and Green Foundation Trust
P.O. Box 61
Glen Arbor, MI   49636   (231) 334-3372
Contact: R. Duncan McPherson, Tr.

Donor: R. Duncan McPherson.

Grantmaker type: Independent foundation.
Financial data (yr. ended 12/31/05): Assets, $32,720 (M); gifts received, $2,000; expenditures, $1,006; total giving, $1,000; qualifying distributions, $1,000; giving activities include $1,000 for grants.
Purpose and activities: The trust supports projects promoting the welfare of children and the conservation and preservation of the northern Michigan landscape.
Fields of interest: Environment, natural resources; Children/youth, services.
Limitations: Giving primarily in northern MI. No grants to individuals.
Application information:
Initial approach: Letter
Deadline(s): None
Trustees: Mary Ann Smith McPherson; R. Duncan McPherson; Mary Vardigan.
EIN: 383380307

535
Evereg-Fenesse Mesrobian-Roupinian Educational Society, Inc.
4140 Tanglewood Ct.
Bloomfield Hills, MI   48301-1218

Grantmaker type: Independent foundation.
Financial data (yr. ended 7/31/03): Assets, $8,706 (M); expenditures, $11,805; total giving, $11,400; qualifying distributions, $11,400; giving activities include $11,400 for 43 grants to individuals.
Purpose and activities: Giving primarily through scholarships to students attending Armenian day schools and to full-time college students attending four-year undergraduate or two-year postgraduate schools.
Type of support: Grants to individuals; Scholarships—to individuals.
Limitations: Giving limited to CA, MI, and NY.
Application information: Submit application to local chapter representative. Application form required.
Deadline(s): Dec. 15
Officers: Vahram Fantazian, Pres.; John Semizian, V.P.; Laura Negosian Lucassian, Secy.; Harry Keoleian, Treas.
Advisors: Jack Kavlakian; George Kouzoujian; Kathy Mekjan.
EIN: 136154468

536
H. T. Ewald Foundation
15450 E. Jefferson Ave., Ste. 180
Grosse Pointe, MI   48230   (313) 821-1278
Contact: Shelagh K. Czuprenski, Secy.
FAX: (313) 821-3299; E-mail: ewaldfndtn@aol.com;
URL: http://www.ewaldfoundation.org

Established in 1928 in MI.
Donor: Henry T. Ewald‡.
Grantmaker type: Independent foundation.
Financial data (yr. ended 12/31/04): Assets, $2,826,168 (M); gifts received, $6,100; expenditures, $149,501; total giving, $81,450; qualifying distributions, $97,444; giving activities include $650 for 2 grants, and $80,800 for 40 grants to individuals (high: $5,500; low: $500).
Purpose and activities: Awards four-year scholarships for undergraduate study to local area high school seniors.

Fields of interest: Education; Human services.
Type of support: General/operating support; Scholarships—to individuals.
Limitations: Giving limited to the metropolitan Detroit, MI, area.
Publications: Informational brochure (including application guidelines).
Application information: Application form required for scholarships; see foundation Web site for application guidelines. Application form required.
  Initial approach: Letter or telephone
  Copies of proposal: 1
  Deadline(s): Mar. 1 for scholarships
  Final notification: Approximately July 10
Officers: Kristi L. Ewald, Pres.; Holly S. Ewald, V.P.; Carolyn Ewald-Kratzet, V.P.; Shirley Ewald-Pfeifer, V.P. Emeritus; Shelagh K. Czuprenski, Secy.; Cliff Ewald, Treas.
Number of staff: 1 part-time support.
EIN: 386007837

537
Eyster Charitable Family Foundation
1475 Epley Rd.
Williamston, MI 48895   (517) 655-3217
Contact: Janet Tolson Eyster, Dir.

Established in 2000 in MI.
Donors: George E. Eyster; Janet Tolson Eyster.
Grantmaker type: Independent foundation.
Financial data (yr. ended 12/31/04): Assets, $29,749 (M); gifts received, $491; expenditures, $352; total giving, $0; qualifying distributions, $0.
Limitations: Giving primarily in Lansing, MI.
Application information:
  Initial approach: Letter
  Deadline(s): None
Directors: George E. Eyster; Janet Tolson Eyster.
EIN: 383501935

538
Ida M. Faigle Charitable Foundation
40 Oak Hollow St., Ste. 120
Southfield, MI 48034-7470

Established in 1978 in MI.
Donor: Ida M. Faigle†.
Grantmaker type: Independent foundation.
Financial data (yr. ended 12/31/05): Assets, $683,409 (M); expenditures, $58,750; total giving, $28,750; qualifying distributions, $28,750; giving activities include $28,750 for grants.
Fields of interest: Cancer; Eye diseases; Human services.
Type of support: General/operating support.
Limitations: Giving primarily in MI. No grants to individuals.
Application information:
  Initial approach: Letter
  Deadline(s): None
  Final notification: Within 4 months
Trustee: Michael M. Wild.
EIN: 237366145

539
The Falk Family Foundation
4628 E. Beltline N.E.
Grand Rapids, MI 49525-9786   (616) 361-6906
Contact: Daniel C. Falk, Pres.

Established in 1998 in MI.
Donors: Daniel C. Falk; Susan G. Falk.
Grantmaker type: Independent foundation.
Financial data (yr. ended 12/31/05): Assets, $121,100 (M); expenditures, $38,123; total giving, $36,329; qualifying distributions, $36,329; giving activities include $36,329 for grants.
Fields of interest: Christian agencies & churches.
Limitations: Giving on a national basis.
Officers: Daniel C. Falk, Pres.; Matthew Falk, V.P.; Michael Falk, V.P.; Susan G. Falk, Secy.-Treas.
EIN: 383441180

540
Family Christian Stores Foundation
5300 Patterson Ave. S.E.
Grand Rapids, MI 49530

Established in 2003 in MI.
Donors: David M. Browne; Family Christian Stores, Inc.
Grantmaker type: Independent foundation.
Financial data (yr. ended 12/31/04): Assets, $289,164 (M); gifts received, $299,967; expenditures, $113,357; total giving, $42,585; qualifying distributions, $177,427; giving activities include $42,585 for grants.
Limitations: Applications not accepted. No grants to individuals.
Application information: Contributes only to pre-selected organizations.
Officers and Trustees: Steve Biondo,* Pres.; Amy Anderson, Secy.; Ruth White, Treas.; Earl C. Bartow; David M. Browne.
EIN: 383673924

541
The Paul Farago Foundation Trust
3518 Erie Dr.
Orchard Lake, MI 48324-1522
Contact: Frank Campanale, Pres.

Established in 1998 in MI.
Grantmaker type: Independent foundation.
Financial data (yr. ended 12/31/04): Assets, $3,888,174 (M); expenditures, $135,252; total giving, $126,000; qualifying distributions, $126,000; giving activities include $126,000 for 5 grants (high: $55,000; low: $1,000).
Purpose and activities: Support to organizations that train dogs to assist the disabled.
Fields of interest: Education; Human services; Christian agencies & churches; Disabilities, people with.
Limitations: Giving primarily in MI. No grants to individuals.
Application information:
  Initial approach: Letter on organization letterhead
  Deadline(s): None
Officer: Frank Campanale, Pres.
EIN: 383378111

542
William and Audrey Farber Family Foundation
32640 Whatley Rd.
Franklin, MI 48025
Application address: c/o William and Audrey Farber, 26211 Central Park Blvd., Ste. 220, Southfield, MI 48076, tel.: (248) 357-2400

Established in 1993 in MI.
Donors: William Farber; Audrey Farber.
Grantmaker type: Independent foundation.
Financial data (yr. ended 12/31/05): Assets, $257,393 (M); gifts received, $159,250; expenditures, $47,242; total giving, $46,716; qualifying distributions, $46,716; giving activities include $46,716 for 14 grants (high: $10,000; low: $200).
Fields of interest: Human services; Jewish federated giving programs.
Limitations: Giving primarily in MI and NY.
Application information:
  Initial approach: Letter
  Deadline(s): None
Officers: William Farber, Pres.; Audrey Farber, Secy.
EIN: 383159762

543
The Farbman Family Foundation
(formerly The Farbman Foundation)
28400 Northwestern Hwy., 4th Fl.
Southfield, MI 48034-1839

Established in 1997 in MI.
Donors: Burton D. Farbman; Susan B. Farbman; The Farbman Group.
Grantmaker type: Independent foundation.
Financial data (yr. ended 12/31/04): Assets, $56,363 (M); gifts received, $300,150; expenditures, $291,772; total giving, $291,600; qualifying distributions, $291,589; giving activities include $291,600 for 15 grants (high: $100,000; low: $100).
Fields of interest: Education; Zoos/zoological societies; YM/YWCAs & YM/YWHAs; Jewish federated giving programs; Jewish agencies & temples.
Limitations: Applications not accepted. Giving primarily in MI, with emphasis on Detroit. No grants to individuals.
Application information: Contributes only to pre-selected organizations.
Directors: Andrew V. Farbman; Burton D. Farbman; David S. Farbman; Susan B. Farbman.
EIN: 383345578
Selected grants: The following grants were reported in 2003.
$60,000 to Jewish Federation of Metropolitan Detroit, Bloomfield Hills, MI. For general support.
$35,000 to YMCA of Metropolitan Detroit, Detroit, MI. For general support.
$5,500 to College for Creative Studies, Detroit, MI. For general support.
$5,000 to Detroit Zoological Society, Royal Oak, MI. For general support.
$1,500 to University of Michigan, Ann Arbor, MI. For general support.
$1,000 to Crooked Tree Arts Council, Crooked Tree Arts Center, Petoskey, MI.
$1,000 to Detroit Historical Society, Detroit, MI. For general support.
$1,000 to Karmanos Cancer Foundation, Lathrup Village, MI. For general support.
$1,000 to Mosaic Youth Theater of Detroit, Detroit, MI. For general support.
$500 to Food Bank of Oakland County, Pontiac, MI. For general support.

THE MICHIGAN FOUNDATION DIRECTORY

544
The Farhan Foundation
26300 Telegraph Rd., 2nd Fl.
Southfield, MI   48034

Established in 2000 in MI.
Grantmaker type: Independent foundation.
Financial data (yr. ended 12/31/05): Assets, $350,353 (M); gifts received, $25,000; expenditures, $16,882; total giving, $10,270; qualifying distributions, $10,270; giving activities include $10,270 for grants.
Officer: Jamal Farhan, Pres.
EIN: 383533248

545
Marcus Martin Farley and Mable Stone Farley Memorial Foundation
121 Pepperidge Ln.
Battle Creek, MI   49015-3109   (269) 963-6750
Contact: Larry L. Payne, Pres.

Established in MI.
Grantmaker type: Independent foundation.
Financial data (yr. ended 12/31/05): Assets, $238,949 (M); expenditures, $11,207; total giving, $0; qualifying distributions, $0.
Fields of interest: Human services.
Type of support: Equipment.
Limitations: Giving limited to Calhoun County, MI.
Application information:
  Initial approach: Letter
  Deadline(s): None
Officers: Larry L. Payne, Pres. and Treas.; Patricia McCully, V.P.; Brenda Payne, Secy.
EIN: 383114865

546
Farrehi Family Foundation, Inc.
P.O. Box 446
Goodrich, MI   48438

Established in 2000 in MI.
Donors: Cyrus Farrehi; Z. Jane Farrehi.
Grantmaker type: Independent foundation.
Financial data (yr. ended 12/31/04): Assets, $588,125 (M); expenditures, $18,517; total giving, $16,900; qualifying distributions, $16,900; giving activities include $16,900 for grants.
Fields of interest: Education.
Type of support: Professorships; General/operating support.
Limitations: Applications not accepted. Giving limited to MI. No grants to individuals.
Application information: Contributes only to pre-selected organizations.
Officers and Directors:* Cyrus Farrehi,* Pres.; Paul Farrehi,* V.P.; Lisa Miserlian,* Secy.; Z. Jane Farrehi,* Treas.; Mary Delzer; Peter Farrehi.
EIN: 383451359

547
The Farver Foundation
626 Depot St.
Blissfield, MI   49228-1399
Contact: Lori Mount, Admin. Asst.

Established in 1988 in MI.
Donors: Orville W. Farver‡; Constance Farver; Herbert Farver.

Grantmaker type: Independent foundation.
Financial data (yr. ended 12/31/04): Assets, $5,143,536 (M); expenditures, $419,793; total giving, $384,550; qualifying distributions, $382,003; giving activities include $384,550 for 57 grants (high: $25,000; low: $50).
Fields of interest: Education; Athletics/sports, baseball; Human services; Community development.
Type of support: General/operating support; Continuing support; Annual campaigns; Capital campaigns; Building/renovation; Equipment; Emergency funds.
Limitations: Giving primarily in Lenawee County, MI, with emphasis on the Adrian and Blissfield areas. No grants to individuals.
Application information: Application form not required.
  Initial approach: Letter
  Deadline(s): None
Trustees: Constance Farver; O. Herbert Farver.
EIN: 386540398

548
Drusilla Farwell Foundation
20600 Eureka Rd., Ste. 401
Taylor, MI   48180
Application address: c/o Leslie Wise, 725 Barclay Cir., Ste. 230, Rochester Hills, MI 48307, tel.: (248) 852-9330

Established in 1937 in MI.
Grantmaker type: Independent foundation.
Financial data (yr. ended 8/31/05): Assets, $3,211,092 (M); expenditures, $241,788; total giving, $184,600; qualifying distributions, $193,079; giving activities include $184,600 for 103 grants (high: $6,300; low: $200).
Purpose and activities: Giving primarily for higher and other education, particularly an intercultural and foreign exchange program; funding also for the arts, health associations, children, youth, and social services, and Christian churches.
Fields of interest: Arts; Higher education; Education; Health organizations; Human services; Children/youth, services; Christian agencies & churches.
Limitations: Giving primarily in FL and MI; funding also in New York, NY.
Application information: Application form not required.
  Initial approach: Letter
  Deadline(s): None
Officers: Randolph Fields, Pres.; Leslie Wise, Secy.-Treas.
Trustees: Helmuth Krave; Charles Peltz.
EIN: 386082430

549
Gaynel L. Fausell Charitable Trust
c/o Citizens Bank, N.A.
328 S. Saginaw St., M/C 002072
Flint, MI   48502

Grantmaker type: Independent foundation.
Financial data (yr. ended 12/31/05): Assets, $590,730 (M); expenditures, $40,686; total giving, $19,000; qualifying distributions, $19,000; giving activities include $19,000 for 6 grants (high: $6,000; low: $2,000).

Fields of interest: Performing arts; Housing/shelter; Youth development, centers/clubs; Salvation Army; YM/YWCAs & YM/YWHAs; Family services.
Limitations: Applications not accepted. Giving primarily in Jackson, MI. No grants to individuals.
Application information: Contributes only to pre-selected organizations.
Trustees: Philip J. Curtis; Citizens Bank, N.A.
EIN: 386516668

550
The Charles and Audrey Faust Charitable Foundation
755 W. Big Beaver Rd.
Troy, MI   48084

Established in 2004 in FL.
Donor: Audrey R. Faust.
Grantmaker type: Independent foundation.
Financial data (yr. ended 12/31/04): Assets, $100,019 (M); gifts received, $100,000; expenditures, $0; total giving, $0; qualifying distributions, $0.
Limitations: Applications not accepted. No grants to individuals.
Application information: Contributes only to pre-selected organizations.
Trustee: Audrey R. Faust.
EIN: 542164110

551
Charles E. Favor Educational Trust
c/o Fifth Third Bank
P.O. Box 3636
Grand Rapids, MI   49501-3636

Established in 1997 in MI.
Donor: Charles Favor Trust.
Grantmaker type: Independent foundation.
Financial data (yr. ended 12/31/05): Assets, $310,212 (M); expenditures, $18,212; total giving, $14,496; qualifying distributions, $14,496; giving activities include $14,496 for grants.
Purpose and activities: Giving limited to public schools in Trenton, MI.
Fields of interest: Elementary/secondary education.
Type of support: Scholarship funds.
Limitations: Giving limited to Trenton, MI. No grants to individuals.
Application information:
  Initial approach: Letter
  Deadline(s): None
Advisory Committee: Chris Dimanin; Hector Garcia; Shirley Hipsher; Donna Jeffers; Linda Mack; John Schulte; Valerie Smith.
Trustee: Fifth Third Bank.
EIN: 386692994

552
The Charles Fay Foundation
228 W. Main St.
P.O. Box 85
Morenci, MI   49256

Established in 1996 in MI.
Grantmaker type: Independent foundation.
Financial data (yr. ended 12/31/04): Assets, $1 (M); expenditures, $16,655; total giving, $8,549;

qualifying distributions, $8,549; giving activities include $8,549 for grants.
Limitations: Applications not accepted. Giving primarily in Morenci, MI. No grants to individuals.
Application information: Contributes only to pre-selected organizations.
Officers: Doyle Collar, Pres.; Dorothy McDowell, Secy.; Roger Porter, Treas.
Trustees: Rod Nelson; Jim Smith.
EIN: 383251025

553
Feather Foundation
728 Indiana Woods
Leland, MI 49654
Contact: Nancy Boynton Fisher, Secy.

Established in 2002 in MI.
Donor: Jeffrey E. Fisher.
Grantmaker type: Independent foundation.
Financial data (yr. ended 9/30/05): Assets, $432,689 (M); gifts received, $118; expenditures, $39,163; total giving, $30,000; qualifying distributions, $30,000; giving activities include $30,000 for grants.
Limitations: Giving limited to MI. No grants to individuals.
Application information:
  Initial approach: Proposal
  Deadline(s): None
Officers: Jeffrey E. Fisher, Pres.; Nancy Boynton Fisher, Secy.; Wayne A. Pahssen, Treas.
EIN: 300141451

554
Albert J. and Helen E. Febbo Family Foundation
2000 Town Ctr., Ste. 2400
Southfield, MI 48075

Established in 2000 in MI.
Donors: Albert J. Febbo; Helen E. Febbo.
Grantmaker type: Independent foundation.
Financial data (yr. ended 12/31/03): Assets, $96,652 (M); expenditures, $6,880; total giving, $6,650; qualifying distributions, $6,650; giving activities include $6,650 for grants.
Limitations: Giving primarily in MA.
Officers: Albert J. Febbo, Pres.; Helen E. Febbo, V.P.
EIN: 311671406

555
The Sergei Federov Foundation
322 N. Old Woodward Ave.
Birmingham, MI 48009-5321   (248) 646-8292
Contact: Brian D. O'Keefe, Secy.-Treas.

Grantmaker type: Independent foundation.
Financial data (yr. ended 12/31/04): Assets, $1,445,179 (M); expenditures, $191,492; total giving, $87,700; qualifying distributions, $87,700; giving activities include $87,700 for grants.
Fields of interest: Scholarships/financial aid; Children, services; Federated giving programs.
Limitations: Giving primarily in MI.
Officers: Sergei Fedorov, Pres.; Victor Fedorov, V.P.; Sergei Kournikov, V.P.; Brian D. O'Keefe, Secy.-Treas.
EIN: 383437116

556
C. Scott Fedewa Foundation
298 W. Chicago St.
Coldwater, MI 49036
Contact: C. Scott Fedewa, Pres.

Established in 1992 in CA.
Donor: C. Scott Fedewa.
Grantmaker type: Independent foundation.
Financial data (yr. ended 12/31/05): Assets, $29 (M); expenditures, $1,753; total giving, $1,000; qualifying distributions, $1,000; giving activities include $1,000 for grants.
Purpose and activities: Scholarship award paid directly to the college or university that the senior of Detroit High School will attended.
Fields of interest: Higher education.
Type of support: Scholarships—to individuals.
Limitations: Giving limited to MI.
Officers: C. Scott Fedewa, Pres. and Treas.; Constance Mettler, Secy.
Directors: Jonathan Fedewa; Philip Fedewa.
EIN: 383040444

557
Frank B. and Virginia V. Fehsenfeld Charitable Foundation
1107 1st Ave., Ste. 1404
Seattle, WA 98101
Contact: H. Warren Smith, V.P.

Established in 1987 in MI.
Donors: Frank Fehsenfeld; Virginia V. Fehsenfeld.
Grantmaker type: Independent foundation.
Financial data (yr. ended 12/31/05): Assets, $1,799,840 (M); expenditures, $94,707; total giving, $93,000; qualifying distributions, $93,000; giving activities include $93,000 for grants.
Purpose and activities: Giving for the arts, education, and human services.
Fields of interest: Arts; Education; Environment, natural resources; Human services; Children/youth, services.
Type of support: Annual campaigns; Building/renovation.
Limitations: Giving primarily in the Grand Rapids, MI, and Seattle, WA, areas. No grants to individuals.
Application information:
  Initial approach: Letter
  Deadline(s): None
Officers: Frank Fehsenfeld, Pres. and Treas.; H. Warren Smith, V.P.; Nancy Fehsenfeld Smith, Secy.
Trustees: John A. Fehsenfeld; Thomas V. Fehsenfeld; William Fehsenfeld.
EIN: 382775201
Selected grants: The following grants were reported in 2003.
$6,000 to Baxter Community Center, Grand Rapids, MI. For annual support.
$6,000 to Land Conservancy of West Michigan, Grand Rapids, MI. For annual support.
$6,000 to Opera Grand Rapids, Grand Rapids, MI. For annual support.
$6,000 to Ryerson Library Foundation, Grand Rapids, MI. For annual support.
$5,000 to Eastern Michigan University, Ypsilanti, MI. For annual support.
$5,000 to Grand Rapids Symphony, Grand Rapids, MI. For annual support.
$5,000 to Steepletown Neighborhood Services, Grand Rapids, MI. For annual support.
$5,000 to University of Michigan, Ann Arbor, MI. For annual support.

$5,000 to Wedgwood Christian Youth and Family Services, Grand Rapids, MI. For annual support.
$4,000 to Heartside Ministry, Grand Rapids, MI. For annual support.

558
Sybil and Morris Fenkell Foundation
411 S. Woodward Ave., Ste. 500
Birmingham, MI 48009-6646

Established in 1999 in MI.
Donor: Morris Fenkell.
Grantmaker type: Independent foundation.
Financial data (yr. ended 12/31/04): Assets, $670,003 (M); expenditures, $36,369; total giving, $12,000; qualifying distributions, $12,000; giving activities include $12,000 for 3 grants (high: $5,000; low: $2,000).
Fields of interest: Health organizations; Jewish federated giving programs; Jewish agencies & temples.
Limitations: Applications not accepted. Giving primarily in MI and NY. No grants to individuals.
Application information: Contributes only to pre-selected organizations.
Officers: Morris Fenkell, Pres.; Lisa Fenkell, V.P.; Robert Fenkell, V.P.; Steven Fenkell, V.P.; Sybil Fenkell, Secy.
EIN: 383505807
Selected grants: The following grants were reported in 2003.
$247,017 to UJA-Federation of New York, New York, NY.
$200,000 to Friendship Circle, West Bloomfield, MI.
$6,300 to Cystic Fibrosis Foundation, Bethesda, MD.
$5,000 to Friends of the Israel Defense Forces, New York, NY.
$2,000 to JARC, Farmington Hills, MI.
$1,000 to International Institute for Secular Humanistic Judaism-North American Section, Farmington Hills, MI. For program support.
$1,000 to Multiple Sclerosis Society, National, Southfield, MI.

559
The Ronda and Ron Ferber Foundation
3000 Pontiac Trail
Commerce Township, MI 48390
(248) 863-3001
Contact: Ron Ferber, Pres.; Ronda Ferber, Secy.

Established in 2000 in MI.
Donors: Ron Ferber; Ronda Ferber.
Grantmaker type: Independent foundation.
Financial data (yr. ended 12/31/04): Assets, $584,561 (M); gifts received, $350,000; expenditures, $145,887; total giving, $145,617; qualifying distributions, $145,617; giving activities include $145,617 for 23 grants (high: $38,600; low: $200).
Purpose and activities: Giving primarily to Jewish federated giving programs; support also for Jewish temples and yeshivas.
Fields of interest: Human services; Children/youth, services; Family services; Jewish federated giving programs; Jewish agencies & temples.
Application information:
  Initial approach: Letter
  Deadline(s): None

Officers and Directors: * Ron Ferber,* Pres. and Treas.; Ronda Ferber,* Secy.
EIN: 383557521

560
The Miriam & Fred Ferber Foundation

3000 Pontiac Trail
Commerce Township, MI 48390
(248) 863-3001
Contact: Roman Ferber, Pres.

Established in 2002 in MI.
Donors: Annette Adalman; Brian Adalman.
Grantmaker type: Independent foundation.
Financial data (yr. ended 12/31/04): Assets, $94,298 (M); gifts received, $300,000; expenditures, $694,726; total giving, $694,300; qualifying distributions, $694,217; giving activities include $694,300 for 11 grants (high: $365,000; low: $1,000).
Purpose and activities: Giving primarily to Jewish organizations.
Fields of interest: Health care; Jewish federated giving programs; Jewish agencies & temples.
Limitations: Giving on a national basis, with some emphasis on MI. No grants to individuals.
Application information:
  Initial approach: Letter
  Deadline(s): None
Officers and Directors: * Roman Ferber,* Pres. and Secy.; Alon Kaufman,* V.P. and Treas.
EIN: 371432758
Selected grants: The following grants were reported in 2003.
  $400,000 to Jewish Federation of Metropolitan Detroit, Bloomfield Hills, MI. For program support.
  $100,000 to Friendship Circle, West Bloomfield, MI. For program support.
  $50,000 to Chabad. For program support.
  $40,000 to Friends of the Israel Defense Forces, New York, NY. For program support.
  $20,000 to Henry Ford Health System, Detroit, MI. For program support.
  $20,000 to Hillel Day School of Metropolitan Detroit, Farmington Hills, MI. For program support.
  $19,000 to Jewish Hospice and Chaplaincy Network, Bloomfield, MI. For program support.
  $6,000 to Friends of AKIM USA, New York, NY. For program support.

561
Robert W. & Caroline A. Fernstrum Scholarship Foundation Trust

P.O. Box 137
Marinette, WI 54143
Application address: c/o Superintendent of Schools, 1230 13th St., Menominee, MI 49858, tel.: (906) 863-9951

Established in 1996 in WI.
Donors: Caroline A. Fernstrum; Robert W. Fernstrum.
Grantmaker type: Independent foundation.
Financial data (yr. ended 12/31/05): Assets, $621,525 (M); gifts received, $431; expenditures, $33,436; total giving, $26,750; qualifying distributions, $26,750; giving activities include $26,750 for grants.

Purpose and activities: Scholarship awards given by the Menominee, MI, area Public School Scholarship distribution to graduating seniors of Menominee High School for college tuition.
Fields of interest: Education.
Type of support: Scholarship funds.
Limitations: Giving limited to Menominee, MI. No grants to individuals.
Application information: Application form not required.
  Initial approach: Letter
  Deadline(s): Apr. 17
Trustees: Richard Doust; Sean Fernstrum; John Reinke.
EIN: 396625465

562
Ferrantino Charitable Foundation, Inc.

36255 Michigan Ave.
Wayne, MI 48184

Established in 1997 in MI.
Donors: Estela Ferrantino; Michael J. Ferrantino, Jr.; Nancy Y. Young.
Grantmaker type: Independent foundation.
Financial data (yr. ended 12/31/04): Assets, $65,663 (M); gifts received, $144,168; expenditures, $79,245; total giving, $78,600; qualifying distributions, $78,600; giving activities include $78,600 for grants.
Fields of interest: Hospitals (general); Medical care, outpatient care; Human services.
Limitations: Applications not accepted. Giving primarily in MI. No grants to individuals.
Application information: Contributes only to pre-selected organizations.
Officers and Directors: * Estela Ferrantino,* Pres.; Michael J. Ferrantino, Jr.,* V.P.; Nancy Y. Young,* Secy.-Treas.
EIN: 383374062

563
Ferries Family Foundation

c/o Northpoint Financial
920 E. Lincoln St.
Birmingham, MI 48009-3608
Contact: John C. Ferries, Pres.
Application address: 80 Chestnut Hill Rd., Wilton, CT 06897; NY tel.: (212) 468-3622

Established in 1998 in DE.
Donor: John C. Ferries.
Grantmaker type: Independent foundation.
Financial data (yr. ended 12/31/05): Assets, $149,045 (M); gifts received, $1,790; expenditures, $24,426; total giving, $22,584; qualifying distributions, $22,584; giving activities include $22,584 for grants.
Fields of interest: Higher education, college; Protestant agencies & churches.
Limitations: Giving primarily in CT and NH.
Application information:
  Initial approach: Proposal
  Deadline(s): June 30
Officers and Directors: * John C. Ferries,* Pres. and Treas.; Donna Ferries,* V.P. and Secy.; Alexander Ferries; Jason Ferries; Karen Ferries.
EIN: 134000700

564
John E. Fetzer Memorial Trust Fund

c/o Michael C. Gergely
P.O. Box 117
Vicksburg, MI 49097-0117

Established in 1991 in MI.
Donor: J.E. Fetzer Revocable Trust.
Grantmaker type: Independent foundation.
Financial data (yr. ended 6/30/05): Assets, $75,803,696 (M); gifts received, $1,000,000; expenditures, $3,675,421; total giving, $3,000,000; qualifying distributions, $3,460,243; giving activities include $3,000,000 for 1 grant.
Fields of interest: Higher education; Human services, mind/body enrichment; Voluntarism promotion; Psychology/behavioral science.
Type of support: General/operating support; Research.
Limitations: Applications not accepted. Giving primarily to Kalamazoo, MI, also and some giving in San Francisco, CA. No grants to individuals.
Application information: Contributes only to 2 pre-selected organizations.
Officers: Robert Lehman, Pres.; Bruce Fetzer, Exec. V.P.; Thomas Beaver, V.P.; Michael Gergely, Secy.; Louis Leeburg, Treas.
Number of staff: 1 full-time professional.
EIN: 383010714

565
Seymour S. & Diana M. Feuer Foundation

4117 Chatfield Ln.
Troy, MI 48098-4327
Contact: Seymour S. Feuer, Tr.
Application address: 1141 Near Ocean Dr., Vero Beach, FL 32963

Donors: Seymour S. Feuer; Diana M. Feuer.
Grantmaker type: Independent foundation.
Financial data (yr. ended 8/31/05): Assets, $68,242 (M); expenditures, $4,735; total giving, $4,616; qualifying distributions, $4,616; giving activities include $4,616 for grants.
Application information: Application form not required.
  Deadline(s): None
Trustees: Diana M. Feuer; Seymour S. Feuer.
EIN: 382690090

566
The Malcolm & Lois Field Foundation

4705 Towne Centre Rd., Ste. 205
Saginaw, MI 48604

Established in 1987 in MI.
Donor: E. Malcolm Field, M.D.
Grantmaker type: Independent foundation.
Financial data (yr. ended 12/31/05): Assets, $2,411,965 (M); gifts received, $396,125; expenditures, $25,805; total giving, $15,000; qualifying distributions, $15,000; giving activities include $15,000 for 2 grants (high: $12,500; low: $2,500).
Fields of interest: Salvation Army; Christian agencies & churches.
Type of support: General/operating support.
Limitations: Applications not accepted. Giving limited to Saginaw, MI. No grants to individuals.
Application information: Contributes only to pre-selected organizations.

Officers and Directors:* E. Malcolm Field, M.D.*, Pres.; Lois J. Field,* Secy.-Treas.
EIN: 382785515
Selected grants: The following grants were reported in 2003.
$100,000 to Field Neurosciences Institute, Saginaw, MI.
$20,509 to First Free Methodist Church, Grand Rapids, MI.

567
Fieldman Sims Foundation
21557 Meadow Ln.
Beverly Hills, MI 48025

Established in 2001 in MI.
Donors: Mark A. Sims; Elaine S. Fieldman.
Grantmaker type: Independent foundation.
Financial data (yr. ended 12/31/04): Assets, $515,481 (M); gifts received, $237,419; expenditures, $4,347; total giving, $1,500; qualifying distributions, $1,500; giving activities include $1,500 for grants.
Limitations: Applications not accepted. No grants to individuals.
Application information: Contributes only to pre-selected organizations.
Officers and Directors:* Elaine S. Fieldman,* Pres.; Mark A. Sims,* V.P.
EIN: 383638470

568
Fike Family Foundation
c/o Gregory L. Fike
46382 Rockledge Dr.
Plymouth, MI 48170

Established in 1993 in MI.
Donors: Marvin N. Fike; Gregory L. Fike.
Grantmaker type: Independent foundation.
Financial data (yr. ended 11/30/05): Assets, $690 (M); expenditures, $10,511; total giving, $10,500; qualifying distributions, $10,500; giving activities include $10,500 for grants.
Purpose and activities: Support only for Adrian First Nazarene Church.
Fields of interest: Religion.
Type of support: Building/renovation.
Limitations: Applications not accepted. Giving limited to Adrian, MI. No grants to individuals.
Application information: Contributes only to a pre-selected organization as specified in the governing instrument.
Officers and Directors:* Marvin N. Fike,* Chair. and Pres.; Gregory L. Fike,* Secy.-Treas.
EIN: 383148616

569
Dr. Leon Fill Foundation
27301 DeQuindre Rd., Ste. 301
Madison Heights, MI 48071-3473

Grantmaker type: Independent foundation.
Financial data (yr. ended 11/30/05): Assets, $103,523 (M); gifts received, $12,836; expenditures, $12,250; total giving, $11,668; qualifying distributions, $11,668; giving activities include $11,668 for grants.
Limitations: Applications not accepted. Giving primarily in MI. No grants to individuals.

Application information: Contributes only to pre-selected organizations.
Trustee: Norman M. Fill.
EIN: 386123163

570
George R. and Elise M. Fink Foundation
377 Fisher Rd., Ste. C-5
Grosse Pointe, MI 48230 (313) 886-8451
Contact: Elyse F. Jones, Pres.
E-mail: finknews@aol.com

Incorporated in 1955 in MI.
Donors: George R. Fink‡; Elise M. Fink‡.
Grantmaker type: Independent foundation.
Financial data (yr. ended 11/30/05): Assets, $2,074,235 (M); expenditures, $225,410; total giving, $179,150; qualifying distributions, $193,818; giving activities include $179,150 for 17 grants (high: $25,000; low: $1,000).
Purpose and activities: Giving for education, health and children's services.
Fields of interest: Education; Health care; Mental health, treatment; Human services; Children, services.
Type of support: General/operating support.
Limitations: Giving primarily in MI. No grants to individuals, or for scholarships or fellowships; no loans.
Application information: Application form not required.
 Initial approach: Letter
 Deadline(s): None
Officers: Elyse F. Jones, Pres.; John M. Fink, V.P.; Lynn Carpenter, Secy.
Number of staff: 1 part-time support.
EIN: 386059952
Selected grants: The following grants were reported in 2005.
$25,000 to Bon Secours Cottage Health Services, Grosse Pointe, MI. For general operating support.
$22,000 to International Association of Cancer Victors and Friends (IACVF), Playa del Rey, CA. For general operating support.
$20,000 to Cradle Foundation, Evanston, IL. For general operating support.
$20,000 to Salvation Army Baltimore Area, Baltimore, MD. For Hurricane Relief Fund.
$16,150 to Friends School in Detroit, Detroit, MI. For general operating support.
$15,000 to Grosse Pointe Animal Adoption Society, Grosse Pointe Farms, MI. For general operating support.
$10,000 to American Red Cross, National Headquarters, DC. For general operating support.
$10,000 to Gleaners Community Food Bank, Detroit, MI. For general operating support.
$10,000 to Save the Children, Westport, CT. For general operating support.
$5,000 to People to People International, Kansas City, MO. For general operating support.

571
Finkel Family Foundation
41200 Bridge St.
Novi, MI 48375-1301

Established in 1990 in MI.
Donors: Seymour D. Finkel; Paul G. Finkel.
Grantmaker type: Independent foundation.

Financial data (yr. ended 12/31/04): Assets, $315,061 (M); gifts received, $25,000; expenditures, $18,274; total giving, $17,675; qualifying distributions, $17,675; giving activities include $17,675 for grants.
Limitations: Applications not accepted. Giving limited to MI. No grants to individuals.
Application information: Contributes only to pre-selected organizations.
Officers: Paul G. Finkel, Pres. and Treas.; Seymour D. Finkel, Secy.
EIN: 382953931

572
Morton M. Finkelstein Family Charitable Foundation
18053 N. Fruitport Rd.
Spring Lake, MI 49456-1573
Contact: Morton M. Finkelstein, Tr.

Established in 1999 in MI.
Donor: Morton M. Finkelstein.
Grantmaker type: Independent foundation.
Financial data (yr. ended 12/31/04): Assets, $169,503 (M); gifts received, $43,139; expenditures, $6,700; total giving, $6,700; qualifying distributions, $6,700; giving activities include $6,700 for grants.
Fields of interest: Jewish federated giving programs.
Application information: Application form not required.
 Initial approach: Letter
 Deadline(s): None
Trustee: Morton M. Finkelstein.
EIN: 383507986

573
Harvey S. Firestone, Jr. No. 2 Fund B
c/o JPMorgan Chase Bank, N.A.
P.O. Box 1308
Milwaukee, WI 53201

Established in OH.
Grantmaker type: Independent foundation.
Financial data (yr. ended 12/31/05): Assets, $378,169 (M); expenditures, $21,369; total giving, $15,000; qualifying distributions, $15,000; giving activities include $15,000 for grants.
Purpose and activities: Support only for the Christ Church, MI, Christ Memorial Chapel, FL, St. Luke's Church, NY.
Fields of interest: Christian agencies & churches.
Type of support: General/operating support.
Limitations: Applications not accepted. Giving limited to Hope Sound, FL, Grosse Pointe Farms, MI, and East Hampton, NY. No grants to individuals.
Application information: Contributes only to 3 pre-selected organizations.
Trustee: JPMorgan Chase Bank, N.A.
EIN: 346743117

574
Harvey S. Firestone, Jr. No. 2 Fund C
c/o JPMorgan Chase Bank, N.A.
P.O. Box 1308
Milwaukee, WI 53201-1308

Established in OH.
Grantmaker type: Independent foundation.

Financial data (yr. ended 12/31/05): Assets, $552,012 (M); expenditures, $29,715; total giving, $23,000; qualifying distributions, $23,000; giving activities include $23,000 for grants.
Fields of interest: Religion, interfaith issues.
Limitations: Applications not accepted. Giving primarily in CT and MI. No grants to individuals.
Application information: Contributes only to pre-selected organizations.
Trustee: JPMorgan Chase Bank, N.A.
EIN: 346743118

575
First Fruits Foundation
3825 Lake Dr. S.E.
Grand Rapids, MI   49546-4344

Established in 1996 in MI.
Donors: Lawrence J. Kuipers; Nancy G. Kuipers.
Grantmaker type: Independent foundation.
Financial data (yr. ended 9/30/04): Assets, $17,025 (M); expenditures, $0; total giving, $0; qualifying distributions, $0.
Fields of interest: Protestant agencies & churches.
Limitations: Applications not accepted. No grants to individuals.
Application information: Contributes only to pre-selected organizations.
Officers: Lawrence J. Kuipers, Pres.; Nancy G. Kuipers, Secy.
EIN: 383314193

576
Fish Foundation
7500 Patterson Rd.
Caledonia, MI   49316
Contact: David J. Smies, Pres.

Established in 1998 in MI.
Donors: David J. Smies; Deborah Smies.
Grantmaker type: Independent foundation.
Financial data (yr. ended 12/31/05): Assets, $285,604 (M); expenditures, $17,864; total giving, $13,792; qualifying distributions, $13,792; giving activities include $13,792 for grants.
Fields of interest: Theological school/education; Christian agencies & churches.
Type of support: General/operating support.
Limitations: Giving primarily in Grand Rapids, MI. No support for political parties, television or radio ministries, non-Christian institutions or causes, or educational facilities. No grants for building projects or other capital expenditures, debt retirement, or educational projects or tuition; no loans to individuals.
Application information:
   Initial approach: Proposal
   Deadline(s): Mar. or Apr. for requests of $2,500 or more; requests of less than $2,500 can be made at any time
   Final notification: Generally in June
Officers: David J. Smies, Pres. and Treas.; Deborah Smies, V.P. and Secy.
EIN: 383419231

577
Max M. and Marjorie S. Fisher Foundation, Inc.
2 Towne Sq., Ste. 920
Southfield, MI   48075-3761

Established in 1955 in MI.
Donors: Max M. Fisher; Marjorie M. Fisher; Martinique Hotel, Inc.
Grantmaker type: Independent foundation.
Financial data (yr. ended 11/30/05): Assets, $13,414,218 (M); gifts received, $7,569,630; expenditures, $4,762,402; total giving, $4,611,027; qualifying distributions, $4,616,657; giving activities include $4,611,027 for 105 grants (high: $2,608,410; low: $100; average: $1,000–$300,000).
Purpose and activities: Giving primarily for education, with emphasis on a university; funding also for Jewish organizations, the arts, including a symphony orchestra, and human services.
Fields of interest: Museums; Performing arts; Arts; Elementary/secondary education; Higher education; Education; Health organizations; Human services; Federated giving programs; Jewish federated giving programs; Jewish agencies & temples.
Limitations: Applications not accepted. Giving on a national basis, with emphasis on MI, OH, and NY. No grants to individuals.
Application information: Contributes only to pre-selected organizations.
Officers and Directors: * Marjorie S. Fisher,* Pres.; Phillip William Fisher,* V.P.; Julie F. Cummings; Marjorie M. Fisher; Mary D. Fisher; Jane Ellen Sherman.
EIN: 381784340

578
Francenia Fisher Trust
c/o Bank of America, N.A.
P.O. Box 40200, MC FL9-100-10-19
Jacksonville, FL   32203-0200

Established in 1994 in FL.
Grantmaker type: Independent foundation.
Financial data (yr. ended 12/31/05): Assets, $201,769 (M); expenditures, $12,046; total giving, $8,151; qualifying distributions, $8,151; giving activities include $8,151 for grants.
Purpose and activities: Support only for Florida State University, Tallahassee, FL, Michigan State University, East Lansing, and International Society of Plant Pathology, Berks, UK.
Fields of interest: Higher education; Environmental education.
Type of support: General/operating support.
Limitations: Applications not accepted. Giving limited to FL, MI, and the United Kingdom. No grants to individuals.
Application information: Contributes only to pre-selected organizations specified in the governing instrument.
Trustee: Bank of America, N.A.
EIN: 596884250

579
The Fisher-Insley Foundation
41110 Fox Run Rd., No. 108
Novi, MI   48377-4804

Grantmaker type: Independent foundation.
Financial data (yr. ended 12/31/05): Assets, $133,775 (M); expenditures, $6,072; total giving, $5,476; qualifying distributions, $5,476; giving activities include $5,476 for grants.

Limitations: Applications not accepted. Giving primarily in MI, with emphasis on Detroit and Bloomfield Hills. No grants to individuals.
Application information: Contributes only to pre-selected organizations.
Officers and Trustees: * Barbara F. Maniscalco,* Pres. and Treas.; Kathleen I. Bartley,* V.P.; Hon. William J. Giovan,* Secy.; Deborah I. Dingell; David N. Insley, Jr.; Joseph Maniscalco.
EIN: 386094589

580
David and Deena Fishman Charitable Foundation
121 W. Long Lake Rd., 3rd Fl.
Bloomfield Hills, MI   48304

Established in 2003 in MI.
Donors: David Fishman; Deena Fishman.
Grantmaker type: Independent foundation.
Financial data (yr. ended 12/31/05): Assets, $323,616 (M); expenditures, $28,478; total giving, $26,067; qualifying distributions, $26,067; giving activities include $26,067 for grants.
Fields of interest: Higher education.
Limitations: Giving primarily in Detroit, MI. No grants to individuals.
Application information: Contributes only to pre-selected organizations.
Officers: David Fishman, Pres.; Deena Fishman, V.P.
EIN: 382188360

581
Fitzgibbon Dermidoff Foundation
1776 S. Bates St.
Birmingham, MI   48009-1905   (248) 433-3527
Contact: Jane Fitzgibbon, Pres.

Established in 1996 in MI.
Donor: Jane Fitzgibbon.
Grantmaker type: Independent foundation.
Financial data (yr. ended 12/31/05): Assets, $164,120 (M); gifts received, $10,000; expenditures, $7,184; total giving, $6,200; qualifying distributions, $7,184; giving activities include $6,200 for 3 grants (high: $2,500; low: $1,500).
Purpose and activities: Giving primarily for education.
Fields of interest: Higher education.
Limitations: Giving on a national basis.
Application information:
   Initial approach: Letter
   Deadline(s): None
Officers: Jane Fitzgibbon, Pres.; Howard Kastner, Secy.; Karen Dermidoff Reilly, Treas.
EIN: 383323499

582
Edward I. Fleischman Foundation
21700 Northwestern Hwy., Ste. 1160
Southfield, MI   48075

Established in 1952 in MI.
Grantmaker type: Independent foundation.
Financial data (yr. ended 12/31/04): Assets, $2,012,322 (M); expenditures, $56,507; total giving, $48,900; qualifying distributions, $48,900; giving activities include $48,900 for grants.

Purpose and activities: Giving primarily to Jewish affiliated organizations.
Fields of interest: Jewish federated giving programs; Jewish agencies & temples.
Limitations: Applications not accepted. Giving primarily in MI. No grants to individuals.
Application information: Contributes only to pre-selected organizations.
Officers: Marvin Fleischman, Pres.; Steven Robinson, Secy.; Fannie Robinson, Treas.
EIN: 386091812

583
Nora Flemington Scholarship Trust
508 Margaret St.
Iron Mountain, MI 49801-1844
Application address: c/o Norma Simone, 1510 W. A St., Iron Mountain, MI 49801-2524, tel.: (906) 774-2066

Grantmaker type: Independent foundation.
Financial data (yr. ended 12/31/05): Assets, $30,677 (M); expenditures, $1,500; total giving, $1,500; qualifying distributions, $1,500; giving activities include $1,500 for grants to individuals.
Type of support: Scholarships—to individuals.
Limitations: Giving limited to Dickinson and Iron counties, MI, and Marinette County, WI.
Application information:
 Initial approach: Letter
 Deadline(s): June 15
Directors: Carol Curtis; Margaret Jones; Martee Trepanier; Susan Youngberg.
EIN: 386509939

584
The Edward J. Fletcher Foundation
1700 S. Park St.
Kalamazoo, MI 49001

Established in 2000 in MI.
Donor: Edward J. Fletcher.
Grantmaker type: Independent foundation.
Financial data (yr. ended 12/31/05): Assets, $10,071 (M); gifts received, $40,760; expenditures, $37,696; total giving, $37,000; qualifying distributions, $37,000; giving activities include $37,000 for grants.
Limitations: Applications not accepted. Giving primarily in FL, MI, and NJ. No grants to individuals.
Application information: Contributes only to pre-selected organizations.
Directors: Andrew J. Fletcher; Edward J. Fletcher; Matthew J. Fletcher; Bruce W. Martin.
EIN: 383558309

585
Ethel and James Flinn Foundation
(formerly Ethel and James Flinn Family Foundation)
500 Woodward Ave., Ste. 3500
Detroit, MI 48226 (313) 965-8580
Contact: Leonard W. Smith, Pres.
E-mail: lws@flinnfoundation.org

Established in 1976 in MI as a public foundation; reclassified in 2005 as an independent foundation.
Donors: Ethel W. Flinn; James H. Flinn, Jr.
Grantmaker type: Independent foundation.
Financial data (yr. ended 12/31/05): Assets, $14,381,675 (M); gifts received, $1,150,000;

expenditures, $1,664,738; total giving, $1,419,460; qualifying distributions, $1,419,460; giving activities include $1,419,460 for grants.
Purpose and activities: The foundation is committed to improving the quality of life of those with mental illness by improving the quality, scope, and delivery of mental health services. The foundation uses its resources through research to develop, evaluate, and implement best practice treatment programs delivered in the community.
Fields of interest: Mental health, treatment; Mental health, disorders.
Type of support: Program development; Curriculum development; Research; Program evaluation.
Limitations: Applications not accepted. Giving limited to MI, with some emphasis in the southeastern portion of the state, to organizations listed in Trust Agreement. No grants to individuals.
Publications: Annual report.
Application information: Contributes only to pre-selected organizations; unsolicited requests for funds not considered.
Officers and Trustees: * Leonard W. Smith,* Pres. and Fdn. Mgr.; David E. Nims,* V.P. and Secy.; J. Peter Smith,* V.P. and Treas.; Lynn Carpenter; Allen Ledyard.
Number of staff: 1 full-time professional.
EIN: 382143122

586
Mary G. & Robert H. Flint Foundation
100 W. Long Lake Rd., Ste. 100
Bloomfield Hills, MI 48304 (248) 647-5111
Contact: L. James Wilson

Established in 1985 in MI.
Donors: Mary G. Flint; Robert H. Flint‡; Robert Flint Trust.
Grantmaker type: Independent foundation.
Financial data (yr. ended 11/30/03): Assets, $3,099,103 (M); gifts received, $502,599; expenditures, $274,881; total giving, $260,000; qualifying distributions, $260,524; giving activities include $260,000 for 6 grants (high: $100,000; low: $20,000).
Purpose and activities: Giving primarily for higher education and human services.
Fields of interest: Performing arts, orchestra (symphony); Animal welfare; Agriculture, farm cooperatives; Human services; Children, services.
Limitations: Giving primarily in MI. No grants to individuals.
Application information:
 Initial approach: Letter
 Deadline(s): None
Officer: Susan E. Cooper, Pres.
EIN: 382641865
Selected grants: The following grants were reported in 2003.
$100,000 to Dawn Farm, Ann Arbor, MI. For unrestricted support.
$50,000 to Detroit Symphony Orchestra, Detroit, MI. For unrestricted support.
$50,000 to Simon House, Detroit, MI. For unrestricted support.
$20,000 to Childrens Home of Detroit, Grosse Pointe Woods, MI. For unrestricted support.
$20,000 to Covenant House Michigan, Detroit, MI. For unrestricted support.
$20,000 to Leader Dogs for the Blind, Rochester, MI. For unrestricted support.

587
Folkert Family Foundation
15626 Bittersweet Ln.
Spring Lake, MI 49456

Established in 1992 in MI.
Donor: David F. Folkert.
Grantmaker type: Independent foundation.
Financial data (yr. ended 8/31/05): Assets, $688,033 (M); expenditures, $44,091; total giving, $36,960; qualifying distributions, $36,960; giving activities include $36,960 for grants.
Fields of interest: Christian agencies & churches.
Limitations: Applications not accepted. Giving primarily in MI.
Application information: Contributes only to pre-selected organizations.
Directors: Carol R. Folkert; David F. Folkert; Lucinda Lea Folkert Havercamp.
EIN: 383084541

588
Jeff Foran Charitable Trust
c/o Frank S. Arval, Tr.
888 W. Big Beaver Rd., Ste. 890
Troy, MI 48084
Contact: William R. "Bill" Nixon, Jr., Tr.
Application address: BHYSL Scholarship Committee, 3845 Woodlake Dr., Bloomfield Hills, MI 48304

Established in 2001 in MI.
Grantmaker type: Independent foundation.
Financial data (yr. ended 12/31/04): Assets, $35,736 (M); expenditures, $2,000; total giving, $2,000; qualifying distributions, $2,000; giving activities include $2,000 for grants.
Purpose and activities: Awards scholarships to students who have played soccer: 1) within the Bloomfield School District boundaries, 2) at least three years in the Bloomfield Hills Youth Soccer League, or 3) played on a high school soccer team.
Fields of interest: Athletics/sports, soccer.
Type of support: Scholarships—to individuals.
Limitations: Giving to residents of the greater Bloomfield, MI, area.
Application information: Application form required.
 Deadline(s): Aug. 15
Trustees: Frank S. Arval; Nancy K. Arval; John F. Lecznar; Mary R. Lecznar; Barbara P. Nixon; William R. Nixon, Jr.
EIN: 386773411

589
Geraldine C. and Emory M. Ford Foundation
P.O. Box 33
Roseville, MI 48066
Contact: Deborah Olinger, Pres.

Established in 1994 in MI.
Donor: Geraldine C. Ford‡.
Grantmaker type: Independent foundation.
Financial data (yr. ended 6/30/05): Assets, $1,242,521 (M); gifts received, $50; expenditures, $107,565; total giving, $94,150; qualifying distributions, $94,150; giving activities include $94,150 for grants.
Purpose and activities: Supports work by American composers and musicians by assisting in establishment of professional careers through programs.

Fields of interest: Performing arts; Performing arts, music; Performing arts, orchestra (symphony).
Type of support: General/operating support.
Limitations: Giving on a national basis. No grants to individuals.
Application information: Must be recommended by director of a symphony or music festival if grant is for a music-related program. Application form not required.
Initial approach: Letter
Copies of proposal): 1
Board meeting date(s): As required
Final notification: 1 month
Officers: Deborah Olinger, Pres.; Allen Olinger, V.P. and Treas.; Donald Thulean, V.P.; Thomas E.K. Cerruti, Secy.
EIN: 383190683

590
The Ford Foundation

320 E. 43rd St.
New York, NY   10017   (212) 573-5000
Contact: Secy.
FAX: (212) 351-3677;
E-mail: office-secretary@fordfound.org; URL: http://www.fordfound.org

Incorporated in 1936 in MI.
Donors: Henry Ford‡; Edsel Ford‡.
Grantmaker type: Independent foundation.
Financial data (yr. ended 9/30/05): Assets, $11,615,906,693 (M); expenditures, $663,979,509; total giving, $516,907,177; qualifying distributions, $621,924,695; giving activities include $515,157,652 for 3,034 grants (high: $15,814,025; low: $2; average: $100,000–$250,000), $619,169 for 21 grants to individuals (high: $100,000; low: $503; average: $5,000–$25,000), $1,130,356 for employee matching gifts, $5,919,996 for 4 foundation-administered programs and $15,672,579 for loans/program-related investments.
Purpose and activities: The foundation's mission is to serve as a resource for innovative people and institutions worldwide. Its goals are to: strengthen democratic values, reduce poverty and injustice, promote international cooperation, and advance human achievement. Grants are made primarily within three broad categories: (1) asset building and community development; (2) knowledge, creativity, and freedom; and (3) peace and social justice. Local needs and priorities, within these subject areas, determine program activities in individual countries.
Fields of interest: Media/communications; Media, film/video; Museums; Performing arts; Performing arts, dance; Performing arts, theater; Performing arts, music; Arts; Education, research; Education, early childhood education; Elementary school/education; Secondary school/education; Higher education; Education; Environment, natural resources; Environment; Reproductive health; Reproductive health, sexuality education; Public health, STDs; AIDS; Crime/violence prevention, abuse prevention; Legal services; Employment; Agriculture; Housing/shelter, development; Youth development; Human services; Women, centers/services; Minorities/immigrants, centers/services; International economic development; International affairs, arms control; International affairs, foreign policy; International human rights; International affairs; Civil rights, race/intergroup relations; Civil rights; Urban/community development; Rural development; Community development;

Philanthropy/voluntarism; Social sciences; Economics; Law/international law; International studies; Public policy, research; Government/public administration; Public affairs, citizen participation; Leadership development; Religion, interfaith issues; Minorities; Women; Immigrants/refugees; Economically disadvantaged.
International interests: Africa; Asia; Latin America; Middle East; Russia; Southeast Asia.
Type of support: Management development/capacity building; Income development; General/operating support; Continuing support; Endowments; Program development; Conferences/seminars; Film/video/radio; Publication; Seed money; Curriculum development; Fellowships; Research; Technical assistance; Consulting services; Program evaluation; Program-related investments/loans; Employee matching gifts; Grants to individuals; Matching/challenge support.
Limitations: Giving on an international basis, including the U.S., Africa and the Middle East, Asia, Russia, Latin America and the Caribbean. No support for programs for which substantial support from government or other sources is readily available, or for religious sectarian activities. No grants for routine operating costs, construction or maintenance of buildings, or undergraduate scholarships; graduate fellowships generally channeled through grants to universities or other organizations; no grants for purely personal or local needs.
Publications: Application guidelines; Annual report (including application guidelines); Informational brochure (including application guidelines); Newsletter; Occasional report.
Application information: Prospective applicants are advised to review the foundation's Web site for information or current funding guidelines. Foreign applicants should contact foundation for addresses of its overseas offices, through which they must apply. Application form not required.
Initial approach: Brief letter of inquiry
Copies of proposal: 1
Deadline(s): None
Board meeting date(s): Jan., May, and Sept.
Final notification: Initial indication as to whether proposal falls within program interests within 6 weeks
Officers and Trustees:* Kathryn S. Fuller,* Chair.; Susan V. Berresford,* Pres.; Barron M. Tenny, Exec. V.P., Secy., and Genl. Counsel; Barry D. Gaberman, Sr. V.P. and Acting V.P., Peace and Social Justice; Linda B. Strumpf, V.P. and C.I.O.; Alison R. Bernstein, V.P., Knowledge, Creativity, and Freedom; Pablo J. Farias, V.P., Asset Building and Community Devel.; Margaret Lourdes Tellado, V.P., Comms.; Nicholas M. Gabriel, Treas. and Dir., Financial Svcs.; Nancy P. Feller, Assoc. Genl. Counsel; Afsaneh M. Beschloss; Anke A. Ehrhardt; Juliet V. Garcia; Irene Y. Hirano; J. Clifford Hudson; Wilmot G. James; Yolanda Kakabadse; Richard Moe; Yolanda T. Moses; Carl B. Weisbrod; W. Richard West.
Number of staff: 281 full-time professional; 220 full-time support; 3 part-time support.
EIN: 131684331
Selected grants: The following grants were reported in 2005.
$3,500,000 to International Center for Transitional Justice, New York, NY. Toward general support for activities to help countries respond to legacy of human rights abuse, to advance accountability, respond to needs of victims, and to prevent recurrence of such violence.

$1,270,000 to African Virtual University, Nairobi, Kenya. To secure and oversee delivery of low-cost bandwidth for research and scholarly activities to consortium comprising Association of African Universities and 33 universities, payable over 3 years.
$1,100,000 to Anti-Defamation League of Bnai Brith, New York, NY. For on-line platform to deliver teacher education programs for A World of Difference Institute.
$800,000 to Public Radio Capital, Englewood, CO. For general support to expand choices for public radio programming in United States by protecting and expanding public radio's scarce broadcast assets, payable over 2 years.
$605,000 to University of Michigan, Ann Arbor, MI. To evaluate effectiveness of student dialogues for bridging inter-group differences in ten universities, payable over 3 years.
$600,000 to National Commission on Violence Against Women, Jakarta, Indonesia. For work to rebuild women's human rights and promote women's legal and economic empowerment in post-tsunami Aceh, payable over 2 years.
$300,000 to Advancement Project, DC. For Voter Protection Program to coordinate nonpartisan efforts to educate public about voting rights policies to ensure that all eligible Americans participate in democratic process.
$260,000 to Charities Aid Foundation (UK), West Malling, England. For small grants competitions and technical assistance to build capacity of self-help groups of people living with HIV-AIDS across Russia, payable over 2 years.
$225,000 to Centre for Research and Innovation in Social Policy and Practice (CENTRIS), Newcastle Upon Thyme, England. To evaluate International Initiative to Strengthen Philanthropy, payable over 2.50 years.
$200,000 to Watershed Research and Training Center, Hayfork, CA. To undertake regional organizing and training for community-based forestry groups, payable over 1.50 years.

591
William & Lisa Ford Foundation

1901 Saint Antoine St., 6th Fl.
Detroit, MI   48226   (313) 259-7777
Contact: David M. Hempstead, Secy.

Established in 1998 in MI.
Donors: William Clay Ford, Jr.; Lisa V. Ford.
Grantmaker type: Independent foundation.
Financial data (yr. ended 12/31/05): Assets, $10,828,359; expenditures, $465,188; total giving, $410,000; qualifying distributions, $412,162; giving activities include $410,000 for 17 grants (high: $250,000; low: $1,000).
Purpose and activities: Giving primarily for children's services and higher education; funding also for human services.
Fields of interest: Museums; Higher education; Education; Environment, land resources; Health care; Human services; Children, services; Federated giving programs; Buddhism.
Limitations: Giving primarily in MI. No grants to individuals.
Application information: Awards are generally limited to charitable organizations already known and of interest to the foundation.
Initial approach: Letter
Deadline(s): None
Board meeting date(s): As necessary

Officers and Trustee: * William Clay Ford, Jr.,* Pres. and Dir.; Lisa V. Ford, V.P.; David M. Hempstead, Secy.; George A. Straitor, Treas.
EIN: 383441138

592
Benson and Edith Ford Fund
1901 Saint Antoine St., 6th Fl.
Detroit, MI 48226 (313) 259-7777
Contact: David M. Hempstead, Secy.

Incorporated in 1943 in MI as the Hotchkiss Fund.
Donor: Benson Ford‡.
Grantmaker type: Independent foundation.
Financial data (yr. ended 12/31/05): Assets, $34,280,463 (M); expenditures, $1,976,757; total giving, $1,815,000; qualifying distributions, $1,819,510; giving activities include $1,815,000 for 44 grants (high: $485,000; low: $2,000).
Purpose and activities: Support for health, human services, education, and arts and culture.
Fields of interest: Arts; Education; Hospitals (general); Youth development, services; Children/youth, services; Federated giving programs; Jewish agencies & temples.
Limitations: Giving primarily in MI. No grants to individuals.
Application information: Awards generally limited to charities already favorably known to substantial contributors of the foundation.
Initial approach: Letter
Deadline(s): None
Officers and Trustees: * Lynn F. Alandt,* Pres.; Benson Ford, Jr.,* V.P.; David M. Hempstead,* Secy.; George A. Straitor, Treas.
EIN: 386066333

593
Eleanor and Edsel Ford Fund
c/o David M. Hempstead
1901 Saint Antoine St., 6th Fl.
Detroit, MI 48226

Incorporated in 1944 in MI.
Donor: Eleanor Clay Ford‡.
Grantmaker type: Independent foundation.
Financial data (yr. ended 12/31/05): Assets, $21,508,135 (M); expenditures, $1,427,674; total giving, $1,390,000; qualifying distributions, $1,391,117; giving activities include $1,390,000 for 7 grants (high: $325,000; low: $20,000).
Purpose and activities: Grants are limited to organizations selected by the trustees from among the charities with which Eleanor Clay Ford was prominently associated during her lifetime.
Fields of interest: Museums; Performing arts; Arts; Elementary/secondary education; Higher education; Medical care, in-patient care; Protestant agencies & churches.
Type of support: General/operating support; Building/renovation; Scholarship funds.
Limitations: Applications not accepted. Giving primarily in MI, with emphasis on Detroit, MI. No grants to individuals.
Application information: Contributes only to pre-selected organizations. Unsolicited requests for funds not considered.
Officers and Trustees: * William Clay Ford,* Pres.; David M. Hempstead,* Secy.; George A. Straitor, Treas.
EIN: 386066331

594
Walter and Josephine Ford Fund
Ford Field
1901 Saint Antoine St., 6th Fl.
Detroit, MI 48226
Contact: David M. Hempstead, Secy.

Incorporated in 1951 in MI.
Donors: Josephine F. Ford‡; Walter B. Ford II.
Grantmaker type: Independent foundation.
Financial data (yr. ended 12/31/05): Assets, $4,436,805 (M); gifts received, $206,170; expenditures, $1,317,331; total giving, $1,298,500; qualifying distributions, $1,302,218; giving activities include $1,298,500 for 45 grants (high: $400,000; low: $500).
Purpose and activities: Giving primarily for arts and culture, particularly to a center for creative studies, as well as for education, health associations, children and youth services, social services, federated giving programs, religious purposes, and for the prevention of cruelty to children and animals.
Fields of interest: Arts; Higher education; Education; Hospitals (general); Health organizations, association; Medical research, institute; Human services; Children/youth, services; Federated giving programs; Religion.
Limitations: Giving primarily in ME, with some emphasis on Northeast Harbor, and MI, with emphasis on Detroit. No grants to individuals.
Application information: Awards generally limited to charities already favorably known to substantial contributors of the foundation.
Initial approach: Letter
Deadline(s): None
Board meeting date(s): Varies
Officers and Trustees: * Walter B. Ford III, V.P.; David M. Hempstead,* Secy.; George A. Straitor, Treas.
EIN: 386066334

595
William and Martha Ford Fund
1901 Saint Antoine St., 6th Fl.
Detroit, MI 48226 (313) 259-7777
Contact: David M. Hempstead, Secy.

Incorporated in 1953 in MI.
Donors: William Clay Ford; Martha Firestone Ford.
Grantmaker type: Independent foundation.
Financial data (yr. ended 12/31/05): Assets, $6,728,675 (M); expenditures, $1,317,283; total giving, $1,285,000; qualifying distributions, $1,286,653; giving activities include $1,285,000 for 63 grants (high: $401,750; low: $250).
Purpose and activities: The fund provides financial support to corporations, trusts, community chests, funds or foundations, organized and operated solely for religious, charitable, scientific, literary or educational purposes, or for the prevention of cruelty to children or animals.
Fields of interest: Museums; Arts; Higher education; Zoos/zoological societies; Hospitals (general); Health care; Substance abuse, services; Boys & girls clubs; Human services; Foundations (community); Federated giving programs.
Limitations: Giving primarily in MI; some giving nationally. No grants to individuals.
Application information: Awards generally limited to charities already favorably known to substantial contributors of the foundation.
Initial approach: Letter
Deadline(s): None

Officers and Trustees: * William Clay Ford,* Pres.; David M. Hempstead,* Secy.; George A. Straitor, Treas.; Martha F. Ford.
EIN: 386066335

596
Edsel B. Ford II Fund
6th Fl. at Ford Field
1901 Saint Antoine St.
Detroit, MI 48226 (313) 259-7777
Contact: David M. Hempstead, Secy.

Established in 1993 in MI.
Donor: Edsel B. Ford II.
Grantmaker type: Independent foundation.
Financial data (yr. ended 12/31/05): Assets, $7,328,302 (M); expenditures, $335,155; total giving, $321,550; qualifying distributions, $321,960; giving activities include $321,550 for 43 grants (high: $31,000; low: $500).
Purpose and activities: Giving primarily for higher education, health, social services, children and youth services, particularly juvenile diabetes, federated giving programs, and a Presbyterian church.
Fields of interest: Arts; Higher education; Education; Zoos/zoological societies; Hospitals (general); Health care; Diabetes; Human services; Children/youth, services; Federated giving programs; Protestant agencies & churches.
Limitations: Giving primarily in MI. No grants to individuals.
Application information: Generally contributes to organizations already known to the donor.
Initial approach: Letter
Deadline(s): None
Board meeting date(s): As needed
Officers and Director: * Edsel B. Ford II,* Pres.; David M. Hempstead, Secy.; George A. Straitor, Treas.
EIN: 383153050

597
The Henry Ford II Fund
Ford Field
1901 Saint Antoine St., 6th Fl.
Detroit, MI 48226 (313) 259-7777
Contact: David M. Hempstead, Secy.

Incorporated in 1953 in MI.
Donor: Henry Ford II‡.
Grantmaker type: Independent foundation.
Financial data (yr. ended 12/31/05): Assets, $30,804,263 (M); expenditures, $2,226,055; total giving, $2,100,000; qualifying distributions, $2,101,629; giving activities include $2,100,000 for 24 grants (high: $650,000; low: $2,500).
Purpose and activities: Giving primarily for education, social services, federated giving programs, and for the prevention of cruelty to children and animals.
Fields of interest: Higher education; Education; Health care; Human services; Federated giving programs.
Limitations: Applications not accepted. Giving primarily in MI, with emphasis on Dearborn, Detroit, and Grosse Pointe Woods. No grants to individuals.
Application information: Unsolicited requests for funds not accepted.
Board meeting date(s): As necessary

Officers and Trustees:* Edsel B. Ford II,* Pres.; David M. Hempstead,* Secy.; George A. Straitor,* Treas.
EIN: 386066332

598
Forevergreen Foundation
c/o Plante & Moran, LLP
1111 Michigan Ave., P. O. Box 2500
East Lansing, MI 48826

Established in 1997 in MI.
Donors: Caryl M. Chocola; J. Byron Chocola.
Grantmaker type: Independent foundation.
Financial data (yr. ended 5/31/05): Assets, $881,157 (M); expenditures, $43,690; total giving, $40,000; qualifying distributions, $40,000; giving activities include $40,000 for grants.
Limitations: Applications not accepted. No grants to individuals.
Application information: Contributes only to pre-selected organizations.
Officers and Directors:* Caryl M. Chocola,* Pres.; J. Byron Chocola,* V.P.; Kelley C. Logan,* Secy.-Treas.; J. Christopher Chocola; Sarah Chocola; John M. Logan.
EIN: 383396202

599
Foss Family Foundation
28834 Oak Point Dr.
Farmington Hills, MI 48331

Established in 1997 in MI.
Donor: Donald A. Foss.
Grantmaker type: Independent foundation.
Financial data (yr. ended 12/31/05): Assets, $1,559,084 (M); expenditures, $839,822; total giving, $834,000; qualifying distributions, $834,000; giving activities include $834,000 for grants.
Purpose and activities: Support only for Scholarship Fund at the Don Foss Annual Northwood University, Midland, MI.
Fields of interest: Higher education, university.
Type of support: Scholarship funds.
Limitations: Applications not accepted. Giving limited to Midland, MI. No grants to individuals.
Application information: Contributes only to a pre-selected organization.
Officers: Jill Foss Watson, Pres.; Stacee L. Foss, V.P. and Secy.
EIN: 383326775

600
Foster Family Foundation
c/o West Michigan National Bank
120 Cypress St.
Manistee, MI 49660

Established in 1997 in MI.
Donors: Kate Foster; Phyliss L. Foster; Robert C. Foster.
Grantmaker type: Independent foundation.
Financial data (yr. ended 12/31/05): Assets, $522,250 (M); gifts received, $113,080; expenditures, $19,628; total giving, $16,000; qualifying distributions, $16,000; giving activities include $16,000 for grants.

Fields of interest: Media, radio; Hospitals (general); Christian agencies & churches.
Limitations: Applications not accepted. Giving primarily in MI. No grants to individuals.
Application information: Contributes only to pre-selected organizations.
Trustees: Thomas A. Baither; Phyliss L. Foster; Robert C. Foster; Henry T. Mather.
EIN: 383357234

601
Foster Family Foundation
P.O. Box 437
St. Clair, MI 48079

Established in 2005 in MI.
Donors: Richard Foster; Virginia Foster; John Foster; Jennifer Foster; Tom Foster; Michele Foster; Marjorie Foster-Cummins.
Grantmaker type: Independent foundation.
Financial data (yr. ended 12/31/05): Assets, $98,700 (M); gifts received, $101,700; expenditures, $3,084; total giving, $0; qualifying distributions, $0.
Limitations: Applications not accepted. No grants to individuals.
Application information: Contributes only to pre-selected organizations.
Officers: Richard Foster, Pres.; Virginia Foster, Secy.-Treas.
Directors: John Foster; Tom Foster; Marjorie Foster-Cummins.
EIN: 203439954

602
Foster Foundation
(formerly Foster Welfare Foundation)
161 Ottawa Ave. N.W., Ste. 511
Grand Rapids, MI 49503-2712
Contact: Karley D. Johns, Exec. Dir.
Application address: 581 Alta Dale S.E., Grand Rapids, MI 49546, tel.: (616) 676-5958

Established in MI.
Donor: Clara J. Foster.
Grantmaker type: Independent foundation.
Financial data (yr. ended 4/30/05): Assets, $56,257 (M); gifts received, $36,246; expenditures, $34,868; total giving, $24,500; qualifying distributions, $32,411; giving activities include $24,500 for grants to individuals.
Purpose and activities: Scholarship awards to students in Kent County, MI, for higher education.
Fields of interest: Education.
Type of support: Scholarships—to individuals.
Limitations: Giving limited to residents of Kent County, MI.
Application information:
   Initial approach: Letter
   Deadline(s): Feb. 1
Officers: John D. Hibbard, Jr., Pres.; Andrea K. Sugiyama, V.P.; Karley D. Johns, Exec. Dir.
Directors: Gilbert Davis; Vern Boss; Emery Freeman; Barbara Jacoboice; Vernis Schad.
EIN: 380831533

603
Foundation for Birmingham Senior Residents
2121 Midvale St.
Birmingham, MI 48009-1509   (248) 619-3400

Established around 1984.
Grantmaker type: Independent foundation.
Financial data (yr. ended 12/31/05): Assets, $366,497 (M); gifts received, $50,327; expenditures, $6,417; total giving, $4,500; qualifying distributions, $4,500; giving activities include $4,500 for grants.
Purpose and activities: Awards granted to Birmingham Area Seniors Coordinating Council and directly to senior residents of Birmingham, MI, for minor home repairs and maintenance.
Fields of interest: Aging.
Type of support: Building/renovation.
Limitations: Giving limited to residents of Birmingham, MI.
Application information: Grants limited to the benefit of Birmingham, MI, homeowners 60 years of age or older with financial need. Application form required.
Officers: Jack Fawcett, V.P.; David E. Hershey, Treas.
Directors: Rackeline Hoff; Claudia Jackson; Benedict J. Smith.
EIN: 382507882

604
The Foundation for Educational Advancement
26200 American Dr., Ste. 500
Southfield, MI 48086

Established in 2003 in MI.
Grantmaker type: Independent foundation.
Financial data (yr. ended 6/30/05): Assets, $32,639 (M); gifts received, $279,275; expenditures, $312,207; total giving, $310,253; qualifying distributions, $310,253; giving activities include $310,253 for 1 grant.
Fields of interest: Education.
International interests: Turks & Caicos Islands.
Limitations: Applications not accepted. Giving primarily in the Turks & Caicos Islands, BWI.
Application information: Unsolicited requests for funds not accepted.
Officers: Gordon R. Follmer, Pres.; Gary L. White, Sr., Secy.-Treas.
Directors: Elias Gennaoui; Danny Knopper.
EIN: 200307479

605
Foundation for the Glory of God
2150 Blueberry Dr. N.W.
Grand Rapids, MI 49504-2507

Donors: George Pawlanta; Marilyn Pawlanta.
Grantmaker type: Independent foundation.
Financial data (yr. ended 12/31/04): Assets, $31,779 (M); expenditures, $370; total giving, $275; qualifying distributions, $275; giving activities include $275 for grants.
Limitations: Applications not accepted. No grants to individuals.
Application information: Contributes only to pre-selected organizations.

Officers: Joseph E. Pawlanta, Pres.; George Pawlanta, Treas.
EIN: 382820930

606
Foundation for Washington & Lee University

39555 Orchard Hill Pl., Ste. 370
Novi, MI 48375

Established in 2001 in MI.
Donor: Walter J. Borda.
Grantmaker type: Independent foundation.
Financial data (yr. ended 12/31/04): Assets, $247,943 (M); gifts received, $98,368; expenditures, $25,500; total giving, $25,500; qualifying distributions, $25,500; giving activities include $25,500 for grants.
Purpose and activities: Support only for Washington & Lee University, Lexington, VA.
Fields of interest: Higher education, university.
Type of support: General/operating support.
Limitations: Applications not accepted. Giving limited to Lexington, VA. No grants to individuals.
Application information: Contributes only to a pre-selected organization.
Officer: Walter J. Borda, Pres.
EIN: 383571954

607
Henry A. Fox, Jr. and Kathleen O'Brien Fox Charitable Foundation

4494 36th St. S.E.
Kentwood, MI 49512

Established in 1986 in MI.
Donors: Henry A. Fox, Jr.; Kathleen O'Brien Fox; Henry A. Fox Sales Co., Inc.
Grantmaker type: Independent foundation.
Financial data (yr. ended 12/31/05): Assets, $70,049 (M); gifts received, $3,057; expenditures, $3,958; total giving, $2,500; qualifying distributions, $2,500; giving activities include $2,500 for grants.
Limitations: Applications not accepted. Giving limited to MI. No grants to individuals.
Application information: Contributes only to pre-selected organizations.
Officer: Henry A. Fox, Jr., Pres.
Director: Kathleen O'Brien Fox.
EIN: 382732553

608
Richard E. Fox Charitable Foundation

P.O. Box 882896
Steamboat Springs, CO 80488-2896

Established in 1999 in PA.
Grantmaker type: Independent foundation.
Financial data (yr. ended 12/31/04): Assets, $2,754,701 (M); expenditures, $269,208; total giving, $174,750; qualifying distributions, $174,081; giving activities include $174,750 for 4 grants (high: $82,500; low: $10,000).
Fields of interest: Higher education, college; Education.
Limitations: Applications not accepted. Giving primarily in MI, NY and PA. No grants to individuals.
Application information: Contributes only to pre-selected organizations.

Trustees: Leonard J. Boss; Wayne Kablack; Joseph Kolter; Michael Pivarnik; Doris J. Regotti.
EIN: 256657059
Selected grants: The following grants were reported in 2004.
$82,500 to Foundation for Economic Education, Irvington, NY.
$42,250 to Grove City College, Grove City, PA.
$40,000 to Hillsdale College, Hillsdale, MI.
$10,000 to Acton Institute for the Study of Religion and Liberty, Grand Rapids, MI.

609
Leon & Rena Frank Memorial Corporation

c/o JPMorgan Chase Bank, N.A.
P.O. Box 1308
Milwaukee, WI 53201

Established in MI.
Grantmaker type: Independent foundation.
Financial data (yr. ended 12/31/05): Assets, $195,819 (M); expenditures, $22,614; total giving, $17,730; qualifying distributions, $17,730; giving activities include $17,730 for grants.
Purpose and activities: Giving primarily for education, Jewish organizations and federated giving programs, the arts, and health and human services.
Fields of interest: Museums; Education; Human services; Jewish federated giving programs; Jewish agencies & temples.
Limitations: Applications not accepted. Giving on a national basis, with emphasis on MI. No grants to individuals.
Application information: Contributes only to pre-selected organizations.
Officers: Levi Smith, Pres.; Robert C. Smith, V.P.; Patricia Frank, Secy.; Bobbette Smith Siegel, Treas.
Trustee: JPMorgan Chase Bank, N.A.
EIN: 386058044

610
William C. Frank Trust

c/o Bank of America, N.A.
P.O. Box 40200, MC FL9-100-10-19
Jacksonville, FL 32203-0200

Established in 1998 in FL.
Grantmaker type: Independent foundation.
Financial data (yr. ended 9/30/05): Assets, $461,473 (M); expenditures, $33,229; total giving, $28,264; qualifying distributions, $28,264; giving activities include $28,264 for grants.
Purpose and activities: Support only for Michigan Masonic Home of Alma, Bloomfield, and Shriners Hospital's for children, Tampa.
Fields of interest: Hospitals (specialty); Residential/custodial care, senior continuing care.
Type of support: General/operating support.
Limitations: Applications not accepted. Giving limited to Tampa, FL and Bloomfield, MI. No grants to individuals.
Application information: Contributes only to 2 pre-selected organizations.
Trustee: Bank of America, N.A.
EIN: 596497938

611
Stanley and Judith Frankel Family Foundation

2301 W. Big Beaver Rd., Ste. 900
Troy, MI 48084

Established in 2000 in MI.
Donors: Stanley Frankel; Judith Frankel.
Grantmaker type: Independent foundation.
Financial data (yr. ended 2/28/05): Assets, $5,521,237 (M); expenditures, $439,789; total giving, $420,000; qualifying distributions, $418,352; giving activities include $420,000 for 9 grants (high: $100,000; low: $5,000).
Fields of interest: Performing arts; Higher education; Education; Jewish federated giving programs.
Limitations: Applications not accepted. Giving limited to MI. No grants to individuals.
Application information: Contributes only to pre-selected organizations.
Directors: Judith Frankel; Stanley Frankel.
EIN: 383531285

612
Maxine and Stuart Frankel Foundation

2301 W. Big Beaver Rd., Ste. 510
Troy, MI 48084

Established in 1998 in MI.
Donors: Maxine Frankel; Stuart Frankel; Jean Frankel; Samuel Frankel.
Grantmaker type: Independent foundation.
Financial data (yr. ended 12/31/04): Assets, $4,369,703 (M); gifts received, $5,000,000; expenditures, $644,697; total giving, $644,300; qualifying distributions, $644,300; giving activities include $644,300 for 60 grants (high: $214,800; low: $300).
Purpose and activities: Giving primarily for the arts, education, health, particularly a children's hospital, as well as for youth, family and social services, and Jewish organizations.
Fields of interest: Museums (art); Arts; Higher education; Education; Hospitals (specialty); Health organizations, association; Human services; Children/youth, services; Family services; Jewish federated giving programs; Jewish agencies & temples.
Limitations: Applications not accepted. Giving primarily in MI. No grants to individuals.
Application information: Contributes only to pre-selected organizations.
Officers: Maxine Frankel, Pres.; Stuart Frankel, Secy.-Treas.
EIN: 383445379
Selected grants: The following grants were reported in 2003.
$204,400 to Childrens Hospital of Michigan, Detroit, MI. For general support.
$100,000 to New Common School Foundation, Detroit, MI. For general support.
$35,000 to Common Ground Sanctuary, Bloomfield Hills, MI. For general support.
$32,500 to Jewish Federation of Metropolitan Detroit, Bloomfield Hills, MI. For general support.
$20,150 to Independent Curators International, New York, NY. For general support.
$12,500 to Storm King Art Center, Mountainville, NY. For general support.
$6,000 to Planned Parenthood Federation of America, New York, NY. For general support.

$4,000 to University of Michigan, Ann Arbor, MI. For general support.
$3,500 to American Friends of the Israel Museum, New York, NY. For general support.
$1,000 to Gildas Club, New York, NY. For general support.

613
Samuel & Jean Frankel Foundation
3875 Lakeland Ln.
Bloomfield Hills, MI   48302

Established around 1970.
Donors: Samuel Frankel; Jean Frankel.
Grantmaker type: Independent foundation.
Financial data (yr. ended 12/31/04): Assets, $33,882,371 (M); gifts received, $597,393; expenditures, $579,550; total giving, $537,231; qualifying distributions, $537,231; giving activities include $537,231 for 92 grants (high: $100,000; low: $15).
Purpose and activities: Giving primarily for Jewish services, the fine and performing arts, health organizations, and human services.
Fields of interest: Museums; Performing arts; Health organizations; Human services; Jewish federated giving programs; Jewish agencies & temples.
Limitations: Applications not accepted. Giving primarily in MI. No grants to individuals.
Application information: Contributes only to pre-selected organizations.
Officers: Samuel Frankel, Pres.; Jean Frankel, V.P. and Secy.; Stanley Frankel, Treas.
Trustees: Bruce Frankel; Stuart Frankel; Joelyn Nyman; Arthur Weiss.
EIN: 386088399

614
The Barbara Frankel Foundation
4912 Fairway Ridge Cir.
West Bloomfield, MI   48323

Established in 2001 in GA.
Donor: Barbara Frankel.
Grantmaker type: Independent foundation.
Financial data (yr. ended 12/31/05): Assets, $450,285 (M); expenditures, $136,466; total giving, $135,229; qualifying distributions, $135,229; giving activities include $135,229 for 14 + grants (high: $41,560).
Purpose and activities: Giving primarily for the performing arts, and health and human services.
Fields of interest: Performing arts, orchestra (symphony); Performing arts, opera; Nursing home/convalescent facility; Health care; Jewish federated giving programs; Jewish agencies & temples.
Type of support: General/operating support.
Limitations: Applications not accepted. Giving primarily in MI. No grants to individuals.
Application information: Contributes only to pre-selected organizations.
Trustee: Barbara Frankel.
EIN: 586432171
Selected grants: The following grants were reported in 2004.
$89,636 to Temple Israel, West Bloomfield, MI. For general support.
$40,300 to Michigan Opera Theater, Detroit, MI. For general support.

$39,450 to Detroit Symphony Orchestra, Detroit, MI. For general support.
$5,270 to Detroit Institute of Arts, Detroit, MI. For general support.
$3,500 to Henry Ford Health System, Detroit, MI. For general support.
$3,000 to Mayo Clinic, Rochester, MN. For general support.
$3,000 to United Way for Southeastern Michigan, Detroit, MI. For general support.
$1,400 to Jewish Home Services, West Bloomfield, MI. For general support.
$1,000 to Beaumont Foundation, Southfield, MI. For general support.
$1,000 to W T V S Detroit Educational Television, Detroit, MI. For general support.

615
The Samuel and Jean Frankel Jewish Heritage Foundation
2301 W. Big Beaver Rd., Ste. 900
Troy, MI   48084

Established in 2004 in MI.
Donors: Samuel Frankel; Jean Frankel.
Grantmaker type: Independent foundation.
Financial data (yr. ended 12/31/04): Assets, $41,959,950 (M); gifts received, $41,775,383; expenditures, $11,438; total giving, $0; qualifying distributions, $0.
Limitations: Applications not accepted. No grants to individuals.
Application information: Contributes only to pre-selected organizations.
Officers and Trustees:* Samuel Frankel,* Pres.; Jean Frankel,* V.P.; Judith Frankel,* Secy.; Stanley Frankel,* Treas.
EIN: 300095016

616
Frazier Fund, Inc.
c/o Wells Fargo Bank Michigan, N.A.
P.O. Box 580, Trust Dept.
Marquette, MI   49855   (906) 228-9500
Contact: Mary C. Nurmi

Established in 1980 in MI.
Donor: Anne M. Frazier‡.
Grantmaker type: Independent foundation.
Financial data (yr. ended 9/30/05): Assets, $1,772,944 (M); expenditures, $85,600; total giving, $73,900; qualifying distributions, $73,900; giving activities include $73,900 for grants.
Purpose and activities: Giving primarily for children's museums and youth services.
Fields of interest: Museums (children's); Housing/shelter; Youth development; Human services; YM/YWCAs & YM/YWHAs; Federated giving programs.
Limitations: Giving limited to Marquette, MI. No grants to individuals.
Application information:
Initial approach: Proposal
Deadline(s): Apr. 30
Officers: Peter W. Frazier, Pres.; Julia Q. Frazier, V.P.; William I. McDonald, Secy.; Robert J. Toutant, Treas.
Director: Lincoln B. Frazier, Jr.
Trustee: Wells Fargo Bank Michigan, N.A.
EIN: 382287345

617
Marshall M. Fredericks Foundation
1301 W. Long Lake Rd., Ste. 320
Troy, MI   48098

Established in MI.
Donor: Marshall M. Fredericks.
Grantmaker type: Independent foundation.
Financial data (yr. ended 12/31/05): Assets, $681,369 (M); expenditures, $55,713; total giving, $40,000; qualifying distributions, $51,097; giving activities include $40,000 for 1 grant.
Purpose and activities: The foundation provides sculptures to various organizations for public display.
Fields of interest: Visual arts, sculpture.
Limitations: Applications not accepted. Giving limited to MI. No grants to individuals.
Application information: Contributes only to pre-selected organizations.
Trustees: Francis F. Ferris; Carl M. Fredericks; Christopher M. Fredericks; Suzanne P. Fredericks; Thomas W. Payne; Rosalind F. Rymal.
EIN: 386154750

618
Freedom Educational Foundation
6340 Autumn Dr.
Hudsonville, MI   49426-9309

Donors: Brian Bosch; Cimberly Bosch.
Grantmaker type: Independent foundation.
Financial data (yr. ended 6/30/05): Assets, $2,797 (M); gifts received, $17,434; expenditures, $23,835; total giving, $23,400; qualifying distributions, $23,400; giving activities include $23,400 for grants.
Fields of interest: Higher education; Protestant agencies & churches.
Type of support: General/operating support.
Limitations: Applications not accepted. Giving primarily in Hudsonville, MI. No grants to individuals.
Application information: Contributes only to pre-selected organizations.
Officers: Timothy Kleis, Pres.; Douglas VandeGuethe, V.P.; Rick Koster, Secy.; Phil Gluoker, Treas.
EIN: 383350883

619
The Freeman Foundation
(formerly Westran Corporation Foundation)
5588 W. 32nd St.
Fremont, MI   49412   (231) 924-3059
Contact: Rebecca Llewellyn, Mgr.

Established in MI.
Grantmaker type: Independent foundation.
Financial data (yr. ended 12/31/03): Assets, $210,828 (M); expenditures, $732; total giving, $0; qualifying distributions, $732.
Type of support: General/operating support.
Limitations: Giving primarily in MI. No grants to individuals.
Application information:
Initial approach: Letter
Deadline(s): None
Officer: Rebecca Llewellyn, Mgr.
EIN: 386048805

620
Freiheit Foundation

1660 International Dr., Ste. 470
McLean, VA 22102
Contact: Peter Nguyen

Established in 1989 in MI.
Donors: Erik D. Prince; Joan Prince; Edgar D. Prince; Elsa D. Prince; Prince Holding Corp.
Grantmaker type: Independent foundation.
Financial data (yr. ended 6/30/03): Assets, $529,229 (M); expenditures, $2,334,646; total giving, $176,500; qualifying distributions, $176,484; giving activities include $176,500 for 8 grants (high: $60,000; low: $500).
Fields of interest: Elementary/secondary education; Human services; Christian agencies & churches.
Type of support: General/operating support; Research.
Limitations: Applications not accepted. Giving primarily in Washington, DC, VA, and New York, NY; some giving also in MI. No grants to individuals.
Application information: Contributes only to pre-selected organizations.
Officers: Erik D. Prince, Pres.; George Mokhiber, Secy.; Joan Prince, Treas.
EIN: 382902413
Selected grants: The following grants were reported in 2003.
$60,000 to Institute of World Politics, DC. For general support.
$50,000 to Intrepid Museum Foundation, New York, NY. For general support.
$30,000 to Christendom College, Front Royal, VA. For general support.
$25,000 to Rooted in Faith-Forward in Hope, Arlington, VA. For general support.
$8,000 to Catholic University of America, DC. For general support.
$2,500 to Acton Institute for the Study of Religion and Liberty, Grand Rapids, MI. For general support.
$500 to Brownson Institute, Crisis Magazine, DC. For general support.
$500 to Childrens Hospital of the Kings Daughters, Norfolk, VA. For general support.

621
Frey Foundation

40 Pearl St. N.W., Ste. 1100
Grand Rapids, MI 49503-3028 (616) 451-0303
Contact: Milton W. Rohwer, Pres.
FAX: (616) 451-8481; E-mail: contact@freyfdn.org;
URL: http://www.freyfdn.org

Established in 1974 in MI; endowed in 1988.
Donors: Edward J. Frey, Sr.†; Frances T. Frey†.
Grantmaker type: Independent foundation.
Financial data (yr. ended 12/31/05): Assets, $131,802,000 (M); expenditures, $5,726,000; total giving, $4,847,000; qualifying distributions, $5,726,000; giving activities include $4,847,000 for grants.
Purpose and activities: Priorities include promoting healthy developmental outcomes for children in their early years (0-6 years); support for land use planning and growth management, and protection of natural resources; stimulating the vitality, effectiveness, and growth of community-based arts; encouraging civic progress and leadership; and strengthening philanthropy.

Fields of interest: Arts, cultural/ethnic awareness; Arts, folk arts; Arts education; Visual arts; Museums; Museums (art); Museums (children's); Museums (ethnic/folk arts); Museums (history); Museums (marine/maritime); Museums (natural history); Museums (science/technology); Museums (specialized); Performing arts; Performing arts centers; Performing arts, dance; Performing arts, ballet; Performing arts, theater; Performing arts, theater (musical); Performing arts, music; Performing arts, orchestra (symphony); Performing arts, opera; Performing arts, music (choral); Performing arts, music ensembles/groups; Performing arts, education; Historic preservation/historical societies; Arts; Education, reform; Education, early childhood education; Child development, education; Libraries (public); Environment, water pollution; Environment, natural resources; Environment, water resources; Environment, land resources; Botanical gardens; Environment, beautification programs; Environment; Animals/wildlife, preservation/protection; Animals/wildlife, fisheries; Zoos/zoological societies; Children/youth, services; Children, day care; Children, services; Child development, services; Family services; Family services, parent education; Community development, neighborhood development; Community development, civic centers; Community development, public/private ventures; Urban/community development; Foundations (community); Philanthropy/voluntarism.
Type of support: Capital campaigns; Land acquisition; Program development; Seed money; Research; Technical assistance; Employee matching gifts.
Limitations: Giving primarily in Emmet, Charlevoix, and Kent counties, MI. No support for sectarian charitable activity. No grants to individuals, or for endowment funds, debt retirement, general operating expenses, scholarships, conferences, speakers, travel, or to cover routine, current, or emergency expenses.
Publications: Application guidelines; Annual report.
Application information: Application form required for all requests; online application available. Application form required.
    Initial approach: Letter of inquiry or telephone
    Copies of proposal: 1
    Deadline(s): Feb. 15, May 15, Aug. 15, and Nov. 15
    Board meeting date(s): Feb., May, Aug., and Nov.
Officers and Trustees: * David G. Frey,* Chair.; John M. Frey,* Vice-Chair.; Milton W. Rohwer, Pres.; Edward J. Frey, Jr.,* Secy.-Treas.; Mary Caroline "Twink" Frey, Tr. Emeritus.
Number of staff: 5 full-time professional; 1 full-time support.
EIN: 237094777
Selected grants: The following grants were reported in 2003.
$1,000,000 to Grand Rapids Art Museum, Grand Rapids, MI. For creation of landmark art museum in downtown Grand Rapids adjacent to Maya Lin's Ecliptic.
$650,000 to Nature Conservancy, Michigan Chapter, Lansing, MI. For land purchase and protection of 390,000 acres in Michigan's Upper Peninsula.
$334,000 to Grand Traverse Regional Land Conservancy, Traverse City, MI. 2 grants: $100,000 (For protection of scenic viewsheds, prime farmland and natural areas along corridor from Traverse City to northern Antrim County),

$234,000 (For the acquisition and preservation of 6,230 acres in northern Michigan).
$150,000 to Grand Action Foundation, Grand Rapids, MI. For DeVos Performance Hall interior renovation project.
$129,700 to Charlevoix County Community Foundation, East Jordan, MI. For support of John M. and Hilda C. Discretionary Fund.
$125,000 to Conservation Resource Alliance, Traverse City, MI. To continue stream bank stabilizations and water quality restoration work (River Care) and pilot concentrated program connecting wildlife habitat with corridor (Wildlink) on Maple River.
$105,000 to Grand Valley State University, Allendale, MI. For digital conversion of GVSU Public Television facility in accordance with federal mandate.
$100,000 to Michigan State University, East Lansing, MI. To establish Guyers/Seevers Endowed Chair in Natural Resources Conservation, focusing on finding comprehensive solutions to land-based problems through teaching, research and serving as a resource to industry, nonprofits and government.
$100,000 to Potters House, Grand Rapids, MI. For Opening Doors capital campaign and specifically for campaign's new preschool elements.

622
The Friedman Family Foundation, Inc.

1215 Southwood Ct.
Ann Arbor, MI 48103

Donor: Jacob Friedman.
Grantmaker type: Independent foundation.
Financial data (yr. ended 12/31/04): Assets, $846,633 (M); expenditures, $57,584; total giving, $55,500; qualifying distributions, $55,000; giving activities include $55,500 for grants.
Fields of interest: Higher education; Jewish federated giving programs; Jewish agencies & temples.
Limitations: Applications not accepted. No grants to individuals.
Application information: Contributes only to pre-selected organizations.
Officer: Susan Cameron, Pres.
EIN: 650384894

623
Robert G. Friedman Foundation

76 Isla Bahia Dr.
Fort Lauderdale, FL 33316-2331

Established in 1977.
Donors: Robert G. Friedman; Eugenie S. Friedman.
Grantmaker type: Independent foundation.
Financial data (yr. ended 12/31/04): Assets, $6,923,267 (M); expenditures, $403,227; total giving, $318,135; qualifying distributions, $318,135; giving activities include $318,135 for 47 grants (high: $35,000; low: $35).
Purpose and activities: Giving primarily for the arts, education, health, and human services.
Fields of interest: Arts; Elementary/secondary education; Higher education; Medical care, in-patient care; Human services; Children/youth, services; Federated giving programs; Roman Catholic agencies & churches.

Type of support: General/operating support; Grants to individuals.
Limitations: Applications not accepted. Giving primarily in FL, MA, MI, OH, and WI.
Application information: Contributes only to pre-selected organizations.
Officers: Robert G. Friedman, Pres.; Eugenie S. Friedman, V.P.
Directors: Jane F. Anspach; Mary Friedman Baske; Jennifer Friedman Hillis; Elizabeth F. O'Connor.
EIN: 591726262

624
The Steven Paul Friedman Foundation
c/o Eli Friedman
6745 Heron Pt.
West Bloomfield, MI   48323

Established in 1998 in MI.
Donors: Eli Friedman; Marc J. Friedman.
Grantmaker type: Independent foundation.
Financial data (yr. ended 12/31/04): Assets, $100,754 (M); gifts received, $4,000; expenditures, $4,042; total giving, $4,000; qualifying distributions, $4,042; giving activities include $4,000 for 3 grants (high: $3,000; low: $500).
Limitations: Applications not accepted. Giving primarily in IL; some giving also in CA and MI. No grants to individuals.
Application information: Contributes only to pre-selected organizations.
Directors: Eli Friedman; Ethelene Friedman; Madalyn Friedman; Marc J. Friedman.
EIN: 383415501

625
Friend Foundation
40 Pearl St. N.W., Ste. 600
Grand Rapids, MI   49503

Donors: Ernestine B. Friend; Barbara B. Friend; Barbara F. Van Ess.
Grantmaker type: Independent foundation.
Financial data (yr. ended 12/31/05): Assets, $86,062 (M); expenditures, $13,936; total giving, $12,500; qualifying distributions, $12,500; giving activities include $12,500 for grants.
Limitations: Applications not accepted. Giving limited to Grand Rapids, MI. No grants to individuals.
Application information: Contributes only to pre-selected organizations.
Trustees: Barbara B. Friend; Barbara F. Van Ess.
EIN: 382283799

626
Friends of Spring Lake District Library
(formerly Friends of the Warner Baird Library)
123 E. Exchange St.
Spring Lake, MI   49456

Donor: Lakeland Library Cooperative.
Grantmaker type: Independent foundation.
Financial data (yr. ended 9/30/05): Assets, $22,405 (M); gifts received, $110; expenditures, $15,332; total giving, $0; qualifying distributions, $0.
Purpose and activities: Support only for the Warner Baird Library in Spring Lake, Michigan.
Fields of interest: Libraries (public).

Limitations: Applications not accepted. Giving limited to Spring Lake, MI. No grants to individuals.
Application information: Contributes only to a pre-selected organization.
Officers: Mary Janusch, Pres.; Francene Crandall, V.P.; Virginia Johnson, Secy.; Lois Matheson, Treas.
EIN: 382412375

627
Friends of Yerevan State University
31506 W. Stonewood Ct.
Farmington Hills, MI   48334

Donors: Lincy Foundation; Armenian Church Endowment Fund.
Grantmaker type: Independent foundation.
Financial data (yr. ended 12/31/05): Assets, $181,967 (M); gifts received, $57,456; expenditures, $177,342; total giving, $173,201; qualifying distributions, $319,995; giving activities include $173,201 for grants.
Purpose and activities: Support only for the Yerevan State University in Armenia.
Fields of interest: Higher education, university.
International interests: Armenia.
Limitations: Applications not accepted. Giving limited to Yerevan, Armenia. No grants to individuals.
Application information: Contributes only to a pre-selected organization.
Officers: Vartkess Balian, Pres.; Rouren Terzian, V.P.; Edmond Azadian, Secy.; Osep Sarafian, Treas.
Director: Armand Arabian.
EIN: 541800204

628
The Kurt C. & Sally S. Frisch Family Foundation
17986 Parke Ln.
Grosse Ile, MI   48138-1042

Established in 1999 in MI.
Donors: Kurt C. Frisch; Sally S. Frisch.
Grantmaker type: Independent foundation.
Financial data (yr. ended 12/31/05): Assets, $265,354 (M); expenditures, $14,713; total giving, $14,040; qualifying distributions, $14,040; giving activities include $14,040 for grants.
Fields of interest: Cancer research; Residential/custodial care, hospices.
Limitations: Applications not accepted. Giving primarily in Ann Arbor, MI. No grants to individuals.
Application information: Contributes only to pre-selected organizations.
Directors: Kurt C. Frisch, Jr.; Sally S. Frisch.
EIN: 383468471

629
David & Barbara Fromm Family Foundation
27777 Franklin Rd., Ste. 2500
Southfield, MI   48034

Established in 2000 in MI.
Donors: David G. Fromm; Barbara S. Fromm.
Grantmaker type: Independent foundation.
Financial data (yr. ended 12/31/05): Assets, $145,687 (M); expenditures, $2,080; total giving, $0; qualifying distributions, $0.
Limitations: Applications not accepted. Giving on a national basis. No grants to individuals.

Application information: Contributes only to pre-selected organizations.
Officers: David G. Fromm, Pres. and Treas.; Barbara S. Fromm, V.P. and Secy.
Trustees: Kathleen Fromm Cohen; Marc A. Fromm; Ken Koltun-Fromm.
EIN: 383523128

630
The Albert & Dorothy Fruman Foundation
P.O. Box 250642
Franklin, MI   48025-0642

Established in 1988 in MI.
Donor: Hubbell Steel.
Grantmaker type: Independent foundation.
Financial data (yr. ended 12/31/04): Assets, $294,126 (M); expenditures, $15,241; total giving, $14,625; qualifying distributions, $14,625; giving activities include $14,625 for grants.
Fields of interest: Higher education; Jewish federated giving programs; Roman Catholic agencies & churches; Jewish agencies & temples.
Limitations: Giving primarily in MI.
Officers: Dorothy Fruman, Pres.; Lee Fruman, V.P. and Secy.-Treas.
EIN: 386109134

631
Golden & Lillian M. Fuller Charitable Trust
c/o Citizens Bank Wealth Mgmt., N.A.
328 S. Saginaw St., M/C 002072
Flint, MI   48502

Established in MI.
Grantmaker type: Independent foundation.
Financial data (yr. ended 2/28/06): Assets, $2,645,577 (M); expenditures, $154,021; total giving, $126,398; qualifying distributions, $126,398; giving activities include $126,398 for grants.
Purpose and activities: Support only for Lutheran Hour Ministries and Lutheran Church, St. Louis.
Fields of interest: Protestant agencies & churches.
Type of support: General/operating support.
Limitations: Applications not accepted. Giving limited to St. Louis, MO. No grants to individuals.
Application information: Contributes only to 2 pre-selected organizations specified in the trust instrument.
Trustee: Citizens Bank.
EIN: 386400225

632
Fund for Indigenous Rights and the Environment
(also known as F.I.R.E.)
(formerly D. R. T. Fund)
c/o Comerica Bank
P.O. Box 75000 M/C 3302
Detroit, MI   48275-3302
E-mail: info@FIREfdn.org; Mailing address: P.O. Box 460, Cordova, AK 99574, tel.: (907) 424-5899, fax: (907) 424-5891; URL: http://www.FIREfdn.org/

Established in 2003 in AK.
Donors: Jack Titcomb; Diana Titcomb.
Grantmaker type: Independent foundation.
Financial data (yr. ended 12/31/04): Assets, $1,623,448 (M); gifts received, $1,550,385;

expenditures, $25,495; total giving, $0; qualifying distributions, $16,920.

Purpose and activities: The mission of the fund is to provide strategic support for indigenous human rights, self-determination, community and ecological health, cultural and environmental protection of indigenous lands, and the preservation of related intact ecosystems and wilderness.

Fields of interest: Environment, natural resources; Indigenous people.

Limitations: Applications not accepted. Giving primarily in AK initially, with plans to gradually expand activities to the national and international level.

Application information: The fund currently does not accept unsolicited proposals.

Officers and Directors:* David R. Titcomb,* Pres.; Susanna Colloredo,* V.P.; Joe Hickey,* Secy.; Peter Titcomb,* Treas.; Dune Lankard, Exec. Dir.; Faith Gemmill; Anna Huntington-Kriska; Peter Van Tuyn.

EIN: 870694911

633
Gabooney Foundation
c/o Michael D. Gibson
500 Woodward Ave., Ste. 2500
Detroit, MI 48226

Established in 1981 in MI.
Donors: David B. Gamble; L. David Gamble Charitable Trust.
Grantmaker type: Independent foundation.
Financial data (yr. ended 3/31/05): Assets, $40,090 (M); gifts received, $27,871; expenditures, $27,400; total giving, $23,700; qualifying distributions, $23,700; giving activities include $23,700 for grants.
Purpose and activities: Giving primarily for hospitals, law enforcement and community service organizations.
Fields of interest: Performing arts; Performing arts, theater; Performing arts, opera; Crime/law enforcement, police agencies; Disasters, fire prevention/control; Big Brothers/Big Sisters; Boy scouts.
Limitations: Applications not accepted. Giving primarily in MI and Livingston, MT. No grants to individuals.
Application information: Contributes only to pre-selected organizations.
Officers and Directors:* David B. Gamble,* Chair.; Regitze Gamble,* Pres.; Christopher L. Gamble,* V.P.; Kimberly N. Fleming,* Secy.-Treas.
EIN: 382382126

634
Carmela Gagliardi Foundation
789 Upper Scotsborough Way
Bloomfield Hills, MI 48304-3827

Established in 1989 in MI.
Donors: Gerald A. Gagliardi; Mrs. Gerald A. Gagliardi; Raymond A. Gagliardi; Mrs. Raymond A. Gagliardi.
Grantmaker type: Independent foundation.
Financial data (yr. ended 12/31/05): Assets, $48,338 (M); expenditures, $27,399; total giving, $25,000; qualifying distributions, $25,000; giving activities include $25,000 for grants to individuals.

Purpose and activities: Scholarship awards primarily to students of Italian descent who have been accepted to a recognized medical school.
Fields of interest: Medical school/education.
Type of support: Scholarship funds.
Limitations: Applications not accepted. Giving on a national basis.
Application information: Unsolicited requests for funds not accepted.
Officers: Raymond A. Gagliardi, Pres.; Gerald A. Gagliardi, V.P.; Patricia D. Gagliardi, Secy.
EIN: 382895105

635
Galencher Nagy Foundation
31555 W. 14 Mile Rd., Ste. 316
Farmington Hills, MI 48334

Established in 1997 in MI.
Donor: Elizabeth Galencher.
Grantmaker type: Independent foundation.
Financial data (yr. ended 12/31/05): Assets, $246,193 (M); gifts received, $20,602; expenditures, $32,439; total giving, $25,000; qualifying distributions, $25,000; giving activities include $25,000 for grants.
Purpose and activities: Giving primarily for children's services.
Fields of interest: Children/youth, services.
Type of support: General/operating support.
Limitations: Applications not accepted. Giving primarily in MI. No grants to individuals.
Application information: Contributes only to pre-selected organizations.
Directors: Elizabeth Galencher.
EIN: 383319580

636
Jon A. Gallant Foundation
3519 Wayland Dr.
P.O. Box 1675
Jackson, MI 49204-1675

Established in 1986 in MI.
Grantmaker type: Independent foundation.
Financial data (yr. ended 9/30/05): Assets, $56,825 (M); expenditures, $3,508; total giving, $3,112; qualifying distributions, $3,112; giving activities include $3,112 for grants.
Limitations: Giving primarily in MI.
Trustee: Thomas Gallant.
EIN: 386511184

637
Frederick Gallo Irrevocable Trust
c/o Comerica Bank
P.O. Box 75000, MC 3302
Detroit, MI 48275-3302

Established in 2000 in MI.
Grantmaker type: Independent foundation.
Financial data (yr. ended 12/31/05): Assets, $598,822 (M); expenditures, $42,259; total giving, $34,176; qualifying distributions, $34,176; giving activities include $34,176 for grants.
Fields of interest: Health organizations, association; Human services.
Limitations: Applications not accepted. Giving primarily in FL. No grants to individuals.

Application information: Contributes only to pre-selected organizations.
Trustee: Comerica Bank.
EIN: 656308278

638
The Gandhi Foundation
4694 Valleyview Dr.
West Bloomfield, MI 48323-3355

Established in 1999 in MI.
Grantmaker type: Independent foundation.
Financial data (yr. ended 12/31/05): Assets, $10,155 (M); gifts received, $9,134; expenditures, $6,845; total giving, $6,725; qualifying distributions, $6,725; giving activities include $6,725 for grants.
Limitations: Applications not accepted. No grants to individuals.
Application information: Contributes only to pre-selected organizations.
Officers: Harendra S. Gandhi, Pres. and Treas.; Yellow H. Gandhi, Secy.
EIN: 383502285

639
Richard L. and Claire A. Gantos Charitable Foundation
71 Wildhorse
Santa Fe, NM 87506

Established in 1989 in MI.
Donors: Richard L. Gantos; Claire A. Gantos.
Grantmaker type: Independent foundation.
Financial data (yr. ended 12/31/04): Assets, $316,953 (M); gifts received, $40,000; expenditures, $40,120; total giving, $40,000; qualifying distributions, $40,020; giving activities include $40,000 for grants.
Purpose and activities: Giving primarily for higher education and a symphony orchestra.
Fields of interest: Higher education, college.
Limitations: Applications not accepted. Giving primarily in MI. No grants to individuals.
Application information: Contributes only to pre-selected organizations.
Officers: Richard L. Gantos, Pres. and Treas.; Claire A. Gantos, Secy.
EIN: 382889548

640
L. Douglas Gantos Family Foundation
2465 Cascade Springs Dr.
Grand Rapids, MI 49546

Established in 1994 in MI.
Donor: L. Douglas Gantos.
Grantmaker type: Independent foundation.
Financial data (yr. ended 10/31/03): Assets, $131,248 (M); expenditures, $3,355; total giving, $1,600; qualifying distributions, $1,600; giving activities include $1,600 for 4 grants.
Type of support: General/operating support.
Limitations: Applications not accepted. Giving primarily in San Diego, CA. No grants to individuals.
Application information: Contributes only to pre-selected organizations.
Officers: L. Douglas Gantos, Pres. and Secy.; Kathy Gantos, Secy.-Treas.
EIN: 333212083

641
Gardner Charitable Enterprises
4061 Lacey Ln.
Fort Gratiot, MI   48059

Established in 2000 in MI.
Grantmaker type: Independent foundation.
Financial data (yr. ended 6/30/05): Assets, $304 (M); expenditures, $858; total giving, $500; qualifying distributions, $500; giving activities include $500 for grants.
Fields of interest: Christian agencies & churches.
Type of support: General/operating support.
Limitations: Giving primarily in TN.
Director: Donald Gardner.
EIN: 383441364

642
Garland-Schut Foundation
487 W. Division St.
P.O. Box 246
Sparta, MI   49345   (616) 887-7301
Contact: Warren H. Schut, Secy.-Treas.

Established in 1986 in MI.
Donors: Warren H. Schut; D. Maxine Schut; Dorothy Schut.
Grantmaker type: Independent foundation.
Financial data (yr. ended 12/31/04): Assets, $283,811 (M); gifts received, $74,082; expenditures, $26,379; total giving, $22,886; qualifying distributions, $22,886; giving activities include $22,886 for grants.
Fields of interest: Education; Community development; Christian agencies & churches.
Limitations: Giving primarily in Sparta, MI. No grants to individuals.
Application information:
  Initial approach: Letter
  Deadline(s): None
Officers: D. Maxine Schut, Pres.; Warren H. Schut, Secy.-Treas.
EIN: 382705026

643
William Albright Garrison Fund f/b/o University of Michigan
(formerly William Albright Garrison Memorial Fund)
c/o Bank of America, N.A.
P.O. Box 40200
Jacksonville, FL   32203-0200

Established in 1997 in FL.
Grantmaker type: Independent foundation.
Financial data (yr. ended 7/31/05): Assets, $513,965 (M); expenditures, $27,966; total giving, $22,690; qualifying distributions, $22,690; giving activities include $22,690 for grants.
Purpose and activities: Support only to the University of Michigan.
Fields of interest: Higher education, university.
Type of support: General/operating support.
Limitations: Applications not accepted. Giving limited to Ann Arbor, MI. No grants to individuals.
Application information: Contributes only to a pre-selected organization.
Trustee: Bank of America, N.A.
EIN: 596694672

644
The Gary Family Foundation
3710 Roger B. Chaffee Blvd.
Grand Rapids, MI   49548

Established in 2004 in MI.
Donors: Brian I. Gary; Kim L. Gray; Shawn E. Gray.
Grantmaker type: Independent foundation.
Financial data (yr. ended 12/31/05): Assets, $227,622 (M); gifts received, $150,000; expenditures, $42,170; total giving, $42,050; qualifying distributions, $42,050; giving activities include $42,050 for grants.
Fields of interest: Community development.
Type of support: Building/renovation.
Limitations: Giving primarily in Grand Rapids, MI.
Directors: Brian I. Gray; Kim L. Gray; Shawn E. Gray.
EIN: 352231209

645
Gary Sisters Foundation
107 W. Michigan Ave., PH
Kalamazoo, MI   49007
Contact: William T. Little, Tr.

Established in 1993 in MI.
Grantmaker type: Independent foundation.
Financial data (yr. ended 12/31/05): Assets, $1,214,773 (M); expenditures, $67,329; total giving, $53,225; qualifying distributions, $53,225; giving activities include $53,225 for grants.
Purpose and activities: Giving primarily for higher and other education, and children, youth, and social services.
Fields of interest: Higher education; Libraries (public); Education; Environment, natural resources; Athletics/sports, golf; Human services; Children/youth, services.
Limitations: Giving primarily in Kalamazoo, MI. No grants to individuals.
Application information:
  Initial approach: Letter
  Deadline(s): None
Officers and Trustees:* George T. Schumacher,* Secy.; Shirley Palmer, Treas.; Mary Delehanty; Fran Little; William T. Little.
EIN: 383109660

646
Warren E. & D. Lou Gast Charitable Foundation
c/o 1st Source Bank
1600 Hilltop Rd.
St. Joseph, MI   49085

Established in 1996 in MI.
Donors: Warren E. Gast; D. Lou Gast.
Grantmaker type: Independent foundation.
Financial data (yr. ended 12/31/05): Assets, $1,525,882 (M); gifts received, $17,969; expenditures, $342,469; total giving, $330,500; qualifying distributions, $336,108; giving activities include $330,500 for 4 grants (high: $260,000; low: $500).
Purpose and activities: Giving primarily for education and to Lutheran agencies and churches.
Fields of interest: Arts; Higher education; Education; Human services; Protestant agencies & churches.

Limitations: Applications not accepted. Giving in the U.S., with some emphasis on MI. No grants to individuals.
Application information: Contributes only to pre-selected organizations.
Trustees: D. Lou Gast; Warren E. Gast; 1st Source Bank.
EIN: 386676317
Selected grants: The following grants were reported in 2003.
$50,000 to Concordia University, Portland, OR. For capital support.
$8,000 to Island Lutheran Church, Hilton Head Island, SC. For general operating support.
$5,000 to Concordia University Foundation, Portland, OR. For capital support.
$5,000 to Curious Kids Museum, Saint Joseph, MI. For general operating support.
$5,000 to Fort Miami Heritage Society of Michigan, Saint Joseph, MI. For general operating support.
$5,000 to Maud Preston Palenske Memorial Library, Saint Joseph, MI. For general operating support.
$4,500 to Michigan Colleges Foundation, Southfield, MI. For general operating support.
$3,000 to Southwest Michigan Symphony Orchestra, Saint Joseph, MI. For general operating support.
$2,800 to Lakeshore Public Schools, Stevensville, MI. For band trip to Washington.
$1,750 to Fernwood Botanical Garden and Nature Preserve, Niles, MI. For general operating support.

647
Gast Foundation
1240 Young Pl.
St. Joseph, MI   49085-2126

Established in 1967 in MI.
Donors: Martha H. Gast‡; Warren E. Gast; Marcella J. Schalon; Gast Manufacturing Corp.
Grantmaker type: Independent foundation.
Financial data (yr. ended 12/31/05): Assets, $2,306,279 (M); expenditures, $157,743; total giving, $134,000; qualifying distributions, $145,871; giving activities include $134,000 for 9 grants (high: $50,000; low: $7,000).
Purpose and activities: Giving primarily to Lutheran organizations and churches; funding also for higher education.
Fields of interest: Higher education; Human services; Protestant agencies & churches.
Type of support: General/operating support; Building/renovation; Scholarship funds.
Limitations: Applications not accepted. Giving primarily in MI; some funding also in River Forest, IL, and Watertown, WI. No grants to individuals.
Application information: Contributes only to pre-selected organizations.
Officer: Warren E. Gast, Pres. and Secy.
Directors: D. Lou Gast; Marcella Schalon.
EIN: 386146354
Selected grants: The following grants were reported in 2005.
$50,000 to Trinity Lutheran Church, Saint Joseph, MI. For general operating support.
$25,000 to Concordia University Foundation, Portland, OR. For general operating support.
$14,000 to Concordia University, Ann Arbor, MI. For general operating support.
$10,000 to Immanuel Lutheran School, Bridgman, MI. For general operating support.

$7,000 to Bethesda Lutheran Homes and Services, Watertown, WI. For general operating support.

$7,000 to Lutheran Child and Family Services of Illinois, River Forest, IL. For general operating support.

$7,000 to Lutheran Homes of Michigan, Frankenmuth, MI. For general operating support.

$7,000 to Lutheran Special Education Ministries, River Forest, IL. For general operating support.

$7,000 to Saint James Evangelical Lutheran Church, Portage, MI. For general operating support.

648
The Gates Foundation
161 Ottawa N.W., Ste. 600
Grand Rapids, MI 49503

Established in 1999 in MI.
Grantmaker type: Independent foundation.
Financial data (yr. ended 12/31/04): Assets, $534,235 (M); expenditures, $46,969; total giving, $36,125; qualifying distributions, $36,125; giving activities include $36,125 for grants.
Fields of interest: Recreation, camps; Youth, services; Protestant agencies & churches.
Limitations: Applications not accepted. Giving primarily in Grand Rapids, MI. No grants to individuals.
Application information: Contributes only to pre-selected organizations.
Officers: Charles M. Gates, Jr., Pres.; Robert J. Dugan, Secy.; Sally Pyper, Treas.
Director: Deborah Lambrix.
EIN: 383453138

649
Paul E. Gau Foundation
30100 Telegraph Rd., Ste. 302
Bingham Farms, MI 48025-4517
(248) 642-3200
Contact: Jacob Alspector, Pres.

Established in 1997.
Donor: Paul Gau.
Grantmaker type: Independent foundation.
Financial data (yr. ended 12/31/04): Assets, $0 (M); expenditures, $109,295; total giving, $100,000; qualifying distributions, $100,000; giving activities include $100,000 for grants.
Fields of interest: Health care, research; Spine disorders research.
Limitations: Giving primarily in Detroit, MI. No grants to individuals.
Application information:
 Initial approach: Letter
 Deadline(s): None
Officers: Jacob Alspector, Pres.; James Barson, Treas.
EIN: 383297161

650
Gavin Family Foundation
c/o 321 N. Clark St.
3 First National Plz., No. 4200
Chicago, IL 60610

Established in IL.
Grantmaker type: Independent foundation.

Financial data (yr. ended 12/31/04): Assets, $52,971 (M); expenditures, $3,610; total giving, $3,600; qualifying distributions, $3,600; giving activities include $3,600 for grants.
Limitations: Applications not accepted. Giving primarily in IL; some giving also in MI. No grants to individuals.
Application information: Contributes only to pre-selected organizations.
Directors: Patricia Gavin Binder; John N. Gavin; Lawrence M. Gavin; Marguerite Robson.
EIN: 257120181

651
The Gayar Foundation
26300 Telegraph Rd., 2nd Fl.
Southfield, MI 48034

Established in 1994 in MI.
Grantmaker type: Independent foundation.
Financial data (yr. ended 12/31/04): Assets, $2,364,605 (M); gifts received, $500,000; expenditures, $326,770; total giving, $324,650; qualifying distributions, $324,648; giving activities include $324,650 for grants.
Purpose and activities: Giving to Islamic centers and medical centers.
Fields of interest: International relief; Islam.
International interests: Africa.
Limitations: Applications not accepted. Giving primarily in MI. No grants to individuals.
Application information: Unsolicited requests for funds not accepted.
Officer: Hesham E. Gayar, Pres.
EIN: 383176739

652
Geenen Family Foundation
c/o Charles Geenen
1276 Beach Dr.
Holland, MI 49423-4483

Established in 2000 in MI.
Donors: Charles Geenen; Julie Geenen.
Grantmaker type: Independent foundation.
Financial data (yr. ended 12/31/04): Assets, $677,982 (M); gifts received, $50,000; expenditures, $12,796; total giving, $11,250; qualifying distributions, $11,250; giving activities include $11,250 for grants.
Limitations: Giving primarily in Holland, MI.
Officer: Charles Geenen, Pres. and Treas.
Director: Julie Geenen.
EIN: 383534246

653
Richard and Sylvia Geenen Foundation
Clinton Realty Bldg.
2876 28th St. S.W.
Grandville, MI 49418-1100

Established in 2001 in MI.
Donors: Sylvia Geenen†; Richard J. Geenen.
Grantmaker type: Independent foundation.
Financial data (yr. ended 12/31/05): Assets, $821,872 (M); expenditures, $42,372; total giving, $40,000; qualifying distributions, $40,000; giving activities include $40,000 for grants.
Fields of interest: Christian agencies & churches.

Limitations: Applications not accepted. Giving primarily in MI. No grants to individuals.
Application information: Contributes only to pre-selected organizations.
Officers: Gary A. Geenen, Pres.; Richard J. Geenen, Secy.-Treas.
EIN: 383600874

654
The Geetha and Govindaraj Foundation
1315 Chissom Trl.
Flint, MI 48532

Established in 2000 in MI.
Donors: Ethiraj G. Raj; Geetha Raj.
Grantmaker type: Independent foundation.
Financial data (yr. ended 12/31/04): Assets, $1,139,134 (M); expenditures, $52; total giving, $0; qualifying distributions, $0.
Limitations: Applications not accepted. No grants to individuals.
Application information: Contributes only to pre-selected organizations.
Officers and Directors: * Ethiraj G. Raj,* Pres. and Treas.; Geetha Raj,* Secy.; Kumar Raj; Padma Raj; Shanthi Raj.
EIN: 912088671

655
Gegax Family Foundation
c/o Comerica Bank
P.O. Box 75000
Detroit, MI 48275-3302

Established in 2000 in MN.
Donor: Thomas L. Gegax.
Grantmaker type: Independent foundation.
Financial data (yr. ended 12/31/04): Assets, $1,050,333 (M); expenditures, $96,204; total giving, $86,985; qualifying distributions, $89,292; giving activities include $86,985 for grants.
Fields of interest: Heart & circulatory diseases.
Type of support: General/operating support.
Limitations: Applications not accepted. Giving primarily in Edina, MN. No grants to individuals.
Application information: Contributes only to pre-selected organizations.
Officers and Directors: * Thomas L. Gegax,* Pres.; T. Trent Gegax,* V.P. and Secy.; Mary Wescott,* V.P. and Treas.; Christopher Gegax.
EIN: 411989478

656
The Geist Foundation of Michigan
31710 Ridgeside Dr., Ste. 1
Farmington Hills, MI 48334-1274

Established in 1996 in MI.
Grantmaker type: Independent foundation.
Financial data (yr. ended 12/31/05): Assets, $986,198 (M); expenditures, $58,304; total giving, $47,700; qualifying distributions, $47,700; giving activities include $47,700 for grants.
Fields of interest: Performing arts; Jewish federated giving programs; Jewish agencies & temples.
Type of support: General/operating support.
Limitations: Applications not accepted. Giving primarily in MI and NY. No grants to individuals.
Application information: Contributes only to pre-selected organizations.

Trustees: Jonathon L. Rones; Rona Rones; Todd I. Rones.
EIN: 383306198

657
Gelman Educational Foundation

201 S. Main St., No. 900
Ann Arbor, MI 48104

Established in 1994 in MI.
Donor: Charles Gelman.
Grantmaker type: Independent foundation.
Financial data (yr. ended 12/31/05): Assets, $5,545,956 (M); expenditures, $321,878; total giving, $183,515; qualifying distributions, $270,592; giving activities include $183,515 for 16 grants (high: $100,000; low: $35).
Fields of interest: Higher education, university; Public health.
Limitations: Applications not accepted. Giving primarily in Ann Arbor, MI. No grants to individuals.
Application information: Contributes only to pre-selected organizations.
Officers: Rita Gelman, Pres.; Charles Gelman, Secy.
EIN: 383197904

658
General Sports Foundation

400 Water St., Ste. 250
Rochester, MI 48307

Established in 2001 in MI.
Donors: Trimas Corp.; RVP Development Corp.
Grantmaker type: Independent foundation.
Financial data (yr. ended 12/31/04): Assets, $209,728 (M); gifts received, $264,552; expenditures, $408,392; total giving, $86,429; qualifying distributions, $224,284; giving activities include $86,429 for grants.
Fields of interest: Health care; Children/youth, services.
Limitations: Applications not accepted. No grants to individuals.
Application information: Contributes only to pre-selected organizations.
Officers: Andrew D. Appleby,* Pres.; Dana L. Schmitt,* Secy.; Kristiana Appleby,* Treas.
Trustees: Lionel Margolick; Kay Ponicall; Michael Ponicall; Lori Robbins; Michael Robbins; Lee Todd.
EIN: 383520154

659
Generation IV Charitable Trust

c/o Comerica Bank
P.O. Box 75000
Detroit, MI 48275-9413

Established in 2001 in MI.
Donor: Earl-Beth Foundation.
Grantmaker type: Independent foundation.
Financial data (yr. ended 12/31/05): Assets, $1,941,060 (M); expenditures, $118,658; total giving, $91,000; qualifying distributions, $92,130; giving activities include $91,000 for grants.
Limitations: Applications not accepted. No grants to individuals.
Application information: Contributes only to pre-selected organizations.

Trustees: Helen M. Fowler; Duane L. Tarnacki; Comerica Bank.
EIN: 386781068

660
George Fund

P.O. Box 930408
Wixom, MI 48393-0408
Contact: Janice Erichsen, Secy.

Established in 1965 in MI.
Donor: Henry E. George‡.
Grantmaker type: Independent foundation.
Financial data (yr. ended 12/31/05): Assets, $1,240,302 (M); expenditures, $75,059; total giving, $53,000; qualifying distributions, $64,029; giving activities include $53,000 for grants.
Fields of interest: Human services; Youth, services; Family services; Aging, centers/services.
Type of support: General/operating support.
Limitations: Giving limited to MI. No grants to individuals.
Application information:
   Initial approach: Letter
   Deadline(s): Sept. 1
Officers: Richard Hinterman, Pres.; Linda L. Wroten, V.P.; Janice Erichsen, Secy.
EIN: 386115722

661
The Gerber Foundation

(formerly The Gerber Companies Foundation)
4747 W. 48th St., Ste. 153
Fremont, MI 49412-8119 (231) 924-3175
Contact: Catherine A. Obits, Prog. Mgr.
FAX: (231) 924-7906; E-mail: tgf@ncresa.org;
Additional E-mail for Catherine A. Obits: cobits@ncresa.org; URL: http://www.gerberfoundation.org

Incorporated in 1952 in MI with funds from Gerber Products Co; in 1995 the foundation became independent from the company.
Grantmaker type: Independent foundation.
Financial data (yr. ended 12/31/05): Assets, $82,646,107 (M); expenditures, $5,141,405; total giving, $4,277,576; qualifying distributions, $4,452,224; giving activities include $3,917,567 for 213 grants (high: $936,246; low: $150), $210,933 for 146 grants to individuals, and $149,076 for 385 employee matching gifts.
Purpose and activities: The foundation seeks to enhance the quality of life for infants and children by focusing on their nutrition, care, and development.
Fields of interest: Health care, infants; Health organizations, association; Pediatrics; Medical research, institute; Pediatrics research; Nutrition; Minorities.
Type of support: Seed money; Research; Scholarships—to individuals; Matching/challenge support.
Limitations: Giving on a national basis. No support for national child welfare or international based programs. No grants to individuals (except for scholarships), or for capital campaigns or operating support.
Publications: Application guidelines; Annual report (including application guidelines); Program policy statement.
Application information: The foundation prefers that applications be submitted only after receiving

approval of a letter of inquiry. Application guidelines are available on foundation Web site. Application form required.
   Initial approach: Letter of inquiry
   Copies of proposal: 16
   Deadline(s): Feb. 15 and Aug. 15; June 1 and Dec. 1 for letter of inquiry
   Board meeting date(s): Feb., May, Aug., Nov.
   Final notification: May and Nov.
Officers and Trustees:* Barbara J. Ivens,* Pres.; Fernando Flores-New,* V.P.; Tracy A. Baker,* Secy.; Stan M. VanderRoest,* Treas.; William L. Bush, M.D.; Ted C. Davis; Michael J. Ebert; John J. James, Esq.; Jane M. Jeannero; David C. Joslin; Carolyn R. Morby; Nancy Nevin-Folino; Steven W. Poole; Randy A. Puff; William B. Weil, Jr., M.D.
Number of staff: 1 full-time professional; 1 part-time support.
EIN: 386068090
Selected grants: The following grants were reported in 2004.
$1,022,827 to University of North Carolina, Chapel Hill, NC. To evaluate effects of chlorine supplementation on short term memory.
$844,397 to Yale University, New Haven, CT. For identification of biomarkers of calcium deficiency in young children.
$753,665 to Van Andel Research Institute, Grand Rapids, MI. For evaluation of congenital chromosomal abnormalities in newborns.
$625,150 to Cincinnati Childrens Hospital Medical Center, Cincinnati, OH. 2 grants: $377,819 (For evaluation of Interleukin-11 as preventive therapy against development of necrotizing entercolitis (NEC)), $247,331 (For evaluation of epidermal growth factor and maturation of the gastrointestinal tract in premature infants).
$529,497 to Memorial Sloan-Kettering Cancer Center, New York, NY. For evaluation of oral beta-glucan therapy as a potential additive to cancer treatment.
$304,200 to Wayne State University, Detroit, MI. For evaluation of harmful effects of fatty acid supplementation on cognitive development.
$223,288 to University of Minnesota, Minneapolis, MN. For evaluation of the harmful effects of oxygen therapy given at birth.
$213,588 to Duke University Medical Center, Durham, NC. To evaluate current methods of diagnosis and treatment of gastroesophageal reflux disease in very low birth weight infants.
$139,668 to Childrens Memorial Hospital, Chicago, IL. For evaluation of risk factors for iron deficiency in Premature infants.

662
The Gerberding/Fackler Family Foundation, Inc.

P.O. Box 6
Arcadia, MI 49613-0006 (231) 882-3203
Contact: Miles C. Gerberding, Pres.

Established in 1999 in MI.
Donors: Miles C. Gerberding; Joan W. Gerberding.
Grantmaker type: Independent foundation.
Financial data (yr. ended 12/31/05): Assets, $252,791; gifts received, $49,126; expenditures, $12,400; total giving, $12,000; qualifying distributions, $12,000; giving activities include $12,000 for grants.
Fields of interest: Education; Family services, domestic violence; Christian agencies & churches.
Limitations: Giving primarily in MI.

Application information: Application form required.
Deadline(s): Dec. 1
Officers: Miles C. Gerberding, Pres.; Joan W. Fackler Gerberding, V.P.; Karla M. Smith, M.D., Secy.; Steven W. Fackler, Treas.
Directors: Greta E. Cowart; Brian K. Gerberding; Kent E. Gerberding; Deborah Holbrook.
EIN: 383493199

663

The Bruce and Suzy Gershenson Family Foundation

31500 Northwestern Hwy., Ste. 300
Farmington Hills, MI 48334-2567

Established in 1996 in MI.
Donors: Bruce Gershenson; Suzy Gershenson.
Grantmaker type: Independent foundation.
Financial data (yr. ended 1/31/05): Assets, $110,410 (M); expenditures, $14,365; total giving, $9,929; qualifying distributions, $9,929; giving activities include $9,929 for grants.
Fields of interest: Higher education; Cancer research; Jewish agencies & temples.
Type of support: General/operating support.
Limitations: Applications not accepted. Giving primarily in MI. No grants to individuals.
Application information: Contributes only to pre-selected organizations.
Directors: Bruce Gershenson; Suzy Gershenson.
EIN: 383312952

664

The Dennis and Nancy Gershenson Family Foundation

31500 Northwestern Hwy., Ste. 300
Farmington Hills, MI 48334-2567

Established in 1996 in MI.
Donors: Dennis Gershenson; Nancy Gershenson.
Grantmaker type: Independent foundation.
Financial data (yr. ended 1/31/05): Assets, $505,390 (M); expenditures, $27,497; total giving, $25,261; qualifying distributions, $25,261; giving activities include $25,261 for grants.
Fields of interest: Health care; Alzheimer's disease.
Type of support: General/operating support.
Limitations: Applications not accepted. Giving primarily in MI. No grants to individuals.
Application information: Contributes only to pre-selected organizations.
Directors: Dennis Gershenson; Nancy Gershenson.
EIN: 383314619

665

The Joel and Linda Gershenson Family Foundation

32500 Northwestern Hwy., Ste. 100
Farmington Hills, MI 48334

Established in 1996 in MI.
Donors: Joel Gershenson; Linda Gershenson.
Grantmaker type: Independent foundation.
Financial data (yr. ended 1/31/05): Assets, $177,697 (M); expenditures, $11,395; total giving, $11,122; qualifying distributions, $11,142; giving activities include $11,122 for grants.
Fields of interest: Human services; Jewish federated giving programs; Jewish agencies & temples.

Limitations: Applications not accepted. No grants to individuals.
Application information: Contributes only to pre-selected organizations.
Directors: Joel Gershenson; Linda Gershenson.
EIN: 383315288

666

The Richard and Sherry Gershenson Family Foundation

31500 Northwestern Hwy.
Farmington Hills, MI 48334

Established in 1996 in MI.
Donors: Richard Gershenson; Sherry Gershenson.
Grantmaker type: Independent foundation.
Financial data (yr. ended 1/31/05): Assets, $149,803 (M); expenditures, $8,663; total giving, $4,670; qualifying distributions, $5,295; giving activities include $4,670 for grants.
Fields of interest: Children, services.
Limitations: Applications not accepted. Giving primarily in MI. No grants to individuals.
Application information: Contributes only to pre-selected organizations.
Directors: Richard Gershenson; Sherry Gershenson.
EIN: 383314501

667

Charles H. Gershenson Foundation

2290 First National Bldg.
Detroit, MI 48226-3583

Established in 1984 in MI.
Grantmaker type: Independent foundation.
Financial data (yr. ended 4/30/04): Assets, $5,153,719 (M); expenditures, $322,941; total giving, $250,000; qualifying distributions, $261,552; giving activities include $250,000 for grants.
Purpose and activities: Giving for higher education, Jewish organizations, and hospitals.
Fields of interest: Higher education; Hospitals (general); Jewish agencies & temples.
Type of support: Capital campaigns; Scholarship funds.
Limitations: Applications not accepted. Giving limited to Ann Arbor, Bloomfield Township, and Detroit, MI. No grants to individuals.
Application information: Contributes only to pre-selected organizations.
Trustee: Maurice S. Binkow.
EIN: 386454423

668

The Rollin M. Gerstacker Foundation

P.O. Box 1945
Midland, MI 48641-1945 (989) 631-6097
Contact: E.N. Brandt, V.P.

Incorporated in 1957 in MI.
Donors: Eda U. Gerstacker†; Carl A. Gerstacker†.
Grantmaker type: Independent foundation.
Financial data (yr. ended 12/31/05): Assets, $210,230,699 (M); expenditures, $11,554,220; total giving, $11,116,969; qualifying distributions, $11,194,051; giving activities include $11,116,969 for 243 grants (high: $500,000; low: $500; average: $10,000–$100,000).

Purpose and activities: Giving to assist community projects, with emphasis on the aged and the youth; grants also for higher education, health care, medical research, and hospitals.
Fields of interest: Higher education; Hospitals (general); Health care; Mental health/crisis services; Health organizations, association; Human services; Children/youth, services; Aging, centers/services; Government/public administration; Aging.
Type of support: General/operating support; Continuing support; Annual campaigns; Capital campaigns; Building/renovation; Equipment; Land acquisition; Endowments; Emergency funds; Seed money; Research; Matching/challenge support.
Limitations: Giving primarily in MI; giving also in OH. No grants to individuals, or for scholarships or fellowships; no loans.
Publications: Annual report.
Application information: Application form not required.
Initial approach: Letter
Copies of proposal: 1
Deadline(s): Apr. 15, Aug. 15, and Nov. 15
Board meeting date(s): May, Sept., and Dec.
Final notification: 1 month
Officers and Trustees:* Gail E. Lanphear,* Pres.; Lisa J. Gerstacker,* V.P. and Secy.; Alan W. Ott,* V.P. and Treas.; E.N. Brandt,* V.P.; William D. Schuette,* V.P.; Alexio R. Baum; Frank Gerace; Paula A. Liveris; Thomas L. Ludington; Paul F. Oreffice; William S. Stavropoulos.
EIN: 386060276
Selected grants: The following grants were reported in 2005.
$1,000,000 to Michigan State University, East Lansing, MI. 2 grants: $500,000 each
$400,000 to Nature Conservancy, Arlington, VA. 2 grants: $200,000 each
$400,000 to University of Michigan, Ann Arbor, MI.
$62,500 to Mid-Michigan Community Action Agency, Clare, MI.
$57,500 to Midland Community Center, Midland, MI.
$40,000 to Little Forks Conservancy, Midland, MI.
$30,000 to Southern University and A & M College, Baton Rouge, LA.
$18,000 to Council on Domestic Violence and Sexual Assault, Midland, MI.

669

Herman & Irene Gertz Foundation

c/o Monroe Bank & Trust
102 E. Front St.
Monroe, MI 48161 (734) 241-3431

Established in 1966.
Donors: Irene Gertz†; Herman F. Gertz†.
Grantmaker type: Independent foundation.
Financial data (yr. ended 12/31/05): Assets, $1,341,218 (M); expenditures, $76,383; total giving, $63,000; qualifying distributions, $63,000; giving activities include $63,000 for grants.
Fields of interest: Historic preservation/historical societies; Higher education; Hospitals (general); Human services; Community development; Christian agencies & churches.
Limitations: Giving primarily in Fort Myers, FL and MI. No grants to individuals.
Application information: Application form not required.
Initial approach: Letter
Deadline(s): None
Officers: Robert Gertz, Pres.; Alice Frank, V.P.

Trustee: Monroe Bank & Trust.
EIN: 386153472

670
Wilmar Geyer Charitable Foundation, Inc.
c/o National City Bank
171 Monroe Ave. N.W., KC17-63
Grand Rapids, MI   49503-2634

Grantmaker type: Independent foundation.
Financial data (yr. ended 12/31/05): Assets, $164,086 (M); expenditures, $11,419; total giving, $6,800; qualifying distributions, $6,800; giving activities include $6,800 for grants.
Limitations: Applications not accepted. Giving primarily in MI. No grants to individuals.
Application information: Contributes only to pre-selected organizations.
Trustee: National City Bank.
EIN: 382803978

671
Ghitalla Foundation
216 E. Washington St.
Ann Arbor, MI   48104   (734) 994-1188

Established in 1998 in MI.
Donor: Armando Ghitalla.
Grantmaker type: Independent foundation.
Financial data (yr. ended 12/31/05): Assets, $248,792 (M); expenditures, $11,058; total giving, $9,787; qualifying distributions, $9,787; giving activities include $9,787 for grants.
Limitations: Applications not accepted. No grants to individuals.
Application information: Contributes only to pre-selected organizations.
Director: Robert Tisch.
EIN: 383427630

672
Ruby L. Gibbs Charitable Trust
c/o Citizens Bank Wealth Mgmt., N.A.
328 S. Saginaw St., M/C 002072
Flint, MI   48502
Application addresses: c/o Ovid-Elsie High School, 8989 E. Colony Rd., Elsie, MI 48831, or c/o Arthur Hill High School, 3115 Mackinaw St., Saginaw, MI 49602-3221

Established in 1995 in MI.
Donor: Ruby Gibbs Trust.
Grantmaker type: Independent foundation.
Financial data (yr. ended 12/31/05): Assets, $1,173,863 (M); gifts received, $6,093; expenditures, $67,758; total giving, $52,605; qualifying distributions, $52,605; giving activities include $52,605 for grants.
Purpose and activities: Scholarship awards to students graduating from Arthur Hill High School attending any accredited Michigan college and students graduating from Ovid-Elsie High School attending Central Michigan University; some giving to two Methodist churches.
Fields of interest: Scholarships/financial aid; Protestant agencies & churches.
Type of support: General/operating support; Scholarships—to individuals.
Limitations: Giving limited to residents of MI.
Application information: Application form required.

Initial approach: Letter
Deadline(s): May 1
Trustee: Citizens Bank.
EIN: 386658848

673
Kirk Gibson Foundation
15135 Charlevoix St.
Grosse Pointe, MI   48230-1007

Grantmaker type: Independent foundation.
Financial data (yr. ended 12/31/05): Assets, $20,237 (M); expenditures, $3,219; total giving, $500; qualifying distributions, $500; giving activities include $500 for grants.
Fields of interest: Education.
Limitations: Giving primarily in MI.
Officers: Kirk Gibson, Pres.; JoAnn Gibson, Secy.; Sandra Kempa, Treas.
EIN: 383353375

674
The Irma Giddey Charitable Fund
c/o JPMorgan Chase Bank, N.A.
P.O. Box 1308
Milwaukee, WI   53201

Established in 1994 in MI.
Grantmaker type: Independent foundation.
Financial data (yr. ended 12/31/04): Assets, $1,238,391 (M); expenditures, $83,855; total giving, $71,770; qualifying distributions, $76,491; giving activities include $71,770 for grants.
Purpose and activities: Support only for the Clarence S. Livingood Lectureship and Education Fund, Detroit, MI, and the American Academy of Dermatology, Schaumburg, IL.
Fields of interest: Education.
Limitations: Applications not accepted. Giving limited to Detroit, MI. No grants to individuals.
Application information: Contributes only to 2 pre-selected organizations.
Officers and Trustees: * Douglas J. Rasmussen,* Pres.; David M. Hempstead,* Treas.
Agent: JPMorgan Chase Bank, N.A.
EIN: 383152222

675
Doris J. Giddey Trust
c/o Charles W. McCallum
1630 Park Dr.
Benton Harbor, MI   49022

Established in 1989 in MI.
Donor: Doris J. Giddey†.
Grantmaker type: Independent foundation.
Financial data (yr. ended 12/31/05): Assets, $1,822,664 (M); expenditures, $127,073; total giving, $69,502; qualifying distributions, $69,502; giving activities include $69,502 for grants.
Purpose and activities: Support only for Michigan State University, E. Lansing, Michigan Osteopathic College, Okemos, Adrian College, and Henry Ford Hospital and Wayne State University, Detroit, MI.
Fields of interest: Medical school/education.
Type of support: General/operating support.
Limitations: Applications not accepted. Giving limited to East Lansing, Adrian, Detroit and Okemos, MI. No grants to individuals.

Application information: Contributes only to pre-selected organizations.
Trustees: Charles W. McCallum; Charles H. Webb.
EIN: 386505877

676
Henry Gieseking Perpetual Trust
c/o U.S. Bank, N.A.
P.O. Box 387
St. Louis, MO   63166

Donor: Henry Gieseking.
Grantmaker type: Independent foundation.
Financial data (yr. ended 11/30/05): Assets, $494,586 (M); expenditures, $29,676; total giving, $22,500; qualifying distributions, $22,500; giving activities include $22,500 for grants.
Purpose and activities: Support only for Bethesda Lutheran Home, WI, Lutheran School of the Deaf, MI, Hillsboro Hospital, IL, and Anne Carlsen School, ND.
Fields of interest: Elementary/secondary education; Hospitals (general); Disabilities, people with.
Type of support: General/operating support.
Limitations: Applications not accepted. Giving limited to IL, MI, ND, and WI. No grants to individuals.
Application information: Contributes only to 4 pre-selected organizations.
Trustee: U.S. Bank, N.A.
EIN: 376205858

677
John P. & Susan E. Giesy Foundation
c/o John P. Giesy
2355 Bravender Rd.
Williamston, MI   48895

Established in 2000 in MI.
Donors: John P. Giesy; Susan E. Giesy.
Grantmaker type: Independent foundation.
Financial data (yr. ended 12/31/05): Assets, $100,759 (M); expenditures, $17,866; total giving, $13,000; qualifying distributions, $13,000; giving activities include $13,000 for grants.
Fields of interest: Higher education.
Limitations: Applications not accepted. Giving primarily in MI. No grants to individuals.
Application information: Contributes only to pre-selected organizations.
Officers and Directors: * John P. Giesy,* Pres.; Susan E. Giesy,* V.P.
EIN: 383517941

678
GII Charities
3333 Evergreen Dr. N.E., Ste. 201
Grand Rapids, MI   49525   (616) 363-9209
Contact: Ronald K. Williams, Pres.

Established in 2002 in MI.
Donor: Gordon Food Service, Inc.
Grantmaker type: Independent foundation.
Financial data (yr. ended 12/31/03): Assets, $184,522 (M); gifts received, $2,000,000; expenditures, $1,878,467; total giving, $1,678,317; qualifying distributions, $1,704,245; giving activities include $1,678,317 for 25 grants (high: $275,000; low: $5,000).

Purpose and activities: Giving limited to Christian non-profit organizations for effective evangelization activities emphasizing proclamation, church planting, discipleship, and leadership development.
Fields of interest: Christian agencies & churches.
Limitations: Giving on a worldwide basis. No grants to individuals.
Application information:
  Initial approach: Letter
Officers: Ronald K. Williams, Pres.; James D. Gordon, V.P.; John M. Gordon, Jr., Secy.-Treas.
EIN: 300129615

679
Muriel Gilbert Memorial Scholarship Fund
c/o KeyBank N.A.
800 Superior Ave., 4th Fl.
Cleveland, OH 44114
Application addresses: c/o James Hause, Prof., Eastern Michigan Univ., Music Dept., 1215 Huron River Dr., Ypsilanti, MI 48197, or c/o Superintendent of Schools, Milan Area Schools, 920 North St., Milan, MI 48160

Established in 1988 in MI.
Grantmaker type: Independent foundation.
Financial data (yr. ended 9/30/05): Assets, $526,151 (M); expenditures, $5,064; total giving, $0; qualifying distributions, $0.
Purpose and activities: Scholarship awards to a full-time music major with a voice concentration at Eastern Michigan University, and to graduating seniors majoring in music from Milan, MI, area high schools.
Fields of interest: Performing arts, music.
Type of support: Scholarship funds.
Limitations: Giving limited to the Milan, MI, area.
Application information: Application form required.
  Deadline(s): Prior to end of academic year
Trustee: KeyBank N.A.
EIN: 386525706

680
Karen L. Gilhooly & Rowan Gilhooly Sanford Educational Foundation
10105 E. Apple Ridge
Traverse City, MI 49684 (231) 946-2843
Contact: Kurt Sanford, Pres.

Established in 2004 in MI.
Donors: David Handleman; Charlene Handleman.
Grantmaker type: Independent foundation.
Financial data (yr. ended 12/31/04): Assets, $38,233 (M); gifts received, $38,213; expenditures, $10; total giving, $0; qualifying distributions, $10.
Officers: Kurt Sanford, Pres.; Todd Sanford, Treas.
EIN: 201848629

681
Herbert & Florence Gilles Scholarship Trust
c/o Citizens Bank
328 S. Saginaw St., M/C 002072
Flint, MI 48502
Application address: c/o Ann Siminowski, Nouvel Catholic Central High School, 2555 Wieneke Rd., Saginaw, MI 48602, tel.: (989) 797-6605

Established in 1999 in MI.

Donor: Herbert A. Gilles†.
Grantmaker type: Independent foundation.
Financial data (yr. ended 12/31/05): Assets, $191,179 (M); expenditures, $11,375; total giving, $8,300; qualifying distributions, $8,300; giving activities include $8,300 for grants to individuals.
Purpose and activities: Scholarship awards to students of Nouvel Catholic Central High School with financial need.
Fields of interest: Scholarships/financial aid.
Type of support: Scholarships—to individuals.
Limitations: Giving to residents of Saginaw, MI.
Application information: Application form required.
  Deadline(s): 2nd Mon. in May
Trustee: Citizens Bank.
EIN: 386738557

682
Gilmore Foundation
c/o Fifth Third Bank
P.O. Box 4019
Kalamazoo, MI 49003

Trust established in 1956 in MI.
Donor: Irving S. Gilmore.
Grantmaker type: Independent foundation.
Financial data (yr. ended 12/31/04): Assets, $41,684 (M); gifts received, $40,000; expenditures, $38,959; total giving, $35,134; qualifying distributions, $37,159; giving activities include $35,134 for 13 grants to individuals (high: $4,620; low: $1,056).
Purpose and activities: Grants to low-income individuals residing in the Kalamazoo, MI, area who are unable to care for themselves due to physical limitations or advanced age.
Fields of interest: Aging, centers/services; Aging; Disabilities, people with; Economically disadvantaged.
Type of support: Grants to individuals.
Limitations: Applications not accepted. Giving primarily in the Kalamazoo, MI, area.
Application information: Unsolicited requests for funds not accepted.
Directors: Dan Baas; Craig Kobylik; John Paul.
Trustee: Fifth Third Bank.
EIN: 386052803

683
Irving S. Gilmore Foundation
136 E. Michigan Ave., Ste. 900
Kalamazoo, MI 49007 (269) 342-6411
Contact: Frederick W. Freund, C.E.O. and Exec. V.P.
FAX: (269) 342-6465; E-mail: fritz@isgilmore.org;
URL: http://www.isgilmore.org

Established in 1972 in MI.
Donor: Irving S. Gilmore†.
Grantmaker type: Independent foundation.
Financial data (yr. ended 12/31/05): Assets, $212,065,300 (M); expenditures, $11,353,748; total giving, $10,000,390; qualifying distributions, $10,688,529; giving activities include $10,000,390 for grants.
Purpose and activities: The mission of the foundation is to support and enrich the cultural, social, and economic life of the greater Kalamazoo, MI, area. The priorities of the foundation are: 1) arts, culture, and humanities; 2) human services; 3) education and youth activities; 4) community development; and 5) health and well-being.

Fields of interest: Performing arts; Arts; Education; Health care; Youth development; Human services; Community development.
Type of support: General/operating support; Continuing support; Annual campaigns; Capital campaigns; Building/renovation; Equipment; Land acquisition; Debt reduction; Emergency funds; Program development; Conferences/seminars; Publication; Seed money; Scholarship funds; Technical assistance; Consulting services; Program evaluation; Employee matching gifts; Matching/challenge support.
Limitations: Giving primarily in the greater Kalamazoo, MI, area. No support for political organizations. No grants to individuals.
Publications: Annual report.
Application information: Please refer to foundation Web site for further guidelines and deadlines. Application form not required.
  Initial approach: Unbound proposal including cover letter
  Copies of proposal: 1
  Deadline(s): 15th of Jan., Mar., May, July, Sept., and Nov.
  Board meeting date(s): Jan., Mar., May, July, Sept., and Nov.
  Final notification: Acknowledgement letter within 2 weeks
Officers and Trustees:* Richard M. Hughey, Sr.,* Chair. and Pres.; Floyd L. Parks,* Vice-Chair., 1st V.P., and Treas.; Frederick W. Freund,* C.E.O. and Exec. V.P.; Janice C. Elliott, V.P., Admin.; Richard M. Hughey, Jr., V.P., Prog.; Russell L. Gabier,* Secy.
Number of staff: 3 full-time professional; 1 full-time support; 2 part-time support.
EIN: 237236057
Selected grants: The following grants were reported in 2004.
$1,000,000 to Kalamazoo Aviation History Museum, Air Zoo, Kalamazoo, MI. For Michigan Space and Science Center.
$1,000,000 to Western Michigan University Foundation, Kalamazoo, MI. For equipment.
$900,000 to Irving S. Gilmore International Keyboard Festival, Kalamazoo, MI. For operating support.
$500,000 to Kalamazoo Valley Community College Foundation, Kalamazoo, MI. To purchase and equip new media center.
$350,000 to Southwest Michigan First Corporation, Kalamazoo, MI. For operating support.
$100,000 to Community Advocates for Persons with Developmental Disabilities, Kalamazoo, MI. For Heersma Initiative programming.
$100,000 to Local Initiatives Support Corporation (LISC), Kalamazoo, MI. For local match funding.
$25,000 to Boys and Girls Club of Kalamazoo, Kalamazoo, MI. For Participating Arts program.
$20,000 to Kairos Dwelling, Kalamazoo, MI. For operating support.
$10,000 to Specialized Language Development (SLD) Learning Center, Kalamazoo, MI. For operating support.

684
Jim Gilmore, Jr. Foundation
c/o National City Bank of The Midwest
108 E. Michigan Ave., K-B01-2A
Kalamazoo, MI 49007

Grantmaker type: Independent foundation.
Financial data (yr. ended 11/30/04): Assets, $405 (M); gifts received, $2,500; expenditures, $3,020;

total giving, $2,500; qualifying distributions, $2,500; giving activities include $2,500 for grants.
Limitations: Applications not accepted. Giving primarily in Kalamazoo, MI. No grants to individuals.
Application information: Contributes only to pre-selected organizations.
Officer and Directors: Mariette Lemieux,* Pres.; Bethany Gilmore; Case Hoogendoorn; George Lennon; Sydney McElduff.
EIN: 363584018

685
The Aaron & Anne Ginsberg Foundation
30875 River Crossing
Bingham Farms, MI 48025-4656

Established in 1996 in MI.
Donors: Aaron Ginsberg; Anne Ginsberg.
Grantmaker type: Independent foundation.
Financial data (yr. ended 9/30/05): Assets, $68,461 (M); gifts received, $14,061; expenditures, $14,050; total giving, $13,035; qualifying distributions, $13,035; giving activities include $13,035 for grants.
Limitations: Applications not accepted. Giving primarily in MI and NY. No grants to individuals.
Application information: Contributes only to pre-selected organizations.
Officers: Anne Ginsberg, Pres.; Aaron Ginsberg, V.P.; Richard Polk, Secy.; Paul P. Baker, Treas.
EIN: 383349855

686
Norbert and Paula Gits Foundation
c/o Bessemer Trust Co., N.A.
630 5th Ave., 37th Fl.
New York, NY 10111
Contact: Philip C. Kalafatis, Trust Off., Bessemer Trust Co., N.A.

Established in 2000 in FL.
Donors: Norbert Gits; Paula Gits.
Grantmaker type: Independent foundation.
Financial data (yr. ended 6/30/05): Assets, $539,806 (M); expenditures, $32,211; total giving, $24,582; qualifying distributions, $26,547; giving activities include $24,582 for grants.
Fields of interest: Museums; Health organizations.
Limitations: Giving primarily in Lake Leelanau, MI; some giving also in FL.
Application information:
  Initial approach: Letter
  Deadline(s): None
Advisory Committee: Norbert Gits; Paula Gits.
Trustee: Bessemer Trust Co., N.A.
EIN: 527109505

687
The Glancy Foundation, Inc.
c/o Alfred R. Glancy III
400 Maple Park Blvd., Ste. 405
St. Clair Shores, MI 48081-3709
FAX: (586) 498-6603;
E-mail: alglancy@glancyfamily.com

Established in 1994 in GA.
Grantmaker type: Independent foundation.
Financial data (yr. ended 12/31/05): Assets, $3,573,954 (M); expenditures, $196,378; total giving, $162,450; qualifying distributions,

$172,999; giving activities include $162,450 for 30 grants (high: $50,000; low: $100).
Purpose and activities: Giving primarily for education, and a zoological society; support also for the arts, natural resource conservation, and social services.
Fields of interest: Museums; Arts; Higher education; Education; Environment, natural resources; Zoos/zoological societies; Human services.
Limitations: Applications not accepted. Giving primarily in MI. No grants to individuals.
Application information: Unsolicited requests for funds not accepted.
Officers and Trustees: * Alfred R. Glancy III,* Chair. and Treas.; Ruth R. Glancy,* Vice-Chair. and Secy.; Alfred R. Glancy IV; Andrew Roby Glancy; Douglas R. Glancy; Joan C. Glancy.
EIN: 582116482
Selected grants: The following grants were reported in 2004.
$27,500 to University Liggett School, Grosse Pointe, MI.
$25,000 to Alternatives for Girls, Detroit, MI.
$25,000 to Detroit Symphony Orchestra, Detroit, MI.
$10,000 to Detroit Zoological Society, Royal Oak, MI.
$5,000 to Detroit Science Center, Detroit, MI.
$2,500 to Detroit Historical Society, Detroit, MI.
$2,000 to Community Foundation for Southeastern Michigan, Detroit, MI.
$2,000 to Detroit Institute of Arts, Detroit, MI.
$1,000 to Edison Institute, Dearborn, MI.
$500 to Detroit Institute for Children, Detroit, MI.

688
Hal & Jean Glassen Memorial Foundation
3603 Breezy Point Dr.
Okemos, MI 48864-5923
Contact: Neil A. McLean, Pres.

Established in 1991 in MI; funded in 1993.
Donor: Harold Glassen†.
Grantmaker type: Independent foundation.
Financial data (yr. ended 12/31/04): Assets, $5,142,033 (M); expenditures, $320,664; total giving, $217,564; qualifying distributions, $469,255; giving activities include $217,564 for 12 grants (high: $50,000; low: $761).
Fields of interest: Education; Environment; Athletics/sports, fishing/hunting.
Limitations: Giving primarily in MI. No grants to individuals.
Application information: Application form not required.
  Deadline(s): None
Officers: Neil A. McLean, Pres.; Frank W. Perrin, V.P.; Tom Huggler, Secy.; Glen Miller, D.V.M., Treas.
Director: C. Allan Stewatt.
EIN: 383012223
Selected grants: The following grants were reported in 2003.
$55,000 to Michigan State University, East Lansing, MI. 2 grants: $5,000 (For scholarships), $50,000 to College of Veterinary Medicine.
$50,000 to Potter Park Zoological Society, Lansing, MI. For Core Project.
$25,000 to National Rifle Association of America, National Rifle Association Museum, DC.
$10,000 to Michigan Legislative Sportsmens Foundation, Saline, MI.

$6,500 to Michigan Youth Hunter Education Challenge, Shelby Township, MI.
$4,000 to Wildflower Association of Michigan, Albion, MI. For general support.
$2,000 to Outdoor Writers Association of America, Missoula, MT. For Norm Strung Youth Writing Contest.
$221 to Onaway Area Schools, Onaway, MI.

689
Glenn Family Foundation
1405 Ballybunion Ct. S.E.
Grand Rapids, MI 49546

Established in 2000 in CO.
Donor: Michael B. Glenn.
Grantmaker type: Independent foundation.
Financial data (yr. ended 12/31/05): Assets, $410,505 (M); gifts received, $29,000; expenditures, $127,430; total giving, $127,280; qualifying distributions, $127,280; giving activities include $127,280 for 16 grants (high: $50,780; low: $100).
Fields of interest: Theological school/education; Education; Medical research; Human services; Christian agencies & churches.
Type of support: General/operating support.
Limitations: Applications not accepted. Giving primarily in MI and NC. No grants to individuals.
Application information: Contributes only to pre-selected organizations.
Officers and Directors: * Michael B. Glenn,* Pres.; Glenda J. Glenn,* Secy.-Treas.; Lindsey A. Glenn; Michael S. Glenn.
EIN: 841569913

690
Joseph Gless Foundation
c/o JPMorgan Chase Bank, N.A.
P.O. Box 1308
Milwaukee, WI 53201

Established in 1994 in MI.
Grantmaker type: Independent foundation.
Financial data (yr. ended 12/31/05): Assets, $739,268 (M); expenditures, $49,946; total giving, $42,000; qualifying distributions, $42,000; giving activities include $42,000 for grants.
Fields of interest: Education; Human services; Children/youth, services; Federated giving programs.
Limitations: Applications not accepted. Giving primarily in Grand Rapids, MI. No grants to individuals.
Application information: Contributes only to pre-selected organizations.
Trustees: Harold Gless; JPMorgan Chase Bank, N.A.
EIN: 383218718

691
The Robert and Rose Glick Charitable Foundation
P.O. Box 1166
Jackson, MI 49204

Established in 2000 in MI.
Donors: Robert A. Glick†; Rose M. Glick.
Grantmaker type: Independent foundation.
Financial data (yr. ended 12/31/05): Assets, $570,311 (M); gifts received, $60,593;

expenditures, $21,472; total giving, $19,994; qualifying distributions, $19,994; giving activities include $19,994 for grants.
Fields of interest: Jewish agencies & temples.
Limitations: Applications not accepted. Giving primarily in Jackson, MI. No grants to individuals.
Application information: Contributes only to pre-selected organizations.
Officers and Directors:* Rose M. Glick,* Pres.; Barry J. Glick,* V.P.; Carlton L. Glick,* Secy.-Treas.; Gary M. Glick; Susan G. Weber.
EIN: 383556345

692
The Alvin L. Glick Foundation
3100 E. High St.
Jackson, MI 49203

Established in 2000 in MI.
Donor: Alvin L. Glick.
Grantmaker type: Independent foundation.
Financial data (yr. ended 12/31/05): Assets, $1,133,951 (M); gifts received, $94,095; expenditures, $128,203; total giving, $123,383; qualifying distributions, $123,383; giving activities include $123,383 for grants.
Limitations: Applications not accepted. Giving primarily in MI. No grants to individuals.
Application information: Contributes only to pre-selected organizations.
Officers: Alvin L. Glick, Pres.; Barry J. Glick, V.P.; Carlton L. Glick, Secy.; Randal L. Glick, Treas.
EIN: 383551619

693
Louis Glick Memorial & Charitable Trust
P.O. Box 1166
Jackson, MI 49204-1166   (517) 787-1900

Established in 1968.
Donors: Glick Iron and Metal Co.; Alro Steel Corp.; Edith Glick†.
Grantmaker type: Independent foundation.
Financial data (yr. ended 12/31/05): Assets, $1,403,435 (M); gifts received, $12,000; expenditures, $34,109; total giving, $28,050; qualifying distributions, $28,050; giving activities include $28,050 for grants.
Purpose and activities: Grants for Jewish organizations, health, and human services. The trust also provides college loans to local high school graduates to attend a college in MI. Funding also for the arts, children, youth and social services, Jewish organizations and temples, and the United Way.
Fields of interest: Arts; Human services; Children/youth, services; Federated giving programs; Jewish federated giving programs; Jewish agencies & temples.
Type of support: Student loans—to individuals.
Limitations: Giving primarily in Jackson County, MI.
Application information: Application form required for loans.
   Deadline(s): May 15 for loans
Trustee: Carlton Glick.
EIN: 386156959

694
The Goad Foundation
(formerly The Louis C. Goad Foundation)
1840 Redding Rd.
Birmingham, MI 48009   (248) 644-2086
Contact: Thomas C. Goad, Pres.

Established in MI.
Donor: Clarissa A. Goad.
Grantmaker type: Independent foundation.
Financial data (yr. ended 12/31/04): Assets, $277,654 (M); gifts received, $5,028; expenditures, $6,760; total giving, $1,500; qualifying distributions, $2,509; giving activities include $1,500 for grants.
Fields of interest: Arts; Education; Health care; Protestant agencies & churches.
Limitations: Giving primarily in MI. No grants to individuals.
Application information:
   Initial approach: Letter
   Deadline(s): Varies
Officers: Thomas C. Goad, Pres.; Clarissa A. Goad, V.P.
Trustees: Elizabeth G. Enders; Douglass C. Goad; Theodore C. Goad; Linda C. Goad Larisch.
EIN: 381678220

695
God's Gift Foundation
4020 Silvergrass Dr. N.E.
Grand Rapids, MI 49525-9551

Established in 2003 in MI.
Donor: God's Gift Foundation of Ohio.
Grantmaker type: Independent foundation.
Financial data (yr. ended 12/31/04): Assets, $1,320,883 (M); gifts received, $6,000; expenditures, $56,025; total giving, $51,872; qualifying distributions, $51,872; giving activities include $51,872 for grants.
Purpose and activities: Giving primarily to Christian churches and national Christian-focused organizations.
Fields of interest: Christian agencies & churches.
Limitations: Giving on a national basis. No grants to individuals.
Application information: Application form not required.
   Initial approach: Letter
   Deadline(s): None
Officers and Trustees:* Jeffrey W. Greene,* Pres.; Bonnie Jane Greene,* V.P.; Amanda L. Greene, Secy.-Treas.; C. Craig Covrett; Kenneth W. Greene.
EIN: 270038384

696
Frank L. & Helen Gofrank Foundation
445 S. Livernois Rd., Ste. 105
Rochester Hills, MI 48307-2575

Established in 1988 in MI.
Donor: Frank L. Gofrank.
Grantmaker type: Independent foundation.
Financial data (yr. ended 12/31/05): Assets, $1,075,821 (M); expenditures, $60,802; total giving, $59,050; qualifying distributions, $59,572; giving activities include $59,050 for grants.
Purpose and activities: Giving for education and medical research, including cancer research.

Fields of interest: Higher education; Medical research, institute; Cancer research.
Limitations: Applications not accepted. Giving in the U.S., with some emphasis on MI. No grants to individuals.
Application information: Contributes only to pre-selected organizations.
Officers: Helen J. Gofrank, Pres.; Ronald F. Gofrank, V.P.; Catherine A. Gofrank, Secy.; Shirley E. Gofrank, Treas.
EIN: 382828028

697
John & Sally Goggins Family Foundation
3301 S. Dort Hwy.
Flint, MI 48507

Established in 1997 in MI.
Donor: John Goggins.
Grantmaker type: Independent foundation.
Financial data (yr. ended 12/31/04): Assets, $135,930 (M); gifts received, $266,255; expenditures, $252,401; total giving, $218,989; qualifying distributions, $222,380; giving activities include $218,989 for 38 grants (high: $99,500; low: $30).
Purpose and activities: Giving primarily to Roman Catholic schools and organizations.
Fields of interest: Elementary/secondary education; Roman Catholic agencies & churches.
Limitations: Applications not accepted. No grants to individuals.
Application information: Contributes only to pre-selected organizations.
Officers: John Goggins, Pres.; Sally Goggins, V.P.; Teresa Goggins Witt, Secy.-Treas.
EIN: 383381100

698
Harry & Bertha A. Goldman Foundation
37684 Enterprise Ct.
Farmington Hills, MI 48331
Contact: Harry Witus, Tr.
Application address: 25800 W. Eleven Mile Rd., Apt. 506, Southfield, MI 48034, tel.: (248) 213-1283

Established in MI.
Grantmaker type: Independent foundation.
Financial data (yr. ended 7/31/05): Assets, $58,467 (M); expenditures, $7,525; total giving, $7,000; qualifying distributions, $7,000; giving activities include $7,000 for grants.
Type of support: Scholarships—to individuals.
Limitations: Giving primarily in Detroit, MI.
Application information:
   Initial approach: Letter with brief resume of academic qualifications
   Deadline(s): None
Trustees: Harry Witus.
EIN: 510147560

699
Irving & Doris Lee Goldman Foundation
26677 W. 12 Mile Rd., Ste. 110
Southfield, MI 48034

Established in 1976 in MI.
Donor: Irving Goldman.
Grantmaker type: Independent foundation.

Financial data (yr. ended 7/31/05): Assets, $1,232,270 (M); expenditures, $66,197; total giving, $65,322; qualifying distributions, $65,322; giving activities include $65,322 for grants.
Purpose and activities: Giving primarily for human services and Jewish organizations.
Fields of interest: Arts; Higher education; Human services; Jewish federated giving programs; Jewish agencies & temples.
Limitations: Applications not accepted. Giving primarily in Detroit, MI. No grants to individuals.
Application information: Contributes only to pre-selected organizations.
Trustees: Doris Lee Goldman; Irving Goldman.
EIN: 510141976

700
Marvin H. & Nola Goldman Foundation
26677 W. 12 Mile Rd., Ste. 110
Southfield, MI 48034-1514

Established in 1975 in MI.
Donor: Marvin H. Goldman.
Grantmaker type: Independent foundation.
Financial data (yr. ended 7/31/05): Assets, $75,488 (M); gifts received, $10,000; expenditures, $18,570; total giving, $18,570; qualifying distributions, $18,570; giving activities include $18,570 for grants.
Purpose and activities: Giving to Jewish agencies and temples.
Fields of interest: Jewish federated giving programs; Jewish agencies & temples.
Limitations: Applications not accepted. Giving limited to MI. No grants to individuals.
Application information: Contributes only to pre-selected organizations.
Trustees: Marvin H. Goldman; Nola Goldman.
EIN: 510141979

701
Sydney Goldstein Foundation
c/o Harvey Kaplan
90 S. 7th St., Ste. 5500
Minneapolis, MN 55402

Established in 1990 in MN as successor to Sydney Goldstein Foundation.
Grantmaker type: Independent foundation.
Financial data (yr. ended 6/30/05): Assets, $66,157 (M); expenditures, $4,311; total giving, $3,448; qualifying distributions, $3,448; giving activities include $3,448 for grants.
Limitations: Applications not accepted. Giving primarily in CA and MI. No grants to individuals.
Application information: Contributes only to pre-selected organizations.
Officers and Directors:* Joanne Goldstein,* Pres.; Allan Goldstein,* V.P.; Marvin Goldstein,* Secy.-Treas.
EIN: 411694014

702
Good News! Foundation
c/o Jack Lousma
2722 Roseland
Ann Arbor, MI 48103

Established in 2004 in MI.
Grantmaker type: Independent foundation.
Financial data (yr. ended 12/31/04): Assets, $50,015 (M); gifts received, $50,000; expenditures, $0; total giving, $0; qualifying distributions, $0.
Fields of interest: Christian agencies & churches.
Limitations: Applications not accepted. No grants to individuals.
Application information: Contributes only to pre-selected organizations.
Officers: Jack Lousma, Pres.; Gratia Lousma, V.P.
EIN: 830409795

703
The Good Part Foundation
7500 Brookville Rd.
Plymouth, MI 48170

Established in 2000 in MI.
Donors: Barton B. Bryant; Lorraine A. Bryant.
Grantmaker type: Independent foundation.
Financial data (yr. ended 12/31/04): Assets, $1,032,812 (M); expenditures, $61,671; total giving, $45,000; qualifying distributions, $45,000; giving activities include $45,000 for grants.
Fields of interest: Christian agencies & churches.
Limitations: Giving primarily in Roanoke, VA. No grants to individuals.
Officer: Barton B. Bryant, Mgr.
Director: Lorraine A. Bryant.
EIN: 383558047

704
Mary V. Good Trust
c/o Citizens Bank, N.A.
328 S. Saginaw St., MC 002072
Flint, MI 48502

Established in MI.
Grantmaker type: Independent foundation.
Financial data (yr. ended 12/31/05): Assets, $581,032 (M); expenditures, $50,223; total giving, $47,932; qualifying distributions, $48,103; giving activities include $47,932 for grants.
Fields of interest: Protestant agencies & churches.
Type of support: General/operating support.
Limitations: Applications not accepted. Giving primarily in Chelsea, MI. No grants to individuals.
Application information: Contributes only to pre-selected organizations.
Trustee: Citizens Bank, N.A.
EIN: 386782799

705
The Goodale Fund
23705 Ravineview Ct.
Bingham Farms, MI 48025-4648
Contact: Stephen L. Goodale, Pres.

Established in 1996 in MI.
Donor: Stephen L. Goodale.
Grantmaker type: Independent foundation.
Financial data (yr. ended 12/31/04): Assets, $764,395 (M); gifts received, $53,522; expenditures, $30,050; total giving, $24,326; qualifying distributions, $27,224; giving activities include $24,326 for grants.
Fields of interest: Education; Human services.
Limitations: Giving primarily in Vero Beach, FL and MI.
Application information:

Initial approach: Letter
Deadline(s): None
Officers: Stephen L. Goodale, Pres. and Treas.; Margery C. Goodale, V.P.
EIN: 383315943

706
Goodnow/Prus Foundation
38 Kerby Rd.
Grosse Pointe Farms, MI 48236

Established in 1998 in MI.
Donor: Nathan B. Goodnow Trust.
Grantmaker type: Independent foundation.
Financial data (yr. ended 6/30/05): Assets, $169,203 (M); expenditures, $9,844; total giving, $9,100; qualifying distributions, $9,100; giving activities include $9,100 for grants.
Limitations: Applications not accepted. Giving primarily in MI.
Application information: Contributes only to pre-selected organizations.
Officers and Trustees:* Judith G. Prus,* Pres. and Secy.; A. Michael Prus,* Treas.; Elizabeth B. Myers; Jeffrey G. Prus; Michael G. Prus.
EIN: 383440580

707
David Goodrich College Education Fund
c/o Fifth Third Bank
P.O. Box 3636
Grand Rapids, MI 49501-3636
Application address: c/o Wayne Petroelje, Elsie Area Superintendent of Schools, 8989 E. Colony Rd., Elsie, MI 48831

Established in 1995 in MI.
Grantmaker type: Independent foundation.
Financial data (yr. ended 12/31/05): Assets, $775,448 (M); expenditures, $47,269; total giving, $39,433; qualifying distributions, $39,433; giving activities include $39,433 for grants to individuals.
Purpose and activities: Scholarship awards to needy students living within a four-mile radius of Ovid, MI.
Fields of interest: Higher education; Education.
Type of support: Scholarships—to individuals.
Limitations: Giving limited to residents of Ovid, MI.
Application information: Application form required.
Deadline(s): May 1
Trustee: Fifth Third Bank.
EIN: 386658237

708
The Goodrich Foundation, Inc.
c/o John L. Cady
46 Summit Ave.
Bronxville, NY 10708

Established in 1998 in NY.
Donor: John K. Goodrich.
Grantmaker type: Independent foundation.
Financial data (yr. ended 12/31/04): Assets, $275,838 (M); expenditures, $1,351; total giving, $0; qualifying distributions, $0.
Limitations: Applications not accepted. Giving primarily in MI. No grants to individuals.
Application information: Contributes only to pre-selected organizations.

Officers: John K. Goodrich, Pres.; John L. Cady, Secy.-Treas.
EIN: 134036967

709
The Googasian Family Foundation
6895 Telegraph Rd.
Bloomfield Hills, MI 48301-3138

Established in 2001 in MI.
Donors: George A. Googasian; Phyllis E. Googasian.
Grantmaker type: Independent foundation.
Financial data (yr. ended 12/31/05): Assets, $398,285 (M); gifts received, $92,170; expenditures, $55,451; total giving, $54,100; qualifying distributions, $54,100; giving activities include $54,100 for grants.
Limitations: Applications not accepted. No grants to individuals.
Application information: Contributes only to pre-selected organizations.
Officers: George A. Googasian, Pres.; Phyllis E. Googasian, Secy.-Treas.
EIN: 383640263

710
Gordon Christian Foundation
3333 Evergreen Dr. N.E., Ste. 201
Grand Rapids, MI 49525-9493 (616) 363-9209
Contact: Ken Kregel

Established in 1967 in MI.
Donors: Paul B. Gordon; Gordon Food Service, Inc.
Grantmaker type: Independent foundation.
Financial data (yr. ended 12/31/05): Assets, $710,704 (M); expenditures, $44,010; total giving, $43,860; qualifying distributions, $43,860; giving activities include $43,860 for grants.
Purpose and activities: Giving for Christian missionary support.
Fields of interest: Protestant agencies & churches.
Type of support: General/operating support.
Limitations: Giving primarily in the U.S. No grants to individuals.
Application information:
  Initial approach: Letter
  Deadline(s): None
Officers: Philip M. Gordon, Pres.; John M. Gordon, Jr., V.P. and Treas.; Joyce G. Williams, Secy.
EIN: 386123463

711
The Harold and Marion Gordon Family Foundation
(formerly The Gordon Family Foundation)
31530 Concord Dr.
Madison Heights, MI 48071

Established in 1987 in MI.
Donors: Harold Gordon; Marion Gordon; Gordon Properties.
Grantmaker type: Independent foundation.
Financial data (yr. ended 7/31/04): Assets, $255,585 (M); gifts received, $25,000; expenditures, $9,134; total giving, $7,670; qualifying distributions, $7,670; giving activities include $7,670 for grants.
Purpose and activities: Giving to Jewish programs and legal education.

Fields of interest: Arts; Education; Jewish federated giving programs; Jewish agencies & temples.
Limitations: Applications not accepted. Giving primarily in FL and MI. No grants to individuals.
Application information: Contributes only to pre-selected organizations.
Officers: Harold Gordon, Pres. and Treas.; Marion Gordon, Secy.
EIN: 382707899

712
The Frank & Doris Gordon Foundation
1917 Cross Bend St., N.E.
Grand Rapids, MI 49505-6397 (616) 361-0412
Contact: Doris M. Gordon, Pres.

Grantmaker type: Independent foundation.
Financial data (yr. ended 12/31/05): Assets, $367,271 (M); expenditures, $16,871; total giving, $16,788; qualifying distributions, $16,788; giving activities include $16,788 for grants.
Purpose and activities: Giving primarily to Protestant organizations, and for education.
Fields of interest: Higher education; Protestant agencies & churches.
Limitations: Giving primarily in IL and MI. No grants to individuals.
Application information:
  Initial approach: Letter
  Deadline(s): None
Officers: Doris M. Gordon, Pres. and Treas.; Joseph P. Gordon, V.P.; David P. DeKoning, Secy.
EIN: 237068918

713
The Seymour & Marilynn Gordon Foundation
31090 Nottingham Dr.
Franklin, MI 48025-1247

Established in 1995 in MI.
Donors: Seymour Gordon; Marilynn Gordon.
Grantmaker type: Independent foundation.
Financial data (yr. ended 12/31/05): Assets, $15,003 (M); gifts received, $20; expenditures, $974; total giving, $700; qualifying distributions, $700; giving activities include $700 for grants.
Fields of interest: Medical care, in-patient care; Heart & circulatory diseases.
Type of support: General/operating support.
Limitations: Applications not accepted. Giving primarily in Southfield, MI. No grants to individuals.
Application information: Contributes only to pre-selected organizations.
Officers: Seymour Gordon, Pres. and Treas.; Marilynn Gordon, Secy.
EIN: 383260671

714
Gordy Foundation, Inc.
2656 W. Grand Blvd.
Detroit, MI 48208-1237 (313) 875-0656
Contact: Robin Terry, Treas.

Established in 1967 in MI.
Donors: Jobete Music Co., Inc.; Berry Gordy.
Grantmaker type: Independent foundation.
Financial data (yr. ended 6/30/05): Assets, $3,223,970 (M); expenditures, $119,464; total giving, $77,000; qualifying distributions, $99,441;

giving activities include $77,000 for 3 grants (high: $75,000; low: $1,000).
Fields of interest: Museums (specialized); Performing arts, music.
Limitations: Giving primarily in Detroit, MI. No grants to individuals.
Application information:
  Initial approach: Letter
  Deadline(s): None
Officers and Directors: * Esther G. Edwards,* C.E.O. and Pres.; Robin Terry, Treas.; Berry Gordy,* Exec. Dir.; Robert Bullock; Elesha Cherry.
EIN: 386149511

715
The Gornick Fund
P.O. Box 957
Bloomfield Hills, MI 48303-0957
Contact: Diana Gornick Day, Pres.

Established about 1957 in MI.
Donor: Alan L. Gornick†.
Grantmaker type: Independent foundation.
Financial data (yr. ended 6/30/05): Assets, $2,113,300 (M); expenditures, $120,456; total giving, $98,428; qualifying distributions, $106,481; giving activities include $98,428 for 40 grants (high: $10,000; low: $100).
Purpose and activities: Giving primarily for arts and cultural programs, and for education.
Fields of interest: Arts; Higher education; Hospitals (general); Health organizations, association; Human services; Children/youth, services.
Type of support: Annual campaigns.
Limitations: Giving primarily in MI. No grants to individuals.
Application information: Application form not required.
  Initial approach: Letter
  Deadline(s): June 30
Officers and Trustees: * Diana Gornick Day,* Pres.; Keith H. Gornick,* V.P. and Secy.; Margaret A. Richard,* V.P.
EIN: 386063404

716
Joseph Gorski Trust
c/o FirstMerit Bank, N.A.
106 S. Main St., Ste. 1600
Akron, OH 44308-1440

Established in 1992 in OH.
Donor: Joseph Gorski†.
Grantmaker type: Independent foundation.
Financial data (yr. ended 4/30/03): Assets, $168,871 (M); expenditures, $12,911; total giving, $10,000; qualifying distributions, $10,666; giving activities include $10,000 for grants.
Fields of interest: Higher education; Christian agencies & churches.
Limitations: Applications not accepted. Giving limited to Orchard Lake, MI and Cleveland, Pepper Pike, Wickliffe, OH. No grants to individuals.
Application information: Contributes only to pre-selected organizations specified in the governing instrument.
Trustee: FirstMerit Bank, N.A.
EIN: 346969492

717
Beatrice I. Goss Educational Testamentary Trust
c/o Fifth Third Bank
P.O. Box 3636
Grand Rapids, MI 49501
Application address: c/o Fifth Third Bank, 56 S. Washington, Valparaiso, IN 46383, tel.: (219) 465-6706

Established around 1980 in IN.
Donor: Beatrice I. Goss‡.
Grantmaker type: Independent foundation.
Financial data (yr. ended 9/30/05): Assets, $174,342 (M); expenditures, $10,859; total giving, $8,400; qualifying distributions, $8,400; giving activities include $8,400 for grants to individuals.
Purpose and activities: Scholarship awards to residents of Marshall County, IN.
Type of support: Scholarships—to individuals.
Limitations: Giving limited to residents of Marshall County, IN.
Application information: Application form required.
  Deadline(s): Mar. 15
Trustee: Fifth Third Bank.
EIN: 356361029

718
Meda Graham Educational Fund, Inc.
c/o Comerica Bank
P.O Box 75000, MC 3462
Detroit, MI 48275-0001

Grantmaker type: Independent foundation.
Financial data (yr. ended 4/30/03): Assets, $785,891 (M); expenditures, $45,746; total giving, $44,000; qualifying distributions, $44,325; giving activities include $44,000 for grants.
Purpose and activities: Support only to Alma College, MI, for its scholarship fund.
Fields of interest: Higher education.
Type of support: Scholarship funds.
Limitations: Applications not accepted. Giving limited to Alma, MI. No grants to individuals.
Application information: Contributes only to a pre-selected organization.
Officers: David Turner, Pres.; Robert Colladay, V.P.
Trustee: Comerica Bank.
EIN: 386261402

719
Grand Rapids Christian Foundation
3129 E. Gatehouse Dr. S.E.
Grand Rapids, MI 49546-7010

Established in 1988 in MI.
Donors: Gene Goulooze; Ruth Goulooze.
Grantmaker type: Independent foundation.
Financial data (yr. ended 12/31/05): Assets, $118,776 (M); gifts received, $12,500; expenditures, $48,026; total giving, $47,175; qualifying distributions, $47,175; giving activities include $47,175 for grants.
Purpose and activities: Giving for Christian organizations, including education, missions, youth programs, and community development.
Fields of interest: Higher education; Recreation, camps; Youth development; Children/youth, services; International affairs; Community development; Christian agencies & churches.
Type of support: General/operating support.

Limitations: Applications not accepted. Giving primarily in MI. No grants to individuals.
Application information: Contributes only to pre-selected organizations.
Directors: Gene Goulooze; Ruth Goulooze.
EIN: 382841568

720
Grand Rapids Elks Philanthropy Fund
2715 Leonard St. N.W.
Grand Rapids, MI 49504-3761

Grantmaker type: Independent foundation.
Financial data (yr. ended 3/31/05): Assets, $271,672 (M); gifts received, $11,425; expenditures, $21,813; total giving, $21,657; qualifying distributions, $21,657; giving activities include $21,657 for grants.
Limitations: Applications not accepted. Giving primarily in Grand Rapids, MI. No grants to individuals.
Application information: Contributes only to pre-selected organizations.
Officer: Michael Nawrocki, Chair.
EIN: 386072417

721
Grand Rapids Kiwanis Foundation
c/o Goodlander and Co.
3900 Costa NE
Grand Rapids, MI 49525 (616) 361-1896

Established in MI.
Grantmaker type: Independent foundation.
Financial data (yr. ended 9/30/04): Assets, $281,129 (M); expenditures, $12,577; total giving, $12,396; qualifying distributions, $12,408; giving activities include $12,396 for grants.
Fields of interest: Youth, services; Disabilities, people with.
Limitations: Giving limited to Grand Rapids, MI. No grants to individuals.
Application information: Application form not required.
  Initial approach: Proposal
  Deadline(s): None
Officers and Trustees:* Donald J. Swierenga,* Pres.; John Tambour,* V.P.; Jim Opperman,* Secy.; Larry Goodlander, Treas.; Gordy Howe; John Hunt; Bob Mills.
EIN: 386056394

722
Granger Foundation
P.O. Box 22185
Lansing, MI 48909-7185 (517) 371-9765
Contact: Ray Easton
E-mail: elee@grangerconstruction.com; URL: http://www.grangerfoundation.org/

Established in 1978.
Donors: Granger Associates, Inc.; Granger Construction Co.; and members of the Granger family.
Grantmaker type: Independent foundation.
Financial data (yr. ended 12/31/04): Assets, $21,228,427 (M); gifts received, $540,500; expenditures, $1,362,605; total giving, $1,231,550; qualifying distributions, $1,231,550;

giving activities include $1,231,550 for 74 grants (high: $100,000; low: $500).
Purpose and activities: The foundation's primary mission is to support Christ-centered activities. It also support efforts that enhance the lives of youth in the community.
Fields of interest: Youth development; Christian agencies & churches; Youth.
Type of support: Annual campaigns; Capital campaigns.
Limitations: Giving primarily in the greater Lansing and the Tri-County (Ingham, Eaton and Clinton counties), MI, areas. No grants to individuals, or for endowments, fundraising, social events, conferences, or exhibits; no grants for capital funds or improvements for churches or public schools.
Publications: Application guidelines; Annual report; Program policy statement.
Application information: Application form required.
  Initial approach: Completed Request for Funding form
  Copies of proposal: 4
  Deadline(s): Apr. 15 and Oct. 15
  Board meeting date(s): Semiannually
Trustees: Alton L. Granger; Donna Granger; Janice Granger; Jerry P. Granger; Lynne Granger; Ronald K. Granger.
EIN: 382251879
Selected grants: The following grants were reported in 2003.
$100,000 to Mission India, Grand Rapids, MI.
$50,000 to Teen Challenge, Lansing, Lansing, MI. For building upgrades.
$50,000 to Youth for Christ, Lansing, MI.
$44,000 to Eaton Community Hospice, Charlotte, MI.
$34,000 to Youth for Christ/USA, Wheaton, IL.
$30,000 to Ingham Regional Healthcare Foundation, Lansing, MI.
$25,000 to Cristo Rey Community Center, Lansing, MI. For capital campaign.
$25,000 to Highfields, Onondaga, MI. For Alternatives to Domestic Violence.
$25,000 to Salvation Army.
$16,000 to City Rescue Mission of Saginaw, Saginaw, MI. To purchase a refrigerated van or truck.

723
Granger III Foundation, Inc.
P.O. Box 27185
Lansing, MI 48909-7185 (571) 371-9717
Contact: Todd J. Granger, Treas.

Established in 2000 in OH.
Donors: Granger Electric; Granger Energy; Granger Associates, Inc.; Granger Holdings, LLC; Granger Energy of Decatur, LLC; Granger Energy of Honeybrook, LLC; Granger Meadows, LLC.
Grantmaker type: Independent foundation.
Financial data (yr. ended 12/31/05): Assets, $3,738,519 (M); gifts received, $1,012,000; expenditures, $771,795; total giving, $752,818; qualifying distributions, $752,818; giving activities include $752,818 for 19 grants (high: $176,000; low: $1,500).
Purpose and activities: Giving primarily for a Christian school as well as for other Christian organizations; funding also for human services, education, volunteer organizations, and YMCAs.
Fields of interest: Theological school/education; Human services; YM/YWCAs & YM/YWHAs;

Philanthropy/voluntarism; Christian agencies & churches.
Limitations: Giving primarily in MI. No grants to individuals.
Application information:
Initial approach: Letter
Deadline(s): None
Officers and Trustees:* Thomas D. Hofman,* Pres.; Ray A. Easton,* V.P.; Dawn M. Granger,* Secy.; Todd J. Granger,* Treas.; Keith L. Granger; Randy J. Russ; Joel M. Zylstra.
EIN: 383555568

724
Grassland Trust
c/o West Michigan National Bank
120 Cypress St.
Manistee, MI   49660-1753

Established in 1997 in MI.
Donors: Lorreva S. Foster; James R. Foster.
Grantmaker type: Independent foundation.
Financial data (yr. ended 12/31/05): Assets, $3,469,596 (M); gifts received, $536,080; expenditures, $145,976; total giving, $132,000; qualifying distributions, $132,000; giving activities include $132,000 for grants.
Limitations: Applications not accepted. Giving primarily in Livingston, MT. No grants to individuals.
Application information: Contributes only to pre-selected organizations.
Trustees: Thomas A. Baither; James R. Foster; Lorreva S. Foster; Henry T. Mather.
EIN: 383357237

725
Greater Lansing Chinese American Association
c/o Mike Ma
3752 Chippendale Cir.
Okemos, MI   48864

Established in 2005 in MI.
Grantmaker type: Independent foundation.
Financial data (yr. ended 12/31/05): Assets, $0 (M); gifts received, $4,369; expenditures, $2,664; total giving, $0; qualifying distributions, $0; giving activities include $2,664 for foundation-administered programs.
Officer: Mike Ma, Pres.
EIN: 113720634

726
Greater Life International
10850 Peerless St.
Detroit, MI   48224-1162

Established in 2000 in MI.
Grantmaker type: Independent foundation.
Financial data (yr. ended 12/31/04): Assets, $0 (M); gifts received, $12,100; expenditures, $12,100; total giving, $0; qualifying distributions, $12,100; giving activities include $12,100 for foundation-administered programs.
Officers: Jeanie Jackson, Pres.; Angela Thomas, Secy.; Robert Walker, Treas.; Charles Needham, Exec. Dir.
EIN: 383246048

727
Leslie H. & Edith C. Green Charitable Trust
c/o Comerica Bank
P.O. Box 75000, M/C 3302
Detroit, MI   48275-3302

Established in 1975 in MI.
Donor: Edith C. Green‡.
Grantmaker type: Independent foundation.
Financial data (yr. ended 12/31/05): Assets, $9,978,449 (M); expenditures, $762,490; total giving, $651,441; qualifying distributions, $651,441; giving activities include $651,441 for grants.
Purpose and activities: Support for Cathedral Church of St. Paul and St. Peter's Home for Boys, Detroit, Michigan.
Fields of interest: Residential/custodial care; Roman Catholic agencies & churches; Boys.
Limitations: Applications not accepted. Giving limited to Detroit, MI. No grants to individuals.
Application information: Contributes only to 2 pre-selected organizations.
Trustees: Dean S. Bancroft; Bishop R. Stewart Wood; Comerica Bank.
EIN: 386162077

728
Albert M. & Lyda M. Green Foundation
c/o JPMorgan Chase Bank, N.A.
P.O. Box 1308
Milwaukee, WI   53201

Grantmaker type: Independent foundation.
Financial data (yr. ended 12/31/05): Assets, $889,247 (M); expenditures, $31,121; total giving, $29,000; qualifying distributions, $29,000; giving activities include $29,000 for grants.
Purpose and activities: Giving primarily for public policy, wildlife, and environmental conservation.
Fields of interest: Environment, natural resources; Animals/wildlife, preservation/protection; Big Brothers/Big Sisters; Children, services; Public policy, research.
Limitations: Applications not accepted. Giving primarily in Washington, DC, and MI. No grants to individuals.
Application information: Contributes only to pre-selected organizations.
Officers and Directors:* David M. Rosenberger,* Pres.; Mark C. Larson,* 1st V.P.; James M. Elsworth,* V.P.; John K. Cannon,* Secy.; Gail A. Moro, Treas.
Trustee: JPMorgan Chase Bank, N.A.
EIN: 382601744

729
Leslie H., Edith C. & Robert C. Green Memorial Endowment Fund
c/o Comerica Bank
P.O. Box 75000
Detroit, MI   48275

Established in 1996.
Grantmaker type: Independent foundation.
Financial data (yr. ended 8/31/05): Assets, $227,410 (M); expenditures, $11,506; total giving, $7,000; qualifying distributions, $7,000; giving activities include $7,000 for grants.
Purpose and activities: Support only for St. Peter's Home for the Boys, Detroit, MI.

Limitations: Applications not accepted. Giving limited to Detroit, MI. No grants to individuals.
Application information: Contributes only to a pre-selected organization.
Trustee: Comerica Bank.
EIN: 386043971

730
Green Vision Foundation
966 Holland St.
Saugatuck, MI   49453   (269) 857-1247
Contact: Suzy A. Richardson, Dir.

Established in 1997 in MI.
Donor: Phillip D. Miller.
Grantmaker type: Independent foundation.
Financial data (yr. ended 12/31/04): Assets, $49,263 (M); gifts received, $21,000; expenditures, $11,071; total giving, $8,301; qualifying distributions, $8,551; giving activities include $8,301 for grants.
Fields of interest: Performing arts, music; Environment; Human services.
Limitations: Giving primarily in MI.
Application information: Application form not required.
Deadline(s): None
Directors: Phillip D. Miller; Suzy A. Richardson.
EIN: 411876575

731
Hugh W. & Carolyn K. Greenberg Foundation
27530 Fairway Hills Dr.
Franklin, MI   48025

Established about 1967 in MI.
Donors: Carolyn K. Greenberg; Hugh W. Greenberg.
Grantmaker type: Independent foundation.
Financial data (yr. ended 1/31/05): Assets, $187,468 (M); expenditures, $121,380; total giving, $121,517; qualifying distributions, $121,503; giving activities include $121,517 for 4 grants (high: $63,967; low: $1,050).
Purpose and activities: Giving primarily for Jewish agencies.
Fields of interest: Cancer; Jewish federated giving programs; Jewish agencies & temples.
Type of support: General/operating support.
Limitations: Applications not accepted. Giving primarily in MI. No grants to individuals.
Application information: Contributes only to pre-selected organizations.
Trustees: Carolyn K. Greenberg; Hugh W. Greenberg.
EIN: 386117983

732
The Patrick T. and Sue C. Greene Family Foundation
992 Lake Shore Rd.
Grosse Pointe Shores, MI   48236

Established in 1999 in MI.
Donor: Patrick T. Greene.
Grantmaker type: Independent foundation.
Financial data (yr. ended 1/31/06): Assets, $25,664 (M); expenditures, $1,360; total giving, $1,360; qualifying distributions, $1,360; giving activities include $1,360 for grants.

Purpose and activities: Support only for the University of Liggett School, Grosse Pointe.
Fields of interest: Higher education, university.
Type of support: General/operating support.
Limitations: Applications not accepted. Giving limited to Grosse Pointe, MI. No grants to individuals.
Application information: Contributes only to a pre-selected organization.
Officers: Patrick T. Greene, Pres. and Treas.; Sue C. Greene, V.P. and Secy.
EIN: 383465666

733
Greene View Foundation
3662 Tartan Cir.
Portage, MI   49024
Contact: Lois A. Stuck, Pres.

Established in 1988 in MI.
Grantmaker type: Independent foundation.
Financial data (yr. ended 12/31/05): Assets, $226,308 (M); expenditures, $9,296; total giving, $9,000; qualifying distributions, $9,031; giving activities include $9,000 for grants.
Fields of interest: Children/youth, services; Christian agencies & churches.
Type of support: General/operating support.
Limitations: Giving primarily in MI, with some emphasis on Kalamazoo.
Application information:
  Initial approach: Proposal
  Deadline(s): June 30
Officers and Director:* Lois A. Stuck,* Pres.; David T. Stuck, Secy.-Treas.
EIN: 382769679

734
Ferris Greeney Family Foundation
2740 Littlefield Dr. N.E.
Grand Rapids, MI   49506

Established in 2003 in MI.
Donor: Edith I. Blodgett Charitable Lead Trust.
Grantmaker type: Independent foundation.
Financial data (yr. ended 12/31/05): Assets, $618,534 (M); gifts received, $280,462; expenditures, $21,039; total giving, $15,350; qualifying distributions, $15,350; giving activities include $15,350 for grants.
Fields of interest: Performing arts, music; Higher education.
Type of support: General/operating support; Program development; Research.
Limitations: Applications not accepted. Giving on a national basis, with some emphasis on MI. No grants to individuals.
Application information: Contributes only to pre-selected organizations.
Officers and Trustees:* Wendy L. Greeney,* Pres. and Secy.; Paul E. Greeney,* V.P. and Treas.; Daniel F. Greeney; Jonathan P. Greeney.
EIN: 300171087

735
Henry Greenspan Foundation
c/o Bruce H. Sobel, C.P.A.
270 Madison Ave., Ste. 1500
New York, NY   10016

Donor: Albert L. Greenspan†.
Grantmaker type: Independent foundation.
Financial data (yr. ended 12/31/04): Assets, $250,793 (M); expenditures, $10,890; total giving, $9,200; qualifying distributions, $10,386; giving activities include $9,200 for grants.
Fields of interest: Human services; Jewish federated giving programs; General charitable giving.
Type of support: General/operating support; Continuing support; Research.
Limitations: Applications not accepted. Giving primarily in IL, MI, and NY. No grants to individuals.
Application information: Contributes only to pre-selected organizations.
Officer: Henry Greenspan, Pres.
EIN: 237416723

736
Seymour & Pearl Greenstein Foundation
17089 Jeanette St.
Southfield, MI   48075

Established in 1985 in MI.
Donors: Pearl Greenstein; Seymour Greenstein; Golden Valley Dairy.
Grantmaker type: Independent foundation.
Financial data (yr. ended 12/31/04): Assets, $1,386,574 (M); gifts received, $880,547; expenditures, $107,033; total giving, $105,151; qualifying distributions, $105,151; giving activities include $105,151 for 100 grants (high: $10,000; low: $20).
Purpose and activities: Giving primarily for Jewish organizations.
Fields of interest: Theological school/education; Human services; Jewish federated giving programs; Jewish agencies & temples.
Limitations: Applications not accepted. Giving primarily in MI, with emphasis on Oak Park and Southfield; funding also in New York, NY. No grants to individuals.
Application information: Contributes only to pre-selected organizations.
Officers: Seymour Greenstein, Pres.; Pearl Greenstein, V.P.
EIN: 382633409
Selected grants: The following grants were reported in 2004.
$10,000 to Jewish Federation of Metropolitan Detroit, Bloomfield Hills, MI.
$5,000 to Kadima Association for Jewish Residential Care, Southfield, MI.
$3,500 to JARC, Farmington Hills, MI.
$1,300 to Akiva Hebrew Day School, Lathrup Village, MI.
$1,000 to Yeshivath Beth Yehudah, Southfield, MI.
$500 to Chinuch Atzmia, Brooklyn, NY.
$200 to Diskin Orphan Home of Israel, Brooklyn, NY.
$180 to Orthodox Union - Union of Orthodox Jewish Congregations of America, New York, NY.
$100 to Yad Ezra, Oak Park, MI.
$20 to Telshe Yeshiva Chicago, Chicago, IL.

737
Griffin Fund, Inc.
3311 Daleview Dr.
Ann Arbor, MI   48105-9685

Donor: Carleton H. Griffin.
Grantmaker type: Independent foundation.

Financial data (yr. ended 12/31/05): Assets, $126,980 (M); expenditures, $7,131; total giving, $6,900; qualifying distributions, $6,900; giving activities include $6,900 for grants.
Purpose and activities: Giving primarily to Christian organizations with emphasis on children and youth, and foreign missions; some giving also for education and health care.
Fields of interest: Higher education; Theological school/education; Hospitals (specialty); Mental health, residential care; Christian agencies & churches.
International interests: India.
Limitations: Applications not accepted. Giving on a national basis. No grants to individuals.
Application information: Contributes only to pre-selected organizations.
Officers: Carleton H. Griffin, Pres. and Treas.; Julia N. Griffin, V.P.; Anne J. Griffin Sloan, V.P.; Mary Lou Griffin, Secy.
EIN: 237425855

738
Donald C. & Doris G. Griffith Foundation
231 Shore Haven Dr. S.E.
Grand Rapids, MI   49546-2255
Contact: Doris G. Griffith, Tr.

Established in 1984 in MI.
Donor: Doris G. Griffith.
Grantmaker type: Independent foundation.
Financial data (yr. ended 12/31/05): Assets, $276,384 (M); gifts received, $50,000; expenditures, $79,277; total giving, $76,250; qualifying distributions, $76,250; giving activities include $76,250 for grants.
Purpose and activities: Giving for conservation, higher education, federated giving programs and the arts.
Fields of interest: Arts; Higher education; Environment, natural resources; Federated giving programs; Christian agencies & churches.
Limitations: Giving primarily in MI. No grants to individuals.
Application information:
  Initial approach: Letter
  Deadline(s): None
Trustees: Doris G. Griffith; Douglas T. Griffith; Kim A. Griffith; Kay G. Hammond; Martha A. O'Brien.
EIN: 382566349

739
The Grimaldi Foundation
29200 Southfield Rd., Ste. 100
Southfield, MI   48076
Application address: c/o Ruth E. Grimaldi, 3925 Oakland Dr., Bloomfield, MI 48301, tel.: (248) 646-5582

Established in 1990 in MI.
Donors: Thomas J. Grimaldi; Ruth E. Grimaldi.
Grantmaker type: Independent foundation.
Financial data (yr. ended 12/31/04): Assets, $1,066,281 (M); gifts received, $113,000; expenditures, $209,415; total giving, $205,750; qualifying distributions, $205,261; giving activities include $205,750 for 13 grants (high: $38,000; low: $250).
Fields of interest: Secondary school/education; Theological school/education; Christian agencies & churches; Roman Catholic agencies & churches.

Type of support: Scholarship funds; Scholarships—to individuals.
Limitations: Giving limited to residents of Macomb, Oakland and Wayne counties, MI.
Application information:
Initial approach: Letter or proposal for grants; essay, copies of academic records, and references for scholarships
Deadline(s): None
Directors: Ruth E. Grimaldi; Paul L. McCoy.
EIN: 382938393

740
Grodman Cure Foundation, Inc.
7325 Willow Oak Dr.
West Bloomfield, MI   48324

Established in 1999 in MI.
Grantmaker type: Independent foundation.
Financial data (yr. ended 12/31/04): Assets, $280,056 (M); gifts received, $60,107; expenditures, $72,694; total giving, $47,590; qualifying distributions, $47,590; giving activities include $47,590 for grants.
Limitations: Applications not accepted. Giving primarily in MI. No grants to individuals.
Application information: Contributes only to pre-selected organizations.
Directors: Karyn J. Grodman; Scott T. Grodman.
EIN: 383477444

741
Robert and Sharon Grooters Foundation
4633 Patterson Ave. S.E., Ste. B
Grand Rapids, MI   49512-5383

Established in 2000 in MI.
Donors: Robert D. Grooters; Sharon L. Grooters.
Grantmaker type: Independent foundation.
Financial data (yr. ended 12/31/05): Assets, $259,998 (M); expenditures, $27,185; total giving, $23,987; qualifying distributions, $23,987; giving activities include $23,987 for grants.
Fields of interest: Higher education; Health organizations, association; Human services.
Limitations: Applications not accepted. No grants to individuals.
Application information: Contributes only to pre-selected organizations.
Officer: Robert D. Grooters, Pres. and Secy.-Treas.
EIN: 383568177

742
The Grosfeld Foundation
2290 First National Bldg.
Detroit, MI   48226-3583

Established in 1984 in MI.
Donors: James Grosfeld; Nancy Grosfeld; Multivest.
Grantmaker type: Independent foundation.
Financial data (yr. ended 11/30/04): Assets, $3,080,085 (M); gifts received, $991,374; expenditures, $2,637,446; total giving, $2,615,231; qualifying distributions, $2,618,086; giving activities include $2,615,231 for grants.
Purpose and activities: Giving primarily for colleges and universities and an employment service agency; support also for human services, including Jewish-affiliated organizations.

Fields of interest: Higher education; Hospitals (general); Employment, services; Human services; Jewish federated giving programs; Jewish agencies & temples.
Limitations: Applications not accepted. Giving primarily in MI. No grants to individuals.
Application information: Contributes only to pre-selected organizations.
Officers: James Grosfeld, Pres. and Treas.; Nancy Grosfeld, V.P. and Secy.
EIN: 382575307
Selected grants: The following grants were reported in 2003.
$456,800 to Jewish Federation of Metropolitan Detroit, Bloomfield Hills, MI. For unrestricted support.
$301,000 to Amherst College, Amherst, MA. For unrestricted support.
$250,000 to Anti-Defamation League of Bnai Brith, New York, NY. For unrestricted support.
$35,000 to Hillel Day School of Metropolitan Detroit, Farmington Hills, MI. For unrestricted support.
$20,000 to Columbia University, New York, NY. For unrestricted support.
$17,000 to Jewish Womens Foundation of Metropolitan Detroit, Bloomfield Hills, MI. For unrestricted support.
$10,000 to Jewish Vocational Service and Community Workshop, Southfield, MI. For unrestricted support.
$10,000 to Washington Institute for Near East Policy, DC. For unrestricted support.
$3,168 to United Jewish Foundation, Bloomfield Hills, MI. For unrestricted support.
$1,000 to Planned Parenthood of Southeast Michigan, Detroit, MI. For unrestricted support.

743
The Gruenberg Foundation, Inc.
50 N. Franklin Tpke., Ste. 206
Ho-Ho-Kus, NJ   07423   (201) 652-0404

Established in 1995 in NJ.
Grantmaker type: Independent foundation.
Financial data (yr. ended 9/30/05): Assets, $6,150,941 (M); expenditures, $306,358; total giving, $140,977; qualifying distributions, $256,736; giving activities include $140,977 for 25 grants to individuals (high: $13,000; low: $2,500).
Purpose and activities: Awards scholarships to students enrolled at Tri-State University in Indiana, and to residents of Ridgewood, New Jersey who are eligible high school seniors or college students seeking renewal at an accredited college or university.
Type of support: Scholarships—to individuals.
Limitations: Giving primarily to residents of IN, MI, NJ, and OH.
Application information: Contract Scholarship Advisory Committee at Tri-State University or Ridgewood High School, NJ, for application form. Application form required.
Deadline(s): Jan. 30 for Ridgewood High School students and Mar. 1 for Tri-State University students
Trustees: William C. Caspare; Ronald G. Collins; Tahra C. Collins.
EIN: 223381175

744
Guiding Shepherd Foundation
1341 Lallendorf Rd.
Oregon, OH   43616

Established in 2001 in OH.
Donor: Orene E. Duvall Trust.
Grantmaker type: Independent foundation.
Financial data (yr. ended 12/31/04): Assets, $1,488,341 (M); expenditures, $142,738; total giving, $118,641; qualifying distributions, $120,470; giving activities include $118,641 for 21 grants (high: $47,200; low: $35).
Purpose and activities: Giving primarily for Christian organizations, including schools.
Fields of interest: Elementary/secondary education; Christian agencies & churches.
Limitations: Applications not accepted. Giving primarily in Chicago, IL, Lakeview, MI, and Bowling Green and Toledo, OH. No grants to individuals.
Application information: Contributes only to pre-selected organizations.
Trustees: Michele L. Mariano; Nicholas A. Mariano.
EIN: 341961400

745
Guilliom Family Foundation
709 Harding St.
Plymouth, MI   48170

Established in KY.
Grantmaker type: Independent foundation.
Financial data (yr. ended 12/31/03): Assets, $14,143 (M); gifts received, $13,362; expenditures, $1,670; total giving, $0; qualifying distributions, $1,671.
Limitations: Applications not accepted. No grants to individuals.
Application information: Contributes only to pre-selected organizations.
Officers: Gregory Guilliom, Chair.; Jennifer Guilliom, Vice-Chair.
Trustees: Anthony Guilliom; Heather Guilliom.
EIN: 616275892

746
Mary L. Gumaer Scholarship Foundation
c/o Fifth Third Bank
P.O. Box 3636
Grand Rapids, MI   49501-3636
Application address: c/o: Superintendent of Schools, Ovid-Elsie Area Schools, 8989 Colony Rd., Elsie, MI 48831, tel.: (989) 834-2271

Established in 2000 in MI.
Donor: Mary L. Grumaer.
Grantmaker type: Independent foundation.
Financial data (yr. ended 12/31/05): Assets, $339,923 (M); expenditures, $19,167; total giving, $15,330; qualifying distributions, $15,330; giving activities include $15,330 for grants.
Purpose and activities: Scholarships awarded to graduating seniors of Ovid-Elsie High School who are entering college as a full-time student.
Type of support: Scholarships—to individuals.
Limitations: Giving limited to residents in the Ovid-Elsie, MI, area.
Application information: Application form required.
Deadline(s): May 1
Trustee: Fifth Third Bank.
EIN: 386751392

747
The June and Robert Gurwin Family Foundation
37000 Woodward Ave., Ste. 200
Bloomfield Hills, MI 48304-0924

Established in 2003 in MI.
Donor: June H. Gurwin.
Grantmaker type: Independent foundation.
Financial data (yr. ended 12/31/05): Assets, $672,159 (M); gifts received, $609,382; expenditures, $258,954; total giving, $249,900; qualifying distributions, $249,900; giving activities include $249,900 for 7 grants (high: $107,500; low: $200).
Fields of interest: Cancer; Diabetes; Human services; Federated giving programs; Jewish agencies & temples.
Limitations: Applications not accepted. Giving primarily in MI.
Application information: Contributes only to pre-selected organizations.
Officers: June H. Gurwin, Pres.; John D. Bell, V.P. and Secy.; Frances G. Bell, V.P. and Treas.
EIN: 300164263

748
Rita Guy Christian Music Ministry, Inc.
5338 Lawn Arbor Dr.
Houston, TX 77066
Contact: Rev. Clara M. Lewis, Treas.

Established in 1985 in CA.
Grantmaker type: Independent foundation.
Financial data (yr. ended 12/31/04): Assets, $134,179 (M); expenditures, $69,052; total giving, $21,500; qualifying distributions, $21,444; giving activities include $21,500 for grants.
Purpose and activities: To support and promote the art form of Christian music and the related performing arts of dance and drama in the worship of God by providing education, instruction, and performance opportunities on a non-denominational basis.
Fields of interest: Performing arts, music; Christian agencies & churches.
Limitations: Giving primarily in MI; giving also in TX. No grants to individuals.
Application information: Application form required.
Initial approach: Proposal
Copies of proposal: 7
Deadline(s): Varies
Officers: Gordon E. Nelson, Pres.; Harry Platt, Secy.; Rev. Clara M. Lewis, Treas.
Director: Erik Winter.
EIN: 770101026

749
H.I.S. Foundation
13919 S. West Bay Shore Dr., Ste. G-1
Traverse City, MI 49684
Contact: Dale M. Nielson, V.P.

Established in 1990.
Donors: Nielson Enterprises Corp.; Dale M. Nielson.
Grantmaker type: Independent foundation.
Financial data (yr. ended 12/31/04): Assets, $22,577 (M); gifts received, $3,041,106; expenditures, $1,142,118; total giving, $833,390; qualifying distributions, $833,390; giving activities

include $833,390 for 71 grants (high: $126,500; low: $250).
Purpose and activities: Giving primarily for Protestant and Roman Catholic agencies, as well as for Christian education, pro-life causes, conservative public policy, and entrepreneurship assistance.
Fields of interest: Education; Youth development, religion; Residential/custodial care, hospices; Civil liberties, right to life; Business/industry; Social sciences, public policy; Christian agencies & churches.
International interests: China; Mexico.
Type of support: Continuing support; Income development; Annual campaigns; Capital campaigns; Building/renovation; Equipment; Land acquisition; Seed money; Fellowships; Scholarship funds; Matching/challenge support.
Limitations: Giving on a national and international basis, with emphasis on Antrim, Bonzie, Crawford, Grant Traverse, Kalkaska and Leelanau counties, MI, and China and Mexico. No support for liberal public policy, and religious organizations other than Christian.
Application information: Application form not required.
Initial approach: Letter
Copies of proposal: 1
Deadline(s): None
Board meeting date(s): Dec.
Officers and Directors:* Melvin K. Nielson,* Pres.; Dale M. Nielson,* V.P.; Barbara A. Nielson, Secy.; Ruth E. Nielson,* Treas.
EIN: 382953594

750
H.O.N.O.R. Foundation
19428 Gill Rd.
Livonia, MI 48152

Established in 2003.
Grantmaker type: Independent foundation.
Financial data (yr. ended 12/31/05): Assets, $0 (M); gifts received, $150; expenditures, $3,348; total giving, $3,348; qualifying distributions, $3,348; giving activities include $3,348 for grants.
Type of support: Grants to individuals.
Officers: Gary R. Thomas, Pres.; Laura L. Thomas, V.P.
EIN: 320080904

751
H.S. Foundation
c/o Carol A. Sigler, C.P.A.
31313 N.W. Hwy., Ste. 223
Farmington Hills, MI 48334

Established in 1987 in MI.
Donors: Jerome Soble; Kenneth Soble.
Grantmaker type: Independent foundation.
Financial data (yr. ended 12/31/05): Assets, $795,589 (M); expenditures, $30,182; total giving, $27,693; qualifying distributions, $27,693; giving activities include $27,693 for grants.
Fields of interest: Higher education; Jewish federated giving programs; Jewish agencies & temples.
Limitations: Applications not accepted. Giving on a national basis. No grants to individuals.
Application information: Contributes only to pre-selected organizations.

Officers: Jerome Soble, Pres.; Kenneth Soble, V.P.; Richard Soble, Secy.-Treas.
EIN: 382706164

752
Oscar and Keturah Haab Foundation
436 Pine Brae St.
Ann Arbor, MI 48105

Grantmaker type: Independent foundation.
Financial data (yr. ended 12/31/05): Assets, $244,653 (M); gifts received, $38,890; expenditures, $11,000; total giving, $11,000; qualifying distributions, $11,000; giving activities include $11,000 for grants.
Fields of interest: Protestant agencies & churches.
Limitations: Applications not accepted. Giving primarily in MI. No grants to individuals.
Application information: Contributes only to pre-selected organizations.
Officer: Keturah Haab, Pres. and Secy.-Treas.
EIN: 383285275

753
Carroll J. Haas Foundation
27020 Simpson Rd.
Mendon, MI 49072
Contact: Carroll J. Haas, Pres.

Established in 1998 in MI.
Donor: Carroll J. Haas.
Grantmaker type: Independent foundation.
Financial data (yr. ended 3/31/05): Assets, $2,196,968 (M); expenditures, $81,045; total giving, $69,255; qualifying distributions, $71,920; giving activities include $69,255 for 6+ grants (high: $50,000).
Fields of interest: Higher education, university; Human services; Roman Catholic agencies & churches.
Limitations: Giving primarily in MI.
Application information: Application form not required.
Initial approach: Letter
Deadline(s): None
Officers: Carroll J. Haas, Pres. and Treas.; Robert G. Haas, Secy.
Directors: Kathleen A. Gray; Carroll J. Haas II; James H. Haas; Theresa Haas; Mary Jo McKee.
EIN: 383415066

754
Clarence & Marion Wiggins Haas Scholarship Fund
c/o Citizens Bank Wealth Mgmt., N.A.
328 S. Saginaw St., MC 002072
Flint, MI 48502
Application address: c/o Saginaw High School, 3100 Webber St., Saginaw, MI 48601, tel.: (989) 776-0421

Established in MI.
Grantmaker type: Independent foundation.
Financial data (yr. ended 12/31/05): Assets, $84,414 (M); expenditures, $4,993; total giving, $2,400; qualifying distributions, $3,627; giving activities include $2,400 for 4 grants to individuals (high: $700; low: $500).
Purpose and activities: Scholarship awards to graduates of Saginaw High School, MI.

Fields of interest: Higher education.
Type of support: Scholarships—to individuals.
Limitations: Giving limited to Saginaw, MI.
Application information: Application form required.
　Deadline(s): May 1
Trustee: Citizens Bank, N.A.
EIN: 386219139

755
Erwin & Virginia Haass Foundation, Inc.
80 Moran Rd.
Grosse Pointe Farms, MI　48236-3607

Donors: Virginia A. Haass; Frederick E. Haass;
Robert O. Haass; Stephen A. Haass; Susan H.
Klonowski.
Grantmaker type: Independent foundation.
Financial data (yr. ended 12/31/05): Assets,
$54,493 (M); gifts received, $100; expenditures,
$4,063; total giving, $3,976; qualifying
distributions, $3,976; giving activities include
$3,976 for grants.
Limitations: Applications not accepted. Giving
primarily in FL and the Detroit, MI, area. No grants
to individuals.
Application information: Contributes only to
pre-selected organizations.
Officers: Frederick E. Haass, Pres.; Stephen A.
Haass, V.P. and Secy.; Robert O. Haass, V.P. and
Treas.
EIN: 381777180

756
The Hadied Foundation
26300 Telegraph Rd., 2nd Fl.
Southfield, MI　48034

Established in 1994 in MI.
Grantmaker type: Independent foundation.
Financial data (yr. ended 12/31/04): Assets,
$169,239 (M); gifts received, $16,000;
expenditures, $8,468; total giving, $5,854;
qualifying distributions, $5,854; giving activities
include $5,854 for grants.
Fields of interest: Islam.
Type of support: General/operating support.
Officer: Ahmed Hadied, Pres.
EIN: 383172507

757
Rowena Hafer Trust f/b/o University of
Michigan
(formerly Hazen A. & Rowena P. Hafer University of
Michigan Scholarship Fund)
c/o National City Bank
P.O. Box 94651
Cleveland, OH　44101-4651

Established in 1996 in MI.
Grantmaker type: Independent foundation.
Financial data (yr. ended 12/31/04): Assets,
$359,953 (M); expenditures, $12,865; total giving,
$10,500; qualifying distributions, $11,812; giving
activities include $10,500 for grants.
Fields of interest: Higher education, university.
Type of support: Scholarship funds.
Limitations: Applications not accepted. Giving
limited to Ann Arbor, MI. No grants to individuals.
Application information: Contributes only to a
pre-selected organization.

Trustee: National City Bank.
EIN: 386531865

758
Hagen Family Foundation
2760 N.E. 16th St.
Fort Lauderdale, FL　33304
Contact: David F. Hagen, Pres.
E-mail: webmaster@hagenfamilyfoundation.org;
URL: http://www.hagenfamilyfoundation.org

Established in 1999 in MI.
Donors: David F. Hagen; Virginia Hagen.
Grantmaker type: Independent foundation.
Financial data (yr. ended 12/31/05): Assets,
$1,351,965 (M); expenditures, $101,013; total
giving, $65,885; qualifying distributions, $70,244;
giving activities include $65,885 for 16 grants (high:
$5,000; low: $2,000).
Fields of interest: Education, reading; Education;
Science; General charitable giving.
Type of support: Program development;
Conferences/seminars; Seed money; Curriculum
development; Scholarship funds; Technical
assistance; Matching/challenge support.
Limitations: Giving in the U.S., with special interest
in the Midwest, the New England area, and FL. No
support for on-going programs. No grants to
individuals, or for annual drives, capital campaigns,
research, or scholarships.
Application information: See foundation Web site
for application guidelines, formats, and timeline for
current grant cycle. Application form required.
　Initial approach: Letter of intent
　Copies of proposal: 4
　Deadline(s): May for letter of intent, July for full
　　proposal
　Board meeting date(s): Aug. 10
　Final notification: Sept.
Officers and Directors:* David F. Hagen,* Pres.;
Virginia Hagen,* V.P.; Christopher Born; Patricia
Born; Rev. Andrew Hagen; Laura C. Hagen; Susan
Dingle Hagen.
EIN: 383482329

759
Hager Family Foundation
c/o Fifth Third Bank
P.O. Box 3636
Grand Rapids, MI　49501-3636
Application address: c/o Hager Lumber Co.,
Attn.: Ted W. Buzalski, 1545 Marquette, Grand
Rapids, MI 49509, tel.: (616) 452-5151

Donor: T. James Hager.
Grantmaker type: Independent foundation.
Financial data (yr. ended 11/30/05): Assets,
$456,155 (M); gifts received, $96,000;
expenditures, $70,143; total giving, $64,000;
qualifying distributions, $64,294; giving activities
include $64,000 for 9 grants (high: $50,000; low:
$1,000).
Purpose and activities: Giving for education,
Christian organizations, and human services.
Fields of interest: Education; YM/YWCAs & YM/
YWHAs; Human services; Federated giving
programs; Christian agencies & churches.
Limitations: Giving primarily in Grand Rapids, MI. No
grants to individuals.
Application information: Application form not
required.

　Initial approach: Letter
　Deadline(s): None
Officers and Trustees:* Titus Ronald Hager,* Pres.;
Ted W. Buzalski,* V.P.; Dan Oumedian,
Secy.-Treas.; Virginia Gearhart; Fifth Third Bank.
EIN: 386050526
Selected grants: The following grants were reported
in 2003.
$200,000 to Grand Valley State University,
　Allendale, MI.
$27,500 to YMCA of Greater Grand Rapids, Grand
　Rapids, MI. 2 grants: $25,000, $2,500
$3,500 to Mel Trotter Ministries, Grand Rapids, MI.
$500 to Michigan Colleges Foundation, Southfield,
　MI.
$500 to Steepletown Neighborhood Services, Grand
　Rapids, MI.

760
The Haggard Foundation
P.O. Box 2256
Traverse City, MI　49685-2256
Contact: Ward M. Haggard, Jr., Pres.
Application address: P.O. Box 56248, Houston, TX
77256

Established in 1986 in MI.
Donors: Ward M. Haggard, Jr.; Dee Bowman
Haggard.
Grantmaker type: Independent foundation.
Financial data (yr. ended 12/31/05): Assets,
$93,561 (M); expenditures, $864; total giving, $0;
qualifying distributions, $0.
Fields of interest: Higher education; Education;
Protestant agencies & churches.
Type of support: General/operating support.
Limitations: Giving primarily in Traverse City, MI, and
Houston, TX. No grants to individuals.
Application information:
　Initial approach: Letter
　Deadline(s): None
Officers: Ward M. Haggard, Jr., Pres.; Dee Bowman
Haggard, Secy.-Treas.
EIN: 382711484

761
Haggarty Foundation
20630 Harper Ave., Ste. 112
Harper Woods, MI　48225-1448

Established in 1985 in MI.
Donor: George A. Haggarty.
Grantmaker type: Independent foundation.
Financial data (yr. ended 6/30/05): Assets, $428
(M); gifts received, $10,030; expenditures,
$16,667; total giving, $16,500; qualifying
distributions, $16,500; giving activities include
$16,500 for grants.
Limitations: Applications not accepted. Giving
primarily in MI, with emphasis on Detroit and Grosse
Pointe. No grants to individuals.
Application information: Contributes only to
pre-selected organizations.
Officers: George A. Haggarty, Pres. and Treas.; Alice
W. Haggarty, V.P. and Secy.
Directors: Sarah H. Chironi-Lubelli; Charles K.
Haggarty; George A. Haggarty, Jr.; Laura I. Haggarty.
EIN: 382630272

762
Hagopian Family Foundation
850 S. Woodward
Birmingham, MI 48009-6722

Established in 1995 in MI.
Donor: Edgar Hagopian.
Grantmaker type: Independent foundation.
Financial data (yr. ended 12/31/04): Assets, $64,260 (M); gifts received, $50,724; expenditures, $46,396; total giving, $16,813; qualifying distributions, $16,813; giving activities include $16,813 for grants.
Purpose and activities: Giving primarily for the benefit of the Armenian-American community.
Limitations: Applications not accepted. Giving on a national basis, with some emphasis on MI. No grants to individuals.
Application information: Contributes only to pre-selected organizations.
Directors: Edgar Hagopian; Edmond Hagopian; Sarah Hagopian; Suzanne Hagopian; Angela Snow.
EIN: 383254491

763
William and Sharon Hahn Foundation, Inc.
500 S. Opdyke Rd.
Pontiac, MI 48343-1046 (248) 332-9300
Contact: Sharon Hahn, Secy.

Established in 2000 in MI.
Donors: Sharon Hahn; William Hahn.
Grantmaker type: Independent foundation.
Financial data (yr. ended 12/31/05): Assets, $5,718 (M); gifts received, $370,000; expenditures, $370,248; total giving, $370,000; qualifying distributions, $370,000; giving activities include $370,000 for 15 grants (high: $35,000; low: $10,000).
Purpose and activities: Giving primarily for family and other human services.
Fields of interest: Arts, association; Crime/violence prevention, child abuse; Human services; Children/youth, services; Family services; Women, centers/services; Federated giving programs.
Limitations: Giving primarily in MI, with emphasis on Pontiac. No grants to individuals.
Application information: Application form is currently in development.
Officers: William Hahn, Pres. and Treas.; Sharon Hahn, Secy.
EIN: 383549321

764
George H. Haines Charitable Trust
P.O. Box 3636
Grand Rapids, MI 49501-3636
Application address: c/o Casey Normandine, St. Joseph County Intermediate School, Dist. 62445, Shimmel Rd., P.O. Box 219, Centerville, MI 49032

Established in 1994 in MI.
Grantmaker type: Independent foundation.
Financial data (yr. ended 12/31/05): Assets, $431,532 (M); expenditures, $19,983; total giving, $16,855; qualifying distributions, $16,855; giving activities include $16,855 for grants.
Purpose and activities: The trust maintains the property of the First United Methodist Church in Three Rivers, MI, and provides scholarships to

students in St. Joseph County enrolled in a school teaching tool and die making.
Fields of interest: Protestant agencies & churches.
Type of support: Scholarships—to individuals.
Limitations: Giving primarily to residents of St. Joseph County, MI.
Application information: Application form required.
    Deadline(s): None
Advisory Committee: Nancy Grabiak; Doug Hunter; Gary Major; Casey Normandine; Jim Romain; Greg Wallman.
Trustee: Fifth Third Bank.
EIN: 386092830

765
The Hakim Foundation
26300 Telegraph Rd., 2nd Fl.
Southfield, MI 48034

Established in 1999.
Grantmaker type: Independent foundation.
Financial data (yr. ended 12/31/04): Assets, $17,646 (M); gifts received, $10,000; expenditures, $450; total giving, $0; qualifying distributions, $0.
Officer: Mohamad M. Hakim, Pres.
EIN: 383434014

766
Halcyon Foundation
663 Halcyon Ct.
Ann Arbor, MI 48103-1579
Contact: Thomas R. Larson, Treas.

Established in 2002 in MI.
Donor: Thomas R. Larson.
Grantmaker type: Independent foundation.
Financial data (yr. ended 12/31/05): Assets, $56,382 (M); expenditures, $3,656; total giving, $3,100; qualifying distributions, $3,100; giving activities include $3,100 for grants.
Fields of interest: Christian agencies & churches.
Limitations: Giving primarily in Ann Arbor, MI. No grants to individuals.
Application information:
    Initial approach: Letter
    Deadline(s): None
Officers and Directors: Claudia K. Larson,* Pres.; Jonathan B. Larson,* V.P.; Scott T. Larson,* V.P.; Elizabeth A. Moraw,* Secy.; Thomas R. Larson,* Treas.
EIN: 300012887

767
The Hale Family Foundation
c/o The Northern Trust Co.
190 Carondelet Plz.
St. Louis, MO 63105

Established in 1997 in MO.
Donor: Douglas Hale.
Grantmaker type: Independent foundation.
Financial data (yr. ended 12/31/04): Assets, $601,876 (M); gifts received, $31,010; expenditures, $31,450; total giving, $29,500; qualifying distributions, $29,291; giving activities include $29,500 for grants.
Fields of interest: Education; Health care; Youth development; Human services; Christian agencies & churches.

Limitations: Applications not accepted. Giving primarily in CT, MI, MO, and VT. No grants to individuals.
Application information: Contributes only to pre-selected organizations.
Trustees: Jennifer Bollinger; L. Franklin Bollinger; Douglas Hale; Joan Jackson Hale; Lou Ellen Tufts; V. Randy Tufts.
EIN: 436741329

768
Hall Family Foundation
429 S. Michigan Ave.
Hastings, MI 49058-2250

Established in 2004 in MI.
Donor: Hall Enterprises.
Grantmaker type: Independent foundation.
Financial data (yr. ended 12/31/05): Assets, $152,687 (M); expenditures, $8,200; total giving, $8,200; qualifying distributions, $8,200; giving activities include $8,200 for grants.
Fields of interest: Libraries (public); Health care.
Type of support: Building/renovation; General/operating support.
Limitations: Applications not accepted. Giving in Hastings, MI. No grants to individuals.
Application information: Contributes only to pre-selected organizations.
Officers: Rowland F. Hall, Pres.; Rodney W. Hall, V.P.; Michael J. Hall, Secy.; Garry L. Hall, Treas.
EIN: 201698041

769
Michael A. Halpin Memorial Law Enforcement Fund, Inc.
200 N. Main St.
Mount Pleasant, MI 48858-2390

Grantmaker type: Independent foundation.
Financial data (yr. ended 12/31/05): Assets, $1,179 (M); expenditures, $0; total giving, $0; qualifying distributions, $0.
Fields of interest: Education; Crime/law enforcement.
Limitations: Giving primarily in Isabella County, MI.
Officers: Larry J. Burdick, Pres.; Robert Holmes, Jr., Secy.; Mark H. Duthie, Treas.
EIN: 382697079

770
Marcella L. Hamar Scholarship
P.O. Box 380
Dollar Bay, MI 49922

Reorganized as a private foundation in 2003.
Grantmaker type: Independent foundation.
Financial data (yr. ended 12/31/05): Assets, $13,756 (M); expenditures, $604; total giving, $0; qualifying distributions, $0.
Purpose and activities: Provides scholarships for higher education for selected graduates of Chassell High School, Michigan.
Type of support: Scholarships—to individuals.
Limitations: Giving limited to residents of Chassell, MI.
Trustee: Douglas Hamar.
EIN: 382314909

771
James & Cleo Hamilton Family Charitable Trust
c/o James L. Hamilton
758 Longfellow
Detroit, MI 48202

Established in 1996 in MI.
Donors: Cleo V. Hamilton; James L. Hamilton.
Grantmaker type: Independent foundation.
Financial data (yr. ended 12/31/05): Assets, $43,603 (M); gifts received, $13,000; expenditures, $12,802; total giving, $12,793; qualifying distributions, $12,902; giving activities include $12,793 for 31 grants (high: $2,400; low: $40).
Fields of interest: Arts; Education; Human services.
Limitations: Applications not accepted. Giving primarily in MI. No grants to individuals.
Application information: Contributes only to pre-selected organizations.
Trustees: Cleo V. Hamilton; James L. Hamilton.
EIN: 383277537

772
Hammel-Delangis Scholarship Trust
c/o Northern Michigan Bank & Trust Co.
1502 W. Washington St.
Marquette, MI 49855-3195
Application address: c/o Scholarship Selection Comm., City of Iron Mountain School Dist., Iron Mountain, MI 49801

Established in 1987 in MI.
Grantmaker type: Independent foundation.
Financial data (yr. ended 9/30/05): Assets, $88,630 (M); expenditures, $6,486; total giving, $3,500; qualifying distributions, $3,500; giving activities include $3,500 for grants to individuals.
Purpose and activities: Scholarship awards to graduates of the Iron Mountain High School, MI, pursuing a baccalaureate degree in the health fields of optometry, medicine, or any similar course of instruction.
Fields of interest: Medical school/education.
Type of support: Scholarships—to individuals.
Limitations: Giving limited to Iron Mountain, MI.
Application information: Applicant must also submit ACT score, high school transcript and 3 letters of recommendation. Application form not required.
Deadline(s): Apr. 25
Trustee: Northern Michigan Bank & Trust Co.
EIN: 386513191

773
The Hammoud Foundation
26300 Telegraph Rd., 2nd Fl.
Southfield, MI 48034

Established in 1998 in MI.
Grantmaker type: Independent foundation.
Financial data (yr. ended 12/31/04): Assets, $104,000 (M); gifts received, $35,000; expenditures, $8,218; total giving, $7,113; qualifying distributions, $7,113; giving activities include $7,113 for grants.
Officer: Yasser T. Hammoud, Pres.
EIN: 383336881

774
Hampson Foundation
800 W. Long Lake Rd., Ste. 210
Bloomfield Hills, MI 48302-2058
Contact: Robert J. Hampson, Pres.
Application address: P.O. Box 250614, Franklin, MI 48025, tel.: (248) 626-3264

Established in MI.
Donors: Robert J. Hampson; Sadie G. Hampson.
Grantmaker type: Independent foundation.
Financial data (yr. ended 12/31/05): Assets, $70,901 (M); expenditures, $1,148,204; total giving, $1,142,185; qualifying distributions, $1,146,744; giving activities include $1,142,185 for 34 grants (high: $997,685; low: $500).
Purpose and activities: Giving primarily for education, particularly to a women's college; funding also for health associations and human services.
Fields of interest: Higher education; Education; Health organizations, association; Human services.
Type of support: General/operating support.
Limitations: Giving primarily in MI; some funding nationally.
Application information:
Initial approach: Letter
Deadline(s): Dec. 1
Officers: Robert J. Hampson, Pres. and Treas.; Jane J. Hampson Berca, V.P.; Sadie G. Hampson, V.P.
EIN: 386066115

775
Bernard and Dorothy Hamstra Charitable Foundation
629 St. Marks Ave.
Westfield, NJ 07090
Contact: Faith H. Bennett, Tr.

Established in 1995 in NJ.
Donor: Bernard Hamstra†.
Grantmaker type: Independent foundation.
Financial data (yr. ended 12/31/04): Assets, $2,448,401 (M); expenditures, $148,501; total giving, $130,495; qualifying distributions, $136,743; giving activities include $130,495 for 15 grants (high: $28,000; low: $2,500).
Purpose and activities: Giving primarily for Christian higher education, as well as Presbyterian churches and organizations; giving also for general mission activities.
Fields of interest: Higher education; Theological school/education; Food services; Human services; Christian agencies & churches; Protestant agencies & churches.
Limitations: Giving primarily in Grand Rapids, MI, and NJ. No support for political organizations. No grants to individuals.
Application information: Application form required.
Initial approach: Letter requesting application form
Deadline(s): None
Trustees: Faith H. Bennett; John K. Bennett; Frances K. Hamstra.
Number of staff: None.
EIN: 223285822
Selected grants: The following grants were reported in 2003.
$28,000 to Calvin College, Grand Rapids, MI.
$26,481 to Presbyterian Church, Westfield, NJ. 2 grants: $21,481, $5,000 to Nursery School

$16,800 to Calvin Theological Seminary, Grand Rapids, MI.
$10,000 to Habitat for Humanity International, Americus, GA.
$10,000 to Zuni Christian Mission School, Zuni, NM.
$5,000 to Creston Christian School, Grand Rapids, MI.
$5,000 to Eastern Christian School Association, North Haledon, NJ.
$2,500 to Christian Appalachian Project, Lancaster, KY.
$2,000 to Grandville Christian School, Grandville, MI.

776
The Hamzavi Foundation
831 Hidden Pine
Bloomfield Hills, MI 48304

Established in 1995 in MI.
Donor: S.L. Husain Hamzavi.
Grantmaker type: Independent foundation.
Financial data (yr. ended 12/31/05): Assets, $230,818 (M); gifts received, $200; expenditures, $46,514; total giving, $39,625; qualifying distributions, $39,625; giving activities include $39,625 for grants.
Fields of interest: Education; Islam.
Type of support: General/operating support.
Limitations: Applications not accepted. Giving primarily in MI. No grants to individuals.
Application information: Contributes only to pre-selected organizations.
Directors: Aquela F. Hamzavi; S.L. Husain Hamzavi.
EIN: 383217655

777
The Hamzeh Foundation
2630 Telegraph Rd., 2nd Fl.
Southfield, MI 48034

Established in 1999.
Grantmaker type: Independent foundation.
Financial data (yr. ended 12/31/05): Assets, $198,341 (M); gifts received, $12,500; expenditures, $4,163; total giving, $2,700; qualifying distributions, $2,700; giving activities include $2,700 for grants.
Fields of interest: Human services.
Limitations: Applications not accepted. Giving primarily in MI. No grants to individuals.
Application information: Contributes only to pre-selected organizations.
Officer: Nancy Hamzeh, Pres.
EIN: 383497160

778
The Hancock Foundation
675 Robinson Rd.
P.O. Box 449
Jackson, MI 49204-0449 (517) 788-8600
Contact: James A. Hildreth, Tr.

Donor: Arline M. Hancock.
Grantmaker type: Independent foundation.
Financial data (yr. ended 11/30/04): Assets, $364,736 (M); expenditures, $35,000; total giving, $35,000; qualifying distributions, $35,000; giving activities include $35,000 for grants.

Fields of interest: Visual arts; Museums; Performing arts; Arts; Elementary/secondary education; Elementary school/education; Education; Human services; Roman Catholic federated giving programs; Roman Catholic agencies & churches; Religion.
Type of support: Building/renovation; Program development; Seed money; Matching/challenge support.
Limitations: Giving primarily in Jackson County, MI.
Application information:
 Initial approach: Letter
 Deadline(s): Oct. 1
 Board meeting date(s): Dec.
Trustees: Jack D. Bunce; James A. Hildreth; Robert H. Moore.
EIN: 386096275

779
Hands of Hope, Inc.
4265 Corporate Exchange Dr.
Hudsonville, MI 49426

Established in 2000 in MI.
Donor: Donald J. Koop.
Grantmaker type: Independent foundation.
Financial data (yr. ended 12/31/05): Assets, $68,117 (M); gifts received, $224,350; expenditures, $189,226; total giving, $175,925; qualifying distributions, $188,978; giving activities include $175,925 for 1 grant.
Fields of interest: International relief; Children/youth.
Limitations: Applications not accepted. Giving primarily in Vietnam; giving also in Mexico. No grants to individuals.
Application information: Contributes only to pre-selected organizations.
Officers and Directors:* Donald J. Koop, Pres.; J.P. Koop,* Secy.-Treas.; Robin Horder-Koop; Al Koop; Dan Koop; Jean Koop; Ray Koop; Ed Vanessendelft.
EIN: 383560968

780
Charles D. & Bessie L. Hannan 1991 Education Trust
c/o Wells Fargo Bank, N.A.
P.O. Box 63954
San Francisco, CA 94163

Established in 1992 in CA.
Grantmaker type: Independent foundation.
Financial data (yr. ended 12/31/05): Assets, $422,987 (M); expenditures, $26,334; total giving, $19,785; qualifying distributions, $19,785; giving activities include $19,785 for grants.
Fields of interest: Secondary school/education; Roman Catholic agencies & churches.
Limitations: Applications not accepted. Giving limited to CA and MI. No grants to individuals.
Application information: Contributes only to 6 pre-selected organizations.
Trustee: Wells Fargo Bank, N.A.
EIN: 330470165

781
Hannan Foundation
8383 Warwick Groves
Grand Blanc, MI 48439
Contact: Ahmad T. Hannan, Pres.

Established in 2002 in MI.
Donor: Ahmad Hannan.
Grantmaker type: Independent foundation.
Financial data (yr. ended 12/31/04): Assets, $31,012 (M); gifts received, $10,000; expenditures, $17,240; total giving, $15,000; qualifying distributions, $15,000; giving activities include $15,000 for grants.
Fields of interest: Human services.
Application information:
 Initial approach: Letter of inquiry
 Deadline(s): None
Officers: Ahmad Hannan, Pres. and Treas.; Samir Rifai, V.P. and Secy.
EIN: 383544600

782
The Bernice Hansen Charitable Foundation
2493 Pettis Ave. N.E.
Ada, MI 49301-9533

Established in 1997 in MI.
Donor: Bernice Hansen.
Grantmaker type: Independent foundation.
Financial data (yr. ended 12/31/05): Assets, $83,816 (M); gifts received, $1,631; expenditures, $505; total giving, $0; qualifying distributions, $0.
Purpose and activities: Giving primarily for a community church.
Fields of interest: Protestant agencies & churches.
Limitations: Applications not accepted. Giving primarily in Grand Rapids, MI. No grants to individuals.
Application information: Contributes only to pre-selected organizations.
Officer: Bernice Hansen, Pres.
EIN: 383386831

783
Jens and Maureen Hansen Charitable Foundation
1230 Monroe Ave. N.W.
Grand Rapids, MI 49505-4620 (616) 458-1414
Contact: Shirley Balk, Pres.

Donors: Jens Hansen Residuary Trust; Jens Hansen Marital Trust; M. Hansen Qualified Domestic Trust; Margaret M. Hansen Trust.
Grantmaker type: Independent foundation.
Financial data (yr. ended 12/31/05): Assets, $2,589,011 (M); expenditures, $123,739; total giving, $122,150; qualifying distributions, $122,150; giving activities include $122,150 for 12 grants (high: $40,000; low: $150).
Fields of interest: Museums; Higher education, college; Federated giving programs; Protestant agencies & churches.
Limitations: Giving primarily in Grand Rapids, MI.
Application information:
 Initial approach: Letter on organization's letterhead
 Deadline(s): None
Officers: Shirley Balk, Pres.; Steven Balk, Secy.-Treas.
Directors: James H. Balk; James H. Balk II; Martin Balk.
EIN: 383220087

784
The Hansen Charitable Foundation
5775 Stonebridge Dr. S.W.
Grandville, MI 49418-3240

Established in 1997 in MI.
Donors: Richard G. Hansen; Sandra E. Hansen.
Grantmaker type: Independent foundation.
Financial data (yr. ended 12/31/04): Assets, $403,526 (M); gifts received, $1,490; expenditures, $21,490; total giving, $20,000; qualifying distributions, $20,480; giving activities include $20,000 for grants.
Limitations: Applications not accepted. Giving primarily in Grand Rapids, MI. No grants to individuals.
Application information: Contributes only to pre-selected organizations.
Officers and Directors:* Richard G. Hansen,* Pres. and Treas.; Sandra E. Hansen,* V.P. and Secy.; Elizabeth A. Hansen; Richard R. Hansen.
EIN: 383350783

785
The Hanson Family Foundation
2900 S. State St., Ste. 5 E.
St. Joseph, MI 49085-0008

Established in 1997 in MI.
Donor: Merlin J. Hanson.
Grantmaker type: Independent foundation.
Financial data (yr. ended 12/31/05): Assets, $509,630 (M); expenditures, $4,885; total giving, $3,100; qualifying distributions, $3,100; giving activities include $3,100 for grants.
Limitations: Applications not accepted. Giving primarily in MI. No grants to individuals.
Application information: Contributes only to pre-selected organizations.
Officers: Merlin J. Hanson, Pres.; Deborah Craig, Secy.; Gail Mathews, Treas.
Directors: Carolyn Hanson; Greg Hanson; Scott Hanson.
EIN: 383030572

786
Harbor Beach Student Loan Fund Association
8118 Section Line Rd.
Harbor Beach, MI 48441-9436
Contact: Marilyn Ritchie, Treas.

Established in 1997 in MI.
Grantmaker type: Independent foundation.
Financial data (yr. ended 6/30/05): Assets, $46,856 (M); expenditures, $1,148; total giving, $1,000; qualifying distributions, $1,000; giving activities include $1,000 for grants.
Purpose and activities: Loans to graduates of Harbor Beach High School, MI.
Type of support: Student loans—to individuals.
Limitations: Giving limited to residents of the Harbor Beach, MI, area.
Application information: Application form required.
 Deadline(s): None
Officers: Beth Bowen, Pres.; Vickie Erdman, Secy.; Marilyn Ritchie, Treas.
EIN: 386091395

787
The Harden Foundation
P.O. Box 38216
Detroit, MI 48238-0216

Established in 2002 in MI.
Grantmaker type: Independent foundation.
Financial data (yr. ended 12/31/04): Assets, $118 (M); gifts received, $1,385; expenditures, $2,144; total giving, $250; qualifying distributions, $250; giving activities include $250 for grants.
Fields of interest: Human services.
Officer and Trustees: * Lisa M. Harden,* Secy.; Jean Harden; Maurice Harden.
EIN: 043701688

788
Charles Stewart Harding Foundation
111 E. Court St., Ste. 3D
Flint, MI 48502-1649 (810) 767-0136
Contact: Frederick S. Kirkpatrick

Established in 1963 in MI.
Donors: C.S. Harding Mott‡; C.S. Harding Mott II‡; Claire Mott White.
Grantmaker type: Independent foundation.
Financial data (yr. ended 6/30/05): Assets, $12,853,818 (M); expenditures, $583,461; total giving, $527,000; qualifying distributions, $531,670; giving activities include $527,000 for 16 grants (high: $250,000; low: $1,000).
Purpose and activities: Giving primarily for the arts.
Fields of interest: Media, television; Performing arts, music; Performing arts, orchestra (symphony); Arts; Human services.
Type of support: General/operating support; Continuing support; Annual campaigns; Scholarship funds.
Limitations: Giving primarily in Flint, MI. No grants to individuals.
Application information: Application form not required.
  Initial approach: Letter
  Deadline(s): None
  Board meeting date(s): Usually Oct.
  Final notification: Dec.
Officers and Trustees: * Claire Mott White,* Pres.; Paula M. Turrentine,* V.P.; C. Edward White, Jr., Secy.; William S. White,* Treas.
EIN: 386081208

789
Jennifer Howell Harding Foundation
2601 John R Rd.
Troy, MI 48083-2365
Contact: Jennifer Harding, Tr.

Established in 1999 in MI.
Donor: Don N. Howell.
Grantmaker type: Independent foundation.
Financial data (yr. ended 12/31/04): Assets, $130,578 (M); gifts received, $16,270; expenditures, $7,786; total giving, $7,100; qualifying distributions, $0; giving activities include $7,100 for grants.
Fields of interest: Protestant agencies & churches.
Application information: Application form not required.
  Initial approach: Letter
  Deadline(s): None

Trustees: Jennifer Harding; Michael Harding.
EIN: 586396643

790
The Harding Foundation
c/o MFO Management Co.
111 E. Court St., Ste. 3D
Flint, MI 48502-1649
Contact: Mark C. Turrentine, Exec. Dir.

Established in 1988 in MI.
Donor: C.S. Harding Mott Trust.
Grantmaker type: Independent foundation.
Financial data (yr. ended 6/30/05): Assets, $59,823,077 (M); gifts received, $30,000; expenditures, $2,657,016; total giving, $2,086,753; qualifying distributions, $2,324,893; giving activities include $2,086,753 for 24 grants (high: $750,000; low: $4,570).
Purpose and activities: Giving primarily to organizations which are dedicated to supporting or contributing to the cause of Christian Science.
Fields of interest: Museums (history); Education, early childhood education; Christian agencies & churches.
Application information: Application form not required.
  Initial approach: Letter
  Copies of proposal: 1
  Deadline(s): None
Officers and Trustee: * Paula K. Turrentine, Chair. and Pres.; Paula M. Switzer, V.P. and Secy.; Milo I. Mott, V.P. and Treas.; Mark C. Turrentine,* Exec. Dir.
Number of staff: 1 full-time professional; 1 full-time support; 1 part-time support.
EIN: 382849003

791
The George Harding Scholarship Fund
c/o Bodman LLP
229 Court St.
P.O. Box 405
Cheboygan, MI 49721 (231) 627-8000
Contact: Lloyd C. Fell, Tr.

Grantmaker type: Independent foundation.
Financial data (yr. ended 12/31/05): Assets, $54,424 (M); gifts received, $10,357; expenditures, $30,697; total giving, $16,000; qualifying distributions, $16,000; giving activities include $16,000 for 16 grants to individuals (high: $1,000; low: $1,000).
Purpose and activities: Scholarship awards to Michigan residents, who are full time students, enrolled in a four-year Michigan college or university, pursuing a finance-related degree. Scholarships are only available for the senior year of college, or first year of graduate school.
Fields of interest: Business school/education; Economics.
Type of support: Scholarships—to individuals.
Limitations: Giving limited to residents of MI.
Application information: Application form required.
  Deadline(s): None
Trustees: Lloyd C. Fell; Gregory J. Hofbauer; Donald B. Jeffery, Jr.; Gerald A. Johnson; James C. Kurt; Mary D. Naz; Lawrence J. Sauter.
EIN: 382527040

792
Harlan Foundation
7769 Clearwater Dr.
Williamsburg, MI 49690-9579
Contact: John M. Harlan, Chair.; Glenn Lowenstein, Secy.-Treas.

Grantmaker type: Independent foundation.
Financial data (yr. ended 12/31/05): Assets, $1,295,262 (M); expenditures, $62,766; total giving, $58,000; qualifying distributions, $60,664; giving activities include $58,000 for 19 grants (high: $10,000; low: $1,000).
Purpose and activities: Giving primarily for education.
Fields of interest: Arts; Higher education; Education; Zoos/zoological societies; Boy scouts; Youth development, business; Community development.
Limitations: Giving primarily in MI; some giving also in PA and WV. No grants to individuals.
Application information:
  Initial approach: Letter
  Deadline(s): None
Officers and Trustees: * John M. Harlan,* Chair. and Pres.; William R. Patterson,* V.P.; Glenn Lowenstein,* Secy.-Treas.
EIN: 386041516

793
Lewis G. Harmon Foundation
300 Park St., Ste. 265
Birmingham, MI 48009-3413

Established in 1998 in MI.
Donor: Lewis G. Harmon.
Grantmaker type: Independent foundation.
Financial data (yr. ended 12/31/05): Assets, $3,106 (M); gifts received, $1,000; expenditures, $755; total giving, $0; qualifying distributions, $0.
Limitations: Giving primarily in Detroit, MI.
Officers and Directors: * Lewis G. Harmon,* Pres.; Charles J. Carson,* V.P. and Secy.; James C. Carson,* V.P.; Gary C. Holvick,* Treas.
EIN: 383416481

794
Harmony Chapel Missionary Church Testamentary Trust
c/o Donald R. France
P.O. Box 247
Marcellus, MI 49067-0247

Established in MI.
Grantmaker type: Independent foundation.
Financial data (yr. ended 12/31/04): Assets, $39,563 (M); expenditures, $5,303; total giving, $4,200; qualifying distributions, $4,751; giving activities include $4,200 for 1 grant.
Purpose and activities: Support only for the Harmony Chapel Missionary Church, MI.
Fields of interest: Christian agencies & churches.
Limitations: Applications not accepted. Giving limited to Marcellus, MI. No grants to individuals.
Application information: Contributes only to a pre-selected organization.
Trustee: Donald R. France.
EIN: 382866911

795
Georgine M. Harper Charitable Trust
(formerly George E. & Georgine M. Harper Charitable Trust)
c/o Comerica Bank
P.O. Box 75000
Detroit, MI   48275

Established in 1986 in NC.
Donors: George E. Harper†; Georgine M. Harper†.
Grantmaker type: Independent foundation.
Financial data (yr. ended 12/31/05): Assets, $1,109,812 (M); expenditures, $57,542; total giving, $36,000; qualifying distributions, $36,000; giving activities include $36,000 for grants.
Fields of interest: Higher education; Protestant agencies & churches.
Type of support: General/operating support; Scholarship funds.
Limitations: Applications not accepted. Giving limited to NC. No grants to individuals.
Application information: Contributes only to pre-selected organizations.
Trustee: Comerica Bank.
EIN: 566259626

796
David Holmden Harris and Anne Wells Harris Charitable Foundation
7433 Palm Dr.
Spring Lake, MI   49456

Established in 1997 in FL.
Donor: David H. Harris.
Grantmaker type: Independent foundation.
Financial data (yr. ended 12/31/05): Assets, $9,000 (M); gifts received, $9,430; expenditures, $479; total giving, $0; qualifying distributions, $0.
Limitations: Applications not accepted. No grants to individuals.
Application information: Contributes only to pre-selected organizations.
Trustees: Carolyn A. Gillotte; Peter A. Harris; Robert W. Harris.
EIN: 656223797

797
The Harris Family Foundation
190 S. LaSalle St., Ste. 3100
Chicago, IL   60603-3441
Contact: John D. Marshall, Tr.

Established in 1999 in IL.
Donor: Charles U. Harris.
Grantmaker type: Independent foundation.
Financial data (yr. ended 12/31/03): Assets, $318,284 (M); expenditures, $204,043; total giving, $200,000; qualifying distributions, $200,000; giving activities include $200,000 for 1 grant.
Fields of interest: Environment, natural resources.
Limitations: Applications not accepted. Giving in the U.S., with emphasis on AZ and MI. No grants to individuals.
Application information: Contributes only to pre-selected organizations.
Trustees: Jack C. Harris; John D. Marshall; Diana H. Melvin.
EIN: 364333755

798
Mort & Brigitte Harris Foundation
(formerly Harris Foundation)
36800 Woodward Ave., Ste. 100
Bloomfield Hills, MI   48304-0916
Contact: Morton E. Harris, Tr.

Established in 1983 in MI.
Donor: Brigitte P. Harris Charitable Lead Trust.
Grantmaker type: Independent foundation.
Financial data (yr. ended 5/31/05): Assets, $3,327,746 (M); gifts received, $1,000; expenditures, $118,961; total giving, $97,635; qualifying distributions, $97,635; giving activities include $97,635 for grants.
Purpose and activities: Giving primarily for religious welfare organizations, including a Jewish welfare fund; giving also for health associations and medical research, hospitals, education, and family services.
Fields of interest: Performing arts, orchestra (symphony); Education; Health care; Human services; Family services; Jewish federated giving programs.
Limitations: Applications not accepted. Giving primarily in MI. No grants to individuals.
Application information: Contributes only to pre-selected organizations.
Trustees: Brigitte P. Harris; Morton E. Harris.
EIN: 382499405

799
Mabel H. Harris Trust
c/o Comerica Bank
P.O. Box 75000
Detroit, MI   48275
Application address: c/o Thomas Mitchell, Trust Off., Comerica Bank, 245 W. Michigan, Jackson, MI 49201

Donor: Mabel M. Harris†.
Grantmaker type: Independent foundation.
Financial data (yr. ended 12/31/05): Assets, $580,999 (M); expenditures, $44,480; total giving, $34,000; qualifying distributions, $34,000; giving activities include $34,000 for grants.
Purpose and activities: Giving primarily for health and social services.
Fields of interest: Museums; Health care; Human services.
Limitations: Giving limited to Jackson County and the south central MI, area. No grants to individuals.
Application information:
   Initial approach: Letter
   Deadline(s): None
Trustees: Philip J. Curtis; Comerica Bank.
EIN: 386145296

800
Vera Marie Hart Irrevocable Trust
c/o Comerica Bank
P.O. Box 75000, 3302
Detroit, MI   48275

Grantmaker type: Independent foundation.
Financial data (yr. ended 12/31/05): Assets, $2,177,599 (M); expenditures, $729,719; total giving, $699,718; qualifying distributions, $699,718; giving activities include $699,718 for 6 grants (high: $279,887; low: $17,493).
Fields of interest: Higher education; Theological school/education; Protestant agencies & churches.

Limitations: Applications not accepted. Giving limited to River Forest, IL, Detroit, MI, Altenburg and St. Louis, MO, and Watertown, WI. No grants to individuals.
Application information: Contributes only to pre-selected organizations specified in the trust instrument.
Trustee: Comerica Bank.
EIN: 386705201

801
The Hartmann Foundation, Inc.
500 Woodward Ave., Ste. 2500
Detroit, MI   48226

Established in 1994 in MI.
Grantmaker type: Independent foundation.
Financial data (yr. ended 12/31/05): Assets, $1,027,806 (M); expenditures, $120,089; total giving, $104,250; qualifying distributions, $104,250; giving activities include $104,250 for 24 grants (high: $30,100; low: $500).
Fields of interest: Arts education; Arts; Higher education; Education; Cancer research.
Type of support: General/operating support.
Limitations: Applications not accepted. No grants to individuals.
Application information: Contributes only to pre-selected organizations.
   Board meeting date(s): Varies
Officers: E. Jan Hartmann, Pres.; Curtis J. DeRoo, Secy.; Patricia C. Hartmann, Treas.
Directors: Carolyn Hartmann; Karin Hartmann; Paul Hartmann.
EIN: 383199761

802
Alice Kales Hartwick Foundation
c/o Gregory V. Dicenso
840 W. Long Lake Rd., Ste. 200
Troy, MI   48098-6358
Contact: Peter A. Dow, Secy.-Treas.
Application address: 191 Ridge Rd., Grosse Pointe Farms, MI 48236, tel.: (313) 886-1424

Donor: Alice Kales Hartwick Unitrust.
Grantmaker type: Independent foundation.
Financial data (yr. ended 12/31/04): Assets, $1,807,770 (M); gifts received, $126,397; expenditures, $314,521; total giving, $276,000; qualifying distributions, $294,956; giving activities include $276,000 for 32 grants (high: $30,000; low: $1,000).
Purpose and activities: Giving primarily for arts and culture, education, and human services.
Fields of interest: Arts, association; Visual arts, ceramic arts; Performing arts; Performing arts, orchestra (symphony); Arts; Libraries (public); Education; Zoos/zoological societies; Human services; Community development; Federated giving programs.
Limitations: Giving primarily in Detroit, MI.
Application information: Application form not required.
   Initial approach: Proposal
   Deadline(s): None
Officers and Trustees:* Frank J. Sladen, Jr.,* Pres.; Carl M. Eckert,* V.P.; Peter A. Dow, Secy.-Treas.
EIN: 382248118

803
The Harvest Foundation
900 Fifth Third Ctr.
111 Lyon St. N.
Grand Rapids, MI 49503-2487 (616) 752-2000
Contact: Geraldine L. Anderson, Pres.
Application address: 3278 Roosevelt Rd.,
Muskegon, MI 49441, tel.: (616) 780-4257

Established in 1985 in MI.
Donor: Thomas Seyferth‡.
Grantmaker type: Independent foundation.
Financial data (yr. ended 12/31/05): Assets,
$269,002 (M); expenditures, $20,805; total giving,
$15,000; qualifying distributions, $15,000; giving
activities include $15,000 for grants.
Fields of interest: Foundations (community).
Limitations: Giving primarily in MI. No grants to
individuals.
Application information:
   Initial approach: Letter
   Deadline(s): None
Officers: Geraldine L. Anderson, Pres.; Donald F.
Seyferth, V.P.; Roger H. Oetting, Secy.-Treas.
EIN: 382642065

804
Harvey Memorial Foundation
300 St. Andrews Rd.
Saginaw, MI 48638-5977 (989) 790-3908
Contact: Albert S. Harvey, Pres.

Established in MI.
Grantmaker type: Independent foundation.
Financial data (yr. ended 12/31/05): Assets,
$284,184 (M); expenditures, $18,859; total giving,
$14,250; qualifying distributions, $14,250; giving
activities include $14,250 for grants.
Fields of interest: Family services; Human services.
Limitations: Giving primarily in Saginaw, MI.
Application information:
   Initial approach: Letter
   Deadline(s): None
Officers: Albert S. Harvey, Pres. and Treas.;
Katherine Almirall, V.P. and Secy.
Directors: Thomas C. Harvey, Jr.; William L. Harvey.
EIN: 386072427

805
Hasey Foundation, Inc.
262 Commercial Blvd.
Lauderdale By The Sea, FL 33308-4439
Contact: Robert J. Fredrikson
Application address: 1877 S. Federal Hwy., Ste.
202, Boca Raton, FL 33432

Established in 1998 in FL.
Grantmaker type: Independent foundation.
Financial data (yr. ended 12/31/04): Assets,
$967,846 (M); expenditures, $53,403; total giving,
$52,500; qualifying distributions, $52,500; giving
activities include $52,500 for grants.
Fields of interest: Education; Medical research;
Christian agencies & churches; Roman Catholic
agencies & churches.
Type of support: General/operating support.
Limitations: Giving primarily in FL; some giving also
in MI and NY. No grants to individuals.
Application information:
   Initial approach: Typewritten letter
   Deadline(s): None

Officers and Directors:* Regina M. Hasey,* Pres.;
Catherine Seydel,* V.P.; Martin J. Hasey,* Secy.
EIN: 591851950

806
Hastings Mutual Insurance Company Charitable Foundation
404 E. Woodlawn Ave.
Hastings, MI 49058

Established in 2004 in MI.
Donor: Hastings Mutual Insurance Co.
Grantmaker type: Independent foundation.
Financial data (yr. ended 12/31/04): Assets,
$1,000,021 (M); gifts received, $1,000,000;
expenditures, $0; total giving, $0; qualifying
distributions, $0.
Limitations: Applications not accepted. No grants to
individuals.
Application information: Contributes only to
pre-selected organizations.
Officers: William H. Wallace, Pres.; Michael W.
Puerner, Secy.; Joseph J. Babiak, Jr., Treas.
Directors: Mark Kolanowski; Bruce Osterink; James
Toburen; James Wiswell.
EIN: 202031029

807
Hauenstein Foundation
3739 Cook Valley Blvd. S.E.
Grand Rapids, MI 49548

Established in 1996 in MI.
Donors: Ralph Hauenstein; Karla Hauenstein; Mary
Gerzanick‡.
Grantmaker type: Independent foundation.
Financial data (yr. ended 12/31/05): Assets,
$1,367,789 (M); expenditures, $425,546; total
giving, $424,383; qualifying distributions,
$424,383; giving activities include $424,383 for 26
grants (high: $52,000; low: $1,000).
Fields of interest: Museums; Human services;
Foundations (private grantmaking).
Limitations: Applications not accepted. Giving
primarily in Grand Rapids, MI. No grants to
individuals.
Application information: Contributes only to
pre-selected organizations.
Officer: Ralph Hauenstein, Pres.
Director: William F. Roth.
EIN: 382898214

808
James & Catherine Haveman Family Foundation
(also known as Haveman Family Foundation, Inc.)
5069 S. Quail Crest Dr. S.E.
Grand Rapids, MI 49546-7507 (616) 975-3416
Contact: James Haveman, Dir.

Established in 1998 in MI.
Donor: Catherine Haveman.
Grantmaker type: Independent foundation.
Financial data (yr. ended 12/31/05): Assets,
$531,310 (M); expenditures, $34,718; total giving,
$23,400; qualifying distributions, $23,400; giving
activities include $23,400 for grants.
Purpose and activities: Giving primarily for Christian
religious counseling and outreach, international
relief, and to Christian churches and schools.

Fields of interest: Education; Animal welfare;
Human services; International relief; Christian
agencies & churches; Economically disadvantaged.
Limitations: Giving limited to MI.
Application information:
   Initial approach: Letter or proposal
   Deadline(s): Aug. 31
Directors: Barbara Haveman; Catherine Haveman;
James Haveman.
EIN: 383419761

809
Havirmill Foundation, Inc.
(formerly Katherine P. & Jerry L. Miller Foundation)
3505 Greenleaf Blvd.
Kalamazoo, MI 49008

Established in 1984 in MI.
Grantmaker type: Independent foundation.
Financial data (yr. ended 12/31/05): Assets,
$118,619 (M); expenditures, $150,068; total
giving, $142,917; qualifying distributions,
$142,917; giving activities include $142,917 for 20
grants (high: $10,000; low: $100).
Fields of interest: Performing arts; Performing arts,
orchestra (symphony); Higher education; Medical
research; Human services; American Red Cross;
YM/YWCAs & YM/YWHAs; Federated giving
programs; Christian agencies & churches.
Limitations: Applications not accepted. Giving
primarily in Kalamazoo, MI. No grants to individuals.
Application information: Contributes only to
pre-selected organizations.
Officers: Jerry L. Miller, Pres. and Treas.; Kenneth
V. Miller, V.P. and Secy.
EIN: 382480744
Selected grants: The following grants were reported
in 2003.
$55,667 to Western Michigan University
   Foundation, Kalamazoo, MI.
$11,750 to Kalamazoo Symphony Orchestra,
   Kalamazoo, MI.
$11,000 to United Way, Greater Kalamazoo,
   Kalamazoo, MI.
$6,875 to YMCA of Kalamazoo, Kalamazoo, MI.
$5,000 to Kalamazoo Community Foundation,
   Kalamazoo, MI.
$5,000 to Northside Association for Community
   Development, Kalamazoo, MI.
$5,000 to Southwest Michigan First Corporation,
   Kalamazoo, MI.
$3,500 to Gryphon Place, Kalamazoo, MI.
$3,000 to Lakeside Treatment and Learning Center,
   Kalamazoo, MI.
$1,000 to University of Michigan, Ann Arbor, MI.

810
HCC Foundation
590 Woodland Ave.
Holland, MI 49424 (616) 399-9505
Contact: Ned Timmer, Tr.

Establishes in 2002 in MI.
Grantmaker type: Independent foundation.
Financial data (yr. ended 12/31/05): Assets,
$93,214 (M); gifts received, $32,440;
expenditures, $46,719; total giving, $45,832;
qualifying distributions, $45,832; giving activities
include $45,832 for grants.

Application information: Application form not required.

Deadline(s): None
Trustee: Ned Timmer.
EIN: 061660898

811
Heartland Foundation
c/o Fifth Third Bank
P.O. Box 630858
Cincinnati, OH   45263

Grantmaker type: Independent foundation.
Financial data (yr. ended 6/30/05): Assets, $463,078 (M); expenditures, $40,808; total giving, $35,617; qualifying distributions, $35,617; giving activities include $35,617 for grants.
Purpose and activities: Support only for the Heartland Consolidated Schools, MI.
Fields of interest: Education.
Limitations: Applications not accepted. Giving limited to Heartland, MI. No grants to individuals.
Application information: Contributes only to a pre-selected organization.
Trustee: Fifth Third Bank.
EIN: 386190071

812
Maurice and Virginia Hecht Scholarship Fund
c/o Citizens Bank Wealth Mgmt., N.A.
328 S. Saginaw St., M/C 002072
Flint, MI   48502   (866) 308-7878
Contact: Donna Sumbera, Trust Off., Citizens Bank, N.A.

Established in 1986 in MI.
Grantmaker type: Independent foundation.
Financial data (yr. ended 3/31/06): Assets, $191,077 (M); expenditures, $9,869; total giving, $6,000; qualifying distributions, $6,000; giving activities include $6,000 for grants to individuals.
Purpose and activities: Scholarship awards to residents of Burr Oak who are seniors at Burr Oak High School, MI.
Type of support: Scholarships—to individuals.
Limitations: Applications not accepted. Giving limited to residents of Burr Oak, MI.
Application information: Recipients are recommended by the superintendent and the principal of Burr Oak High School. Unsolicited requests for funds not accepted.
Trustee: Citizens Bank Wealth Management, N.A.
EIN: 382923150

813
The George and Lucile Heeringa Foundation
P.O. Box 9016
Holland, MI   49422-9016

Established in 1991 in MI.
Donor: Trendway Corp.
Grantmaker type: Independent foundation.
Financial data (yr. ended 12/31/04): Assets, $731,806 (M); expenditures, $37,419; total giving, $35,000; qualifying distributions, $35,000; giving activities include $19,000 for 6 grants (high: $6,000; low: $500), and $16,000 for 19 grants to individuals (high: $1,000; low: $250).

Purpose and activities: Giving primarily for education, including scholarships to western MI area high school students.
Fields of interest: Higher education; Education; Youth development.
Type of support: General/operating support; Scholarships—to individuals.
Limitations: Applications not accepted. Giving limited to western MI.
Application information: Unsolicited requests for funds not accepted.
Director: Harlan J. Sprik.
EIN: 383024217

814
The Hees Family Foundation
P.O. Box 458
Gaylord, MI   49734-0458
Contact: Ronald D. Hees, Pres.
Tel./FAX: (989) 939-8500

Established in 1997 in MI.
Donor: Ronald D. Hees.
Grantmaker type: Independent foundation.
Financial data (yr. ended 8/31/05): Assets, $452,737 (M); expenditures, $25,900; total giving, $23,000; qualifying distributions, $24,916; giving activities include $23,000 for 3 grants (high: $10,000; low: $5,000).
Fields of interest: Human services.
Limitations: Giving limited to MI. No grants to individuals.
Application information:
    Initial approach: Letter
    Deadline(s): Aug. 31
Officers: Ronald D. Hees, Pres.; Kathleen A. Hees, V.P.; Mildred M. McGuire, Secy.-Treas.
Directors: Daniel A. Hees; David G. Hees; Michael D. Hees.
EIN: 383368989

815
The Hehl Family Foundation
6935 Langle Ct.
Clarkston, MI   48346

Established in 1997 in MI.
Donor: Fred T. Hehl.
Grantmaker type: Independent foundation.
Financial data (yr. ended 12/31/05): Assets, $182,355 (M); expenditures, $17,632; total giving, $12,555; qualifying distributions, $12,555; giving activities include $12,555 for grants.
Limitations: Applications not accepted. Giving primarily in MI. No grants to individuals.
Application information: Contributes only to pre-selected organizations.
Officers: Fred T. Hehl, Pres.; Carol Lee Hehl, Secy.
EIN: 383348608

816
Helping Others Foundation
31555 W. Fourteen Mile Rd., Ste. 316
Farmington Hills, MI   48334

Established in 2004 in MI.
Grantmaker type: Independent foundation.
Financial data (yr. ended 12/31/04): Assets, $25,585 (M); gifts received, $25,259;

expenditures, $0; total giving, $0; qualifying distributions, $0.
Officers: Bruce Clayton, Pres.; Lisa Clayton, V.P.; Lori Lipsitz, Secy.-Treas.
EIN: 202017811

817
Helppie Family Charitable Foundation
5225 Auto Club Dr.
Dearborn, MI   48126
Contact: Susan M. Synor, Secy.-Treas.
Application address: c/o Susan M. Synor, Secy.-Treas., 17570 W. 12 Mile Rd., Southfield, MI 48076, tel.: (248) 386-8300

Established in 1997 in MI.
Donors: Richard Helppie; Richard D. Helppie Trust.
Grantmaker type: Independent foundation.
Financial data (yr. ended 12/31/04): Assets, $1,002,630 (M); gifts received, $89,873; expenditures, $23,043; total giving, $16,525; qualifying distributions, $16,525; giving activities include $16,525 for 15 grants (high: $7,850; low: $50).
Purpose and activities: Giving for organizations involved with the disadvantaged, medically impaired children, community improvement, and education.
Fields of interest: Education; Health care; Children, services; Community development; Protestant agencies & churches.
Limitations: Giving limited to MI. No support for private foundations. No grants to individuals.
Application information:
    Initial approach: Letter
    Deadline(s): None
Officers and Directors:* Richard D. Helppie, Jr.,* Pres.; Leslie S. Helppie,* V.P.; Susan M. Synor,* Secy.-Treas.
EIN: 383374687

818
The Ernest Hemingway Foundation, Inc.
c/o Fred Svoboda
2761 Roseland Ave.
East Lansing, MI   48823

Established in NY.
Grantmaker type: Independent foundation.
Financial data (yr. ended 12/31/04): Assets, $534,991 (M); gifts received, $14,420; expenditures, $96,162; total giving, $16,000; qualifying distributions, $89,816; giving activities include $16,000 for 16 grants to individuals (high: $7,500; low: $500).
Purpose and activities: Grant awards to American first-time novelists.
Fields of interest: Literature.
Type of support: Grants to individuals.
Limitations: Applications not accepted.
Application information: Unsolicited requests for funds not accepted.
Officers: James H. Meredith, Pres.; J. Gerald Kennedy, V.P.; Fred Svoboda, Treas.
Board Members: Susan Beegel; Jackson R. Bryer; Scott Donaldson; Hilary Justice; Linda Miller; Rena Sanderson.
EIN: 136195832

819
The John C. Hendry Foundation
40 Oak Hollow St., Ste. 120
Southfield, MI 48034-7470 (248) 353-1530

Established in 1997 in MI.
Grantmaker type: Independent foundation.
Financial data (yr. ended 12/31/05): Assets, $1,647,572 (M); expenditures, $120,122; total giving, $88,500; qualifying distributions, $88,500; giving activities include $88,500 for grants.
Fields of interest: Scholarships/financial aid; Human services; Christian agencies & churches.
Limitations: Applications not accepted. No grants to individuals.
Application information: Contributes only to pre-selected organizations.
Officers: John G. Gibbons, Pres.; Michael M. Wild, Treas.
EIN: 383246883

820
Keith S. & Marcelle M. Henley Foundation
307 Wildwood Ave.
Ann Arbor, MI 48103
Contact: Keith S. Henley, Pres.

Established in 1997 in MI.
Grantmaker type: Independent foundation.
Financial data (yr. ended 12/31/04): Assets, $14,141 (M); gifts received, $48,000; expenditures, $46,551; total giving, $45,000; qualifying distributions, $46,350; giving activities include $45,000 for 3 grants (high: $15,000; low: $15,000).
Purpose and activities: Giving limited to disaster and hardship relief, Jewish philanthropy, and medical research, with emphasis on gastroenterology.
Fields of interest: Health care; Digestive disorders research; Medical research; Children/youth, services; International relief.
International interests: Vietnam.
Type of support: Continuing support; Emergency funds; Conferences/seminars; Seed money; Fellowships; Research; Scholarships—to individuals; Exchange programs.
Application information: Application form required.
  Initial approach: Letter requesting application form
  Copies of proposal: 3
  Deadline(s): None
  Board meeting date(s): Apr.
  Final notification: Within 3 months
Officers and Directors:* Keith S. Henley,* Pres.; Marcelle M. Henley,* Secy.-Treas.; Roy H. Henley.
EIN: 383388570

821
Hennessee Floyd Foundation
6285 N. McKinley Rd.
Flushing, MI 48433

Established in 1989 in MI; funded in 1990.
Donors: Greg Floyd; Trina Floyd.
Grantmaker type: Independent foundation.
Financial data (yr. ended 12/31/05): Assets, $39 (M); gifts received, $19,027; expenditures, $19,033; total giving, $13,058; qualifying distributions, $13,058; giving activities include $13,058 for grants.

Limitations: Applications not accepted. Giving primarily in GA, IN, and MI. No grants to individuals.
Application information: Contributes only to pre-selected organizations.
Officers: Trina Floyd, Pres.; Greg Floyd, V.P.
Directors: Barbara Floyd; Clarence Floyd; Earline Hennessee; Maurice Hennessee.
EIN: 382908948

822
Jacob & Kate Henock Foundation
26788 Farmbrook Villa Dr.
Southfield, MI 48034-5707 (248) 827-1935
Contact: Mildred Grossman, Tr.

Grantmaker type: Independent foundation.
Financial data (yr. ended 12/31/05): Assets, $32,278 (M); expenditures, $7,954; total giving, $4,645; qualifying distributions, $4,645; giving activities include $4,645 for grants.
Application information:
  Initial approach: Letter
  Deadline(s): None
Trustees: Fred Grossman; Mildred Grossman.
EIN: 386519840

823
Paul B. Henry Foundation
16 Campau Cir. N.W.
Grand Rapids, MI 49501-0352 (616) 336-6000
Contact: Karen Henry Stokes, Pres.

Established in 1994 in MI.
Grantmaker type: Independent foundation.
Financial data (yr. ended 12/31/05): Assets, $295,057 (M); gifts received, $300; expenditures, $16,639; total giving, $15,600; qualifying distributions, $15,600; giving activities include $15,600 for 11 grants (high: $2,500; low: $300).
Fields of interest: Performing arts; Higher education; Human services.
Type of support: Continuing support; Endowments; Internship funds; Scholarship funds.
Limitations: Giving primarily in Grand Rapids, MI. No grants to individuals.
Application information: Application form not required.
  Initial approach: Letter
  Deadline(s): June 30
  Board meeting date(s): Fall
Officers and Directors:* Karen Henry Stokes,* Pres.; Jordan Henry, V.P.; Megan Henry, Secy.; Kara Henry,* Treas.; Hilary Snell.
EIN: 383158473

824
Elizabeth A. Herdegen Trust
c/o Comerica Bank
P.O. Box 75000
Detroit, MI 48275 (313) 222-9067
Application address: c/o Taylor Statten Camps, 59 Hoyle Ave., Toronto, Canada M4S 2X5, tel.: (416) 486-6959

Grantmaker type: Independent foundation.
Financial data (yr. ended 12/31/05): Assets, $178,966 (M); expenditures, $11,367; total giving, $8,500; qualifying distributions, $8,500; giving activities include $8,500 for grants to individuals.

Purpose and activities: Grants given to campers between the ages of 7 and 17 in financial need.
Type of support: Grants to individuals.
Application information: Application form required.
  Deadline(s): Feb. 15
Trustee: Comerica Bank.
EIN: 386461176

825
Heritage Mark Foundation
P.O. Box 980
East Lansing, MI 48826-0980

Established in 1968 in MI.
Donors: David R. Foote; Frederick C. Foote; Shirley A. Foote; Kenneth J. Foote; Marnie Foote; Steven M. Foote; Lynne Foote; Cheryl F. Groenendyke; First National Bancshares, Inc.; 1889 Bankcorp, Inc.
Grantmaker type: Independent foundation.
Financial data (yr. ended 9/30/05): Assets, $55,360,390 (M); gifts received, $2,990,953; expenditures, $8,080,706; total giving, $7,681,917; qualifying distributions, $7,897,888; giving activities include $7,681,917 for 136 grants (high: $3,200,500; low: $250; average: $1,000–$350,000).
Purpose and activities: Giving primarily for Christian agencies and churches, with emphasis on evangelism.
Fields of interest: Performing arts centers; Education, research; Health care, single organization support; Human services; Economics; Public policy, research; Christian agencies & churches.
Limitations: Applications not accepted. Giving on a national basis. No grants to individuals.
Application information: Contributes only to pre-selected organizations.
Officers: Shirley A. Foote, Chair.; Cheryl F. Groenendyke, Pres.; Barbara Shingleton, V.P.; Frederick C. Foote, Secy.-Treas.
Trustees: David R. Foote; Kenneth J. Foote; Steven M. Foote; Susan L. Foote; Rhonda F. Judy.
EIN: 237017100
Selected grants: The following grants were reported in 2004.
$1,652,200 to Rest Haven Homes, Grand Rapids, MI.
$1,145,000 to Cleveland Clinic Foundation, Cleveland, OH.
$260,000 to School of American Research, Santa Fe, NM.
$240,060 to Truth and Tidings Gospel Trust USA, Wadsworth, OH.
$193,400 to Christian Missions in Many Lands, Spring Lake, NJ.
$181,800 to Boston Trinity Academy, Brookline, MA.
$122,700 to Christian Workers Fellowship Fund, Kansas City, KS.
$112,350 to Navigators, The, Colorado Springs, CO.
$100,000 to Berachah Church, Houston, TX.
$100,000 to New School, New York, NY.

826
Stanley F. Herman Charitable Trust f/b/o Vicksburg Foundation
c/o Fifth Third Bank
P.O. Box 3636
Grand Rapids, MI 49501-3636

Established in MI.
Grantmaker type: Independent foundation.
Financial data (yr. ended 7/31/05): Assets, $1,043,494 (M); expenditures, $37,801; total giving, $26,895; qualifying distributions, $27,958; giving activities include $26,895 for grants.
Purpose and activities: Support only for the Vicksburg Foundation, Kalamazoo.
Fields of interest: Philanthropy/voluntarism, single organization support.
Type of support: General/operating support.
Limitations: Applications not accepted. Giving limited to Kalamazoo, MI. No grants to individuals.
Application information: Contributes only to a pre-selected organization.
Trustee: Fifth Third Bank.
EIN: 386567489

827
The F. B. Heron Foundation
100 Broadway, 17th Fl.
New York, NY 10005
Contact: Mary Jo Mullan, V.P., Progs.
URL: http://www.heronfdn.org

Established in 1992 in DE.
Grantmaker type: Independent foundation.
Financial data (yr. ended 12/31/05): Assets, $279,896,147 (M); expenditures, $19,043,843; total giving, $11,658,023; qualifying distributions, $17,157,532; giving activities include $11,623,340 for 293 grants (high: $200,000; low: $25; average: $25,000–$125,000), $34,683 for 39 employee matching gifts, $78,512 for foundation-administered programs and $3,383,834 for 8 loans/program-related investments (high: $500,000; low: $250,000).
Purpose and activities: The foundation focuses its grantmaking and mission-related investing on five wealth-creation strategies for low-income families and communities. These five areas are: 1) access to capital; 2) quality and affordable child care; 3) comprehensive community development; 4) enterprise development; and 5) home ownership. The foundation concentrates its support on organizations with a national focus and in some cases, regional focus where these organizations are advancing solutions that have broad application for Heron's Wealth Creation Strategies.
Fields of interest: Housing/shelter, home owners; Children, day care; Community development, neighborhood development; Community development, citizen coalitions; Economic development.
Type of support: General/operating support; Continuing support; Program development; Technical assistance; Program evaluation; Program-related investments/loans; Employee matching gifts; Matching/challenge support.
Limitations: Giving primarily in Appalachia; CA; Chicago, IL; MI; Kansas City, MO; Twin Cities, MN; the Mississippi Delta; NC; NJ; New York, NY; and TX. No grants to individuals, or for endowments or capital campaigns.
Publications: Application guidelines; Annual report (including application guidelines); Grants list; Occasional report.
Application information: Information is also available on the foundation's Web site. Videotapes, CDs, DVDs, etc. will not be accepted. Application form not required.
Initial approach: Letter of inquiry (2 - 3 pages)
Copies of proposal: 1

Deadline(s): None
Board meeting date(s): Quarterly
Final notification: 1 week to initial letter of inquiry; 4 weeks max to full proposal, if requested
Officers and Directors:* William M. Dietel,* Chair.; Sharon B. King,* Pres.; Mary Jo Mullan, V.P., Progs. and Secy.-Treas.; Patricia J. Kozu, V.P., Finance and Admin.; Luther M. Ragin, Jr., V.P., Investments; John Otterlei; Buzz Schmidt; Tom Tinsley.
Number of staff: 9 full-time professional; 1 part-time professional; 4 full-time support.
EIN: 133647019
Selected grants: The following grants were reported in 2004.
$300,000 to Calvert Social Investment Foundation, Bethesda, MD. To support National Rural Funders' Collaborative that seeks to expand resources available to low-income rural areas and improve the practice of rural grantmaking, payable over 2 years.
$250,000 to Delaware Valley Community Reinvestment Fund, Philadelphia, PA. For Public Policy and Program Assessment Department's efforts to track impact of Fund's lending and investments, payable over 2 years.
$250,000 to Enterprise Corporation of the Delta, Jackson, MS. For general support to improve access to capital that finances creation and expansion of commercial enterprises and home ownership in the Delta regions of Arkansas, Louisiana, and Mississippi, payable over 2 years.
$250,000 to Paraprofessional Healthcare Institute, Bronx, NY. For general support to expand and strengthen worker-owned enterprises in home health care industry, payable over 2 years.
$200,000 to Boston Community Capital, Boston, MA. For general support to increase access to capital for affordable housing, community facilities, and business start-ups and expansions to benefit low-income residents and low-income communities, payable over 2 years.
$200,000 to Low Income Investment Fund, San Francisco, CA. For general support to increase access to capital in low-income communities for strategies including home ownership and child care, payable over 2 years.
$200,000 to North Carolina Community Development Initiative, Raleigh, NC. For general support to strengthen capacity, impact, and sustainability of community development corporations in low-resource communities in North Carolina, payable over 2 years.
$150,000 to Associated Early Care and Education, Boston, MA. For general support to expand the number of nationally accredited programs serving low-income children in the metropolitan Boston area, payable over 2 years.
$150,000 to New School, New York, NY. For Capital Markets Access Project that provides technical assistance to community development corporations, community development finance institutions, and other nonprofits seeking to access private capital markets.
$150,000 to Shorebank Enterprise Group Pacific, Ilwaco, WA. For general support to provide financing and technical assistance for small-business development in low-income, coastal regions of the Pacific Northwest, payable over 2 years.

828
Heron Oaks Foundation
432 N. Saginaw St., Ste. 417
Flint, MI 48502

Established in 1999 in MI.
Grantmaker type: Independent foundation.
Financial data (yr. ended 12/31/05): Assets, $287,727 (M); expenditures, $15,999; total giving, $13,500; qualifying distributions, $13,500; giving activities include $13,500 for grants.
Fields of interest: Education; Environment; Health care.
Type of support: Building/renovation; Program development.
Limitations: Applications not accepted. Giving in the U.S. and Brazil. No grants to individuals.
Application information: Contributes only to pre-selected organizations.
Officers: Olivia P. Maynard, Pres.; Sten Karlstrom, Secy.; S. Olof Karlstrom, Treas.
Trustees: Kiersten DeKorne; Elizabeth Lund; Ben Maynard.
EIN: 383482525

829
Herrick Foundation
150 W. Jefferson Ave., Ste. 2500
Detroit, MI 48226
Contact: Todd W. Herrick, Pres.

Incorporated in 1949 in MI.
Donors: Ray W. Herrick†; Hazel M. Herrick†.
Grantmaker type: Independent foundation.
Financial data (yr. ended 9/30/05): Assets, $178,431,140 (M); expenditures, $10,321,013; total giving, $9,167,959; qualifying distributions, $9,295,006; giving activities include $9,167,959 for 37 grants (high: $2,000,000; low: $250; average: $5,000–$150,000).
Purpose and activities: Emphasis on higher education, including research grants, scholarship programs (made through college and postgraduate educational institutions, not individual scholarships), and capital funding; grants also for church support, youth, health and welfare agencies, hospitals, and libraries.
Fields of interest: Secondary school/education; Higher education; Hospitals (general); Health care; Human services; Children/youth, services; Aging, centers/services.
Type of support: General/operating support; Continuing support; Annual campaigns; Capital campaigns; Building/renovation; Equipment; Land acquisition; Endowments; Emergency funds; Program development; Professorships; Curriculum development; Scholarship funds; Research; Matching/challenge support.
Limitations: Giving primarily in MI; giving also in the New York Metropolitan area, Washington, DC, IN, MS, OH, OK, TN, and WI. No support for international organizations, or for domestic organizations for international programs. No grants to individuals.
Publications: Application guidelines.
Application information: Application form not required.
Initial approach: 1- to -3 page grant proposal letter
Copies of proposal: 1
Deadline(s): None
Board meeting date(s): Monthly
Final notification: By letter

Officers and Trustees: * Todd W. Herrick,* Chair., Pres. and Treas.; Kent B. Herrick,* V.P.; Michael A. Indenbaum,* Secy.
Number of staff: 1 part-time support.
EIN: 386041517
Selected grants: The following grants were reported in 2005.
$2,000,000 to Henry Ford Health System, Detroit, MI. 2 grants: $1,000,000 each (For Herrick Center for Translational Neuro-oncology and Neuroregeneration Research).
$2,000,000 to Heritage Foundation, DC. To establish Bernard and Barbara Lomas Fellow at Margaret Thatcher Center for Freedom.
$1,500,000 to Herrick Memorial Hospital Foundation, Tecumseh, MI. To renovate Herrick Birthing Center.
$1,000,000 to Chamber of Commerce of the United States, DC. For educational program, Creating a Competitive American Economy.
$1,000,000 to University of Michigan, Ann Arbor, MI. 2 grants: $500,000 to Kelsey Museum of Archeology (For National Endowment for Humanities Challenge Grant for Conservation Internship Program Endowment), $500,000 to Kelsey Museum of Archeology (For National Endowment for the Humanities Challenge Grant for Exhibits Preparator Endowment).
$250,000 to Clifford H Ted Rees Jr Scholarship Foundation, Arlington, VA. For Clifford H Ted Rees, Jr. Scholarship Fund.
$100,000 to Focus: Hope, Detroit, MI. For Machinist Training Institute program.
$100,000 to National Ovarian Cancer Coalition, Georgia Division, Buckhead, GA. For unrestricted support.

830
The Herrington-Fitch Family Foundation, Inc.
c/o Leslie Lee
204 River St.
P.O. Box 605
Elk Rapids, MI 49629

Established in 1996 in MI.
Donor: Leslie Lee.
Grantmaker type: Independent foundation.
Financial data (yr. ended 12/31/05): Assets, $2,800,463 (M); expenditures, $145,748; total giving, $139,050; qualifying distributions, $139,050; giving activities include $139,050 for 42 grants (high: $29,000; low: $100).
Purpose and activities: Giving for art and cultural programs, education, and nature conservation.
Fields of interest: Arts; Education; Environment, natural resources; Environment, land resources; Environment.
Type of support: General/operating support.
Limitations: Applications not accepted. Giving primarily in MI. No grants to individuals.
Application information: Contributes only to pre-selected organizations.
Officer: Leslie Lee, Pres.
EIN: 383331023

831
Myrtle E. & William G. Hess Charitable Trust
c/o JPMorgan Chase Bank, N.A.
P.O. Box 1308
Milwaukee, WI 53201
Contact: Matthew Wasmund
Application address: c/o JPMorgan Chase Bank, N.A., 611 Woodward Ave., Ste. MI1-8113, Detroit, MI 48226-3408, tel.: (313) 225-3454, FAX: (313) 225-3948

Established in 1984 in MI.
Donor: Myrtle E. Hess†.
Grantmaker type: Independent foundation.
Financial data (yr. ended 9/30/05): Assets, $7,877,329 (M); expenditures, $420,229; total giving, $390,000; qualifying distributions, $398,763; giving activities include $390,000 for 27 grants (high: $100,000; low: $5,000).
Purpose and activities: Giving only to Roman Catholic institutions and agencies located in Oakland County, MI, including Roman Catholic hospitals and schools, or to those institutions that received grants during the donor's lifetime or that were designated for support in donor's will.
Fields of interest: Elementary/secondary education; Child development, education; Education; Hospitals (general); Alcoholism; Recreation; Human services; Child development, services; Roman Catholic federated giving programs; Roman Catholic agencies & churches; Religion.
Type of support: General/operating support; Annual campaigns; Building/renovation; Endowments; Program development; Scholarship funds.
Limitations: Giving limited to Oakland County, MI.
Application information: Application form not required.
Initial approach: Proposal
Copies of proposal: 2
Deadline(s): Mar. 1
Board meeting date(s): Mar.
Trustees: Thomas W. Payne; JPMorgan Chase Bank, N.A.
EIN: 382617770
Selected grants: The following grants were reported in 2003.
$100,000 to Saint Patrick Catholic Church. For general support.
$45,000 to Angels Place, Southfield, MI. For general support.
$25,000 to Archdiocese of Detroit, Detroit, MI. For general support.
$20,000 to Dominican Sisters of Oxford, Oxford, MI. For general support.
$15,000 to Guest House, Lake Orion, MI. For general support.
$10,000 to Camp Sancta Maria Trust, Gaylord, MI. For general support.
$10,000 to Lighthouse of Oakland County, Pontiac, MI. For general support.
$10,000 to Marygrove College, Detroit, MI. For general support.
$10,000 to Saint Joseph Mercy Hospital, Ann Arbor, MI. For emergency center.
$5,000 to Academy of the Sacred Heart, Bloomfield Hills, MI. For after school learning center.

832
William G. and Myrtle E. Hess Charitable Trust
c/o JPMorgan Chase Bank, N.A.
P.O. Box 1308
Milwaukee, WI 53201
Application address: c/o JPMorgan Chase Bank, N.A., 1116 W. Long Lake Rd., Bloomfield Hills, MI 48302, tel.: (313) 225-3454

Established in 1969 in MI.
Donors: William Hess†; Myrtle Hess†.
Grantmaker type: Independent foundation.
Financial data (yr. ended 12/31/04): Assets, $3,823,069 (M); expenditures, $128,906; total giving, $108,500; qualifying distributions, $113,999; giving activities include $108,500 for 26 grants (high: $10,000; low: $1,000).
Fields of interest: Arts; Health care; Health organizations; Youth development; Youth, services.
Limitations: Giving limited to Oakland County, MI. No support for religious or political organizations. No grants to individuals.
Application information: Application form not required.
Initial approach: Proposal
Copies of proposal: 1
Deadline(s): None
Trustee: JPMorgan Chase Bank, N.A.
EIN: 386166831
Selected grants: The following grants were reported in 2003.
$10,000 to Oakland Family Services, Pontiac, MI.
$7,500 to Oakland Livingston Human Service Agency, Howell, MI. For expansion of computer training program.
$7,500 to Saint Joseph Mercy Oakland, Pontiac, MI.
$5,000 to Common Ground Sanctuary, Bloomfield Hills, MI.
$5,000 to Epilepsy Foundation of Michigan, Southfield, MI. For new educational and therapeutic art program for children with epilepsy.
$5,000 to Eton Academy, Birmingham, MI.
$5,000 to Lighthouse of Oakland County, Pontiac, MI.
$3,000 to Judson Center, Royal Oak, MI.
$3,000 to South Oakland Shelter, Royal Oak, MI.
$1,000 to Womens Survival Center of Oakland County, Bloomfield Hills, MI. For general operating support.

833
Frances Hess Scholarship Fund
c/o Fifth Third Bank
P.O. Box 3636
Grand Rapids, MI 49501
Application address: c/o Fifth Third Bank, Chris Lukas, 640 Pasquinelli Dr., Westmont, IL 60559

Established in 1995 in IL.
Donor: Frances P. Hess†.
Grantmaker type: Independent foundation.
Financial data (yr. ended 12/31/05): Assets, $334,362 (M); expenditures, $4,354; total giving, $0; qualifying distributions, $0.
Type of support: Scholarships—to individuals.
Application information:
Initial approach: Proposal
Deadline(s): May 1
Trustee: Fifth Third Bank.
EIN: 364006773

834
Hibbert Family Foundation
7425 Pelican Bay Blvd., Ste. 1404
Naples, FL 34108

Established in 1997 in FL.
Donors: Donald R. Hibbert; Marilyn V. Hibbert.
Grantmaker type: Independent foundation.
Financial data (yr. ended 11/30/05): Assets,
$262,899 (M); expenditures, $3,500; total giving,
$0; qualifying distributions, $0.
Purpose and activities: Giving primarily to a
business school and for education.
Fields of interest: Higher education; Student
services/organizations; Health care; Health
organizations, association; Christian agencies &
churches.
Type of support: General/operating support;
Scholarship funds.
Limitations: Applications not accepted. Giving
primarily in FL, MI, TX, and WI. No grants to
individuals.
Application information: Contributes only to
pre-selected organizations.
Trustees: Donald R. Hibbert; Marilyn V. Hibbert.
EIN: 656253128

835
The Stephen L. Hickman Family Foundation
2711 E. Maumee St.
Adrian, MI 49221 (734) 662-5726
Contact: Sally D. Hickman, V.P.

Established in 1997.
Donors: Sally D. Hickman; Stephen L. Hickman.
Grantmaker type: Independent foundation.
Financial data (yr. ended 12/31/04): Assets,
$1,200,539 (M); gifts received, $43,951;
expenditures, $53,727; total giving, $48,454;
qualifying distributions, $48,454; giving activities
include $48,454 for grants.
Purpose and activities: Giving primarily for youth
services, education and for health and human
services.
Fields of interest: Arts; Education; Environment;
Health care; Cancer research; Boys & girls clubs;
Human services; YM/YWCAs & YM/YWHAs;
Children/youth, services.
Type of support: Capital campaigns; Endowments;
Scholarships—to individuals.
Limitations: Giving in Adrian and Lenawee County,
MI.
Application information:
  Initial approach: Proposal
  Deadline(s): Apr. and Oct.
  Board meeting date(s): Annually in Oct.
Officers: Tracy L. Hickman, Pres.; Sally D. Hickman,
V.P. and Treas.; Stephanie L. Hickman, Secy.
Trustee: Stephen L. Hickman.
EIN: 383349206

836
Samuel J. Hicks Charitable Trust
c/o Comerica Bank
P.O. Box 75000, MC 3302
Detroit, MI 48275-3302

Established in 1997 in FL.
Grantmaker type: Independent foundation.

Financial data (yr. ended 12/31/05): Assets,
$1,549,780 (M); expenditures, $109,402; total
giving, $94,411; qualifying distributions, $94,411;
giving activities include $94,411 for grants.
Purpose and activities: Giving for 3 Episcopal
organizations.
Fields of interest: Protestant agencies & churches.
Limitations: Applications not accepted. Giving
limited to FL. No grants to individuals.
Application information: Contributes only to 3
pre-selected organizations.
Trustee: Comerica Bank.
EIN: 597039374

837
The Bobby Higginson Foundation
c/o Edward J. Hayes
2000 Market St., 10th Fl.
Philadelphia, PA 19103-3291

Established in 1998 in PA.
Donor: Bobby Higginson.
Grantmaker type: Independent foundation.
Financial data (yr. ended 12/31/05): Assets,
$2,245 (M); expenditures, $3; total giving, $0;
qualifying distributions, $0.
Fields of interest: Cancer; Children, services.
Limitations: Applications not accepted. Giving
primarily in MI. No grants to individuals.
Application information: Contributes only to
pre-selected organizations.
Officers: Bobby Higginson, Pres.; Edward J. Hayes,
Secy.
EIN: 232975350

838
Hildreth Foundation, Inc.
41 S. High St.
Columbus, OH 43215-3406
Contact: Mark Merkle, V.P.

Established in 1949.
Donor: Helen R. Davies.
Grantmaker type: Independent foundation.
Financial data (yr. ended 12/31/04): Assets,
$1,153,390 (M); expenditures, $92,535; total
giving, $50,670; qualifying distributions, $50,670;
giving activities include $50,670 for grants.
Purpose and activities: Giving for museums,
education, health, and the environment.
Fields of interest: Museums; Libraries (public);
Education; Environment, natural resources; Medical
care, rehabilitation; Cancer.
Type of support: Annual campaigns; General/
operating support.
Limitations: Giving primarily in Columbus, OH, and
MI. No grants to individuals.
Officers: Louis H. Sanford, Pres.; Louis Hildreth II,
V.P. and Secy.; Mark Merkle, V.P. and Treas.
EIN: 316026444

839
Arthur W. Hill Foundation
c/o Robert W. Gillett
1133 Willow Ln.
Northbrook, IL 60062

Established in IL.
Grantmaker type: Independent foundation.

Financial data (yr. ended 10/31/05): Assets,
$1,156,474 (M); expenditures, $61,907; total
giving, $44,545; qualifying distributions, $44,545;
giving activities include $44,545 for grants.
Fields of interest: Higher education; Hospitals
(general); Christian agencies & churches.
Limitations: Applications not accepted. Giving
primarily in IL and MI. No grants to individuals.
Application information: Contributes only to
pre-selected organizations.
Officers and Directors: * Robert W. Gillett,* Pres.;
Mary H. Gillett,* V.P.; Nancy Tefft,* V.P.; Doryce
Maher,* Secy.
EIN: 366050191

840
Robert D. Hill Foundation
10539 Whispering Brook N.W.
Grand Rapids, MI 49544-9535
Contact: Priscilla Hill Gregels

Grantmaker type: Independent foundation.
Financial data (yr. ended 12/31/05): Assets,
$118,583 (M); expenditures, $16,745; total giving,
$16,000; qualifying distributions, $16,000; giving
activities include $16,000 for grants.
Fields of interest: Elementary/secondary
education; Reproductive health, family planning;
Cerebral palsy; Federated giving programs.
Limitations: Giving primarily in Coopersville, MI. No
grants to individuals.
Application information:
  Initial approach: Letter
  Deadline(s): Oct. 31
Officers and Trustees: * Barbara Hill Newby,* Pres.;
Priscilla Hill Gregels,* V.P. and Secy.-Treas.
EIN: 386071614

841
Jack E. and Eleanor Cannon Hill Foundation
P.O. Box 864
Jackson, MI 49204-0864

Established in 1993 in MI.
Donor: Jack E. Hill.
Grantmaker type: Independent foundation.
Financial data (yr. ended 12/31/04): Assets,
$80,052 (M); expenditures, $3,611; total giving,
$2,500; qualifying distributions, $2,950; giving
activities include $2,500 for grants.
Fields of interest: Heart & circulatory research.
Type of support: Research.
Limitations: Applications not accepted. Giving
primarily in Ann Arbor, MI. No grants to individuals.
Application information: Contributes only to
pre-selected organizations.
Officers: Jack E. Hill, Pres. and Treas.; Eleanor C.
Hill, V.P. and Secy.
Directors: Patricia C. Haughton; Debra A. Jamieson;
David Lucas.
EIN: 383119249

842
Hiller Charitable Foundation
24359 Northwestern Hwy., Ste. 150
Southfield, MI 48075

Established in 2001 in MI.
Donor: James A. Hiller.

Grantmaker type: Independent foundation.
Financial data (yr. ended 12/31/04): Assets, $287,769 (M); gifts received, $25,000; expenditures, $22,404; total giving, $22,100; qualifying distributions, $22,100; giving activities include $22,100 for 2 grants (high: $12,100; low: $10,000).
Fields of interest: Higher education; ALS research.
Limitations: Applications not accepted. Giving primarily in MI. No grants to individuals.
Application information: Contributes only to pre-selected organizations.
Director: James A. Hiller.
EIN: 383615500

843
The Hilt Foundation
P.O. Box 5200
North Muskegon, MI   49445

Established in 1997 in MI.
Donor: George E. Hilt.
Grantmaker type: Independent foundation.
Financial data (yr. ended 12/31/05): Assets, $233,005 (M); expenditures, $53,790; total giving, $46,127; qualifying distributions, $46,127; giving activities include $46,127 for grants.
Fields of interest: Higher education; Human services; Community development.
Limitations: Applications not accepted. Giving primarily in MI. No grants to individuals.
Application information: Contributes only to pre-selected organizations.
Directors: Fred C. Culver, Jr.; Heather Hensell; David Hilt; George E. Hilt; Robert Hilt.
EIN: 383306839

844
Clarence and Jack Himmel Foundation
3000 Town Ctr., Ste. 2150
Southfield, MI   48075-1313

Established in 1975 in MI.
Donor: Clarence Himmel‡.
Grantmaker type: Independent foundation.
Financial data (yr. ended 10/31/05): Assets, $2,018,117 (M); expenditures, $125,418; total giving, $73,100; qualifying distributions, $73,100; giving activities include $73,100 for 21 grants (high: $7,500; low: $1,000).
Fields of interest: Arts; Education; Health care; Health organizations, association; Human services; Children/youth, services; Jewish agencies & temples.
Limitations: Giving primarily in MI, with emphasis on the greater Detroit metropolitan area. No grants to individuals.
Application information:
  Deadline(s): None
Officers: Robert A. Karbel, Pres. and Secy.; David Wallace, V.P.; Ronald A. Rothstein, Treas.
EIN: 510140773
Selected grants: The following grants were reported in 2003.
$16,000 to Hillel.
$10,500 to Childrens Center of Wayne County, Detroit, MI.
$10,000 to W T V S Detroit Educational Television, Detroit, MI.
$7,500 to Kadima Association for Jewish Residential Care, Southfield, MI.

$5,500 to Jewish Association for Residential Care.
$5,000 to Anti-Defamation League of Bnai Brith, Southfield, MI.
$5,000 to Common Ground.
$4,000 to Planned Parenthood of Southeast Michigan, Detroit, MI.
$3,500 to Yad Ezra, Oak Park, MI.
$2,500 to Saint Vincent and Sarah Fisher Center, Farmington Hills, MI.

845
Joy C. Hinson-Rider Foundation
136 E. Michigan Ave., Ste. 1201
Kalamazoo, MI   49007-3918   (269) 382-5800

Established in 1994 in MI.
Donor: Joy C. Hinson-Rider.
Grantmaker type: Independent foundation.
Financial data (yr. ended 12/31/05): Assets, $698,506 (M); expenditures, $37,032; total giving, $23,500; qualifying distributions, $30,341; giving activities include $23,500 for grants.
Fields of interest: Performing arts, music; Reproductive health, family planning; Population studies.
Limitations: Applications not accepted. Giving primarily in NJ, NM, and NY. No grants to individuals.
Application information: Contributes only to pre-selected organizations.
Officers and Trustees:* James S. Hilboldt,* Pres.; James C. Melvin,* V.P.; Loyal A. Eldridge III,* Secy.; David S. Kruis, Treas.
EIN: 383163729

846
The Hire Family Foundation
26 E. Main St., Ste. 2
Lexington, OH   44904   (419) 884-3522
Contact: Jackie Fulk

Established in 2003 in OH.
Donor: Phyllis F. Hire.
Grantmaker type: Independent foundation.
Financial data (yr. ended 12/31/05): Assets, $74,356 (M); gifts received, $150,000; expenditures, $169,687; total giving, $169,637; qualifying distributions, $169,637; giving activities include $169,637 for 10 grants (high: $78,000; low: $250).
Fields of interest: Performing arts, ballet; Health care; Salvation Army; Residential/custodial care, hospices.
Limitations: Giving primarily in Garfield and Pitkin counties, CO, Charlotte County, FL, Inverness Township, MI and Richland County, OH. No grants to individuals, or for operating expenses, debt reduction, capital campaigns, or endowments.
Application information: Application form required.
  Initial approach: Letter
  Deadline(s): July 31
  Final notification: Dec. 31
Officers and Directors:* Phyllis F. Hire,* Pres.; John S. Hire,* Secy.; Lawrence M. Wolf,* Treas.
EIN: 770590536

847
Ray & Peg Hirvonen Charitable Foundation
451 Lakewood Ln.
Marquette, MI   49855
Contact: Mark Hirvonen, Secy.

Established in 1993.
Donors: Ray Hirvonen; Peg Hirvonen.
Grantmaker type: Independent foundation.
Financial data (yr. ended 12/31/05): Assets, $1,928,977 (M); gifts received, $63,000; expenditures, $77,831; total giving, $76,200; qualifying distributions, $77,831; giving activities include $76,200 for grants.
Purpose and activities: Giving for youth, family services, and community service organizations.
Fields of interest: Higher education; Human services.
Limitations: Giving primarily in Marquette, MI. No grants to individuals.
Application information: Application form required.
  Initial approach: Letter
  Deadline(s): None
Officers: Linda Hirvonen, Pres.; Matt Hirvonen, V.P.; Mark Hirvonen, Secy.; Ray Hirvonen, Treas.
EIN: 311388018

848
His Work Private Foundation
333 Bridge St. N.W., Ste. 810
Grand Rapids, MI   49504

Established in 1998 in MI.
Donor: Gary Granger.
Grantmaker type: Independent foundation.
Financial data (yr. ended 11/30/05): Assets, $403,677 (M); expenditures, $2,502; total giving, $0; qualifying distributions, $0.
Purpose and activities: Support for Mission India, headquartered in Grand Rapids, Michigan.
Fields of interest: International development; Christian agencies & churches.
International interests: India.
Limitations: Applications not accepted. Giving limited for the benefit of India. No grants to individuals.
Application information: Contributes only to a pre-selected organization.
Officer: Gary Granger, Pres.
EIN: 383444500
Selected grants: The following grants were reported in 2003.
$215,000 to Mission India, Grand Rapids, MI. 3 grants: $15,000 (For Bible teacher's training school), $100,000 (For National Plan), $100,000 (For Tamil Nadu State).

849
The Hitchens Family Foundation
10161 E. Pickwick Ct.
Traverse City, MI   49684

Established in 2001 in MI.
Donor: Jessie Z. Hitchens.
Grantmaker type: Independent foundation.
Financial data (yr. ended 11/30/05): Assets, $243,360 (M); gifts received, $25,670; expenditures, $20,638; total giving, $18,000; qualifying distributions, $18,000; giving activities include $18,000 for grants.
Fields of interest: Human services.
Limitations: Applications not accepted. Giving primarily in Traverse City, MI. No grants to individuals.
Application information: Contributes only to pre-selected organizations.

Officers: Thomas E. Hitchens, Pres.; J. Daniel Hitchens, Secy.; Julie M. Paron, Treas.
EIN: 383577617

850
The Hodgkins Family Fund, Inc.
1274 Westwood Dr.
Birmingham, MI   48009

Established in 1999 in MI.
Donor: Charles D. Hodgkins.
Grantmaker type: Independent foundation.
Financial data (yr. ended 12/31/05): Assets, $94,064 (M); expenditures, $6,927; total giving, $5,450; qualifying distributions, $5,450; giving activities include $5,450 for grants.
Limitations: Applications not accepted. Giving primarily in MI. No grants to individuals.
Application information: Contributes only to pre-selected organizations.
Officers: Charles D. Hodgkins, Pres.; Shelby S. Hodgkins, Secy.
Directors: Charles D. Hodgkins III; Whitney S. Hodgkins.
EIN: 383503443

851
Helmut and Ellen Hof Charitable Foundation
3452 Charlevoix Dr. S.E.
Grand Rapids, MI   49546
Contact: Helmut Hof, Pres.

Established in 1989 in MI.
Grantmaker type: Independent foundation.
Financial data (yr. ended 12/31/05): Assets, $43,403 (M); gifts received, $10,000; expenditures, $6,523; total giving, $6,170; qualifying distributions, $6,170; giving activities include $6,170 for grants.
Limitations: Giving primarily in MI.
Application information:
  Initial approach: Letter or proposal
  Deadline(s): None
Officers: Helmut Hof, Pres. and Treas.; Ellen Hof, Secy.
EIN: 382920772

852
Holcomb Family Foundation
P.O. Box 60
Mayville, MI   48744

Established in 1986 in VA.
Grantmaker type: Independent foundation.
Financial data (yr. ended 12/31/05): Assets, $261,386 (M); expenditures, $6,048; total giving, $5,000; qualifying distributions, $5,000; giving activities include $5,000 for grants.
Limitations: Applications not accepted. Giving primarily in Winchester, VA. No grants to individuals.
Application information: Contributes only to pre-selected organizations.
Officer: Mary Jo Stout, Pres. and Secy.-Treas.
Directors: Keith A. Holcomb; Steven J. Holcomb.
EIN: 541386760

853
James and Lynelle Holden Fund
802 E. Big Beaver Rd.
Troy, MI   48083-1404   (313) 962-8710
Contact: Donald J. Miller, Pres.
FAX: (313) 962-5792;
E-mail: hmmlaw@sbcglobal.net

Incorporated in 1941 in MI.
Donors: James S. Holden†; Lynelle A. Holden†.
Grantmaker type: Independent foundation.
Financial data (yr. ended 10/31/05): Assets, $3,529,893 (M); expenditures, $287,329; total giving, $154,000; qualifying distributions, $196,461; giving activities include $154,000 for 21 grants (high: $17,500; low: $2,000).
Purpose and activities: Support for medical research, including medical schools and children's hospitals, youth agencies, minority and underprivileged children, higher education, and cultural programs.
Fields of interest: Arts; Higher education; Hospitals (specialty); Medical research, institute; Children/ youth, services.
Type of support: General/operating support; Continuing support; Building/renovation; Equipment; Publication; Scholarship funds; Research; Matching/challenge support.
Limitations: Giving primarily in Macomb, Oakland, Washtenaw, and Wayne counties, MI; giving to colleges and universities throughout MI. No support for religious or ethnic organizations, or for disease-specific organizations. No grants to individuals, or for endowment funds; no loans.
Application information: Application form not required.
  Initial approach: Letter or proposal
  Copies of proposal: 1
  Deadline(s): None
  Board meeting date(s): Feb., May, Aug., and Nov.
  Final notification: Several weeks, or until the next board meeting
Officers and Trustees:* Donald J. Miller,* Pres.; Herbert E. Weston,* V.P. and Treas.; Ingrid O. Vernier, Secy.; Daniel T. Lis.
Number of staff: 3 part-time professional; 1 part-time support.
EIN: 386052154
Selected grants: The following grants were reported in 2003.
$25,150 to Boys and Girls Clubs of Southeastern Michigan, Farmington Hills, MI. For general support.
$10,000 to Detroit Zoological Society, Royal Oak, MI. For general support.
$10,000 to Michigan State University, East Lansing, MI. For general support.
$10,000 to University of Detroit Mercy, Detroit, MI. For general support.
$10,000 to University of Michigan, School of Law, Ann Arbor, MI. For general support.
$5,000 to Childrens Hospital of Michigan, Detroit, MI. For general support.
$5,000 to Detroit Institute of Arts, Detroit, MI. For general support.
$5,000 to Detroit Symphony Orchestra, Detroit, MI. For general support.
$5,000 to Michigan Opera Theater, Detroit, MI. For general support.
$5,000 to Wayne State University, School of Law, Detroit, MI. For general support.

854
The Holl Foundation
2911 E. Ten Mile Rd.
Warren, MI   48091

Established in 2001 in MI.
Donors: Dale S. Holl; Patricia M. Holl.
Grantmaker type: Independent foundation.
Financial data (yr. ended 12/31/05): Assets, $152,685 (M); gifts received, $50,000; expenditures, $25,118; total giving, $25,000; qualifying distributions, $25,000; giving activities include $25,000 for grants.
Purpose and activities: Support for the arts and a church.
Fields of interest: Arts; Christian agencies & churches.
Type of support: Building/renovation.
Limitations: Applications not accepted. Giving primarily in NC. No grants to individuals.
Application information: Contributes only to pre-selected organizations.
Officers: Dale S. Holl, Pres.; Patricia M. Holl, V.P.; Marina Meriggi-Gibbons, Secy.; Timothy P. Heacock, Treas.
EIN: 383558909

855
The Laura Ludington Hollenbeck Foundation
c/o Deloitte & Touche, LLP
3320 Ridgecrest Dr., Ste. 400
Midland, MI   48642   (989) 631-2370
Contact: Laura L. Hollenbeck, Pres.

Donor: John S. Ludington.
Grantmaker type: Independent foundation.
Financial data (yr. ended 12/31/05): Assets, $533,541 (M); gifts received, $43,740; expenditures, $27,233; total giving, $22,900; qualifying distributions, $22,900; giving activities include $22,900 for grants.
Purpose and activities: Giving primarily to a community foundation, and for health and human services.
Fields of interest: Health care; Human services; Foundations (community); Protestant agencies & churches.
Limitations: Giving primarily in MI.
Application information:
  Initial approach: Letter
  Deadline(s): None
Officers: Laura L. Hollenbeck, Pres.; Martyn T. Hollenbeck, V.P.; John S. Ludington, Treas.
EIN: 383323698

856
The Holley Foundation
c/o The Private Bank of Bloomfield Hills
38505 Woodward Ave., Ste. 1300
Bloomfield Hills, MI   48304
Contact: Stefanie Nesi
E-mail: george.holley@cox.net; Application address: c/o Rev. George M. Holley III, 1846 Heydon Ct., Henderson, NV 89014, e-mail: george.holley@att.net

Established in 1944 in MI.
Donor: George M. Holley†.
Grantmaker type: Independent foundation.

Financial data (yr. ended 12/31/05): Assets, $3,084,583 (M); expenditures, $197,148; total giving, $149,000; qualifying distributions, $164,785; giving activities include $149,000 for grants.
Purpose and activities: Supports education and various other programs for young people, primarily in southeastern MI. The foundation is interested in programs, other than bricks and mortar, which are imaginative and well-articulated and that can enable, enhance, or heal.
Fields of interest: Arts; Education; Human services; Children/youth, services.
Type of support: Endowments; Program development; Seed money.
Limitations: Giving primarily in southeastern MI.
Publications: Application guidelines.
Application information: Application form may be obtained from the foundation by e-mail. Application form required.
  Initial approach: E-mail using required form
  Copies of proposal: 1
  Deadline(s): Apr. 1
  Board meeting date(s): May and Nov.
  Final notification: About 2 months
Officers and Trustees:* Margaret E. Holley,* Pres.; Rev. George M. Holley III,* V.P. and Progs. Comm. Chair.; Gregg Kuehn, Jr.,* Secy.; Jack Kuehn, Treas. and Finance Comm. Chair.; Daane deVries; Barbara K. Frank; John C. Holley, Sr.; Stephen Holley; Lynn Krugman; Edward J. Miller; Margery H. Uihlein.
EIN: 386055168
Selected grants: The following grants were reported in 2004.
$31,000 to Student Mentor Partners, Harper Woods, MI. For administrative support.
$27,000 to Project SEED (Special Elementary Education for the Disadvantaged), Detroit, MI. 2 grants: $12,000 (For program support), $15,000 (For program support).
$15,000 to Big Brothers/Big Sisters of Detroit, Detroit, MI. For mentoring project in a Southeastern Village school.
$10,000 to Community Foundation for Southeastern Michigan, Detroit, MI.
$10,000 to Gleaners Community Food Bank, Detroit, MI. For the Kidsnack program in Southeastern Village schools.
$10,000 to National Conference for Community and Justice. For program support.
$10,000 to Santa Fe Symphony Orchestra and Chorus, Santa Fe, NM. For unrestricted support.
$7,500 to Southeastern Village, Detroit, MI. For Parent Engagement in Education program.
$7,500 to University of Detroit Jesuit High School and Academy, Detroit, MI. For the Southeastern Village scholarship.

857
Home & Building Association Foundation
(also known as HBA Foundation)
(formerly Greater Grand Rapids Home Builders Association Foundation)
c/o Housing Center of West Michigan
1633 E. Beltline Ave., N.E.
Grand Rapids, MI 49525-4509 (616) 447-7262
Contact: Bobbie Talsma, Exec. Dir.
FAX: (616) 281-6002; URL: http://hbaggr.com/CommunityInvolvement/HBAFoundation/tabid/92/Default.aspx

Established in 1988 in MI.
Grantmaker type: Independent foundation.

Financial data (yr. ended 12/31/04): Assets, $245,984 (M); gifts received, $50,249; expenditures, $62,397; total giving, $35,250; qualifying distributions, $47,392; giving activities include $2,350 for grants, and $12,000 for grants to individuals.
Purpose and activities: The foundation's mission is to provide scholarships for students pursuing a career related to the building industry, and to provide assistance and grants to community service programs focusing on education and special needs housing.
Fields of interest: Housing/shelter, development; Housing/shelter, rehabilitation; Housing/shelter, temporary shelter; Housing/shelter, homeless; Housing/shelter, repairs; Community development, business promotion; Economically disadvantaged; Homeless.
Type of support: Building/renovation; Program development; Scholarships—to individuals.
Limitations: Giving limited to the greater Grand Rapids, MI, area.
Publications: Annual report; Newsletter.
Application information: Foundation Grants and Community Projects Committee reviews all requests. Application form required.
  Initial approach: Request application form by telephone
  Deadline(s): Feb. 9 and Oct. 31 for grants; Mar. 24 for scholarships
Officers and Directors:* Judy Barnes,* C.E.O. and Exec. V.P.; Dan Diephuis,* Pres.; Daniel N. Grzywacz,* V.P.; Clutch Holtvluwer,* Secy.; Anne VanTol,* Treas.; Bobbie Talsma, Exec. Dir.; Jake Groot; Lee Kitson; Elizabeth Lykins; Nick Nicola; Tim Rottschafer; Ken Van Haaften; Benham R. Wrigley.
Advisory Committee: Bill Kaluske; Harry Mika.
EIN: 382836920

858
Max and Lucille Cortright Homer Education Foundation
203 E. Michigan Ave.
Marshall, MI 49068

Donors: Max Cortright; Lucille Cortright.
Grantmaker type: Independent foundation.
Financial data (yr. ended 12/31/05): Assets, $459,953 (M); expenditures, $18,694; total giving, $17,849; qualifying distributions, $18,694; giving activities include $17,849 for grants.
Fields of interest: Education.
Limitations: Applications not accepted. No grants to individuals.
Application information: Contributes only to pre-selected organizations.
Officers: Lisa M. Ridgeway, Pres.; Thomas Petredean, V.P.; David J. DeGraw, Secy.
EIN: 201289687

859
Honigman Foundation, Inc.
19195 Eastwood Dr.
Harper Woods, MI 48225

Incorporated in 1955 in MI.
Donors: Jason L. Honigman; Edith Honigman.
Grantmaker type: Independent foundation.
Financial data (yr. ended 10/31/05): Assets, $4,631,481 (M); expenditures, $213,227; total giving, $202,550; qualifying distributions,

$201,822; giving activities include $202,550 for 19 grants (high: $111,500; low: $100).
Purpose and activities: Giving primarily for Jewish agencies, temples, and federated giving programs.
Fields of interest: Elementary/secondary education; Higher education; Health organizations, association; Human services; Jewish federated giving programs; Jewish agencies & temples.
Limitations: Applications not accepted. Giving primarily in MI. No grants to individuals.
Application information: Contributes only to pre-selected organizations.
  Board meeting date(s): 1st Mon. in May
Officers: Daniel M. Honigman, Pres.; David M. Honigman, Secy.; Kay Honigman-Singer, Treas.
EIN: 386059254
Selected grants: The following grants were reported in 2003.
$110,000 to Allied Jewish Campaign, Detroit, MI.
$15,000 to Detroit Country Day School, Beverly Hills, MI.
$10,000 to Michigan Association for Emotionally Disturbed Children, Southfield, MI.
$4,000 to University of Michigan, Ann Arbor, MI.
$3,100 to Yad Ezra, Oak Park, MI.
$2,500 to Most Holy Trinity Parish, Detroit, MI.
$1,100 to Temple Israel, West Bloomfield, MI.
$1,000 to Cranbrook Educational Community, Bloomfield Hills, MI. For Horizons-Upward Bound program.
$1,000 to Cystic Fibrosis Foundation, Palm Beach, FL.
$1,000 to Wayne State University, Detroit, MI.

860
The Joseph W. Hood Foundation
11636 Highland Rd., Ste. 104
Hartland, MI 48353
Contact: Joseph W. Hood, Pres.
Application address: 5161 Harp Dr., Linden, MI 48451

Established in 2001 in MI.
Donors: Joseph Chevrolet, Inc.; Joseph Pontiac, Inc.
Grantmaker type: Independent foundation.
Financial data (yr. ended 12/31/04): Assets, $7,147 (M); gifts received, $10,200; expenditures, $13,317; total giving, $12,990; qualifying distributions, $12,990; giving activities include $12,990 for grants.
Purpose and activities: Giving primarily for St. Judes Hospital, Detroit, MI.
Fields of interest: Hospitals (specialty).
Limitations: Giving primarily in Detroit, MI. No grants to individuals.
Application information:
  Initial approach: Letter
  Deadline(s): None
Officers and Directors:* Joseph W. Hood,* Pres.; Nancy Hood,* V.P.; Cheryl Luttman,* Secy.; Kevin Hood.
EIN: 383564128

861
Hoogerwerf Foundation
P.O. Box 704
Grand Haven, MI 49417-0704

Established in 1994 in MI.
Donor: Dave Hoogerwerf.
Grantmaker type: Independent foundation.

Financial data (yr. ended 12/31/05): Assets, $51,665 (M); gifts received, $2,925; expenditures, $17,942; total giving, $17,500; qualifying distributions, $17,500; giving activities include $17,500 for grants.
Fields of interest: Human services; Christian agencies & churches.
Type of support: General/operating support.
Limitations: Applications not accepted. Giving primarily in MI. No grants to individuals.
Application information: Contributes only to pre-selected organizations.
Directors: Bryan Hoogerwerf; Dave Hoogerwerf; Lynn Hoogerwerf.
EIN: 383183915

862
Hoogland Family Foundation
1022 E. Adams St.
Springfield, IL   62703

Established in 2000 in IL.
Donors: Charles R. Hoogland; Kathleen Hoogland.
Grantmaker type: Independent foundation.
Financial data (yr. ended 12/31/03): Assets, $2,494,646 (M); gifts received, $340,505; expenditures, $155,053; total giving, $113,000; qualifying distributions, $111,049; giving activities include $113,000 for 8 grants (high: $105,000; low: $1,000).
Fields of interest: Higher education; Health care; Foundations (public).
Limitations: Applications not accepted. Giving primarily in Hillsdale, MI. No grants to individuals.
Application information: Contributes only to pre-selected organizations.
Directors: Charles E. Hoogland; Charles R. Hoogland; Kathleen Hoogland; Keith A. Hoogland.
EIN: 364427146

863
David S. and Leslie A. Hooker Foundation
2747 Bonnell Ave. S.E.
East Grand Rapids, MI   49506

Established in 2000 in MI.
Donors: David S. Hooker; Leslie A. Hooker.
Grantmaker type: Independent foundation.
Financial data (yr. ended 12/31/05): Assets, $37,038 (M); expenditures, $3,760; total giving, $3,500; qualifying distributions, $3,500; giving activities include $3,500 for grants.
Fields of interest: Education; Hospitals (general); Children/youth, services.
Limitations: Applications not accepted. Giving primarily in Grand Rapids, MI. No grants to individuals.
Application information: Contributes only to pre-selected organizations.
Officers: David S. Hooker, Pres. and Secy.-Treas.; Leslie A. Hooker, V.P.
EIN: 383531809

864
Robert L. and Judith S. Hooker Foundation
618 Kenmoor Ave. S.E., Ste. 100
Grand Rapids, MI   49546

Established in 1989 in MI as successor to Robert L. and Judith S. Hooker Charitable Trust.

Donors: Robert L. Hooker; Judith S. Hooker; Transnational Motors, Inc.
Grantmaker type: Independent foundation.
Financial data (yr. ended 12/31/05): Assets, $188,208 (M); expenditures, $66,708; total giving, $64,150; qualifying distributions, $64,150; giving activities include $64,150 for 46 grants (high: $15,000; low: $200).
Fields of interest: Arts; Higher education; Health organizations; Human services; Christian agencies & churches.
Limitations: Applications not accepted. Giving primarily in MI, with emphasis in the Grand Rapids area. No grants to individuals.
Application information: Contributes only to pre-selected organizations.
Officer: Robert L. Hooker, Pres. and Secy.-Treas.
Directors: Anne E. Ernst; David S. Hooker; Joseph J. Hooker; Judith S. Hooker; Robert L. Hooker, Jr.
EIN: 382846736
Selected grants: The following grants were reported in 2003.
$25,000 to Blodgett Butterworth Health Care Foundation, Grand Rapids, MI. For general support.
$20,500 to University of Michigan, Ann Arbor, MI. For general support.
$6,300 to Grand Rapids Symphony, Grand Rapids, MI. For general support.
$4,000 to Frederick Meijer Gardens and Sculpture Park, Grand Rapids, MI. For general support.
$3,500 to Crooked Tree Arts Council, Petoskey, MI. For general support.
$3,500 to Western Theological Seminary, Holland, MI. For general support.
$3,000 to Central Reformed Church, Grand Rapids, MI. For general support.
$2,500 to Grand Rapids Christian Schools, Grand Rapids, MI. For general support.
$2,500 to Heartside Ministry, Grand Rapids, MI. For general support.
$2,100 to Association for the Blind and Visually Impaired, Grand Rapids, MI. For general support.

865
Hope Charitable Foundation
9461 Coleman Rd.
Haslett, MI   48840

Established in 2001.
Donor: DL Assocs.
Grantmaker type: Independent foundation.
Financial data (yr. ended 12/31/04): Assets, $439,134 (M); gifts received, $381,500; expenditures, $268,209; total giving, $171,675; qualifying distributions, $239,280; giving activities include $171,675 for 16 grants (high: $116,150; low: $75).
Fields of interest: Human services; Christian agencies & churches.
Limitations: Applications not accepted. Giving on a national basis, with some emphasis in the Lansing, MI, area. No grants to individuals.
Application information: Contributes only to pre-selected organizations.
Director: Lorraine K. Puuri.
Trustee: Barbara J. Van Hal.
EIN: 383585035
Selected grants: The following grants were reported in 2004.
$116,150 to Mount Hope Church and International Outreach Ministries, Lansing, MI.
$10,000 to Living Water Teaching, Caddo Mills, TX.

$7,200 to Gospel for Asia, Carrollton, TX.
$6,800 to His Mansion Ministries, Hillsboro, NH.
$5,050 to Navigators, The, Colorado Springs, CO.
$4,800 to Lansing City Rescue Mission, Lansing, MI.
$4,400 to Pregnancy Services of Greater Lansing, East Lansing, MI.
$3,600 to Mission of Mercy, Colorado Springs, CO.
$2,400 to General Council of the Assemblies of God, Springfield, MO.
$1,200 to Focus on the Family, Colorado Springs, CO.

866
Hope Human Resources
20516 Chapel St.
Detroit, MI   48219

Grantmaker type: Independent foundation.
Financial data (yr. ended 12/31/04): Assets, $500 (M); gifts received, $500; expenditures, $0; total giving, $0; qualifying distributions, $0.
Director: Geraldine Cobb.
EIN: 383448765

867
Hospitalers Committee of Detroit Commandery No. 1 Knights Templar
500 Temple Ave.
Detroit, MI   48201   (313) 831-7072
Contact: Don J. Williams, Treas.

Established in 1998 in MI.
Grantmaker type: Independent foundation.
Financial data (yr. ended 12/31/05): Assets, $1,419,967 (M); gifts received, $9,416; expenditures, $142,064; total giving, $68,050; qualifying distributions, $68,050; giving activities include $68,050 for grants.
Purpose and activities: Giving primarily for human services; some giving also for scholarships.
Fields of interest: Education; Health care; Human services; Children/youth, services.
Application information: Application form required.
Initial approach: Letter
Deadline(s): None
Officers: Gilbert A. Rice, Pres.; Jerry Bush, V.P.; Theodore Monolidis, Secy.; Don J. Williams, Treas.
EIN: 383476671

868
Hougen Foundation
P.O. Box 2005
Flint, MI   48501-2005

Established in 1981 in MI.
Donors: Everett D. Hougen; Therese Y. Hougen.
Grantmaker type: Independent foundation.
Financial data (yr. ended 12/31/05): Assets, $2,559,666 (M); expenditures, $76,886; total giving, $71,000; qualifying distributions, $76,795; giving activities include $71,000 for 5 grants (high: $40,000; low: $2,000).
Fields of interest: Higher education; Health care; Arthritis.
Limitations: Applications not accepted. Giving primarily in Flint and Troy, MI. No grants to individuals.
Application information: Contributes only to pre-selected organizations.

Officers: Therese Y. Hougen, Pres. and Secy.-Treas.; Randall B. Hougen, V.P.
Directors: Bradley Hougen; Douglas S. Hougen; Victor L. Hougen.
EIN: 382388686
Selected grants: The following grants were reported in 2003.
$40,000 to Arthritis Foundation, Troy, MI.
$40,000 to Kettering University, Flint, MI.
$15,000 to Michigan Dyslexia Institute, Lansing, MI.
$5,000 to Flint Classroom Support Fund, Flint, MI.
$5,000 to Hurley Foundation, Flint, MI.
$2,000 to American Lung Association of Michigan, Flint, MI.
$2,000 to American Red Cross, Flint, MI.
$1,000 to Charter Township of Flint K-9 Unit, Flint, MI.
$1,000 to Council of Michigan Foundations, Grand Haven, MI.
$1,000 to McLaren Regional Medical Center, Flint, MI.

869
House Family Foundation
(formerly Dave House Family Foundation)
1600 Saratoga Ave., No. 403
PMB 269
San Jose, CA   95129

Established in 1999 in CA.
Donor: David House.
Grantmaker type: Independent foundation.
Financial data (yr. ended 6/30/05): Assets, $23,221,029 (M); expenditures, $2,405,393; total giving, $1,843,153; qualifying distributions, $1,953,794; giving activities include $1,843,153 for 19 grants (high: $1,050,000; low: $1,000).
Purpose and activities: Giving primarily for higher and other education, children, youth, and social services, and to a museum specializing in computers.
Fields of interest: Museums (specialized); Higher education, university; Education; Boys & girls clubs; Human services; Children/youth, services.
Limitations: Applications not accepted. Giving primarily in CA; funding also in MI. No grants to individuals.
Application information: Contributes only to pre-selected organizations.
Officers: David House, C.E.O. and Pres.; Robert Olsen, V.P.; Shelley Cargill, Secy.; Robert House, Treas.
Director: Karla House.
EIN: 522207366
Selected grants: The following grants were reported in 2003.
$1,100,000 to Computer History Museum, Mountain View, CA. For general support.
$125,530 to San Jose State University Foundation, San Jose, CA. For general support.
$124,280 to Boys and Girls Clubs of the Peninsula, Menlo Park, CA. For general support.
$100,000 to Foothill College, Los Altos Hills, CA. For general support.
$50,000 to Silicon Valley Childrens Fund, San Jose, CA. For general support.
$25,996 to Rock-It Science, Moffett Field, CA. For general support.
$24,160 to Muskegon Public Schools, Muskegon, MI. For general support.
$10,000 to Girls Inc. of Alameda County, San Leandro, CA. For general support.

$6,830 to Girl Scouts of the U.S.A., Michigan Pine and Dunes Council, Muskegon, MI. For general support.
$6,830 to Muskegon Area Intermediate School District, Muskegon, MI. For general support.

870
Leon & Audrey Hovarter Scholarship Fund Trust
P.O. Box 247
Marcellus, MI   49067-0247
Contact: Donald R. France, Tr.

Established in 2004 in MI.
Grantmaker type: Independent foundation.
Financial data (yr. ended 12/31/04): Assets, $424,524 (M); expenditures, $4,170; total giving, $4,000; qualifying distributions, $3,969; giving activities include $4,000 for 5 grants to individuals.
Purpose and activities: Scholarship awards to graduating seniors from Marcellus High School, MI, and must attend full-time in the State of MI, any accredited community college or university.
Type of support: Scholarships—to individuals.
Limitations: Giving primarily in MI.
Application information:
  Deadline(s): Apr. 15
Trustee: Donald R. France.
EIN: 616309487

871
Howard City Action Center for Senior Citizens
P.O. Box 399
Howard City, MI   49329

Grantmaker type: Independent foundation.
Financial data (yr. ended 12/31/05): Assets, $46,957 (M); gifts received, $4,153; expenditures, $13,035; total giving, $0; qualifying distributions, $12,826; giving activities include $12,826 for foundation-administered programs.
Limitations: Applications not accepted. No grants to individuals.
Application information: Contributes only to pre-selected organizations.
Officers and Director:* Duane Voss, Chair.; Thomas Farrell, Vice-Chair.; Dawny Kniffen,* Secy.-Treas.
EIN: 382427409

872
John C. and Mary Jane Howard Foundation
180 S. Union St.
Battle Creek, MI   49014

Established in 1999 in MI.
Donor: Mary Jane Howard.
Grantmaker type: Independent foundation.
Financial data (yr. ended 12/31/05): Assets, $1,735,744 (M); expenditures, $90,074; total giving, $70,000; qualifying distributions, $73,796; giving activities include $70,000 for grants.
Fields of interest: Education; Health organizations; Human services; American Red Cross; Federated giving programs; Christian agencies & churches; Protestant agencies & churches.
Type of support: General/operating support.
Limitations: Applications not accepted. Giving primarily in MI and NY. No grants to individuals; no loans.

Application information: Contributes only to pre-selected organizations.
Officers and Directors:* Winship C. Howard,* Pres. and Treas.; Ann E. Beckos,* Secy.; Andrew T. Howard; Michael J. Howard; Mary E. Keyser.
EIN: 383452536

873
Marjorie W. Howe & Howard C. Howe Scholarship Trust
c/o Fifth Third Bank
111 Lyon St. N.W.
P.O. Box 3636
Grand Rapids, MI   49501   (847) 354-7248

Established in 1995 in IL.
Grantmaker type: Independent foundation.
Financial data (yr. ended 12/31/05): Assets, $806,451 (M); expenditures, $63,684; total giving, $48,000; qualifying distributions, $56,375; giving activities include $48,000 for grants to individuals.
Purpose and activities: Scholarship awards to residents of Waukegan who are graduates of Waukegan High School, IL.
Fields of interest: Higher education.
Type of support: Scholarships—to individuals.
Limitations: Giving limited to residents of Waukegan, IL.
Application information: Application form required.
  Deadline(s): Apr. 1
Trustees: Robert Bollman; Fifth Third Bank.
EIN: 364005689

874
HP Foundation
32606 Pine Ridge Dr.
Warren, MI   48093-1000

Established in 2001 in MI.
Donor: Earl-Beth Foundation.
Grantmaker type: Independent foundation.
Financial data (yr. ended 12/31/05): Assets, $2,106,265 (M); expenditures, $102,368; total giving, $67,175; qualifying distributions, $67,175; giving activities include $67,175 for grants.
Limitations: Applications not accepted. No grants to individuals.
Application information: Contributes only to pre-selected organizations.
Officers and Directors:* Deborah Holley Palms,* Pres.; Helen M. Fowler, Secy.; Jeffrey Palms,* Treas.
EIN: 383577492

875
Robert P. & Ella B. Hudson Foundation, Inc.
P.O. Box 699
Sault Sainte Marie, MI   49783-0699
(906) 635-5696
Contact: Frank Fazi, Pres.
Application address: 801 Summit St., Sault Sainte Marie, MI 49783

Established in 1948 in MI.
Grantmaker type: Independent foundation.
Financial data (yr. ended 12/31/04): Assets, $1,749,298 (M); expenditures, $94,901; total giving, $72,455; qualifying distributions, $83,678; giving activities include $72,455 for grants.

Fields of interest: Museums (history); Higher education; Health organizations, association; Human services; Community development.
Type of support: General/operating support; Scholarship funds; Scholarships—to individuals.
Limitations: Giving limited to Chippewa County, MI.
Publications: Annual report.
Application information: Application form not required.
Initial approach: Proposal
Copies of proposal: 1
Deadline(s): None
Board meeting date(s): 3rd Thurs. of each month
Officer: Frank Fazi, Pres.
Directors: James Halvorsen; William Oberman; Roger L. Paris; Don Wilson.
Number of staff: 1 part-time support.
EIN: 386057714

876
Hudson-Webber Foundation
333 W. Fort St., Ste. 1310
Detroit, MI 48226-3149 (313) 963-7777
Contact: David O. Egner, Pres.
FAX: (313) 963-2818;
E-mail: HWF@hudson-webber.org; URL: http://www.hudson-webber.org

Incorporated in 1943 in MI; on Jan. 1, 1984 absorbed the Richard H. and Eloise Jenks Webber Charitable Fund, Inc., and the Eloise and Richard Webber Foundation.
Donors: Eloise Webber‡; Richard Webber‡; The J.L. Hudson Co.; Mary Webber Parker; and members of the Webber family.
Grantmaker type: Independent foundation.
Financial data (yr. ended 12/31/05): Assets, $150,376,115 (M); gifts received, $654,322; expenditures, $8,608,489; total giving, $7,299,369; qualifying distributions, $7,949,973; giving activities include $6,928,821 for 83+ grants (high: $1,000,000; average: $5,000–$250,000), $370,548 for 183 employee matching gifts, and $21,721 for 1 foundation-administered program.
Purpose and activities: Concentrates efforts and resources in support of projects within five program missions that impact the vitality and quality of life of the metropolitan Detroit, MI community: 1) growth and development of the Detroit Medical Center; 2) economic development of southeastern Michigan, with emphasis on assisting chronically unemployed Detroiters obtain and retain employment; 3) physical revitalization of the central city; 4) enhancement of major art and cultural resources in Detroit; and 5) reduction of crime in Detroit. The foundation also provides charitable assistance to qualified J.L. Hudson Co. employees or ex-employees needing help in overcoming personal crises and misfortunes.
Fields of interest: Arts; Crime/violence prevention; Urban/community development.
Type of support: General/operating support; Continuing support; Annual campaigns; Capital campaigns; Building/renovation; Program development; Seed money; Consulting services; Program evaluation; Employee matching gifts; Matching/challenge support.
Limitations: Giving primarily in the city of Detroit, and the tri-county Wayne, Oakland, and Macomb area of southeastern MI. No support for educational institutions or neighborhood organizations (except for projects that fall within current program missions). No grants to individuals (except for J.L. Hudson Co. employees and their families), or for

emergency funds, deficit financing, endowment funds, scholarships, fellowships, publications, conferences, fundraising, social events, or exhibits; no loans.
Publications: Biennial report (including application guidelines); Financial statement; Grants list.
Application information: Accepts CMF Common Grant Application Form. Application form not required.
Initial approach: Letter of request or proposal
Copies of proposal: 1
Deadline(s): Apr. 15, Aug. 15 (for July and Dec. meetings), and Dec. 15 (for meeting in Apr. of following year)
Board meeting date(s): Apr., July, and Dec.
Final notification: 1 week after board decision
Officers and Trustees:* Jennifer Hudson Parke,* Chair.; David O. Egner,* Pres.; Hudson Holland, Jr.,* Secy.; Alfred R. Glancy III,* Treas.; Matthew P. Cullen; Stephen R. D'Arcy; W. Frank Fountain; Frank M. Hennessey; Gilbert Hudson; Joseph L. Hudson, Jr.; Joseph L. Hudson IV; Reginald M. Turner; Amanda Van Dusen.
Number of staff: 2 full-time professional; 1 part-time professional; 1 full-time support; 1 part-time support.
EIN: 386052131
Selected grants: The following grants were reported in 2005.
$1,000,000 to Detroit Institute of Arts, Detroit, MI. For Campaign for Detroit Institute of Arts Transformation Initiative.
$620,000 to Detroit Symphony Orchestra, Detroit, MI. 2 grants: $20,000 to Detroit Symphony Orchestra Hall (For general program support), $600,000 to Detroit Symphony Orchestra Hall (For Summer in the City Programming Initiative).
$517,000 to Goodwill Industries of Greater Detroit, Detroit, MI. For Reducing Chronic Unemployment Initiative.
$500,000 to United Way for Southeastern Michigan, Detroit, MI. 2 grants: $200,000 (For Torch Drive), $300,000 (For 2-1-1 Call Center).
$300,000 to Habitat for Humanity of Metropolitan Detroit, Detroit, MI. For partnership to build capacity initiative.
$300,000 to Women A.R.I.S.E., Detroit, MI. For Women ARISE and Goodwill Industries collaborative.
$200,000 to Detroit Renaissance Foundation, Detroit, MI. For Super Bowl Downtown Improvement Plan Project.
$44,000 to New Detroit, Detroit, MI. For general program support.

877
Julius and Cynthia Huebner Foundation
491 Lincoln Rd.
Grosse Pointe, MI 48230-1608

Established in 1996 in MI.
Donor: Julius J. Huebner.
Grantmaker type: Independent foundation.
Financial data (yr. ended 5/31/05): Assets, $814,242 (M); gifts received, $79,400; expenditures, $31,570; total giving, $31,300; qualifying distributions, $31,425; giving activities include $31,300 for 9 grants (high: $10,000; low: $200).
Fields of interest: Museums; Performing arts; Arts.
Type of support: General/operating support.

Limitations: Applications not accepted. Giving primarily in MI, with some emphasis on Detroit. No grants to individuals.
Application information: Contributes only to pre-selected organizations.
Officers: Julius J. Huebner, Pres. and Treas.; Cynthia K. Huebner, V.P. and Secy.
Trustee: Peter F. Huebner.
EIN: 383321090

878
Huizenga Foundation
2215 York Rd., Ste. 500
Oak Brook, IL 60523

Established in 1988 in IL.
Donor: Peter H. Huizenga.
Grantmaker type: Independent foundation.
Financial data (yr. ended 12/31/04): Assets, $6,069,827 (M); gifts received, $45,000; expenditures, $1,549,530; total giving, $1,396,056; qualifying distributions, $1,396,056; giving activities include $1,396,056 for 146 grants (high: $156,000; low: $25).
Purpose and activities: Giving primarily to Protestant organizations, including a prison ministry, and churches, and for Protestant education, as well as for higher education, environmental conservation, and for children, youth, families, and social services.
Fields of interest: Historic preservation/historical societies; Arts; Elementary/secondary education; Higher education; Theological school/education; Environment; Animals/wildlife, preservation/protection; Human services; Family services; Christian agencies & churches.
Limitations: Applications not accepted. Giving in the U.S., primarily in IL, Washington, DC, PA, and MI. No grants to individuals.
Application information: Contributes only to pre-selected organizations.
Officers and Directors:* Peter H. Huizenga,* Pres.; David A. Bradley, Secy.; Heidi A. Huizenga,* Treas.; Betsy Bradley; Greta Giesen; P.J. Huizenga; Tim Huizenga.
EIN: 363582536
Selected grants: The following grants were reported in 2003.
$186,100 to Christ Church of Oak Brook, Oak Brook, IL. For general support.
$140,100 to Hope College, Holland, MI. For general support.
$110,100 to Trinity Christian College, Palos Heights, IL. For general support.
$25,000 to Loyola University of Chicago, Chicago, IL. For general support.
$15,000 to DePauw University, Greencastle, IN. For general support.
$10,000 to University of Illinois Foundation, Champaign, IL. For general support.
$1,000 to North Central College, Naperville, IL. For general support.
$950 to Friends of Conservation, Oak Brook, IL. For general support.
$250 to Nature Conservancy, Chicago, IL. For general support.
$200 to Conservation Foundation of DuPage County, Naperville, IL. For general support.

879
George M. Hull Memorial Foundation
c/o Citizens Bank, N.A.
3075 Washtenaw Ave.
Ypsilanti, MI 48197 (734) 434-7056

Established in MI.
Grantmaker type: Independent foundation.
Financial data (yr. ended 12/31/04): Assets, $52,016 (M); expenditures, $1,282; total giving, $908; qualifying distributions, $1,089; giving activities include $908 for grants to individuals.
Purpose and activities: provides medical assistance to indigent residents of Ypsilanti, MI.
Fields of interest: Health care.
Type of support: Grants to individuals.
Limitations: Giving limited to residents of Ypsilanti, MI.
Application information: Application form required.
Initial approach: Contact one of the officers
Deadline(s): Varies
Officers: Thomas Willoughby, Pres.; James B. Nelson, V.P.; Barbara Robb, Secy.; Arlene Lalonde, Treas.
Directors: Ann Kettles; Richard Wagner.
EIN: 386089896

880
Humane Society of Macomb Foundation, Inc.
11350 22 Mile Rd.
Utica, MI 48317 (586) 739-6870
Contact: George Fox, Pres.

Established in 1994 in MI.
Grantmaker type: Independent foundation.
Financial data (yr. ended 12/31/05): Assets, $1,470,256 (M); expenditures, $72,109; total giving, $69,750; qualifying distributions, $69,750; giving activities include $69,750 for grants.
Purpose and activities: Giving for animal welfare organizations; also awards scholarships to veterinary students.
Fields of interest: Graduate/professional education; Animal welfare; Veterinary medicine.
Type of support: Scholarships—to individuals.
Limitations: Giving primarily in MI.
Application information: Application form not required.
Deadline(s): None
Officers: George Fox, Pres.; Eric Puff, V.P.; Bob Wiedenbach, V.P.
EIN: 383183238

881
Paul A. Humbert Scholarship Trust
c/o Fifth Third Bank
P.O. Box 3636
Grand Rapids, MI 49501-3636
Application address: c/o Culver Community High School, Guidance Off., N. School St., Culver, IN 46511, tel.: (219) 842-3391

Established in 1988 in IN.
Donor: Ines M. Humbert.
Grantmaker type: Independent foundation.
Financial data (yr. ended 6/30/05): Assets, $641,730 (M); expenditures, $37,626; total giving, $34,015; qualifying distributions, $34,265; giving activities include $34,015 for grants to individuals.

Purpose and activities: Scholarship awards to graduates of Culver Community High School, IN.
Type of support: Scholarships—to individuals.
Limitations: Giving limited to residents of the Culver, IN area.
Application information: Application form required.
Deadline(s): Apr. 15
Scholarship Committee: Don Adams; M. Karen Mendenhall; Brenda Sheldon; Barbara Winters.
Trustee: Fifth Third Bank.
EIN: 356505726

882
Humphrey-Admore Foundation, Inc.
(formerly Glenn E. & Malvina S. Humphrey Foundation, Inc.)
10 W. Square Lake Rd., Ste. 220
Bloomfield Hills, MI 48302-0466

Established in 1986 in MI.
Donors: Glenn E. Humphrey; Malvina S. Humphrey.
Grantmaker type: Independent foundation.
Financial data (yr. ended 11/30/04): Assets, $103,504 (M); gifts received, $86,000; expenditures, $116,293; total giving, $106,500; qualifying distributions, $106,493; giving activities include $106,500 for 2 grants (high: $101,500; low: $5,000).
Purpose and activities: Giving for health, human services, and religious organizations.
Fields of interest: Protestant agencies & churches.
Limitations: Applications not accepted. Giving limited to CA. No grants to individuals.
Application information: Contributes only to pre-selected organizations.
Officers and Directors:* Glenn E. Humphrey,* Pres.; Malvina S. Humphrey,* V.P.
EIN: 382705140

883
Hunter Charitable Trust
94 Southlawn Ave.
Dobbs Ferry, NY 10522

Established in NY in 1997.
Donor: Harriette E. Hunter.
Grantmaker type: Independent foundation.
Financial data (yr. ended 12/31/04): Assets, $206,915 (M); expenditures, $9,001; total giving, $8,500; qualifying distributions, $8,500; giving activities include $8,500 for grants.
Fields of interest: Education; Science; Religion, interfaith issues.
Type of support: General/operating support.
Limitations: Applications not accepted. Giving primarily in Dobbs Ferry, Ossining, Poughkeepsie, and Yonkers, NY; some giving also in DE, MA, MI, NH, and PA. No grants to individuals.
Application information: Contributes only to pre-selected organizations.
Trustees: David H. Hunter; Stephen K. Hunter.
EIN: 383326883

884
Edward and Irma Hunter Foundation
423 Sycamore St., Ste. 101
Niles, MI 49120-0960
Contact: James F. Keenan, Pres.
Additional address: P.O. Box 906, Niles, MI 49120

Established in 1968 in MI.
Donors: Edward Hunter†; Irma Hunter†.
Grantmaker type: Independent foundation.
Financial data (yr. ended 12/31/05): Assets, $5,230,280 (M); expenditures, $349,914; total giving, $223,376; qualifying distributions, $280,276; giving activities include $223,376 for 13 grants (high: $50,000; low: $2,000).
Fields of interest: Employment; Human services; Community development; Government/public administration.
Type of support: Annual campaigns; Building/renovation; Equipment; Land acquisition; Emergency funds; Matching/challenge support.
Limitations: Giving limited to the Buchanan and Niles, MI, area. No grants to individuals, or for operating budgets, continuing support, seed money, deficit financing, endowment funds, scholarships, fellowships, program support, research, demonstration projects, publications, or conferences; no loans.
Publications: Informational brochure (including application guidelines).
Application information: Application form not required.
Initial approach: Letter
Copies of proposal: 7
Deadline(s): 2nd week of Feb., May, Aug., and Nov.
Board meeting date(s): 4th Mon. of Feb., May, Aug., and Nov.
Final notification: 1 week
Officer: James F. Keenan, Pres.
Trustees: Jerry E. French; Gary Gaynor; David L. Lawrence; William Racine; Donald F. Walter.
EIN: 237065471
Selected grants: The following grants were reported in 2003.
$75,000 to Niles, City of, Niles, MI. For city redevelopment projects.
$56,900 to Greater Niles Community Development, Niles, MI.
$25,000 to Southwestern Michigan Economic Growth Alliance, Niles, MI. For annual support.
$15,000 to United Way of Greater Niles, Niles, MI. For general support.
$10,000 to Lakeland Health Foundation, Saint Joseph, MI. For general support.
$7,500 to Fernwood Botanical Garden and Nature Preserve, Niles, MI.
$6,150 to Goodwill Industries. For general support.
$6,000 to Junior Achievement of the Michigan Great Lakes, Grand Rapids, MI. For general support.
$2,500 to Meals on Wheels, Niles-Buchanan, Niles, MI.
$2,500 to Salvation Army, Niles, MI. For Christmas baskets.

885
Hunting Foundation
2820 Pioneer Club Rd. S.E.
Grand Rapids, MI 49506

Established in 1998 in MI.
Donor: John R. Hunting.
Grantmaker type: Independent foundation.
Financial data (yr. ended 12/31/05): Assets, $1,364,384 (M); expenditures, $82,954; total giving, $74,400; qualifying distributions, $74,400; giving activities include $74,400 for grants.
Purpose and activities: Giving primarily for the arts and human services.

Fields of interest: Arts; Education; Environment, pollution control; Medical research, institute; Human services.
Type of support: General/operating support.
Limitations: Applications not accepted. Giving primarily in MI, IL, and MN. No grants to individuals.
Application information: Contributes only to pre-selected organizations.
Officers: Helen J. Hunting, Pres.; Allen I. Hunting, Secy.; Allen I. Hunting, Jr., Treas.
Director: Anne Hunting.
EIN: 383412588

886

The Hurst Foundation

675 Robinson Rd.
Jackson, MI   49203   (517) 788-8600

Trust established in 1955 in MI.
Donors: Peter F. Hurst†; Elizabeth S. Hurst†.
Grantmaker type: Independent foundation.
Financial data (yr. ended 12/31/04): Assets, $9,002,638 (M); expenditures, $330,099; total giving, $321,500; qualifying distributions, $321,500; giving activities include $321,500 for 39 grants (high: $75,000; low: $1,000).
Fields of interest: Museums; Arts; Secondary school/education; Higher education; Human services; Youth, services; Community development; Protestant agencies & churches.
Type of support: General/operating support; Building/renovation; Equipment; Program development; Seed money.
Limitations: Giving primarily in Jackson County, MI. No grants to individuals, or for endowment funds, scholarships, fellowships, or matching gifts; no loans.
Application information: Application form not required.
  Initial approach: Letter
  Copies of proposal: 2
  Deadline(s): Oct. 1
  Board meeting date(s): Dec. and as necessary
  Final notification: Within 60 days for favorable decisions
Officer: Anthony P. Hurst, Pres.
EIN: 386089457

887

The Dick and Mary Ann Hurst Foundation

8310 Rum Creek Trail N.E.
Rockford, MI   49341

Established in 2000 in MI.
Donors: Richard Hurst; Mary Ann Hurst.
Grantmaker type: Independent foundation.
Financial data (yr. ended 12/31/04): Assets, $2,316 (M); expenditures, $2,030; total giving, $1,927; qualifying distributions, $1,927; giving activities include $1,927 for grants.
Limitations: Applications not accepted. No grants to individuals.
Application information: Contributes only to pre-selected organizations.
Officers: Richard Hurst, Pres.; Mary Ann Hurst, V.P.; Jennifer Kramarz, Secy.; Todd Hurst, Treas.
EIN: 383502330

888

Theodore Huss, Sr. and Elsie Endert Huss Memorial Fund

c/o Citizens Bank Wealth Mgmt., N.A.
328 S. Saginaw St., M/C 002072
Flint, MI   48502
Application address: c/o Helen James, Citizens Bank, N.A., Wealth Mgmt., 101 N. Washington Ave., Saginaw, MI 48607, tel.: (989) 776-7368

Established in 1985 in MI.
Grantmaker type: Independent foundation.
Financial data (yr. ended 12/31/05): Assets, $392,240 (M); expenditures, $25,411; total giving, $16,600; qualifying distributions, $16,600; giving activities include $16,600 for grants to individuals.
Purpose and activities: Scholarships awarded only to full time undergraduate students of Saginaw County, Michigan.
Type of support: Scholarships—to individuals.
Limitations: Giving limited to Saginaw County, MI.
Application information: Application form required.
  Deadline(s): June 1
Trustee: Citizens Bank.
EIN: 386476850

889

Hutchcroft Perpetual Charitable Trust

c/o Alan Hutchcroft
4203 Tallwood Ave.
Rockford, IL   61114

Established in 1998 in IL.
Donor: Elizabeth B. Hutchcroft.
Grantmaker type: Independent foundation.
Financial data (yr. ended 12/31/04): Assets, $0 (M); expenditures, $65,303; total giving, $56,000; qualifying distributions, $56,000; giving activities include $56,000 for 3 grants (high: $36,000; low: $5,000).
Purpose and activities: Giving to educational institution for specific departments of learning.
Fields of interest: Higher education.
Type of support: General/operating support.
Limitations: Applications not accepted. Giving primarily to Rockford, IL, South Hadley, MA, and Kalamazoo, MI. No grants to individuals.
Application information: Contributes only to pre-selected organizations.
Trustee: Alan C. Hutchcroft.
EIN: 364226779

890

Ruahmah J. Hutchings Fund Irrevocable Charitable Trust

c/o Howell Public Schools
411 N. Highlander Way
Howell, MI   48843-1021

Established in 2000 in MI.
Grantmaker type: Independent foundation.
Financial data (yr. ended 12/31/05): Assets, $426,545 (M); expenditures, $27,785; total giving, $22,238; qualifying distributions, $22,238; giving activities include $22,238 for grants.
Purpose and activities: Scholarships for seniors at Howell High School, MI, who possess mechanical ability or have special needs.
Type of support: Scholarships—to individuals.
Limitations: Giving limited to residents of Howell, MI.

Application information: Application form not required.
  Initial approach: Letter
  Deadline(s): Apr. 1
Trustee: Richard P. Terres, Assoc. Supt.
EIN: 386743523

891

I Have a Dream Foundation - Port Huron

5538 Lakeshore Rd.
Fort Gratiot, MI   48059
Contact: Chris M. Kurzweil, Pres.

Established in 1994 in MI.
Donor: Chris M. Kurzweil.
Grantmaker type: Independent foundation.
Financial data (yr. ended 6/30/05): Assets, $73,529 (M); expenditures, $136,666; total giving, $119,267; qualifying distributions, $136,423; giving activities include $119,267 for 32 grants to individuals (high: $9,309; low: $278), and $17,399 for foundation-administered programs.
Purpose and activities: To provide comprehensive educational support and guidance to selected disadvantaged elementary school children.
Fields of interest: Education; Minorities; Economically disadvantaged.
Type of support: Grants to individuals; Scholarships—to individuals.
Limitations: Giving primarily in Port Huron, MI.
Officers: Chris M. Kurzweil, Pres.; Joanne Kurzweil, Secy.; Richard F. Dufner, Treas.
Number of staff: 1 full-time professional.
EIN: 383193498

892

Iacobelli Family Foundation

2375 Hunt Club Dr.
Bloomfield Hills, MI   48304

Established in 1999 in MI.
Donors: Mario F. Iacobelli; Celia J. Iacobelli.
Grantmaker type: Independent foundation.
Financial data (yr. ended 12/31/04): Assets, $556,156 (M); expenditures, $18,504; total giving, $17,350; qualifying distributions, $17,350; giving activities include $17,350 for grants.
Limitations: Applications not accepted. Giving primarily in Detroit, MI. No grants to individuals.
Application information: Contributes only to pre-selected organizations.
Officers: Celia J. Iacobelli, Pres.; Mario F. Iacobelli, V.P. and Secy.
EIN: 383505771

893

ICN Foundation

1 Riverfront Plz.
55 Campau N.W.
Grand Rapids, MI   49503   (616) 458-1150
Contact: Sidney J. Jansma, Jr., Pres.

Established in 1986.
Donors: Sidney J. Jansma, Jr.; Sidney J. Jansma III.
Grantmaker type: Independent foundation.
Financial data (yr. ended 12/31/05): Assets, $7,478,536 (M); gifts received, $25,000; expenditures, $1,221,388; total giving, $1,064,039; qualifying distributions, $1,065,014;

giving activities include $1,064,039 for 82 grants (high: $182,600; low: $25).

Purpose and activities: Giving primarily for evangelical Christian organizations and churches.

Fields of interest: Christian agencies & churches; Protestant agencies & churches.

Limitations: Giving primarily in MI. No grants to individuals.

Application information:
Initial approach: Letter or proposal
Deadline(s): None

Officers: Sidney J. Jansma, Jr., Pres. and Treas.; Joanne R. Jansma, V.P. and Secy.

EIN: 382638771

894
Bill and Bea Idema Foundation

(formerly Wren Foundation)
c/o Fifth Third Bank
P.O. Box 3636
Grand Rapids, MI   49501-3636
Application address: c/o Phil P. Versluis, 75 Collindale S.W., Grand Rapids, MI 49504

Established in 1986 in MI.

Donors: Beatrice A. Idema; William W. Idema.

Grantmaker type: Independent foundation.

Financial data (yr. ended 6/30/05): Assets, $4,011,574 (M); expenditures, $240,834; total giving, $199,500; qualifying distributions, $201,855; giving activities include $199,500 for 17 grants (high: $30,000; low: $2,000).

Purpose and activities: Giving primarily to Christian causes, education, and the arts.

Fields of interest: Performing arts; Secondary school/education; Higher education; Education; Health care, blood supply; Girl scouts; Human services; Children/youth, services; Christian agencies & churches.

Type of support: General/operating support; Capital campaigns; Building/renovation; Program development; Seed money; Scholarship funds.

Limitations: Giving primarily in the Grand Rapids, MI, area.

Application information: Application form required.
Initial approach: Letter
Copies of proposal: 1
Deadline(s): June and Dec.
Board meeting date(s): June and Dec.

Officers: William W. Idema, Pres.; Beatrice A. Idema, V.P.; Philip P. Versluis, Secy.

Trustees: Paul Ryan; Joyce Versluis.

Manager: Fifth Third Bank.

EIN: 382653272

Selected grants: The following grants were reported in 2003.

$25,000 to Calvin College, Life Sciences Center, Grand Rapids, MI. For DeVries Hall of Science.

$15,000 to Grand Valley State University, Allendale, MI. For New Center for Health Professions.

$10,000 to Camp Tall Turf, Grand Rapids, MI. For capital project.

$10,000 to Dutton Christian School, Caledonia, MI. For renovations.

$10,000 to Grand Rapids Ballet Company, Grand Rapids, MI. For general support.

$10,000 to Mel Trotter Ministries, Grand Rapids, MI. For children and youth program.

$10,000 to Opera Grand Rapids, Grand Rapids, MI. For general support.

$10,000 to Potters House, Grand Rapids, MI. For capital campaign.

$10,000 to Steepletown Neighborhood Services, Grand Rapids, MI. For capital project.

$10,000 to Van Andel Education Institute, Grand Rapids, MI. For general support.

895
IDM Foundation

136 E. Michigan Ave., Ste. 1201
Kalamazoo, MI   49007
Contact: James C. Melvin, Secy.-Treas.

Established in 1997 in MI.

Donor: David C. Rigsby.

Grantmaker type: Independent foundation.

Financial data (yr. ended 12/31/05): Assets, $1,587,972 (M); gifts received, $499,294; expenditures, $104,344; total giving, $76,500; qualifying distributions, $76,500; giving activities include $76,500 for grants.

Fields of interest: Education; Environment, natural resources; Foundations (community).

Limitations: Applications not accepted. Giving primarily in MI. No grants to individuals.

Application information: Contributes only to pre-selected organizations.

Officers: David C. Rigsby, Pres.; James S. Hilboldt, V.P.; James C. Melvin, Secy.-Treas.

EIN: 383348061

896
The Ikhlas Foundation

26300 Telegraph Rd., 2nd Fl.
Southfield, MI   48034

Established in 2003.

Grantmaker type: Independent foundation.

Financial data (yr. ended 12/31/05): Assets, $88,778 (M); gifts received, $35,000; expenditures, $67,699; total giving, $67,030; qualifying distributions, $67,030; giving activities include $67,030 for grants.

Officer: Joffer H. Hakim, Pres.

EIN: 371462479

897
John & Ella Imerman Foundation

1505 E. 11 Mile Rd.
Royal Oak, MI   48067-2027
Contact: John Bloom, Pres.

Established in MI.

Grantmaker type: Independent foundation.

Financial data (yr. ended 12/31/04): Assets, $352,051 (M); expenditures, $19,087; total giving, $9,767; qualifying distributions, $9,767; giving activities include $9,767 for grants.

Fields of interest: Arts; Education; Health organizations, association; Volunteers of America; Jewish agencies & temples.

Type of support: General/operating support; Endowments.

Limitations: Giving limited to the Detroit, MI, area.

Application information:
Initial approach: Letter
Deadline(s): None

Officer: John Bloom, Pres. and Treas.

Director: Harriet Friedman.

EIN: 386088885

898
Stanley Imerman Memorial Foundation

121 W. Long Lake Rd., 2nd Fl.
Bloomfield Hills, MI   48304

Established in 1971 in MI.

Donor: Stanley Imerman†.

Grantmaker type: Independent foundation.

Financial data (yr. ended 12/31/04): Assets, $2,116,599 (M); expenditures, $320,943; total giving, $217,317; qualifying distributions, $281,363; giving activities include $217,317 for 45 grants (high: $50,000; low: $150).

Purpose and activities: Giving primarily to Jewish organizations, including welfare funds, yeshivas, and universities.

Fields of interest: Higher education; Law school/education; Human services; Jewish federated giving programs; Jewish agencies & temples.

Type of support: General/operating support; Continuing support; Annual campaigns; Building/renovation.

Limitations: Applications not accepted. Giving primarily in MI. No grants to individuals, or for endowment funds, scholarships, fellowships, or matching gifts; no loans.

Application information: Contributes only to pre-selected organizations.

Officers and Trustees:* Lawrence S. Jackier,* Pres. and Treas.; Dale G. Rands,* V.P.; Mark Schlussel,* Secy.

EIN: 237152760

Selected grants: The following grants were reported in 2004.

$50,000 to Childrens Hospital of Michigan, Detroit, MI.

$12,500 to Jewish Academy of Metropolitan Detroit, West Bloomfield, MI.

$10,000 to Jewish Vocational Service and Community Workshop, Southfield, MI.

$4,000 to Holocaust Memorial Center, Farmington Hills, MI.

$2,500 to Hillel Day School of Metropolitan Detroit, Farmington Hills, MI.

$2,500 to Hospice of Michigan, Detroit, MI.

$1,500 to Ecumenical Institute for Jewish-Christian Studies, Southfield, MI.

$1,000 to Akiva Hebrew Day School, Lathrup Village, MI.

$1,000 to American ORT Federation, New York, NY. For general support.

$1,000 to Counterterrorism and Security Educational Research Foundation, DC.

899
Frances B. Imoberstag Charitable Foundation

22211 W. Warren St.
Dearborn Heights, MI   48127-2531
Contact: Margaret Campbell, Tr.

Established in 1994 in MI.

Donor: Frances B. Imoberstag†.

Grantmaker type: Independent foundation.

Financial data (yr. ended 12/31/05): Assets, $247,550 (M); expenditures, $21,553; total giving, $20,000; qualifying distributions, $20,000; giving activities include $20,000 for grants.

Fields of interest: Higher education, university; Children, services.

Limitations: Giving primarily in Dearborn Heights, MI. No grants to individuals.

Application information:

Initial approach: Letter
Deadline(s): None
Trustee: Margaret Campbell.
EIN: 383172291

900
In His Love Foundation
6617 Crossing Dr.
Grand Rapids, MI 49508-7378

Established in 1998 in MI.
Donors: Internet Services Corp.; Michael & Associates, Inc.; Puryear & Associates; Trinity Motivation, LLC; Yager Freedom Foundation; Yager Personal Development, Inc.
Grantmaker type: Independent foundation.
Financial data (yr. ended 12/31/05): Assets, $113,325 (M); gifts received, $45,000; expenditures, $38,773; total giving, $36,800; qualifying distributions, $36,800; giving activities include $36,800 for grants.
Purpose and activities: Giving primarily to Baptist and other Christian organizations.
Fields of interest: Christian agencies & churches; Protestant agencies & churches.
Limitations: Applications not accepted. Giving primarily in MI. No grants to individuals.
Application information: Contributes only to pre-selected organizations.
Officers: William J. Zeoli, Pres. and Treas.; John W. Tromp, V.P.; William H. Heritage, Jr., Secy.
EIN: 383437817

901
India Foundation
3505 Coolidge Rd.
East Lansing, MI 48823-6377
Contact: Shrikumar Poddar, Pres.

Established in 1970 in MI.
Donors: Shrikumar Poddar; Mayurika Poddar; Devesh Darshan Poddar.
Grantmaker type: Independent foundation.
Financial data (yr. ended 12/31/04): Assets, $1,667,302 (M); expenditures, $80,409; total giving, $19,781; qualifying distributions, $31,195; giving activities include $19,781 for grants.
Purpose and activities: Giving primarily for East Indian religious and charitable organizations.
Fields of interest: Education; Crime/violence prevention, domestic violence; Religion; Asians/Pacific Islanders; Economically disadvantaged.
International interests: India.
Type of support: Conferences/seminars; Seed money; Technical assistance; In-kind gifts; Matching/challenge support.
Limitations: Giving primarily in MI. No grants to individuals.
Application information: Application form not required.
Copies of proposal: 1
Deadline(s): Apr. 1 and Aug. 1
Board meeting date(s): Semiannually in June and Sept.
Officers: Shrikumar Poddar, Pres. and Treas.; Mayurika Poddar, V.P.; Daniel J. Warmels, Secy.
Director: Kaushik Shah.
EIN: 237300230

902
The Barton J. & Gail G. Ingraham Foundation
10203 E. Shady Ln.
Suttons Bay, MI 49682

Established in 2000 in MI.
Grantmaker type: Independent foundation.
Financial data (yr. ended 12/31/05): Assets, $1 (M); gifts received, $1,000; expenditures, $100; total giving, $100; qualifying distributions, $100; giving activities include $100 for grants.
Trustees: Barton Ingraham; Gail Ingraham.
EIN: 383597295

903
The Inman Family Foundation
400 Talon Centre
Detroit, MI 48207-5035

Established in 1992 in MI.
Donor: Wayne C. Inman.
Grantmaker type: Independent foundation.
Financial data (yr. ended 12/31/04): Assets, $92,046 (M); gifts received, $2,250; expenditures, $7,823; total giving, $7,000; qualifying distributions, $7,000; giving activities include $7,000 for grants.
Fields of interest: Secondary school/education; Higher education; Cancer.
Type of support: General/operating support.
Limitations: Applications not accepted. No grants to individuals.
Application information: Contributes only to pre-selected organizations.
Officers: Wayne C. Inman, Pres. and Secy.; Amelia P. Inman, Treas.
EIN: 383082729

904
Inter City Oil Foundation
c/o ICO
P.O. Box 3048
Duluth, MN 55803-3048 (218) 728-3641
Contact: Donna K. Flesher, Secy.-Treas.

Established in 1995 in MN.
Grantmaker type: Independent foundation.
Financial data (yr. ended 12/31/05): Assets, $21,906 (M); expenditures, $8,512; total giving, $8,500; qualifying distributions, $8,500; giving activities include $8,500 for grants.
Fields of interest: Higher education; Youth development; YM/YWCAs & YM/YWHAs; Community development.
Limitations: Giving primarily in MI, MN, and WI. No grants to individuals.
Application information:
Initial approach: Proposal
Deadline(s): Nov. 1
Final notification: Dec. 31
Officers: Judith L. Weber, C.E.O. and Pres.; Donna K. Flesher, Secy.-Treas.
Director: Susan J. Weber.
EIN: 411817691

905
International Society of Barristers Foundation
c/o University of Michigan Law School
625 S. State St., Ste. 806
Ann Arbor, MI 48109-1215 (734) 763-0165
FAX: (734) 764-8309;
E-mail: info@internationalsocietyofbarristers.org;
URL: http://www.internationalsocietyofbarristers.com/foundation.html

Established in 2002 in CO and MI.
Donors: Robert F. Ritter; International Society of Barristers.
Grantmaker type: Independent foundation.
Financial data (yr. ended 12/31/05): Assets, $160,403 (M); gifts received, $53,950; expenditures, $25,500; total giving, $25,500; qualifying distributions, $25,500; giving activities include $25,500 for grants.
Purpose and activities: Grants awarded to preserve the adversary system, to retain trial by jury in litigated matters, to help young lawyers improve their advocacy skills, and to improve the justice system and its components.
Fields of interest: Law school/education; Legal services.
Type of support: General/operating support.
Limitations: Applications not accepted. Giving on a national basis.
Application information: Contributes only to pre-selected organizations.
Officers: Myron J. Bromberg, Pres.; James K. Robinson, V.P.; John T. Crowder,* Secy.; Joe McLeod,* Treas.; John W. Reed,* Exec. Secy.
Directors: Kevin D. Krist; John G. Lancione; Joseph K. Meusey; Joel E. Pink; Henry J. Price.
EIN: 300112645

906
Irish American Information Service
c/o John McInerny
10001 Creekwood Cir.
Plymouth, MI 48170

Grantmaker type: Independent foundation.
Financial data (yr. ended 12/31/05): Assets, $1 (M); gifts received, $91,671; expenditures, $94,403; total giving, $6,435; qualifying distributions, $6,435; giving activities include $6,435 for grants.
Limitations: Applications not accepted. No grants to individuals.
Application information: Contributes only to pre-selected organizations.
Officers: Patrick O'Kennedy, Pres.; Tom Kennedy, Secy.; John McInerny, Treas.
EIN: 383050471

907
The Irwin Foundation
19701 Vernier Rd., Ste. 290
Harper Woods, MI 48225 (313) 886-0795
Contact: Sharon L. Potter, Secy.-Treas.
FAX: (313) 886-0795;
E-mail: info@irwinfoundation.com; URL: http://www.irwinfoundation.com/

Established in 1996 in MI.
Donors: Claire Irwin†; James Irwin†.

Grantmaker type: Independent foundation.
Financial data (yr. ended 12/31/05): Assets, $724,559 (M); gifts received, $550; expenditures, $235,460; total giving, $100,000; qualifying distributions, $110,699; giving activities include $100,000 for 3 grants (high: $50,000; low: $25,000).
Purpose and activities: Giving for the promotion of veterinary education, including the funding of student scholarships in schools, departments, or units accredited in veterinary medicine or veterinary technology, within a major university. Other support includes use of foundation mobile veterinary facility for remote medical programs and various veterinary-related activities and events.
Fields of interest: Medical school/education; Education; Veterinary medicine.
Type of support: Building/renovation; Equipment; Fellowships; Scholarship funds.
Limitations: Giving in the U.S., with emphasis on East Lansing, MI. No grants to individuals.
Application information:
Initial approach: Letter
Deadline(s): None
Officers and Directors:* Sean P. Kelly,* Pres.; William J. Cari,* V.P.; Sharon L. Potter,* Secy.-Treas.; Russell M. Paquette.
EIN: 383262167

908
Isaac 880130 Foundation
3009 Crownview Ct. N.E.
Grand Rapids, MI 49525-2079
Contact: Kaplin S. Jones, Pres.

Established in 1988.
Donor: Kaplin S. Jones.
Grantmaker type: Independent foundation.
Financial data (yr. ended 12/31/04): Assets, $0 (M); expenditures, $3,030; total giving, $3,030; qualifying distributions, $3,030; giving activities include $3,030 for grants.
Limitations: Giving primarily in Salt Lake City, UT.
Officer: Kaplin S. Jones, Pres.
EIN: 382789597

909
The Isabel Foundation
111 E. Court St., Ste. 3D
Flint, MI 48502-1649 (810) 767-0136
Contact: C. Edward White, Jr.

Established in 1988 in MI.
Grantmaker type: Independent foundation.
Financial data (yr. ended 6/30/05): Assets, $59,112,952 (M); gifts received, $30,000; expenditures, $2,948,087; total giving, $2,665,580; qualifying distributions, $2,711,761; giving activities include $2,665,580 for 52 grants (high: $300,000; low: $1,280).
Purpose and activities: Funding primarily for community foundations and to churches and other religious organizations dedicated to supporting or contributing to the cause of Christian Science.
Fields of interest: Recreation, camps; Foundations (community); Christian agencies & churches.
Type of support: Equipment; General/operating support; Continuing support; Annual campaigns.
Limitations: Giving in the U.S. No grants to individuals.

Application information: Application form not required.
Initial approach: Letter
Copies of proposal: 1
Deadline(s): No set deadline, but grants are primarily made in June
Officers and Trustees:* Claire Mott White,* Chair. and Treas.; William S. White,* Pres. and Secy.; Tiffany W. Lovett; Ridgeway H. White.
EIN: 382853004
Selected grants: The following grants were reported in 2003.
$315,000 to First Church of Christ Scientist, Boston, MA.
$300,000 to Adventure Unlimited, Greenwood Village, CO.
$250,000 to Flint Institute of Arts, Flint, MI.
$200,000 to Hobart College, Geneva, NY.
$200,000 to Principia Corporation, Saint Louis, MO.
$100,000 to Leaves, The, Richardson, TX.
$75,000 to High Ridge House, Riverdale, NY.
$60,000 to Flint Institute of Music, Flint, MI.
$50,000 to Arden Wood Benevolent Association, San Francisco, CA.
$50,000 to Cedars Camps, Manchester, MO.

910
Isabella Foundation, Inc.
c/o Fifth Third Bank
P.O. Box 3636
Grand Rapids, MI 49501-3636

Established in 1994 in MI.
Grantmaker type: Independent foundation.
Financial data (yr. ended 9/30/05): Assets, $1,464,804 (M); expenditures, $98,023; total giving, $82,000; qualifying distributions, $82,000; giving activities include $82,000 for grants.
Purpose and activities: Giving primarily for Protestant-affiliated human services groups, with emphasis on programs assisting the elderly.
Fields of interest: Human services; Aging, centers/services; Protestant agencies & churches; Aging.
Limitations: Applications not accepted. Giving primarily in Grand Rapids, MI. No grants to individuals.
Application information: Contributes only to pre-selected organizations.
Officers: Calvin Owen, Pres.; Samuel H. Metcalf, V.P. and Treas.; Ken Tiews, Secy.
Trustees: Lois Deboer; Caroline Dellenbusch; Charlene Glerum; Samuel C. Metcalf; Mary Remien; Fifth Third Bank.
EIN: 381387662

911
Isakow Foundation
4405 Oakgrove Dr.
Bloomfield Hills, MI 48302 (248) 737-0600

Established in 1990 in MI.
Donor: Selwyn Isakow.
Grantmaker type: Independent foundation.
Financial data (yr. ended 1/31/05): Assets, $932,797 (M); expenditures, $59,850; total giving, $51,886; qualifying distributions, $51,886; giving activities include $51,886 for grants.
Purpose and activities: Giving primarily for health and human services and Jewish organizations.

Fields of interest: Education; Human services; Jewish federated giving programs; Jewish agencies & temples.
Limitations: Applications not accepted. Giving primarily in Detroit, MI. No grants to individuals.
Application information: Contributes only to pre-selected organizations.
Officer: Selwyn Isakow, Pres.
Trustee: Hilary Isakow.
EIN: 382948092

912
Keith A. Iverson Foundation
300 E. Huron St.
Milford, MI 48381

Established in 1998 in MI.
Donor: Keith A. Iverson.
Grantmaker type: Independent foundation.
Financial data (yr. ended 12/31/05): Assets, $1,188 (M); gifts received, $10,000; expenditures, $9,695; total giving, $9,500; qualifying distributions, $9,500; giving activities include $9,500 for grants.
Limitations: Giving limited to MI.
Officers: Keith A. Iverson, Pres. and Treas.; Mark D. Hamlin, Secy.
Directors: John M. Foster; Amy M. Iverson; Clifford T. Iverson; Michael H. Russell.
EIN: 383378231

913
John Ivkov Foundation
24416 Cubberness St.
St. Clair Shores, MI 48080

Established in 2002 in MI.
Donors: John Ivkov Memorial; Black River Country Club.
Grantmaker type: Independent foundation.
Financial data (yr. ended 12/31/05): Assets, $1,286 (M); gifts received, $1,500; expenditures, $5,470; total giving, $5,000; qualifying distributions, $5,000; giving activities include $5,000 for grants.
Fields of interest: Children/youth, services.
Limitations: Applications not accepted. Giving primarily in MI. No grants to individuals.
Application information: Contributes only to pre-selected organizations.
Directors: Michelle Davis; John C. Ivkov; Tracy M. Ivkov.
EIN: 364496562

914
J.C. Charitable Trust Fund
P.O. Box 513189
Los Angeles, CA 90051-1189
Contact: Lawrence J. Wiegand, Tr.
Application address: 5672 Sugarloaf Trail, Cave Creek, AZ 85331

Established in 1992 in MI.
Donor: Lawrence J. Wiegand.
Grantmaker type: Independent foundation.
Financial data (yr. ended 10/31/05): Assets, $464,348 (M); gifts received, $45,000; expenditures, $46,722; total giving, $43,160; qualifying distributions, $43,160; giving activities include $43,160 for grants.

Fields of interest: Higher education; Education.
Type of support: Scholarship funds.
Limitations: Giving limited to AZ and MI. No grants to individuals.
Application information: Application form not required.
  Deadline(s): None
Trustee: Lawrence J. Wiegand.
EIN: 383083137

915
Jackson Audubon Society, Inc.
c/o Cheryl DeGroote
P.O. Box 6453
Jackson, MI 49204-6453

Established in 1989 in MI.
Grantmaker type: Independent foundation.
Financial data (yr. ended 5/31/05): Assets, $101,819 (M); gifts received, $6,559; expenditures, $5,657; total giving, $900; qualifying distributions, $900; giving activities include $900 for grants.
Fields of interest: Environment, natural resources.
Limitations: Applications not accepted. Giving primarily in MI. No grants to individuals.
Application information: Contributes only to pre-selected organizations.
Officers and Directors:* Connie Spotts,* Pres.; Susan Larson,* V.P.; Diane Valen,* Secy.; Cheryl DeGroote,* Treas.; Barbara Anderson; Nancy Lapinski; and 7 additional directors.
EIN: 386065102

916
Corwill and Margie Jackson Foundation
c/o Comerica Bank
P.O. Box 75000, M/C 3302
Detroit, MI 48275-3302
Application address: c/o David J. Hall, 6954 W. Jackson Rd., Ludington, MI 49431-9428

Donors: Corwill Jackson†; Margie Jackson†.
Grantmaker type: Independent foundation.
Financial data (yr. ended 12/31/05): Assets, $2,539,025 (M); expenditures, $160,311; total giving, $130,000; qualifying distributions, $131,940; giving activities include $130,000 for 68 grants to individuals (high: $6,000; low: $300).
Purpose and activities: Four-year scholarships awarded to graduating high school seniors in Mason County, MI, starting their first year of college.
Type of support: Scholarships—to individuals.
Limitations: Giving limited to residents of Mason County, MI.
Application information: Application form required.
  Deadline(s): May 1
Officers: David J. Hall, Pres.; Margie N. Bach, Secy.; Thomas Hall, Treas.
Director: Jens Bach; Susan Meyers.
EIN: 386064502

917
The Jacob Family Foundation Corporation
31920 Mountain View
Franklin, MI 48025
Contact: Arnold M. Jacob, Tr.

Established in 1987 in OH.
Grantmaker type: Independent foundation.

Financial data (yr. ended 12/31/04): Assets, $2,263,613 (M); expenditures, $141,051; total giving, $136,104; qualifying distributions, $140,814; giving activities include $136,104 for 5 grants (high: $50,000; low: $500).
Fields of interest: Education; Human services; Federated giving programs; Jewish federated giving programs; Jewish agencies & temples.
Limitations: Giving primarily in FL, MI, and Dayton, OH.
Application information: Application form not required.
  Initial approach: Letter
  Copies of proposal: 1
Trustees: Arnold M. Jacob; Louise M. Jacob; Richard J. Jacob; Patricia Vanartsdalen.
EIN: 311214668
Selected grants: The following grants were reported in 2004.
$50,000 to Campaign for Crainbrook School, Dayton, OH. For general support.
$34,000 to Jewish Federation of Metropolitan Detroit, Bloomfield Hills, MI. For general support.
$26,604 to Islamorada Firefighters Benevolent Association, Islamorada, FL. For general support.
$25,000 to University of Michigan, Ann Arbor, MI. For general support.
$500 to Humane Society of Greater Dayton, Dayton, OH. For general support.

918
Fredrica, Neva & Abraham Jaffe Scholarship Fund f/b/o Colon High School
(formerly Jaffe Charitable Trust f/b/o Colon High School)
c/o Citizens Bank Wealth Mgmt., N.A.
328 S. Saginaw St., M/C 002072
Flint, MI 48502-2401
Application address: c/o Lloyd Kirby, Superintendent, Colon Community Schools, 400 Dallas St., Colon, MI 49040-9318, tel.: (269) 432-3231

Established in 1992 in MI.
Grantmaker type: Independent foundation.
Financial data (yr. ended 12/31/05): Assets, $191,553 (M); expenditures, $4,835; total giving, $0; qualifying distributions, $0.
Purpose and activities: Scholarships awarded to graduates of Colon High School, MI, pursuing an R.N. or L.P.N. nursing degree.
Fields of interest: Nursing school/education; Scholarships/financial aid.
Type of support: Scholarship funds; Scholarships—to individuals.
Limitations: Giving limited to residents of Colon, MI.
Application information: Application form required.
  Deadline(s): May 1
Trustee: Citizens Bank.
EIN: 316447467

919
The Jampel Family Foundation
4363 Barchester Dr.
Bloomfield Hills, MI 48302

Established in MI in 1998.
Donor: Robert S. Jampel.
Grantmaker type: Independent foundation.

Financial data (yr. ended 12/31/04): Assets, $345,111 (M); gifts received, $200,583; expenditures, $226,118; total giving, $223,020; qualifying distributions, $222,595; giving activities include $223,020 for 15 grants (high: $105,200; low: $100).
Purpose and activities: Giving primarily for education.
Fields of interest: Higher education; Jewish federated giving programs; Jewish agencies & temples.
Type of support: General/operating support.
Limitations: Applications not accepted. Giving primarily in MI. No grants to individuals.
Application information: Contributes only to pre-selected organizations.
  Board meeting date(s): Dec. 15
Officers: Robert S. Jampel, Pres.; Joan M. Jampel, Secy.
Directors: Delia Ellen Jampel Frank; Henry David Jampel; James Meyers Jampel; Emily Sharon Sherman.
Number of staff: None.
EIN: 383432413
Selected grants: The following grants were reported in 2004.
$105,200 to Wayne State University, Detroit, MI.
$100,000 to United Jewish Foundation, Bloomfield Hills, MI.
$8,750 to Jewish Federation of Metropolitan Detroit, Bloomfield Hills, MI.
$2,600 to Temple Beth El, Bloomfield Hills, MI.
$1,250 to Detroit Symphony Orchestra, Detroit, MI.
$1,000 to ARVO Foundation for Eye Research, Rockville, MD.
$1,000 to Johns Hopkins Medical Institutions, Wilmer Eye Institute, Baltimore, MD.
$750 to University of Michigan, Ann Arbor, MI. For Heinz Prechter Fund.
$500 to Columbia University, College of Physicians and Surgeons, New York, NY.
$500 to Princeton University, Princeton, NJ.

920
The Janes Family Foundation
1485 Lochridge Rd.
Bloomfield Hills, MI 48302

Established in 1997 in MI.
Donor: Richard J. Janes.
Grantmaker type: Independent foundation.
Financial data (yr. ended 12/31/04): Assets, $188,035 (M); expenditures, $150; total giving, $0; qualifying distributions, $0.
Fields of interest: Education; Community development.
Limitations: Applications not accepted. Giving primarily in MI. No grants to individuals.
Application information: Contributes only to pre-selected organizations.
Officers: Richard J. Janes, Pres.; Mary Louise Jane, Secy.; Robert Anthony Janes, Treas.
Director: Joanna Janes Boeckl.
EIN: 383352169

921
The Jas Foundation
25216 Pierce St.
Southfield, MI 48075-2059

Established in 2003 in MI.

Donor: Julius & Senta Buck Memorial Trust.
Grantmaker type: Independent foundation.
Financial data (yr. ended 12/31/05): Assets, $558,519 (M); expenditures, $8,940; total giving, $7,700; qualifying distributions, $7,700; giving activities include $7,700 for grants.
Fields of interest: Jewish agencies & temples.
Limitations: Applications not accepted. Giving on a national basis. No grants to individuals.
Application information: Contributes only to pre-selected organizations.
Trustee: Henry S. Baum.
EIN: 352198588

922
Jasam Foundation Fund B

1002 N. Dalian Pl.
Tucson, AZ 85748-2070
Contact: Joan D. Guylas, Admin.

Established in 2002 in AR.
Grantmaker type: Independent foundation.
Financial data (yr. ended 12/31/04): Assets, $8,501,420 (M); expenditures, $520,949; total giving, $461,098; qualifying distributions, $461,098; giving activities include $461,098 for 17 grants (high: $161,641; low: $3,000).
Purpose and activities: Giving to support U.S. troops.
Fields of interest: Hospitals (general); Human services; Children/youth, services; Christian agencies & churches.
Limitations: Applications not accepted. Giving limited to western MI, and the greater Tucson, AZ, area. No grants to individuals.
Application information: Contributes only to pre-selected organizations.
    Board meeting date(s): Varies
Officer: Joan D. Guylas, Admin.
Number of staff: 1 part-time support.
EIN: 383637370

923
Karen Sokolof Javitch Charitable Foundation

c/o Comerica Bank
P.O. Box 75000, M/C 3302
Detroit, MI 48275-3302
Application address: c/o Comerica Bank, Attn: Ted Stumpp, P.O. Box 75000, M/C 5124, Detroit, MI 48275-5124, Colorado tel.: (303) 294-3349

Established in 2004 in NE.
Donor: Phil Sokolof‡.
Grantmaker type: Independent foundation.
Financial data (yr. ended 12/31/05): Assets, $1,945,623 (M); expenditures, $162,713; total giving, $140,000; qualifying distributions, $140,500; giving activities include $140,000 for 15 grants (high: $90,327; low: $48).
Fields of interest: Jewish agencies & temples; Children/youth; Blind/visually impaired.
Limitations: Giving primarily in Omaha, NE. No support for organizations lacking 501(c)(3) status. No grants to individuals.
Application information: Application form not required.
    Deadline(s): None
Trustee: Comerica Bank.
EIN: 746536463

924
Jaya Charitable Foundation

26500 Northwestern Hwy., Ste. 260
Southfield, MI 48076

Established in 2002 in MI.
Donors: Arvind Shah; Akshay Shah; Priya Velji.
Grantmaker type: Independent foundation.
Financial data (yr. ended 12/31/05): Assets, $222,151 (M); gifts received, $165,000; expenditures, $105,074; total giving, $105,000; qualifying distributions, $105,000; giving activities include $105,000 for 2 grants (high: $80,000; low: $25,000).
Type of support: General/operating support.
Limitations: Applications not accepted. No grants to individuals.
Application information: Contributes only to pre-selected organizations.
Officer: Arvind Shah, Pres.
Directors: Vrajesh Patel; Akshay Shah; Jayshree Shah.
EIN: 320027023

925
The JCM Foundation

c/o U.S. Trust
1600 Tysons Blvd., Ste. 250
McLean, VA 22102

Donors: James F. Macguidwin; Cheryl Y. Macguidwin.
Grantmaker type: Independent foundation.
Financial data (yr. ended 9/30/05): Assets, $3,378,774 (M); expenditures, $184,476; total giving, $161,500; qualifying distributions, $161,500; giving activities include $161,500 for 11 grants (high: $75,000; low: $1,000).
Fields of interest: Education; Health organizations; Human services; Protestant agencies & churches.
Limitations: Applications not accepted. Giving primarily in MI and VA. No grants to individuals.
Application information: Contributes only to pre-selected organizations.
Directors: Cheryl Y. Macguidwin; James F. Macguidwin.
EIN: 611409457

926
JCT Foundation

6812 Farrell Dr. N.E.
Rockford, MI 49341-9410
Contact: Jeff Power

Established in 1997 in MI.
Donors: William W. Idema; P. Craig Welch, Jr.
Grantmaker type: Independent foundation.
Financial data (yr. ended 12/31/05): Assets, $12,421,092 (M); gifts received, $68,400; expenditures, $413,701; total giving, $396,400; qualifying distributions, $399,521; giving activities include $396,400 for 32 grants (high: $70,500; low: $2,500).
Purpose and activities: Giving primarily to Christian agencies and churches.
Limitations: Applications not accepted. Giving on a national basis.
Application information: Unsolicited requests for funds not accepted.

Officers and Trustees:* P. Craig Welch, Jr.,* Pres.; Mary K. Welch,* V.P.; Julie W. Regan; P. Craig Welch III; Thomas J. Welch.
EIN: 383386697
Selected grants: The following grants were reported in 2003.
$63,000 to North Hills Classical Academy, Grand Rapids, MI. For operating support.
$47,500 to Gildas Club Grand Rapids, Grand Rapids, MI. For building fund.
$28,000 to First Assembly of God of Fort Myers, Fort Myers, FL. For debt retirement.
$25,000 to Eagle Forum Education and Legal Defense Fund, DC. For operating support.
$22,000 to Grand Rapids Baptist Schools, Grand Rapids, MI. For operating support.
$15,000 to Campus Crusade for Christ International, Orlando, FL. For operating support.
$15,000 to Free Congress Research and Education Foundation, DC. For operating support.
$10,000 to Grand Rapids Art Museum, Grand Rapids, MI. For building fund.
$10,000 to Michigan State University, East Lansing, MI. For building fund.
$10,000 to Potters House, Grand Rapids, MI. For operating support.

927
Michael Jeffers Memorial Education Fund

c/o Citizens Bank Wealth Mgmt., N.A.
328 S. Saginaw St., M/C 002072
Flint, MI 48502
Application address: c/o Helen James, Citizens Bank, N.A., Wealth Mgmt., 101 N. Washington Ave., Saginaw, MI 48607, tel.: (989) 776-7368

Established in 1999 in MI.
Donor: Michael Jeffers Memorial Fund.
Grantmaker type: Independent foundation.
Financial data (yr. ended 12/31/05): Assets, $6,433,338 (M); expenditures, $104,948; total giving, $0; qualifying distributions, $0.
Purpose and activities: Student loans to residents of Saginaw, MI, ages 16 to 19, with a need for economic aid.
Type of support: Student loans—to individuals.
Limitations: Giving primarily to residents of Saginaw, MI.
Application information: Application form required.
    Deadline(s): June 1 for renewals, June 15 for new loans
Trustee: Citizens Bank.
EIN: 383431990

928
John Michael Jeffers Memorial Fund

c/o Citizens Bank
325 S. Saginaw St., M/C 002072
Flint, MI 48502
Application address: c/o Helen James, Citizens Bank Wealth Mgmt., N.A., 101 N. Washington Ave., Saginaw, MI 48607, tel.: (989) 776-7368

Established in 1994 in MI.
Grantmaker type: Independent foundation.
Financial data (yr. ended 4/30/04): Assets, $2,529,065 (M); expenditures, $123,987; total giving, $93,353; qualifying distributions, $98,867; giving activities include $93,353 for 5 grants (high: $30,000; low: $5,000).

Fields of interest: Hospitals (general); Food services; Boys & girls clubs; Community development; Foundations (community).
Limitations: Giving limited to Saginaw County, MI. No grants to individuals.
Application information:
Initial approach: Letter or telephone requesting application guidelines
Deadline(s): None
Trustee: Citizens Bank.
EIN: 237425043

929
Jennings Memorial Foundation

c/o Citizens Bank Wealth Mgmt., N.A.
328 S. Saginaw St., Ste. 001051
Flint, MI   48502
Contact: Donald A. Snide, Dir.

Established in 1997 in MI.
Donors: Edith Jennings Trust; Wyman Jennings Trust.
Grantmaker type: Independent foundation.
Financial data (yr. ended 12/31/05): Assets, $5,043,370 (M); expenditures, $330,352; total giving, $204,200; qualifying distributions, $271,829; giving activities include $204,200 for 27 grants (high: $24,000; low: $1,000).
Purpose and activities: The foundation supports charities in the area of Montrose, Michigan, with emphasis on public education, Protestant churches, and municipal agencies.
Fields of interest: Elementary/secondary education; Disasters, fire prevention/control; Human services; Government/public administration; Protestant agencies & churches.
Type of support: General/operating support; Equipment.
Limitations: Giving primarily in Montrose, MI, and surrounding areas. No support for political organizations.
Publications: Application guidelines.
Application information: Grant suggestions are made by the Board of Directors. Application form not required.
Copies of proposal: 1
Deadline(s): None
Board meeting date(s): 3rd Thurs. in Feb., Apr., June, Oct., and Dec.
Directors: James McCartney; Donald A. Snide; Donald W. Snide; John C. Wendling.
Trustee: Citizens Bank.
EIN: 386684041
Selected grants: The following grants were reported in 2004.
$27,000 to Montrose Area Historical Association, Montrose, MI. For museum.
$10,000 to Montrose Community Schools, Montrose, MI. For science kits.
$8,500 to Food Bank of Eastern Michigan, Flint, MI.
$8,500 to Salvation Army Flint, Flint, MI.
$8,500 to Shelter of Flint, Flint, MI.
$5,000 to Catholic Charities of Shiawassee and Genesee Counties, Flint, MI. To replace boiler.
$4,000 to Carriage Town Mission, Flint, MI.
$4,000 to Christian Faith Church, Montrose, MI.
$4,000 to Good Shepherd Church, Montrose, MI.
$4,000 to Montrose Baptist Church, Montrose, MI.

930
Jensen Foundation

1702 Hill St.
Ann Arbor, MI   48104   (734) 995-0694
Contact: James Jensen, Pres.

Established in MI.
Donors: Keith D. Jensen; A. Paul Jensen.
Grantmaker type: Independent foundation.
Financial data (yr. ended 12/31/04): Assets, $162,460 (M); expenditures, $9,232; total giving, $8,000; qualifying distributions, $8,000; giving activities include $8,000 for grants.
Fields of interest: Health care, clinics/centers.
Limitations: Giving primarily in MI. No grants to individuals.
Application information: Application form not required.
Initial approach: Proposal
Deadline(s): None
Officers: James Jensen, Pres.; Keith C. Jensen, V.P.; Patricia Verhage, Secy.; Thomas Jensen, Treas.
EIN: 386082462

931
The Jentes Family Foundation

c/o William R. Jentes
1500 N. Lake Shore Dr., Ste. 4C
Chicago, IL   60610-6686

Established in 1987 in IL.
Donors: Janet O. Jentes; William R. Jentes.
Grantmaker type: Independent foundation.
Financial data (yr. ended 12/31/05): Assets, $6,441,083 (M); gifts received, $299,981; expenditures, $238,003; total giving, $233,579; qualifying distributions, $235,700; giving activities include $233,579 for 16 grants (high: $202,229; low: $100).
Purpose and activities: Giving primarily for the arts and higher education.
Fields of interest: Performing arts, opera; Arts; Higher education.
Limitations: Applications not accepted. Giving primarily in Chicago, IL, and Ann Arbor, MI. No grants to individuals.
Application information: Contributes only to pre-selected organizations.
Officers and Directors:* William R. Jentes, Pres. and Treas.; Donald G. Kempf, Jr.,* Secy.; Janet O. Jentes; Justine D. Jentes.
EIN: 363566107

932
The JKO Foundation Charitable Trust

c/o Mr. & Mrs. Kenneth Ozinga
1580 Thorofare Rd., P.O. Box 169
Minocqua, WI   54548

Established in 1999 in IL.
Donors: Kenneth J. Zinga; Judith A. Zinga.
Grantmaker type: Independent foundation.
Financial data (yr. ended 12/31/04): Assets, $371,021 (M); gifts received, $1,638; expenditures, $231,757; total giving, $225,000; qualifying distributions, $224,708; giving activities include $225,000 for 3 grants (high: $100,000; low: $25,000).
Fields of interest: Christian agencies & churches.

Limitations: Applications not accepted. Giving primarily in IL and MI. No grants to individuals.
Application information: Contributes only to pre-selected organizations.
Trustees: Charles J. Ozinga; Judith A. Ozinga; Kenneth J. Ozinga.
EIN: 367293190
Selected grants: The following grants were reported in 2004.
$100,000 to Advocate Charitable Foundation, Park Ridge, IL. For unrestricted support.
$100,000 to Christ Church of Oak Brook, Oak Brook, IL. For unrestricted support.
$25,000 to Calvin College, Grand Rapids, MI. For unrestricted support.

933
Conrad & Caroline Jobst Foundation

c/o KeyBank N.A.
P.O. Box 10099
Toledo, OH   43699-0099   (419) 259-8655
Contact: Diane Ohns, V.P., KeyBank N.A.

Established in 1986 in OH.
Grantmaker type: Independent foundation.
Financial data (yr. ended 12/31/04): Assets, $12,868,314 (M); gifts received, $32; expenditures, $608,838; total giving, $540,000; qualifying distributions, $585,046; giving activities include $540,000 for 4 grants (high: $210,000; low: $60,000).
Purpose and activities: Giving primarily for health associations and medical education; funding also for an Episcopal church, and the symphony.
Fields of interest: Performing arts, orchestra (symphony); Higher education; Medical research, institute; Protestant agencies & churches.
Limitations: Giving primarily in Toledo, OH; funding also in Ann Arbor, MI. No grants to individuals.
Application information:
Initial approach: Letter
Deadline(s): July 31
Trustees: John M. Curphey; Douglas Metz; Orval Seydlitz; KeyBank N.A.
EIN: 346872214

934
Donald L. Johns Family Foundation

2000 Town Ctr., Ste. 900
Southfield, MI   48075-1100

Established in MI in 1998.
Donor: Donald L. Johns.
Grantmaker type: Independent foundation.
Financial data (yr. ended 12/31/04): Assets, $73,726 (M); expenditures, $9,184; total giving, $1,000; qualifying distributions, $1,000; giving activities include $1,000 for grants.
Fields of interest: Food services.
Limitations: Applications not accepted. Giving primarily in MI. No grants to individuals.
Application information: Contributes only to pre-selected organizations.
Officer: H. Rollin Allen, Pres.; Lynn Hoskins, V.P.; Janice L. Johns, V.P.; Clare A. Allen, Secy.-Treas.
Director: Tracy L. Allen.
EIN: 383388669

935
Wilburn L. & Barbara J. Johnson Family Foundation

445 S. Livernois Rd., Ste. 105
Rochester Hills, MI   48307-2575

Established in 1998 in MI.
Donor: Wilburn L. Johnson.
Grantmaker type: Independent foundation.
Financial data (yr. ended 12/31/05): Assets, $71,327 (M); gifts received, $96,354; expenditures, $48,000; total giving, $48,000; qualifying distributions, $48,000; giving activities include $48,000 for grants.
Limitations: Applications not accepted. Giving primarily in Lapeer, MI. No grants to individuals.
Application information: Contributes only to pre-selected organizations.
Officers: Wilburn L. Johnson, Pres.; Barbara J. Johnson, Secy.
Director: Joan Cowan.
EIN: 383417875

936
The Lloyd and Mabel Johnson Foundation

10315 Grand River
Brighton, MI   48116

Established in 1990 in FL.
Donors: Lloyd R. Johnson‡; Mabel K. Johnson.
Grantmaker type: Independent foundation.
Financial data (yr. ended 9/30/05): Assets, $5,468,010 (M); gifts received, $85,792; expenditures, $269,011; total giving, $115,400; qualifying distributions, $120,891; giving activities include $115,400 for 22 grants (high: $20,000; low: $900).
Fields of interest: Museums; Education; Health care; Eye research; Alzheimer's disease research; American Red Cross; Christian agencies & churches.
Type of support: Scholarship funds.
Limitations: Applications not accepted. Giving on a national basis.
Application information: Contributes only to pre-selected organizations.
Officer: Gordon H. Kummer,* Pres.
Director: Linda Kummer*.
Trustees: Catherine Kalman; Anna Miller; Daniel Miller; Karen Townsley.
EIN: 593009032

937
Paul A. Johnson Foundation

c/o Bari Stanton Johnson
41 Washington Ave., Ste. 349
Grand Haven, MI   49417-1378

Established around 1955 in MI.
Donor: Paul A. Johnson‡.
Grantmaker type: Independent foundation.
Financial data (yr. ended 12/31/04): Assets, $453,669 (M); gifts received, $10,003; expenditures, $20,866; total giving, $6,230; qualifying distributions, $14,498; giving activities include $6,230 for grants.
Fields of interest: Historical activities; Higher education; Human services; Christian agencies & churches.
Type of support: Continuing support; Annual campaigns; Program development.

Limitations: Applications not accepted. Giving primarily in MI. No grants to individuals.
Application information: Contributes only to pre-selected organizations.
Officer and Trustees:* Bari S. Johnson,* Pres.; Charlotte A. Johnson; Donald A. Johnson; JoAnn R. Johnson.
EIN: 386048818

938
The Paul T. and Frances B. Johnson Foundation

787 Michigan Ave.
P.O. Box 203
Benzonia, MI   49616-0203   (231) 882-4681
Contact: Jon M. Haugen, Chair.

Established in 1997.
Donors: Paul Johnson; Frances Johnson.
Grantmaker type: Independent foundation.
Financial data (yr. ended 6/30/05): Assets, $3,653,256 (M); expenditures, $203,217; total giving, $193,900; qualifying distributions, $193,900; giving activities include $10,000 for 4 grants (high: $7,000; low: $1,000), and $183,900 for 111 grants to individuals (high: $8,000; low: $600).
Purpose and activities: Giving primarily for college scholarships; some giving also for human services and community services.
Fields of interest: Education; Human services; Community development.
Type of support: General/operating support; Scholarships—to individuals.
Limitations: Giving limited to residents of Benzie, Grand Traverse, and Leelanau counties, MI.
Application information:
  Initial approach: Application form required for scholarships
  Deadline(s): May 1 for scholarships and honoraria
  Final notification: No later than July 30 for scholarships and honoraria
Officers and Directors:* Jon M. Haugen,* Chair. and Treas.; Lawrence I. McKay III,* Secy.; Ingrid K. Brey; James Kaiser; Dale A. Penny.
EIN: 383382755

939
The Johnson Foundation

225 Merrill St.
Birmingham, MI   48009

Established in 1986 in MI.
Donors: Paul H. Johnson; Pamela Callam; Scott A. Melby; Colleen M. Wolford; Kevin P. Johnson; Drew Wolford; Karen Melby; Lisa Johnson.
Grantmaker type: Independent foundation.
Financial data (yr. ended 11/30/05): Assets, $849,017 (M); gifts received, $795,267; expenditures, $770,563; total giving, $729,370; qualifying distributions, $746,502; giving activities include $729,370 for 106 grants (high: $202,500; low: $100).
Purpose and activities: Giving primarily for Christian religious organizations including churches, schools, and missions.
Fields of interest: Education; Human services; Christian agencies & churches; Protestant agencies & churches.

Limitations: Applications not accepted. Giving on a national basis, with some emphasis on MI. No grants to individuals.
Application information: Contributes only to pre-selected organizations.
Officers: Paul H. Johnson, Pres.; Marilyn B. Johnson, V.P.; Kevin P. Johnson, Secy.
EIN: 382706960
Selected grants: The following grants were reported in 2004.
$192,000 to Walk Thru the Bible Ministries, Atlanta, GA.
$71,100 to Maranatha Bible and Missionary Conference, Muskegon, MI.
$60,000 to Crown Ministries, Longwood, FL.
$47,000 to OMS International, Greenwood, IN.
$35,000 to Highland Park Baptist Church, Southfield, MI.
$27,000 to Southfield Christian School, Southfield, MI.
$26,000 to Judson College, Elgin, IL.
$15,300 to Moody Bible Institute of Chicago, Chicago, IL.
$15,000 to Peter Deyneka Russian Ministries, Wheaton, IL.
$14,000 to Sanctuary Community Church, Greenwood, IN.

940
Joie de Vivre Foundation

(formerly Dennis & Eileen Ellens Foundation)
345 E. 48th St., Ste. 200
Holland, MI   49423

Established in 1989 in MI.
Donors: Dennis Ellens; Eileen Ellens; Edgar Prince; Elsa Prince; Prince Holding Corp.
Grantmaker type: Independent foundation.
Financial data (yr. ended 12/31/05): Assets, $1,238 (M); gifts received, $265,000; expenditures, $266,041; total giving, $266,000; qualifying distributions, $266,038; giving activities include $266,000 for 18 grants (high: $75,000; low: $500).
Purpose and activities: Giving primarily to Christian organizations, including churches, schools, and youth and family services.
Fields of interest: Education; Human services; Children/youth, services; Family services; Christian agencies & churches.
Type of support: General/operating support.
Limitations: Applications not accepted. Giving primarily in MI, with emphasis on Holland. No grants to individuals.
Application information: Contributes only to pre-selected organizations.
Officers: Eileen Ellens, Pres.; Kenneth Filippini, Secy.; Dennis Ellens, Treas.
EIN: 382902415
Selected grants: The following grants were reported in 2005.
$75,000 to Winning at Home, Holland, MI. For general operating support.
$51,000 to Calvary Christian Reformed Church, Holland, MI. For general operating support.
$25,000 to Childrens Assessment Center, Childrens Advocacy Center of Ottawa County, Holland, MI. For general operating support.
$25,000 to Providence Youth Outreach, Pontiac, MI. For general operating support.
$20,000 to Holland Rescue Mission, Holland, MI. For general operating support.

$11,000 to Youth Life, Colorado Springs, CO. For general operating support.

$10,000 to Authentic Leadership, Holland, MI. For general operating support.

$10,000 to Detroit Sports Ministry, Oakland, MI. For general operating support.

$8,000 to Community Foundation of the Holland Zeeland Area, Holland, MI. For general operating support.

$3,000 to Central Wesleyan Church, Holland, MI. For general operating support.

941
Jonathan & David Foundation
c/o Bill Biel
9365 Vergennes St. N.E.
Ada, MI 49301

Established in 1982 in MI.
Donors: Samuel Butcher; William Biel.
Grantmaker type: Independent foundation.
Financial data (yr. ended 12/31/05): Assets, $557,523 (M); expenditures, $40,588; total giving, $28,500; qualifying distributions, $28,500; giving activities include $28,500 for grants.
Fields of interest: Elementary/secondary education; Christian agencies & churches; Protestant agencies & churches; Religion.
International interests: Philippines.
Limitations: Applications not accepted. Giving on a national basis; some giving in the Philippines. No grants to individuals.
Application information: Contributes only to pre-selected organizations.
Trustee: William Biel.
EIN: 382443692

942
The Jonathan Foundation
2006 S. Cross Creek Dr. S.E.
Grand Rapids, MI 49508-8780

Established in 1995 in MI.
Donor: James Velting.
Grantmaker type: Independent foundation.
Financial data (yr. ended 12/31/05): Assets, $3,376,513 (M); gifts received, $7,500; expenditures, $181,342; total giving, $108,170; qualifying distributions, $108,170; giving activities include $108,170 for 15 grants (high: $45,800; low: $100).
Purpose and activities: Giving primarily for Christian organizations, including missions and theology colleges.
Fields of interest: Higher education; Recreation, camps; Christian agencies & churches.
Type of support: General/operating support; Building/renovation.
Limitations: Applications not accepted. Giving primarily in MI. No grants to individuals.
Application information: Contributes only to pre-selected organizations.
Officers: James Velting, Pres.; Phyllis Velting, V.P.; Kim Velting, Secy.; Vicki Bickel, Treas.
EIN: 383246029

943
The Jondy Foundation
26300 Telegraph Rd., 2nd Fl.
Southfield, MI 48034

Established in 2003.
Grantmaker type: Independent foundation.
Financial data (yr. ended 12/31/04): Assets, $359,689 (M); gifts received, $250,000; expenditures, $37,561; total giving, $36,000; qualifying distributions, $36,000; giving activities include $36,000 for grants.
Fields of interest: Religious federated giving programs; Islam.
Limitations: Giving primarily in MI.
Officer: Abdelmajid Jondy, Pres.
EIN: 364530214

944
Calvin and Deborah A. Jones Family Foundation
5061 Retha Ct.
Flint, MI 48504

Established in 2002 in MI.
Grantmaker type: Independent foundation.
Financial data (yr. ended 12/31/05): Assets, $11,553 (M); gifts received, $10,100; expenditures, $3,016; total giving, $850; qualifying distributions, $3,016; giving activities include $850 for grants.
Limitations: Applications not accepted. No grants to individuals.
Application information: Contributes only to pre-selected organizations.
Officer and Trustees: Deborah Jones,* Secy.; Calvin Jones, Exec. Dir.
EIN: 550806892

945
Jones Foundation
936 Sycamore Ave.
Holland, MI 49424

Established in 1993 in MI.
Donors: Walter T. Jones; Marion J. Jones.
Grantmaker type: Independent foundation.
Financial data (yr. ended 12/31/04): Assets, $16,000 (M); gifts received, $40,000; expenditures, $35,137; total giving, $34,000; qualifying distributions, $34,000; giving activities include $34,000 for grants.
Purpose and activities: Giving primarily to education, human services, and Roman Catholic churches and agencies.
Fields of interest: Education; Boys & girls clubs; Human services; Family services; Roman Catholic agencies & churches.
Limitations: Applications not accepted. Giving primarily in MI. No grants to individuals.
Application information: Contributes only to pre-selected organizations.
Officers: Walter T. Jones, Pres.; Marion J. Jones, Secy.; David W. Jones, Treas.
Director: Karen M. Richelsen.
EIN: 383148994

946
Mary Bartush Jones Foundation
22140 Orchard Way
Beverly Hills, MI 48025

Established in 1986 in MI.
Donor: Mary Bartush Jones.
Grantmaker type: Independent foundation.

Financial data (yr. ended 10/31/05): Assets, $764,373 (M); expenditures, $27,232; total giving, $25,750; qualifying distributions, $25,750; giving activities include $25,750 for grants.
Fields of interest: Arts; Education; Hospitals (general).
Type of support: General/operating support.
Limitations: Applications not accepted. Giving primarily in MI. No grants to individuals.
Application information: Contributes only to pre-selected organizations.
Officers: Mary Bartush Jones, Pres.; Michael Douglas Jones, Secy.
EIN: 386505469

947
Sherrie L. Jones Foundation
16845 Kercheval St., Ste. 5
Grosse Pointe, MI 48230-1551
Contact: Sherrie L. Jones, Pres.

Established in 1998 in MI.
Donor: Sherrie L. Jones.
Grantmaker type: Independent foundation.
Financial data (yr. ended 12/31/05): Assets, $5,310 (M); gifts received, $30,000; expenditures, $37,000; total giving, $33,000; qualifying distributions, $33,000; giving activities include $33,000 for grants.
Fields of interest: Higher education.
Type of support: General/operating support.
Limitations: Giving primarily in MI. No grants to individuals.
Application information: Application form not required.
   Deadline(s): None
Officers and Trustees:* Sherrie L. Jones,* Pres.; Jennifer Shapiro,* Secy.
EIN: 383407495

948
Joseph Foundation
3741 Monarch Dr. N.E.
Grand Rapids, MI 49525

Established in 2001 in MI.
Donor: Betty Smyth.
Grantmaker type: Independent foundation.
Financial data (yr. ended 12/31/05): Assets, $188,638 (M); expenditures, $13,533; total giving, $10,500; qualifying distributions, $10,500; giving activities include $10,500 for grants.
Application information:
   Initial approach: Letter
   Deadline(s): None
Officer: Roy G. Smyth, Pres.
EIN: 300002540

949
The Joslin Foundation, Inc.
P.O Box 7212
Sturgis, MI 49091

Established in 1999.
Donor: Burr G. Joslin.
Grantmaker type: Independent foundation.
Financial data (yr. ended 12/31/05): Assets, $603,532 (M); expenditures, $44,853; total giving, $35,415; qualifying distributions, $35,415; giving activities include $35,415 for grants.

Fields of interest: Education; Protestant agencies & churches.
Type of support: General/operating support.
Limitations: Applications not accepted. Giving primarily in MI. No grants to individuals.
Application information: Contributes only to pre-selected organizations.
Officers and Directors:* Burr G. Joslin,* Pres.; Judith Joslin-Page,* V.P.; Nancy Joslin Kaleel,* V.P.; Elizabeth A. Joslin,* Treas.
EIN: 383484334

950
Marjorie and Maxwell Jospey Foundation
1 Towne Sq., Ste. 600
Southfield, MI 48076-3710
Contact: Maxwell Jospey, Pres.; Marjorie R. Jospey, V.P.

Established in 1948 in MI.
Donor: Maxwell Jospey.
Grantmaker type: Independent foundation.
Financial data (yr. ended 11/30/05): Assets, $18,862 (M); expenditures, $12,591; total giving, $12,500; qualifying distributions, $12,500; giving activities include $12,500 for 3 grants (high: $5,000; low: $2,500).
Fields of interest: Performing arts; Animals/wildlife, special services; Federated giving programs; Blind/visually impaired.
Limitations: Giving primarily in MI. No grants to individuals.
Application information:
  Initial approach: Proposal
  Deadline(s): None
Officers: Maxwell Jospey, Pres.; Marjorie R. Jospey, V.P.
EIN: 386061846

951
Joy Foundation
350 24th St.
Hudsonville, MI 49426-8673
Contact: Steven C. Windemuller, Dir.

Donors: Steven C. Windemuller; Debra Windemuller.
Grantmaker type: Independent foundation.
Financial data (yr. ended 12/31/05): Assets, $80,158 (M); gifts received, $16; expenditures, $103,061; total giving, $102,770; qualifying distributions, $102,770; giving activities include $102,770 for grants.
Fields of interest: Christian agencies & churches.
Type of support: General/operating support.
Limitations: Giving primarily in MI. No grants to individuals.
Application information:
  Initial approach: Letter
  Deadline(s): None
Directors: Debra Windemuller; Steven C. Windemuller.
EIN: 382898700

952
George W. & Sadie Marie Juhl Scholarship Fund
c/o Southern Michigan Bank & Trust
51 W. Pearl St.
Coldwater, MI 49036-1933
Contact: Mary Guthrie

Established in 1983 in MI.
Grantmaker type: Independent foundation.
Financial data (yr. ended 3/31/06): Assets, $2,836,692 (M); expenditures, $158,059; total giving, $134,000; qualifying distributions, $134,000; giving activities include $134,000 for 68 grants to individuals (high: $2,000; low: $1,000).
Purpose and activities: Awards scholarships for Branch County, MI, students to attend schools of higher education in MI.
Type of support: Scholarships—to individuals.
Limitations: Giving limited to residents of Branch County, MI, attending schools of higher education in MI.
Application information: Applications available through Branch County High School counseling offices. Application form required.
  Initial approach: Contact local high school
  Deadline(s): None
Trustee: Southern Michigan Bank & Trust.
EIN: 386372257

953
The Julius Family Foundation
c/o George P. Julius, Jr.
186 S. River Ave.
Holland, MI 49423

Established in 1998 in MI.
Donors: George P. Julius, Jr.; Terene Julius.
Grantmaker type: Independent foundation.
Financial data (yr. ended 12/31/05): Assets, $4,221 (M); gifts received, $10,000; expenditures, $9,526; total giving, $8,000; qualifying distributions, $8,000; giving activities include $8,000 for grants.
Fields of interest: Human services; Roman Catholic agencies & churches.
Type of support: General/operating support.
Limitations: Applications not accepted. Giving primarily in MI. No grants to individuals.
Application information: Contributes only to pre-selected organizations.
Officers: George P. Julius, Jr., Pres.; Terene Julius, Secy.
EIN: 383441966

954
Jim and Ginger Jurries Family Foundation
c/o James Jurries
347 Settlers Rd., Ste. 120
Holland, MI 49423-3704

Established in 1997 in MI.
Donors: James Jurries; Virginia Jurries; E.I. Huizenga Foundation.
Grantmaker type: Independent foundation.
Financial data (yr. ended 12/31/04): Assets, $5,748,556 (M); gifts received, $419,563; expenditures, $541,431; total giving, $389,300; qualifying distributions, $392,831; giving activities include $389,300 for 80 grants (high: $40,000; low: $1,000).

Purpose and activities: Giving to Christian schools, churches and organizations, higher education, and for boys and girls clubs.
Fields of interest: Higher education; Theological school/education; Education; Boys & girls clubs; Christian agencies & churches.
Type of support: Endowments; Capital campaigns; General/operating support.
Limitations: Applications not accepted. Giving in the U.S. primarily in MI, with emphasis on Grand Rapids and Holland. No grants to individuals.
Application information: Contributes only to pre-selected organizations.
Directors: James L. Jurries; Virginia L. Jurries.
EIN: 383342545
Selected grants: The following grants were reported in 2003.
$100,000 to Holland Christian Schools, Holland, MI. For general support.
$100,000 to Hope College, DeVos Fieldhouse, Holland, MI. For capital campaign.
$22,000 to Young Life, Holland, MI. For general support.
$5,000 to Boys and Girls Club of Greater Holland, Holland, MI. For general support.
$2,500 to Christian Schools International, Grand Rapids, MI. For general support.
$1,500 to Northwestern College, Orange City, IA. For general support.
$1,000 to Borculo Christian School, Zeeland, MI. For general support.
$1,000 to Christian Counseling Center, Grand Rapids, MI. For general support.
$1,000 to Grand Rapids Christian Schools, Grand Rapids, MI. For annual fund.
$1,000 to United Way, Greater Ottawa County, Holland, MI. For general support.

955
The Jury Foundation
5799 Dunrovin Dr.
Saginaw, MI 48603-5408   (989) 793-5527
Contact: Sarah Jury, Pres.
E-mail: sbjury@aol.com

Established in 2004 in MI.
Donors: Michael Jury; Sarah Jury; Burke E. Porter Machinery Co.
Grantmaker type: Independent foundation.
Financial data (yr. ended 12/31/05): Assets, $2,551,731 (M); gifts received, $84,500; expenditures, $122,828; total giving, $115,400; qualifying distributions, $119,496; giving activities include $115,400 for 21 grants (high: $20,400; low: $1,000).
Fields of interest: Museums; Performing arts; Higher education; Environment, natural resources; Zoos/zoological societies; Human services; Children/youth, services.
Type of support: General/operating support; Debt reduction; Program development; Scholarship funds.
Limitations: Giving primarily in MI, with some emphasis on Grand Rapids and Saginaw.
Application information:
  Initial approach: Letter
  Deadline(s): None
Officers: Sarah Jury, Pres. and Treas.; Michael Jury, V.P. and Secy.
EIN: 200748605

956
Justice Foundation of West Michigan
(formerly Grand Rapids Bar Foundation)
c/o Grand Rapids Bar Assn.
161 Ottawa Ave. N.W., Ste. 203B
Grand Rapids, MI 49503 (616) 454-5550
Contact: Mark Petz

Established in 1978 in MI.
Grantmaker type: Independent foundation.
Financial data (yr. ended 12/31/05): Assets, $549,217 (M); gifts received, $74,857; expenditures, $240,700; total giving, $175,849; qualifying distributions, $175,849; giving activities include $175,849 for 4 grants (high: $168,349; low: $1,000).
Purpose and activities: Support for programs that promote or provide legal services to the disadvantaged, improve the administration of justice, and educate the public about democratic values.
Fields of interest: Courts/judicial administration.
Type of support: Seed money; Program development.
Limitations: Giving limited to western MI, primarily in Kent County. No support for partisan political organizations. No grants to individuals, or for capital campaigns or endowments.
Publications: Application guidelines.
Application information: Application form required.
Initial approach: Letter
Copies of proposal: 2
Deadline(s): Mar. 1 and Sept. 1
Board meeting date(s): Mar. and Sept.
Final notification: 60 days
Officers: Patrick Miles, Jr., Pres.; Hon. Paul J. Sullivan, Pres.-Elect.; Paul T. Sorensen, V.P.; Miles J. Postema, Secy.; Terence J. Ackert, Treas.
Trustees: Jane M. Beckering; Karl W. Butterer; Charles E. Chamberlain; Scott E. Dwyer; Anthony P. Gauthier, Jr.; Dwight K. Hamilton; Wendell P. Russell, Jr.; Kristin M. Vandenberg; Matthew L. Vicari.
EIN: 382245940
Selected grants: The following grants were reported in 2003.
$258,872 to Grand Rapids Bar Association, Grand Rapids, MI. 2 grants: $256,372 (For general support for legal assistance center), $2,500 to Legal Assistance Center (For general support).
$1,250 to East Grand Rapids, City of, East Grand Rapids, MI. For legal assistance.

957
Thomas E. Kaczperski Foundation
P.O. Box 46997
Mount Clemens, MI 48046-6997

Established in 1997 in MI.
Donor: Thomas E. Kaczperski.
Grantmaker type: Independent foundation.
Financial data (yr. ended 1/31/06): Assets, $13,325 (M); expenditures, $2,890; total giving, $1,950; qualifying distributions, $2,420; giving activities include $1,950 for 5 grants (high: $500; low: $200).
Purpose and activities: Giving to organizations that improve the quality of life of needy families where the Omega Plastics, Inc., operates. Some scholarships awards children of Omega Plastics employees.
Fields of interest: Human services; Salvation Army; Christian agencies & churches.

Type of support: General/operating support.
Limitations: Applications not accepted. Giving primarily in MI. No grants to individuals.
Application information: Contributes only to pre-selected organizations.
Officers: Thomas E. Kaczperski, Pres.; Paulette M. Kaczperski, V.P.
Directors: Susan L. Jex; Jeffrey T. Kaczperski; Jill Marie Kaczperski.
EIN: 383319669

958
Leo A. Kahan and Emelie O. Kahan Charitable Foundation
77 Benton Rd.
Saginaw, MI 48602-1905 (989) 799-3320
Contact: Leo A. Kahan, Pres.

Established in 1997 in MI.
Donors: Emelie O. Kahan; Leo A. Kahan.
Grantmaker type: Independent foundation.
Financial data (yr. ended 12/31/04): Assets, $170,666 (M); expenditures, $248,292; total giving, $246,671; qualifying distributions, $246,671; giving activities include $246,671 for grants.
Fields of interest: Arts; Higher education; Human services; Jewish agencies & temples.
Limitations: Giving primarily in MI, with emphasis on Saginaw.
Officer: Leo A. Kahan, Pres.
Directors: Kathleen Fehrman; Bill J. Thomas.
EIN: 383341030

959
The Mark & Gayle Kahn Family Foundation
(formerly The Mark S. Kahn Family Foundation)
725 Vaughn Rd.
Bloomfield Hills, MI 48304-2666

Established in 1997 in MI.
Donor: Mark S. Kahn.
Grantmaker type: Independent foundation.
Financial data (yr. ended 12/31/05): Assets, $1 (M); expenditures, $0; total giving, $0; qualifying distributions, $0.
Fields of interest: Jewish federated giving programs.
Limitations: Applications not accepted. Giving primarily in MI. No grants to individuals.
Application information: Contributes only to pre-selected organizations.
Officers and Trustees: * Mark S. Kahn,* Pres.; Lawrence A. Wolfe,* Secy.
EIN: 383324668

960
The D. Dan and Betty Kahn Foundation
(formerly Kahn Family Foundation)
8655 E. 8 Mile Rd.
Warren, MI 48089
Contact: David D. Kahn, Pres.

Established in 1986 in MI.
Donor: David D. Kahn.
Grantmaker type: Independent foundation.
Financial data (yr. ended 11/30/05): Assets, $3,290,191 (M); expenditures, $690,027; total giving, $685,763; qualifying distributions, $685,783; giving activities include $685,763 for 12 + grants (high: $256,009).

Purpose and activities: Giving primarily for higher education as well as for Jewish organizations and Jewish federated giving programs; some funding for children and human services.
Fields of interest: Education; Health care; Human services; Children/youth, services; Jewish federated giving programs; Jewish agencies & temples.
Type of support: General/operating support; Building/renovation; Scholarship funds.
Limitations: Applications not accepted. Giving primarily in MI and NY. No grants to individuals.
Application information: Contributes only to pre-selected organizations.
Officers and Trustees: * David D. Kahn,* Pres.; Patrice Aaron, Secy.; Lawrence A. Wolfe,* Treas.
EIN: 382712361

961
Kahn Sovel Mertz Fund
3405 Pine Estates Dr.
Orchard Lake, MI 48323 (248) 682-1172
Contact: Susan Sovel, Secy.-Treas.

Established in 2000 in MI.
Donor: Kopel I. Kahn.
Grantmaker type: Independent foundation.
Financial data (yr. ended 12/31/05): Assets, $144,781 (M); gifts received, $15,693; expenditures, $10,462; total giving, $7,500; qualifying distributions, $7,500; giving activities include $7,500 for 4 grants (high: $3,000; low: $500).
Fields of interest: Jewish agencies & temples.
Limitations: Giving primarily in MI. No grants to individuals.
Application information:
Initial approach: Letter
Deadline(s): None
Officers: Kopel I. Kahn, Pres.; Alyssa Mertz, V.P.; Susan Sovel, Secy.-Treas.
EIN: 383570641

962
Kakarala Foundation
2871 Troy Ctr. Dr., Apt. P5
Troy, MI 48084-4712
Contact: Ramani Kakarala, Pres.

Established in 1986 in MI.
Donors: Sriman N. Kakarala; Bhavani P. Garapati.
Grantmaker type: Independent foundation.
Financial data (yr. ended 12/31/05): Assets, $80,661 (M); expenditures, $2,547; total giving, $2,291; qualifying distributions, $2,291; giving activities include $2,291 for grants.
Fields of interest: Education, fund raising/fund distribution; Federated giving programs.
International interests: India.
Type of support: General/operating support; Building/renovation.
Limitations: Giving primarily in India; giving also in the Midwest. No grants to individuals.
Application information:
Initial approach: Proposal
Deadline(s): None
Officers: Ramani Kakarala, Pres.; Vijaya Kakarala, Secy.
Trustees: Raghuram Kakarala; Ramesh Kakarala.
EIN: 382703534

963
Kaleidoscope Foundation
5099 Williams Lake Rd.
Waterford, MI 48329

Established in MI.
Donor: Tammy Sue V. Sikora.
Grantmaker type: Independent foundation.
Financial data (yr. ended 12/31/04): Assets, $61,392 (M); expenditures, $10,345; total giving, $0; qualifying distributions, $0.
Officer: Marc Cooper, V.P.
EIN: 383597924

964
Kanaan Family Foundation
6495 Pepperidge Cir.
Portage, MI 49024

Established in 2004 in MI.
Donors: Azzam S. Kanaan; Shadi A. Kanaan.
Grantmaker type: Independent foundation.
Financial data (yr. ended 12/31/05): Assets, $90,083 (M); gifts received, $60,000; expenditures, $20,700; total giving, $20,000; qualifying distributions, $20,000; giving activities include $20,000 for grants.
Limitations: Applications not accepted. No grants to individuals.
Application information: Contributes only to pre-selected organizations.
Officers and Directors:* Azzam S. Kanaan,* Pres.; Shadi A. Kanaan,* Secy.-Treas.
EIN: 320121980

965
Louis J. & Golda I. Kanitz Scholarship Memorial Fund
c/o Wells Fargo Bank, N.A.
P.O. Box 63954, MAC 0103-179
San Francisco, CA 94163

Established in 1994 in CA.
Grantmaker type: Independent foundation.
Financial data (yr. ended 12/31/04): Assets, $6,160,992 (M); expenditures, $252,994; total giving, $203,419; qualifying distributions, $215,542; giving activities include $40,000 for grants, and $163,419 for grants to individuals.
Purpose and activities: Giving primarily for higher education.
Fields of interest: Higher education; Higher education, college (community/junior); Higher education, college; Higher education, university; Business school/education; Medical school/education; Scholarships/financial aid; Education; Roman Catholic agencies & churches.
Limitations: Applications not accepted. Giving primarily in CA and MI.
Application information: Unsolicited requests for funds not accepted.
Trustee: Wells Fargo Bank, N.A.
EIN: 946665743

966
The Kantzler Foundation
900 Center Ave.
Bay City, MI 48708 (989) 892-0591

Incorporated in 1974 in MI.

Donor: Leopold J. Kantzler†.
Grantmaker type: Independent foundation.
Financial data (yr. ended 12/31/04): Assets, $5,695,622 (M); gifts received, $54,948; expenditures, $316,389; total giving, $295,167; qualifying distributions, $301,324; giving activities include $295,167 for 13 grants (high: $75,000; low: $6,000).
Purpose and activities: To support projects and capital improvements of charitable, artistic, educational, and cultural organizations in the greater metropolitan Bay City, MI, area.
Fields of interest: Media, television; Performing arts, theater; Historical activities; Arts; Libraries (public); Education; Environment, natural resources; Housing/shelter, homeless; Human services; Community development; Foundations (community).
Type of support: Capital campaigns; Building/renovation; Equipment; Land acquisition; Program development; Seed money; Scholarship funds; Matching/challenge support.
Limitations: Giving limited to the greater Bay City, MI, area. No grants to individuals, or for endowment funds, operating budgets, continuing support, annual campaigns, special projects, publications, conferences, emergency funds, deficit financing, research, scholarships, or fellowships; no loans.
Publications: Financial statement; Informational brochure (including application guidelines).
Application information: Application form not required.
  Initial approach: Proposal
  Copies of proposal: 1
  Deadline(s): 2 weeks before board meeting
  Board meeting date(s): Approximately 6 times per year
  Final notification: 2 months
Officers: Dominic Monastiere, Pres.; Joseph Sasiela, V.P.; Robert D. Sarow, Secy.
Trustees: Meade A. Gougeon; Linda R. Heemstra; Ruth M. Jaffe; D. Brian Law; Clifford C. Van Dyke; Jerome L. Yantz.
EIN: 237422733
Selected grants: The following grants were reported in 2004.
$75,000 to CORY Place, Bay City, MI. To construct Runaway Youth Shelter.
$50,000 to Bay County Library System, Bay City, MI. For library construction.
$33,334 to State Theater of Bay City, Bay County, Bay City, MI. To renovate Historic Theater.
$25,000 to Delta College, University Center, MI. For conversion of public TV to analog.
$25,000 to Saginaw Valley State University, University Center, MI. For scholarships.
$20,000 to Great Lakes Center Foundation, Bay City, MI. For operating support.
$15,000 to Baysail, Bay City, MI. To purchase new schooner Westwind.
$10,000 to Bay County CAN Council, Bay City, MI. For Child Advocacy Center.
$10,000 to Community Clothing Center, Pinconning, MI. To renovate facility.
$10,000 to Little Forks Conservancy, Midland, MI.

967
Ernest and Rosemarie Kanzler Foundation
1901 Saint Antoine St.
6th Fl. at Ford Field
Detroit, MI 48226 (313) 259-7777

Established in 2001 in MI.
Grantmaker type: Independent foundation.

Financial data (yr. ended 12/31/05): Assets, $7,035,093 (M); gifts received, $3,999,971; expenditures, $20,108,726; total giving, $20,000,000; qualifying distributions, $20,039,500; giving activities include $20,000,000 for 1 grant.
Fields of interest: Arts; Education.
Limitations: Applications not accepted. Giving primarily in MI. No grants to individuals.
Application information: Contributes only to pre-selected organizations.
Officers and Directors:* Edsel B. Ford II,* Pres. and Treas.; David M. Hempstead, Secy.
EIN: 383624601

968
The Kashlan Foundation
26300 Telegraph Rd., 2nd Fl.
Southfield, MI 48034

Established in 2004 in MI.
Grantmaker type: Independent foundation.
Financial data (yr. ended 12/31/05): Assets, $189,470 (M); gifts received, $145,000; expenditures, $22,515; total giving, $21,900; qualifying distributions, $21,900; giving activities include $21,900 for grants.
Officers: Muhammad Kashlan, Pres.; Rana Alsabbagh, Treas.
EIN: 383703162

969
The Joseph & Ann Katz Foundation
141 Harrow Ln.
Saginaw, MI 48603-6093

Established in 1987 in MI.
Donors: Joseph Katz; Ann Katz.
Grantmaker type: Independent foundation.
Financial data (yr. ended 3/31/05): Assets, $286,686 (M); gifts received, $1,519; expenditures, $21,524; total giving, $20,000; qualifying distributions, $20,623; giving activities include $20,000 for grants.
Purpose and activities: Giving for Jewish organizations.
Fields of interest: Jewish federated giving programs; Jewish agencies & temples.
Type of support: General/operating support.
Limitations: Applications not accepted. Giving primarily in CA and NY. No grants to individuals.
Application information: Contributes only to pre-selected organizations.
Officers: Ann Katz, Pres. and Treas.; Sara R. Borin, V.P. and Secy.
EIN: 382414613

970
Samuel P. & Martha L. Katz Foundation, Inc.
31841 Franklin Fairway
Farmington Hills, MI 48334

Established in 2001 in MI.
Donor: Martha L. Katz.
Grantmaker type: Independent foundation.
Financial data (yr. ended 12/31/05): Assets, $8,392 (M); expenditures, $619; total giving, $434; qualifying distributions, $434; giving activities include $434 for grants.

Limitations: Applications not accepted. No grants to individuals.
Application information: Contributes only to pre-selected organizations.
Officer and Trustee: * Martha L. Katz,* Pres. and Treas.
EIN: 383557921

971
The Paul & Lois Katzman Foundation
4547 Kiftsgate Bend
Bloomfield Hills, MI 48302

Established in 1993 in MI.
Grantmaker type: Independent foundation.
Financial data (yr. ended 12/31/05): Assets, $126,795 (M); gifts received, $150,517; expenditures, $67,339; total giving, $67,168; qualifying distributions, $67,168; giving activities include $67,168 for grants.
Purpose and activities: Giving primarily to Jewish organizations, temples, and federated giving programs.
Fields of interest: Health organizations, association; Human services; Children, services; Jewish federated giving programs; Jewish agencies & temples.
Limitations: Applications not accepted. Giving primarily in MI. No grants to individuals.
Application information: Contributes only to pre-selected organizations.
Trustees: Lois Katzman; Paul Katzman.
EIN: 383124580

972
Barney Katzman Foundation
5655 Wing Lake Rd.
Bloomfield Hills, MI 48301
Contact: Barney Katzman, Pres.

Grantmaker type: Independent foundation.
Financial data (yr. ended 12/31/04): Assets, $112,931 (M); expenditures, $9,231; total giving, $9,011; qualifying distributions, $9,011; giving activities include $9,011 for grants.
Fields of interest: Performing arts; Higher education; Medical research, institute; Jewish agencies & temples.
Type of support: General/operating support.
Limitations: Giving primarily in MI.
Application information:
   Initial approach: Proposal
   Deadline(s): None
Officers and Directors: * Barney Katzman,* Pres. and Treas.; Jeanette Katzman,* V.P.; Richard Katzman,* Secy.; Jane Glass.
EIN: 386064688

973
Sidney and Robert Katzman Foundation
(formerly Sidney Katzman Foundation)
30100 Telegraph Rd., Ste. 320
Bingham Farms, MI 48025-4516
Contact: Robert Katzman, Pres.

Donor: Betty Katzman.
Grantmaker type: Independent foundation.
Financial data (yr. ended 12/31/04): Assets, $387,600 (M); expenditures, $43,353; total giving,

$40,574; qualifying distributions, $40,574; giving activities include $40,574 for grants.
Fields of interest: Arts; Health organizations, association; Jewish federated giving programs; Jewish agencies & temples.
Type of support: General/operating support.
Limitations: Giving primarily in MI. No grants to individuals.
Application information:
   Initial approach: Proposal
   Deadline(s): None
Officers: Robert Katzman, Pres.; Betty Katzman, V.P.; Martin Stoneman, Secy.-Treas.
EIN: 386064687
Selected grants: The following grants were reported in 2003.
$104,438 to Detroit Institute of Arts, Detroit, MI.
$1,615 to Temple Emanu-El, Troy, MI.
$1,000 to American Friends of the Israel Museum, Beverly Hills, CA.
$1,000 to Buddy Program, Aspen, CO.
$1,000 to Santa Monica Museum of Art, Santa Monica, CA.
$840 to Temple Beth El, Bloomfield Hills, MI.
$750 to Modern and Contemporary Art Council, Los Angeles, CA.
$300 to Synagogue for the Performing Arts, Los Angeles, CA.
$100 to American Heart Association, Chicago, IL.
$25 to American Cancer Society, Southfield, MI.

974
Louis G. Kaufman Endowment Fund
c/o Wells Fargo Bank Michigan, N.A.
P.O. Box 580
Marquette, MI 49855-0580 (906) 228-1244
Contact: James F. Duranceau, Fund Comm., Wells Fargo Bank Michigan, N.A.

Established in 1927 in MI.
Donor: L.G. Kaufman Trust.
Grantmaker type: Independent foundation.
Financial data (yr. ended 12/31/05): Assets, $3,403,000 (M); expenditures, $119,000; total giving, $91,885; qualifying distributions, $91,885; giving activities include $91,885 for grants (high: $60,000).
Purpose and activities: Giving primarily for education and human services.
Fields of interest: Secondary school/education; Education; Recreation; Human services; Children/youth, services; Family services; Community development.
Type of support: General/operating support; Annual campaigns; Program development; Scholarship funds.
Limitations: Giving primarily in Marquette, MI. No grants to individuals, or for continuing support, deficit financing, land acquisition, endowment funds, matching gifts, research, publications, or conferences; no loans.
Publications: Application guidelines.
Application information: Application form required.
   Initial approach: Letter
   Copies of proposal: 7
   Deadline(s): May 1
   Board meeting date(s): As required
Officer and Fund Committee: * Peter Kaufman,* Chair.; Henry Bothwell; Ann Kaufman Jordan; Audrey Kaufman; Stephen Mattson; Kenneth Seavoy.
Trustee: Wells Fargo Bank Michigan, N.A.
EIN: 386048505

Selected grants: The following grants were reported in 2004.
$65,000 to Marquette Area Public Schools, Marquette, MI. 2 grants: $50,000 (For high school scholarship program), $15,000 (For middle school scholarship program).
$10,000 to Marquette Junior Hockey, Marquette, MI. For youth scholarship program.
$8,000 to Bay Cliff Health Camp, Big Bay, MI. For scholarships for Marquette youth.
$5,000 to YMCA of Marquette County, Marquette, MI. For shiras pool and strong kids campaign.
$4,000 to Upper Peninsula Childrens Museum, Marquette, MI. For good lung/bad lung and supplies.
$2,500 to Father Marquette Catholic Central Schools System, Marquette, MI. 2 grants: $1,000 (For scholarship program), $1,500 (For scholarship program).
$1,900 to Pine Mountain Music Festival, Hancock, MI. For childrens symphony concert.
$1,000 to Liberty Childrens Art Project, Negaunee, MI. For City of Marquette youth scholarships.

975
Kaufman Foundation
297 W. Clay Ave., Ste. 106
Muskegon, MI 49440 (231) 727-3415
Contact: Richard F. Kaufman, Tr.; Sylvia C. Kaufman, Tr.

Established in 1959 in MI.
Grantmaker type: Independent foundation.
Financial data (yr. ended 12/31/03): Assets, $3,169,606 (M); expenditures, $162,812; total giving, $158,775; qualifying distributions, $154,396; giving activities include $158,775 for 29 grants (high: $80,000; low: $50).
Purpose and activities: Giving to museums, the arts, and Jewish agencies.
Fields of interest: Museums; Arts; Jewish federated giving programs; Jewish agencies & temples.
Limitations: Giving primarily in MI.
Application information:
   Initial approach: Letter
   Deadline(s): None
Trustees: Richard F. Kaufman; Sylvia C. Kaufman.
EIN: 386091556

976
Alan Jay & Sue Kaufman Foundation
30833 Northwestern Hwy., Ste. 200
Farmington Hills, MI 48334-2582

Established in 1987 in MI.
Donor: Alan Jay Kaufman.
Grantmaker type: Independent foundation.
Financial data (yr. ended 8/31/05): Assets, $303,142 (M); gifts received, $16,976; expenditures, $11,671; total giving, $11,671; qualifying distributions, $11,671; giving activities include $11,671 for grants.
Fields of interest: Elementary/secondary education; Jewish agencies & temples.
Type of support: General/operating support.
Limitations: Applications not accepted. Giving primarily in MI. No grants to individuals.
Application information: Contributes only to pre-selected organizations.
Directors: Alan Jay Kaufman; Susan Kaufman.
EIN: 382770140

977
The Chaim, Fanny, Louis, Benjamin and Anne Florence Kaufman Memorial Trust
c/o JPMorgan Chase Bank, N.A.
685 St. Clair Ave.
Grosse Pointe, MI 48230 (313) 343-8575
Contact: Andrew L. Camden, Sr. V.P., Bank One Turst Co., N.A.

Established in 1986 in MI.
Donor: Anne F. Kaufman†.
Grantmaker type: Independent foundation.
Financial data (yr. ended 5/31/05): Assets, $3,035,471 (M); expenditures, $200,555; total giving, $168,833; qualifying distributions, $171,950; giving activities include $168,833 for 30 grants (high: $20,833; low: $500).
Fields of interest: Visual arts; Performing arts; Performing arts, dance; Arts; Education; Reproductive health, family planning; Health organizations, association; Human services; Family services; Jewish federated giving programs.
Type of support: General/operating support; Building/renovation; Program development; Seed money; Research.
Limitations: Giving primarily in southeastern MI, with emphasis on Detroit. No grants to individuals.
Application information: Application form not required.
Initial approach: Letter
Copies of proposal: 1
Deadline(s): None
Trustee: JPMorgan Chase Bank, N.A.
EIN: 386504432

978
Helen L. Kay Charitable Trust
(formerly Helen L. Kay Foundation)
c/o Comerica Bank
101 N. Main St., Ste. 100
Ann Arbor, MI 48104 (877) 405-1091
Contact: Scott Drogs, V.P., Comerica Charitable Services Group

Established in 2000 in MI.
Grantmaker type: Independent foundation.
Financial data (yr. ended 12/31/05): Assets, $8,758,586 (M); expenditures, $593,514; total giving, $465,000; qualifying distributions, $484,335; giving activities include $465,000 for 7 grants (high: $100,000; low: $50,000).
Purpose and activities: Giving primarily to a school and a Presbyterian church.
Fields of interest: Elementary/secondary education; Hospitals (specialty); Goodwill Industries; Human services; Salvation Army; Protestant agencies & churches.
Limitations: Giving primarily in FL, MI, and PA. No grants to individuals.
Application information: Application form not required.
Initial approach: Letter
Deadline(s): None
Trustees: George D. Miller, Jr.; Comerica Bank.
EIN: 383047073

979
Ryan Michael Kay Scholarship Foundation
4820 Leonard Ct.
West Bloomfield, MI 48322

Established in 2004 in MI.
Donors: Kay Family; Harriet Dryburgh; Mandel Stanley; Iola Stanley; Marion Moorehead; Gwen Leach.
Grantmaker type: Independent foundation.
Financial data (yr. ended 12/31/05): Assets, $95,627 (M); gifts received, $500; expenditures, $18,181; total giving, $15,000; qualifying distributions, $15,521; giving activities include $15,000 for 3 grants to individuals.
Type of support: Scholarships—to individuals.
Limitations: Applications not accepted. Giving primarily in MI.
Application information: Unsolicited requests for funds not accepted.
Officers: Christine Kay, Pres. and Secy.; Neil Kay, V.P. and Treas.
EIN: 320102123

980
Kebok Foundation
6500 W. 6 Mile Rd.
Northville, MI 48167
Contact: Soon K. Kim

Established in 2002 in MI.
Grantmaker type: Independent foundation.
Financial data (yr. ended 12/31/05): Assets, $5,925 (M); expenditures, $955; total giving, $655; qualifying distributions, $655; giving activities include $655 for grants.
Application information:
Initial approach: Letter
Deadline(s): None
Final notification: Within 2 months
Officer: Bouh H. Kim, Pres.
EIN: 300106301

981
Kee Foundation
c/o David K. Ellis
221 W. Webster Ave., Ste 400
Muskegon, MI 49440

Established in 2004 in MI.
Grantmaker type: Independent foundation.
Financial data (yr. ended 12/31/04): Assets, $213 (M); expenditures, $0; total giving, $0; qualifying distributions, $0.
Officers: David K. Elllis, Pres.; Andrew Matinus, V.P.; Ryan Martinus, Secy.-Treas.
Directors: Jeffrey Buck; Michele Buckley; David K. Ellis; Robert Jacobs; Jerry Peterman; John Pridnia.
EIN: 320041703

982
The Keeler Foundation
(formerly The Miner S. & Mary Ann Keeler Fund)
200 Monroe Ave. N.W., Ste. 240
Grand Rapids, MI 49503-2213
Contact: Mary Ann Keeler, Pres.

Incorporated in 1985 in MI as successor to the First Keeler Fund established in 1953, which transferred its assets to the new Keeler Fund in 1986.
Donors: Mary Ann Keeler; Miner S. Keeler II†; The Keeler Fund.
Grantmaker type: Independent foundation.
Financial data (yr. ended 7/31/05): Assets, $1,607,994 (M); expenditures, $734,532; total giving, $710,669; qualifying distributions, $710,008; giving activities include $710,669 for 60 grants (high: $220,000; low: $25).
Purpose and activities: Giving primarily to organizations that are artistic or scholastic in nature.
Fields of interest: Museums (art); Performing arts; Arts; Secondary school/education; Higher education; Libraries (public); Environment; Health organizations, association; Human services; YM/YWCAs & YM/YWHAs; Christian agencies & churches.
Limitations: Giving primarily in MI, with emphasis on Grand Rapids; some giving in NY. No grants to individuals.
Application information:
Initial approach: Letter
Deadline(s): None
Officers: Mary Ann Keeler, Pres.; Isaac S. Keeler, V.P.; Rita L. Miller, Secy.-Treas.
Director: Donald Johnson.
EIN: 382625402
Selected grants: The following grants were reported in 2003.
$1,030,000 to Grand Valley State University, Allendale, MI. 2 grants: $1,000,000, $30,000
$300,000 to Grand Action Foundation, Grand Rapids, MI.
$260,000 to Ryerson Library Foundation, Grand Rapids, MI.
$138,000 to Frederick Meijer Gardens and Sculpture Park, Grand Rapids, MI.
$50,000 to Saint Johns Home, Grand Rapids, MI.
$36,000 to Aquinas College, Grand Rapids, MI.
$35,000 to Pathfinder Resources, Grand Rapids, MI.
$25,000 to Saint Anns Home, Grand Rapids, MI.
$10,000 to Calvin College, Grand Rapids, MI.

983
Hattie Hannah Keeney Trust
c/o JPMorgan Chase Bank, N.A.
P.O. Box 1308
Milwaukee, WI 53201
Application address: c/o Richard Jung, 120 S. Hough St., Barrington, IL 60010

Established in 1950 in IL.
Donor: Hattie Hannah Keeney†.
Grantmaker type: Independent foundation.
Financial data (yr. ended 12/31/05): Assets, $4,989,668 (M); expenditures, $51,730; total giving, $0; qualifying distributions, $0.
Purpose and activities: Support for the benefit of disabled children.
Fields of interest: Hospitals (general); Children/youth, services; Disabilities, people with.
Limitations: Giving primarily in the Traverse City, MI, area. No grants to individuals.
Application information:
Deadline(s): None
Trustee: JPMorgan Chase Bank, N.A.
EIN: 366016171
Selected grants: The following grants were reported in 2003.
$86,100 to Munson Medical Center, Traverse City, MI. For general support.
$84,000 to Child Guidance Center, Traverse City, MI. For general support.

984
Kegel Family Foundation
c/o Paul S. Gravenhorst
P.O. Box 14070
Fort Lauderdale, FL   33302-4070

Established in 1993.
Grantmaker type: Independent foundation.
Financial data (yr. ended 2/28/05): Assets, $450,456 (M); expenditures, $38,708; total giving, $25,000; qualifying distributions, $25,000; giving activities include $25,000 for grants.
Fields of interest: Secondary school/education; Education, special.
Limitations: Applications not accepted. Giving primarily in Ann Arbor, MI, and Mill Neck, NY. No grants to individuals.
Application information: Contributes only to pre-selected organizations.
Trustees: Paul S. Gravenhorst; Margaret Miller; Rosemary Pemberton.
EIN: 656117841

985
Lenna M. Keith Charitable Trust
c/o Standard Federal Bank N.A.
135 S. LaSalle St., Ste. 2060
Chicago, IL   60603

Established in MI.
Grantmaker type: Independent foundation.
Financial data (yr. ended 6/30/04): Assets, $191,451 (M); expenditures, $4,221; total giving, $600; qualifying distributions, $2,745; giving activities include $600 for 1 grant to an individual.
Purpose and activities: Financial assistance to individuals who have demonstrated a need for assistance for health care and housing costs while residing at Burcham Hills Retirement Center, Lansing, MI.
Fields of interest: Aging, centers/services; Aging.
Type of support: Grants to individuals.
Limitations: Applications not accepted. Giving limited to Lansing, MI.
Application information: Unsolicited requests for funds not accepted.
Trustee: Standard Federal Bank N.A.
EIN: 386468026

986
Keller Foundation
5225 33rd St. S.E.
Grand Rapids, MI   49512
Contact: Anne Williamson, Exec. Dir.
E-mail: fndanne@iserv.net; URL: http://www.kellerfoundation.org

Established around 1980 in MI.
Donor: Paragon Die & Engineering Co.
Grantmaker type: Independent foundation.
Financial data (yr. ended 6/30/05): Assets, $5,784,159 (M); gifts received, $28,816; expenditures, $291,715; total giving, $236,235; qualifying distributions, $254,377; giving activities include $214,985 for 93 grants (high: $21,000; low: $150), and $21,250 for 44 employee matching gifts.
Purpose and activities: The Keller Foundation seeks to support innovative programs for Grand Rapids' core city youth that foster nurturing environments,

spark curiosity, enhance opportunities for self-sufficiency, and inspire high aspirations.
Fields of interest: Performing arts; Education; Botanical/horticulture/landscape services; Zoos/zoological societies; Health care; Human services; Children/youth, services.
Type of support: General/operating support; Continuing support; Capital campaigns; Building/renovation; Program development; Seed money; Curriculum development; Scholarship funds; Matching/challenge support.
Limitations: Giving primarily in the Grand Rapids, MI, area. No support for political organizations. No grants to individuals.
Publications: Application guidelines.
Application information: Application form available on foundation Web site. Application form required.
  Initial approach: Letter of request
  Copies of proposal: 1
  Deadline(s): None
  Board meeting date(s): Nov., Mar. and June
Officers and Directors:* Kathleen K. Muir,* Chair.; Lorissa K. MacAllister,* Vice-Chair.; William M. Muir,* Secy.; David F. Muir,* Treas.; Anne Williamson, Exec. Dir.; Bernedine J. Keller; Christina L. Keller; Frederick P. Keller; Linn Maxwell Keller; Wes MacAllister; Cathy Muir; Elizabeth M. Muir; William W. Muir, Jr.; Lars Whitman; Susan T.K. Whitman.
Number of staff: 1 part-time professional.
EIN: 382331693
Selected grants: The following grants were reported in 2005.
$21,000 to Grand Rapids Art Museum, Grand Rapids, MI. For general support.
$15,000 to Grand Rapids Symphony, Grand Rapids, MI. For general support.
$12,250 to United Methodist Community House, Grand Rapids, MI. For general support.
$10,250 to Grand Rapids Ballet Company, Grand Rapids, MI. For general support.
$10,000 to Garrett-Evangelical Theological Seminary, Evanston, IL. For general support.
$10,000 to Spectrum Health, Grand Rapids, MI. For general support.
$5,000 to Grand Action Foundation, Grand Rapids, MI. For general support.
$5,000 to Grand Valley State University, Grand Rapids, MI. For general support.
$4,250 to Grand Rapids Community College Foundation, Grand Rapids, MI. For general support.
$3,750 to Girl Scouts of the U.S.A., Michigan Trails Council, Grand Rapids, MI. For general support.

987
Edward and June Kellogg Foundation, Inc.
1250 Byron Rd.
Howell, MI   48843

Established in 2001 in MI.
Donor: June Kellogg.
Grantmaker type: Independent foundation.
Financial data (yr. ended 6/30/05): Assets, $420,877 (M); expenditures, $23,488; total giving, $18,000; qualifying distributions, $18,000; giving activities include $18,000 for grants.
Limitations: Applications not accepted. Giving primarily in MI. No grants to individuals.
Application information: Contributes only to pre-selected organizations.

Officers: June Kellogg, Pres.; Thomas Kellogg, V.P. and Secy.-Treas.
EIN: 300057241

988
W. K. Kellogg Foundation
1 Michigan Ave. E.
Battle Creek, MI   49017-4058   (269) 968-1611
Contact: Debbie Rey, Supervisor of Proposal Processing
FAX: (269) 968-0413; URL: http://www.wkkf.org

Incorporated in 1930 in MI.
Donors: W.K. Kellogg†; W.K. Kellogg Foundation Trust; Carrie Staines Kellogg Trust.
Grantmaker type: Independent foundation.
Financial data (yr. ended 8/31/05): Assets, $7,298,383,532 (M); gifts received, $198,722,966; expenditures, $291,302,569; total giving, $219,862,847; qualifying distributions, $285,275,828; giving activities include $216,920,112 for 1,001 grants, $2,942,735 for 1,738 employee matching gifts, and $9,969,356 for 2 foundation-administered programs.
Purpose and activities: The W.K. Kellogg Foundation was established in 1930 "to help people help themselves through the practical application of knowledge and resources to improve their quality of life and that of future generations." The foundation bases its programming on the following values: 1) The foundation believes all people have the inherent capacity to effect change in their lives, their organizations, and their communities. The foundation respects individuals and values their collective interests, strengths, and insights. 2) The foundation believes stewardship requires fidelity to the spirit and intent of the founder, and the wise use of resources. The foundation believes in being responsible, prudent, selfless, and exercising good judgment. 3) The foundation believes innovation of thought and action leads to enduring and positive change in both formal and informal systems. 4) The foundation values integrity of purpose and action and believes it is essential to all of its affairs. To achieve the greatest impact, the foundation targets its grants toward specific areas: health; food systems and rural development; youth and education; and philanthropy and volunteerism. Within these areas, attention is given to exploring learning opportunities in leadership; information and communication technology; capitalizing on diversity; and social and economic community development.
Fields of interest: Education, early childhood education; Elementary school/education; Secondary school/education; Adult/continuing education; Education; Health care, reform; Health care; Health organizations, association; Agriculture; Agriculture/food; Youth development, services; Youth, services; Minorities/immigrants, centers/services; Community development, neighborhood development; Rural development; Community development; Voluntarism promotion; Leadership development; Minorities; African Americans/Blacks.
International interests: Botswana; Caribbean; Latin America; Lesotho; Malawi; Mozambique; South Africa; Swaziland; Zimbabwe.
Type of support: Program development; Seed money; Program evaluation; Employee matching gifts; Matching/challenge support.
Limitations: Giving primarily in the U.S., Latin America and the Caribbean, and the South African countries of Botswana, Lesotho, Malawi, South

Africa, Swaziland, Zimbabwe and Mozambique. No support for religious purposes or for capital facilities. No grants to individuals (except through fellowship programs), or for endowment funds, development campaigns, films, equipment, publications, conferences, or radio and television programs unless they are an integral part of a project already being funded; no grants for operating budgets.

Publications: Application guidelines; Annual report (including application guidelines); Financial statement; Grants list; Informational brochure (including application guidelines); Newsletter; Occasional report; Program policy statement.

Application information: Proposals must conform to specified program priorities. Application form not required.

   Initial approach: Pre-proposal letter (1 to 2 pages) or letter of inquiry
   Copies of proposal: 1
   Deadline(s): None
   Board meeting date(s): Monthly
   Final notification: 3 months

Officers and Trustees:* Cynthia H. Milligan,* Chair.; Sterling Speirn, C.E.O. and Pres.; Gregory A. Lyman, Sr. V.P. and Corp. Secy.; James E. McHale, Sr. V.P., Progs.; La June Montgomery-Talley, V.P., Finance and Treas.; Richard M. Foster, V.P., Progs.; C. Patrick Babcock, V.P., Progs.; Paul J. Lawler, V.P. and C.I.O.; Robert F. Long, V.P., Progs.; Gail D. McClure, V.P., Progs.; Mary Carole Cotter, Genl. Counsel; Shirley D. Bowser; Dorothy A. Johnson; Fred P. Keller; Hanmin Liu; Wenda Weekes Moore; Howard F. Sims; Joseph M. Stewart.

Number of staff: 115 full-time professional; 1 part-time professional; 73 full-time support; 2 part-time support.

EIN: 381359264

Selected grants: The following grants were reported in 2005.

$16,220,000 to Institute of American Indian Arts, Santa Fe, NM. To create home and place of permanency for learning for diverse tribal communities in U.S. and worldwide, payable over 4 years.

$6,800,000 to Great Lakes Center for Youth Development, Marquette, MI. To serve as catalyst for healthy development of youth in rural northern Michigan communities by establishing itself as resource to youth-serving organizations operating in state's Upper Peninsula and Lower Northern Region, payable over 5 years.

$6,000,000 to North Carolina Community Foundation, Raleigh, NC. To nurture and increase private giving for public good in North Carolina and strengthen organizations that support it, payable over 5 years.

$4,070,000 to Tides Center, San Francisco, CA. To provide projects and nonprofits with fiscal sponsorship and affordable, quality management support services through developing shared standards, operating procedures, regional geographic centers, and technology infrastructure, payable over 3 years.

$4,000,000 to Battle Creek Community Foundation, Battle Creek, MI. To create endowed community-based, collaborative scholarship program to ensure that underserved, low-income, and minority students graduate from high school and successfully complete post-secondary education program.

$4,000,000 to Morehouse College, Atlanta, GA. To eliminate racial and ethnic health disparities by uniting communities, grassroots organizations,

and students and faculty at Historically Black Colleges and Universities (HBCU) in Georgia through partnerships that effect sustainable community change, payable over 5 years.

$1,975,000 to Northeast-Midwest Institute, DC. To advance food and farm policy to enhance economic viability of farms, ranches, and rural communities, reward environmental stewardship, and increase access to healthy food, payable over 2.75 years.

$198,000 to Southern Africa Microfinance and Enterprise Enhancement Facility, Harare, Zimbabwe. To build capacity of Chimanimani Business Trust's mission as micro-finance and micro-enterprise development organization, payable over 2 years.

$195,000 to City at Peace, New York, NY. To strengthen capacity of current youth community engagement and service learning programs, enhance resource base for future, and improve management and organizational development effectiveness.

$109,260 to Center for Studies on Public Policies, Centro de Estudos de Politicas Publicas, Ipanema, Brazil. To strengthen arts and cultural component of development strategies in micro-regions of northeast Brazil.

989
C. L. Kelly Charitable Trust

c/o Comerce Bank, Agent
P.O. Box 75000
Detroit, MI 48275-3302
Contact: Claudia Moore, Trust Rep., RBC Centura Bank

Established in 1980 in NC.
Donor: C.L. Kelly, Sr.†.
Grantmaker type: Independent foundation.
Financial data (yr. ended 1/31/06): Assets, $1,533,560 (M); expenditures, $90,779; total giving, $70,000; qualifying distributions, $70,000; giving activities include $70,000 for grants.
Purpose and activities: Grants primarily to Protestant churches, and educational loans to residents of Brinkleyville, Butterwood, or Faucette Townships, Halifax County, NC.
Fields of interest: Education; Protestant agencies & churches.
Type of support: Student loans—to individuals.
Limitations: Giving primarily in NC.
Application information: Application form required.
   Deadline(s): June 15
   Board meeting date(s): June
Trustee: RBC Centura Bank.
EIN: 566218777

990
The Joseph D. and Suzanne G. Kelly Family Foundation

26877 Northwestern Hwy., Ste. 305
Southfield, MI 48034-8417

Established in 2000 in MI.
Donors: Joseph D. Kelly; Suzanne G. Kelly.
Grantmaker type: Independent foundation.
Financial data (yr. ended 12/31/04): Assets, $474,712 (M); expenditures, $88,700; total giving, $88,700; qualifying distributions, $88,700; giving activities include $88,700 for grants.

Fields of interest: Higher education; Education; Health organizations, association; Human services.
Limitations: Applications not accepted. Giving on a national basis. No grants to individuals.
Application information: Contributes only to pre-selected organizations.
Directors: Joseph D. Kelly; Suzanne G. Kelly.
EIN: 383489366

991
The Larry and Doris Kelly Foundation

142 Lakeview Dr.
Wayland, MI 49348

Established in 1993 in MI.
Donors: Lawrence O. Kelly; Doris L. Kelly.
Grantmaker type: Independent foundation.
Financial data (yr. ended 12/31/05): Assets, $254,982 (M); gifts received, $6,500; expenditures, $22,693; total giving, $19,565; qualifying distributions, $19,565; giving activities include $19,565 for grants.
Fields of interest: Human services; Protestant agencies & churches.
Type of support: General/operating support.
Limitations: Applications not accepted. Giving primarily in FL and MI. No grants to individuals.
Application information: Contributes only to pre-selected organizations.
Directors: Doris L. Kelly; Lawrence O. Kelly; Lynn M. Zevenbergen.
EIN: 383126025

992
Charles Kelly Foundation

c/o Charles A. Kelly, Jr.
807 Asa Gray Dr., Ste. 304
Ann Arbor, MI 48105

Established in 1997 in MI.
Donors: Charles A. Kelly, Jr.; Serendipity Books; Blue Hill Development.
Grantmaker type: Independent foundation.
Financial data (yr. ended 5/31/05): Assets, $4,053 (M); gifts received, $5,000; expenditures, $4,100; total giving, $4,100; qualifying distributions, $4,100; giving activities include $4,100 for grants.
Purpose and activities: The foundation's primary activity is the Kelly Foundation Scholarship for the Study of English Literature in Ireland; other activities include sponsorship of an exchange of lectures between the American Society for Eighteenth Century Studies (ASECS) and its British counterpart.
Limitations: Applications not accepted. No grants to individuals.
Application information: Contributes only to pre-selected organizations.
Trustee: Charles A. Kelly, Jr.
EIN: 383263391

993
Kelter Foundation, Inc.

210 S. Old Woodward Ave., Ste. 200
Birmingham, MI 48012

Grantmaker type: Independent foundation.
Financial data (yr. ended 12/31/03): Assets, $111,315 (M); gifts received, $7,115; expenditures, $5,957; total giving, $5,125;

qualifying distributions, $5,125; giving activities include $5,125 for grants.
Purpose and activities: Support only for Jewish Community Federation, San Francisco, CA.
Limitations: Applications not accepted. Giving limited to San Francisco, CA. No grants to individuals.
Application information: Contributes only to a pre-selected organization.
Officers: Theodore R. Kelter, Pres.; Marilyn R. Chernoff, Secy.-Treas.
EIN: 237003469

994
W. J. and Lillian Kemler Foundation
39300 W. 12 Mile Rd., Ste. 100
Farmington Hills, MI 48331
Contact: Margaret Savage, Pres.
Application address: 5328 Mirror Lake Ct., West Bloomfield, MI 48323

Established in 1997 in MI.
Donor: Lillian Kemler.
Grantmaker type: Independent foundation.
Financial data (yr. ended 11/30/04): Assets, $1,750,290 (M); gifts received, $984,424; expenditures, $110,996; total giving, $53,000; qualifying distributions, $53,000; giving activities include $53,000 for grants.
Fields of interest: Christian agencies & churches; General charitable giving.
Application information:
  Initial approach: Letter
  Deadline(s): None
Officer: Margaret Savage, Pres.
EIN: 383384888

995
Kemp, Klein, Umphrey, Endelman & May Foundation
(formerly Kemp, Klein, Umphrey & Endelman Foundation)
201 W. Big Beaver Rd., Ste. 600
Troy, MI 48084-4161   (248) 528-1111
Contact: Ralph A. Castelli, Jr., Pres.

Established in 1994 in MI.
Donors: Kemp, Klein, Umphrey, Endelman & May, PC; Turner & Turner, P.C.
Grantmaker type: Independent foundation.
Financial data (yr. ended 12/31/05): Assets, $20,716 (M); gifts received, $22,539; expenditures, $19,310; total giving, $19,255; qualifying distributions, $19,255; giving activities include $19,255 for grants.
Purpose and activities: Giving primarily for education, and for health and human services.
Fields of interest: Law school/education; Education, reading; Education; Health care; Food banks; Human services; Jewish federated giving programs; Jewish agencies & temples.
Limitations: Giving primarily in MI. No grants to individuals.
Application information:
  Initial approach: Letter
  Deadline(s): None
Officers: John B. Kemp, Chair.; Ralph A. Castelli, Jr., Pres. and Treas.; Thomas J. O'Conner, Secy.

Directors: Irwin Alterman; Tom Boyer; Cynthia E. Brazzil; Marie Goedtel; Sue Halligan; Margaret Sagese.
EIN: 383169464

996
John C. & Nancy G. Kennedy Family Foundation
4070 E. Paris Ave. S.E.
Kentwood, MI 49512-3909

Established in 1993 in MI.
Donors: John C. Kennedy; Nancy G. Kennedy.
Grantmaker type: Independent foundation.
Financial data (yr. ended 12/31/04): Assets, $1,279,179 (M); gifts received, $1,937,177; expenditures, $1,029,334; total giving, $1,029,334; qualifying distributions, $1,029,334; giving activities include $1,029,334 for grants (high: $250,000).
Fields of interest: Elementary/secondary education; Higher education; Hospitals (general); Roman Catholic agencies & churches.
Type of support: General/operating support; Building/renovation; Program development.
Limitations: Applications not accepted. Giving primarily in Grand Rapids, MI. No grants to individuals.
Application information: Contributes only to pre-selected organizations.
Officers: John C. Kennedy, Pres.; Nancy G. Kennedy, V.P.
Director: Stuart F. Cheney.
EIN: 383099643

997
Kent Charitable Trust
c/o Fifth Third Bank
P.O. Box 3636
Grand Rapids, MI 49501-3636
Application address: c/o Brian Deuby, 111 Lyon St., Grand Rapids, MI 49504, tel.: (616) 771-5627

Grantmaker type: Independent foundation.
Financial data (yr. ended 11/30/05): Assets, $374,337 (M); expenditures, $32,326; total giving, $28,564; qualifying distributions, $28,564; giving activities include $28,564 for grants.
Fields of interest: Federated giving programs.
Limitations: Giving limited to the Grand Rapids, MI, area. No grants to individuals.
Application information:
  Initial approach: Letter
  Deadline(s): None
Trustee: Fifth Third Bank.
EIN: 386050486

998
Kent Family Charitable Foundation
8814 New Castle Dr.
Fort Myers, FL 33908

Established in 2000 in MI.
Donors: Joseph A. Kent; Sheree A. Kent.
Grantmaker type: Independent foundation.
Financial data (yr. ended 12/31/05): Assets, $465,004 (M); expenditures, $35,964; total giving, $32,750; qualifying distributions, $32,750; giving activities include $32,750 for grants.

Fields of interest: Higher education; Environment, water resources; Cancer.
Limitations: Applications not accepted. Giving primarily in MI. No grants to individuals.
Application information: Contributes only to pre-selected organizations.
Officers: Joseph A. Kent, Pres.; Sheree A. Kent, Secy.; Thomas R. Kent, Treas.
Directors: Adam J. Kent; Ashlee E. Kent; Brian J. Kent; Michele A. Kent.
EIN: 912090674

999
The Kent Foundation
500 Westridge Dr., Unit No. 5
Harbor Springs, MI 49740   (231) 526-9342
Contact: Gary A. Kent, Pres.

Donor: Ralph E. Kent.
Grantmaker type: Independent foundation.
Financial data (yr. ended 8/31/05): Assets, $996,947 (M); expenditures, $63,996; total giving, $58,500; qualifying distributions, $58,500; giving activities include $58,500 for grants.
Fields of interest: Higher education; Health care.
Type of support: General/operating support.
Limitations: Giving in the U.S., with some emphasis on FL, MI, and NC. No grants to individuals.
Application information: Application form not required.
  Initial approach: Letter
  Deadline(s): None
Officers: Gary A. Kent, Pres. and Treas.; Gregory D. Kent, V.P.; Janice D. Kent, Secy.
Directors: Betty K. Kent; Ralph E. Kent.
EIN: 136126351

1000
Floyd Kent Foundation
5141 Ramsey Rd.
Oxford, MI 48371-3922

Established in MI.
Grantmaker type: Independent foundation.
Financial data (yr. ended 12/31/05): Assets, $32,985 (M); expenditures, $134,301; total giving, $130,000; qualifying distributions, $132,122; giving activities include $130,000 for 4 grants (high: $78,000; low: $5,000).
Fields of interest: Education; Human services.
Type of support: General/operating support.
Limitations: Applications not accepted. Giving limited to MI. No grants to individuals.
Application information: Contributes only to pre-selected organizations.
Officers: Dorris E. Gaines, Pres. and Treas.; Kevin J. Gaines, V.P.; Jerry D. Gaines, Jr., Secy.
EIN: 386089793

1001
Kent Medical Foundation
1400 Michigan N.E.
Grand Rapids, MI 49503-2032   (616) 458-4157
Contact: William G. McClimans, Jr., Exec. Dir.

Established in 1961 in MI.
Donors: Matilda Crane; Kent County Medical Society.
Grantmaker type: Independent foundation.

Financial data (yr. ended 12/31/05): Assets, $475,393 (M); gifts received, $17,080; expenditures, $31,405; total giving, $0; qualifying distributions, $0.
Purpose and activities: Scholarships and loans to high school graduates, who are residents of the Kent County, MI, area pursuing an education in nursing.
Type of support: Scholarships—to individuals; Student loans—to individuals.
Limitations: Giving limited to Kent, MI, and its bordering counties.
Application information: Application form required.
   Deadline(s): None
Officers: Wayne L. Creelman, Chair.; Dana E. Sommers, Vice-Chair; Amy L. Manley, M.D., Secy.-Treas.; William G. McClimans, Jr., Exec. Dir.
Trustees: Michael J. Dejong, M.D.; William R. Jewell; Robert C. Richard, M.D.; Jack L. Romence, M.D.; Valerie P. Simmons; Bruce C. Springer, M.D.; Willard S. Stawski, M.D.; Andrea Sugiyama.
EIN: 386089794

1002
Kentwood Foundation

(formerly Stauffer Kentwood Foundation)
c/o Law, Weathers & Richardson
333 Bridge St. N.W., Ste. 800
Grand Rapids, MI   49504-5360   (616) 459-1171
Contact: John P. Schneider, Secy.

Established around 1978 in MI.
Grantmaker type: Independent foundation.
Financial data (yr. ended 12/31/05): Assets, $217,994 (M); gifts received, $48; expenditures, $6,635; total giving, $0; qualifying distributions, $0.
Limitations: Giving limited to Kentwood, MI.
Application information:
   Initial approach: Letter
   Deadline(s): None
Officers and Directors: * David C. Bottrall,* Pres.; Hon. William G. Kelly,* V.P.; John P. Schneider,* Secy.; James J. Obermiller,* Treas.; William Hardiman.
EIN: 386378785

1003
Keough Family Foundation

12238 Newburgh Rd.
Livonia, MI   48150

Established in 2004 in MI.
Grantmaker type: Independent foundation.
Financial data (yr. ended 12/31/04): Assets, $12,506 (M); gifts received, $17,500; expenditures, $5,000; total giving, $5,000; qualifying distributions, $5,000; giving activities include $5,000 for grants.
Limitations: Applications not accepted. No grants to individuals.
Application information: Contributes only to pre-selected organizations.
Officers: John R. Keough, Pres.; Nancy E. Keough, Secy.-Treas.
Trustees: Ian M. Keough; Joshua R. Keough; Lane A. Keough.
EIN: 364563657

1004
Kerkstra Family Charitable Foundation

8609 Cedar Lake Dr.
Jenison, MI   49428-9559   (616) 224-6176
Contact: Lawrence Kerkstra, Pres.

Established in 1999 in MI.
Donors: Lawrence Kerkstra; Virginia Kerkstra.
Grantmaker type: Independent foundation.
Financial data (yr. ended 12/31/04): Assets, $383,367 (M); gifts received, $121,450; expenditures, $77,040; total giving, $76,370; qualifying distributions, $76,995; giving activities include $76,370 for grants.
Fields of interest: Education; Christian agencies & churches.
Limitations: Giving primarily in MI. No grants to individuals.
Application information:
   Initial approach: Proposal
   Deadline(s): Sept. 30
Officers: Lawrence Kerkstra, Pres.; Virginia Kerkstra, Secy.-Treas.
EIN: 383502922

1005
Key-Hope Foundation

1821 Sheridan Dr.
Ann Arbor, MI   48104

Established in 1997 in MI.
Donors: Robert G. Ause; Martha R. Ause.
Grantmaker type: Independent foundation.
Financial data (yr. ended 12/31/05): Assets, $222,525 (M); gifts received, $31,234; expenditures, $32,024; total giving, $30,350; qualifying distributions, $30,350; giving activities include $30,350 for grants.
Purpose and activities: Giving primarily for higher education and Christian agencies and churches.
Fields of interest: Higher education; Housing/shelter, alliance; Federated giving programs; Christian agencies & churches.
Limitations: Applications not accepted. Giving primarily in MI. No grants to individuals.
Application information: Contributes only to pre-selected organizations.
Officers: Robert G. Ause, Pres.; Martha R. Ause, Treas.
EIN: 383382529

1006
The Prem & Urmilla Khilanani Foundation

4592 Misty Morning Ct.
Bloomfield Hills, MI   48302

Established in 1997 in MI.
Donors: Prem Khilanani; Urmilla Khilanani.
Grantmaker type: Independent foundation.
Financial data (yr. ended 12/31/05): Assets, $1,654 (M); expenditures, $120; total giving, $0; qualifying distributions, $0.
Type of support: General/operating support.
Limitations: Applications not accepted. Giving primarily in PA. No grants to individuals.
Application information: Contributes only to pre-selected organizations.
Officers: Prem Khilanani, Pres.; Urmilla Khilanani, V.P.
EIN: 383345289

1007
Kid Rock Foundation

P.O. Box 1230
Clarkston, MI   48347

Established in 2004 in MI.
Donor: Robert J. Ritchie.
Grantmaker type: Independent foundation.
Financial data (yr. ended 12/31/05): Assets, $148,500 (M); gifts received, $50,000; expenditures, $1,500; total giving, $1,000; qualifying distributions, $1,000; giving activities include $1,000 for grants.
Limitations: Applications not accepted. No grants to individuals.
Application information: Contributes only to pre-selected organizations.
Officers and Directors: * Robert J. Ritchie,* Pres. and Secy.; Carol A. Ritchie,* Treas.
EIN: 201967749

1008
KidRelief Foundation

4045 W. 13 Mile Rd., Ste. A
Royal Oak, MI   48073

Established in 1999 in MI.
Donor: Carl Karoub, M.D.
Grantmaker type: Independent foundation.
Financial data (yr. ended 12/31/04): Assets, $6,515 (M); gifts received, $164,338; expenditures, $274,389; total giving, $274,187; qualifying distributions, $273,896; giving activities include $274,187 for grants (high: $113,500).
Purpose and activities: Support primarily for an international right to life organization; giving also for education.
Fields of interest: Education; Health care; Children/youth, services; Pregnancy centers; International relief; Civil liberties, right to life.
Limitations: Applications not accepted. Giving primarily in MI. No grants to individuals.
Application information: Contributes only to pre-selected organizations.
Directors: Carl Karoub, M.D.; Constance Karoub; Richard Karoub.
EIN: 383423013

1009
Kierstead Foundation

5600 Mt. Hope Hwy.
Lansing, MI   48917

Grantmaker type: Independent foundation.
Financial data (yr. ended 12/31/04): Assets, $0 (M); expenditures, $16,969; total giving, $10,265; qualifying distributions, $10,265; giving activities include $10,265 for grants.
Fields of interest: Animal welfare; Christian agencies & churches.
Limitations: Applications not accepted. Giving primarily in CA and MI. No grants to individuals.
Application information: Contributes only to pre-selected organizations.
Trustees: Glenn Kierstead; Lorraine Puuri.
EIN: 100004460

1010
Kindred Spirit
11533 Liberty St.
Clio, MI 48420

Established in 1997 in MI.
Donors: Lois Montague; Bella Vista Church; The Harvey & Elizabeth Mackey Foundation.
Grantmaker type: Independent foundation.
Financial data (yr. ended 12/31/05): Assets, $581,448 (M); gifts received, $272,090; expenditures, $96,782; total giving, $0; qualifying distributions, $292,140; giving activities include $292,140 for foundation-administered programs.
Purpose and activities: Support for a group home.
Limitations: Applications not accepted. No grants to individuals.
Application information: Contributes only to pre-selected organizations.
Officer and Directors:* Lois Montague,* Pres.; James Montague; Michael E. Thomas.
EIN: 383361146

1011
Ronald F. Kinney Foundation, Inc.
c/o David S. Kruis, Treas.
136 E. Michigan Ave., Ste. 1201
Kalamazoo, MI 49007

Established in 1990 in MI.
Donors: Ronald F. Kinney; Eva J. Kinney.
Grantmaker type: Independent foundation.
Financial data (yr. ended 12/31/05): Assets, $8,455,329 (M); gifts received, $300,482; expenditures, $314,103; total giving, $220,250; qualifying distributions, $281,239; giving activities include $220,250 for 15 grants (high: $100,000; low: $250).
Purpose and activities: Giving primarily for education and medical research.
Fields of interest: Higher education; Mental health/crisis services; Medical research; Human services; Roman Catholic agencies & churches.
Type of support: General/operating support; Annual campaigns; Capital campaigns; Building/renovation; Research.
Limitations: Applications not accepted. Giving on a national basis, with emphasis on MI.
Application information: Unsolicited requests for funds not accepted.
Officers and Trustees:* Ronald F. Kinney,* Chair.; Eva J. Kinney,* Pres.; James C. Melvin, V.P.; Bradley E. Weller, V.P.; Loyal A. Eldridge III, Secy.; David S. Kruis, Treas.
EIN: 382956566
Selected grants: The following grants were reported in 2003.
$200,000 to Lake Michigan Catholic Schools, Saint Joseph, MI. For capital campaign.
$100,000 to Mayo Foundation, Rochester, MN. For general support.
$50,000 to Birthright of Saint Joseph, Saint Joseph, MI. For general operating support.
$25,000 to John Carroll University, University Heights, OH. For general support.
$25,000 to Mercy-Memorial Health Foundation, Benton Harbor, MI. For general support.
$25,000 to Saint Malachy Church, Philadelphia, PA. For general support.
$10,000 to Carleton College, Northfield, MN. For Ronald F. Kinney Jr. Library Fund.
$10,000 to Hamilton College, Arts Department, Clinton, NY.

$10,000 to University of Notre Dame, Notre Dame, IN. For annual support.
$1,000 to Brooks School, North Andover, MA. For annual support.

1012
KINSHIP Foundation
(formerly Columbine Foundation)
P.O. Box 399
Ada, MI 49301-9798
Contact: Mary Goodwillie Nelson, Pres.

Established in 1998 in MI.
Donor: Mary Goodwillie Nelson.
Grantmaker type: Independent foundation.
Financial data (yr. ended 12/31/04): Assets, $596,700 (M); expenditures, $85,190; total giving, $79,049; qualifying distributions, $79,375; giving activities include $79,049 for 4 grants (high: $49,999; low: $2,000).
Fields of interest: Visual arts; Performing arts; Elementary/secondary education.
Type of support: General/operating support.
Limitations: Giving primarily in Forest Hills and Grand Rapids, MI. No grants to individuals.
Application information:
   Initial approach: Letter
   Deadline(s): None
Officers: Mary Goodwillie Nelson, Pres. and Secy.; James E. Nelson, V.P. and Treas.
EIN: 383444860

1013
The Kirt Foundation
1033 Valley Stream Dr.
Rochester Hills, MI 48309

Established in 2003 in MI.
Donors: Robert Kirt; Rosemary Kirt.
Grantmaker type: Independent foundation.
Financial data (yr. ended 12/31/05): Assets, $56,842 (M); expenditures, $5,322; total giving, $4,220; qualifying distributions, $4,220; giving activities include $4,220 for grants.
Limitations: Applications not accepted. Giving primarily in Grand Rapids, MI. No grants to individuals.
Application information: Contributes only to pre-selected organizations.
Officers: Robert Kirt, Pres.; Rosemary Kirt, V.P.; Edith Hetling, Secy.; Joseph Kirt, Treas.
EIN: 300191393

1014
Kiwanis Club of Shorewood Foundation
21055 E. 12 Mile Rd.
Roseville, MI 48066-2205

Established in 2002 in MI.
Grantmaker type: Independent foundation.
Financial data (yr. ended 9/30/03): Assets, $89,328 (M); gifts received, $8,000; expenditures, $8,000; total giving, $8,000; qualifying distributions, $8,000; giving activities include $8,000 for grants.
Limitations: Giving primarily in St. Clair Shores, MI.
Directors: Jack Cascione; Larry Lozo; Lenny Palermino; Carl Papa; Howard Robinson; Hal Schafer; Sam Ventimiglia.
EIN: 383545748

1015
Kiwanis of Michigan Foundation
P.O. Box 572
Petoskey, MI 49770

Grantmaker type: Independent foundation.
Financial data (yr. ended 9/30/04): Assets, $685,073 (M); gifts received, $255,745; expenditures, $339,489; total giving, $325,234; qualifying distributions, $336,412; giving activities include $325,234 for grants.
Purpose and activities: Support primarily for the C.S. Mott Hospital, Ann Arbor, MI.
Fields of interest: Hospitals (general); Children/youth, services.
Limitations: Applications not accepted. Giving limited to MI. No grants to individuals.
Application information: Contributes only to pre-selected organizations.
Officers and Trustees:* Thomas A. Mann,* Pres.; Allen J. LaFurgey,* 1st V.P.; Wendell Meyer,* 2nd V.P.; David L. Meyer,* Secy.-Treas.; Carl Romano; and 15 additional trustees.
EIN: 381723513

1016
The Harvey and Aileen Kleiman Family Foundation
24201 Bingham Ct.
Bingham Farms, MI 48025

Established in 1996 in MI.
Donors: Aileen Kleiman; Harvey Kleiman.
Grantmaker type: Independent foundation.
Financial data (yr. ended 9/30/05): Assets, $314,750 (M); expenditures, $17,248; total giving, $16,948; qualifying distributions, $16,948; giving activities include $16,948 for grants.
Limitations: Applications not accepted. Giving primarily in MI. No grants to individuals.
Application information: Contributes only to pre-selected organizations.
Officers: Harvey Kleiman, Pres.; Gary Kleinman, V.P.; Mark Kleiman, V.P.; Robert Kleinman, V.P.; Aileen Kleiman, Secy.
EIN: 383320168

1017
Verne O. & Dorothy M. Kling Scholarship Fund
c/o Comerica Bank
P.O. Box 7500, M/C 8280
Detroit, MI 48275
Application address: c/o Comerica Bank, 101 N Main St., Ste. 100, Ann Arbor, MI 48104, tel.: (734) 930-2413

Grantmaker type: Independent foundation.
Financial data (yr. ended 6/30/05): Assets, $59,249 (M); expenditures, $15,875; total giving, $11,500; qualifying distributions, $11,937; giving activities include $11,500 for 18 grants to individuals.
Purpose and activities: Scholarship awards to members of the Protestant Church and who are residents of the following states, with preference given to following order 1) Shelby County, IN, 2) IN, 3) MI, and then 4) nationally.
Fields of interest: Higher education.
Type of support: Scholarships—to individuals.

Limitations: Giving primarily in Shelby County, IN, and MI.
Application information: Application form required.
Deadline(s): Apr. 1
Trustee: Comerica Bank.
EIN: 386302950

1018
John E. Klobucar and Joseph D. Klobucher Foundation
P.O. Box 404
Frankenmuth, MI 48734
Contact: Joseph D. Klobucher, Pres.

Established in 2002.
Donors: John E. Klobucar; Joseph D. Klobucher.
Grantmaker type: Independent foundation.
Financial data (yr. ended 12/31/05): Assets, $186,397 (M); gifts received, $62,000; expenditures, $42,261; total giving, $41,500; qualifying distributions, $41,500; giving activities include $41,500 for grants.
Application information:
Initial approach: Letter
Deadline(s): None
Officers: Joseph D. Klobucher, Pres.; Wayne Stewart, Secy.; John E. Klobucar, Treas.
EIN: 383605623

1019
Klopcic Family Foundation
5400 Patterson Ave. S.E.
Grand Rapids, MI 49512

Established in 1994 in MI.
Donors: Donald L. Klopcic, Sr.; Elizabeth M. Klopcic.
Grantmaker type: Independent foundation.
Financial data (yr. ended 12/31/05): Assets, $2,594,313 (M); gifts received, $200,558; expenditures, $145,961; total giving, $127,500; qualifying distributions, $127,900; giving activities include $127,500 for 12 grants (high: $50,000; low: $1,500).
Purpose and activities: Giving primarily for education, the arts and community programs.
Fields of interest: Arts; Education; Health care; Crime/violence prevention, abuse prevention; Youth development; Community development.
Limitations: Applications not accepted. Giving limited to MI, with emphasis on Grand Rapids. No grants to individuals.
Application information: Contributes only to pre-selected organizations.
Officers: Donald L. Klopcic, Sr., Pres. and Secy.; Donald L. Klopcic, Jr., V.P.; Keith C. Klopcic, V.P.; Elizabeth M. Klopcic, Treas.
EIN: 383211779
Selected grants: The following grants were reported in 2004.
$50,000 to Kent County Parks Foundation, Grand Rapids, MI.
$25,000 to Forest Hills Public Schools, Grand Rapids, MI. For Fine Arts Center.
$15,000 to Blodgett Butterworth Health Care Foundation, Grand Rapids, MI.
$12,500 to D. A. Blodgett Services for Children and Families, Grand Rapids, MI.
$9,000 to Grand Rapids Art Museum, Grand Rapids, MI.
$5,000 to Gildas Club Grand Rapids, Grand Rapids, MI.

$5,000 to Operation Resources, Grand Rapids, MI.
$5,000 to West Michigan Academy of Music for Girls, Grand Rapids, MI.
$2,500 to Grand Rapids Childrens Museum, Grand Rapids, MI.
$1,500 to YMCA of Greater Grand Rapids, Grand Rapids, MI.

1020
KMD Foundation
1 S. Ocean Blvd., Ste. 305
Boca Raton, FL 33432

Established in 1981 in MI.
Donors: Irving A. Smokler; Toba Smokler Trust.
Grantmaker type: Independent foundation.
Financial data (yr. ended 8/31/03): Assets, $3,947,112 (M); expenditures, $148,586; total giving, $113,400; qualifying distributions, $117,400; giving activities include $113,400 for 12 grants (high: $50,000; low: $500).
Purpose and activities: Giving primarily to Jewish agencies, temples, schools, and federated giving programs.
Fields of interest: Higher education; Education; Human services; Jewish federated giving programs; Jewish agencies & temples.
Limitations: Applications not accepted. Giving primarily in Ann Arbor, MI. No grants to individuals; no loans or program-related investments.
Application information: Contributes only to pre-selected organizations.
Trustees: Carol S. Smokler; Irving A. Smokler.
EIN: 382378958

1021
Edward M. and Henrietta M. Knabusch Charitable Trust No. 1
c/o Monroe Bank & Trust
102 E. Front St.
Monroe, MI 48161

Established in 1994 in MI.
Donor: Edward M. Knabusch.
Grantmaker type: Independent foundation.
Financial data (yr. ended 12/31/05): Assets, $15,405,575 (M); expenditures, $2,560,672; total giving, $2,465,463; qualifying distributions, $2,482,510; giving activities include $2,465,463 for 15 grants (high: $470,133; low: $14,702; average: $58,717–$117,435).
Purpose and activities: Giving primarily to Lutheran churches and organizations; support also for a YMCA.
Fields of interest: Historic preservation/historical societies; Higher education; Nursing home/convalescent facility; YM/YWCAs & YM/YWHAs; Children/youth, services; Protestant agencies & churches.
Type of support: General/operating support.
Limitations: Applications not accepted. Giving limited to Watertown, IA, Ann Arbor, Bay City, Detroit and Monroe, MI and St. Louis, MO. No grants to individuals.
Application information: Contributes only to pre-selected organizations.
Trustee: Monroe Bank & Trust.
EIN: 386643327

1022
Edward M. and Henrietta M. Knabusch Charitable Trust No. 2
c/o Monroe Bank & Trust
102 E. Front St.
Monroe, MI 48161 (734) 242-2066
Contact: John F. Weaver, Tr.

Established in 1995 in MI.
Donor: Edward M. Knabusch Marital Trust.
Grantmaker type: Independent foundation.
Financial data (yr. ended 12/31/05): Assets, $10,733,308 (M); expenditures, $882,126; total giving, $817,000; qualifying distributions, $839,707; giving activities include $817,000 for 34 grants (high: $50,000; low: $5,000).
Fields of interest: Performing arts centers; Higher education.
Limitations: Giving primarily in Monroe, MI, and High Point, NC. No grants to individuals.
Application information: Application form not required.
Deadline(s): None
Trustees: John F. Weaver; Betty Lou White.
EIN: 386643328

1023
Edward M. and Henrietta M. Knabusch Scholarship Foundation
c/o Monroe Bank & Trust
102 E. Front St.
Monroe, MI 48161

Established in 1998 in MI.
Donors: La-Z-Boy Foundation; Edward M. & Henrietta M. Knabusch Charitable Trust No. 2.
Grantmaker type: Independent foundation.
Financial data (yr. ended 12/31/05): Assets, $2,336,155 (M); expenditures, $156,103; total giving, $134,349; qualifying distributions, $144,899; giving activities include $134,349 for 71 grants to individuals (high: $4,000; low: $1,000).
Purpose and activities: Scholarships awarded to high school seniors who are children of La-Z-Boy, Inc., employees.
Type of support: Scholarships—to individuals.
Limitations: Giving limited to children of La-Z-Boy employees in the following locations: Siloam Springs, AR, Redlands, CA, Monroe, MI, Neosho, MO, Leland and Newton, MS, Hudson, Lenoir, and Lincolnton, NC, Florence, SC, Dayton and New Tazewell, TN, Tremonton, UT, Bedford, VA, and Waterloo, Ontario, Canada.
Application information: Application form required.
Deadline(s): None
Trustees: John F. Weaver; Betty Lou White.
EIN: 383450698

1024
Stewart and Lenore Kniff Family Foundation, Inc.
c/o Gerald L. Horton
4112 20th St.
White Cloud, MI 49349-9534

Established in 1997 in MI.
Donors: Stewart Kniff; Lenore Kniff.
Grantmaker type: Independent foundation.
Financial data (yr. ended 12/31/05): Assets, $869,204 (M); expenditures, $79,165; total giving, $70,000; qualifying distributions, $70,000; giving

activities include $70,000 for 3 grants (high: $35,000; low: $10,000).
Fields of interest: Christian agencies & churches.
International interests: India.
Limitations: Applications not accepted. Giving primarily for the benefit of India. No grants to individuals.
Application information: Contributes only to pre-selected organizations.
Officers: Stewart Kniff, Pres. and Treas.; Lenore Kniff, V.P. and Secy.; Gerald L. Horton, Mgr.
EIN: 383338626

1025
Knight Family Charitable and Educational Foundation

(formerly Kings Point Richmond Foundation, Inc.)
215 N. Talbot St.
P.O. Box 255
Addison, MI 49220-0255 (517) 547-6131
Contact: N.J. Glasser, Secy.-Treas.

Established in 1984 in MI.
Donors: J.A. Knight; V.C. Knight†; Heat Controller, Inc.
Grantmaker type: Independent foundation.
Financial data (yr. ended 12/31/04): Assets, $1,933,810 (M); expenditures, $104,038; total giving, $102,500; qualifying distributions, $102,500; giving activities include $102,500 for 38 grants (high: $12,000; low: $500).
Purpose and activities: Funding for education, religion, health, and human services.
Fields of interest: Higher education; Education; Health organizations, association; Human services; Christian agencies & churches.
Limitations: Giving primarily in MI.
Application information: Application form required.
  Deadline(s): None
  Final notification: 2 months
Officers and Directors:* M.K. Underhill,* Pres.; D.S. MacLennan,* V.P.; N.J. Glasser,* Secy.-Treas.; L.K. Dully; L.J. Mosley.
EIN: 382564732

1026
James A. and Faith Knight Foundation

180 Little Lake Dr., Ste. 6B
Ann Arbor, MI 48103 (734) 769-5653
Contact: Margaret A. Talburtt Ph.D., Exec. Dir.
FAX: (734) 769-8383;
E-mail: info@knightfoundationmi.org; URL: http://www.knightfoundationmi.org

Established in 1999 in MI.
Donor: James A. Knight Trust.
Grantmaker type: Independent foundation.
Financial data (yr. ended 12/31/04): Assets, $15,245,744 (L); gifts received, $81,106; expenditures, $799,074; total giving, $622,182; qualifying distributions, $709,233; giving activities include $622,182 for 31 grants (high: $50,000; low: $3,477).
Purpose and activities: Primarily serving Jackson and Washtenaw counties, the James A. & Faith Knight Foundation is dedicated to improving communities by providing grant support to qualified nonprofit organizations including, but not limited to, those that address the needs of women and girls, animals and the natural world, and internal capacity. Giving primarily for human services, including a

neighborhood center, women's organizations, and family services; support also for nonprofit management, the United Way, housing, the arts, education, and environmental conservation.
Fields of interest: Performing arts, theater; Arts; Adult education—literacy, basic skills & GED; Education; Environment, natural resources; Housing/shelter, development; Human services; Neighborhood centers; Family services; Women, centers/services; Nonprofit management; Women.
Type of support: General/operating support; Capital campaigns; Building/renovation; Debt reduction; Program development.
Limitations: Giving limited to MI, with some emphasis on Ann Arbor and Jackson. No support for religious or political organizations. No grants to individuals, or for conferences or special events, or for annual campaigns.
Publications: Application guidelines; Grants list; Occasional report; Program policy statement.
Application information: Application form available on foundation Web site. Application form required.
  Initial approach: 2-page concept letter
  Copies of proposal: 3
  Deadline(s): Jan. 10 and Aug. 29
  Board meeting date(s): 10 times per year
  Final notification: Approximately 90 days
Officers: Carol Knight-Drain, Pres. and Secy.; David Knight, V.P.; Scott Drain, Treas.
Number of staff: 1 part-time professional.
EIN: 383465904

1027
Ann G. Knooihuizen Irrevocable Trust

c/o Comerica Bank
P.O. Box 75000
Detroit, MI 48275

Established in 1996 in MI.
Grantmaker type: Independent foundation.
Financial data (yr. ended 12/31/05): Assets, $199,116 (M); expenditures, $11,565; total giving, $7,269; qualifying distributions, $7,944; giving activities include $7,269 for grants.
Purpose and activities: Support only for the Calvary Baptist Church, Hackley Hospital, and Muskegon City Rescue Mission, Muskegon, MI.
Fields of interest: Hospitals (general); Human services; Protestant agencies & churches.
Type of support: General/operating support.
Limitations: Applications not accepted. Giving limited to Muskegon, MI. No grants to individuals.
Application information: Contributes only to 3 pre-selected organizations.
Trustee: Comerica Bank.
EIN: 386436167

1028
Robert & Margaret Koch Bomarko Founders Scholarship Fund

c/o Fifth Third Bank
P.O. Box 3636
Grand Rapids, MI 49501-3636

Established in 1989 in IN.
Donors: Robert Koch; Margaret Koch.
Grantmaker type: Independent foundation.
Financial data (yr. ended 9/30/05): Assets, $111,081 (M); expenditures, $7,181; total giving, $5,735; qualifying distributions, $5,735; giving activities include $5,735 for grants to individuals.

Purpose and activities: Scholarship awards to students or graduates of the Argos, Bremen, Culver, LaVille, Plymouth or Triton schools; scholarships also to employees of Bomarko, Plymouth high, IN, who will attend Ancilla College, Donaldson, IN.
Type of support: Scholarships—to individuals.
Limitations: Giving limited to residents of IN.
Application information: Application form required.
  Deadline(s): Apr. 15
Trustee: Fifth Third Bank.
EIN: 351781577

1029
Hulda M. Koch Charitable Foundation, Inc.

c/o National City Bank
171 Monroe Ave., N.W.
Grand Rapids, MI 49503

Grantmaker type: Independent foundation.
Financial data (yr. ended 12/31/05): Assets, $82,566 (M); expenditures, $4,868; total giving, $2,679; qualifying distributions, $2,679; giving activities include $2,679 for grants.
Purpose and activities: Support only to Michigan Lutheran Seminary in Saginaw, Martin Luther College in New Ulm, Minnesota, and Luther Preparatory School in Watertown, Wisconsin.
Fields of interest: Secondary school/education; Theological school/education; Protestant agencies & churches.
Limitations: Applications not accepted. Giving limited to Saginaw, MI, New Ulm, MN, and Watertown, WI. No grants to individuals.
Application information: Contributes only to 3 pre-selected organizations.
Trustee: National City Bank.
EIN: 382803976

1030
Arnold J. and Irene B. Kocurek Family Foundation, 1986

c/o Comerica Bank
P.O. Box 75000, M/C 3302
Detroit, MI 48275-3302
Application address: c/o Latrinda Chumley, Comerica Bank, P.O. Box 6596, Detroit, MI 48275-6596, tel.: (972) 361-2578

Established in 1986 in TX.
Donors: Arnold J. Kocurek†; Irene B. Kocurek.
Grantmaker type: Independent foundation.
Financial data (yr. ended 2/28/05): Assets, $3,001,334 (M); expenditures, $154,365; total giving, $108,000; qualifying distributions, $109,865; giving activities include $108,000 for 21 grants (high: $16,000; low: $2,000).
Fields of interest: Education; Hospitals (general); Human services; Roman Catholic agencies & churches.
Type of support: General/operating support.
Limitations: Giving limited to TX, with emphasis on San Antonio.
Application information: Application form not required.
  Initial approach: Letter
  Deadline(s): None
Managers: Irene B. Kocurek; Karen Kocurek; Suzanne Kocurek.
Trustee: Comerica Bank.
EIN: 746345100

Selected grants: The following grants were reported in 2004.
$25,000 to Saint Peter-Saint Joseph Childrens Home, San Antonio, TX.
$15,000 to Assumption Seminary, San Antonio, TX.
$12,000 to San Antonio State School, San Antonio, TX.
$3,000 to Any Baby Can of San Antonio, San Antonio, TX.
$3,000 to Battered Womens Shelter, San Antonio, TX.
$3,000 to Discalced Carmelite Nuns, San Antonio, TX.
$3,000 to Saint Vincent de Paul Society, San Antonio, TX.
$3,000 to Sisters of Divine Providence, San Antonio, TX.
$3,000 to Winston School, San Antonio, TX.
$2,000 to Sacred Heart School, Library, Hallettsville, TX.

1031
John and Ann L. Koester Charitable Trust
P.O. Box 180
Frankenmuth, MI   48734-0180

Established in 1994 in MI.
Donors: John C. Koester; Ann Leone Koester.
Grantmaker type: Independent foundation.
Financial data (yr. ended 12/31/05): Assets, $210,575 (M); expenditures, $45,706; total giving, $42,050; qualifying distributions, $42,050; giving activities include $42,050 for grants.
Purpose and activities: Giving primarily to Evangelical Lutheran churches and schools.
Fields of interest: Elementary/secondary education; Protestant agencies & churches.
Limitations: Giving primarily in FL and MI.
Application information:
Initial approach: Letter
Deadline(s): None
Trustees: Ann Leone Koester; John C. Koester.
EIN: 383150475

1032
Ivan H. Koetje & Carolyn J. Koetje Foundation
7425 40th Ave.
Hudsonville, MI   49426-9258

Established in 1999 in MI.
Donors: Carolyn J. Koetje; Ivan H. Koetje; C & I Properties, LLC.
Grantmaker type: Independent foundation.
Financial data (yr. ended 12/31/05): Assets, $324,982 (M); expenditures, $43,488; total giving, $38,570; qualifying distributions, $38,570; giving activities include $38,570 for grants.
Purpose and activities: Giving primarily to promote Christian education.
Fields of interest: Elementary/secondary education.
Limitations: Giving primarily in Hudsonville, MI.
Officers: Ivan H. Koetje, Pres. and Treas.; Carolyn J. Koetje, Secy.
Directors: Julie Boetsma; Sue Glashower.
EIN: 383447359

1033
John F. Koetje & Delia Koetje Foundation
P.O. Box 339
Belmont, MI   49306

Established in 1999 in MI.
Donors: John F. Koetje; Delia Koetje.
Grantmaker type: Independent foundation.
Financial data (yr. ended 12/31/05): Assets, $502,657 (M); gifts received, $64,570; expenditures, $137,710; total giving, $132,850; qualifying distributions, $132,850; giving activities include $132,850 for 9 grants (high: $60,000; low: $250).
Fields of interest: Human services; Christian agencies & churches.
Limitations: Applications not accepted. Giving primarily in MI. No grants to individuals.
Application information: Contributes only to pre-selected organizations.
Officers: John F. Koetje, Pres.; Delia Koetje, Secy.
Directors: Mary Brower; Scott Van Popering; Gerard Winkle.
EIN: 383445373
Selected grants: The following grants were reported in 2004.
$49,610 to Young Life, Timber Wolf Lake Young Life Camp, Colorado Springs, CO.
$45,000 to Bible League, Chicago, IL.
$25,000 to Freedom Baptist Schools, Hudsonville, MI.
$10,000 to Georgetown Harmony Homes, Jenison, MI.
$10,000 to Unity Christian High School, Hudsonville, MI.
$5,000 to Project Canefire, Lake City, MI.
$1,400 to Lake City Christian Reformed Church, Lake City, MI.
$500 to Bethany United Reformed Church, Wyoming, MI.
$500 to International Messengers, Clear Lake, IA.

1034
Kogan Foundation
c/o Kogan Co. Oakland Mall
39577 Woodward Ave., Ste. 110
Bloomfield Hills, MI   48304-5083

Established in 1943 in MI.
Donors: Jay Kogan; Oakland Mall Ltd.
Grantmaker type: Independent foundation.
Financial data (yr. ended 12/31/04): Assets, $2,750,905 (M); expenditures, $558,632; total giving, $552,402; qualifying distributions, $557,896; giving activities include $552,402 for 8 + grants (high: $405,297).
Purpose and activities: Support primarily for Jewish federated giving programs and temples.
Fields of interest: Performing arts, orchestra (symphony); Human services; Jewish federated giving programs; Jewish agencies & temples.
Limitations: Applications not accepted. Giving primarily in MI, with emphasis on Bloomfield Hills, Detroit, and Southfield. No grants to individuals.
Application information: Contributes only to pre-selected organizations.
Officers: Lauren Daitch, Pres. and Treas.; Douglas Mossman, Secy.
EIN: 386064802
Selected grants: The following grants were reported in 2003.
$250,000 to Massachusetts Institute of Technology, Cambridge, MA.

$140,750 to Jewish Federation of Metropolitan Detroit, Bloomfield Hills, MI.
$35,000 to Kadima Jewish Support Services for Adults with Mental Illness, Southfield, MI.
$25,000 to American School in London Foundation, Princeton, NJ.
$15,000 to Temple Israel, Long Beach, CA.
$7,500 to Interlochen Center for the Arts, Interlochen, MI.
$6,300 to JARC, Farmington Hills, MI.
$5,900 to Detroit Symphony Orchestra, Detroit, MI.
$5,000 to Wexner Center Foundation, Columbus, OH.
$4,322 to Congregation Shaarey Zedek, Southfield, MI.

1035
The Kohn-Bancroft Family Foundation
9813 Weko Dr., Box E-1
Bridgman, MI   49106-9703
Application address: 3389 Linco Rd., Stevensville, MI 49127

Established in 2000 in MI.
Donors: Robert A. Kohn; Elizabeth J. Kohn.
Grantmaker type: Independent foundation.
Financial data (yr. ended 12/31/05): Assets, $366,507 (M); expenditures, $31,972; total giving, $31,902; qualifying distributions, $31,902; giving activities include $31,902 for grants.
Purpose and activities: Scholarship awards to employees of Supreme Casting, Inc., Stevensville, and their dependents.
Fields of interest: Higher education.
Type of support: Employee-related scholarships.
Limitations: Giving primarily in MI.
Application information: Application form required.
Deadline(s): May 1 and Oct. 1
Officers: Robert A. Kohn, Pres.; Robert W. Bancroft, V.P.; William R. Bancroft, Jr., V.P.; Elizabeth J. Kohn, Secy.-Treas.
EIN: 383537827

1036
Louis and Ella I. Kondur Memorial Foundation, Inc.
2945 Orchard Pl.
Orchard Lake, MI   48324

Established in 1996 in MI.
Donor: Louis Kondur Trust.
Grantmaker type: Independent foundation.
Financial data (yr. ended 12/31/04): Assets, $441,348 (M); expenditures, $53,120; total giving, $52,500; qualifying distributions, $52,458; giving activities include $52,500 for 21 grants to individuals (high: $2,500; low: $2,500).
Purpose and activities: Scholarship awards to the ten students with the highest GPA in academic courses at West Bloomfield High School; scholarship awards also to qualified students at St. Mary's High School, MI.
Type of support: Scholarships—to individuals.
Limitations: Applications not accepted. Giving primarily to residents of MI.
Application information: Recipient selected by school high school staff.
Officers: Bruce H. Tobin, Pres.; Msgr. Stanley Milewski, V.P.; James K. Talpos, Secy.
EIN: 383314192

1037
The Korff Foundation
455 Cherry St. S.E.
Grand Rapids, MI 49503

Established in 1994 in MI.
Donor: Jack J. Korff.
Grantmaker type: Independent foundation.
Financial data (yr. ended 12/31/04): Assets, $1,128,048 (M); gifts received, $280,545; expenditures, $222,413; total giving, $217,550; qualifying distributions, $219,981; giving activities include $217,550 for 65 grants (high: $50,000; low: $500).
Purpose and activities: Giving for museums, education, and Roman Catholic and Protestant churches.
Fields of interest: Museums; Arts; Higher education; Education; Human services; Federated giving programs; Protestant agencies & churches; Roman Catholic agencies & churches.
Limitations: Applications not accepted. Giving primarily in Grand Rapids, MI. No grants to individuals.
Application information: Contributes only to pre-selected organizations.
Officer: Jack J. Korff, Pres. and Treas.
Director: Marcae Johnson.
EIN: 383190927

1038
Harry B. & Anna Korman Foundation
c/o Larry Zietz
30445 Northwestern Hwy., Ste. 230
Farmington Hills, MI 48334
Contact: Ingeborg Schuetz, Pres.

Established in 1956 in MI.
Donor: Harry B. Korman.
Grantmaker type: Independent foundation.
Financial data (yr. ended 12/31/05): Assets, $2,072,749 (M); expenditures, $217,149; total giving, $179,000; qualifying distributions, $179,000; giving activities include $179,000 for 11 grants (high: $34,000; low: $1,000).
Fields of interest: Cancer; Jewish federated giving programs; Jewish agencies & temples.
Limitations: Giving primarily in Detroit, MI. No grants to individuals.
Application information:
Initial approach: Letter
Deadline(s): None
Officers and Directors:* Ingeborg Schuetz, Pres.; Helen Braverman,* V.P.; Lawrence D. Zietz,* Secy.; Eunice Ring.
EIN: 386078083
Selected grants: The following grants were reported in 2003.
$50,000 to Hadassah, The Womens Zionist Organization of America, New York, NY.
$25,000 to Karmanos Cancer Foundation, Lathrup Village, MI.
$15,000 to American Society for Technion-Israel Institute of Technology, New York, NY.
$10,000 to University of Michigan, Ann Arbor, MI.

1039
The Korybalski Family Foundation
1801 Hermitage Rd.
Ann Arbor, MI 48104

Established in 2002 in MI.
Donor: Michael E. Korybalski.
Grantmaker type: Independent foundation.
Financial data (yr. ended 12/31/04): Assets, $79,084 (M); expenditures, $18,273; total giving, $17,550; qualifying distributions, $17,725; giving activities include $17,550 for grants.
Limitations: Applications not accepted. No grants to individuals.
Application information: Contributes only to pre-selected organizations.
Officer and Directors:* Phyllis Korybalski,* Secy.; Michael E. Korybalski.
EIN: 300127755

1040
Donald & Mary Kosch Foundation
(formerly Donald F. Kosch Foundation)
P.O. Box 687
Dearborn, MI 48121
Application address: c/o Donald F. Kosch, 2450 Wyoming St., Dearborn, MI 48126, tel.: (313) 842-2375

Established in 1994 in MI.
Donor: Donald F. Kosch.
Grantmaker type: Independent foundation.
Financial data (yr. ended 12/31/05): Assets, $824,953 (M); gifts received, $75,000; expenditures, $61,274; total giving, $53,000; qualifying distributions, $53,000; giving activities include $53,000 for grants.
Purpose and activities: Giving primarily to a community fund; funding also for Christian and Presbyterian churches and human services.
Fields of interest: Human services; Foundations (community); Federated giving programs; Christian agencies & churches; Protestant agencies & churches.
Type of support: General/operating support.
Limitations: Giving primarily in MI, with emphasis on Dearborn.
Application information:
Initial approach: Letter
Deadline(s): None
Officers and Directors:* Donald F. Kosch,* Pres. and Treas.; Mary T. Kosch,* Secy.; Susan L. Kosch-Meier.
EIN: 383147426

1041
The Kosins Family Foundation
141 Harrow Ln.
Saginaw, MI 48663

Established in 1988 in MI.
Donor: Benjamin Kosins.
Grantmaker type: Independent foundation.
Financial data (yr. ended 6/30/05): Assets, $518,934 (M); expenditures, $42,480; total giving, $39,250; qualifying distributions, $39,270; giving activities include $39,250 for grants.
Limitations: Applications not accepted. Giving primarily in MI, with emphasis on West Bloomfield and Farmington Hills. No grants to individuals.
Application information: Contributes only to pre-selected organizations.
Officers and Trustee:* Frank Polasky,* Chair. and Pres.; Donald Sharfman, Secy.-Treas.
EIN: 382634177

1042
Daniel J. & Ardith A. Koster Foundation
2015 8th Ave.
Byron Center, MI 49315 (616) 878-5554
Contact: Ardith A. Koster, Pres.; Greg Koster, Exec. Dir.

Established in 1992 in MI.
Donors: Daniel J. Koster†; Ardith A. Koster.
Grantmaker type: Independent foundation.
Financial data (yr. ended 12/31/05): Assets, $141,399 (M); gifts received, $185,200; expenditures, $131,670; total giving, $131,169; qualifying distributions, $131,169; giving activities include $131,169 for 15 grants (high: $29,800; low: $2,400).
Purpose and activities: Giving primarily to education and Christian organizations.
Fields of interest: Elementary/secondary education; Education; Children/youth, services; Christian agencies & churches.
Limitations: Giving on a national basis, with some emphasis on MI. No grants to individuals.
Application information:
Initial approach: Letter
Deadline(s): None
Board meeting date(s): Jan. and June
Officers: Ardith A. Koster, Pres.; Greg Koster, Exec. Dir.
Board Members: Cheryl Koster; Kurt Koster; Linda Koster; Rick Koster; Susan Koster.
EIN: 383067600

1043
Fannie Kraft Foundation
17515 W. 9 Mile Rd., No. 550
Southfield, MI 48075

Donors: Eugene Kraft; Lawrence H. Kraft.
Grantmaker type: Independent foundation.
Financial data (yr. ended 12/31/05): Assets, $1,486,902 (M); expenditures, $75,720; total giving, $71,150; qualifying distributions, $71,150; giving activities include $71,150 for grants.
Purpose and activities: Giving to hospitals, health associations and Jewish agencies.
Fields of interest: Hospitals (general); Health organizations, association; Jewish agencies & temples.
Limitations: Applications not accepted. Giving primarily in MI. No grants to individuals.
Application information: Contributes only to pre-selected organizations.
Officers and Trustees: Lawrence H. Kraft,* Pres.; Jackie Kraft, V.P.; Milton Einstandig,* Secy-Treas.
EIN: 386070179

1044
R. & W. Krause Foundation, Inc.
140 Krause St.
Rockford, MI 49341 (616) 866-1515
Contact: Barbara K. Bunbury, Pres.

Established in MI.
Grantmaker type: Independent foundation.
Financial data (yr. ended 10/31/05): Assets, $198,750 (M); gifts received, $10,500; expenditures, $11,874; total giving, $10,500; qualifying distributions, $10,500; giving activities include $10,500 for grants.

THE MICHIGAN FOUNDATION DIRECTORY 149

Purpose and activities: Giving primarily for a Protestant church and agency, and education.
Fields of interest: Education; Protestant agencies & churches.
Type of support: General/operating support.
Limitations: Giving primarily in MI. No grants to individuals.
Application information:
 Initial approach: Letter
 Deadline(s): None
Officers: Barbara K. Bunbury, Pres.; John D. Bunbury, V.P.
EIN: 386111582

1045
Cmdr. and Mrs. Robert Krause Foundation
132 State St.
Harbor Beach, MI 48441
Contact: Marilyn S. Townley, Tr.

Established in 2003 in MI.
Grantmaker type: Independent foundation.
Financial data (yr. ended 12/31/04): Assets, $792,367 (M); expenditures, $57,049; total giving, $35,600; qualifying distributions, $35,600; giving activities include $35,600 for 26 grants to individuals (high: $2,000; low: $500).
Purpose and activities: Scholarship awards to graduates of Harbor Beach Community School, Harbor Beach, MI, for post-secondary education.
Fields of interest: Higher education.
Type of support: Scholarships—to individuals.
Limitations: Giving limited to residents of Harbor Beach, MI.
Application information: Application form required.
 Deadline(s): Apr. 30
Trustees: Robert W. Krause; Marilyn S. Townley.
EIN: 527317516

1046
Jenny H. & Otto F. Krauss Charitable Foundation
c/o Michael R. Ries, C.P.A.
409 Burrows Ave.
Roscommon, MI 48653

Donor: Otto F. Krauss.
Grantmaker type: Independent foundation.
Financial data (yr. ended 12/31/04): Assets, $5,955,651 (M); expenditures, $144,367; total giving, $120,400; qualifying distributions, $120,450; giving activities include $120,400 for 22 grants (high: $17,000; low: $200).
Purpose and activities: Giving primarily to schools and churches.
Fields of interest: Higher education; Higher education, college; Protestant agencies & churches.
Type of support: General/operating support.
Limitations: Applications not accepted. Giving primarily in FL and MI. No grants to individuals.
Application information: Contributes only to pre-selected organizations.
Trustees: A.G. Edwards; Alan F. Krauss; Frederick G. Krauss.
EIN: 382837174

1047
Sam & Jane Kravitz Foundation
23 Campau Cir. N.W.
Grand Rapids, MI 49503

Donors: Sam Kravitz; Jane Kravitz.
Grantmaker type: Independent foundation.
Financial data (yr. ended 12/31/05): Assets, $104,754 (M); gifts received, $4,546; expenditures, $16,165; total giving, $15,115; qualifying distributions, $15,115; giving activities include $15,115 for grants.
Fields of interest: Higher education; Human services; American Red Cross; Federated giving programs; Jewish federated giving programs; Jewish agencies & temples.
Limitations: Applications not accepted. Giving primarily in Grand Rapids, MI. No grants to individuals.
Application information: Contributes only to pre-selected organizations.
Trustees: Jane Kravitz; M. Paul Kravitz; Norman Kravitz; Sam Kravitz.
EIN: 386061359

1048
Kreilick Family Foundation, Inc.
717 St. Joseph Dr., PMB 120
St. Joseph, MI 49085

Established in 1999 in WI.
Donor: Thomas K. Kreilick.
Grantmaker type: Independent foundation.
Financial data (yr. ended 12/31/04): Assets, $941,844 (M); expenditures, $47,590; total giving, $45,750; qualifying distributions, $46,985; giving activities include $45,750 for grants.
Fields of interest: Education; Environment, natural resources; Christian agencies & churches.
Type of support: General/operating support.
Limitations: Applications not accepted. Giving primarily in MI. No grants to individuals.
Application information: Contributes only to pre-selected organizations.
Officer: Thomas K. Kreilick, Pres.
Directors: Katherine L. Gatewood; Eric P. Kreilick.
EIN: 391979909

1049
The Kresge Foundation
3215 W. Big Beaver Rd.
Troy, MI 48084 (248) 643-9630
Contact: Richard "Rip" Rapson, C.E.O. and Pres.
FAX: (248) 643-0588; E-mail: info@kresge.org;
URL: http://www.kresge.org

Incorporated in 1924 in MI.
Donor: Sebastian S. Kresge†.
Grantmaker type: Independent foundation.
Financial data (yr. ended 12/31/04): Assets, $2,752,257,750 (M); expenditures, $37,171,023; total giving, $97,714,540; qualifying distributions, $126,405,652; giving activities include $96,687,354 for 178 grants (high: $5,000,000; low: $50,000; average: $100,000–$1,000,000), and $1,027,186 for employee matching gifts.
Purpose and activities: The foundation seeks to strengthen nonprofit organizations by catalyzing their growth, connecting them to their stake holders, and challenging greater support through grants. The foundation believes that strong, sustainable, high capacity organizations are positioned to achieve their missions and strengthen communities. Grants are awarded to nonprofit organizations operating in the fields of education, health and long-term care,

human services, arts and humanities, public affairs, and science, nature, and the environment.
Fields of interest: Humanities; Arts; Higher education; Environment; Health care; Human services; Science; Public affairs.
Type of support: Capital campaigns; Building/renovation; Equipment; Land acquisition; Employee matching gifts; Matching/challenge support.
Limitations: No support for religious organizations, (unless applicant is operated by a religious organization and it serves secular needs and has financial and governing autonomy separate from the parent organization with space formally dedicated to its programs) community colleges, private foundations, or elementary or secondary schools (unless they predominantly serve individuals with physical and/or developmental disabilities). No grants to individuals, or for debt retirement or minor equipment, furnishings, operating/program support, or endowment funds by themselves; no loans.
Publications: Application guidelines; Annual report.
Application information: See foundation Web site for more application information. Application procedures vary for each foundation program area. Application form required.
 Initial approach: Letter or proposal
 Copies of proposal: 1
 Deadline(s): None
 Board meeting date(s): Mar., June, Sept., and Dec.
 Final notification: Generally within 4 to 6 months; decisions announced after each board meeting, applicants notified in writing
Officers and Trustees:* Irene Y. Hirano,* Chair.; Richard "Rip" Rapson, C.E.O. and Pres.; Edward M. Hunia, Sr. V.P. and Secy.-Treas.; Elizabeth C. Sullivan, V.P., Prog. and Admin.; Amy B. Coleman, Cont. and Dir., Finance; James L. Bildner; Lee C. Bollinger; Jane L. Delgado, Ph.D.; Steven K. Hamp; Paul C. Hillegonds; David W. Horvitz; Robert C. Larson; Katherine A. Lutey; Elaine D. Rosen; Nancy M. Schlichting; Robert D. Storey.
Number of staff: 23 full-time professional.
EIN: 381359217
Selected grants: The following grants were reported in 2005.
$3,000,000 to United Negro College Fund, Fairfax, VA. For challenge grant toward Phase I implementation of Historically Black Colleges and Universities (HBCU) Institutional Advancement Program as part of capacity-building initiative for selected HBCU's.
$2,500,000 to Detroit Educational Television Foundation-W T V S Channel 56, Detroit, MI. For challenge grant toward creation of classical music station to be owned by Detroit Public Schools with studios in Detroit School of the Arts and managed by Detroit Public Television.
$2,000,000 to Minneapolis Institute of Arts, Minneapolis, MN. For challenge grant toward renovation and expansion of museum.
$2,000,000 to W G B H Educational Foundation, Boston, MA. For challenge grant toward purchase of property and renovation and construction of facilities.
$1,500,000 to Institute of Contemporary Art, Boston, MA. For challenge grant toward construction of museum.
$1,500,000 to Nashville Symphony Association, Nashville, TN. For challenge grant toward construction of replacement symphony hall.

$1,500,000 to University of Michigan, Ann Arbor, MI. For challenge grant toward renovation and expansion of Alumni Memorial Hall.

$1,500,000 to Virginia Museum of Fine Arts Foundation, Richmond, VA. For challenge grant toward museum's expansion and renovation.

$1,250,000 to Cleveland Institute of Music, Cleveland, OH. For challenge grant for renovation and expansion of conservatory.

$1,000,000 to Associated Catholic Charities, Baltimore, MD. For challenge grant for renovation of Saint Vincent's Center, providing therapeutic care for emotionally and physically abused children.

1050
Krishnamurti Rajghat Foundation, Inc.
5549 Blue Spruce Ln.
Kalamazoo, MI 49009-4568
Contact: Krishna M. Jain, Pres.

Established in 1989 in MI.
Donors: Suresh Bazaj; Alka Bazaj.
Grantmaker type: Independent foundation.
Financial data (yr. ended 1/31/05): Assets, $10,675 (M); gifts received, $85,910; expenditures, $86,466; total giving, $84,622; qualifying distributions, $84,622; giving activities include $84,622 for 3 grants (high: $55,000; low: $2,870).
Fields of interest: Education.
International interests: India.
Limitations: Giving primarily in India, with some giving in CA.
Application information:
Initial approach: Letter
Deadline(s): None
Officers and Director:* Krishna M. Jain,* Pres.; Armand M. Clark, Treas.
EIN: 382799825

1051
Kronlund Foundation Charitable Trust
c/o JPMorgan Chase Bank, N.A.
P.O. Box 1308
Milwaukee, WI 53201
Application address: c/o M. Wasmund, JPMorgan Chase Bank, N.A., 611 Woodward Ave., Ste. MI18038, Detroit, MI 48226, tel.: (313) 225-3454

Established in MI.
Donor: Louise B. Kronlund†.
Grantmaker type: Independent foundation.
Financial data (yr. ended 12/31/05): Assets, $638,424 (M); expenditures, $28,505; total giving, $26,000; qualifying distributions, $26,000; giving activities include $26,000 for grants.
Purpose and activities: Giving primarily to Lutheran and Episcopal churches.
Fields of interest: Human services; Protestant agencies & churches.
Limitations: Giving primarily in MI. No grants to individuals.
Application information: Application form not required.
Deadline(s): None
Trustees: Thomas W. Payne; JPMorgan Chase Bank, N.A.
EIN: 382117538

1052
KT Family Foundation
P.O. Box 337
Fraser, MI 48026-0337

Established in 1992 in MI.
Donor: Orville K. Thompson†.
Grantmaker type: Independent foundation.
Financial data (yr. ended 12/31/04): Assets, $3,032,088 (M); gifts received, $64,200; expenditures, $164,526; total giving, $131,525; qualifying distributions, $155,525; giving activities include $131,525 for 23 grants (high: $25,000; low: $2,000).
Purpose and activities: Giving for educational, religious, and community organizations.
Fields of interest: Human services; Family services; Protestant agencies & churches.
Type of support: General/operating support; Continuing support; Emergency funds.
Limitations: Applications not accepted. Giving primarily in MI. No grants to individuals.
Application information: Contributes only to pre-selected organizations.
Directors: Lauri A. Palazzolo; Janice L. Thompson; Kristen L. Thompson.
Number of staff: 1 part-time professional.
EIN: 383085402
Selected grants: The following grants were reported in 2004.
$25,000 to Shepherds Gate Lutheran Church, Shelby Township, MI.
$15,000 to Turning Point, Mount Clemens, MI.
$7,500 to Rhema International Ministries, Rochester, MI.
$7,000 to Baldwin Church and Center, Pontiac, MI.
$7,000 to Make-A-Wish Foundation of Michigan, Lansing, MI.
$5,000 to Open Door Outreach Center, Union Lake, MI.
$5,000 to Samaritan Counseling Center of Southeastern Michigan, Farmington Hills, MI.
$5,000 to Special Olympics of Michigan, Detroit, MI.
$4,000 to Boys Hope Girls Hope, Detroit, MI.
$2,000 to Reading for the Blind, Southfield, MI.

1053
Elizabeth Kulma Private Foundation
c/o Comerica Bank
P.O. Box 75000 MC 3302
Detroit, MI 48275-3302

Established in 2003 in MI.
Donor: Elizabeth Kulma†.
Grantmaker type: Independent foundation.
Financial data (yr. ended 6/30/05): Assets, $426,305 (M); expenditures, $29,138; total giving, $20,000; qualifying distributions, $20,693; giving activities include $20,000 for grants.
Limitations: Applications not accepted. No grants to individuals.
Application information: Contributes only to pre-selected organizations.
Trustee: Comerica Bank.
EIN: 386815983

1054
Kutsche Charitable Trust
c/o Fifth Third Bank
P.O. Box 3636
Grand Rapids, MI 49501-3636

Established in 1993 in MI.
Donor: Kutsche Trust.
Grantmaker type: Independent foundation.
Financial data (yr. ended 12/31/05): Assets, $2,521,311 (M); expenditures, $159,328; total giving, $128,979; qualifying distributions, $129,304; giving activities include $128,979 for 3 grants (high: $42,993; low: $42,993).
Purpose and activities: Support only for Blodgett Memorial Medical Center, Mary Free Bed Hospital, and St. Mary's Health Services, Grand Rapids, MI.
Fields of interest: Hospitals (general); Health care.
Limitations: Applications not accepted. Giving limited to Grand Rapids, MI. No grants to individuals.
Application information: Contributes only to 3 pre-selected organizations.
Trustee: Fifth Third Bank.
EIN: 386610379

1055
Robert Kutz Foundation
(formerly Robert Kutz Charitable Trust)
c/o Comerica Bank
P.O. Box 75000
Detroit, MI 48275-3300
Contact: Paula M. Gralewski

Established in 1987 in OH.
Donor: Robert A. Kutz†.
Grantmaker type: Independent foundation.
Financial data (yr. ended 12/31/05): Assets, $1,832,115 (M); expenditures, $308,870; total giving, $237,700; qualifying distributions, $263,853; giving activities include $237,700 for 7 grants (high: $207,500; low: $1,500).
Purpose and activities: Funding for local youth oriented programs.
Fields of interest: Education; Youth development; Children/youth, services; Federated giving programs.
Type of support: Program development; Equipment; Scholarship funds.
Limitations: Applications not accepted. Giving limited to Summit County, OH.
Application information: Unsolicited requests for funds not accepted.
Board meeting date(s): Varies
Officer and Trustees:* W. Paul Jeffery,* Managing Dir.; Comerica Bank.
EIN: 346977068
Selected grants: The following grants were reported in 2004.
$7,000 to South Street Mission, Akron, OH.
$6,000 to Return to Home, Barberton, OH.
$5,000 to CYO and Community Services, Akron, OH.
$5,000 to Hattie Larlham Fund, Mantua, OH.
$5,000 to Inner-City Soccer Team, Akron, OH.
$5,000 to Salvation Army, OH.
$5,000 to Victory Gallop, Cleveland, OH.
$4,500 to Cuyahoga Valley National Park, Brecksville, OH.
$4,000 to Boy Scouts of America.
$4,000 to Western Reserve Historical Society, Cleveland, OH.

1056
Kymal Family Foundation
4301 Ann Arbor Saline Rd.
Ann Arbor, MI 48103

Donor: Chad Kymal.

Grantmaker type: Independent foundation.
Financial data (yr. ended 12/31/04): Assets, $62,505 (M); gifts received, $500; expenditures, $1,355; total giving, $608; qualifying distributions, $608; giving activities include $608 for grants.
Fields of interest: Religion.
Type of support: General/operating support.
Limitations: Applications not accepted. Giving primarily in CA and MI. No grants to individuals.
Application information: Contributes only to pre-selected organizations.
Officer: Chad Kymal, Pres.
EIN: 383210794

1057
L & D Foundation
A-5228 147th Ave.
Holland, MI 49423-9304

Established in 1989 in MI.
Donor: Leon R. Slikkers.
Grantmaker type: Independent foundation.
Financial data (yr. ended 12/31/05): Assets, $10,641 (M); gifts received, $26,000; expenditures, $26,811; total giving, $26,811; qualifying distributions, $26,811; giving activities include $26,811 for grants.
Fields of interest: Christian agencies & churches.
Limitations: Applications not accepted. Giving primarily in MI. No grants to individuals.
Application information: Contributes only to pre-selected organizations.
Trustees: Dolores E. Slikkers; Leon R. Slikkers.
EIN: 382902434

1058
L & H Foundation
32606 Pine Ridge Dr.
Warren, MI 48093-1100 (586) 795-2653
Contact: Lisa C. Holley, Pres.

Established in 1997 in MI.
Donor: Earl-Beth Foundation.
Grantmaker type: Independent foundation.
Financial data (yr. ended 12/31/05): Assets, $1,379,702 (M); expenditures, $97,783; total giving, $80,000; qualifying distributions, $81,644; giving activities include $80,000 for 40 grants (high: $12,000; low: $100).
Fields of interest: Arts; Education; Youth development; Human services.
Type of support: General/operating support.
Limitations: Giving primarily in ID, MI and Portland, OR.
Application information: Application form required.
   Initial approach: Letter
   Deadline(s): None
Officers and Trustees:* Holley R. Shepard,* Pres.; Lisa C. Holley,* V.P. and Treas.; Helen M. Fowler,* Secy.
EIN: 383348542

1059
Labaro Family Foundation, Inc.
P.O. Box 427
Potterville, MI 48876

Established in 2004 in MI.
Grantmaker type: Independent foundation.

Financial data (yr. ended 6/30/05): Assets, $604,554 (M); expenditures, $6,416; total giving, $0; qualifying distributions, $0.
Limitations: Applications not accepted. No grants to individuals.
Application information: Contributes only to pre-selected organizations.
Director: Keith Labard.
EIN: 300024663

1060
Laboratory for Education & Research in Neuroscience
615 Griswold St., Ste. 1616
Detroit, MI 48226-3991

Established in 1988 in MI.
Grantmaker type: Independent foundation.
Financial data (yr. ended 6/30/03): Assets, $52,373 (M); expenditures, $37,414; total giving, $33,000; qualifying distributions, $33,000; giving activities include $33,000 for grants.
Fields of interest: Neuroscience research.
Limitations: Applications not accepted. Giving primarily in MI. No grants to individuals.
Application information: Contributes only to pre-selected organizations.
Officers and Trustees:* Richard F. Freeman, M.D.*, Pres.; Bernyce Edwards,* V.P.; Eugenie Durant,* Secy.; Joseph P. Zanglin,* Treas.; Miriam Imerman.
EIN: 382170401

1061
The Lachimi Foundation
3270 W. Big Beaver Rd.
Troy, MI 48084

Established in 1998 in MI.
Donors: Madhava Reddy; HTC Global Svcs., Inc.
Grantmaker type: Independent foundation.
Financial data (yr. ended 12/31/05): Assets, $544,348 (M); gifts received, $2,200,000; expenditures, $2,134,026; total giving, $2,132,000; qualifying distributions, $2,132,000; giving activities include $2,132,000 for 3 grants (high: $2,106,000; low: $1,000).
Purpose and activities: Giving primarily for the education and enhancement of knowledge and spirituality.
Fields of interest: Human services, mind/body enrichment; Spirituality.
Limitations: Applications not accepted. No grants to individuals.
Application information: Contributes only to pre-selected organizations.
Officer: Madhava G. Reddy, Pres.
Director: Sobha Reddy.
EIN: 383429963

1062
William T. Laflin Scholarship Fund, Inc.
c/o Trustees
3226 Arthur Rd.
Remus, MI 49340-9541

Established in MI.
Grantmaker type: Independent foundation.
Financial data (yr. ended 12/31/05): Assets, $86,382 (M); expenditures, $4,498; total giving,

$4,050; qualifying distributions, $4,050; giving activities include $4,050 for grants to individuals.
Purpose and activities: Scholarship awards to high school graduates and residents of the Chippewa Hills School District, MI.
Fields of interest: Higher education.
Type of support: Scholarships—to individuals.
Limitations: Giving limited to MI.
Application information: Application form required.
   Deadline(s): None
Officers: Cheryl Hahnenberg, Pres.; Linda Travis, V.P.; Kathy Gaffner, Secy.; John Ruddell, Treas.
EIN: 381579001

1063
Lahti Family Foundation
c/o Comerica Bank
P.O. Box 75000, M/C 3302
Detroit, MI 48275-3302
Application address: c/o Comerica Bank, P.O. Box 75000, M/C 5100, Detroit, MI 48275-5100, tel.: (612) 215-3603

Established in 2004 in MI.
Donor: Martha Lahti.
Grantmaker type: Independent foundation.
Financial data (yr. ended 12/31/05): Assets, $2,194,645 (M); expenditures, $191,546; total giving, $145,500; qualifying distributions, $151,179; giving activities include $145,500 for 12 grants (high: $20,000; low: $1,000).
Fields of interest: Arts; Human services; YM/YWCAs & YM/YWHAs; Children/youth, services.
Limitations: Giving primarily in MN. No grants to individuals.
Application information: Application form not required.
   Deadline(s): None
Trustee: Comerica Bank.
EIN: 202988335

1064
Maxine Sprague Lahti Foundation for the Performing Arts
c/o National City Bank
P.O. Box 94651
Cleveland, OH 44101-4651
Application address: c/o M. P. Allen, 1900 E. 9th St., LOC 01-2111, Cleveland, OH 44114, tel.: (216) 222-2799

Established in 1987 in MI.
Grantmaker type: Independent foundation.
Financial data (yr. ended 12/31/04): Assets, $116,409 (M); expenditures, $6,049; total giving, $4,800; qualifying distributions, $5,725; giving activities include $4,800 for grants.
Fields of interest: Performing arts; Performing arts, theater; Performing arts, music; Libraries/library science.
Type of support: General/operating support.
Limitations: Giving limited to the Monroe, MI, area. No grants to individuals.
Application information: Application form required.
   Initial approach: Letter or telephone
   Deadline(s): Oct. 31
Trustee: National City Bank.
EIN: 382720188

1065
The Helen Laidlaw Foundation
314 Newman St.
East Tawas, MI 48730 (989) 362-5911
Contact: Nancy E. Huck, Pres.
FAX: (989) 362-7675

Established in 1989 in MI.
Grantmaker type: Independent foundation.
Financial data (yr. ended 12/31/05): Assets,
$540,313 (M); gifts received, $3,425;
expenditures, $43,459; total giving, $27,500;
qualifying distributions, $27,500; giving activities
include $27,500 for grants to individuals.
Purpose and activities: Scholarship awards limited
to those pursuing an education in the health care
field.
Fields of interest: Medical school/education;
Nursing school/education; Public health school/
education; Health sciences school/education.
Type of support: Scholarships—to individuals.
Limitations: Giving limited to northeast MI.
Application information: Application form required.
Deadline(s): Mar. 1
Officers and Directors:* Nancy E. Huck,* Pres.;
James C. Laidlaw,* V.P.; Brenda Redding,* Secy.;
W. William Laidlaw,* Treas.; Thomas B. Huck;
Barbara G. Laidlaw; Margaret K. Laidlaw.
EIN: 382901107

1066
James and Louise Laing Camp Ba-Ta-Wa-Ga-Ma Irrevocable Trust
P.O. Box 8
Crystal Falls, MI 49920

Grantmaker type: Independent foundation.
Financial data (yr. ended 12/31/05): Assets,
$536,850 (M); expenditures, $52,826; total giving,
$27,461; qualifying distributions, $27,461; giving
activities include $27,461 for grants.
Limitations: Giving primarily in Crystal Falls, MI.
Trustees: Lorna C. Addison; John L. Harrison; Brian
D. Schultze.
EIN: 386664953

1067
The Irving and Beverly Laker Family Foundation
4764 N. Chipping Glen
Bloomfield Hills, MI 48302-2390

Established in 1999 in MI.
Donors: Irving Laker; Beverly Laker.
Grantmaker type: Independent foundation.
Financial data (yr. ended 12/31/04): Assets,
$123,931 (M); gifts received, $91,386;
expenditures, $121,990; total giving, $120,926;
qualifying distributions, $120,319; giving activities
include $120,926 for 1 grant.
Fields of interest: Christian agencies & churches.
Limitations: Applications not accepted. Giving
primarily in MI. No grants to individuals.
Application information: Contributes only to
pre-selected organizations.
Directors: Beverly Laker; Irving Laker.
EIN: 383432423

1068
Gordon and Evon Laman Charitable Foundation for Theological Education
145 Columbia Ave., Ste. 565
Holland, MI 49423-2980 (616) 394-7144

Established in 2003.
Donors: Gordon Laman; Evon Laman.
Grantmaker type: Independent foundation.
Financial data (yr. ended 12/31/04): Assets,
$53,711 (M); gifts received, $26,000;
expenditures, $1,917; total giving, $1,000;
qualifying distributions, $1,000; giving activities
include $1,000 for grants.
Trustees: Evon Laman; Gordon Laman.
EIN: 320064869

1069
Frank and Mary Lamberson Foundation
c/o JPMorgan Chase Bank, N.A.
P.O. Box 1308
Milwaukee, WI 53201
Application address: c/o Gary W. Gomoll, JPMorgan
Chase Bank, N.A., 3399 PGA Blvd., Ste.100, Palm
Beach, FL 33410, tel.: (561) 627-9400

Established in 1997 in FL.
Grantmaker type: Independent foundation.
Financial data (yr. ended 12/31/05): Assets,
$1,460,930 (M); expenditures, $54,219; total
giving, $27,119; qualifying distributions, $27,119;
giving activities include $27,119 for grants.
Purpose and activities: Giving primarily to museums
and education.
Fields of interest: Museums; Higher education;
Environment; Zoos/zoological societies.
Limitations: Giving primarily in FL, MI, Asheville, NC,
and Poughkeepsie, NY. No grants to individuals.
Application information: Application form required.
Initial approach: Letter
Deadline(s): None
Trustees: Frank A. Lamberson; Mary T. Lamberson;
JPMorgan Chase Bank, N.A.
EIN: 597096409

1070
Patricia A. & William E. LaMothe Foundation
620 Jennings Ln.
Battle Creek, MI 49015
Contact: Patricia A. LaMothe, Pres.

Established in 1986 in MI.
Donors: Patricia A. LaMothe; William E. LaMothe;
Sydney McManus.
Grantmaker type: Independent foundation.
Financial data (yr. ended 12/31/05): Assets,
$4,942,757 (M); gifts received, $35,358;
expenditures, $423,883; total giving, $399,909;
qualifying distributions, $402,971; giving activities
include $399,909 for 84 grants (high: $60,000;
low: $50).
Purpose and activities: Giving primarily for higher
education, Roman Catholic organizations, and
conservation.
Fields of interest: Education; Environment, natural
resources; Health organizations, association;
Human services; Roman Catholic agencies &
churches.
Limitations: Giving primarily in Battle Creek and
Kalamazoo, MI.

Application information:
Initial approach: Letter
Deadline(s): None
Officers and Trustees:* Patricia A. LaMothe,* Pres.;
Alexis LaMothe,* V.P.; Sydney McManus,* Secy.;
William E. LaMothe,* Treas.
EIN: 386517929

1071
Carol and Kent H. Landsberg Foundation
(formerly Kent H. Landsberg Foundation)
701 Ocean Ave., Ste. 303
Santa Monica, CA 90402
Contact: Carol Landsberg, C.E.O.
FAX: (310) 899-9584

Established in 1989 in CA.
Donor: Kent H. Landsberg‡.
Grantmaker type: Independent foundation.
Financial data (yr. ended 12/31/04): Assets,
$1,833,500 (M); expenditures, $106,494; total
giving, $84,035; qualifying distributions, $81,995;
giving activities include $84,035 for grants.
Purpose and activities: Giving for education, special
education, environmental enterprises, community
health, personal growth and development, and
scientific research related to deafness and
alternative medicine.
Type of support: Building/renovation; Equipment;
Program development; Conferences/seminars;
Seed money; Curriculum development; Scholarship
funds; Research.
Limitations: Giving primarily in CA, with emphasis on
southern CA, and MI. No support for redundant
community services, or for programs that derive
income from government or public funding. No
grants to individuals, or for capital campaigns, debt
reduction, operating funds, memberships, or
computer equipment.
Publications: Application guidelines.
Application information: 6-month progress report
required in June. Application form required.
Initial approach: Letter requesting application
form
Copies of proposal: 2
Deadline(s): Aug. 28
Board meeting date(s): Oct., and as needed
Final notification: Dec. 15
Officers and Board Members:* Carol P.
Landsberg,* C.E.O. and Pres.; Jon P. Talarico,*
Secy.; Alin H. Wall,* C.F.O.
EIN: 330353391

1072
W. & A. Lane Music Education Trust
c/o Citizens Bank Wealth Mgmt., N.A.
328 S. Saginaw St., M/C 002027
Flint, MI 48502

Established in 2001 in MI.
Grantmaker type: Independent foundation.
Financial data (yr. ended 5/31/05): Assets,
$226,627 (M); expenditures, $6,308; total giving,
$2,982; qualifying distributions, $2,982; giving
activities include $2,982 for grants.
Fields of interest: Performing arts, music.
Type of support: General/operating support.
Limitations: Applications not accepted. Giving
primarily in Flint, MI. No grants to individuals.
Application information: Contributes only to
pre-selected organizations.

Trustee: Citizens Bank.
EIN: 386431899

1073
Arnold G. & Martha M. Langbo Foundation
20137 Evans Ct.
Beverly Hills, MI 48025
Application address: c/o Martha M. Langbo, 5606
Baltusrol Ct., Sanibel Island, FL 33957

Established in 1991 in MI.
Donors: Arnold G. Langbo; Martha M. Langbo.
Grantmaker type: Independent foundation.
Financial data (yr. ended 12/31/05): Assets,
$919,258 (M); gifts received, $194,490;
expenditures, $393,101; total giving, $386,216;
qualifying distributions, $388,719; giving activities
include $386,216 for 64 grants (high: $250,041;
low: $10).
Purpose and activities: Giving for education, human
services, and Catholic organizations.
Fields of interest: Higher education; Human
services; Federated giving programs; Roman
Catholic agencies & churches.
Limitations: Giving limited to MI. No grants to
individuals.
Application information:
Initial approach: Letter
Deadline(s): None
Officers: Martha M. Langbo, Pres. and Secy.-Treas.;
Arnold G. Langbo, V.P.
Directors: Sharon A. Bateman; Maureen Langbo;
Susan C. Maks.
EIN: 383026270
Selected grants: The following grants were reported
in 2004.
$110,250 to Blessed Sacrament Church, Stowe,
VT. For general operating support.
$28,000 to Saint Isabel Catholic Church, Sanibel,
FL. For general operating support.
$12,500 to Lahey Clinic Hospital, Burlington, MA.
For general operating support.
$10,000 to Our Lady of the Mississippi Abbey,
Dubuque, IA. For general operating support.
$5,000 to Battle Creek Area Catholic Schools,
Battle Creek, MI. For general operating support.
$5,000 to YMCA, Sherman Lake, Augusta, MI. For
general operating support.
$250 to Christian Foundation for Children and Aging,
Kansas City, KS. For general operating support.
$185 to Saint Lawrence Seminary High School,
Mount Calvary, WI. For general operating support.
$150 to Mercy Home for Boys and Girls, Chicago, IL.
For general operating support.
$100 to Helen Day Art Center, Stowe, VT. For
general operating support.

1074
Ann H. and Robert C. Lange Foundation
1388 S. Manitou Trail
Lake Leelanau, MI 49653

Established in 2004 in MI.
Grantmaker type: Independent foundation.
Financial data (yr. ended 12/31/05): Assets, $1
(M); expenditures, $10; total giving, $10; qualifying
distributions, $10; giving activities include $10 for
grants.
Fields of interest: Animal welfare.
Type of support: General/operating support.

Limitations: Giving primarily in MI. No grants to
individuals.
Officers: Robert Lange, Pres.; Ann H. Lange, Secy.
EIN: 201804898

1075
The Greater Lansing Foundation
c/o National City Bank
120 N. Washington Sq., Ste. 650
Lansing, MI 48933-1619
Contact: Steven J. Peters

Established as a community foundation in 1947 in
MI; status changed in 1980 to independent
foundation.
Grantmaker type: Independent foundation.
Financial data (yr. ended 12/31/04): Assets,
$13,067,273 (M); expenditures, $598,013; total
giving, $457,972; qualifying distributions,
$469,806; giving activities include $457,972 for 80
grants (high: $56,575; low: $24).
Purpose and activities: Support for charitable,
public, or educational institutions, including support
for health and the handicapped.
Fields of interest: Arts; Education; Health care;
Health organizations, association; Disabilities,
people with; Economically disadvantaged.
Type of support: Annual campaigns; Capital
campaigns; Building/renovation; Equipment;
Emergency funds; Program development;
Conferences/seminars; Publication; Seed money;
Scholarship funds; Research; Consulting services;
Matching/challenge support.
Limitations: Applications not accepted. Giving
limited to Ingham, Clinton, and Eaton counties, MI.
No grants to individuals, or for operating budgets,
endowment funds, continuing support, deficit
financing, land acquisition, or technical assistance;
no loans.
Application information: Unsolicited requests for
funds not considered.
Board meeting date(s): May and Nov.
Trustee Bank: National City Bank.
EIN: 386057513
Selected grants: The following grants were reported
in 2003.
$54,400 to Woldumar Nature Center, Lansing, MI.
For general support.
$25,000 to Interlochen Center for the Arts,
Interlochen, MI. For general support.
$25,000 to Jupiter Medical Center Foundation,
Jupiter, FL. For general support.
$25,000 to Stetson University, DeLand, FL. For
operating support.
$23,000 to American Red Cross, Lansing, MI. For
general support.
$20,000 to Eles Place, Lansing, MI. For general
support.
$17,000 to R. E. Olds Transportation Museum
Association, Lansing, MI. For general support.
$11,000 to National Council on Alcoholism and
Drug Dependence, Lansing, MI. For general
support.
$10,000 to Saint Vincent Home for Children,
Lansing, MI. For general support.
$6,000 to Highfields, Onondaga, MI. For general
support.

1076
Lanting Foundation
151 Central Ave., Ste. 220
Holland, MI 49423

Established in 1996 in MI.
Donor: Arlyn Lanting.
Grantmaker type: Independent foundation.
Financial data (yr. ended 12/31/05): Assets,
$274,542 (M); gifts received, $36,536;
expenditures, $77,369; total giving, $75,000;
qualifying distributions, $75,000; giving activities
include $75,000 for grants.
Purpose and activities: Giving to Christian schools
and organizations.
Fields of interest: Education; Christian agencies &
churches.
Limitations: Applications not accepted. Giving
primarily in MI. No grants to individuals.
Application information: Contributes only to
pre-selected organizations.
Trustees: Arlyn Lanting; Marcia Lanting.
EIN: 383320436

1077
Lapham Foundation, Inc.
18412 Blue Heron Dr.
Northville, MI 48167

Established in 1999 in MI.
Grantmaker type: Independent foundation.
Financial data (yr. ended 12/31/04): Assets, $177
(M); gifts received, $1,400; expenditures, $5,767;
total giving, $0; qualifying distributions, $5,764.
Limitations: Applications not accepted. No grants to
individuals.
Application information: Contributes only to
pre-selected organizations.
Officer: Charles P. Lapham, Pres.
Directors: Darcy Connolly; John A. Gallina.
EIN: 383451390

1078
The Lawrence W. Larsen Charitable Trust
2652 Middleboro Ln. N.E.
Grand Rapids, MI 49506

Established in 1986 in MI.
Donor: Lawrence W. Larsen.
Grantmaker type: Independent foundation.
Financial data (yr. ended 12/31/04): Assets,
$2,878 (M); gifts received, $12,500; expenditures,
$13,178; total giving, $13,178; qualifying
distributions, $13,178; giving activities include
$13,178 for grants.
Fields of interest: Education; Health organizations,
association; Human services; Christian agencies &
churches.
Limitations: Applications not accepted. Giving
primarily in Grand Rapids, MI. No grants to
individuals.
Application information: Contributes only to
pre-selected organizations.
Trustee: Lawrence W. Larsen.
EIN: 382711094

1079
The Larson Family Fund
(formerly The Larson Family Foundation)
38500 Woodward Ave., Ste. 250
Bloomfield Hills, MI   48304-5050
Contact: Robert C. Larson, Chair.

Established in 1987 in MI.
Donor: Robert C. Larson.
Grantmaker type: Independent foundation.
Financial data (yr. ended 12/31/04): Assets, $6,801 (M); gifts received, $500; expenditures, $279,936; total giving, $272,686; qualifying distributions, $272,686; giving activities include $272,686 for grants.
Purpose and activities: Support to organizations of interest to the family.
Limitations: Giving primarily in MI.
Officers: Robert C. Larson, Chair.; Elizabeth L. Willoughby, Pres.; Eric B. Larson, V.P. and Secy.; Kathryn W. Larson, V.P. and Treas.
EIN: 382711975

1080
The Robert C. and Bonnie Ann Larson Foundation
38500 Woodward Ave., Ste. 250
Bloomfield Hills, MI   48304   (248) 593-0710
Contact: Robert C. Larson, V.P.

Established in 2000 in MI.
Donor: Robert C. Larson.
Grantmaker type: Independent foundation.
Financial data (yr. ended 11/30/04): Assets, $493,781 (M); gifts received, $270; expenditures, $21,521; total giving, $18,110; qualifying distributions, $18,110; giving activities include $18,110 for grants.
Limitations: Giving primarily in MI.
Application information:
   Initial approach: Letter
   Deadline(s): None
Officers: Bonnie Ann Larson, Pres.; Robert C. Larson, V.P. and Secy.-Treas.
EIN: 383532074

1081
Larson Land Foundation
c/o Comerica Bank
P.O. Box 75000
Detroit, MI   48275-8280
Application address: c/o Kim Fulgenzi, 3131 E. Camelback Rd., Ste. 226, Phoenix, AZ 85016, tel.: (602) 606-5791

Established in 2001 in MI.
Donor: Ruth L. Chartier‡.
Grantmaker type: Independent foundation.
Financial data (yr. ended 12/31/05): Assets, $2,187,915 (M); gifts received, $340,101; expenditures, $169,117; total giving, $132,000; qualifying distributions, $132,825; giving activities include $132,000 for 9 grants (high: $65,000; low: $2,000).
Purpose and activities: Giving to programs that protect and preserve land.
Fields of interest: Environment, natural resources; Environment, land resources.
Limitations: Giving limited to NJ. No grants to individuals.
Application information:

Initial approach: Letter
Deadline(s): None
Advisory Committee: Edith Hillman; Wade Martin; Robert Sajdak.
Trustee: Comerica Bank.
EIN: 386776837

1082
Henry E. & Annabel Larzelere Foundation
1944 Winchester Dr.
East Lansing, MI   48823

Established in 2000 in MI.
Grantmaker type: Independent foundation.
Financial data (yr. ended 12/31/05): Assets, $1,203 (M); gifts received, $150; expenditures, $157; total giving, $142; qualifying distributions, $142; giving activities include $142 for grants.
Limitations: Giving primarily in MI. No grants to individuals.
Directors: Martha Larzelere Campbell; Mary Larzelere Dygert; Annabel S. Larzelere; Henry E. Larzelere; John H. Larzelere.
EIN: 383530833

1083
The Las Milpas Scholarship Fund
c/o Marc Robinson
3587 Salem Rd.
Troy, MI   48084-1145   (248) 649-5609
Contact: Elizabeth K. Briody, Pres.

Grantmaker type: Independent foundation.
Financial data (yr. ended 6/30/03): Assets, $14,230 (M); gifts received, $10; expenditures, $3,792; total giving, $3,750; qualifying distributions, $4,022; giving activities include $3,750 for 5 grants to individuals (high: $750; low: $750).
Purpose and activities: Scholarships given to residents of Las Milpas Colonia, TX, who are graduates of Pharr or Hidalgo school districts.
Type of support: Scholarships—to individuals.
Limitations: Giving limited to residents of Las Milpas Colonia, TX.
Application information: Application form required.
   Deadline(s): Mar. 31
Officers: Elizabeth K. Briody, Pres.; Marc Robinson, V.P.; Martha Knies, Secy.; Lile Briones, Treas.
EIN: 760162558

1084
John C. Lasko Foundation
c/o Charles Zimmerman
P.O. Box 339
Belleville, MI   48112-0339

Established in 1998 in MI.
Donors: John C. Lasko; Republic Die and Tool Co.
Grantmaker type: Independent foundation.
Financial data (yr. ended 12/31/05): Assets, $42,264,033 (M); gifts received, $6,310,563; expenditures, $1,972,967; total giving, $1,836,875; qualifying distributions, $1,836,875; giving activities include $1,836,875 for 11 grants (high: $1,095,000; low: $200).
Purpose and activities: Giving primarily to Christian and Protestant churches.
Fields of interest: Christian agencies & churches; Protestant agencies & churches.

Limitations: Giving primarily in MI.
Application information:
   Initial approach: Letter
   Deadline(s): None
Officers: John C. Lasko, Pres.; William Kren, V.P.; Barbara T. Huston, Secy.; Charles Zimmerman, Treas.
Directors: Barton Bryant; Gordon Cook; Brian Eckhardt; Gary Lasko; James J. Walker.
EIN: 383440640

1085
Thomara Latimer Cancer Foundation
21500 Greenfield, Ste. 211
Oak Park, MI   48237   (248) 557-2346
E-mail: info@thomlatimercares.org; URL: http://www.thomlatimercares.org/
Application address: c/o Franklin Plaza Ctr., 29193 Northwestern Hwy., No. 528, Southfield, MI 48034

Grantmaker type: Independent foundation.
Financial data (yr. ended 12/31/03): Assets, $3,762 (M); gifts received, $8,462; expenditures, $38,261; total giving, $12,000; qualifying distributions, $12,000; giving activities include $12,000 for grants to individuals, and $4,772 for foundation-administered programs.
Purpose and activities: Scholarship awards to students engaged in any area of medical study, including biomedical research, pediatrics, oncology, nursing and pharmacology.
Fields of interest: Medical school/education; Nursing school/education.
Type of support: Scholarships—to individuals.
Application information: See foundation Web site for full application requirements, including downloadable form. Award must be used within 1 year of issue. Application form required.
   Deadline(s): Dec.
   Final notification: Jan.
Officers and Directors:* Mashonda Griffin,* Acting Chair.; Shirley Davis,* Secy.; Thomas Latimer,* Treas.; Barbara Latimer; Jaira Latimer; Helen Byrd Pinnah, M.D.; Jacquelyn Sneed.
EIN: 383610986

1086
Latzer-Keydel Foundation
535 Griswold, Ste. 1900
Detroit, MI   48226-3679   (313) 496-1200
Contact: Harvey B. Wallace II, Tr.

Donor: Roberta L. Keydel.
Grantmaker type: Independent foundation.
Financial data (yr. ended 11/30/05): Assets, $5,502 (M); expenditures, $1,000; total giving, $1,000; qualifying distributions, $1,000; giving activities include $1,000 for 1 grant.
Fields of interest: Christian agencies & churches.
Limitations: Giving primarily in MI. No grants to individuals.
Application information:
   Initial approach: Letter
   Deadline(s): None
Trustees: Roberta L. Keydel; Harvey B. Wallace II.
EIN: 237089654

1087
Daisy Harder LaVictoire Memorial Scholarship
c/o John Schaefer
7254 Michigan Ave.
Pigeon, MI 48755 (989) 453-2097
Contact: Robert Drury, Tr.

Established in 1993.
Donor: Daisy Harder Lavictoire Trust.
Grantmaker type: Independent foundation.
Financial data (yr. ended 3/31/05): Assets, $234,912 (M); expenditures, $7,427; total giving, $5,069; qualifying distributions, $7,382; giving activities include $5,069 for 5 grants to individuals (high: $1,267; low: $634).
Purpose and activities: Scholarship awards to students of Laker High School, MI.
Fields of interest: Higher education.
Type of support: Scholarships—to individuals.
Limitations: Giving limited to residents of MI.
Application information: Recipient submission by area high schools. Application form required.
Deadline(s): Mar. 31
Trustees: Paul Clabuesch; Dwight Gascho; John Raab.
EIN: 386629469

1088
Dolores & Paul Lavins Foundation
15230 Windmill Pointe Dr.
Grosse Pointe Park, MI 48230

Established in 2000 in MI.
Donors: Paul N. Lavins; Dolores Lavins.
Grantmaker type: Independent foundation.
Financial data (yr. ended 12/31/04): Assets, $22,336 (M); gifts received, $246,333; expenditures, $241,733; total giving, $240,460; qualifying distributions, $240,460; giving activities include $240,460 for 17 grants (high: $151,000; low: $500).
Fields of interest: Arts; Education; Community development; Federated giving programs; Religion.
Limitations: Applications not accepted. Giving primarily in Detroit, MI. No grants to individuals.
Application information: Contributes only to pre-selected organizations.
Officers: Paul N. Lavins, Pres. and Treas.; Dolores Lavins, Secy.
EIN: 383426007
Selected grants: The following grants were reported in 2004.
$151,000 to Grosse Pointe Park Foundation, Grosse Pointe, MI.
$40,000 to Carmichaels Area School District, Carmichaels, PA.
$10,000 to Ohio Roundtable, Strongsville, OH.
$2,000 to Grosse Pointe War Memorial Association, Grosse Pointe Farms, MI.
$1,000 to Detroit Institute of Arts, Detroit, MI.
$1,000 to Disabled American Veterans, Cincinnati, OH.
$1,000 to Make-A-Wish Foundation of South Florida, Fort Lauderdale, FL.
$1,000 to Neighborhood Club, Grosse Pointe, MI.
$1,000 to Salvation Army of Southfield, Southfield, MI.
$1,000 to United Way of Lee County, Fort Myers, FL.

1089
Richard Barton Law Memorial Trust
227 Lagoon Beach Dr.
Bay City, MI 48706

Grantmaker type: Independent foundation.
Financial data (yr. ended 12/31/05): Assets, $680,441 (M); gifts received, $2,000; expenditures, $31,334; total giving, $25,000; qualifying distributions, $25,000; giving activities include $25,000 for grants.
Fields of interest: Education; Medical specialty research; Boys clubs.
Limitations: Giving limited to MI.
Application information:
Initial approach: Proposal
Deadline(s): Nov. 15
Trustees: Bruce Law; Jacquelyn D. Law.
EIN: 386081726

1090
Leaven International, Inc.
c/o J.C. Huizenga
618 Kenmoor Ave. S.E., Ste. 120
Grand Rapids, MI 49546-2375

Established in 1994 in MI.
Donors: J.C. Huizenga; Al Lettinga.
Grantmaker type: Independent foundation.
Financial data (yr. ended 12/31/04): Assets, $11,567 (M); gifts received, $46,000; expenditures, $42,623; total giving, $41,812; qualifying distributions, $41,812; giving activities include $41,812 for 3 grants (high: $15,304; low: $12,500).
Fields of interest: Christian agencies & churches.
International interests: Latin America.
Limitations: Applications not accepted. Giving on an international basis, primarily in Latin America. No grants to individuals.
Application information: Contributes only to pre-selected organizations.
Officer: J.C. Huizenga, Pres. and Secy.-Treas.
Directors: Ross Luurtsema; Jason Pater.
EIN: 383158585

1091
C. & W. Lee Foundation
1902 Chevy Chase Blvd.
Kalamazoo, MI 49008-2255

Established in 1996 in MI.
Donor: Carl E. Lee.
Grantmaker type: Independent foundation.
Financial data (yr. ended 6/30/05): Assets, $301,809 (M); expenditures, $9,714; total giving, $8,700; qualifying distributions, $8,700; giving activities include $8,700 for grants.
Limitations: Applications not accepted. Giving primarily in Kalamazoo, MI. No grants to individuals.
Application information: Contributes only to pre-selected organizations.
Officers: Carl E. Lee, Pres. and Treas.; E. Winifred Lee, V.P.; Cheryl Lee Weedman, Secy.
Director: Jeff Weedman.
EIN: 383352719

1092
Whilma B. Lee Scholarship Trust Fund
P.O. Box 247
Marcellus, MI 49067-0247
Contact: Donald R. France, Tr.

Established in 1988 in MI.
Donor: Whilma B. Lee†.
Grantmaker type: Independent foundation.
Financial data (yr. ended 12/31/04): Assets, $128,198 (M); expenditures, $13,043; total giving, $9,225; qualifying distributions, $11,113; giving activities include $9,225 for 25 grants to individuals (high: $500; low: $100).
Purpose and activities: Scholarship awards to graduating seniors at public or private high schools in Van Buren, Cass, Kalamazoo, and St. Joseph counties, MI.
Fields of interest: Higher education.
Type of support: Scholarships—to individuals.
Limitations: Giving limited to residents of Cass, Kalamazoo, St. Joseph and Van Buren counties, MI.
Application information: Application form required.
Deadline(s): Apr. 15
Trustee: Donald R. France.
EIN: 386547465

1093
The Legion Foundation
1750 S. Telegraph Rd., Ste. 301
Bloomfield Hills, MI 48302
Contact: James E. Mulvoy, Tr.

Established in 1997 in MI.
Donors: The Thewes Charitable Annuity Lead Trust; The TT Charitable Annuity Lead Trust.
Grantmaker type: Independent foundation.
Financial data (yr. ended 12/31/05): Assets, $2,400,972 (M); gifts received, $1,498,400; expenditures, $574,751; total giving, $478,863; qualifying distributions, $504,097; giving activities include $7,300 for 1 grant, and $471,563 for 43 grants to individuals (high: $49,120; low: $189).
Purpose and activities: Scholarships to individuals and grant awards to facilitate and encourage the study and maintenance of their Christian faith.
Fields of interest: Education; Christian agencies & churches.
Type of support: General/operating support; Scholarships—to individuals.
Limitations: Giving on a national basis.
Application information: Application form required.
Deadline(s): None
Trustee: James E. Mulvoy.
EIN: 383330588

1094
The Alvin Lehman Foundation, Inc.
c/o Ari Lehman
24556 Perceval Ln.
Novi, MI 48375

Donor: Hanna L. Albert.
Grantmaker type: Independent foundation.
Financial data (yr. ended 6/30/05): Assets, $135,646 (M); expenditures, $7,214; total giving, $6,000; qualifying distributions, $6,000; giving activities include $6,000 for grants.
Limitations: Applications not accepted. Giving primarily in NY. No grants to individuals.

Application information: Contributes only to pre-selected organizations.
Officers: John Lehman, Pres.; Alan Lehman, Secy.
Director: Ari Lehman.
EIN: 237304122

1095
Sara M. Leki Trust
c/o National City Bank
P.O. Box 94651
Cleveland, OH 44101-4651

Established in 1999 in MI.
Grantmaker type: Independent foundation.
Financial data (yr. ended 12/31/04): Assets, $433,139 (M); expenditures, $21,972; total giving, $17,041; qualifying distributions, $19,358; giving activities include $17,041 for grants.
Purpose and activities: Support only for American Heart Association, IL, American Cancer Society, Delta College, Saginaw Valley State University, and Salvation Army, MI.
Limitations: Applications not accepted. Giving limited to Chicago, IL and Lansing, Delta, and Saginaw, MI. No grants to individuals.
Application information: Contributes only to 5 pre-selected organizations specified in the trust instrument.
Trustee: National City Bank.
EIN: 386703010

1096
Wayne E. Lemmen, Helene Lemmen & B. J. Lemmen Foundation
(formerly The Bernie J. Lemmen Foundation)
633 Center St.
Coopersville, MI 49404
Contact: Wayne E. Lemmen, Treas.

Grantmaker type: Independent foundation.
Financial data (yr. ended 3/31/05): Assets, $497,433 (M); expenditures, $26,465; total giving, $26,000; qualifying distributions, $26,000; giving activities include $26,000 for grants.
Purpose and activities: Support for Christian organizations, including educational institutions.
Fields of interest: Education; Christian agencies & churches.
Limitations: Giving limited to MI, primarily in Coopersville and Allendale. No grants to individuals.
Application information:
Initial approach: Letter
Deadline(s): None
Officers: Helene Lemmen, Pres.; Wayne E. Lemmen, Treas.
EIN: 386069061

1097
Jeffrey D. Leonard Memorial Foundation
31217 Adams Ct.
Gibraltar, MI 48173

Established in 1995 in MI.
Donor: Jerry F. Leonard, Jr.
Grantmaker type: Independent foundation.
Financial data (yr. ended 12/31/04): Assets, $16,931 (M); expenditures, $20,000; total giving, $20,000; qualifying distributions, $19,999; giving activities include $20,000 for grants.

Limitations: Applications not accepted. Giving primarily in MI. No grants to individuals.
Application information: Contributes only to pre-selected organizations.
Officers: Michelle R. Leonard-Licari, Pres.; Janice F. Leonard, Secy.
EIN: 383142153

1098
The Leppien Foundation
815 N. State St.
Alma, MI 48801-1155

Established in 1987 in MI.
Donors: Cleo M. Leppien; John C. Leppien; Garr Tool Co.
Grantmaker type: Independent foundation.
Financial data (yr. ended 12/31/04): Assets, $0 (M); gifts received, $950,000; expenditures, $427,687; total giving, $420,000; qualifying distributions, $420,000; giving activities include $420,000 for 14 grants (high: $75,000; low: $5,000).
Purpose and activities: Giving primarily for Christian organizations, and children and youth services.
Fields of interest: Higher education; Children/youth, services; Christian agencies & churches.
Limitations: Applications not accepted. Giving primarily in MI. No grants to individuals.
Application information: Contributes only to pre-selected organizations.
Trustees: Cleo M. Leppien; John C. Leppien.
EIN: 382692343

1099
Eugene H. Leslie Trust
c/o JPMorgan Chase Bank, N.A.
P.O. Box 1308
Milwaukee, WI 53201

Established in MI.
Grantmaker type: Independent foundation.
Financial data (yr. ended 12/31/05): Assets, $763,683 (M); expenditures, $42,179; total giving, $34,285; qualifying distributions, $34,285; giving activities include $34,285 for grants.
Purpose and activities: Support only for the Leslie Science Center, MI.
Fields of interest: Museums (science/technology).
Limitations: Applications not accepted. Giving limited to Ann Arbor, MI. No grants to individuals.
Application information: Contributes only to a pre-selected organization.
Trustee: JPMorgan Chase Bank, N.A.
EIN: 386377398

1100
Norman & Marilyn Leven Foundation
(formerly Norman J. Leven Family Foundation)
14 Campau Cir.
Grand Rapids, MI 49503

Established in 1985 in MI.
Donors: Norman J. Leven; Marilyn Leven.
Grantmaker type: Independent foundation.
Financial data (yr. ended 12/31/04): Assets, $663,894 (M); expenditures, $57,299; total giving, $55,560; qualifying distributions, $55,560; giving activities include $55,560 for grants.

Fields of interest: Higher education; Federated giving programs; Jewish federated giving programs; Jewish agencies & temples.
Type of support: General/operating support.
Limitations: Applications not accepted. Giving primarily in Grand Rapids, MI. No grants to individuals.
Application information: Contributes only to pre-selected organizations.
Officers and Trustees:* Norman J. Leven,* Pres.; Marilyn Leven,* Secy.; Norton P. Remes.
EIN: 382639116

1101
The Myron P. Leven Foundation
25899 W. 12 Mile Rd., Ste. 350
Southfield, MI 48034-8315
Contact: Arnold P. Garber, Secy.

Established in 1998 in MI.
Donor: Myron P. Leven†.
Grantmaker type: Independent foundation.
Financial data (yr. ended 12/31/04): Assets, $2,069,424 (M); expenditures, $150,863; total giving, $120,400; qualifying distributions, $119,878; giving activities include $120,400 for 8 + grants (high: $46,600).
Fields of interest: Museums; Performing arts; Arts; Higher education; Jewish federated giving programs.
Type of support: Program development; Scholarship funds.
Limitations: Giving limited to MI. No grants to individuals.
Officer: Arnold P. Garber, Secy.
EIN: 383443921

1102
The Ellen Levy Foundation
9300 Dix Ave.
Dearborn, MI 48120

Established in 1997 in MI.
Grantmaker type: Independent foundation.
Financial data (yr. ended 12/31/05): Assets, $1,050,215 (M); expenditures, $78,129; total giving, $68,000; qualifying distributions, $68,000; giving activities include $68,000 for grants.
Purpose and activities: Giving for legal services, employment, and human services, with some focus on services for people with AIDS.
Fields of interest: Media, film/video; Museums (specialized); Legal services; Employment, sheltered workshops; Human services; AIDS, people with.
Limitations: Applications not accepted. Giving primarily in Astoria and New York, NY, and Nashville, TN. No grants to individuals.
Application information: Contributes only to pre-selected organizations.
Officers: Ellen Levy, Pres.; Gregg M. Horowitz, Secy.-Treas.
EIN: 311498912

1103
The Carol Anne Levy Foundation
9300 Dix Ave.
Dearborn, MI 48120

Established in 1996 in MI.
Donor: Carol Anne Levy.

Grantmaker type: Independent foundation.
Financial data (yr. ended 12/31/05): Assets, $1,804,046 (M); expenditures, $91,294; total giving, $75,500; qualifying distributions, $77,000; giving activities include $75,500 for 6 grants (high: $55,000; low: $1,000).
Purpose and activities: Giving primarily for international development and AIDS funding.
Fields of interest: AIDS; AIDS research; International development; International human rights; Civil rights, advocacy.
Limitations: Applications not accepted. Giving primarily in New York, NY, and CA, with emphasis in Los Angeles. No grants to individuals.
Application information: Contributes only to pre-selected organizations.
Officers and Directors:* Carol Anne Levy, Pres.; John D. Johnstone,* Secy.; Ellen Levy,* Treas.
EIN: 383331960

1104
Julie & Edward Levy, Jr. Foundation
(formerly Edward C. Levy Foundation)
9300 Dix Ave.
Dearborn, MI 48120

Established in 1973 in MI.
Donors: Carol Levy; Ellen Levy; Edward C. Levy, Jr.; Edward C. Levy Co.; The Charitable Lead Trust.
Grantmaker type: Independent foundation.
Financial data (yr. ended 9/30/05): Assets, $17,177,472 (M); expenditures, $1,130,307; total giving, $1,044,626; qualifying distributions, $1,046,776; giving activities include $1,044,626 for 54 grants (high: $250,226; low: $100).
Purpose and activities: Giving for health, education, and Jewish organizations.
Fields of interest: Higher education; Health care; Health organizations, association; Neuroscience; Cancer research; Jewish federated giving programs; Jewish agencies & temples.
Limitations: Applications not accepted. Giving primarily in MI, with emphasis on Detroit; some giving in Washington, DC, and Cambridge, MA. No grants to individuals.
Application information: Contributes only to pre-selected organizations.
Officer: Edward C. Levy, Jr., Pres.
Trustees: Patrick Duerr; Ellen Levy Horowitz; Carol Levy Johnstone.
EIN: 386091368

1105
Pam Lewis Foundation
c/o S. Gary Spicer
16845 Kercheval St., Ste. 5
Grosse Pointe, MI 48230-1551

Established in 1997 in MI.
Donor: Pam Lewis.
Grantmaker type: Independent foundation.
Financial data (yr. ended 12/31/05): Assets, $84,361 (M); gifts received, $60,524; expenditures, $35,085; total giving, $29,739; qualifying distributions, $29,739; giving activities include $29,739 for grants.
Purpose and activities: Giving primarily for the arts, health and human services, the environment, and animal welfare.

Fields of interest: Arts; Education; Environment; Animals/wildlife; Human services; Children/youth, services.
Limitations: Giving primarily in TN.
Application information: Contact foundation for application guidelines.
Deadline(s): None
Officers and Trustees:* Pam Lewis,* Pres.; S. Gary Spicer, Secy.; John Lewis,* Treas.
EIN: 383278908

1106
Liebler Family Foundation, Inc.
c/o Arthur C. Liebler
1099 Orchard Ridge Rd.
Bloomfield Hills, MI 48304

Established in 1997 in MI.
Donor: Arthur C. Liebler.
Grantmaker type: Independent foundation.
Financial data (yr. ended 12/31/04): Assets, $852,138 (M); expenditures, $81,264; total giving, $75,750; qualifying distributions, $75,750; giving activities include $75,750 for grants.
Fields of interest: Arts; Education; Federated giving programs.
Type of support: General/operating support; Annual campaigns; Building/renovation.
Limitations: Applications not accepted. Giving primarily in Detroit, MI. No grants to individuals.
Application information: Contributes only to pre-selected organizations.
Officers: Arthur C. Liebler, Pres.; Nancy C. Liebler, Secy.; Patrick Liebler, Treas.
Directors: Mary Francis Liebler Beauregard; Michael Beauregard; Catherine Liebler Trevino; Paul Trevino.
EIN: 383346936

1107
Lileikis Family Foundation
3417 Roger B Chaffee Memorial Dr. S.E.
Wyoming, MI 49548-2323
Contact: Frank Lileikis, Pres.

Grantmaker type: Independent foundation.
Financial data (yr. ended 12/31/05): Assets, $216,515 (M); expenditures, $11,960; total giving, $11,450; qualifying distributions, $11,450; giving activities include $11,450 for grants.
Limitations: Giving primarily in Grand Rapids, MI.
Application information: Application form not required.
Deadline(s): None
Officers: Frank Lileikis, Pres. and Treas.; Thomas Lileikis, V.P. and Secy.
Directors: Christine Erskine; Katherine Erskine.
EIN: 383390415

1108
August Lilja Family Memorial Fund
c/o Northern Michigan Bank & Trust Co.
1502 W. Washington St.
Marquette, MI 49855
Application address: c/o Judge John A. Torreano, Probate/Juvenile Court Div., P.O. Box 609, Iron Mountain, MI 49801

Grantmaker type: Independent foundation.
Financial data (yr. ended 12/31/05): Assets, $545,934 (M); expenditures, $99,025; total giving,

$84,317; qualifying distributions, $84,317; giving activities include $84,317 for grants.
Limitations: Giving primarily in MI. No grants to individuals.
Application information:
Initial approach: Letter
Deadline(s): None
Trustee: Northern Michigan Bank & Trust Co.
EIN: 386648816

1109
Lincoln Health Care Foundation
550 Stephenson Hwy., Ste. 202
Troy, MI 48083

Established in MI.
Grantmaker type: Independent foundation.
Financial data (yr. ended 12/31/05): Assets, $2,741,432 (M); expenditures, $168,665; total giving, $118,000; qualifying distributions, $120,038; giving activities include $118,000 for 2 grants (high: $100,000; low: $18,000).
Purpose and activities: Giving primarily for health care services and education.
Fields of interest: Higher education; Medical school/education; Hospitals (general); Health care; Health organizations.
Type of support: Capital campaigns; Program development; Scholarship funds; Research.
Limitations: Applications not accepted. Giving primarily in NC; some giving also in MI. No grants to individuals.
Application information: Contributes only to pre-selected organizations.
Officers and Trustees:* Maurice B. Landers III, M.D.*, Chair., Pres., and Treas.; Stephen D. Landers,* V.P. and Secy.
EIN: 381359220
Selected grants: The following grants were reported in 2003.
$27,000 to Starr Commonwealth, Albion, MI.
$25,000 to Dana College, Blair, NE. For health science scholarships.
$25,000 to Mecklenburg County Medical Society, Charlotte, NC. For Physicians Reach Out Program.
$20,000 to Queens University, Charlotte, NC. For scholarships and capital support.
$10,000 to South Tryon Community Church, Charlotte, NC. For program support.

1110
J. Stewart Linden Foundation
33776 Old Timber Rd.
Farmington Hills, MI 48331
Contact: Sanford J. Linden, Secy.-Treas.

Established in MI.
Donor: J. Stewart Linden†.
Grantmaker type: Independent foundation.
Financial data (yr. ended 12/31/05): Assets, $304,263 (M); expenditures, $13,645; total giving, $13,100; qualifying distributions, $13,100; giving activities include $13,100 for grants.
Fields of interest: Higher education; Human services; Jewish agencies & temples.
Type of support: General/operating support.
Limitations: Giving primarily in MI. No grants to individuals.
Application information:

Initial approach: Letter
Deadline(s): None
Officers and Trustees:* Hanna Linden,* Pres.; Allan J. Linden,* V.P.; Sanford J. Linden,* Secy.-Treas.
EIN: 386109122

1111
The Linse Bock Foundation
(formerly The Ralph and Maggie Klingenmeyer Foundation)
c/o John P. Schneider
333 Bridge St. N.W., Ste. 800
Grand Rapids, MI 49504

Established in 1992 in MI.
Donors: Ralph E. Klingenmeyer; Maggie Klingenmeyer.
Grantmaker type: Independent foundation.
Financial data (yr. ended 12/31/04): Assets, $5,781,124 (M); expenditures, $302,367; total giving, $270,000; qualifying distributions, $267,864; giving activities include $270,000 for 6 grants (high: $150,000; low: $15,000).
Fields of interest: Higher education, university; Health care, single organization support.
Limitations: Applications not accepted. Giving on a national basis. No grants to individuals.
Application information: Contributes only to pre-selected organizations.
Officers and Directors:* Maggie Klingenmeyer,* Pres.; Amy E. Iverson,* Secy.; John D. Klingenmeyer; Joseph R. Klingenmeyer.
EIN: 383078569
Selected grants: The following grants were reported in 2004.
$150,000 to Mayo Foundation, Rochester, MN.
$40,000 to Middle Tennessee State University Foundation, Murfreesboro, TN. For Linse Bock Endowed Scholarship.
$25,000 to Providence Day School, Charlotte, NC. For endowment fund.
$20,000 to PKD Foundation, Kansas City, MO.
$20,000 to Ronald McDonald House of Western Michigan, Grand Rapids, MI.
$15,000 to Christ Lutheran Church, Charlotte, NC. For Fill the Gap building fund.

1112
Linway Foundation
7299 152nd Ave.
West Olive, MI 49460

Established in 1998.
Donors: Wayne E. Pynnonen; Linda A. Pynnonen.
Grantmaker type: Independent foundation.
Financial data (yr. ended 12/31/05): Assets, $149,976 (M); expenditures, $4,595; total giving, $3,790; qualifying distributions, $3,790; giving activities include $3,790 for grants.
Limitations: Applications not accepted. No grants to individuals.
Application information: Contributes only to pre-selected organizations.
Officer: Linda A. Pynnonen, Pres.
Trustee: Wayne E. Pynnonen.
EIN: 383416613

1113
William Tedrow Little Foundation
107 W. Michigan Ave., PH
Kalamazoo, MI 49007
Contact: William Tedrow Little, Pres.

Established in 1998 in MI.
Donor: William Tedrow Little.
Grantmaker type: Independent foundation.
Financial data (yr. ended 12/31/05): Assets, $41,128 (M); expenditures, $1,387; total giving, $0; qualifying distributions, $0.
Fields of interest: Cancer; Muscular dystrophy; Big Brothers/Big Sisters; Residential/custodial care, hospices.
Type of support: General/operating support.
Application information:
Initial approach: Letter
Deadline(s): None
Officers and Trustees:* William Tedrow Little,* Pres. and Treas; Virginia S. Little,* V.P.; Frances A. Little,* Secy.; James M. Elsworth.
EIN: 383443723

1114
The Earle and Elsie Little Scholarship Trust
c/o Monroe Bank & Trust
102 E. Front St.
Monroe, MI 48161-2162

Established in 1998 in MI.
Donor: Elsie Little.
Grantmaker type: Independent foundation.
Financial data (yr. ended 12/31/05): Assets, $346,030 (M); expenditures, $19,467; total giving, $9,550; qualifying distributions, $9,550; giving activities include $9,550 for grants to individuals.
Purpose and activities: Scholarships awarded to U.S. citizens for undergraduate studies in an accredited Michigan college or university.
Type of support: Scholarships—to individuals.
Limitations: Giving limited to U.S. citizens, with preference to residents of MI.
Application information: Application form required.
Deadline(s): None
Trustee: Monroe Bank & Trust.
EIN: 386729055

1115
The Litvak Foundation
c/o Ackerman, Dynkowski and Ackerman
100 W. Long Lake Rd., Ste. 210
Bloomfield Hills, MI 48304-2774

Established in 1983 in MI.
Donors: Alan T. Ackerman; Sheldon Stone.
Grantmaker type: Independent foundation.
Financial data (yr. ended 12/31/04): Assets, $156,980 (M); expenditures, $30,785; total giving, $24,000; qualifying distributions, $24,000; giving activities include $24,000 for 7 grants (high: $10,000; low: $500).
Fields of interest: Education; Human services; Children/youth, services; Jewish federated giving programs; Jewish agencies & temples.
Limitations: Applications not accepted. Giving primarily in MI. No grants to individuals.
Application information: Contributes only to pre-selected organizations.

Officers: Alan T. Ackerman, Pres.; Sharyl Ackerman, Secy.
EIN: 382489585
Selected grants: The following grants were reported in 2003.
$50,000 to University of Michigan, Ann Arbor, MI.
$25,000 to Edison Institute, Dearborn, MI.
$10,000 to American Israel Education Foundation (AIEF), DC.
$8,000 to Wayne State University, Detroit, MI.
$5,641 to Charlevoix Area Community Pool, Charlevoix, MI.
$3,765 to Temple Beth El, Bloomfield Hills, MI.
$2,198 to Leukemia & Lymphoma Society, White Plains, NY.
$2,000 to Hillel Day School of Metropolitan Detroit, Farmington Hills, MI.
$1,500 to YMCA of Metropolitan Detroit, Detroit, MI.
$350 to Jewish National Fund, New York, NY.

1116
The David & Sheryl Livingston Family Foundation
1003 Parchment Dr.
Grand Rapids, MI 49546

Established in 1996 in MI.
Donor: David Livingston.
Grantmaker type: Independent foundation.
Financial data (yr. ended 12/31/04): Assets, $3,897 (M); gifts received, $28,460; expenditures, $44,512; total giving, $39,969; qualifying distributions, $39,969; giving activities include $39,969 for grants.
Fields of interest: Higher education; Health organizations; Christian agencies & churches.
Limitations: Applications not accepted. Giving primarily in East Lansing and Grand Rapids, MI. No grants to individuals.
Application information: Contributes only to pre-selected organizations.
Officers and Directors:* David Livingston,* Mgr.; Sheryl Livingston,* Mgr.
EIN: 311486754

1117
LMC Foundation
48690 Harbor Dr.
Chesterfield, MI 48047

Established in 2004 in MI.
Donor: TLC Foundation.
Grantmaker type: Independent foundation.
Financial data (yr. ended 12/31/04): Assets, $2,673,600 (M); expenditures, $0; total giving, $0; qualifying distributions, $0.
Director: Linda M. Calliea.
EIN: 200442102

1118
Stella & Frederick Loeb Charitable Trust
c/o Citizens Bank
328 S. Saginaw St., MC 000041
Saginaw, MI 48602
Contact: Dawn Bentley, Trust Off.

Established in 1990 in MI.
Donor: Frederick Loeb‡.
Grantmaker type: Independent foundation.

Financial data (yr. ended 8/31/05): Assets, $5,293,936 (M); gifts received, $9,564; expenditures, $322,501; total giving, $272,904; qualifying distributions, $311,814; giving activities include $272,904 for 57 grants (high: $20,000; low: $1,000).
Purpose and activities: Giving primarily for human services.
Fields of interest: Arts; Education; Human services; Children/youth, services; Federated giving programs; Christian agencies & churches; Jewish agencies & temples.
Type of support: Program development.
Limitations: Giving primarily in Flint, MI.
Publications: Application guidelines.
Application information: Application form required.
  Initial approach: Letter
  Deadline(s): None
Trustee: Citizens Bank.
EIN: 386571896

1119
Loichle Family Foundation
7418 E. High Point Dr.
Scottsdale, AZ   85262

Established in 1999 in MI.
Donors: Leon J. Loichle; Janice E. Loichle.
Grantmaker type: Independent foundation.
Financial data (yr. ended 12/31/05): Assets, $144,383 (M); gifts received, $70; expenditures, $8,538; total giving, $6,000; qualifying distributions, $6,000; giving activities include $6,000 for grants.
Fields of interest: Higher education; Christian agencies & churches.
Type of support: General/operating support.
Limitations: Applications not accepted. Giving primarily in MI and MN. No grants to individuals.
Application information: Contributes only to pre-selected organizations.
Officers: Leon J. Loichle, Jr., Pres.; Janice E. Loichle, Secy.
Directors: Ann L. Loichle; Eric B. Loichle.
EIN: 383503173

1120
Lone Pine Foundation
3253 Avalon Pl.
Houston, TX   77019

Established in 2000 in MI.
Donor: Jacque H. Passino, Jr.
Grantmaker type: Independent foundation.
Financial data (yr. ended 12/31/04): Assets, $588,813 (M); gifts received, $249,300; expenditures, $11,057; total giving, $7,500; qualifying distributions, $7,500; giving activities include $7,500 for grants.
Limitations: Applications not accepted. Giving primarily in MI and TX. No grants to individuals.
Application information: Contributes only to pre-selected organizations.
Officers: Jacque H. Passino, Jr., Pres. and Treas.; Pamela A. Passino, Secy.
EIN: 383562808

1121
Charles W. Loosemore Foundation
(formerly Loosemore Foundation)
15 Ionia Ave. S.W., Ste. 400
Grand Rapids, MI   49503

Established in 1966 in MI.
Donor: Charles W. Loosemore.
Grantmaker type: Independent foundation.
Financial data (yr. ended 12/31/05): Assets, $4,001,665 (M); expenditures, $224,480; total giving, $197,600; qualifying distributions, $197,600; giving activities include $197,600 for 28 grants (high: $60,100; low: $100).
Purpose and activities: Giving primarily to universities, museums, and the performing arts; support also for federated giving programs, human services, and community development.
Fields of interest: Museums; Performing arts; Higher education; Health organizations; Human services; Community development; Federated giving programs.
Limitations: Applications not accepted. Giving primarily in Grand Rapids, MI. No grants to individuals.
Application information: Contributes only to pre-selected organizations.
Officers: David M. Hecht, Pres.; Joyce F. Hecht, V.P.
EIN: 386140749

1122
Lot Foundation
13151 Lakeshore Dr.
Grand Haven, MI   49417

Donor: Judith Van Kampen.
Grantmaker type: Independent foundation.
Financial data (yr. ended 12/31/04): Assets, $1,866,853 (M); gifts received, $2,140,000; expenditures, $297,593; total giving, $297,500; qualifying distributions, $297,594; giving activities include $297,500 for 6 grants (high: $100,000; low: $1,500).
Fields of interest: Elementary/secondary education; Christian agencies & churches; Protestant agencies & churches.
Limitations: Giving primarily in MI and IL.
Directors: David Wisen; Kristen Wisen.
EIN: 421561347

1123
Frank B. Lounsberry Educational Foundation Trust
c/o Bank of America, N.A.
P.O. Box 40200, MC F19-100-10-19
Jacksonville, FL   32203-0200

Established in 1998 in FL.
Grantmaker type: Independent foundation.
Financial data (yr. ended 6/30/05): Assets, $98,713 (M); expenditures, $6,054; total giving, $1,945; qualifying distributions, $1,945; giving activities include $1,945 for grants.
Purpose and activities: Support only for Hope College, Holland, MI.
Fields of interest: Higher education.
Limitations: Applications not accepted. Giving limited to Holland, MI. No grants to individuals.
Application information: Contributes only to a pre-selected organization.

Trustee: Bank of America, N.A.
EIN: 596596474

1124
The Loutit Foundation
c/o LaSalle Bank, N.A.
135 S. LaSalle St., Ste. 2060
Chicago, IL   60603
Application address: c/o LaSalle Bank, N.A., P.O. Box 1707, Grand Rapids, MI 49501-1707

Incorporated in 1957 in MI.
Donors: William R. Loutit†; William Loutit Memorial Trust.
Grantmaker type: Independent foundation.
Financial data (yr. ended 6/30/05): Assets, $868,479 (M); gifts received, $128,271; expenditures, $175,947; total giving, $153,679; qualifying distributions, $155,252; giving activities include $153,679 for 43 grants (high: $20,000; low: $50).
Fields of interest: Museums; Museums (history); Higher education; Human services; Community development; Foundations (community); Federated giving programs.
Type of support: Capital campaigns; Building/renovation; Equipment; Land acquisition; Program development; Seed money.
Limitations: Giving limited to western MI, with emphasis on the Grand Haven/Spring Lake area. No grants to individuals, or for research; no loans.
Publications: Biennial report.
Application information: Application form not required.
  Initial approach: Letter
  Copies of proposal: 5
  Deadline(s): None
Officers and Trustees:* Jon W. Eshleman,* Pres.; Thomas M. Boven,* V.P.; Sharon Burtrum, Secy.-Treas.; Kennard Creason; Bari Johnson; LaSalle Bank, N.A.
EIN: 386053445

1125
William Loutit Memorial Trust
c/o Standard Federal Bank N.A.
135 S. Lasalle St., Ste. 2060
Chicago, IL   60603

Grantmaker type: Independent foundation.
Financial data (yr. ended 6/30/04): Assets, $2,232,785 (M); expenditures, $120,586; total giving, $99,810; qualifying distributions, $110,342; giving activities include $99,810 for 4 grants (high: $45,810; low: $10,000).
Fields of interest: Museums (history); Higher education; Foundations (private independent).
Limitations: Applications not accepted. Giving primarily in MI. No grants to individuals.
Application information: Contributes only to pre-selected organizations.
Trustee: Standard Federal Bank N.A.
EIN: 386047716

1126
Arthur J. and Josephine W. Lowell Charitable Foundation
c/o Fifth Third Bank
P.O. Box 3636
Grand Rapids, MI   49501-3636

Established in 1989 in IL.
Grantmaker type: Independent foundation.
Financial data (yr. ended 10/31/05): Assets, $3,188,043 (M); expenditures, $296,924; total giving, $277,422; qualifying distributions, $277,422; giving activities include $277,422 for grants.
Fields of interest: Scholarships/financial aid; Health organizations, association; Youth development, centers/clubs; American Red Cross; Salvation Army; Federated giving programs.
Type of support: General/operating support.
Limitations: Applications not accepted. Giving limited to Fort Lauderdale, FL. No grants to individuals.
Application information: Contributes only to 14 pre-selected organizations.
Trustees: Barbara H. Harvill; David T. Hughes; Fifth Third Bank.
EIN: 366911813

1127
Malcolm & Beth Lowenstein Foundation
c/o Acme Mills
1750 S. Telegraph, Ste. 304
Bloomfield Hills, MI 48304-0166

Established in 1963 in MI.
Grantmaker type: Independent foundation.
Financial data (yr. ended 12/31/05): Assets, $2,049,906 (M); expenditures, $98,233; total giving, $88,780; qualifying distributions, $88,780; giving activities include $88,780 for grants.
Purpose and activities: Giving for education, health associations, human services, and Jewish organizations.
Fields of interest: Elementary/secondary education; Education; Health organizations, association; Human services; Jewish federated giving programs; Jewish agencies & temples.
Limitations: Applications not accepted. Giving primarily in MI. No grants to individuals.
Application information: Contributes only to pre-selected organizations.
Officers and Directors:* Betsy Lowenstein Feld,* Pres.; James A. Colman,* V.P.; James M. Feld,* V.P.; Linda Gawel, Secy.; Connie Lowenstein Colman,* Treas.
EIN: 386092530

1128
Lubin, Schwartz & Goldman Foundation
2369 Franklin Rd.
P.O. Box 3000
Bloomfield Hills, MI 48302   (248) 332-3100

Established in 1996 in MI.
Donors: Sheldon Goldman; Joel Lubin; Robert Schwartz; Mark Fisher.
Grantmaker type: Independent foundation.
Financial data (yr. ended 3/31/05): Assets, $4,694 (M); gifts received, $92,938; expenditures, $88,679; total giving, $88,659; qualifying distributions, $88,659; giving activities include $88,659 for grants.
Purpose and activities: Giving primarily for hospitals and Jewish federated giving programs.
Fields of interest: Hospitals (general); American Red Cross; Jewish federated giving programs; Jewish agencies & temples.

Limitations: Giving primarily in MI. No grants to individuals.
Application information: Application form not required.
  Deadline(s): None
Directors: David Colburn; Robert Colburn; Mark Fisher; Sheldon Goldman*; Jay Schreibman; Robert Schwartz.
EIN: 382777749

1129
The Thomas L. Ludington Foundation
c/o Deloitte & Touche, LLP
3320 Ridgecrest Dr.
Midland, MI 48642
Contact: Thomas L. Ludington, Pres.

Donor: John S. Ludington.
Grantmaker type: Independent foundation.
Financial data (yr. ended 12/31/05): Assets, $565,939 (M); gifts received, $43,740; expenditures, $28,781; total giving, $24,410; qualifying distributions, $24,410; giving activities include $24,410 for grants.
Limitations: Giving primarily in MI. No grants to individuals.
Application information:
  Initial approach: Letter
  Deadline(s): None
Officers: Thomas L. Ludington, Pres.; Katrina K. Ludington, V.P.; John S. Ludington, Treas.
EIN: 383323700

1130
The Ludy Family Foundation
(formerly The Ernest & Carmen Ludy Charitable Foundation)
c/o EGL Investments LLC
801 Laurel Oak Dr., No. 610
Naples, FL 34108-2766

Established in 1994 in MI.
Donor: Ernest G. Ludy.
Grantmaker type: Independent foundation.
Financial data (yr. ended 12/31/04): Assets, $2,412,287 (M); expenditures, $158,078; total giving, $73,000; qualifying distributions, $91,097; giving activities include $73,000 for 6 grants (high: $40,000; low: $1,000).
Fields of interest: Performing arts, orchestra (symphony); Elementary/secondary education; Higher education, university; Hospitals (general); Health care; International development; Philanthropy/voluntarism.
Type of support: Annual campaigns; Endowments; Program development.
Limitations: Applications not accepted. Giving on a national basis, with emphasis on MI. No grants to individuals.
Application information: Contributes only to pre-selected organizations.
Officer: Ernest G. Ludy, Pres. and Secy.-Treas.
EIN: 383211299

1131
Lugers Family Foundation
288 McVea Rd.
Douglas, MI 49406
Contact: Janet Lugers, Dir.

Application address: P.O. Box 820, Douglas, MI 49406

Established in 1999 in MI.
Grantmaker type: Independent foundation.
Financial data (yr. ended 12/31/05): Assets, $582,076 (M); expenditures, $37,090; total giving, $30,518; qualifying distributions, $30,518; giving activities include $30,518 for grants.
Fields of interest: Education; Animal welfare; Human services; Children/youth, services; Residential/custodial care, hospices.
Type of support: General/operating support.
Limitations: Giving limited to Holland, MI, and its surrounding areas. No grants to individuals.
Application information:
  Initial approach: Letter
  Deadline(s): None
Directors: Marilyn Hoffer; Janet Lugers; Leona S. Lugers.
EIN: 383369937

1132
Lukens Family Foundation
2432 Camelot Ct. S.E.
Grand Rapids, MI 49546

Established in 1997 in MI.
Donors: Jack Lukens; Katherine Lukens.
Grantmaker type: Independent foundation.
Financial data (yr. ended 12/31/05): Assets, $330,223 (M); expenditures, $20,116; total giving, $18,835; qualifying distributions, $18,835; giving activities include $18,835 for grants.
Limitations: Applications not accepted. No grants to individuals.
Officers: Jack Lukens, Pres.; Katherine Lukens, Secy.
EIN: 593486468

1133
Lundstrom Family Foundation
c/o Charles C. Lundstrom
111 Lyon St. N.W., Ste. 900
Grand Rapids, MI 49503-2413

Established in 1997 in MI.
Donors: Charles C. Lundstrom; Janice C. Lundstrom.
Grantmaker type: Independent foundation.
Financial data (yr. ended 12/31/05): Assets, $523,033 (M); gifts received, $45,820; expenditures, $20,191; total giving, $20,000; qualifying distributions, $20,000; giving activities include $20,000 for grants.
Fields of interest: Animal welfare.
Type of support: General/operating support.
Limitations: Applications not accepted. Giving primarily in AZ and MI. No grants to individuals.
Application information: Contributes only to pre-selected organizations.
Officers and Trustees:* Charles C. Lundstrom,* Pres.; Scott C. Lundstrom,* V.P.; Janice B. Lundstrom,* Secy.; Eric T. Lundstrom,* Treas.; Craig C. Lundstrom.
EIN: 383368451

1134
J. Edward Lundy Foundation
2855 Coolidge Hwy., Ste. 109
Troy, MI 48084

Established in 1987 in MI.
Donor: J. Edward Lundy.
Grantmaker type: Independent foundation.
Financial data (yr. ended 12/31/05): Assets, $4,857 (M); expenditures, $30,715; total giving, $29,350; qualifying distributions, $29,350; giving activities include $29,350 for grants.
Fields of interest: Health care; Eye diseases; Protestant agencies & churches.
Type of support: General/operating support.
Limitations: Applications not accepted. Giving primarily in IA, MA, and MI. No grants to individuals.
Application information: Contributes only to pre-selected organizations.
Officers: J. Edward Lundy, Pres.; W. Robert Chandler, Secy.
EIN: 382707749

1135
Luneack Family Foundation
308 Gratiot Ave.
Alma, MI 48801

Established in 2005 in MI.
Donor: Ken Luneack.
Grantmaker type: Independent foundation.
Financial data (yr. ended 12/31/05): Assets, $100,464 (M); gifts received, $101,000; expenditures, $536; total giving, $0; qualifying distributions, $0.
Officers: Ken Luneack, Pres.; Paul Luneack, V.P.; Charles Fortino, Secy.; Doug Hoard, Treas.
EIN: 202784486

1136
Ann and Robert H. Lurie Family Foundation
2 N. Riverside Plz., Ste. 1500
Chicago, IL 60606 (312) 466-3997
Contact: Janet V. Ecker, C.A.O.

Established in 1986 in IL.
Donor: Robert Lurie†.
Grantmaker type: Independent foundation.
Financial data (yr. ended 12/31/04): Assets, $16,740,389 (M); expenditures, $5,575,031; total giving, $5,317,017; qualifying distributions, $5,317,017; giving activities include $5,317,017 for 37 grants (high: $2,500,000; low: $250; average: $2,500–$100,000).
Purpose and activities: Giving primarily for education, human services, and health.
Fields of interest: Higher education; Environment, research; Environment, natural resources; Health care; Health organizations, association; Children/youth, services.
Type of support: Endowments.
Limitations: Applications not accepted. Giving primarily in Chicago, IL, and MI. No grants to individuals.
Application information: Contributes only to pre-selected organizations.
Officers and Directors:* Ann Lurie,* Pres. and Treas.; Sheli Z. Rosenberg,* V.P. and Secy.; Andrew Lurie,* V.P.; Mark Slezak,* V.P.; Benjamin Lurie; Robert M. Levin.
EIN: 363486274

Selected grants: The following grants were reported in 2004.
$2,500,000 to University of Michigan, College of Engineering, Ann Arbor, MI. For unrestricted support.
$1,771,190 to Africa Infectious Disease Village Clinics, Chicago, IL. For unrestricted support.
$244,563 to Riders for Health II, Rockville, MD. 2 grants: $219,563 (For unrestricted support), $25,000 (For unrestricted support).
$155,000 to Infant Welfare Society of Chicago, Chicago, IL. For unrestricted support.
$50,000 to Chicago Public Library Foundation, Chicago, IL. For unrestricted support.
$50,000 to Choate Rosemary Hall, Wallingford, CT. For unrestricted support.
$47,000 to Childrens Memorial Foundation, Chicago, IL. 2 grants: $35,000 (For unrestricted support), $12,000 (For unrestricted support).
$25,000 to Children Affected by AIDS Foundation, Los Angeles, CA. For unrestricted support.

1137
Lutjens Family Foundation
c/o John P. Schneider
333 Bridge St. N.W., Ste. 800
Grand Rapids, MI 49504

Established in 1994 in MI.
Donors: Larry R. Lutjens; Louette R. Lutjens.
Grantmaker type: Independent foundation.
Financial data (yr. ended 12/31/05): Assets, $174,161 (M); expenditures, $18,070; total giving, $14,550; qualifying distributions, $14,550; giving activities include $14,550 for grants.
Fields of interest: Secondary school/education; Environment; Human services; Roman Catholic agencies & churches.
Limitations: Giving primarily in MI; some giving also in La Quinta, CA. No grants to individuals.
Officers: Larry R. Lutjens, Pres.; Louette R. Lutjens, V.P.; Heidi L. Schmitt, Secy.; Chad A. Lutjens, Treas.
Director: Eric Schmitt.
EIN: 383139336

1138
Ray J. & Leila M. Lynch Charitable Trust
15 Windemere Pl.
Grosse Pointe Farms, MI 48236-9080
Contact: Ray J. Lynch, Tr.

Established in 1985 in MI.
Donors: Ray J. Lynch; Leila M. Lynch.
Grantmaker type: Independent foundation.
Financial data (yr. ended 12/31/04): Assets, $468,635 (M); expenditures, $40,200; total giving, $39,750; qualifying distributions, $39,750; giving activities include $39,750 for grants.
Fields of interest: Human services; Children/youth, services; Roman Catholic agencies & churches.
Limitations: Giving primarily in the Detroit and southeastern MI, area. No grants to individuals.
Application information:
Initial approach: Proposal
Deadline(s): Dec. 31
Trustees: Leila M. Lynch; Ray J. Lynch; Tim J. Lynch; Richard E. Rassel.
EIN: 382637861

1139
Lyon Foundation, Inc.
c/o A. Randolph Judd
1592 Redding Rd.
Birmingham, MI 48009-1029

Incorporated in 1951 in MI.
Donor: G. Albert Lyon, Sr.
Grantmaker type: Independent foundation.
Financial data (yr. ended 12/31/05): Assets, $2,943,983 (M); expenditures, $164,093; total giving, $144,877; qualifying distributions, $152,069; giving activities include $144,877 for 34 grants (high: $20,000; low: $250).
Purpose and activities: Support primarily for the Community Foundation for Southeast Michigan.
Fields of interest: Education; Human services; Foundations (community).
Limitations: Applications not accepted. Giving limited to southeastern MI. No grants to individuals.
Application information: Contributes only to pre-selected organizations.
Officers: Albert Randolph Judd, Pres. and Secy.; Winn Lyon Moore, V.P.; John Terrill Judd, Treas.
Number of staff: 1 full-time support.
EIN: 386121075

1140
Maryann & Wayne B. Lyon Foundation
65 Lone Pine Rd.
Bloomfield Hills, MI 48304

Established in 1986 in MI.
Donors: Wayne B. Lyon; Maryann Lyon.
Grantmaker type: Independent foundation.
Financial data (yr. ended 6/30/05): Assets, $3,430,047 (M); expenditures, $228,957; total giving, $180,825; qualifying distributions, $226,961; giving activities include $180,825 for 11 grants (high: $157,000; low: $25).
Fields of interest: Education; Human services; Federated giving programs; Protestant agencies & churches.
Limitations: Applications not accepted. Giving primarily in MI, with some emphasis on Bloomfield Hills. No grants to individuals.
Application information: Contributes only to pre-selected organizations.
Officers: Wayne B. Lyon, Pres.; Maryann Lyon, V.P.; Eugene A. Gargaro, Jr., Secy.
EIN: 382680420
Selected grants: The following grants were reported in 2005.
$157,000 to Cranbrook Educational Community, Bloomfield Hills, MI. For capital support.
$10,000 to Village Club, Bloomfield Hills, MI. For operating support.
$6,500 to Kirk in the Hills Presbyterian Church, Bloomfield Hills, MI. For operating support.
$2,000 to Patient Advocates for Advanced Cancer Treatments, Grand Rapids, MI. For operating support.
$1,500 to Luther High School South, Chicago, IL. For operating support.
$1,000 to Community House Association, Birmingham, MI. For operating support.
$1,000 to Copeland Oaks, Sebring, OH. For operating support.
$1,000 to Winona United Methodist Church, Salem, OH. For operating support.
$600 to First Presbyterian Church, Naples, FL. For operating support.

$200 to Salvation Army of Naples, Naples, FL. For operating support.

1141
Bob and Jan Lyons Foundation
3549 Pine View Dr.
Dexter, MI 48130

Established in 1999 in MI.
Grantmaker type: Independent foundation.
Financial data (yr. ended 12/31/05): Assets, $1,414,010 (M); expenditures, $91,769; total giving, $73,000; qualifying distributions, $73,000; giving activities include $73,000 for 18 grants (high: $25,000; low: $1,000).
Fields of interest: Museums; Higher education; Hospitals (general); Health care; Human services.
Type of support: General/operating support.
Limitations: Applications not accepted. Giving primarily in MI, with some emphasis on Ann Arbor and Dexter. No grants to individuals.
Application information: Contributes only to pre-selected organizations.
Officers and Director:* Rolland B. Lyons,* Pres.
EIN: 383423247

1142
M & M Foundation
1614 Hoit Tower Dr.
Bloomfield Hills, MI 48302
Contact: Mohamad Al-Hadidi, Pres.

Established in 2001 in MI.
Grantmaker type: Independent foundation.
Financial data (yr. ended 12/31/05): Assets, $511,344 (M); gifts received, $15,000; expenditures, $18,048; total giving, $12,827; qualifying distributions, $12,827; giving activities include $12,827 for grants.
Officers: Mohamad Al-Hadidi, Pres. and Treas.; Samir S. Al-Hadidi, V.P. and Secy.
EIN: 383586757

1143
M & S Foundation, Inc.
c/o Douglas McArthur
550 E. Main St.
Hudson, MI 49247 (517) 448-2026
Contact: Douglas McArthur

Established in 1986 in MI.
Grantmaker type: Independent foundation.
Financial data (yr. ended 3/31/05): Assets, $75,917 (M); gifts received, $24,000; expenditures, $24,020; total giving, $24,000; qualifying distributions, $24,000; giving activities include $24,000 for grants.
Fields of interest: Higher education.
Type of support: Scholarship funds.
Limitations: Giving primarily in MI.
Application information: Application form required.
   Deadline(s): 1st Fri. in Jan.
Officer: James D. Sayre, Pres.
EIN: 386074333

1144
Arlin E. Maas Family Foundation
c/o Arlin E. Maas
11440 Fulton St. E.
Lowell, MI 49331-9425

Established in 1997.
Grantmaker type: Independent foundation.
Financial data (yr. ended 12/31/04): Assets, $0 (M); gifts received, $510,000; expenditures, $134,035; total giving, $133,563; qualifying distributions, $133,354; giving activities include $133,563 for 18 grants (high: $95,182; low: $50).
Purpose and activities: Giving primarily to Christian churches, agencies, and schools.
Fields of interest: Education; Human services; Christian agencies & churches.
Limitations: Applications not accepted. Giving primarily in MI, with emphasis on Grand Rapids. No grants to individuals.
Application information: Contributes only to pre-selected organizations.
Officer: Arlin E. Maas, Pres.
EIN: 383351934
Selected grants: The following grants were reported in 2004.
$95,182 to Cary Christian Center, Cary, MS. For general support and building.
$31,834 to Ada Christian Reformed Church, Ada, MI. For general support.
$1,960 to Ada Christian School, Grand Rapids, MI. For general support.
$1,200 to Navigators, The, Colorado Springs, CO. For general support.
$850 to Missionary Flights International, West Palm Beach, FL. For general support.
$525 to Calvin College, Grand Rapids, MI. For general support.
$500 to Youth for Christ, Anchorage, Anchorage, AK. For general support.
$252 to Worldwide Christian Schools, Grand Rapids, MI. For general support.
$250 to Volunteers in Service (VIS), Grand Rapids, MI. For general support.
$200 to Asbury United Methodist Church, York, PA. For general support.

1145
Benard L. Maas Foundation
715 Barclay Ct.
Ann Arbor, MI 48105

Established in 1942 in MI.
Donor: Benard L. Maas‡.
Grantmaker type: Independent foundation.
Financial data (yr. ended 12/31/05): Assets, $7,928,130 (M); expenditures, $583,311; total giving, $380,680; qualifying distributions, $380,680; giving activities include $380,680 for 98 grants (high: $43,000; low: $200).
Purpose and activities: Giving primarily for Jewish organizations.
Fields of interest: Performing arts; Law school/education; Hospitals (specialty); Health organizations, association; Human services; Children/youth, services; Jewish federated giving programs; Jewish agencies & temples.
Limitations: Applications not accepted. Giving primarily in MI. No grants to individuals.
Application information: Contributes only to pre-selected organizations. Unsolicited requests for funds not accepted.

Officers and Directors:* David E. Engelbert,* Pres. and Treas.; Matthew Engelbert,* V.P.; Lynn H. Engelbert,* Secy.
EIN: 386096405

1146
Edward E. MacCrone Trust
c/o Comerica Bank
P.O. Box 75000, MC 3302
Detroit, MI 48275-3302
Application address: c/o Comerica Bank, 101 N. Main St., Ste. 100, Ann Arbor, MI 48104, tel.: (734) 930-2416

Established in 1959 in MI.
Donor: Edward E. MacCrone‡.
Grantmaker type: Independent foundation.
Financial data (yr. ended 12/31/05): Assets, $1,776,943 (M); expenditures, $109,065; total giving, $90,000; qualifying distributions, $91,767; giving activities include $90,000 for grants.
Fields of interest: Museums (art); Performing arts, orchestra (symphony); Higher education; Hospitals (general); Mental health, residential care; Boy scouts.
Type of support: General/operating support.
Limitations: Giving primarily in MI. No grants to individuals.
Application information:
   Initial approach: Letter
   Deadline(s): None
Trustee: Comerica Bank.
EIN: 386043730

1147
George R. and Doris Engblom MacDonald Scholarship Trust
c/o Northern Michigan Bank & Trust Co.
1502 W. Washington St.
Marquette, MI 49855-3195

Established in 1987 in MI.
Grantmaker type: Independent foundation.
Financial data (yr. ended 9/30/05): Assets, $25,792 (M); expenditures, $2,581; total giving, $1,000; qualifying distributions, $1,000; giving activities include $1,000 for grants.
Purpose and activities: Scholarship to a graduate of Iron Mountain High School, MI to pursue an education in the field of social studies; scholarship also to a graduate of Norway-Vulcan High School, MI for higher education.
Type of support: Scholarships—to individuals.
Limitations: Giving limited to MI.
Application information: Application form not required.
   Deadline(s): None
Trustee: Northern Michigan Bank & Trust Co.
EIN: 386462968

1148
Thomas A. Mackey Charitable Foundation
c/o Thomas A. Mackey
515 Rivard Blvd.
Grosse Pointe, MI 48230-1630

Established in 1998 in MI.
Donor: Thomas A. Mackey.
Grantmaker type: Independent foundation.

Financial data (yr. ended 12/31/05): Assets, $1,159,024 (M); gifts received, $737,000; expenditures, $37,969; total giving, $33,111; qualifying distributions, $33,111; giving activities include $33,111 for grants.
Fields of interest: Human services.
Limitations: Applications not accepted. Giving primarily in MI. No grants to individuals.
Application information: Contributes only to pre-selected organizations.
Officers: Thomas A. Mackey, Pres.; Roberta M. Rigger, Secy.; Albert M. Mackey, Jr., Treas.
EIN: 383383525

1149
Helen H. Mackey Educational Awards Foundation

c/o National City Bank of the Midwest
P.O. Box 94651
Cleveland, OH 44101-9957
Application address: c/o Senior Counselor, Bay City Central High School, 1624 Columbus Ave., Bay City, MI 48708, tel.: (989) 893-9541

Established in MI.
Donor: Helen Mackey†.
Grantmaker type: Independent foundation.
Financial data (yr. ended 12/31/04): Assets, $120,189 (M); expenditures, $4,140; total giving, $2,500; qualifying distributions, $3,602; giving activities include $2,500 for 10 grants to individuals (high: $250; low: $250).
Purpose and activities: Scholarship awards to graduating seniors at T.L. Handy High School, MI.
Fields of interest: Higher education.
Type of support: Scholarships—to individuals.
Limitations: Giving limited to Bay City, MI.
Application information: Application form required.
   Deadline(s): Varies
Trustee: National City Bank.
EIN: 386058127

1150
The Mackey Foundation

(formerly The Harvey and Elizabeth Mackey Foundation)
c/o Bruce Mackey
3181 Tri-Park Dr.
Grand Blanc, MI 48439

Established in 1993 in MI.
Donor: Bruce B. Mackey.
Grantmaker type: Independent foundation.
Financial data (yr. ended 12/31/05): Assets, $3,355,542 (M); gifts received, $1,600,000; expenditures, $512,664; total giving, $510,000; qualifying distributions, $510,000; giving activities include $510,000 for 12 grants (high: $100,000; low: $10,000).
Fields of interest: Housing/shelter, homeless; Boys & girls clubs; Human services; Homeless, human services; Christian agencies & churches; Protestant agencies & churches; Economically disadvantaged.
Limitations: Applications not accepted. Giving primarily in Flint, MI. No grants to individuals.
Application information: Contributes only to pre-selected organizations.
Officers: Marilyn Johnson, Pres.; Bruce B. Mackey, Secy.-Treas.
Trustee: Stanley D. Mackey.

Board Member: Robert B. Mackey.
EIN: 383134945
Selected grants: The following grants were reported in 2003.
$75,000 to Christ Episcopal Center, Flint, MI.
$70,000 to Young Life, Flint, MI.
$50,000 to Potters Clay Ministries, Hot Springs, AR.
$50,000 to Shelter of Flint, Flint, MI.
$40,000 to Boys and Girls Club of Greater Flint, Flint, MI.
$20,000 to Crossover Downtown Outreach Ministry, Flint, MI.
$20,000 to Saint Andrews Episcopal Church, Flint, MI.

1151
Macomb County Rotary Foundation

2 Crocker Blvd., Ste. 302
Mount Clemens, MI 48043-2528

Grantmaker type: Independent foundation.
Financial data (yr. ended 6/30/05): Assets, $451,553 (M); expenditures, $17,021; total giving, $10,825; qualifying distributions, $10,825; giving activities include $10,825 for grants.
Purpose and activities: Support primarily for the Sterling Heights Rotary Club, MI.
Limitations: Applications not accepted. Giving limited to MI. No grants to individuals.
Application information: Contributes only to pre-selected organizations.
Directors: Hank Charbeneau; Jim Corke; James Davey; Ted De Vantier; Bill Deyo; John Foster; Ronald Getz; Christine Latour; Eric Lundquist; Midge Lusardi; Frank Mallon; Dennis McCarron; Robert Shugart.
EIN: 381579780

1152
Anna M. MacRae Scholarship Trust

c/o National City Bank
2322 Tittabawassee Rd.
Saginaw, MI 48604-9476

Established in 2000 in MI.
Grantmaker type: Independent foundation.
Financial data (yr. ended 12/31/05): Assets, $176,202 (M); expenditures, $13,332; total giving, $10,050; qualifying distributions, $10,050; giving activities include $10,050 for grants to individuals.
Limitations: Giving limited to Cass City, MI, area.
Application information: Application form required.
   Deadline(s): Apr. 15
Trustee: National City Bank.
EIN: 386706105

1153
The Mahmud Foundation

c/o Ramla Mahmud, Pres.
475 S. Adams Rd., Unit 9
Birmingham, MI 48009-6752

Established in 1999 in MI.
Grantmaker type: Independent foundation.
Financial data (yr. ended 12/31/05): Assets, $207,934 (M); expenditures, $12,393; total giving, $11,600; qualifying distributions, $11,600; giving activities include $11,600 for 2 grants (high: $10,400; low: $1,200).
Fields of interest: Islam.

Limitations: Applications not accepted. Giving primarily in MI. No grants to individuals.
Application information: Contributes only to pre-selected organizations.
Officers: Ramla Mahmud, Pres.
EIN: 383439266

1154
Mahogany Foundation

9612 Walkabout Ln.
Traverse City, MI 49684 (231) 946-5320
Contact: Erik J. Falconer, Pres.

Established in 2003 in MI.
Donors: Daniel P. Falconer; Erik J. Falconer.
Grantmaker type: Independent foundation.
Financial data (yr. ended 12/31/04): Assets, $3,252,498 (M); gifts received, $100; expenditures, $176,155; total giving, $150,000; qualifying distributions, $149,391; giving activities include $150,000 for 3 grants (high: $75,000; low: $25,000).
Fields of interest: Environment, recycling; Environment, natural resources.
Limitations: Giving primarily in MI, NY and WA. No grants to individuals, or for annual campaigns or endowments.
Application information:
   Initial approach: Proposal
   Deadline(s): June 1 and Nov. 1
Officers and Trustees:* Daniel P. Falconer,* Chair.; Erik J. Falconer,* Pres. and Secy.-Treas.; Leslie M. Falconer,* V.P.; Meridith Falconer,* V.P.
EIN: 200126179

1155
R. C. Mahon Foundation

176 Windwood Pointe
St. Clair Shores, MI 48080-1582
(586) 777-2091
Contact: Karl Mallard, Pres.

Established in 1951 in MI.
Grantmaker type: Independent foundation.
Financial data (yr. ended 12/31/05): Assets, $1,458,845 (M); expenditures, $83,752; total giving, $75,100; qualifying distributions, $75,100; giving activities include $75,100 for grants.
Purpose and activities: Giving for health associations, human services, and higher education.
Fields of interest: Historic preservation/historical societies; Higher education; Libraries/library science; Zoos/zoological societies; Hospitals (general); Cancer; Human services; Children/youth, services.
Limitations: Giving primarily in MI. No grants to individuals.
Application information: Application form not required.
   Deadline(s): None
Officers: Karl Mallard, Pres.; Carolyn D. Mallard, V.P.; Judith M. Mallard, Secy.; Thomas M. Mallard, Treas.
EIN: 381598951

1156
Lorene and Ben Maibach Foundation
(formerly Maibach Foundation)
26500 American Dr.
Southfield, MI 48034

Established in 1966 in MI.
Donor: Benjamin C. Maibach, Jr.
Grantmaker type: Independent foundation.
Financial data (yr. ended 12/31/04): Assets,
$897,990 (M); gifts received, $50,000;
expenditures, $70,707; total giving, $64,057;
qualifying distributions, $64,057; giving activities
include $64,057 for 53 grants (high: $26,500; low:
$20).
Fields of interest: Health organizations,
association; Christian agencies & churches.
Limitations: Applications not accepted. Giving
primarily in MI. No grants to individuals.
Application information: Contributes only to
pre-selected organizations.
Trustee: Benjamin C. Maibach, Jr.
EIN: 386146651

1157
Anna Main Charitable Trust
c/o Victor R. Hayes and Gerald R. Gase
18263 E. 10 Mile Rd., Ste. A
Roseville, MI 48066-5805

Established in 1998 in MI.
Donor: Anna Main.
Grantmaker type: Independent foundation.
Financial data (yr. ended 9/30/05): Assets,
$7,518,339 (M); expenditures, $267,410; total
giving, $245,000; qualifying distributions,
$267,410; giving activities include $245,000 for 11
grants (high: $37,500; low: $5,000).
Purpose and activities: Giving primarily for
handicapped and disabled children.
Fields of interest: Animal welfare; Children,
services; Aging, centers/services; Developmentally
disabled, centers & services; Roman Catholic
agencies & churches; Disabilities, people with.
Limitations: Applications not accepted. Giving
primarily in KY, MI, and OH. No grants to individuals.
Application information: Contributes only to
pre-selected organizations.
Trustees: Gerald R. Gase; Victor R. Hayes.
EIN: 383336530
Selected grants: The following grants were reported
in 2004.
$37,500 to Our Mother of Good Counsel Church,
   Hazard, KY.
$37,500 to Saint Aloysius Parish, Detroit, MI.
$37,500 to Sisters of Mercy, Cincinnati, OH.
$30,000 to Healing Hands, Grand Rapids, MI. For
   handicapped children's programs.
$25,000 to Diocese of Montego Bay, Montego Bay,
   Jamaica. .
$17,500 to Christian Service Program Institute,
   Shreveport, LA.
$15,000 to Peace Place for Children, Inc.,
   Williamsburg, KY.
$10,000 to Michigan Anti-Cruelty Society, Detroit,
   MI.
$10,000 to Special Olympics Michigan, Mount
   Clemens, MI.
$5,000 to Fowler Center, Mayville, MI.

1158
The Maisel Foundation
c/o Geneva Maisel, Pres.
29260 Franklin Rd., Apt. 611
Southfield, MI 48034-1178

Established in 1993 in MI.
Donors: Emanuel N. Maisel Marital Trust; Geneva
Maisel.
Grantmaker type: Independent foundation.
Financial data (yr. ended 12/31/04): Assets,
$861,298 (M); expenditures, $95,113; total giving,
$75,000; qualifying distributions, $84,513; giving
activities include $75,000 for grants.
Purpose and activities: Giving primarily for Jewish
agencies and temples, human services, and
education.
Fields of interest: Education; Human services;
Children/youth, services; Jewish agencies &
temples.
Limitations: Applications not accepted. Giving
primarily in CA. No grants to individuals.
Application information: Contributes only to
pre-selected organizations.
Officers: Geneva Maisel, Pres.; Alan Maisel, V.P.;
Donald Maisel, V.P.; Jan Maisel, V.P.; Richard
Maisel, V.P.; Robin Maisel, V.P.; Marion August,
Secy.
EIN: 383133484

1159
W. E. Maldonado Charitable Foundation
Trust
4722 Huron Hills Dr.
Okemos, MI 48864

Established in 1989 in MI.
Donor: Wilford E. Maldonado.
Grantmaker type: Independent foundation.
Financial data (yr. ended 12/31/04): Assets,
$29,444 (M); gifts received, $5,000; expenditures,
$12,655; total giving, $11,480; qualifying
distributions, $11,480; giving activities include
$11,480 for grants.
Fields of interest: Media, television; Media, radio;
Higher education; Education, services; Animal
welfare; Animals/wildlife, preservation/protection;
Cancer; Human services; Salvation Army; Youth,
services; Federated giving programs.
Type of support: General/operating support; Grants
to individuals.
Limitations: Giving primarily in MI.
Application information:
   Initial approach: Letter
   Deadline(s): None
Trustee: Wilford E. Maldonado.
EIN: 386550486

1160
Malloure Family Foundation
c/o Donald H. Malloure
22630 N. Nottingham Dr.
Beverly Hills, MI 48025-3523

Donor: D.H. Malloure.
Grantmaker type: Independent foundation.
Financial data (yr. ended 9/30/04): Assets,
$17,238 (M); gifts received, $151,528;
expenditures, $145,700; total giving, $145,700;
qualifying distributions, $145,700; giving activities
include $145,700 for 25 grants (high: $50,000;
low: $50).
Purpose and activities: Giving primarily for higher
education, as well as for social services, hospitals
and health associations, and federated giving
programs.
Fields of interest: Higher education; Animal welfare;
Hospitals (general); Health organizations,
association; Human services; Family services;
Federated giving programs.
Limitations: Applications not accepted. Giving
primarily in MI. No grants to individuals.
Application information: Contributes only to
pre-selected organizations.
Officers and Directors:* Lucille A. Malloure,* Pres.;
D.H. Malloure,* Secy.; Susan L. Whitaker.
EIN: 383505870
Selected grants: The following grants were reported
in 2004.
$50,000 to Saint Joseph Mercy Hospital, Ann Arbor,
   MI.
$50,000 to University of Michigan, Ann Arbor, MI.
$16,000 to Angels Place, Southfield, MI.
$15,000 to United Way of Michigan, Lansing, MI.
$3,000 to Salvation Army, MI.
$2,000 to American Red Cross, MI.
$1,500 to Detroit Symphony Orchestra, Detroit, MI.
$1,500 to Edison Institute, Dearborn, MI.
$1,500 to Oakland Family Services, Pontiac, MI.
$500 to Humane Society, Michigan, Southfield, MI.

1161
Chester F. and Laura L. Mally Foundation
97 N. Cass Ave.
Pontiac, MI 48342-2003
Contact: C. Lane Mally

Established in 1986 in MI.
Grantmaker type: Independent foundation.
Financial data (yr. ended 8/31/05): Assets,
$308,956 (M); expenditures, $16,362; total giving,
$15,512; qualifying distributions, $15,512; giving
activities include $15,512 for grants.
Fields of interest: Human services.
Limitations: Giving limited to MI, with emphasis on
Pontiac.
Application information:
   Initial approach: Letter
   Deadline(s): None
Officer and Trustees:* C. Lane Mally,* Pres.;
Steven Jones; Mark A. Kaminski.
EIN: 382709513

1162
Fred J. Maloof Family Foundation
28525 Harper St.
St. Clair Shores, MI 48081
Contact: Fred J. Maloof, Pres.

Established in 2001 in MI.
Donor: Fred J. Maloof.
Grantmaker type: Independent foundation.
Financial data (yr. ended 12/31/05): Assets,
$845,519 (M); expenditures, $40,042; total giving,
$40,000; qualifying distributions, $40,000; giving
activities include $40,000 for grants.
Limitations: Applications not accepted. Giving
primarily in Detroit, MI. No grants to individuals.
Application information: Contributes only to
pre-selected organizations.

Officer: Fred J. Maloof, Pres.
EIN: 383618043

1163
Malpass Foundation
c/o William J. Lorne
301 Spring St., P.O. Box 1206
East Jordan, MI   49727-1206

Established in 1953 in MI.
Donors: Frederick F. Malpass; William E. Malpass†;
East Jordan Iron Works, Inc.
Grantmaker type: Independent foundation.
Financial data (yr. ended 10/31/05): Assets,
$575,735 (M); gifts received, $100,000;
expenditures, $20,156; total giving, $19,107;
qualifying distributions, $19,107; giving activities
include $19,107 for grants.
Purpose and activities: Support for community
development and education in the East Jordan
School District and city of East Jordan.
Fields of interest: Education; Community
development; Government/public administration.
Type of support: General/operating support;
Building/renovation; Equipment.
Limitations: Applications not accepted. Giving
primarily in Charlevoix County, MI, with a very strong
preference for the East Jordan School District. No
grants to individuals.
Application information: Contributes only to
pre-selected organizations.
Officers: Frederick F. Malpass, Pres.; Tracy K.
Malpass, V.P.; Tad M. Malpass, V.P.; William J.
Lorne, Secy.
EIN: 386048813

1164
Manat Foundation
26877 Northwestern Hwy., Ste. 413
Southfield, MI   48034

Established in 1986 in MI.
Donors: Manuel Charach; Natalie Charach; Jeffrey
Charach; Michael Berman; Sherrill Berman.
Grantmaker type: Independent foundation.
Financial data (yr. ended 7/31/05): Assets,
$4,341,598 (M); gifts received, $351,000;
expenditures, $471,245; total giving, $389,370;
qualifying distributions, $389,370; giving activities
include $389,370 for 39 grants (high: $250,000;
low: $250).
Purpose and activities: Giving primarily for health
associations, particularly a cancer institute, and to
Jewish organizations; funding also for education,
and children, youth and social services.
Fields of interest: Higher education; Hospitals
(general); Health organizations, association; Cancer
research; Human services; Children/youth,
services; Jewish federated giving programs; Jewish
agencies & temples.
Limitations: Applications not accepted. Giving
primarily in MI and NY. No grants to individuals.
Application information: Contributes only to
pre-selected organizations.
Managers: Manuel Charach; Natalie Charach.
Trustees: Michael Berman; Joel Shulman.
EIN: 382710511

1165
Mandelbaum Family Foundation
14610 Sherwood Ct.
Oak Park, MI   48237

Established in 1998 in MI.
Donor: Sheldon Mandelbaum.
Grantmaker type: Independent foundation.
Financial data (yr. ended 12/31/05): Assets,
$4,941 (M); gifts received, $9,090; expenditures,
$11,560; total giving, $11,540; qualifying
distributions, $11,540; giving activities include
$11,540 for grants.
Fields of interest: Jewish federated giving programs;
Jewish agencies & temples.
Limitations: Applications not accepted. No grants to
individuals.
Application information: Contributes only to
pre-selected organizations.
Officers: Sheldon Mandelbaum, Pres.; Mina D.
Mandelbaum, Secy.
Directors: Andrew J. Mandelbaum; David S.
Mandelbaum; Esther L. Mandelbaum; Michael A.
Mandelbaum.
EIN: 383451413

1166
James & Laurie Manhardt Foundation, Inc.
400 Monmouth Ave.
Spring Lake, NJ   07762

Established in 2000.
Donors: James Manhardt; Laurie Manhardt.
Grantmaker type: Independent foundation.
Financial data (yr. ended 12/31/05): Assets, $0
(M); expenditures, $125,541; total giving,
$122,740; qualifying distributions, $122,740;
giving activities include $122,740 for 11+ grants
(high: $46,000).
Fields of interest: Education; Roman Catholic
agencies & churches.
Limitations: Applications not accepted. Giving on a
national basis, with emphasis on FL, MI, NJ, and OH.
No grants to individuals.
Application information: Contributes only to
pre-selected organizations.
Officers: James H. Manhardt, Pres.; Laurie
Manhardt, Secy.
Advisor: Fr. John Gordon.
EIN: 223760415
Selected grants: The following grants were reported
in 2004.
$37,300 to Franciscan University of Steubenville,
   Steubenville, OH.
$16,000 to Renewal Ministries, Ann Arbor, MI.
$5,100 to Saint Helens Catholic Church, Vero
   Beach, FL.
$5,000 to Bishops Annual Appeal, Trenton, NJ.
$5,000 to Brotherhood of Hope, Somerville, MA.
$5,000 to Catholic Mens Fellowship, Cincinnati, OH.
$5,000 to Diocese of Camden, Camden, NJ.
$5,000 to Diocese of Palm Beach, Palm Beach
   Gardens, FL.
$2,600 to Legatus, Ann Arbor, MI.
$2,000 to Huron Valley Catholic School, Ypsilanti,
   MI.

1167
Manistee Catholic Central Schools
   Foundation
1500 Manistee Hwy.
Manistee, MI   49660

Grantmaker type: Independent foundation.
Financial data (yr. ended 9/30/05): Assets,
$515,663 (M); gifts received, $6,700;
expenditures, $33,990; total giving, $28,710;
qualifying distributions, $28,710; giving activities
include $28,710 for grants.
Purpose and activities: Support only for the
Manistee Catholic Central School, MI.
Fields of interest: Elementary/secondary
education.
Type of support: General/operating support.
Limitations: Applications not accepted. Giving
limited to Manistee, MI. No grants to individuals.
Application information: Contributes only to a
pre-selected organization specified in the trust
instrument.
Officers: Steven Ennis, Pres.; Phil Etheridge, V.P.;
Kay Fortier, Secy.; Bernie A. Pieczynski, Treas.
Directors: John Bartosz; Dean Etheridge; Tom
Kaminski; Dale Kowalkowski; and 9 additional
directors.
EIN: 382606921

1168
The Manix Family Foundation
1478 High Ct.
Bloomfield Hills, MI   48302-2328

Established in 2000 in MI.
Grantmaker type: Independent foundation.
Financial data (yr. ended 12/31/04): Assets,
$5,307 (M); expenditures, $1,245; total giving,
$1,200; qualifying distributions, $1,200; giving
activities include $1,200 for grants.
Limitations: Applications not accepted. No grants to
individuals.
Application information: Contributes only to
pre-selected organizations.
Officers: Ann Manix, Pres. and Treas.; Douglas W.
Manix, V.P.
Director: John T. Manix.
EIN: 383521766

1169
Katherine Mann Charitable Trust
c/o Citizens Bank Wealth Mgmt., N.A.
328 S. Saginaw St., M/C 002072
Flint, MI   48502

Established in MI.
Grantmaker type: Independent foundation.
Financial data (yr. ended 5/31/05): Assets,
$631,427 (M); expenditures, $19,055; total giving,
$10,752; qualifying distributions, $10,752; giving
activities include $10,752 for grants.
Purpose and activities: Support only for Easter Seal
Society, Salvation Army, and Visually Impaired
Center, Inc., Flint.
Fields of interest: Federated giving programs.
Type of support: General/operating support.
Limitations: Applications not accepted. Giving
limited to Flint, MI. No grants to individuals.
Application information: Contributes only to 3
pre-selected organizations specified in the trust
instrument.

Trustee: Citizens Bank.
EIN: 386653802

1170
Jessie Ellen Mann Trust
c/o Citizens Bank, Wealth Mgmt.
328 S. Saginaw St.
Flint, MI 48502-2401

Grantmaker type: Independent foundation.
Financial data (yr. ended 12/31/05): Assets, $186,251 (M); expenditures, $8,846; total giving, $2,051; qualifying distributions, $5,063; giving activities include $2,051 for grants.
Purpose and activities: Support only for Michigan Historical Society-Mann House, Lansing, MI.
Fields of interest: Historical activities.
Limitations: Applications not accepted. Giving limited to Lansing, MI. No grants to individuals.
Application information: Contributes only to a pre-selected organization.
Trustees: Albert Aldrich; Philip J. Curtis; Citizens Bank.
EIN: 386191020

1171
Alex and Marie Manoogian Foundation
21001 Van Born Rd.
Taylor, MI 48180 (313) 274-7400

Incorporated in 1942 in MI.
Donors: Alex Manoogian†; Marie Manoogian.
Grantmaker type: Independent foundation.
Financial data (yr. ended 12/31/05): Assets, $96,323,619 (M); expenditures, $1,394,474; total giving, $261,815; qualifying distributions, $7,089,038; giving activities include $261,815 for 8 grants (high: $80,000; low: $1,000).
Purpose and activities: Support primarily for an affiliated foundation, Armenian welfare funds and religious institutions, and higher and secondary education; support also for cultural programs and human services.
Fields of interest: Arts; Secondary school/education; Higher education; Human services; Minorities/immigrants, centers/services; Foundations (private grantmaking); Religion; Minorities.
Type of support: General/operating support; Continuing support; Building/renovation; Equipment; Endowments; Emergency funds; Seed money; Fellowships; Scholarship funds; Research; Matching/challenge support.
Limitations: Applications not accepted. Giving primarily in MI. No grants to individuals or for annual campaigns, deficit financing, land acquisition, publications, or conferences or seminars.
Application information: Contributes only to pre-selected organizations.
    Board meeting date(s): Twice per year
Officers and Directors:* Richard A. Manoogian,* Chair.; Eugene A. Gargaro, Jr.,* Secy.
EIN: 386089952

1172
Richard & Jane Manoogian Foundation
21001 Van Born Rd.
Taylor, MI 48180-1300

Established in 1984 in MI.

Donors: Alex Manoogian†; Marie Manoogian.
Grantmaker type: Independent foundation.
Financial data (yr. ended 6/30/05): Assets, $228,638,216 (M); expenditures, $10,319,837; total giving, $8,334,005; qualifying distributions, $38,213,301; giving activities include $8,334,005 for 48 grants (high: $6,079,140; low: $500; average: $5,000–$100,000).
Purpose and activities: Giving primarily for the arts, with emphasis on an art museum; funding also for education, health care, human services, community development, and federated giving programs.
Fields of interest: Museums; Performing arts; Performing arts, orchestra (symphony); Historic preservation/historical societies; Arts; Higher education; Education; Zoos/zoological societies; Health organizations, association; Human services; Children/youth, services; Community development; Foundations (private grantmaking); Foundations (community); Federated giving programs.
Type of support: General/operating support.
Limitations: Applications not accepted. Giving primarily in MI. No grants to individuals.
Application information: Contributes only to pre-selected organizations.
Officers: Richard A. Manoogian, Pres. and Treas.; Eugene A. Gargaro, Jr., Secy.
Director: Jane C. Manoogian.
EIN: 382531814
Selected grants: The following grants were reported in 2005.
$6,079,140 to Detroit Institute of Arts, Detroit, MI. For operating support.
$1,000,000 to College for Creative Studies, Detroit, MI. For operating support.
$225,000 to Detroit Symphony Orchestra, Detroit, MI. For operating support.
$125,000 to W T V S Detroit Educational Television, Detroit, MI. For operating support.
$50,000 to San Francisco Artspace, San Francisco, CA. For operating support.
$45,000 to University Cultural Center Association, Detroit, MI. 2 grants: $35,000 (For operating support), $10,000 (For operating support).
$25,000 to Detroit Artists Market, Detroit, MI. For operating support.
$12,500 to Jewish Ensemble Theater, West Bloomfield, MI. For operating support.
$10,000 to Crooked Tree Arts Council, Crooked Tree Arts Center, Petoskey, MI. For operating support.

1173
Manoogian Simone Foundation
(formerly Louise Manoogian Simone Foundation)
21001 Van Born Rd.
Taylor, MI 48180

Established in 1962 in MI.
Donors: Alex Manoogian†; Marie Manoogian; Masco Corp.
Grantmaker type: Independent foundation.
Financial data (yr. ended 12/31/05): Assets, $169,166,081 (M); expenditures, $8,308,856; total giving, $8,194,600; qualifying distributions, $8,196,211; giving activities include $8,194,600 for 25 grants (high: $4,814,000; low: $1,000; average: $10,000–$250,000).
Purpose and activities: Giving for Armenian organizations, including Armenian churches and cultural organizations, and education.
Fields of interest: Arts; Education; Orthodox Catholic agencies & churches.
International interests: Armenia.

Limitations: Applications not accepted. Giving primarily in CA, MI, NJ, and NY. No grants to individuals.
Application information: Contributes only to pre-selected organizations.
Officers and Directors:* Louise M. Simone,* Pres.; David Simone,* V.P.; Christine M. Simone, Secy.-Treas.; Mark Simone.
EIN: 381799107
Selected grants: The following grants were reported in 2004.
$1,501,000 to Armenian Apostolic Society, Southfield, MI. For operating support.
$416,000 to American University of Armenia, Oakland, CA. For operating support.
$50,000 to Armenian Assembly of America, DC. For operating support and Armenian Tree Project.
$15,000 to Gomidas Institute, Princeton, NJ. For operating support.
$10,000 to MSAADA, Minneapolis, MN. For operating support.

1174
Manthei Charitable Trust
3996 U.S. 31 S.
Petoskey, MI 49770-9801

Established in 1960.
Donors: Theodore W. Manthei; Mary Manthei; Dan Manthei; Tim Manthei.
Grantmaker type: Independent foundation.
Financial data (yr. ended 12/31/04): Assets, $1,546,709 (M); gifts received, $309,787; expenditures, $351,443; total giving, $347,348; qualifying distributions, $347,348; giving activities include $347,348 for 17+ grants (high: $101,000).
Purpose and activities: Support for Christian agencies and churches.
Fields of interest: Education; Christian agencies & churches.
Type of support: General/operating support.
Limitations: Applications not accepted. Giving on a national basis. No grants to individuals.
Application information: Contributes only to pre-selected organizations.
Trustees: Daniel R. Manthei; Mark Manthei; Thomas Manthei.
EIN: 381204856

1175
Maranatha Foundation, Inc.
1500 E. Maple Rd.
Milford, MI 48381

Established about 1965 in MI.
Donors: JIC Electric, Inc.; Members of the Pew family.
Grantmaker type: Independent foundation.
Financial data (yr. ended 12/31/05): Assets, $1,455,886 (M); expenditures, $323,696; total giving, $169,484; qualifying distributions, $169,484; giving activities include $169,484 for 26 grants (high: $40,000; low: $384).
Purpose and activities: Giving primarily for family services.
Fields of interest: Performing arts, orchestra (symphony); Education; Human services; Family services; Christian agencies & churches.
Limitations: Applications not accepted. No grants to individuals.

Application information: Contributes only to pre-selected organizations.
Officers: Ronald K. Pew, Pres. and Treas.; Margaret E. Pew, V.P. and Secy.
EIN: 386108739
Selected grants: The following grants were reported in 2003.
$80,000 to Alliance Defense Fund, Scottsdale, AZ. For general support.
$16,000 to Prison Fellowship Ministries, DC. For general support.
$6,000 to Focus on the Family, Colorado Springs, CO. For general support.
$5,000 to Philharmonic Center for the Arts, Naples, FL. For general support.
$5,000 to Protected Harbor, Bonita Springs, FL. For general support.
$3,500 to Insight for Living, Anaheim, CA. For general support.
$2,000 to Eagle Forum Education and Legal Defense Fund, Alton, IL. For general support.
$1,500 to Right to Life Committee Educational Trust Fund, National, DC. For general support.
$1,000 to American Family Association, Tupelo, MS. For general support.
$1,000 to Heritage Foundation, DC. For general support.

1176
Oliver Dewey Marcks Foundation
645 Griswold St., Ste. 3180
Detroit, MI 48226-4250
Contact: John M. Chase, Jr., Pres.

Established in 1960.
Donors: Eula D. Marcks†; Oliver Dewey Marcks†.
Grantmaker type: Independent foundation.
Financial data (yr. ended 12/31/04): Assets, $12,818,965 (M); expenditures, $582,436; total giving, $495,000; qualifying distributions, $553,742; giving activities include $495,000 for 29 grants (high: $150,000; low: $5,000).
Fields of interest: Arts; Education; Environment, natural resources; Animal welfare.
Type of support: General/operating support; Program development.
Limitations: Giving limited to Detroit, MI, and surrounding communities. No grants to individuals.
Publications: Application guidelines.
Application information: Application form required.
  Initial approach: Letter, including a 1-page summary
  Copies of proposal: 4
  Board meeting date(s): May, July and Oct.
Officers and Board Members:* John M. Chase, Jr.,* Pres.; Marion Valentine,* Secy.; Michael J. Predhomme,* Treas.
EIN: 386081311

1177
Edward & Helen Mardigian Foundation
c/o Comerica Bank
P.O. Box 75000, MC 3302
Detroit, MI 48275-3302 (248) 647-0077
Contact: Edward Mardigian, Jr.
Application address: 39400 N. Woodward Ave., Bloomfield Hills, MI 48304

Incorporated in 1955 in MI.
Donors: Edward S. Mardigian†; Helen Mardigian; Arman Mardigian†.

Grantmaker type: Independent foundation.
Financial data (yr. ended 12/31/05): Assets, $21,699,559 (M); gifts received, $350,000; expenditures, $1,045,671; total giving, $976,650; qualifying distributions, $1,013,056; giving activities include $976,650 for 48 grants (high: $200,000; low: $100).
Purpose and activities: Giving primarily for Armenian organizations and churches in the U.S.; funding also for children, youth and social services, and health associations.
Fields of interest: Arts; Higher education; Zoos/zoological societies; Health organizations, association; Human services; Children/youth, services; Christian agencies & churches; Minorities.
Limitations: Giving in the U.S., primarily in MI. No grants to individuals.
Application information:
  Initial approach: Letter
  Deadline(s): None
Officers: Helen Mardigian, Pres. and Secy.; Edward S. Mardigian, V.P. and Treas.
Director: Robert D. Mardigian.
EIN: 386048886

1178
Mariel Foundation
c/o U.S. Bank, N.A.
P.O. Box 1118, CN-OH-WIOX
Cincinnati, OH 45201

Established in 1997 in MI.
Donors: Carolyn T. Hoagland; James H. Hoagland; John T. Hoagland; Nancy L. Hoagland; Anne H. Magoun.
Grantmaker type: Independent foundation.
Financial data (yr. ended 9/30/05): Assets, $2,968,292 (M); expenditures, $163,592; total giving, $128,554; qualifying distributions, $138,030; giving activities include $128,554 for 38 grants (high: $18,000; low: $250).
Purpose and activities: Giving for the fine and performing arts, education, and youth services.
Fields of interest: Museums; Performing arts; Higher education; Youth development; Children/youth, services.
Limitations: Applications not accepted. Giving primarily in MI. No grants to individuals.
Application information: Contributes only to pre-selected organizations.
Directors: Carolyn T. Hoagland; James H. Hoagland; John H. Hoagland; John T. Hoagland; Nancy L. Hoagland; Anne H. Magoun.
Trustee: U.S. Bank, N.A.
EIN: 383334050
Selected grants: The following grants were reported in 2003.
$11,000 to Leelanau Conservancy, Leland, MI.
$10,779 to Vajradhatu, Boulder, CO.
$10,000 to Interlochen Center for the Arts, Interlochen, MI.
$9,000 to Foothill Theater Company, Nevada City, CA.
$6,014 to Glen Arbor Art Association, Glen Arbor, MI.
$6,000 to Arts Council of Greater Lansing, Lansing, MI.
$5,250 to Inland Seas Education Association, Suttons Bay, MI.
$5,000 to Childrens Literacy Initiative, Philadelphia, PA.
$5,000 to Northern California Center for the Arts, Grass Valley, CA.

$3,200 to Imaginarium of Nevada County, CA.

1179
David and Stacy Markel Charitable Foundation
3060 Dover Pl.
Ann Arbor, MI 48104

Established in 2004 in MI.
Donors: David Markel; Stacy Markel.
Grantmaker type: Independent foundation.
Financial data (yr. ended 12/31/04): Assets, $81,108 (M); gifts received, $80,453; expenditures, $0; total giving, $0; qualifying distributions, $0.
Limitations: Applications not accepted. No grants to individuals.
Application information: Contributes only to pre-selected organizations.
Officers: David Markel, Pres.; Stacy Markel, V.P.
EIN: 202000896

1180
Marsh Trust for Cryobiological Research & Development
c/o Jane Devine
1705 E. Main Ave.
Morgan Hill, CA 95037
Contact: Earle M. Marsh, Tr.

Established in 1994 in CA.
Donor: Richard P. Marsh†.
Grantmaker type: Independent foundation.
Financial data (yr. ended 12/31/04): Assets, $643,193 (M); expenditures, $79,422; total giving, $20,000; qualifying distributions, $20,000; giving activities include $20,000 for grants.
Purpose and activities: Giving only to the field of cryobiological research and development.
Fields of interest: Medical research.
Limitations: Giving primarily in CA and MI. No grants to individuals.
Application information:
  Initial approach: Letter
  Deadline(s): None
Trustee: Earle M. Marsh.
EIN: 686103786

1181
Edward H. & Diana H. Marsilje Charitable Foundation
P.O. Box 2308
Holland, MI 49422-2308
Contact: Edward H. Marsilje, Pres.
FAX: (616) 396-7859;
E-mail: marsilje@macatawa.org

Established in 1989 in MI.
Donors: Diana H. Marsilje; Edward H. Marsilje; The Title Office, Inc.
Grantmaker type: Independent foundation.
Financial data (yr. ended 12/31/04): Assets, $3,579,358 (M); gifts received, $157,245; expenditures, $194,912; total giving, $169,250; qualifying distributions, $169,250; giving activities include $169,250 for grants.
Purpose and activities: Giving for the arts, higher education and religion.
Fields of interest: Arts; Higher education; Christian agencies & churches.

Type of support: General/operating support; Annual campaigns; Capital campaigns; Endowments.
Limitations: Applications not accepted. Giving limited to residents of MI. No grants to individuals.
Application information: Contributes only to pre-selected organizations.
Board meeting date(s): Annually in Dec.
Officer and Trustees:* Edward H. Marsilje,* Pres.; Diana H. Marsilje.
Number of staff: None.
EIN: 382889205

1182
Marstrand Foundation
755 W. Big Beaver Rd., Ste. 2300
Troy, MI 48084
Contact: Craig G. Gombolay, Secy.-Treas.

Established in 1966 in MI.
Grantmaker type: Independent foundation.
Financial data (yr. ended 12/31/04): Assets, $623,641 (M); expenditures, $36,218; total giving, $32,000; qualifying distributions, $32,000; giving activities include $32,000 for grants.
Fields of interest: Arts, folk arts; Arts education; Museums; Performing arts, music; Higher education; Animals/wildlife; Housing/shelter, development; American Red Cross.
Limitations: Applications not accepted. Giving primarily in NY. No grants to individuals.
Application information: Contributes only to pre-selected organizations.
Officers: Siri von Reis, Vice-Chair.; Craig G. Gombolay, Secy.-Treas.
EIN: 386121574

1183
Donald J. & Catherine D. Martin Benefit Fund f/b/o Augustinian Scholarship Fund
25901 W. Ten Mile Rd., Ste. 128
Southfield, MI 48034

Established in 2004 in MI.
Donor: Catherine D. Martin Trust.
Grantmaker type: Independent foundation.
Financial data (yr. ended 12/31/05): Assets, $290,222 (M); expenditures, $12,046; total giving, $9,235; qualifying distributions, $9,235; giving activities include $9,235 for grants.
Purpose and activities: Support only for the Augustinian Scholarship Fund, Chula Vista.
Fields of interest: Scholarships/financial aid.
Type of support: Scholarship funds.
Limitations: Applications not accepted. Giving limited to Chula Vista, CA. No grants for inidividuals.
Application information: Contributes only to a pre-selected organization.
Trustees: Arthur J. Balamucki; Frances Martin Hay.
EIN: 347177766

1184
Donald J. & Catherine D. Martin Benefit Fund f/b/o Real Life Children's Ranch
25901 W. Ten Mile Rd., Ste. 128
Southfield, MI 48034

Established in 2004 in MI.
Donor: Catherine D. Martin Trust.
Grantmaker type: Independent foundation.

Financial data (yr. ended 12/31/05): Assets, $499,344 (M); expenditures, $21,397; total giving, $16,520; qualifying distributions, $16,520; giving activities include $16,520 for grants.
Purpose and activities: Support only for the Real Life Children's Ranch, Okeechobee, FL.
Fields of interest: Residential/custodial care.
Type of support: General/operating support.
Limitations: Applications not accepted. Giving limited to Okeechobee, FL. No grants to individuals.
Application information: Contributes only to a pre-selected organization.
Trustees: Arthur J. Balamucki; Frances Martin Hay.
EIN: 347177767

1185
W. Ross Martin Family Foundation, Inc.
5180 Zeeb Rd.
Dexter, MI 48130

Established in 1999 in MI.
Donor: W. Ross Martin.
Grantmaker type: Independent foundation.
Financial data (yr. ended 12/31/05): Assets, $192,417 (M); expenditures, $17,074; total giving, $16,800; qualifying distributions, $16,800; giving activities include $16,800 for grants.
Fields of interest: Youth, services.
Limitations: Applications not accepted. Giving primarily in CO and MI. No grants to individuals.
Application information: Contributes only to pre-selected organizations.
Officers: W. Ross Martin, Pres. and V.P.; Patricia J. Martin, Secy.-Treas.
EIN: 383505450

1186
The Martin Family Foundation
c/o Sally A. Martin
115 Depot St.
Ann Arbor, MI 48104

Established in 1998 in MI.
Donor: William C. Martin.
Grantmaker type: Independent foundation.
Financial data (yr. ended 12/31/05): Assets, $758,008 (M); expenditures, $49,341; total giving, $46,140; qualifying distributions, $48,085; giving activities include $46,140 for 23 grants (high: $10,000; low: $500).
Purpose and activities: Giving primarily to colleges and universities for programs and scholarship funds and for environmental conservation organizations.
Fields of interest: Higher education; Environment, natural resources.
Type of support: Capital campaigns; Scholarship funds.
Limitations: Applications not accepted. Giving limited to MI, primarily in Ann Arbor, Keweenaw County, and the upper Peninsula area. No grants to individuals.
Application information: Contributes only to pre-selected organizations.
Officers and Board Members:* Sally A. Martin,* Pres.; William C. Martin,* V.P. and Secy.-Treas.
EIN: 383340278

1187
Jason Mark Martin TCB Foundation
5069 Did Dr.
Cedar Springs, MI 49319   (616) 696-8313

Established in 2002 in MI.
Donor: Judy A. Cristensen.
Grantmaker type: Independent foundation.
Financial data (yr. ended 12/31/05): Assets, $61,266 (M); gifts received, $100; expenditures, $3,486; total giving, $3,000; qualifying distributions, $3,000; giving activities include $3,000 for grants.
Purpose and activities: Support for Milford High School, Michigan, for its scholarship fund.
Fields of interest: Secondary school/education; Scholarships/financial aid.
Type of support: Scholarship funds.
Limitations: Applications not accepted. Giving limited to Milford, MI.
Application information: Contributes only to a pre-selected organization.
Officer: Judy Christensen, Pres.
EIN: 383576219

1188
Edward G. Martin Trust
c/o Wells Fargo Bank Nevada, N.A.
P.O. Box 95021
Henderson, NV 89009

Established in 1996 in AZ & NV.
Grantmaker type: Independent foundation.
Financial data (yr. ended 12/31/04): Assets, $132,163 (M); expenditures, $6,745; total giving, $4,325; qualifying distributions, $5,309; giving activities include $4,325 for grants.
Purpose and activities: Support only for the Battle Creek Symphony Orchestra, MI.
Fields of interest: Performing arts, orchestra (symphony).
Limitations: Applications not accepted. Giving limited to Battle Creek, MI. No grants to individuals.
Application information: Contributes only to a pre-selected organization.
Trustee: Wells Fargo Bank Nevada, N.A.
EIN: 866118597

1189
Vernon A. Martin Trust
c/o Citizens Bank Wealth Mgmt., N.A.
328 S. Saginaw St., M/C 002072
Flint, MI 48502

Established in 2000 in MI.
Grantmaker type: Independent foundation.
Financial data (yr. ended 12/31/05): Assets, $243,724 (M); expenditures, $14,164; total giving, $11,584; qualifying distributions, $11,584; giving activities include $11,584 for grants.
Fields of interest: Higher education; Christian agencies & churches.
Limitations: Applications not accepted. Giving primarily in Flint, MI. No grants to individuals.
Application information: Contributes only to pre-selected organizations.
Trustee: Citizens Bank.
EIN: 386194394

1190
Gertrude E. Martin Trust
c/o Comerica Bank
P.O. Box 75000
Detroit, MI 48275
Application address: c/o Scholarship Comm., Santa
Cruz High School, 415 Walnut Ave., Santa Cruz, CA
95060, tel.: (408) 429-3977

Established in CA.
Grantmaker type: Independent foundation.
Financial data (yr. ended 12/31/05): Assets,
$126,276 (M); expenditures, $6,413; total giving,
$4,000; qualifying distributions, $4,000; giving
activities include $4,000 for grants.
Purpose and activities: Scholarship awards to
graduates of Santa Cruz High School, CA.
Type of support: Scholarships—to individuals.
Limitations: Applications not accepted. Giving
limited to residents of Santa Cruz, CA.
Application information: Unsolicited requests for
funds not accepted.
Trustee: Comerica Bank.
EIN: 946113526

1191
William and Carol Martz Foundation
6340 Drakeshire Ln.
West Bloomfield, MI 48322-2050

Established in 2003 in MI.
Donors: Carol Martz; William Martz.
Grantmaker type: Independent foundation.
Financial data (yr. ended 12/31/04): Assets,
$623,249 (M); gifts received, $30,000;
expenditures, $21,817; total giving, $17,000;
qualifying distributions, $17,000; giving activities
include $17,000 for grants.
Limitations: Applications not accepted. No grants to
individuals.
Application information: Contributes only to
pre-selected organizations.
Officers and Directors: * William Martz,* Pres. and
Treas.; Carol Martz,* Secy.; Elizabeth Martz.
EIN: 200464172

1192
The Marzke Family Foundation
1207 Broad St.
St. Joseph, MI 49085

Established in 2001 in MI.
Donors: Nancy Ann Marzke; L. Richard Marzke;
Christopher J. Marzke; Craig S. Marzke; Kurt R.
Marzke; Kevin W. Marzke; Lynn Ann
Marzke-Schmidt.
Grantmaker type: Independent foundation.
Financial data (yr. ended 12/31/05): Assets,
$431,565 (M); gifts received, $190,823;
expenditures, $67,192; total giving, $65,850;
qualifying distributions, $65,850; giving activities
include $65,850 for grants.
Purpose and activities: Giving primarily for Catholic
schools and other organizations.
Fields of interest: Education; Health care; Human
services; Protestant agencies & churches; Roman
Catholic agencies & churches.
Type of support: General/operating support;
Fellowships; Scholarship funds.
Limitations: Applications not accepted. Giving
primarily in MI. No grants to individuals.

Application information: Contributes only to
pre-selected organizations.
Officers: L. Richard Marzke, Pres.; Christopher J.
Marzke, V.P.; Craig S. Marzke, V.P.; Kevin W.
Marzke, V.P.; Kurt R. Marzke, V.P.; Lynn Ann
Marzke-Schmidt, V.P.; Nancy Ann Marzke,
Secy.-Treas.
EIN: 383584852

1193
Peter Mason Charitable Foundation
c/o Peter Mason, Pres.
P.O. Box 2738
Grand Rapids, MI 49501-2738

Established in 1998 in MI.
Donor: Peter Mason.
Grantmaker type: Independent foundation.
Financial data (yr. ended 12/31/05): Assets,
$28,083 (M); expenditures, $4,420; total giving,
$3,500; qualifying distributions, $3,500; giving
activities include $3,500 for grants.
Limitations: Applications not accepted. Giving
limited to Grand Rapids, MI. No grants to individuals.
Application information: Contributes only to
pre-selected organizations.
Officer: Peter Mason, Pres.
EIN: 383454017

1194
Marilyn Mason Foundation
2108 Scottwood Ave.
Ann Arbor, MI 48104-4511

Established in 1996 in MI.
Donor: Marilyn Mason.
Grantmaker type: Independent foundation.
Financial data (yr. ended 12/31/05): Assets,
$169,260 (M); expenditures, $4,346; total giving,
$0; qualifying distributions, $0.
Purpose and activities: Giving primarily to a center
for church music.
Type of support: General/operating support.
Limitations: Applications not accepted. Giving
limited to Ann Arbor, MI. No grants to individuals.
Application information: Contributes only to
pre-selected organizations.
Directors: Edward A. Brown; M. Christian Brown;
Marilyn Mason.
EIN: 383317749

1195
The Mast Foundation
2095 72nd St. S.W.
Byron Center, MI 49315

Established in 1998 in MI.
Donor: Henry Mast, Jr.
Grantmaker type: Independent foundation.
Financial data (yr. ended 12/31/05): Assets,
$55,599 (M); gifts received, $130,423;
expenditures, $113,713; total giving, $113,563;
qualifying distributions, $113,563; giving activities
include $113,563 for grants.
Fields of interest: Christian agencies & churches.
Limitations: Applications not accepted. Giving
primarily in MI. No grants to individuals.
Application information: Contributes only to
pre-selected organizations.
Officer: Henry Mast, Jr., Mgr.

Trustee: Constance M. Mast.
EIN: 383443209

1196
The Marshall Mathers Foundation
c/o Howard Hertz
1760 S. Telegraph Rd., Ste. 300
Bloomfield Hills, MI 48302

Established in 2002 in MI.
Donor: Marshall B. Mathers III.
Grantmaker type: Independent foundation.
Financial data (yr. ended 12/31/04): Assets,
$2,058 (M); gifts received, $120,500;
expenditures, $120,622; total giving, $120,500;
qualifying distributions, $120,500; giving activities
include $120,500 for 14 grants (high: $25,000;
low: $500).
Fields of interest: Food services; Youth
development; Human services.
Limitations: Giving limited to MI, with emphasis on
Detroit.
Application information:
 Initial approach: Letter
 Deadline(s): None
Officers: Marshall B. Mathers III, Pres.; Paul
Rosenberg, V.P.; Howard Hertz, Secy.; Bruce
Seckendorf, Treas.
EIN: 010706738

1197
Rose & K. V. Mathew Foundation
P.O. Box 320379
Flint, MI 48532

Established in 1994 in MI.
Donors: K.V. Mathew; Rosamma S. Nidhiry.
Grantmaker type: Independent foundation.
Financial data (yr. ended 12/31/05): Assets,
$79,130 (M); gifts received, $15,000;
expenditures, $11,425; total giving, $412;
qualifying distributions, $412; giving activities
include $412 for grants.
Fields of interest: Roman Catholic agencies &
churches.
Limitations: Applications not accepted. No grants to
individuals.
Application information: Contributes only to
pre-selected organizations.
Officers: K.V. Mathew, Pres.; Rosamma S. Nidhiry,
Secy.-Treas.
EIN: 383210681

1198
Lorraine D. Matson Trust
c/o Comerica Bank
P.O. Box 75000
Detroit, MI 48275
Application addresses: c/o Avondale High School,
Attn.: Principal, 2800 Waukegan St., Auburn Hills,
MI 48326, or c/o Auburn Hills Presbyterian Church,
3456 Primary St., Auburn Hills, MI 48236

Established in MI.
Grantmaker type: Independent foundation.
Financial data (yr. ended 11/30/05): Assets,
$211,562 (M); expenditures, $11,160; total giving,
$6,900; qualifying distributions, $6,900; giving
activities include $6,900 for grants.

Purpose and activities: Scholarships awards to graduates of Avondale High School or members of the Auburn Hills Presbyterian Church, MI.
Fields of interest: Higher education.
Type of support: Scholarships—to individuals.
Limitations: Giving limited to residents of Auburn Hills, MI.
Application information: Application form required.
 Deadline(s): Jan. 1 to Apr. 1
Advisory Committee: Carol Baldwin; Cindy Edwards; Jeanne Lang; Jerry Sadowski.
Trustee: Comerica Bank.
EIN: 386523330

1199
The Matthews Family Foundation
28001 Hickory Dr.
Farmington Hills, MI 48331

Established in MI.
Donor: Robert E. Matthews.
Grantmaker type: Independent foundation.
Financial data (yr. ended 12/31/05): Assets, $46,022 (M); gifts received, $66,000; expenditures, $57,485; total giving, $40,000; qualifying distributions, $78,568; giving activities include $40,000 for grants.
Limitations: Applications not accepted. No grants to individuals.
Application information: Contributes only to pre-selected organizations.
Officer and Director:* Robert E. Matthews,* Pres.
EIN: 383527757

1200
Joseph and Gloria Matthews Private Foundation
28001 Hickory Dr.
Farmington Hills, MI 48331-2952

Established in 2000 in MI.
Donor: Robert E. Matthews.
Grantmaker type: Independent foundation.
Financial data (yr. ended 12/31/04): Assets, $35,230 (M); gifts received, $89,570; expenditures, $55,812; total giving, $40,000; qualifying distributions, $93,128; giving activities include $40,000 for 1 grant.
Purpose and activities: Giving to the Jewish Federation of Metropolitan Detroit.
Fields of interest: Jewish federated giving programs.
Limitations: Applications not accepted. Giving limited to Bloomfield Hills, MI. No grants to individuals.
Application information: Contributes only to pre-selected organizations.
Officer and Director:* Robert E. Matthews,* Pres.
EIN: 383257757

1201
Mauser Harmony with Nature Foundation, Inc.
9911 Fairfield St.
Livonia, MI 48150-2707
Contact: William T. Cook, Pres.

Established in 1999 in MI.
Grantmaker type: Independent foundation.
Financial data (yr. ended 12/31/04): Assets, $1,144,434 (M); gifts received, $65; expenditures,

$86,676; total giving, $27,350; qualifying distributions, $72,201; giving activities include $27,350 for grants.
Purpose and activities: Giving primarily for genetic research and wildlife; funding also for higher education.
Fields of interest: Higher education; Animals/wildlife; Health organizations, association; Genetics/birth defects research.
Limitations: Giving primarily in MI.
Officers: William T. Cook, Pres.; Rose M. Cook, Secy.
EIN: 383408710

1202
Maust Foundation
c/o Joseph J. Maust
7564 Pigeon Rd.
Pigeon, MI 48755

Established in 1991 in MI.
Donors: Joseph Maust; Joseph J. Maust.
Grantmaker type: Independent foundation.
Financial data (yr. ended 9/30/05): Assets, $232,006 (M); gifts received, $9,750; expenditures, $15,052; total giving, $14,521; qualifying distributions, $14,521; giving activities include $14,521 for grants.
Fields of interest: Religion.
Limitations: Applications not accepted. Giving primarily in MI. No grants to individuals.
Application information: Contributes only to pre-selected organizations.
Officers: Joseph J. Maust, Pres.; Joseph Maust, Secy.-Treas.
EIN: 383022006

1203
Richard H. May Charitable Trust
P.O. Box 1134
Bloomfield Hills, MI 48303-1134

Established in 1986 in MI.
Donor: Richard H. May.
Grantmaker type: Independent foundation.
Financial data (yr. ended 12/31/05): Assets, $708 (M); gifts received, $4,000; expenditures, $4,535; total giving, $4,350; qualifying distributions, $4,350; giving activities include $4,350 for grants.
Fields of interest: Education; Human services; Federated giving programs.
Limitations: Applications not accepted. Giving primarily in MI. No grants to individuals.
Application information: Contributes only to pre-selected organizations.
Trustees: Mary E. May; Richard H. May.
EIN: 382628862

1204
May Family Foundation
600 Columbia Ctr.
201 W. Big Beaver Rd.
Troy, MI 48084

Established in 1990 in MI.
Donor: Alan A. May.
Grantmaker type: Independent foundation.
Financial data (yr. ended 12/31/05): Assets, $34,771 (M); gifts received, $12,000; expenditures, $25,621; total giving, $21,850;

qualifying distributions, $21,850; giving activities include $21,850 for grants.
Fields of interest: Arts, association; Alzheimer's disease; Jewish federated giving programs; Jewish agencies & temples.
Limitations: Applications not accepted. Giving primarily in MI. No grants to individuals.
Application information: Contributes only to pre-selected organizations.
Officers: Elizabeth May, Secy.; Alan A. May, Mgr.
EIN: 382928784

1205
The Edwin J. May Foundation
615 Abbey St.
Birmingham, MI 48009-5620
Contact: Brian May, Tr.

Established in 1994 in FL.
Donors: Daniel May Clut; Dianne L. May.
Grantmaker type: Independent foundation.
Financial data (yr. ended 12/31/05): Assets, $1,592,831 (M); gifts received, $226,628; expenditures, $179,766; total giving, $170,000; qualifying distributions, $170,921; giving activities include $170,000 for 3 grants (high: $100,000; low: $30,000).
Purpose and activities: Giving primarily for a relief organization for Haiti and the American Red Cross.
Fields of interest: American Red Cross; International relief; Christian agencies & churches.
International interests: Haiti.
Limitations: Giving to U.S.-based organizations, with some emphasis on Washington, DC, and Naples, FL. No grants to individuals.
Application information:
 Deadline(s): None
Trustees: Brian S. May; Daniel May; Dianne L. May.
EIN: 650501566

1206
Doeren Mayhew Foundation
755 W. Big Beaver Rd., Ste. 2300
Troy, MI 48084-0231
Contact: Joseph C. DeGennaro, V.P.

Grantmaker type: Independent foundation.
Financial data (yr. ended 12/31/05): Assets, $17,637 (M); expenditures, $23; total giving, $0; qualifying distributions, $0.
Type of support: Scholarships—to individuals.
Limitations: Giving primarily in MI.
Application information: Application form not required.
 Deadline(s): None
Officers: Mark Crawford, Pres.; Joseph C. DeGennaro, V.P.; Michael J. Berry, Secy.-Treas.
EIN: 386147314

1207
Robert J. McBain Foundation
654 Crofton St. S.E.
Grand Rapids, MI 49507-1819
Contact: Robert J. McBain, Pres.

Established in MI.
Donor: Robert J. McBain†.
Grantmaker type: Independent foundation.
Financial data (yr. ended 12/31/05): Assets, $35,233 (M); expenditures, $4,347; total giving,

$1,800; qualifying distributions, $4,275; giving activities include $1,800 for 12 grants (high: $500; low: $100).
Fields of interest: Education; Human services.
Limitations: Giving primarily in Grand Rapids, MI. No grants to individuals.
Application information: Application form not required.
  Initial approach: Proposal
  Deadline(s): None
Officer and Trustee:* Robert J. McBain,* Pres. and Treas.
EIN: 237114594

1208
McBrearty Associates
1139 Park Place Ct.
Bloomfield, MI 48302

Donor: John H. McBrearty.
Grantmaker type: Independent foundation.
Financial data (yr. ended 12/31/05): Assets, $69,470 (M); gifts received, $15,295; expenditures, $36,438; total giving, $36,400; qualifying distributions, $36,419; giving activities include $36,400 for grants.
Limitations: Applications not accepted. Giving on a national basis, with emphasis on MI. No grants to individuals.
Application information: Contributes only to pre-selected organizations.
Officers: John H. McBrearty, Pres.; Kathleen Wild, V.P. and Secy.; Susan Tomba, V.P. and Treas.; John D. McBrearty, V.P.; Marianne McBrearty, V.P.
EIN: 383329902

1209
Donald C. and Helene Marienthal McCabe Charitable Foundation
c/o National City Bank
171 Monroe Ave. N.W.
Grand Rapids, MI 49503
Contact: Scott E. Campbell

Established in 1994 in MI.
Grantmaker type: Independent foundation.
Financial data (yr. ended 12/31/05): Assets, $905,055 (M); expenditures, $77,963; total giving, $67,976; qualifying distributions, $67,976; giving activities include $67,976 for grants.
Purpose and activities: Scholarship awards to students of Delta Community College, Saginaw Valley State University, MI, with preference to needy Jewish and Presbyterian students in Bay, Saginaw, and Midland counties, Michigan. Annual support also for a public library system.
Fields of interest: Libraries (public); Protestant agencies & churches; Jewish agencies & temples.
Type of support: Scholarships—to individuals.
Limitations: Giving for the benefit of MI organizations and residents, with emphasis on Bay, Saginaw, and Midland counties.
Application information: Application form required.
  Deadline(s): Apr. 30
Trustee: National City Bank.
EIN: 383184550

1210
Helen McCalla Foundation
c/o KeyBank N.A.
800 Superior Ave., 4th Fl.
Cleveland, OH 44114
Contact: Bill Dunlap, Admin.

Established in 1995 in MI.
Donor: Helen McCalla†.
Grantmaker type: Independent foundation.
Financial data (yr. ended 12/31/05): Assets, $2,281,400 (M); expenditures, $134,921; total giving, $105,930; qualifying distributions, $114,294; giving activities include $105,930 for grants.
Purpose and activities: Giving to organizations that provide assistance to the elderly or handicapped children.
Fields of interest: Hospitals (general); Aging, centers/services.
Limitations: Giving limited to the Washtenaw County, MI, area. No grants to individuals.
Application information:
  Initial approach: Letter
  Deadline(s): Mar. 31
Trustee: KeyBank N.A.
EIN: 383195451

1211
The W. B. McCardell Family Foundation
355 Olivewood Ct.
Rochester, MI 48306
Contact: Bradley W. McCardell, Pres.

Established in 1994 in MI.
Donor: Willard B. McCardell, Jr.
Grantmaker type: Independent foundation.
Financial data (yr. ended 12/31/05): Assets, $1,008,621 (M); expenditures, $127,180; total giving, $117,000; qualifying distributions, $118,413; giving activities include $117,000 for 9 grants (high: $102,500; low: $500).
Purpose and activities: Giving in areas that promote spiritual values and support familiy independence.
Fields of interest: Physical therapy; Athletics/sports, equestrianism; Disabilities, people with.
Type of support: Endowments; General/operating support.
Limitations: Giving primarily in MI.
Application information: Accepts CMF Common Grant Application Form. Application form required.
  Initial approach: Letter
  Deadline(s): Oct. 1
Officers: Willard B. McCardell, Jr., Chair.; Sheran M. McCardell, Vice-Chair.; Bradley W. McCardell, Pres.; Michael D. Mulcahy, Secy.; Tracy L. McCardell, Treas.
Trustees: Scott I. Andrews; Tina M. Andrews; Ann-Marie McCardell; Kenneth W. McCardell; Steven R. McCardell.
EIN: 383211106
Selected grants: The following grants were reported in 2004.
$350,000 to Oak Arbor Church of the New Jerusalem, Rochester, MI. For unrestricted support.
$103,500 to Banbury Cross Therapeutic Equestrian Center, Metamora, MI. For unrestricted support.
$14,500 to General Church of the New Jerusalem, Bryn Athyn, PA. 4 grants: $3,500, $3,500, $3,500, $4,000
$2,000 to Focus on the Family, Colorado Springs, CO. For unrestricted support.

$1,500 to Crisis Pregnancy Center of Rochester, Rochester, MI. For unrestricted support.
$1,000 to HAVEN (Help Against Violent Encounters Now), Pontiac, MI. For unrestricted support.
$1,000 to Humane Society, Michigan, Southfield, MI. For unrestricted support.

1212
E. Jerome and Joanne McCarthy Foundation
c/o E. Jerome McCarthy
623 Kensington Dr.
East Lansing, MI 48823

Established in 1994 in MI.
Donors: E. Jerome McCarthy; Joanne McCarthy.
Grantmaker type: Independent foundation.
Financial data (yr. ended 12/31/05): Assets, $419,165 (M); gifts received, $23,400; expenditures, $30,465; total giving, $30,400; qualifying distributions, $30,400; giving activities include $30,400 for grants.
Limitations: Applications not accepted. Giving primarily in IL and MI; some giving also in Canada. No grants to individuals.
Application information: Contributes only to pre-selected organizations.
Officers: E. Jerome McCarthy, Pres.; Joanne McCarthy, Secy.-Treas.
Directors: Robin Childress; William Hodgman; Janet McCarthy; Roxanne McCarthy; Steve Plunkett.
EIN: 383184846

1213
The Pamela T. McClelland Family Foundation
1111 W. Long Lake Rd., Ste. 202
Troy, MI 48098

Established in 2000.
Donor: Pamela T. McClelland.
Grantmaker type: Independent foundation.
Financial data (yr. ended 6/30/05): Assets, $251,338 (M); expenditures, $19,051; total giving, $14,000; qualifying distributions, $14,000; giving activities include $14,000 for grants.
Limitations: Giving primarily in MI. No grants to individuals.
Officers: Pamela T. McClelland, Pres.; James McClelland III, V.P.; Pamela K. McClelland, V.P.; R. Keith Stark, Secy.-Treas.
EIN: 383568733

1214
McClendon Family Foundation
2 Chestnut St.
South Haven, MI 49090
Contact: Joanne McClendon, Pres.; Robert McClendon, Dir.

Established in 1997 in MI.
Donors: Robert "Bob" McClendon; Joanne McClendon.
Grantmaker type: Independent foundation.
Financial data (yr. ended 12/31/05): Assets, $449,068 (M); expenditures, $29,217; total giving, $25,000; qualifying distributions, $25,000; giving activities include $25,000 for grants.
Limitations: Giving primarily in South Haven, MI. No grants to individuals.

Application information:
Initial approach: Letter
Deadline(s): None
Officers: Joanne McClendon, Pres.; Holly Beck, V.P.; Margaret McClendon, V.P.; G. Philip Dietrich, Secy.-Treas.
Directors: Vearl Beck; Mark McClendon; Robert McClendon.
EIN: 383403655

1215
Theo & Mable McClendon Scholarship Foundation
(formerly Theo and Mable McClendon Scholarship Fund)
c/o Sherry M. Pickett
P.O. Box 2623
Southfield, MI   48037-2623

Grantmaker type: Independent foundation.
Financial data (yr. ended 3/31/04): Assets, $0 (M); gifts received, $362; expenditures, $687; total giving, $500; qualifying distributions, $500; giving activities include $500 for grants.
Officers: Sherry Pickett, Pres.; Kiatra Pickett, Secy.; Jason Pickett, Treas.
EIN: 383174912

1216
William T. and Ann D. McCormick Educational and Charitable Foundation
17190 Denver Ave.
Detroit, MI   48224

Established in 1989 in MI.
Donors: William T. McCormick, Jr.; Ann D. McCormick.
Grantmaker type: Independent foundation.
Financial data (yr. ended 9/30/05): Assets, $9,762 (M); expenditures, $855; total giving, $0; qualifying distributions, $0.
Purpose and activities: Giving primarily to schools and churches.
Fields of interest: Higher education; Hospitals (general); Christian agencies & churches.
Type of support: General/operating support; Building/renovation; Scholarship funds.
Limitations: Applications not accepted. Giving primarily in Cambridge, MA, and Detroit, MI. No grants to individuals.
Application information: Contributes only to pre-selected organizations.
Trustees: Ann D. McCormick; William T. McCormick, Jr.
EIN: 382902481

1217
The Ruby McCoy Foundation
19790 Mack Ave.
Grosse Pointe Woods, MI   48236

Established in 2000 in MI.
Donor: Ruby Amanda Nelson McCoy‡.
Grantmaker type: Independent foundation.
Financial data (yr. ended 12/31/04): Assets, $752,577 (M); expenditures, $45,011; total giving, $43,000; qualifying distributions, $43,000; giving activities include $43,000 for grants.
Fields of interest: Alzheimer's disease; Human services.

Limitations: Applications not accepted. Giving primarily in MI. No grants to individuals.
Application information: Contributes only to pre-selected organizations.
Directors: Antonio G. Cueter; Charles T. Gabel; John D. Lundy; Patrick M. Simasko.
EIN: 383529307

1218
McCurdy Memorial Scholarship Foundation
c/o Comerica Bank
49 W. Michigan Ave.
Battle Creek, MI   49017-3603
Contact: Lori Hill, Treas.

Established in 1961 in MI.
Grantmaker type: Independent foundation.
Financial data (yr. ended 12/31/05): Assets, $665,165 (M); expenditures, $43,265; total giving, $36,000; qualifying distributions, $36,000; giving activities include $36,000 for grants to individuals.
Purpose and activities: Scholarships to high school graduates from Calhoun County, MI, for undergraduate study in a college or other post-high school education, for a period of not more than four years.
Type of support: Scholarships—to individuals.
Limitations: Giving limited to residents of Calhoun County, MI.
Application information: Application form required.
Deadline(s): Apr. 1
Board meeting date(s): Jan., Mar., June, and Sept.
Final notification: May 25
Officers: Sandra Morgan, Pres.; Thomas Shively, V.P.; Edward Tersteeg, Secy.; Lori Hill, Treas.
Trustees: Karen Atkinson; Sonja Dotson; Robin Reed; Louis Ryason.
EIN: 381687120

1219
Leon A. McDermott Charitable Trust
c/o KeyBank N.A.
800 Superior, 4th Fl.
Cleveland, OH   44114

Established in 1995 in MI.
Grantmaker type: Independent foundation.
Financial data (yr. ended 12/31/03): Assets, $763,471 (M); expenditures, $45,901; total giving, $38,355; qualifying distributions, $40,090; giving activities include $38,355 for 1 grant.
Purpose and activities: Support for Central Michigan University.
Fields of interest: Higher education.
Limitations: Applications not accepted. Giving limited to Mount Pleasant, MI. No grants to individuals.
Application information: Contributes only to a pre-selected organization.
Trustee: KeyBank N.A.
EIN: 341832860

1220
The June and Cecil McDole Foundation
40 Oak Hollow St., Ste. 120
Southfield, MI   48034

Established in 1993 in MI.
Donor: June McDole.

Grantmaker type: Independent foundation.
Financial data (yr. ended 12/31/05): Assets, $576,160 (M); expenditures, $32,685; total giving, $26,000; qualifying distributions, $26,000; giving activities include $26,000 for grants.
Purpose and activities: Giving primarily to a Christian church, as well as for federated giving programs.
Fields of interest: Health care; Cancer research; Federated giving programs; Christian agencies & churches.
Type of support: General/operating support.
Limitations: Applications not accepted. Giving primarily in FL and MI. No grants to individuals.
Application information: Contributes only to pre-selected organizations.
Officers: June McDole, Pres.; E. James Gamble, V.P. and Secy.; Michael M. Wild, Treas.
EIN: 383145381

1221
McDonald Agape Foundation
380 N. Old Woodward Ave., Ste. 314
Birmingham, MI   48009

Established in 1988 in MI.
Donor: Alonzo L. McDonald, Jr.
Grantmaker type: Independent foundation.
Financial data (yr. ended 12/31/04): Assets, $8,775,402 (M); gifts received, $129,460; expenditures, $1,249,245; total giving, $1,159,773; qualifying distributions, $1,184,771; giving activities include $1,159,773 for 20 grants (high: $604,594; low: $500).
Purpose and activities: Giving primarily for Christian organizations and education.
Fields of interest: Higher education; Theological school/education; Human services; Children, services; Religious federated giving programs; Christian agencies & churches.
Limitations: Applications not accepted. Giving on a national basis. No grants to individuals.
Application information: Contributes only to pre-selected organizations.
Officers: Alonzo L. McDonald, Chair.; R. Jamison Williams, Secy.; Mark A. Maurice, Treas.
Trustees: Peter McDonald; Suzanne M. McDonald; Jennifer McDonald Peters; Robert M. Pool.
EIN: 382840692
Selected grants: The following grants were reported in 2003.
$247,987 to Emory University, Atlanta, GA.
$209,553 to Harvard University, Cambridge, MA. 2 grants: $194,553 (For chair endowment), $15,000.
$30,000 to Trinity Forum, Orlando, FL.
$12,120 to Young Life Ministries, Southfield, MI.
$9,686 to McLean Presbyterian Church, McLean, VA. For general support.
$7,732 to Our Lady of the Mississippi Abbey, Dubuque, IA.
$1,719 to Compassion International, Colorado Springs, CO.
$1,000 to International Justice Mission, Alexandria, VA.
$480 to Heifer Project International, Little Rock, AR.

1222
Timothy McElroy Foundation
43902 Woodward Ave., Ste. 104
Bloomfield Hills, MI   48302

Established in 2002 in MI.
Donors: Karyn A. Hopp; Christopher McElroy; Lucian G. McElroy; Patricia McElroy; Kimberly McElroy-Pawel.
Grantmaker type: Independent foundation.
Financial data (yr. ended 12/31/05): Assets, $1,140,617 (M); gifts received, $61,050; expenditures, $53,146; total giving, $51,640; qualifying distributions, $51,640; giving activities include $51,640 for grants.
Limitations: Applications not accepted. No grants to individuals.
Application information: Contributes only to pre-selected organizations.
Officers: Lucian G. McElroy, Pres. and Treas.; Patricia McElroy, V.P. and Secy.
Directors: Karyn A. Hopp; Christopher McElroy; Kimberly McElroy-Pawel.
EIN: 300040762

1223
Harry J. McFalls Charitable Foundation, Inc.
14738 Hannebauer Ln.
Sterling Heights, MI 48313

Established in 2003 in MI.
Grantmaker type: Independent foundation.
Financial data (yr. ended 12/31/04): Assets, $800 (M); expenditures, $100; total giving, $100; qualifying distributions, $100; giving activities include $100 for grants.
Limitations: Giving primarily in MI.
Officer: Robert VanGoethem, Pres.
EIN: 364532316

1224
Daniel J. McGillen Foundation for Down Syndrome, Inc.
6046 Bynthrop Dr.
Shelby Township, MI 48316-4301

Established in 2002 in MI.
Donors: Stanton K. Smith; Mary Beth Smith.
Grantmaker type: Independent foundation.
Financial data (yr. ended 12/31/05): Assets, $45,508 (M); gifts received, $9,638; expenditures, $4,200; total giving, $2,936; qualifying distributions, $2,936; giving activities include $2,936 for grants.
Limitations: Applications not accepted. No grants to individuals.
Application information: Contributes only to pre-selected organizations.
Officers: Mary Beth Smith, Chair.; Dana Smith McGillen, Pres.; Sean Patrick McGillen, Sr., V.P.; Kathryn Smith Sigman, Secy.; Staton E. Smith, Sr., Treas.
EIN: 383619039

1225
The McGrae Charitable Foundation
4532 Cross Creek Dr.
Ann Arbor, MI 48108

Donor: Carmen McGrae.
Grantmaker type: Independent foundation.
Financial data (yr. ended 12/31/05): Assets, $1 (M); gifts received, $137,884; expenditures, $6,934; total giving, $0; qualifying distributions, $0.
Officer: Carmen McGrae, Pres.
EIN: 383572138

1226
McGregor Fund
333 W. Fort St., Ste. 2090
Detroit, MI 48226-3134 (313) 963-3495
Contact: C. David Campbell, Pres.
FAX: (313) 963-3512;
E-mail: info@mcgregorfund.org; URL: http://www.mcgregorfund.org

Incorporated in 1925 in MI.
Donors: Tracy W. McGregor†; Katherine W. McGregor†.
Grantmaker type: Independent foundation.
Financial data (yr. ended 6/30/05): Assets, $172,095,146 (M); expenditures, $11,229,395; total giving, $8,773,181; qualifying distributions, $9,399,596; giving activities include $8,583,909 for 78 grants (high: $500,000; low: $4,500; average: $50,000–$100,000), and $189,272 for 82 employee matching gifts.
Purpose and activities: A private foundation organized to relieve misfortune and improve the well-being of people. The foundation provides grants to support activities in human services, education, health care, arts and culture, and public benefit.
Fields of interest: Arts; Higher education; Education; Medical care, in-patient care; Health organizations, association; Human services; Youth, services; Homeless.
Type of support: General/operating support; Continuing support; Capital campaigns; Building/renovation; Equipment; Program development; Seed money; Employee matching gifts.
Limitations: Giving primarily in the metropolitan Detroit, MI, area, including Wayne, Oakland, and Macomb counties. No support for disease-specific organizations (or their local affiliates). No grants to individuals, or for scholarships directly, fellowships, travel, workshops, seminars, special events, film or video projects, or conferences; no loans.
Publications: Application guidelines; Annual report (including application guidelines); Grants list.
Application information: Grantmaking guidelines and application procedures are available on the foundation's Web site. Potential applicants are encouraged to contact the foundation to discuss proposed projects before submitting a proposal. Organizations are limited to submitting one grant application per year. Application form required.
> *Initial approach:* Cover letter and proposal
> *Copies of proposal:* 1
> *Deadline(s):* Applicants are encouraged to submit proposals at least 3 months in advance of board meetings
> *Board meeting date(s):* Mar., June, Sept., and Dec.
> *Final notification:* 90 to 120 days
Officers and Trustees:* Eugene A. Miller,* Chair.; Ruth R. Glancy,* Vice-Chair.; C. David Campbell,* Pres. and Secy.; William W. Shelden, Jr.,* Treas.; Bruce W. Steinhauer, M.D.*, Tr. Emeritus; Dave Bing; Cynthia N. Ford; Ira J. Jaffe; James B. Nicholson; Susan Schooley, M.D.
Number of staff: 2 full-time professional; 1 part-time professional; 1 full-time support.
EIN: 380808800
Selected grants: The following grants were reported in 2005.
$2,000,000 to Detroit Institute of Arts, Detroit, MI. For Great Art-New Start, campaign to complete structural renovations, reinstall art, and carry on daily operation of museum, payable over 5 years.
$1,200,000 to Local Initiatives Support Corporation (LISC), New York, NY. To support Neighborhoods NOW, initiative of Detroit LISC, to encourage inter-neighborhood cooperation and collaboration between community development corporations, businesses, institutions, and residents to make impact on targeted neighborhoods within Detroit and inner-ring suburbs, payable over 3 years.
$900,000 to Starfish Family Services, Inkster, MI. For implementation of Family Success Model, to help families break cycle of intergenerational poverty and achieve lasting success, payable over 3 years.
$500,000 to Community Health and Social Services Center, Detroit, MI. For capital campaign to build new facility in southwest Detroit, payable over 2 years.
$486,000 to University of Michigan, Ann Arbor, MI. For Geriatric Social Work Fellows Program and fieldwork in metropolitan Detroit, payable over 3 years.
$250,000 to Kenyon College, Gambier, OH. For Food for Thought, collaboration between students and faculty of college's Rural Life Center and local farmers to include applied student research across disciplines, aimed at raising consumer interest in locally produced foods.
$150,000 to Saint John Health System, Detroit, MI. To support renovation costs to prepare facility for operation as Northeast Health Center, Federally Qualified Health Center operated by Advantage Health in collaboration with Detroit Department of Health and Wellness Promotion and Saint John's Health.
$100,000 to Detroit Science Center, Detroit, MI. For program support.
$60,000 to Calvin College, Grand Rapids, MI. For trustee designated grant.
$50,000 to Volunteer Accounting Service Team of Michigan, Detroit, MI. To support Tax Assistance Program, providing volunteers to prepare and file tax returns for low-income residents of metropolitan Detroit.

1227
B. D. and Jane E. McIntyre Foundation
c/o JPMorgan Chase Bank, N.A.
P.O. Box 1308
Milwaukee, WI 53201
Application address: c/o JPMorgan Chase Bank, N.A., 611 Woodward Ave., Ste. MI18038, Detroit, MI 48226, tel.: (313) 225-3454, FAX: (313) 225-3948

Trust established in 1961 in MI.
Donor: Members of the McIntyre family.
Grantmaker type: Independent foundation.
Financial data (yr. ended 11/30/05): Assets, $4,534,875 (M); expenditures, $241,502; total giving, $216,100; qualifying distributions, $229,817; giving activities include $216,100 for 24 grants (high: $45,000; low: $1,000).
Purpose and activities: Giving primarily for higher education and to Episcopal and other churches; support also for the arts and health organizations.
Fields of interest: Arts; Higher education; Education; Health organizations; Medical research; Christian agencies & churches.

Type of support: Continuing support; Scholarship funds.
Limitations: Giving primarily in MI, with some emphasis on Monroe and Midland. No grants to individuals.
Application information: Application form not required.
  Initial approach: Proposal
  Copies of proposal: 1
  Deadline(s): None
  Board meeting date(s): As required
  Final notification: Oct. 31
Trustee and Advisory Committee: Rocque L. Lipford; C.S. McIntyre III; JPMorgan Chase Bank, N.A.
EIN: 386046718

1228
C. S. and Marion F. McIntyre Foundation
c/o JPMorgan Chase Bank, N.A.
P.O. Box 1308
Milwaukee, WI   53201
Contact: Matthew Wasmund, Trust Off.
Application address: c/o JPMorgan Chase Bank, N.A., 611 Woodward Ave., Ste. MI18038, Detroit, MI 48226, tel.: (313) 225-3183, FAX: (313) 225-3948

Trust established in 1961 in MI.
Donor: Members of the McIntyre family.
Grantmaker type: Independent foundation.
Financial data (yr. ended 11/30/05): Assets, $2,995,709 (M); expenditures, $153,694; total giving, $131,000; qualifying distributions, $142,186; giving activities include $131,000 for 11 grants (high: $35,000; low: $1,000).
Purpose and activities: Support primarily for a college and other education.
Fields of interest: Arts; Higher education, college; Education; Housing/shelter, development; Human services; Christian agencies & churches.
Limitations: Giving primarily in MI, with emphasis on the Monroe area. No grants to individuals.
Application information: Application form not required.
  Initial approach: Letter
  Copies of proposal: 1
  Deadline(s): None
  Board meeting date(s): As required
  Final notification: Oct. 31
Advisory Committee: Don Korn; Rocque L. Lipford; David L. McIntyre.
Trustee: JPMorgan Chase Bank, N.A.
EIN: 386046733
Selected grants: The following grants were reported in 2004.
$85,000 to Alma College, Alma, MI. 2 grants: $75,000, $10,000
$20,000 to Meadow Montessori School, Monroe, MI.
$12,000 to Boy Scouts of America, Ann Arbor, MI. 2 grants: $10,000 to Great Sauk Trail Council, $2,000 to Great Sauk Trail Council
$10,000 to First Presbyterian Church of Monroe, Monroe, MI.
$9,000 to Monroe County Community College, Monroe, MI.
$1,100 to Council of Michigan Foundations, Grand Haven, MI.
$1,000 to Humane Society of Monroe, Monroe, MI.
$1,000 to Veterans of Foreign Wars, Monroe, MI. For Memorial Day Parade.

1229
W. D. & Prudence McIntyre Foundation
c/o JPMorgan Chase Bank, N.A.
P.O. Box 1308
Milwaukee, WI   53201
Contact: Matthew Wasmund, Trust Off., JPMorgan Chase Bank, N.A.
Application address: c/o JPMorgan Chase Bank, N.A., Attn.: Don Korn, 611 Woodward Ave., Ste. MI18038, Detroit, MI 48226, tel.: (313) 225-3454, FAX: (313) 225-3948

Established in 1960 in MI.
Grantmaker type: Independent foundation.
Financial data (yr. ended 11/30/05): Assets, $1,221,644 (M); expenditures, $48,674; total giving, $42,000; qualifying distributions, $42,000; giving activities include $42,000 for grants.
Purpose and activities: Giving for Catholic organizations.
Fields of interest: Human services; Roman Catholic agencies & churches.
Limitations: Giving primarily in MI, with emphasis on Monroe. No grants to individuals.
Application information: Application form required.
  Initial approach: Letter
  Deadline(s): None
Advisory Committee: Don Korn; Rocque E. Lipford; William D. McIntyre, Jr.
Trustee: JPMorgan Chase Bank, N.A.
EIN: 386046659

1230
The McKeen Foundation
c/o Comerica Bank
P.O. Box 75000, M/C 3317
Detroit, MI   48275-3317   (313) 222-5576
Contact: David C. Wind

Established in 2001 in MI.
Grantmaker type: Independent foundation.
Financial data (yr. ended 12/31/05): Assets, $1,166,064 (M); expenditures, $62,775; total giving, $53,000; qualifying distributions, $53,000; giving activities include $53,000 for grants.
Application information:
  Initial approach: Letter
  Deadline(s): None
Advisory Committee: Alexander McKeen; Evelyn McKeen.
Trustee: Comerica Bank.
EIN: 912119007

1231
Brian J. McKeen Foundation
c/o Barry R. Bess
2000 Town Ctr., Ste. 1500
Southfield, MI   48075-1195

Established in 2000 in MI.
Donor: Brian J. McKeen.
Grantmaker type: Independent foundation.
Financial data (yr. ended 12/31/04): Assets, $202,716 (M); expenditures, $40,867; total giving, $40,248; qualifying distributions, $40,175; giving activities include $40,248 for 2 grants to individuals.
Purpose and activities: Primarily makes scholarship awards for tuition and books for graduating students of Royal Oak, schools.
Type of support: Scholarships—to individuals.

Limitations: Applications not accepted. Giving primarily in Royal Oak, MI.
Application information: Unsolicited requests for funds not accepted.
Officers: Brian J. McKeen, Pres.; Brenda Ann McKeen, Secy.
EIN: 383574592

1232
Verna McKibben Memorial Foundation
c/o Comerica Bank
P.O. Box 75000
Detroit, MI   48275-3302
Contact: Joel R. Aberth, Tr.
Application address: 3296 W. Market St., Akron, OH 44333-3355, tel.: (330) 865-7722

Established in 1999 in OH.
Donor: Verna McKibben†.
Grantmaker type: Independent foundation.
Financial data (yr. ended 4/30/05): Assets, $577,502 (M); expenditures, $41,253; total giving, $15,000; qualifying distributions, $15,000; giving activities include $15,000 for grants.
Purpose and activities: Giving for health organizations and human services.
Fields of interest: Arts; Health organizations, association; Human services.
Limitations: Giving primarily in OH.
Application information:
  Initial approach: Letter
  Deadline(s): None
Board Members: Donna Longfellow; Lisa Heeler Neely.
Trustees: Joel R. Aberth; Comerica Bank.
EIN: 316608261

1233
Russell McLauchlin Foundation
c/o Comerica Bank
P.O. Box 75000, MC 3302
Detroit, MI   48275

Grantmaker type: Independent foundation.
Financial data (yr. ended 12/31/05): Assets, $342,172 (M); expenditures, $22,376; total giving, $16,000; qualifying distributions, $16,000; giving activities include $16,000 for grants.
Purpose and activities: Support only for the Wayne State University Theater Dept., Detroit, MI.
Fields of interest: Arts education; Higher education, university.
Type of support: General/operating support.
Limitations: Applications not accepted. Giving limited to Detroit, MI. No grants to individuals.
Application information: Contributes only to a pre-selected organization.
Trustee: Comerica Bank.
EIN: 386377743

1234
Helen Metzger McLean Foundation
233 Lewiston Rd.
Grosse Pointe Farms, MI   48236

Established in 1995.
Donor: Helen McLean Carter Trust.
Grantmaker type: Independent foundation.
Financial data (yr. ended 8/31/05): Assets, $4,758,057 (M); expenditures, $358,500; total

giving, $302,488; qualifying distributions, $324,113; giving activities include $302,488 for grants.
Purpose and activities: Support only for the Alpha Chi Omega Foundation, Inc., IN.
Fields of interest: Higher education, university.
Limitations: Applications not accepted. Giving limited to Indianapolis, IN. No grants to individuals.
Application information: Contributes only to a pre-selected organizations.
Officers and Trustees:* John A. MacLeod,* Pres.; Lois M. MacLeod,* Secy.; Andrew W. MacLeod,* Treas.
EIN: 383257148

1235
McLennan Family Foundation
29516 Southfield Rd., Ste. 102
Southfield, MI 48076-2029

Established in 2001 in MI.
Donors: James McLennan; Rebecca McLennan.
Grantmaker type: Independent foundation.
Financial data (yr. ended 1/31/05): Assets, $393,249 (M); expenditures, $21,062; total giving, $20,000; qualifying distributions, $20,000; giving activities include $20,000 for grants.
Limitations: Applications not accepted. No grants to individuals.
Application information: Contributes only to pre-selected organizations.
Directors: James McLennan; Lisa F. McLennan; Rebecca A. McLennan; Rebecca W. McLennan.
EIN: 383604317

1236
Mary I. McLeod Foundation
16845 Kercheval St., Ste. 5
Grosse Pointe, MI 48230-1551
Contact: Mary I. McLeod, Pres.

Established in 1998 in MI.
Donor: Mary I. McLeod.
Grantmaker type: Independent foundation.
Financial data (yr. ended 12/31/05): Assets, $100,251 (M); gifts received, $6,750; expenditures, $7,806; total giving, $7,000; qualifying distributions, $7,000; giving activities include $7,000 for grants.
Fields of interest: Arts; Animals/wildlife, special services; General charitable giving.
Type of support: General/operating support.
Limitations: Giving primarily in Detroit, MI. No grants to individuals.
Application information: Application form required.
Deadline(s): None
Officers and Trustees:* Mary I. McLeod,* Pres.; S. Gary Spicer,* Secy.
EIN: 383407098

1237
The McLoughlin Family Foundation
P.O. Box 295
Cassopolis, MI 49031-0295

Established in 1997 in MI.
Donors: K&M Machine Fabricating; Michael T. McLoughlin.
Grantmaker type: Independent foundation.

Financial data (yr. ended 12/31/05): Assets, $518,377 (M); gifts received, $205,500; expenditures, $27,027; total giving, $26,025; qualifying distributions, $26,025; giving activities include $26,025 for grants.
Fields of interest: Children/youth, services; Family services.
Limitations: Applications not accepted. Giving primarily in MI. No grants to individuals.
Application information: Contributes only to pre-selected organizations.
Directors: C. Derek McLoughlin; Emily J. McLoughlin; Kevin M. McLoughlin; M. Katherine McLoughlin; Michael T. McLoughlin; Patrick J. McLoughlin.
EIN: 383335768

1238
The Michael F. McManus Foundation
(formerly The Header Foundation)
P.O. Box 74188
Romulus, MI 48174-0188

Established in 1969 in MI.
Donors: Header Products, Inc.; Michael F. McManus.
Grantmaker type: Independent foundation.
Financial data (yr. ended 12/31/04): Assets, $848,988 (M); gifts received, $30,000; expenditures, $46,343; total giving, $46,170; qualifying distributions, $46,170; giving activities include $46,170 for grants.
Fields of interest: Higher education; Human services; Roman Catholic agencies & churches.
Limitations: Applications not accepted. Giving primarily in the greater Detroit, MI, area. No grants to individuals.
Application information: Contributes only to pre-selected organizations.
Officer: Michael F. McManus, Jr., Pres. and Secy.-Treas.
Trustees: J. Rodney Guest; Mary Ann Harahan.
EIN: 386174305

1239
Donald E. and Shirley M. McMinn Family Foundation
64527 Kildare Dr.
Washington, MI 48095-2522

Established in 1997.
Donors: Donald E. McMinn; Shirley M. McMinn.
Grantmaker type: Independent foundation.
Financial data (yr. ended 12/31/05): Assets, $87,147 (M); expenditures, $6,707; total giving, $6,300; qualifying distributions, $6,300; giving activities include $6,300 for grants.
Limitations: Applications not accepted. No grants to individuals.
Application information: Contributes only to pre-selected organizations.
Trustees: Bonnie L. McMinn; Dean R. McMinn; Donald E. McMinn; Donna M. McMinn; Kevin J. McMinn; Mark J. McMinn.
EIN: 383270332

1240
William F. McNally Family Foundation
(formerly William F. and Marjorie A. McNally Memorial Foundation)
5825 Dixie Hwy.
Saginaw, MI 48601
Contact: William F. McNally, Pres.

Established in 1982 in MI.
Donor: William F. McNally.
Grantmaker type: Independent foundation.
Financial data (yr. ended 12/31/05): Assets, $3,520,606 (M); gifts received, $199,765; expenditures, $165,351; total giving, $163,025; qualifying distributions, $163,025; giving activities include $163,025 for 26 grants (high: $100,000; low: $50).
Purpose and activities: Giving for education, hospitals, and human services.
Fields of interest: Museums (art); Higher education; Theological school/education; Hospitals (general); Human services; Protestant agencies & churches.
Limitations: Giving primarily in MI.
Application information: Application form not required.
Initial approach: Letter
Deadline(s): None
Officer: William F. McNally, Pres. and Treas.
Trustees: Brian McNally; Dwight McNally.
EIN: 382429175
Selected grants: The following grants were reported in 2003.
$30,000 to Valley Lutheran High School, Saginaw, MI. For general support.
$20,000 to Mayo Clinic, Rochester, MN. For general support.
$10,000 to Covenant Hospital Foundation, Saginaw, MI. For general support.
$10,000 to Faith Lutheran Church, Bridgeport, MI. For general support.
$10,000 to Saginaw Valley State University, University Center, MI. For general support.
$8,000 to Bridgeport-Spaulding Community School District, Bridgeport, MI. For general support.
$6,000 to Saginaw Community Concert Association, Kawkawlin, MI. For general support.
$5,750 to Mount Calvary Lutheran Church, Detroit, MI. For general support.
$5,000 to Taymouth Township Historical Association, Burt, MI. For general support.
$3,000 to Salvation Army of Saginaw, Saginaw, MI. For general support.

1241
Margaret McNally Memorial Fund
c/o Citizens Bank Wealth Mgmt., N.A.
328 S. Saginaw St., M/C 002072
Flint, MI 48501
Application address: c/o Helen James, Citizens Bank, N.A., Wealth Mgmt., 101 N. Washington Ave., Saginaw, MI 48607, tel.: (989) 776-7368

Established in 1985 in MI.
Grantmaker type: Independent foundation.
Financial data (yr. ended 12/31/05): Assets, $110,470 (M); expenditures, $7,835; total giving, $5,500; qualifying distributions, $5,500; giving activities include $5,500 for grants.
Purpose and activities: Grants to organizations to provide assistance to blind residents of Saginaw County, Michigan.
Fields of interest: Blind/visually impaired.

Type of support: General/operating support; Equipment.
Limitations: Giving limited to benefit Saginaw County, MI. No grants to individuals.
Application information: Application form required.
Initial approach: Letter or telephone
Deadline(s): None
Trustee: Citizens Bank.
EIN: 386234122

1242
McNish Family Foundation
26622 Woodward Ave., Ste. 200
Royal Oak, MI 48067 (248) 544-4800
Contact: Carol A. McNish, Pres.
FAX: (248) 544-4801;
E-mail: christinemcnish@sbcglobal.net

Established in 2003 in MI.
Grantmaker type: Independent foundation.
Financial data (yr. ended 12/31/05): Assets, $47,159 (M); gifts received, $29,894; expenditures, $21,452; total giving, $21,432; qualifying distributions, $21,432; giving activities include $21,432 for grants.
Purpose and activities: Giving to Catholic educational facilities and organizations conducting youth education and athletic programs; also provides for scholarship funding.
Fields of interest: Elementary/secondary education; Athletics/sports, training; Youth development; Roman Catholic agencies & churches.
Type of support: Scholarship funds.
Limitations: Giving primarily in MI. No grants to individuals.
Application information: Most funding goes to pre-selected organizations. Application form not required.
Initial approach: Letter
Deadline(s): None
Officers and Directors: * Carol A. McNish,* Pres.; Suzanne McNish Moceri,* V.P.; Christine McNish,* Secy.; Megan Curoe,* Treas.; Colleen McNish; Elizabeth McNish.
EIN: 300184715

1243
R. S. McPherson Trust
c/o Citizens Bank
328 S. Saginaw St.
Flint, MI 48502

Established in 2004 in MI.
Grantmaker type: Independent foundation.
Financial data (yr. ended 12/31/05): Assets, $243,772 (M); expenditures, $9,258; total giving, $4,920; qualifying distributions, $7,549; giving activities include $4,920 for grants to individuals.
Fields of interest: Children/youth; Disabilities, people with.
Type of support: Grants to individuals.
Limitations: Applications not accepted. Giving limited to residents of Clinton and Gratiot counties, MI.
Application information: Eligibility for assistance is determined by the Clinton County Court.
Trustee: Citizens Bank.
EIN: 386140246

1244
Mary McVicar Trust
c/o Hillsdale County Comm. Foundation
P.O. Box 276
Hillsdale, MI 49242

Donor: Mary McVicar†.
Grantmaker type: Independent foundation.
Financial data (yr. ended 12/31/04): Assets, $72,781 (M); expenditures, $7,503; total giving, $6,447; qualifying distributions, $6,747; giving activities include $6,447 for 3 grants (high: $2,149; low: $2,149).
Purpose and activities: Support only for Starr Commonwealth, Albion, Hillsdale College and Mitchell Library, Hillsdale, MI.
Fields of interest: Education.
Type of support: General/operating support.
Limitations: Applications not accepted. Giving limited to Albion and Hillsdale, MI. No grants to individuals.
Application information: Contributes only to 3 pre-selected organizations.
Trustee: Hillsdale County Community Foundation.
EIN: 386105310

1245
Meadlock Foundation, Inc.
18311 E. 9 Mile Rd.
Eastpointe, MI 48021

Grantmaker type: Independent foundation.
Financial data (yr. ended 12/31/04): Assets, $135,862 (M); expenditures, $8,674; total giving, $8,674; qualifying distributions, $8,674; giving activities include $8,674 for grants.
Purpose and activities: Support only for the M.D. Anderson Center, Houston, TX.
Fields of interest: Cancer research.
Type of support: Research.
Limitations: Applications not accepted. Giving limited to Houston, TX. No grants to individuals.
Application information: Contributes only to a pre-selected organization.
Officers: William A. Meadlock, Pres. and Treas.; Concetta Meadlock, V.P. and Secy.
EIN: 581655986

1246
Madeline Sweeney Meeks Foundation
1001 Warrenville Rd., Ste. 105
Lisle, IL 60532
Contact: Robert Meeks, Dir.

Established in 1998 in IL.
Donors: Robert Meeks; Debra Meeks.
Grantmaker type: Independent foundation.
Financial data (yr. ended 12/31/05): Assets, $81,451 (M); expenditures, $7,196; total giving, $6,500; qualifying distributions, $6,500; giving activities include $6,500 for grants.
Fields of interest: Education.
Type of support: General/operating support; Scholarship funds.
Limitations: Giving primarily in IL and MI. No grants to individuals.
Application information:
Initial approach: Letter
Deadline(s): None

Directors: Andrew Meeks; Debra Meeks; Jenny Lynn Meeks; Robert Meeks.
EIN: 364258774

1247
The Meer Family Foundation
26081 Stratford Pl.
Oak Park, MI 48237-1029

Established in 1998 in MI.
Donors: Robert D. Meer; Sondra Meer.
Grantmaker type: Independent foundation.
Financial data (yr. ended 12/31/04): Assets, $154,053 (M); gifts received, $182,400; expenditures, $59,675; total giving, $57,962; qualifying distributions, $59,675; giving activities include $57,962 for 86 grants (high: $8,680; low: $10).
Fields of interest: Jewish federated giving programs; Jewish agencies & temples.
Type of support: General/operating support; Program development.
Limitations: Applications not accepted. Giving primarily in Oak Park, MI, and New York, NY. No grants to individuals.
Application information: Contributes only to pre-selected organizations.
Officers and Directors: * Robert D. Meer,* Pres. and Treas.; Sondra Meer,* Secy.
EIN: 383442773
Selected grants: The following grants were reported in 2003.
$51,237 to Yeshivas Darchei Torah, Southfield, MI.
$1,500 to Jewish Federation of Metropolitan Detroit, Bloomfield Hills, MI.
$248 to Agudath Israel of America, New York, NY.
$150 to Chai Lifeline, New York, NY.
$118 to American Red Magen David for Israel, Southfield, MI.
$100 to Boys Town Jerusalem Foundation of America, New York, NY.
$100 to Holocaust Memorial Center, Farmington Hills, MI.
$60 to Lubavitch Foundation, Farmington Hills, MI.
$50 to Cincinnati Community Kollel, Cincinnati, OH.
$18 to Belz Institutions of Israel, Brooklyn, NY.

1248
Lisa and Brian Meer Foundation
3020 Middlebelt Rd.
West Bloomfield, MI 48323-1932

Established in 2001 in MI.
Donors: Brian Meer; Lisa Meer.
Grantmaker type: Independent foundation.
Financial data (yr. ended 12/31/05): Assets, $69,585 (M); gifts received, $49,188; expenditures, $34,073; total giving, $32,938; qualifying distributions, $32,938; giving activities include $32,938 for grants.
Fields of interest: Arts; Jewish agencies & temples.
Limitations: Applications not accepted. Giving limited to MI. No grants to individuals.
Application information: Contributes only to pre-selected organizations.
Officers and Directors: * Brian Meer,* Pres. and Treas.; Lisa Meer,* Secy.
EIN: 383605133

1249
MEG Tuition Reimbursement Program
6153 S. Dort Hwy.
Grand Blanc, MI 48439

Established in 2001.
Grantmaker type: Independent foundation.
Financial data (yr. ended 12/31/05): Assets,
$60,388 (M); gifts received, $8,550; expenditures,
$11,850; total giving, $9,313; qualifying
distributions, $9,313; giving activities include
$9,313 for grants.
Purpose and activities: Tuition reimbursement
program for active employees of a UAW MEG local
who are members in good standing of OPEIU.
Type of support: Scholarships—to individuals.
Officer: Ann M. Hunt, Treas.
EIN: 383547803

1250
David P. & Linda M. Mehney Foundation
3049 Mary St. S.E.
Grand Rapids, MI 49506

Established in 1985 in MI.
Donors: David P. Mehney; Linda M. Mehney; KMW
Group, Inc.
Grantmaker type: Independent foundation.
Financial data (yr. ended 12/31/05): Assets,
$749,292 (M); gifts received, $51,957;
expenditures, $75,060; total giving, $73,000;
qualifying distributions, $73,000; giving activities
include $73,000 for grants.
Fields of interest: Higher education; Education;
Recreation, parks/playgrounds.
Type of support: General/operating support.
Limitations: Applications not accepted. Giving
primarily in Grand Rapids, MI. No grants to
individuals.
Application information: Contributes only to
pre-selected organizations.
Officers: David P. Mehney, Pres.; Linda M. Mehney,
V.P.
EIN: 386484168

1251
Anita and Santosh Mehra Foundation
c/o Santosh Mehra
1419 Burgundy Rd.
Ann Arbor, MI 48105

Established in 2001 in MI.
Donors: Anita Mehra; Santosh Mehra.
Grantmaker type: Independent foundation.
Financial data (yr. ended 11/30/05): Assets,
$955,508 (M); expenditures, $5,289; total giving,
$5,231; qualifying distributions, $5,231; giving
activities include $5,231 for grants.
Limitations: Applications not accepted. Giving
limited to MI. No grants to individuals.
Application information: Contributes only to
pre-selected organizations.
Officers: Santosh Mehra, Pres.; Anita Mehra,
Secy.-Treas.
EIN: 383638221

1252
The Meijer Foundation
c/o Fifth Third Bank
P.O. Box 3636
Grand Rapids, MI 49501-3636

Established in 1990 in MI.
Donors: Frederik G.H. Meijer; Meijer, Inc.; Lena
Meijer.
Grantmaker type: Independent foundation.
Financial data (yr. ended 9/30/04): Assets,
$78,473,710 (M); gifts received, $420,000;
expenditures, $8,766,407; total giving,
$8,350,502; qualifying distributions, $8,351,415;
giving activities include $8,350,502 for 34 grants
(high: $2,000,000; low: $2,336; average:
$100,000–$400,000).
Purpose and activities: Giving primarily to a
horticultural society, and to a charitable trust;
funding also for community foundations and an art
museum. The foundation administers a
donor-advised fund.
Fields of interest: Museums (art); Botanical
gardens; Horticulture/garden clubs; Foundations
(community).
Limitations: Applications not accepted. Giving
primarily in Grand Rapids, MI, some giving also in
Greenville, MI. No grants to individuals.
Application information: Contributes only to
pre-selected organizations.
Trustee: Frederik G.H. Meijer.
EIN: 386575227
Selected grants: The following grants were reported
in 2004.
$3,910,756 to Frederick Meijer Gardens and
Sculpture Park, Grand Rapids, MI. 8 grants:
$300,000 (For elephant sculpture), $160,000
(For purchase of The Kiss sculpture),
$2,000,000 (For operating support), $365,000,
$272,756, $420,000 (For purchase of Male/
Female sculpture), $150,000 (For Degas
Exhibition), $243,000 (For purchase of B-Tree II
sculpture).
$400,000 to Grand Rapids Art Museum, Grand
Rapids, MI. 2 grants: $200,000 (For expansion
of capital campaign), $200,000 (For general
support).

1253
The Melgaard Family Foundation
128 Heights Ave.
Holland, MI 49424

Established in 1992 in MI.
Donor: Barbara Melgaard Grisson.
Grantmaker type: Independent foundation.
Financial data (yr. ended 12/31/05): Assets,
$52,489 (M); expenditures, $10,297; total giving,
$9,360; qualifying distributions, $9,360; giving
activities include $9,360 for grants.
Fields of interest: Girl scouts; Salvation Army;
Protestant agencies & churches; Women.
Limitations: Applications not accepted. Giving
primarily in MI. No grants to individuals.
Application information: Contributes only to
pre-selected organizations.
Trustee: Barbara Melgaard Grisson.
EIN: 383051247

1254
Louis Mentlikowski Charitable Trust
c/o Comerica Bank
P.O. Box 75000
Detroit, MI 48275-3302

Established in 1999 in MI.
Donor: Bernadine Ment†.
Grantmaker type: Independent foundation.
Financial data (yr. ended 10/31/05): Assets,
$151,819 (M); expenditures, $33,034; total giving,
$30,000; qualifying distributions, $30,000; giving
activities include $30,000 for grants.
Limitations: Applications not accepted. No grants to
individuals.
Application information: Contributes only to
pre-selected organizations.
Trustee: Comerica Bank.
EIN: 912053777

1255
Orville D. & Ruth A. Merillat Foundation
1800 W. U.S. Hwy. 223
Adrian, MI 49221-8479

Established in 1983 in MI.
Donors: Orville D. Merillat†; Ruth A. Merillat.
Grantmaker type: Independent foundation.
Financial data (yr. ended 2/28/05): Assets,
$82,292,161 (M); gifts received, $150,000;
expenditures, $6,187,154; total giving,
$5,508,132; qualifying distributions, $5,508,152;
giving activities include $5,508,132 for 90 grants
(high: $2,698,000; low: $300; average: $3,000–
$250,000).
Purpose and activities: Support primarily for
churches and religious welfare.
Fields of interest: Elementary/secondary
education; Human services; Religious federated
giving programs; Religion.
Type of support: General/operating support;
Building/renovation; Equipment.
Limitations: Applications not accepted. Giving
primarily in MI. No grants to individuals.
Application information: Contributes only to
pre-selected organizations.
Officers and Directors: * Ruth A. Merillat,* Pres. and
Secy.; Richard D. Merillat,* V.P.; John D. Thurman,
Treas.
EIN: 382476813
Selected grants: The following grants were reported
in 2004.
$2,597,000 to Lenawee Christian Ministries,
Adrian, MI. For operating support.
$1,562,500 to Huntington College, Huntington, IN.
2 grants: $1,000,000 (For operating support),
$562,500 (For building support).
$900,000 to Winebrenner Theological Seminary,
Findlay, OH. For building support.
$250,000 to Emmanuel Community Church, Fort
Wayne, IN. For building support.
$180,000 to New Common School Foundation,
Detroit, MI. For operating support.
$100,000 to Church of the United Brethren in
Christ, Huntington, IN. For operating support.
$100,000 to Clarkston Community Church of God,
Clarkston, MI. For building support.
$100,000 to Harvest Community United Brethren in
Christ Church, Toledo, OH. For building support.
$92,000 to Campus Crusade for Christ
International, Orlando, FL. For operating support.

1256
Richard D. & Lynette S. Merillat Private Foundation

c/o Merrill Lynch Trust Co.
P.O. Box 1525
Pennington, NJ 08534
Contact: Richard D. Merillat, Pres.
Application address: 2600 Gordon Dr., Naples, FL 34102

Established in 1993 in MI.
Donors: Richard D. Merillat; Lynette S. Merillat.
Grantmaker type: Independent foundation.
Financial data (yr. ended 6/30/04): Assets, $22,885,377 (M); gifts received, $2,264,898; expenditures, $1,031,063; total giving, $767,000; qualifying distributions, $771,510; giving activities include $767,000 for 19 grants (high: $150,000; low: $2,000).
Purpose and activities: Grants primarily to organizations promoting Christian values.
Fields of interest: Higher education; Human services; Family services; Christian agencies & churches.
Limitations: Giving primarily in Adrian, MI; some giving nationally. No grants to individuals.
Application information:
  Initial approach: Letter
  Deadline(s): None
Officers and Trustees: Richard D. Merillat,* Pres.; Lynette S. Merillat,* Secy.
EIN: 383148627

1257
Merkley Charitable Trust

c/o Citizens Bank Wealth Mgmt., N.A.
328 S. Saginaw St., MC 00041
Flint, MI 48502 (810) 342-7390
Contact: Dawn Bentley, Trust Off., Citizens Bank

Established in 1986.
Donor: Martha K. Merkley†.
Grantmaker type: Independent foundation.
Financial data (yr. ended 11/30/05): Assets, $4,684,682 (M); expenditures, $278,365; total giving, $220,875; qualifying distributions, $257,225; giving activities include $220,875 for 16 grants (high: $122,509; low: $1,000).
Fields of interest: Education; Human services; Youth, services; Christian agencies & churches; Aging.
Type of support: Continuing support; Program development.
Limitations: Giving limited to Genesee County, MI. No grants to individuals.
Publications: Application guidelines.
Application information: Application form not required.
  Initial approach: Letter
  Copies of proposal: 1
  Deadline(s): None
  Board meeting date(s): Quarterly
Trustee: Citizens Bank.
EIN: 386528749
Selected grants: The following grants were reported in 2003.
$101,756 to Genesee County Parks and Recreation Commission, Flint, MI. For operating support.
$33,919 to Humane Society of Genesee County, Burton, MI. For operating support.
$16,500 to Jewish Community Services, Flint, MI. For operating support.

$12,000 to YMCA, Flint, Flint, MI. For general support.
$8,000 to Food Bank of Eastern Michigan, Flint, MI. For operating support.
$7,500 to Valley Area Agency on Aging, Flint, MI. For operating support.
$5,000 to Alzheimers Association, Flint, MI. For general support.
$5,000 to Kettering University, Flint, MI. For operating support.
$3,000 to Flint Institute of Music, Flint, MI. For general support.
$1,500 to Flint Community Schools, Flint, MI. For operating support.

1258
Arthur J. & Kathryn D. Mervenne Foundation

c/o Laurie Hekman
11500 Riley St.
Holland, MI 49424

Established in 1994 in MI.
Donor: Kathryn D. Mervenne.
Grantmaker type: Independent foundation.
Financial data (yr. ended 12/31/05): Assets, $940,995 (M); expenditures, $46,605; total giving, $46,000; qualifying distributions, $46,000; giving activities include $46,000 for grants.
Purpose and activities: Giving for human services, and higher education.
Fields of interest: Higher education; Salvation Army.
Limitations: Applications not accepted. Giving limited to MI. No grants to individuals.
Application information: Contributes only to pre-selected organizations.
Officers: Laurie M. Hekman, Pres.; A. John Mervenne, Secy.-Treas.
EIN: 383212164

1259
Frances Williams Messer Trust f/b/o Pennock Hospital & McKinley Home for Boys

c/o Fifth Third Bank
P.O. Box 3636
Grand Rapids, MI 49501-3636

Established in 1939 in MI.
Grantmaker type: Independent foundation.
Financial data (yr. ended 12/31/05): Assets, $166,453 (M); expenditures, $5,377; total giving, $1,500; qualifying distributions, $1,750; giving activities include $1,500 for 2 grants (high: $750; low: $750).
Purpose and activities: Support only for the McKinley Home for Boys, San Dimas, CA, and Pennock Hospital, Hastings, MI.
Fields of interest: Hospitals (general); Residential/custodial care.
Limitations: Applications not accepted. Giving limited to San Dimas, CA, and Hastings, MI. No grants to individuals.
Application information: Contributes only to 2 pre-selected organizations.
Trustee: Fifth Third Bank.
EIN: 386050417

1260
Richard B. Messer Trust f/b/o Pennock Hospital

c/o Fifth Third Bank
P.O. Box 3636
Grand Rapids, MI 49501-3636

Grantmaker type: Independent foundation.
Financial data (yr. ended 12/31/05): Assets, $1,606,916 (M); gifts received, $168; expenditures, $50,450; total giving, $30,376; qualifying distributions, $31,037; giving activities include $30,376 for 7 grants (high: $10,000; low: $1,000).
Purpose and activities: Giving primarily for Family & Children Services, Battle Creek MI, and Pennock Hospital, Hastings, MI; some giving for youth services.
Fields of interest: Hospitals (general); Children/youth, services.
Type of support: General/operating support.
Limitations: Applications not accepted. Giving primarily to Battle Creek and Hastings, MI. No grants to individuals.
Application information: Contributes only to pre-selected organizations.
Trustee: Fifth Third Bank.
EIN: 386051680

1261
Metro Health Foundation

333 W. Fort St., Ste. 1370
Detroit, MI 48226-3134 (313) 965-4220
Contact: Theresa L. Sondys, Sr. Prog. Off.
FAX: (313) 965-3626;
E-mail: metrohealthfdn@aol.com; Additional E-mail: theresasondys@aol.com

Incorporated in 1986 in MI; converted from Group Health Plan of Southeast Michigan.
Grantmaker type: Independent foundation.
Financial data (yr. ended 12/31/05): Assets, $8,083,692 (M); expenditures, $513,483; total giving, $210,128; qualifying distributions, $365,004; giving activities include $210,128 for 16 grants (high: $30,000; low: $3,000).
Purpose and activities: Dedicated to helping metropolitan Detroit organizations meet the community's health care needs. Grants support a wide variety of health-related services for people of all ages. Collaborative programs which make comprehensive, primary health care accessible to at-risk urban groups are a priority. Areas of primary interest include: teenage pregnancy crisis; health care transportation for the elderly and homeless; in-home healthcare assistance; medically-related assistance to the homeless; healthcare equipment and medical supplies in limited amounts, preferably for underfunded organizations; medical education in special situations in the tri-county Detroit, Michigan, area; and start-up and support money for projects such as AIDS, epilepsy, cancer, heart disease, leukemia, and other major ills of substantial public concern. Note: AIDS-related grants are made through Michigan AIDS Fund.
Fields of interest: Nursing school/education; Health care; Health organizations, association; AIDS; Children/youth, services; Aging, centers/services; Homeless, human services; Aging; Disabilities, people with; African Americans/Blacks; Women; Economically disadvantaged; Homeless.

Type of support: Program development; General/operating support; Equipment; Scholarship funds; Matching/challenge support.
Limitations: Giving limited to Macomb, Oakland and Wayne counties, MI, with primary emphasis on the city of Detroit. No support for religious organizations or government agencies (except by specific Board action), or for organizations which discriminate because of age, race, ethnic origin, religion, sexual orientation, handicap or sex. No grants to individuals, or for building campaigns, conferences or seminars, or for research projects; no loans.
Publications: Application guidelines; Annual report (including application guidelines); Grants list; Program policy statement (including application guidelines).
Application information: Application form required.
  Initial approach: Telephone for application and to discuss proposal idea
  Copies of proposal: 6
  Deadline(s): Aug. 1 and Feb. 1
  Board meeting date(s): Oct. and Apr.
  Final notification: Within 90 days
Officers and Trustees:* Randy Walainis,* Pres.; Lillie M. Tabor,* V.P.; Raymond Cochran,* Treas.; Glenn F. Kossick,* Exec. Dir.; Judith Bean, Ph.D.; Valerie Herod Belay; Laura Champagne; Cheryl Chandler; Robert Doll; Doris M. Fell; Barbara Justice; Jacqueline Majors; Gloria Robinson.
Number of staff: 2 full-time professional; 1 part-time support.
EIN: 382100939
Selected grants: The following grants were reported in 2005.
$30,000 to Saint John Health Foundation, Madison Heights, MI. To equip dental clinic within Northeast Community Health Center, renovated facility which will provide access to primary medical care, pediatrics, OB/GYN, behavioral health, and dental services to uninsured and under-insured people in Northeast Detroit.
$25,000 to Michigan AIDS Fund, Southfield, MI. To provide technical assistance to AIDS Walk Michigan to: maintain coalition of walk sites; ensure statewide coordination of walks; maintain capacity to offer community-based education through walk sites; and maintain local fundraising efforts for each walk site.
$20,000 to United Way for Southeastern Michigan, Detroit, MI. For 2-1-1 Initiative to be used for partial salary support of a Follow-Up Specialist to assess caller satisfaction, utilization of referred health care services, and impact on their lives.
$19,031 to Hope Medical Clinic, Ypsilanti, MI. To provide partial salary support for Medical Clinic Coordinator, to provide adequate administrative oversight and ensure that Clinic operates as efficiently and effectively as possible.
$15,000 to Joy-Southfield Community Development Corporation, Detroit, MI. For costs of laboratory services and clinical supplies used during course of providing primary health care services to low-income and uninsured individuals.
$15,000 to Saint Joseph Mercy Oakland, Pontiac, MI. To provide portion of salary of family support specialist who will provide services to Hispanic community through newly established La Clinica, in partnership with Saint Joseph Mercy Oakland, Healthy Start/Healthy Care, and El Centro La Familia.
$15,000 to World Medical Relief, Detroit, MI. For Senior Prescription Medication Assistance Program.

$14,610 to National Kidney Foundation of Michigan, Ann Arbor, MI. For "Dodge the Punch: African American Male health Campaign," barbershop-based intervention campaign designed to provide information and education to African American men in the city of Detroit at risk for kidney disease, diabetes and hypertension.
$12,000 to Crossroads of Michigan, Detroit, MI. For provision of emergency prescription medication assistance to agency clients.
$8,000 to Macomb Community College Foundation, Warren, MI. To provide scholarships for students in MCC nursing program who successfully complete at least 12 credit hours of study in nursing curriculum each term, maintain a 3.0 GPA, and demonstrate financial need with preference given to minority students.
$7,000 to Starfish Family Services, Inkster, MI. To support work of Inkster Teen Health Center, by providing medical supplies and lab fees.
$6,500 to Freedom House, Detroit, MI. To support Physical Health Team by providing portion of salary of Physical Health Team Coordinator, and providing dental care, prescription medication assistance, physician visits, and other miscellaneous medical care for indigent, homeless refugees temporarily residing at Freedom House.
$6,000 to Central United Methodist Church, N.O.A.H. Project, Detroit, MI. For purchase of medical supplies/equipment for parish nurse use in treating patients, and emergency prescription medication assistance for clients.
$5,000 to Lighthouse Emergency Services, Pontiac, MI. For Emergency Medical Assistance Program, to provide emergency medication and medical assistance (including dental care) for low/limited income residents of Oakland County.
$5,000 to Wayne County SAFE Program, Detroit, MI. For training of minimum of ten nurses as sexual assault nurse examiners.
$3,000 to Mariners Inn, Detroit, MI. For financial assistance for prescription over-the-counter medications not otherwise available for program participants (homeless and chemically dependent men) through existing programs. In addition, MHF staff will provide technical assistance in connecting agency into existing safety net organizations that can serve clients and help meet needs presented on a long-term, cost-effective basis.

1262
Mette Foundation, Inc.
c/o John S. Snyder, Comerica Bank-Detroit
P.O. Box 75000
Detroit, MI 48275-1021

Established in MI.
Donor: Norman H. Mette†.
Grantmaker type: Independent foundation.
Financial data (yr. ended 11/30/05): Assets, $2,215,884 (M); expenditures, $187,794; total giving, $130,000; qualifying distributions, $130,000; giving activities include $130,000 for grants.
Purpose and activities: Support only for the schools of medicine and dentistry at the University of Michigan.
Fields of interest: Dental school/education; Medical school/education.
Type of support: General/operating support; Scholarship funds.

Limitations: Applications not accepted. Giving limited to Ann Arbor, MI. No grants to individuals.
Application information: Contributes only to 2 pre-selected organizations.
Officers: John S. Snyder, Pres. and Treas.; Ronald B. Schwach, V.P.; Marilyn Knickerbocker, Secy.
EIN: 510177958

1263
Meyer Family Foundation
30150 Telegraph Rd., Ste. 444
Bingham Farms, MI 48025

Established in 2000 in MI.
Donor: Rosalind Meyer.
Grantmaker type: Independent foundation.
Financial data (yr. ended 12/31/05): Assets, $7,831 (M); gifts received, $20,475; expenditures, $18,185; total giving, $17,500; qualifying distributions, $17,500; giving activities include $17,500 for grants.
Fields of interest: Arts councils; Human services; Children, services; Religion.
Type of support: General/operating support.
Limitations: Applications not accepted. Giving primarily in MI. No grants to individuals.
Application information: Contributes only to pre-selected organizations.
Officers: Rosalind Meyer, Pres.; William Meyer, Treas.
EIN: 383463253

1264
Allen H. and Nydia Meyers Foundation
(formerly Allen H. Meyers Foundation)
P.O. Box 100
Tecumseh, MI 49286-0100 (517) 423-8086

Established in MI.
Donor: Nydia Meyers†.
Grantmaker type: Independent foundation.
Financial data (yr. ended 4/30/05): Assets, $548,862 (M); expenditures, $26,002; total giving, $21,000; qualifying distributions, $25,008; giving activities include $21,000 for 21 grants.
Purpose and activities: Scholarships limited to graduating students who also reside in a Lenawee County school district and planning college studies in the sciences and allied fields.
Fields of interest: Higher education, college.
Type of support: Scholarships—to individuals.
Limitations: Giving limited to residents of Lenawee County, MI.
Application information: Application form required.
  Deadline(s): Mar. 1
Officers: Timothy Husband, Pres.; Jerry Nelson, V.P. and Treas.; Ann Hindsdale-Kinsel, Secy.
Directors: Michael Beil; Dianne Froelich; Kim Koch; Lloyd Miller; Sharon Weber; Pareese Young.
EIN: 386143278

1265
Roy G. Michell Charitable Foundation and Trust
c/o Janz & Knight, PLC
300 E. Long Lake Rd., Ste. 360
Bloomfield Hills, MI 48304-2377

Established in 1963 in MI.
Donor: Roy G. Michell†.

Grantmaker type: Independent foundation.
Financial data (yr. ended 4/30/05): Assets, $5,298,725 (M); expenditures, $257,666; total giving, $224,000; qualifying distributions, $224,000; giving activities include $224,000 for 90 grants (high: $38,000; low: $250).
Purpose and activities: Giving primarily to Christian ministries and organizations.
Fields of interest: Higher education; Education; Health care; Human services; Children/youth, services; Community development, neighborhood development; Christian agencies & churches.
Limitations: Applications not accepted. Giving on a national basis, primarily in AL, MI and VA. No grants to individuals.
Application information: Contributes only to pre-selected organizations.
Trustees: Frederick C. Janz; Roy G. Michell, Jr.; William Michell.
EIN: 386071109
Selected grants: The following grants were reported in 2004.
$68,300 to Charles Simpson Ministries, Mobile, AL.
$4,000 to University of Michigan, School of Public Health, Ann Arbor, MI.
$3,000 to Christ Community Church, Rochester, MI.
$2,000 to Foundation for Mentally Ill Children, Bloomfield Hills, MI.
$1,000 to Henry Ford Hospital, Detroit, MI.
$1,000 to Leader Dogs for the Blind, Rochester, MI.
$1,000 to Saint Thomas More Parish, Troy, MI.
$800 to Hillsdale College, Hillsdale, MI.
$500 to American Red Cross, Detroit, MI.
$500 to Pontiac Area Transitional Housing, Pontiac, MI.

1266
Michigan Agri-Business Association Educational Trust Fund

(also known as Michigan Agri-Dealers Educational Trust)
1501 Northshore Dr., Ste. A
East Lansing, MI 48823-7622   (517) 336-0223
Contact: James E. Byrum, Pres.

Established in MI.
Grantmaker type: Independent foundation.
Financial data (yr. ended 12/31/04): Assets, $370,971 (M); gifts received, $18,471; expenditures, $17,989; total giving, $16,500; qualifying distributions, $16,500; giving activities include $16,500 for 21 grants to individuals (high: $1,150; low: $550).
Purpose and activities: Scholarship awards to students enrolled in grain elevator management and related courses.
Fields of interest: Higher education.
Type of support: Scholarships—to individuals.
Limitations: Giving limited to MI.
Application information: Application form required.
  Initial approach: Letter
  Deadline(s): None
Officers: James R. Suchodolski, Chair.; James Byrum, Pres.
Trustees: Bill Drushel; John P. Kohr; Ward Forquer; Phil Schmiege.
EIN: 382086180

1267
Michigan Elks Association Charitable Grant Fund

43904 Lee Ann Ln.
Canton, MI 48187-2822

Donor: Michigan Elks Assn.
Grantmaker type: Independent foundation.
Financial data (yr. ended 3/31/05): Assets, $333,143 (M); expenditures, $36,186; total giving, $31,017; qualifying distributions, $31,017; giving activities include $31,017 for 16 grants to individuals (high: $3,000; low: $1,017).
Purpose and activities: Scholarship awards to disabled college students who are residents of MI and members of an Elk's Lodge.
Fields of interest: Higher education.
Type of support: Scholarships—to individuals.
Limitations: Giving limited to residents of MI.
Application information: Applications are made to members of Elks Lodges. Application form required.
  Deadline(s): Jan. 31
Officers: John Kuptz, Pres.; Chad V. High, 1st V.P.; Rodney Bellman, 2nd V.P.
EIN: 382599208

1268
Michigan State Medical Society Foundation

(formerly Health Education Foundation)
c/o Michigan State Medical Society
120 W. Saginaw St.
East Lansing, MI 48823   (517) 336-5745
Contact: Sheri W. Greenhoe, Tr.
E-mail: msms@msms.org; FAX: (517) 337-2490;
E-mail: sgreenhoe@msms.org; URL: http://www.msms.org/msmsto/msmsfoundation/foundation.html

Established in 1945 as Michigan Foundation for Medical & Health Education.
Grantmaker type: Independent foundation.
Financial data (yr. ended 11/30/04): Assets, $880,747 (M); gifts received, $166,380; expenditures, $618,681; total giving, $142,370; qualifying distributions, $618,681; giving activities include $142,370 for grants.
Purpose and activities: Support for community-based programs promoting volunteerism and public health. The foundation supports both research programs and demonstration programs with short-term or start-up costs. A current focus is on wellness and healthy lifestyles.
Fields of interest: Public health; Community development; Voluntarism promotion.
Type of support: Annual campaigns; Equipment; Emergency funds; Program development; Publication; Seed money; Technical assistance; Matching/challenge support.
Limitations: Giving limited to MI.
Publications: Informational brochure; Occasional report (including application guidelines).
Application information: Accepts CMF Common Grant Application Form. See foundation Web site for full application guidelines and downloadable application form. Application form required.
  Copies of proposal: 14
  Deadline(s): Mar. 25 and Sept. 25
  Board meeting date(s): Feb., Apr., and Oct.
Officers: Dorothy J. Kahkonen, M.D., Pres.; William E. Madigan, V.P.; Kevin A. Kelly, Secy.

Trustees: Busharat Ahmad, M.D.; Rudy Ansbacher; Thomas J. Archambeau, M.D.; Billy Ben Baumann; Gilbert Bluhm, M.D.; Henry M. Domzalski, M.D.; Curtis DeRoo; Peter A. Duhamel; Gregory J. Forzley; Alan M. Mindlin; Anne M. Nachazel; Suzanne H. Pederson; Richard D. Weber.
Number of staff: 1 part-time support.
EIN: 386069432

1269
Joseph & Lottie Michner Educational Foundation

P.O. Box 1128
Jackson, MI 49204-1128
Contact: Charles C. McClafferty, Tr.

Established in MI.
Grantmaker type: Independent foundation.
Financial data (yr. ended 12/31/05): Assets, $356,030 (M); expenditures, $21,425; total giving, $21,425; qualifying distributions, $21,425; giving activities include $21,425 for grants to individuals.
Purpose and activities: Scholarship awards to students who attend Lumen Christi High School, Jackson, MI, for high education.
Fields of interest: Higher education.
Type of support: Scholarships—to individuals.
Limitations: Giving limited to residents of Jackson, MI.
Application information: Application form required.
  Initial approach: Request application form
  Deadline(s): Apr. 30
Directors: Camilla A. Cavanaugh; Charles C. McClafferty; Walter J. Michner.
EIN: 382346759

1270
Margaret W. Midgett Charitable Trust

c/o Comerica Bank
P.O. Box 75000 M/C 3302
Detroit, MI 48275-3302

Established in 2000 in NC.
Grantmaker type: Independent foundation.
Financial data (yr. ended 12/31/05): Assets, $351,002 (M); expenditures, $19,219; total giving, $13,000; qualifying distributions, $13,000; giving activities include $13,000 for grants.
Limitations: Applications not accepted. No grants to individuals.
Application information: Contributes only to pre-selected organizations.
Trustee: Comerica Bank.
EIN: 316648798

1271
Margaret W. & Lorimer W. Midgett Trust

c/o Comerica Bank
P.O. Box 75000, M/C 3302
Detroit, MI 48275-3302

Grantmaker type: Independent foundation.
Financial data (yr. ended 12/31/05): Assets, $2,901,851 (M); expenditures, $168,095; total giving, $131,184; qualifying distributions, $132,329; giving activities include $131,184 for 3 grants (high: $65,592; low: $32,796).
Fields of interest: Higher education; Scholarships/financial aid; Federated giving programs.

Limitations: Applications not accepted. No grants to individuals.
Application information: Contributes only to pre-selected organizations.
Trustee: Comerica Bank.
EIN: 527100207

1272
Charles & Florence Milan Foundation
6700 Ridgefield Cir. , Ste. 105
West Bloomfield, MI   48322

Established in 1953 in MI.
Donors: Charles Milan†; Florence Milan.
Grantmaker type: Independent foundation.
Financial data (yr. ended 10/31/05): Assets, $746,416 (M); expenditures, $73,810; total giving, $71,200; qualifying distributions, $71,200; giving activities include $71,200 for grants.
Purpose and activities: Giving to Jewish agencies.
Fields of interest: Jewish federated giving programs; Jewish agencies & temples.
Limitations: Applications not accepted. Giving primarily in MI. No grants to individuals.
Application information: Contributes only to pre-selected organizations.
Officers: Henry Milan, Pres.; Nancy West, V.P.; Robert Rubinstein, Secy.-Treas.
EIN: 386059346

1273
E. Ronald & Estelle M. Milan Foundation, Inc.
30400 Telegraph Rd., Ste. 100
Bingham Farms, MI   48025-4537

Established around 1980 in MI.
Donor: E. Ronald Milan.
Grantmaker type: Independent foundation.
Financial data (yr. ended 11/30/05): Assets, $1 (M); expenditures, $7,362; total giving, $3,600; qualifying distributions, $3,600; giving activities include $3,600 for grants.
Fields of interest: Jewish agencies & temples.
Limitations: Applications not accepted. Giving primarily in Farmington Hills, MI. No grants to individuals.
Application information: Contributes only to pre-selected organizations.
Officers: E. Ronald Milan, Pres.; Estelle M. Milan, Secy.
Directors: Hannah Gottsegen; David M. Milan; Ruth M. Milan; Susan V. Milan-Houser.
EIN: 382257536

1274
Mill Steel Foundation
5116 36th St. S.E.
Grand Rapids, MI   49512

Established in 1999 in MI.
Grantmaker type: Independent foundation.
Financial data (yr. ended 12/31/04): Assets, $137,333 (M); gifts received, $7,260; expenditures, $61,220; total giving, $61,220; qualifying distributions, $61,220; giving activities include $61,220 for 6 grants (high: $25,000; low: $720).

Fields of interest: Big Brothers/Big Sisters; Jewish federated giving programs; Jewish agencies & temples.
Limitations: Applications not accepted. Giving primarily in MI. No grants to individuals.
Application information: Contributes only to pre-selected organizations.
Officer: David Samrick, Pres.
EIN: 383507526

1275
C. John and Reva Miller Charitable Foundation, Inc.
261 E. Kalamazoo Ave., Ste. 100
Kalamazoo, MI   49007-3866

Established in 1985 in MI.
Donors: C. John Miller; Michael J. Miller; Cynthia J. Martin; Sara J. Southwicke; Sally J. Buxton; Miller Energy, Inc.; Providence Energy, Inc.
Grantmaker type: Independent foundation.
Financial data (yr. ended 9/30/05): Assets, $11,484 (M); gifts received, $240,000; expenditures, $227,114; total giving, $226,975; qualifying distributions, $226,975; giving activities include $226,975 for 53 grants (high: $33,500; low: $100).
Purpose and activities: Giving primarily to Christian churches and organizations; funding also for youth, family and social services, health associations, and education.
Fields of interest: Higher education; Education; Health care; Health organizations; Youth, services; Family services; Christian agencies & churches.
Limitations: Applications not accepted. Giving primarily in MI; some funding nationally. No grants to individuals.
Application information: Contributes only to pre-selected organizations.
Officers: C. John Miller, Pres.; Michael J. Miller, V.P. and Secy.-Treas.
Directors: James R. Carl; Reva A. Miller.
EIN: 382623333
Selected grants: The following grants were reported in 2005.
$33,500 to Shepherds Home, Union Grove, WI.
$20,714 to Youth for Christ, Kalamazoo, MI.
$15,500 to Association of Baptists for World Evangelism, Harrisburg, PA.
$14,200 to Northbridge Church, Kalamazoo, MI.
$13,750 to North Pointe Christian Schools, Grand Rapids, MI.
$10,000 to Michigan Family Forum, Lansing, MI.
$9,000 to Cornerstone University, Grand Rapids, MI.
$4,050 to Richland Bible Church, Richland, MI.
$1,500 to Stephens Children Foundation, Atlanta, GA.
$500 to Temple Hill Baptist Church, Cadillac, MI.

1276
Stanley O. Miller Charitable Fund
P.O. Box 737
St. Joseph, MI   49085

Established in 1953 in MI.
Donor: Stanley O. Miller.
Grantmaker type: Independent foundation.
Financial data (yr. ended 9/30/05): Assets, $217,661 (M); expenditures, $12,963; total giving,

$12,000; qualifying distributions, $12,000; giving activities include $12,000 for grants.
Limitations: Applications not accepted. Giving primarily in MI. No grants to individuals, nor for scholarships, fellowships, or prizes; no loans.
Application information: Contributes only to pre-selected organizations.
Trustee: Phyllis Miller.
EIN: 386062439

1277
C. E. Miller Family Foundation
(formerly Clyde & Betty Miller Charitable Foundation)
P.O. Box 348
Traverse City, MI   49685   (231) 941-0004
Contact: Kelly E. Miller, Secy.- Treas.

Established in 1985 in MI.
Donors: C.E. Miller; Betty E. Miller.
Grantmaker type: Independent foundation.
Financial data (yr. ended 9/30/04): Assets, $425,385 (M); gifts received, $288,978; expenditures, $79,890; total giving, $77,500; qualifying distributions, $77,500; giving activities include $77,500 for grants.
Purpose and activities: Giving primarily for higher education, as well as for Christian elementary and secondary education.
Fields of interest: Elementary/secondary education; Higher education, college; Christian agencies & churches.
Type of support: General/operating support; Capital campaigns; Building/renovation; Scholarship funds.
Limitations: Giving primarily in MI; some giving also in OH.
Application information: Application form not required.
  Initial approach: Individuals applying for scholarships should submit letter indicating field of interest, colleges of choice, religious background, scholastic aptitude, and athletic ability
  Deadline(s): None
Officers: C.E. Miller, Pres.; Betty E. Miller, V.P.; Kelly E. Miller, Secy.-Treas.
Directors: Sue E. Bell; Daniel R. Miller.
EIN: 382620981

1278
Hurley Miller Family Foundation
2581 W. Buno Rd.
Milford, MI   48380-4417

Established in 2004 in MI.
Donor: Michael Miller.
Grantmaker type: Independent foundation.
Financial data (yr. ended 12/31/04): Assets, $100,041 (M); gifts received, $100,000; expenditures, $0; total giving, $0; qualifying distributions, $0.
Limitations: Applications not accepted. No grants to individuals.
Application information: Contributes only to pre-selected organizations.
Officers: Michael Miller, Pres.; Margaret Miller, Secy.-Treas.
EIN: 202016743

1279
J. William & Lorraine M. Miller Family Foundation

2814 Canterbury Dr.
Midland, MI 48642 (989) 832-3454
Contact: Lorraine M. Miller, Secy.-Treas.

Established in 1992 in MI.
Donors: J. William Miller; Lorraine M. Miller.
Grantmaker type: Independent foundation.
Financial data (yr. ended 12/31/05): Assets, $717,294 (M); expenditures, $42,799; total giving, $42,000; qualifying distributions, $42,000; giving activities include $42,000 for grants to individuals.
Purpose and activities: Scholarship awards to high school graduates from Saginaw, Bay, and Midland counties, MI.
Fields of interest: Higher education.
Type of support: Scholarships—to individuals.
Limitations: Giving limited to Saginaw, Bay, and Midland counties, MI.
Application information: Application form required.
   Initial approach: Application with high school transcript
   Deadline(s): Apr. 10
Officers: Jan Stevens, Pres.; Lorraine M. Miller, Secy.-Treas.
Directors: Virginia Morrison; L.A. Preston.
EIN: 383009465

1280
Milton J. and Jeanette X. Miller Foundation

2290 First National Bldg.
Detroit, MI 48226-3583
Contact: Milton J. Miller, Pres.

Donor: Milton J. Miller.
Grantmaker type: Independent foundation.
Financial data (yr. ended 12/31/04): Assets, $0 (M); expenditures, $67,596; total giving, $64,871; qualifying distributions, $64,839; giving activities include $64,871 for grants.
Fields of interest: Performing arts, music; Jewish federated giving programs; Jewish agencies & temples; General charitable giving.
Limitations: Giving primarily in Detroit, MI. No grants to individuals.
Application information: Application information available upon request.
   Deadline(s): None
Officer and Director:* Milton J. Miller,* Pres.
EIN: 386076903

1281
Howard Miller Foundation

860 E. Main Ave.
Zeeland, MI 49464-0301

Established in 1976 in MI.
Donors: Howard Miller Clock Co.; Herman Furniture Co.
Grantmaker type: Independent foundation.
Financial data (yr. ended 12/31/05): Assets, $14,036,428 (M); gifts received, $594,037; expenditures, $655,792; total giving, $593,000; qualifying distributions, $598,140; giving activities include $567,000 for 45 grants (high: $52,500; low: $2,500), and $26,000 for 13 grants to individuals (high: $2,000; low: $2,000).

Purpose and activities: Giving primarily for education, Christian missionary work, the arts, health, and human services; also awards college scholarships.
Fields of interest: Arts; Higher education; Education; Hospitals (general); Health care; Mental health/crisis services; Human services; Christian agencies & churches.
Type of support: General/operating support; Scholarships—to individuals.
Limitations: Applications not accepted. Giving primarily in IA and MI.
Application information: Unsolicited requests for funds not accepted.
Officers: Philip D. Miller, Pres.; Jack H. Miller, V.P.; Howard J. Miller, Secy.-Treas.
EIN: 382137226

1282
Philip D. Miller Foundation

860 E. Main St.
Zeeland, MI 49464

Established in 1987 in MI.
Donor: Philip D. Miller.
Grantmaker type: Independent foundation.
Financial data (yr. ended 12/31/05): Assets, $2,890,709 (M); expenditures, $227,216; total giving, $215,100; qualifying distributions, $215,100; giving activities include $215,100 for 24 grants (high: $25,000; low: $1,000).
Fields of interest: Christian agencies & churches.
Limitations: Applications not accepted. Giving primarily in Grand Rapids, MI. No grants to individuals.
Application information: Contributes only to pre-selected organizations.
Officers: Philip D. Miller, Pres.; Nancy J. Miller, Secy.-Treas.
EIN: 382709490

1283
Roger D. Miller & Donna M. Miller Foundation

4677 5th St.
Caledonia, MI 49316

Established in 2000 in MI.
Donors: Roger D. Miller; Donna M. Miller.
Grantmaker type: Independent foundation.
Financial data (yr. ended 12/31/05): Assets, $123,444 (M); gifts received, $179,164; expenditures, $82,605; total giving, $80,500; qualifying distributions, $80,500; giving activities include $80,500 for 3 grants (high: $48,500; low: $1,000).
Fields of interest: Christian agencies & churches.
Limitations: Applications not accepted. Giving primarily in Grand Rapids, MI. No grants to individuals.
Application information: Contributes only to pre-selected organizations.
Officers: Roger D. Miller, Pres. and Treas.; Donna M. Miller, V.P. and Secy.
EIN: 383506830

1284
The Miller Foundation

(formerly Albert L. and Louise B. Miller Foundation, Inc.)
310 WahWahTaySee Way
Battle Creek, MI 49015 (269) 964-3542
Contact: Diane Thompson, Exec. Dir.
FAX: (269) 964-8455;
E-mail: dthompson@millerfdn.org; URL: http://www.willard.lib.mi.us/npa/miller

Incorporated in 1963 in MI.
Donors: Louise B. Miller†; Robert B. Miller†.
Grantmaker type: Independent foundation.
Financial data (yr. ended 12/31/05): Assets, $32,755,296 (M); expenditures, $1,703,280; total giving, $932,630; qualifying distributions, $1,386,023; giving activities include $879,810 for 30 grants (high: $325,000; low: $500), and $52,820 for employee matching gifts.
Purpose and activities: Giving mainly to improve the quality of life in the Battle Creek, MI, community area by supporting local organizations and government agencies that provide for economic development, neighborhood improvement, improving educational outcomes for youth, and eliminating barriers to employment for all in Battle Creek, MI, and the surrounding area.
Fields of interest: Adult/continuing education; Human services; Children/youth, services; Community development, neighborhood development; Economic development.
Type of support: Annual campaigns; Capital campaigns; Building/renovation; Equipment; Land acquisition; Emergency funds; Program development; Seed money; Consulting services; Program-related investments/loans; Matching/challenge support.
Limitations: Giving limited to the greater Battle Creek, MI, area. No support for religious or political organizations. No grants to individuals, or for endowments.
Publications: Application guidelines; Annual report.
Application information: Application guidelines available on foundation Web site. Application form required.
   Initial approach: Initial letter
   Copies of proposal: 12
   Deadline(s): Jan. 1, Mar.1, May 1, July 1, Sept. 1, and Nov. 1
   Board meeting date(s): Jan., Mar., May, July, Sept., and Nov.
   Final notification: 2 months
Officers and Trustees:* Barbara L. Comai,* Chair.; Greg D. Dotson,* Vice-Chair.; Gloria J. Robertson,* Secy.; John J. Gallagher,* Treas.; Arthur W. Angood; Rance L. Leaders; Allen B. Miller; Robert B. Miller, Jr.; Paul R. Ohm.
Number of staff: 1 full-time professional; 1 part-time support.
EIN: 386064925
Selected grants: The following grants were reported in 2003.
$175,000 to Robert B. Miller College, Battle Creek, MI.
$163,078 to Neighborhoods, Inc. of Battle Creek, Battle Creek, MI.
$33,100 to Habitat for Humanity, Battle Creek Area, Battle Creek, MI.
$15,650 to Food Bank of South Central Michigan, Battle Creek, MI.
$15,650 to Junior Achievement of South Central Michigan, Battle Creek, MI.

$15,000 to Michigan Colleges Foundation,
Southfield, MI.
$8,500 to Battle Creek Community Foundation,
Battle Creek, MI.
$5,000 to Charitable Union, Battle Creek, MI.
$5,000 to Urban League, Southwestern Michigan,
Battle Creek, MI.
$100 to Family and Childrens Service of Calhoun
County, Battle Creek, MI.

1285
Rhea E. Miller Music Education Endowment Fund

c/o National City Bank
P.O. Box 94651
Cleveland, OH   44101

Donor: Rhea E. Miller Trust.
Grantmaker type: Independent foundation.
Financial data (yr. ended 12/31/04): Assets,
$1,585,787 (M); expenditures, $47,413; total
giving, $26,767; qualifying distributions, $37,203;
giving activities include $26,767 for grants.
Purpose and activities: Giving limited to Saginaw
Valley State University for scholarships and concert
series.
Fields of interest: Performing arts, music; Higher
education, university.
Type of support: Scholarship funds.
Limitations: Applications not accepted. Giving
limited to University Center, MI. No grants to
individuals.
Application information: Contributes only to a
pre-selected organization.
Trustees: Jane E. Brenner; Carl H. Smith, Jr.; Diane
C. Smith; National City Bank.
EIN: 386637604

1286
Louise Tuller Miller Trust

c/o JPMorgan Chase Bank, N.A.
611 Woodward Ave. MI1-8113
Detroit, MI   48226   (313) 225-2549
Contact: Harry L. Hunter, Asst. V.P., Bank One,
Michigan
FAX: (313) 225-3948;
E-mail: harry_hunter@bancone.com

Established in 1961 in MI.
Donor: Louise Tuller Miller†.
Grantmaker type: Independent foundation.
Financial data (yr. ended 6/30/05): Assets,
$1,408,874 (M); expenditures, $98,985; total
giving, $84,390; qualifying distributions, $84,390;
giving activities include $84,390 for grants.
Purpose and activities: Giving primarily for civic and
educational organizations.
Fields of interest: Arts; Education; Human services;
Children/youth, services.
Type of support: General/operating support;
Continuing support; Annual campaigns; Capital
campaigns; Endowments; Program development;
Curriculum development; Scholarship funds.
Limitations: Giving limited to Traverse City and
southeastern MI.
Publications: Application guidelines.
Application information: Application form not
required.
Initial approach: Letter
Copies of proposal: 2

Deadline(s): None
Board meeting date(s): Varies
Trustees: Harry S. Stark; JPMorgan Chase Bank,
N.A.
EIN: 386046007

1287
The Millman-Harris-Romano Foundation

10 Circular Rd.
Poughkeepsie, NY   12601

Established in 2001 in NY.
Donors: Salvatore Romano†; Jode Millman; Michael
C. Harris.
Grantmaker type: Independent foundation.
Financial data (yr. ended 12/31/05): Assets,
$1,116,709 (M); expenditures, $72,978; total
giving, $66,401; qualifying distributions, $72,978;
giving activities include $66,401 for grants.
Fields of interest: Arts; Education; Medical
research.
Type of support: Annual campaigns; Equipment;
Program development; Matching/challenge support.
Limitations: Applications not accepted. Giving
primarily in Ann Arbor, MI, and NY. No grants to
individuals.
Application information: Contributes only to
pre-selected organizations.
Officers and Directors:* Jode Millman,* Pres.; Ellin
R. Millman,* V.P.; Michael C. Harris,* Secy.-Treas.
Number of staff: 1 full-time professional; 1 part-time
support.
EIN: 141833603

1288
Frances Goll Mills Fund

c/o Citizens Bank Wealth Management, N.A.
328 S. Saginaw St., MC 002072
Flint, MI   48502
Application address: c/o Citizens Bank Wealth
Mgmt., N.A., Attn.: Helen James, 101 N. Washington
Ave., Saginaw, MI 48607, tel.: (989) 776-7368

Established in 1982 in MI.
Donor: Frances Goll Mills†.
Grantmaker type: Independent foundation.
Financial data (yr. ended 9/30/05): Assets,
$5,431,538 (M); expenditures, $289,992; total
giving, $225,325; qualifying distributions,
$252,769; giving activities include $225,325 for 13
grants (high: $50,000; low: $4,000).
Purpose and activities: Giving primarily for social
services and churches.
Fields of interest: Museums (marine/maritime);
Performing arts, theater; Arts; Libraries/library
science; Education; Health care; Boy scouts;
Salvation Army; Federated giving programs;
Protestant agencies & churches.
Type of support: General/operating support;
Continuing support; Building/renovation;
Equipment; Emergency funds; Seed money;
Consulting services; Matching/challenge support.
Limitations: Giving limited to MI. No grants to
individuals, or for annual campaigns, deficit
financing, endowments, special programs,
scholarships, fellowships, professorships, or
internships; no loans.
Publications: Application guidelines.
Application information: Application form required.
Initial approach: Letter or proposal requesting
application guidelines

Copies of proposal: 1
Deadline(s): None
Board meeting date(s): 3rd Thurs. of Mar., June,
Sept., and Dec.
Final notification: 1 week after meeting
Trustee: Citizens Bank, N.A.
EIN: 382434002

1289
The Millward Family Foundation

c/o Daniel Millward
606 Hidden Valley Rd.
Traverse City, MI   49686-1671

Established in 1998 in MI.
Donors: Daniel Millward; Laura Millward.
Grantmaker type: Independent foundation.
Financial data (yr. ended 12/31/04): Assets,
$62,072 (M); gifts received, $14,000;
expenditures, $4,046; total giving, $3,325;
qualifying distributions, $4,036; giving activities
include $3,325 for 2 grants (high: $2,175; low:
$1,150).
Fields of interest: Protestant agencies & churches.
Type of support: General/operating support.
Limitations: Applications not accepted. Giving
primarily in Traverse City, MI. No grants to
individuals.
Application information: Contributes only to
pre-selected organizations.
Officers: Daniel Millward, Pres.; Christopher
Millward, V.P.; Laura Millward, Secy.-Treas.
EIN: 383419904

1290
Allan C. Mims & Margaret L. Mims Charitable Trust

c/o Comerica Bank
P.O. Box 75000, MC 3302
Detroit, MI   48275-3302

Established in 2000 in NC.
Grantmaker type: Independent foundation.
Financial data (yr. ended 12/31/05): Assets,
$1,453,321 (M); expenditures, $98,344; total
giving, $65,000; qualifying distributions, $65,000;
giving activities include $65,000 for grants.
Fields of interest: Higher education; Scholarships/
financial aid.
Type of support: Scholarship funds.
Limitations: Applications not accepted. Giving
primarily in Rocky Mount, NC. No grants to
individuals.
Application information: Contributes only to
pre-selected organizations.
Trustees: Thomas A. Betts, Jr.; Lou Uzzle Blackman;
William S. Carver II; Joseph Manning; Patricia Uzzle;
Comerica Bank.
EIN: 566207750

1291
Katharine B. Miner Charitable

c/o JPMorgan Chase Bank, N.A.
P.O. Box 1308
Milwaukee, WI   53201
Contact: Hal Boyd
Application address: c/o JPMorgan Chase Bank,
N.A., 111 E. Court St., Flint, MI 48502, tel.: (810)
237-3801

Established in MI.
Grantmaker type: Independent foundation.
Financial data (yr. ended 10/31/05): Assets, $783,862 (M); expenditures, $42,725; total giving, $33,929; qualifying distributions, $33,929; giving activities include $33,929 for grants.
Fields of interest: Arts; Health care; Youth development.
Limitations: Giving limited to MI, with emphasis on Flint. No grants to individuals.
Application information:
  Initial approach: Letter
  Deadline(s): None
Trustee: JPMorgan Chase Bank, N.A.
EIN: 386419379

1292
The Minkin Family Foundation
c/o S. Sam Tootalian
37000 Woodward Ave., Ste. 200
Bloomfield Hills, MI   48304-0924

Established in 1995 in MI.
Donors: Philip S. Minkin; Edna Minkin.
Grantmaker type: Independent foundation.
Financial data (yr. ended 12/31/04): Assets, $1,712,794 (M); gifts received, $98,996; expenditures, $73,089; total giving, $61,435; qualifying distributions, $61,435; giving activities include $61,435 for 41 grants (high: $20,000; low: $100).
Purpose and activities: Giving primarily to Jewish agencies, temples, schools and federated giving programs, and for health care and health associations.
Fields of interest: Elementary/secondary education; Theological school/education; Hospitals (general); Health organizations, association; Jewish federated giving programs; Jewish agencies & temples.
Limitations: Applications not accepted. Giving primarily in MI. No grants to individuals.
Application information: Contributes only to pre-selected organizations.
Officer and Directors:* Philip S. Minkin,* Pres. and Secy.-Treas.; Edna Minkin; Jerold R. Minkin; Richard A. Minkin.
EIN: 383259421

1293
Mirafzali Foundation
1125 Country Club Rd.
Ann Arbor, MI   48105

Established in 1998 in MI.
Donors: Hamid Mirafzali; Shadan Mirafzali.
Grantmaker type: Independent foundation.
Financial data (yr. ended 12/31/04): Assets, $0 (M); expenditures, $105,058; total giving, $105,000; qualifying distributions, $105,000; giving activities include $105,000 for 1 grant.
Fields of interest: Bahai; Religion.
Limitations: Applications not accepted. Giving primarily in MI. No grants to individuals.
Application information: Contributes only to pre-selected organizations.
Officers: Hamid Mirafzali, Pres.; Shadan Mirafzali, Secy.
EIN: 383439162

1294
The Marsha and Jeffrey H. Miro Foundation
38500 N. Woodward Ave., Ste. 100
Bloomfield Hills, MI   48304

Established in 1987 in MI.
Donors: Jeffrey H. Miro; Marsha Miro.
Grantmaker type: Independent foundation.
Financial data (yr. ended 11/30/05): Assets, $23,751 (M); expenditures, $2,978; total giving, $2,750; qualifying distributions, $2,750; giving activities include $2,750 for grants.
Fields of interest: Arts; Education; Jewish federated giving programs; Jewish agencies & temples.
Limitations: Applications not accepted. Giving primarily in Detroit, MI. No grants to individuals.
Application information: Contributes only to pre-selected organizations.
Officers and Directors:* Jeffrey H. Miro,* Chair. and Treas.; Marsha Miro,* Pres. and Secy.
EIN: 382782958

1295
Missad Foundation
3987 Bridge Stone Dr. N.E.
Grand Rapids, MI   49546

Established in 1991 in MI.
Donors: Matthew J. Missad; Universal Forest Products, Inc.
Grantmaker type: Independent foundation.
Financial data (yr. ended 12/31/04): Assets, $273,094 (M); gifts received, $48,360; expenditures, $19,895; total giving, $19,471; qualifying distributions, $19,895; giving activities include $19,471 for grants.
Fields of interest: Education; Health care; Human services; Christian agencies & churches.
Limitations: Applications not accepted. Giving primarily in Grand Rapids, MI. No grants to individuals.
Application information: Contributes only to pre-selected organizations.
Directors: John E. Missad; Matthew J. Missad; Scott N. Missad.
EIN: 383016826

1296
Neelam-Popat Mistry Memorial Foundation
6862 Cambridge St.
West Bloomfield, MI   48322

Established in 2001 in MI.
Donors: Satish Mistry; Suhasini Mistry; Praveen Soni.
Grantmaker type: Independent foundation.
Financial data (yr. ended 12/31/04): Assets, $119,478 (M); gifts received, $10,000; expenditures, $6,064; total giving, $5,676; qualifying distributions, $5,676; giving activities include $5,676 for grants.
Limitations: Applications not accepted. No grants to individuals.
Application information: Contributes only to pre-selected organizations.
Directors: Mehul Mistry; Satish Mistry; Suhasini Mistry.
EIN: 383624652

1297
Misuraca Family Fund
316 1/2 S. Main St., Ste. 202
Royal Oak, MI   48067

Established in 2000 in MI.
Donor: Samuel Misuraca.
Grantmaker type: Independent foundation.
Financial data (yr. ended 12/31/05): Assets, $6,547 (M); expenditures, $351; total giving, $0; qualifying distributions, $0.
Fields of interest: Human services.
Limitations: Applications not accepted. Giving primarily in Detroit, MI. No grants to individuals.
Application information: Contributes only to pre-selected organizations.
Officer: Samuel Misuraca, Pres.
EIN: 383544754

1298
The Mitchell Family Foundation
c/o Daniel J. LaValley
5800 Monroe St., Bldg. F
Sylvania, OH   43560
Application address: c/o William C. Mitchell, 3150 N. Republic Blvd., Ste. 3, Toledo, OH 43615, tel.: (419) 841-2512

Established in 1995 in OH.
Donor: William C. Mitchell.
Grantmaker type: Independent foundation.
Financial data (yr. ended 12/31/05): Assets, $200,948 (M); expenditures, $8,685; total giving, $7,250; qualifying distributions, $7,250; giving activities include $7,250 for grants.
Fields of interest: Arts; Federated giving programs.
Type of support: General/operating support.
Limitations: Giving primarily in northwest OH and southeast MI. No grants to individuals.
Application information:
  Initial approach: Letter
  Deadline(s): None
Officers and Trustees:* William C. Mitchell,* Pres.; Stephen B. Mitchell,* V.P.; Daniel J. LaValley,* Secy.
EIN: 311422869

1299
Mitchell Foundation
P.O. Box 1592
Owosso, MI   48867
Contact: Lara Wetzel, Tr.

Established in 1962 in MI.
Grantmaker type: Independent foundation.
Financial data (yr. ended 12/31/05): Assets, $125,766 (M); expenditures, $6,751; total giving, $5,937; qualifying distributions, $5,937; giving activities include $5,937 for grants.
Fields of interest: Crime/law enforcement, administration/regulation; Crime/violence prevention, domestic violence; Youth development, services; Human services.
Type of support: Building/renovation; Equipment; Program development.
Limitations: Giving primarily in Benzie, Shiawassee, and Wexford counties, MI. No grants to individuals.
Application information: Application form not required.
  Initial approach: Letter

Trustees: Christine L. Mitchell; William F. Mitchell; Lara Wetzel.
EIN: 386091190

1300
The Celia Moh Foundation
23232 Peralta Dr., Ste. 210
Laguna Hills, CA   92653

Established in 2002 in NC.
Grantmaker type: Independent foundation.
Financial data (yr. ended 12/31/03): Assets, $3,329,640 (M); gifts received, $1,331,890; expenditures, $759,993; total giving, $723,676; qualifying distributions, $723,676; giving activities include $723,676 for 5 grants (high: $615,022; low: $11,294).
Purpose and activities: Scholarship awards to college students in a home furnishing program.
Fields of interest: Higher education; Scholarships/financial aid.
Limitations: Giving primarily in MI and NC.
Application information: Application form required.
    Deadline(s): Last Fri. in Feb.
Officers: Joe Carroll, Pres.; Lyle T. Lansdell, Treas.
Directors: Celia Moh; Michael Moh; R. Ted Weschler.
EIN: 680492736

1301
Ramesh K. and Hem P. Mohindra Foundation
(formerly Cancer Foundation of India)
4403 Landing Dr.
West Bloomfield, MI   48323

Established in 1984.
Grantmaker type: Independent foundation.
Financial data (yr. ended 8/31/05): Assets, $1,336,238 (M); expenditures, $10,770; total giving, $2,084; qualifying distributions, $10,770; giving activities include $2,084 for grants.
Fields of interest: Religion.
Type of support: General/operating support.
Limitations: Applications not accepted. Giving primarily in MI. No support for political organizations. No grants to individuals.
Application information: Contributes only to pre-selected organizations.
Officers: Ramesh K. Mohindra, Pres.; Hem P. Mohindra, Secy.
EIN: 382554784

1302
Mohler Family Foundation
c/o A.G. Edwards Trust Co.
P.O. Box 66734
St. Louis, MO   63166

Established in 1998 in MO.
Donor: A.G. Edwards.
Grantmaker type: Independent foundation.
Financial data (yr. ended 12/31/05): Assets, $895,343 (M); expenditures, $50,828; total giving, $43,218; qualifying distributions, $43,218; giving activities include $43,218 for grants.
Fields of interest: Education; Roman Catholic agencies & churches.
Limitations: Applications not accepted. Giving limited to MI. No grants to individuals.

Application information: Contributes only to pre-selected organizations.
Trustee: A.G. Edwards Trust Co.
EIN: 436782973

1303
Mojo Foundation
5940 Tahoe Dr. S.E.
Grand Rapids, MI   49546-7121   (616) 455-0200
Contact: Michael A. McGraw, Pres.

Established in 1996 in MI.
Donor: Michael A. McGraw.
Grantmaker type: Independent foundation.
Financial data (yr. ended 12/31/04): Assets, $3,573,850 (M); gifts received, $1,344,716; expenditures, $106,440; total giving, $82,500; qualifying distributions, $82,520; giving activities include $82,500 for grants.
Fields of interest: Children, services; Christian agencies & churches.
Limitations: Giving primarily in Grand Rapids, MI. No grants to individuals.
Application information:
    Initial approach: Letter
    Deadline(s): None
Officers: Michael A. McGraw, Pres.; Joshua D. McGraw, V.P.; Michael R. McGraw, V.P.; Kenneth R. Besteman, Secy.-Treas.
EIN: 383325750

1304
Mol Family Foundation
P.O. Box 261024
Highlands Ranch, CO   80163
Contact: Ronald M. Mol, Chair.

Established in 1993 in MI.
Donor: Edward K. Mol‡.
Grantmaker type: Independent foundation.
Financial data (yr. ended 12/31/04): Assets, $2,981,520 (M); expenditures, $315,388; total giving, $290,600; qualifying distributions, $292,170; giving activities include $290,600 for 17 grants (high: $100,000; low: $1,000).
Fields of interest: Christian agencies & churches.
Limitations: Applications not accepted. Giving primarily in Grand Rapids, MI. No grants to individuals.
Application information: Contributes only to pre-selected organizations.
    Board meeting date(s): June and Dec.
Officer and Trustees:* Ronald M. Mol,* Chair.; Jeffrey Batchelder; Brant Cuthbert; Edward T. Mol.
EIN: 383152069
Selected grants: The following grants were reported in 2003.
$67,300 to Association of Baptists for World Evangelism, New Cumberland, PA.
$50,000 to Cornerstone University, Grand Rapids, MI.
$20,000 to Grand Rapids Baptist Schools, Grand Rapids, MI.
$17,000 to Words of Hope, Grand Rapids, MI.
$15,000 to Cadence International, Englewood, CO.
$15,000 to Caleb Project, Littleton, CO.
$15,000 to Trans World Radio, Cary, NC.
$6,000 to Radio Bible Class, Grand Rapids, MI.
$5,000 to Baptists for Life, Grand Rapids, MI.
$4,000 to Childrens Bible Hour, Grand Rapids, MI.

1305
Molinello Family Foundation
P.O. Box 721067
Berkley, MI   48072-0067   (248) 544-2775
Contact: Earl C. Bossenberry, Pres.

Established in 2000 in MI.
Donors: Richard Molinello Revocable Trust; John Molinello Revocable Trust.
Grantmaker type: Independent foundation.
Financial data (yr. ended 12/31/05): Assets, $16,751,432 (M); expenditures, $803,056; total giving, $664,690; qualifying distributions, $803,056; giving activities include $664,690 for 26 grants (high: $47,130; low: $2,000).
Fields of interest: Health care; Medical research, institute; Human services; Christian agencies & churches; Blind/visually impaired; Economically disadvantaged.
Limitations: Giving primarily in MI.
Application information:
    Initial approach: Letter
    Deadline(s): None
Officers: Earl C. Bossenberry, Pres.; Rita Morelli, V.P.
EIN: 383494266
Selected grants: The following grants were reported in 2003.
$35,000 to National Shrine of the Little Flower Catholic Church, Royal Oak, MI.
$24,576 to Barbara Ann Karmanos Cancer Institute, Detroit, MI.
$24,576 to Capuchin Soup Kitchen, Detroit, MI.
$24,576 to Guest House, Lake Orion, MI. For program support.
$24,576 to Leader Dogs for the Blind, Rochester, MI.
$24,576 to Little Sisters of the Poor, Detroit, MI.
$24,576 to March of Dimes Birth Defects Foundation, Southfield, MI.
$24,576 to Saint Jude Childrens Research Hospital, Memphis, TN.
$24,576 to Saint Vincent de Paul Society, Detroit, MI.
$2,000 to Angels Place, Southfield, MI.

1306
Molitor Family Foundation
53196 N. Main St.
Mattawan, MI   49071

Established in 2003 in MI.
Donors: Joan A. Molitor; Ronald A. Molitor.
Grantmaker type: Independent foundation.
Financial data (yr. ended 12/31/04): Assets, $4,927 (M); gifts received, $114,500; expenditures, $115,721; total giving, $112,875; qualifying distributions, $112,875; giving activities include $112,875 for 78 grants (high: $36,000; low: $75).
Fields of interest: Education; Medical research; Crime/violence prevention, abuse prevention; Housing/shelter; Human services; Children/youth, services; International relief; Federated giving programs; Protestant agencies & churches.
Limitations: Applications not accepted. Giving on a national basis, with some emphasis on MI. No grants to individuals.
Application information: Contributes only to pre-selected organizations.
Officers and Trustees:* Ronald A. Molitor,* Pres.; Christine J. Molitor,* V.P.; Derek R. Molitor,* V.P.;

Matthew R. Molitor,* V.P.; Michelle L. Molitor,* V.P.; Joan A. Molitor,* Secy.-Treas.
EIN: 352199665

1307
Molloy Foundation, Inc.
P.O. Box 200
St. Clair Shores, MI   48080

Established in 1962 in MI.
Donor: Brian J. Molloy‡.
Grantmaker type: Independent foundation.
Financial data (yr. ended 1/31/05): Assets, $1,012,583 (M); expenditures, $97,664; total giving, $23,325; qualifying distributions, $23,325; giving activities include $23,325 for grants.
Fields of interest: Education; Human services; Roman Catholic agencies & churches.
Type of support: General/operating support; Continuing support.
Limitations: Giving primarily in MI. No grants to individuals.
Application information: Application form not required.
Initial approach: Letter
Deadline(s): None
Officers: Therese M. Molloy, Pres.; Brian J. Molloy, Jr., V.P.; Stephen P. Molloy, Secy.; Constance M. Kinnear, Treas.
Director: Mary Alice Molloy.
EIN: 386061859

1308
William and Marie Molnar Foundation Corp.
3565 Roland Dr.
Bloomfield Hills, MI   48301

Donors: Marie Molnar; William Molnar.
Grantmaker type: Independent foundation.
Financial data (yr. ended 12/31/05): Assets, $1,078,582 (M); gifts received, $202,389; expenditures, $46,555; total giving, $45,000; qualifying distributions, $45,000; giving activities include $45,000 for grants.
Limitations: Applications not accepted. Giving primarily in MI. No grants to individuals.
Application information: Contributes only to pre-selected organizations.
Officers: Marie Molnar, Mgr.; William Molnar, Mgr.
EIN: 383567851

1309
Ira and Gail Mondry Family Foundation
(formerly David and Miriam Mondry & Ira and Gail Mondry Family Foundation)
31098 Oakleaf Ln.
Franklin, MI   48025-1262

Established in 1978 in MI.
Donor: David Mondry.
Grantmaker type: Independent foundation.
Financial data (yr. ended 11/30/05): Assets, $236,383 (M); gifts received, $20; expenditures, $35,671; total giving, $35,701; qualifying distributions, $35,701; giving activities include $35,701 for grants.
Purpose and activities: Giving primarily for human services, and to Jewish organizations.

Fields of interest: Performing arts, music; Human services; Jewish federated giving programs.
Limitations: Applications not accepted. Giving primarily in MI. No grants to individuals.
Application information: Contributes only to pre-selected organizations.
Officers: Ira Mondry, Pres. and Treas.; Gail Mondry, Secy.
EIN: 382241543

1310
Eugene & Sheila Mondry Family Foundation
2727 S. Ocean Blvd., Ste. 1203
Highland Beach, FL   33487

Donor: Eugene Mondry.
Grantmaker type: Independent foundation.
Financial data (yr. ended 11/30/05): Assets, $1,464,541 (M); gifts received, $760,272; expenditures, $109,303; total giving, $108,786; qualifying distributions, $108,786; giving activities include $108,786 for 12 grants (high: $77,286; low: $1,000).
Purpose and activities: Giving for education and Jewish organizations.
Fields of interest: Arts; Education; Jewish federated giving programs; Jewish agencies & temples.
Limitations: Applications not accepted. Giving primarily in MI. No grants to individuals.
Application information: Contributes only to pre-selected organizations.
Officers: Eugene Mondry, Pres.; Sheila Mondry, Secy.
EIN: 382241542
Selected grants: The following grants were reported in 2003.
$81,500 to Jewish Welfare Federation, Bloomfield Hills, MI. For general support.
$11,000 to University of Michigan, Ann Arbor, MI. 2 grants: $10,000 (For general support), $1,000 (For Hillel).
$4,000 to American Committee for the Weizmann Institute of Science, New York, NY. For general support.
$2,000 to Jewish Womens Foundation of Metropolitan Detroit, Bloomfield Hills, MI. For general support.
$2,000 to Kadima Jewish Support Services for Adults with Mental Illness, Southfield, MI. For general support.
$2,000 to United Jewish Foundation, Bloomfield Hills, MI. For general support.
$1,250 to Detroit Symphony Orchestra, Detroit, MI. For general support.
$1,000 to Cedars-Sinai Medical Center, Los Angeles, CA. For general support.
$1,000 to Michigan Association for Children with Emotional Disorders (MACED), Southfield, MI. For general support.

1311
Monroe Catholic Central High School Scholarship Fund
c/o National City Bank
P.O. Box 94651
Cleveland, OH   44101-4651

Grantmaker type: Independent foundation.
Financial data (yr. ended 12/31/05): Assets, $1,204,553 (M); expenditures, $65,569; total

giving, $56,000; qualifying distributions, $56,000; giving activities include $56,000 for grants.
Purpose and activities: Support only to St. Mary's Catholic Central High School, MI, for their scholarship program.
Fields of interest: Secondary school/education; Roman Catholic agencies & churches.
Type of support: Scholarship funds.
Limitations: Applications not accepted. Giving limited to Monroe, MI. No grants to individuals.
Application information: Contributes only to a pre-selected organization.
Trustee: National City Bank.
EIN: 386177355

1312
George and Amy Monroe Foundation, Inc.
c/o National City Bank of the Midwest
108 E. Michigan Ave.
Kalamazoo, MI   49007

Established in 1986 in MI.
Donor: Amy C. Monroe.
Grantmaker type: Independent foundation.
Financial data (yr. ended 12/31/05): Assets, $2,132,966 (M); expenditures, $150,945; total giving, $133,000; qualifying distributions, $133,605; giving activities include $133,000 for 26 grants (high: $20,000; low: $1,000).
Fields of interest: Education; Human services; Youth, services; Family services; Christian agencies & churches.
Limitations: Applications not accepted. Giving primarily in Kalamazoo, MI. No grants to individuals.
Application information: Contributes only to pre-selected organizations.
Advisors: Amy W. Mehaffie; Constance Monroe Mehaffie; Hugh Mehaffie; Stephen Blackmar Monroe II.
Trustee: National City Bank of the Midwest.
EIN: 382701662

1313
Monroe-Brown Foundation
7950 Moorsbridge Rd.
Portage, MI   49024   (269) 324-5586
Contact: Jane Baker, Dir.
FAX: (269) 324-0686;
E-mail: info@monroebrown.org; e-mail for Jane Baker: jbaker@monroebrown.org; URL: http://www.monroebrown.org

Incorporated in 1983 in MI.
Donors: Albertine M. Brown‡; Robert J. Brown‡; Robert M. Brown; Gail B. Kasdorf; Jane B. Todd; Robert J. Brown Charitable Lead Trust.
Grantmaker type: Independent foundation.
Financial data (yr. ended 12/31/05): Assets, $15,820,156 (M); gifts received, $153,562; expenditures, $946,452; total giving, $760,906; qualifying distributions, $831,318; giving activities include $760,906 for 39 grants (high: $146,000; low: $100).
Purpose and activities: Support primarily for education and community improvement.
Fields of interest: Arts; Higher education; Education; Human services; Urban/community development; Foundations (community).
Type of support: Annual campaigns; Capital campaigns; Building/renovation; Program development; Matching/challenge support.

Limitations: Giving primarily in the Kalamazoo, MI area. No grants to individuals.
Publications: Application guidelines.
Application information: Application guidelines and form available on foundation Web site. Application form required.
  Initial approach: Letter
  Copies of proposal: 7
  Deadline(s): Mar. 31, June 30, Sept. 30, and Nov. 20
  Board meeting date(s): Apr., July, Oct. and Dec.
Officers and Trustees:* Robert M. Brown,* Pres.; Gail B. Kasdorf,* V.P.; Jane B. Todd,* Treas.; Frederick O. Brown; Robert M. Brown, Jr.; A. John Todd; John C. Wattles.
Director: Jane Baker.
Number of staff: 1 full-time professional.
EIN: 382513263

1314
Montague Foundation
1 Hillside Ct.
Ann Arbor, MI   48104

Established in 1996 in MI.
Donors: Menakka W. Bailey; Essel W. Bailey, Jr.
Grantmaker type: Independent foundation.
Financial data (yr. ended 9/30/05): Assets, $1 (M); expenditures, $17,405; total giving, $15,000; qualifying distributions, $15,000; giving activities include $15,000 for grants.
Fields of interest: Human services.
Type of support: General/operating support.
Limitations: Applications not accepted. Giving primarily in Ann Arbor, MI. No grants to individuals.
Application information: Contributes only to pre-selected organizations.
Officers and Trustees:* Menakka W. Bailey,* Pres.; Dyanthe McDougal,* V.P.; Essel W. Bailey, Jr.,* Treas.
EIN: 383315791

1315
Moore Brower Charitable Foundation
2153 Wealthy St., S.E.
P.O. Box 206
East Grand Rapids, MI   49506

Grantmaker type: Independent foundation.
Financial data (yr. ended 12/31/05): Assets, $42,515 (M); gifts received, $1,000; expenditures, $14; total giving, $0; qualifying distributions, $0.
Limitations: Applications not accepted. Giving primarily in Grand Rapids, MI. No grants to individuals.
Application information: Contributes only to pre-selected organizations.
Officers and Directors:* Katherine M. Brower,* Pres.; Robert D. Brower,* V.P. and Secy.-Treas.; Amy K. Brower; Andrew M. Brower; Jennifer J. Brower.
EIN: 383530460

1316
Frederick S. & Lezlynne P. Moore Family Foundation
970 N. Riverside Ave.
St. Clair, MI   48079   (810) 329-9096
Contact: Frederick S. Moore

Established in 1998 in MI.
Donors: Lezlynne P. Moore; Frederick S. Moore.
Grantmaker type: Independent foundation.
Financial data (yr. ended 12/31/04): Assets, $978,601 (M); expenditures, $46,915; total giving, $45,500; qualifying distributions, $45,750; giving activities include $45,500 for 9 grants (high: $30,000; low: $500).
Purpose and activities: Giving primarily for Protestant churches and the United Way.
Fields of interest: Human services; Federated giving programs; Protestant agencies & churches.
Type of support: General/operating support; Continuing support; Annual campaigns; Capital campaigns; Building/renovation; Equipment; Land acquisition; Emergency funds; Program-related investments/loans; Matching/challenge support.
Limitations: Giving primarily in St. Clair County, MI. No grants to individuals.
Application information: Application form not required.
  Initial approach: Letter
  Copies of proposal: 1
Trustee: Fifth Third Bank.
EIN: 383440665

1317
The C. F. Moore Foundation
c/o Lori Breyman, M & I Trust
800 Laurel Oak Dr., Ste. 101
Naples, FL   34108

Established in 1954 in MI.
Donor: Charles F. Moore†.
Grantmaker type: Independent foundation.
Financial data (yr. ended 12/31/04): Assets, $2,836,653 (M); expenditures, $192,195; total giving, $169,798; qualifying distributions, $169,465; giving activities include $169,798 for 39 grants (high: $17,500; low: $100).
Purpose and activities: Giving primarily for education, youth programs, and religious organizations.
Fields of interest: Education; Health organizations, association; Children/youth, services; Federated giving programs; Protestant agencies & churches.
Limitations: Applications not accepted. Giving primarily in Naples, FL, and St. Clair County, MI. No grants to individuals.
Application information: Contributes only to pre-selected organizations.
Trustees: Barbara W. Moore; Franklin H. Moore, Jr.; Frederick S. Moore.
EIN: 386055559
Selected grants: The following grants were reported in 2004.
$17,500 to First Church of Christ Scientist, Naples, FL.
$10,000 to First Congregational Church, Saint Clair, MI.
$5,000 to American Red Cross, Collier County Chapter, Naples, FL.
$5,000 to Salvation Army of Naples, Naples, FL.
$5,000 to United Way of Collier County, Naples, FL.
$4,000 to Hospice of Naples, Naples, FL.
$4,000 to YMCA of Collier County, Bonita Springs, FL.
$4,000 to Youth Haven, Naples, FL.
$2,000 to Conservancy of Southwest Florida, Naples, FL.
$1,000 to Philharmonic Center for the Arts, Naples, FL.

1318
The Franklin H. and Nancy S. Moore Foundation
633 E. Meldrum Cir.
St. Clair, MI   48079

Established in MI in 1997; funded in 2004.
Grantmaker type: Independent foundation.
Financial data (yr. ended 12/31/05): Assets, $1,124,263 (M); expenditures, $40,615; total giving, $35,500; qualifying distributions, $34,742; giving activities include $35,500 for grants.
Fields of interest: Human services.
Type of support: General/operating support.
Limitations: Applications not accepted. Giving primarily in MI. No grants to individuals.
Application information: Contributes only to pre-selected organizations.
Officers: Franklin H. Moore, Jr.,* Pres. and Treas.; Nancy S. Moore,* Secy.
Directors: Elizabeth Bishop; Franklin H. Moore; Walter E. Moore; Jennifer M. Rynne.
EIN: 383388238

1319
Mary Moore Foundation
c/o Fifth Third Bank
P.O. Box 630858
Cincinnati, OH   45263
Contact: Franklin H. Moore, Jr., Pres.
Application address: 200 S. Riverside, St. Clair, MI 48079

Established in 1950.
Grantmaker type: Independent foundation.
Financial data (yr. ended 12/31/04): Assets, $1,140,183 (M); expenditures, $47,219; total giving, $40,000; qualifying distributions, $40,000; giving activities include $40,000 for grants.
Purpose and activities: Giving primarily to Christian organizations and churches and for health and human services.
Fields of interest: Health care; Human services; YM/YWCAs & YM/YWHAs; Children/youth, services; Community development; Federated giving programs; Christian agencies & churches.
Type of support: General/operating support; Program development.
Limitations: Giving primarily in St. Clair, MI. No grants to individuals.
Application information:
  Initial approach: Letter
  Deadline(s): None
Officers: Franklin H. Moore, Jr., Pres.; Frederick S. Moore, V.P.; Charles W. Staiger, Secy.-Treas.
Agent: Fifth Third Bank.
EIN: 386097348

1320
Joan I. & John R. Moore III Foundation
c/o Comerica Bank
P.O. Box 75000, MC 3300
Detroit, MI   48275-3300   (313) 222-5257
Contact: Paula Gralewski, Trust Off., Comerica Bank

Established in 2000 in OH.
Grantmaker type: Independent foundation.
Financial data (yr. ended 12/31/05): Assets, $246,101 (M); expenditures, $15,367; total giving, $12,000; qualifying distributions, $12,000; giving activities include $12,000 for grants.

Fields of interest: Roman Catholic agencies & churches.
Application information:
Initial approach: Letter
Deadline(s): None
Trustee: Comerica Bank.
EIN: 386752915

1321
Carl & Irene Morath Foundation, Inc.
3502 Country Club Dr.
St. Clair Shores, MI 48082
Contact: Carl Morath, Pres.

Donors: Carl Morath; Irene Morath.
Grantmaker type: Independent foundation.
Financial data (yr. ended 12/31/04): Assets, $658,974 (M); gifts received, $5,000; expenditures, $45,636; total giving, $45,680; qualifying distributions, $45,680; giving activities include $45,680 for grants.
Purpose and activities: Giving primarily for Roman Catholic missionary work.
Fields of interest: Higher education; Food banks; Human services; Religious federated giving programs; Roman Catholic agencies & churches.
International interests: Mexico; Taiwan.
Limitations: Giving on a national and international basis. No grants to individuals.
Application information:
Initial approach: Letter
Deadline(s): None
Officers: Carl Morath, Pres.; Irene Morath, V.P.; Paul Morath, Secy.-Treas.
EIN: 382421500

1322
The London and Mary Morawski Charitable Foundation
15850 Common Rd.
Roseville, MI 48066

Established in 1998 in MI.
Donors: London Morawski; Mary Morawski.
Grantmaker type: Independent foundation.
Financial data (yr. ended 12/31/05): Assets, $469,418 (M); expenditures, $37,270; total giving, $36,000; qualifying distributions, $36,000; giving activities include $36,000 for grants.
Type of support: General/operating support.
Limitations: Applications not accepted. No grants to individuals.
Application information: Contributes only to pre-selected organizations.
Officers: London Morawski, Pres.; Mary Morawski, Secy.-Treas.
EIN: 382974496

1323
The Morey Foundation
P.O. Box 1000
Winn, MI 48896
Contact: Lon Morey, Pres.

Established in 1990 in MI.
Donor: Norval Morey.
Grantmaker type: Independent foundation.
Financial data (yr. ended 12/31/05): Assets, $37,432,216 (M); expenditures, $854,067; total giving, $422,564; qualifying distributions,

$422,564; giving activities include $422,564 for grants.
Purpose and activities: Giving to the Central Michigan University, for its scholarship program for qualified students.
Fields of interest: Higher education; Education; Human services.
Type of support: Scholarship funds.
Limitations: Giving primarily in MI. No grants to individuals directly.
Application information: Application form required for scholarship requests.
Initial approach: Letter
Deadline(s): Mar. 15 for Scholarships; none for grants
Officers and Trustee: * Lon Morey,* Pres.; Jeffery Power, Secy.; Larry H. Hoch, Treas.
Directors: Krista Morey; Terra Morey.
EIN: 382965346

1324
Barbara Morgan Memorial Trust
c/o Citizens Bank Wealth Mgmt., N.A.
328 S. Saginaw St., M/C 002072
Flint, MI 48502 (989) 776-7369
Application address: c/o Helen James, Citizens Bank Wealth Mgmt., N.A., 101 N. Washington Ave., Saginaw, MI 48607, tel.: (989) 776-7368

Established in 1998 in MI.
Donor: Barbara Morgan Trust.
Grantmaker type: Independent foundation.
Financial data (yr. ended 12/31/05): Assets, $126,510 (M); expenditures, $10,554; total giving, $7,797; qualifying distributions, $7,797; giving activities include $7,797 for grants.
Fields of interest: Elementary/secondary education; Community development, public education.
Type of support: General/operating support.
Limitations: Giving limited to Saginaw, MI. No grants to individuals.
Application information: Application form required.
Deadline(s): None
Trustee: Citizens Bank.
EIN: 383413062

1325
Morley Foundation
(formerly Morley Brothers Foundation)
P.O. Box 2485
Saginaw, MI 48605-2485 (989) 753-3438
Contact: Robert S. Morley, Pres.

Incorporated in 1948 in MI.
Donors: Ralph Chase Morley, Sr.†; Mrs. Ralph Chase Morley, Sr.†.
Grantmaker type: Independent foundation.
Financial data (yr. ended 12/31/04): Assets, $5,953,546 (M); expenditures, $353,187; total giving, $264,794; qualifying distributions, $305,722; giving activities include $264,794 for 65 grants (high: $75,000; low: $100).
Purpose and activities: Giving primarily for arts and culture, including museums and fine arts, secondary and higher education, organizations providing assistance to students, youth and welfare, health and hospitals, community development, and civic improvement. Ninety-five percent of grants are restricted to the greater Saginaw County, MI, area.

Fields of interest: Museums; Performing arts; Arts; Elementary school/education; Secondary school/ education; Higher education; Business school/ education; Education; Hospitals (general); Health care; Health organizations, association; Human services; Children/youth, services; Community development.
Type of support: General/operating support; Continuing support; Annual campaigns; Capital campaigns; Building/renovation; Equipment; Emergency funds; Program development; Seed money; Research; Employee matching gifts; Matching/challenge support.
Limitations: Giving primarily in the greater Saginaw County, MI, area. No grants to individuals, or for endowment funds, deficit financing, land acquisition, renovation projects, publications, or conferences; no loans.
Publications: Application guidelines; Informational brochure.
Application information: No renewal grants will be made for longer than 3 years. Application form required.
Initial approach: Letter
Copies of proposal: 1
Deadline(s): None
Board meeting date(s): Feb., May, Aug., and Nov.
Final notification: 3 months
Officers and Trustees: * Robert S. Morley,* Pres.; Mark B. Morley,* V.P.; Lois K. Guttowsky,* Secy.; David H. Morley,* Treas.; Carol Morley Beck; Michael M. Brand; Burrows Morley, Jr.; Christopher Morley; George B. Morley, Jr.; Katharyn Morley; Peter B. Morley; Richard B. Thomson, Jr.
Number of staff: 1 part-time professional.
EIN: 386055569
Selected grants: The following grants were reported in 2004.
$75,000 to Saginaw Art Museum, Saginaw, MI.
$14,800 to Delta College, University Center, MI.
$14,500 to Napoleon Athletic Boosters, Napoleon, OH.
$14,000 to Council of Michigan Foundations, Grand Haven, MI.
$10,000 to Interlochen Center for the Arts, Interlochen, MI.
$10,000 to Opportunities Industrialization Center of Metropolitan Saginaw, Saginaw, MI.
$5,000 to Boys and Girls Club of Saginaw County, Saginaw, MI.
$3,500 to Child Abuse and Neglect Council of Saginaw County, Saginaw, MI.
$3,000 to Child and Family Service of Saginaw County, Saginaw, MI.
$3,000 to Good Neighbor Mission, Saginaw, MI.

1326
Mary D. Morman Trust
c/o Comerica Bank
P.O. Box 75000
Detroit, MI 48275-0001

Donor: Mary D. Morman†.
Grantmaker type: Independent foundation.
Financial data (yr. ended 2/28/05): Assets, $295,938 (M); expenditures, $17,891; total giving, $13,500; qualifying distributions, $13,500; giving activities include $13,500 for grants.
Purpose and activities: Support only for Grand Rapids Foundation, MI.
Fields of interest: Foundations (community).
Type of support: General/operating support.

Limitations: Applications not accepted. Giving limited to Grand Rapids, MI. No grants to individuals.
Application information: Contributes only to a pre-selected organization.
Trustee: Comerica Bank.
EIN: 386535128

1327
James K. Morrill Scholarship Fund
c/o Fifth Third Bank
P.O. Box 3636
Grand Rapids, MI 49501-3636
Application address: c/o Brattleboro Union High School District, Attn.: Guidance Counselor, 131 Fairground Rd., Brattleboro, VT 05301 or c/o Holyoke High School, Attn.: Guidance Counselor, 500 Beech St., Holyoke, MA 01040

Established in 1995 in IL.
Grantmaker type: Independent foundation.
Financial data (yr. ended 12/31/05): Assets, $1,342,523 (M); expenditures, $55,846; total giving, $33,740; qualifying distributions, $33,740; giving activities include $33,740 for grants.
Purpose and activities: Scholarship awards to female graduates from Brattleboro Union High School District, VT or Holyoke High School, MA; giving also for Holyoke High School.
Fields of interest: Secondary school/education; Higher education.
Type of support: Scholarships—to individuals.
Limitations: Giving only to Brattleboro, VT and Holyoke, MA.
Application information: Application form required.
  Initial approach: Format provided by schools
  Deadline(s): May 10
Trustee: Fifth Third Bank.
EIN: 367112892

1328
Morrison Family Foundation
1825 Monroe Ave. N.W.
Grand Rapids, MI 49505-6240

Established in 1996 in MI.
Grantmaker type: Independent foundation.
Financial data (yr. ended 12/31/05): Assets, $189,996 (M); gifts received, $25,000; expenditures, $6,839; total giving, $6,200; qualifying distributions, $6,200; giving activities include $6,200 for grants.
Fields of interest: Arts.
Type of support: General/operating support.
Limitations: Applications not accepted. No grants to individuals.
Application information: Contributes only to pre-selected organizations.
Officers: Mary F. Morrison, Pres.; John W. Morrison, V.P.; William J. Morrison, Secy.; Richard G. Morrison, Treas.
EIN: 383324749

1329
The Mosaic Foundation of R. & P. Heydon
2394 Winewood St.
P.O. Box 7801
Ann Arbor, MI 48107-7801

Established in 1990 in MI.

Donors: Kenneth F. Montgomery; Peter N. Heydon; Henrietta M. Heydon.
Grantmaker type: Independent foundation.
Financial data (yr. ended 12/31/04): Assets, $2,778,320 (M); expenditures, $400,809; total giving, $365,529; qualifying distributions, $366,984; giving activities include $365,529 for 118 grants (high: $37,500; low: $100), and $1,445 for 1 loan/program-related investment.
Purpose and activities: Giving primarily for the arts and education.
Fields of interest: Media, radio; Museums; Performing arts; Arts; Elementary/secondary education; Higher education; Environment; Animals/wildlife; Human services.
Limitations: Applications not accepted. Giving in the U.S., with emphasis on MI. No grants to individuals.
Application information: Contributes only to pre-selected organizations.
Directors: James R. Beuche; Henrietta M. Heydon; Peter N. Heydon.
EIN: 382910797

1330
Moscone Family Foundation
382 Cranbrook Ct.
Bloomfield Hills, MI 48304

Established in 2003 in MI.
Donor: M. Michael Moscone.
Grantmaker type: Independent foundation.
Financial data (yr. ended 12/31/04): Assets, $3,034,296 (M); expenditures, $163,046; total giving, $153,000; qualifying distributions, $150,189; giving activities include $153,000 for grants.
Trustees: Elaine Moscone; M. Michael Moscone.
EIN: 200202931

1331
Arno & Caroline Mossner Memorial Foundation
515 S. Main St.
Frankenmuth, MI 48734-1617
Contact: William A. Mossner, Tr.

Donor: Caroline Mossner.
Grantmaker type: Independent foundation.
Financial data (yr. ended 12/31/05): Assets, $318,753 (M); expenditures, $18,493; total giving, $17,500; qualifying distributions, $17,500; giving activities include $17,500 for grants.
Fields of interest: Higher education; Human services; Protestant agencies & churches.
Limitations: Giving primarily in MI. No grants to individuals.
Application information:
  Initial approach: Letter
  Deadline(s): None
Trustees: Caroline Mossner; William A. Mossner; Lloyd J. Yeo.
EIN: 237444484

1332
Charles Stewart Mott Foundation
c/o Office of Proposal Entry
Mott Foundation Bldg.
503 S. Saginaw St., Ste. 1200
Flint, MI 48502-1851   (810) 238-5651
FAX: (810) 766-1753; E-mail: info@mott.org;
Additional E-mail: publications@mott.org;
URL: http://www.mott.org

Incorporated in 1926 in MI.
Donors: Charles Stewart Mott†; and family.
Grantmaker type: Independent foundation.
Financial data (yr. ended 12/31/05): Assets, $2,480,562,766 (M); expenditures, $137,952,616; total giving, $113,334,381; qualifying distributions, $126,989,113; giving activities include $111,716,462 for grants, $1,036,470 for 688 employee matching gifts, and $581,449 for 12 foundation-administered programs.
Purpose and activities: To support efforts that promote a just, equitable and sustainable society with the primary focus on civil society, the environment, the area of Flint, MI and poverty. The foundation makes grants for a variety of purposes within these program areas including: philanthropy and voluntarism; assisting emerging civil societies in Central/Eastern Europe, Russia and South Africa; conservation of fresh water ecosystems in North America; reform of international finance and trade; improving the outcomes for children, youth and families at risk of persistent poverty; education and neighborhood and economic development. The foundation also makes grants to strengthen the capacity of local institutions in its home community of Flint, MI.
Fields of interest: Education; Environment, pollution control; Environment, natural resources; Human services; Children, services; Child development, services; Family services, parent education; Civil rights, race/intergroup relations; Economic development; Urban/community development; Rural development; Community development; Voluntarism promotion; Leadership development; Minorities; Economically disadvantaged.
International interests: Eastern Europe; Latin America; Russia; South Africa.
Type of support: General/operating support; Continuing support; Program development; Conferences/seminars; Seed money; Technical assistance; Program evaluation; Employee matching gifts; Matching/challenge support.
Limitations: Giving nationally and to emerging countries in Central and Eastern Europe, Russia, and South Africa. No support for religious organizations for religious purposes. No grants to individuals, or for building or endowment funds in general or for research, film or video projects, books, scholarships, or fellowships.
Publications: Annual report (including application guidelines); Financial statement; Informational brochure (including application guidelines); Newsletter; Occasional report; Program policy statement.
Application information: Applicants strongly encouraged to submit proposals during first quarter of the year. Application form not required.
  Initial approach: Letter of inquiry or proposal
  Copies of proposal: 1
  Deadline(s): None; grants are determined by Aug. 31 of any given year

Board meeting date(s): Mar., June, Sept., and Dec.

Final notification: 60 to 90 days

Officers and Trustees:* William S. White,* Chair., C.E.O., and Pres.; William H. Piper,* Vice-Chair.; Maureen H. Smyth, Sr. V.P., Progs. and Comms.; Phillip H. Peters, V.P., Admin. Group, and Secy.-Treas.; Michael J. Smith, V.P., Investments, and C.I.O.; Gavin T. Clabaugh, V.P., Inf. Services; Marilyn S. LeFeber, V.P., Comms.; A. Marshall Acuff, Jr.; Rushworth M. Kidder; Tiffany W. Lovett; Webb F. Martin; Olivia P. Maynard; John Morning; Maryanne Mott; Douglas X. Patino; John W. Porter; Marise M.M. Stewart; Claire M. White.

Number of staff: 60 full-time professional; 1 part-time professional; 26 full-time support.

EIN: 381211227

Selected grants: The following grants were reported in 2005.

$2,500,000 to Foundations, Inc., Moorestown, NJ. For technical assistance for After-School Academies which will create system of services that enables after-school staff to design, implement, evaluate and manage programs that promote student success, payable over 3 years.

$2,500,000 to Nature Conservancy, Arlington, VA. For land acquisition as part of Northern Great Lakes Forest Project, payable over 6 years.

$1,500,000 to Foundation for the Uptown Reinvestment Corporation, Flint, MI. For mixed use development of three buildings in downtown Flint for use as office, restaurant and residential space adding jobs and redevelopment activity in Flint.

$1,225,000 to Collaborative Communications Group, DC. For Statewide After-School Network Meetings, initiative to promote learning and development for elementary school-age children through quality programs that provide safety and enrichment outside the traditional classroom, payable over 2 years.

$1,000,000 to Southern Education Foundation, Atlanta, GA. For regranting project which will establish Presidential Leadership Fund to benefit historically black Dillard and Xavier Universities which were forced to close due to Hurricane Katrina. Rebuilding efforts will include salaries for core administrators, faculty and staff and consulting support related to damage assessment and rebuilding and restoration of campus facilities.

$751,000 to Jobs for the Future, Boston, MA. For demonstration project/study to address challenges facing community colleges in helping low-income adults increase their skills and earnings. Study will identify better ways to move from adult basic education programs directly into college credit programs, and also try to identify effective strategies to enhance abilities of students in remedial programs to complete occupational certificates or associate degree programs.

$700,000 to Commonwealth Corporation, Boston, MA. For support for Diploma Plus, program that reconnects young people who have dropped out of school to the economy and higher education, payable over 3 years.

$652,000 to Tip of the Mitt Watershed Council, Petoskey, MI. For Great Lakes Aquatic Habitat Network and Fund, organization providing information and financial support to grassroots citizen initiatives working to protect and restore Great Lakes shorelines, inland lakes, rivers,

wetlands, and other aquatic habitats in the Great Lakes Basin, payable over 2 years.

$600,000 to Center on Budget and Policy Priorities, DC. For continued support for State Fiscal Project, effort to build state-based capacity to address issues of state budget priorities, revenue systems and program design and for State Low-Income Initiatives designed to meet challenges devolution poses by helping state organizations and policymakers develop policy options, analyze emerging proposals and consider promising new approaches to alleviating poverty, payable over 2 years.

$600,000 to Youth Law Center, San Francisco, CA. To expand policies for educational opportunities for vulnerable youth, payable over 3 years.

1333
Ruth Mott Foundation

111 E. Court St., Ste. 3C
Flint, MI 48502-1649 (810) 233-0170
Contact: Joy Murray, Fdn. Secy.
FAX: (810) 233-7022; E-mail: rmf@rmfdn.org; E-mail (for Joy Murray): jmurray@rmfdn.org; URL: http://www.ruthmottfoundation.org

Established in 1989 in MI.

Donor: Ruth R. Mott‡.

Grantmaker type: Independent foundation.

Financial data (yr. ended 12/31/04): Assets, $212,620,490 (M); gifts received, $400,000; expenditures, $9,238,493; total giving, $5,875,517; qualifying distributions, $8,725,477; giving activities include $5,875,517 for 134 grants (high: $254,000; low: $136; average: $25,000–$100,000), and $1,613,464 for 4 foundation-administered programs.

Purpose and activities: Giving primarily for community arts, community health promotion, and community beautification.

Fields of interest: Arts, cultural/ethnic awareness; Arts; Higher education; Libraries (public); Education; Health care; Youth development; Human services; Children/youth, services; Community development; Foundations (community); Federated giving programs; Protestant agencies & churches.

Type of support: General/operating support; Continuing support; Management development/capacity building; Program development; Scholarship funds; Technical assistance; Program evaluation; Matching/challenge support.

Limitations: Giving primarily in Genesee County and Flint, MI. No support for religious programs for religious purposes. No grants to individuals.

Publications: Informational brochure (including application guidelines).

Application information: Application form not required.

Initial approach: Letter (2 - 3 pages)
Deadline(s): Jan. 15, Apr. 15, and Aug. 15
Board meeting date(s): Mar., June, and Oct.
Final notification: 1 month

Officers & Trustees: Susan S. Pool, C.O.O.; Maryanne T. Mott, Pres.; Sandra K. Butler, Secy.; Herman E. Warsh, Tr. Emeritus; Charles B. Webb, Jr., Tr. Emeritus; Joseph R. Robinson; Virginia M. Sullivan.

Number of staff: 9 full-time professional; 12 full-time support; 4 part-time support.

EIN: 382876435

Selected grants: The following grants were reported in 2003.

$1,230,218 to Community Foundation of Greater Flint, Flint, MI. 4 grants: $234,000 (For Downtown Facade Improvement Program), $252,550 (For Ruth Mott Foundation Donor Advised Fund/Uptown Reinvestment Corporation/ Republic Bank Building), $550,000 (For Ruth Mott Foundation Donor Advised Fund/Meeting), $193,668 (For Summer Youth Initiative).

$500,000 to Genesee Intermediate School District, Flint, MI. For Project SKIP.

$415,788 to Genesee Coalition on Adolescent Pregnancy, Parenting, and Prevention, Flint, MI. 2 grants: $263,588 (For Carrera Model replication), $152,200 (For Parents in Process program expansion in Flint, Beecher and Mount Morris schools).

$233,000 to Flint Cultural Center Corporation, Flint, MI. For continued development of engaged community.

$175,000 to Michigan Association of Community Arts Agencies, Ann Arbor, MI. For artists in residency.

$157,943 to Michigan Primary Care Association, Okemos, MI. For school-community health alliance (nutrition, tobacco prevention and physical activity in schools).

1334
Michael & Susan Mousigian Foundation

15 Shady Hollow Dr.
Dearborn, MI 48124-1129

Established in 1987 in MI.

Donors: Michael E. Mousigian; Susan R. Mousigian.

Grantmaker type: Independent foundation.

Financial data (yr. ended 12/31/02): Assets, $85 (M); gifts received, $2,600; expenditures, $4,077; total giving, $4,077; qualifying distributions, $4,077; giving activities include $4,077 for grants.

Purpose and activities: Support for Armenian churches and related charities.

Fields of interest: Education; Health care; Health organizations; Medical research; Human services; Children, services; Orthodox Catholic agencies & churches; Religion.

Type of support: General/operating support.

Limitations: Applications not accepted. Giving on a national basis. No grants to individuals.

Application information: Contributes only to pre-selected organizations.

Officers: Susan R. Mousigian, Secy.; Mike M. Mousigian, Treas.; Michael E. Mousigian, Exec. Dir.

EIN: 382777981

1335
The Mozer Foundation

500 Woodward Ave., Ste 2500
Detroit, MI 48226

Established in 2001 in MI.

Donor: Rudolf W. Mozer.

Grantmaker type: Independent foundation.

Financial data (yr. ended 12/31/05): Assets, $9,307 (M); expenditures, $527,964; total giving, $518,000; qualifying distributions, $518,000; giving activities include $518,000 for grants.

Limitations: Applications not accepted.

Application information: Contributes only to pre-selected organizations.

Officers and Directors:* Rudolf W. Mozer,* Chair.; Eleanor M. Wagner,* Secy.; Karen M. Hoke,* Treas.; Eric Mozer.
EIN: 383573403

1336
MPS Foundation
51116 Lake Park Ave.
Grand Beach, MI 49117-9051
Contact: Lawrence A. Walsh, Pres.

Donor: Lawrence A. Walsh.
Grantmaker type: Independent foundation.
Financial data (yr. ended 12/31/04): Assets, $95,306 (M); expenditures, $11,480; total giving, $11,350; qualifying distributions, $11,350; giving activities include $11,350 for grants.
Fields of interest: Education; Human services; Christian agencies & churches.
Type of support: General/operating support.
Limitations: Giving primarily in IL and IN. No grants to individuals.
Application information:
Initial approach: Letter
Deadline(s): None
Officer: Lawrence A. Walsh,* Pres.
EIN: 510141393

1337
MPS Foundation
39533 Woodward Ave., Ste. 200
Bloomfield Hills, MI 48304

Established in 1997 in MI.
Grantmaker type: Independent foundation.
Financial data (yr. ended 12/31/05): Assets, $3,028,945 (M); expenditures, $184,718; total giving, $149,250; qualifying distributions, $149,250; giving activities include $149,250 for 18 grants (high: $100,000; low: $250).
Purpose and activities: Support primarily for environmental conservation.
Fields of interest: Environment, natural resources; Animals/wildlife.
Limitations: Applications not accepted. Giving on a national basis, with emphasis on MI. No grants to individuals.
Application information: Contributes only to pre-selected organizations.
Officers: Joanne N. Arbaugh, Pres. and Secy.-Treas.; Steven L. Arbaugh, V.P.
EIN: 383421778
Selected grants: The following grants were reported in 2004.
$106,000 to SEE-North, Petoskey, MI. For general operating support.
$6,500 to Corkscrew Swamp Sanctuary, Naples, FL. For general operating support.
$5,000 to Little Traverse Conservancy, Harbor Springs, MI. For general operating support.
$5,000 to Michigan Environmental Council, Lansing, MI. For general operating support.
$3,000 to Humane Society, Little Traverse Bay, Harbor Springs, MI. For general operating support.
$3,000 to National Wildlife Federation, Reston, VA. For general operating support.
$3,000 to Tip of the Mitt Watershed Council, Petoskey, MI. For general operating support.
$2,000 to Mackinaw Forest Council, Petoskey, MI. For general operating support.

$2,000 to Northern Michigan Hospital Foundation, Petoskey, MI. For general operating support.
$1,000 to Planned Parenthood Northern Michigan, Petoskey, MI. For general operating support.

1338
MSJ Foundation
c/o John Schneider
333 Bridge St. N.W., Ste. 800
Grand Rapids, MI 49504

Established in 1992 in MI.
Donor: Michael J. Jandernoa.
Grantmaker type: Independent foundation.
Financial data (yr. ended 12/31/05): Assets, $3,601,306 (M); expenditures, $123,084; total giving, $121,709; qualifying distributions, $121,709; giving activities include $121,709 for grants.
Purpose and activities: Giving primarily for Roman Catholic education.
Fields of interest: Secondary school/education; Higher education; Roman Catholic federated giving programs.
Limitations: Applications not accepted. Giving primarily in Grand Rapids, MI. No grants to individuals.
Application information: Contributes only to pre-selected organizations.
Officers and Directors:* Michael J. Jandernoa,* Pres.; Susan M. Jandernoa,* V.P. and Treas.; John R. Nichols,* Secy.
EIN: 383083625

1339
Mt. Zion Lutheran Church Foundation
c/o Robert Hughes
6336 Vernmoor Dr.
Troy, MI 48098-1843 (248) 879-2098

Established in 1997 in MI.
Grantmaker type: Independent foundation.
Financial data (yr. ended 9/30/05): Assets, $503,115 (M); gifts received, $3,145; expenditures, $24,427; total giving, $20,980; qualifying distributions, $20,980; giving activities include $20,980 for grants.
Purpose and activities: Giving primarily for Lutheran churches and community programs.
Fields of interest: Protestant agencies & churches.
Type of support: Building/renovation; Program development; Publication; Seed money.
Limitations: Applications not accepted. Giving primarily in Macomb, Oakland and Wayne counties, MI. No grants to individuals.
Publications: Annual report; Financial statement; Grants list; Newsletter.
Application information: Contributes only to pre-selected organizations.
Officers: Harold Schlachtenhaufen, Pres.; Robert Hughes, V.P.; Kari Schlachtenhaufen, V.P.; Arlene Kangas, Secy.; Evelyne Russell, Secy.; David Fox, Treas.
Directors: Gustav Jensen; Diane Rotha; Norman Rotha.
EIN: 383364539

1340
MTC Foundation
622 E. Grand River Ave.
Howell, MI 48843

Established in 2001 in MI.
Donor: Kenneth J. Lingenfelter.
Grantmaker type: Independent foundation.
Financial data (yr. ended 12/31/04): Assets, $164,771 (M); expenditures, $10,562; total giving, $9,725; qualifying distributions, $9,725; giving activities include $9,725 for grants.
Limitations: Applications not accepted. No grants to individuals.
Application information: Contributes only to pre-selected organizations.
Officers and Directors:* Kenneth J. Lingfelter,* Pres.; Robin Gilroy,* V.P.; Becky Alverson, Secy.
EIN: 300003592

1341
Karl and Nancy Mueller Family Foundation
5512 Bostall Woods Dr.
Rochester, MI 48306-2612

Established in 2003 in MI.
Donors: Karl Mueller; Nancy Mueller.
Grantmaker type: Independent foundation.
Financial data (yr. ended 12/31/05): Assets, $746,407 (M); gifts received, $180,000; expenditures, $19,378; total giving, $17,000; qualifying distributions, $17,000; giving activities include $17,000 for grants.
Limitations: Applications not accepted. No grants to individuals.
Application information: Contributes only to pre-selected organizations.
Officers and Directors:* Karl Mueller,* Pres.; Nancy Mueller,* Secy.-Treas.
EIN: 352190695

1342
Chuck Muer and Chef Larry Memorial Scholarship Fund
21 Beacon Hil Rd.
Grosse Pointe Farms, MI 48236-3001
Contact: Leo J. Beil, Pres.

Grantmaker type: Independent foundation.
Financial data (yr. ended 12/31/04): Assets, $120,599 (M); expenditures, $9,845; total giving, $7,000; qualifying distributions, $7,000; giving activities include $7,000 for grants.
Purpose and activities: Funding for training at culinary institutes.
Fields of interest: Vocational education.
Application information:
Initial approach: Letter
Deadline(s): None
Officers: Leo J. Beil, Pres.; Greg Ochoa, V.P.
EIN: 382508826

1343
John N. Muirhead Foundation
1 Pembroke Ct.
Dearborn, MI 48126

Established in MI.
Donor: Alberta A. Muirhead.
Grantmaker type: Independent foundation.

Financial data (yr. ended 12/31/05): Assets, $64,987 (M); gifts received, $900; expenditures, $2,127; total giving, $1,000; qualifying distributions, $1,000; giving activities include $1,000 for grants.
Fields of interest: Higher education.
Limitations: Applications not accepted. Giving primarily in Dearborn, MI. No grants to individuals.
Application information: Contributes only to pre-selected organizations.
Officers: Alberta A. Muirhead, Pres.; Robert S. Ketchum, Secy.; John R. Mach, Treas.
EIN: 382284287

1344
Mukkamala Family Foundation
4545 Warwick Cir.
Grand Blanc, MI 48439
Contact: Apparao Mukkamala, Pres.

Established in 1995 in MI.
Donors: Apparao Mukkamala; Sumathi Mukkamala.
Grantmaker type: Independent foundation.
Financial data (yr. ended 12/31/05): Assets, $113,079 (M); gifts received, $112,100; expenditures, $27,207; total giving, $25,651; qualifying distributions, $26,284; giving activities include $25,651 for 3 grants (high: $23,650; low: $1,000).
Fields of interest: Medical school/education; Hospitals (general).
International interests: India.
Type of support: General/operating support.
Limitations: Giving on a national and international basis; with emphasis on India.
Application information:
Initial approach: Letter
Deadline(s): None
Officer: Apparao Mukkamala, Pres.
Directors: Aparna Mukkamala; Srinivas Mukkamala; Sumathi Mukkamala.
EIN: 383224822

1345
Mark B. & Carol S. Muller Charitable Fund
(formerly Mark B. & Carol S. Muller Family Foundation)
98 Ottawa Ave. N.W.
Grand Rapids, MI 49503

Donors: Mark Muller; Carol Muller; Leone Muller‡; Leone Muller Trust.
Grantmaker type: Independent foundation.
Financial data (yr. ended 12/31/04): Assets, $5,101,678 (M); gifts received, $87; expenditures, $353,728; total giving, $208,629; qualifying distributions, $248,552; giving activities include $208,629 for 22 grants (high: $110,000; low: $100).
Purpose and activities: Giving primarily for education and Christian organizations.
Fields of interest: Higher education; Higher education, college; Education; Christian agencies & churches.
Limitations: Applications not accepted. Giving primarily in MI, with emphasis on Grand Rapids. No grants to individuals.
Application information: Contributes only to pre-selected organizations.

Officers: Mark Muller, Pres. and Treas.; Carol Muller, V.P. and Secy.
EIN: 383443809
Selected grants: The following grants were reported in 2003.
$145,000 to Calvin College, Grand Rapids, MI.
$40,200 to Grand Rapids Christian Schools, Grand Rapids, MI.
$16,500 to Inner City Christian Federation, Grand Rapids, MI.
$10,000 to Spectrum Health, Grand Rapids, MI.
$6,500 to Church of the Servant, Grand Rapids, MI.
$3,000 to Young Life, Holland, MI.
$2,500 to Gildas Club Grand Rapids, Grand Rapids, MI.
$850 to Oakdale Christian School, Grand Rapids, MI.
$500 to InterVarsity Christian Fellowship/USA, Madison, WI.
$300 to Interfaith Hospitality Network of Greater Grand Rapids, Grand Rapids, MI.

1346
The Munn Foundation, Inc.
P.O. Box 3232
Steamboat Springs, CO 80477
Application address: c/o John Munn, 425 Park Place Cir., Ste. 100, Mishawaka, IN 46545, tel.: (574) 272-1680

Established in 1987 in IN.
Grantmaker type: Independent foundation.
Financial data (yr. ended 6/30/05): Assets, $499,130 (M); expenditures, $137,775; total giving, $137,000; qualifying distributions, $136,639; giving activities include $137,000 for 2 grants (high: $135,000; low: $2,000).
Purpose and activities: The foundation is currently funding only cancer research and children's programs.
Fields of interest: Higher education; Cancer research; Children, services.
Limitations: Giving primarily in Steamboat Springs, CO and Ann Arbor, MI. No grants to individuals.
Application information: Application form not required.
Initial approach: Letter
Deadline(s): None
Officers: John Munn, Pres.; Suzanne Munn, Secy.-Treas.
Directors: Lauren Davis; Laura Seagram.
EIN: 311220336
Selected grants: The following grants were reported in 2003.
$132,500 to University of Michigan, Ann Arbor, MI.
$40,000 to Ann Arbor Hands-On Museum, Ann Arbor, MI.
$3,000 to North Routt Fire Protection District, Clark, CO.
$2,000 to Yampatika Outdoor Awareness Association, Steamboat Springs, CO.

1347
Wanda Muntwyler Foundation For Animals
P.O. Box 3636
Grand Rapids, MI 49501-3636

Established in 1996 in IL.
Donor: Wanda Muntwyler‡.
Grantmaker type: Independent foundation.

Financial data (yr. ended 12/31/05): Assets, $2,082,071 (M); gifts received, $15; expenditures, $147,169; total giving, $120,217; qualifying distributions, $123,427; giving activities include $120,217 for 21 grants (high: $12,500; low: $600).
Purpose and activities: Giving primarily for animal welfare.
Fields of interest: Higher education; Animal welfare; Veterinary medicine.
Type of support: General/operating support; Scholarship funds.
Limitations: Applications not accepted. Giving primarily in IL. No grants to individuals.
Application information: Contributes only to pre-selected organizations.
Trustee: Fifth Third Bank.
EIN: 367155124

1348
The Murdock Foundation
4298 Cedar Point Rd.
Manitou Beach, MI 49253

Established in 1985 in MI.
Donors: Donald L. Murdock; Marcia Jean Murdock.
Grantmaker type: Independent foundation.
Financial data (yr. ended 11/30/05): Assets, $1,358,293 (M); gifts received, $150,000; expenditures, $64,289; total giving, $59,420; qualifying distributions, $59,420; giving activities include $59,420 for 3 grants (high: $30,000; low: $420).
Fields of interest: Museums; Higher education; Federated giving programs.
Type of support: General/operating support.
Limitations: Applications not accepted. Giving primarily in MI. No grants to individuals.
Application information: Contributes only to pre-selected organizations.
Officer and Director:* Donald L. Murdock,* Pres. and Secy.-Treas.
EIN: 382638239

1349
T. B. Murphy Foundation Charitable Trust
21420 Greater Mack Ave.
St. Clair Shores, MI 48080

Established in 1984 in MI.
Donor: Thomas B. Murphy.
Grantmaker type: Independent foundation.
Financial data (yr. ended 12/31/05): Assets, $185,661 (M); gifts received, $99,070; expenditures, $85,779; total giving, $80,500; qualifying distributions, $80,500; giving activities include $80,500 for 6 grants (high: $70,000; low: $1,000).
Fields of interest: Higher education; Roman Catholic agencies & churches.
Type of support: General/operating support; Building/renovation; Research.
Limitations: Applications not accepted. Giving primarily in Boston, MA. No grants to individuals.
Application information: Contributes only to pre-selected organizations.
Trustees: Jacquelyn Murphy; Thomas B. Murphy; Thomas B. Murphy, Jr.
EIN: 382531815
Selected grants: The following grants were reported in 2004.
$100,000 to Boston College, Chestnut Hill, MA.

$20,000 to Madonna University, Livonia, MI.
$20,000 to Weston Jesuit School of Theology, Cambridge, MA.
$2,600 to Knights of Malta, DC.
$2,000 to Rose Hill Center, Holly, MI.
$1,000 to Diocese of Palm Beach, Palm Beach Gardens, FL. For Diocesan Service Appeal.
$1,000 to Legionaries of Christ.
$100 to Jesuit Community at Boston College, Newton, MA.

1350
Henry C. and Audrienne Murray Foundation
c/o James J. Murray
1000 Grand Ave.
Petoskey, MI 49770

Established in 1993 in MI.
Donor: Henry C. Murray.
Grantmaker type: Independent foundation.
Financial data (yr. ended 12/31/04): Assets, $2,273,583 (M); expenditures, $116,717; total giving, $89,000; qualifying distributions, $90,707; giving activities include $89,000 for grants.
Fields of interest: Foundations (community); General charitable giving.
Type of support: General/operating support.
Limitations: Applications not accepted. Giving primarily in MI, with some emphasis on Petoskey. No grants to individuals.
Application information: Contributes only to pre-selected organizations.
Officers: James J. Murray, Pres.; Mary S. O'Connell, Secy.
Directors: Brian F. Murray; J. Henry Murray; Joseph P. Murray; Maria Murray; Stephen P. Murray.
EIN: 383085171

1351
Mutter Private Foundation Trust
c/o Comerica Bank
P.O. Box 75000, M/C 3302
Detroit, MI 48275-3302

Established in 2003 in FL.
Donor: Dolores Mutter Charitable Remainder Unitrust.
Grantmaker type: Independent foundation.
Financial data (yr. ended 11/30/04): Assets, $604,519 (M); gifts received, $612,852; expenditures, $36,919; total giving, $15,321; qualifying distributions, $25,783; giving activities include $15,321 for 2 grants (high: $9,193; low: $6,128).
Fields of interest: Protestant agencies & churches.
Limitations: Applications not accepted. Giving primarily in FL and NJ. No grants to individuals.
Application information: Contributes only to pre-selected organizations.
Trustee: Comerica Bank.
EIN: 611471620

1352
Myers Church Scholarship
c/o Fifth Third Bank
P.O. Box 630858
Cincinnati, OH 45263
Application address: c/o Rev. William Collins, 6108 Barnhart Rd., Ludington, MI 49431, tel.: (616) 843-9275

Established in 1995 in MI.
Donor: Keith T. Myers.
Grantmaker type: Independent foundation.
Financial data (yr. ended 12/31/05): Assets, $195,581 (M); expenditures, $7,100; total giving, $3,750; qualifying distributions, $4,000; giving activities include $3,750 for 6 grants to individuals.
Purpose and activities: Scholarship awards to graduates of high schools located in Mason County, MI, or to graduates whose parents reside in Mason County, MI.
Fields of interest: Higher education.
Type of support: Scholarships—to individuals.
Limitations: Giving limited to residents of Mason County, MI.
Application information: Application form required.
    Deadline(s): Mar. 1
Scholarship Committee: Sally Barbo; James H. Brammer; Richard Loerup; John Pavlick; Dick Powell; Scott Sitler; Jeff Wooster.
Trustee: Fifth Third Bank.
EIN: 383288570

1353
David & Carol Myers Foundation
(formerly David G. & Carol P. Myers Charitable Foundation)
c/o Carol P. Myers
109 W. 12th St.
Holland, MI 49423

Established in 1989 in MI.
Donors: David G. Myers; Carol P. Myers.
Grantmaker type: Independent foundation.
Financial data (yr. ended 12/31/04): Assets, $17,478,282 (M); gifts received, $1,500; expenditures, $362,069; total giving, $194,892; qualifying distributions, $195,312; giving activities include $194,892 for 12 grants (high: $35,000; low: $225).
Fields of interest: Higher education; Theological school/education; Human services; Religion.
Limitations: Applications not accepted. Giving on a national basis. No grants to individuals.
Application information: Contributes only to pre-selected organizations.
    Board meeting date(s): Spring
Officers: Carol P. Myers, Pres.; David G. Myers, V.P.
EIN: 382884733

1354
Marigowda Nagaraju, M.D. & Renuka Nagaraju Charitable Family Foundation
1614 Lexington Dr.
Troy, MI 48084-5707

Donors: Marigowda Nagaraju, M.D.; Renuka Nagaraju.
Grantmaker type: Independent foundation.
Financial data (yr. ended 12/31/04): Assets, $1,565,947 (M); gifts received, $201,000; expenditures, $203,744; total giving, $203,744;

qualifying distributions, $203,307; giving activities include $203,744 for 5 grants (high: $198,044; low: $1,000).
Fields of interest: Higher education, university; Medical school/education; Health care.
International interests: Global programs; India.
Limitations: Giving primarily in India. No grants to individuals.
Officer: Marigowda Nagaraju, M.D., Pres.
Trustees: Priya Amaresh; Sunil Jayaraj; Pradeep Nagaraju; Renuka Nagaraju; Prameela Patel.
EIN: 382493868

1355
The Nagy Family Charitable Foundation
17560 N. Laurel Park Dr.
Livonia, MI 48152

Established in 2000 in MI.
Donor: Kathy S. Nagy.
Grantmaker type: Independent foundation.
Financial data (yr. ended 12/31/05): Assets, $388,951 (M); gifts received, $100,000; expenditures, $50,051; total giving, $50,000; qualifying distributions, $50,000; giving activities include $50,000 for grants.
Limitations: Applications not accepted. No grants to individuals.
Application information: Contributes only to pre-selected organizations.
Officer: Kathy S. Nagy, Pres.
EIN: 383568853

1356
Judith and Edward Narens Family Foundation
c/o Narens Assocs., Inc.
29200 Northwestern Hwy., Ste. 200
Southfield, MI 48034-1060

Established in 1985 in MI.
Donors: Edward Narens; Judith Narens.
Grantmaker type: Independent foundation.
Financial data (yr. ended 11/30/05): Assets, $580,416 (M); gifts received, $100,000; expenditures, $101,849; total giving, $100,781; qualifying distributions, $101,651; giving activities include $100,781 for 29 grants (high: $66,000; low: $36).
Purpose and activities: Giving primarily for Jewish agencies and services.
Fields of interest: Arts; Human services; Jewish federated giving programs; Jewish agencies & temples.
Limitations: Applications not accepted. Giving primarily in MI. No grants to individuals.
Application information: Contributes only to pre-selected organizations.
Officers: Judith Narens, Pres.; Edward Narens, Secy.-Treas.
EIN: 382661323

1357
Nartel Family Foundation
(formerly Werner and Ruth Nartel Foundation)
6040 Belmont Ct.
Grand Blanc, MI 48439

Grantmaker type: Independent foundation.

Financial data (yr. ended 6/30/05): Assets, $5,310,987 (M); expenditures, $348,530; total giving, $267,296; qualifying distributions, $298,268; giving activities include $267,296 for 15 grants (high: $80,096; low: $500).
Fields of interest: Museums (history); Breast cancer; Heart & circulatory diseases; Alzheimer's disease; Human services; Jewish federated giving programs; Jewish agencies & temples.
Type of support: General/operating support.
Limitations: Applications not accepted. Giving on a national basis, with some emphasis on Washington, DC, IL, MI, NY, and TX. No grants to individuals.
Application information: Contributes only to pre-selected organizations.
Officers: Evelyn Nartelski, Pres. and Treas.; Mary Church, Secy.
EIN: 382477768
Selected grants: The following grants were reported in 2005.
$80,096 to Whaley Childrens Center, Flint, MI. For general support.
$50,000 to Alzheimers Association, Chicago, IL. For general support.
$30,000 to Museum of Jewish Heritage, New York, NY. For general support.
$20,000 to Mott Community College, Flint, MI. For general support.
$18,000 to Chabad House - Lubavitch of Eastern Michigan, Flint, MI. For general support.
$10,000 to Boy Scouts of America, Tall Pine Council, Flint, MI. For general support.
$10,000 to International Crane Foundation, Baraboo, WI. For general support.
$10,000 to Veterans of Foreign Wars, Davison, MI. For general support.
$8,000 to Chamber Foundation, Genesee, Flint, MI. For general support.
$1,200 to Muscular Dystrophy Association of America, Flint, MI. For general support.

1358
National Center for Community Education
1017 Avon St.
Flint, MI   48503-2701   (810) 238-0463
Contact: Daniel J. Cady, Exec. Dir.
FAX: (810) 238-9211; E-mail: info@nccenet.org;
Additional tel. (toll-free): (800) 811-1105;
URL: http://www.nccenet.org/

Donor: Charles Stewart Mott Foundation.
Grantmaker type: Independent foundation.
Financial data (yr. ended 6/30/05): Assets, $1,115,149 (M); gifts received, $590,244; expenditures, $1,396,260; total giving, $0; qualifying distributions, $0.
Purpose and activities: The mission of the center is to promote community and educational change emphasizing community schools by providing state-of-the-art leadership development, training and technical assistance.
Fields of interest: Education, community/cooperative.
Limitations: Giving primarily in MI. No grants to individuals.
Application information:
    Initial approach: Letter
    Deadline(s): None
Officers and Directors:* Gloria Rubio-Cortes,* Chair.; Ellen Sushak,* Secy.; Daniel J. Cady, Exec. Dir.; A. Donald Duncan; Paul Heckman; Donald Weaver.
EIN: 382526543

1359
National Healthcare Scholars Foundation
(formerly United American Healthcare Foundation)
300 River Pl., Rm. 4700
Detroit, MI   48207   (313) 393-4549
Contact: J.V. Combs, M.D., Pres.
FAX: (313) 393-3394; E-mail: info@nhsfonline.org;
URL: http://www.nhsfonline.org/
Additional tel.: (313) 393-7944

Established in 1987 in MI.
Donors: United American Healthcare Corp.; Julius V. Combs, M.D.; OmniCare Health Plan; Ford Motor Co.; Chrysler Motor Co.; General Motors Corp.; MGM Grand Casino; Atwater Entertainment; Greektown Casino; Comerica Bank; Standard Federal Bank N.A.
Grantmaker type: Independent foundation.
Financial data (yr. ended 9/30/04): Assets, $1,528 (M); gifts received, $44,265; expenditures, $159,261; total giving, $92,000; qualifying distributions, $91,895; giving activities include $92,000 for 10 grants.
Purpose and activities: To serve the community by providing financial assistance to educate minority health care professionals through scholarships and to support those institutions and organizations dedicated to enriching the community through programs and education. Scholarships assist qualified African-American, Asian, Hispanic, and Native American students in the fields of medicine, nursing, pharmacy, and allied health professions.
Fields of interest: Medical school/education; Nursing school/education; Pharmacy/prescriptions; Minorities; Asians/Pacific Islanders; African Americans/Blacks; Hispanics/Latinos; Native Americans/American Indians.
Type of support: Annual campaigns; General/operating support; Scholarships—to individuals.
Limitations: Giving on a national basis.
Publications: Biennial report (including application guidelines); Grants list; Informational brochure.
Application information: See foundation Web site for list of participating educational institutions. Application form not required.
    Deadline(s): None
    Board meeting date(s): Feb., June, and Sept.
Officers and Directors:* Julius V. Combs, M.D.*, Chair. and Pres.; Milton H. Watson,* Vice-Chair. and V.P.; Ronald R. Dobbins,* Secy.-Treas.; Monica Y. Allen; Hon. Norma Y. Dotson; Marie Draper Dykes; Henry W. Foster, M.D.; Lorna L. Thomas, M.D.
Advisory Board: Alice G. Combs; Tonya Corbin; Tonya M. Corbitt; Sharon Simpson; Kimberly Combs Voss; and 9 additional advisory members.
Number of staff: 1 part-time support.
EIN: 382894517

1360
Neal Sisters Foundation
c/o JPMorgan Chase Bank, N.A.
P.O. Box 1308
Milwaukee, WI   53201
Contact: Carl Holmes, Treas.
Application address: 1080 W. Northwood Dr., Caro, MI 48723

Established in 1991 in MI.
Donor: Eleanor Neal.
Grantmaker type: Independent foundation.
Financial data (yr. ended 12/31/05): Assets, $1,483,099 (M); expenditures, $90,220; total giving, $81,000; qualifying distributions, $81,000; giving activities include $81,000 for grants.

Purpose and activities: Giving primarily for higher education and human services, including an adult care center and an assault crisis center. Preference given to qualified charities in the education field with priority in the Caro, MI, area.
Fields of interest: Higher education; Libraries/library science; Human services; Residential/custodial care, special day care; Foundations (private grantmaking).
Limitations: Giving primarily in the Caro, MI, area. No grants to individuals.
Application information:
    Initial approach: Letter
    Copies of proposal: 2
    Deadline(s): None
Officers: Steve Fillion, Pres.; Martha Thurston, Secy.; Carl Holmes, Treas.
Trustees: Dolores Rock Hutchinson; JPMorgan Chase Bank, N.A.
EIN: 382942765

1361
The Bruce and Susan Neckers Foundation
34 Bel Air Dr. N.E.
Grand Rapids, MI   49503-3916

Grantmaker type: Independent foundation.
Financial data (yr. ended 12/31/05): Assets, $23,603 (M); gifts received, $2,100; expenditures, $1,675; total giving, $1,500; qualifying distributions, $1,500; giving activities include $1,500 for grants.
Fields of interest: Theological school/education.
Limitations: Applications not accepted. No grants to individuals.
Application information: Contributes only to pre-selected organizations.
Officer: Bruce W. Neckers, Pres.
EIN: 383442952

1362
Neighbors Concerned About Yacht Club Expansion
824 Lake Shore Rd.
Grosse Pointe Shores, MI   48236

Established in MI.
Donors: Warren Wilkinson; Ralph C. Wilson, Jr.; J. Kay Felt; Martha F. Ford; Elaine Peck; Peck Family Foundation.
Grantmaker type: Independent foundation.
Financial data (yr. ended 12/31/05): Assets, $90 (M); gifts received, $49,168; expenditures, $73,021; total giving, $0; qualifying distributions, $0.
Officers: Warren Wilkinson, Pres.; Rebecca C. Booth, V.P.; Mary Anne Lahood, Secy.; J. Kay Felt, Treas.
Directors: John Lord Booth; John F. Monahan; Ralph C. Wilson, Jr.
EIN: 383436576

1363
The Nelson Family Charitable Foundation
6024 Hillsborough Ct. S.W.
Grandville, MI   49418-3237

Established in 2000 in MI.
Donor: Gerald R. Nelson.
Grantmaker type: Independent foundation.

Financial data (yr. ended 12/31/05): Assets, $95,547 (M); gifts received, $74; expenditures, $16,622; total giving, $16,060; qualifying distributions, $16,060; giving activities include $16,060 for grants.
Fields of interest: Protestant agencies & churches.
Limitations: Applications not accepted. Giving primarily in MI. No grants to individuals.
Application information: Contributes only to pre-selected organizations.
Officers: Gerald R. Nelson, Pres. and Treas.; Constance M. Nelson, V.P. and Secy.
Directors: Chad M. Nelson; Gerald R. Nelson, Jr.; Todd J. Nelson.
EIN: 383550494

1364
J. N. Nelson Family Foundation
9095 S. Saginaw Rd., Unit 13
Grand Blanc, MI   48439   (810) 767-7800
Contact: Jay N. Nelson, Pres.

Established in 1997 in MI.
Donors: Jay N. Nelson; Marilyn S. Nelson.
Grantmaker type: Independent foundation.
Financial data (yr. ended 12/31/05): Assets, $432,552 (M); expenditures, $20,178; total giving, $17,000; qualifying distributions, $17,000; giving activities include $17,000 for grants.
Fields of interest: Arts; Education.
Type of support: Grants to individuals; Scholarship funds; Capital campaigns.
Limitations: Giving primarily in MI.
Application information: Application form required.
  Deadline(s): None
Officers: Jay N. Nelson, Pres. and Treas.; Marilyn S. Nelson, V.P. and Secy.
Directors: Bonnie S. Nelson; David N. Nelson; Robin N. Nelson.
EIN: 383342652

1365
Linden David Nelson Foundation
2100 E. Maple Rd., Ste. 200
Birmingham, MI   48009   (248) 458-5000

Established in 1986 in MI.
Donor: Linden David Nelson.
Grantmaker type: Independent foundation.
Financial data (yr. ended 12/31/03): Assets, $34,278 (M); gifts received, $111,834; expenditures, $66,062; total giving, $65,426; qualifying distributions, $65,426; giving activities include $65,426 for 21 grants (high: $10,000; low: $100).
Purpose and activities: Giving primarily for Jewish organizations and temples.
Fields of interest: Children/youth, services; Jewish agencies & temples.
Limitations: Giving primarily in MI.
Application information:
  Initial approach: Letter
  Deadline(s): None
Officers: Linden David Nelson, Pres.; Lois Nelson, Secy.; Harry Nelson, Treas.
EIN: 386505470

1366
Donald E. and Margaret L. Nelson Scholarship Fund
W9473 H. Lucas Dr.
Iron Mountain, MI   49801-9409
Application address: c/o North Dickinson County School, Attn.: Daniel J. Nurmi, Principal, Felch, MI 49831-8890, tel.: (906) 542-9281

Established in 1987 in MI.
Donors: Allen J. Nelson; Irving T. Nelson; Merlin A. Nelson.
Grantmaker type: Independent foundation.
Financial data (yr. ended 12/31/05): Assets, $105,338 (M); gifts received, $5,236; expenditures, $4,619; total giving, $4,525; qualifying distributions, $4,525; giving activities include $4,525 for grants to individuals.
Purpose and activities: Scholarship awards to residents of Felch, MI, and who are graduates of North Dickinson County School.
Type of support: Scholarships—to individuals.
Limitations: Giving limited to Felch, MI.
Application information: Application form required.
  Deadline(s): May 1
Officers and Directors:* Alice M. Brown,* Chair.; Merlin A. Nelson,* Admin.; Allen J. Nelson; Donald J. Nelson; Irving T. Nelson; Patricia A. Nolf; Mavis C. Powell; Norma T. Scolatti; Carol R. Trautner.
EIN: 382731508

1367
Nelson-Marsh Charitable Foundation
3300 Norton Rd.
Howell, MI   48843

Donors: Roger L. Nelson; Marilyn K. Nelson.
Grantmaker type: Independent foundation.
Financial data (yr. ended 12/31/05): Assets, $79,915 (M); expenditures, $4,062; total giving, $3,362; qualifying distributions, $3,537; giving activities include $3,362 for grants.
Fields of interest: Medical research; American Red Cross.
Type of support: General/operating support.
Limitations: Applications not accepted. Giving on a national basis. No grants to individuals.
Application information: Contributes only to pre-selected organizations.
Officers and Directors:* Marilyn K. Nelson,* Pres.; Stewart R. Hicks,* Secy.; Roger L. Nelson,* Treas.
EIN: 383465239

1368
Neuroscience Research Foundation
29100 Northwestern Hwy., Ste. 399
Southfield, MI   48034

Established in 2004 in MI.
Grantmaker type: Independent foundation.
Financial data (yr. ended 12/31/04): Assets, $320 (M); gifts received, $4,225; expenditures, $3,905; total giving, $0; qualifying distributions, $3,905.
Officers: Harold D. Portnoy, M.D., Pres.; John Marshall, Treas.; H. James Zack, Treas.
Directors: Morrie Bednarsh; Mick Perez-Cruet.
EIN: 382626205

1369
Newaygo Public Schools Educational Advancement Foundation
c/o Selection Comm.
360 S. Mill St.
Newaygo, MI   49337

Established in 1990 in MI.
Grantmaker type: Independent foundation.
Financial data (yr. ended 6/30/05): Assets, $319,300 (M); gifts received, $1,000; expenditures, $28,587; total giving, $17,526; qualifying distributions, $17,526; giving activities include $17,526 for 16 grants to individuals (high: $4,500; low: $26).
Purpose and activities: Scholarship awards to graduating seniors of Newaygo, MI, for higher education; some grants for teachers of the Newaygo school system for higher education.
Fields of interest: Higher education.
Type of support: Grants to individuals; Scholarships—to individuals.
Limitations: Giving primarily in Newaygo, MI.
Application information: Application form required.
  Deadline(s): Apr. 1
Officers: Larry J. Lethorn, Pres.; Mary Reese-Pumford, V.P.; Tom Kowalski, Secy.; Paul Eno, Treas.
Trustees: Jelanie Bush; Ed Grodus.
EIN: 382989275

1370
The Newman Family Foundation
5455 Corporate Dr., Ste. 300
Troy, MI   48098-2620
Contact: Craig S. Skulsky, Treas.

Established in 1990 in MI.
Donors: Max K. Newman; Donald L. Newman; Steven E. Newman.
Grantmaker type: Independent foundation.
Financial data (yr. ended 12/31/05): Assets, $1,945,212 (M); expenditures, $75,553; total giving, $67,950; qualifying distributions, $67,950; giving activities include $67,950 for grants.
Purpose and activities: Giving primarily for higher education, health associations, medicine, human services, and Jewish federated giving programs.
Fields of interest: Higher education; Scholarships/financial aid; Health organizations, association; Biomedicine; Medical research, institute; Human services; Jewish federated giving programs; Jewish agencies & temples.
Limitations: Giving primarily in MI.
Application information:
  Initial approach: Letter
  Deadline(s): None
Officers: Max Karl Newman, Pres.; Donald L. Newman, M.D., V.P.; Steven E. Newman, M.D., Secy.; Craig S. Skulsky, Treas.
EIN: 382986180

1371
The Nickless Family Charitable Foundation
2121 University Park Dr., Ste. 150
Okemos, MI   48864
Contact: James E. McCartney, Secy.
Application address: P.O. Box 23125, Lansing, MI 48909-3125, tel.: (517) 347-5000

Established in 2000 in MI.
Grantmaker type: Independent foundation.
Financial data (yr. ended 12/31/05): Assets, $674,497 (M); gifts received, $959,502; expenditures, $504,280; total giving, $500,000; qualifying distributions, $500,000; giving activities include $500,000 for 1 grant.
Fields of interest: Higher education; Hospitals (general); Protestant agencies & churches.
Limitations: Giving primarily in the Sun City West, AZ, and Bay City, MI, areas. No grants to individuals.
Application information: Application form not required.
   Deadline(s): None
Officers: Arthur H. Nickless, Pres.; James E. McCartney, Secy.; Janet Royce, Treas.
EIN: 383501091

1372
Allen E. & Marie A. Nickless Memorial Foundation

3023 Davenport Ave.
Saginaw, MI 48602
Contact: Lloyd J. Yeo, Treas.
Application address: P.O. Box 3275, Saginaw, MI 48605-3275

Established about 1971.
Donors: Marie A. Nickless; Allen E. Nickless†.
Grantmaker type: Independent foundation.
Financial data (yr. ended 12/31/05): Assets, $1,594,037 (M); gifts received, $192,416; expenditures, $78,070; total giving, $62,786; qualifying distributions, $62,786; giving activities include $62,786 for grants.
Purpose and activities: Giving for education and Christian organizations.
Fields of interest: History/archaeology; Historic preservation/historical societies; Education; Voluntarism promotion; Government/public administration; Christian agencies & churches.
Type of support: General/operating support.
Limitations: Giving primarily in Saginaw County, MI. No loans or program-related investments.
Application information: Application form not required.
   Initial approach: Letter
   Deadline(s): None
Officers: Marie A. Nickless, Pres.; Charles Nickless, V.P.; Lloyd J. Yeo, Treas.
EIN: 237011258

1373
Ernest L. Nicolay Family Foundation

c/o Comerica Bank
P.O. Box 75000
Detroit, MI 48275-3317
Contact: Ernest L. Nicolay III, Tr.
Application address: 866 Westchester Way, Birmingham, MI 48009-2918

Established in 1962 in MI.
Grantmaker type: Independent foundation.
Financial data (yr. ended 12/31/05): Assets, $953,141 (M); expenditures, $78,959; total giving, $65,000; qualifying distributions, $65,000; giving activities include $65,000 for grants.
Fields of interest: Higher education; Human services; Salvation Army.
Type of support: General/operating support.
Limitations: Giving primarily in MI.

Application information: Application form not required.
   Deadline(s): None
   Board meeting date(s): Dec.
Trustees: Ernest L. Nicolay, Jr.; Ernest L. Nicolay III; JoAnn Nicolay; Keith Shreve; Chuck Wood; Comerica Bank.
EIN: 386096839

1374
Joanne Nicolay Foundation

c/o S. Gary Spicer
16845 Kercheval St., Ste. 5
Grosse Pointe Park, MI 48230 (313) 884-3700

Established in 1997 in MI.
Donor: Joanne Nicolay.
Grantmaker type: Independent foundation.
Financial data (yr. ended 12/31/05): Assets, $36,471 (M); gifts received, $20,700; expenditures, $10,056; total giving, $10,000; qualifying distributions, $10,000; giving activities include $10,000 for grants.
Fields of interest: Historical activities; Education; Residential/custodial care.
Type of support: General/operating support.
Limitations: Giving primarily in MI and TN. No grants to individuals.
Application information:
   Initial approach: Proposal
   Deadline(s): None
   Final notification: 3 months
Officers and Trustees:* Joanne Nicolay,* Pres.; S. Gary Spicer,* Secy.
EIN: 383302112

1375
The Niemiec Family Foundation

17583 Stonebrook Dr.
Northville, MI 48167-4327

Established in 1997 in MI.
Donors: Brian G. Niemiec; Valerie J. Niemiec.
Grantmaker type: Independent foundation.
Financial data (yr. ended 12/31/04): Assets, $231,117 (M); expenditures, $15,740; total giving, $14,940; qualifying distributions, $14,940; giving activities include $14,940 for grants.
Fields of interest: Hospitals (general); Health organizations; Protestant agencies & churches.
Type of support: General/operating support.
Limitations: Applications not accepted. No grants to individuals.
Application information: Contributes only to pre-selected organizations.
Officers: Brian G. Niemiec, Pres.; Valerie J. Niemiec, Secy.
EIN: 383338112

1376
Dr. William F. and Mabel E. Nill Foundation, Inc.

39288 Dodge Pk.
Sterling Heights, MI 48313
Contact: Wayne Stewart, Dir.
Application address: 41700 Hayes Rd., Ste. A, Clinton Township, MI 48038

Established in 2003 in MI.
Donor: Mabel E. Nill Trust.

Grantmaker type: Independent foundation.
Financial data (yr. ended 12/31/04): Assets, $1,305,100 (M); gifts received, $1,385,426; expenditures, $154,332; total giving, $100,850; qualifying distributions, $100,850; giving activities include $20,850 for 8 grants (high: $6,000; low: $100), and $80,000 for 7 grants to individuals (high: $20,000; low: $5,000).
Purpose and activities: Giving primarily for medical research and scholarships for medical school.
Fields of interest: Medical school/education; Cancer research; Brain research.
Type of support: Scholarships—to individuals; Research.
Limitations: Giving primarily in MI.
Directors: Jean Chapaton; Oscar Chapaton; Wayne Stewart.
EIN: 383546563

1377
Nimrod Society

400 Applejack Ct.
Sparta, MI 49345

Established in 2003 in MI.
Donor: Alan Taylor.
Grantmaker type: Independent foundation.
Financial data (yr. ended 12/31/04): Assets, $109,950 (M); gifts received, $150; expenditures, $709; total giving, $150; qualifying distributions, $150; giving activities include $150 for grants.
Limitations: Applications not accepted. No grants to individuals.
Application information: Contributes only to pre-selected organizations.
Officers: Alan Taylor, Pres.; David Samuel, Secy.
Directors: Robert Radocy; Steven Vanderark.
EIN: 412120406

1378
The Nine Tuna Foundation

P.O. Box 4551
East Lansing, MI 48826-4551
E-mail: info@ninetuna.org; URL: http://www.ninetuna.org

Established in 2000 in MI.
Donor: Dale Grover.
Grantmaker type: Independent foundation.
Financial data (yr. ended 7/31/05): Assets, $966,022 (M); gifts received, $48,000; expenditures, $106,070; total giving, $96,900; qualifying distributions, $96,900; giving activities include $96,900 for 23 grants (high: $20,000; low: $500).
Purpose and activities: Giving for science education, the arts, the environment/animals, and rehabilitative engineering.
Fields of interest: Arts; Higher education; Environment, natural resources; Animals/wildlife; Science; Engineering.
Type of support: Program development.
Limitations: Applications not accepted. Giving on a national basis, with some emphasis on CA and MI. No grants to individuals.
Application information: Unsolicited requests for funds will not be accepted. Grants are identified by internal process.

Officers and Directors:* Dale Grover,* Chair., Pres., and Treas.; Debbi Schaubman,* Secy.; Christine Reagen-Rosales; Becky Grover.
EIN: 383551073

1379
Walter J. and Lela M. Nock Family Foundation
2192 Clinton View Cir.
Rochester Hills, MI 48309

Established in 2000 in MI.
Donor: Lela M. Nock.
Grantmaker type: Independent foundation.
Financial data (yr. ended 12/31/05): Assets, $321,489 (M); gifts received, $300,471; expenditures, $25,498; total giving, $10,600; qualifying distributions, $10,600; giving activities include $10,600 for grants.
Limitations: Applications not accepted. Giving primarily in MI. No grants to individuals.
Application information: Contributes only to pre-selected organizations.
Officers: Lela M. Nock, Chair.; Walter Ronald Nock, Pres., V.P. and Secy.
EIN: 383556868

1380
NOI Foundation, Inc.
20480 Vernier Rd.
Harper Woods, MI 48225-1411
Application address: c/o Franco Iaderosa, 37135 Aspen Dr., Farmington Hills, MI 48335, tel.: (248) 426-8676

Established in 1997 in MI.
Donor: Italian Ministry of Foreign Affairs.
Grantmaker type: Independent foundation.
Financial data (yr. ended 12/31/04): Assets, $104,685 (M); gifts received, $160,522; expenditures, $155,436; total giving, $0; qualifying distributions, $144,596; giving activities include $144,596 for foundation-administered programs.
Limitations: Giving limited to MI.
Application information:
  Initial approach: Letter
  Deadline(s): None
Officers and Directors:* Anthony J. Bellanca,* Chair.; Teresa Nascimbeni,* Secy.; Maria Harris,* Treas.; Brigida Bianco; Rudy Colombi; Andrea DiTommaso; Louis Kibler; Paolo Nervo; Lino Scamardella.
EIN: 383378136

1381
The Nokomis Foundation
161 Ottawa Ave. N.W., Ste. 305-C
Grand Rapids, MI 49503 (616) 451-0267
Contact: Kymberly Mulhern, C.E.O.
FAX: (616) 451-9914;
E-mail: info@nokomisfoundation.org; Additional E-mail for Kymberly Mulhern, C.E.O.: kmulhern@nokomisfoundation.org; URL: http://www.nokomisfoundation.org

Established in 1989 in MI.
Donor: Mary Caroline "Twink" Frey.
Grantmaker type: Independent foundation.
Financial data (yr. ended 12/31/04): Assets, $17,872,735 (M); expenditures, $1,275,576; total giving, $714,812; qualifying distributions, $786,211; giving activities include $714,812 for grants, and $64,173 for foundation-administered programs.
Purpose and activities: Giving to organizations whose efforts are directed primarily toward women and girls, and who are working in advocacy, community awareness and education, and public policy. Preference is given to social change efforts rather than to social services.
Fields of interest: Women, centers/services; Civil rights, advocacy; Community development, women's clubs; Women.
Type of support: General/operating support; Management development/capacity building; Program development; Seed money; Technical assistance; Program evaluation.
Limitations: Applications not accepted. Giving primarily in the greater Grand Rapids area and in Allegan, Kent, and Ottawa counties in western MI. No support for religious purposes. No grants to individuals, or for capital requests, endowments, equipment, renovations, medical research, fellowships, scholarships, or conferences.
Publications: Biennial report; Grants list; Informational brochure; Occasional report.
Application information: The foundation will not accept new unsolicited grant proposals while it undergoes a comprehensive planning and renewal process. The foundation will continue to award grants during this time, but such awards will be limited to pre-selected funding partners. See foundation Web site for periodic updates about the renewal process.
  Board meeting date(s): Quarterly
Officers and Trustees:* Mary Caroline "Twink" Frey,* Chair.; Kymberly Mulhern,* C.E.O. and Pres.; James E. McKay,* Treas.; Patricia Oldt; Joel J. Orosz; Faye Richardson; Mary Alice Williams.
Number of staff: 2 full-time professional; 1 part-time professional; 2 part-time support.
EIN: 382882220

1382
Amos Nordman Foundation Charitable Trust
(also known as Amos Nordman Charitable Trust)
P.O. Box 1242
Muskegon, MI 49443-1242
Contact: Charles E. Silky, Jr., Tr.

Established in 1973 in MI.
Grantmaker type: Independent foundation.
Financial data (yr. ended 12/31/04): Assets, $484,227 (M); expenditures, $82,350; total giving, $12,952; qualifying distributions, $28,933; giving activities include $9,750 for 10 grants (high: $3,500; low: $250), and $3,202 for 5 grants to individuals (high: $889; low: $417).
Purpose and activities: Giving primarily to institutions of higher education; some scholarship awards to students in Muskegon, MI.
Fields of interest: Higher education.
Type of support: Scholarship funds; Scholarships—to individuals.
Limitations: Giving limited to MI.
Application information: Application form required.
  Deadline(s): None
Trustees: Richard C. Gillard; Henry Olah; Jacob Shoemaker; Charles E. Silky, Jr.
EIN: 237251583

1383
The Northern Cross Foundation
7790 Harmony Cove S.E.
Byron Center, MI 49315

Established in 1999 in MI.
Grantmaker type: Independent foundation.
Financial data (yr. ended 12/31/04): Assets, $1,983,871 (M); expenditures, $157,196; total giving, $139,415; qualifying distributions, $149,537; giving activities include $139,415 for 8 grants (high: $50,000; low: $1,500).
Fields of interest: Roman Catholic agencies & churches.
Limitations: Applications not accepted. No grants to individuals.
Application information: Contributes only to pre-selected organizations.
Officers and Directors:* Robert Spica,* Pres.; Beth J. Spica,* V.P.; Amanda Spica,* Secy.
EIN: 383518590
Selected grants: The following grants were reported in 2004.
$50,000 to International Aid, Spring Lake, MI.
$41,000 to Grace Youth Camp of Michigan, Mears, MI.
$21,200 to Holy Family Catholic Church, Caledonia, MI.
$10,215 to International Steward, Grand Rapids, MI.
$9,000 to Kentwood Community Church, Kentwood, MI.
$5,000 to Catholic Foundation of West Michigan, Grand Rapids, MI.
$1,500 to Equest Center for Therapeutic Riding, Rockford, MI.
$1,500 to W A Y K, Kalamazoo, MI.

1384
Noster Foundation
512 Lafayette St.
Dearborn, MI 48128

Established in 2003 in MI.
Donor: Thomas J. Myler, Sr.
Grantmaker type: Independent foundation.
Financial data (yr. ended 12/31/05): Assets, $0 (M); expenditures, $78,909; total giving, $77,000; qualifying distributions, $77,000; giving activities include $77,000 for grants.
Officers: Marylyn Stanhope, Pres.; David G. Myler, Treas.
Board Member: Carl B. Myler.
EIN: 562434413

1385
Nowak Family Foundation
2325 Patrick Blvd.
Beavercreek, OH 45431-8486
Contact: John M. Nowak, Pres.
Application address: 18143 N. Fruitport Rd., Spring Lake, MI 49456

Established in 2001 in OH.
Donor: John M. Nowak.
Grantmaker type: Independent foundation.
Financial data (yr. ended 12/31/04): Assets, $526,862 (M); gifts received, $150,000; expenditures, $41,718; total giving, $41,400; qualifying distributions, $41,400; giving activities include $41,400 for grants.

Fields of interest: Hospitals (specialty); Roman Catholic agencies & churches.
Type of support: General/operating support.
Limitations: Giving primarily in Grand Rapids, MI. No grants to individuals.
Application information:
Initial approach: Letter
Deadline(s): None
Officers: John M. Nowak, Pres. and Treas.; Maureen K. Nowak, V.P. and Secy.
EIN: 311813059

1386
NSF Foundation
4800 Willow Ln.
Orchard Lake, MI   48324

Established in 1997 in MI.
Donor: Warren F. Boos.
Grantmaker type: Independent foundation.
Financial data (yr. ended 4/30/05): Assets, $1,069,098 (M); expenditures, $54,876; total giving, $51,750; qualifying distributions, $51,750; giving activities include $51,750 for grants.
Limitations: Applications not accepted. No grants to individuals.
Application information: Contributes only to pre-selected organizations.
Directors: Beverly B. Boos; Donald B. Boos; Douglas N. Boos; Janet L. Boos; Judith A. Boos; Warren F. Boos; Richard Trapp, Jr.; Sally Jo Trapp.
EIN: 383364306

1387
Lillian A. Nugent Trust f/b/o Confraternity of the Precious Blood
221 W. Webster Ave., Ste. 400
Muskegon, MI   49440

Established in 1995 in MI.
Grantmaker type: Independent foundation.
Financial data (yr. ended 2/28/06): Assets, $41,093 (M); expenditures, $2,295; total giving, $1,595; qualifying distributions, $1,595; giving activities include $1,595 for grants.
Limitations: Applications not accepted. Giving limited to Brooklyn, NY. No grants to individuals.
Application information: Contributes only to a pre-selected organization.
Trustee: Ellis Management Svcs.
EIN: 386376782

1388
Nusbaum Family Foundation
26575 Willowgreen Dr.
Franklin, MI   48025
Application address: c/o Irving Nusbaum, 27750 Stansbury, Farmington Hills, MI 48334, tel.: (248) 473-5511

Established in 1990 in MI.
Donors: Irving Nusbaum; Barbara Nusbaum.
Grantmaker type: Independent foundation.
Financial data (yr. ended 12/31/04): Assets, $1,019,654 (M); expenditures, $222,245; total giving, $210,650; qualifying distributions, $210,938; giving activities include $210,650 for 91 grants (high: $35,000; low: $16).

Purpose and activities: Giving primarily for Jewish federated giving programs and other Jewish organizations.
Fields of interest: Child development, education; Residential/custodial care, hospices; Jewish federated giving programs; Jewish agencies & temples.
Limitations: Giving primarily in MI.
Application information:
Initial approach: Letter
Deadline(s): None
Officers and Directors:* Irving Nusbaum,* Pres.; Barbara Nusbaum, Secy.; Michael Roth; Bruce H. Seyburn.
EIN: 382917028

1389
Sol and Anna Nusbaum Family Foundation, Inc.
15041 Burton St.
Oak Park, MI   48237-1542   (248) 968-0725
Contact: Joseph Nusbaum, Pres.

Donors: Joseph Nusbaum; Dov Loketch; Anna Nusbaum.
Grantmaker type: Independent foundation.
Financial data (yr. ended 12/31/03): Assets, $309,487 (M); expenditures, $70,495; total giving, $62,467; qualifying distributions, $62,467; giving activities include $62,467 for grants.
Purpose and activities: Giving primarily to Jewish agencies, temples, and schools.
Fields of interest: Education; Jewish federated giving programs; Jewish agencies & temples.
Application information:
Initial approach: Letter
Deadline(s): None
Officers: Joseph Nusbaum, Pres.; Dov Loketch, Secy.; Anna Nusbaum, Treas.
EIN: 382277103

1390
The O'Brien-VRBA Scholarship Trust
c/o National City Bank
P.O. Box 94651
Cleveland, OH   44101-4651
Application address: c/o Jo Ann Harlan, National City Bank, P.O. Box 749, Peoria, IL 61652-0749, tel.: (309) 655-5000

Established in 1991 in IL.
Grantmaker type: Independent foundation.
Financial data (yr. ended 12/31/04): Assets, $3,698,282 (M); expenditures, $291,431; total giving, $248,000; qualifying distributions, $272,980; giving activities include $16,000 for 4 grants (high: $4,000; low: $4,000), and $232,000 for 236 grants to individuals (high: $1,000; low: $1,000).
Purpose and activities: Giving for higher education, primarily to individuals of Roman Catholic faith.
Fields of interest: Higher education; Roman Catholic agencies & churches.
Type of support: Scholarship funds; Scholarships—to individuals.
Limitations: Giving primarily to residents of IA, IL, IN, MI, and WI.
Application information: Application form required for scholarship program. Application form required.
Initial approach: Letter for grants
Deadline(s): Apr. 1 for scholarship

Trustee: National City Bank.
EIN: 376277500

1391
The Stella Matutina O'Connor Foundation
54653 Billingham Dr.
Shelby Township, MI   48316

Established in MI.
Donor: Stella Matutina O'Connor.
Grantmaker type: Independent foundation.
Financial data (yr. ended 9/30/05): Assets, $538,632 (M); expenditures, $33,410; total giving, $14,500; qualifying distributions, $14,500; giving activities include $14,500 for grants.
Fields of interest: Human services.
Type of support: General/operating support.
Limitations: Applications not accepted. No grants to individuals.
Application information: Contributes only to pre-selected organizations.
Officer and Trustees:* Fr. Norman J. O'Connor,* Pres.; N. James O'Connor; Patrick D. O'Connor.
EIN: 383267209

1392
O'Donovan Family Foundation
4245 N. Oak Pointe Ct., N.E.
Grand Rapids, MI   49525

Established in 2004 in MI.
Donors: Timothy J. O'Donovan; Karen J. O'Donovan.
Grantmaker type: Independent foundation.
Financial data (yr. ended 12/31/04): Assets, $240,694 (M); gifts received, $231,068; expenditures, $0; total giving, $0; qualifying distributions, $0.
Limitations: Applications not accepted. No grants to individuals.
Application information: Contributes only to pre-selected organizations.
Officers and Trustees:* Timothy J. O'Donovan,* Pres. and Secy.; Karen J. O'Donovan,* Treas.
EIN: 383704443

1393
Leo A. Obloy and Bernice Obloy Foundation
2161 Clinton View Cir.
Rochester Hills, MI   48309-2984

Established in 1987 in MI.
Donors: Leo A. Obloy; Bernice Obloy.
Grantmaker type: Independent foundation.
Financial data (yr. ended 12/31/04): Assets, $35,236 (M); expenditures, $5,287; total giving, $5,200; qualifying distributions, $5,200; giving activities include $5,200 for grants.
Fields of interest: Higher education; Education; Health care; Protestant agencies & churches.
Type of support: General/operating support.
Limitations: Applications not accepted. Giving primarily in MI. No grants to individuals.
Application information: Contributes only to pre-selected organizations.
Officers: Michael H. Obloy, Pres.; Phillis Hudsek, V.P.
EIN: 382805957

1394
The Offield Family Foundation
400 N. Michigan Ave., Rm. 407
Chicago, IL 60611

Incorporated in 1940 in IL.
Donor: Dorothy Wrigley Offield.
Grantmaker type: Independent foundation.
Financial data (yr. ended 6/30/04): Assets,
$101,000,616 (M); gifts received, $1,805,716;
expenditures, $8,033,158; total giving,
$7,241,133; qualifying distributions, $7,321,310;
giving activities include $7,241,133 for 68 grants
(high: $1,026,369; low: $500; average: $5,000–
$100,000).
Purpose and activities: Emphasis on hospitals, a
family planning agency, education, and cultural
programs.
Fields of interest: Arts; Education; Hospitals
(general).
Limitations: Applications not accepted. Giving
primarily in AZ, CA, the Chicago, IL, area and MI. No
grants to individuals.
Application information: Contributes only to
pre-selected organizations.
Officers and Directors:* Paxson H. Offield,* Pres.;
James S. Offield,* V.P. and Treas.; Gail Hodge,*
Secy.; Chase Offield; Meighan Offield.
EIN: 366066240
Selected grants: The following grants were reported
in 2004.
$510,000 to Northern Michigan Hospital
Foundation, Petoskey, MI.
$125,000 to Crooked Tree Arts Council, Petoskey,
MI.
$100,000 to Planned Parenthood Northern
Michigan, Petoskey, MI.
$40,000 to Northwestern Memorial Hospital,
Chicago, IL.
$40,000 to Protocare, Petoskey, MI.
$40,000 to University of Washington, Seattle, WA.
$25,000 to Allied EMS Systems, Harbor Springs,
MI.
$25,000 to Catalina Island Performing Arts
Foundation, Avalon, CA.
$25,000 to Dry Creek Arts Fellowship, Flagstaff, AZ.
$25,000 to Michigan Dyslexia Institute, Lansing,
MI.

1395
The Wayne L. and Patricia M. Ogne Foundation
104 Brady Ln.
Bloomfield Hills, MI 48304-2804

Established in 1998 in MI.
Donors: Wayne L. Ogne; Patricia M. Ogne.
Grantmaker type: Independent foundation.
Financial data (yr. ended 12/31/04): Assets,
$90,266 (M); expenditures, $2,292; total giving,
$400; qualifying distributions, $400; giving
activities include $400 for grants.
Fields of interest: Diabetes; Protestant agencies &
churches.
Type of support: General/operating support.
Limitations: Applications not accepted. Giving
primarily in MI. No grants to individuals.
Application information: Contributes only to
pre-selected organizations.
Officers: Wayne L. Ogne, Pres. and Treas.; Patricia
M. Ogne, V.P. and Secy.
EIN: 383380011

1396
The Clark J. Okulski Charitable Foundation
15366 Windmill Pointe Dr.
Grosse Pointe, MI 48230-1744

Established in 2000 in MI.
Donor: Clark J. Okulski.
Grantmaker type: Independent foundation.
Financial data (yr. ended 12/31/04): Assets,
$161,272 (M); expenditures, $39,892; total giving,
$11,975; qualifying distributions, $11,975; giving
activities include $11,975 for 18 grants (high:
$5,000; low: $50).
Fields of interest: Medical school/education;
Education; Human services; Roman Catholic
agencies & churches.
Limitations: Applications not accepted. Giving in the
U.S., with emphasis on MI and Kansas City, MO. No
grants to individuals.
Application information: Contributes only to
pre-selected organizations.
Officers and Directors:* Clark J. Okulski,* Pres.;
Marvin Redlawski,* Secy.-Treas.
EIN: 912082042

1397
Marvin and Rosalie Okun Foundation
527 S. Rose St.
Kalamazoo, MI 49007 (269) 349-9603
Contact: Marvin Okun, Pres.

Donors: Marvin Okun; Rosalie Okun.
Grantmaker type: Independent foundation.
Financial data (yr. ended 12/31/04): Assets,
$140,348 (M); gifts received, $10,000;
expenditures, $8,207; total giving, $7,000;
qualifying distributions, $8,156; giving activities
include $7,000 for grants.
Fields of interest: Jewish agencies & temples.
Type of support: General/operating support.
Application information: Application form not
required.
Deadline(s): Nov. 15
Officers: Marvin Okun, Pres.; Rosalie Okun,
Secy.-Treas.
EIN: 383323820

1398
R. E. Olds Foundation
(formerly Ransom Fidelity Company)
P.O. Box 4900
East Lansing, MI 48826-4900
Contact: Doris Anderson, V.P.

Incorporated in 1915 in MI.
Donor: Ransom E. Olds†.
Grantmaker type: Independent foundation.
Financial data (yr. ended 12/31/05): Assets,
$3,274,811 (M); expenditures, $139,831; total
giving, $124,140; qualifying distributions,
$135,399; giving activities include $124,140 for 38
grants (high: $17,500; low: $250).
Purpose and activities: Giving primarily for
education, health, social services, religion, and
YWCAs.
Fields of interest: Museums (specialized); Arts;
Higher education; Education; Environment, natural
resources; Hospitals (general); Health
organizations; Human services; YM/YWCAs & YM/
YWHAs; Residential/custodial care, hospices;
Community development; Protestant agencies &
churches; Roman Catholic agencies & churches.
Type of support: Annual campaigns; Capital
campaigns; Building/renovation; Equipment;
Endowments; Emergency funds; Conferences/
seminars; Internship funds; Scholarship funds;
Matching/challenge support.
Limitations: Giving in the U.S., with emphasis on MI.
No grants to individuals.
Publications: Annual report; Financial statement;
Grants list.
Application information: Application form required.
Deadline(s): None
Officers: Edward B. McRee, Pres.; Doris B.
Anderson, V.P.; Diane M. Tarpoff, Secy.
Directors: Ronald Beckwith; Deborah Stephens.
Number of staff: 2 full-time professional.
EIN: 381485403

1399
Oleson Foundation
6645 N. Long Lake Rd.
Traverse City, MI 49684-9607
Contact: John R. Spencer M.D., Dir.

Established in 1959 in MI.
Donors: Gerald W. Oleson†; Frances M. Oleson†.
Grantmaker type: Independent foundation.
Financial data (yr. ended 12/31/04): Assets,
$17,299,255 (M); expenditures, $1,155,268; total
giving, $833,046; qualifying distributions,
$835,900; giving activities include $833,046 for 77
grants (high: $75,000; low: $300).
Purpose and activities: Giving primarily for
education and human services.
Fields of interest: Historic preservation/historical
societies; Elementary/secondary education; Higher
education; Environment; Health care; Youth
development, centers/clubs; Human services;
Federated giving programs; Christian agencies &
churches.
Type of support: General/operating support;
Continuing support; Annual campaigns; Capital
campaigns; Building/renovation; Equipment; Land
acquisition; Curriculum development; Matching/
challenge support.
Limitations: Giving primarily in northwestern MI's
Lower Peninsula region. No grants to individuals.
Application information: Application form required.
Initial approach: 1-page letter
Copies of proposal: 1
Deadline(s): Apr. 15
Board meeting date(s): June
Final notification: Usually in late June
Officers and Directors:* Donald W. Oleson,* Pres.;
Gerald E. Oleson,* V.P.; Richard Ford,*
Secy.-Treas.; John R. Spencer, M.D.; John Tobin.
Number of staff: 1 part-time professional.
EIN: 386083080
Selected grants: The following grants were reported
in 2004.
$35,000 to Boy Scouts of America, Scenic Trails
Council, Traverse City, MI.
$35,000 to Grand Traverse Regional Land
Conservancy, Traverse City, MI.
$34,500 to Traverse City Area Public Schools,
Traverse City, MI.
$25,000 to Inland Seas Education Association,
Suttons Bay, MI.
$25,000 to Munson Healthcare Regional
Foundation, Traverse City, MI.
$25,000 to Traverse Area District Library, Traverse
City, MI.

$21,250 to Saint Marys School, Lake Leelanau, MI.
$20,000 to Michigan Community Blood Centers Foundation, Grand Rapids, MI.
$17,461 to Northwestern Michigan College, Traverse City, MI.
$17,000 to Mount Holiday, Traverse City, MI.

1400
Iona Olson Trust
4647 Thistle Mill Ct.
Kalamazoo, MI   49006   (269) 544-2946
Contact: Ronald Olson, Tr.

Established in 1993 in KS.
Grantmaker type: Independent foundation.
Financial data (yr. ended 12/31/05): Assets, $386,955 (M); expenditures, $25,009; total giving, $18,347; qualifying distributions, $18,347; giving activities include $18,347 for grants.
Purpose and activities: Scholarships awards to graduating high school seniors and are members of the Potwin Christian Church; an annual award to the church.
Fields of interest: Higher education; Christian agencies & churches.
Type of support: Scholarships—to individuals.
Limitations: Giving limited to Potwin, KS.
Application information:
  Initial approach: Proposal
  Deadline(s): None
Trustee: Ronald Olson.
EIN: 486328340

1401
Olson-Kulka Foundation
(formerly Robert G. & Celia S. Olson Foundation)
2000 Town Ctr., Ste. 1500
Southfield, MI   48075-1195
Contact: Barry R. Bess, Secy.

Grantmaker type: Independent foundation.
Financial data (yr. ended 12/31/05): Assets, $767,388 (M); expenditures, $45,243; total giving, $41,550; qualifying distributions, $45,243; giving activities include $41,550 for grants.
Fields of interest: Education; Human services; Federated giving programs.
Type of support: General/operating support.
Limitations: Giving primarily in MI. No grants to individuals.
Application information:
  Initial approach: Proposal
  Deadline(s): None
Officers and Trustees:* Justine Olson Kulka,* Pres. and Treas.; Robert Kulka,* V.P.; Barry R. Bess,* Secy.
EIN: 386074650

1402
Paul F. and Franca G. Oreffice Foundation
2204 Oakfield Dr.
Midland, MI   48640

Established in 1986 in MI.
Donors: Paul F. Oreffice; Franca G. Oreffice.
Grantmaker type: Independent foundation.
Financial data (yr. ended 12/31/05): Assets, $2,645,029 (M); expenditures, $169,750; total giving, $164,200; qualifying distributions,

$169,160; giving activities include $164,200 for 13 grants (high: $40,000; low: $500).
Purpose and activities: Giving primarily to a public policy institute and health organizations.
Fields of interest: Hospitals (general); Health organizations, association; Cancer; Parkinson's disease; Athletics/sports, equestrianism; Public policy, research.
Limitations: Applications not accepted. Giving on a national basis. No grants to individuals.
Application information: Contributes only to pre-selected organizations.
Officer: Paul F. Oreffice, Pres.
Director: Franca G. Oreffice.
EIN: 382705906
Selected grants: The following grants were reported in 2004.
$37,500 to National Parkinson Foundation, New York, NY. For general support.
$35,000 to American Enterprise Institute for Public Policy Research, DC. For general support.
$35,000 to University of Texas M. D. Anderson Cancer Center, Houston, TX. For general support.
$11,500 to Grayson-Jockey Club Research Foundation, Lexington, KY. For general support.
$8,200 to National Museum of Racing, Saratoga Springs, NY. For general support.
$5,000 to Mayo Foundation, Rochester, MN. For general support.
$5,000 to Spring Hill Camps, Evart, MI. For general support.
$5,000 to Steadman Hawkins Sports Medicine Foundation, Vail, CO. For general support.
$1,000 to Blinded Veterans Association, DC. For general support.
$1,000 to Smile Train, New York, NY. For general support.

1403
Gregg Orley Family Foundation
40900 N. Woodward Ave., Ste. 130
Bloomfield Hills, MI   48304-5117

Established in 2003 in MI.
Donors: Gregg C. Orley; Harriet Orley.
Grantmaker type: Independent foundation.
Financial data (yr. ended 12/31/05): Assets, $45,378 (M); expenditures, $2,376; total giving, $0; qualifying distributions, $0.
Officer: Gregg C. Orley.
EIN: 320087856

1404
The Joseph & Suzanne Orley Foundation
201 W. Big Beaver Rd., Ste. 720
Troy, MI   48084

Established in 1997 in MI.
Donors: Joseph H. Orley; Suzanne E. Orley.
Grantmaker type: Independent foundation.
Financial data (yr. ended 12/31/04): Assets, $2,160,869 (M); gifts received, $123,520; expenditures, $158,602; total giving, $154,480; qualifying distributions, $154,480; giving activities include $154,480 for grants (high: $100,000).
Fields of interest: Performing arts; Education; Medical research; Human services; Jewish agencies & temples.
Limitations: Applications not accepted. Giving in MI. No grants to individuals.

Application information: Contributes only to pre-selected organizations.
Trustees: Joseph H. Orley; Suzanne E. Orley.
EIN: 383343679

1405
The Sally A. & Graham A. Orley Foundation
201 W. Big Beaver Rd., Ste. 720
Troy, MI   48084-4162

Established in 2000 in MI.
Donors: Graham A. Orley; Sally A. Orley.
Grantmaker type: Independent foundation.
Financial data (yr. ended 12/31/04): Assets, $1,755,011 (M); gifts received, $148,520; expenditures, $160,870; total giving, $160,300; qualifying distributions, $159,940; giving activities include $160,300 for 13 grants (high: $100,000; low: $1,000).
Fields of interest: Arts; Education; Medical research; Human services; Jewish federated giving programs; Jewish agencies & temples.
Limitations: Applications not accepted. Giving primarily in MI. No grants to individuals.
Application information: Contributes only to pre-selected organizations.
Officers: Sally A. Orley, Pres.; Graham A. Orley, Secy.
EIN: 383525344

1406
Dr. Donald J. Orris Memorial Scholarship Trust Fund
c/o Comerica Bank
P.O. Box 75000
Detroit, MI   48275-3302
Application addresses: c/o Central Christian High School, Attn.: Principal, 204 Hospital Ave., Du Bois, PA 15801, c/o Du Bois Area Senior High School, Attn.: Principal, 500 Liberty Blvd., Du Bois, PA 15801, c/o Punxytawney Area High School, Attn.: Principal, 600 N. Findley St., Punxytawney, PA 15767, c/o Brookville Area High School, Attn.: Principal, P.O. Box 479, Brookville, PA 15825

Established in 1998 in PA.
Donor: Albert J. Orris.
Grantmaker type: Independent foundation.
Financial data (yr. ended 12/31/05): Assets, $26,970 (M); expenditures, $16,750; total giving, $14,000; qualifying distributions, $14,000; giving activities include $14,000 for grants to individuals.
Purpose and activities: Scholarship awards to Central Christian, Du Bois Area, Punxytawny Area and Brookville Area high schools, PA.
Fields of interest: Higher education.
Type of support: Scholarships—to individuals.
Limitations: Giving limited to residents of PA.
Application information:
  Initial approach: Letter
  Deadline(s): May 22
Trustee: Comerica Bank.
EIN: 383406443

1407
Aline Underhill Orten Foundation, Inc.
1 Galleria Blvd., Ste. 1100
Metairie, LA   70001

Established in 2000 in LA.
Donor: Aline Underhill Orten Trust.

Grantmaker type: Independent foundation.
Financial data (yr. ended 12/31/05): Assets, $3,301,016 (M); gifts received, $73; expenditures, $213,438; total giving, $104,700; qualifying distributions, $148,340; giving activities include $104,700 for 33 grants (high: $20,000; low: $1,000).
Fields of interest: Higher education; Medical school/education; Botanical/horticulture/ landscape services; Cancer; Food services; Disasters, fire prevention/control; Human services; Children/youth, services; Developmentally disabled, centers & services; Blind/visually impaired.
Limitations: Applications not accepted. Giving primarily in MI. No grants to individuals.
Application information: Contributes only to pre-selected organizations.
Officers and Directors:* Joyce A. Roehl,* Pres.; Allen McCreedy,* Secy.-Treas.; David M. Kenny; Kathleen Roehl; Michele Ann Worden.
EIN: 721477797

1408
Armando and Joan Ortiz Foundation
2488 Inglehill Pointe
Bloomfield Hills, MI   48304

Established in 1999 in MI.
Donors: Armando Ortiz; Joan Ortiz.
Grantmaker type: Independent foundation.
Financial data (yr. ended 12/31/05): Assets, $108,699 (M); gifts received, $300; expenditures, $7,237; total giving, $5,550; qualifying distributions, $5,550; giving activities include $5,550 for grants.
Fields of interest: Arts education; Education.
Limitations: Applications not accepted. Giving primarily in MI. No grants to individuals.
Application information: Contributes only to pre-selected organizations.
Directors: Armando Ortiz, M.D.; Joan Ortiz.
EIN: 383504731

1409
Annette L. Ott Scholarship Fund
18620 Fort St.
Riverview, MI   48192

Established in 2004 in MI.
Grantmaker type: Independent foundation.
Financial data (yr. ended 12/31/04): Assets, $785 (M); gifts received, $785; expenditures, $0; total giving, $0; qualifying distributions, $0.
Officers: Richard E. Ott, Chair.; Alise Welsh, Pres. and Treas.; Richard E. Ott, Jr., V.P. and Secy.
EIN: 201978806

1410
Otto Family Foundation
795 Fairway Ct.
Gaylord, MI   49735

Donor: Fred Otto.
Grantmaker type: Independent foundation.
Financial data (yr. ended 12/31/05): Assets, $16,802 (M); gifts received, $3,000; expenditures, $3,035; total giving, $3,015; qualifying distributions, $3,015; giving activities include $3,015 for grants.

Limitations: Applications not accepted. No grants to individuals.
Application information: Contributes only to pre-selected organizations.
Trustees: Sandra Fisher; Pamela Jacques; Barbara Otto; Fred Otto.
EIN: 383327783

1411
Our Greatest Gift Foundation
c/o Mark Craig
15450 E. Jefferson Ave., Ste. 150
Grosse Pointe Park, MI   48230-2030

Established in 2000 in MI as a public charity; became an independent foundation in 2003.
Donor: Mark Craig.
Grantmaker type: Independent foundation.
Financial data (yr. ended 12/31/05): Assets, $0 (M); gifts received, $20,000; expenditures, $19,759; total giving, $5,000; qualifying distributions, $19,759; giving activities include $5,000 for grants.
Purpose and activities: The foundation seeks to foster Christian-based child development programming and resources.
Fields of interest: Child development, services; Christian agencies & churches.
Limitations: Applications not accepted.
Application information: Unsolicited requests for funds not accepted.
Officer: Mark Craig, Pres.
EIN: 383509422

1412
Overlook International Foundation, Inc.
500 Woodward Ave., Ste. 2500
Detroit, MI   48226

Established in 2004 in MI.
Donors: Richard H. Lawrence; Dee M. Lawrence.
Grantmaker type: Independent foundation.
Financial data (yr. ended 12/31/04): Assets, $529,838 (M); gifts received, $520,050; expenditures, $73,379; total giving, $70,182; qualifying distributions, $70,182; giving activities include $70,182 for grants.
Officers: Richard H. Lawrence, Pres.; Dee M. Lawrence, V.P.; Philip S. Lawrence, Secy.-Treas.
EIN: 201164239

1413
Owen Scholarship Trust
c/o Fifth Third Bank
P.O. Box 3636
Grand Rapids, MI   49501-3636
Contact: Kathyrn Dlabach, Secy.
Application address: c/o Plano High School, W. Abe St., Plano, IL 60545, tel.: (708) 552-3178

Established in MI.
Grantmaker type: Independent foundation.
Financial data (yr. ended 12/31/05): Assets, $44,616 (M); expenditures, $4,708; total giving, $2,400; qualifying distributions, $2,400; giving activities include $2,400 for grants to individuals.
Purpose and activities: Scholarship awards to graduates of Plano High School, IL.
Fields of interest: Scholarships/financial aid.

Type of support: Scholarship funds; Scholarships—to individuals.
Limitations: Giving limited to Plano, IL.
Application information: Application form required. *Deadline(s):* Apr. 15
Officer: Kathyrn Dlabach, Secy.
Scholarship Committee: Jeff Cooper; Denise Helmers; Donna Henningsen; Mike Nedeau; Fran Sauer.
Trustee: Fifth Third Bank.
EIN: 386080449

1414
Ralph L. Owens Trust
c/o Citizens Bank Wealth Mgmt., N.A.
328 S. Saginaw St., MC 002072
Flint, MI   48502

Established in MI.
Donor: Ralph L. Owens†.
Grantmaker type: Independent foundation.
Financial data (yr. ended 12/31/05): Assets, $125,072 (M); expenditures, $11,561; total giving, $9,484; qualifying distributions, $9,688; giving activities include $9,484 for 1 grant.
Purpose and activities: Support only for the City of Hillsdale, MI.
Type of support: General/operating support.
Limitations: Applications not accepted. Giving limited to Hillsdale, MI. No grants to individuals.
Application information: Contributes only to a pre-selected organization.
Trustee: Citizens Bank, N.A.
EIN: 386121838

1415
Esther and Seymour Padnos Foundation
c/o Seymour K. Padnos
P.O. Box 1979
Holland, MI   49422-1979

Established in 1992 in MI.
Donors: Seymour Padnos; Esther Padnos.
Grantmaker type: Independent foundation.
Financial data (yr. ended 12/31/05): Assets, $959,885 (M); gifts received, $206,460; expenditures, $36,174; total giving, $33,146; qualifying distributions, $33,146; giving activities include $33,146 for grants.
Fields of interest: Museums; Arts; Health organizations; Children/youth, services; Jewish agencies & temples.
Limitations: Applications not accepted. Giving on a national basis. No grants to individuals.
Application information: Contributes only to pre-selected organizations.
Officers: Seymour Padnos, Pres.; Esther Padnos, Secy.-Treas.
EIN: 383072505

1416
Louis and Helen Padnos Foundation
P.O. Box 1979
Holland, MI   49422-1979

Established in 1999 in MI.
Donors: Louis & Helen Padnos Foundation; Louis Padnos Iron and Metal Co.
Grantmaker type: Independent foundation.

Financial data (yr. ended 5/31/05): Assets, $7,008,757 (M); gifts received, $645,480; expenditures, $377,402; total giving, $358,726; qualifying distributions, $360,342; giving activities include $358,726 for 121 grants (high: $91,000; low: $50).
Purpose and activities: Giving primarily to Jewish organizations and a community foundation; funding also for health care, education, youth and social services, and the arts.
Fields of interest: Museums; Arts; Education; Hospitals (general); Reproductive health, family planning; Cancer; Health organizations; Boys & girls clubs; Human services; Residential/custodial care, hospices; Jewish federated giving programs; Jewish agencies & temples.
Limitations: Applications not accepted. Giving primarily in MI, with emphasis on Grand Rapids and Holland. No grants to individuals.
Application information: Contributes only to pre-selected organizations.
Officers and Trustees: * Jeffrey S. Padnos,* Pres.; Shelley E. Padnos,* Secy.; Mitchell W. Padnos,* Treas.; Cynthia B. Padnos; Daniel P. Padnos; Douglas B. Padnos; William R. Padnos.
EIN: 383476218

1417
Stuart and Barbara Padnos Foundation
P.O. Box 1979
Holland, MI   49422-1979

Established in 1995 in MI.
Donors: Stuart Padnos; Barbara Padnos.
Grantmaker type: Independent foundation.
Financial data (yr. ended 12/31/05): Assets, $15,718 (M); expenditures, $330; total giving, $230; qualifying distributions, $250; giving activities include $230 for 5 grants (high: $50; low: $35).
Type of support: General/operating support.
Limitations: Applications not accepted. Giving primarily in MI. No grants to individuals.
Application information: Contributes only to pre-selected organizations.
Director: Stuart Padnos.
EIN: 383237340

1418
Arlene and Forrest Winston Page Foundation, Inc.
30450 Oakview Way
Bingham Farms, MI   48025

Established in 1998 in MI.
Donors: Forrest Page; Arlene Page.
Grantmaker type: Independent foundation.
Financial data (yr. ended 12/31/05): Assets, $1,218,163 (M); gifts received, $184,309; expenditures, $49,927; total giving, $48,500; qualifying distributions, $48,500; giving activities include $48,500 for grants.
Fields of interest: Education.
Type of support: Scholarship funds.
Limitations: Applications not accepted. No grants to individuals.
Application information: Contributes only to pre-selected organizations.
Officers: Forrest Page, Pres. and Treas.; Arlene Page, V.P. and Secy.
EIN: 383444161

1419
Paideia Foundation
P.O. Box 130-980
Ann Arbor, MI   48113-0980   (734) 741-9720
Contact: John Psarouthakis, Dir.

Established in 1986.
Donor: John Psarouthakis.
Grantmaker type: Independent foundation.
Financial data (yr. ended 10/20/03): Assets, $0 (M); expenditures, $7,286; total giving, $4,000; qualifying distributions, $5,643; giving activities include $4,000 for 1 grant.
Fields of interest: Higher education, university.
Application information: Application form required.
    Deadline(s): None
Director: John Psarouthakis.
EIN: 382711090

1420
Paine Family Foundation
c/o Northwest Investment and Trust
P.O. Box 1380
Traverse City, MI   49685-1380
Application address: c/o Carol Paine-McGovern, 2445 Hall St. S.E., Grand Rapids, MI 49506, tel.: (616) 285-0409

Established in 1991 in MI.
Donors: Martha L. Paine; G. William Paine; Carol Paine-McGovern.
Grantmaker type: Independent foundation.
Financial data (yr. ended 12/31/05): Assets, $5,488,819 (M); expenditures, $327,055; total giving, $265,691; qualifying distributions, $290,272; giving activities include $265,691 for 31 grants (high: $78,000; low: $100).
Purpose and activities: Giving primarily for education; funding also for community foundations and federated giving programs, historical preservation, hospitals, and human services.
Fields of interest: Historic preservation/historical societies; Higher education; Education; Hospitals (general); Human services; Foundations (community); Federated giving programs.
Type of support: General/operating support; Endowments; Scholarship funds.
Limitations: Giving primarily in Mason and Manistee counties., MI.
Application information: Application form not required.
    Deadline(s): None
Officers: Carol Paine-McGovern, Pres.; G. William Paine, V.P.; Martha L. Paine, Secy.-Treas.
EIN: 382996404

1421
C. H. & G. F. Pajeau Foundation
c/o The Northern Trust Co.
50 S. LaSalle St., M-14
Chicago, IL   60675

Grantmaker type: Independent foundation.
Financial data (yr. ended 12/31/05): Assets, $1,012,691 (M); expenditures, $52,506; total giving, $50,000; qualifying distributions, $50,000; giving activities include $50,000 for grants.
Purpose and activities: Supports organizations that advocate the comfort of birds and animals.
Fields of interest: Animal welfare; Animals/wildlife, preservation/protection.

Type of support: General/operating support.
Limitations: Giving primarily in MI and NY. No grants to individuals; no program-related investments.
Application information: Application form not required.
    Deadline(s): None
Trustee: The Northern Trust Co.
EIN: 366791307

1422
The Irving and Ethel Palman Foundation
c/o Jonathan D. Lowe
P.O. Box 251431
West Bloomfield, MI   48325

Established in 1998 in MI.
Donor: Irving Palman†.
Grantmaker type: Independent foundation.
Financial data (yr. ended 12/31/05): Assets, $3,704,317 (M); expenditures, $206,721; total giving, $143,800; qualifying distributions, $155,398; giving activities include $143,800 for 22 grants (high: $17,000; low: $500).
Fields of interest: Jewish agencies & temples.
Limitations: Applications not accepted. No grants to individuals.
Application information: Contributes only to pre-selected organizations.
Officers and Trustees: * Jonathan D. Lowe,* Pres.; Stanley Levy,* Secy.
EIN: 383452975

1423
Ronald Palmer Family Foundation
4261 13th St.
Wyandotte, MI   48192-7002
Contact: Heather Gardner, Secy.
E-mail: gardnerh@horizonet.com

Established in 1997 in MI.
Donor: Ronald Palmer.
Grantmaker type: Independent foundation.
Financial data (yr. ended 12/31/04): Assets, $1 (M); expenditures, $3,800; total giving, $3,599; qualifying distributions, $3,800; giving activities include $3,599 for grants.
Fields of interest: Performing arts, theater; Education; Human services.
Limitations: Giving limited to MI. No grants to individuals.
Application information: Application form not required.
    Initial approach: Letter
    Copies of proposal: 1
    Deadline(s): None
Officers: Ronald Palmer, Pres.; Heather Gardner, Secy.; Susan Urdahl, Treas.
Directors: Nathan Forbes; Richard Vlasic.
EIN: 383373231

1424
Walter E. and Maria F. Palmer Foundation
P.O. Box 312
Frankenmuth, MI   48734   (989) 652-6648
Contact: Walter E. Palmer, Pres.

Established in 1990 in MI.
Donors: Walter E. Palmer; Maria F. Palmer.
Grantmaker type: Independent foundation.

Financial data (yr. ended 12/31/05): Assets, $584,977 (M); gifts received, $40,008; expenditures, $27,516; total giving, $23,246; qualifying distributions, $26,266; giving activities include $23,246 for grants.
Fields of interest: Human services; Community development; Government/public administration; Roman Catholic agencies & churches.
Type of support: Program development; Building/ renovation.
Limitations: Giving primarily in Frankenmuth, MI. No grants to individuals.
Application information:
  Initial approach: Letter
  Deadline(s): None
Officers: Walter E. Palmer,* Pres.; Maria F. Palmer,* V.P.
Directors: Thomas A. Jaffke; Franklin Rittmueller; W. Don Zehnder.
EIN: 382962926

1425
Pappas Foundation, Inc.
30301 Northwestern Hwy., Ste. 200
Farmington Hills, MI   48334-3278

Established in 1997 in MI.
Donor: Norman A. Pappas.
Grantmaker type: Independent foundation.
Financial data (yr. ended 12/31/05): Assets, $869,415 (M); gifts received, $310,336; expenditures, $43,238; total giving, $43,238; qualifying distributions, $43,238; giving activities include $43,238 for grants.
Fields of interest: Jewish agencies & temples.
Limitations: Applications not accepted. Giving primarily in MI. No grants to individuals.
Application information: Contributes only to pre-selected organizations.
Directors: Charles N. Pappas; Norman A. Pappas; Susan L. Pappas.
EIN: 383386198

1426
Paradise Foundation
c/o Huntington Bank
P.O. Box 1350
Traverse City, MI   49685-1350

Established in 1994 in MI.
Donors: Sally W. Zublin; Sally W. Andreatta.
Grantmaker type: Independent foundation.
Financial data (yr. ended 12/31/05): Assets, $1,363,759 (M); expenditures, $144,594; total giving, $43,664; qualifying distributions, $43,664; giving activities include $33,664 for 9 grants (high: $12,000; low: $1,200), and $10,000 for 1 grant to an individual.
Fields of interest: Education; Recreation; Children, services.
Limitations: Giving primarily in CA.
Directors: Sally W. Andreatta; John H. Martin.
EIN: 383182229

1427
Charles A. Parcells Foundation
178 Lothrop Rd.
Grosse Pointe Farms, MI   48236
Contact: Charles A. Parcells, Jr., Pres.

Established in 2000 in MI.
Donor: William Lyon Phelps Foundation.
Grantmaker type: Independent foundation.
Financial data (yr. ended 12/31/04): Assets, $150,343 (M); expenditures, $25,648; total giving, $23,975; qualifying distributions, $23,975; giving activities include $23,975 for grants.
Fields of interest: Performing arts, opera.
Limitations: Applications not accepted. Giving primarily in Detroit, MI. No grants to individuals.
Application information: Contributes only to pre-selected organizations.
Officers and Directors:* Charles A. Parcells, Jr.,* Pres.; Kathryn H. Parcells,* V.P. and Treas.
EIN: 383521926

1428
Elsa U. Pardee Foundation
P.O. Box 2767
Midland, MI   48641-2767   (989) 832-3691
Contact: James A. Kendall, Secy.
FAX: (989) 832-8842; E-mail: lucille@tm.net;
URL: http://www.pardeefoundation.org

Incorporated in 1944 in MI.
Donor: Elsa U. Pardee‡.
Grantmaker type: Independent foundation.
Financial data (yr. ended 12/31/05): Assets, $106,019,850 (M); gifts received, $100; expenditures, $5,449,762; total giving, $5,100,135; qualifying distributions, $5,153,240; giving activities include $5,100,135 for 48 grants (high: $247,122; low: $6,000; average: $50,000–$225,000).
Purpose and activities: Giving primarily to support: 1) research programs directed toward discovering new approaches for cancer treatment and cure; and 2) financial support for cancer treatment.
Fields of interest: Cancer; Medical research, institute; Cancer research.
Type of support: Research.
Publications: Annual report (including application guidelines).
Application information: Application form is available on foundation Web site. Application form required.
  Initial approach: Letter
  Copies of proposal: 8
  Deadline(s): None
  Board meeting date(s): 3 times per year
  Final notification: 4 to 6 months
Officers and Trustees:* Gail E. Lanphear,* Pres.; Lisa J. Gerstacker,* V.P.; James A. Kendall,* Secy.; Alan W. Ott,* Treas.; W. James Allen; Richard J. Kociba; Mary M. Neely; Patrick J. Oriel; William D. Schuette.
Number of staff: 1 part-time support.
EIN: 386065799
Selected grants: The following grants were reported in 2004.
$280,000 to Pardee Cancer Treatment Fund of Midland/Gladwin, Midland, MI. For program support.
$200,000 to Pardee Cancer Treatment Fund of Clare County, Clare, MI. For program support.
$200,000 to Pardee Cancer Treatment Fund of Isabella County, Mount Pleasant, MI. For program support.
$150,000 to Manitoba Institute of Cell Biology, Winnipeg, Canada. For study of identification of mutations in pro-cell death and putative tumor suppressor gene BNIP3 in oligodendroglioma.

$142,500 to Pardee Cancer Treatment Fund of Bay County, Bay City, MI. For program support.
$126,316 to Yale University, School of Medicine, New Haven, CT. For study on improving survival with growth hormone in a mouse model of human ovarian cancer.
$125,000 to Pardee Cancer Treatment Association of Greater Brazosport, Lake Jackson, TX. For program support.
$125,000 to Pardee Cancer Treatment Fund of Gratiot County, Alma, MI. For program support.
$125,000 to Wayne State University, Detroit, MI. For study of role of phosphatase MKP1 in cisplatin resistance of ovarian cancer.
$124,754 to University of Pittsburgh, Pittsburgh, PA. For study of base excision repair as global tumor suppressor mechanism.

1429
The Parekh-Vora Charitable Foundation
5214 Great Oaks Ct.
West Bloomfield, MI   48323

Established in 1988 in MI.
Donors: Kamlesh K. Parekh; Deepika K. Parekh.
Grantmaker type: Independent foundation.
Financial data (yr. ended 12/31/04): Assets, $1,955,256 (M); gifts received, $47,664; expenditures, $74,288; total giving, $72,248; qualifying distributions, $74,288; giving activities include $72,248 for grants.
Fields of interest: Education; Hospitals (general); Human services; Federated giving programs; Religion.
International interests: India.
Limitations: Applications not accepted. Giving on a national basis. No grants to individuals.
Application information: Contributes only to pre-selected organizations.
Directors: Deepika K. Parekh; Kamlesh K. Parekh.
EIN: 382779568

1430
Donald and Ann Parfet Family Foundation
259 E. Michigan Ave., Ste. 409
Kalamazoo, MI   49007-5902   (269) 349-8483
Contact: Wendy Van Peenan, Compt.
FAX: (269) 349-8993;
E-mail: wvanpeenan@ameritech.net

Established in 1996 in MI.
Donor: Donald R. Parfet.
Grantmaker type: Independent foundation.
Financial data (yr. ended 12/31/04): Assets, $2,130,347 (M); expenditures, $276,410; total giving, $244,287; qualifying distributions, $263,289; giving activities include $244,287 for 136 grants (high: $20,000; low: $50).
Purpose and activities: Giving primarily for health, human services, and educational organizations.
Fields of interest: Arts; Education; Health care; Human services; Community development.
Type of support: Program development; General/ operating support; Continuing support; Annual campaigns; Capital campaigns; Building/ renovation; Endowments; Emergency funds; Scholarship funds; Employee matching gifts.
Limitations: Giving primarily in Kalamazoo, MI, and surrounding communities. No grants to individuals.
Application information: Application form not required.

Initial approach: Letter with accompanying information.
Copies of proposal: 6
Deadline(s): 3 weeks prior to board meetings
Board meeting date(s): 2006: Mar. 2, May 15, Sept. 11, Oct. 30 and Dec. 12
Final notification: 2 weeks after a board meeting
Officers and Trustees:* Ann V. Parfet,* Pres.; Andrew Worgess,* V.P.; Rachel E. Worgess,* V.P.; Sydney E. Waldorf,* Secy.; Donald R. Parfet,* Co-Treas.; C. MacKenzie Waldorf,* Co-Treas.
Number of staff: 1 part-time professional.
EIN: 383326370

1431
Suzanne Upjohn Delano Parish Foundation

(formerly Suzanne D. Parish Foundation)
100 W. Michigan Ave., Ste. 100
Kalamazoo, MI 49007   (269) 388-9800
Contact: Ronald N. Kilgore, V.P.

Established in MI.
Donor: Suzanne U.D. Parish.
Grantmaker type: Independent foundation.
Financial data (yr. ended 12/31/04): Assets, $7,582,816 (M); expenditures, $522,404; total giving, $500,000; qualifying distributions, $508,105; giving activities include $500,000 for 1 grant.
Purpose and activities: Support primarily to an aviation history museum.
Fields of interest: Museums (history); Space/aviation.
Type of support: General/operating support.
Limitations: Giving primarily in Kalamazoo, MI. No grants to individuals; no loans.
Application information:
Initial approach: Letter
Deadline(s): None
Officers and Directors:* Suzanne U.D. Parish,* Pres. and Secy.; Ronald N. Kilgore,* V.P. and Treas.; Katharine P. Miller; Preston L. Parish.
EIN: 382484268

1432
Barbara E. Parish Foundation

244 N. Rose St., Ste. 100
Kalamazoo, MI 49007-3824

Established in 1997 in MI.
Donor: Barbara E. Parish.
Grantmaker type: Independent foundation.
Financial data (yr. ended 12/31/05): Assets, $369,610 (M); gifts received, $116,095; expenditures, $66,350; total giving, $60,720; qualifying distributions, $60,720; giving activities include $60,720 for grants.
Fields of interest: Elementary/secondary education; Higher education; Health care, single organization support.
Type of support: Annual campaigns; Capital campaigns.
Limitations: Applications not accepted. Giving primarily in CO, with emphasis on Telluride. No grants to individuals.
Application information: Contributes only to pre-selected organizations.
Trustee: Barbara E. Parish.
EIN: 367166378

1433
Preston S. Parish Foundation

c/o Barbara J. Parish
244 N. Rose St., Ste. 100
Kalamazoo, MI 49007
Contact: Barbara J. Parish, V.P.
FAX: (269) 343-1542;
E-mail: ParishAssociates@msn.com

Established in 1984 in MI.
Donor: Preston S. Parish.
Grantmaker type: Independent foundation.
Financial data (yr. ended 12/31/05): Assets, $70,627 (M); gifts received, $229,788; expenditures, $193,214; total giving, $182,475; qualifying distributions, $187,323; giving activities include $182,475 for 78 grants (high: $16,000; low: $125).
Purpose and activities: Giving for the arts, community development, the environment, higher education, and Christian organizations.
Fields of interest: Arts; Higher education; Environment, natural resources; Health organizations, association; Community development; Federated giving programs; Christian agencies & churches; Women.
Type of support: Annual campaigns; Capital campaigns.
Limitations: Applications not accepted. Giving primarily in Kalamazoo, MI. No grants to individuals.
Application information: Contributes only to pre-selected organizations.
Board meeting date(s): First Mon. in Dec.
Officers: Preston S. Parish, Pres. and Secy.; Barbara J. Parish, V.P.; Kathy A. Roschek, Treas.
Number of staff: 1 part-time support.
EIN: 363249490
Selected grants: The following grants were reported in 2004.
$20,000 to Heritage Community of Kalamazoo, Kalamazoo, MI. For general support.
$16,000 to Kalamazoo Symphony Orchestra, Kalamazoo, MI. For general support.
$15,000 to Kalamazoo Nature Center, Kalamazoo, MI. For general support.
$10,000 to Michigan State University, College of Veterinary Medicine, East Lansing, MI. For general support.
$9,000 to Saint Timothy Episcopal Church, Richland, MI. For general support.
$6,000 to YMCA, Sherman Lake, Augusta, MI. For general support.
$5,000 to Binder Park Zoological Society, Battle Creek, MI. For general support.
$5,000 to Holderness School, Plymouth, NH. For general support.
$5,000 to Little Traverse Conservancy, Harbor Springs, MI. For general support.
$5,000 to Western Michigan University Foundation, Kalamazoo, MI. For general support.

1434
John M. Parker Educational Memorial Foundation

c/o John J. Raymond, Jr.
300 E. Long Lake Rd., Ste. 360
Bloomfield Hills, MI 48304-2377
Contact: James B. Zellen, Pres.
Application address: 1520 N. Woodward, Bloomfield Hills, MI 48304, tel.: (248) 647-8878

Established in 1999 in MI.
Grantmaker type: Independent foundation.

Financial data (yr. ended 12/31/02): Assets, $395,524 (M); expenditures, $15,919; total giving, $0; qualifying distributions, $0.
Fields of interest: Higher education; Higher education, college.
Type of support: Student loans—to individuals.
Limitations: Giving limited to residents of Pontiac, MI.
Application information:
Initial approach: Letter
Deadline(s): None
Officers: James B. Zellen, Pres.; John J. Raymond, Jr., Secy.-Treas.
Directors: Clarence G. Carlson; John M. Foster.
EIN: 383438767

1435
Robert W. and Maxine C. Parker Foundation, Inc.

4777 W. Liberty Rd.
Ann Arbor, MI 48103-9707

Established in 1988 in MI.
Donor: Robert W. Parker✝.
Grantmaker type: Independent foundation.
Financial data (yr. ended 12/31/05): Assets, $4,135,321 (M); expenditures, $226,038; total giving, $209,234; qualifying distributions, $217,203; giving activities include $209,234 for 19 grants (high: $72,500; low: $1,000).
Purpose and activities: Giving to religion, education, humanitarian organizations and medical services.
Fields of interest: Libraries/library science; Hospitals (general); Boy scouts; Military/veterans' organizations; Christian agencies & churches.
Type of support: Equipment.
Limitations: Applications not accepted. Giving primarily in MI. No grants to individuals.
Application information: Contributes only to pre-selected organizations.
Officers and Trustees:* Andrew D. Parker,* Pres.; T. Gilbert Parker,* V.P.; Johanna C. Johnson,* Secy.-Treas.
EIN: 382795440
Selected grants: The following grants were reported in 2005.
$72,500 to Howell Department of Recreation, Howell, MI.
$27,500 to First Presbyterian Church, Howell, MI.
$10,000 to American Legion Riders Post 141, Howell, MI.
$10,000 to Boy Scouts of America, Great Sauk Trail Council, Ann Arbor, MI.
$10,000 to Family Impact Center, Fowlerville, MI.
$10,000 to Livingston County Nutrition Program, Howell, MI.
$6,824 to Howell Carnegie District Library, Howell, MI.
$6,500 to Livingston Arts Council, Howell, MI.
$5,410 to Michigan Masonic Home, Alma, MI.
$5,000 to Humane Society of Livingston County, Howell, MI.

1436
Henry & Louise Parker Scholarship Trust

c/o Comerica Bank
P.O. Box 75000
Detroit, MI 48275
Application addresses: c/o Santa Cruz High School, Attn: Principal, 415 Walnut Ave., Santa Cruz, CA 95060, c/o Harbor High School, Attn: Principal, 300

LaFonda Ave., Santa Cruz, CA 95062, c/o Soquel High School, Attn: Principal, 401 Old San Jose Rd., Soquel, CA 95073

Established in CA.
Grantmaker type: Independent foundation.
Financial data (yr. ended 12/31/05): Assets, $295,029 (M); expenditures, $17,767; total giving, $14,900; qualifying distributions, $14,900; giving activities include $14,900 for grants.
Purpose and activities: Scholarship awards to graduates of Santa Cruz, Harbor, and Soquel high schools, CA.
Fields of interest: Higher education.
Type of support: Scholarships—to individuals.
Limitations: Giving limited to CA.
Application information: Application form required.
  Deadline(s): Varies
Trustee: Comerica Bank.
EIN: 946347991

1437
Edward Parks Charitable Trust
727 Harmon St.
Birmingham, MI 48009-1329

Established in 2000 in MI.
Donor: Edward M. Parks.
Grantmaker type: Independent foundation.
Financial data (yr. ended 12/31/05): Assets, $162,543 (M); gifts received, $36,225; expenditures, $38,288; total giving, $38,198; qualifying distributions, $38,198; giving activities include $38,198 for grants.
Limitations: Applications not accepted. No grants to individuals.
Application information: Contributes only to pre-selected organizations.
Trustee: Edward M. Parks.
EIN: 383507050

1438
Athanase & Shirley Pasant Family Foundation
c/o George H. McCrimlisk & Co.
201 S. Lake Ave., Ste. 508
Pasadena, CA 91101

Established in 1992 in CA.
Donor: Shirley K. Pasant.
Grantmaker type: Independent foundation.
Financial data (yr. ended 12/31/05): Assets, $683,058 (M); expenditures, $205,750; total giving, $200,000; qualifying distributions, $200,000; giving activities include $200,000 for 1 grant.
Fields of interest: Performing arts, theater.
Limitations: Applications not accepted. Giving primarily in MI. No grants to individuals.
Application information: Contributes only to pre-selected organizations.
Officers: Shirley K. Pasant, Pres.; George H. McCrimlisk, Secy.
Director: David A. Pasant.
EIN: 954397285

1439
Beatrice & Reymont Paul Foundation
c/o Comerica Bank
P.O. Box 75000, M/C 3302
Detroit, MI 48275-3302
Contact: Janet Stanfield, Trust Off., Commerica Bank

Established in 2004 in MI.
Donor: Beatrice Paul.
Grantmaker type: Independent foundation.
Financial data (yr. ended 12/31/05): Assets, $1,130,949 (M); gifts received, $185,685; expenditures, $58,909; total giving, $31,500; qualifying distributions, $31,500; giving activities include $31,500 for grants.
Application information: Application form not required.
  Deadline(s): None
Officers: Beatrice Paul, Chair.; Susan H. Garin, Pres.; Joseph P. Garin, Treas.
EIN: 201279991

1440
Anna Paulina Foundation
3400 W. Bristol Rd.
Flint, MI 48507-3112
Contact: Albert J. Koegel, Treas.

Established in 1961 in MI.
Donors: Albert J. Koegel; Anne Rocco; Kathryn Koegel; Jane Koegel; John Koegel; Sunset Hills Assn.
Grantmaker type: Independent foundation.
Financial data (yr. ended 12/31/05): Assets, $12,024,605 (M); gifts received, $794,200; expenditures, $893,541; total giving, $877,891; qualifying distributions, $893,541; giving activities include $877,891 for 98 grants (high: $500,000; low: $25).
Fields of interest: Arts; Education; Human services; YM/YWCAs & YM/YWHAs; Federated giving programs; Christian agencies & churches.
Limitations: Applications not accepted. Giving primarily in the Genesee County, MI, area. No grants to individuals.
Application information: Contributes only to pre-selected organizations. Unsolicited applications not considered.
Officers: Kathryn Koegel, Pres.; Elizabeth M. Neithercut, V.P.; Jeffry D. Rocco, Secy.; Albert J. Koegel, Treas.
Trustees: Barbara L. Koegel; Jane Koegel; John C. Koegel; Lisa A. Koegel; Edward J. Neithercut; Anne Koegel Rocco.
EIN: 386061335

1441
Paulsen Trust
5230 Village Dr. S.W.
Wyoming, MI 49509-5147
Contact: Nelson R. Allen, Tr.
Application address: 2121 Pantano Rd., No. 267, Tucson, AZ 85710, tel.: (520) 751-7897

Established in 1988 in MI.
Grantmaker type: Independent foundation.
Financial data (yr. ended 12/31/05): Assets, $194,288 (M); expenditures, $7,821; total giving, $7,000; qualifying distributions, $7,000; giving activities include $7,000 for grants to individuals.

Purpose and activities: Scholarship awards to graduating seniors in MI, to attend an accredited state institution.
Fields of interest: Higher education.
Type of support: Scholarships—to individuals.
Limitations: Giving limited to residents of MI.
Application information: Application form required.
  Deadline(s): None
Trustees: Nelson R. Allen; John Barnett; Agnes Karas.
EIN: 386537948

1442
PAV Foundation
c/o JPMorgan Chase Bank, N.A.
P.O. Box 1103
Dayton, OH 45401

Established in 1957 in OH.
Grantmaker type: Independent foundation.
Financial data (yr. ended 12/31/04): Assets, $1,830,053 (M); expenditures, $95,121; total giving, $85,000; qualifying distributions, $84,889; giving activities include $85,000 for grants.
Purpose and activities: Giving for the arts, education, and human services.
Fields of interest: Arts; Higher education; Human services.
Type of support: General/operating support.
Limitations: Applications not accepted. Giving limited to FL, KY, MI, MN, OH, TN, and VT. No grants to individuals.
Application information: Contributes only to pre-selected organizations.
Officers: Albert F. Polk, Sr., Pres. and Mgr.; Patricia Polk, V.P. and Mgr.
Trustee: JPMorgan Chase Bank, N.A.
EIN: 316029349

1443
Peace Camp, Inc.
22240 M-66 N.
Battle Creek, MI 49017

Grantmaker type: Independent foundation.
Financial data (yr. ended 12/31/05): Assets, $1 (M); expenditures, $5,747; total giving, $300; qualifying distributions, $300; giving activities include $300 for grants.
Limitations: Applications not accepted. Giving primarily in Battle Creek, MI. No grants to individuals.
Application information: Contributes only to pre-selected organizations.
Officers: Kenneth Rabbitt, Pres.; Patricia Rabbitt, Secy.
EIN: 382401688

1444
J. Red Peach Foundation
1999 Morris Dr.
Niles, MI 49120
Contact: Robin Oare Brown, Pres.

Established in 2003 in MI.
Donor: Nancy Oare Butler.
Grantmaker type: Independent foundation.
Financial data (yr. ended 12/31/05): Assets, $41,632 (M); gifts received, $20,000; expenditures, $9,281; total giving, $1,412;

qualifying distributions, $9,281; giving activities include $1,412 for grants.
Fields of interest: Human services; Economically disadvantaged.
Limitations: Giving primarily in Niles, MI. No grants to individuals.
Application information:
  Initial approach: Letter
  Deadline(s): None
Officers and Directors:* Robin Oare Brown,* Pres.; Donald E. Hill, Jr.,* V.P.; James H. Brown,* V.P.; Ericka L. Hill,* Secy.-Treas.
EIN: 200530854

1445
Louise Peacock Educational Trust
c/o Fifth Third Bank
200 S. Riverside Ave.
St. Clair, MI 48079
Application address: c/o Corunna High School, Guidance Office, 417 E. King St., Corunna, MI 48817

Grantmaker type: Independent foundation.
Financial data (yr. ended 4/30/02): Assets, $219,428 (M); gifts received, $14,000; expenditures, $17,142; total giving, $14,000; qualifying distributions, $14,440; giving activities include $14,000 for 14 loans to individuals (high: $1,000; low: $1,000).
Purpose and activities: Scholarships and loans limited to high school students of the Corunna High School District, MI, who attend senior or junior colleges.
Type of support: Scholarships—to individuals; Student loans—to individuals.
Limitations: Giving limited to Corunna, MI.
Application information: Application form required.
  Deadline(s): May 15
Officer: Lyle Thomas, Admin.
Trustee: Fifth Third Bank.
EIN: 386215314

1446
Peak Street Foundation
c/o Michael Van Haren
111 Lyon St. N.W., Ste. 900
Grand Rapids, MI 49503-2487

Established in 1997 in MI.
Donors: Barbara Malpass; Frederick F. Malpass.
Grantmaker type: Independent foundation.
Financial data (yr. ended 3/31/05): Assets, $2,315,452 (M); expenditures, $130,364; total giving, $105,000; qualifying distributions, $104,408; giving activities include $105,000 for 2 grants (high: $100,000; low: $5,000).
Fields of interest: Foundations (community).
Limitations: Applications not accepted. Giving limited to MI, with emphasis on East Jordan and Petoskey. No grants to individuals.
Application information: Contributes only to pre-selected organizations.
Officers: Barbara J. Malpass, Pres.; Frederick F. Malpass, Secy.-Treas.
EIN: 383350363
Selected grants: The following grants were reported in 2003.
$70,160 to Charlevoix County Community Foundation, East Jordan, MI. 6 grants: $25,000 (For Boswell Stadium), $5,000 (For Father Bill

McKeon fund), $5,000 (For East Jordan Pageant), $5,000 (For Rotary Scholarship Fund), $25,000 (For operation endowment fund), $5,160 (For rotary student exchange fund).
$25,000 to Charlevoix Area Hospital, Charlevoix, MI. For enlargement of emergency department and obstetrical.
$5,000 to Petoskey-Harbor Springs Area Community Foundation, Petoskey, MI. For Jerolene and Lewis Brown Charitable Youth Fund.
$5,000 to Raven Hill Discovery Center, East Jordan, MI.

1447
Joseph H. and Maxine F. Pearlman Foundation
29100 Northwestern Hwy., Ste. 205
Southfield, MI 48034

Established in 1999 in MI.
Donor: Joseph H. Pearlman.
Grantmaker type: Independent foundation.
Financial data (yr. ended 12/31/04): Assets, $532,190 (M); expenditures, $46,772; total giving, $43,292; qualifying distributions, $43,292; giving activities include $43,292 for grants.
Limitations: Applications not accepted. No grants to individuals.
Application information: Contributes only to pre-selected organizations.
Officers: Joseph H. Pearlman, Pres.; Maxine Pearlman, V.P.
EIN: 383505226

1448
The Pearson Family Foundation
2025 W. Long Lake Rd., Ste. 100
Troy, MI 48098

Established in 1993 in MI.
Donor: Richard E. Pearson.
Grantmaker type: Independent foundation.
Financial data (yr. ended 3/31/06): Assets, $169,358 (M); gifts received, $15,000; expenditures, $55,770; total giving, $55,000; qualifying distributions, $55,000; giving activities include $55,000 for grants.
Fields of interest: Higher education; Salvation Army; Roman Catholic agencies & churches.
Type of support: Building/renovation; Scholarship funds.
Limitations: Applications not accepted. Giving primarily in MI, with emphasis on Detroit and Troy. No grants to individuals.
Application information: Contributes only to pre-selected organizations.
Officers: Richard E. Pearson, Pres.; Elaine A. Pearson, V.P.; James L. Baker, Secy.; Paul P. Baker, Treas.
EIN: 383139129

1449
Elaine and Rankin Peck Family Foundation
200 Maple Park Blvd., Ste. 201
St. Clair Shores, MI 48081-2211

Established in 1996 in MI.
Donor: Elaine Z. Peck.
Grantmaker type: Independent foundation.

Financial data (yr. ended 9/30/05): Assets, $752,346 (M); expenditures, $47,629; total giving, $39,731; qualifying distributions, $39,731; giving activities include $39,731 for grants.
Purpose and activities: Giving for education, health and religion.
Fields of interest: Education; Hospitals (general); Health care; Christian agencies & churches.
Limitations: Applications not accepted. Giving primarily in MI. No grants to individuals.
Application information: Contributes only to pre-selected organizations.
Officers: Rankin Peck, Pres.; Sheila Pettee, Exec. V.P.; Lisa P. Cruikshank, V.P.; George R. Peck, V.P.; Jennifer Eckrich, Secy.; Elaine Z. Peck, Treas.
EIN: 383354189

1450
Lee and Maxine Peck Foundation
17145 Garfield Ave., No. 4B
Redford, MI 48240-2108

Established in 2004 in MI.
Donor: Lee P. Peck.
Grantmaker type: Independent foundation.
Financial data (yr. ended 12/31/04): Assets, $70 (M); gifts received, $25,570; expenditures, $25,500; total giving, $25,000; qualifying distributions, $25,000; giving activities include $25,000 for grants.
Limitations: Applications not accepted. No grants to individuals.
Application information: Contributes only to pre-selected organizations.
Officer: Lee P. Peck, Pres. and Secy.-Treas.
EIN: 371474765

1451
Pellerito, Manzella, Certa & Cusmano Family Foundation
30295 Embassy St.
Beverly Hills, MI 48025-5021
Contact: Frank A. Pellerito, Tr.

Established in 1988 in MI.
Grantmaker type: Independent foundation.
Financial data (yr. ended 12/31/05): Assets, $613,007 (M); expenditures, $40,819; total giving, $40,024; qualifying distributions, $40,024; giving activities include $40,024 for grants.
Fields of interest: Education; Human services; Children/youth, services; Roman Catholic agencies & churches.
Type of support: General/operating support; Equipment; Emergency funds; Seed money; Research; Matching/challenge support.
Limitations: Giving primarily in MI.
Application information:
  Initial approach: Letter or in person
  Deadline(s): None
  Board meeting date(s): Annually
  Final notification: 60 days
Trustees: Coleen O. Pellerito; Frank A. Pellerito.
EIN: 382776130

1452
The Peninsula Foundation
c/o Scholarship Comm.
1512 Pacheco St., Ste. D-203
Santa Fe, NM 87505 (505) 986-6874
Application address: c/o Guidance Dept.,
Menominee High School, 2101 18th St.,
Menominee, MI 49858; tel.: (906) 863-7814

Established in TX.
Donors: Ame Vennema†; Catherine S. Vennema.
Grantmaker type: Independent foundation.
Financial data (yr. ended 12/31/05): Assets,
$28,545 (M); gifts received, $10,000;
expenditures, $11,128; total giving, $10,000;
qualifying distributions, $10,000; giving
activities include $10,000 for grants to individuals.
Purpose and activities: Scholarship awards to
graduating seniors at Menominee High School, MI.
Fields of interest: Higher education.
Type of support: Scholarships—to individuals.
Limitations: Giving limited to Menominee, MI.
Application information: Application form can be
obtained from Menominee High, MI School
Guidance Dept. Application form required.
   Deadline(s): Feb. 1
Trustees: Margaret K. Lemen; John Vennema; Peter
A. Vennema; Linda V. White.
EIN: 742028228

1453
Clarence & Ella Pennell Memorial Trust
(formerly Ella M. & Clarence A. Pennell Memorial
Foundation)
c/o Citizens Bank Wealth Mgmt., N.A.
328 S. Saginaw St., MC 002072
Flint, MI 48502

Established in MI.
Grantmaker type: Independent foundation.
Financial data (yr. ended 12/31/05): Assets,
$598,518 (M); expenditures, $31,841; total giving,
$24,258; qualifying distributions, $30,989; giving
activities include $24,258 for 2 grants (high:
$12,129; low: $12,129).
Purpose and activities: Support only for the
Saginaw Society for Crippled Children and St.
Vincent Home, MI.
Fields of interest: Medical care, rehabilitation;
Children/youth, services; Disabilities, people with.
Type of support: General/operating support.
Limitations: Applications not accepted. Giving
limited to Clinton and Saginaw, MI. No grants to
individuals.
Application information: Contributes only to 2
pre-selected organizations.
Trustee: Citizens Bank, N.A.
EIN: 386040423

1454
Penner Foundation
10133 Diamond Park Rd.
Interlochen, MI 49643

Established in 1991.
Donor: Leroy King.
Grantmaker type: Independent foundation.
Financial data (yr. ended 12/31/05): Assets,
$91,528 (M); expenditures, $14,454; total giving,
$14,225; qualifying distributions, $14,225; giving
activities include $14,225 for grants.

Fields of interest: Higher education, college.
Limitations: Applications not accepted. Giving
limited to Wheaton, IL. No grants to individuals.
Application information: Contributes only to
pre-selected organizations.
Trustees: James Bowen; Susan Bowen; Andrew
Engel; Kristine Engel; Jonathan Penner; Ruth M.
Penner; Terri Penner; Robert Raese; Shirley Raese;
Linda Samelson; Randon Samelson; Ann Usey;
Michael Usey.
EIN: 382974470

1455
Lucille A. Penniman Revocable Trust
c/o A.G. Edwards Trust Co.
P.O. Box 66734
St. Louis, MO 63166

Established in 1999 in MO.
Donor: Lucille Penniman Revocable Trust.
Grantmaker type: Independent foundation.
Financial data (yr. ended 12/31/05): Assets,
$492,777 (M); expenditures, $176,223; total
giving, $168,222; qualifying distributions,
$168,622; giving activities include $168,222 for 3
grants (high: $56,074; low: $56,074).
Purpose and activities: Support only for St. Paul's
Episcopal Church, Lansing, Michigan, American
Cancer Society, Oklahoma City, Oklahoma, and
Arthritis Foundation, Troy, Michigan.
Fields of interest: Cancer; Arthritis; Protestant
agencies & churches.
Limitations: Applications not accepted. Giving
limited to MI and OK. No grants to individuals.
Application information: Contributes only to 3
pre-selected organizations.
Trustee: A.G. Edwards Trust Co.
EIN: 436797255

1456
Pennock Hospital Endowment Fund
c/o Fifth Third Bank
P.O. Box 3636
Grand Rapids, MI 49501-3636

Established in 1923 in MI.
Grantmaker type: Independent foundation.
Financial data (yr. ended 12/31/05): Assets,
$253,202 (M); expenditures, $5,654; total giving,
$0; qualifying distributions, $250.
Purpose and activities: Support only for Pennock
Hospital, Hastings, MI.
Fields of interest: Hospitals (general).
Type of support: Endowments.
Limitations: Applications not accepted. Giving
limited to Hastings, MI. No grants to individuals.
Application information: Contributes only to a
pre-selected organization.
Trustee: Fifth Third Bank.
EIN: 386050351

1457
Joe D. Pentecost Foundation
1331 E. Grand River, Ste. 225
East Lansing, MI 48823 (517) 336-5000
Contact: Rita F. Stoskopf, Pres.
FAX: (517) 336-5882; E-mail: bpi@arq.net

Established in 2002 in MI.
Donor: Joe D. Pentecost‡.

Grantmaker type: Independent foundation.
Financial data (yr. ended 12/31/04): Assets,
$2,074,171 (M); gifts received, $966,734;
expenditures, $64,461; total giving, $52,800;
qualifying distributions, $52,800; giving activities
include $52,800 for grants.
Fields of interest: Higher education; Protestant
agencies & churches.
Type of support: Endowments; Building/renovation.
Limitations: Giving primarily in MI.
Officers and Directors:* Rita F. Stoskopf,* Pres.;
Robert J. Phipps,* Secy.-Treas.; Calvin C. Lutz.
EIN: 352178154

1458
Perri Family Foundation
66 Sunningdale Dr.
Grosse Pointe Shores, MI 48236

Established in 1997 in IL.
Donor: Katherine Perniciaro Trust.
Grantmaker type: Independent foundation.
Financial data (yr. ended 12/31/04): Assets,
$1,647,459 (M); expenditures, $98,638; total
giving, $95,500; qualifying distributions, $95,500;
giving activities include $95,500 for grants.
Fields of interest: Hospitals (general); Eye
diseases; Heart & circulatory diseases; Eye
research; Heart & circulatory research.
Limitations: Giving primarily in Detroit, MI. No grants
to individuals.
Officers: Anita Penta, Pres. and Treas.; Anastasia
M. Wilson, V.P. and Secy.
Directors: Alexander N. Masters; Anthony C. Penta
III; Thia A. Penta.
EIN: 364143117

1459
Perrone Charitable Foundation, Inc.
38570 Northfarm Dr.
Northville, MI 48167
Contact: John Perrone, Pres.

Established in 1997 in MI.
Donor: John Perrone.
Grantmaker type: Independent foundation.
Financial data (yr. ended 12/31/05): Assets,
$125,235 (M); expenditures, $11,319; total giving,
$10,730; qualifying distributions, $10,730; giving
activities include $10,730 for grants.
Fields of interest: Education; Health organizations,
association; Human services.
Limitations: Giving primarily in MI.
Application information:
   Initial approach: Letter
   Deadline(s): None
Officers: John Perrone, Pres.; Christine Bartlett, V.P.
and Treas.; Dianne C. Perrone, Secy.
EIN: 383378779

1460
Alexander Petrellis Perry Trust
c/o Comerica Bank
P.O. Box 75000, MC3300
Detroit, MI 48275

Established in 1985 in MI.
Grantmaker type: Independent foundation.
Financial data (yr. ended 1/31/05): Assets,
$864,247 (M); expenditures, $35,219; total giving,

$25,000; qualifying distributions, $25,000; giving activities include $25,000 for grants.
Purpose and activities: Support only for the Diocese Philanthropika, Greece; also support for Anatolia College, MA, and Athens College, NE, for Greek instruction.
Fields of interest: Secondary school/education; Higher education; Orthodox Catholic agencies & churches.
International interests: Greece.
Limitations: Applications not accepted. Giving limited to Athens, Greece, with some giving in Boston, MA, and New York, NY. No grants to individuals.
Application information: Contributes only to pre-selected organizations specified in the trust instrument.
Trustee: Comerica Bank.
EIN: 386475645

1461
Perry-Morrice-Shaftsburg Emergency Relief Council
P.O. Box 783
Perry, MI 48872

Grantmaker type: Independent foundation.
Financial data (yr. ended 12/31/05): Assets, $5,900 (M); gifts received, $13,754; expenditures, $500; total giving, $500; qualifying distributions, $500; giving activities include $500 for grants.
Purpose and activities: Provides emergency assistance, including cash and food, to residents of Shiawassee County, MI.
Fields of interest: Human services; Economically disadvantaged.
Type of support: Emergency funds; In-kind gifts.
Limitations: Applications not accepted. Giving primarily in the Morrice and Perry, MI, areas. No grants to individuals.
Officers: David Robertson, Pres.; Shirley Shaw, V.P.; Alilah Smith, Secy.
Director: Sharon Ledy.
EIN: 382417568

1462
The Persia Family Foundation
1515 Addaleen Rd.
Highland, MI 48357 (248) 478-1182

Established in 1994 in MI.
Donor: Raymond J. Persia.
Grantmaker type: Independent foundation.
Financial data (yr. ended 12/31/05): Assets, $384,951 (M); expenditures, $9,714; total giving, $5,616; qualifying distributions, $5,616; giving activities include $5,616 for grants.
Fields of interest: Roman Catholic agencies & churches.
Limitations: Applications not accepted. No grants to individuals.
Application information: Contributes only to pre-selected organizations.
Officers: Raymond J. Persia, Pres.; Sonya K. Persia, Secy.
Director: Kimber Persia Laur.
EIN: 383191845

1463
The Karen & Drew Peslar Foundation
280 W. Maple Rd., Ste. 212
Birmingham, MI 48009 (248) 594-6294
Contact: Virginia Webster-Smith, Exec. Dir.

Established in 1997 in MI.
Donors: Drew Peslar; Karen Peslar.
Grantmaker type: Independent foundation.
Financial data (yr. ended 12/31/05): Assets, $7,801,899 (M); expenditures, $491,982; total giving, $305,560; qualifying distributions, $358,776; giving activities include $305,560 for 25 grants (high: $100,000; low: $400).
Purpose and activities: Giving primarily for education, religion, human services, and arts and culture.
Fields of interest: Museums; Arts; Secondary school/education; Youth development; Human services; Christian agencies & churches.
Limitations: Applications not accepted. Giving limited to MI. No grants to individuals.
Application information: Contributes only to pre-selected organizations.
Officers and Directors:* Drew Peslar,* Pres.; Samantha Cairns,* Secy.; Karen Peslar,* Treas.; Virginia Webster-Smith, Exec. Dir.
EIN: 383374272

1464
The Herman & Katherine Peters Foundation Corp.
67 E. Madison St., Ste. 1515
Chicago, IL 60603-3014 (312) 782-4415
Contact: Scot A. Leonard, Pres.

Established in 1998 in IL.
Donors: Katherine Peters†; Katherine Peters Trust.
Grantmaker type: Independent foundation.
Financial data (yr. ended 12/31/04): Assets, $9,800,669 (M); gifts received, $5,418,338; expenditures, $211,685; total giving, $157,200; qualifying distributions, $157,200; giving activities include $73,200 for grants, and $84,000 for 32 grants to individuals.
Purpose and activities: Scholarship awards to financially needy students pursuing studies relating to environmental concerns or Christian-based religious instruction. Some giving for educational field trips for underprivileged children to heighten their awareness about the importance of conservation.
Fields of interest: Higher education; Environmental education; Christian agencies & churches.
Type of support: Scholarships—to individuals.
Limitations: Giving primarily in AZ, CO, IL, MI, and WI.
Application information: Application form required.
  Deadline(s): None
Officers and Directors:* Scot A. Leonard,* Pres.; James P. Devine, Jr.,* V.P.; Jeanine Holtsford,* Secy.-Treas.; George Carroll; Inge Dominis.
EIN: 364180010

1465
Ruth and Lovett Peters Foundation
(formerly Lovett Peters Foundation)
c/o Daniel S. Peters
1500 Chiquita Ctr.
250 E. 5th St.
Cincinnati, OH 45202

Established in 1992 in MA.
Donor: Lovett C. Peters.
Grantmaker type: Independent foundation.
Financial data (yr. ended 12/31/04): Assets, $3,804,826 (M); expenditures, $1,287,783; total giving, $941,947; qualifying distributions, $1,215,990; giving activities include $941,947 for 23 grants (high: $250,000; low: $4,573).
Purpose and activities: Giving primarily for public policy organizations and research; funding also for education.
Fields of interest: Education, alliance; Education, reform; Higher education; Education; Human services; Foundations (private grantmaking); Public policy, research; Public affairs.
Limitations: Applications not accepted. Giving primarily to national organizations, with emphasis on AZ, Washington, DC, and MI.
Application information: Unsolicited requests for funds not accepted.
Officer and Trustees:* Daniel S. Peters,* Pres.; Lovett C. Peters; Ruth Stott Peters.
EIN: 046748820

1466
Mabel & Ray Petersen Master Craftsman Scholarship Trust
c/o Comerica Bank
P.O. Box 75000, M/C 3302
Detroit, MI 48275

Established in 1995 in MI.
Donor: Ray Petersen†.
Grantmaker type: Independent foundation.
Financial data (yr. ended 9/30/05): Assets, $332,095 (M); expenditures, $19,409; total giving, $14,498; qualifying distributions, $14,498; giving activities include $14,498 for grants.
Fields of interest: Higher education, college.
Type of support: Scholarship funds.
Limitations: Applications not accepted. Giving primarily in Grand Rapids, MI. No grants to individuals.
Application information: Contributes only to pre-selected organizations.
Trustee: Comerica Bank.
EIN: 383261371

1467
Peterson Family Foundation
c/o McDonnell, Conley, Arslanian & Neveux, LLP
38500 Woodward Ave., Ste. 300
Bloomfield Hills, MI 48304-5051
(248) 540-7500
Contact: Paul Arslanian, Dir.

Established in 1999 in MI.
Donor: Robert Peterson†.
Grantmaker type: Independent foundation.
Financial data (yr. ended 12/31/05): Assets, $2,459,243 (M); expenditures, $150,469; total giving, $100,013; qualifying distributions, $100,013; giving activities include $100,013 for grants.
Fields of interest: Foundations (community); Protestant agencies & churches.
Limitations: Giving limited to MI.
Application information:
  Initial approach: Letter
  Deadline(s): None

Directors: Paul Arslanian; Mark R. Peterson.
EIN: 383457564

1468
Julie A. Peterson Foundation
c/o Michael D. Gibson
500 Woodward Ave., Ste. 2500
Detroit, MI 48226

Established in 1987 in MI.
Grantmaker type: Independent foundation.
Financial data (yr. ended 3/31/03): Assets, $1 (M); expenditures, $35,110; total giving, $35,110; qualifying distributions, $35,110; giving activities include $35,110 for grants.
Purpose and activities: Support only for Seven Ponds Nature Center, Michigan Audubon Society,.
Fields of interest: Animals/wildlife, preservation/protection.
Limitations: Applications not accepted. Giving limited to Dryden, MI. No grants to individuals.
Application information: Contributes only to a pre-selected organization.
Officers and Trustees:* Harry S. Peterson, Jr.,* Pres. and Treas.; Michael D. Gibson,* Secy. and Mgr.; Donald R. Naish; Kevin Peterson.
EIN: 382713870

1469
Dean & Diane Petitpren Family Foundation
44500 N. Groesbeck Hwy.
Clinton Township, MI 48036-1111

Established in 2003 in MI.
Donors: Dean Petitpren; Diane Petitpren.
Grantmaker type: Independent foundation.
Financial data (yr. ended 12/31/05): Assets, $41,753 (M); gifts received, $350,000; expenditures, $326,600; total giving, $326,600; qualifying distributions, $326,600; giving activities include $326,600 for 4+ grants (high: $250,000).
Fields of interest: Arts; Education; Human services; Federated giving programs.
Limitations: Applications not accepted. Giving primarily in MI. No grants to individuals.
Application information: Contributes only to pre-selected organizations.
Officers and Directors:* Dean Petitpren,* Pres.; Diane Petitpren,* Secy.-Treas.
EIN: 200129571

1470
Phantom Foundation
113 W. Michigan Ave., Ste. 301
Jackson, MI 49201

Established in 1998 in MI.
Donor: William B. Holmes.
Grantmaker type: Independent foundation.
Financial data (yr. ended 12/31/05): Assets, $151,079 (M); expenditures, $15,000; total giving, $15,000; qualifying distributions, $15,000; giving activities include $15,000 for grants.
Purpose and activities: The foundation gives only to the Ann Arbor YMCA.
Fields of interest: YM/YWCAs & YM/YWHAs.
Limitations: Applications not accepted. Giving limited to Ann Arbor, MI. No grants to individuals.
Application information: Contributes only to pre-selected organizations.

Officers: William B. Holmes, Pres.; Wendy B. Holmes, Secy.-Treas.
EIN: 383353208

1471
Robert J. Phelps Foundation, Inc.
c/o Gerald H. Lakritz
30100 Telegraph Rd., Ste. 440
Bingham Farms, MI 48025-5809

Established in 1996 in MI.
Grantmaker type: Independent foundation.
Financial data (yr. ended 12/31/05): Assets, $7,377 (M); gifts received, $1,000; expenditures, $0; total giving, $300; qualifying distributions, $300; giving activities include $300 for grants.
Purpose and activities: Support only for the American Heart Association.
Fields of interest: Heart & circulatory diseases.
Type of support: General/operating support.
Limitations: Applications not accepted. Giving limited to Chicago, IL. No grants to individuals.
Application information: Contributes only to a pre-selected organization.
Officers and Directors:* Gerald H. Lakritz,* Pres.; Jim R. Drake,* Secy.-Treas.; Paul R. Dunbar.
Trustee: Standard Federal Bank N.A.
EIN: 383258350

1472
Winifred Y. Phelps Trust
c/o Comerica Bank
P.O. Box 75000
Detroit, MI 48275
Application address: c/o Antioch High School, Attn.: Scholarship Comm., 700 W. 18th St., Antioch, CA 94509, tel.: (415) 757-6560

Established in CA.
Grantmaker type: Independent foundation.
Financial data (yr. ended 12/31/05): Assets, $330,953 (M); expenditures, $8,090; total giving, $4,500; qualifying distributions, $4,500; giving activities include $4,500 for grants.
Purpose and activities: Scholarship funds for graduates of Antioch High School and San Lorenzo Valley High School, CA.
Type of support: Scholarship funds.
Limitations: Giving limited to CA.
Application information: Application form required.
Deadline(s): Varies
Trustee: Comerica Bank.
EIN: 946087426

1473
The Phinny Family Foundation
c/o Founders Trust Personal Bank
5200 Cascade Rd. S.E.
Grand Rapids, MI 49546

Established in 1991 in MI.
Donors: Robert H. Phinny; Sally G. Phinny.
Grantmaker type: Independent foundation.
Financial data (yr. ended 12/31/05): Assets, $34,479 (M); expenditures, $3,140; total giving, $1,850; qualifying distributions, $1,850; giving activities include $1,850 for grants.
Limitations: Applications not accepted. Giving primarily in CA, MI, and WY. No grants to individuals.

Application information: Contributes only to pre-selected organizations.
Officer: Sally G. Phinny, Pres.
Trustee: Stephen D. Phinny.
EIN: 382966992

1474
Physician Educational & Practice Associates, P.C.
2384 Heronwood Dr.
Bloomfield Hills, MI 48302

Established in 1998.
Grantmaker type: Independent foundation.
Financial data (yr. ended 6/30/05): Assets, $267,581 (M); expenditures, $2,554; total giving, $0; qualifying distributions, $0.
Purpose and activities: Giving limited to Grace Hospital in Detroit, and St. Joseph Mercy Hospital in Pontiac, Michigan.
Fields of interest: Hospitals (general).
Limitations: Applications not accepted. Giving limited to Detroit and Pontiac, MI. No grants to individuals.
Application information: Contributes only to 2 pre-selected organizations.
Officers: Thomas Petinga, D.O., Pres.; Leonard Alexander, M.D., V.P.; Ahmad Aburashed, M.D., Secy.; Edward Klimkowski, M.D., Treas.
Directors: Mark Brantigon, M.D.; Jason Cortez, M.D.; Alfonso Diaz, M.D.; John Harm, M.D.; Raymond Jungwirth, M.D.; Ratanatar Kini, M.D.; Lakshmi Kottamasu, M.D.; Gloria Kuhn, M.D.; John Malone, M.D.; Ceres Morales, M.D.; Maheshkumar Patel, M.D.; Guthinkonda Rao, M.D.; Kirit Shan, M.D.; Andrew Stefani, M.D.; Robert Toal, M.D.
EIN: 382462815

1475
Physician's Organization of Western Michigan Foundation, Inc.
233 E. Fulton, Ste. 101
Grand Rapids, MI 49503-3200
Contact: David Silliven
Application address: 121 Michigan N.E., Grand Rapids, MI 49503

Established in 2000 in MI.
Donor: Physician's Organization of Western Michigan.
Grantmaker type: Independent foundation.
Financial data (yr. ended 12/31/05): Assets, $52,881 (M); expenditures, $1,141; total giving, $0; qualifying distributions, $0.
Limitations: Giving primarily in Grand Rapids, MI.
Application information: Application form not required.
Deadline(s): None
Officers: Peter A. Kuhl, M.D., Pres.; Andrew M. Welch, M.D., V.P.; Alan Siegel, M.D., Secy.-Treas.
Directors: Randall Clark, M.D.; Steven Crane, M.D.; Vincent A. Dubravec, M.D.; Kenneth Dudley, M.D.; Roger Edvenson, M.D.; Mark A. Frederickson, M.D.; David D. Hamm, M.D.; Gregory Johnson, M.D.; John Keller, M.D.; David E. Langholz, M.D.; Charles Lawrence, M.D.; David F. McCorry, D.O.; Henry J. Mulder; Khan J. Nedd, M.D.; Kenneth Nelson, M.D.; David Thompson, M.D.; Douglas Vandrie, M.D.; Darryl J. Varda; Philip J. Weighner, M.D.; Jeffrey A.

Wolfson, M.D.; Terrence P. Wright, M.D.; Ivars Zadvinskis, M.D.
EIN: 383522988

1476
Milton & Sylvia Pierce Foundation
20800 Southfield Rd.
Southfield, MI 48075

Established in 2000 in MI.
Donors: Milton J. Pierce; Sylvia Pierce.
Grantmaker type: Independent foundation.
Financial data (yr. ended 12/31/05): Assets, $667,394 (M); expenditures, $36,189; total giving, $35,000; qualifying distributions, $35,000; giving activities include $35,000 for grants.
Fields of interest: Jewish agencies & temples.
Limitations: Applications not accepted. No grants to individuals.
Application information: Contributes only to pre-selected organizations.
Officer: Milton J. Pierce, Pres.
EIN: 383515181

1477
Carol C. Pierson Trust
c/o JPMorgan Chase Bank, N.A.
P.O. Box 1308
Milwaukee, WI 53201

Established in 2003 in MI.
Donor: Carol C. Pierson.
Grantmaker type: Independent foundation.
Financial data (yr. ended 12/31/04): Assets, $1,061,126 (M); expenditures, $62,858; total giving, $52,968; qualifying distributions, $53,993; giving activities include $52,968 for grants.
Purpose and activities: Support only for the Flint Institute for the Arts and the Sloan Museum, Flint.
Fields of interest: Museums (art).
Type of support: General/operating support.
Limitations: Applications not accepted. Giving limited to Flint, MI. No grants to individuals.
Application information: Contributes only to 2 pre-selected organizations.
Trustee: JPMorgan Chase Bank, N.A.
EIN: 386364457

1478
The Pietrasiuk Family Foundation
2395 S. Huron Pkwy., Ste. 100
Ann Arbor, MI 48104-5129 (734) 971-8008
Contact: Catherine M. Miller, Pres.

Donor: Catherine M. Miller.
Grantmaker type: Independent foundation.
Financial data (yr. ended 12/31/04): Assets, $118,820 (M); expenditures, $9,592; total giving, $6,200; qualifying distributions, $6,200; giving activities include $6,200 for grants.
Limitations: Giving limited to southeastern MI.
Application information:
  Initial approach: Letter
  Deadline(s): None
Officers and Directors:* Catherine M. Miller,* Pres.; Patrick D. Miller,* V.P.; Preston Murray.
EIN: 383348405

1479
Pilgrim Foundation
c/o S. Gunnar Klarr
401 S. Old Woodward Ave., Ste. 465
Birmingham, MI 48009-6622

Established in 1996 in MI.
Donors: Louise S. Klarr; S. Gunnar Klarr; Salwil Foundation.
Grantmaker type: Independent foundation.
Financial data (yr. ended 12/31/04): Assets, $3,916,239 (M); gifts received, $20,000; expenditures, $271,646; total giving, $246,926; qualifying distributions, $246,926; giving activities include $246,926 for 10 grants (high: $165,000; low: $1,426).
Fields of interest: Human services; International development; International relief; Christian agencies & churches; Economically disadvantaged.
Type of support: General/operating support.
Limitations: Applications not accepted. Giving on a national basis. No grants to individuals.
Application information: Contributes only to pre-selected organizations.
Trustees: Louise S. Klarr; S. Gunnar Klarr.
EIN: 367159136
Selected grants: The following grants were reported in 2003.
$135,000 to Questscope, Winfield, IL.
$6,000 to Campus Crusade for Christ International, Orlando, FL.
$5,000 to A Strictly Biblical Perspective Ministries, Dacula, GA. For general support.
$5,000 to InterVarsity Christian Fellowship/USA, Madison, WI. For Collins Ministry.
$3,500 to Discipleship Network of America-DNA Ministries, Signal Mountain, TN. For outreach and training.
$3,500 to Navigators, The, Colorado Springs, CO.
$3,000 to Great Commission Ministries, Ohio State University Ministry, Winter Park, FL.
$3,000 to International Foundation, DC. For Katalaso Ministry.
$3,000 to Wellspring, Detroit, MI. For employment opportunity program.
$2,500 to SAT-7 North American, Easton, MD. For Analog Air.

1480
Bernard E. & Marilyn Pincus Foundation
21711 W. Ten Mile Rd., Ste. 114
Southfield, MI 48075

Established in 1985 in MI.
Donors: Bernard E. Pincus; Marilyn Pincus.
Grantmaker type: Independent foundation.
Financial data (yr. ended 12/31/05): Assets, $18,498 (M); expenditures, $918; total giving, $500; qualifying distributions, $500; giving activities include $500 for grants.
Fields of interest: Performing arts; Arts; Health organizations, association; Human services; Jewish federated giving programs; Jewish agencies & temples.
Limitations: Applications not accepted. Giving primarily in Detroit, MI. No grants to individuals.
Application information: Contributes only to pre-selected organizations.
Officer: Marilyn Pincus, Pres. and Secy.-Treas.
EIN: 382641854

1481
Irwin Jack & Lena Pincus Foundation
21711 W. 10 Mile Rd., Ste. 114
Southfield, MI 48075-1027

Established in 1987 in MI.
Donors: Irwin Jack Pincus; Lena Pincus.
Grantmaker type: Independent foundation.
Financial data (yr. ended 12/31/05): Assets, $164,872 (M); expenditures, $5,130; total giving, $5,000; qualifying distributions, $5,000; giving activities include $5,000 for grants.
Fields of interest: Higher education; General charitable giving.
Limitations: Applications not accepted. Giving primarily in southern CA. No grants to individuals.
Application information: Contributes only to pre-selected organizations.
Officers: Lena Pincus, Pres.; Robert Pincus, Treas.
EIN: 382639189

1482
Pinney Foundation
c/o Chemical Bank & Trust
P.O. Box 231
Midland, MI 48640

Established in 1984 in MI.
Donor: Lottie W. Pinney Irrevocable Trust.
Grantmaker type: Independent foundation.
Financial data (yr. ended 12/31/05): Assets, $1,476,427 (M); expenditures, $87,796; total giving, $75,050; qualifying distributions, $78,327; giving activities include $75,050 for 11 grants (high: $19,375; low: $1,000).
Fields of interest: Education, public education; Libraries (public); Recreation, parks/playgrounds; Urban/community development.
Type of support: General/operating support; Building/renovation; Equipment; Land acquisition.
Limitations: Applications not accepted. Giving limited to the Cass City, MI, area. No grants to individuals.
Publications: Informational brochure.
Application information: Contributes only to pre-selected organizations.
Officers and Directors:* Michael Weaver,* Pres.; Annette L. Pinney,* V.P.; Jude T. Patnaude,* Secy.; Cheryl Whitman,* Treas.; Robert Hirn; David Milligan; Beverly Perry; Theresa Rabideau; Barbara Tuckey; Ben Varney; Kathryn Ziemba.
EIN: 382517070

1483
Murray C. and Ina C. Pitt Charitable Trust
2000 Town Ctr., Ste. 1350
Southfield, MI 48075

Established in 1995 in MI.
Donor: Murray C. Pitt.
Grantmaker type: Independent foundation.
Financial data (yr. ended 11/30/05): Assets, $1,905,889 (M); expenditures, $630,699; total giving, $550,068; qualifying distributions, $551,008; giving activities include $550,068 for 49 grants (high: $203,056; low: $100).
Purpose and activities: Giving primarily to Jewish agencies, temples, and federated giving programs; funding also for education, health, and human services.

Fields of interest: Arts; Higher education; Education; Mental health/crisis services; Health organizations; Cancer research; Human services; Civil rights; Federated giving programs; Jewish federated giving programs; Jewish agencies & temples.
Limitations: Applications not accepted. Giving primarily in MI; some funding in CO and NY. No grants to individuals.
Application information: Contributes only to pre-selected organizations.
Officers: Murray C. Pitt, Pres.; Ina C. Pitt, V.P.; Carleen F. Lunsford, Secy.-Treas.
Directors: Erin R. Frankel; Jeffery S. Pitt.
EIN: 383268352

1484
Albert and Doris Pitt Foundation
8019 Concord Rd.
Huntington Woods, MI 48070-1303

Established in 1992 in MI.
Donor: Doris Pitt.
Grantmaker type: Independent foundation.
Financial data (yr. ended 12/31/05): Assets, $2,383,483 (M); expenditures, $257,227; total giving, $234,750; qualifying distributions, $235,362; giving activities include $234,750 for 26 grants (high: $53,500; low: $1,000).
Fields of interest: Human services; Civil liberties, advocacy; Federated giving programs; Jewish federated giving programs.
Limitations: Applications not accepted. Giving primarily in MI. No grants to individuals.
Application information: Contributes only to pre-selected organizations.
Officers: Michael L. Pitt, Pres.; Janice B. Buchanan, Secy.; Peggy Pitt, Treas.
EIN: 383080424
Selected grants: The following grants were reported in 2003.
$25,000 to Lance Armstrong Foundation, Austin, TX. For general support.
$15,000 to American Civil Liberties Union Fund of Michigan, Detroit, MI. For general support.
$15,000 to Doctors Without Borders USA, New York, NY. For general support.
$10,000 to Anti-Defamation League of Bnai Brith, New York, NY. For general support.
$10,000 to Willow House, Deerfield, IL. For general support.
$7,000 to Michigan Legal Services, Detroit, MI. For general support.
$6,000 to Ruth Alden Childrens Clothing Drive. For general support.
$5,000 to Americas Second Harvest, Chicago, IL. For general support.
$5,000 to Food Bank of South Central Michigan, Battle Creek, MI. For general support.
$5,000 to Leader Dogs for the Blind, Rochester, MI. For general support.

1485
Pivnick Family Foundation
31380 Stonewood Ct. W.
Farmington Hills, MI 48333

Established in 1964.
Donors: Ben Pivnick; Lorraine Pivnick.
Grantmaker type: Independent foundation.

Financial data (yr. ended 12/31/04): Assets, $941,838 (M); gifts received, $195,000; expenditures, $89,999; total giving, $88,928; qualifying distributions, $239,999; giving activities include $88,928 for grants.
Purpose and activities: Giving primarily for education and to Jewish organizations.
Fields of interest: Arts; Human services; Jewish federated giving programs; Jewish agencies & temples.
Limitations: Applications not accepted. Giving primarily in MI. No grants to individuals.
Application information: Contributes only to pre-selected organizations.
Trustees: Ben Pivnick; Lorraine Pivnick; Sherwin T. Wine.
EIN: 386105067

1486
PJM Charitable Foundation, Inc.
2 Sound View Dr., Ste. 100
Greenwich, CT 06830

Established in 1986 in NY.
Donor: Phillip J. Meek.
Grantmaker type: Independent foundation.
Financial data (yr. ended 11/30/05): Assets, $3,807,858 (M); gifts received, $108,000; expenditures, $32,607; total giving, $30,000; qualifying distributions, $30,000; giving activities include $30,000 for grants.
Purpose and activities: Support only for Ohio Wesleyan University, Delaware, Ohio, and Grand Traverse Regional Land Conservancy, Traverse City, Michigan.
Fields of interest: Higher education, university; Environment, land resources.
Limitations: Applications not accepted. Giving limited to Delaware, OH, and Traverse City, MI, with emphasis on OH. No grants to individuals.
Application information: Contributes only to pre-selected organizations.
Officer: Phillip J. Meek, Pres. and Mgr.
EIN: 133406169

1487
Platinum Charitable Foundation
30521 Schoenherr Rd.
Warren, MI 48088
Application address: c/o Betty R. Bess, 2000 Town Ctr., Ste. 1500, Southfield, MI 48075

Established in 2001 in MI.
Donor: Ralph Roberts.
Grantmaker type: Independent foundation.
Financial data (yr. ended 12/31/04): Assets, $804,342 (M); gifts received, $6,025; expenditures, $41,503; total giving, $6,050; qualifying distributions, $18,192; giving activities include $6,050 for grants.
Application information:
  Initial approach: Letter
  Deadline(s): None
Officers: Ralph Roberts, Pres.; Robert Van Goethem, V.P. and Treas.; Kathleen Ann Roberts, Secy.
EIN: 300003211

1488
Plym Foundation
423 Sycamore St., Ste. 101
Niles, MI 49120-2330 (269) 683-3982
Contact: Donald F. Walter, V.P.
Application address: P.O. Box 906, Niles, MI 49120

Incorporated in 1952 in MI.
Donor: Mrs. Francis J. Plym†.
Grantmaker type: Independent foundation.
Financial data (yr. ended 12/31/05): Assets, $6,664,919 (M); expenditures, $549,711; total giving, $420,050; qualifying distributions, $446,650; giving activities include $420,050 for 14 grants (high: $75,000; low: $750).
Purpose and activities: Giving primarily for the arts and human services.
Fields of interest: Arts; Education; Human services.
Type of support: Building/renovation; Program development; Matching/challenge support.
Limitations: Giving primarily in MI. No grants to individuals.
Application information: Application form not required.
  Initial approach: Letter
  Copies of proposal: 1
  Deadline(s): None
  Board meeting date(s): May
Officers and Directors:* J. Eric Plym,* Pres.; Donald F. Walter,* V.P. and Treas.; Sarah P. Campbell,* V.P.; Andrew J. Plym,* V.P.; James F. Keenan, Secy.; John M. Campbell; John E. Plym, Jr.
EIN: 386069680

1489
John Polakovic Charitable Trust
32100 Telegraph Rd., Ste. 200
Bingham Farms, MI 48025
Contact: James B. Tintera, Tr.
Application address: 117 Scissortail Trail, Georgetown, TX 78628

Established in MI.
Grantmaker type: Independent foundation.
Financial data (yr. ended 12/31/05): Assets, $134,175 (M); gifts received, $3,135; expenditures, $14,292; total giving, $13,500; qualifying distributions, $13,500; giving activities include $13,500 for grants to individuals.
Purpose and activities: Scholarship awards to graduating seniors at J. Sterling Morton High School, IL.
Fields of interest: Higher education.
Type of support: Scholarships—to individuals.
Limitations: Giving primarily to residents of IL.
Application information:
  Initial approach: Letter
  Deadline(s): None
Trustees: Evelyn Tintera; James B. Tintera.
EIN: 386390004

1490
Jennifer Gordon Polan Foundation
27340 Willowgreen Ct.
Franklin, MI 48025 (248) 626-2231
Contact: Jesse N. Polan, Tr.

Established in MI.
Donors: Alfred Berkowitz Foundation; Jesse N. Polan.
Grantmaker type: Independent foundation.

Financial data (yr. ended 12/31/05): Assets, $44,219 (M); gifts received, $281; expenditures, $3,581; total giving, $3,000; qualifying distributions, $3,000; giving activities include $3,000 for grants.
Limitations: Giving primarily in MI.
Application information:
  Initial approach: Letter
  Deadline(s): May 1 for scholarships
Trustee: Jesse N. Polan.
EIN: 383540779

1491
Polasky Family Foundation
(formerly Lurie-Polasky Foundation)
141 Harrow Ln.
Saginaw, MI 48603

Established in 1988 in MI.
Donors: Buddy McLaughlin; Frank M. Polasky; Frumeth Hirsh Polasky.
Grantmaker type: Independent foundation.
Financial data (yr. ended 6/30/05): Assets, $26,491 (M); gifts received, $47,048; expenditures, $46,441; total giving, $30,271; qualifying distributions, $30,271; giving activities include $30,271 for grants.
Fields of interest: Arts; Higher education; Hospitals (general); Health organizations; Medical research; Girl scouts; Human services; Jewish federated giving programs; Jewish agencies & temples.
Limitations: Applications not accepted. Giving primarily in MI. No grants to individuals.
Application information: Contributes only to pre-selected organizations.
Officers: Frank M. Polasky, Pres.; Frumeth Hirsh Polasky, V.P.
EIN: 386107372

1492
Ralph L. and Winifred E. Polk Foundation
26955 Northwestern Hwy.
Southfield, MI 48034

Incorporated in 1962 in MI.
Donors: Ralph L. Polk‡; Winifred E. Polk.
Grantmaker type: Independent foundation.
Financial data (yr. ended 12/31/04): Assets, $4,064,994 (M); expenditures, $248,088; total giving, $223,500; qualifying distributions, $229,045; giving activities include $223,500 for 41 grants (high: $15,000; low: $1,000).
Purpose and activities: Giving primarily for education and youth programs.
Fields of interest: Arts; Education; Environment, natural resources; Zoos/zoological societies; Human services; Children/youth, services; Christian agencies & churches.
Type of support: General/operating support; Capital campaigns.
Limitations: Applications not accepted. Giving primarily in MI, with some emphasis on Detroit. No grants to individuals.
Application information: Contributes only to pre-selected organizations.
Officers and Trustees:* Stephen R. Polk,* Pres. and Treas.; Joe Walker, Secy.; Kathy Polk Osborne; Julie A. Polk; Susan E. Polk; Janet P. Read.
EIN: 386080075
Selected grants: The following grants were reported in 2003.

$15,000 to Michigans Thanksgiving Parade Foundation, Detroit, MI. For general support.
$10,000 to Beaumont Foundation, Southfield, MI. 2 grants: $5,000 (For Center for Human Development), $5,000 (For Positive Parenting Program).
$4,000 to Crossroads for Youth, Oxford, MI. For general support.
$4,000 to Detroit Historical Society, Detroit, MI. For general support.
$4,000 to Interlochen Center for the Arts, Interlochen, MI. For general support.
$4,000 to Minerva Education and Development Foundation, Detroit, MI. For general support.
$4,000 to New Detroit Science Center, Detroit, MI. For general support.
$4,000 to Orchard Childrens Services, Southfield, MI. For general support.
$4,000 to Spectrum Human Services, Livonia, MI. For general support.

1493
Sara Pollack Educational Trust
345 Sumac Ln.
Ann Arbor, MI 48105-3012
Application address: c/o Margaret Guire, 2108 Shadford Rd., Ann Arbor, MI 48104-4552, tel.: (734) 662-2040

Grantmaker type: Independent foundation.
Financial data (yr. ended 12/31/05): Assets, $55,091 (M); gifts received, $500; expenditures, $2,880; total giving, $2,880; qualifying distributions, $2,880; giving activities include $2,880 for 3 grants to individuals.
Purpose and activities: Grants are awarded to elementary and high school students in southeast Michigan for music education or other educational purposes.
Fields of interest: Arts education; Performing arts, music.
Type of support: Grants to individuals.
Limitations: Giving primarily in Ann Arbor and southeast MI.
Application information:
  Initial approach: Proposal
  Deadline(s): None
  Final notification: Within 3 months
Trustees: Henry N. Pollack; Lana B. Pollack.
EIN: 386424735

1494
Herbert and Elsa Ponting Foundation
535 Griswold St., Ste. 1900
Detroit, MI 48226   (313) 496-1200
Contact: John L. King, Pres.
FAX: (313) 496-1300;
E-mail: jking@berrymoorman.com

Established in 1987 in MI.
Donor: The William Fitzherbert Ponting Trust.
Grantmaker type: Independent foundation.
Financial data (yr. ended 12/31/05): Assets, $2,485,421 (M); expenditures, $206,498; total giving, $155,500; qualifying distributions, $155,500; giving activities include $155,500 for 31 grants (high: $15,000; low: $1,000).
Purpose and activities: Giving primarily for academic scholarships, educational equipment, and specific educational programs for the staff of

agencies that have been in existence for at least five years, within the state of Michigan.
Fields of interest: Elementary school/education; Secondary school/education; Higher education; Business school/education; Law school/education; Education.
Type of support: General/operating support; Equipment; Program development; Scholarship funds.
Limitations: Giving primarily in MI. No grants to individuals.
Publications: Application guidelines; Informational brochure (including application guidelines).
Application information: Application form not required.
  Initial approach: Letter
  Copies of proposal: 1
  Deadline(s): Mar. 1 and Oct. 1
  Board meeting date(s): May and Nov.
Officers and Directors:* John L. King,* Pres.; Shiela P. Geier,* V.P.; Dennis M. Mitzel,* Secy.-Treas.
Number of staff: 1 part-time professional.
EIN: 386058868
Selected grants: The following grants were reported in 2004.
$11,000 to University of Michigan, Kresge Hearing Research Institute, Ann Arbor, MI.
$10,000 to Loyola High School, Detroit, MI.
$7,000 to Detroit Waldorf School, Detroit, MI.
$5,000 to Academy of the Sacred Heart, Bloomfield Hills, MI.
$5,000 to Battle Creek Academy, Battle Creek, MI.
$5,000 to Friends School in Detroit, Detroit, MI.
$5,000 to Huron Valley Catholic School, Ypsilanti, MI.
$5,000 to Japhet School, Madison Heights, MI.
$5,000 to Northwood University, Midland, MI.
$5,000 to Walsh College of Accountancy and Business Administration, Troy, MI.

1495
The Porter Family Foundation
200 Orchard Hills Dr.
Ann Arbor, MI 48104

Established in 1999 in MI.
Donor: Thomas S. Porter.
Grantmaker type: Independent foundation.
Financial data (yr. ended 11/30/05): Assets, $1,324,016 (M); expenditures, $54,590; total giving, $37,900; qualifying distributions, $37,900; giving activities include $37,900 for 10 grants (high: $25,900; low: $500).
Fields of interest: Human services; Philanthropy/voluntarism.
Type of support: General/operating support.
Limitations: Applications not accepted. Giving primarily in MI. No grants to individuals.
Application information: Contributes only to pre-selected organizations.
Director: Thomas S. Porter.
EIN: 383503967

1496
Porter Foundation
P.O. Box 6484
Grand Rapids, MI 49516-6484
Contact: Margaret Beusse, Pres. and Secy.

Established in 1966.

Donors: Burke E. Porter Machinery Co.; Burke Porter Trust.
Grantmaker type: Independent foundation.
Financial data (yr. ended 6/30/05): Assets, $2,366,178 (M); gifts received, $44,500; expenditures, $145,952; total giving, $155,000; qualifying distributions, $155,000; giving activities include $155,000 for 29 grants (high: $20,000; low: $1,000).
Fields of interest: Museums (art); Performing arts, theater; Performing arts, orchestra (symphony); Arts; Higher education; Higher education, college; Education; Human services.
Type of support: General/operating support; Matching/challenge support.
Limitations: Giving primarily in Grand Rapids, MI. Generally prefers programs with no religious affiliation.
Application information:
Initial approach: Letter, including letter from school counselor
Deadline(s): None
Officers and Director:* Margaret Beusse,* Pres. and Secy.; Heather Beusse, V.P.; Blake Beusse, Treas.
EIN: 386118663

1497
Posey Family Foundation
15303 Dallas Pkwy., No. 999
Addison, TX 75001

Established in 1998 in TX.
Donors: Lee Posey; Sally Posey.
Grantmaker type: Independent foundation.
Financial data (yr. ended 3/31/05): Assets, $900,047 (M); expenditures, $173,135; total giving, $152,379; qualifying distributions, $152,379; giving activities include $152,379 for 6 grants (high: $50,000; low: $1,000).
Fields of interest: Performing arts, opera; Language/linguistics; Higher education; Education; Foundations (public).
Limitations: Applications not accepted. Giving primarily in MI, TX, and WA. No grants to individuals.
Application information: Contributes only to pre-selected organizations.
Officers: Lee Posey, Pres.; Tim Smith, V.P.; Gina Betts, Secy.; Pattie Keath, Treas.
Directors: Jennifer P. Ahearn; Jill M. Posey; Sally Posey.
EIN: 752768325

1498
John W. Post, Jr. and Arden R. Post Family Foundation
3545 Lakeshore Dr.
Holland, MI 49424-6201

Established in 2000 in MI.
Donors: John W. Post, Jr.; Arden R. Post.
Grantmaker type: Independent foundation.
Financial data (yr. ended 12/31/05): Assets, $75,044 (M); expenditures, $5,260; total giving, $4,000; qualifying distributions, $4,000; giving activities include $4,000 for grants.
Fields of interest: Higher education.
Type of support: General/operating support.
Limitations: Applications not accepted. No grants to individuals.

Application information: Contributes only to pre-selected organizations.
Directors: Arden R. Post; John W. Post, Jr.
EIN: 383515682

1499
Richard & Ruth Postema Family Foundation
4776 Pinnacle Ct. S.W.
Wyoming, MI 49509

Established in 2002 in MI.
Donors: Richard R. Postema; Ruth E. Postema.
Grantmaker type: Independent foundation.
Financial data (yr. ended 12/31/05): Assets, $57,794 (M); gifts received, $15,300; expenditures, $6,023; total giving, $5,250; qualifying distributions, $5,250; giving activities include $5,250 for grants.
Limitations: Applications not accepted. No grants to individuals.
Application information: Contributes only to pre-selected organizations.
Directors: Richard R. Postema; Ruth E. Postema.
EIN: 300064759

1500
Norine E. Potts Scholarship Trust
c/o National City Bank of MI/IL
P.O. Box 94651
Cleveland, OH 44101-4651

Established in 2003 in MI.
Donor: Norine Potts Trust.
Grantmaker type: Independent foundation.
Financial data (yr. ended 12/31/04): Assets, $166,609 (M); expenditures, $20,108; total giving, $14,807; qualifying distributions, $14,807; giving activities include $14,807 for 6 grants to individuals.
Type of support: Scholarships—to individuals.
Limitations: Applications not accepted. Giving primarily in MI.
Application information: Unsolicited requests for fund not accepted.
Trustee: National City Bank.
EIN: 201094587

1501
Bernard F. & Mary Ann Powell Foundation, Inc.
P.O. Box 1368
Clearwater, FL 33756-1368

Established in 2000 in FL.
Donors: B.F. Powell; C & B Foundation.
Grantmaker type: Independent foundation.
Financial data (yr. ended 12/31/05): Assets, $4,647,692 (M); gifts received, $500,000; expenditures, $213,476; total giving, $201,000; qualifying distributions, $213,262; giving activities include $201,000 for 26 grants (high: $20,000; low: $1,000).
Fields of interest: Higher education; Education; Cancer; Human services; Salvation Army; Youth, services; Residential/custodial care, hospices; Roman Catholic agencies & churches.
Limitations: Applications not accepted. Giving primarily in FL and MI. No grants to individuals.

Application information: Contributes only to pre-selected organizations.
Officers: Bernard F. Powell, Pres.; Mary Ann Powell, Secy.
EIN: 593575091

1502
The Power Foundation
c/o James C. Melvin, Secy.
136 E. Michigan Ave., Ste. 1201
Kalamazoo, MI 49007

Established in 1967 in MI.
Donors: Eugene B. Power†; Sadye H. Power†; Philip H. Power.
Grantmaker type: Independent foundation.
Financial data (yr. ended 12/31/05): Assets, $8,151,904 (M); gifts received, $858,846; expenditures, $441,481; total giving, $326,364; qualifying distributions, $382,806; giving activities include $326,364 for 33 grants (high: $100,000; low: $500).
Purpose and activities: Giving for higher education, the arts, social services, and natural resource preservation and enhancement.
Fields of interest: Arts; Higher education; Education; Mental health/crisis services; Community development.
Type of support: General/operating support; Continuing support; Annual campaigns; Capital campaigns; Building/renovation; Research.
Limitations: Applications not accepted. Giving primarily in MI, with emphasis on Ann Arbor.
Application information: Unsolicited requests for funds not accepted.
Officers and Trustees:* Philip H. Power,* Pres.; Kathleen K. Power,* V.P.; James C. Melvin,* Secy.; James S. Hilboldt,* Treas.
EIN: 386119490

1503
The Powers Family Foundation
3635 29th St.
Grand Rapids, MI 49512

Established in 1997 in MI.
Donor: Robert J. Powers.
Grantmaker type: Independent foundation.
Financial data (yr. ended 12/31/04): Assets, $49,548 (M); expenditures, $154,212; total giving, $136,500; qualifying distributions, $136,496; giving activities include $136,500 for 8 grants (high: $75,000; low: $1,000).
Purpose and activities: Giving primarily for Christian agencies and churches, for ministry support.
Fields of interest: Education; Christian agencies & churches.
Limitations: Applications not accepted. Giving primarily in MI. No grants to individuals.
Application information: Contributes only to pre-selected organizations.
Officers: Robert J. Powers, Pres. and Treas.; Carol A. Powers, Secy.
Directors: Janet L. Jepsen; Sharon C. Meerman; Linda A. Powers; Lisa M. Wilbur.
EIN: 383377775
Selected grants: The following grants were reported in 2004.
$75,000 to Saint Philip Neri House, Kalamazoo, MI.
$28,000 to Diocese of Grand Rapids, Grand Rapids, MI.

$12,500 to Inner City Christian Federation, Grand Rapids, MI.
$10,000 to Patrick Murphy Scholarship Foundation.
$6,000 to Franciscan Sisters of the Eucharist, Lowell, MI.
$2,000 to Go Fore Golf, Grand Ledge, MI.
$2,000 to Saint John Vianney, Wyoming, MI.
$1,000 to University of Michigan, Ann Arbor, MI.

1504
The Preede Foundation
c/o Roger B. Preede
5901 Stonehaven Blvd.
Oakland Township, MI   48306

Established in 1992 in MI.
Donor: Roger B. Preede.
Grantmaker type: Independent foundation.
Financial data (yr. ended 11/30/05): Assets, $128,470 (M); gifts received, $7,300; expenditures, $5,495; total giving, $5,400; qualifying distributions, $5,400; giving activities include $5,400 for 13 grants (high: $1,000; low: $100).
Fields of interest: Human services.
Limitations: Applications not accepted. Giving primarily in MI, with some emphasis on Rochester. No grants to individuals.
Application information: Contributes only to pre-selected organizations.
Officers: Roger B. Preede, Pres.; Linda C. Preede, Secy.
Directors: Phillip D. Preede; Stephen R. Preede.
EIN: 383019445

1505
Ed & June Prein Foundation
c/o H. Edward Prein
156 Hidden Lake Ct. S.E.
Grand Rapids, MI   49546

Established in 1996 in MI.
Donors: Ed Prein; June Prein.
Grantmaker type: Independent foundation.
Financial data (yr. ended 12/31/05): Assets, $824,724 (M); expenditures, $46,573; total giving, $44,750; qualifying distributions, $44,750; giving activities include $44,750 for grants.
Fields of interest: Performing arts, orchestra (symphony); Higher education; Education; Hospitals (general).
Type of support: General/operating support.
Limitations: Applications not accepted. Giving primarily in MI; giving also in FL, IN, and MN. No grants to individuals.
Application information: Contributes only to pre-selected organizations.
Officers: Barbara J. Prein, Secy.; H. Edward Prein, Treas.
EIN: 383325135

1506
The Meyer and Anna Prentis Family Foundation, Inc.
P.O. Box 7055
Huntington Woods, MI   48070
Application address: c/o Mark L. Silverman, 401 S. Old Woodward Ave., Ste. 435, Birmingham, MI 48009-6611

Incorporated in 1955 in MI.
Donor: Members of the Prentis family.
Grantmaker type: Independent foundation.
Financial data (yr. ended 12/31/04): Assets, $4,921,073 (M); expenditures, $223,560; total giving, $173,600; qualifying distributions, $219,564; giving activities include $173,600 for 71 grants (high: $24,400; low: $50).
Purpose and activities: Giving primarily for Jewish organizations, as well as for the performing arts, education, hospitals and health care, and human services.
Fields of interest: Performing arts; Historic preservation/historical societies; Arts; Education, early childhood education; Elementary school/education; Higher education; Education; Hospitals (general); Health care; Human services; Residential/custodial care, senior continuing care; Jewish federated giving programs; Jewish agencies & temples.
Limitations: Giving primarily in MI. No grants to individuals, or for endowment funds, scholarships, fellowships, or matching gifts; no loans.
Application information:
  Initial approach: Letter
  Copies of proposal: 1
  Deadline(s): None
  Board meeting date(s): July and Dec.
Officers: Dale P. Frenkel, Pres.; Denise L. Brown, V.P.; Ronald E.P. Frenkel, M.D., V.P.; Marvin A. Frenkel, Secy.-Treas.; Cindy F. Kanter, Secy.
Trustee: Nelson P. Lande.
EIN: 386090332

1507
The Preston Foundation
c/o James E. Preston
6059 Champagne Ct. S.E.
Grand Rapids, MI   49546-6430

Established in 1993 in MI.
Donors: James E. Preston; Marie C. Preston.
Grantmaker type: Independent foundation.
Financial data (yr. ended 12/31/05): Assets, $72,736 (M); gifts received, $41,337; expenditures, $75,945; total giving, $74,775; qualifying distributions, $74,775; giving activities include $74,775 for grants.
Fields of interest: Health organizations, association; Human services; Federated giving programs; Protestant agencies & churches.
Limitations: Applications not accepted. Giving primarily in Grand Rapids, MI. No grants to individuals.
Application information: Contributes only to pre-selected organizations.
Officers: James E. Preston, Pres.; Marie C. Preston, V.P.
EIN: 383146740

1508
Dan R. and Pamela M. Prevo Foundation
16243 Arbor Trail
Traverse City, MI   49686   (231) 223-4669
Contact: Dan R. Prevo, Pres.

Established in 1999 in MI.
Donor: Prevo's Family Markets, Inc.
Grantmaker type: Independent foundation.
Financial data (yr. ended 11/30/04): Assets, $466,080 (M); expenditures, $29,224; total giving,

$20,695; qualifying distributions, $20,695; giving activities include $20,695 for grants.
Fields of interest: Education; Human services; Women.
Limitations: Giving limited to MI. No grants to individuals.
Application information: Application form required.
  Deadline(s): None
  Final notification: Within 2 months
Officers: Dan R. Prevo, Pres.; Pamela M. Prevo, V.P.; Aaron P. Prevo, Treas.
EIN: 383454586

1509
Maxwell Pribil Memorial Trust
c/o Citizens Bank Wealth Mgmt., N.A.
328 S. Saginaw St., M/C 002072
Flint, MI   48502
Application Address: c/o Helen James, Citizens Bank Wealth Mgmt., N.A., 101 N. Washington Ave., Saginaw, MI 48607, tel.: (989) 776-7368

Established in 1998 in MI.
Grantmaker type: Independent foundation.
Financial data (yr. ended 12/31/05): Assets, $3,171,385 (M); expenditures, $135,970; total giving, $102,845; qualifying distributions, $128,724; giving activities include $102,845 for 9 grants (high: $30,000; low: $1,000).
Fields of interest: Arts; Education.
Limitations: Giving primarily in Bay City and Saginaw, MI.
Application information: Application form required.
  Deadline(s): None
Trustee: Citizens Bank.
EIN: 386723513
Selected grants: The following grants were reported in 2003.
$100,000 to Saginaw Art Museum, Saginaw, MI.
$15,000 to State Theater of Bay City, Bay County, Bay City, MI.
$10,000 to Saginaw Choral Society, Saginaw, MI.
$9,000 to Saginaw, City of, Saginaw, MI. 2 grants: $4,000 (For Saginaw Community Enrichment Commission), $5,000 (For Andersen Enrichment Center).
$5,500 to Saginaw Valley State University, University Center, MI. 2 grants: $4,000, $1,500
$5,000 to Bay City Players, Bay City, MI.
$5,000 to Midland Center for the Arts, Midland, MI.
$4,500 to Bullock Creek School District, Midland, MI.

1510
Maxwell Pribil Trust f/b/o Hoyt Library
c/o Citizens Bank Wealth Mgmt., N.A.
328 S. Saginaw St., M/C 002072
Flint, MI   48502

Established in 1998 in MI.
Donor: Maxwell Pribil Trust.
Grantmaker type: Independent foundation.
Financial data (yr. ended 12/31/05): Assets, $719,585 (M); expenditures, $35,022; total giving, $25,999; qualifying distributions, $25,999; giving activities include $25,999 for grants.
Purpose and activities: Support only for the Hoyt Library, MI.
Fields of interest: Libraries (public).
Limitations: Applications not accepted. Giving limited to Saginaw, MI. No grants to individuals.

Application information: Contributes only to a pre-selected organization.
Trustee: Citizens Bank.
EIN: 386723514

1511
Maxwell Pribil Trust f/b/o Saginaw Symphony
c/o Citizens Bank Wealth Mgmt., N.A.
328 S. Saginaw St., M/C 002072
Flint, MI 48502

Established in 1998 in MI.
Donor: Maxwell Pribil Trust.
Grantmaker type: Independent foundation.
Financial data (yr. ended 12/31/05): Assets, $528,074 (M); expenditures, $30,173; total giving, $22,657; qualifying distributions, $22,657; giving activities include $22,657 for grants.
Purpose and activities: Support only for the Saginaw Bay Orchestra, MI.
Fields of interest: Performing arts, music; Performing arts, orchestra (symphony).
Limitations: Applications not accepted. Giving limited to Saginaw, MI. No grants to individuals.
Application information: Contributes only to a pre-selected organization.
Trustee: Citizens Bank.
EIN: 386723515

1512
The Robert E. Price Foundation, Inc.
P.O. Box 605
Adrian, MI 49221 (517) 265-6168
Contact: Robert E. Price, Pres.

Established in 1995 in MI.
Donor: Robert E. Price.
Grantmaker type: Independent foundation.
Financial data (yr. ended 12/31/04): Assets, $3,378,975 (M); gifts received, $70,000; expenditures, $174,324; total giving, $172,074; qualifying distributions, $174,324; giving activities include $172,074 for 12 grants (high: $76,000; low: $250).
Purpose and activities: Giving primarily for education and health; funding also for YMCAs.
Fields of interest: Performing arts, orchestra (symphony); Higher education; Health organizations; Cancer research; YM/YWCAs & YM/YWHAs; Residential/custodial care, hospices.
Limitations: Giving primarily in Adrian, MI. No grants to individuals.
Application information:
Initial approach: Letter
Deadline(s): None
Officers: Robert E. Price, Pres.; Henry E. Mistele, Secy.-Treas.
EIN: 383247629

1513
Edgar and Elsa Prince Foundation
(formerly Prince Foundation)
190 River Ave., Ste. 300
Holland, MI 49423 (616) 494-8143

Established in 1977.
Donors: Edgar D. Prince†; Elsa D. Prince; Prince Corp.
Grantmaker type: Independent foundation.

Financial data (yr. ended 6/30/05): Assets, $23,256,168 (M); expenditures, $5,365,145; total giving, $4,948,250; qualifying distributions, $4,954,103; giving activities include $4,948,250 for 157 grants (high: $500,000; low: $250; average: $1,000–$100,000).
Purpose and activities: Giving to Christian organizations, churches, and schools and community activities.
Fields of interest: Elementary/secondary education; Health organizations, association; Family services; Aging, centers/services; Community development, neighborhood development; Christian agencies & churches; Aging.
Type of support: General/operating support.
Limitations: Applications not accepted. Giving primarily in MI. No grants to individuals.
Application information: Contributes only to pre-selected organizations.
Officers: Elsa D. Prince, Pres.; Elisabeth DeVos, V.P.; Eileen Ellens, V.P.; Erik D. Prince, V.P.; Emilie Wierda, V.P.; Robert Haveman, Secy.-Treas.
EIN: 382190330
Selected grants: The following grants were reported in 2004.
$750,000 to Hope College, Holland, MI. For general operating support.
$500,000 to Family Research Council, DC. For general operating support.
$500,000 to Haggai Institute for Advanced Leadership Training, Atlanta, GA. For general operating support.
$462,000 to Focus on the Family, Colorado Springs, CO. 2 grants: $250,000 (For general operating support), $212,000 (For general operating support).
$400,000 to Gospel Communications International, Muskegon, MI. 2 grants: $250,000 (For general operating support), $150,000 (For general operating support).
$300,000 to Rehoboth Christian School, Rehoboth, NM. 2 grants: $150,000 each (For general operating support).
$100,000 to Grand Rapids Christian Schools, Grand Rapids, MI. For general operating support.

1514
Leslie Prince Memorial Scholarship Fund
c/o Fifth Third Bank
P.O. Box 3636
Grand Rapids, MI 49501
Application address: c/o Financial Aid/Counseling Offices, Morton East High Schools, 2423 S. Austin Blvd., Cicero, IL 60804

Established around 1993.
Grantmaker type: Independent foundation.
Financial data (yr. ended 6/30/04): Assets, $15,715 (M); gifts received, $80; expenditures, $1,017; total giving, $0; qualifying distributions, $265.
Purpose and activities: Scholarship awards to graduating seniors of East and West Morton high schools attending IL State University.
Type of support: Scholarships—to individuals.
Limitations: Giving limited to residents of Cicero, IL.
Application information:
Initial approach: Letter
Deadline(s): 1st Tues. in May
Officers and Directors:* J. Frank Daly,* Senior V.P.; John Pindiak,* V.P.
Trustee: Fifth Third Bank.
EIN: 366934253

1515
Providence Foundation
P.O. Box 510208
Livonia, MI 48150-9998

Established in 1986 in MI.
Donor: Wayne E. Whitney.
Grantmaker type: Independent foundation.
Financial data (yr. ended 12/31/05): Assets, $190,767 (M); expenditures, $15,439; total giving, $12,750; qualifying distributions, $12,750; giving activities include $12,750 for grants.
Fields of interest: Christian agencies & churches.
Limitations: Applications not accepted. Giving primarily in FL and MI. No grants to individuals.
Application information: Contributes only to pre-selected organizations.
Officers and Directors:* Wayne E. Whitney,* Pres. and Treas.; Robert Myers,* V.P.; Taki Anagnostou, Secy.; Royce Shelton, Secy.
EIN: 386510130

1516
The Pryor Foundation
c/o Frederic L. Pryor
740 Harvard Ave.
Swarthmore, PA 19081
E-mail: fpryor1@swarthmore.edu

Established in 1947 in MI.
Donors: Mary S. Pryor†; Millard H. Pryor†; Corey Kienholz.
Grantmaker type: Independent foundation.
Financial data (yr. ended 1/31/05): Assets, $4,072,794 (M); expenditures, $293,696; total giving, $262,500; qualifying distributions, $272,836; giving activities include $262,500 for 26 grants (high: $25,000; low: $500).
Purpose and activities: Giving to the arts, culture and education.
Fields of interest: Arts; Higher education; Human services; Federated giving programs.
Type of support: Annual campaigns; Capital campaigns; Emergency funds; Consulting services.
Limitations: Applications not accepted. Giving primarily in Hartford, CT, Ann Arbor, MI, Mansfield, OH, and Philadelphia, PA. No support for religious or political organizations. No grants for building funds or land acquisition.
Application information: Contributes to organizations in which Pryor family members are involved.
Board meeting date(s): Nov.
Officer and Trustees:* Frederic L. Pryor,* Mgr.; F. Loyal Bemiller; H. Elizabeth Bradley; Daniel A. Pryor; Esther A. Pryor.
Number of staff: None.
EIN: 386056108
Selected grants: The following grants were reported in 2005.
$60,000 to Tougaloo College, Tougaloo, MS. For general support.
$25,000 to Peace Neighborhood Center, Ann Arbor, MI. For general support.
$10,000 to Amistad Foundation, Hartford, CT. For general support.
$10,000 to Asylum Hill Boys and Girls Club Development Association, West Hartford, CT. For general support.
$10,000 to Connecticut Opera Association, Hartford, CT. For general support.
$10,000 to Hartford Symphony Orchestra, Hartford, CT. For general support.

$10,000 to University of Connecticut Foundation, West Hartford, CT. For general support.

$10,000 to Wadsworth Atheneum, Hartford, CT. For general support.

$7,500 to NARAL Pro-Choice America Foundation, DC. For general support.

$5,000 to University of Michigan, Ann Arbor, MI. For general support.

1517
George Puschelberg Foundation
20100 Mack Ave., 2nd Fl.
Grosse Pointe Woods, MI 48236-1820
(313) 343-9200
Contact: Allan Neef, Tr.

Grantmaker type: Independent foundation.
Financial data (yr. ended 4/30/06): Assets, $320,231 (M); expenditures, $23,416; total giving, $11,000; qualifying distributions, $11,000; giving activities include $11,000 for grants.
Purpose and activities: Giving to hospitals, medical training facilities, and organizations doing cancer or arthritis research.
Fields of interest: Medical school/education; Hospitals (general); Cancer research; Arthritis research.
Limitations: Giving primarily in MI. No grants to individuals.
Application information: Application form not required.
  Initial approach: Letter
  Deadline(s): None
Trustees: Allan Neef; Jack Porter.
EIN: 382319247

1518
The Pyle Foundation
3020 Charlevoix Dr.
Grand Rapids, MI 49546

Established in 1986 in MI.
Donors: Owen Pyle, Jr.; Margaret Pyle.
Grantmaker type: Independent foundation.
Financial data (yr. ended 12/31/05): Assets, $439,808 (M); expenditures, $18,690; total giving, $15,627; qualifying distributions, $15,627; giving activities include $15,627 for grants.
Purpose and activities: Giving primarily for natural resource conservation; funding also for education and human services.
Fields of interest: Arts; Higher education; Education; Environment, natural resources; Health organizations; Human services; Federated giving programs.
Type of support: General/operating support.
Limitations: Applications not accepted. Giving primarily in MI. No grants to individuals.
Application information: Contributes only to pre-selected organizations.
Trustees: Margaret Pyle; Owen Pyle, Jr.
EIN: 382678280

1519
The Qazi Foundation
c/o Ciena Healthcare Management, Inc.
4000 Town Ctr., Ste. 300
Southfield, MI 48075

Established in 2003 in MI.

Donor: Mohammad Qazi.
Grantmaker type: Independent foundation.
Financial data (yr. ended 12/31/04): Assets, $6,214 (M); gifts received, $10,000; expenditures, $53,858; total giving, $53,678; qualifying distributions, $53,678; giving activities include $53,678 for grants.
Fields of interest: Higher education; Human services; Islam.
Limitations: Applications not accepted. No grants to individuals.
Application information: Contributes only to pre-selected organizations.
Officer: Mohammad Qazi, Pres.
EIN: 352166479

1520
Mary Anne S. Quiachon Memorial & Ernesto Quiachon, M.D. Foundation
3897 Breckinridge Dr.
Okemos, MI 48864

Established in 1997 in MI.
Donors: Ernesto B. Quiachon, M.D.; Rose S. Quiachon, Ph.D.
Grantmaker type: Independent foundation.
Financial data (yr. ended 9/30/04): Assets, $52,623 (M); gifts received, $12,065; expenditures, $26,068; total giving, $22,588; qualifying distributions, $22,588; giving activities include $22,588 for grants.
Fields of interest: Elementary school/education; Higher education; Education; Children/youth, services; Christian agencies & churches; Roman Catholic agencies & churches.
International interests: Philippines.
Type of support: General/operating support.
Limitations: Applications not accepted. Giving primarily for the benefit of the Philippines. No grants to individuals.
Application information: Contributes only to pre-selected organizations.
Officers and Directors:* Ernesto B. Quiachon, M.D.*, Pres.; Vincent Louis Quiachon,* V.P.; Rose S. Quiachon, Ph.D.*, Secy.-Treas.; Thomas Graham Bell; Wanderly Demendonca-Calaca; Florencia M. Lazaro; Antonio J.A. Pido, Ph.D.; Teresa G. Pido; Vincent Shunsky.
EIN: 383384926

1521
The Rabahy Foundation
12932 Farmington Rd.
Livonia, MI 48150

Donor: Rosemary Rabahy.
Grantmaker type: Independent foundation.
Financial data (yr. ended 12/31/05): Assets, $217,129 (M); expenditures, $13,443; total giving, $11,000; qualifying distributions, $11,000; giving activities include $11,000 for grants.
Limitations: Applications not accepted. No grants to individuals.
Application information: Contributes only to pre-selected organizations.
Officers: David Rabahy, Pres. and Treas.; Donald L. Rabahy, Secy.
EIN: 383420555

1522
Rachor Family Foundation, Ltd.
(formerly Michael Garry Rachor Professional School Scholarship Fund, Ltd.)
P.O. Box 320100
Flint, MI 48532-0002

Established in 1996 in MI.
Donor: Michael Garry Rachor.
Grantmaker type: Independent foundation.
Financial data (yr. ended 12/31/04): Assets, $1,792,168 (M); gifts received, $154,900; expenditures, $69,682; total giving, $56,775; qualifying distributions, $56,775; giving activities include $25,675 for grants, and $31,100 for 5 grants to individuals.
Fields of interest: Higher education; Law school/education; Medical school/education.
Type of support: Scholarships—to individuals; Scholarship funds.
Limitations: Applications not accepted. Giving on a national basis.
Application information: Unsolicited requests for funds not accepted.
Officer and Directors:* Michael Garry Rachor,* Pres.; James Michael Rachor; Terese Marie Rachor-Beste.
EIN: 383264828

1523
Rainbow Foundation
5131 Rosabelle Beach Ave.
Holland, MI 49424-1034
Contact: Marjorie G. Hoogeboom, Secy.-Treas.

Established in 1990 in MI.
Donors: Thomas J. Hoogeboom; Marjorie G. Hoogeboom.
Grantmaker type: Independent foundation.
Financial data (yr. ended 12/31/04): Assets, $897,179 (M); gifts received, $14,736; expenditures, $34,187; total giving, $32,250; qualifying distributions, $32,250; giving activities include $32,250 for 4 grants (high: $20,000; low: $500).
Purpose and activities: Giving primarily to Christian organizations and schools.
Fields of interest: Higher education; Education; Christian agencies & churches.
Limitations: Giving primarily in the western MI area.
Application information:
  Initial approach: Letter or proposal
  Deadline(s): None
  Final notification: Within 3 months
Officers: Thomas J. Hoogeboom, Pres.; Cheryl L. Hoogewind, V.P.; Karen J. Vanderlaan, V.P.; Marjorie G. Hoogeboom, Secy-Treas.
Director: Robert P. Egly, Jr.
EIN: 382939744

1524
Walter J. and Natalie M. Rais Charitable Trust Foundation
35560 Grand River Ave., Ste. 318
Farmington, MI 48335-3123

Established in 2003 in MI.
Grantmaker type: Independent foundation.
Financial data (yr. ended 10/31/05): Assets, $1,459,981 (M); expenditures, $75,982; total

giving, $40,000; qualifying distributions, $75,982; giving activities include $40,000 for 1 grant.
Purpose and activities: Support for medical research to develop an early detection test and cure for ovarian cancer.
Fields of interest: Cancer research; Women.
Limitations: Applications not accepted. Giving primarily in MI. No grants to individuals.
Application information: Contributes only to pre-selected organizations.
Trustees: Joseph H. Clancy; Ursula Clancy.
EIN: 326021410

1525
Rajput-Dasgupta Family Charitable Foundation
3339 Pine Estate Dr.
West Bloomfield, MI 48323
Contact: Hemant Rajput, Treas.
Application address: 37895 Ann Arbor Rd., Livonia, MI 48150

Established in 1999 in MI.
Grantmaker type: Independent foundation.
Financial data (yr. ended 12/31/04): Assets, $27,879 (M); gifts received, $200; expenditures, $4,471; total giving, $4,451; qualifying distributions, $4,451; giving activities include $4,451 for grants.
Limitations: Applications not accepted. No grants to individuals.
Application information: Contributes only to pre-selected organizations.
Officer: Minoti H. Rajput, Pres.; Hemant Rajput, Treas.
EIN: 383488234

1526
Ram Foundation, Ltd.
P.O. Box 80695
Rochester, MI 48308-0695

Established in MI.
Grantmaker type: Independent foundation.
Financial data (yr. ended 12/31/04): Assets, $658,500 (M); expenditures, $300,370; total giving, $300,000; qualifying distributions, $300,000; giving activities include $300,000 for 1 grant.
Purpose and activities: Giving primarily to a center for obesity research.
Fields of interest: Medical research, association.
Limitations: Applications not accepted. Giving primarily in Rochester Hills, MI. No grants to individuals.
Application information: Contributes only to pre-selected organizations.
Director: Raymond J. Nicholson.
EIN: 383504442

1527
Ramser-Morgan Foundation
c/o Comerica Bank
P.O. Box 75000, MC 3300
Detroit, MI 48275 (313) 222-6105
Contact: Robert Sajdak, Pres.

Established in 1991 in MI.
Donor: M. Louise Morgan.
Grantmaker type: Independent foundation.

Financial data (yr. ended 12/31/05): Assets, $1,174,163 (M); expenditures, $81,000; total giving, $65,000; qualifying distributions, $66,670; giving activities include $65,000 for 10 grants (high: $10,000; low: $2,500).
Fields of interest: Higher education; Cancer; Human services; Federated giving programs; Military/veterans' organizations.
Limitations: Giving in MI, primarily in Detroit.
Application information: Application form not required.
Deadline(s): None
Officers: Robert Sajdak, Pres.; Steve Milbeck, V.P. and Treas.; Thomas W. Payne, Secy.
EIN: 383003280

1528
Ran Family Foundation
1425 Clarendon Rd.
Bloomfield Hills, MI 48302

Established in 2000 in MI.
Donor: Gary L. Ran.
Grantmaker type: Independent foundation.
Financial data (yr. ended 8/31/05): Assets, $1,228 (M); gifts received, $26,000; expenditures, $26,577; total giving, $25,527; qualifying distributions, $25,527; giving activities include $25,527 for grants.
Fields of interest: Jewish agencies & temples.
Limitations: Applications not accepted. Giving primarily in MI. No grants to individuals.
Application information: Contributes only to pre-selected organizations.
Officers: Gary L. Ran, Pres. and Treas.; Rhonda S. Ran, V.P. and Secy.
EIN: 383569240

1529
Ranger Foundation
c/o Erik Serr
101 N. Main St., 7th Fl.
Ann Arbor, MI 48104-1481

Established in 1999 in MI.
Grantmaker type: Independent foundation.
Financial data (yr. ended 12/31/04): Assets, $947,417 (M); expenditures, $56,572; total giving, $40,000; qualifying distributions, $40,000; giving activities include $40,000 for grants.
Limitations: Applications not accepted. Giving primarily in MI. No grants to individuals.
Application information: Contributes only to pre-selected organizations.
Director: Howard S. Holmes.
EIN: 383499187

1530
The Rankauf Foundation
121 W. Long Lake Rd., 3rd Fl.
Bloomfield Hills, MI 48304

Established in 2000 in MI.
Donors: Dale C. Rands; Stuart M. Kaufman.
Grantmaker type: Independent foundation.
Financial data (yr. ended 12/31/05): Assets, $8,539 (M); expenditures, $4,470; total giving, $4,450; qualifying distributions, $4,450; giving activities include $4,450 for grants.

Limitations: Applications not accepted. No grants to individuals.
Application information: Contributes only to pre-selected organizations.
Officers and Directors:* Stuart M. Kaufman,* Pres.; Dale G. Rands,* V.P. and Treas.; Susan A. Kaufman,* Secy.
EIN: 383572477

1531
Grace Rapinchuk Charitable Foundation, Inc.
4001 Glacier Hills Dr., Ste. 227
Ann Arbor, MI 48105
Contact: Grace Rapinchuk, Tr.

Established in 2000 in NJ.
Donor: Grace Rapinchuk.
Grantmaker type: Independent foundation.
Financial data (yr. ended 6/30/05): Assets, $261,694 (M); gifts received, $50,000; expenditures, $13,670; total giving, $11,825; qualifying distributions, $11,825; giving activities include $11,825 for grants.
Limitations: Giving primarily in NJ.
Application information: Application form not required.
Deadline(s): None
Trustees: Grace Rapinchuk; James Rapinchuk; Jane Rapinchuk; John Rapinchuk.
EIN: 522277126

1532
Milton M. Ratner Foundation
P.O. Box 250628
Franklin, MI 48025-0628
Contact: Therese M. Thorn, Treas.
E-mail: ratner_foundation@sbcglobal.net

Incorporated in 1968 in MI.
Donor: Milton M. Ratner†.
Grantmaker type: Independent foundation.
Financial data (yr. ended 8/31/05): Assets, $8,502,386 (M); expenditures, $516,837; total giving, $410,300; qualifying distributions, $457,069; giving activities include $410,300 for 51 grants.
Purpose and activities: Giving primarily for higher education, and health and human services for children, families, and the elderly. Giving also for research to fight heart disease, for aid and training for the blind, and to aid physically handicapped children.
Fields of interest: Higher education; Scholarships/financial aid; Hospitals (general); Health organizations, association; Medical research, institute; Heart & circulatory research; Blind/visually impaired.
Type of support: General/operating support; Continuing support; Building/renovation; Equipment; Endowments; Program development; Scholarship funds; Research; Matching/challenge support.
Limitations: Giving primarily in GA and MI. No grants to individuals.
Application information: Application form not required.
Initial approach: Letter no more than 3 pages
Copies of proposal: 1
Deadline(s): Aug. 31

Board meeting date(s): Oct.
Final notification: Dec. 31
Officers and Trustees: * Mary Jo Rossen,* Pres.;
Charles R. McDonald,* V.P. and Secy.; Therese M.
Thorn,* Treas.
Agent: Meadowbrook Investment Advisors.
EIN: 386160330
Selected grants: The following grants were reported
in 2004.
$20,000 to Calhouns GEM Theater, Friends of,
   Calhoun, GA. For capital campaign.
$20,000 to Gordon Hospital Foundation, Calhoun,
   GA. For capital campaign.
$15,000 to United Way of Gordon County, Calhoun,
   GA. For general operating support.
$10,000 to Child Abuse and Neglect Council of
   Oakland County, Pontiac, MI. For general
   operating support.
$10,000 to Eastern Michigan University Foundation,
   Ypsilanti, MI. For scholarships.
$10,000 to Foundation of Wesley Woods, Atlanta,
   GA. For general operating support.
$10,000 to Judson Center, Royal Oak, MI. For
   general operating support.
$10,000 to Michigan Colleges Foundation,
   Southfield, MI. For general operating support.
$10,000 to Oglethorpe University, Atlanta, GA. For
   scholarships.
$10,000 to Shepherd Center, Atlanta, GA. For
   general operating support.

1533
The Ruth F. Rattner and the Ann F. and Norman D. Katz Charitable Foundation
(formerly The William Henry and Ruth Lambert Frank
Charitable Foundation)
c/o Norman D. Katz
401 S. Old Woodward Ave., Ste. 333
Birmingham, MI   48009-6612

Donors: William H. Frank‡; Ruth L. Frank‡.
Grantmaker type: Independent foundation.
Financial data (yr. ended 12/31/05): Assets,
$949,401 (M); expenditures, $44,020; total giving,
$42,500; qualifying distributions, $42,500; giving
activities include $42,500 for grants.
Fields of interest: Performing arts; Cancer research.
Type of support: General/operating support;
Building/renovation; Scholarship funds.
Limitations: Applications not accepted. Giving
limited to MI, with emphasis on Detroit. No grants
to individuals.
Application information: Contributes only to
pre-selected organizations.
Officers: Norman D. Katz, Pres.; Ann Katz, Secy.;
Ruth Rattner, Treas.
EIN: 386065115

1534
The Raval Education Foundation, Inc.
1004 Browns Lake Rd.
Jackson, MI   49203
Contact: Harish Rawal, Pres.

Established in 2001 in MI.
Donor: Harish Rawal.
Grantmaker type: Independent foundation.
Financial data (yr. ended 12/31/05): Assets,
$68,898 (M); gifts received, $650; expenditures,
$14,020; total giving, $13,000; qualifying

distributions, $13,000; giving activities include
$13,000 for grants.
Purpose and activities: Scholarship awards to
graduates of Jackson High School, MI.
Limitations: Giving primarily in Jackson, MI.
Application information:
   Initial approach: Letter
   Deadline(s): None
Officers: Harish Rawal, Pres.; Tejas H. Raval, V.P.;
Sudha Rawal, Secy.
EIN: 383624064

1535
The Ravitz Foundation
P.O. Box 5058
Southfield, MI   48086-5058

Established in 2001 in MI.
Donor: The Edward Ravitz Revocable Living Trust.
Grantmaker type: Independent foundation.
Financial data (yr. ended 12/31/04): Assets,
$21,867,435 (M); gifts received, $680,604;
expenditures, $1,064,074; total giving, $798,600;
qualifying distributions, $1,064,074; giving
activities include $798,600 for 12 grants (high:
$250,000; low: $3,600).
Purpose and activities: Giving primarily for medical
services and research.
Fields of interest: Dental school/education; Health
care; Mental health, treatment; Cancer; Medical
research; Boys & girls clubs; Residential/custodial
care, hospices; Jewish agencies & temples.
Limitations: Applications not accepted. Giving
primarily in MI; some funding also in New York, NY.
No grants to individuals.
Application information: Contributes only to
pre-selected organizations.
Directors: Bruce Gelbaugh; Burton R. Shifman; Neil
Zales.
EIN: 383508943

1536
Rawson Foundation, Inc.
6943 N. Cemetery Rd.
Cass City, MI   48726
Contact: Delbert E. Rawson, Secy.

Grantmaker type: Independent foundation.
Financial data (yr. ended 12/31/05): Assets,
$321,183 (M); expenditures, $16,246; total giving,
$15,935; qualifying distributions, $15,935; giving
activities include $15,935 for grants.
Purpose and activities: Scholarships primarily to
graduates of Cass City High School for attendance
at Central Michigan University.
Fields of interest: Higher education.
Type of support: General/operating support;
Scholarship funds.
Limitations: Giving primarily in MI and VA.
Application information: Application form not
required.
   Deadline(s): None
Officers: Daniel Derfiny, Pres.; Robert L. Tuckey,
V.P.; Delbert E. Rawson, Secy.; Robert Green, Treas.
EIN: 386060361

1537
The Rayes Foundation
26300 Telegraph Rd., 2nd Fl.
Southfield, MI   48034

Established in 1994 in MI.
Donor: Ayman Rayes.
Grantmaker type: Independent foundation.
Financial data (yr. ended 12/31/03): Assets,
$60,866 (M); expenditures, $9,012; total giving,
$6,600; qualifying distributions, $6,600; giving
activities include $6,600 for grants.
Fields of interest: International relief; Islam.
Limitations: Applications not accepted. No grants to
individuals.
Application information: Contributes only to
pre-selected organizations.
Officer: Ayman Rayes, Pres.
EIN: 383128284

1538
The Razzak Foundation
26300 Telegraph Rd., 2nd Fl.
Southfield, MI   48034

Established in 1999.
Grantmaker type: Independent foundation.
Financial data (yr. ended 12/31/05): Assets,
$668,861 (M); gifts received, $215,000;
expenditures, $162,776; total giving, $159,485;
qualifying distributions, $159,485; giving activities
include $159,485 for grants.
Purpose and activities: Giving primarily to Islamic
organizations and for health care.
Fields of interest: Health care; Islam.
Type of support: General/operating support.
Limitations: Applications not accepted. Giving
primarily in MI. No grants to individuals.
Officer: Abdulkader Abdulrazzak, M.D., Pres.
EIN: 383436519

1539
RBS Foundation
6553 Creekwood Ln.
Holland, MI   49423

Established in 1988 in MI.
Donors: Robert Slikkers; Barbara Slikkers.
Grantmaker type: Independent foundation.
Financial data (yr. ended 12/31/05): Assets,
$133,682 (M); gifts received, $236,316;
expenditures, $160,272; total giving, $160,272;
qualifying distributions, $160,272; giving activities
include $160,272 for 10+ grants (high: $85,844).
Purpose and activities: Giving primarily for Christian
evangelism.
Fields of interest: Education; Christian agencies &
churches.
Type of support: General/operating support.
Limitations: Applications not accepted. Giving
primarily in CA and MI. No grants to individuals.
Application information: Contributes only to
pre-selected organizations.
Trustee: Robert L. Slikkers.
EIN: 382859894

1540
Recreational Boating Industries Educational Foundation
32398 Five Mile Rd.
Livonia, MI   48154-6109   (734) 261-0123
Contact: Van W. Snider, Jr., Dir.

Donor: Michigan Boating Industries Assn.
Grantmaker type: Independent foundation.

Financial data (yr. ended 12/31/05): Assets, $80,645 (M); gifts received, $25,000; expenditures, $62,916; total giving, $28,500; qualifying distributions, $28,500; giving activities include $28,500 for grants.
Purpose and activities: Support for higher education, including scholarships given to permanent residents of Michigan, based on merit and financial need.
Fields of interest: Higher education.
Type of support: Scholarship funds; Scholarships—to individuals.
Limitations: Giving limited to MI.
Application information:
  Initial approach: Letter
  Deadline(s): Apr. 20
Officers: John Hatfield, Pres.; Robert G. Liggett, Jr., V.P.; Gregory Krueger, Secy.; Horst Sherriff, Treas.
Directors: James A. Coburn; Theodore Sampanes; Van W. Snider, Jr.; Ray L. Underwood.
EIN: 382704909

1541
The Reem Foundation
26300 Telegraph Rd., 2nd Fl.
Southfield, MI 48034

Established in 2003.
Grantmaker type: Independent foundation.
Financial data (yr. ended 12/31/04): Assets, $57,250 (M); gifts received, $35,000; expenditures, $650; total giving, $0; qualifying distributions, $0.
Officer: Fayez Shukairy, Pres.
EIN: 364495768

1542
David E. Reese Family Foundation
7348 Red Ledge Dr.
Paradise Valley, AZ 85253-2880

Established in 1994 in AZ.
Donors: David E. Reese; Caleb F. Reese; Everett D. Reese II; Everett Reese†.
Grantmaker type: Independent foundation.
Financial data (yr. ended 12/31/04): Assets, $20,411,634 (M); expenditures, $993,760; total giving, $954,000; qualifying distributions, $954,000; giving activities include $954,000 for 32 grants (high: $189,500; low: $1,000).
Fields of interest: Arts; Higher education; Education; Environment, land resources; Environment; Human services; Foundations (private grantmaking); Foundations (community).
Limitations: Applications not accepted. Giving primarily in Scottsdale and Phoenix, AZ; some giving also in MI. No grants to individuals.
Application information: Contributes only to pre-selected organizations.
Officers: David E. Reese, Pres.; Louise R. Reese, V.P. and Secy.; Everett D. Reese, Treas.
EIN: 860763892
Selected grants: The following grants were reported in 2003.
$250,000 to Denison University, Granville, OH.
$151,000 to Arizona Community Foundation, Phoenix, AZ.
$100,000 to Grand Traverse Regional Land Conservancy, Traverse City, MI.
$100,000 to Lawrenceville School, Lawrenceville, NJ.

$50,000 to Heard Museum, Phoenix, AZ.
$50,000 to Wheaton Club Philadelphia, Philadelphia, PA.
$25,000 to Hospice of the Valley, Phoenix, AZ.
$25,000 to Humane Society, Arizona, Phoenix, AZ.
$25,000 to Painted Turtle, Santa Monica, CA.
$10,000 to Phoenix Art Museum, Phoenix, AZ.

1543
Wallace O. Refke Trust
c/o National City Bank
P.O. Box 94651
Cleveland, OH 44101-4651

Established in 1997 in MI.
Grantmaker type: Independent foundation.
Financial data (yr. ended 12/31/04): Assets, $737,139 (M); expenditures, $35,025; total giving, $30,500; qualifying distributions, $30,500; giving activities include $30,500 for grants.
Purpose and activities: Support only for the Manistee County Library, MI.
Fields of interest: Libraries (public).
Limitations: Applications not accepted. Giving limited to Manistee, MI. No grants to individuals.
Application information: Contributes only to a pre-selected organization.
Trustee: National City Bank.
EIN: 386679358

1544
The Regal Dean Family Foundation
8338 S. Kostner Ave.
Chicago, IL 60652 (773) 582-9565
Contact: Ella Armstrong, Tr.

Established in 2003 in IL.
Donor: Ella Armstrong.
Grantmaker type: Independent foundation.
Financial data (yr. ended 12/31/04): Assets, $23,161 (M); gifts received, $800; expenditures, $2,053; total giving, $2,000; qualifying distributions, $2,053; giving activities include $2,000 for grants.
Fields of interest: Education; Human services; Children/youth, services; Minorities.
Limitations: Giving primarily in the Midwest. No grants for annual campaigns, endowments, or sectarian religious activities.
Application information: Application form required.
  Initial approach: Proposal
  Deadline(s): Mar. 1 and Sept. 1
Trustees: Ella Armstrong; Fairy D. Armstrong.
EIN: 200382606

1545
C. & A. Reid Charitable Trust
(formerly Carrie M. & Alex A. Reid Trust)
c/o Citizens Bank Wealth Mgmt., N.A.
328 S. Saginaw St., M/C 002072
Flint, MI 48502

Established in MI.
Donor: Alex A. Reid†.
Grantmaker type: Independent foundation.
Financial data (yr. ended 8/31/05): Assets, $630,133 (M); expenditures, $36,164; total giving, $27,593; qualifying distributions, $27,593; giving activities include $27,593 for grants.
Fields of interest: Human services.

Type of support: General/operating support.
Limitations: Applications not accepted. Giving limited to Saginaw, Lansing, Albion, Hemlock, Auburn, Alma, and Southfield, MI and Tucson, AZ. No grants to individuals.
Application information: Contributes only to 21 pre-selected organizations specified in the trust instrument.
Trustee: Citizens Bank.
EIN: 386339147

1546
M. C. & A. A. Reid Educational Trust
c/o Citizens Bank Wealth Mgmt., N.A.
328 S. Saginaw St., M/C 002072
Flint, MI 48502
Application address: c/o Helen James, Citizens Bank Wealth Mgmt., N.A., 101 N. Washington Ave., Saginaw, MI 48607, tel.: (989) 776-7368

Established in 1976 in MI.
Donor: Alex Reid†.
Grantmaker type: Independent foundation.
Financial data (yr. ended 8/31/05): Assets, $527,457 (M); gifts received, $25,013; expenditures, $11,318; total giving, $0; qualifying distributions, $0.
Purpose and activities: Student loans to Saginaw County, MI, residents, age 15-30, to be used to attend a college or university.
Type of support: Student loans—to individuals.
Limitations: Giving limited to residents of Saginaw County, MI.
Application information: Application form required.
  Deadline(s): June 1
Trustee: Citizens Bank.
Number of staff: 2 full-time support.
EIN: 386347006

1547
The Joseph D. Reid Family Charitable Foundation
222 N. Washington Sq., Ste. 210
Lansing, MI 48933

Established in 1996 in MI.
Donors: Joseph D. Reid; Jerry Reid.
Grantmaker type: Independent foundation.
Financial data (yr. ended 12/31/05): Assets, $5,240,148 (M); gifts received, $930,000; expenditures, $275,018; total giving, $255,000; qualifying distributions, $255,000; giving activities include $255,000 for 7 grants (high: $100,000; low: $5,000).
Fields of interest: Libraries (public); Education; Federated giving programs; Roman Catholic agencies & churches.
Type of support: General/operating support.
Limitations: Applications not accepted. Giving primarily in Lansing, MI. No grants to individuals.
Application information: Contributes only to pre-selected organizations.
Officers: Jerry Reid, C.E.O.; Colleen Reid, Pres.
Directors: Brian English; Cristin Reid; Joseph D. Reid; Joseph D. Reid III.
EIN: 383327108
Selected grants: The following grants were reported in 2005.
$100,000 to Saint Vincent Catholic Charity.
$75,000 to United Way.
$50,000 to Capital Regional Community.

$15,000 to Saint Thomas Aquinas Foundation. For Adopt-A-Student.
$5,000 to Lansing Community College, Lansing, MI.
$5,000 to Our Lady of the Snows.
$5,000 to Saint Marys Catholic Church.

1548
Florence M. Rennie Scholarship Trust
c/o Fifth Third Bank
P.O. Box 3636
Grand Rapids, MI   49501-3636
Contact: Kirsten Willis, Chair.
Application address: University of Michigan, 1255 Angell Hall, Ann Arbor, MI 48109

Grantmaker type: Independent foundation.
Financial data (yr. ended 12/31/05): Assets, $290,346 (M); expenditures, $29,190; total giving, $21,056; qualifying distributions, $21,056; giving activities include $21,056 for grants.
Purpose and activities: Scholarships to students of the University of Michigan.
Type of support: Scholarship funds.
Limitations: Giving limited to Ann Arbor, MI.
Application information: Application form required.
Deadline(s): Jan. and Feb.
Officers: Kirsten Willis, Chair.; Harry Marsden, Admin.
Trustee: Fifth Third Bank.
EIN: 386111647

1549
Resnal Foundation
7010 76th St. S.E.
Caledonia, MI   49316   (616) 772-5959
Contact: Peter L. Lanser, Pres.; Janet L. Lanser, Secy.-Treas.

Established in 2000 in MI.
Donors: Peter L. Lanser; Janet L. Lanser.
Grantmaker type: Independent foundation.
Financial data (yr. ended 12/31/04): Assets, $202,361 (M); gifts received, $16,912; expenditures, $18,738; total giving, $17,893; qualifying distributions, $17,893; giving activities include $17,893 for grants.
Purpose and activities: Giving primarily for Christian agencies and churches.
Fields of interest: Christian agencies & churches.
Limitations: Giving primarily in MI; some giving also in NC.
Application information: Application form not required.
Initial approach: Letter
Deadline(s): None
Officers: Peter L. Lanser, Pres.; Janet L. Lanser, Secy.-Treas.
EIN: 383533081

1550
Loraine & Melinese Reuter Foundation
c/o Comerica Bank
P.O. Box 75000 M/C 3302
Detroit, MI   48275-3302
Contact: Scott Frogs
Application address: c/o Comerica Bank, P.O. Box 75000 M/C 9413, Detroit, MI 48275-9416, tel.: (734) 930-2416

Established in 2003 in MI.

Donor: Loraine Reuter Estate Trust.
Grantmaker type: Independent foundation.
Financial data (yr. ended 8/31/05): Assets, $860,403 (M); gifts received, $536,443; expenditures, $30,078; total giving, $15,000; qualifying distributions, $15,000; giving activities include $15,000 for grants.
Purpose and activities: Funding to assist students of music.
Fields of interest: Arts education; Performing arts, music.
Type of support: Grants to individuals.
Application information:
Initial approach: Letter
Deadline(s): None
Trustee: Comerica Bank.
EIN: 201535256

1551
Phyllis and Max Reynolds Foundation
c/o Wells Fargo Bank Michigan, N.A.
P.O. Box 580
Marquette, MI   49855   (906) 228-1244
Contact: Mary Nurmi

Established in 1997 in MI.
Donor: Phyllis M. Reynolds.
Grantmaker type: Independent foundation.
Financial data (yr. ended 12/31/04): Assets, $1,608,317 (M); expenditures, $89,604; total giving, $77,530; qualifying distributions, $77,530; giving activities include $77,530 for grants.
Purpose and activities: Giving for youth and human services, higher and public education, and for recreation.
Fields of interest: Arts; Education; Recreation; Youth development, centers/clubs; Human services; Children/youth, services.
Limitations: Giving primarily in MI.
Application information: Application form required.
Deadline(s): None
Officers and Directors:* Phyllis M. Reynolds,* Chair.; Robert J. Toutant,* Treas.; John F. Marshall; William McDonald; Patricia L. Micklow; Joan R. Miller; Alice M. Reynolds.
EIN: 383354883

1552
Chi Sun Rhee Foundation
811 N. Macomb St.
Monroe, MI   48161

Established in 1984 in MI.
Donors: Chi Sun Rhee; Sung Hi Rhee.
Grantmaker type: Independent foundation.
Financial data (yr. ended 9/30/05): Assets, $104,626 (M); expenditures, $2,915; total giving, $1,800; qualifying distributions, $1,800; giving activities include $1,800 for grants.
Limitations: Applications not accepted. Giving primarily in Toledo, OH. No grants to individuals.
Application information: Contributes only to pre-selected organizations.
Officers: Chi Sun Rhee, Pres.; Hyun A. Rhee Steward, V.P.; Sung Hi Rhee, Secy.-Treas.
Directors: Robert Rhee; Stephan Rhee.
EIN: 382485264

1553
James B. Richardson Trust
c/o Comerica Bank
P.O. Box 75000
Detroit, MI   48275

Established in CA.
Grantmaker type: Independent foundation.
Financial data (yr. ended 12/31/05): Assets, $472,270 (M); expenditures, $25,320; total giving, $20,000; qualifying distributions, $20,000; giving activities include $20,000 for grants.
Purpose and activities: Support only for Cornell University, Ithaca, NY and Santa Cruz City Library, CA.
Fields of interest: Higher education, university; Libraries (public).
Type of support: General/operating support.
Limitations: Applications not accepted. Giving limited to Ithaca, NY and Santa Cruz, CA. No grants to individuals.
Application information: Contributes only to 2 pre-selected organizations specified in the governing instrument.
Trustee: Comerica Bank.
EIN: 946505556

1554
R. Gene and Nancy D. Richter Foundation, Inc.
48741 Wildrose Dr.
Canton, MI   48187-5641

Established in 2003 in MI.
Donor: Nancy D. Richter.
Grantmaker type: Independent foundation.
Financial data (yr. ended 12/31/04): Assets, $430,313 (M); gifts received, $67,280; expenditures, $108,015; total giving, $30,000; qualifying distributions, $30,000; giving activities include $30,000 for grants.
Purpose and activities: The foundation will provide a scholarship of up to $5,000 per year to individuals seeking education and training in the area of Supply Chain Management.
Type of support: Scholarships—to individuals.
Application information: Application form required.
Deadline(s): Feb. 15
Officers and Directors:* Nancy D. Richter,* Pres. and Secy.; Linda J. Obrec, V.P.; Paul J. Staffaroni, Treas.; Kerry Richter; O. Frank Richter.
EIN: 161679880

1555
Rickert Family Foundation
28835 Hidden Trail
Farmington Hills, MI   48331

Established in 2000 in MI.
Donor: Herbert E. Rickert.
Grantmaker type: Independent foundation.
Financial data (yr. ended 12/31/05): Assets, $2,061 (M); gifts received, $100,000; expenditures, $141,999; total giving, $141,000; qualifying distributions, $141,000; giving activities include $141,000 for 24 grants (high: $31,000; low: $500).
Fields of interest: Higher education, university; Human services; Christian agencies & churches.
Limitations: Applications not accepted. Giving primarily in MI. No grants to individuals.

Application information: Contributes only to pre-selected organizations.
Officers and Directors: Herbert E. Rickert,* Pres. and Treas.; Donna J. Rickert,* V.P. and Secy.
EIN: 383525090
Selected grants: The following grants were reported in 2004.
$30,000 to SEND International, Farmington, MI.
$20,000 to Indiana Wesleyan University, Marion, IN.
$16,000 to Community Living Centers, Farmington, MI.
$8,000 to Samaritans Purse, Boone, NC.
$4,000 to Evangelical Presbyterian Church, Livonia, MI.
$4,000 to Grace Centers of Hope, Pontiac, MI.
$3,000 to Detroit Rescue Mission Ministries, Detroit, MI.
$1,000 to Joy of Jesus, Detroit, MI.
$1,000 to World Impact, Los Angeles, CA.
$500 to William Tyndale College, Farmington Hills, MI.

1556
The Nan Jean Riekse Foundation
136 Maple St.
Fruitport, MI 49415

Established in 2002 in MI.
Donor: Nan Jean Riekse.
Grantmaker type: Independent foundation.
Financial data (yr. ended 12/31/03): Assets, $252 (M); expenditures, $50; total giving, $50; qualifying distributions, $50; giving activities include $50 for grants.
Trustee: Nan Jean Riekse.
EIN: 320025267

1557
Philip and Joane Riley Foundation
c/o Lisa A. Perlos
1903 W. Liberty Rd.
Clarklake, MI 49234

Established in 2000 in MI.
Donors: Philip A. Riley, Jr.; Joane Riley.
Grantmaker type: Independent foundation.
Financial data (yr. ended 12/31/05): Assets, $109,732 (M); gifts received, $30,000; expenditures, $31,000; total giving, $31,000; qualifying distributions, $31,000; giving activities include $31,000 for grants.
Fields of interest: Education.
Type of support: General/operating support; Endowments.
Limitations: Applications not accepted. Giving on a national basis. No grants to individuals.
Application information: Contributes only to pre-selected organizations.
Trustee: Lisa A. Perlos.
EIN: 383573766

1558
The Riley Foundation
c/o Comerica Bank
P.O. Box 75000, MC 3302
Detroit, MI 48275-3302
Application address: c/o Comerica Bank, P.O. Box 75000, MC 7806, Detroit, MI 48275

Established in 1998 in MI.

Donors: George Riley; Dolores Riley.
Grantmaker type: Independent foundation.
Financial data (yr. ended 9/30/05): Assets, $8,683,258 (M); expenditures, $1,292,211; total giving, $1,205,427; qualifying distributions, $1,225,334; giving activities include $1,205,427 for 12 grants (high: $1,000,000; low: $300).
Purpose and activities: Giving primarily to a public television station, as well as for human services, community development, and to Roman Catholic organizations and churches.
Fields of interest: Media, television; Higher education; Human services; Community development; Roman Catholic agencies & churches.
Limitations: Giving primarily in MI, with emphasis on Detroit and Farmington. No grants to individuals; or for scholarships.
Application information: Application form not required.
   Deadline(s): None
Board of Managers: Daniel G. Riley; George K. Riley; Michael J. Riley; William D. Riley.
Trustees: Kimberly A. Fouts; Comerica Bank.
EIN: 383439851

1559
Sigurd & Jarmila Rislov Foundation
206 S. Main St., Ste. 218
Ann Arbor, MI 48104
Contact: Sue Ann Savas, Dir.
URL: http://www.rislovfoundation.org

Established in 1998 in MI.
Grantmaker type: Independent foundation.
Financial data (yr. ended 12/31/05): Assets, $1,129,679 (M); expenditures, $131,553; total giving, $103,500; qualifying distributions, $104,550; giving activities include $57,500 for 6 grants (high: $25,000; low: $500), and $46,000 for 22 grants to individuals (high: $4,000; low: $2,000).
Purpose and activities: Giving for classical music in the form of grants to organizations and grant awards to students.
Fields of interest: Performing arts, music; Performing arts, music composition; Performing arts, education.
Type of support: General/operating support; Scholarships—to individuals.
Limitations: Giving on a national basis, with some emphasis on MI and OR.
Application information: See foundation Web site for application requirements. Application form not required.
   Deadline(s): None
   Board meeting date(s): Mar., June, Sept., and Dec.
Officers: Zachary Savas, Pres.; Sue Ann Savas, Secy.; Martha Post, Treas.
EIN: 931247286

1560
River City Foundation
c/o Kenneth Betz
3860 Rector Ave. N.E.
Rockford, MI 49341-7929

Established in 1989 in MI.
Donors: Kenneth Betz; Judy Betz.
Grantmaker type: Independent foundation.

Financial data (yr. ended 11/30/05): Assets, $666,297 (M); gifts received, $105,965; expenditures, $23,065; total giving, $17,500; qualifying distributions, $20,416; giving activities include $17,500 for 16 grants (high: $2,500; low: $1,000).
Limitations: Applications not accepted. Giving primarily in Grand Rapids, MI. No grants to individuals.
Application information: Contributes only to pre-selected organizations.
Officers: Kenneth Betz, Pres.; Judy Betz, Secy.
EIN: 382966996

1561
RJK Foundation
c/o Andrew Camden
685 St. Clair Ave., 2nd Fl.
Grosse Pointe, MI 48230

Established in 1987 in MI.
Donor: Richard J. Kelly.
Grantmaker type: Independent foundation.
Financial data (yr. ended 11/30/05): Assets, $2,251,454 (M); expenditures, $172,464; total giving, $133,000; qualifying distributions, $142,798; giving activities include $133,000 for 3 grants (high: $88,000; low: $20,000).
Purpose and activities: Giving primarily for community foundations.
Fields of interest: Foundations (community).
Limitations: Applications not accepted. Giving primarily in Detroit, MI. No grants to individuals.
Application information: Contributes only to pre-selected organizations.
Officers: Richard J. Kelly, Pres.; Andrew L. Camden, V.P. and Secy.; Nancy Meconi, Treas.
Number of staff: 1 part-time support.
EIN: 382812719
Selected grants: The following grants were reported in 2004.
$81,000 to Community Foundation for Southeastern Michigan, Detroit, MI.
$25,000 to Hazelden Foundation, Center City, MN.
$20,000 to Youth for Tomorrow New Life Center, Bristow, VA.

1562
RNR Foundation, Inc.
3025 Exmoor Rd.
Ann Arbor, MI 48104

Established in 1994 in FL.
Donor: Rhoda Newberry Reed.
Grantmaker type: Independent foundation.
Financial data (yr. ended 7/31/05): Assets, $8,927,554 (M); expenditures, $551,088; total giving, $424,504; qualifying distributions, $465,504; giving activities include $424,504 for 5 grants (high: $197,231; low: $570).
Purpose and activities: Giving primarily for education and health and human services.
Fields of interest: Museums (art); Education; Health care, EMS; Health care; Human services; Foundations (community).
Limitations: Applications not accepted. Giving primarily in FL and MI. No grants to individuals.
Application information: Contributes only to pre-selected organizations.

Officers: David Lord, Pres.; Charles Lord, V.P.; Edith Lord-Wolff, Secy.; Richard Lord, Treas.
EIN: 650539370
Selected grants: The following grants were reported in 2004.
$202,094 to Morton Plant Mease Health Care Foundation, Clearwater, FL. 3 grants: $107,211, $94,425, $458
$40,209 to Rollins College, Winter Park, FL. 2 grants: $40,020 to Public Service Program, $189 to Public Service Program
$15,417 to Jodi House, Santa Barbara, CA.
$15,255 to Ann Arbor Area Community Foundation, Ann Arbor, MI.
$450 to Council on Foundations, DC.

1563
Roan Universal Foundation
20416 Harper Ave.
Harper Woods, MI   48225

Established in 2003 in MI.
Donors: Leland D. Blatt; Tracy A. Blatt.
Grantmaker type: Independent foundation.
Financial data (yr. ended 12/31/05): Assets, $154,033 (M); gifts received, $111,500; expenditures, $25,054; total giving, $25,000; qualifying distributions, $25,000; giving activities include $25,000 for grants.
Limitations: Applications not accepted. No grants to individuals.
Application information: Contributes only to pre-selected organizations.
Officers and Directors:* Brian D. Blatt,* Pres.; Lauren E. Marchal,* V.P.; Tracy A. Blatt,* Secy.; Leland D. Blatt,* Treas.; Callie A. Blatt.
EIN: 200504187

1564
The J. Marshall Robbins Foundation
2641 Indian Mound S.
Bloomfield Hills, MI   48301-2257

Donor: J. Marshall Robbins.
Grantmaker type: Independent foundation.
Financial data (yr. ended 12/31/05): Assets, $90,446 (M); gifts received, $100; expenditures, $4,622; total giving, $4,150; qualifying distributions, $4,150; giving activities include $4,150 for grants.
Limitations: Applications not accepted. Giving primarily in MI. No grants to individuals.
Application information: Contributes only to pre-selected organizations.
Officer: J. Marshall Robbins, Pres.
EIN: 386151483

1565
Frank E. Robbins Memorial Scholarship Fund
c/o Bank of America, N.A.
P.O. Box 1802
Providence, RI   02940-1802
Application address: c/o Augusta Haydock, Bank of America, N.A., 100 Federal St., Boston, MA 02110

Established in MA.
Donor: Edith M. Robbins.
Grantmaker type: Independent foundation.

Financial data (yr. ended 12/31/04): Assets, $931,331 (M); expenditures, $43,828; total giving, $39,045; qualifying distributions, $41,704; giving activities include $39,045 for grants.
Purpose and activities: Scholarship funds to the University of Michigan, Ann Arbor, MI.
Fields of interest: Higher education.
Type of support: Scholarship funds.
Limitations: Giving limited to Ann Arbor, MI.
Application information:
    Initial approach: Letter
    Deadline(s): None
Trustee: Bank of America, N.A.
EIN: 046072097

1566
Robell Foundation
P.O. Box 6367
Grand Rapids, MI   49516-6367

Established in 1997 in MI.
Donors: Robert Ellis; Susan Ellis.
Grantmaker type: Independent foundation.
Financial data (yr. ended 12/31/05): Assets, $273,308 (M); gifts received, $42,000; expenditures, $66,801; total giving, $64,500; qualifying distributions, $64,500; giving activities include $64,500 for grants.
Fields of interest: Elementary/secondary education; Christian agencies & churches.
Type of support: General/operating support; Building/renovation.
Limitations: Applications not accepted. Giving primarily in Grand Rapids, MI; some giving also in FL and WA. No grants to individuals.
Application information: Contributes only to pre-selected organizations.
Officers: Brian R. Ellis, Pres.; Cynthia Ellis Vanscoyk, V.P. and Treas.
Director: Susan Ellis.
EIN: 383386380

1567
The Robideau Foundation, Inc.
153 E. Maumee St.
Adrian, MI   49221-7882

Established in 1978 in MI.
Grantmaker type: Independent foundation.
Financial data (yr. ended 9/30/05): Assets, $1,399,061 (M); gifts received, $100,000; expenditures, $600,000; total giving, $587,574; qualifying distributions, $586,697; giving activities include $587,574 for 21 grants (high: $300,000; low: $300).
Purpose and activities: Giving primarily for Christian churches, education, human services, and YMCAs.
Fields of interest: Arts; Education; Hospitals (general); Human services; Christian agencies & churches.
Limitations: Giving primarily in MI. No grants to individuals.
Officers: James J. Robideau, Pres.; Gladys E. Robideau, V.P. and Secy.; Jeffrey T. Robideau, V.P.; Margaret Jeffery, Treas.
EIN: 382241755

1568
Robinson Family Foundation
2921 10th St.
P.O. Box 23
Bradley, MI   49311

Established in 2001.
Grantmaker type: Independent foundation.
Financial data (yr. ended 12/31/04): Assets, $113,686 (M); gifts received, $5,249; expenditures, $4,484; total giving, $2,500; qualifying distributions, $2,500; giving activities include $2,500 for grants.
Limitations: Applications not accepted. No grants to individuals.
Application information: Contributes only to pre-selected organizations.
Officers: Gregory A. Robinson, Pres.; Kimberly K. Robinson, V.P.
EIN: 383563868

1569
Hattie, Anna and Harley Robinson Foundation
3910 Telegraph Rd., Ste. 200
Bloomfield Hills, MI   48302

Established in 1997 in MI.
Grantmaker type: Independent foundation.
Financial data (yr. ended 12/31/04): Assets, $1,654,696 (M); expenditures, $135,276; total giving, $115,723; qualifying distributions, $115,211; giving activities include $115,723 for 11 + grants (high: $34,600).
Fields of interest: Education; Animals/wildlife; Hospitals (specialty).
Type of support: General/operating support.
Limitations: Applications not accepted. Giving on a national basis, with some emphasis on CA and MI. No grants to individuals.
Application information: Contributes only to pre-selected organizations.
Directors: Denise Dutrow; Jane Hanna; Jeffrey T. Neilson.
EIN: 382646236

1570
Harold & Carolyn Robison Foundation
500 Woodward Ave.
Detroit, MI   48226
Contact: Norma Kumbier, Pres.
Application address: 32918 Vermont St., Livonia, MI 48150, tel.: (734) 422-4084

Established in 1966.
Donor: Harold Robison†.
Grantmaker type: Independent foundation.
Financial data (yr. ended 6/30/05): Assets, $1,552,832 (M); expenditures, $74,614; total giving, $55,500; qualifying distributions, $59,826; giving activities include $55,500 for 25 grants (high: $3,000; low: $1,000).
Fields of interest: Education; Hospitals (general); Food services; Human services.
Type of support: General/operating support; Continuing support; Capital campaigns; Building/ renovation; Equipment; Scholarship funds; Research.
Limitations: Giving primarily in Detroit, MI. No grants to individuals.

Application information: Application form not required.
Initial approach: Letter
Deadline(s): None
Board meeting date(s): Spring and fall
Officers and Trustees: * Norma Kumbier,* Pres. and Treas.; Marcy Carolyn Seymour,* V.P.; Martin C. Oetting, Secy.; George Carter; Daniel Gwinn; Laura Mastracci.
EIN: 386105557

1571
James M. and Louise C. Roche Foundation
c/o Douglas D. Roche
500 Woodward Ave., Ste. 4000
Detroit, MI 48226-3425

Donor: James M. Roche.
Grantmaker type: Independent foundation.
Financial data (yr. ended 12/31/04): Assets, $1,160,672 (M); expenditures, $58,605; total giving, $41,700; qualifying distributions, $49,700; giving activities include $41,700 for grants.
Purpose and activities: Giving to Christian agencies and education.
Fields of interest: Higher education; Education; Health care; Health organizations; Christian agencies & churches; General charitable giving.
Type of support: General/operating support.
Limitations: Applications not accepted. Giving primarily in MI. No grants to individuals.
Application information: Contributes only to pre-selected organizations.
Trustee: Douglas D. Roche.
EIN: 386069143

1572
Rock Foundation
13919 S.W. Bayshore Dr., Ste. G01
Traverse City, MI 49684 (231) 946-8772
Contact: Dale M. Nielson, Tr.

Established in 2001 in MI.
Grantmaker type: Independent foundation.
Financial data (yr. ended 12/31/04): Assets, $6,186,074 (M); gifts received, $6,486,389; expenditures, $35,451; total giving, $27,000; qualifying distributions, $28,292; giving activities include $27,000 for grants.
Purpose and activities: Giving primarily to Christian churches and institutions.
Fields of interest: Education; Health organizations, association; Human services; Christian agencies & churches.
Limitations: Giving on a national basis, with some emphasis on MI.
Application information:
Initial approach: Letter
Deadline(s): None
Trustee: Dale M. Nielson.
EIN: 916526685

1573
George Rockwell Trust
c/o Harper L. Camp
P.O. Box 1907
Midland, MI 48641-1907

Established in 1999 in MI.
Grantmaker type: Independent foundation.

Financial data (yr. ended 12/31/05): Assets, $549,850 (M); expenditures, $25,778; total giving, $25,278; qualifying distributions, $25,778; giving activities include $25,278 for grants.
Fields of interest: Human services; Economically disadvantaged; Homeless.
Limitations: Applications not accepted. Giving primarily in Midland, MI.
Application information: Contributes only to pre-selected organizations.
Officers: Harper L. Camp, Pres. and Treas.; Herbert Camp, V.P.; John Riecker, V.P.; Virginia Dorrien, Secy.
EIN: 386064436

1574
The Rodney Fund
19100 W. 8 Mile Rd.
Southfield, MI 48075-5726
Contact: James M. Rodney, Pres.

Established in 1992 in MI.
Donor: James M. Rodney.
Grantmaker type: Independent foundation.
Financial data (yr. ended 12/31/05): Assets, $8,555,580 (M); gifts received, $1,007,551; expenditures, $667,894; total giving, $631,281; qualifying distributions, $631,281; giving activities include $631,281 for 33 grants (high: $131,100; low: $1,000).
Purpose and activities: Giving primarily for public affairs institutes and centers. The fund supports libertarian principles: limited government, private property, free markets, individual liberty, free trade, and rule by law, as established by the U.S. Constitution.
Fields of interest: Education, research; Higher education; Education; Employment, public policy; Human services; Federated giving programs; Social sciences; Public affairs.
Limitations: Giving on a national basis.
Application information:
Initial approach: Letter
Deadline(s): None
Officer and Directors: * James M. Rodney,* Pres.; Lawrence Reed; Leigh Rodney; Steven Thomas.
EIN: 383030437

1575
Otto & Helen Roethke Scholarship Fund
c/o Citizens Bank, Wealth Mgmt.
101 N. Washington Ave.
Saginaw, MI 48607
Application address: c/o Mercedes Perez, Selection Comm., 3115 Mackinaw, Saginaw, MI 48602, tel.: (989) 797-4815

Established in 1999 in MI.
Donor: Otto Roethke‡.
Grantmaker type: Independent foundation.
Financial data (yr. ended 7/31/05): Assets, $121,348 (M); expenditures, $8,440; total giving, $5,400; qualifying distributions, $7,786; giving activities include $5,400 for 1 grant to an individual.
Purpose and activities: Scholarships awarded to Arthur Hill High School students attending the University of Michigan; preference given to students majoring in English.
Type of support: Scholarships—to individuals.
Limitations: Giving limited to residents of Saginaw, MI.

Application information: Application form required.
Deadline(s): May 1
Trustee: Citizens Bank.
EIN: 386720940

1576
Wendell & Doris Rogers Charitable Foundation
500 Woodward Ave., Ste. 3500
Detroit, MI 48226-3435 (313) 965-8417

Established in 1997 in MI.
Donors: Doris Rogers; Wendell Rogers.
Grantmaker type: Independent foundation.
Financial data (yr. ended 12/31/05): Assets, $454,041 (M); expenditures, $105,528; total giving, $100,000; qualifying distributions, $100,000; giving activities include $100,000 for grants.
Purpose and activities: Support only for the American Diabetes Association, MI.
Fields of interest: Diabetes.
Type of support: General/operating support.
Limitations: Applications not accepted. Giving limited to Bingham Farms, MI. No grants to individuals.
Application information: Contributes only to a pre-selected organization.
Officers: Wendell Rogers, Pres.; Doris Rogers, Secy.-Treas.
EIN: 383383862

1577
The Robert G. Rogers and Jane E. Rogers Family Foundation, Inc.
3 Sovereign Dr.
Bay City, MI 48708

Established in 1998 in MI.
Grantmaker type: Independent foundation.
Financial data (yr. ended 12/31/05): Assets, $10,939 (M); expenditures, $1,671; total giving, $1,650; qualifying distributions, $1,650; giving activities include $1,650 for grants.
Fields of interest: Education.
Type of support: General/operating support.
Limitations: Applications not accepted. Giving primarily in Bay City, MI. No grants to individuals.
Application information: Contributes only to pre-selected organizations.
Officers: Robert G. Rogers, Pres. and Treas.; Jane E. Rogers, V.P. and Secy.
Trustees: Adam M. Rogers; Alexander J. Rogers; Erin L. Rogers.
EIN: 043436740

1578
Edward and Elyse Rogers Family Foundation
5809 Windy Gyle
Midland, MI 48640-6945 (989) 631-8621
Contact: Elyse M. Rogers, Pres.
FAX: (989) 839-9393;
E-mail: rogersfoundation@aol.com

Established in 2002 in MI.
Donors: Elyse M. Rogers; Edward W. Rogers.
Grantmaker type: Independent foundation.
Financial data (yr. ended 12/31/04): Assets, $122,165 (M); gifts received, $16,720;

expenditures, $15,284; total giving, $14,252; qualifying distributions, $14,198; giving activities include $14,252 for grants.
Limitations: Applications not accepted.
Application information: Contributes only to pre-selected organizations.
Officers: Elyse M. Rogers,* Pres.; Edward W. Rogers, Treas.
Directors: Pamela Butcher; Cynthia Tate; Jenifer Rogers.
EIN: 611411391

1579
S. Dennis and Leslie L. Rogers Foundation Corporation
32400 Telegraph Rd., No. 202
Bingham Farms, MI 48025-2460

Established in 1986 in MI.
Donors: S. Dennis Rogers; Leslie L. Rogers; Darryl Rogers.
Grantmaker type: Independent foundation.
Financial data (yr. ended 12/31/05): Assets, $540,570 (M); gifts received, $1,000,000; expenditures, $1,013,127; total giving, $1,008,787; qualifying distributions, $1,009,327; giving activities include $1,008,787 for 31 grants (high: $1,000,000; low: $15).
Fields of interest: Arts; Higher education, university; Education; Health organizations, association; Cancer research; Human services; Children/youth, services; Jewish agencies & temples.
Limitations: Applications not accepted. Giving primarily in MI. No grants to individuals.
Application information: Contributes only to pre-selected organizations.
Officers: S. Dennis Rogers, Pres. and Treas.; Leslie L. Rogers, V.P. and Secy.
Directors: Darryl Rogers; Irvin Rogers.
EIN: 382710391

1580
Charles A. Rogers Testamentary Trust
7175 Lindenmere Dr.
Bloomfield, MI 48301-3527

Grantmaker type: Independent foundation.
Financial data (yr. ended 12/31/05): Assets, $343,747; expenditures, $29,028; total giving, $23,671; qualifying distributions, $23,671; giving activities include $23,671 for grants.
Purpose and activities: Support only for the Friends School, Detroit, and Hillsdale College, MI.
Fields of interest: Secondary school/education; Higher education.
Limitations: Applications not accepted. Giving limited to Detroit and Hillsdale, MI. No grants to individuals.
Application information: Contributes only to 2 pre-selected organizations.
Trustee: William D. Belski.
EIN: 386434903

1581
Sigmund and Sophie Rohlik Foundation
2025 W. Long Lake Rd., Ste. 100
Troy, MI 48098-4100

Established in 1956 in MI.
Donors: Sigmund Rohlik†; Sophie Rohlik.

Grantmaker type: Independent foundation.
Financial data (yr. ended 6/30/05): Assets, $2,540,248 (M); expenditures, $163,544; total giving, $111,050; qualifying distributions, $119,808; giving activities include $111,050 for 43 grants (high: $20,000; low: $250).
Purpose and activities: Giving primarily to Jewish organizations.
Fields of interest: Human services; Jewish federated giving programs; Jewish agencies & temples.
Limitations: Applications not accepted. Giving primarily in MI. No grants to individuals.
Application information: Contributes only to pre-selected organizations.
Officers and Trustees:* Charles L. Levin,* Pres.; David Hertzberg,* V.P.; Richard A. Polk, Secy.; Paul P. Baker, Treas.; Joseph Levin; Bernard H. Stollman; Helene N. White.
EIN: 386056443

1582
Rolka Scholarship Foundation
c/o James L. Rolka
1619 Van Geisen Rd.
Caro, MI 48723-1344

Donor: James Rolka.
Grantmaker type: Independent foundation.
Financial data (yr. ended 12/31/04): Assets, $383,658 (M); expenditures, $18,000; total giving, $18,000; qualifying distributions, $18,000; giving activities include $18,000 for grants.
Type of support: Scholarships—to individuals.
Limitations: Applications not accepted.
Application information: Unsolicited requests for funds not accepted.
Officers: James L. Rolka, Pres.; Paul Langlois, V.P.; Cindie Dubs, Secy.-Treas.
Directors: Gary R. Anderson; Gary J. Crews.
EIN: 383448069

1583
Jack and Lija Romence Family Foundation
2654 Shadowbrook Dr. S.E.
Grand Rapids, MI 49546-7460

Donors: Jack L. Romence; Lija Romence.
Grantmaker type: Independent foundation.
Financial data (yr. ended 12/31/05): Assets, $12,853 (M); gifts received, $20,250; expenditures, $17,859; total giving, $16,950; qualifying distributions, $16,950; giving activities include $16,950 for grants.
Limitations: Applications not accepted. No grants to individuals.
Application information: Contributes only to pre-selected organizations.
Trustees: Jack L. Romence; Lija Romence.
EIN: 383147551

1584
The Roney Foundation
1075 Timberlake Dr.
Bloomfield Hills, MI 48302

Grantmaker type: Independent foundation.
Financial data (yr. ended 12/31/05): Assets, $408,361 (M); expenditures, $21,100; total giving,

$18,325; qualifying distributions, $18,325; giving activities include $18,325 for grants.
Purpose and activities: Giving primarily to Christian organizations and churches; support also for health and human services.
Fields of interest: Education, services; Hospitals (general); Human services; Christian agencies & churches.
Limitations: Applications not accepted. Giving primarily in MI. No grants to individuals.
Application information: Contributes only to pre-selected organizations.
Officers: William C. Roney, Jr., Pres.; Catherine Roney, V.P.; William C. Roney III, Secy.; Brian Roney, Treas.
EIN: 386091222

1585
The Joseph and Rose Rontal Foundation
28300 Orchard Lake Rd., Ste. 100
Farmington Hills, MI 48334

Established in 1993 in MI.
Donors: Joseph Rontal†; Robert A. Karbel.
Grantmaker type: Independent foundation.
Financial data (yr. ended 3/31/05): Assets, $509,455 (M); expenditures, $25,402; total giving, $22,745; qualifying distributions, $22,745; giving activities include $22,745 for grants.
Fields of interest: Medical school/education; Ear & throat diseases; Jewish agencies & temples.
Type of support: General/operating support.
Limitations: Applications not accepted. Giving primarily in Ann Arbor, MI. No grants to individuals.
Application information: Contributes only to pre-selected organizations.
Officer: Robert A. Karbel, Mgr.
Directors: Eugene Rontal; Michael Rontal.
EIN: 383106698

1586
Pierson J. Roon Family Foundation
11355 Ripple Dr.
P.O. Box 86
Allendale, MI 49401
Contact: Pierson J. Roon, Dir.

Established in 2000 in MI.
Donors: Idamarie Roon; Pierson J. Roon.
Grantmaker type: Independent foundation.
Financial data (yr. ended 10/31/05): Assets, $623,636 (M); expenditures, $31,218; total giving, $31,000; qualifying distributions, $31,000; giving activities include $31,000 for grants.
Fields of interest: Education; Religion.
Application information:
  Initial approach: Letter
  Deadline(s): None
Directors: Idamarie Roon; Pierson J. Roon.
EIN: 383628676

1587
Ropp Foundation
1314 Long Lake Dr.
Brighton, MI 48114-9639

Established in 2000 in MI.
Grantmaker type: Independent foundation.
Financial data (yr. ended 12/31/05): Assets, $621 (M); expenditures, $70; total giving, $50; qualifying

distributions, $70; giving activities include $50 for grants.
Limitations: Giving primarily in Akron, PA.
Officer: Leland Ropp, Pres. and Treas.
Trustees: Daron C. Showalter; H.D. Hollins Showalter.
EIN: 383542802

1588
The Rordor Foundation
P.O. Box 202
Grand Rapids, MI   49501

Established in 1983 in MI.
Donors: Donald O. Roskam; Robert O. Roskam; Harold Zeigler Chrysler; Don Roskam†; Bakers Food.
Grantmaker type: Independent foundation.
Financial data (yr. ended 12/31/04): Assets, $812,618 (M); gifts received, $525,469; expenditures, $823,908; total giving, $823,559; qualifying distributions, $823,419; giving activities include $823,559 for 23 grants (high: $500,000; low: $1,000).
Purpose and activities: Giving primarily for health, education, Christian organizations, and human services.
Fields of interest: Higher education; Education; Hospitals (general); Cancer; Health organizations; Human services; Christian agencies & churches.
Limitations: Applications not accepted. Giving limited to Grand Rapids, MI. No grants to individuals.
Application information: Contributes only to pre-selected organizations.
Officers: Robert O. Roskam, Pres.
EIN: 382500050

1589
Carl F. & Donna M. Rose Family Foundation
1976 S. Telegraph Rd.
Bloomfield Hills, MI   48302

Established in 2001 in MI.
Donors: Carl F. Rose; Donna M. Rose.
Grantmaker type: Independent foundation.
Financial data (yr. ended 12/31/05): Assets, $156,110 (M); gifts received, $10,000; expenditures, $8,858; total giving, $7,495; qualifying distributions, $7,495; giving activities include $7,495 for grants.
Purpose and activities: Giving primarily for Protestant churches.
Fields of interest: Protestant agencies & churches.
Limitations: Giving primarily in FL and MI. No grants to individuals.
Officers: Carl F. Rose, Pres.; Donna M. Rose, V.P.
EIN: 383547473

1590
The Bruce H. and Rosalie N. Rosen Family Foundation
38200 Amrhein St.
Livonia, MI   48150

Established in 1994 in MI.
Donors: Bruce H. Rosen; Rosalie N. Rosen.
Grantmaker type: Independent foundation.
Financial data (yr. ended 12/31/04): Assets, $2,076,129 (M); gifts received, $420,537; expenditures, $181,878; total giving, $162,252;

qualifying distributions, $162,252; giving activities include $162,252 for 22 grants (high: $30,000; low: $500).
Fields of interest: Higher education; Hospitals (general); Health organizations, association; Jewish federated giving programs; Jewish agencies & temples.
Limitations: Applications not accepted. No grants to individuals.
Application information: Contributes only to pre-selected organizations.
Officers and Trustees:* Bruce H. Rosen,* Pres. and Treas.; Rosalie N. Rosen,* Secy.; Joel S. Golden; Pam Roberts; Julie Weiner.
EIN: 383161453

1591
Ann & Mike Rosenthal Family Foundation
(formerly Rosenthal Family Foundation)
1225 Stuyvesant Rd.
Bloomfield Hills, MI   48301

Established in 1986 in MI.
Donors: Ann Rosenthal; Marvin Rosenthal.
Grantmaker type: Independent foundation.
Financial data (yr. ended 10/31/05): Assets, $1,355,203 (M); expenditures, $93,246; total giving, $93,226; qualifying distributions, $93,226; giving activities include $93,226 for grants.
Purpose and activities: Giving to human services, health associations and youth development.
Fields of interest: Arts; Zoos/zoological societies; Health organizations, association; Human services; Federated giving programs; Jewish federated giving programs; Jewish agencies & temples.
Limitations: Applications not accepted. Giving primarily in MI. No grants to individuals.
Application information: Contributes only to pre-selected organizations.
Officers and Directors:* Ann Rosenthal,* Pres.; Rochelle Forester,* V.P.; James Rosenthal,* Secy.
EIN: 382702954

1592
The Rosenzweig Coopersmith Foundation
c/o Vanderwerff Law Office PC, Robert VanDongen
2666 Capilano Dr., S.E.
Grand Rapids, MI   49546-5517

Established in 1997 in MI.
Donors: Dora Rosenzweig; Leonard Rosenzweig.
Grantmaker type: Independent foundation.
Financial data (yr. ended 12/31/04): Assets, $11,865,577 (M); expenditures, $487,362; total giving, $446,050; qualifying distributions, $477,213; giving activities include $446,050 for 18 grants (high: $75,500; low: $1,000).
Purpose and activities: Support primarily for Jewish organizations.
Fields of interest: Jewish federated giving programs; Jewish agencies & temples.
Limitations: Applications not accepted. Giving on a national basis. No grants to individuals.
Application information: Contributes only to pre-selected organizations.
Officer: Robert Van Dongen, Mgr.
Trustees: Monica Armour; Suzanne Fenster; Harry Rosenzweig; Herschel Rosenzweig; Joseph Rosenzweig.
EIN: 383393545

1593
Arthur & Honoria Roshak Foundation
80 Lakeshore Dr.
Grosse Pointe Farms, MI   48236

Established in 2000 in MI.
Donors: Arthur J. Roshak; Honoria Roshak.
Grantmaker type: Independent foundation.
Financial data (yr. ended 12/31/05): Assets, $248,348 (M); expenditures, $19,515; total giving, $17,565; qualifying distributions, $18,010; giving activities include $17,565 for grants.
Limitations: Applications not accepted. No grants to individuals.
Application information: Contributes only to pre-selected organizations.
Officers: Arthur J. Roshak, Pres. and Treas.; Honoria Roshak, Secy.
Directors: Barbara Bucko; Cheryl Roshak.
EIN: 383505346

1594
Sydney and Elizabeth Ross Family Foundation
3045 Chestnut Run
Bloomfield Township, MI   48302

Established in 2002.
Donors: Elizabeth Ross; Sydney L. Ross.
Grantmaker type: Independent foundation.
Financial data (yr. ended 12/31/04): Assets, $396,767 (M); gifts received, $100,000; expenditures, $40,000; total giving, $0; qualifying distributions, $0.
Officers: Sydney L. Ross, Pres.; Elizabeth Ross, Secy.
EIN: 743070613

1595
Grace P. Ross Foundation
c/o JPMorgan Chase Bank, N.A.
111 E. Wisconsin Ave., Ste. 940
Milwaukee, WI   53202

Established in MI.
Grantmaker type: Independent foundation.
Financial data (yr. ended 12/31/05): Assets, $594,282 (M); expenditures, $32,832; total giving, $24,326; qualifying distributions, $28,525; giving activities include $24,326 for grants.
Purpose and activities: Support only for the Humane Society of Southwestern MI.
Fields of interest: Animal welfare.
Type of support: General/operating support.
Limitations: Applications not accepted. Giving limited to Benton Harbor, MI. No grants to individuals.
Application information: Contributes only to a pre-selected organization.
Trustee: JPMorgan Chase Bank, N.A.
EIN: 386040221

1596
Rosso Family Foundation
1122 Cole St.
Birmingham, MI   48009

Established in 1986 in MI.
Donors: John M. Rosso; William A. Rosso; Linda Rosso.

Grantmaker type: Independent foundation.
Financial data (yr. ended 11/30/05): Assets, $967,575 (M); expenditures, $64,242; total giving, $62,500; qualifying distributions, $62,500; giving activities include $62,500 for grants.
Fields of interest: Museums (history); Libraries (public); Education; Health care; YM/YWCAs & YM/YWHAs; Children/youth, services; Community development; Federated giving programs.
Limitations: Applications not accepted. Giving primarily in Bellaire, Birmingham, Eastport, and Oxford, MI. No grants to individuals.
Application information: Contributes only to pre-selected organizations.
Trustee: John M. Rosso.
EIN: 386510662

1597
Thomas and Nancy Rost Foundation, Ltd.
1208 Copperwood Dr.
Bloomfield Hills, MI   48302-1926

Established in 2002 in MI.
Donor: Thomas F. Rost.
Grantmaker type: Independent foundation.
Financial data (yr. ended 12/31/04): Assets, $18,855 (M); gifts received, $30,000; expenditures, $16,465; total giving, $16,465; qualifying distributions, $16,463; giving activities include $16,465 for 17 grants (high: $3,000; low: $65).
Fields of interest: Christian agencies & churches.
Limitations: Applications not accepted. No grants to individuals.
Application information: Contributes only to pre-selected organizations.
Officers and Directors:* Thomas F. Rost,* Pres. and Treas.; David M. Thoms, V.P.; Nancy L. Rost,* Secy.
EIN: 383328273

1598
A. Frank and Dorothy B. Rothschild Fund
37 Mountain Meadow Dr.
Woodside, CA   94062

Established in 1952 in IL.
Donor: Dorothy B. Rothschild.
Grantmaker type: Independent foundation.
Financial data (yr. ended 12/31/04): Assets, $2,812,460 (M); expenditures, $110,459; total giving, $103,300; qualifying distributions, $107,593; giving activities include $103,300 for 39 grants (high: $25,000; low: $100).
Purpose and activities: Giving primarily for health care and various medical disciplines.
Fields of interest: Arts; Education; Environment; Animals/wildlife, preservation/protection; Hospitals (general); Health care; Health organizations, association; Human services; Jewish agencies & temples.
Limitations: Applications not accepted. Giving primarily in IL, MI, and NY. No grants to individuals.
Application information: Contributes only to pre-selected organizations.
Officers: A. Frank Rothschild, Jr., V.P. and Treas.; David N. Rothschild, V.P.; Holly B. Rothschild, V.P.; Lee J. Strauss, Jr., V.P.; Henry DeVos Lawrie, Jr., Secy.
EIN: 366049231

1599
Rotter Family Foundation
c/o Harriet B. Rotter
24265 Bingham Ct.
Bingham Farms, MI   48025-3420

Established in 2002 in MI.
Donors: Norman J. Rotter; Harriet B. Rotter.
Grantmaker type: Independent foundation.
Financial data (yr. ended 12/31/05): Assets, $45,218 (M); gifts received, $37,274; expenditures, $26,626; total giving, $24,270; qualifying distributions, $24,270; giving activities include $24,270 for grants.
Limitations: Applications not accepted. No grants to individuals.
Application information: Contributes only to pre-selected organizations.
Officers and Directors:* Harriet B. Rotter,* Pres. and Treas.; Norman J. Rotter,* V.P. and Secy.; David Rotter; Michael Rotter; Steven Rotter.
EIN: 300051699

1600
Rottman Family Charitable Foundation
(formerly Fritz and Carol Rottman Charitable Foundation)
11300 Hart St. N.E.
Greenville, MI   48838

Established in 2000 in MI.
Donors: Francis M. Rottman; Carol J. Rottman.
Grantmaker type: Independent foundation.
Financial data (yr. ended 12/31/04): Assets, $342,123 (M); gifts received, $190,000; expenditures, $20,220; total giving, $5,000; qualifying distributions, $5,000; giving activities include $5,000 for grants.
Limitations: Applications not accepted. No grants to individuals.
Application information: Contributes only to pre-selected organizations.
Officers: Francis M. Rottman, Pres.; Carol J. Rottman, Secy.-Treas.
EIN: 383566006

1601
Rowan Foundation
c/o R. Desmond Rowan
5296 Arbor Bay Dr.
Brighton, MI   48116-7779

Established in 1992 in MI.
Donor: R. Desmond Rowan.
Grantmaker type: Independent foundation.
Financial data (yr. ended 12/31/04): Assets, $96,046 (M); expenditures, $20,581; total giving, $20,500; qualifying distributions, $20,581; giving activities include $20,500 for grants.
Fields of interest: Arts; Higher education; Human services.
Limitations: Applications not accepted. Giving limited to MI. No grants to individuals.
Application information: Contributes only to pre-selected organizations.
Officers and Directors:* R. Desmond Rowan,* Pres.; Joanne P. Rowan,* Secy.-Treas.; John W. Rowan; Pamela Rowan Sparks.
EIN: 383031254

1602
The Robert D. Rowan Foundation
18868 Warwick St.
Beverly Hills, MI   48025-4069

Grantmaker type: Independent foundation.
Financial data (yr. ended 12/31/05): Assets, $34,482 (M); expenditures, $5,532; total giving, $5,000; qualifying distributions, $5,000; giving activities include $5,000 for grants.
Limitations: Applications not accepted. Giving limited to MI. No grants to individuals.
Application information: Contributes only to pre-selected organizations.
Officers and Directors:* Richard P. Rowan,* Pres. and Treas.; Ruth A. Rowan,* Secy.
EIN: 386048912

1603
May Mitchell Royal Foundation
c/o Comerica Bank
P.O. Box 75000, MC 3302
Detroit, MI   48275
Application address: c/o Richard Hartley, 11735 Quail Village Way, Naples, FL 34119-8802

Established in 1981 in MI.
Donor: May Mitchell Royal Trust.
Grantmaker type: Independent foundation.
Financial data (yr. ended 9/30/05): Assets, $2,793,961 (M); expenditures, $209,529; total giving, $155,530; qualifying distributions, $177,091; giving activities include $155,530 for 12 grants (high: $26,800; low: $2,500).
Purpose and activities: Giving for the research and treatment of cancer, vision, and heart disease; support also for hospital equipment and nursing training.
Fields of interest: Higher education, university; Hospitals (general); Cancer; Eye diseases; Heart & circulatory diseases; Eye research.
Type of support: Equipment; Scholarship funds; Research.
Limitations: Giving primarily in FL, HI, and MI. No grants to individuals.
Application information: Application form required.
   Initial approach: Letter
   Deadline(s): May 30
Grants Committee: Richard O. Hartley, Chair.; Susan J. Hartley; Michael Kennerly; Ruth Lishman.
Trustee: Comerica Bank.
EIN: 382387140

1604
Royal Oak Foundation for Public Education
3070 Normandy Rd.
Royal Oak, MI   48073

Established in 1995.
Grantmaker type: Independent foundation.
Financial data (yr. ended 12/31/04): Assets, $0 (M); gifts received, $4,835; expenditures, $37,944; total giving, $17,098; qualifying distributions, $17,098; giving activities include $9,589 for 3 grants (high: $7,589; low: $1,000), and $7,509 for 38 grants to individuals (high: $1,195; low: $50).
Purpose and activities: Giving to the Royal Oak public school system, including grants to teachers for educational projects in the teachers' classrooms.

Fields of interest: Elementary/secondary education.
Type of support: General/operating support; Grants to individuals.
Limitations: Applications not accepted. Giving limited to Royal Oak, MI.
Application information: Unsolicited request for funds not accepted.
Officers and Trustees:* Fred Meinberg,* Chair.; Gary Houck,* Vice-Chair.; Stan Harris,* Secy.; Tom Zamberlan,* Treas.; Anne Hoyt.
EIN: 383147156

1605
Ruch Family Foundation
975 Sunflower Ct.
Holland, MI   49424

Established in 1997 in MI.
Donors: Patricia L. Ruch; Richard H. Ruch.
Grantmaker type: Independent foundation.
Financial data (yr. ended 12/31/05): Assets, $1,948,740 (M); expenditures, $97,036; total giving, $95,000; qualifying distributions, $95,000; giving activities include $95,000 for grants.
Purpose and activities: Giving for education, human services, and religious organizations.
Fields of interest: Education; Human services; Religion.
Limitations: Applications not accepted. Giving primarily in MI. No grants to individuals.
Application information: Contributes only to pre-selected organizations.
Officers: Richard H. Ruch, Pres. and Secy.-Treas.; Patricia L. Ruch, V.P.
Directors: Christine M. Ruch; Douglas C. Ruch; Michael D. Ruch; Richard S. Ruch.
EIN: 383345296

1606
The Rita G. Rudel Foundation
81 Cross Ridge Rd.
Chappaqua, NY   10514-2117   (914) 238-6428
Application address: c/o International Neuropsychological Society, 700 Ackerman Rd., Ste. 550, Columbus, OH 43202

Established in 1985 in NY.
Donor: Julius Rudel.
Grantmaker type: Independent foundation.
Financial data (yr. ended 12/31/05): Assets, $12,492 (M); gifts received, $10,000; expenditures, $1,058; total giving, $0; qualifying distributions, $0.
Purpose and activities: Grants awards paid to the university for an individuals research in fields related to childhood neurological and neuropsychological disorders, including developmental disabilities, and for training programs educating professionals in the care and guidance of such children.
Fields of interest: Neuroscience research.
Type of support: Research; Grants to individuals.
Limitations: Giving primarily in IL and MI.
Publications: Application guidelines.
Application information: Applicants must hold a Ph.D. or M.D. degree and should be in post-doctoral or at mid-career at the time of application. Awards not granted to persons holding tenure.
Initial approach: Letter or proposal
Deadline(s): May 31

Trustees: Martha Bridge Denckla, M.D.; Darryl DeVivo, M.D.; Madelene R. Grant; Rita Haggerty; Bettyann Kevles, Ph.D.; Rose Lynn Sherr, Ph.D.; Lewis P. Rowland, M.D.; Anthony J. Rudel; Kristy W. Rudel; Paula Tallal, Ph.D.; Joan R. Weinreich, Ph.D.; John R. Weinreich, Ph.D.; Ralph Wharton, M.D.
EIN: 133262903

1607
Rudlaff Family Foundation
263 Horizon St.
White Lake, MI   48386
Contact: John Rudzewicz
Application address: P.O. Box 5004, Southfield, MI 48086-5004, tel.: (248) 355-1040

Established in 1997 in MI.
Donor: F. Richard Rudlaff III.
Grantmaker type: Independent foundation.
Financial data (yr. ended 12/31/05): Assets, $9,698 (M); expenditures, $9,910; total giving, $8,250; qualifying distributions, $8,250; giving activities include $8,250 for grants.
Fields of interest: Youth, services.
Type of support: General/operating support.
Limitations: Giving primarily in MI. No grants to individuals.
Application information:
Initial approach: Letter
Deadline(s): None
Officer and Trustee:* F. Richard Rudlaff III,* Pres.
EIN: 383391369

1608
Clara A. Ruf Scholarship Trust
207 S. Saginaw St.
St. Charles, MI   48655

Established in 1985 in MI.
Grantmaker type: Independent foundation.
Financial data (yr. ended 12/31/05): Assets, $88,621 (M); gifts received, $235; expenditures, $4,547; total giving, $4,000; qualifying distributions, $4,000; giving activities include $4,000 for grants to individuals.
Purpose and activities: Scholarship awards to graduates of St. Charles High School, MI.
Fields of interest: Higher education.
Type of support: Scholarships—to individuals.
Limitations: Giving limited to the St. Charles, MI, area.
Application information: Application form not required.
Initial approach: Letter
Deadline(s): Varies
Officers: Robert F. Loomis,* Chair.; Anne Marie Loubert, Secy.; Kathy Borough, Treas.
Trustees: Arthur E. Fields; Doris A. Loomis; Michael Olson.
EIN: 382587560

1609
The Ruffner Foundation
c/o Peter E. Ruffner
615 Griswold St., Ste. 1400
Detroit, MI   48226-3993

Established in 1982 in MI.
Donors: Frederick G. Ruffner; Mary E. Ruffner.
Grantmaker type: Independent foundation.

Financial data (yr. ended 12/31/05): Assets, $99,341 (M); gifts received, $10,000; expenditures, $37,725; total giving, $33,000; qualifying distributions, $33,000; giving activities include $33,000 for 5 grants (high: $25,000; low: $1,000).
Fields of interest: Libraries/library science; Community development.
Limitations: Applications not accepted. Giving primarily in MI, with some emphasis on Grosse Pointe. No grants to individuals.
Application information: Contributes only to pre-selected organizations.
Officer: Frederick G. Ruffner, Jr., Pres.
Director: Mary E. Ruffner.
Trustees: Catherine Parrot Ruffner; Frederick G. Ruffner III; Peter E. Ruffner.
EIN: 382416462

1610
Rukibai & Rijhumal Foundation
4087 W. Maple Rd.
Bloomfield Hills, MI   48301-3100

Established in 1999 in MI.
Donor: Dayal R. Gopwani.
Grantmaker type: Independent foundation.
Financial data (yr. ended 12/31/04): Assets, $162,824 (M); expenditures, $126,368; total giving, $124,408; qualifying distributions, $124,393; giving activities include $124,408 for grants.
Purpose and activities: Giving to support disadvantaged communities in India.
Fields of interest: Community development.
International interests: India.
Type of support: General/operating support.
Limitations: Applications not accepted. Giving primarily in India. No grants to individuals.
Application information: Contributes only to pre-selected organizations.
Officers and Directors:* Dayal R. Gopwani,* Pres. and Treas.; Kailash Gurnani,* V.P.; Troy Lindsey,* Secy.; Vineeta D. Gopwani.
EIN: 383494291

1611
The John Rusch Family Scholarship
126 W. Chicago Rd.
Sturgis, MI   49091   (269) 651-7861
Contact: Donald S. Eaton, Tr.

Established in 1994 in MI.
Grantmaker type: Independent foundation.
Financial data (yr. ended 4/30/05): Assets, $25,308 (M); expenditures, $11,908; total giving, $10,500; qualifying distributions, $10,500; giving activities include $10,500 for grants to individuals.
Purpose and activities: Scholarships awarded annually to graduates of Mason High School, Mason, MI.
Type of support: Scholarships—to individuals.
Limitations: Giving limited to residents in Mason, MI.
Application information:
Initial approach: Letter
Deadline(s): May
Trustee: Donald S. Eaton.
EIN: 386635264

1612
Herman Russell Foundation
c/o Comerica Bank
P.O. Box 75000, MC 3302
Detroit, MI 48275-3302
Contact: Herman Russell, Tr.
Application address: 504 Fair St. S.W., Atlanta, GA
30313-1206

Donor: Herman Russell.
Grantmaker type: Independent foundation.
Financial data (yr. ended 12/31/05): Assets,
$61,158 (M); expenditures, $3,250; total giving,
$0; qualifying distributions, $500.
Fields of interest: Higher education; Human
services; Christian agencies & churches.
Limitations: Giving primarily in Atlanta and Marietta,
GA.
Application information:
Initial approach: Letter
Deadline(s): None
Trustee: Herman Russell.
EIN: 586343476

1613
Dorothy M. Russell Medical Education Fund
c/o Comerica Bank
P.O. Box 75000, M/C 3302
Detroit, MI 48275-3302

Established in 1994 in MI.
Grantmaker type: Independent foundation.
Financial data (yr. ended 12/31/04): Assets,
$426,764 (M); expenditures, $20,658; total giving,
$14,000; qualifying distributions, $16,905; giving
activities include $14,000 for grants.
Limitations: Applications not accepted. Giving
primarily in MI. No grants to individuals.
Application information: Contributes only to
pre-selected organizations.
Trustee: Comerica Bank.
EIN: 386644248

1614
Ryals Foundation
2018 Caniff St.
Flint, MI 48504

Established in 2002 in MI.
Grantmaker type: Independent foundation.
Financial data (yr. ended 12/31/04): Assets,
$1,109 (M); gifts received, $1,822; expenditures,
$805; total giving, $0; qualifying distributions, $0.
Trustees: Kassondra Ryals; Marqueretta Ryals;
Patrick L. Ryals, Sr.
EIN: 383639184

1615
James R. Ryan Family Foundation
c/o James R. Ryan, M.D.
9420 Whim Trail
Richland, MI 49083-9594

Established in 1999 in MI.
Donor: James R. Ryan, M.D.
Grantmaker type: Independent foundation.
Financial data (yr. ended 12/31/05): Assets,
$191,649 (M); gifts received, $10,000;
expenditures, $10,669; total giving, $10,000;

qualifying distributions, $10,000; giving activities
include $10,000 for grants.
Purpose and activities: Giving primarily for the arts,
and education.
Fields of interest: Museums (art); Performing arts,
orchestra (symphony); Higher education.
Limitations: Applications not accepted. Giving
primarily in MI. No grants to individuals.
Application information: Contributes only to
pre-selected organizations.
Officer: James R. Ryan, M.D., Pres.
Directors: Deborah Ryan; Thomas G. Ryan.
EIN: 383495184

1616
Edward J. Sackerson Charitable Foundation
P.O. Box 716
Escanaba, MI 49829
Contact: Matt N. Smith, Jr., Tr.
Tel.: (906) 786-0220, ext. 112

Established in 1997 in MI.
Donor: Edward J. Sackerson.
Grantmaker type: Independent foundation.
Financial data (yr. ended 12/31/04): Assets,
$4,794,919 (M); expenditures, $251,272; total
giving, $229,341; qualifying distributions,
$229,341; giving activities include $229,341 for 29
grants (high: $133,877; low: $1,000).
Fields of interest: Elementary/secondary
education; Youth development; Human services;
Community development; Christian agencies &
churches.
Limitations: Giving in Escanaba, MI. No grants to
individuals.
Application information:
Initial approach: Letter
Deadline(s): None
Trustees: Paul Kangas; Gary Olsen; Helen A.
Sackerson; Matt N. Smith, Jr.
EIN: 383351811

1617
Sacred Family Causes Foundation
110 Merriweather Rd.
Grosse Pointe, MI 48236 (313) 882-8266
Contact: Daniel Goodnow, Chair.

Established in 1999 in MI.
Grantmaker type: Independent foundation.
Financial data (yr. ended 12/31/05): Assets,
$739,520 (M); expenditures, $48,542; total giving,
$40,689; qualifying distributions, $40,689; giving
activities include $40,689 for grants.
Purpose and activities: Giving primarily to Christian
organizations.
Fields of interest: Christian agencies & churches.
Limitations: Giving primarily in MI.
Application information:
Initial approach: Letter
Deadline(s): None
Officers and Trustees:* Daniel Goodnow,* Chair.;
Susan Goodnow,* Secy.
EIN: 383417814

1618
Sadaqa Foundation
c/o Khawaja M. Ikram
P.O. Box 885
Jackson, MI 49204-0885

Established in 2002 in MI; funded in 2004.
Donors: Khawaja H. Ikram; Khawaja N. Ikram;
Khawaja M. Ikram; Farhat S. Ikram.
Grantmaker type: Independent foundation.
Financial data (yr. ended 12/31/05): Assets,
$25,085 (M); gifts received, $48,000;
expenditures, $32,020; total giving, $32,000;
qualifying distributions, $32,000; giving activities
include $32,000 for grants.
Fields of interest: Islam.
Type of support: General/operating support.
Limitations: Applications not accepted. Giving
primarily in MI. No grants to individuals.
Application information: Contributes only to
pre-selected organizations.
Officers: Khawaja M. Ikram, Pres.; Khawaja H.
Ikram, V.P.; Khawaja N. Ikram, Secy.; Tahir Alvi,
Treas.
EIN: 611430641

1619
Saddle Foundation
101 N. Main St., 7th Fl.
Ann Arbor, MI 48104-1400
Contact: Erik H. Serr, Dir.

Established in 1997 in MI.
Donor: Kathryn W. Holmes.
Grantmaker type: Independent foundation.
Financial data (yr. ended 12/31/05): Assets,
$7,227,516 (M); gifts received, $108,150;
expenditures, $502,026; total giving, $480,000;
qualifying distributions, $486,415; giving activities
include $480,000 for 8 grants (high: $110,000;
low: $20,000; average: $50,000–$90,000).
Purpose and activities: Giving primarily for the arts,
higher education, the environment, and human
services.
Fields of interest: Museums; Performing arts;
Higher education; Environment, natural resources;
Animals/wildlife, preservation/protection; Human
services; YM/YWCAs & YM/YWHAs.
Limitations: Applications not accepted. Giving
primarily in MI; some giving also in San Francisco,
CA. No grants to individuals.
Application information: Contributes only to
pre-selected organizations.
Officer: Kathryn W. Holmes, Pres. and Secy.-Treas.
Directors: Howard S. "Howdy" Holmes; Erik H. Serr.
EIN: 383347262

1620
John & Margaret Sagan Foundation
c/o Margaret Sagan, V.P.
1 Calvin Cir., Apt. B305
Evanston, IL 60201-1929

Established in 1985 in MI.
Donors: John Sagan; Margaret Sagan.
Grantmaker type: Independent foundation.
Financial data (yr. ended 12/31/05): Assets,
$981,210 (M); gifts received, $25,000;
expenditures, $64,431; total giving, $60,000;
qualifying distributions, $60,000; giving activities
include $60,000 for grants.

Fields of interest: Health care; Children/youth, services; Christian agencies & churches; Protestant agencies & churches.
Limitations: Applications not accepted. Giving primarily in CA, IL, and MI. No grants to individuals.
Application information: Contributes only to pre-selected organizations.
Officers and Trustees:* John Sagan,* Pres. and Secy.-Treas.; Linda Sagan Harrier,* V.P.; Margaret Sagan, V.P.; Scott D. Sagan, V.P.
EIN: 382638868

1621
Sage Foundation
P.O. Box 1919
Brighton, MI   48116
Contact: Melissa Sage Fadim, Chair.

Incorporated in 1954 in MI.
Donors: Charles F. Sage†; Effa L. Sage†.
Grantmaker type: Independent foundation.
Financial data (yr. ended 12/31/04): Assets, $57,068,154 (M); expenditures, $3,236,665; total giving, $2,659,000; qualifying distributions, $2,883,648; giving activities include $2,659,000 for 158 grants (high: $250,000; low: $500).
Purpose and activities: Emphasis on higher and secondary education and hospitals; grants also for aid to the handicapped, Roman Catholic religious and charitable organizations, youth and child welfare agencies, church support, and cultural programs.
Fields of interest: Arts; Secondary school/education; Higher education; Hospitals (general); Human services; Children/youth, services; Roman Catholic federated giving programs; Roman Catholic agencies & churches; Disabilities, people with.
Type of support: General/operating support; Continuing support; Annual campaigns; Capital campaigns; Building/renovation; Equipment; Endowments; Program development; Scholarship funds; Research; Matching/challenge support.
Limitations: Giving on a national basis.
Application information: Application form not required.
  Initial approach: Letter
  Copies of proposal: 1
  Deadline(s): None
  Board meeting date(s): Quarterly
  Final notification: 12 weeks
Officers and Trustees:* Melissa Sage Fadim,* Chair., Pres., and Treas.; John J. Ayaub,* V.P. and Secy.; Anne Sage Price; James E. Van Doren.
Number of staff: 1 part-time professional.
EIN: 386041518

1622
Saginaw Community Foundation Depository, Inc.
100 S. Jefferson St., Ste. 201
Saginaw, MI   48607   (989) 755-0545

Grantmaker type: Independent foundation.
Financial data (yr. ended 12/31/05): Assets, $1 (M); gifts received, $15,585; expenditures, $27,743; total giving, $27,171; qualifying distributions, $27,171; giving activities include $27,171 for grants.
Fields of interest: Human services; Federated giving programs; Christian agencies & churches.
Limitations: Applications not accepted. Giving primarily in Saginaw, MI. No grants to individuals.

Application information: Contributes only to pre-selected organizations.
Officers: Larry L. Preston, Chair.; Linda L. Sims, Vice-Chair.; Lucy Allen, Pres.; Renee Johnston, Pres.; Joseph Madison, Secy.; Richard T. Watson, Secy.; David J. Abbs, Treas.; David Butts, Treas.
Trustees: Raana Akbar, M.D.; Heidi Bolger; David Carbajal; Morrall Claramunt; Hurley Coleman; and 21 additional trustees.
EIN: 382765862

1623
Saginaw Public Libraries Foundation
505 Janes St.
Saginaw, MI   48607-1236

Established in 1988 in MI.
Donor: Gladys J. Diekman†.
Grantmaker type: Independent foundation.
Financial data (yr. ended 6/30/05): Assets, $305,911 (M); gifts received, $28,569; expenditures, $32,045; total giving, $14,607; qualifying distributions, $14,607; giving activities include $14,607 for grants.
Purpose and activities: Support only to the Saginaw Public Library, Saginaw, MI.
Fields of interest: Libraries (public).
Limitations: Applications not accepted. Giving limited to Saginaw, MI.
Application information: Contributes only to a pre-selected organization.
Officers: Carol Selby, Pres.; Tina Gutierrez, V.P. and Secy.; Joan B. Brownell, Treas.
Directors: Ann Schneider Branch; Neville Britto; Pamela Clark; Ralph Martin.
EIN: 382816474

1624
Dr. Shanti Swarup & Mrs. Chawli Devi Saini Memorial Foundation
4337 Bender Ct.
Troy, MI   48098   (248) 641-1822
Contact: Inder Jit Saini M.D., Pres.

Established in 1998 in MI.
Donor: Inder Jit Saini, M.D.
Grantmaker type: Independent foundation.
Financial data (yr. ended 9/30/04): Assets, $49,809 (M); gifts received, $9,823; expenditures, $3,856; total giving, $3,425; qualifying distributions, $5,000; giving activities include $3,425 for grants.
Limitations: Giving primarily in MI.
Application information: Application form required.
  Deadline(s): None
Officers: Inder Jit Saini, M.D., Pres.; Mrs. Inder Saini, V.P.; Robert Saini, Secy.; Rashmi Saini, Treas.
Director: Krishan Saini.
EIN: 383408285

1625
The Salahi Foundation
26300 Telegraph Rd., 2nd Fl.
Southfield, MI   48034

Grantmaker type: Independent foundation.
Financial data (yr. ended 12/31/05): Assets, $2,841 (M); gifts received, $20,000; expenditures, $20,416; total giving, $19,916; qualifying

distributions, $19,916; giving activities include $19,916 for grants.
Fields of interest: Human services.
Type of support: General/operating support.
Officer: Farouk Salahi, Pres.
EIN: 383452435

1626
The Saleh Foundation
26300 Telegraph Rd., 2nd Fl.
Southfield, MI   48034

Established in 2003.
Grantmaker type: Independent foundation.
Financial data (yr. ended 12/31/05): Assets, $270,565 (M); gifts received, $23,000; expenditures, $6,915; total giving, $5,600; qualifying distributions, $5,600; giving activities include $5,600 for grants.
Officer: Husain Saleh, Pres.
EIN: 383679147

1627
Burl E. Salisbury Memorial Scholarship Fund
c/o Southern Michigan Bank & Trust
51 W. Pearl St.
Coldwater, MI   49036
Contact: Mary Guthrie, Trust Off., Southern Michigan Bank & Trust

Grantmaker type: Independent foundation.
Financial data (yr. ended 4/30/05): Assets, $308,237 (M); expenditures, $37,017; total giving, $30,000; qualifying distributions, $30,000; giving activities include $30,000 for grants to individuals.
Purpose and activities: Loans to students of Bronson High School, MI.
Type of support: Student loans—to individuals.
Limitations: Giving limited to residents of Bronson, MI.
Application information: Application form required.
  Deadline(s): May 1
Trustee: Southern Michigan Bank & Trust.
EIN: 386429664

1628
Fritchof T. Sallness and Marian M. Sallness Memorial Scholarship Fund
c/o Citizens Bank
328 S. Saginaw St., M/C 002072
Saginaw, MI   48602
Application address: Helen James, 101 N. Washington Ave., Saginaw, MI 48607-1206, tel.: (989) 776-7368

Established in 1990 in MI.
Grantmaker type: Independent foundation.
Financial data (yr. ended 12/31/05): Assets, $229,859 (M); expenditures, $5,471; total giving, $1,000; qualifying distributions, $1,000; giving activities include $1,000 for grants to individuals.
Purpose and activities: Scholarships and student loans awarded to Saginaw County residents attending a Michigan school, college, or university.
Type of support: Student loans—to individuals; Scholarships—to individuals.
Limitations: Giving limited to residents of Saginaw County, MI.
Application information:

Initial approach: Letter
Deadline(s): May 1
Trustee: Citizens Bank.
EIN: 386565588

1629
Alex Saltsman Family Foundation
2000 Town Ctr., Ste. 1500
Southfield, MI 48075-1195

Established in 1997 in MI.
Grantmaker type: Independent foundation.
Financial data (yr. ended 12/31/05): Assets, $613,733 (M); expenditures, $34,615; total giving, $34,200; qualifying distributions, $34,200; giving activities include $34,200 for grants.
Fields of interest: Jewish agencies & temples.
Type of support: General/operating support.
Limitations: Giving primarily in MI. No grants to individuals.
Officers: Alex Saltsman, Pres.; Elaine Miller, V.P.; Sara Bricker, Secy.; Jerry Saltsman, Treas.
EIN: 383301275

1630
The Samaritan Foundation
(formerly DeLapa Family Foundation)
2505 E. Paris St., Ste. 195
Grand Rapids, MI 49546
Application address: c/o John M. DeLapa, 2935 Division St., St. Joseph, MI 49085

Established in 1991 in MI.
Donors: Gina DeLapa; James DeLapa; John DeLapa; Judy DeLapa.
Grantmaker type: Independent foundation.
Financial data (yr. ended 12/31/05): Assets, $367,803 (M); gifts received, $259,585; expenditures, $135,679; total giving, $127,000; qualifying distributions, $128,721; giving activities include $127,000 for 33 grants (high: $15,500; low: $400).
Purpose and activities: Awards scholarships for education, preferably to southwest MI residents; also awards grants to organizations that serve low income groups and assist with arts and community recreation programs.
Fields of interest: Arts; Education; Human services; Children/youth, services; Economically disadvantaged.
Limitations: Giving primarily in southwestern MI.
Application information:
Initial approach: Letter requesting questionnaire
Deadline(s): June 30. No deadline for individuals
Board meeting date(s): Apr. and Nov.
Officers: Judith DeLapa, Pres.; Joseph DeLapa, V.P.; James DeLapa, Secy.; John M. DeLapa, Treas.
EIN: 382173249

1631
Joseph W. Samuels, M.D. and Clarence E. Thompson Scholarship Fund, Inc.
2310 W. McNichols Rd.
Detroit, MI 48221-3120

Established in 1995 in MI.
Grantmaker type: Independent foundation.
Financial data (yr. ended 12/31/04): Assets, $237 (M); gifts received, $500; expenditures, $1,000;

total giving, $1,000; qualifying distributions, $1,000; giving activities include $1,000 for grants.
Type of support: Scholarships—to individuals.
Officers: James Womack, Pres.; Sophie Womack, V.P.
EIN: 383244740

1632
San Pablo Foundation, Inc.
c/o Comerica Bank
P.O. Box 75000, MC 3302
Detroit, MI 48275-3302
Application address: c/o James Karnegis, 100 N.E. 3rd Ave., Fort Lauderdale, FL 33301, tel.: (954) 468-0613

Established in 1998 in FL.
Donor: Guido Mendoza.
Grantmaker type: Independent foundation.
Financial data (yr. ended 12/31/05): Assets, $576,898 (M); expenditures, $34,711; total giving, $26,000; qualifying distributions, $26,000; giving activities include $26,000 for grants.
Fields of interest: Education.
Type of support: Scholarship funds.
Limitations: Giving primarily in the Dominican Republic.
Application information: Application form not required.
Deadline(s): None
Directors: Amelia Mendoza; Pablo Mendoza; Gloria Rodriguez; Veronica Silva.
EIN: 650803135

1633
Jack & Marguerite Sanders Memorial Fund
c/o Citizens Bank
101 N. Washington Ave.
Saginaw, MI 48607

Established in 1989 in MI.
Donor: Jack Sanders†.
Grantmaker type: Independent foundation.
Financial data (yr. ended 12/31/05): Assets, $1,702,055 (M); expenditures, $107,697; total giving, $12,050; qualifying distributions, $12,050; giving activities include $12,050 for grants.
Fields of interest: Health care; Human services; Christian agencies & churches; General charitable giving.
Type of support: General/operating support.
Limitations: Applications not accepted. No grants to individuals.
Application information: Contributes only to 14 pre-selected organizations as specified in the trust instrument.
Trustee: Citizens Bank.
EIN: 382881468

1634
Sandy Family Foundation, Inc.
10 W. Long Lake Rd.
Bloomfield Hills, MI 48304

Donors: William H. Sandy; Marjorie M. Sandy.
Grantmaker type: Independent foundation.
Financial data (yr. ended 12/31/05): Assets, $475,039 (M); expenditures, $52,902; total giving, $39,510; qualifying distributions, $39,510; giving activities include $39,510 for grants.

Fields of interest: Performing arts, opera; Elementary/secondary education; Higher education; Jewish federated giving programs; Jewish agencies & temples.
Type of support: General/operating support.
Limitations: Applications not accepted. Giving primarily in MI. No grants to individuals.
Application information: Contributes only to pre-selected organizations.
Officers and Trustees:* William H. Sandy, Pres.; Marjorie M. Sandy, V.P. and Secy.; Alan M. Sandy,* Treas.; Barbara Golub; Lewis G. Sandy.
EIN: 383208309

1635
Sankrithi Foundation
1437 Sodon Lake Dr.
Bloomfield Hills, MI 48302-2356

Established in 2002.
Donors: Mahalakshmi Honasoge; Nataraj Honasoge.
Grantmaker type: Independent foundation.
Financial data (yr. ended 12/31/05): Assets, $1 (M); gifts received, $4,000; expenditures, $1,520; total giving, $1,500; qualifying distributions, $1,500; giving activities include $1,500 for grants.
Officers: Nataraj Honasoge, Pres.; Mahalakshmi Honasoge, Secy.
EIN: 522380135

1636
Santa Maria Charitable Foundation
743 S. Renaud Rd.
Grosse Pointe Woods, MI 48236-1731

Donors: James R. Guest; Maryanne M. Guest.
Grantmaker type: Independent foundation.
Financial data (yr. ended 11/30/05): Assets, $128,985 (M); gifts received, $3,000; expenditures, $3,217; total giving, $3,112; qualifying distributions, $3,112; giving activities include $3,112 for grants.
Limitations: Applications not accepted. Giving primarily in Detroit, MI. No grants to individuals.
Application information: Contributes only to pre-selected organizations.
Officers: James R. Guest, Pres.; Maryanne M. Guest, Secy.
Trustees: Alan J. Guest; David R. Guest.
EIN: 386074753

1637
Saranac Education Foundation
685 Wildwood Dr.
Saranac, MI 48881   (616) 642-6606

Established in 1992 in MI.
Donors: Joseph E. Brown; Sandra J. Brown.
Grantmaker type: Independent foundation.
Financial data (yr. ended 12/31/04): Assets, $1,507,464 (M); expenditures, $55,333; total giving, $52,000; qualifying distributions, $54,689; giving activities include $52,000 for grants.
Purpose and activities: Support only for Saranac Community Schools, MI, for its programs and scholarship awards.
Fields of interest: Education.
Limitations: Applications not accepted. Giving limited to Saranac, MI. No grants to individuals.

Application information: Contributes only to a pre-selected organization.
Officers: Ed Brown, Pres. and Treas.; Sandra J. Brown, V.P.; Adele Williams, V.P.; Bruce Chadwick, Secy.
EIN: 383076816

1638
Glenn and Elizabeth Sargent Endowment Fund

c/o Citizens Bank Wealth Mgmt., N.A.
328 S. Saginaw St., M/C 002072
Flint, MI   48502

Established in 2001 in MI.
Donor: Elizabeth Sargent†.
Grantmaker type: Independent foundation.
Financial data (yr. ended 8/31/05): Assets, $2,397,394 (M); expenditures, $110,748; total giving, $88,744; qualifying distributions, $88,744; giving activities include $88,744 for grants.
Purpose and activities: Support only for the Saginaw Art Museum.
Fields of interest: Museums (art).
Type of support: General/operating support.
Limitations: Applications not accepted. Giving limited to Saginaw, MI. No grants to individuals.
Application information: Contributes only to a pre-selected organization.
Trustee: Citizens Bank.
EIN: 386794787
Selected grants: The following grants were reported in 2004.
$105,017 to Saginaw Art Museum, Saginaw, MI.

1639
Sarin Family Foundation

12792 Sleigh Trail
Milford, MI   48380-1261   (248) 685-9914

Established in 2002 in MI.
Donor: Susan Sarin.
Grantmaker type: Independent foundation.
Financial data (yr. ended 6/30/05): Assets, $50,904 (M); gifts received, $30,000; expenditures, $48,560; total giving, $46,000; qualifying distributions, $46,000; giving activities include $46,000 for grants.
Officer: Susan Sarin, Pres.
EIN: 020638745

1640
Jerome & Caecilia Sarnowski Foundation

P.O. Box 158
Vulcan, MI   49892

Established in 2000 in WI.
Grantmaker type: Independent foundation.
Financial data (yr. ended 12/31/05): Assets, $393,235 (M); expenditures, $51,142; total giving, $51,000; qualifying distributions, $51,000; giving activities include $51,000 for grants.
Fields of interest: Secondary school/education.
Limitations: Applications not accepted. Giving primarily in WI. No grants to individuals.
Application information: Contributes only to pre-selected organizations.
Directors: John R. Nelson; Caecilia K. Sarnowski; Jerome T. Sarnowski.
EIN: 392012968

1641
The Saugatuck-Douglas Lions Club Charitable Foundation

434 Butler St.
Saugatuck, MI   49453

Established in 1989 in MI.
Donor: Saugatuck-Douglas Lions Club.
Grantmaker type: Independent foundation.
Financial data (yr. ended 12/31/05): Assets, $55,589 (M); gifts received, $100; expenditures, $960; total giving, $500; qualifying distributions, $500; giving activities include $500 for grants to individuals.
Purpose and activities: Scholarship awards only to seniors at Saugatuck High School, MI.
Type of support: Scholarships—to individuals.
Limitations: Applications not accepted. Giving limited to residents of the Saugatuck, MI, area.
Application information: Unsolicited requests for funds not accepted.
Officers: Marty Bickel, Pres.; G. Darryl Meyer, V.P.; Tom Nowak, Secy.; John Geier, Treas.
Directors: Jim Chamberlain; Ray Jonakait.
EIN: 382825072

1642
Marjorie Shuman Saulson Foundation

26662 Scenic Dr.
P.O. Box 250123
Franklin, MI   48025

Established in 2004 in MI.
Donor: Marjorie Shuman Saulson.
Grantmaker type: Independent foundation.
Financial data (yr. ended 12/31/05): Assets, $296 (M); gifts received, $25,500; expenditures, $26,655; total giving, $25,825; qualifying distributions, $25,825; giving activities include $25,825 for grants.
Fields of interest: Jewish agencies & temples; Women.
Limitations: Applications not accepted. Giving on a national basis, with some emphasis on MI. No grants to individuals.
Application information: Contributes only to pre-selected organizations.
Officer: Marjorie Shuman Saulson, Pres.
EIN: 201602289

1643
Savage Foundation

P.O. Box 843
East Lansing, MI   48826-0843

Established in 1996 in MI.
Donor: James M. Savage.
Grantmaker type: Independent foundation.
Financial data (yr. ended 12/31/05): Assets, $438,145 (M); expenditures, $24,258; total giving, $22,730; qualifying distributions, $22,730; giving activities include $22,730 for 14 grants (high: $7,780; low: $450).
Fields of interest: Higher education; Youth development, centers/clubs; Human services; Roman Catholic agencies & churches.
Type of support: General/operating support.
Limitations: Applications not accepted. Giving primarily in Lansing, MI. No grants to individuals.
Application information: Contributes only to pre-selected organizations.

Officers: James M. Savage, Pres.; Mary T. Savage, Secy.-Treas.
EIN: 383226603

1644
Scears Foundation of Akron Michigan

c/o Jan Holik
998 N. Graf Rd.
Caro, MI   48723

Established in 2001 in MI.
Donor: Gweneth M. Scears.
Grantmaker type: Independent foundation.
Financial data (yr. ended 12/31/05): Assets, $34,431 (M); expenditures, $5,500; total giving, $5,500; qualifying distributions, $5,500; giving activities include $5,500 for grants to individuals.
Limitations: Applications not accepted.
Application information: Unsolicited request for funds not accepted.
Directors: Jan Holik; Heather Holik.
EIN: 383593135

1645
George E. and Agnes M. Schael Trust Fund

c/o Fifth Third Bank
P.O. Box 3636
Grand Rapids, MI   49501-3636

Grantmaker type: Independent foundation.
Financial data (yr. ended 7/31/05): Assets, $290,725 (M); expenditures, $3,635; total giving, $0; qualifying distributions, $0.
Purpose and activities: Giving only for scholarships at the University of Chicago.
Type of support: Scholarship funds.
Limitations: Applications not accepted. Giving limited to Chicago, IL. No grants to individuals (directly).
Application information: Contributes only to pre-selected organizations.
Trustee: Fifth Third Bank.
EIN: 356383161

1646
The Schalon Foundation

4418 Tanglewood Trail
St. Joseph, MI   49085
Contact: Susan K. Schalon, Secy.

Established in 1997 in MI.
Donors: Edward I. Schalon; Marcella J. Schalon.
Grantmaker type: Independent foundation.
Financial data (yr. ended 12/31/04): Assets, $3,297,515 (M); expenditures, $246,457; total giving, $225,500; qualifying distributions, $224,730; giving activities include $225,500 for 14 grants (high: $30,000; low: $2,000).
Fields of interest: Performing arts, orchestra (symphony); Performing arts, opera; Arts; Education; Housing/shelter, development; Recreation, community facilities; Human services; Christian agencies & churches.
Type of support: Building/renovation.
Limitations: Giving primarily in St. Joseph, MI. No grants to individuals.
Application information:
   Initial approach: Letter

Officers and Directors:* Edward I. Schalon,* Pres.; Scott Schalon,* V.P.; Susan Schalon,* Secy.; Marcella J. Schalon,* Treas.
EIN: 383341098

1647
Conrad Schanz and Nellie Grant Schanz Family Memorial Trust
124 Fulton St. E., Ste. 100
Grand Rapids, MI 49503-3230

Established in 1992 in MI.
Grantmaker type: Independent foundation.
Financial data (yr. ended 12/31/05): Assets, $1,625,989 (M); expenditures, $183,217; total giving, $140,000; qualifying distributions, $140,000; giving activities include $140,000 for grants.
Fields of interest: Human services; Christian agencies & churches.
Type of support: General/operating support.
Limitations: Applications not accepted. No grants to individuals.
Application information: Contributes only to 5 pre-selected organizations.
Trustees: Brian J. Plachta; Mary Catherine Pollack; Donald C. Schanz; Donald K. Schanz.
EIN: 383066991

1648
The Morris and Emma Schaver Foundation, Inc.
29100 Northwestern Hwy., Ste. 399
Southfield, MI 48034-1092

Donor: Emma Schaver.
Grantmaker type: Independent foundation.
Financial data (yr. ended 12/31/05): Assets, $1,431,489 (M); expenditures, $92,730; total giving, $90,000; qualifying distributions, $90,000; giving activities include $90,000 for grants.
Purpose and activities: Giving primarily for Jewish education.
Fields of interest: Arts; Higher education; Education.
Limitations: Applications not accepted. Giving primarily in MI. No grants to individuals.
Application information: Contributes only to pre-selected organizations.
Officers: Harvey M. Beim, Secy.-Treas.; Isaac Schaver, Pres.
Director: Beryl Shemtov.
EIN: 386091306

1649
Maude Ripley Schemm Scholarship Trust
c/o Citizens Bank Wealth Mgmt., N.A.
328 S. Saginaw St., M/C 002072
Flint, MI 48502
Application address: c/o Arthur Hill High School, 3115 Mackinaw St., Saginaw, MI 48602-3221, tel.: (989) 797-4815

Established in MI.
Grantmaker type: Independent foundation.
Financial data (yr. ended 12/31/05): Assets, $198,913 (M); expenditures, $8,233; total giving, $4,500; qualifying distributions, $6,574; giving activities include $4,500 for 2 grants to individuals (high: $2,500; low: $2,000).

Purpose and activities: Scholarship awards to graduates of Arthur Hill High School, Saginaw, MI.
Fields of interest: Higher education.
Type of support: Scholarships—to individuals.
Limitations: Giving limited to residents of Saginaw, MI.
Application information: Application form required.
Deadline(s): May 1
Trustee: Citizens Bank.
EIN: 386095919

1650
Olga Schiefer Charitable Trust
c/o National City Bank
1900 E. 9th St.
Cleveland, OH 44114

Established in 1992 in MI.
Grantmaker type: Independent foundation.
Financial data (yr. ended 12/31/03): Assets, $152,535 (M); expenditures, $7,603; total giving, $4,057; qualifying distributions, $6,841; giving activities include $4,057 for 5 grants (high: $1,623; low: $203).
Purpose and activities: Support only for Bethesda Lutheran Homes, WI, and the Lutheran Home, Lutheran Homes of Michigan, Lutheran Special Education, and St. Lorenz Evangelical Church, MI.
Fields of interest: Protestant agencies & churches.
Type of support: General/operating support.
Limitations: Applications not accepted. Giving limited to Detroit, Frankenmuth, and Monroe, MI, and Watertown, WI. No grants to individuals.
Application information: Contributes only to 5 pre-selected organizations.
Trustee: National City Bank.
EIN: 383078080

1651
The Shirley K. Schlafer Foundation
1465 Clarendon Rd.
Bloomfield Hills, MI 48302-2604

Established in 1985 in MI.
Donors: Shirley K. Schlafer; Shirley K. Schlafer Trust.
Grantmaker type: Independent foundation.
Financial data (yr. ended 10/31/05): Assets, $9,183,157 (M); expenditures, $571,969; total giving, $505,529; qualifying distributions, $505,529; giving activities include $505,529 for 40 grants (high: $200,000; low: $50).
Purpose and activities: Giving primarily for the arts, particularly to museums, including a folk art museum; some giving also for health care including hospitals, and education.
Fields of interest: Visual arts; Museums (art); Museums (ethnic/folk arts); Performing arts; Arts; Higher education; Education; Health care; Medical research, institute; Cancer research.
Limitations: Applications not accepted. Giving primarily in MI and in New York, NY. No grants to individuals.
Application information: Contributes only to pre-selected organizations.
Officers: Edith S. Briskin, Chair. and Treas.; Barry D. Briskin, Pres. and Secy.; Andrew Briskin, V.P.; Susannah M. Briskin, V.P.
EIN: 382637259

1652
John Schleider Education Fund
100 E. Main St.
Owosso, MI 48867-3133
Application address: c/o Celia Woodworth, Owosso High School, Counsel Dept., 765 E. North St., Owosso, MI 48867, tel.: (989) 723-8231

Grantmaker type: Independent foundation.
Financial data (yr. ended 6/30/03): Assets, $31,493 (M); expenditures, $986; total giving, $600; qualifying distributions, $986; giving activities include $600 for 1 grant to an individual.
Purpose and activities: Scholarships only to high school students of the Owosso School District.
Type of support: Scholarships—to individuals.
Limitations: Giving limited to the Owosso, MI, area.
Application information: Application form required.
Deadline(s): May 15
Trustees: Larry Audet; Jack Harrison; Thomas E. Moorehead.
EIN: 237321206

1653
The Frederick E. Schmid Charitable Foundation, Inc.
P.O. Box 157
Jackson, MI 49204-0157

Established in 1989 in MI.
Donor: Frederick E. Schmid.
Grantmaker type: Independent foundation.
Financial data (yr. ended 12/31/05): Assets, $1,801,730 (M); expenditures, $245,152; total giving, $239,864; qualifying distributions, $239,864; giving activities include $239,864 for 25 grants (high: $37,400; low: $400).
Purpose and activities: Giving for tuition assistance to schools of religion.
Fields of interest: Higher education; Theological school/education; Education; Christian agencies & churches.
Type of support: General/operating support; Scholarship funds.
Limitations: Applications not accepted. Giving primarily in MI, with some emphasis on Ann Arbor and Harper Woods. No grants to individuals (except through designated scholarship funds).
Application information: Contributes only to pre-selected organizations.
Officers: Frederick E. Schmid, Pres.; Heidi M. Woell, V.P.; Jim L. Drake, Secy.-Treas.
Director: Andy Woell.
EIN: 382875531

1654
Leslie & Regene Schmier Foundation
c/o Walnut Svcs., Inc.
30100 Telegraph Rd., No. 403
Bingham Farms, MI 48025 (248) 645-2300
Contact: Regene Schmier, Pres.

Established in 1953 in MI.
Donor: Regene Schmier.
Grantmaker type: Independent foundation.
Financial data (yr. ended 12/31/04): Assets, $278,604 (M); gifts received, $20,000; expenditures, $41,137; total giving, $30,279; qualifying distributions, $30,279; giving activities include $30,279 for grants.

...uation; Health
; &
...ort.

Stoneman,

1655
The Art and Mary Schmuckal Family Foundation
4249 U.S. 31 S.
Traverse City, MI 49684 (231) 943-8544
Contact: Arthur M. Schmuckal, Pres.

Established in 1999 in MI.
Donors: Arthur M. Schmuckal; Schmuckal Land Co.
Grantmaker type: Independent foundation.
Financial data (yr. ended 6/30/05): Assets, $4,449,408 (M); expenditures, $341,668; total giving, $231,760; qualifying distributions, $280,138; giving activities include $231,760 for 34 grants (high: $50,000; low: $550).
Purpose and activities: Giving primarily to enhance the well-being of children, and to strengthen the economic ability of Traverse City, MI, citizens; funding also for community development.
Fields of interest: Theological school/education; Human services; Residential/custodial care, hospices; Community development.
Limitations: Giving primarily in Traverse City, MI.
Application information:
Initial approach: Letter
Deadline(s): None
Officers: Arthur M. Schmuckal, Pres.; Barbara F. Benson, V.P.; Donald A. Schmuckal, V.P.; Evelyn K. Richardson, Secy.; Paul M. Schmuckal, Treas.
EIN: 383498264
Selected grants: The following grants were reported in 2005.
$50,000 to Munson Healthcare Regional Foundation, Traverse City, MI. For building construction.
$33,750 to Grand Traverse Pavilions Foundation, Traverse City, MI.
$22,000 to Area Agency on Aging, Grand Rapids, MI. For computer purchases.
$5,000 to Fife Lake Public Library, Fife Lake, MI. For capital campaign.
$5,000 to Great Lakes Childrens Museum, Traverse City, MI.
$5,000 to House of Hope, Northwest Michigan, Traverse City, MI.
$2,000 to Father Fred Foundation, Traverse City, MI.
$2,000 to Saint Francis High School, Traverse City, MI.
$1,000 to Michigan Leadership Institute, Old Mission, MI.
$1,000 to Third Level Crisis Intervention Center, Traverse City, MI.

1656
Philip H. Schneider Trust for Village of Lowell
c/o Fifth Third Bank
P.O. Box 3636
Grand Rapids, MI 49501-3636

Grantmaker type: Independent foundation.
Financial data (yr. ended 10/31/03): Assets, $2,167,972 (M); expenditures, $116,898; total giving, $105,884; qualifying distributions, $106,446; giving activities include $105,884 for grants.
Purpose and activities: Support only for Lowell Area Housing, Inc., Lowell, MI.
Fields of interest: Residential/custodial care.
Limitations: Applications not accepted. Giving limited to Lowell, MI. No grants to individuals.
Application information: Contributes only to a pre-selected organization.
Trustee: Fifth Third Bank.
EIN: 386513806

1657
Schneider-Engstrom Foundation
3039 Vincent Rd.
Clyde, MI 48049-4436

Grantmaker type: Independent foundation.
Financial data (yr. ended 12/31/05): Assets, $33,275 (L); expenditures, $1,931; total giving, $1,400; qualifying distributions, $1,917; giving activities include $1,400 for grants.
Limitations: Applications not accepted. Giving primarily in MI. No grants to individuals.
Application information: Contributes only to pre-selected organizations.
Officers: Maria E.S. Kuznia, Pres.; Anna B. Schneider, V.P.; Raymond L. Kuznia, Secy.-Treas.
Trustee: Susan Borovich.
EIN: 386106819

1658
Scholarship Fund of Flint Plumbing and Pipefitting Industry
6525 Centurion Dr.
Lansing, MI 48917
Application address: 906 Woodbridge, Flint, MI 48504

Established in 1987 in MI.
Donor: Flint Plumbers & Pipefitting.
Grantmaker type: Independent foundation.
Financial data (yr. ended 4/30/05): Assets, $19,961 (M); gifts received, $22,743; expenditures, $23,326; total giving, $21,100; qualifying distributions, $21,100; giving activities include $21,100 for grants to individuals.
Type of support: Scholarships—to individuals.
Limitations: Giving primarily in MI.
Application information: Application form required.
Deadline(s): Mar. 1
Trustees: Domonic Goyette; Vic Gross; Mike Tomaszewski; John D. Walter.
EIN: 386522581

1659
Schoonbeck Family Foundation
705 Kent Hills Rd. N.E.
Grand Rapids, MI 49505 (616) 682-4655
Contact: Katherine S. Miller, Secy.
Application address: 310 Riders Trail, N.E., Ada, MI 49301

Established in 1997 in MI.
Grantmaker type: Independent foundation.

Financial data (yr. ended 12/31/05): Assets, $1,097,501 (M); expenditures, $62,599; total giving, $56,500; qualifying distributions, $56,500; giving activities include $56,500 for grants.
Purpose and activities: Giving to fund libraries.
Limitations: Giving limited to western MI.
Application information:
Initial approach: Letter
Deadline(s): None
Officers and Directors:* Caroline P. Schoonbeck,* Pres.; Katherine S. Miller,* Secy.; Fredrick Schoonbeck,* Treas.
EIN: 383382133

1660
The Schregardus Family Foundation, Inc.
1800 E. Fox Ln.
Fox Point, WI 53217
Contact: Ralph Schregardus, Pres.

Established in 1996 in WI.
Donor: Ralph Schregardus.
Grantmaker type: Independent foundation.
Financial data (yr. ended 12/31/05): Assets, $895,110 (M); expenditures, $53,595; total giving, $48,992; qualifying distributions, $48,992; giving activities include $48,992 for grants.
Fields of interest: Education; Human services; Children/youth, services; Religion.
Type of support: General/operating support.
Limitations: Applications not accepted. Giving primarily in MI and WI. No grants to individuals.
Application information: Contributes only to pre-selected organizations.
Officers: Ralph Schregardus, Pres.; Randall Schregardus, V.P.; Andrea Votava, Secy.
EIN: 391868672

1661
Herb & Cece Schreiber Foundation
2239 Fenkell St.
Detroit, MI 48238-2852

Established in 1987 in MI.
Grantmaker type: Independent foundation.
Financial data (yr. ended 5/31/05): Assets, $1,303,409 (M); gifts received, $2,000; expenditures, $65,060; total giving, $65,060; qualifying distributions, $65,060; giving activities include $65,060 for grants.
Fields of interest: Jewish federated giving programs; Jewish agencies & temples.
Type of support: General/operating support.
Limitations: Applications not accepted. Giving primarily in MI and NY. No grants to individuals.
Application information: Contributes only to pre-selected organizations.
Officers: Herbert L. Schreiber, Pres.; Cece Schreiber, Secy.-Treas.
EIN: 382472420

1662
Schriber Family Foundation
2116 Dorset Rd.
Ann Arbor, MI 48104-2604

Established in 2003 in MI.
Donors: Ann S. Schriber; Thomas J. Schriber.
Grantmaker type: Independent foundation.

Financial data (yr. ended 9/30/04): Assets, $437,229 (M); gifts received, $5,000; expenditures, $635; total giving, $0; qualifying distributions, $0.
Limitations: Applications not accepted. No grants to individuals.
Application information: Contributes only to pre-selected organizations.
Officers and Directors: Ann S. Schriber,* Pres.; Thomas J. Schriber,* Secy.; John C. Schriber, Treas.; Maria A. Schriber; Sarah E. Schriber.
EIN: 542135622

1663
Fred D. & Evelyn A. Schroeder Foundation
146 Flag Point Dr.
Roscommon, MI   48653

Donors: Fred D. Schroeder; Bobbe Dale Morley.
Grantmaker type: Independent foundation.
Financial data (yr. ended 9/30/05): Assets, $441,884 (M); expenditures, $27,898; total giving, $17,600; qualifying distributions, $17,600; giving activities include $17,600 for grants.
Limitations: Applications not accepted. Giving limited to MI, primarily in Roscommon. No grants to individuals.
Application information: Contributes only to pre-selected organizations.
Officer: Bobbe Dale Morley, Pres.
EIN: 382558752

1664
E. Schultz Memorial Fund
c/o Comerica Bank
P.O. Box 75000
Detroit, MI   48275-3302

Established in 2000 in MI.
Grantmaker type: Independent foundation.
Financial data (yr. ended 12/31/05): Assets, $60,408 (M); expenditures, $8,757; total giving, $7,400; qualifying distributions, $7,400; giving activities include $7,400 for 2 grants (high: $4,440; low: $2,960).
Purpose and activities: Support only for St. Thomas Lutheran Church and St. Paul's Evangelical Lutheran Church, MI.
Fields of interest: Protestant agencies & churches.
Type of support: General/operating support.
Limitations: Applications not accepted. Giving limited to Eastpointe and Grosse Pointe, MI. No grants to individuals.
Application information: Contributes only to 2 pre-selected organizations.
Trustee: Comerica Bank.
EIN: 386182506

1665
Schulz Family Foundation
1270 Rickett Rd.
Brighton, MI   48116

Established in 2002 in MI.
Donors: Donald J. Schulz; Bobbie F. Shulz.
Grantmaker type: Independent foundation.
Financial data (yr. ended 12/31/05): Assets, $253 (M); gifts received, $9,800; expenditures, $9,570; total giving, $9,100; qualifying distributions, $9,100; giving activities include $9,100 for grants.

Fields of interest: Environment, land resources; Christian agencies & churches.
Officers: Donald J. Schulz, Pres. and Treas.; Bobbie F. Schulz, V.P.; Joseph A. Schulz, Secy.
Director: Kelly M. Schulz.
EIN: 383637877

1666
Carrie E. Smith Schuyler Estate Trust
20100 Mack Ave., 2nd Fl.
Grosse Pointe Farms, MI   48236
Contact: Allan Neef, Tr.

Grantmaker type: Independent foundation.
Financial data (yr. ended 12/31/05): Assets, $350,646 (M); expenditures, $17,770; total giving, $14,500; qualifying distributions, $14,500; giving activities include $14,500 for grants.
Purpose and activities: Scholarships for needy girls pursuing an education in music or commercial skills.
Type of support: Scholarship funds.
Limitations: Giving limited to MI. No grants to individuals.
Application information: Application form not required.
  Initial approach: Letter
  Deadline(s): None
Trustees: Allan Neef; Josephine M. Wunsch; Gladys M. Young.
EIN: 386093210

1667
Schwartz Family Foundation
2290 First National Bldg.
Detroit, MI   48226
Contact: Alan E. Schwartz, Pres.

Established in 1959 in MI.
Grantmaker type: Independent foundation.
Financial data (yr. ended 12/31/05): Assets, $468,121 (M); expenditures, $36,930; total giving, $32,104; qualifying distributions, $32,104; giving activities include $32,104 for grants.
Purpose and activities: Giving for the arts, education, health, community development, and Jewish organizations.
Fields of interest: Arts; Higher education; Education; Health care; Health organizations, association; Cancer; Human services; Community development; Jewish agencies & temples.
Limitations: Giving primarily in MI. No loans, program-related investments, or direct charitable giving.
Application information: Application form not required.
  Initial approach: Letter
  Deadline(s): None
Officers and Directors: Alan E. Schwartz,* Pres. and Treas.; Marianne S. Schwartz,* V.P.; Marc A. Schwartz,* Secy.
EIN: 386059415

1668
Robert and Caroline Schwartz Foundation
c/o Metropolitan Life Insurance Co.
200 Park Ave., 32nd Fl.
New York, NY   10166-0114
Contact: Robert G. Schwartz, Pres.

Established in 1986 in DE.

Donors: Robert G. Schwartz; Caroline Schwartz.
Grantmaker type: Independent foundation.
Financial data (yr. ended 12/31/04): Assets, $1,253,944 (M); expenditures, $120,454; total giving, $49,850; qualifying distributions, $49,850; giving activities include $49,850 for grants.
Fields of interest: Health care; Human services; Federated giving programs.
Limitations: Applications not accepted. Giving primarily in MI, NJ, NY, and VA. No grants to individuals.
Application information: Contributes only to pre-selected organizations.
Officers: Robert G. Schwartz, Pres. and Treas.; Caroline Schwartz, V.P. and Secy.
Directors: Joanne Schwartz Carter; Tracy Schwartz Parks; Robert G. Schwartz, Jr.
EIN: 133386282

1669
The Schwarz Family Foundation
4 Meadow Gate Ln.
Harbor Springs, MI   49740

Established in 2000 in MI.
Donor: Patricia D. Schwarz.
Grantmaker type: Independent foundation.
Financial data (yr. ended 12/31/04): Assets, $176,505 (M); expenditures, $11,709; total giving, $8,000; qualifying distributions, $11,515; giving activities include $8,000 for grants.
Limitations: Applications not accepted. No grants to individuals.
Application information: Contributes only to pre-selected organizations.
Trustees: Wendy Crawford; Frank W. Schwarz, Jr.; Frank W. Schwarz III; Patricia D. Schwarz.
EIN: 383507999

1670
Emily Scofield Trust
142 W. Van Buren St.
Battle Creek, MI   49017   (269) 962-9591
Contact: Michael C. Jordan, Tr.

Donor: Emily Scofield†.
Grantmaker type: Independent foundation.
Financial data (yr. ended 12/31/05): Assets, $183,608 (M); expenditures, $10,498; total giving, $5,600; qualifying distributions, $5,600; giving activities include $5,600 for grants to individuals.
Purpose and activities: Scholarship awards to graduates of Calhoun County High School, MI.
Type of support: Scholarships—to individuals.
Limitations: Giving primarily to residents of Calhoun County, MI.
Application information: Application form not required.
  Initial approach: Letter
  Deadline(s): None
Trustee: Michael C. Jordan.
EIN: 386087167

1671
John Scully Foundation
c/o Comerica Bank
P.O. Box 75000
Detroit, MI   48275-5100
Contact: Susan Anderson

Established in 2002 in SD.
Donor: John Scully.
Grantmaker type: Independent foundation.
Financial data (yr. ended 12/31/05): Assets, $504,837 (M); expenditures, $40,947; total giving, $23,927; qualifying distributions, $23,927; giving activities include $23,927 for grants.
Purpose and activities: Giving to seminary schools.
Fields of interest: Higher education, college; Theological school/education.
Type of support: General/operating support.
Application information: Application form required.
  Initial approach: Letter
  Deadline(s): None
Trustee: Comerica Bank.
EIN: 266003516

1672
Sea Dog Foundation
43455 Schoenherr Rd., Ste. 18
Sterling Heights, MI 48313

Established in 2001 in MI.
Donor: Louis D. Cataldo.
Grantmaker type: Independent foundation.
Financial data (yr. ended 12/31/04): Assets, $6,156 (M); expenditures, $700; total giving, $700; qualifying distributions, $700; giving activities include $700 for grants.
Limitations: Applications not accepted. No grants to individuals.
Application information: Contributes only to pre-selected organizations.
Officer: Louis D. Cataldo, Exec. Dir.
EIN: 383604915

1673
The Seabury Foundation
1111 N. Wells St., Ste. 503
Chicago, IL 60610
Contact: Boyd McDowell III
FAX: (312) 587-7332;
E-mail: seabury@seaburyfoundation.org

Trust established in 1947 in IL.
Donors: Charles Ward Seabury†; Louise Lovett Seabury†.
Grantmaker type: Independent foundation.
Financial data (yr. ended 12/31/04): Assets, $25,336,971 (M); expenditures, $1,196,643; total giving, $907,550; qualifying distributions, $1,146,590; giving activities include $907,550 for 82 grants (high: $80,000; low: $1,000).
Purpose and activities: Giving primarily for community and social services.
Fields of interest: Performing arts, theater; Arts; Secondary school/education; Higher education; Education; Environment; Health care; Employment, training; Human services; Children/youth, services; Family services; Community development.
Type of support: Seed money; Matching/challenge support; Equipment; General/operating support; Program development; Scholarship funds; Technical assistance.
Limitations: Giving primarily in Chicago, IL; giving also in MI. No grants to individuals, or for benefits; no loans.
Publications: Application guidelines; Program policy statement; Program policy statement (including application guidelines).

Application information: See application guidelines. Application form not required.
  Initial approach: Letter of inquiry at least 30 days in advance of deadlines
  Copies of proposal: 1
  Deadline(s): Nov. 1, Mar. 1, and Aug. 1
  Board meeting date(s): Feb., May, and Oct.
  Final notification: Feb. 28, May 31, and Oct. 31
Officers and Trustees:* Louise F. Morris,* Exec. Secy.; Seabury J. Hibben, Exec. Dir.; Robert S. Boone; Charles B. Fisk; Richard D. Fisk; William C. Fisk; Deborah S. Holloway; The Northern Trust Co.
Director: Boyd McDowell III.
Number of staff: 2 full-time professional.
EIN: 366027398

1674
Fred and Lizzie Sears Scholarship Fund
c/o Citizens Bank Wealth Mgmt., N.A.
328 S. Saginaw St., M/C 002072
Flint, MI 48502

Grantmaker type: Independent foundation.
Financial data (yr. ended 4/30/03): Assets, $273,899 (M); expenditures, $14,478; total giving, $10,930; qualifying distributions, $14,124; giving activities include $10,930 for grants.
Purpose and activities: Support only for Spring Arbor College.
Limitations: Applications not accepted. Giving limited to Spring Arbor, MI. No grants to individuals.
Application information: Contributes only to a pre-selected organization specified in the governing instrument.
Trustee: Citizens Bank.
EIN: 386447142

1675
Sebastian Foundation
3333 Evergreen Dr. N.E., Ste. 110
Grand Rapids, MI 49525-9756
Contact: David S. Sebastian, Exec. Dir.

Established in 1980 in MI.
Donors: Audrey M. Sebastian; James R. Sebastian.
Grantmaker type: Independent foundation.
Financial data (yr. ended 8/31/05): Assets, $25,810,757 (M); expenditures, $1,606,625; total giving, $1,345,100; qualifying distributions, $1,423,797; giving activities include $1,345,100 for 62 grants (high: $150,000; low: $500).
Purpose and activities: Supports human services and public benefit organizations, education, and the arts.
Fields of interest: Arts; Education; Human services.
Limitations: Giving primarily in the Grand Rapids, MI, area. No support for religious programs. No grants to individuals.
Application information: Application form not required.
  Initial approach: Proposal
  Copies of proposal: 1
  Deadline(s): None
Officer: David S. Sebastian, Exec. Dir.
Trustees: Audrey M. Sebastian; John O. Sebastian.
Number of staff: 2 full-time support.
EIN: 382340219

1676
Secchia Family Foundation
(formerly Peter F. Secchia Foundation)
c/o Universal Forest Products, Inc.
220 Lyon St. N.W., Ste. 510
Grand Rapids, MI 49503-2210

Established in 1985 in MI.
Donor: Peter F. Secchia.
Grantmaker type: Independent foundation.
Financial data (yr. ended 12/31/04): Assets, $12,753,284 (M); expenditures, $699,862; total giving, $602,726; qualifying distributions, $602,726; giving activities include $602,276 for 50 grants (high: $200,000; low: $100).
Purpose and activities: Giving for education, health associations, youth programs, and religion; some giving also in Italy.
Fields of interest: Education; Health organizations, association; Children/youth, services; Christian agencies & churches.
International interests: Italy.
Type of support: Building/renovation; Equipment; Scholarship funds.
Limitations: Applications not accepted. Giving on a national and international basis. No grants to individuals.
Application information: Contributes only to pre-selected organizations.
Officers: Peter F. Secchia, Pres.; Mark A. Schut, Treas.
Director: Sandra Secchia Aslanian.
EIN: 382641093

1677
Seed the World, Inc.
6066 Champagne Ct. S.E.
Grand Rapids, MI 49546-6431

Grantmaker type: Independent foundation.
Financial data (yr. ended 12/31/04): Assets, $416,910 (M); gifts received, $8,973; expenditures, $20,057; total giving, $16,616; qualifying distributions, $19,599; giving activities include $16,616 for grants.
Limitations: Applications not accepted. Giving on an international basis, primarily in India. No grants to individuals.
Application information: Contributes only to pre-selected organizations.
Officers: Renu Sophat Malhotra, Pres.; S.K. Malhotra, V.P.
Trustee: Bithika S. Kheterpal, M.D.
EIN: 383333880

1678
SEED Thompson Family Foundation
1071 Royal Crest Dr.
Flint, MI 48532

Established in 2003 in MI.
Donor: Stanley Thompson.
Grantmaker type: Independent foundation.
Financial data (yr. ended 12/31/04): Assets, $5,840 (M); gifts received, $7,101; expenditures, $6,361; total giving, $2,225; qualifying distributions, $4,136; giving activities include $2,225 for grants.
Limitations: Applications not accepted. No grants to individuals.

Application information: Contributes only to pre-selected organizations.
Officer and Trustees:* DeAnna Thompson,* Secy.; Stanley Thompson.
EIN: 200382485

1679
The Mike and Sharon Seelye Family Foundation
3820 Stadium Dr.
Kalamazoo, MI   49008

Established in 2003 in MI.
Donors: Michael N. Seelye; Sharon K. Seelye.
Grantmaker type: Independent foundation.
Financial data (yr. ended 6/30/05): Assets, $337,397 (M); expenditures, $28,650; total giving, $27,250; qualifying distributions, $27,250; giving activities include $27,250 for grants.
Limitations: Applications not accepted. Giving primarily in MI. No grants to individuals.
Application information: Contributes only to pre-selected organizations.
Officers: Michael N. Seelye, Pres.; Sharon K. Seelye, V.P. and Secy.-Treas.
Directors: Lindsey M. Seelye; Mauri E. Seelye; Michael T. Seelye; Michelle N. Seelye.
EIN: 200488026

1680
Seevers Family Foundation
c/o BCRS Assocs., LLP
100 Wall St., 11th Fl.
New York, NY   10005

Established in 1987 in NY.
Donor: Gary L. Seevers.
Grantmaker type: Independent foundation.
Financial data (yr. ended 7/31/05): Assets, $3,309,872 (M); gifts received, $104,300; expenditures, $600,509; total giving, $542,507; qualifying distributions, $545,948; giving activities include $542,507 for 22 grants (high: $250,000; low: $250).
Purpose and activities: Giving primarily for the arts, education, environmental conservation, and human service organizations.
Fields of interest: Museums; Performing arts, opera; Higher education; Libraries (public); Education; Environment, natural resources; Hospitals (general); Human services.
Limitations: Applications not accepted. Giving on a national basis, with emphasis on MI and NY. No grants to individuals.
Application information: Contributes only to pre-selected organizations.
Trustees: Gary L. Seevers; Gary L. Seevers, Jr.; Sharon Seevers.
EIN: 133437890

1681
Martha R. and Susan I. Seger Foundation
c/o Susan I. Seger
1734 Washtenaw Rd.
Ypsilanti, MI   48197-2040

Established in 1999.
Donor: Susan I. Seger.
Grantmaker type: Independent foundation.

Financial data (yr. ended 10/31/05): Assets, $185,533 (M); gifts received, $50,000; expenditures, $61,534; total giving, $61,500; qualifying distributions, $61,500; giving activities include $61,500 for grants.
Fields of interest: Higher education; Libraries (school); Children, services; Christian agencies & churches.
Type of support: General/operating support.
Limitations: Applications not accepted. No grants to individuals.
Application information: Contributes only to pre-selected organizations.
Trustees: Martha R. Seger; Susan I. Seger.
EIN: 383500489

1682
The Sehn Foundation
3515 Brookside Dr., Ste. A
Bloomfield Hills, MI   48302-1501

Established in 1968 in MI.
Donors: Francis J. Sehn; James T. Sehn.
Grantmaker type: Independent foundation.
Financial data (yr. ended 12/31/04): Assets, $6,363,854 (M); gifts received, $40,800; expenditures, $411,111; total giving, $331,450; qualifying distributions, $331,470; giving activities include $331,450 for 15+ grants (high: $100,000).
Purpose and activities: Giving primarily for Roman Catholic organizations and education.
Fields of interest: Higher education; Education; Human services; Roman Catholic agencies & churches.
Type of support: General/operating support.
Limitations: Applications not accepted. Giving primarily in Detroit, MI. No grants to individuals.
Application information: Contributes only to pre-selected organizations.
Officers: Francis J. Sehn, Pres.; Barbara S. Day, Mgr.
EIN: 386160784
Selected grants: The following grants were reported in 2004.
$100,000 to Sacred Heart Seminary. For general support.
$50,000 to Saint Vincent de Paul Society. For general support.
$13,000 to Saint Hugo of the Hills Church, Bloomfield Hills, MI. For general support.
$5,000 to Equestrian Order of the Holy Sepulchre of Jerusalem. For general support.
$5,000 to Leukemia & Lymphoma Society, West Michigan Chapter, Grand Rapids, MI. For general support.
$4,000 to Saint Joseph Mercy Hospital, Ann Arbor, MI.
$2,000 to Michigan Catholic Radio, Troy, MI. For general support.
$2,000 to West Point Fund, West Point, NY. For general support.
$1,500 to University of Detroit Jesuit High School and Academy, Detroit, MI. For general support.
$1,400 to Middleburg Community Center, Middleburg, VA. For general support.

1683
Seidman Family Foundation
(formerly The Thomas Erler Seidman Foundation)
c/o Balancing Act
8316 Calle Petirrojo N.W.
Albuquerque, NM   87120
Contact: Jane R. Volock, Tr.
FAX: (505) 898-4977

Trust established in 1950 in MI.
Donors: Frank E. Seidman†; Esther L. Seidman†.
Grantmaker type: Independent foundation.
Financial data (yr. ended 12/31/04): Assets, $3,684,942 (M); expenditures, $267,876; total giving, $250,850; qualifying distributions, $253,163; giving activities include $250,850 for 70 grants (high: $30,000; low: $50).
Purpose and activities: Funding for the health, welfare, development, and happiness of children.
Fields of interest: Arts; Higher education; Medical research, institute; Children, services.
Type of support: General/operating support; Annual campaigns; Capital campaigns; Building/renovation; Equipment; Endowments; Seed money.
Limitations: Applications not accepted. Giving on a national basis, with emphasis on MI. No grants to individuals.
Application information: Unsolicited requests for funds not accepted.
Board meeting date(s): Dec.
Trustees: Tracy Seidman Hephner; B. Thomas Seidman; L. William Seidman; Nancy C. Seidman; Sarah B. Seidman; Sarah L. Seidman; Jane R. Volock; Margaret Ann Williams.
Number of staff: 1 part-time professional.
EIN: 136098204
Selected grants: The following grants were reported in 2004.
$30,000 to University of Michigan, Ann Arbor, MI. For general support.
$25,000 to Corcoran Gallery of Art, DC. For general support.
$10,000 to Gerald R. Ford Foundation, Grand Rapids, MI. For general support.
$10,000 to Nantucket Conservation Foundation, Nantucket, MA. For general support.
$5,000 to Grand Valley State University, Allendale, MI. For general support.
$3,000 to Albuquerque Public Schools Foundation, Albuquerque, NM. For general support.
$1,500 to Planned Parenthood of Nebraska and Council Bluffs, Lincoln, NE. For general support.
$1,500 to Southwest Indian Foundation, Gallup, NM. For general support.
$1,000 to American Civil Liberties Union (ACLU), New York, NY. For general support.
$1,000 to Rocky Mountain Elk Foundation, Missoula, MT. For general support.

1684
The George & Elizabeth Seifert Foundation
1300 Mead Rd.
Rochester, MI   48306-3524
Contact: George H. Seifert, Pres.

Established in 1996 in MI.
Donors: Elizabeth J. Seifert; George H. Seifert; Sid Mitra.
Grantmaker type: Independent foundation.
Financial data (yr. ended 12/31/05): Assets, $262,464 (M); gifts received, $15,000; expenditures, $45,187; total giving, $18,837;

qualifying distributions, $18,837; giving activities include $18,837 for grants.
Fields of interest: Arts; Education; Community development.
Application information: Application form not required.
Board meeting date(s): Oct.
Officers and Directors:* George H. Seifert,* Pres. and Treas.; Elizabeth J. Seifert,* Secy.; Elizabeth L. Calcei; George K. Seifert; Gail J. Strunk.
EIN: 383313644

1685
Seizert Family Foundation
1716 Heron Ridge Rd.
Bloomfield Hills, MI 48302

Donors: Gerald L. Seizert; Candace C. Seizert.
Grantmaker type: Independent foundation.
Financial data (yr. ended 12/31/05): Assets, $70,086 (M); gifts received, $7,500; expenditures, $3,400; total giving, $3,250; qualifying distributions, $3,250; giving activities include $3,250 for grants.
Purpose and activities: Giving primarily for education, religious organizations, and health care.
Fields of interest: Education; Health care; Religion.
Limitations: Applications not accepted. No grants to individuals.
Application information: Contributes only to pre-selected organizations.
Officers: Gerald L. Seizert, Pres. and Treas.; Candace C. Seizert, V.P. and Secy.
EIN: 383326716

1686
The Sekkarie Foundation
26300 Telegraph Rd., 2nd Fl.
Southfield, MI 48034

Grantmaker type: Independent foundation.
Financial data (yr. ended 12/31/05): Assets, $68,971 (M); gifts received, $51,136; expenditures, $545; total giving, $0; qualifying distributions, $0.
Fields of interest: Hospitals (general); General charitable giving.
Type of support: General/operating support.
Officer: Mohamed A. Sekkarie, Pres.
EIN: 383306444

1687
The Seligman Family Foundation
1 Towne Sq., Ste. 1913
Southfield, MI 48076

Established in 1991 in MI.
Donor: Irving Seligman.
Grantmaker type: Independent foundation.
Financial data (yr. ended 12/31/05): Assets, $2,491,290 (M); expenditures, $920,969; total giving, $919,951; qualifying distributions, $919,951; giving activities include $919,951 for 43 grants (high: $300,000; low: $250; average: $5,000–$10,000).
Fields of interest: Arts; Higher education; Health organizations, association; Human services; Jewish federated giving programs; Jewish agencies & temples.

Limitations: Applications not accepted. Giving primarily in San Francisco, CA, and Detroit, MI. No grants to individuals.
Application information: Contributes only to pre-selected organizations.
Officers: Irving Seligman, Pres.; Mary K. Seligman, Secy.-Treas.
EIN: 382972397

1688
Prewitt & Valerie D. Semmes Foundation
584 E. Highland Rd.
P.O. Box 547
Highland, MI 48357

Grantmaker type: Independent foundation.
Financial data (yr. ended 12/31/04): Assets, $692,273 (M); expenditures, $37,055; total giving, $34,545; qualifying distributions, $34,545; giving activities include $34,545 for grants.
Purpose and activities: Giving for the arts, education, and health care.
Fields of interest: Arts; Medical school/education; Education; Animal welfare; Health care; Medical research, institute; Protestant agencies & churches.
Limitations: Applications not accepted. Giving primarily in VA. No grants to individuals.
Application information: Contributes only to pre-selected organizations.
Trustee: Prewitt Semmes, Jr.
EIN: 386052364

1689
Thomas E. Sequin, Jr. Family Foundation
3375 Anna Dr.
Bay City, MI 48706   (989) 684-0087
Contact: Thomas E. Sequin, Jr., Pres.

Established in 1990 in MI.
Donors: Thomas E. Sequin, Jr.; Sequin Lumber Corp.
Grantmaker type: Independent foundation.
Financial data (yr. ended 12/31/05): Assets, $472,686 (M); gifts received, $74,000; expenditures, $79,118; total giving, $70,000; qualifying distributions, $70,000; giving activities include $70,000 for grants.
Fields of interest: Protestant agencies & churches.
Limitations: Giving primarily in MI; some giving in IL. No grants to individuals.
Application information:
Initial approach: Proposal
Deadline(s): None
Officers: Thomas E. Sequin, Jr., Pres.; Denise A. Sequin, V.P.; Peter A. Sequin, Secy.
EIN: 382931537

1690
Serra Family Foundation
5644 N. Rainbow Ln.
Waterford, MI 48329

Established in 1997 in MI.
Donors: Albert Serra; Lois Serra.
Grantmaker type: Independent foundation.
Financial data (yr. ended 12/31/04): Assets, $4,489,510 (M); gifts received, $200,000; expenditures, $202,806; total giving, $171,100; qualifying distributions, $171,100; giving activities

include $171,100 for 14 grants (high: $30,000; low: $3,000).
Fields of interest: Higher education; Environment, natural resources; Health care; Christian agencies & churches.
Type of support: General/operating support.
Limitations: Giving in the U.S., primarily in MI.
Officers and Directors:* Amy Albright,* V.P.; Ann Lowney,* V.P.; Mary McMahon,* V.P.; Alice Serra Reid,* V.P.; Lynne Parker, Treas.
EIN: 383352324

1691
Otto & Alma Seyferth Trust
P.O. Box 133
Fremont, MI 49412

Established in MI.
Grantmaker type: Independent foundation.
Financial data (yr. ended 7/31/05): Assets, $147,577 (M); expenditures, $10,430; total giving, $7,000; qualifying distributions, $8,659; giving activities include $7,000 for grants.
Fields of interest: Human services.
Type of support: General/operating support.
Limitations: Applications not accepted. Giving primarily in MI. No grants to individuals.
Application information: Contributes only to pre-selected organizations.
Trustees: Anna Jane Seyferth; Eric Seyferth; James R. Seyferth.
EIN: 386091424

1692
Seymour and Troester Foundation
20630 Harper Ave., No. 117
Harper Woods, MI 48225

Incorporated in 1945 in MI.
Donor: Charles E. Troester†.
Grantmaker type: Independent foundation.
Financial data (yr. ended 12/31/05): Assets, $1,953,737 (M); expenditures, $154,846; total giving, $53,000; qualifying distributions, $53,000; giving activities include $53,000 for grants.
Purpose and activities: Giving for higher education, human services, and Catholic organizations.
Fields of interest: Higher education; Food services, congregate meals; Human services; Roman Catholic agencies & churches.
Limitations: Applications not accepted. Giving primarily in MI. No grants to individuals.
Application information: Contributes only to pre-selected organizations. Unsolicited requests for funds not accepted.
Officers and Trustees:* B.A. Seymour, Jr.,* Pres. and Treas.; Kathleen Anderson,* V.P.; B.A. Seymour III, Secy.; William P. Seymour, Treas.
EIN: 386062647

1693
Azeez Shaheen Charitable Trust
3625 Cumberland Blvd.
Atlanta, GA 30339

Established in 1996 in GA.
Grantmaker type: Independent foundation.
Financial data (yr. ended 12/31/05): Assets, $2,394,864 (M); expenditures, $110,678; total giving, $107,482; qualifying distributions,

$107,482; giving activities include $107,482 for grants.
Fields of interest: Education; Human services; Children/youth, services; Roman Catholic agencies & churches.
Type of support: General/operating support.
Limitations: Applications not accepted. Giving limited to GA, IA, IL, IN, MI, and NY. No grants to individuals.
Application information: Contributes only to 7 pre-selected organizations.
Trustees: Shaheen A. Shaheen; Shouky A. Shaheen.
Number of staff: 1 part-time support.
EIN: 586323197

1694
Charles M. Shander Trust f/b/o St. Cyril & Methodius Seminary
c/o PNC Advisors
620 Liberty Ave., P2-PTPP-10-2
Pittsburgh, PA   15222-2705

Established in 1999 in PA.
Donor: Josephine Shander.
Grantmaker type: Independent foundation.
Financial data (yr. ended 12/31/05): Assets, $543,865 (M); expenditures, $12,630; total giving, $7,363; qualifying distributions, $7,363; giving activities include $7,363 for grants.
Purpose and activities: Support only for St. Cyril & Methodius Seminary, Orchard Lake, MI.
Fields of interest: Christian agencies & churches.
Type of support: General/operating support.
Limitations: Applications not accepted. Giving limited to Orchard Lake, MI. No grants to individuals.
Application information: Contributes only to a pre-selected organization specified in the governing instrument.
Trustee: PNC Bank, N.A.
EIN: 237991562

1695
The Nate S. and Ruth B. Shapero Foundation
660 Woodward Ave., Ste. 2290
Detroit, MI   48226-3506

Established in 1949 in MI.
Donor: Nate S. Shapero†.
Grantmaker type: Independent foundation.
Financial data (yr. ended 4/30/05): Assets, $910,163 (M); expenditures, $206,767; total giving, $197,314; qualifying distributions, $199,228; giving activities include $197,314 for 38 grants (high: $75,000; low: $49).
Purpose and activities: Funding primarily for the arts and culture; some giving for Jewish agencies and temples and human services.
Fields of interest: Visual arts; Museums; Performing arts; Performing arts, music; Humanities; Arts; Higher education; Education; Human services; Jewish federated giving programs; Jewish agencies & temples.
Type of support: General/operating support; Matching/challenge support.
Limitations: Applications not accepted. Giving primarily in MI. No grants to individuals.
Application information: Contributes only to pre-selected organizations.

Officers and Trustees:* Marianne S. Schwartz,* Chair.; A.E. Schwartz,* Vice-Chair.; Marc A. Schwartz; Jean E. Shapero.
Number of staff: 1 part-time support.
EIN: 386041567

1696
Mickey Shapiro Charitable Trust
31550 Northwestern Hwy., Ste. 200
Farmington Hills, MI   48334

Established in 2003 in MI.
Donor: Mickey Shapiro.
Grantmaker type: Independent foundation.
Financial data (yr. ended 12/31/05): Assets, $1,143,394 (M); gifts received, $500,000; expenditures, $211,740; total giving, $205,959; qualifying distributions, $205,959; giving activities include $205,959 for 23 grants (high: $95,709; low: $50).
Fields of interest: Museums (specialized); Prostate cancer; Eye research; Human services; Residential/custodial care, hospices; Jewish agencies & temples.
Limitations: Applications not accepted. No grants to individuals.
Application information: Contributes only to pre-selected organizations.
Trustee: Mickey Shapiro.
EIN: 306068151

1697
The Sharp Family Foundation, Inc.
c/o Comerica Bank
P.O. Box 75000, M/C 8280
Detroit, MI   48275-8280

Established in 1999 in FL.
Grantmaker type: Independent foundation.
Financial data (yr. ended 12/31/03): Assets, $53,061 (M); expenditures, $20,304; total giving, $16,893; qualifying distributions, $17,529; giving activities include $16,893 for 1 grant.
Purpose and activities: Support only for the University of Kentucky, Lexington, for its scholarship fund.
Fields of interest: Higher education, university.
Type of support: Scholarship funds.
Limitations: Applications not accepted. Giving limited to Lexington, KY. No grants to individuals.
Application information: Contributes only to a pre-selected organization.
Trustees: Barton W. Sharp; Margaret B. Sharp; William K. Sharp.
EIN: 593302952

1698
Shelby Family Foundation
559 Oak St.
Winnetka, IL   60093
Contact: Carole Shelby, Pres.

Established in 1995 in IL.
Donors: David T. Shelby; Carole Shelby.
Grantmaker type: Independent foundation.
Financial data (yr. ended 11/30/05): Assets, $861,888 (M); expenditures, $49,905; total giving, $37,600; qualifying distributions, $37,600; giving activities include $37,600 for grants.

Purpose and activities: Giving for scientific and medical research.
Fields of interest: Health care, research; Social sciences, research.
Limitations: Giving primarily in IL; some giving also in MI. No grants to individuals.
Application information:
Initial approach: Letter
Deadline(s): None
Officers: Carole Shelby, Pres.; Kaylynn Shelby, V.P.; Sarah Shelby, V.P.; David Shelby, Secy.-Treas.
Directors: Christian Shelby; Justin Shelby; Paige Shelby.
EIN: 364055432

1699
Elizabeth, Allan and Warren Shelden Fund
17152 Kercheval St.
Grosse Pointe Farms, MI   48230
Contact: William W. Shelden, Jr., Pres.

Incorporated in 1937 in MI.
Donors: Elizabeth Warren Shelden†; Allan Shelden III†; W. Warren Shelden†.
Grantmaker type: Independent foundation.
Financial data (yr. ended 12/31/05): Assets, $38,878,888 (M); gifts received, $237,083; expenditures, $2,175,254; total giving, $2,075,500; qualifying distributions, $2,075,500; giving activities include $2,075,500 for grants (high: $700,000; low: $5,000; average: $5,000–$25,000).
Purpose and activities: Giving primarily for the arts, education, and health care.
Fields of interest: Performing arts, music; Arts; Higher education; Hospitals (general); Health care; Children/youth, services; Economically disadvantaged.
Type of support: General/operating support; Continuing support; Annual campaigns; Capital campaigns; Building/renovation; Equipment; Endowments; Research.
Limitations: Giving primarily in the metropolitan Detroit, MI, area. No grants to individuals, or for scholarships, fellowships, or matching gifts; no loans.
Publications: Annual report.
Application information: Application form not required.
Initial approach: Proposal
Copies of proposal: 1
Deadline(s): Submit proposal preferably in Nov.; no set deadline
Board meeting date(s): Nov. or Dec.
Final notification: Positive replies only
Officers and Trustees:* William W. Shelden, Jr.,* Pres. and Treas.; David M. Hempstead.
Number of staff: 1 part-time professional; 1 part-time support.
EIN: 386052198

1700
Leon and Josephine Wade Shepard Scholarship Fund Foundation, Inc.
c/o National City Bank
171 Monroe Ave. N.W., KC17063
Grand Rapids, MI   49503-2634
Application address: c/o Alan Hogenmiller, 4 Memorial Dr., Fennville, MI 49408

Grantmaker type: Independent foundation.

Financial data (yr. ended 3/31/05): Assets, $816,391 (M); expenditures, $44,212; total giving, $38,292; qualifying distributions, $38,292; giving activities include $38,292 for grants to individuals.
Purpose and activities: Scholarships only to needy and qualified graduates of Fennville High School for full-time study at an institution of higher education in Michigan.
Type of support: Scholarships—to individuals.
Limitations: Giving limited to residents of Fennville, MI.
Application information: Application form required.
 Initial approach: Letter
 Deadline(s): Between late Feb. and early Mar.
Officers: Scott Campbell, Pres.; Karen Keller, V.P.; Donna Bruner, Secy.-Treas.
Trustee: National City Bank.
EIN: 386101349

1701
Shepherd Area Historical Society
P.O. Box 505
Shepherd, MI   48883-0505

Grantmaker type: Independent foundation.
Financial data (yr. ended 5/31/05): Assets, $29,100 (M); expenditures, $2,251; total giving, $100; qualifying distributions, $100; giving activities include $100 for grants.
Officers: Sue Sazima, Pres.; Beverly Kalmar, Secy.; Loretta Koester, Treas.
Trustees: Sarah Ayris; Max Berry; Rose Cohoon; Steve Davidson; Leorna Lynch; Clayton Lyons; Newell Oren.
EIN: 382851556

1702
The Shepherd Foundation
2967 Lakeshore Dr.
Holland, MI   49423
Contact: Max O. DePree, Dir.

Established in 1992 in MI.
Donors: Barbara DePree; Esther DePree; Kris DePree; Max O. DePree.
Grantmaker type: Independent foundation.
Financial data (yr. ended 12/31/05): Assets, $47,867 (M); gifts received, $55,868; expenditures, $6,276,319; total giving, $6,258,050; qualifying distributions, $6,259,000; giving activities include $6,258,050 for 33 grants (high: $5,000,000; low: $1,000; average: $2,000–$5,000).
Purpose and activities: Giving primarily to Christian programs, including theological education and Christian youth groups.
Fields of interest: Theological school/education; Housing/shelter, services; Youth development; Human services; Christian agencies & churches.
Type of support: Capital campaigns; General/operating support.
Limitations: Giving in the U.S., primarily in MI.
Application information:
 Initial approach: Letter
 Deadline(s): None
Officers: Kris DePree, Pres. and Secy.; Jody VanDerwel, Treas.
Directors: Esther DePree; Max O. DePree.
EIN: 383046929

1703
The Keith Shereda Foundation, Inc.
3561 Magnolia Ct.
Oakland Township, MI   48363

Established in 2001 in MI.
Grantmaker type: Independent foundation.
Financial data (yr. ended 12/31/04): Assets, $109,580 (M); gifts received, $119,687; expenditures, $95,763; total giving, $90,000; qualifying distributions, $90,000; giving activities include $90,000 for grants.
Purpose and activities: Giving for research to cure spinal cord injuries.
Fields of interest: Spine disorders research.
Limitations: Applications not accepted. No grants to individuals.
Application information: Contributes only to pre-selected organizations.
Officer: Martin Shereda, Pres.
EIN: 383582350

1704
The Sherman Family Foundation
25001 River Dr.
Franklin, MI   48025

Established in 2000 in MI.
Donors: Max M. and Marjorie S. Fisher Foundation, Inc.; Jane F. Sherman.
Grantmaker type: Independent foundation.
Financial data (yr. ended 12/31/05): Assets, $305,361 (M); gifts received, $133,082; expenditures, $213,891; total giving, $210,715; qualifying distributions, $210,715; giving activities include $210,715 for 39 grants (high: $100,000; low: $25).
Fields of interest: Arts; Education; Jewish federated giving programs; Jewish agencies & temples.
Limitations: Applications not accepted. No grants to individuals.
Application information: Contributes only to pre-selected organizations.
Officers: D. Larry Sherman, Pres.; Jane Sherman, Secy.-Treas.
Directors: David F. Sherman; Scott R. Sherman; Sylvia S. Wolf.
EIN: 383505951

1705
Sherwood Family Foundation
636 Cascade Hills Hollow S.E.
Grand Rapids, MI   49546

Established in 1998 in MI.
Donors: Marilyn W. Sherwood; B.P. Sherwood.
Grantmaker type: Independent foundation.
Financial data (yr. ended 12/31/05): Assets, $221,970 (M); gifts received, $14,375; expenditures, $29,664; total giving, $29,000; qualifying distributions, $29,000; giving activities include $29,000 for grants.
Fields of interest: Reproductive health, family planning; Civil rights, women; Protestant agencies & churches; Women.
Limitations: Applications not accepted. Giving primarily in MI. No grants to individuals.
Application information: Contributes only to pre-selected organizations.

Officers: Marilyn W. Sherwood, Pres.; B.P. Sherwood, Secy.-Treas.
EIN: 383393640

1706
Lynne Sherwood Foundation
15760 Prospect Pt.
Spring Lake, MI   49456

Established in 1986 in NY.
Donor: Lynne Sherwood.
Grantmaker type: Independent foundation.
Financial data (yr. ended 11/30/05): Assets, $573,682 (M); gifts received, $4,621; expenditures, $47,057; total giving, $45,600; qualifying distributions, $45,600; giving activities include $45,600 for grants.
Limitations: Applications not accepted. Giving primarily in MI and New York, NY. No grants to individuals.
Application information: Contributes only to pre-selected organizations.
Trustees: Martha A. Erickson; Lynne Sherwood; Peter K. Sherwood.
EIN: 133385644

1707
The Shiffman Foundation
18135 Hamilton Rd.
Detroit, MI   48203   (313) 345-1225
Contact: Richard H. Levey, Pres.
FAX: (313) 345-1930; E-mail: ShiffmanFd@aol.com

Incorporated in 1948 in MI.
Donors: Abraham Shiffman†; Richard H. Levey.
Grantmaker type: Independent foundation.
Financial data (yr. ended 9/30/04): Assets, $404,644 (M); expenditures, $25,296; total giving, $12,495; qualifying distributions, $12,495; giving activities include $12,495 for grants.
Purpose and activities: Giving to program-related investments for community development and economic justice through the Episcopal Diocese of MI and other suitable institutions.
Fields of interest: Arts; Higher education; Education; International human rights; Civil rights, race/intergroup relations; Urban/community development; Community development; Minorities; Economically disadvantaged.
Type of support: General/operating support; Continuing support; Building/renovation; Conferences/seminars; Seed money; Technical assistance; Program-related investments/loans; In-kind gifts.
Limitations: Giving primarily in MI. No grants to individuals.
Publications: Occasional report.
Application information:
 Initial approach: 1- to 2-page letter outlining purpose of request
 Copies of proposal: 1
 Deadline(s): None
 Board meeting date(s): Annually and as needed
Officer: Richard H. Levey, Pres.
EIN: 381396850

1708
Shin Foundation for Medical Research and Betterment of Mankind
c/o Dong H. Shin
1872 Golf Ridge Dr. S.
Bloomfield, MI 48302-1737 (248) 851-4856
Contact: Chae S. Shin, Pres.

Established in 1998 in MI.
Grantmaker type: Independent foundation.
Financial data (yr. ended 12/31/04): Assets, $518,434 (M); expenditures, $166,696; total giving, $164,000; qualifying distributions, $166,608; giving activities include $164,000 for 3 grants (high: $104,000; low: $10,000).
Purpose and activities: Giving primarily to a Christian Church; support also for education.
Fields of interest: Education; Christian agencies & churches.
Limitations: Giving primarily in MI and NY.
Application information: Application form not required.
Initial approach: Resume and proposal
Deadline(s): None
Officer: Chae S. Shin, Pres. and Secy.-Treas.
EIN: 383267984

1709
Shir Chadash Foundation
26240 Raine
Oak Park, MI 48237

Established in 1999 in MI.
Donors: Mark Phillips; Renee Phillips.
Grantmaker type: Independent foundation.
Financial data (yr. ended 12/31/02): Assets, $7,864 (M); expenditures, $11; total giving, $0; qualifying distributions, $0.
Limitations: Giving primarily in MI.
Application information:
Initial approach: Letter
Deadline(s): None
Officers: Renee Phillips,* Pres.; Mark Phillips,* Secy.-Treas.
EIN: 383489697

1710
Ruth M. Shoemaker Charitable Trust
c/o Monroe Bank & Trust
102 E. Front St.
Monroe, MI 48161

Established in 2001 in MI.
Donor: Ruth M. Shoemaker Marital Trust.
Grantmaker type: Independent foundation.
Financial data (yr. ended 12/31/05): Assets, $839,128 (M); expenditures, $103,372; total giving, $95,583; qualifying distributions, $99,099; giving activities include $95,583 for 21 grants (high: $28,675; low: $1,912).
Purpose and activities: Giving primarily for Lutheran churches and agencies.
Fields of interest: Theological school/education; Education; Human services; Protestant agencies & churches.
Limitations: Applications not accepted. Giving primarily in MI and MO. No grants to individuals.
Application information: Contributes only to pre-selected organizations.
Trustee: Monroe Bank & Trust.
EIN: 383439276

1711
Edwin J. & Ruth M. Shoemaker Foundation
214 E. Elm Ave., Ste. 100
Monroe, MI 48162

Established in 1998 in MI.
Donors: Edwin J. Shoemaker‡; Dale Shoemaker.
Grantmaker type: Independent foundation.
Financial data (yr. ended 12/31/05): Assets, $16,038,543 (M); expenditures, $868,415; total giving, $772,500; qualifying distributions, $816,872; giving activities include $772,500 for 24 grants (high: $150,000; low: $2,500).
Purpose and activities: The foundation supports organizations that pursue and further the tenets of the Christian faith.
Fields of interest: Civil liberties, right to life; Christian agencies & churches.
Limitations: Applications not accepted. Giving primarily in MI, NC, and TX.
Application information: Contributes only to pre-selected organizations.
Officers and Directors:* Robert L. Shoemaker,* Pres.; Dale A. Shoemaker,* V.P.; Mary Kaye Johnston,* Secy.-Treas.; David S. Johnston; Rocque E. Lipford; Erich C. Shoemaker.
EIN: 383137832

1712
John R. Shofnitz Charitable Trust
c/o Fifth Third Bank
P.O. Box 3636
Grand Rapids, MI 49501-3636

Established in 1994 in MI.
Grantmaker type: Independent foundation.
Financial data (yr. ended 12/31/05): Assets, $1,723,455 (M); expenditures, $113,490; total giving, $91,720; qualifying distributions, $91,720; giving activities include $91,720 for grants.
Fields of interest: Education; Human services; Protestant agencies & churches.
Type of support: General/operating support.
Limitations: Applications not accepted. Giving limited to Owosso, New Lothrop, Roscommon, Corunna, MI, Tampa , FL, and the Bronx, NY. No grants to individuals.
Application information: Contributes only to 7 pre-selected organizations.
Trustee: Fifth Third Bank.
EIN: 383206767

1713
Francis M. Shook Trust
c/o Wells Fargo Bank, N.A., Trust Tax Dept.
P.O. Box 63954
San Francisco, CA 94163

Established in CA.
Grantmaker type: Independent foundation.
Financial data (yr. ended 12/31/05): Assets, $1,479,491 (M); expenditures, $95,042; total giving, $72,972; qualifying distributions, $72,972; giving activities include $72,972 for grants.
Purpose and activities: Support only for Stanford University and Alta Bates Summit Foundation, Berkeley, CA, Manhattan Eye, Ear, & Throat Hospital, New York, NY, and University of Michigan, Ann Arbor.
Fields of interest: Higher education; Medical school/education; Medical care, in-patient care.

Type of support: General/operating support.
Limitations: Applications not accepted. Giving limited to CA, MI, and NY. No grants to individuals.
Application information: Contributes only to 4 pre-selected organizations.
Trustee: Wells Fargo Bank, N.A.
EIN: 946057023

1714
The Martin and Diana Shoushanian Foundation
26982 Hampstead Blvd.
Farmington Hills, MI 48331

Donors: Martin Shoushanian; Diana Shoushanian.
Grantmaker type: Independent foundation.
Financial data (yr. ended 12/31/05): Assets, $17,361 (M); expenditures, $3,021; total giving, $3,000; qualifying distributions, $3,000; giving activities include $3,000 for grants.
Limitations: Applications not accepted. No grants to individuals.
Application information: Contributes only to pre-selected organizations.
Officers: Martin Shoushanian, Pres.; Diana Shoushanian, V.P.
EIN: 383213292

1715
Shubeck Monsour Foundation
1500 Long Rd.
Kalamazoo, MI 49008-1322 (269) 343-1452
Contact: Michael B. Shubeck, Dir.

Established in 1994 in MI.
Donors: Michael B. Shubeck; Nancy A. Monsour.
Grantmaker type: Independent foundation.
Financial data (yr. ended 12/31/04): Assets, $444,330 (M); expenditures, $15,920; total giving, $13,650; qualifying distributions, $13,650; giving activities include $13,650 for grants.
Fields of interest: Arts; Education; Human services.
Type of support: General/operating support.
Limitations: Giving primarily in western MI, with emphasis on Kalamazoo.
Application information:
Initial approach: Letter
Deadline(s): None
Directors: Nancy A. Monsour; Michael B. Shubeck.
EIN: 383211370

1716
Arthur S. and Norma J. Shufro Family Foundation
c/o Arthur S. Shufro
28585 Rivercrest Dr.
Southfield, MI 48034

Established in 1986 in MI.
Grantmaker type: Independent foundation.
Financial data (yr. ended 12/31/04): Assets, $83,195 (M); gifts received, $31,696; expenditures, $9,434; total giving, $8,085; qualifying distributions, $8,085; giving activities include $8,085 for 25 grants (high: $2,700; low: $25).
Fields of interest: Arts; Multiple sclerosis; Alzheimer's disease; Medical research; American Red Cross; Jewish federated giving programs; Jewish agencies & temples.

Limitations: Applications not accepted. Giving primarily in Detroit, MI. No grants to individuals.
Application information: Contributes only to pre-selected organizations.
Officers: Arthur S. Shufro, Pres.; Norma Shufro, V.P.
EIN: 382705934

1717
The Shukairy Foundation

26300 Telegraph Rd., 2nd Fl.
Southfield, MI 48034

Established in 1998.
Grantmaker type: Independent foundation.
Financial data (yr. ended 12/31/05): Assets, $13,789 (M); gifts received, $14,000; expenditures, $14,941; total giving, $14,000; qualifying distributions, $14,000; giving activities include $14,000 for grants.
Purpose and activities: Giving primarily for Islamic activities.
Fields of interest: Islam.
Officer: Khaled Shukairy, Pres.
EIN: 383381987

1718
The John and Matilda Shumsky Foundation

c/o Thomas E. Gartland
P.O. Box 947
Traverse City, MI 49685-0947

Donor: Matilda Shumsky.
Grantmaker type: Independent foundation.
Financial data (yr. ended 12/31/04): Assets, $592,773 (M); expenditures, $33,544; total giving, $30,500; qualifying distributions, $30,500; giving activities include $30,500 for 18 grants (high: $5,000; low: $500).
Fields of interest: Elementary/secondary education; Human services; Roman Catholic agencies & churches.
Type of support: Scholarship funds; Program development; General/operating support.
Limitations: Applications not accepted. Giving primarily in Traverse City, MI. No grants to individuals.
Application information: Contributes only to pre-selected organizations.
Officers: Kenneth Kleinrichert, Pres.; Mary Oosterhouse, V.P.; Kay O'Brien, Secy.; Thomas E. Gartland, Treas.
Director: Bill Brady.
EIN: 382806447

1719
The Bill and Wanda Shurlow Foundation

3333 Egypt Valley N.E.
Ada, MI 49301

Established in 1999 in MI.
Donors: William Shurlow; Wanda Shurlow.
Grantmaker type: Independent foundation.
Financial data (yr. ended 12/31/04): Assets, $184,303 (M); gifts received, $2,000; expenditures, $8,765; total giving, $7,150; qualifying distributions, $7,170; giving activities include $7,150 for grants.
Purpose and activities: Giving primarily for community development and medical research.

Fields of interest: Cancer, leukemia research; Medical research; Community development.
Limitations: Applications not accepted. No grants to individuals.
Application information: Contributes only to pre-selected organizations.
Officers: William Shurlow, Pres.; Wanda Shurlow, Secy.-Treas.
EIN: 383504642

1720
Charles J. Sibert, Clarissa B. Sibert & Virginia D. Aemisegger Charitable Trust

(formerly Charles J. & Clarissa B. Sibert Trust)
444 W. University Dr.
Rochester, MI 48307

Grantmaker type: Independent foundation.
Financial data (yr. ended 12/31/05): Assets, $6,560 (M); expenditures, $756; total giving, $750; qualifying distributions, $750; giving activities include $750 for grants.
Purpose and activities: Support only for the First Congregational Church of Rochester, MI.
Fields of interest: Protestant agencies & churches.
Type of support: General/operating support.
Limitations: Applications not accepted. Giving limited to Rochester, MI. No grants to individuals.
Application information: Contributes only to a pre-selected organization.
Trustees: Susan B. Menko; Charles M. Sibert.
EIN: 386495050

1721
The Qamar Tawakul Siddiqui Charitable Foundation

428 S. Grove Rd.
Ypsilanti, MI 48198

Established in 1999 in MI.
Grantmaker type: Independent foundation.
Financial data (yr. ended 12/31/03): Assets, $37,930 (L); gifts received, $25,000; expenditures, $25,042; total giving, $25,000; qualifying distributions, $25,000; giving activities include $25,000 for 2 grants (high: $20,000; low: $5,000).
Fields of interest: International affairs, foreign policy; International affairs.
Limitations: Applications not accepted. Giving primarily in MI. No grants to individuals.
Application information: Contributes only to pre-selected organizations.
Officer: Athar Siddiqui, Pres.
EIN: 383429611

1722
Thomas Sidlik & Rebecca Boylan Foundation

c/o Northern Trust
P.O. Box 803878
Chicago, IL 60680

Established in 1998 in MI.
Donors: Rebecca A. Boylan; Thomas W. Sidlik.
Grantmaker type: Independent foundation.
Financial data (yr. ended 12/31/04): Assets, $468,915 (M); gifts received, $188,653; expenditures, $194,200; total giving, $191,118; qualifying distributions, $191,422; giving activities

include $191,118 for 22 grants (high: $100,000; low: $100).
Fields of interest: Secondary school/education; Higher education; Human services; Family services; Federated giving programs.
Limitations: Applications not accepted. Giving primarily in MI. No grants to individuals.
Application information: Contributes only to pre-selected organizations.
Directors: Rebecca A. Boylan; Thomas W. Sidlik.
EIN: 383447404
Selected grants: The following grants were reported in 2004.
$100,000 to University of Chicago, Chicago, IL.
$25,000 to Starfish Family Services, Inkster, MI.
$20,000 to New York University, New York, NY.
$13,200 to Oakland University, Rochester, MI.
$10,000 to United Way, Washtenaw, Ann Arbor, MI.
$5,550 to Detroit Institute of Arts, Detroit, MI.
$5,000 to University of Michigan, Ann Arbor, MI.
$1,000 to Detroit Science Center, Detroit, MI.
$200 to Salvation Army of Ann Arbor, Ann Arbor, MI.
$200 to Womens Committee for Hospice Care, Bloomfield Hills, MI.

1723
Siebenthaler Foundation

225 N.W. Torch Lake Dr.
Kewadin, MI 49648
Contact: Jessica E. Thompson, V.P.

Established in 2002 in MI.
Donor: William A. Siebenthaler.
Grantmaker type: Independent foundation.
Financial data (yr. ended 12/31/05): Assets, $326,775 (M); gifts received, $69,110; expenditures, $65,347; total giving, $47,692; qualifying distributions, $47,692; giving activities include $47,692 for grants.
Application information: Application form not required.
Deadline(s): None
Officers: William A. Siebenthaler, Pres.; Jessica E. Thompson, V.P. and Secy.; Jeffrey D. Terrell, V.P.; Elizabeth C. Siebenthaler, Treas.
EIN: 043662001

1724
Bill & Vi Sigmund Foundation

P.O. Box 1128
Jackson, MI 49204-1128 (517) 784-5464
Contact: Carolyn M. Pratt, Projects and Prog. Dir.

Established in 2002.
Donors: William A. Sigmund†; Violet S. Sigmund Trust; W.A. Sigmund Trust.
Grantmaker type: Independent foundation.
Financial data (yr. ended 12/31/05): Assets, $5,611,897 (M); gifts received, $1,231; expenditures, $443,542; total giving, $256,660; qualifying distributions, $422,359; giving activities include $143,500 for grants, and $113,160 for grants to individuals.
Fields of interest: Education; Youth development; Human services.
Type of support: General/operating support.
Limitations: Giving limited to Jackson and Lenawee counties, MI.
Application information: Application information is provided only after a Letter of Intent has been reviewed.

Initial approach: Letter of intent
Deadline(s): Mar. 31
Officers and Directors:* Charles C. McClafferty,* Pres. and Treas.; Ralph L. Bodman,* V.P.; Carolyn M. Pratt, Secy.; Kenneth A. Dillon; John Macchia; Marcia Pickford.
EIN: 380002491

1725
Sills Foundation, Inc.
6960 Orchard Lake Rd., Ste. 300
West Bloomfield, MI 48322

Established in 1997 in MI.
Donors: Arthur M. Sills; Rhoda Sills.
Grantmaker type: Independent foundation.
Financial data (yr. ended 4/30/05): Assets, $2,271,502 (M); gifts received, $1,615,000; expenditures, $174,401; total giving, $168,981; qualifying distributions, $168,981; giving activities include $168,981 for 53 grants (high: $50,000; low: $25).
Purpose and activities: Giving primarily for Jewish organizations.
Fields of interest: Health organizations, association; Human services; Jewish federated giving programs; Jewish agencies & temples.
Limitations: Applications not accepted. Giving primarily in MI. No grants to individuals.
Application information: Contributes only to pre-selected organizations.
Officers: Susan Sills, Pres.; Claudia Sills, Secy.; Douglas Sills, Treas.
EIN: 383352516

1726
The Silver Lining Foundation
10643 Arbour Dr.
Brighton, MI 48114-9095

Donor: Darlene Domanik.
Grantmaker type: Independent foundation.
Financial data (yr. ended 12/31/05): Assets, $27,277 (M); gifts received, $370; expenditures, $1,870; total giving, $1,500; qualifying distributions, $1,500; giving activities include $1,500 for grants.
Limitations: Applications not accepted. Giving primarily in Birmingham and Whitmore Lake, MI. No grants to individuals.
Application information: Contributes only to pre-selected organizations.
Officers: Darlene Domanik, Pres. and Treas.; Gary March, Secy.
Director: Mark Wilson.
EIN: 383384663

1727
Gilbert B. & Lila Silverman Foundation
26500 Telegraph Rd.
Southfield, MI 48034

Established in 1966 in MI.
Donors: Gilbert B. Silverman; Lila Silverman.
Grantmaker type: Independent foundation.
Financial data (yr. ended 9/30/05): Assets, $292,393 (M); gifts received, $100,000; expenditures, $109,960; total giving, $106,913; qualifying distributions, $106,913; giving activities include $106,913 for grants.

Fields of interest: Museums (ethnic/folk arts); Arts; Health organizations, association; Cancer; Medical research, institute; Jewish federated giving programs; Jewish agencies & temples.
Limitations: Applications not accepted. Giving primarily in Detroit, MI. No grants to individuals.
Application information: Contributes only to pre-selected organizations.
Officers: Gilbert B. Silverman, Pres.; Lila Silverman, V.P. and Secy.
EIN: 381796145

1728
Walter P. and Carroll B. Simmons Family Foundation
2351 River Rd.
St. Clair, MI 48079

Established in 1998.
Donors: Walter P. Simmons; Carroll B. Simmons.
Grantmaker type: Independent foundation.
Financial data (yr. ended 12/31/05): Assets, $1,457 (M); gifts received, $175; expenditures, $1,070; total giving, $400; qualifying distributions, $400; giving activities include $400 for grants.
Purpose and activities: Giving primarily to a Protestant church.
Fields of interest: Arts; Health care; American Red Cross; Salvation Army; Protestant agencies & churches.
Type of support: General/operating support.
Limitations: Applications not accepted. Giving primarily in St. Clair, MI. No grants to individuals.
Application information: Contributes only to pre-selected organizations.
Officers: Carroll B. Simmons, Pres. and Treas.; Walter P. Simmons, Secy.
Directors: Jill K. Hilty; Michael S. Simmons; Timothy P. Simmons.
EIN: 383449073

1729
Simmons Foundation
3390 Travis Pointe Rd., Ste. B
Ann Arbor, MI 48108 (734) 996-0900
Contact: David T. Simmons, Secy.

Established in 1961 in MI.
Grantmaker type: Independent foundation.
Financial data (yr. ended 12/31/05): Assets, $1,109,274 (M); expenditures, $58,266; total giving, $51,850; qualifying distributions, $51,850; giving activities include $51,850 for grants.
Fields of interest: Higher education.
Type of support: General/operating support; Equipment; Scholarship funds.
Limitations: Applications not accepted. Giving primarily in MI, with emphasis on Ann Arbor. No grants to individuals.
Application information: Contributes only to pre-selected organizations.
Officers: Constance M. Simmons, Pres.; David T. Simmons, Secy.; Steve M. Simmons, Treas.
EIN: 386075922

1730
Sinai Medical Staff Foundation
3000 Southfield Town Ctr., Ste. 2150
Southfield, MI 48075-1313 (248) 353-0150

Established in 2000 in MI.
Grantmaker type: Independent foundation.
Financial data (yr. ended 6/30/05): Assets, $3,383,002 (M); expenditures, $212,527; total giving, $183,775; qualifying distributions, $182,373; giving activities include $183,775 for 11 grants (high: $40,200; low: $100).
Purpose and activities: Support for medical research and dissemination of medical information and education in MI.
Fields of interest: Education; Health care; Medical research, institute.
Limitations: Giving limited to MI.
Application information:
Initial approach: Letter
Deadline(s): None
Officers: Robert S. Michaels, Pres.; Hugh Beckman, V.P.; Gaylord D. Alexander, Secy.-Treas.
EIN: 237078893
Selected grants: The following grants were reported in 2004.
$55,000 to Michigan State University, East Lansing, MI. 2 grants: $27,500 each to College of Osteopathic Medicine (For scholarships).
$46,400 to Rehabilitation Institute, Detroit, MI. For general support.
$27,500 to University of Michigan, School of Medicine, Ann Arbor, MI. For scholarships.
$27,500 to Wayne State University, School of Medicine, Detroit, MI. For scholarships.
$15,000 to Deaf and Hearing Impaired Service, Farmington Hills, MI. Toward Guide My Hand Project.
$900 to Council of Michigan Foundations, Grand Haven, MI. For operating support.
$100 to Beaumont Foundation, Southfield, MI. For operating support.
$100 to Planned Parenthood of Southeast Michigan, Detroit, MI. For operating support.
$100 to Womens American ORT, Detroit, MI. For operating support.

1731
Kris Sirchio Foundation
c/o Sherri Stephens
5206 Gateway Ctr., Ste. 300
Flint, MI 48507

Established in 1998 in MI.
Donor: John Kristin Sirchio.
Grantmaker type: Independent foundation.
Financial data (yr. ended 5/31/05): Assets, $12,973 (M); gifts received, $2,535; expenditures, $5,976; total giving, $5,000; qualifying distributions, $5,000; giving activities include $5,000 for grants.
Limitations: Applications not accepted. No grants to individuals.
Application information: Contributes only to pre-selected organizations.
Officer: John Kristin Sirchio, Pres.
EIN: 383416159

1732
Harry A. Sisson Charitable Trust
c/o Comerica Bank, Trust Tax Div.
P.O. Box 75000, MC 3462
Detroit, MI 48275-3462 (313) 222-4085
Contact: Janis Dudek

Established in 1952.

Donor: Harry A. Sisson†.
Grantmaker type: Independent foundation.
Financial data (yr. ended 12/31/05): Assets, $674,330 (M); expenditures, $31,998; total giving, $30,000; qualifying distributions, $30,000; giving activities include $30,000 for grants.
Type of support: Annual campaigns; Scholarship funds.
Limitations: Giving primarily in Detroit, MI. No grants to individuals.
Application information: Application form not required.
   Deadline(s): None
Trustee: Comerica Bank.
EIN: 386043587

1733
Harvey and Verdi Sjaarda Family
c/o Harvey Sjaarda
4822 Havana Ave S.W.
Wyoming, MI   49509-5028

Established in 1999 in MI.
Donors: Harvey Sjaarda; Verdi Sjaarda.
Grantmaker type: Independent foundation.
Financial data (yr. ended 12/31/05): Assets, $8,491 (M); gifts received, $15,624; expenditures, $21,499; total giving, $20,998; qualifying distributions, $20,998; giving activities include $20,998 for grants.
Fields of interest: Zoos/zoological societies; Religion.
Type of support: General/operating support.
Limitations: Applications not accepted. Giving primarily in MI. No grants to individuals.
Application information: Contributes only to pre-selected organizations.
Officers and Directors:* Verdi Sjaarda,* Pres. and Treas.; Russell Sjaarda,* V.P. and Secy.
EIN: 383465076

1734
Skandalaris Family Foundation
P.O. Box 2061
Venice, FL   34284   (941) 544-8659
FAX: (941) 408-9526;
E-mail: info@skandalaris.com; Application address for Future Leaders Merit Scholarship: 33 Bloomfield Hills Pkwy., Ste. 240, Bloomfield Hills, MI 48304, tel.: (248) 220-2004; fax: (248) 220-2038;
URL: http://www.skandalaris.com

Established in 1997 in MI.
Grantmaker type: Independent foundation.
Financial data (yr. ended 12/31/05): Assets, $24,833 (M); gifts received, $271,000; expenditures, $270,596; total giving, $238,500; qualifying distributions, $238,500; giving activities include $238,500 for 115 grants to individuals (high: $2,500; low: $2,000).
Purpose and activities: The foundation awards scholarships to a group of students, characterized by their special talents, leadership skills, unselfish ways, strong values and commitment to excellence.
Type of support: Scholarships—to individuals.
Limitations: Giving primarily to residents of MI. No support for candidates attending trade or foreign schools.

Application information: Application guidelines available on foundation Web site. Application form required.
   Deadline(s): College scholarships: Previous scholarship recipients: Apr. 15; current college students who are first time applicants and current high school students: May 1. Future Leaders Merit Scholarship: May 31
Officer: Robert J. Skandalaris, Pres.
EIN: 383394567

1735
Velma M. Skeen French Trust
c/o Southern Michigan Bank & Trust
51 W. Pearl St.
Coldwater, MI   49036

Established in 1994 in MI.
Grantmaker type: Independent foundation.
Financial data (yr. ended 12/31/05): Assets, $977,926 (M); expenditures, $73,963; total giving, $65,488; qualifying distributions, $65,488; giving activities include $65,488 for grants.
Purpose and activities: Support only for the American Cancer Society and the Michigan Heart Association.
Fields of interest: Cancer; Heart & circulatory diseases.
Limitations: Applications not accepted. Giving limited to MI. No grants to individuals.
Application information: Contributes only to 2 pre-selected organizations.
Trustee: Southern Michigan Bank & Trust.
EIN: 386418911

1736
Skendzel Family Foundation
10338 Western Hills Dr.
Traverse City, MI   49684

Established in 1999 in MI.
Donor: Jean Skendzel.
Grantmaker type: Independent foundation.
Financial data (yr. ended 12/31/05): Assets, $146,765 (M); gifts received, $26,716; expenditures, $22,490; total giving, $14,000; qualifying distributions, $14,000; giving activities include $14,000 for grants.
Limitations: Applications not accepted. Giving primarily in MI, IN, and TN. No grants to individuals.
Application information: Contributes only to pre-selected organizations.
Officers: Jean Skendzel, Pres. and Treas.; Laurence Skendzel, V.P. and Secy.
EIN: 383445050

1737
Lloyd Skillin Charitable Foundation
c/o Wells Fargo Bank West, N.A.
P.O. Box 5825, MAC 4931-022
Denver, CO   80217   (303) 293-5365

Established in 1996.
Grantmaker type: Independent foundation.
Financial data (yr. ended 12/31/02): Assets, $1,528,157 (M); expenditures, $160,291; total giving, $138,893; qualifying distributions, $138,893; giving activities include $138,893 for 1 grant.

Purpose and activities: Giving primarily for education.
Fields of interest: Higher education, university; Education.
Limitations: Applications not accepted. Giving primarily in MI. No grants to individuals.
Application information: Contributes only to pre-selected organizations.
Trustee: Wells Fargo Bank West, N.A.
EIN: 846296012

1738
Skilling and Andrews Foundation
11720 E. Shore Dr.
Whitmore Lake, MI   48189
Contact: Ann Skilling Andrews, Pres.

Established in 1996 in MI.
Donors: Hazel D. Skilling†; Hugh H. Skilling Trust.
Grantmaker type: Independent foundation.
Financial data (yr. ended 12/31/05): Assets, $1 (M); expenditures, $471,276; total giving, $469,100; qualifying distributions, $469,100; giving activities include $469,100 for 15 grants (high: $100,000; low: $500).
Purpose and activities: Giving primarily to aid new secondary schools; some support also for conservation.
Fields of interest: Secondary school/education; Environment, natural resources.
Limitations: Applications not accepted. Giving primarily in the central U.S. No grants to individuals.
Application information: Contributes only to pre-selected organizations.
Officers and Trustees:* Ann Skilling Andrews,* Pres. and Treas.; Kenneth Andrews,* V.P.; Steven Andrews,* Secy.
EIN: 383335356

1739
The Skillman Foundation
100 Talon Centre Dr., Ste. 100
Detroit, MI   48207   (313) 393-1185
Contact: Prog. Off.
FAX: (313) 393-1187; E-mail: mailbox@skillman.org; URL: http://www.skillman.org

Incorporated in 1960 in MI.
Donor: Rose P. Skillman†.
Grantmaker type: Independent foundation.
Financial data (yr. ended 12/31/04): Assets, $507,839,550 (M); expenditures, $28,321,026; total giving, $21,588,613; qualifying distributions, $24,895,508; giving activities include $21,092,046 for 150 grants (high: $1,200,000; low: $40), $496,567 for employee matching gifts, and $500,000 for loans/program-related investments.
Purpose and activities: The foundation is a resource for improving the lives of children in metropolitan Detroit, MI. Children in disadvantaged situations are of special concern. The foundation applies its resources to foster positive relationships between children and adults, support high quality learning opportunities and strengthen healthy, safe and supportive homes and communities.
Fields of interest: Visual arts; Performing arts; Arts; Education, early childhood education; Education, reading; Education; Health care; Substance abuse, services; Crime/violence prevention, youth; Food services;

Recreation; Human services; Children/youth, services; Child development, services; Family services; Homeless, human services; Economically disadvantaged; Homeless.

Type of support: General/operating support; Program development; Seed money; Scholarship funds; Employee matching gifts.

Limitations: Giving primarily in southeastern MI, with emphasis on metropolitan Detroit, and Macomb, Oakland, and Wayne counties. No support for long-term projects not being aided by other sources, sectarian religious activities, political lobbying or legislative activities, or new organizations which do not have an operational and financial history. The foundation does not make grants to organizations that had public support and revenues of less than $100,000 for the preceding year. No grants to individuals, or for endowment funds, annual campaigns, purchase, construct or renovate facilities, basic research or deficit financing; no loans.

Publications: Application guidelines; Annual report; Informational brochure (including application guidelines); Newsletter; Occasional report; Program policy statement.

Application information: The foundation accepts grant applications online. Application form required.

> *Initial approach:* Letter of intent
> *Copies of proposal:* 1
> *Deadline(s):* None
> *Board meeting date(s):* Feb., Apr., June, Sept., and Nov.
> *Final notification:* 6 weeks after board meeting

Officers and Trustees:* Lillian Bauder,* Chair.; Stephen E. Ewing,* Vice-Chair.; Carol A. Goss, C.E.O. and Pres.; Andrea Cole, Treas. and Dir., Finance; Alan Harris, C.I.O.; Lizabeth Ardisana; Ralph W. Babb, Jr.; William M. Brodhead; Walter E. Douglas; Edsel B. Ford II; David Baker Lewis; Amyre Makupson; Robert S. Taubman; Jane R. Thomas.

Number of staff: 10 full-time professional; 5 full-time support.

EIN: 381675780

Selected grants: The following grants were reported in 2005.

$1,500,000 to Local Initiatives Support Corporation (LISC), New York, NY. For Neighborhoods NOW, effort to develop public safety, education, workforce development, child care, health care, business assistance and other community services, payable over 3 years.

$500,000 to Communication and Media Arts High School, Detroit, MI. To transform Communication and Media Arts High School into small high school model of success.

$500,000 to Michigan Womens Foundation, Livonia, MI. To expand Young Women for Change youth grantmaking program in four Detroit neighborhoods (Brightmoor, Cody/Rouge, Chadsey/Condon and Vernor), payable over 3 years.

$450,000 to Wayne State University, Detroit, MI. For evaluation of Good Schools Making the Grade Initiative, payable over 3 years.

$400,000 to High Tech High Foundation, San Diego, CA. To provide technical assistance to new urban High Tech High inspired school, payable over 3 years.

$380,000 to Marygrove College, Detroit, MI. To expand Marygrove College Technical Assistance Center for Good Schools Initiative.

$373,500 to Southwest Counseling and Development Services, Detroit, MI. To offer family literacy programs to low-income Latino

families and build capacity of community to increase awareness and access to early childhood education programs, payable over 3 years.

$300,000 to Focus: Hope, Detroit, MI. To expand youth photography program and offer high school students opportunities to work with professional artists as instructors and mentors, payable over 3 years.

$300,000 to Michigans Children, Lansing, MI. To increase public awareness of public investments in children in state budget and to enhance ability of policymakers and public to be involved in budget advocacy, payable over 3 years.

$300,000 to Oakland Livingston Human Service Agency, Pontiac, MI. To align multiple social service agencies support systems for children of incarcerated and probationer parents, particularly fathers, payable over 3 years.

1740
Michael S. and Jill S. Skrzypczak Foundation
1059 Pointe Place Dr.
Rochester, MI 48307

Established in 1998 in MI.
Grantmaker type: Independent foundation.
Financial data (yr. ended 12/31/04): Assets, $6,398 (M); expenditures, $2,119; total giving, $1,345; qualifying distributions, $1,345; giving activities include $1,345 for grants.
Limitations: Applications not accepted. No grants to individuals.
Application information: Contributes only to pre-selected organizations.
Officers: Michael S. Skrzypczak, Pres.; Jill S. Skrzypczak, Secy.
EIN: 383385885

1741
The D. Jerome and Margery C. Slack Foundation
3687 Courtney Pl.
Traverse City, MI 49684-8810
Contact: D. Jerome Slack, Pres.

Established in 1995 in MI.
Donor: D. Jerome Slack.
Grantmaker type: Independent foundation.
Financial data (yr. ended 12/31/05): Assets, $314,124 (M); expenditures, $21,102; total giving, $16,200; qualifying distributions, $16,200; giving activities include $16,200 for grants.
Fields of interest: Higher education; Christian agencies & churches.
Type of support: Scholarship funds.
Limitations: Giving limited to MI.
Officers: D. Jerome Slack, Pres.; Margery C. Slack, V.P.
EIN: 383265519

1742
Stephan F. & Mary E. Slavik Foundation Charitable Trust
5152 Mirror Lake Ct.
West Bloomfield, MI 48323

Established in 1984 in MI.
Grantmaker type: Independent foundation.

Financial data (yr. ended 12/31/04): Assets, $601,447 (M); expenditures, $32,205; total giving, $31,100; qualifying distributions, $31,156; giving activities include $31,100 for grants.
Fields of interest: Hospitals (general); Cancer research; Boy scouts; American Red Cross; Salvation Army.
Limitations: Applications not accepted. Giving primarily in MI. No grants to individuals.
Application information: Contributes only to pre-selected organizations.
Trustees: Lawrence Carey; Mary E. Slavik; Richard Slavik; Stephan F. Slavik, Sr.
EIN: 382746844

1743
Joseph F. & Edna Slavik Foundation
32605 W. 12 Mile Rd., Ste. 350
Farmington Hills, MI 48334

Established in 1980 in MI.
Donor: Joseph F. Slavik.
Grantmaker type: Independent foundation.
Financial data (yr. ended 12/31/04): Assets, $1,216,526 (M); expenditures, $108,645; total giving, $97,530; qualifying distributions, $97,586; giving activities include $97,530 for 30 grants (high: $25,000; low: $130).
Fields of interest: Arts; Education; Health care; Medical research, institute; Children/youth, services; Christian agencies & churches.
Type of support: General/operating support.
Limitations: Applications not accepted. Giving in the U.S., primarily in MA. No grants to individuals.
Application information: Contributes only to pre-selected organizations.
Directors: Berneda Meeks; Edna Slavik.
Number of staff: 1 full-time support.
EIN: 382744923

1744
Slemons Foundation
c/o Standard Federal Bank N.A., Wealth Mgmt.
P.O. Box 1707
Grand Rapids, MI 49501-1707
Contact: John Bergstrom, Pres.
Additional address: c/o Kate Luckert, Grand Rapids Community Foundation, 209C Waters Bldg., Grand Rapids, MI 49503

Established in 1995 in MI.
Donor: Elmer & Mabel Slemons Trust.
Grantmaker type: Independent foundation.
Financial data (yr. ended 8/31/05): Assets, $1,894 (M); gifts received, $178,000; expenditures, $178,950; total giving, $162,000; qualifying distributions, $178,924; giving activities include $162,000 for 19 grants (high: $25,000; low: $1,000).
Purpose and activities: Support primarily for a library foundation, a Congregational church, and human services.
Fields of interest: Museums; Libraries (public); Health organizations, association; Human services; Community development; Protestant agencies & churches.
Type of support: General/operating support; Capital campaigns; Building/renovation; Program development.
Limitations: Applications not accepted. Giving limited to Grand Rapids, MI. No grants to individuals.

Application information: Contributes only to pre-selected organizations.

Officers: John Bergstrom, Pres.; Brian Heaney, V.P.; Sharon Burtrum, Secy.-Treas.

EIN: 386107913

Selected grants: The following grants were reported in 2003.

$100,000 to Saint Marys Doran Foundation, Grand Rapids, MI.

$66,250 to Michigan Family Independence Agency, Lansing, MI. For Kent County early impact program.

$50,000 to Public Museum of Grand Rapids, Grand Rapids, MI. For Dead Sea Scrolls Exhibition.

$43,000 to Steepletown Neighborhood Services, Grand Rapids, MI.

$37,328 to Family Outreach Center, Grand Rapids, MI.

$33,000 to ArtWorks, Grand Rapids, MI. For job skills program.

$25,000 to American Lung Association of Michigan, Grand Rapids, MI. For anti-tobacco program.

$25,000 to Gildas Club Grand Rapids, Grand Rapids, MI.

$25,000 to Lighthouse Communities, Grand Rapids, MI.

$20,000 to Mayflower Congregational Church, Grand Rapids, MI. For shuttle bus.

1745
Slikkers Foundation

725 E. 40th St.
Holland, MI   49423

Established in 1998 in MI.

Donors: David A. Slikkers; Mary B. Slikkers; Leon R. Slikkers; Dolores E. Slikkers; Mark Ringwelski; Susan Ringwelski; S 2 Yachts; L&D Foundation; RBS Foundation.

Grantmaker type: Independent foundation.

Financial data (yr. ended 12/31/05): Assets, $2,185,210 (M); gifts received, $2,051,880; expenditures, $733,151; total giving, $731,848; qualifying distributions, $731,848; giving activities include $731,848 for 24+ grants (high: $300,000).

Purpose and activities: Giving primarily to Seventh-day Adventist churches, agencies, and schools.

Fields of interest: Arts; Human services; Protestant agencies & churches.

Type of support: General/operating support.

Limitations: Applications not accepted. Giving in the U.S., with emphasis on in MI. No grants to individuals.

Application information: Contributes only to pre-selected organizations.

Officer and Trustees:* Robert L. Slikkers,* Pres. and Secy.; David A. Slikkers; Dolores E. Slikkers; Leon R. Slikkers; Thomas B. Slikkers; Susan K. Slikkers-Ringwelski.

EIN: 383431246

1746
The David and Mary Slikkers Foundation

c/o David A. Slikkers
13 Carousel Ln.
Holland, MI   49423-8930

Established in 1999 in MI.

Donors: David A. Slikkers; Mary B. Slikkers.

Grantmaker type: Independent foundation.

Financial data (yr. ended 12/31/05): Assets, $259,725 (M); gifts received, $252,254; expenditures, $16,290; total giving, $16,290; qualifying distributions, $16,290; giving activities include $16,290 for grants.

Fields of interest: Community development, volunteer services; Foundations (private grantmaking).

Type of support: General/operating support.

Limitations: Applications not accepted. No grants to individuals.

Application information: Contributes only to pre-selected organizations.

Officer and Directors:* David A. Slikkers,* Pres.; Lee Slikkers; Mary B. Slikkers; Steve Slikkers.

EIN: 383470751

1747
Suzanne Sloat and Ray Okonski Foundation

25050 Skye Dr.
Farmington Hills, MI   48336
Contact: Raymond N. Okonski, Chair.

Established in 1997 in MI.

Donors: Raymond N. Okonski; Suzanne M. Sloat.

Grantmaker type: Independent foundation.

Financial data (yr. ended 4/30/05): Assets, $164,037 (M); gifts received, $10,000; expenditures, $43,663; total giving, $39,945; qualifying distributions, $39,945; giving activities include $39,945 for grants.

Fields of interest: Higher education; Education; Cancer; Multiple sclerosis; Alzheimer's disease; Food services; Boy scouts; Religion.

Type of support: General/operating support.

Limitations: Applications not accepted. Giving primarily in MI. No grants to individuals.

Application information: Contributes only to pre-selected organizations.

Officers: Raymond N. Okonski, Chair., V.P. and Treas.; Suzanne M. Sloat, Pres. and Secy.

EIN: 383352871

1748
George M. & Mabel H. Slocum Foundation

114 Moorings Park Dr., No. A-401
Naples, FL   34105
Contact: William W. Slocum, Jr., Tr.

Established in 1957 in MI.

Donor: Mabel H. Slocum†.

Grantmaker type: Independent foundation.

Financial data (yr. ended 7/31/05): Assets, $258,783 (M); expenditures, $182,562; total giving, $179,120; qualifying distributions, $181,265; giving activities include $179,120 for 58 grants (high: $50,000; low: $250).

Purpose and activities: Giving to art and culture, education, youth and family services, and health and human services.

Fields of interest: Higher education; Education; Environment, natural resources; Environment; Reproductive health, family planning; Health care; Health organizations, association; Children/youth, services; Family services; Residential/custodial care, hospices.

Type of support: General/operating support.

Limitations: Giving primarily in FL, MI, and NY. No grants to individuals.

Application information:

Initial approach: Letter
Deadline(s): None

Trustees: Elizabeth Slocum; Jody Slocum; William W. Slocum, Jr.

EIN: 386092065

1749
Faith F. Small Foundation

P.O. Box 572
Jackson, MI   49204-0572

Established in 2002 in MI.

Donor: Faith F. Small.

Grantmaker type: Independent foundation.

Financial data (yr. ended 12/31/05): Assets, $4,500 (M); gifts received, $1,992; expenditures, $1,060; total giving, $500; qualifying distributions, $500; giving activities include $500 for grants.

Fields of interest: Museums (art); Performing arts, orchestra (symphony); Higher education; Children/youth, services.

Limitations: Applications not accepted. No grants to individuals.

Application information: Contributes only to pre-selected organizations.

Trustees: Lawrence L. Bullen; S. Brian Jurasek; Faith F. Small.

EIN: 016185817

1750
R. V. Small Trust f/b/o Cascades Humane Society

c/o Comerica Bank
P.O. Box 75000, MC 3302
Detroit, MI   48275

Established in 1996 in MI.

Donor: R.V. Small†.

Grantmaker type: Independent foundation.

Financial data (yr. ended 12/31/05): Assets, $86,179 (M); expenditures, $6,449; total giving, $5,000; qualifying distributions, $5,000; giving activities include $5,000 for grants.

Purpose and activities: Support only for Cascades Humane Society.

Limitations: Applications not accepted. Giving limited to MI. No grants to individuals.

Application information: Contributes only to a pre-selected organization.

Trustee: Comerica Bank.

EIN: 386677649

1751
The Florence J. Smallegan Family Foundation

c/o Kenneth D. Smallegan
2698 32nd Ave.
Hudsonville, MI   49426-9684

Established in 2002 in MI.

Donor: Florence J. Smallegan Charitable Remainder Unitrust.

Grantmaker type: Independent foundation.

Financial data (yr. ended 12/31/05): Assets, $433,609 (M); gifts received, $64,359; expenditures, $251,632; total giving, $60,496; qualifying distributions, $60,496; giving activities include $60,496 for grants.

Limitations: Applications not accepted. No grants to individuals.

Application information: Contributes only to pre-selected organizations.
Officers: Kenneth D. Smallegan, Pres.; Judith Smallegan, V.P.
Board Members: Dana Brower; Karen Smallegan; Kevin Smallegan; Lisa Smallegan.
EIN: 412055038

1752
Russell H. & Maxine E. Smith Charitable Foundation
900 Center Ave.
Bay City, MI   48708

Established in 1998 in MI.
Donor: Maxine E. Smith.
Grantmaker type: Independent foundation.
Financial data (yr. ended 12/31/05): Assets, $2,376,524 (M); expenditures, $122,213; total giving, $101,653; qualifying distributions, $120,525; giving activities include $101,653 for grants.
Fields of interest: Libraries (public); Foundations (public).
Limitations: Applications not accepted. Giving primarily in MI. No grants to individuals.
Application information: Contributes only to pre-selected organizations.
Officers and Trustees:* Dominic Monastiere,* Pres. and Treas.; Jean Hill,* V.P.; Robert D. Sarow,* Secy.; James W. Patterson.
EIN: 382978504

1753
Jason L. and Carrie M. Smith Charitable Trust
c/o Comerica Bank
P.O. Box 75000
Detroit, MI   48275-3302

Grantmaker type: Independent foundation.
Financial data (yr. ended 3/31/05): Assets, $749,685 (M); expenditures, $50,469; total giving, $40,000; qualifying distributions, $40,000; giving activities include $40,000 for grants.
Fields of interest: Education; Hospitals (general); Health organizations, association; Children/youth, services.
Limitations: Applications not accepted. Giving limited to FL. No grants to individuals.
Application information: Contributes only to pre-selected organizations.
Trustee: Comerica Bank.
EIN: 591952016

1754
Earla B. Smith Educational Foundation
c/o Stephen W. Jones
200 E. Long Lake Rd., Ste. 110
Bloomfield Hills, MI   48304
Contact: Earla B. Smith, Pres.
Application address: 2434 Evergreen Dr., Royal Oak, MI 48073

Established in 1994 in MI.
Donor: Earla B. Smith.
Grantmaker type: Independent foundation.
Financial data (yr. ended 12/31/04): Assets, $125,221 (M); gifts received, $17,467; expenditures, $4,665; total giving, $1,000;

qualifying distributions, $1,000; giving activities include $1,000 for grants.
Purpose and activities: Scholarship award paid directly to the college or university on behalf of a graduating student of Troy High School or Athens High School in Troy, MI.
Type of support: Scholarship funds.
Limitations: Applications not accepted. Giving limited to residents of Troy, MI. No grants to individuals directly.
Application information: Unsolicited requests for funds not accepted.
Officers: Earla B. Smith, Pres.; Stephen W. Jones, Secy.; Kendal McKinney, Treas.; Doris Rains, Treas.
EIN: 383149017

1755
Arthur L. & Carra J. Smith Family Foundation
428 Yale Ave.
Alma, MI   48801   (989) 463-3779
Contact: Karen L. Smith, Secy.-Treas.

Established in 2002 in MI.
Donors: Arthur L. Smith; Carra J. Smith.
Grantmaker type: Independent foundation.
Financial data (yr. ended 12/31/04): Assets, $2,702,383 (M); gifts received, $992,268; expenditures, $379,057; total giving, $378,859; qualifying distributions, $378,859; giving activities include $378,859 for 1 grant.
Purpose and activities: Giving primarily to a liberal arts college.
Fields of interest: Higher education; American Red Cross.
Limitations: Giving primarily in MI.
Application information:
   Initial approach: Letter
   Deadline(s): None
Officers: Arthur L. Smith, Pres.; Carra J. Smith, V.P.; Karen L. Smith, Secy.-Treas.
EIN: 371451908

1756
Bill & Lois Smith Family Foundation
1108 Lincoln Rd.
Allegan, MI   49010

Established in 1999 in MI.
Donors: Billy W. Smith; Wesley H. Smith; Cassandra J. Aitkens.
Grantmaker type: Independent foundation.
Financial data (yr. ended 12/31/05): Assets, $3,092,846 (M); expenditures, $45,499; total giving, $11,500; qualifying distributions, $15,445; giving activities include $11,500 for 3 grants (high: $8,000; low: $500).
Fields of interest: Education; Christian agencies & churches; Protestant agencies & churches; Religion.
Type of support: Continuing support; Capital campaigns.
Limitations: Applications not accepted. Giving primarily in western MI. No grants to individuals.
Application information: Contributes only to pre-selected organizations.
Officers: Billy W. Smith, Pres.; Lois Smith, V.P.; Cassandra J. Atkins, Secy.; Wesley H. Smith, Treas.
EIN: 383472742
Selected grants: The following grants were reported in 2004.

$157,500 to Otsego Christian School, Gaylord, MI. 2 grants: $35,000 (For operating support), $122,500 (For general support).
$50,000 to First Baptist Church of Allegan, Allegan, MI. For operating support.
$30,000 to Beechpoint Christian Camp, Allegan, MI. For operating support.
$4,500 to Closed Door Ministries, Grand Rapids, MI. For operating support.
$2,500 to International Aid, Spring Lake, MI. For operating support.
$1,000 to Salvation Army National Headquarters, Alexandria, VA. For operating support.

1757
Don & Dolly Smith Foundation
P.O. Box 187
Grosse Ile, MI   48138-0187

Grantmaker type: Independent foundation.
Financial data (yr. ended 6/30/05): Assets, $165,276 (M); expenditures, $4,405; total giving, $1,270; qualifying distributions, $1,270; giving activities include $1,270 for grants.
Limitations: Applications not accepted. Giving primarily in MI. No grants to individuals.
Application information: Contributes only to pre-selected organizations.
Officers: Dolly Smith, Pres.; Gary Spicer, V.P.; Roger D. Smith, Secy.-Treas.
Director: Jan Smith.
EIN: 386077425

1758
Isabel Francis Smith and Ralph Lawrence Smith Foundation
7110 Paterese Dr.
Bloomfield Hills, MI   48301

Established in 1997 in MI.
Donors: Ralph L. Smith; Isabel F. Smith.
Grantmaker type: Independent foundation.
Financial data (yr. ended 4/30/05): Assets, $396,595 (M); gifts received, $36,020; expenditures, $20,722; total giving, $19,190; qualifying distributions, $19,190; giving activities include $19,190 for grants.
Limitations: Applications not accepted. Giving primarily in MI. No grants to individuals.
Application information: Contributes only to pre-selected organizations.
Officers and Directors:* Isabel F. Smith,* Pres.; Ralph L. Smith,* Treas.; Hugh M. Smith; Mark L. Smith; Isabel Claire Smith-Hornung.
EIN: 383348122

1759
Jay C. and Dariel S. Smith Foundation, Inc.
1780 Vernier, Ste. 2
Grosse Pointe Woods, MI   48236

Donors: Jay C. Smith; Dariel S. Smith.
Grantmaker type: Independent foundation.
Financial data (yr. ended 12/31/05): Assets, $408,396 (M); expenditures, $25,166; total giving, $25,000; qualifying distributions, $25,000; giving activities include $25,000 for grants.
Fields of interest: Ear & throat diseases; Alzheimer's disease.

Limitations: Applications not accepted. Giving primarily in MI and OR. No grants to individuals.
Application information: Contributes only to pre-selected organizations.
Officers: Jay C. Smith, Pres. and Treas.; Dariel S. Smith, V.P.; E. Peter Drolet, Secy.
EIN: 383494423

1760
William H. and Patricia M. Smith Foundation
26479 Greythorne Trail
Farmington Hills, MI 48334

Established in 1994 in MI.
Donor: William H. Smith.
Grantmaker type: Independent foundation.
Financial data (yr. ended 6/30/05): Assets, $2,171,789 (M); expenditures, $62,768; total giving, $40,100; qualifying distributions, $40,100; giving activities include $40,100 for grants.
Fields of interest: Museums; Performing arts; Arts; General charitable giving.
Limitations: Applications not accepted. Giving primarily in Detroit, MI. No grants to individuals.
Application information: Contributes only to pre-selected organizations.
Officers and Trustees:* William H. Smith,* Pres.; Patricia M. Smith,* V.P.; Wendy A. Kubitskey, Secy.-Treas.; Kendall A. Smith; Scott D. Smith.
EIN: 383213042

1761
Jean M. R. Smith Foundation
c/o Robert A. Sajdak
1200 Earhart Rd., No. 506
Ann Arbor, MI 48105-2768 (734) 663-4385
Contact: Edward J. Moore, Treas.
Application address: 64 Westland Dr., Bad Axe, MI 48413, tel.: (989) 269-9909

Established in 1997 in MI.
Donor: Jean M.R. Smith.
Grantmaker type: Independent foundation.
Financial data (yr. ended 12/31/05): Assets, $1,144,679 (M); expenditures, $69,065; total giving, $47,106; qualifying distributions, $47,106; giving activities include $47,106 for grants to individuals.
Purpose and activities: Scholarships awards given to residents of Huron County, MI.
Type of support: Scholarships—to individuals.
Limitations: Giving primarily to residents of Huron County, MI.
Application information: Individual applicants should submit academic records and 2 letters of reference.
Deadline(s): Senior year of high school
Officers: Jean M.R. Smith, Pres.; Robert Sajdak, Secy.; Edward J. Moore, Treas.
Directors: Richard M. Mieitinen; John Schwedler.
EIN: 383323030

1762
Sneed Foundation, Inc.
Philtower Bldg.
427 S. Boston Ave., Ste. 309
Tulsa, OK 74103-4167

Established in 1982 in OK.

Donor: Cornelia L. Sneed†.
Grantmaker type: Independent foundation.
Financial data (yr. ended 6/30/05): Assets, $716,016 (M); gifts received, $1,622; expenditures, $35,158; total giving, $28,050; qualifying distributions, $28,050; giving activities include $28,050 for grants.
Purpose and activities: Giving primarily for religion and education.
Fields of interest: Arts; Education; Pediatrics research; Human services; Protestant agencies & churches.
Type of support: General/operating support.
Limitations: Applications not accepted. Giving in the U.S., primarily in CO, MI, and OK. No grants to individuals.
Application information: Contributes only to pre-selected organizations.
Officers and Directors:* James Sneed,* Chair. and Pres; Ann S. Schriber,* V.P.; Jane B. Sneed,* V.P; Robert E. Sneed,* V.P.; Mary L. Martin, Secy.; Patti P. Brown, Treas.
EIN: 731168046

1763
The Joanie and Ira Snider Family Foundation
35980 Woodward Ave., Ste. 325
Bloomfield Hills, MI 48304-0903

Established in 1991 in MI.
Donors: Joan Snider; Ira Snider.
Grantmaker type: Independent foundation.
Financial data (yr. ended 12/31/04): Assets, $10,824 (M); expenditures, $870; total giving, $325; qualifying distributions, $325; giving activities include $325 for grants.
Fields of interest: Jewish federated giving programs; Jewish agencies & temples.
Limitations: Applications not accepted. No grants to individuals.
Application information: Contributes only to pre-selected organizations.
Officers: Ira Snider, Pres.; Joan Snider, Secy.-Treas.
EIN: 383002955

1764
Snyder Christian Environmental Preservation Foundation
7628 Sunset Trail
Mancelona, MI 49659-9802

Donor: Harold Z. Snyder.
Grantmaker type: Independent foundation.
Financial data (yr. ended 4/30/05): Assets, $68,677 (M); gifts received, $15,707; expenditures, $67,732; total giving, $0; qualifying distributions, $0.
Limitations: Applications not accepted. Giving primarily in Spring Arbor, MI. No grants to individuals.
Application information: Contributes only to pre-selected organizations.
Officers: Rev. Mark Willey, Pres.; James A. Snyder, V.P.; Steve Snyder, Secy.; Charles Stankey, Treas.
Trustee: Rick Duerksen.
EIN: 382385269

1765
The Snyder Foundation, Inc.
7029 Gilroy Ct.
Spring Arbor, MI 49283-9662 (517) 750-2778
Contact: Clarence A. Snyder, Treas.

Established in 1944 in MI.
Donors: Clarence A. Snyder†; Mrs. Clarence A. Snyder†.
Grantmaker type: Independent foundation.
Financial data (yr. ended 12/31/04): Assets, $217,172 (M); gifts received, $13,981; expenditures, $25,095; total giving, $21,250; qualifying distributions, $21,250; giving activities include $21,250 for grants.
Purpose and activities: Giving to the Free Methodist Missions in Africa. Giving includes scholarship programs for worthy national students in Rwanda, Africa, for advanced training based on a selection process and criteria established at Mission Hospital in Kibogora, Africa.
Fields of interest: Medical school/education; Education; Hospitals (general); Health care; Human services; Religious federated giving programs; Christian agencies & churches; Religion.
International interests: Africa.
Type of support: General/operating support; Scholarship funds.
Limitations: Giving primarily in Africa. No grants to individuals.
Application information:
Initial approach: Letter
Deadline(s): None
Officers: Arthur H. Snyder, Pres.; Ruth E. White, V.P.; Harold F. Snyder, Secy.; Clarence A. Snyder, Treas.
EIN: 381710360

1766
Peter & Dorothy Solomon Foundation
(formerly Peter Solomon Foundation)
2855 Coolidge Hwy., No. 101A
Troy, MI 48084

Established in 1991 in MI.
Grantmaker type: Independent foundation.
Financial data (yr. ended 12/31/04): Assets, $4,611,372 (M); gifts received, $1,890,852; expenditures, $233,166; total giving, $18,000; qualifying distributions, $187,013; giving activities include $18,000 for grants.
Limitations: Applications not accepted. Giving primarily in MI. No grants to individuals.
Application information: Contributes only to pre-selected organizations.
Officers and Directors:* Richard E. Penoyar, Jr.,* Pres. and Treas.; Doris E. Wenban,* V.P.; Darlene Hood,* Secy.; Thomas Houghtaling; Helen Ison.
EIN: 382956333

1767
The Sonneveldt Foundation
18042 Wildwood Springs Pkwy.
Spring Lake, MI 49456
Contact: Carol A. Sonneveldt, Pres.

Established in 1988 in MI.
Grantmaker type: Independent foundation.
Financial data (yr. ended 12/31/05): Assets, $1,108,478 (M); gifts received, $1,900; expenditures, $69,203; total giving, $54,200;

qualifying distributions, $54,200; giving activities include $54,200 for grants.
Purpose and activities: Giving for higher education tuition assistance scholarships directly to the institution for persons or children of persons who have been involved in substantial Christian service resulting in the need for financial assistance to attend college or trade school.
Fields of interest: Higher education; Theological school/education; Scholarships/financial aid; Christian agencies & churches.
Limitations: Giving primarily in the Midwest.
Application information: Application form required.
Initial approach: Letter
Deadline(s): June 1
Officers and Directors:* Carol A. Sonneveldt,* Pres. and Treas.; Sharon S. Everest; Lance C. Sonneveldt; Robyn J. Sonneveldt.
EIN: 382835613

1768
Souder Family Foundation
c/o The Northern Trust Bank of FL
P.O. Box 803878
Chicago, IL 60680
Application address: c/o The Northern Trust Bank of FL, 700 Brickell Ave., Miami, FL 33131

Established in 1986 in FL.
Donors: William F. Souder, Jr. Charitable Lead Trust; Susanna J. Souder.
Grantmaker type: Independent foundation.
Financial data (yr. ended 12/31/04): Assets, $12,728,098 (M); gifts received, $565,513; expenditures, $629,445; total giving, $556,271; qualifying distributions, $558,101; giving activities include $556,271 for 37 grants (high: $115,000; low: $500).
Purpose and activities: Giving primarily for education and health care, and to Protestant organizations, particularly to a Presbyterian church.
Fields of interest: Museums (children's); Historic preservation/historical societies; Higher education; Medical school/education; Education; Zoos/zoological societies; Aquariums; Hospitals (general); Health care; Human services; Children/youth, services; Protestant agencies & churches.
Type of support: General/operating support; Annual campaigns; Building/renovation.
Limitations: Giving primarily in FL, IL, MI, and WI. No grants to individuals.
Application information: Application form not required.
Deadline(s): None
Directors: Paul Schwab; Susanna J. Souder; William F. Souder, Jr.
EIN: 391560019

1769
Southeastern Michigan Chapter NECA Educational and Research Foundation
25180 Lahser Rd.
Southfield, MI 48037 (248) 355-3500
Application address: c/o Scholarship Committee, P.O. Box 385, Southfield, MI 48037

Established in 2003 in MI.
Donor: Electrical Industry Educational Fund.
Grantmaker type: Independent foundation.
Financial data (yr. ended 12/31/05): Assets, $673,205 (M); expenditures, $79,294; total giving,

$68,788; qualifying distributions, $68,788; giving activities include $68,788 for grants.
Purpose and activities: Scholarship awards paid directly to college or university for employees of SMC/NECA and their relatives.
Fields of interest: Higher education.
Type of support: Scholarship funds.
Application information: Application form required.
Deadline(s): Apr. 15
Directors: Art Ashley; John Colley; John Munro; Tim Shaw; Daniel T. Tripp.
EIN: 300134735

1770
The Southeastern Michigan Tarbut Foundation
1301 W. Long Lake Rd., Ste. 200
Troy, MI 48098-6348
Contact: Joel M. Nass, Pres.

Established in 1998 in MI.
Grantmaker type: Independent foundation.
Financial data (yr. ended 12/31/04): Assets, $20,594 (M); gifts received, $3,145; expenditures, $2,185; total giving, $2,145; qualifying distributions, $2,145; giving activities include $2,145 for grants.
Fields of interest: Jewish agencies & temples.
Application information:
Initial approach: Letter
Deadline(s): None
Officer: Joel M. Nass, Pres.
Directors: Hugh Parks; Rabbi Norman T. Roman.
EIN: 383360386

1771
Southfield Radiology Association Foundation
23100 Providence Dr., Ste. 420
Southfield, MI 48075

Established in 2004 in MI.
Donor: Members of the Southfield Radiology Assn.
Grantmaker type: Independent foundation.
Financial data (yr. ended 12/31/05): Assets, $213,976 (M); gifts received, $126,928; expenditures, $24,698; total giving, $10,000; qualifying distributions, $24,698; giving activities include $10,000 for grants.
Limitations: Applications not accepted. No grants to individuals.
Application information: Contributes only to pre-selected organizations.
Officers: Roger L. Gonda, Jr., M.D., Pres.; Allan D. Frailberg, M.D., V.P. and Treas.; Henry M. Nirenberg, Secy.
EIN: 201752541

1772
Southwest Michigan Rehab Foundation
100 Peet's Cove
Battle Creek, MI 49015
Contact: Cheryl Humbarger, Grant Coord.

Established in 1991 in MI.
Donor: Southwest Regional Rehabilitation Center.
Grantmaker type: Independent foundation.
Financial data (yr. ended 12/31/05): Assets, $1,973,342 (M); expenditures, $435,699; total giving, $427,571; qualifying distributions,

$433,801; giving activities include $404,871 for 4 grants (high: $400,000; low: $500), and $22,699 for 45 grants to individuals (high: $2,000; low: $30; average: $130–$1,000).
Purpose and activities: Aid to people with temporary or permanent conditions related to handicap, including prosthetics and equipment for home enablement.
Fields of interest: Physical therapy; Disabilities, people with.
Type of support: Equipment.
Limitations: Giving limited to residents of southwestern MI, with emphasis on the Battle Creek area, including Calhoun County.
Publications: Informational brochure.
Application information: Application form required.
Initial approach: Request application form
Copies of proposal: 1
Deadline(s): Fri. prior to board meetings
Board meeting date(s): 3rd Thurs. of each month
Final notification: 2 weeks after board meeting
Officers and Directors:* Carl F. Greene,* Pres.; Richard Allen, M.D.*, V.P.; Robert Humbarger,* Secy.; William Comai, M.D.*, Treas.; David Marousek; Roger Mattens; Marilyn Sharp; Jan Smith.
Number of staff: 1 part-time support.
EIN: 382939930

1773
The Spark Foundation
2414 Red Maple Ct.
Troy, MI 48084

Established in 2004 in MI.
Grantmaker type: Independent foundation.
Financial data (yr. ended 12/31/05): Assets, $8,893 (M); gifts received, $17,879; expenditures, $16,124; total giving, $15,935; qualifying distributions, $15,935; giving activities include $15,935 for grants.
Limitations: Giving primarily in Troy and Detroit, MI. No grants to individuals.
Trustees: Lawrence D. Piotrowski; Nancy Piotrowski.
EIN: 201524555

1774
William F. Sparling Trust
c/o Citizens Bank Wealth Mgmt., N.A.
328 S. Saginaw St., M/C 002072
Flint, MI 48502

Established in MI.
Grantmaker type: Independent foundation.
Financial data (yr. ended 4/30/05): Assets, $98,379 (M); expenditures, $2,286; total giving, $0; qualifying distributions, $218.
Purpose and activities: Support only for the Children's Home of Detroit, Grosse Pointe Woods, MI.
Fields of interest: Residential/custodial care.
Limitations: Applications not accepted. Giving limited to Grosse Pointe Woods, MI. No grants to individuals.
Application information: Contributes only to a pre-selected organization specified in the trust instrument.
Trustee: Citizens Bank.
EIN: 382437047

1775
The Spartan Motors Private Foundation
1000 Reynolds Rd.
Charlotte, MI   48813
Contact: Janine L. Nierenberger, Dir.

Established in 1995 in MI.
Donor: Spartan Motors, Inc.
Grantmaker type: Independent foundation.
Financial data (yr. ended 12/31/04): Assets, $5,988 (M); gifts received, $100,000; expenditures, $187,845; total giving, $185,322; qualifying distributions, $187,841; giving activities include $185,322 for 65 grants (high: $104,748; low: $75).
Fields of interest: Higher education; Hospitals (general); Health organizations, association; Cancer; Aging, centers/services; Federated giving programs.
Limitations: Giving primarily in MI.
Application information:
   Initial approach: Letter
   Deadline(s): None
Officers: George W. Sztykiel, Pres.; John R. Gaedert, Secy.; Richard J. Schalter, Treas.
Director: Janine L. Nierenberger.
EIN: 383212131

1776
Speckhard-Knight Charitable Foundation
771 Bogey Ct.
Ann Arbor, MI   48103   (734) 761-8752
Contact: Gerald Knight, Pres.
E-mail: info@skcf.org; fax for completed applications: (734) 827-0091; URL: http://www.skcf.org

Established in 1999 in MI.
Donors: Gerald Knight; Maureen Knight.
Grantmaker type: Independent foundation.
Financial data (yr. ended 12/31/05): Assets, $5,174,244 (M); gifts received, $44,838; expenditures, $236,179; total giving, $201,100; qualifying distributions, $205,746; giving activities include $201,100 for 16 grants (high: $60,000; low: $900).
Purpose and activities: The foundation is dedicated to improving the quality of life in Jackson and Washtenaw Counties in MI, and aiding environmental efforts in the third world. The foundation strives to assist nonprofit organizations that work in the important areas of adoption, foster care, at risk families and the environment.
Fields of interest: Education; Environment; Health care; Human services; Children, adoption; Children, foster care.
Type of support: General/operating support; Land acquisition; Program development.
Limitations: Giving primarily in MI.
Application information: Council of Michigan Foundations Common Grant Application Form accepted. Application form required.
   Initial approach: E-mail
   Copies of proposal: 1
   Deadline(s): None
Directors: Gerald Knight; Maureen Knight.
EIN: 383466344

1777
Peter and Evelyn Speerstra Scholarship Fund Trust
c/o Fifth Third Bank
P.O. Box 3636
Grand Rapids, MI   49501-3636
Application address: c/o Lowell High School, Attn: Barbara Pierce, 750 Foreman St., Lowell, MI 49331, tel.: (616) 897-4125

Established in 1985 in MI.
Grantmaker type: Independent foundation.
Financial data (yr. ended 2/28/06): Assets, $269,006 (M); expenditures, $15,237; total giving, $12,000; qualifying distributions, $12,000; giving activities include $12,000 for grants to individuals.
Purpose and activities: Scholarship awards to high school graduates from the Lowell, MI, public school district.
Fields of interest: Higher education.
Type of support: Scholarships—to individuals.
Limitations: Giving limited to the Lowell, MI, area.
Application information: Application form required.
   Deadline(s): Apr. 1
Scholarship Committee: Tania Devries; Barbara Pierce; Errolyn Weeks.
Trustee: Fifth Third Bank.
EIN: 386480250

1778
Spencer Family Foundation
909 Cascade Hills Dr. S.E.
Grand Rapids, MI   49546-3678   (616) 942-4743
Contact: Kenneth Spencer, Pres.

Established in 1993 in MI.
Grantmaker type: Independent foundation.
Financial data (yr. ended 12/31/05): Assets, $1,063 (M); gifts received, $33,000; expenditures, $44,024; total giving, $43,300; qualifying distributions, $43,300; giving activities include $43,300 for grants.
Fields of interest: Education; Christian agencies & churches.
Limitations: Giving on a national basis, with some emphasis on MI.
Application information: Application form not required.
   Deadline(s): None
Officers: Kenneth Spencer, Pres.; Carol Spencer, Secy.-Treas.
EIN: 383076355

1779
S. Gary Spicer, Sr. Foundation
16845 Kercheval St., Ste. 5
Grosse Pointe, MI   48230

Established in 1997 in MI.
Donor: S. Gary Spicer.
Grantmaker type: Independent foundation.
Financial data (yr. ended 12/31/05): Assets, $795,000 (M); gifts received, $23,495; expenditures, $24,319; total giving, $18,822; qualifying distributions, $18,822; giving activities include $18,822 for grants.
Fields of interest: Historical activities; Higher education; Environment; Health organizations; Protestant agencies & churches.
Type of support: General/operating support.

Limitations: Giving primarily in MI. No grants to individuals.
Application information:
   Initial approach: Letter
   Deadline(s): None
Officers and Trustee:* S. Gary Spicer,* Pres.; Ed Zionkowski, Secy.
EIN: 383341391

1780
John and Judy Spoelhof Foundation
341 Waukazoo Dr.
Holland, MI   49424

Established in 1984 in MI.
Donors: John Spoelhof; Judy Spoelhof; Prince Holding Corp.; JJS Partnership.
Grantmaker type: Independent foundation.
Financial data (yr. ended 12/31/04): Assets, $17,993,417 (M); gifts received, $248,500; expenditures, $1,518,390; total giving, $1,378,450; qualifying distributions, $1,402,454; giving activities include $1,378,450 for 92 grants (high: $500,000; low: $50).
Purpose and activities: Support primarily for higher education, Christian schools and churches, and community foundations.
Fields of interest: Elementary/secondary education; Higher education; Theological school/education; Youth development, religion; Human services; Children/youth, services; Federated giving programs; Christian agencies & churches; Protestant agencies & churches.
Type of support: General/operating support; Building/renovation.
Limitations: Applications not accepted. Giving primarily in MI, with emphasis on Holland. No grants to individuals.
Application information: Contributes only to pre-selected organizations.
Officers: John Spoelhof, Pres.; Judith Spoelhof, Secy.
Trustee: Scott Spoelhof.
EIN: 382492821
Selected grants: The following grants were reported in 2003.
$100,000 to Davenport University, Grand Rapids, MI. For general operating support.
$100,000 to Geneva Camp and Retreat Center, Holland, MI. For general operating support.
$100,000 to Hope College, Holland, MI. For general operating support.
$60,000 to Friendship Ministries, Grand Rapids, MI. For general operating support.
$50,000 to Holland Christian Schools, Holland, MI. For general operating support.
$45,000 to Luke Society, Sioux Falls, SD. For general operating support.
$25,000 to Lakeshore Pregnancy Center, Holland, MI. For general operating support.
$25,000 to Wildlife Unlimited of Allegan and Ottawa Counties, Holland, MI. For general operating support.
$20,000 to Family Research Council, DC. For general operating support.
$20,000 to Focus on the Family, Colorado Springs, CO. For general operating support.

1781
Springview Foundation
1 Haworth Ctr.
Holland, MI   49423   (616) 393-3551
Contact: Richard G. Haworth, Tr.

Established in 1998 in MI.
Donors: Ethelyn L. Haworth; Richard G. Haworth; Richard and Ethelyn Haworth Foundation; Anna Haworth.
Grantmaker type: Independent foundation.
Financial data (yr. ended 12/31/05): Assets, $4,536,339 (M); gifts received, $50,000; expenditures, $283,867; total giving, $281,000; qualifying distributions, $282,837; giving activities include $281,000 for 14 grants (high: $63,500; low: $500).
Fields of interest: Theological school/education; Human services; Children/youth, services; Family services; Christian agencies & churches; Protestant agencies & churches.
Limitations: Giving primarily in Grand Rapids and Holland, MI.
Application information: Application form required.
  Initial approach: Letter
  Copies of proposal: 6
  Deadline(s): Sept. 30
  Board meeting date(s): 1st half of Nov.
  Final notification: Mid-Dec.
Trustees: Sara E. Dykema; Timothy J. Dykema; Anna C. Haworth; Ethelyn L. Haworth; Jennifer L. Haworth; Matthew R. Haworth; Richard G. Haworth.
EIN: 383422204
Selected grants: The following grants were reported in 2004.
$75,000 to DeVos Childrens Hospital Foundation, Grand Rapids, MI.
$20,000 to Words of Hope, Grand Rapids, MI.
$18,000 to Harbor House Ministries, Jenison, MI.
$15,000 to Gildas Club Grand Rapids, Grand Rapids, MI.
$15,000 to Holland Rescue Mission, Holland, MI.
$10,000 to Wedgwood Christian Youth and Family Services, Grand Rapids, MI.
$10,000 to Wildlife Unlimited of Allegan and Ottawa Counties, Outdoor Discovery Center, Holland, MI.
$9,000 to Child and Family Services of Western Michigan, Holland, MI.
$8,000 to Center for Women in Transition, Holland, MI.
$8,000 to Kids Hope USA, Holland, MI.

1782
St. Clair Charitable Trust
c/o Butzel Long
100 Bloomfield Hills Pkwy., Ste. 200
Bloomfield Hills, MI   48304

Established in 1986 in MI.
Grantmaker type: Independent foundation.
Financial data (yr. ended 12/31/04): Assets, $99,429 (M); expenditures, $9,673; total giving, $8,850; qualifying distributions, $8,850; giving activities include $8,850 for grants.
Fields of interest: Arts; Education; Christian agencies & churches.
Type of support: General/operating support.
Limitations: Applications not accepted. Giving primarily in the Detroit, MI, area. No grants to individuals.
Application information: Contributes only to pre-selected organizations.

Trustees: Henrietta Fridholm; Roger T. Fridholm; David W. Sommerfield.
EIN: 382709935

1783
St. Clair Foundation
c/o Fifth Third Bank
P.O. Box 630858
Cincinnati, OH   45263
Contact: Franklin H. Moore, Jr., Tr.
Application address: c/o Fifth Third Bank, 200 S. Riverside Ave., St. Clair, MI 48079

Established in 1956 in MI.
Donors: Alice W. Moore; John Emig Trust A; John Emig Trust B.
Grantmaker type: Independent foundation.
Financial data (yr. ended 12/31/04): Assets, $2,291,796 (M); gifts received, $650,000; expenditures, $89,802; total giving, $77,745; qualifying distributions, $79,556; giving activities include $77,745 for 20 grants (high: $22,000; low: $645).
Fields of interest: Arts; Elementary school/education; Secondary school/education; Youth development; Human services; Community development; Government/public administration.
Type of support: Annual campaigns; Equipment; Scholarship funds.
Limitations: Giving limited to the city of St. Clair, MI, and its immediate vicinity. No grants to individuals.
Application information:
  Initial approach: Letter
  Deadline(s): None
Trustees: Gerald M. Emig; James Fredericks; Richard Groff; Bernard Kuhn; Franklin H. Moore, Jr.
EIN: 386064622

1784
St. Deny's Foundation, Inc.
(formerly Tremble Foundation, Inc.)
P.O. Box 704
Dowagiac, MI   49047
Contact: Kelly Deritter

Established in 1988 in MI.
Donor: Helen R. Tremble†.
Grantmaker type: Independent foundation.
Financial data (yr. ended 12/31/05): Assets, $7,137,323 (M); gifts received, $202,320; expenditures, $418,325; total giving, $316,250; qualifying distributions, $316,250; giving activities include $316,250 for 41 grants (high: $40,000; low: $1,000).
Fields of interest: Higher education; Environment; Animal welfare.
Type of support: General/operating support; Program development; Scholarship funds.
Limitations: Giving primarily in MI, with emphasis on the Dowagiac area.
Application information: Application form not required.
  Initial approach: Proposal
  Copies of proposal: 1
  Deadline(s): Feb. 1 and Aug. 1
  Board meeting date(s): Spring and fall
  Final notification: 6 months
Officers and Directors: * Thomas Dalton,* Pres.; Lynn Dalton, V.P.; Robert Sajdak, Secy.-Treas.; Cara Carrabine-Dalton; Dillon Dalton; Dusty Dalton; Jim McWilliams.

Trustee: Comerica Bank.
EIN: 382869889

1785
St. Joseph Kiwanis Foundation
c/o Jonathan B. Sauer
414 Main St.
St. Joseph, MI   49085-1235

Established in MI.
Grantmaker type: Independent foundation.
Financial data (yr. ended 12/31/05): Assets, $514,085 (M); expenditures, $24,148; total giving, $18,000; qualifying distributions, $24,148; giving activities include $18,000 for 18 grants to individuals.
Purpose and activities: Scholarship awards to graduates of Lakeshore, St. Joseph, and Lake Michigan Catholic high schools, MI.
Fields of interest: Higher education.
Type of support: Scholarships—to individuals.
Limitations: Applications not accepted. Giving limited to residents of the St. Joseph, MI, area.
Application information: Unsolicited requests for funds not accepted.
Officers: Edward E. Meny, Pres.; Louis A. Pinderski, Secy.; Jonathan B. Sauer, Treas.
Directors: Daryl Godke; Nancy Holloway; Bruce Molineaux; Joe Moore; Garry Sisson.
EIN: 386117678

1786
St. Joseph the Worker Foundation
3716 Merriweather Ln.
Rochester, MI   48306

Established in 2004 in MI.
Donor: Valentina Lopez.
Grantmaker type: Independent foundation.
Financial data (yr. ended 12/31/04): Assets, $22,428 (M); gifts received, $63,000; expenditures, $50,642; total giving, $45,000; qualifying distributions, $45,000; giving activities include $45,000 for grants.
Fields of interest: Roman Catholic agencies & churches.
Type of support: General/operating support.
Limitations: Applications not accepted. Giving primarily in the Philippines. No grants to individuals.
Application information: Contributes only to pre-selected organizations.
Officers: Valentina Lopez, Pres.; Ruben Lopez, Secy.
Director: Minda Menor.
EIN: 200414135

1787
Mary G. Stange Charitable Trust
201 W. Big Beaver Rd., Ste. 500
Troy, MI   48084

Established in 1999 in MI.
Donor: Mary G. Stange Trust.
Grantmaker type: Independent foundation.
Financial data (yr. ended 12/31/05): Assets, $14,229,712 (M); gifts received, $190,419; expenditures, $760,975; total giving, $618,300; qualifying distributions, $685,099; giving activities include $618,300 for 15 grants (high: $155,000; low: $2,500; average: $10,000–$50,000).

Purpose and activities: Giving primarily for education.
Fields of interest: Elementary/secondary education; Higher education; Health care; Human services; Christian agencies & churches.
Limitations: Applications not accepted. Giving primarily in MI; some giving also in NC. No grants to individuals.
Application information: Contributes only to pre-selected organizations.
Trustee: David C. Stone.
EIN: 386739773

1788
The James and Dorothy Stanton Foundation
174 S. Wilson Blvd.
Mount Clemens, MI 48043

Established in 2000 in MI.
Donors: James B. Stanton; Dorothy Stanton.
Grantmaker type: Independent foundation.
Financial data (yr. ended 12/31/05): Assets, $203,922 (M); gifts received, $10,000; expenditures, $10,661; total giving, $9,200; qualifying distributions, $9,200; giving activities include $9,200 for grants.
Limitations: Applications not accepted. Giving primarily in MI. No grants to individuals.
Application information: Contributes only to pre-selected organizations.
Officers: James B. Stanton, Pres.; Martha J. Casale, V.P.; Michael J. Stanton, Secy.; Dorothy M. Stanton, Treas.
Directors: Mary E. Sessions; Paul A. Stanton.
EIN: 912077094

1789
The Stanton Foundation
714 W. Michigan Ave.
Jackson, MI 49201-1909

Established in 1999 in MI.
Donor: David J. Stanton.
Grantmaker type: Independent foundation.
Financial data (yr. ended 6/30/05): Assets, $438,408 (M); expenditures, $23,091; total giving, $21,991; qualifying distributions, $21,991; giving activities include $21,991 for grants.
Limitations: Giving primarily in MI. No grants to individuals.
Officers: David J. Stanton, Pres.; Laura M. Stanton, Secy.
EIN: 383448185

1790
Clarence Elbert Stanton Memorial Scholarship Foundation
c/o Bert Quinn, Secy.-Treas.
523 N. Broadway St.
Lake Orion, MI 48362
Application address: c/o Marilyn Gaskins, Pres., 2375 Cedar Key Dr., Lake Orion, MI 48360, tel.: (248) 391-0192

Established around 1982.
Grantmaker type: Independent foundation.
Financial data (yr. ended 12/31/04): Assets, $571,987 (M); expenditures, $125,640; total giving, $124,250; qualifying distributions,

$125,640; giving activities include $124,250 for 179 grants to individuals (high: $1,050; low: $450).
Purpose and activities: Scholarships only to students in the Orion and Oxford, MI, area.
Type of support: Scholarships—to individuals.
Limitations: Giving limited to residents of the Orion and Oxford, MI, area.
Application information: Application form required. *Deadline(s):* Apr. 1
Officers: Marilyn Gaskins, Pres.; Paul Bailey, V.P.; Bert Quinn, Secy.-Treas.
EIN: 382962898

1791
The Stauffer Foundation
68645 Birch Rd.
Union, MI 49130

Donors: Stauffer & Co.; Donald R. Stauffer.
Grantmaker type: Independent foundation.
Financial data (yr. ended 10/31/05): Assets, $13,901 (M); gifts received, $12,600; expenditures, $10,060; total giving, $10,040; qualifying distributions, $10,040; giving activities include $10,040 for 11 grants (high: $5,000; low: $90).
Purpose and activities: The foundation supports Christian agencies and churches and organizations involved with health.
Fields of interest: Health care; Christian agencies & churches.
Limitations: Applications not accepted. Giving limited to IN, MI, and PA. No grants to individuals.
Application information: Contributes only to pre-selected organizations.
Officers: Donald R. Stauffer, Pres. and Treas.; Elizabeth Stauffer, V.P. and Secy.
EIN: 382300195

1792
The Steele Foundation
4977 New Carlisle St. Paris Rd.
New Carlisle, OH 45344-9500

Donor: Harold E. Steele.
Grantmaker type: Independent foundation.
Financial data (yr. ended 12/31/05): Assets, $210,450 (M); gifts received, $4,000; expenditures, $10,392; total giving, $10,000; qualifying distributions, $10,000; giving activities include $10,000 for grants.
Fields of interest: Education; Children, services.
Type of support: General/operating support; Building/renovation.
Limitations: Applications not accepted. Giving primarily in IN, MI, and OH. No grants to individuals.
Application information: Contributes only to pre-selected organizations.
Officers: Harold E. Steele, Pres.; Thelma M. Streber, V.P.; Esther L. Steele, Secy.-Treas.
EIN: 237204460

1793
William & Marie Stehouwer Family Foundation
500 Parkside Dr., Ste. 268
Zeeland, MI 49464
Contact: William H. Stehouwer, Pres.

Established in 2000 in MI.

Donor: William H. Stehouwer.
Grantmaker type: Independent foundation.
Financial data (yr. ended 12/31/05): Assets, $44,793 (M); expenditures, $37,346; total giving, $37,000; qualifying distributions, $37,000; giving activities include $37,000 for grants.
Limitations: Applications not accepted. Giving limited to MI.
Application information: Contributes only to pre-selected organizations.
Officers: William H. Stehouwer, Pres.; Joanne M. Vandenbosch, V.P.; Earl J. Schipper, Secy.-Treas.
Director: Alyce J. Schipper.
EIN: 383506023

1794
The Steinmann Family Foundation
3 Park Ave.
St. Clair, MI 48079

Established in 1999 in MI.
Donor: Karl Steinmann.
Grantmaker type: Independent foundation.
Financial data (yr. ended 12/31/04): Assets, $1,547 (M); gifts received, $1,000; expenditures, $195; total giving, $175; qualifying distributions, $175; giving activities include $175 for grants.
Limitations: Applications not accepted. No grants to individuals.
Application information: Contributes only to pre-selected organizations.
Officers: Karl M. Steinmann, Pres.; Diane J. Steinmann, Secy.
EIN: 383480177

1795
Richard A. and Donna L. Sterban Foundation
16845 Kercheval St., Ste. 5
Grosse Pointe, MI 48230

Established in 1997 in MI.
Donors: Donna L. Sterban; Richard A. Sterban.
Grantmaker type: Independent foundation.
Financial data (yr. ended 12/31/05): Assets, $226,000 (M); gifts received, $12,191; expenditures, $11,191; total giving, $10,185; qualifying distributions, $10,185; giving activities include $10,185 for grants.
Fields of interest: Education; Protestant agencies & churches.
Limitations: Giving primarily in TN.
Application information: Contact foundation for application guidelines.
Officers and Trustees:* Richard A. Sterban,* Pres.; S. Gary Spicer, Secy.; Donna L. Sterban,* Treas.
EIN: 383383414

1796
Sterk Family Foundation
804 Hazelwood Dr.
Holland, MI 49424-2758

Established around 1994 in MI.
Donors: Marlene J. Sterk; William Sterk.
Grantmaker type: Independent foundation.
Financial data (yr. ended 12/31/04): Assets, $303,128 (M); gifts received, $186,000; expenditures, $62,047; total giving, $61,215;

qualifying distributions, $61,215; giving activities include $61,215 for grants.
Fields of interest: Protestant agencies & churches.
Limitations: Applications not accepted. Giving primarily in Grand Rapids and Bryon Center, MI. No grants to individuals.
Application information: Contributes only to pre-selected organizations.
Officers: Marlene Sterk, Pres. and Secy.; William Sterk, V.P. and Treas.
EIN: 383097975

1797
The Helmut Stern Foundation
c/o Helmut F. Stern
P.O. Box 1733
Ann Arbor, MI 48106

Established in 1983 in MI.
Donor: Helmut F. Stern.
Grantmaker type: Independent foundation.
Financial data (yr. ended 11/30/05): Assets, $1,866,841 (M); expenditures, $276,970; total giving, $260,000; qualifying distributions, $260,000; giving activities include $260,000 for 3 grants (high: $100,000; low: $60,000).
Purpose and activities: Giving primarily for higher education; support also for social services, museums, hospitals, and conservation.
Fields of interest: Museums; Arts; Higher education; Medical school/education; Education; Environment, natural resources; Hospitals (general); Human services; Federated giving programs.
Type of support: Land acquisition; Fellowships; Scholarship funds.
Limitations: Applications not accepted. Giving primarily in MI. No grants to individuals.
Application information: Contributes only to pre-selected organizations.
Officer: Helmut F. Stern, Pres.
EIN: 382515772
Selected grants: The following grants were reported in 2004.
$115,000 to University of Michigan, Ann Arbor, MI. For operating support.
$40,000 to YMCA, Ann Arbor, Ann Arbor, MI. For operating support.
$15,000 to American Red Cross, Ann Arbor, MI. For operating support.
$5,000 to Dance Gallery Foundation, Ann Arbor, MI. For operating support.
$5,000 to Dawn Farm, Ann Arbor, MI. For operating support.
$5,000 to Performance Network of Ann Arbor, Ann Arbor, MI. For operating support.
$2,500 to Ann Arbor Area Community Foundation, Ann Arbor Art Center, Ann Arbor, MI. For operating support.
$1,000 to Humane Society of Huron Valley, Ann Arbor, MI. For operating support.

1798
Mervyn H. and Leslie D. Sternberg
Foundation, Inc.
2275 Cameo Lake Dr.
Bloomfield Hills, MI 48302

Established in 1986 in MI.
Donors: Mervyn H. Sternberg; Leslie D. Sternberg.
Grantmaker type: Independent foundation.

Financial data (yr. ended 11/30/05): Assets, $515,995 (M); expenditures, $31,161; total giving, $26,264; qualifying distributions, $26,264; giving activities include $26,264 for grants.
Limitations: Applications not accepted. Giving primarily in MI. No grants to individuals.
Application information: Contributes only to pre-selected organizations.
Officer: Mervyn H. Sternberg, Pres. and Treas.
Director: Leslie D. Sternberg.
EIN: 382707908

1799
Walter H. and Ella Stevenson Foundation
c/o Comerica Bank
P.O. Box 75000, M/C 3302
Detroit, MI 48275

Established in 1994 in MI.
Grantmaker type: Independent foundation.
Financial data (yr. ended 7/31/05): Assets, $799,955 (M); expenditures, $47,408; total giving, $38,848; qualifying distributions, $38,848; giving activities include $38,848 for grants.
Purpose and activities: Support only for the American Heart Association, Lathrup Village, Detroit Chapter of Hadassah, Bloomfield, and Jewish Home for the Aged, and Michigan Cancer Foundation, Detroit.
Fields of interest: Heart & circulatory diseases; Cancer research; Residential/custodial care, senior continuing care; Jewish agencies & temples.
Type of support: General/operating support.
Limitations: Applications not accepted. Giving limited to Bloomfield, Detroit, and Lathrup Village, MI. No grants to individuals.
Application information: Contributes only to 4 pre-selected organizations.
Trustee: Comerica Bank.
EIN: 364063285

1800
The Stewardship Foundation
2540 Floral Dr.
Zeeland, MI 49464-9106

Established in 1997 in MI.
Donor: Kenneth Decker.
Grantmaker type: Independent foundation.
Financial data (yr. ended 12/31/05): Assets, $138,651 (M); gifts received, $7,685; expenditures, $884; total giving, $0; qualifying distributions, $0.
Limitations: Applications not accepted. Giving primarily in MI. No grants to individuals.
Application information: Contributes only to pre-selected organizations.
Directors: Kenneth Decker; Marlene Decker.
EIN: 383355391

1801
Robert A. Stewart Family Foundation
2000 Town Ctr., Ste. 1500
Southfield, MI 48075

Established in 2003.
Grantmaker type: Independent foundation.
Financial data (yr. ended 12/31/05): Assets, $913,099 (M); gifts received, $30,000; expenditures, $57,670; total giving, $57,300;

qualifying distributions, $57,300; giving activities include $57,300 for grants.
Fields of interest: Jewish federated giving programs.
Limitations: Giving primarily in MI.
Officers: Robert Stewart, Pres.; Philip Stewart, V.P.; Alexander Stewart, Secy.
EIN: 200105460

1802
Stewart Management Group Charitable
Foundation
31850 Ford Rd.
Garden City, MI 48135-1506
Contact: Gordon L. Stewart, Pres.

Established in 1994 in MI.
Grantmaker type: Independent foundation.
Financial data (yr. ended 11/30/05): Assets, $151,254 (M); gifts received, $9,000; expenditures, $6,710; total giving, $6,136; qualifying distributions, $6,136; giving activities include $6,136 for grants.
Purpose and activities: Scholarship awards to local area residents who are students of the Westland and Garden City, MI.
Fields of interest: Scholarships/financial aid.
Type of support: Scholarships—to individuals.
Limitations: Giving limited to Garden City and Westland, MI.
Application information: Selection based on recommendations of the committee at each school. Application form required.
Deadline(s): None
Officers: Gordon L. Stewart, Pres.; Linda A. Stewart, Secy.; Craig M. Hale, Treas.
EIN: 383189964

1803
Stieg Family Foundation
c/o Harold E. Stieg
333 W. Fort St., Ste. 1940
Detroit, MI 48226

Established in 1996 in MI.
Donor: Harold E. Stieg.
Grantmaker type: Independent foundation.
Financial data (yr. ended 12/31/05): Assets, $194,538 (M); expenditures, $6,874; total giving, $4,000; qualifying distributions, $4,000; giving activities include $4,000 for grants.
Fields of interest: Environment, land resources; Protestant agencies & churches.
Limitations: Applications not accepted. No grants to individuals.
Application information: Contributes only to pre-selected organizations.
Officers and Directors:* Harold E. Stieg,* Pres. and Treas.; Elizabeth A. Stieg,* V.P. and Secy.; Annette D. Stieg,* V.P.; Edward C. Stieg,* V.P.; William H. Stieg,* V.P.
EIN: 383324822

1804
Stockbridge Foundation
3717 Wards Pt.
Orchard Lake, MI 48324
Contact: Mahmoud Alhadidi, Pres.

Established in 2003 in MI.

Donors: Mahmoud Alhadidi, M.D.; Stockbridge Enterprise Inc.
Grantmaker type: Independent foundation.
Financial data (yr. ended 12/31/05): Assets, $53,716 (M); gifts received, $50,000; expenditures, $6,806; total giving, $6,725; qualifying distributions, $6,725; giving activities include $6,725 for grants.
Fields of interest: Education; Islam.
Limitations: Giving limited to MI.
Application information:
Initial approach: Letter
Deadline(s): 60 days prior to the fiscal year end
Officer: Mahmoud Alhadidi, M.D., Pres. and Treas.
EIN: 352191395

1805
North J. and Florence Stockton Charitable Foundation

c/o JPMorgan Chase Bank, N.A.
P.O. Box 1308
Milwaukee, WI 53201

Established in 1995 in FL.
Donor: Florence Stockton.
Grantmaker type: Independent foundation.
Financial data (yr. ended 12/31/05): Assets, $1,261,798 (M); gifts received, $747,244; expenditures, $15,707; total giving, $10,000; qualifying distributions, $10,000; giving activities include $10,000 for grants.
Fields of interest: Eye diseases; Alzheimer's disease; Food services; Roman Catholic agencies & churches.
Type of support: General/operating support.
Limitations: Giving limited to Broward County, FL, and Wayne County, MI.
Application information: Application form not required.
Initial approach: Letter
Deadline(s): None
Trustees: Florence Stockton; JPMorgan Chase Bank, N.A.
EIN: 386662894

1806
Jennie C. Stoddard Charitable Foundation

126 Ottawa Ave. N.W.
Grand Rapids, MI 49503-2829

Established in 1992 in MI.
Donor: Jennie C. Stoddard.
Grantmaker type: Independent foundation.
Financial data (yr. ended 7/31/05): Assets, $542,491 (M); expenditures, $58,734; total giving, $56,500; qualifying distributions, $56,500; giving activities include $56,500 for grants.
Fields of interest: Arts education; Higher education, university.
Limitations: Applications not accepted. Giving primarily in MI. No grants to individuals.
Application information: Contributes only to pre-selected organizations.
Trustees: Charles C. Stoddard; Stanford C. Stoddard.
EIN: 382937192

1807
Stoddard Family Foundation, Inc.

29600 Southfield Rd.
Southfield, MI 48076-2039

Established in 2000 in MI.
Donor: Stanford C. Stoddard.
Grantmaker type: Independent foundation.
Financial data (yr. ended 12/31/05): Assets, $1,755,129 (M); gifts received, $292,210; expenditures, $409,106; total giving, $331,010; qualifying distributions, $336,980; giving activities include $331,010 for 14 grants (high: $100,000; low: $200).
Purpose and activities: Support primarily for higher education.
Fields of interest: Museums; Arts; Higher education; Student services/organizations; Community development, business promotion.
Type of support: Program development; General/operating support.
Limitations: Applications not accepted. Giving in the U.S., with some emphasis on VA. No grants to individuals.
Application information: Contributes only to pre-selected organizations.
Officers and Director:* Stanford C. Stoddard,* Pres.; M. Richard Olson, Secy.-Treas.
EIN: 383539927

1808
Charles and Janet Stoddard Foundation

c/o Charles C. Stoddard
111 Lyon St. N.W., Ste. 900
Grand Rapids, MI 49503-2487

Established in 2002 in MI.
Donors: Charles C. Stoddard; Janet O. Stoddard.
Grantmaker type: Independent foundation.
Financial data (yr. ended 12/31/05): Assets, $2,738,029 (M); expenditures, $182,440; total giving, $145,766; qualifying distributions, $148,961; giving activities include $145,766 for 9 grants (high: $117,736; low: $500).
Fields of interest: Education; Human services; Children/youth, services; Jewish agencies & temples.
Limitations: Applications not accepted. Giving primarily in MI.
Application information: Unsolicited requests for funds not accepted.
Officers and Trustees:* Charles C. Stoddard,* Pres. and Treas.; Janet O. Stoddard,* V.P.; Jeffrey B. Power, Secy.
EIN: 300074233

1809
Alice A. Stoddard Trust

c/o Monroe Bank & Trust
102 E. Front St.
Monroe, MI 48161
Application address: c/o University of Michigan, Medical Research Program, Medical Admin., Box 0624, Ann Arbor, MI 48109, tel.: (734) 763-9600

Donor: Alice A. Stoddard†.
Grantmaker type: Independent foundation.
Financial data (yr. ended 6/30/03): Assets, $296,668 (M); expenditures, $20,209; total giving, $14,025; qualifying distributions, $15,346; giving activities include $14,025 for 1 grant.

Purpose and activities: Scholarships limited to students attending the University of Michigan for research on lymph gland diseases.
Fields of interest: Medical school/education; Medical specialty research.
Type of support: Scholarship funds.
Limitations: Giving limited to Ann Arbor, MI.
Application information: Application form required.
Initial approach: Proposal
Deadline(s): Feb. 1
Trustee: Monroe Bank & Trust.
EIN: 386052244

1810
Margaret Jane Stoker Charitable Trust

c/o Citizens Bank Wealth Mgmt., N.A.
328 S. Saginaw St., MC 002072
Flint, MI 48502
Application address: c/o Karen McNish, Citizens Bank Wealth Mgmt., 101 N. Washington Ave., Saginaw, MI 48607, tel.: (989) 776-1416

Established in 2001 in MI.
Grantmaker type: Independent foundation.
Financial data (yr. ended 9/30/05): Assets, $2,687,890 (M); expenditures, $142,893; total giving, $115,408; qualifying distributions, $126,100; giving activities include $115,408 for 9 grants (high: $35,000; low: $1,170).
Fields of interest: Higher education, university; Zoos/zoological societies; Human services.
Limitations: Giving primarily in the Saginaw County, MI area.
Application information: Application form required.
Deadline(s): None
Trustee: Citizens Bank.
EIN: 320000318
Selected grants: The following grants were reported in 2004.
$50,000 to Saginaw Valley State University, Regional Education Center, University Center, MI.
$30,000 to Child Abuse and Neglect Council of Saginaw County, Saginaw, MI.
$25,675 to Chamber Foundation, Saginaw County, Saginaw, MI. 2 grants: $15,000, $10,675
$10,000 to Saginaw Valley Zoological Society, Saginaw, MI.
$10,000 to Teen Challenge of Saginaw, Saginaw, MI.
$6,220 to Child and Family Service of Saginaw County, Saginaw, MI.
$5,000 to Saginaw, City of, Fire Department, Saginaw, MI.
$2,500 to Saint Marys Medical Center, Saginaw, MI.

1811
Olive A. Stokes Scholarship Trust

c/o Comerica Bank
P.O. Box 75000, M/C 3302
Detroit, MI 48275-3302
Application address: c/o RBC Centura Bank, Attn.: Sharon Stephens, P.O. Box 1220, Rocky Mount, NC 27804, tel.: (252) 454-4025

Established in 2001 in NC.
Grantmaker type: Independent foundation.
Financial data (yr. ended 9/30/05): Assets, $545,213 (M); expenditures, $29,104; total giving, $19,500; qualifying distributions, $19,500; giving activities include $19,500 for grants to individuals.

Purpose and activities: Scholarship awards to U.S. citizen who are residents of Nash or Edgecombe counties with a GAP'S. C plus or better.
Fields of interest: Scholarships/financial aid.
Type of support: Scholarships—to individuals.
Limitations: Giving primarily in Nash and Edgecombe Counties, NC.
Application information: Application form not required.
  Deadline(s): June 1
Trustee: RBC Centura Bank; Comerica Bank.
EIN: 316646001

1812
The Vivian Vivio Stolaruk and Steve Stolaruk Foundation
1928 Star Batt Dr., Ste. E
Rochester Hills, MI 48309-3722

Established in 2003 in MI.
Donor: Steve Stolaruk.
Grantmaker type: Independent foundation.
Financial data (yr. ended 12/31/05): Assets, $262,422 (M); gifts received, $160,000; expenditures, $395,660; total giving, $395,350; qualifying distributions, $395,350; giving activities include $395,350 for 14 grants (high: $340,000; low: $200).
Fields of interest: Cancer; Human services; Roman Catholic agencies & churches.
Type of support: Building/renovation; General/operating support.
Limitations: Applications not accepted. Giving primarily in MI. No grants to individuals.
Application information: Contributes only to pre-selected organizations.
Officers: Steve Stolaruk, Pres.; Marc J. Stolaruk, Secy.-Treas.
EIN: 200515908

1813
The Stollman Foundation
2025 W. Long Lake Rd., Ste. 104
Troy, MI 48098-4100

Incorporated in 1953 in MI.
Donors: Phillip Stollman†; Max Stollman; Melvyn J. Stollman.
Grantmaker type: Independent foundation.
Financial data (yr. ended 4/30/05): Assets, $563,493 (M); expenditures, $152,881; total giving, $148,821; qualifying distributions, $148,549; giving activities include $148,821 for 18 + grants (high: $56,900).
Purpose and activities: Grants for education, including religious education and higher education in Israel, temple support, and Jewish welfare.
Fields of interest: Arts; Elementary/secondary education; Human services; Jewish federated giving programs; Jewish agencies & temples.
International interests: Israel.
Type of support: General/operating support.
Limitations: Applications not accepted. Giving primarily in MI and NY. No grants to individuals.
Application information: Contributes only to pre-selected organizations.
Officers: Bernard H. Stollman, Pres. and Treas.; Gerald H. Stollman, V.P. and Secy.
EIN: 386086417

1814
John Franklin Stone Trust
c/o Comerica Bank
P.O. Box 75000, M/C 3302
Detroit, MI 48275

Established in 1995.
Grantmaker type: Independent foundation.
Financial data (yr. ended 7/31/05): Assets, $1,720,849 (M); expenditures, $110,975; total giving, $88,000; qualifying distributions, $88,000; giving activities include $88,000 for grants.
Purpose and activities: Support only for American Cancer Society, Hospice of Southeastern, and the University of MI.
Fields of interest: Higher education; Cancer; Residential/custodial care, hospices.
Limitations: Applications not accepted. Giving limited to MI. No grants to individuals.
Application information: Contributes only to 3 pre-selected organizations.
Trustees: Anne H. Krom; Comerica Bank.
EIN: 386658355

1815
Stonisch Foundation
545 W. Brown St.
Birmingham, MI 48009-1458

Established in 1961 in MI.
Donor: Helen Stonisch.
Grantmaker type: Independent foundation.
Financial data (yr. ended 12/31/05): Assets, $21,700,530 (M); expenditures, $1,332,874; total giving, $865,000; qualifying distributions, $865,000; giving activities include $865,000 for 8 + grants (high: $415,000).
Purpose and activities: Giving primarily for health care, education, and to Christian agencies and churches.
Fields of interest: Secondary school/education; Higher education; Cancer; Cancer research; Medical research; Children/youth, services; Christian agencies & churches.
Type of support: Research.
Limitations: Applications not accepted. Giving primarily in MI.
Application information: Contributes only to pre-selected organizations.
  Board meeting date(s): Nov.
Officers: Gail Riggs, Pres.; Rudy Stonisch, V.P.; Mary Sue Stonisch, Secy.
EIN: 386088638

1816
Emma Stowe Trust
c/o Citizens Bank Wealth Mgmt., N.A.
328 S. Saginaw St., MC 002072
Flint, MI 48502

Established in MI.
Grantmaker type: Independent foundation.
Financial data (yr. ended 12/31/05): Assets, $890,849 (M); expenditures, $66,015; total giving, $55,260; qualifying distributions, $59,206; giving activities include $55,260 for 9 grants (high: $21,260; low: $4,125).
Fields of interest: Human services; Federated giving programs; Protestant agencies & churches.
Type of support: General/operating support.

Limitations: Applications not accepted. Giving limited to MI and MO, with emphasis on Jackson, MI. No grants to individuals.
Application information: Contributes only to 9 pre-selected organizations.
Trustee: Citizens Bank, N.A.
EIN: 386054053

1817
The Stratton Foundation
450 Oak Ave., Ste. 101
Birmingham, MI 48009

Established in 2001 in MI.
Donor: Douglas G. Stratton.
Grantmaker type: Independent foundation.
Financial data (yr. ended 12/31/05): Assets, $25,460 (M); gifts received, $1,000; expenditures, $2,482; total giving, $1,000; qualifying distributions, $1,000; giving activities include $1,000 for grants.
Officer: Douglas G. Stratton, Pres.; Bryan D. Stratton, V.P.; Kaoru Chatani, Secy.
EIN: 383571442

1818
The Stricof Family Foundation
30100 Telegraph Rd., Ste. 120
Bingham Farms, MI 48025

Grantmaker type: Independent foundation.
Financial data (yr. ended 4/30/05): Assets, $18,795 (M); expenditures, $2,127; total giving, $2,100; qualifying distributions, $2,100; giving activities include $2,100 for grants.
Limitations: Applications not accepted. Giving limited to Ann Arbor and Lathrup Village, MI. No grants to individuals.
Application information: Contributes only to pre-selected organizations.
Officer: Norman Stricof, Pres.
EIN: 383353548

1819
The Wally and Jo Strobel Foundation
3 Weber Ct.
Frankenmuth, MI 48734

Established in 2004 in MI.
Donor: Josephine Strobel.
Grantmaker type: Independent foundation.
Financial data (yr. ended 12/31/05): Assets, $461,489 (M); expenditures, $26,160; total giving, $25,394; qualifying distributions, $25,394; giving activities include $25,394 for grants.
Officers: John Strobel, Pres.; Josephine Strobel, V.P.; Sarah King, Secy.-Treas.
EIN: 201570905

1820
Chester A. Strong Trust
c/o Comerica Bank
P.O. Box 75000, M/C 3302
Detroit, MI 48275-0001

Established around 1987.
Grantmaker type: Independent foundation.
Financial data (yr. ended 4/30/05): Assets, $263,880 (M); expenditures, $15,994; total giving,

$11,000; qualifying distributions, $11,000; giving activities include $11,000 for grants.
Fields of interest: Recreation, government agencies.
Limitations: Applications not accepted. Giving limited to Lake Worth, FL. No grants to individuals.
Application information: Contributes only to pre-selected organizations.
Trustee: Comerica Bank.
EIN: 596830306

1821
The Charles J. Strosacker Foundation
P.O. Box 471
Midland, MI   48640-0471
Contact: Marian L. Cimbalik, Tr.

Incorporated in 1957 in MI.
Donors: Charles J. Strosacker†; Ula G. Shaffer Administration Trust.
Grantmaker type: Independent foundation.
Financial data (yr. ended 12/31/05): Assets, $61,186,503 (M); gifts received, $237,555; expenditures, $2,973,950; total giving, $2,741,450; qualifying distributions, $2,796,070; giving activities include $2,741,450 for 109 grants (high: $225,000; low: $250).
Purpose and activities: Giving to assist and benefit political subdivisions of the state of Michigan, educational organizations, and social services.
Fields of interest: Performing arts; Education; Health organizations, association; Human services; Economic development; Engineering/technology; Science.
Type of support: Continuing support; Building/ renovation; Equipment; Endowments; Program development; Seed money; Research.
Limitations: Giving primarily in MI, with emphasis on Midland County. No grants to individuals, or for matching gifts; no loans.
Publications: Annual report (including application guidelines).
Application information: Application form not required.
   Initial approach: Letter
   Copies of proposal: 1
   Board meeting date(s): May, Aug., and Nov.
Officers and Trustees:* David J. Arnold,* Chair.; Bobbie N. Arnold, C.E.O. and Pres.; Donna T. Morris,* V.P., Fin. and Secy.; Richard M. Reynolds, Treas.; Kimberlee K. Arnold; John N. Bartos; James L. Borin; Lawrence E. Burks; Marian L. Cimbalik; John S. Ludington; Charles J. Thrune; Charlie C. Thrune; Carolyn Thrune-Durand; Eugene C. Yehle.
Number of staff: 1 part-time support.
EIN: 386062787

1822
Strunk Foundation
37671 Fiore Trail
Clinton Township, MI   48036

Established in 1995 MI.
Donors: Arthur E. Strunk, Jr.; Erika L. Strunk.
Grantmaker type: Independent foundation.
Financial data (yr. ended 6/30/05): Assets, $726,739 (M); expenditures, $31,555; total giving, $28,800; qualifying distributions, $28,800; giving activities include $28,800 for grants.
Limitations: Giving primarily in Detroit, MI.

Officer: Arthur E. Strunk, Jr., Pres.
EIN: 383245852

1823
The Ronda E. Stryker and William D. Johnston Foundation
100 W. Michigan Ave., Ste. 100
Kalamazoo, MI   49007
Contact: William D. Johnston, Secy.-Treas.

Established in 1995 in MI.
Donors: Ronda E. Stryker; William Johnston.
Grantmaker type: Independent foundation.
Financial data (yr. ended 12/31/05): Assets, $14,799,653 (M); gifts received, $1,934,000; expenditures, $4,878,103; total giving, $4,687,824; qualifying distributions, $4,688,764; giving activities include $4,687,824 for 35 grants (high: $700,000; low: $500; average: $1,000–$250,000).
Purpose and activities: Giving primarily for the arts, museums, higher education and human services.
Fields of interest: Museums; Arts; Higher education; Education; Human services; YM/YWCAs & YM/YWHAs; Community development; Foundations (community).
Limitations: Giving primarily in Kalamazoo, MI. No grants to individuals.
Application information:
   Initial approach: Letter
   Deadline(s): None
Officers: Ronda E. Stryker, Pres.; William D. Johnston, Secy.-Treas.
EIN: 383224966

1824
Maurice & Dorothy Stubnitz Foundation
153 E. Maumee St.
Adrian, MI   49221-2703

Established in 1981 in MI.
Grantmaker type: Independent foundation.
Financial data (yr. ended 9/30/05): Assets, $6,999,063 (M); expenditures, $384,487; total giving, $301,548; qualifying distributions, $301,548; giving activities include $301,548 for 18 grants (high: $62,500; low: $1,750).
Purpose and activities: Giving primarily for higher education and human services.
Fields of interest: Performing arts, orchestra (symphony); Higher education; Housing/shelter, development; Human services; Community development.
Type of support: Building/renovation; Equipment; Land acquisition; Emergency funds; Program development; Seed money; Scholarship funds.
Limitations: Applications not accepted. Giving primarily in Adrian, MI. No grants to individuals.
Application information: Contributes only to pre-selected organizations.
   Board meeting date(s): Semiannually
Officers: Charles E. Gross, Pres. and Treas.; Betty Gross, V.P.; Gaylord L. Baker, Secy.
Directors: James L. Feeney; Hildreth Spencer.
EIN: 382392373

1825
The Stucki Family Foundation, Inc.
c/o Greenleaf Trust
100 W. Michigan Ave., Kalamazoo Ctr.
Kalamazoo, MI   49007-3963

Established in 1998 in MI.
Donors: Jacob C. Stucki; Naomi Stucki.
Grantmaker type: Independent foundation.
Financial data (yr. ended 12/31/05): Assets, $215,542 (M); expenditures, $12,259; total giving, $9,980; qualifying distributions, $9,980; giving activities include $9,980 for grants.
Purpose and activities: Giving primarily for health and human services.
Fields of interest: Reproductive health, family planning; Human services; Children/youth, services; Federated giving programs.
Limitations: Giving primarily in Kalamazoo, MI. No grants to individuals.
Officers and Directors:* Naomi Stucki,* Pres.; Heidi E. Stucki,* V.P. and Secy.; Jacob C. Stucki,* V.P. and Treas.; J. Christopher Stucki,* V.P.; Marcia V. Stucki,* V.P.
Trustee: Greenleaf Trust.
EIN: 383385788

1826
Stulberg Family Foundation
c/o David Stulberg
505 N. Lake Shore Dr., Ste. 2806
Chicago, IL   60611

Established in 2003 in IL.
Donors: S. David Stulberg; Joseph Stulberg.
Grantmaker type: Independent foundation.
Financial data (yr. ended 12/31/04): Assets, $10,474 (M); gifts received, $32,000; expenditures, $21,526; total giving, $20,000; qualifying distributions, $21,455; giving activities include $20,000 for grants.
Fields of interest: Performing arts, orchestra (symphony).
Type of support: General/operating support.
Limitations: Applications not accepted. Giving primarily in Kalamazoo, MI. No grants to individuals.
Application information: Contributes only to pre-selected organizations.
Officers and Directors:* S. David Stulberg,* Pres.; Joseph Stulberg,* V.P.; Mira Halpert,* Secy.; Bernard Stulberg,* Treas.
EIN: 300153499

1827
David & Lois Stulberg Foundation
1497 Lochridge Rd.
Bloomfield Hills, MI   48302-0734
(248) 334-5353
Contact: Lois Stulberg, Pres.

Established in 1984 in MI.
Donors: Margaret Dunning; David A. Stulberg; Lois Stulberg.
Grantmaker type: Independent foundation.
Financial data (yr. ended 12/31/05): Assets, $3,859,248 (M); expenditures, $175,486; total giving, $154,250; qualifying distributions, $154,250; giving activities include $154,250 for grants (high: $121,500; low: $1,000).

Fields of interest: Arts; Health care; Jewish federated giving programs; Jewish agencies & temples; Women.
Limitations: Giving primarily in FL and MI.
Application information:
  Initial approach: Letter
  Deadline(s): None
Officers: Lois Stulberg, Pres. and Treas.; Robert M. Stulberg, Secy.
Trustees: Robert Appel; Susan A. Rosenstein.
EIN: 382575785

1828
W. & H. Sturdevant Charitable Trust
c/o Comerica Bank
P.O. Box 75000, MC 3302
Detroit, MI 48275-3302

Established in 2004 in MI.
Donor: Harriet Sturdevant‡.
Grantmaker type: Independent foundation.
Financial data (yr. ended 12/31/05): Assets, $274,718 (M); expenditures, $4,411; total giving, $0; qualifying distributions, $4,411.
Limitations: Applications not accepted. No grants to individuals.
Application information: Contributes only to pre-selected organizations.
Trustees: Wayne Seitl; Comerica Bank.
EIN: 656395712

1829
Jerome P. Subar Foundation
P.O. Box 8037
Grand Rapids, MI 49518-8037

Established in 1983 in MI.
Donor: Jerome P. Subar.
Grantmaker type: Independent foundation.
Financial data (yr. ended 12/31/04): Assets, $1,547,253 (M); gifts received, $56,970; expenditures, $72,795; total giving, $72,536; qualifying distributions, $72,556; giving activities include $72,536 for grants (high: $30,000; low: $250).
Purpose and activities: Giving to higher education, Jewish organizations and youth programs.
Fields of interest: Higher education; Jewish federated giving programs; Jewish agencies & temples.
Limitations: Applications not accepted. Giving primarily in MI. No grants to individuals.
Application information: Contributes only to pre-selected organizations.
Officer: Jerome P. Subar, Pres.
Trustees: Jonathon E. Subar; Judith H. Subar.
EIN: 382445793

1830
Anup and Parul Sud Family Foundation
1126 Millcreek Rd.
Flint, MI 48532
Contact: Anup Sud, Pres.

Established in 1995 in MI.
Donors: Anup Sud; Parul Sud.
Grantmaker type: Independent foundation.
Financial data (yr. ended 12/31/05): Assets, $229,869 (M); expenditures, $12,938; total giving,

$10,125; qualifying distributions, $10,125; giving activities include $10,125 for grants.
Limitations: Giving primarily in Flint, MI.
Application information:
  Initial approach: Letter
  Deadline(s): None
Officers: Anup Sud, Pres.; Parul Sud, V.P.
EIN: 383206403

1831
Suleiman Foundation
26300 Telegraph Rd., 2nd Fl.
Southfield, MI 48034

Established in 2003.
Grantmaker type: Independent foundation.
Financial data (yr. ended 12/31/03): Assets, $47,925 (M); gifts received, $50,000; expenditures, $2,075; total giving, $0; qualifying distributions, $0.
Officer: Jiab Suleiman, Pres.
EIN: 300211566

1832
J. Samir Sulieman Charitable Foundation
15 Heritage Park Cir.
North Little Rock, AR 72116

Established in 2001 in AR.
Grantmaker type: Independent foundation.
Financial data (yr. ended 12/31/03): Assets, $107,405 (M); expenditures, $3,446; total giving, $2,910; qualifying distributions, $2,910; giving activities include $2,910 for grants.
Fields of interest: Christian agencies & churches; Roman Catholic agencies & churches.
Type of support: General/operating support.
Limitations: Applications not accepted. Giving primarily in AR, MD, and MI. No grants to individuals.
Application information: Contributes only to pre-selected organizations.
Director: J. Samir Sulieman.
EIN: 716185614

1833
Sullivan and Taylor Family Foundation
1490 Skyline Blvd.
Reno, NV 89509

Established in 1999 in NV.
Donors: J.D. Taylor; Nancy S. Taylor.
Grantmaker type: Independent foundation.
Financial data (yr. ended 12/31/04): Assets, $543,577 (M); gifts received, $10,027; expenditures, $27,729; total giving, $26,575; qualifying distributions, $26,575; giving activities include $26,575 for grants.
Limitations: Applications not accepted. Giving primarily in AZ, CA, MI, and NV. No grants to individuals.
Application information: Contributes only to pre-selected organizations.
Trustees: Barbara Ann Becker; Brigid S. Pierce; Barbara Sullivan; Nancy S. Taylor.
EIN: 880448358

1834
The Ann Ludington Sullivan Foundation
c/o Currie & Kendall
3320 Ridgecrest Dr., Ste. 400
Midland, MI 48642-5864   (989) 631-2370
Contact: Ann L. Sullivan, Pres.

Established in 1996 in MI.
Donor: John S. Ludington.
Grantmaker type: Independent foundation.
Financial data (yr. ended 12/31/04): Assets, $498,661 (M); gifts received, $42,870; expenditures, $23,083; total giving, $19,000; qualifying distributions, $19,000; giving activities include $19,000 for grants.
Fields of interest: Higher education; Substance abuse, services.
Limitations: Giving primarily in NC.
Application information: Application form required.
  Initial approach: Letter
  Deadline(s): None
Officers: Ann L. Sullivan,* Pres.; Patrick M. Sullivan,* V.P.; John S. Ludington, Treas.
EIN: 383323702

1835
Robert and Timothy Sullivan Scholarship Fund Trust
(formerly Sullivan Scholarship Fund Trust)
2745 DeHoop Ave. S.W.
Wyoming, MI 49509-1867   (616) 538-6380
Contact: Dana L. Snoap, Tr.

Grantmaker type: Independent foundation.
Financial data (yr. ended 9/30/05): Assets, $84,532 (M); gifts received, $16,768; expenditures, $11,110; total giving, $8,000; qualifying distributions, $8,000; giving activities include $8,000 for grants.
Purpose and activities: Scholarship awards through Calvin College, Davenport College, Aquinas College, Grand Rapids Community College, and Grand Valley State University in Michigan.
Fields of interest: Scholarships/financial aid.
Type of support: Scholarship funds.
Limitations: Giving limited to the metropolitan Grand Rapids, MI, area.
Application information:
  Initial approach: Letter
  Deadline(s): May 1
Trustee: Dana L. Snoap.
EIN: 382448544

1836
Summerfield Family Foundation
c/o JPMorgan Chase Bank, N.A.
P.O. Box 1308
Milwaukee, WI 53201
Application address: c/o JPMorgan Chase Bank, N.A., 3245 Elizabeth Lake Rd., Waterford, MI 48328-3004, tel.: (888) 354-3907

Established in 1997 in MI.
Grantmaker type: Independent foundation.
Financial data (yr. ended 7/31/04): Assets, $108,243 (M); expenditures, $9,523; total giving, $7,150; qualifying distributions, $8,347; giving activities include $7,150 for grants.
Fields of interest: Performing arts, music; Education.
Type of support: General/operating support.

Limitations: Giving primarily in MI. No grants to individuals.
Application information:
Initial approach: Letter
Deadline(s): None
Trustee: JPMorgan Chase Bank, N.A.
EIN: 386689271

1837
Summerfield-MacArthur Foundation
c/o JPMorgan Chase Bank, N.A.
P.O. Box 1308
Milwaukee, WI 53201
Application address: c/o Hal Boyd, 111 E. Court St., Flint, MI 48502, tel.: (810) 237-3801

Established in 1997 in MI.
Grantmaker type: Independent foundation.
Financial data (yr. ended 7/31/05): Assets, $214,597 (M); expenditures, $16,130; total giving, $10,975; qualifying distributions, $10,975; giving activities include $10,975 for grants.
Fields of interest: Arts; Higher education; Education; Children/youth, services; Protestant agencies & churches.
Limitations: Giving primarily in Flint, MI. No grants to individuals.
Application information:
Initial approach: Letter
Deadline(s): None
Trustees: Gertrude S. MacArthur; JPMorgan Chase Bank, N.A.
EIN: 386689302

1838
Summerland Foundation
300 Golfview Dr.
Saginaw, MI 48603

Donor: Kenneth W. LeCureux.
Grantmaker type: Independent foundation.
Financial data (yr. ended 12/31/05): Assets, $18,909 (M); expenditures, $3,858; total giving, $3,538; qualifying distributions, $3,538; giving activities include $3,538 for grants.
Fields of interest: Human services; Religion.
Type of support: General/operating support.
Limitations: Applications not accepted. No grants to individuals.
Application information: Contributes only to pre-selected organizations.
Officers: Kenneth W. LeCureux, Pres.; Janet M. LeCureux, Secy.
EIN: 383353813

1839
The Summers Foundation, Inc.
254 Grosse Pointe Blvd.
Grosse Pointe Farms, MI 48236-3358

Established in 1998 in MI.
Donors: Emmet and Frances Tracy Fund; Denice T. Summers.
Grantmaker type: Independent foundation.
Financial data (yr. ended 12/31/04): Assets, $1,107,466 (M); expenditures, $68,576; total giving, $54,300; qualifying distributions, $68,576; giving activities include $54,300 for grants.

Fields of interest: Elementary/secondary education; Higher education; Children/youth, services; Protestant agencies & churches.
Type of support: General/operating support; Program development.
Limitations: Applications not accepted. Giving on a national basis, with emphasis on MI. No grants to individuals.
Application information: Contributes only to pre-selected organizations.
Officers: David S. Summers, Pres.; Elizabeth Skau, Secy.; Loren A. Summers, Treas.
Directors: Gregory Skau; David S. Summers, Jr.; Denice T. Summers; Denice T. Summers II; Marcie Summers; Matthew Summers; Michael Summers; Paul G. Summers.
EIN: 383403606

1840
Bernice B. Mayes Sunal Scholarship Foundation
P.O. Box 335
Greencastle, PA 17225-0335
Contact: Dale D. Ruohomaki, Pres.

Grantmaker type: Independent foundation.
Financial data (yr. ended 12/31/03): Assets, $48,738 (M); expenditures, $8,489; total giving, $3,000; qualifying distributions, $3,000; giving activities include $3,000 for 4 grants to individuals (high: $1,500; low: $500).
Purpose and activities: Scholarship awards to high school graduates residing in the geographical area of the North Huron High School District in Kinde, Michigan, who are enrolled on a full-time basis at a college or university.
Fields of interest: Higher education.
Type of support: Scholarships—to individuals.
Limitations: Giving limited to residents of the Kinde, MI, area.
Application information: Application form required.
Deadline(s): Dec. 31 for nominations; Jan. 31 for applications
Officers and Trustees: Dale D. Ruohomaki,* Pres. and Secy.-Treas.; John M. Sunal,* V.P.
EIN: 382598111

1841
Ralph & Elaine Sundquist Charitable & Educational Trust
c/o Comerica Bank
P.O. Box 75000 M/C 3302
Detroit, MI 48275-3302
Application address: c/o Marvin F. Sundquist, P.O. Box 1308, Takima, WA 98907, tel.: (303) 294-3349

Established in 1954 in WA.
Donor: Marvin Sundquist.
Grantmaker type: Independent foundation.
Financial data (yr. ended 12/31/05): Assets, $2,633,100 (M); gifts received, $2,537; expenditures, $153,289; total giving, $124,500; qualifying distributions, $125,375; giving activities include $124,500 for 15 grants (high: $25,250; low: $900).
Purpose and activities: Giving for education, social welfare services, performing arts, and for graphic arts.
Fields of interest: Arts; Education; Recreation, camps; Human services; Protestant agencies & churches.

Type of support: General/operating support; Capital campaigns; Endowments.
Limitations: Giving limited to WA, primarily in Yakima Valley. No grants to individuals.
Application information: Application form not required.
Initial approach: Letter
Deadline(s): None
Trustees: Marvin F. Sundquist; Comerica Bank.
EIN: 916025654

1842
Sunrise Community Foundation
8546 Eastbeach Trail
Traverse City, MI 49686-1674
Contact: Ronald R. Pohl, Dir.

Established in 2004 in MI.
Donors: Ronald R. Pohl; Judy C. Pohl.
Grantmaker type: Independent foundation.
Financial data (yr. ended 12/31/05): Assets, $193,592 (M); expenditures, $11,153; total giving, $8,000; qualifying distributions, $8,000; giving activities include $8,000 for grants.
Application information:
Initial approach: Letter
Deadline(s): None
Directors: Judy C. Pohl; Ronald R. Pohl.
EIN: 202005328

1843
Sunshine Foundation
26300 Telegraph Rd., 2nd Fl.
Southfield, MI 48034

Established in 2002 in MI.
Grantmaker type: Independent foundation.
Financial data (yr. ended 12/31/05): Assets, $188,987 (M); gifts received, $200,000; expenditures, $18,115; total giving, $12,500; qualifying distributions, $12,500; giving activities include $12,500 for grants.
Officer: Ahmed Zaki, M.D., Pres.
EIN: 300007313

1844
Superior Consultant Charitable Foundation
5225 Auto Club Dr.
Dearborn, MI 48126
Application Address: c/o Susan Synor, 17570 W. 12 Mile Rd., Southfield, MI 48076, tel: (248) 386-8300

Established in 1997 in MI.
Donor: Richard D. Helppie, Jr.
Grantmaker type: Independent foundation.
Financial data (yr. ended 12/31/04): Assets, $1,760,329 (M); gifts received, $1,235; expenditures, $259,440; total giving, $247,310; qualifying distributions, $247,228; giving activities include $247,310 for 34 grants (high: $100,000; low: $100).
Purpose and activities: Giving primarily to organizations involved with disadvantaged and medically impaired children, community improvement, and education.
Fields of interest: Education; Health care; Health organizations, association; Housing/shelter; Children/youth, services; Community development.

Limitations: Giving primarily in MI. No support for private foundations. No grants to individuals.
Application information:
 Initial approach: Written request
 Deadline(s): None
Officers and Directors:* Richard D. Helppie, Jr.,* Pres.; Leslie S. Helppie,* V.P.; Susan M. Synor,* Secy.-Treas.
EIN: 383374688

1845
Sutaruk Foundation
c/o Jacob & Weingarten
2301 W. Big Beaver Rd., Ste. 777
Troy, MI 48084

Established in 2003 in MI.
Donor: Catherine Sutar‡.
Grantmaker type: Independent foundation.
Financial data (yr. ended 12/31/05): Assets, $3,850,678 (M); gifts received, $2,612,329; expenditures, $264,078; total giving, $256,000; qualifying distributions, $256,000; giving activities include $256,000 for grants.
Fields of interest: Medical research; Human services.
Limitations: Applications not accepted. Giving in MI, primarily in Detroit and Southfield. No grants to individuals.
Application information: Contributes only to pre-selected organizations.
Directors: Walter Cwysyshyn; Olga Sutaruk Meyer; Tom Meyer; William Sutar.
EIN: 113673305

1846
H. W. Suter Foundation
807 Yarmouth Rd.
Bloomfield Hills, MI 48301

Established in MI.
Donor: Margaret A.B. Suter.
Grantmaker type: Independent foundation.
Financial data (yr. ended 12/31/05): Assets, $322,997 (M); expenditures, $12,436; total giving, $10,200; qualifying distributions, $10,200; giving activities include $10,200 for grants.
Fields of interest: Education; Protestant agencies & churches.
Type of support: General/operating support; Scholarship funds.
Limitations: Applications not accepted. Giving primarily in MI. No grants to individuals.
Application information: Contributes only to pre-selected organizations.
Trustees: Rose V. Marsh; Herbert W. Suter II; Margaret A.B. Suter.
EIN: 316028514

1847
Swanson Foundation
806 E. Grand Blvd.
Detroit, MI 48207-2552 (313) 272-9000

Established in 1968.
Donor: Swanson Funeral Home.
Grantmaker type: Independent foundation.
Financial data (yr. ended 6/30/05): Assets, $26,717 (M); gifts received, $55,000; expenditures, $66,448; total giving, $65,898;

qualifying distributions, $65,898; giving activities include $65,898 for grants.
Purpose and activities: Giving primarily for higher education and Baptist organizations.
Fields of interest: Higher education; Protestant agencies & churches.
Limitations: Applications not accepted. Giving primarily in Detroit, MI. No grants to individuals.
Application information: Contributes only to pre-selected organizations.
Officer: O'Neal D. Swanson, Pres.
EIN: 237007629

1848
William & Sally Swets Family Foundation
757 Plymouth S.E.
East Grand Rapids, MI 49506
Contact: William T. Swets, Pres.; Sally J. Swets, V.P.

Established in 1998 in MI.
Donors: William T. Swets; Sally J. Swets.
Grantmaker type: Independent foundation.
Financial data (yr. ended 12/31/05): Assets, $162,861 (M); gifts received, $7,750; expenditures, $19,622; total giving, $19,566; qualifying distributions, $19,566; giving activities include $19,566 for grants.
Limitations: Giving primarily in MI.
Application information:
 Initial approach: Letter
 Deadline(s): None
Officers and Directors:* William T. Swets,* Pres. and Treas.; Sally J. Swets,* V.P. and Secy.
EIN: 383439027

1849
The Richard J. and Frances B. Swiat Foundation
1615 W. Centre Ave.
Portage, MI 49024-5379
Contact: Richard G. Swiat, Pres.

Established in 1987 in MI.
Donor: Richard J. Swiat.
Grantmaker type: Independent foundation.
Financial data (yr. ended 12/31/04): Assets, $1,138,329 (M); expenditures, $50,955; total giving, $19,100; qualifying distributions, $20,543; giving activities include $19,100 for grants.
Purpose and activities: Giving primarily to organizations that will aid mentally impaired individuals on the states of IL, MI, and WI.
Fields of interest: Mental health, disorders.
Limitations: Giving limited to Lake County, IL, and Kalamazoo and Lelanau counties, MI; giving also in WI. No grants to individuals.
Application information:
 Initial approach: Letter
 Deadline(s): None
Officers: Richard G. Swiat, Pres. and Treas.; Shelly Swiat, V.P. and Secy.
EIN: 382813470

1850
William and Mary Swift Foundation
13956 Peninsula Dr.
Traverse City, MI 49686-8458

Established in 2000 in MI.
Donors: William A. Swift; Mary Swift.

Grantmaker type: Independent foundation.
Financial data (yr. ended 12/31/05): Assets, $1,485 (M); gifts received, $9,873; expenditures, $11,580; total giving, $10,200; qualifying distributions, $10,200; giving activities include $10,200 for grants.
Fields of interest: Environment.
Type of support: General/operating support.
Limitations: Applications not accepted. Giving primarily in MI. No grants to individuals.
Application information: Contributes only to pre-selected organizations.
Officers and Directors:* William A. Swift,* Pres. and Treas.; Mary E. Swift,* V.P. and Secy.
EIN: 364360800

1851
Sol & Doris Swiss Foundation
619 N. Sheldon Rd.
Plymouth, MI 48170

Established in MI.
Grantmaker type: Independent foundation.
Financial data (yr. ended 12/31/05): Assets, $218,690 (M); expenditures, $12,668; total giving, $11,455; qualifying distributions, $11,455; giving activities include $11,455 for grants.
Fields of interest: Education; Civil liberties, advocacy; Jewish agencies & temples.
Type of support: General/operating support.
Limitations: Applications not accepted. Giving primarily in MI. No grants to individuals.
Application information: Contributes only to pre-selected organizations.
Trustees: Irene Bach; Sandra McClennen; Shana Swiss.
EIN: 386147689

1852
SYTA Youth Foundation, Inc.
936 S. Baldwin Rd., Ste. 104
Clarkston, MI 48348

Established in 2001.
Grantmaker type: Independent foundation.
Financial data (yr. ended 6/30/03): Assets, $39,230 (M); gifts received, $30,317; expenditures, $27,244; total giving, $12,000; qualifying distributions, $11,999; giving activities include $12,000 for 2 grants (high: $10,000; low: $2,000).
Officers and Directors:* Rip Hunter,* Chair.; Cindy Brown,* Vice-Chair.; Karla Wilson, Secy.-Treas.; Michael Palmer, Exec. Dir.; Fred Dixon; Norm Hull.
EIN: 383605887

1853
Take Time Out
22701 Drake Rd.
Farmington Hills, MI 48335-3916

Established in 2002.
Grantmaker type: Independent foundation.
Financial data (yr. ended 6/30/03): Assets, $1,076 (M); gifts received, $1,076; expenditures, $0; total giving, $0; qualifying distributions, $0.
Officer: Doris Webber, Exec. Dir.
EIN: 383129158

1854
Anne Talen Foundation
c/o North Central Trust Co.
P.O. Box 489
La Crosse, WI   54602-0489

Established in 1991 in WI.
Grantmaker type: Independent foundation.
Financial data (yr. ended 12/31/05): Assets,
$407,773 (M); expenditures, $23,686; total giving,
$19,495; qualifying distributions, $19,495; giving
activities include $19,495 for grants.
Fields of interest: Libraries (public); Hospitals
(general); Religion.
Limitations: Applications not accepted. Giving
primarily in MI and WI. No grants to individuals.
Application information: Contributes only to
pre-selected organizations.
Trustee: North Central Trust Co.
EIN: 396511259

1855
Tamer Foundation
56 S. Groesbeck Hwy.
Clinton Township, MI   48036

Established in 1986 in MI.
Donors: James Tamer; James Tamer Restated
Living Trust.
Grantmaker type: Independent foundation.
Financial data (yr. ended 4/30/05): Assets,
$10,966,925 (M); expenditures, $617,831; total
giving, $585,950; qualifying distributions,
$582,925; giving activities include $521,550 for 47
grants (high: $65,000; low: $500), and $64,400 for
24 grants to individuals (high: $6,008; low: $691).
Purpose and activities: Giving primarily for higher
education, health and human services, and
Christian organizations, primarily Maronite Catholic
agencies and churches.
Fields of interest: Higher education; Hospitals
(general); Health organizations, association; Food
services; Human services; Christian agencies &
churches.
Type of support: General/operating support;
Scholarship funds; Scholarships—to individuals.
Limitations: Applications not accepted. Giving
primarily in Detroit, MI.
Application information: Unsolicited requests for
funds not considered.
Officer and Trustees:* Josephine Saigh,* Mgr.;
James George; Joseph Thomas.
EIN: 382679633

1856
The Keith W. Tantlinger Foundation
c/o JPMorgan Chase Bank, N.A.
P.O. Box 1308
Milwaukee, WI   53201
Application address: c/o Matthew H. Wasmund,
V.P., JPMorgan Chase Bank, N.A., Div., 611
Woodward Ave., Detroit, MI 48226, tel.: (313)
225-3454, fax: (313) 225-3948,
matthew_h_wasmund@bankone.com

Established in MI.
Grantmaker type: Independent foundation.
Financial data (yr. ended 12/31/05): Assets,
$101,801 (M); expenditures, $6,925; total giving,
$6,100; qualifying distributions, $6,925; giving

activities include $6,100 for 9 grants (high: $1,050;
low: $300).
Fields of interest: Historical activities; Education;
Salvation Army.
Limitations: Giving on a national basis, with
emphasis on CA. No grants to individuals.
Application information: Application form not
required.
   Initial approach: Proposal
   Deadline(s): None
Trustee: JPMorgan Chase Bank, N.A.
EIN: 386046660

1857
The Tapestry Foundation
1717 W. 6th St., Ste. 460
Austin, TX   78703-4778
E-mail: mctmb@aol.com

Established in 1994 in MI.
Donor: Thomas P. Borders.
Grantmaker type: Independent foundation.
Financial data (yr. ended 12/31/04): Assets,
$4,662,133 (M); expenditures, $194,114; total
giving, $161,250; qualifying distributions,
$161,270; giving activities include $161,250 for 19
grants (high: $20,000; low: $1,000).
Purpose and activities: The foundation primarily
partners with innovative literacy groups.
Fields of interest: Adult education—literacy, basic
skills & GED; Education, reading; Family services.
Limitations: Applications not accepted. Giving
primarily in the Austin, TX, metropolitan area; some
giving also in Louisville, KY, and MI. No grants to
individuals.
Application information: Contributes only to
pre-selected organizations.
Officers: Mary Carmel Borders, Pres.; Joshua T.
Borders, V.P.; Thomas P. Borders, Secy.-Treas.
Director: Samantha C. Borders.
EIN: 383196007
Selected grants: The following grants were reported
in 2004.
$50,000 to Childrens Medical Center Foundation of
   Central Texas, Austin, TX. For program support.
$20,000 to Passionist Nuns, Owensboro, KY. For
   program support.
$20,000 to Seton Fund of the Daughters of Charity
   of Saint Vincent de Paul, Austin, TX. For program
   support.
$16,000 to University of Texas, Austin, TX. 2 grants:
   $6,000 (For program support), $10,000 to Harry
   Ransom Center (For program support).
$10,000 to Texas Book Festival, Austin, TX. For
   program support.
$10,000 to University of Louisville, Department of
   Pediatrics, Louisville, KY. For program support.
$6,000 to Laura Bush Foundation for Americas
   Libraries, DC. For program support.
$5,000 to Austin Project, Austin, TX. For program
   support.
$5,000 to Greenlights for Nonprofit Success,
   Austin, TX. For program support.

1858
Tarakji Foundation
26300 Telegraph Rd., 2nd Fl.
Southfield, MI   48034

Established in 1999.
Donor: N. Tarakji.

Grantmaker type: Independent foundation.
Financial data (yr. ended 12/31/04): Assets,
$1,461,327 (M); gifts received, $530,000;
expenditures, $51,290; total giving, $50,550;
qualifying distributions, $50,408; giving activities
include $50,550 for grants.
Officer: N. Tarakji, Pres.
EIN: 383478158

1859
Tarnoff Family Foundation
2025 W. Long Lake Rd., Ste. 100
Troy, MI   48098-4100

Donors: Esther Cooper; Muriel Tarnoff.
Grantmaker type: Independent foundation.
Financial data (yr. ended 11/30/05): Assets,
$148,509 (M); expenditures, $12,258; total giving,
$10,800; qualifying distributions, $10,800; giving
activities include $10,800 for grants.
Limitations: Applications not accepted. Giving
primarily in MI. No grants to individuals.
Application information: Contributes only to
pre-selected organizations.
Officers: Lynn B. Lipman, Pres.; James L. Baker,
V.P. and Secy.; Paul P. Baker, Treas.
EIN: 382412636

1860
The Leslie E. Tassell Foundation
3439 Quiggle Ave. S.E.
Ada, MI   49301-9237
Contact: Joyce Wisner, Tr.

Established in 1994 in MI.
Donors: Leslie E. Tassell†; The Leslie Metal Arts
Co., Inc.
Grantmaker type: Independent foundation.
Financial data (yr. ended 12/31/03): Assets,
$8,992,127 (M); expenditures, $214,314; total
giving, $170,286; qualifying distributions,
$170,296; giving activities include $122,420 for 11
grants (high: $30,000; low: $1,500), and $47,866
for 14 grants to individuals (high: $7,214; low:
$1,500).
Purpose and activities: Support primarily for higher
education, including scholarships to individuals;
giving also for health and community services.
Fields of interest: Higher education; Health care;
Community development.
Type of support: Scholarships—to individuals.
Limitations: Giving primarily in Grand Rapids, MI.
Application information: Application form required.
   Initial approach: Write for application form
   Deadline(s): None
Trustees: David C. Bottrall; Carolyn J. Brown;
Michael R. Julien; Hilary F. Shell; Joyce S. Wisner.
EIN: 383186818

1861
Tauber Family Foundation
27777 Franklin Rd., Ste. 1630
Southfield, MI   48034

Established in 1993 in MI.
Donor: Joel D. Tauber.
Grantmaker type: Independent foundation.
Financial data (yr. ended 12/31/04): Assets,
$3,167,667 (M); expenditures, $341,883; total
giving, $334,190; qualifying distributions,

$331,168; giving activities include $334,190 for 30 grants (high: $91,000; low: $25).

Purpose and activities: Giving for education, medical education and research, federated giving programs and for Jewish organizations.

Fields of interest: Higher education; Medical school/education; Education; Human services; Federated giving programs; Jewish federated giving programs; Jewish agencies & temples.

Type of support: Scholarship funds; Building/renovation; General/operating support.

Limitations: Applications not accepted. Giving in the U.S., with emphasis on MI. No grants to individuals.

Application information: Contributes only to pre-selected organizations.

Officers: Joel D. Tauber, Chair. and Pres.; Julie T. McMahon, V.P.; Shelley J. Tauber, V.P.; Benjamin Brian Tauber, Secy.; Ellen T. Horing, Treas.

EIN: 383092417

Selected grants: The following grants were reported in 2003.

$200,000 to Jewish Federation of Metropolitan Detroit, Bloomfield Hills, MI. For unrestricted support.

$35,000 to American Friends of Shalom Hartman Institute, New York, NY. For unrestricted support.

$10,000 to Detroit Zoological Society, Royal Oak, MI. For unrestricted support.

$10,000 to Jewish Community Center of Metropolitan Detroit, West Bloomfield, MI.

$5,000 to Salk Institute for Biological Studies, San Diego, CA. For unrestricted support.

$2,000 to United Way for Southeastern Michigan, Detroit, MI. For capital campaign.

$1,865 to Temple Beth El of Marquette, Detroit, MI. For unrestricted support.

$1,500 to Aspen Music Festival, Aspen, CO. For unrestricted support.

$1,500 to Jewish Academy of Metropolitan Detroit, West Bloomfield, MI. For unrestricted support.

$1,000 to University of Michigan, Edward Ginsburg Center for Community Service Learning, Ann Arbor, MI. For unrestricted support.

1862
The Taubman Endowment for the Arts
200 E. Long Lake Rd.
P.O. Box 200
Bloomfield Hills, MI   48304-0200
(248) 258-7207
Contact: Fred Henshaw

Established in 1985 in MI.

Donor: A. Alfred Taubman.

Grantmaker type: Independent foundation.

Financial data (yr. ended 12/31/05): Assets, $128 (M); gifts received, $28,160; expenditures, $28,172; total giving, $27,050; qualifying distributions, $27,050; giving activities include $27,050 for grants.

Purpose and activities: Giving for arts and cultural institutes.

Fields of interest: Museums; Historic preservation/historical societies; Arts.

Limitations: Giving primarily in MI; some giving in Columbus, OH, and elsewhere in the U.S. No grants to individuals.

Application information:
Initial approach: Proposal
Deadline(s): None

Officers and Trustees:* A. Alfred Taubman,* Chair., Pres., and Treas.; Jeffrey H. Miro,* Secy.

EIN: 382590370

1863
A. Alfred Taubman Foundation
200 E. Long Lake Rd., Ste. 300
Bloomfield Hills, MI   48304   (248) 258-7207
Contact: J. Fred Henshaw

Established in 1979 in MI.

Donor: A. Alfred Taubman.

Grantmaker type: Independent foundation.

Financial data (yr. ended 7/31/05): Assets, $438 (M); gifts received, $82,114; expenditures, $82,137; total giving, $81,040; qualifying distributions, $82,134; giving activities include $81,040 for 70 grants (high: $20,000; low: $10).

Purpose and activities: Giving for education, Jewish welfare funds, medical research, and human services.

Fields of interest: Education; Medical research, institute; Human services; Jewish federated giving programs.

Type of support: General/operating support.

Limitations: Giving primarily in MI, with emphasis on Detroit.

Application information: Application form not required.
Deadline(s): None
Board meeting date(s): As necessary
Final notification: 4 weeks

Officers and Trustees:* A. Alfred Taubman,* Chair. and Treas.; Gayle T. Kalisman, Pres.; Jeffrey H. Miro,* Secy.; Judith M. Taubman; Robert S. Taubman; William S. Taubman.

EIN: 382219625

Selected grants: The following grants were reported in 2003.

$1,000,000 to Jewish Federation of Metropolitan Detroit, Bloomfield Hills, MI. For general operating support.

$2,500 to Tomorrows Childrens Fund, Hackensack, NJ. For general operating support.

$1,000 to Bnai Brith Foundation of United States, Detroit, MI. For general operating support.

$1,000 to NARAL/NY Foundation, New York, NY. For general operating support.

$1,000 to Southampton Association, Southampton, NY. For general operating support.

$500 to Venetian Heritage, New York, NY. For general operating support.

$500 to Washington Legal Foundation, DC. For general operating support.

$200 to Boy Scouts of America, Enid, OK. For general operating support.

$200 to Kadima Jewish Support Services for Adults with Mental Illness, Southfield, MI. For general operating support.

$100 to Special Olympics Michigan, Mount Pleasant, MI. For general operating support.

1864
The Taubman Foundation
200 E. Long Lake Rd., Ste. 180
Bloomfield Hills, MI   48304
Contact: Jeffrey M. Davidson
FAX: (248) 258-7684;
E-mail: jdavidson@taubman.com

Established in 1985 in MI.

Donor: A. Alfred Taubman.

Grantmaker type: Independent foundation.

Financial data (yr. ended 1/31/05): Assets, $723 (M); gifts received, $5,525,460; expenditures, $5,525,482; total giving, $5,523,200; qualifying distributions, $5,525,479; giving activities include $5,523,200 for 8 grants (high: $5,010,000; low: $200; average: $500–$10,000).

Purpose and activities: Giving primarily for higher education.

Fields of interest: Higher education.

Limitations: Applications not accepted. Giving primarily in MI.

Application information: The foundation has suspended its new grantmaking, current commitments will be honored.

Officers and Trustees:* A. Alfred Taubman,* Chair., Pres., and Treas.; Jeffrey H. Miro,* Secy.

EIN: 382590369

Selected grants: The following grants were reported in 2005.

$5,010,000 to University of Michigan, Ann Arbor, MI. For general operating support.

$500,000 to Lawrence Technological University, Southfield, MI. For general operating support.

$10,000 to Tougaloo College, Tougaloo, MS. For general operating support.

1865
The Taunt Foundation
700 E. Maple Rd., Lower Level
Birmingham, MI   48009-6357

Established in 1999 in MI.

Grantmaker type: Independent foundation.

Financial data (yr. ended 12/31/05): Assets, $0 (M); expenditures, $5,000; total giving, $5,000; qualifying distributions, $5,000; giving activities include $5,000 for grants.

Limitations: Applications not accepted. No grants to individuals.

Application information: Contributes only to pre-selected organizations.

Officers: J. Lawrence Taunt, Pres. and Treas.; Charles J. Taunt, V.P.

Directors: Rosaleen T. Borton; Marjorie E. Carlisle; Jeannie L. Taunt; Michael L. Taunt.

EIN: 383403270

1866
Maurice and Michelle Taylor Foundation
268 Provencal Rd.
Grosse Pointe Farms, MI   48236

Established in 1998 in IL.

Donors: Maurice M. Taylor, Jr.; Michelle Taylor.

Grantmaker type: Independent foundation.

Financial data (yr. ended 12/31/04): Assets, $1,216,645 (M); gifts received, $592; expenditures, $41,305; total giving, $322; qualifying distributions, $40,322; giving activities include $322 for grants.

Fields of interest: Scholarships/financial aid; Hospitals (general).

Limitations: Applications not accepted. Giving primarily in Detroit, MI. No grants to individuals.

Application information: Contributes only to pre-selected organizations.

Directors: Cheri T. Holley; Maureen McClayton; Anthony Soave; Maurice M. Taylor, Jr.; Michelle Taylor.

EIN: 364224065

1867
P. & H. Taylor Scholarship Trust
c/o Century Bank and Trust
100 W. Chicago St.
Coldwater, MI   49036
Contact: Alicia Cole, Trust Off.

Established in 2004 in MI.
Donors: Helen Taylor Irrevocable Trust; Percy Taylor Unitrust.
Grantmaker type: Independent foundation.
Financial data (yr. ended 12/31/05): Assets, $2,573,124 (M); expenditures, $118,101; total giving, $97,500; qualifying distributions, $97,500; giving activities include $97,500 for 49 grants to individuals.
Purpose and activities: Scholarship awards to residents of Branch County, MI.
Fields of interest: Higher education.
Type of support: Scholarships—to individuals.
Limitations: Giving limited to residents of Branch County, MI.
Application information: Application form required.
   Initial approach: Letter
   Deadline(s): None
Trustee: Century Bank and Trust.
EIN: 326030259

1868
H. Taylor Trust f/b/o American Cancer Society
c/o Century Bank and Trust
100 W. Chicago St.
Coldwater, MI   49036

Established in 2004 in MI.
Donor: Helen Taylor Irrevocable Trust.
Grantmaker type: Independent foundation.
Financial data (yr. ended 12/31/05): Assets, $896,142 (M); expenditures, $52,749; total giving, $44,682; qualifying distributions, $44,682; giving activities include $44,682 for grants.
Purpose and activities: Support only for the American Cancer Society.
Fields of interest: Cancer.
Type of support: General/operating support.
Limitations: Applications not accepted. No grants to individuals.
Application information: Contributes only to a pre-selected organization.
Trustee: Century Bank and Trust.
EIN: 326037377

1869
TDR, Inc.
P.O. Box 700034
Plymouth, MI   48170

Established in MI.
Grantmaker type: Independent foundation.
Financial data (yr. ended 12/31/05): Assets, $4,358 (M); gifts received, $13,953; expenditures, $12,817; total giving, $9,800; qualifying distributions, $9,800; giving activities include $9,800 for grants.
Fields of interest: Hospitals (general); Athletics/sports, school programs.
Type of support: General/operating support; Scholarships—to individuals.
Limitations: Applications not accepted. Giving primarily in MI.

Application information: Unsolicited requests for funds not accepted.
Officers: Patrick M. Donnelly, Pres.; Shannon A. Baron, V.P.; Michelle A. Snyder, Secy.; Theresa A. Brackenbury, Treas.
EIN: 522094084

1870
Ben N. Teitel Charitable Trust
2290 First National Bldg.
Detroit, MI   48226
Contact: Gerald S. Cook, Tr.

Established in 1987 in MI.
Donor: Ben N. Teitel†.
Grantmaker type: Independent foundation.
Financial data (yr. ended 9/30/05): Assets, $4,558,547 (M); expenditures, $269,435; total giving, $258,109; qualifying distributions, $261,140; giving activities include $258,109 for 43 grants (high: $45,000; low: $100).
Purpose and activities: The trust supports a variety of Jewish community programs for children and the elderly, including camping, teen touring to Israel, and educational programs to train social workers for Jewish agency work.
Fields of interest: Human services; Aging, centers/services; Jewish federated giving programs; Jewish agencies & temples.
International interests: Israel.
Type of support: General/operating support; Continuing support; Annual campaigns; Capital campaigns; Building/renovation; Endowments; Emergency funds; Program development; Seed money; Scholarship funds; Matching/challenge support.
Limitations: Applications not accepted. Giving primarily in southeast MI, and for the benefit of Israel. No grants to individuals.
Application information: Contributes only to pre-selected organizations.
Trustee: Gerald S. Cook.
EIN: 386512136

1871
Temple-Krick YFU Scholarship Fund, Inc.
2345 Delaware Dr.
Ann Arbor, MI   48103-6170   (734) 663-6472
Contact: Barbara T. Krick, Pres.

Established in 1988 in MI.
Donor: Barbara T. Krick.
Grantmaker type: Independent foundation.
Financial data (yr. ended 3/31/05): Assets, $8,505 (M); gifts received, $5,000; expenditures, $3,869; total giving, $3,848; qualifying distributions, $3,848; giving activities include $3,848 for 1 grant to an individual.
Purpose and activities: Scholarship awards to individuals to participate in the Youth for Understanding Cultural Exchange program.
Fields of interest: International exchange, students.
Type of support: Scholarships—to individuals.
Limitations: Giving limited to residents of MI.
Application information: Application form not required.
   Deadline(s): None
Officer and Directors:* Barbara T. Krick,* Pres.; Mary Alvery; Ken Clover; James H. Krick.
EIN: 382808315

1872
The Ten Talents Foundation, Ltd.
2435 Waite Ave.
Kalamazoo, MI   49008
URL: http://www.tentalentsfoundation.org

Established in 1995 in WI.
Donors: Andrew S. Cupps; Danielle Cupps.
Grantmaker type: Independent foundation.
Financial data (yr. ended 12/31/04): Assets, $232,961 (M); gifts received, $10,000; expenditures, $10,248; total giving, $8,500; qualifying distributions, $9,393; giving activities include $8,500 for 2 grants.
Purpose and activities: The mission of the foundation is to support individuals and organizations that take initiative to improve their skills to achieve excellence and self-reliance. The foundation seeks to educate individuals about the principles of a free-market economy and financial responsibility, and works to assist individuals in identifying and pursuing careers.
Fields of interest: Education, services; Economics.
Type of support: General/operating support.
Limitations: Applications not accepted. Giving primarily in MI. No grants to individuals.
Application information: Contributes only to pre-selected organizations.
Officers: Andrew S. Cupps, Pres.; Steve M. Donoghue, V.P.; Carole D. Cupps, Secy.; Samuel H. Cupps, Treas.
Directors: Danielle Cupps; Laura Donoghue.
EIN: 391822359

1873
The Krishnapilla Thavarajah and Puvaneswary Thavarajah Family Foundation
15 Pine Gate Ct.
Bloomfield Hills, MI   48304

Established in MI.
Donors: Krishnapilla Thavarajah; Puvaneswary Thavarajah; Ranesh C. Mandavo; Sabala Mandavo; Downriver Kidney Center.
Grantmaker type: Independent foundation.
Financial data (yr. ended 12/31/05): Assets, $436 (M); gifts received, $20,085; expenditures, $152,340; total giving, $150,244; qualifying distributions, $150,987; giving activities include $150,244 for 6 grants (high: $76,524; low: $21).
Fields of interest: Religion.
Limitations: Applications not accepted. No grants to individuals.
Application information: Contributes only to pre-selected organizations.
Officers: Krishnapilla Thavarajah, Pres. and Treas.; Puvaneswary Thavarajah, Secy.
Directors: Brian Thavarajah; Indrajit T. Thavarajah; Krishna Thavarajah; Sumeska Thavarajah.
EIN: 912080709

1874
Bhagwani Thawani Foundation
6145 Brookstone Ln.
Grand Blanc, MI   48439
Contact: Hemant Thawani, Pres.

Established in 2002 in MI.
Donor: Hermant Thawani.
Grantmaker type: Independent foundation.

Financial data (yr. ended 12/31/05): Assets, $15,052 (M); expenditures, $5,630; total giving, $4,901; qualifying distributions, $4,901; giving activities include $4,901 for grants.
Application information:
   Initial approach: Letter
   Deadline(s): None
Officer: Hermant Thawani, Pres. and Secy.-Treas.
EIN: 320057659

1875
The Theuerkorn Foundation
29469 Groesbeck Hwy.
Roseville, MI   48066-1942

Established in 1997 in MI.
Donor: Hillside Tool & Die.
Grantmaker type: Independent foundation.
Financial data (yr. ended 12/31/05): Assets, $225,552 (M); expenditures, $11,927; total giving, $11,600; qualifying distributions, $11,600; giving activities include $11,600 for grants.
Purpose and activities: Giving primarily to Protestant organizations.
Fields of interest: International relief; Protestant agencies & churches.
Limitations: Applications not accepted. No grants to individuals.
Application information: Contributes only to pre-selected organizations.
Officers and Directors:* Gary Theuerkorn,* Pres. and Treas.; David Theuerkorn,* V.P. and Secy.; Marshall Rosquin; Tracy Rosquin; Christine Theuerkorn; Sandy Theuerkorn.
EIN: 383330001

1876
Jean and Stewart Thiemkey Scholarship Foundation
9363 Riverside Dr.
St. Louis, MI   48880   (989) 681-5912
Contact: William Thiemkey, Secy.-Treas

Established in 1999 in MI.
Donors: William Thiemkey; Roberta Thiemkey.
Grantmaker type: Independent foundation.
Financial data (yr. ended 12/31/05): Assets, $49,220 (M); gifts received, $7,000; expenditures, $3,774; total giving, $3,300; qualifying distributions, $3,300; giving activities include $3,300 for grants to individuals.
Purpose and activities: Scholarship awards to graduates of Lapeer West High School with an interest in pursuing teaching as a career. Preference given to those attending Eastern Michigan University, the University of Michigan, or Alma College, MI.
Type of support: Scholarships—to individuals.
Limitations: Giving limited to residents of Lapeer, MI.
Application information: Application form not required.
   Initial approach: Letter
   Deadline(s): None
Officers: Richard Thiemkey, Pres.; William Thiemkey, Secy.-Treas.
EIN: 383461005

1877
The Carl and Elinor Glyn Thom Charitable Foundation
206 Bridge St.
Charlevoix, MI   49720-1404

Established in 1993 in MI.
Donor: Carl Thom.
Grantmaker type: Independent foundation.
Financial data (yr. ended 12/31/05): Assets, $1,465,743 (M); gifts received, $2,000; expenditures, $62,421; total giving, $56,000; qualifying distributions, $56,000; giving activities include $56,000 for 23 grants to individuals (high: $4,000; low: $2,000).
Fields of interest: Education.
Type of support: Scholarships—to individuals.
Limitations: Applications not accepted. Giving primarily to residents of Hazel Park, MI.
Application information: Unsolicited requests for funds not accepted.
Director: William C. Thom.
EIN: 383105784

1878
W. B. & Candace Thoman Foundation
222 N. Washington Sq., Ste. 400
Lansing, MI   48933-1800   (517) 377-0710
Contact: Benjamin O. Schwendener, Jr., Pres.

Established in 1968 in MI.
Donors: W.B. Thoman†; Candace Thoman†.
Grantmaker type: Independent foundation.
Financial data (yr. ended 12/31/04): Assets, $2,888,842 (M); expenditures, $33,206; total giving, $4,000; qualifying distributions, $12,400; giving activities include $4,000 for 1 grant.
Purpose and activities: Giving primarily for education, orphans and the economically disadvantaged.
Fields of interest: Arts; Education, special; Higher education; Adult education—literacy, basic skills & GED; Education; Human services; Economically disadvantaged.
Type of support: Continuing support; Program development; Seed money; Scholarship funds; Program-related investments/loans; Matching/challenge support.
Limitations: Giving primarily in Clinton, Eaton, and Ingham counties, MI. No support for political organizations, churches, or religious organizations or programs. No grants to individuals.
Publications: Application guidelines; Program policy statement.
Application information:
   Initial approach: Letter requesting guidelines
   Copies of proposal: 6
   Deadline(s): 2 weeks prior to board meetings
   Board meeting date(s): Quarterly
Officers and Trustees:* Benjamin O. Schwendener, Jr.,* Pres. and Secy.; Louis E. Legg, Jr.,* V.P.; Dorothy Silk,* Treas.; Frederick M. Baker; Richard Chapin.
Number of staff: 1 part-time support.
EIN: 237029842

1879
The Thomas Foundation
201 W. Big Beaver Rd., Ste. 600
Troy, MI   48084-4161   (248) 528-1111
Contact: Jay Howard Brody, Dir.

Established in 1984 in MI.
Donor: Harriet Kay Thomas Revocable Trust.
Grantmaker type: Independent foundation.
Financial data (yr. ended 3/31/05): Assets, $10,564,624 (M); expenditures, $520,760; total giving, $277,865; qualifying distributions, $491,447; giving activities include $277,865 for 38 grants (high: $100,000; low: $1,000).
Purpose and activities: Giving primarily for medical research, particularly diabetes; funding also for children and youth services.
Fields of interest: Higher education; Medical school/education; Health organizations; Medical research, institute; Diabetes research; Boys & girls clubs; Human services; Children/youth, services.
Limitations: Giving primarily in southeast MI.
Application information:
   Initial approach: Letter
   Deadline(s): None
   Final notification: Within 60 days
Directors: Jay Howard Brody; Chester L. Uncapher.
EIN: 382510591

1880
Russ Thomas Scholarship Fund
3707 W. Maple St., Ste. 13
Bloomfield Hills, MI   48301-3212
(248) 216-4050
Contact: Dorothy S. Thomas, Tr.

Established in 1991 in MI.
Donors: Dorothy S. Thomas; John R. Thomas; James E. Thomas.
Grantmaker type: Independent foundation.
Financial data (yr. ended 11/30/05): Assets, $697,917 (M); gifts received, $55,418; expenditures, $62,435; total giving, $53,500; qualifying distributions, $53,500; giving activities include $53,500 for grants.
Purpose and activities: Scholarship awards for undergraduate studies.
Fields of interest: Scholarships/financial aid.
Type of support: Scholarships—to individuals.
Limitations: Giving limited to the greater Detroit, MI area.
Application information: Application form required.
   Initial approach: Letter
   Deadline(s): None
Trustees: Dorothy S. Thomas; James E. Thomas; John Thomas, Jr.
EIN: 382984958

1881
Jack W. Thompson Community Charitable Trust
c/o Citizens Bank Wealth Management, N.A.
328 S. Saginaw St.
Flint, MI   48502

Established in 2004 in MI.
Donor: Jack W. Thompson Trust.
Grantmaker type: Independent foundation.
Financial data (yr. ended 7/31/05): Assets, $616,716 (M); gifts received, $527,042; expenditures, $6,973; total giving, $0; qualifying distributions, $2,439.
Limitations: Applications not accepted. No grants to individuals.
Application information: Contributes only to pre-selected organizations.

Trustee: Citizens Bank, N.A.
EIN: 364554615

1882
Thompson Educational Foundation
P.O. Box 6349
Plymouth, MI 48170

Established in 2002 in MI.
Donors: Ellen A. Thompson; Robert M. Thompson.
Grantmaker type: Independent foundation.
Financial data (yr. ended 12/31/03): Assets, $30,621,639 (M); gifts received, $5,500,000; expenditures, $226,701; total giving, $152,000; qualifying distributions, $11,337,206; giving activities include $152,000 for 2 grants (high: $150,000; low: $2,000), $10,947,645 for foundation-administered programs and $200,000 for 2 loans/program-related investments.
Fields of interest: Higher education; Education.
Limitations: Applications not accepted. Giving primarily in MI. No grants to individuals.
Application information: Contributes only to pre-selected organizations.
Officers and Trustees:* Robert M. Thompson,* Chair. and Pres.; Ellen A. Thompson,* V.P.; Joseph G. Horonzy,* Secy.; Edward M. Parks,* Secy.-Treas.
EIN: 300107259

1883
Lucille S. Thompson Family Foundation
c/o Comerica Bank
P.O. Box 75000 MC 3302
Detroit, MI 48275-3302
Contact: Mrs. Lila K. Pfleger, Exec. Dir.
Application address: 4823 Old Kingston Pike, Ste. 140, Knoxville, TN 37919, tel.: (865) 558-8654

Established in 1988 in TN.
Donor: Lucille S. Thompson.
Grantmaker type: Independent foundation.
Financial data (yr. ended 2/28/05): Assets, $19,173,961 (M); expenditures, $3,078,815; total giving, $2,564,922; qualifying distributions, $2,751,650; giving activities include $2,564,922 for 174 grants (high: $200,000; low: $50).
Purpose and activities: Support primarily for human services, youth services, education, medical services, and arts and culture for individuals and families of the east TN region.
Fields of interest: Museums; Historic preservation/historical societies; Arts; Health care; Health organizations, association; Cancer; Cancer research; Human services; Children/youth, services.
Type of support: General/operating support; Equipment.
Limitations: Giving primarily in the east TN region. No grants to individuals or for endowment funds, or deficit operating budgets.
Application information: Application form required.
Initial approach: Letter or proposal
Deadline(s): Jan. 31, Apr. 30, July 31, and Oct. 31
Final notification: within 2 weeks after board meeting
Officer and Trust Committee:* Sandra K. Bishop,* Chair.; John W. Baker, Jr.; Archer W. Bishop III; Baker O'Neil Bishop; Sandra K. Bishop; Thompson A. Bishop; Kristin B. MacDermott; Lindsay Young.
Trustee: Comerica Bank.
EIN: 581788548

Selected grants: The following grants were reported in 2003.
$225,000 to Duke University, Durham, NC.
$200,000 to Episcopal Schools of Knoxville, Knoxville, TN.
$200,000 to Webb School of Knoxville, Knoxville, TN.
$118,750 to Music Associates of Aspen, Aspen, CO.
$100,000 to Child and Family, Knoxville, TN.
$100,000 to Knox Area Rescue Ministries, Knoxville, TN.
$100,000 to Maryville College, Maryville, TN.
$100,000 to Pellissippi State Technical Community College Foundation, Knoxville, TN.
$100,000 to West End Academy, Knoxville, TN.
$100,000 to YMCA of Knoxville, Knoxville, TN.

1884
Thompson Foundation
(formerly Thompson-McCully Foundation)
c/o Bridget Makridakis
P.O. Box 6349
Plymouth, MI 48170
FAX: (734) 453-6475;
E-mail: bmakridakis@thompsonfdn.org; URL: http://www.thompsonfdn.org

Established in 1999 in MI.
Donors: Robert M. Thompson; Ellen Anne Thompson.
Grantmaker type: Independent foundation.
Financial data (yr. ended 12/31/04): Assets, $59,643,368 (M); gifts received, $825,883; expenditures, $3,130,561; total giving, $2,694,647; qualifying distributions, $2,936,795; giving activities include $2,694,647 for 63 grants (high: $496,800; low: $500; average: $11,000–$125,000).
Purpose and activities: The foundation has narrowed its focus to a specific educational initiative.
Fields of interest: Elementary/secondary education; Higher education; Education.
Type of support: Program development; Scholarship funds.
Limitations: Applications not accepted. Giving in the metropolitan Detroit, MI, area. No grants to individuals.
Application information: Unsolicited requests for funds not accepted.
Board meeting date(s): Feb., Apr., June, Aug., Oct., Dec.
Officers and Trustees:* Robert M. Thompson,* Pres.; Ellen Anne Thompson,* V.P.; Joseph G. Horonzy; Edward M. Parks.
Number of staff: 1 full-time professional.
EIN: 383452577
Selected grants: The following grants were reported in 2003.
$745,000 to Salvation Army of Detroit, Detroit, MI. 2 grants: $735,000 (For purchase of Aurora facility to transfer Harbor Light and Booth operations), $10,000 (For Summer Day Camp program).
$600,000 to Focus: Hope, Detroit, MI. For Student Loan Fund.
$91,000 to Detroit Youth Foundation, Detroit, MI. For Detroit Parent Network.
$88,000 to Lighthouse of Oakland County, Pontiac, MI. For financial training and education program.

$60,000 to Southwest Counseling and Development Services, Detroit, MI. For Friends of the Homeless project.
$50,000 to Saint Patrick Senior Center, Detroit, MI. For general operating support.
$27,000 to Saint Rose Senior Citizens Center, Detroit, MI. For Project Aging Well Program.

1885
Margaret C. Thompson Foundation
c/o National City Bank
P.O. Box 94651
Cleveland, OH 44101-4651

Established in 1986 in MI.
Donor: Margaret C. Thompson.
Grantmaker type: Independent foundation.
Financial data (yr. ended 12/31/05): Assets, $1,558,138 (M); expenditures, $95,126; total giving, $74,730; qualifying distributions, $74,730; giving activities include $74,730 for grants.
Fields of interest: Higher education, university; Hospitals (general); Boys & girls clubs; American Red Cross; Salvation Army; YM/YWCAs & YM/YWHAs; Foundations (community); Protestant agencies & churches.
Type of support: General/operating support.
Limitations: Applications not accepted. Giving limited to Bay City, Essexville, and University Center, MI. No grants to individuals.
Application information: Contributes only to 8 pre-selected organizations.
Trustee: National City Bank.
EIN: 386500422

1886
The Richard K. Thompson Foundation
24417 Groesbeck Hwy.
Warren, MI 48089-4786

Grantmaker type: Independent foundation.
Financial data (yr. ended 12/31/05): Assets, $893,870 (M); gifts received, $364,200; expenditures, $37,120; total giving, $36,760; qualifying distributions, $36,760; giving activities include $36,760 for grants.
Fields of interest: Media, television; Health care; Down syndrome; Lung diseases; Food services; Human services; American Red Cross; Salvation Army.
Type of support: General/operating support.
Limitations: Applications not accepted. Giving primarily in Detroit, MI. No grants to individuals.
Application information: Contributes only to pre-selected organizations.
Officer: Richard K. Thompson, Pres. and Secy.-Treas.
Director: Linda Davis Vaughn.
EIN: 383447218

1887
William G. Thompson Foundation
c/o William G. Thompson
153 E. Maumee St.
Adrian, MI 49221-2703

Donor: William G. Thompson.
Grantmaker type: Independent foundation.
Financial data (yr. ended 9/30/04): Assets, $0 (M); gifts received, $25,000; expenditures, $30,364;

total giving, $27,370; qualifying distributions, $27,370; giving activities include $27,370 for grants.
Fields of interest: Libraries/library science; Community development; Protestant agencies & churches.
Limitations: Applications not accepted. Giving limited to MI, with emphasis on Hudson. No grants to individuals.
Application information: Contributes only to pre-selected organizations.
Officers: William G. Thompson, Pres.; Daniel Cummiskey, V.P.; James K. Whitehouse, Secy.
Trustees: David S. Hickman; Claude Rowley.
EIN: 383123960

1888
Mary Thompson Foundation
c/o Comerica Bank
P.O. Box 75000, MC 3302
Detroit, MI   48275
Contact: Mrs. Douglas F. Roby, Jr., Grant Chair.
Application address: P.O. Box 568, St. Clair Shores, MI 48080-0568

Established in 1979.
Donor: Mary Thompson‡.
Grantmaker type: Independent foundation.
Financial data (yr. ended 12/31/05): Assets, $3,351,944 (M); expenditures, $183,189; total giving, $146,260; qualifying distributions, $147,536; giving activities include $146,260 for 19 grants (high: $15,000; low: $100).
Purpose and activities: Giving primarily to assist the frail and elderly in Michigan.
Fields of interest: Nursing home/convalescent facility; Geriatrics; Aging, centers/services; Aging.
Type of support: General/operating support; Continuing support; Equipment; Program development; Conferences/seminars.
Limitations: Giving limited to Detroit, MI.
Publications: Application guidelines.
Application information: Application form required.
   Initial approach: Letter
   Copies of proposal: 1
   Deadline(s): None
   Board meeting date(s): Spring and fall
   Final notification: 1 month from receipt
Officers and Trustees:* Mrs. William D. Dahling,* Pres.; Mrs. E. Irving Book,* V.P.; Antoinette P. Book,* Secy.; Lynn Cameron,* Treas.; Mrs. David S. Cameron; Mrs. George E. Cartmill; Mrs. Ernest S. Kratzet; Mrs. William H. Ledyard; Mrs. Douglas F. Roby, Jr.; Mrs. John S. Snyder; Mrs. David Viger.
Trustee Bank: Comerica Bank.
EIN: 381359097

1889
Jack W. Thompson Visiting Professorship Foundation
c/o Citizens Bank Wealth Management, N.A
328 S. Saginaw St.
Flint, MI   48502

Established in 2004 in MI.
Donor: Jack W. Thompson Trust.
Grantmaker type: Independent foundation.
Financial data (yr. ended 7/31/05): Assets, $623,169 (M); gifts received, $536,886; expenditures, $6,991; total giving, $0; qualifying distributions, $2,448.

Limitations: Applications not accepted. No grants to individuals.
Application information: Contributes only to pre-selected organizations.
Trustee: Citizens Bank, N.A.
EIN: 352231295

1890
Floyd B. & Helen M. Thormann Foundation, Inc.
41700 Hayes Rd., Ste A
Clinton Township, MI   48038

Established in 1998.
Donor: Helen M. Thormann‡.
Grantmaker type: Independent foundation.
Financial data (yr. ended 12/31/05): Assets, $640,032 (M); expenditures, $58,710; total giving, $36,520; qualifying distributions, $36,520; giving activities include $36,520 for grants.
Fields of interest: Higher education; Education; Medical research, institute; Athletics/sports, Special Olympics; Children, services.
Type of support: General/operating support.
Limitations: Applications not accepted. Giving primarily in FL and MI. No grants to individuals.
Application information: Contributes only to pre-selected organizations.
Officer: Wayne Stewart, Mgr.
EIN: 383342992

1891
Thorrez Foundation
126 Hanover St.
P.O. Box 307
Concord, MI   49237   (517) 750-3160
Contact: Camiel E. Thorrez, Pres.
Application address: 6750 Pulaski Rd., Concord, MI 49237

Donors: Camiel E. Thorrez; C. Thorrez Industries, Inc.
Grantmaker type: Independent foundation.
Financial data (yr. ended 6/30/03): Assets, $121,424 (M); gifts received, $2,459; expenditures, $20; total giving, $0; qualifying distributions, $0.
Limitations: Giving primarily in MI.
Application information: Application form not required.
   Deadline(s): None
Officers: Camiel E. Thorrez, Pres.; Theresa J. Stevens, V.P.; Phyllis J. Thorrez, Secy.-Treas.
Trustees: Jeoffrey A. Thorrez; Mary C. Wheeler.
EIN: 237231150

1892
Thy Kingdom Come Foundation
c/o John Worst
10760 52nd Ave.
Allendale, MI   49401-9309

Established in 1997 in MI.
Donor: Clarence Worst.
Grantmaker type: Independent foundation.
Financial data (yr. ended 12/31/04): Assets, $216,789 (M); expenditures, $15,417; total giving, $14,500; qualifying distributions, $15,005; giving activities include $14,500 for grants.

Limitations: Applications not accepted. Giving primarily in CA, MI, and NY. No grants to individuals.
Application information: Contributes only to pre-selected organizations.
Trustees: Joann Holwerda; Annette Siebelink; John Worst.
EIN: 383325596

1893
Gerald C. Timmis & Dorothy S. Timmis Foundation
4733 W. Wickford
Bloomfield Hills, MI   48302

Established in 1996 in MI.
Donors: Dorothy S. Timmis; Gerald C. Timmis.
Grantmaker type: Independent foundation.
Financial data (yr. ended 12/31/05): Assets, $1,297 (M); gifts received, $300; expenditures, $225; total giving, $0; qualifying distributions, $0.
Fields of interest: Human services.
Type of support: General/operating support.
Limitations: Applications not accepted. No grants to individuals.
Application information: Contributes only to pre-selected organizations.
Officers: Gerald C. Timmis, Pres. and Treas.; Dorothy S. Timmis, Secy.
EIN: 383246399

1894
Michael T. & Nancy E. Timmis Foundation
400 Talon Ctr.
Detroit, MI   48207-5037

Established in 1984 in MI.
Donor: Michael T. Timmis.
Grantmaker type: Independent foundation.
Financial data (yr. ended 12/31/04): Assets, $5,038,536 (M); gifts received, $1,000; expenditures, $1,456,293; total giving, $1,317,345; qualifying distributions, $1,317,345; giving activities include $1,316,345 for 57 grants (high: $457,195; low: $50), and $1,000 for 1 grant to an individual.
Purpose and activities: Giving primarily to Roman Catholic churches and organizations, and affiliated programs.
Fields of interest: Education; Human services; Children/youth, services; International affairs; Federated giving programs; Roman Catholic agencies & churches.
Type of support: General/operating support.
Limitations: Applications not accepted. Giving in the U.S., primarily in Washington, DC, and MI.
Application information: Contributes only to pre-selected organizations.
Officers: Michael T.O. Timmis, Pres.; Nancy E. Timmis, V.P.; Justin P. Blomberg, Secy.-Treas.
EIN: 382519177
Selected grants: The following grants were reported in 2003.
$397,960 to International Foundation, DC. For general support.
$103,707 to Prison Fellowship International, DC. For general support.
$75,000 to Cornerstone Schools, Detroit, MI. For general support.
$32,500 to Navigators, The, Colorado Springs, CO. For general support.

$31,000 to Wayne State University, Detroit, MI. For general support.

$3,000 to Loyola High School, Detroit, MI. For general support.

$1,000 to American Heart Association, Southfield, MI. For general support.

$1,000 to Campus Crusade for Christ International, Orlando, FL. For general support.

$500 to Franciscan University of Steubenville, Steubenville, OH. For general support.

$200 to Childrens Home of Detroit, Grosse Pointe Woods, MI. For general support.

1895
The Timothy Foundation
P.O. Box 67
East Lansing, MI 48826-0067

Established in 2003 in MI.
Donor: Benjamin J. Falconer.
Grantmaker type: Independent foundation.
Financial data (yr. ended 12/31/05): Assets, $516,415 (M); gifts received, $500; expenditures, $161,866; total giving, $155,000; qualifying distributions, $155,020; giving activities include $155,000 for 1 grant (high: $155,000).
Fields of interest: Food banks; Christian agencies & churches.
Limitations: Applications not accepted. No grants to individuals.
Application information: Contributes only to pre-selected organizations.
Officers and Trustees: * Benjamin J. Falconer,* Pres. and Treas.; Kimberly R. Falconer,* V.P. and Secy.
EIN: 200126144

1896
TIR Foundation
P.O. Box 806150
St. Clair Shores, MI 48080-6150

Established in MI.
Donor: Sunil Palchaudhuri.
Grantmaker type: Independent foundation.
Financial data (yr. ended 12/31/05): Assets, $140,000 (M); gifts received, $5,000; expenditures, $6,775; total giving, $2,200; qualifying distributions, $8,975; giving activities include $2,200 for grants.
Purpose and activities: Giving primarily for the research and studying of infectious diseases in India.
Fields of interest: Higher education.
International interests: India.
Limitations: Applications not accepted. Giving primarily in India. No grants to individuals.
Application information: Contributes only to pre-selected organizations.
Directors: Raj Palchaudhuri; Sunil Palchaudhuri; Titir Palchaudhuri.
EIN: 912144774

1897
The Tiscornia Foundation, Inc.
1010 Main St., Ste. A
St. Joseph, MI 49085   (269) 983-4711
Contact: Laurianne T. Davis, Pres.

Incorporated in 1942 in MI.

Donors: James W. Tiscornia†; Waldo V. Tiscornia†; Auto Specialties Manufacturing Co.; Lambert Brake Corp.
Grantmaker type: Independent foundation.
Financial data (yr. ended 12/31/04): Assets, $3,862,702 (M); expenditures, $451,339; total giving, $263,964; qualifying distributions, $356,544; giving activities include $155,964 for 15 grants (high: $75,000; low: $295), and $108,000 for 27 grants to individuals (high: $4,000; low: $4,000).
Fields of interest: Arts; Higher education; Reproductive health, family planning; Health care; Health organizations; Human services; Youth, services.
Type of support: Continuing support; Capital campaigns; Building/renovation; Equipment; Emergency funds; Seed money; Scholarship funds; Scholarships—to individuals.
Limitations: Giving limited to North Berrien County, MI. No grants to individuals (except committee-selected scholarship recipients), or for research or matching gifts; no loans.
Publications: Annual report (including application guidelines).
Application information: Scholarships only for northern Berrien County high school seniors at the following schools: St. Joseph, Benton Harbor, Coloma, Watervliet, Lake Shore, Lake Michigan Catholic, and Lake Michigan Lutheran. Application form not required.
  Initial approach: Letter or proposal
  Copies of proposal: 1
  Deadline(s): Apr. 1 for scholarships; Oct. 1 for grants
  Board meeting date(s): Jan.
Officers: Laurianne T. Davis, Pres. and Exec. Dir.; Bernice Tiscornia, V.P.; James Tiscornia, V.P.; Lesli D. Nadolski, Secy.; Henry Tippet, Treas.
Number of staff: 1 full-time professional; 1 part-time support.
EIN: 381777343

1898
Titche Family Foundation
675 Manhattan Rd. S.E.
Grand Rapids, MI 49506

Grantmaker type: Independent foundation.
Financial data (yr. ended 11/30/05): Assets, $599,617 (M); gifts received, $9,000; expenditures, $28,828; total giving, $28,000; qualifying distributions, $28,000; giving activities include $28,000 for grants.
Fields of interest: Libraries (public).
Limitations: Applications not accepted. Giving limited to MI. No grants to individuals.
Application information: Contributes only to pre-selected organizations.
Directors: Cynthia A. Kogelschatz; Claude A. Titche III; Marilyn A. Titche; Wayne A. Titche.
EIN: 382693221

1899
TLC Foundation
(also known as The Calliea Family Foundation)
48384 Forbes St.
Chesterfield, MI 48047-3948

Established in 2001 in MI.
Donors: Anthony C. Calliea; Linda M. Calliea.

Grantmaker type: Independent foundation.
Financial data (yr. ended 12/31/04): Assets, $2,279,777 (M); expenditures, $94,508; total giving, $90,733; qualifying distributions, $94,508; giving activities include $90,733 for 1 grant.
Fields of interest: Recreation, centers; Children/youth.
Limitations: Applications not accepted. Giving in the U.S., with emphasis on MI. No grants to individuals.
Application information: Contributes only to pre-selected organizations.
Trustees: Michael S. Bommarito; Anthony C. Calliea.
EIN: 383624956
Selected grants: The following grants were reported in 2003.
$90,373 to Blue Water Hockey League, Port Huron, MI. For general support.
$75,000 to Ronald McDonald House Charities, Oak Brook, IL. For general support.
$25,000 to Saint Jude Childrens Research Hospital, Memphis, TN. For general support.
$25,000 to Turning Point, Mount Clemens, MI. For general support.
$20,000 to Alternative Solutions School for Children with Autism, Pinellas Park, FL. For general support.
$20,000 to Humane Society, Macomb County, Utica, MI. For general support.
$20,000 to Macomb County Child Advocacy Center, Care House, Mount Clemens, MI. For general support.
$20,000 to Make-A-Wish Foundation of America, Phoenix, AZ. For general support.
$20,000 to SOS Childrens Villages-USA, Alexandria, VA. For general support.

1900
The Steve Toth, Jr. Family Foundation
300 E. Maple Rd., Ste. 350
Birmingham, MI 48009

Established in 1994 in MI.
Donor: Steve Toth, Jr.
Grantmaker type: Independent foundation.
Financial data (yr. ended 7/31/05): Assets, $228,878 (M); gifts received, $2,355; expenditures, $173,868; total giving, $83,660; qualifying distributions, $83,660; giving activities include $83,660 for 6 grants (high: $40,000; low: $160).
Fields of interest: Hospitals (general); Neuroscience.
Limitations: Applications not accepted. Giving primarily in MI. No grants to individuals.
Application information: Contributes only to pre-selected organizations.
Officers: Steve Toth, Jr., Pres. and Treas.; Margaret A. Toth, V.P.; Margaret J. Toth, Exec. Dir.
EIN: 383207824

1901
The Harry A. and Margaret D. Towsley Foundation
140 Ashman St.
P.O. Box 349
Midland, MI 48640   (989) 837-1100
Contact: Lynn T. White, Pres.

Incorporated in 1959 in MI.
Donor: Margaret D. Towsley†.
Grantmaker type: Independent foundation.

Financial data (yr. ended 12/31/05): Assets, $69,709,596 (M); expenditures, $3,130,534; total giving, $2,808,843; qualifying distributions, $2,902,743; giving activities include $2,808,843 for 49 grants (high: $400,000; low: $500; average: $5,000–$50,000).
Purpose and activities: Support for medical and preschool education, social services, and continuing education and research in the health sciences.
Fields of interest: Arts; Education, early childhood education; Higher education; Medical school/education; Education; Medical research, institute; Human services.
Type of support: General/operating support; Continuing support; Annual campaigns; Capital campaigns; Building/renovation; Endowments; Program development; Professorships; Seed money; Research; Employee matching gifts; Matching/challenge support.
Limitations: Giving limited to MI, primarily within Ann Arbor and Washtenaw County. No grants to individuals, or for travel, scholarships, fellowships, conferences, books, publications, films, tapes, audio-visual, or other communication media; no loans.
Publications: Annual report (including application guidelines).
Application information: Environmental Impact Statement is required for all capital projects. Application form not required.
   Initial approach: Letter and proposal
   Copies of proposal: 2
   Deadline(s): Mar. 31
   Board meeting date(s): Apr., July, Sept., and Dec.
   Final notification: 60 to 90 days
Officers and Trustees:* Margaret Ann Riecker,* Chair.; Lynn T. White,* Pres.; Judith D. Rumelhart,* V.P.; John E. Riecker, Secy.; Wendell Dunbar,* Treas.; Bruce Benner, Tr. Emeritus; David Inglish; Jennifer R. Poteat-Flores; Steven Towsley Riecker; Margaret E. Thompson, M.D.
Number of staff: 1 part-time support.
EIN: 386091798
Selected grants: The following grants were reported in 2004.
$850,130 to University of Michigan, Ann Arbor, MI. 2 grants: $425,065 each
$212,365 to Saint Joseph Mercy Health System, Ann Arbor, MI.
$200,000 to Kalamazoo College, Kalamazoo, MI.
$150,000 to Hope College, Holland, MI.
$125,000 to Culver Educational Foundation, Culver, IN.
$50,000 to Catholic Social Services of Washtenaw County, Ann Arbor, MI.
$50,000 to HelpSource, Ann Arbor, MI.
$50,000 to Hillsdale College, Hillsdale, MI.
$45,000 to West Midland Family Center, Shepherd, MI.

1902
The Thomas J. Tracy Family Foundation
38525 N. Woodward Ave., Ste. 1300
Bloomfield Hills, MI   48304-5089

Established in 1998 in MI.
Donors: Emmet and Frances Tracy Fund; Thomas J. Tracy; Tracy Industries, Inc.
Grantmaker type: Independent foundation.
Financial data (yr. ended 12/31/04): Assets, $1,769,142 (M); gifts received, $1,000,076; expenditures, $614,905; total giving, $610,640;

qualifying distributions, $610,640; giving activities include $610,640 for 31 grants (high: $120,000; low: $100), and $72,000 for foundation-administered programs.
Purpose and activities: Giving primarily for education, hospitals and medical research, human services, and Roman Catholic organizations.
Fields of interest: Higher education; Education; Hospitals (general); Medical research, institute; Human services; Federated giving programs; Roman Catholic agencies & churches.
Limitations: Applications not accepted. Giving on a national basis. No grants to individuals.
Application information: Contributes only to pre-selected organizations.
Officers: Thomas J. Tracy, Pres.; Katherine McCanna, V.P.; David M. Rosenberger, Secy.; Erma Jean Tracy, Treas.
Trustee: Cynthia Tracy.
EIN: 383390017

1903
Emmet E. Tracy, Jr. and Marilyn H. Tracy Foundation, Inc.
1111 W. Long Lake Rd., Ste. 101
Troy, MI   48098

Established in 1999 in FL.
Donors: Emmet E. Tracy, Jr.; Marilyn E. Tracy.
Grantmaker type: Independent foundation.
Financial data (yr. ended 12/31/03): Assets, $12,005 (M); gifts received, $173,000; expenditures, $183,794; total giving, $179,900; qualifying distributions, $183,784; giving activities include $179,900 for 28 grants (high: $35,000; low: $400).
Fields of interest: Performing arts; Secondary school/education; Higher education; Hospitals (general); Boys & girls clubs; Human services; Federated giving programs; Roman Catholic agencies & churches.
Limitations: Applications not accepted. Giving in the U.S., with emphasis on MI. No grants to individuals.
Application information: Contributes only to pre-selected organizations.
Officers and Directors:* Emmet E. Tracy, Jr.,* Pres.; Marilyn E. Tracy,* V.P.; Tiffany T. Klaasen,* Secy.-Treas.
EIN: 650893016

1904
Trapp Family Foundation, Inc.
3272 Erie Dr.
Orchard Lake, MI   48324   (248) 681-8294
Contact: Richard E. Trapp, Pres.

Established in 2000 in MI.
Donor: George W. Trapp.
Grantmaker type: Independent foundation.
Financial data (yr. ended 12/31/05): Assets, $2,429,169 (M); gifts received, $181; expenditures, $134,712; total giving, $125,000; qualifying distributions, $125,000; giving activities include $125,000 for 4 grants (high: $75,000; low: $15,000).
Fields of interest: Human services; American Red Cross; Federated giving programs.
Type of support: General/operating support.
Limitations: Giving primarily in MI.
Application information:

Initial approach: Letter
Deadline(s): None
Officers and Directors:* Richard E. Trapp,* Pres.; Rosemary R. Trapp,* Secy.-Treas.; Andrew Trapp; Richard Trapp II; William Trapp.
EIN: 383558679

1905
The Trico Foundation
29100 Northwestern Hwy., Ste. 290
Southfield, MI   48034

Established in 1986 in MI.
Donors: Warren J. Coville; Margot E. Coville; Joseph Blass; Trico Family Partnership.
Grantmaker type: Independent foundation.
Financial data (yr. ended 6/30/05): Assets, $107,197 (M); gifts received, $864,060; expenditures, $171,171; total giving, $90,954; qualifying distributions, $118,745; giving activities include $90,954 for 28+ grants (high: $11,000).
Fields of interest: Performing arts, theater; Arts; Education; Jewish federated giving programs; Jewish agencies & temples.
Limitations: Applications not accepted. Giving primarily in FL and MI. No grants to individuals.
Application information: Contributes only to pre-selected organizations.
Officers: Warren J. Coville, Chair. and Treas.; Brent S. Triest, Pres.; Margot E. Coville, V.P.; Betsy Coville, Secy.
Board Members: Harold Berry; Barry Rosenbaum; Glenn Triest.
EIN: 382702725
Selected grants: The following grants were reported in 2003.
$115,000 to United Jewish Foundation, Bloomfield Hills, MI. For unrestricted support.
$25,000 to Asolo Theater Company, Sarasota, FL. For unrestricted support.
$13,000 to Childrens Hospital of Michigan, Detroit, MI. For unrestricted support.
$10,260 to Machon L'Torah: The Jewish Learning Network of Michigan, Oak Park, MI. For unrestricted support.
$10,000 to Cornerstone Schools, Detroit, MI. For scholarships.
$10,000 to Detroit Institute of Arts, Detroit, MI. For A New Day project.
$8,000 to Van Wezel Foundation, Sarasota, FL. For unrestricted support.
$6,000 to Kadima Jewish Support Services for Adults with Mental Illness, Southfield, MI. For unrestricted support.
$6,000 to Orangutan Foundation International, Los Angeles, CA. For unrestricted support.
$5,500 to Jewish Vocational Service and Community Workshop, Southfield, MI. For unrestricted support.

1906
Triford Foundation
17713 E. 14 Mile Rd., Ste. B
Fraser, MI   48026-2290

Established in 1968 in MI.
Grantmaker type: Independent foundation.
Financial data (yr. ended 12/31/05): Assets, $5,268,135 (M); expenditures, $307,283; total giving, $275,000; qualifying distributions,

$278,068; giving activities include $275,000 for 96 grants (high: $25,000; low: $250).
Fields of interest: Elementary/secondary education; Education; Hospitals (general); Health care; Human services; Protestant agencies & churches.
Type of support: General/operating support; Annual campaigns.
Limitations: Applications not accepted. Giving on a national basis, with some emphasis on MI. No grants to individuals, or for building funds.
Application information: Funds currently committed. Contributes only to pre-selected organizations.
Officers and Trustees: * Frederick S. Ford, Jr.,* Pres. and Secy.; Horace C. Ford,* V.P. and Treas.; Frederick B. Ford,* V.P. and Mgr.; James W. Ford,* V.P.
Number of staff: 1 part-time professional; 1 part-time support.
EIN: 237003478
Selected grants: The following grants were reported in 2003.
$15,000 to Crown Financial Ministries, Gainesville, GA.
$15,000 to Jupiter Medical Center Foundation, Jupiter, FL.
$15,000 to Northern Michigan Hospitals, Petoskey, MI. For capital campaign.
$10,000 to Focus on the Family, Colorado Springs, CO.
$10,000 to Jupiter Island Medical Fund, Hobe Sound, FL.
$7,500 to Harbor Hall Fund, Harbor Springs, MI.
$5,000 to Berkshire School, Sheffield, MA. For annual campaign.
$5,000 to Boys and Girls Club of Martin County, Hobe Sound, FL.
$5,000 to University Liggett School, Grosse Pointe, MI.
$4,000 to American Cancer Society, Lansing, MI.

1907
The Trillium Foundation
500 Dogwood Ln. N.E.
Ada, MI 49301-9523

Established in 1981 in MI.
Donors: George M. McAleenan; Katherine H. McAleenan.
Grantmaker type: Independent foundation.
Financial data (yr. ended 12/31/04): Assets, $327,905 (M); gifts received, $34; expenditures, $39,905; total giving, $37,730; qualifying distributions, $37,784; giving activities include $37,730 for grants.
Fields of interest: Higher education; Health organizations; Human services.
Limitations: Applications not accepted. Giving primarily in Grand Rapids, MI. No grants to individuals.
Application information: Contributes only to pre-selected organizations.
Officers and Directors: * George M. McAleenan, Pres.; Katherine H. McAleenan,* V.P.; G. Mark McAleenan, Jr., Secy.; Karin M. Turmelle, Treas.; Gary F. McAleenan; Gregory W. McAleenan.
EIN: 382403460

1908
Otto Trinklein Educational Trust
c/o Citizens Bank Wealth Mgmt., N.A.
328 S. Saginaw St., M/C 002072
Flint, MI 48502
Application address: c/o Donald J. Zoeller, Frankenmuth High School, 525 E. Genesee, Frankenmuth, MI 48734, tel.: (989) 652-9955

Established in MI.
Grantmaker type: Independent foundation.
Financial data (yr. ended 12/31/05): Assets, $165,590 (M); expenditures, $11,520; total giving, $7,300; qualifying distributions, $10,382; giving activities include $7,300 for 10 grants to individuals (high: $800; low: $700).
Purpose and activities: Scholarship awards to graduates of Frankenmuth, MI, public schools.
Type of support: Scholarships—to individuals.
Limitations: Giving limited to residents of Frankenmuth, MI.
Application information: Application form required.
Deadline(s): May 1
Trustee: Citizens Bank, N.A.
EIN: 386040607

1909
Trixie Puff Foundation
c/o Comerica Bank
P.O. Box 75000, MC 3302
Detroit, MI 48275

Established in 2000 in PA.
Donor: Mary Lou Campana.
Grantmaker type: Independent foundation.
Financial data (yr. ended 3/31/05): Assets, $1,630,606 (M); gifts received, $906,843; expenditures, $52,715; total giving, $30,000; qualifying distributions, $30,000; giving activities include $30,000 for grants.
Fields of interest: Libraries/library science.
Limitations: Applications not accepted. Giving primarily in WV. No grants to individuals.
Application information: Contributes only to pre-selected organizations.
Trustees: Mary Lou Campana; Comerica Bank.
EIN: 226866487

1910
Blanche Barr Trone Scholarship Trust
20152 East Ave. N.
Battle Creek, MI 49017 (269) 964-7348
Contact: Stig Renstrom, Tr.

Grantmaker type: Independent foundation.
Financial data (yr. ended 12/31/05): Assets, $584,339 (M); expenditures, $28,840; total giving, $23,000; qualifying distributions, $23,000; giving activities include $23,000 for grants to individuals.
Purpose and activities: Scholarships to residents of the Battle Creek, MI, area.
Type of support: Scholarships—to individuals.
Limitations: Giving limited to residents of Battle Creek, MI, area.
Application information: Application form required.
Deadline(s): June
Trustee: Stig Renstrom.
EIN: 386500164

1911
Trudell Scholarship Trust
c/o First National Bank & Trust Co.
P.O. Box 370
Iron Mountain, MI 49801

Established in 2004 in MI.
Grantmaker type: Independent foundation.
Financial data (yr. ended 12/31/05): Assets, $124,559 (M); expenditures, $3,431; total giving, $1,400; qualifying distributions, $3,431; giving activities include $1,400 for grants to individuals.
Purpose and activities: Scholarship awards to students at Bay College, Escanaba, MI.
Fields of interest: Higher education.
Type of support: Scholarship funds.
Limitations: Giving limited to Escanaba, MI.
Trustee: First National Bank & Trust Co.
EIN: 726230453

1912
Trumbull Family Foundation
c/o Jack A. Trumbull
1102 Manitou Trail W.
Leland, MI 49654-9723

Established in OH.
Donors: Jack A. Trumbull; Mary Lou Trumbull.
Grantmaker type: Independent foundation.
Financial data (yr. ended 11/30/04): Assets, $10,192 (M); gifts received, $21,203; expenditures, $26,907; total giving, $25,620; qualifying distributions, $26,264; giving activities include $25,620 for grants.
Purpose and activities: Giving primarily to churches, housing development programs, and for education.
Fields of interest: Education; Housing/shelter, development; Christian agencies & churches.
Limitations: Giving in the U.S., with emphasis on FL and MI.
Officers and Trustees: * Jack A. Trumbull,* Pres.; Mary Lou Trumbull,* V.P.; Thomas A. Trumbull,* Secy.
EIN: 383385222

1913
Jerry L. & Marcia D. Tubergen Foundation
P.O. Box 230257
Grand Rapids, MI 49523-0257 (616) 643-4700
Contact: Ginny Vander Hart, Exec. Dir.

Established in 1996 in MI.
Donors: Jerry L. Tubergen; Helen J. DeVos.
Grantmaker type: Independent foundation.
Financial data (yr. ended 12/31/04): Assets, $18,927,220 (M); gifts received, $2,551,250; expenditures, $3,131,617; total giving, $2,856,500; qualifying distributions, $2,858,975; giving activities include $2,856,500 for 43 grants (high: $1,900,000; low: $100).
Purpose and activities: Giving primarily for Christian-based programs and services.
Fields of interest: Medical care, rehabilitation; Human services; Christian agencies & churches.
Type of support: General/operating support; Annual campaigns; Capital campaigns.
Limitations: Applications not accepted. Giving primarily in the U.S., with emphasis on western MI; giving also internationally. No grants to individuals.
Application information: Contributes only to pre-selected organizations.

Officers: Jerry L. Tubergen, Pres. and Treas.; Marcia D. Tubergen, V.P and Secy.
EIN: 383297265
Selected grants: The following grants were reported in 2003.
$357,650 to Grand Rapids Baptist Schools, Grand Rapids, MI. For general support.
$25,000 to New Horizons Foundation, Colorado Springs, CO. For general support.
$20,000 to United Way, Heart of West Michigan, Grand Rapids, MI. For general support.
$17,200 to CURE International, Harrisburg, PA. For general support.
$4,000 to Education Freedom Fund, Grand Rapids, MI. For general support.
$2,500 to Indian Trails Camp, Grand Rapids, MI. For general support.
$2,500 to Stephens Children Foundation, Atlanta, GA. For general support.
$1,000 to Grand Action Foundation, Grand Rapids, MI. For general support.
$500 to Council of Michigan Foundations, Grand Haven, MI. For general support.
$200 to Oral Roberts University, Tulsa, OK. For general support.

1914
Reginald L. Tucker Scholarship Fund
c/o Richard T. Zwirner
130 E. Randolph St., Ste. 3800
Chicago, IL 60601

Established in 1985 in IL.
Grantmaker type: Independent foundation.
Financial data (yr. ended 12/31/05): Assets, $49,473 (M); expenditures, $5,000; total giving, $5,000; qualifying distributions, $5,000; giving activities include $5,000 for grants.
Purpose and activities: Giving only for a scholarship fund at the University of Michigan Law School.
Type of support: Scholarship funds.
Limitations: Applications not accepted. Giving limited to Ann Arbor, MI.
Application information: Unsolicited requests for funds not accepted.
Trustees: Michael B. Roche; Richard T. Zwirner.
EIN: 366837760

1915
The Doris Tuinstra Foundation
3737 Wentworth Dr. SW
Wyoming, MI 49509-3142
Contact: Kenneth Vander Molen, Dir.

Established in 2003.
Grantmaker type: Independent foundation.
Financial data (yr. ended 12/31/05): Assets, $17,726 (M); gifts received, $5,000; expenditures, $1,528; total giving, $1,000; qualifying distributions, $1,000; giving activities include $1,000 for grants.
Fields of interest: Christian agencies & churches.
Type of support: General/operating support.
Limitations: Giving primarily in MI.
Application information:
Initial approach: Letter
Deadline(s): None
Director: Kenneth Vander Molen.
EIN: 043670914

1916
Tuktawa Foundation
4812 Willow Ln.
Orchard Lake, MI 48324
Contact: Charles J. Andrews, Pres.

Established in 1998 in MI.
Donor: Delphine J. Andrews.
Grantmaker type: Independent foundation.
Financial data (yr. ended 12/31/05): Assets, $6,977,679 (M); expenditures, $282,094; total giving, $215,204; qualifying distributions, $215,204; giving activities include $215,204 for 30 grants (high: $60,000; low: $1,000).
Fields of interest: Youth development; Human services.
Type of support: General/operating support.
Application information: Application form not required.
Deadline(s): None
Officers: Charles J. Andrews, Pres.; Adelaide Ford, Secy.-Treas.
Director: Delphine J. Andrews.
EIN: 383393453

1917
Jeremiah Tumey Fund
(also known as Jeremiah Tumey & Grand Lodge)
c/o Comerica Bank
P.O. Box 75000, MC 3302
Detroit, MI 48275-3302

Established in MI.
Grantmaker type: Independent foundation.
Financial data (yr. ended 12/31/05): Assets, $211,797 (M); expenditures, $11,733; total giving, $9,000; qualifying distributions, $9,000; giving activities include $9,000 for grants to individuals.
Purpose and activities: Provides financial assistance to members or spouses of Masons.
Type of support: Grants to individuals.
Limitations: Applications not accepted. Giving limited to MI.
Application information: Unsolicited requests for funds not accepted.
Officers: Joseph Moore, Co-Chair.; Daniel Potter, Co-Chair.; Zachary Swam, Secy.
Board Members: Henry Hildreth; John Jakacki; Winston Miller.
EIN: 386043299

1918
Berndine MacMullen Tuohy-University of Michigan Student Loan Fund
c/o West Michigan National Bank & Tr.
120 Cypress St., Trust Off.
Manistee, MI 49660 (231) 723-8867

Grantmaker type: Independent foundation.
Financial data (yr. ended 12/31/05): Assets, $1,051,772 (M); expenditures, $51,505; total giving, $13,232; qualifying distributions, $13,232; giving activities include $13,232 for grants.
Purpose and activities: Loans to residents of Manistee, Mason, Wexford or Benzie counties, MI, who must attend the University of Michigan for at least one year.
Fields of interest: Education.
Type of support: Student loans—to individuals.
Limitations: Giving limited to residents of Benzie, Manistee, Mason, and Wexford counties, MI.

Application information: Application form required.
Deadline(s): None
Directors: Evelyn Stege; David Wild; Nathan Williams.
EIN: 382528185

1919
The Turfah Foundation
26300 Telegraph Rd., 2nd Fl.
Southfield, MI 48034

Established in 2002.
Grantmaker type: Independent foundation.
Financial data (yr. ended 12/31/05): Assets, $64,061 (M); gifts received, $50,000; expenditures, $38,741; total giving, $38,150; qualifying distributions, $38,150; giving activities include $38,150 for grants.
Officer: Fuad Turfah, Pres.
EIN: 383615130

1920
Turn 2 Foundation, Inc.
215 Park Ave. S., Ste. 1905
New York, NY 10003 (212) 475-2339
FAX: (212) 475-3378;
E-mail: mail@turn2foundation.org; URL: http://derekjeter.mlb.com/NASApp/mlb/players/jeter_derek/turn2/overview.jsp
Alternate URL: http://www.turn2foundation.org

Established in 1996 MI.
Donors: Derek S. Jeter; Daniel Keith; Thomas Terrill; Philip Rogers; Raniero Cortina, Jr.; Drew Doscher; Adele Smithers-Fornaci; Chris Sullivan; Bestfoods; Pharmacia & Upjohn, Inc.; Kellogg Co.; Christopher D. Smithers Foundation; FleetBoston Financial Corp.; Steiner Sports Memorabilia; Collins Building Services; AXA Foundation Charitable Gift Fund; Turn 2, Inc.; Rockmont Mgmt. Partners; All American Collectibles; Dittman Incentive Marketing; Fleer Trading Cards; 78/79 York Assocs., LLC; Forbes Foundation; Interviewing Services of America; Omdusa, Inc.; Disney Worldwide Services, Inc.; PricewaterhouseCoopers, LLC; IMG; Quaker Oats Co.; Nike, Inc.; Partnership for a Drug-Free America; Time, Inc.; Sport Fun, Inc.; Turn 2 Enterprises, Inc.; Visual Architectural Designs; BBDO; Acclaim Entertainment; ConAgra Foods, Inc.; Credit Suisse First Boston LLC; Ernest & Young, LLP; Fenway Partners; Pfizer Inc.; Millsport; Marquis Jet; Del Frisco's New York; Goldman Sachs; Pepsi Cola Company; The Packer Family Foundation; The Promotions Network; The Upper Deck Co.; Twenty Ones Inc.
Grantmaker type: Independent foundation.
Financial data (yr. ended 12/31/04): Assets, $2,506,922 (M); gifts received, $1,810,737; expenditures, $1,552,686; total giving, $1,126,109; qualifying distributions, $1,547,530; giving activities include $1,126,109 for 30 grants (high: $206,200; low: $2,000).
Purpose and activities: Giving primarily to organizations which focus on substance abuse prevention and treatment for youth, and programs that promote healthy lifestyles, academics and leadership development among youth in the Tampa, FL, Kalamazoo, MI, and New York, NY, areas.
Fields of interest: Secondary school/education; Substance abuse, prevention; Substance abuse, treatment; Recreation, parks/playgrounds; Boys &

girls clubs; Human services; Children/youth, services; Foundations (community).
Limitations: Giving primarily in and around the Tampa, FL, Kalamazoo, MI, and New York, NY, areas. No support for organizations lacking 501(c)(3) status. No grants to individuals, or for endowment funds, building or renovation projects, or conferences or travel expenses.
Application information: See foundation Web site for application guidelines and requirements.
  Initial approach: Letter or telephone requesting guidelines
  Board meeting date(s): Jan. and July
Officers: Derek S. Jeter, Pres.; Sanderson Charles Jeter, V.P.; Dorothy Jeter, Secy.-Treas.
EIN: 341847687

1921
Amherst and Janeth Turner Foundation
401 E. Stadium Blvd.
Ann Arbor, MI 48104

Established in 1997 in MI; funded in 1998.
Donors: Amherst Turner; Janeth Turner.
Grantmaker type: Independent foundation.
Financial data (yr. ended 6/30/05): Assets, $619,542 (M); expenditures, $36,037; total giving, $27,900; qualifying distributions, $27,900; giving activities include $27,900 for grants.
Fields of interest: Animals/wildlife, preservation/protection; Federated giving programs; General charitable giving.
Type of support: General/operating support.
Limitations: Applications not accepted. Giving on a national basis, with some emphasis on MI. No grants to individuals.
Application information: Contributes only to pre-selected organizations.
Officers: Janeth L. Turner, Pres.; Amherst H. Turner, Jr., Secy.-Treas.
Directors: Laura Turner; Matthew Turner.
EIN: 383383667

1922
Jane Smith Turner Foundation, Inc.
500 Woodward Ave., Ste. 2500
Detroit, MI 48226

Established in 1994 in MI.
Grantmaker type: Independent foundation.
Financial data (yr. ended 12/31/05): Assets, $9,540,523 (M); expenditures, $412,608; total giving, $348,500; qualifying distributions, $364,527; giving activities include $348,500 for 54 grants (high: $20,000; low: $1,000).
Purpose and activities: Giving primarily to arts and cultural programs, education, wildlife preservation, health associations, and natural resource conservation.
Fields of interest: Arts; Education; Environment, natural resources; Animals/wildlife, preservation/protection; Hospitals (general); Health organizations, association; Children/youth, services; Protestant agencies & churches.
Limitations: Applications not accepted. Giving in the U.S., primarily in the South, with emphasis on GA and SC. No grants to individuals.
Application information: Contributes only to pre-selected organizations.
Officers and Directors:* Jane Smith Turner, Pres. and Secy.; David W. Laughlin,* Treas.; Sarah Jane

Turner Garlington; Laura Turner Seydel; Reed Beauregard Turner; Rhett Lee Turner; Robert E. Turner IV; John Wilson.
EIN: 383199326

1923
Alice E. Turner Memorial Trust
4800 Fashion Sq. Blvd., Ste. 410A
Plaza North
Saginaw, MI 48604
Contact: B.J. Humphreys, Pres.

Established in 1996 in MI.
Donor: Alice E. Turner‡.
Grantmaker type: Independent foundation.
Financial data (yr. ended 12/31/05): Assets, $1,280,240 (M); expenditures, $65,987; total giving, $53,671; qualifying distributions, $53,671; giving activities include $53,671 for grants.
Purpose and activities: Giving for Lutheran organizations, health and medical services, education, youth groups, human services, and community improvement.
Fields of interest: Education; Health care; Youth development; Human services; Community development; Protestant agencies & churches.
Limitations: Giving primarily in Saginaw, MI.
Application information:
  Initial approach: Letter
  Deadline(s): None
Officers: B.J. Humphreys, Pres.; Lloyd J. Yeo, Treas.
Trustees: John Humphreys; Michael Tribble.
EIN: 386501366

1924
Dr. William A. Turner, Jr. Memorial Scholarship Foundation
100 N. Main St., Ste. 350
Chagrin Falls, OH 44022
Application address: c/o Greg Kish, Wayne State Univ., Science Store, Detroit, MI 48202

Established in 1996 in OH.
Donors: William A. Turner; Miriam D. Turner; Michael Raggio; David Szlag.
Grantmaker type: Independent foundation.
Financial data (yr. ended 12/31/04): Assets, $48,081 (M); expenditures, $3,260; total giving, $2,500; qualifying distributions, $2,500; giving activities include $2,500 for 2 grants to individuals.
Purpose and activities: Scholarship awards to graduate students or prospective graduate students in the field of biological science.
Type of support: Scholarships—to individuals.
Limitations: Giving limited to residents of MI.
Application information:
  Initial approach: Proposal
  Deadline(s): June
Trustees: Miriam D. Turner; Thomas M. Turner; William D. Turner.
EIN: 341818265

1925
The Turtle Lake Wildlife Foundation
P.O. Box 99027
Troy, MI 48099-9027

Established in 2003 in MI.
Grantmaker type: Independent foundation.

Financial data (yr. ended 12/31/05): Assets, $193,563 (M); gifts received, $270,000; expenditures, $183,201; total giving, $0; qualifying distributions, $0.
Officers: F. James McDonald, Pres.; J. Michael Campbell, Secy.; Arvin F. Mueller, Treas.
EIN: 743070493

1926
Alice & Ed Brickman Tzedukah Family Foundation
P.O. Box 75000, MC 3302
Detroit, MI 48275-3302

Established in 1999 in FL.
Donors: Edward Brickman; Alice Brickman.
Grantmaker type: Independent foundation.
Financial data (yr. ended 6/30/05): Assets, $318,216 (M); expenditures, $72,441; total giving, $64,935; qualifying distributions, $64,935; giving activities include $64,935 for grants.
Fields of interest: Museums; Performing arts, theater; Libraries/library science; Health organizations; Children, services; Jewish agencies & temples.
Type of support: General/operating support.
Limitations: Applications not accepted. No grants to individuals.
Application information: Contributes only to pre-selected organizations.
Trustees: Alice Brickman; Edward Brickman.
EIN: 650950239

1927
U.S. Asia Medical Foundation
(formerly U.S. India Medical Foundation)
598 Canterbury Rd.
Grosse Pointe Woods, MI 48236-1200

Donor: Mohd S. Jafri.
Grantmaker type: Independent foundation.
Financial data (yr. ended 12/31/04): Assets, $10,188 (M); gifts received, $9,262; expenditures, $25; total giving, $0; qualifying distributions, $25.
Limitations: Applications not accepted. No grants to individuals.
Application information: Contributes only to pre-selected organizations.
Directors: Mohd S. Jafri; Najma S. Jafri.
EIN: 382862228

1928
U.S.-China Cultural Foundation
920 E. Lincoln St.
Birmingham, MI 48009-3608

Established in 1993 in MI.
Donor: Shirley Young.
Grantmaker type: Independent foundation.
Financial data (yr. ended 12/31/04): Assets, $2,657,131 (M); gifts received, $12,277; expenditures, $168,240; total giving, $141,350; qualifying distributions, $160,270; giving activities include $141,350 for 9 grants (high: $110,000; low: $500).
Purpose and activities: Giving primarily for humanitarian causes; support also for music and other cultural programs, and education.

Fields of interest: Arts, cultural/ethnic awareness; Museums; Performing arts, music; Higher education; International human rights.
International interests: China.
Limitations: Applications not accepted. Giving in the U.S., with some emphasis on NY and MI. No grants to individuals.
Application information: Contributes only to pre-selected organizations.
Officer and Trustees:* Shirley Young,* Pres.; Doug Hsieh; Min-Duo Li; Gene Young.
EIN: 383155351

1929
The University of Michigan Club of Grand Rapids Scholarship Fund
2634 Beechwood Dr. S.E.
Grand Rapids, MI   49506-4207

Established in 1987 in MI.
Donor: The University of Michigan Club of Grand Rapids Club.
Grantmaker type: Independent foundation.
Financial data (yr. ended 12/31/05): Assets, $769,746 (M); gifts received, $4,943; expenditures, $34,879; total giving, $29,505; qualifying distributions, $29,505; giving activities include $29,505 for grants.
Purpose and activities: Support only for a scholarship fund at the University of Michigan.
Fields of interest: Higher education, university.
Type of support: Scholarship funds.
Limitations: Applications not accepted. Giving limited to MI. No grants to individuals.
Application information: Contributes only to a pre-selected organization.
Officers and Board Members:* Robert Boylan,* Chair.; Laird Burns; Bruce Courtade; James K. Goebel; Steve Marshall.
EIN: 382707702

1930
University of Michigan Scholarship Fund of Bay City
(also known as U of M Scholarship Fund of Bay City)
900 Center Ave.
Bay City, MI   48708-6118
Contact: D. Keith Birchler, Secy.
Application address: 305 Scheurmann St., Essexville, MI 48732, tel.: (989) 892-0591

Grantmaker type: Independent foundation.
Financial data (yr. ended 12/31/05): Assets, $7,319 (M); gifts received, $1,838; expenditures, $1,967; total giving, $1,950; qualifying distributions, $1,950; giving activities include $1,950 for grants to individuals.
Purpose and activities: Scholarship awards limited to residents of Bay County, MI, enrolling at the University of Michigan, Ann Arbor campus.
Type of support: Scholarships—to individuals.
Limitations: Giving limited to residents of Bay City, MI.
Application information: Application form required.
  Deadline(s): Apr. 15
Officers: Marge Marchlewicz, Pres.; Nancy Penpraze Cusick, V.P.; D. Keith Birchler, Secy.; Earl J. Mast, Treas.
EIN: 386118064

1931
University of Strathclyde USA Foundation
c/o Chapel & York, PMB 293
601 Penn Ave. NW 900, S. Bldg.
Washington, DC   20004   (202) 220-3012

Established in DC.
Grantmaker type: Independent foundation.
Financial data (yr. ended 12/31/04): Assets, $10,922 (M); gifts received, $10,500; expenditures, $10,949; total giving, $10,870; qualifying distributions, $10,870; giving activities include $10,870 for grants.
Purpose and activities: Giving primarily to an affiliated family foundation.
Fields of interest: Foundations (private independent).
Limitations: Applications not accepted. Giving primarily in MI. No grants to individuals.
Application information: Contributes only to a pre-selected organization.
Officers and Directors:* Donald M. Cresswell,* Pres.; Nancy Bikson, V.P.; Ian Jones, Secy.; David Stirling.
EIN: 521596191

1932
The UNOVA Foundation
(formerly The Western Atas Foundation)
6001 36th Ave. W.
Everett, WA   98203-1264   (425) 265-2499
Contact: Cathy D. Younger, Pres.

Established in 1993.
Grantmaker type: Independent foundation.
Financial data (yr. ended 12/31/04): Assets, $19,070,191 (M); expenditures, $646,891; total giving, $564,962; qualifying distributions, $594,948; giving activities include $564,962 for 93 grants (high: $150,000; low: $500).
Purpose and activities: Giving primarily for education; funding also for the Boy Scouts of America, a performing arts center, and the United Way.
Fields of interest: Performing arts centers; Elementary/secondary education; Higher education; Education; Boy scouts; YM/YWCAs & YM/YWHAs; Federated giving programs.
Type of support: Employee matching gifts.
Limitations: Giving primarily in CA, IA, MI, and WA; some giving also in OH.
Application information:
  Initial approach: Letter
  Deadline(s): None
Officer: Cathy D. Younger, Pres.
Directors: Dan S. Bishop; Larry Brady; Michael E. Keane.
EIN: 954453230

1933
Burton & Elizabeth Upjohn Charitable Trust
c/o Barbara James
4139 Lake Terrace Dr.
Kalamazoo, MI   49008   (269) 384-0219

Established in 1967 in MI.
Donor: Elizabeth S. Upjohn Mason.
Grantmaker type: Independent foundation.
Financial data (yr. ended 12/31/04): Assets, $1,065,543 (M); gifts received, $15,000;

expenditures, $70,543; total giving, $65,000; qualifying distributions, $65,974; giving activities include $65,000 for grants.
Purpose and activities: Giving for health care, children and youth services and family services.
Fields of interest: Health care; Children/youth, services; Family services.
Limitations: Applications not accepted. Giving primarily in Kalamazoo, MI. No grants to individuals.
Application information: Contributes only to pre-selected organizations.
Trustees: Elizabeth S. Upjohn Mason; Caroline E. Orosz; Florence U. Orosz; Joel E. Orosz; Amy Upjohn; Henry L. Upjohn II; Martha Means Upjohn; Bradley E. Vandenberg.
EIN: 382341573

1934
Harold and Grace Upjohn Foundation
136 E. Michigan Ave., Ste. 9B
Kalamazoo, MI   49007   (269) 344-2818
Contact: Floyd L. Parks, Secy.-Treas.

Incorporated in 1958 in MI.
Donors: Grace G. Upjohn†; Edwin Meader; Mary Meader.
Grantmaker type: Independent foundation.
Financial data (yr. ended 10/31/05): Assets, $12,541,087 (M); gifts received, $195,962; expenditures, $651,696; total giving, $585,000; qualifying distributions, $598,435; giving activities include $585,000 for 50 grants (high: $40,000; low: $500).
Purpose and activities: Grants primarily to promote scientific research for the alleviation of human suffering; to care for the sick, aged, and helpless whose private resources are inadequate; to conduct research for and otherwise assist in the improvement of living, moral and working conditions; to promote the spread of education and to provide scholarships for deserving young men and women; to promote and aid in the mental, moral, intellectual and physical improvement, assistance and relief of the poor, indigent or deserving inhabitants of the U.S., regardless of race, color or creed.
Fields of interest: Arts; Higher education; Environment; Family services; Aging, centers/services; Community development; neighborhood development; Christian agencies & churches.
Type of support: Program development; Seed money; Scholarship funds; Research.
Limitations: Giving limited to Kalamazoo, MI. No grants to individuals, or for operating budgets or annual campaigns.
Publications: Application guidelines; Annual report.
Application information: Application form required.
  Initial approach: Call or write for application form and instructions
  Copies of proposal: 6
  Deadline(s): Apr. 1 and Sept. 1
  Board meeting date(s): Spring and fall
  Final notification: 30 days after board meeting
Officers and Trustees:* Janet J. Deal-Koestner,* Pres.; Jon L. Stryker,* V.P.; Floyd L. Parks,* Secy.-Treas.; Timothy Light; Mary U. Meader; Florence Upjohn Orosz.
EIN: 386052963
Selected grants: The following grants were reported in 2005.
$40,000 to Ministry with Community, Kalamazoo, MI.
$30,000 to Housing Resources, Kalamazoo, MI.

$25,000 to Goodwill Industries of Southwestern Michigan, Kalamazoo, MI.

$25,000 to Kalamazoo Civic Theater, Kalamazoo, MI.

$25,000 to Mount Zion Safe House, Kalamazoo, MI.

$25,000 to United Way, Greater Kalamazoo, Kalamazoo, MI.

$25,000 to University of Michigan, Ann Arbor, MI. For Radio Tower in Hastings, MI.

$23,000 to Kalamazoo Communities in Schools Foundation, Kalamazoo, MI.

$20,000 to Hispanic American Council, Kalamazoo, MI.

$20,000 to W. E. Upjohn Unemployment Trustee Corporation, Kalamazoo, MI.

1935
Frederick S. Upton Foundation
100 Ridgeway St.
St. Joseph, MI   49085-1047
Contact: Stephen E. Upton, Chair.
FAX: (269) 982-0323;
E-mail: fsuptonfdn@opexonline.com

Trust established in 1954 in IL.
Donor: Frederick S. Upton†.
Grantmaker type: Independent foundation.
Financial data (yr. ended 12/31/05): Assets, $37,985,021 (M); expenditures, $1,907,268; total giving, $1,593,377; qualifying distributions, $1,666,726; giving activities include $1,593,377 for 183 grants (high: $100,000; low: $200).
Type of support: Research; Seed money; Management development/capacity building; General/operating support; Annual campaigns; Capital campaigns; Building/renovation; Equipment; Program development.
Limitations: Giving primarily in MI and SC.
Publications: Application guidelines.
Application information: Application form required.
   Initial approach: Letter
   Copies of proposal: 9
   Deadline(s): Mar. 15, June 15, Aug. 15 and Oct. 15
   Board meeting date(s): Varies
   Final notification: All applicants will be notified
Officers and Trustees:* Stephen E. Upton,* Chair.; Sylvia Upton Wood,* Secy.; Priscilla Upton Byrns; Steven Byrns; Sarah duPont; Margaret Trumbull; David F. Upton; Michael Upton; JPMorgan Chase Bank, N.A.
Number of staff: 1 part-time professional.
EIN: 366013317

1936
Hui-Keng Pua Uyham Memorial Foundation
1173 Dyemeadow Ln.
Flint, MI   48532   (810) 733-7560
Contact: Rodolfo Uyham, Pres.

Established in 1989 in MI; funded in 1990.
Donors: Rodolfo Uyham; Lily Uyham.
Grantmaker type: Independent foundation.
Financial data (yr. ended 12/31/05): Assets, $359,069 (M); gifts received, $2,330; expenditures, $3,347; total giving, $0; qualifying distributions, $0.
Fields of interest: Secondary school/education.
International interests: China.
Type of support: Scholarship funds.
Limitations: Giving on an international basis.

Application information: Application form required.
   Deadline(s): None
Officers and Directors:* Rodolfo Uyham,* Pres.; Lily Uyham,* Secy.; Cecilie To.
EIN: 382891672

1937
V Care Jainism & Jivdaya Foundation
27208 Hampstead Blvd.
Farmington Hills, MI   48331

Established in 2004 in MI.
Donors: Kirti M. Vora; Mahesh H. Vora; Sejal Parag Vora; Ami Anand Vora; Kalpanaben Ashokbhai Choksi; Koradia Chetan Anantbhai.
Grantmaker type: Independent foundation.
Financial data (yr. ended 12/31/05): Assets, $285,657 (M); gifts received, $192,633; expenditures, $21,071; total giving, $21,071; qualifying distributions, $21,071; giving activities include $21,071 for grants.
Fields of interest: Human services; Religion.
Limitations: Giving primarily in India.
Trustees: Kirti M. Vora; Mahesh H. Vora.
EIN: 030544707

1938
The Valenti Foundation
21001 Van Born Rd., Ste. 100
Taylor, MI   48180

Established in 1993 in MI.
Donors: Samuel Valenti III; Kathleen M. Valenti.
Grantmaker type: Independent foundation.
Financial data (yr. ended 11/30/05): Assets, $702,374 (M); gifts received, $151,520; expenditures, $190,160; total giving, $188,640; qualifying distributions, $188,660; giving activities include $188,640 for 25 grants (high: $100,000; low: $100).
Fields of interest: Performing arts; Higher education; Libraries (academic/research); Education; Human services; Children/youth, services; Christian agencies & churches.
Type of support: General/operating support; Program development; Seed money; Scholarship funds.
Limitations: Applications not accepted. Giving in the U.S., primarily in IN, MI and NY. No grants to individuals.
Application information: Contributes only to pre-selected organizations.
Officers: Samuel Valenti III, Chair.; Kathleen M. Valenti, Pres.; Eugene A. Gargaro, Secy.
EIN: 382729523
Selected grants: The following grants were reported in 2003.
$50,000 to University of Notre Dame, Notre Dame, IN.
$30,000 to Cornerstone Schools, Detroit, MI.
$3,000 to Childhelp USA, Scottsdale, AZ.
$2,000 to Michigan Opera Theater, Detroit, MI.
$1,165 to Christ Child Society, National, Bethesda, MD.
$1,000 to Academy of the Sacred Heart, Bloomfield Hills, MI.
$1,000 to Childrens Hospital of Michigan, Detroit, MI.
$500 to Lighthouse of Oakland County, Pontiac, MI.
$200 to Sanctuary for Families, New York, NY.

$100 to Junior League of Birmingham, Birmingham, MI.

1939
Jay and Betty Van Andel Foundation
3133 Orchard Vista Dr. S.E.
Grand Rapids, MI   49546
Contact: Casey Wondergern, Exec. Dir.

Established in 1963.
Donors: Jay Van Andel†; Betty Jean Van Andel†; Amway Corp.
Grantmaker type: Independent foundation.
Financial data (yr. ended 12/31/04): Assets, $137,756,955 (M); gifts received, $3,156,789; expenditures, $20,930,979; total giving, $18,294,313; qualifying distributions, $18,294,313; giving activities include $18,294,313 for 126 grants (high: $11,752,180; low: $100; average: $2,500–$1,000,000).
Purpose and activities: Emphasis on Christian religious activities, including higher and secondary education; giving also for a museum foundation and other cultural programs.
Fields of interest: Museums; Arts; Secondary school/education; Higher education; Christian agencies & churches.
Limitations: Applications not accepted. Giving primarily in MI, with some emphasis on Grand Rapids. No grants to individuals.
Application information: Contributes only to pre-selected organizations.
Officers and Trustee:* David Van Andel, V.P.; James Rosloniec,* Secy.-Treas.; Mark Bugge, Cont.; Casey Wondergern, Exec. Dir.
Number of staff: 1 part-time professional.
EIN: 237066716
Selected grants: The following grants were reported in 2004.
$1,027,500 to Grand Rapids Art Museum, Grand Rapids, MI.
$250,000 to Grand Valley State University, Grand Rapids, MI.
$153,000 to Ada Christian School, Grand Rapids, MI.
$150,000 to Calvin Theological Seminary, Grand Rapids, MI.
$115,000 to Grand Rapids Symphony, Grand Rapids, MI.
$86,500 to LaGrave Avenue Christian Reformed Church, Grand Rapids, MI.
$75,000 to Public Museum of Grand Rapids, Grand Rapids, MI.
$65,000 to Hope College, Holland, MI.
$60,000 to Frederick Meijer Gardens and Sculpture Park, Grand Rapids, MI.
$50,000 to Creation Research Society, Chino Valley, AZ. For general support.

1940
James and Alma Van Camp Family Foundation
P.O. Box 290
St. Clair Shores, MI   48080-0290

Established in 1996 in MI.
Grantmaker type: Independent foundation.
Financial data (yr. ended 6/30/05): Assets, $1,864,135 (M); expenditures, $113,355; total giving, $100,000; qualifying distributions,

$100,000; giving activities include $100,000 for grants.

Purpose and activities: Giving for education.

Fields of interest: Elementary/secondary education; Higher education.

Limitations: Applications not accepted. Giving limited to Clemens, Houghton, and Marine City, MI. No grants to individuals.

Application information: Contributes only to 3 pre-selected organizations.

Officers: James L. Van Camp, Pres.; Alma Van Camp, V.P. and Secy.; Michelle M. Van Camp, Treas.

EIN: 383324843

1941
Van Curler Foundation
2008 Hogback Rd.
Ann Arbor, MI 48105

Established in 2000 in MI.

Donors: Donald E. Van Curler; Carol Van Curler.

Grantmaker type: Independent foundation.

Financial data (yr. ended 12/31/05): Assets, $732,562 (M); gifts received, $750,000; expenditures, $368,784; total giving, $353,050; qualifying distributions, $353,050; giving activities include $344,050 for 6 grants (high: $311,000; low: $500), and $9,000 for 7 grants to individuals (high: $2,500; low: $500).

Fields of interest: Education; Christian agencies & churches.

Type of support: General/operating support; Scholarships—to individuals.

Limitations: Giving on a national basis.

Officers and Directors: * Donald E. Van Curler,* Pres. and Treas.; Carol Van Curler,* Secy.

EIN: 383529339

1942
The W. S. & Lois Van Dalson Foundation
151 S. Rose St., Ste. 800
Kalamazoo, MI 49048-9560

Established in 2001 in MI.

Donors: William S. Van Dalson; Lois Van Dalson; Virginia Van Dalson.

Grantmaker type: Independent foundation.

Financial data (yr. ended 12/31/04): Assets, $1,188,753 (M); gifts received, $333,352; expenditures, $35,874; total giving, $15,000; qualifying distributions, $18,850; giving activities include $15,000 for grants.

Fields of interest: Children, services; Family services.

Limitations: Applications not accepted. Giving primarily in MI. No grants to individuals.

Application information: Contributes only to pre-selected organizations.

Officers: William S. Van Dalson, Chair.; Alfred J. Gemrich, Secy.; Lois Van Dalson, Treas.

EIN: 383607246

1943
Van Dam Charitable Foundation
c/o Doris M. Van Dam
145 Columbia Ave., No. 601
Holland, MI 49423

Established in 1996 in MI.

Donor: Doris M. Van Dam.

Grantmaker type: Independent foundation.

Financial data (yr. ended 12/31/05): Assets, $536,894 (M); gifts received, $50,000; expenditures, $26,130; total giving, $23,510; qualifying distributions, $23,510; giving activities include $23,510 for grants.

Purpose and activities: Support primarily for Christian churches and orders.

Fields of interest: Human services; Protestant agencies & churches; Roman Catholic agencies & churches.

Limitations: Applications not accepted. Giving primarily in MI. No grants to individuals.

Application information: Contributes only to pre-selected organizations.

Officer: Doris M. Van Dam, Pres. and Secy.-Treas.

EIN: 383328175

1944
William and Anna Van Den Bosch Gospel Foundation
111 Lyon St. N.W., Ste. 900
Grand Rapids, MI 49503-2487
Contact: William Van Den Bosch, Jr., Pres.
Application address: 1000 Hancock St. S.E., Grand Rapids, MI 49507

Established in 2000 in MI.

Donors: William Van Den Bosch†; Anna Van Den Bosch.

Grantmaker type: Independent foundation.

Financial data (yr. ended 12/31/05): Assets, $1,097,824 (M); gifts received, $578,075; expenditures, $16,739; total giving, $9,950; qualifying distributions, $9,950; giving activities include $9,950 for 6 grants (high: $3,000; low: $500).

Purpose and activities: The foundation's mission is to provide funds and encouragement of Bible-based Christian organizations for projects that promote the spread of the Gospel of Jesus Christ.

Fields of interest: Christian agencies & churches.

Limitations: Giving primarily in MI.

Application information:

 Initial approach: Letter

 Deadline(s): Nov. 15

Officers and Directors: * William Van Den Bosch, Jr.,* Pres.; Linda Van Den Bosch,* V.P., Fdn. Grants; Mark Van Den Bosch,* V.P.; Michael Veenstra,* Secy.; Janice Veenstra, Treas.; Sarah Hoogeboom; Kristen Van Andel; Joel Veenstra; Timothy W. Veenstra.

EIN: 383509996

1945
Van Dyke Family Charitable Foundation
c/o Janice Van Dyke, Pres.
11900 W. Roosevelt Rd.
Hillside, IL 60162

Established around 1995.

Grantmaker type: Independent foundation.

Financial data (yr. ended 12/31/03): Assets, $481,979 (M); gifts received, $85,250; expenditures, $119,093; total giving, $118,437; qualifying distributions, $118,991; giving activities include $118,437 for 80 grants (high: $23,600; low: $25).

Purpose and activities: Giving primarily for Christian agencies and churches, education, and human services.

Fields of interest: Elementary/secondary education; Human services; Christian agencies & churches.

Limitations: Applications not accepted. Giving primarily in IL, with some giving in MI. No grants to individuals.

Application information: Contributes only to pre-selected organizations.

Officers and Directors: * Janice K. Van Dyke,* Pres. and Treas.; Brandon Van Dyke,* V.P. and Secy.; Troy Van Dyke,* V.P.

EIN: 363978469

Selected grants: The following grants were reported in 2003.

$23,600 to Elmhurst Christian Reformed Church, Elmhurst, IL. For general support.

$18,000 to Calvin College, Grand Rapids, MI. For general support.

$10,050 to Calvary Community Church, Schaumburg, IL. For general support.

$6,300 to Elim Christian Services, Palos Heights, IL. For general support.

$6,200 to Timothy Christian Schools, Elmhurst, IL. For general support.

$5,650 to Chicago West Side Christian School, Chicago, IL. For general support.

$5,500 to Lampstand Ministries, Elmwood Park, IL. For general support.

$5,500 to Trinity Christian College, Palos Heights, IL. For general support.

$5,000 to Free the Children Chicago, Barrington, IL. For general support.

$2,000 to Rehoboth Christian School, Rehoboth, NM. For general support.

1946
Van Elslander Family Foundation
6500 E. Fourteen Mile Rd.
Warren, MI 48092

Established in 1993 in MI.

Donors: Archie A. Van Elslander; Comfort Mattress, Inc.

Grantmaker type: Independent foundation.

Financial data (yr. ended 12/31/04): Assets, $997,878 (M); gifts received, $1,400,000; expenditures, $1,405,020; total giving, $1,403,100; qualifying distributions, $1,403,595; giving activities include $1,403,100 for 11 grants (high: $600,000; low: $100).

Purpose and activities: Giving primarily to Roman Catholic agencies and churches.

Fields of interest: Roman Catholic agencies & churches.

Limitations: Applications not accepted. Giving primarily in MI. No grants to individuals.

Application information: Contributes only to pre-selected organizations.

Officers: Archie A. Van Elslander, Pres.; Kenneth Van Elslander, V.P.; Mary Ann Van Elslander, Secy.; Debra A. Van Elslander, Treas.

EIN: 383144274

1947
Van Gessel Scholarship Foundation
c/o Fifth Third Bank
P.O. Box 3636
Grand Rapids, MI 49501-3636

Established in MI.

Grantmaker type: Independent foundation.

Financial data (yr. ended 12/31/05): Assets, $844,626 (M); expenditures, $51,614; total giving, $41,396; qualifying distributions, $42,593; giving activities include $41,396 for grants.
Purpose and activities: Support only for Aquinas College, Holy Cross Mission Band, and St. Anthony of Padua Church, Grand Rapids, MI.
Fields of interest: Higher education; Roman Catholic agencies & churches.
Type of support: General/operating support.
Limitations: Applications not accepted. Giving limited to Grand Rapids, MI. No grants to individuals.
Application information: Contributes only to 3 pre-selected organizations.
Trustees: Ernest A. Mika; Fifth Third Bank.
EIN: 386527749

1948
Homer J. Van Hollenbeck Foundation
13231 23 Mile Rd.
Shelby Township, MI 48315 (586) 726-4300
Contact: Stefan Wanczyk, Pres.

Established in 1992 in MI.
Donor: Homer J. Van Hollenbeck.
Grantmaker type: Independent foundation.
Financial data (yr. ended 12/31/05): Assets, $1,065,113 (M); expenditures, $45,386; total giving, $38,000; qualifying distributions, $38,000; giving activities include $38,000 for grants to individuals.
Purpose and activities: Scholarships only to graduates of Macomb County, MI, high schools.
Type of support: Scholarships—to individuals.
Limitations: Giving limited to residents of Macomb County, MI.
Application information: Application form required.
Deadline(s): Prior to graduation day
Officers: Stefan Wanczyk, Pres.; Michael G. Cumming, Secy.; Paul F. Rhoders, Treas.
EIN: 383085929

1949
Van Wormer Family Foundation
311 River Dr.
Bay City, MI 48706

Established in 2002 in MI.
Donors: Norman C. Van Wormer; Melissa Van Wormer; Globe Technologies, Inc.; Bay Fire Protection, Inc.
Grantmaker type: Independent foundation.
Financial data (yr. ended 12/31/05): Assets, $811 (M); gifts received, $75,685; expenditures, $76,500; total giving, $69,074; qualifying distributions, $69,074; giving activities include $69,074 for grants.
Officers: Norman C. Van Wormer, Pres.; Jason S. Van Wormer, Secy.
EIN: 300048447

1950
VanAntwerp Family Foundation
79185 Memphis Ridge
P.O. Box 398
Memphis, MI 48041

Established in 1996 in MI.
Donor: Robert Gary VanAntwerp.
Grantmaker type: Independent foundation.

Financial data (yr. ended 12/31/04): Assets, $24,914 (M); expenditures, $2,047; total giving, $0; qualifying distributions, $0.
Fields of interest: Education.
Limitations: Applications not accepted. No grants to individuals.
Application information: Contributes only to pre-selected organizations.
Trustees: Gretchen Hencek; Gary VanAntwerp; Margaret VanAntwerp; Robert Gary VanAntwerp.
EIN: 383309572

1951
Glen D. VandenBelt Trust No. II
c/o JPMorgan Chase Bank, N.A.
P.O. Box 1308
Milwaukee, WI 53201

Established in MI.
Grantmaker type: Independent foundation.
Financial data (yr. ended 3/31/04): Assets, $1,388,199 (M); expenditures, $65,286; total giving, $52,342; qualifying distributions, $56,833; giving activities include $52,342 for grants.
Purpose and activities: Support only for the Christian Have Home, Second Reformed Church, and Western Theological Seminary, Grand Haven, and Hope College, Holland.
Fields of interest: Higher education; Theological school/education; Christian agencies & churches.
Type of support: General/operating support.
Limitations: Applications not accepted. Giving limited to Grand Haven and Holland, MI. No grants to individuals.
Application information: Contributes only to 4 pre-selected organizations specified in the trust instrument.
Trustee: JPMorgan Chase Bank, N.A.
EIN: 386423998

1952
Simon and Mary Vander Kooy Foundation
c/o Vander Kooy Mgmt. Co.
5300 Northland Dr.
Grand Rapids, MI 49525

Established in 1995 in MI.
Donors: Simon Vander Kooy; Mary Vander Kooy; Vander Kooy Foods, Inc.
Grantmaker type: Independent foundation.
Financial data (yr. ended 12/31/05): Assets, $920,857 (M); gifts received, $45,020; expenditures, $56,839; total giving, $55,600; qualifying distributions, $55,600; giving activities include $55,600 for grants.
Fields of interest: Protestant agencies & churches.
Type of support: General/operating support.
Limitations: Applications not accepted. No grants to individuals.
Application information: Contributes only to pre-selected organizations.
Officers: Simon Vander Kooy, Pres.; Mary Vander Kooy, Secy.; Janis Vander Kooy, Treas.
Directors: Susan Despres; Brian Vander Kooy.
EIN: 383245131

1953
Vander Laan Family Foundation
1925 Lockmere Dr. S.E.
Kentwood, MI 49508

Established in 1998 in MI.
Donors: Allen J. Vander Laan; Nancy D. Vander Laan.
Grantmaker type: Independent foundation.
Financial data (yr. ended 12/31/05): Assets, $2,278,219 (M); gifts received, $245,847; expenditures, $159,090; total giving, $130,500; qualifying distributions, $130,500; giving activities include $130,500 for 37 grants (high: $14,000; low: $1,000).
Purpose and activities: Giving primarily for human services and religious organizations.
Fields of interest: Human services; Family services; Religion.
Type of support: General/operating support.
Limitations: Applications not accepted. No grants to individuals.
Application information: Contributes only to pre-selected organizations.
Officers: Allen J. Vander Laan, Pres. and Treas.; Nancy D. Vander Laan, V.P. and Secy.
EIN: 383440120
Selected grants: The following grants were reported in 2005.
$14,000 to Campus Crusade for Christ.
$5,000 to Children of the Promise, Prinsburg, MN.
$5,000 to Focus on the Family, Colorado Springs, CO.
$5,000 to Hope Network, Grand Rapids, MI.
$5,000 to Pine Rest Foundation, Grand Rapids, MI.
$5,000 to Saint Johns Home, Grand Rapids, MI.
$5,000 to Salvation Army.
$3,000 to Cherry Street Health Services, Grand Rapids, MI.
$3,000 to Gods Kitchen, Grand Rapids, MI.
$2,000 to Habitat for Humanity International.

1954
VanderArk Foundation
c/o Gary D. VanderArk
79 Glenmoor Dr.
Englewood, CO 80110

Established in 1993.
Donor: Gary D. VanderArk.
Grantmaker type: Independent foundation.
Financial data (yr. ended 6/30/05): Assets, $132,474 (M); gifts received, $21,000; expenditures, $24,846; total giving, $23,250; qualifying distributions, $23,250; giving activities include $23,250 for grants.
Purpose and activities: Giving to Christian institutions, higher education, human services and health associations.
Fields of interest: Elementary/secondary education; Higher education; Health care; Christian agencies & churches.
Limitations: Applications not accepted. Giving primarily in Denver, CO; some giving also in MI. No grants to individuals.
Application information: Contributes only to pre-selected organizations.
Officers and Directors:* Gary D. VanderArk,* Pres.; Phyllis J. VanderArk,* V.P. and Secy.; Jillane Kalkman,* V.P.; Thomas J. VanderArk,* V.P.
EIN: 841262856

1955
James and Almeda Vanderwaals Foundation

c/o Fifth Third Bank
P.O. Box 3636
Grand Rapids, MI 49501-3636
Application address: c/o Fifth Third Bank, 111 Lyon St. N.W., Grand Rapids, MI 49503, tel.: (888) 218-7878

Established in 1986 in MI.
Grantmaker type: Independent foundation.
Financial data (yr. ended 12/31/05): Assets, $876,340 (M); expenditures, $75,713; total giving, $66,000; qualifying distributions, $66,000; giving activities include $66,000 for grants.
Purpose and activities: Giving for religious, scientific, educational, and charitable purposes, including art, music, libraries and benefits to the poor. All for the public welfare, and no other purpose.
Fields of interest: Museums; Youth development; Human services; Salvation Army; Children/youth, services.
Limitations: Giving limited to the greater Grand Rapids, MI, area.
Application information: Application form not required.
  Initial approach: Letter
  Deadline(s): None
Officers: Hon. J. Robert Smolenski, Pres.; Conrad A. Bradshaw, Secy.-Treas.
Trustees: David Keyser; Fifth Third Bank.
EIN: 382683671

1956
Robert & Cheri Vanderweide Foundation

P.O. Box 230257
Grand Rapids, MI 49523 (616) 643-4700
Contact: Ginny Vander Hart, Exec. Dir.
FAX: (616) 774-0116; Application address: 126 Ottawa N.W., Ste. 500, Grand Rapids, MI 49503; E-mail (for Ginny Vander Hart): virginiav@rdvcorp.com

Established in 1992 in MI.
Donor: Suzanne DeVos Vanderweide.
Grantmaker type: Independent foundation.
Financial data (yr. ended 12/31/04): Assets, $2,115,343 (M); expenditures, $1,026,965; total giving, $970,034; qualifying distributions, $1,005,714; giving activities include $970,034 for 45 grants (high: $130,000; low: $500).
Purpose and activities: The foundation seeks to create a legacy of caring and stewardship through their support of projects that build community and improve the quality of people's lives. To carry out this commitment, it focuses on organizations, projects, or programs that demonstrate Christian charity to meet both the spiritual and physical needs of people, which strengthen the bond of families and communities, and bring opportunity to disadvantaged persons. Giving primarily for Christian churches; giving also for education and human services.
Fields of interest: Education; Human services; Community development; Federated giving programs; Christian agencies & churches; Protestant agencies & churches.
Type of support: General/operating support; Continuing support; Annual campaigns; Capital campaigns; Building/renovation; Program development; Matching/challenge support.

Limitations: Giving primarily in west MI and central FL. No grants to individuals.
Publications: Application guidelines.
Application information: Application form not required.
  Initial approach: Letter or request application guidelines
  Copies of proposal: 1
  Deadline(s): 2 weeks prior to review
  Board meeting date(s): 3 times annually
  Final notification: 3 to 5 months
Officers: Suzanne C. Vanderweide, Pres.; Jerry L. Tubergen, C.O.O., V.P., and Secy.; Robert A. Vanderweide, V.P.; Robert H. Schierbeek, Treas.
Number of staff: 3 full-time professional.
EIN: 383035978

1957
The William and Katherine Vandomelen Foundation

P.O. Box 20216
Kalamazoo, MI 49019

Established in 1992 in MI.
Donor: William F. Vandomelen.
Grantmaker type: Independent foundation.
Financial data (yr. ended 12/31/05): Assets, $6,762,154 (M); gifts received, $532,980; expenditures, $374,346; total giving, $372,100; qualifying distributions, $372,100; giving activities include $372,100 for 14 grants (high: $125,000; low: $1,000).
Fields of interest: Education; Health care; Human services; Children/youth, services; Family services; Roman Catholic agencies & churches.
Limitations: Applications not accepted. Giving primarily in Kalamazoo, MI. No grants to individuals.
Application information: Contributes only to pre-selected organizations.
Officers and Directors:* William F. Vandomelen,* Pres.; Mark W. Vandomelen,* V.P.; Julia Vandomelen,* Secy.; Arthur E. Albin, Treas.; George Lennon.
EIN: 382916030

1958
Dr. Lavern and Betty VanKley Educational Foundation

20 Princeton Ct.
Zeeland, MI 49464

Established in 1986 in MI.
Donors: Lavern VanKley; Betty VanKley.
Grantmaker type: Independent foundation.
Financial data (yr. ended 12/31/05): Assets, $351,836 (M); expenditures, $4,051; total giving, $0; qualifying distributions, $0.
Purpose and activities: Loans only to members and children of members who attend First Reformed Church, MI.
Type of support: Scholarships—to individuals.
Limitations: Applications not accepted. Giving limited to residents of Zeeland, MI.
Application information: Unsolicited requests for funds not accepted.
Trustees: Betty VanKley; Lavern VanKley.
EIN: 386500707

1959
Peter J. and Anne Vanwingen Memorial Fund

c/o Fifth Third Bank
P.O. Box 3636
Grand Rapids, MI 49501-3636

Established in 1994 in MI.
Grantmaker type: Independent foundation.
Financial data (yr. ended 12/31/05): Assets, $356,449 (M); expenditures, $10,583; total giving, $5,068; qualifying distributions, $5,068; giving activities include $5,068 for grants.
Fields of interest: Nursing home/convalescent facility; Federated giving programs; Christian agencies & churches.
Type of support: General/operating support.
Limitations: Applications not accepted. Giving limited to Grand Rapids, MI. No grants to individuals.
Application information: Contributes only to pre-selected organizations.
Trustee: Fifth Third Bank.
EIN: 386491228

1960
Hulda Vates Charitable Foundation, Inc.

c/o National City Bank
171 Monroe Ave. N.W., KC17-63
Grand Rapids, MI 49503-2634

Established in 1987 in MI.
Grantmaker type: Independent foundation.
Financial data (yr. ended 12/31/05): Assets, $794,115 (M); expenditures, $42,541; total giving, $36,700; qualifying distributions, $36,700; giving activities include $36,700 for grants.
Fields of interest: Human services; Protestant agencies & churches.
Limitations: Applications not accepted. Giving primarily in Frankenmuth, MI; some giving also in St. Louis, MO. No grants to individuals.
Application information: Contributes only to pre-selected organizations.
Trustee: National City Bank.
EIN: 382803977

1961
The Vattikuti Foundation

3350 Eastpointe Ln.
Bloomfield Hills, MI 48302

Established in 1997 in MI.
Donor: Rajendra B. Vattikuti.
Grantmaker type: Independent foundation.
Financial data (yr. ended 12/31/05): Assets, $4,783,948 (M); expenditures, $88,534; total giving, $50,000; qualifying distributions, $71,237; giving activities include $50,000 for 4 grants (high: $25,000; low: $5,000).
Purpose and activities: Giving primarily to organizations focusing on social and economic change in India.
Fields of interest: American Red Cross; International development; International relief, 2004 tsunami.
International interests: India.
Limitations: Applications not accepted. Giving primarily in the U.S., with some emphasis on MI. No grants to individuals.
Application information: Contributes only to pre-selected organizations.

Officers: Rajendra B. Vattikuti, Pres.; Padmaja Vattikuti, V.P.; Nicolas Stasevich, Secy.; Frank Stella, Treas.
EIN: 383380162

1962
Vaughan Foundation
c/o Erik H. Serr
101 N. Main St., 7th Fl.
Ann Arbor, MI 48104

Established in 1997 in MI.
Donor: Christine M. Holmes.
Grantmaker type: Independent foundation.
Financial data (yr. ended 12/31/05): Assets, $6,418,529 (M); gifts received, $143,691; expenditures, $373,458; total giving, $360,000; qualifying distributions, $360,000; giving activities include $360,000 for 23 grants (high: $40,000; low: $5,000).
Purpose and activities: Funding primarily for arts and culture, human services, and animal welfare.
Fields of interest: Arts; Animal welfare; Human services; American Red Cross.
Limitations: Applications not accepted. Giving primarily in MI. No grants to individuals.
Application information: Contributes only to pre-selected organizations.
Officer: Christine Holmes, Pres. and Secy.-Treas.
EIN: 383355160
Selected grants: The following grants were reported in 2004.
$30,000 to Humane Society of Huron Valley, Ann Arbor, MI.
$30,000 to YMCA, Ann Arbor, Ann Arbor, MI.
$20,000 to Paws With A Cause, Wayland, MI.
$20,000 to Peace Neighborhood Center, Ann Arbor, MI.
$20,000 to Saint Louis Center, Chelsea, MI.
$20,000 to Washtenaw Literacy, Ypsilanti, MI.
$15,000 to American Red Cross, Ann Arbor, MI.
$15,000 to Great Lakes Rabbit Sanctuary, Whittaker, MI.
$15,000 to Horses Haven, South Lyon, MI.
$15,000 to Leader Dogs for the Blind, Rochester, MI.

1963
Harry & Eleanor Vellmure Family Foundation
c/o JPMorgan Chase Bank, N.A.
P.O. Box 1308
Milwaukee, WI 53201

Established in 2000 in MI.
Grantmaker type: Independent foundation.
Financial data (yr. ended 8/31/05): Assets, $583,547 (M); expenditures, $54,302; total giving, $40,500; qualifying distributions, $40,500; giving activities include $40,500 for grants.
Fields of interest: Arts councils; Performing arts, orchestra (symphony); Hospitals (general); Food services; Human services; American Red Cross; Salvation Army.
Type of support: General/operating support.
Limitations: Applications not accepted. Giving primarily in MI. No grants to individuals.
Application information: Contributes only to pre-selected organizations.

Officers: Eleanor Vellmure, Pres.; Timothy Vellmure, V.P.; Elizabeth Garey, Secy.; Harry Vellmure, Jr., Treas.
Trustee: JPMorgan Chase Bank, N.A.
EIN: 383496200

1964
Verduin Charitable Foundation
7887 Pine Island Dr.
Belmont, MI 49306-9719

Established in 1988 in MI as successor to the Calvin J. and Patricia M. Verduin Charitable Trust.
Donors: Calvin Verduin; Patricia Verduin; Transnational Motors, Inc.
Grantmaker type: Independent foundation.
Financial data (yr. ended 12/31/04): Assets, $46,008 (M); gifts received, $30,374; expenditures, $32,575; total giving, $31,826; qualifying distributions, $32,645; giving activities include $31,826 for grants.
Limitations: Applications not accepted. Giving primarily in Grand Rapids, MI. No grants to individuals.
Application information: Contributes only to pre-selected organizations.
Officers: Calvin Verduin, Pres.; Patricia Verduin, Secy.-Treas.
EIN: 382798628

1965
Danny and Claudine Veri Family Foundation
c/o Danny Veri
47893 Jake Ln.
Canton, MI 48187-5837

Established in 2002 in MI.
Donors: Claudine Veri; Danny Veri.
Grantmaker type: Independent foundation.
Financial data (yr. ended 12/31/05): Assets, $297,172 (M); gifts received, $10,000; expenditures, $13,079; total giving, $11,729; qualifying distributions, $11,729; giving activities include $11,729 for grants.
Limitations: Applications not accepted. Giving in the U.S., primarily in MI. No grants to individuals.
Application information: Contributes only to pre-selected organizations.
Officers: Danny Veri, Pres. and Treas.; Claudine Veri, V.P. and Secy.
EIN: 383623613

1966
The Melvin and Helen Verwys Foundation
2105 Raybrook St. S.E., Ste. 5039
Grand Rapids, MI 49546-7731

Established in 1995 in MI.
Donors: Melvin Verwys; Helen Verwys.
Grantmaker type: Independent foundation.
Financial data (yr. ended 7/31/05): Assets, $11,454 (M); gifts received, $125,050; expenditures, $114,940; total giving, $114,500; qualifying distributions, $114,500; giving activities include $114,500 for 68 grants (high: $10,500; low: $100).
Purpose and activities: Giving primarily to evangelical organizations, churches, and schools, MI.

Fields of interest: Christian agencies & churches.
Type of support: General/operating support.
Limitations: Applications not accepted. Giving primarily in MI.
Application information: Contributes only to pre-selected organizations.
Officers: Melvin Verwys, Pres.; Helen Verwys, Secy.
Director: William Verwys.
EIN: 383252349

1967
Vetowich Family Foundation
c/o William Felosak
26026 Telegraph Rd., Ste. 200
Southfield, MI 48034

Established in 1999 in MI.
Donors: Peter C. Vetowich; Connie L. Vetowich.
Grantmaker type: Independent foundation.
Financial data (yr. ended 8/31/05): Assets, $250,782 (M); expenditures, $14,118; total giving, $13,700; qualifying distributions, $13,700; giving activities include $13,700 for grants.
Purpose and activities: Support for education, including scholarships to individuals.
Fields of interest: Education.
Type of support: Scholarships—to individuals.
Limitations: Applications not accepted. Giving primarily in Rochester, MI.
Application information: Contributes only to pre-selected organizations.
Officers: Peter C. Vetowich, Pres.; William R. Felosak, V.P.; Peter M. Vetowich, V.P.; Leanne Vetowich-Weinerth, V.P.; Connie L. Vetowich, Secy.
EIN: 386750824

1968
Vicksburg Foundation
P.O. Box 177
Vicksburg, MI 49097
Contact: William Oswalt, Pres.

Incorporated in 1943 in MI.
Grantmaker type: Independent foundation.
Financial data (yr. ended 12/31/05): Assets, $3,413,733 (M); gifts received, $16,863; expenditures, $207,658; total giving, $180,682; qualifying distributions, $192,367; giving activities include $180,682 for grants.
Purpose and activities: To coordinate and unify the charitable and benevolent activities of the incorporators; emphasis on community programs, education, and libraries.
Fields of interest: Education, association; Education, fund raising/fund distribution; Libraries/library science; Education; Human services; Community development.
Type of support: General/operating support; Continuing support; Annual campaigns; Capital campaigns; Building/renovation; Equipment; Endowments; Program development; Conferences/seminars; Seed money; Curriculum development; Scholarship funds; Matching/challenge support.
Limitations: Applications not accepted. Giving limited to MI, with emphasis on Vicksburg, Kalamazoo, and Schoolcraft.
Publications: Informational brochure.
Application information: Contributes only to pre-selected organizations.
Board meeting date(s): Mar., June, Sept., and Dec.

Officers and Directors:* William Oswalt,* Pres. and Treas.; Lloyd Appell,* V.P.; Warren Lawrence,* Secy.; Dana Downing; Jim Shaw; Didik Sockarmoen.
Number of staff: None.
EIN: 386065237

1969
The Victor Foundation
2601 Cambridge Ct., Ste. 310
Auburn Hills, MI 48326-2575

Established in 1988 in MI.
Donor: David V. Johnson.
Grantmaker type: Independent foundation.
Financial data (yr. ended 6/30/05): Assets, $5,148 (M); gifts received, $108,900; expenditures, $133,700; total giving, $124,650; qualifying distributions, $125,603; giving activities include $124,650 for grants.
Fields of interest: Higher education; Graduate/ professional education; Agriculture; Youth development, religion; Christian agencies & churches.
Limitations: Applications not accepted. Giving limited to East Lansing and Southfield, MI. No grants to individuals.
Application information: Contributes only to pre-selected organizations specified in the governing instrument.
Officers: David V. Johnson, Pres.; Cameron H. Piggott, V.P.; Richard L. Pifer, Treas.
Directors: Pamela J. Dykehouse; Linda Munson; Steve Radom.
EIN: 382843599

1970
Paul N. & Lorena C. Vincent Charitable Foundation
(also known as Paul N. & Lorena C. Vincent Charitable Scholarship Fund)
c/o Comerica Bank
P.O. Box 75000, MC 3302
Detroit, MI 48275-3302

Established in 1988 in MI.
Grantmaker type: Independent foundation.
Financial data (yr. ended 10/31/05): Assets, $26,527 (M); expenditures, $31,045; total giving, $26,500; qualifying distributions, $26,500; giving activities include $26,500 for grants.
Purpose and activities: Giving only to the Resurrection School, Lansing, MI, for their scholarship program.
Type of support: Scholarship funds.
Limitations: Giving limited to Lansing, MI. No grants to individuals.
Application information: Application form not required.
 Deadline(s): None
Trustee: Comerica Bank.
EIN: 386539926

1971
Vineyard Foundation
c/o The Northern Trust Co.
50 S. LaSalle St., Ste. L-5
Chicago, IL 60675

Established in 1994 in MI and FL.
Donor: Hugh DePree.

Grantmaker type: Independent foundation.
Financial data (yr. ended 12/31/04): Assets, $1,324,812 (M); expenditures, $70,017; total giving, $57,000; qualifying distributions, $57,000; giving activities include $57,000 for grants.
Fields of interest: Elementary school/education; Housing/shelter.
Type of support: General/operating support.
Limitations: Applications not accepted. Giving primarily in FL; some giving also in MI. No grants to individuals.
Application information: Contributes only to pre-selected organizations.
Trustees: Hugh DePree; Phyllis DePree.
EIN: 383211939

1972
The Wayne and Marcia Visbeen Family Foundation
1328 Old Lake Ct. S.E.
Grand Rapids, MI 49508

Established in 2004 in MI.
Donors: Wayne Visbeen; Marcia Visbeen.
Grantmaker type: Independent foundation.
Financial data (yr. ended 12/31/04): Assets, $12,000 (M); gifts received, $12,000; expenditures, $1,000; total giving, $1,000; qualifying distributions, $1,000; giving activities include $1,000 for grants.
Limitations: Applications not accepted. Giving primarily in MI. No grants to individuals.
Application information: Contributes only to pre-selected organizations.
Directors: Marcia Visbeen; Wayne Visbeen.
EIN: 201652950

1973
Vision Care of West Michigan
750 E. Beltline Ave. N.E.
Grand Rapids, MI 49525

Established in MI in 1994.
Donor: Mark Sheldon, M.D.
Grantmaker type: Independent foundation.
Financial data (yr. ended 12/31/04): Assets, $18,351 (M); gifts received, $20,411; expenditures, $3,787; total giving, $3,712; qualifying distributions, $3,787; giving activities include $3,712 for grants.
Limitations: Applications not accepted. No grants to individuals.
Application information: Contributes only to pre-selected organizations.
Directors: Kenyon Kendall; Mark Sheldon, M.D.; Scott Weber, M.D.; Robert Wolford.
EIN: 383183669

1974
Vlasic Foundation
38710 Woodward, Ste. 100
Bloomfield Hills, MI 48304

Established in 1958 in MI.
Donors: Robert J. Vlasic; Joseph Vlasic†.
Grantmaker type: Independent foundation.
Financial data (yr. ended 12/31/05): Assets, $1,857,665 (M); expenditures, $127,413; total giving, $121,750; qualifying distributions,

$121,750; giving activities include $121,750 for 21 grants (high: $25,000; low: $500).
Purpose and activities: Giving primarily to educational, health, and cultural programs in which members of the Vlasic families have a personal interest.
Fields of interest: Arts; Higher education; Education; Health care; Cancer; Human services; Federated giving programs; Roman Catholic agencies & churches.
Limitations: Applications not accepted. Giving primarily in MI. No grants to individuals.
Application information: Contributes only to pre-selected organizations.
Officers: Robert J. Vlasic, Pres.; Paul A. Vlasic, V.P.; Richard R. Vlasic, V.P.; William J. Vlasic, V.P.; James J. Vlasic, Secy.; Michael A. Vlasic, Treas.
EIN: 386077329
Selected grants: The following grants were reported in 2004.
$20,000 to Cranbrook Schools, Bloomfield Hills, MI.
$20,000 to Sacred Heart Major Seminary, Detroit, MI.
$19,333 to Henry Ford Health System, Detroit, MI.
$10,000 to Detroit Country Day School, Beverly Hills, MI.
$7,250 to Lighthouse P.A.T.H., Pontiac, MI.
$5,000 to Boston University, Boston, MA.
$3,500 to Cranbrook Academy of Art, Bloomfield Hills, MI.
$2,000 to Brewster Academy, Wolfeboro, NH.
$2,000 to Cornerstone Schools, Detroit, MI.
$1,000 to United Negro College Fund, Fairfax, VA.

1975
Vogt Foundation
c/o JPMorgan Chase Bank, N.A.
P.O. Box 1308
Milwaukee, WI 53210
Contact: James B. Vogt, Pres.
Application address: c/o Vogt Industries, 4542 Roger B. Chaffee Blvd. S.E., Grand Rapids, MI 49548-7522

Established in MI.
Grantmaker type: Independent foundation.
Financial data (yr. ended 12/31/05): Assets, $670,362 (M); expenditures, $31,678; total giving, $23,000; qualifying distributions, $23,000; giving activities include $23,000 for grants.
Fields of interest: Performing arts, orchestra (symphony); Higher education; Human services; Federated giving programs; Christian agencies & churches.
Limitations: Giving primarily in Grand Rapids, MI. No grants to individuals.
Application information:
 Initial approach: Letter
 Deadline(s): None
Officers: James B. Vogt, Pres.; Frederick J. Vogt, Jr., V.P.; Hillary F. Snell, Secy.; Joseph McCormick, Treas.
EIN: 386083816

1976
Frederick A. Vollbrecht Foundation
31700 Telegraph Rd., Ste. 220
Bingham Farms, MI 48025-3466
(248) 646-0627
Contact: Kenneth J. Klebba, Pres.

Incorporated in 1959 in MI.
Donor: Frederick A. Vollbrecht†.
Grantmaker type: Independent foundation.
Financial data (yr. ended 11/30/04): Assets, $2,180,829 (M); expenditures, $258,491; total giving, $201,850; qualifying distributions, $200,998; giving activities include $201,850 for 22 grants (high: $20,000; low: $800).
Purpose and activities: Giving for education, health, and human services.
Fields of interest: Child development, education; Higher education; Education; Health care; Human services; Children/youth, services; Child development, services; Disabilities, people with.
Type of support: General/operating support; Continuing support; Scholarship funds.
Limitations: Giving primarily in MI. No grants to individuals.
Publications: Annual report.
Application information: Application form not required.
Initial approach: Proposal
Copies of proposal: 1
Deadline(s): None
Board meeting date(s): June
Officers: Kenneth J. Klebba, Pres. and Treas.; Richard E. Mida, V.P. and Secy.
EIN: 386056173
Selected grants: The following grants were reported in 2004.
$150,000 to Walsh College of Accountancy and Business Administration, Troy, MI. For general support, payable over 8 years.
$14,350 to Childrens Leukemia Foundation of Michigan, Southfield, MI. For general support.
$12,500 to YMCA of Metropolitan Detroit, Detroit, MI. For StrYvers Program.
$5,000 to Williams Syndrome Association, Clawson, MI. For music and arts camp.
$3,000 to American Diabetes Association, Bingham Farms, MI. For education.
$3,000 to North Oakland SCAMP Funding Corporation, Clarkston, MI. For camperships.
$3,000 to Old Newsboys Goodfellow Fund of Detroit, Detroit, MI. For general support.
$2,000 to Lighthouse of Oakland County, Lighthouse North, Pontiac, MI. For general support.
$2,000 to Stagecrafters, Royal Oak, MI. For general support.
$2,000 to Variety Club Charity for Children, Southfield, MI. For holiday program.

1977
The Vomberg Foundation
c/o Olivet College
320 S. Main St.
Olivet, MI   49076-9406   (269) 749-7585
Contact: Christina M. Heisler, Secy.

Established in MI.
Grantmaker type: Independent foundation.
Financial data (yr. ended 12/31/05): Assets, $644,958 (M); expenditures, $41,151; total giving, $31,608; qualifying distributions, $31,608; giving activities include $31,608 for grants to individuals.
Purpose and activities: Scholarship awards to students in Eaton County, MI, of good academic standing who can demonstrate financial need.
Fields of interest: Higher education.
Type of support: Scholarships—to individuals.
Limitations: Giving limited to residents of Eaton County, MI, area.

Application information: Application form required.
Deadline(s): Dec. 1 of senior year in high school
Officers: Richard L. Trumley, Pres.; Christina M. Heisler, Secy.-Treas.
Trustees: Thomas C. Blesch; Christi Dutcher; Gary Rogers; Anthony G. Sommer; Thomas R. Winquist.
EIN: 386072845

1978
Giorgio & Laurel Vozza Family Foundation
13721 S.W. Bay Shore Dr.
Traverse City, MI   49684-6203   (231) 941-9005
Contact: Giorgio Vozza, V.P.

Established in 1997 in MI.
Donors: Giorgio Vozza; Laurel Vozza.
Grantmaker type: Independent foundation.
Financial data (yr. ended 12/31/04): Assets, $967 (M); expenditures, $0; total giving, $0; qualifying distributions, $0.
Purpose and activities: Support primarily for Christian schools.
Fields of interest: Education; Protestant agencies & churches.
Limitations: Giving primarily in Traverse City, MI.
Application information: Application form not required.
Initial approach: Letter
Deadline(s): None
Officers: Laurel Vozza, Pres.; Giorgio Vozza, V.P.
EIN: 383384497

1979
Shaw and Betty Walker Foundation
(formerly Shaw Walker Foundation)
c/o Stephanie L. Geoghan
P.O. Box 5100
North Muskegon, MI   49445

Established in 1993 in MI.
Donors: Shaw Walker; Betty Walker.
Grantmaker type: Independent foundation.
Financial data (yr. ended 12/31/05): Assets, $16,706,582 (M); expenditures, $299,355; total giving, $196,389; qualifying distributions, $256,619; giving activities include $196,389 for 27 grants (high: $35,000; low: $500).
Purpose and activities: Giving primarily for education.
Fields of interest: Scholarships/financial aid; Education.
Type of support: General/operating support; Continuing support; Annual campaigns; Scholarship funds; Research; In-kind gifts.
Limitations: Applications not accepted. Giving primarily in the upper Midwestern U.S., including the Great Lakes region. No grants to individuals.
Application information: Unsolicited requests for funds not accepted.
Board meeting date(s): Fall
Officers and Directors:* Shaw Walker, Jr.,* Pres.; Bruce Walker,* V.P.; Stephanie Geoghan, Secy.; Shaw Walker, Sr.,* Treas.; Betty Walker.
Number of staff: 1 part-time professional.
EIN: 383125893
Selected grants: The following grants were reported in 2004.
$25,000 to Hospice of Muskegon-Oceana, Muskegon, MI. For general support.
$15,000 to Muskegon Rescue Mission, Muskegon, MI. For general support.

$10,000 to Wings of Mercy, Holland, MI. For general support.
$5,000 to American Red Cross, Muskegon, MI. For general support.
$5,000 to Citizens Against Government Waste, DC. For general support.
$5,000 to Make-A-Wish Foundation, Traverse City, MI. For general support.
$5,000 to Oceana, DC. For general support.
$5,000 to W B L V-FM-Blue Lake Public Radio, Twin Lake, MI. For general support.
$5,000 to West Shore Symphony Orchestra, Muskegon, MI. For general support.
$3,000 to Salvation Army, Muskegon, MI. For general support.

1980
David and Zella Bueker Wallace Foundation Charitable Trust
39 E. Hannum Blvd.
Saginaw, MI   48602

Grantmaker type: Independent foundation.
Financial data (yr. ended 12/31/05): Assets, $145,279 (M); expenditures, $11,850; total giving, $10,650; qualifying distributions, $10,650; giving activities include $10,650 for grants.
Fields of interest: Food services; Human services; Homeless, human services; Economically disadvantaged; Homeless.
Limitations: Applications not accepted. Giving primarily in Saginaw, MI. No grants to individuals.
Application information: Contributes only to pre-selected organizations.
Directors: Gwendoline A. Maisch; David A. Wallace; James K. Wallace; Zella B. Wallace.
EIN: 386510703

1981
Richard T. and Marianne H. Walsh Charitable Trust
5039 Van Ness Dr.
Bloomfield Hills, MI   48302   (248) 626-9610
Contact: Marianne H. Walsh, Tr.

Established in 1997 in MI.
Donors: Marianne H. Walsh; Richard T. Walsh.
Grantmaker type: Independent foundation.
Financial data (yr. ended 4/30/05): Assets, $92,293 (M); expenditures, $10,060; total giving, $9,960; qualifying distributions, $9,960; giving activities include $9,960 for grants.
Limitations: Giving primarily in MI. No grants to individuals.
Application information:
Initial approach: Letter
Deadline(s): None
Trustees: Marianne H. Walsh; Richard T. Walsh.
EIN: 386692940

1982
Emil Walter Charitable Foundation, Inc.
c/o National City Bank
171 Monroe Ave., N.W.
Grand Rapids, MI   49503

Grantmaker type: Independent foundation.
Financial data (yr. ended 12/31/05): Assets, $332,516 (M); expenditures, $17,478; total giving,

$13,655; qualifying distributions, $13,655; giving activities include $13,655 for grants.
Purpose and activities: Support only for Church Extension Fund Michigan District of the Lutheran Church-Missouri Synod in Ann Arbor, Lutheran Homes of Michigan in Frankenmuth, and St. Michael's Lutheran Church in Richville.
Fields of interest: Protestant agencies & churches.
Limitations: Applications not accepted. Giving limited to Ann Arbor, Frankenmuth, and Richville, MI. No grants to individuals.
Application information: Contributes only to 3 pre-selected organizations.
Trustee: National City Bank.
EIN: 386401179

1983
Walters Family Foundation, Inc.
22268 Lake St.
Cassopolis, MI   49031

Established in 1998 in IN.
Donor: Nole L. Walters.
Grantmaker type: Independent foundation.
Financial data (yr. ended 12/31/05): Assets, $49,839 (M); expenditures, $83,520; total giving, $82,500; qualifying distributions, $82,500; giving activities include $82,500 for grants.
Fields of interest: Education; Human services; Christian agencies & churches.
Type of support: General/operating support; Building/renovation; Scholarship funds.
Limitations: Applications not accepted. Giving primarily in IN. No grants to individuals.
Application information: Contributes only to pre-selected organizations.
Officers: Nole L. Walters, Pres.; Rosalyn M. Walters, Secy.-Treas.
Directors: Debra M. Hanigoski; Steven M. Walters.
EIN: 352056390

1984
Walzel-Frick Foundation, Inc.
5212 Briar Dr. E.
Houston, TX   77056-1102

Established in 1999 in TX.
Donor: F. Alan Frick.
Grantmaker type: Independent foundation.
Financial data (yr. ended 12/31/04): Assets, $20,417 (M); expenditures, $17,735; total giving, $16,735; qualifying distributions, $16,735; giving activities include $16,735 for grants.
Limitations: Applications not accepted. Giving primarily in MI and TX. No grants to individuals.
Application information: Contributes only to pre-selected organizations.
Officers: F. Alan Frick, Pres.; Cheryl Walzel, Secy.-Treas.
Director: Max Hendrick.
EIN: 760616075

1985
The Stefan Wanczyk Foundation
38505 Woodward Ave., Ste. 2000
Bloomfield Hills, MI   48304   (248) 901-4006
Application address: 13231 23 Mile Rd., Shelby Township, MI 48315

Established in 2004 in MI.

Donor: Stefan Wanczyk.
Grantmaker type: Independent foundation.
Financial data (yr. ended 12/31/04): Assets, $100,000 (M); gifts received, $100,000; expenditures, $0; total giving, $0; qualifying distributions, $0.
Purpose and activities: Scholarship awards paid directly to the college or university for graduating seniors at Oakland, Macomb, and Wayne counties, MI high schools.
Type of support: Scholarship funds.
Limitations: Giving primarily in Oakland, Macomb, and Wayne counties, MI.
Application information: Application form required.
  Deadline(s): May 31
Officer and Directors: * Stefan Wanczyk, * Pres.; Patrick J. Alandt; John Balardo.
EIN: 251906097

1986
Jane and Frank Warchol Foundation
43033 W. Kirkwood Dr.
Clinton Township, MI   48038-1220
Contact: Frank L. Warchol, Pres.
E-mail: puttygut1@aol.com

Established in 1993 in MI.
Donors: Frank L. Warchol; Virginia J. Warchol.
Grantmaker type: Independent foundation.
Financial data (yr. ended 12/31/05): Assets, $719,909 (M); expenditures, $80,090; total giving, $78,900; qualifying distributions, $79,220; giving activities include $78,900 for 30 grants (high: $20,000; low: $200).
Purpose and activities: Giving for scholarship funds and education, human services, women, religion, and arts and culture.
Fields of interest: Historic preservation/historical societies; Arts; Higher education; Zoos/zoological societies; Human services; Science; Christian agencies & churches; Women.
Type of support: General/operating support; Continuing support; Annual campaigns; Building/renovation; Emergency funds; Curriculum development; Scholarship funds; Exchange programs; In-kind gifts; Matching/challenge support.
Limitations: Giving primarily in southeastern MI. No support for political organizations. No grants to individuals.
Publications: Grants list; Informational brochure (including application guidelines).
Application information: Application form required.
  Initial approach: Letter
  Copies of proposal: 1
  Deadline(s): None
  Board meeting date(s): Varies
Officers: Frank L. Warchol, Pres.; Virginia J. Warchol, Secy.
Director: Karen Wudcoski.
Number of staff: None.
EIN: 383148034

1987
The Warner Foundation
c/o JPMorgan Chase Bank, N.A.
P.O. Box 6089
Newark, DE   19714-6089

Established in 2001 in NY.
Donors: Douglas A. Warner III; Patricia G. Warner.

Grantmaker type: Independent foundation.
Financial data (yr. ended 12/31/04): Assets, $5,428,992 (M); expenditures, $310,694; total giving, $255,500; qualifying distributions, $253,807; giving activities include $255,500 for 35 grants (high: $27,500; low: $1,000).
Fields of interest: Education; Health care; Cancer.
Limitations: Applications not accepted. Giving primarily in MI and NY. No grants to individuals.
Application information: Contributes only to pre-selected organizations.
Trustees: Douglas A. Warner III; Patricia G. Warner; JPMorgan Chase Bank, N.A.
EIN: 516522857
Selected grants: The following grants were reported in 2004.
$55,000 to Saint Andrews School of Delaware, Middletown, DE. For general operating support.
$27,500 to Miss Porters School, Farmington, CT. For general operating support.
$25,000 to Hospital for Special Surgery Fund, New York, NY. For general operating support.
$25,000 to Memorial Sloan-Kettering Cancer Center, New York, NY. For general operating support.
$20,000 to Peer Health Exchange, New York, NY. For general operating support.
$13,500 to Yale University, New Haven, CT. For general operating support.
$10,000 to Little Traverse Conservancy, Harbor Springs, MI. For general operating support.
$10,000 to Memorial Sloan-Kettering Cancer Center, Society of, New York, NY. For general operating support.
$2,500 to American Museum of Natural History, New York, NY. For general operating support.
$2,000 to Breast Cancer Research Foundation, New York, NY. For general operating support.

1988
The Alvin and Edith Wasserman Family Education Foundation
453 Merrill St.
Birmingham, MI   48009

Established in 1997 in MI.
Donors: Alvin Wasserman; Edith Wasserman.
Grantmaker type: Independent foundation.
Financial data (yr. ended 12/31/04): Assets, $861,684 (M); expenditures, $42,885; total giving, $33,658; qualifying distributions, $34,478; giving activities include $33,658 for grants.
Purpose and activities: Giving primary to Jewish organizations.
Fields of interest: Performing arts, orchestra (symphony); Performing arts, opera; Education; Health organizations; Jewish agencies & temples.
Limitations: Applications not accepted. Giving primarily in MI, with emphasis on Detroit. No grants to individuals.
Application information: Contributes only to pre-selected organizations.
Officers: Edith Wasserman, Pres. and Treas.; Gary L. Wasserman, V.P.; Rodger D. Wasserman, V.P.; Linda Wasserman Aviv, Secy.
EIN: 383343567

1989
L. P. Wasserman Family Foundation
30 Griffin Ave.
Scarsdale, NY   10583-7661

Established in 2003 in NY.
Grantmaker type: Independent foundation.
Financial data (yr. ended 12/31/04): Assets, $2,454,204 (M); expenditures, $117,429; total giving, $107,485; qualifying distributions, $117,429; giving activities include $107,485 for 73 grants (high: $40,000; low: $50).
Fields of interest: Arts; Education; Human services.
Limitations: Applications not accepted. Giving primarily in MI. No grants to individuals.
Application information: Contributes only to pre-selected organizations.
Officers: Judy Soley, Pres. and Treas.; Jill Soley, V.P.; Robert L. Soley, V.P.
Director: John Soley.
EIN: 010722403

1990
Rodger and Loree Wasserman Foundation
(formerly The Rodger D. Wasserman Family Foundation)
111 Willits St., Ste. 201
Birmingham, MI 48009

Established in 1987 in MI.
Donor: Rodger D. Wasserman.
Grantmaker type: Independent foundation.
Financial data (yr. ended 11/30/04): Assets, $1,736 (M); gifts received, $27,500; expenditures, $27,401; total giving, $25,495; qualifying distributions, $25,495; giving activities include $25,495 for grants.
Limitations: Applications not accepted. Giving primarily in Birmingham and Detroit, MI. No grants to individuals.
Application information: Contributes only to pre-selected organizations.
Officers: Rodger D. Wasserman, Pres. and Secy.-Treas.; Loree Wasserman, V.P.
EIN: 382787503

1991
John W. and Rose E. Watson Foundation
c/o Citizens Bank Wealth Mgmt., N.A.
328 S. Saginaw St., MC 002072
Flint, MI 48502
Application address: c/o Jean Seman, 5800 Weiss St., Saginaw, MI 48602

Established about 1959 in MI.
Grantmaker type: Independent foundation.
Financial data (yr. ended 12/31/05): Assets, $7,056,922 (M); gifts received, $30; expenditures, $371,586; total giving, $284,000; qualifying distributions, $342,952; giving activities include $5,000 for 6 grants (high: $2,000; low: $500), and $279,000 for 190 grants to individuals (high: $7,100; low: $200).
Purpose and activities: Support primarily for Roman Catholic organizations; scholarship awards limited to Saginaw, MI, residents graduating from one local Roman Catholic high school.
Fields of interest: Human services; Children/youth, services; Roman Catholic agencies & churches.
Type of support: General/operating support; Scholarships—to individuals.
Limitations: Giving primarily in Saginaw, MI; scholarships limited to residents of Saginaw, MI.
Application information: Application form required.
Deadline(s): 1 month prior to academic year

Officers: William L. Ruger, Pres.; Anne Hamilton, V.P.; Don Popielarz, Secy.; Jean Seman, Treas.
Trustee: Citizens Bank.
EIN: 386091611

1992
Raymond E. & Evona Watson Foundation
c/o Comerica Bank, Tr.
P.O. Box 75000, MC 3302
Detroit, MI 48275-3302
Application address: c/o Colorado School of Mines, Attn.: Financial aid Office, 1500 Illinois St., Golden, CO 80401, tel.: (800) 446-9488

Established in 1999 in OH.
Grantmaker type: Independent foundation.
Financial data (yr. ended 12/31/05): Assets, $194,929 (M); expenditures, $26,466; total giving, $18,000; qualifying distributions, $18,000; giving activities include $18,000 for grants to individuals.
Purpose and activities: Scholarship awards paid directly to the Colorado School of Mines, who will be attending after graduation from high school.
Type of support: Scholarships—to individuals.
Limitations: Giving limited to CO.
Application information: Application forms should be requested from the Colorado School of Mines, as well as all forms must be pre-approved by the school's financial aid office. Application form required.
Deadline(s): Before the end of each school term and/or semester
Officer: Evona Watson, Mgr.
Trustee: Comerica Bank.
EIN: 383493259

1993
Clermont and Kathryn Watson Scholarship Trust
c/o Bank of America, N.A.
P.O. Box 40200, FL9-100-10-19
Jacksonville, FL 32203-0200

Grantmaker type: Independent foundation.
Financial data (yr. ended 12/31/05): Assets, $403,337 (M); expenditures, $15,515; total giving, $10,638; qualifying distributions, $10,638; giving activities include $10,638 for grants.
Purpose and activities: Support only for Central High School in Springfield, MO, Grinnell High School, IA, and Ishpeming High School, MI.
Fields of interest: Secondary school/education.
Type of support: Scholarship funds.
Limitations: Applications not accepted. Giving limited to Grinnell, IA, Springfield, MO, and Ishpeming, MI. No grants to individuals.
Application information: Contributes only to 3 pre-selected organizations.
Trustee: Bank of America, N.A.
EIN: 656300887

1994
Wattles Family Foundation
P.O. Box 50311
Kalamazoo, MI 49005-0311

Established in 1999 in MI.
Donors: John C. Wattles; Helen F. Wattles.
Grantmaker type: Independent foundation.

Financial data (yr. ended 12/31/05): Assets, $531,180 (M); gifts received, $102,044; expenditures, $56,500; total giving, $55,000; qualifying distributions, $55,000; giving activities include $55,000 for grants.
Fields of interest: Higher education; YM/YWCAs & YM/YWHAs.
Limitations: Applications not accepted. No grants to individuals.
Application information: Unsolicited requests for funds not accepted.
Officers: John C. Wattles, Pres.; Sara W. Perry, V.P. and Secy.; Charles D. Wattles, V.P. and Treas.; Catherine W. Barnes, V.P.; Helen F. Wattles, V.P.
Number of staff: None.
EIN: 383501111

1995
The Way Foundation
1501 Pine Ave. N.W.
Grand Rapids, MI 49504

Donor: Arthur Decker.
Grantmaker type: Independent foundation.
Financial data (yr. ended 12/31/05): Assets, $1,047,313 (M); gifts received, $36,886; expenditures, $50,145; total giving, $49,100; qualifying distributions, $49,100; giving activities include $49,100 for grants.
Fields of interest: Protestant agencies & churches.
Type of support: General/operating support.
Limitations: Applications not accepted. Giving primarily in Grand Rapids, MI. No grants to individuals.
Application information: Contributes only to pre-selected organizations.
Director: Arthur Decker.
EIN: 383374797

1996
Weatherwax Foundation
P.O. Box 1111
Jackson, MI 49204
Application address: c/o Maria M. Dotterweich, Exec. Dir., 245 W. Michigan Ave., 4th Fl., Jackson, MI 49201-2265, tel.: (517) 787-2117

Established in 1981 in MI.
Donor: K.A. Weatherwax Trust I†.
Grantmaker type: Independent foundation.
Financial data (yr. ended 9/30/05): Assets, $21,297,496 (M); expenditures, $1,553,796; total giving, $1,264,792; qualifying distributions, $1,400,445; giving activities include $1,235,592 for 48 grants (high: $125,000; low: $1,000), and $29,200 for 3 employee matching gifts.
Purpose and activities: Support primarily for arts and culture, education, human services, and health care.
Fields of interest: Museums; Performing arts, orchestra (symphony); Arts; Higher education; Education; Health care; Human services; Federated giving programs.
Type of support: General/operating support; Annual campaigns; Capital campaigns; Building/renovation; Equipment; Emergency funds; Conferences/seminars; Curriculum development; Scholarship funds; Technical assistance; Consulting services; Program evaluation; Matching/challenge support.

Limitations: Giving primarily in Hillsdale, Lenawee, and Jackson counties, MI. No grants to individuals, or for computer purchases.
Publications: Application guidelines; Grants list.
Application information: Application form required.
  Initial approach: Proposal (not to exceed 2 pages)
  Copies of proposal: 3
  Deadline(s): None
  Board meeting date(s): Monthly
  Final notification: Acknowledgement within 60 days
Officer: Maria Miceli Dotterweich, Exec. Dir.
Trustees: Lawrence Bullen; Comerica Bank.
Number of staff: 1 part-time professional.
EIN: 386439807

1997
The Wayne and Joan Webber Foundation
44710 Morley Dr.
Clinton Township, MI   48036

Established in 1998 in MI.
Donors: Joan Webber; Wayne Webber; Hanson Aggregates West, Inc.; Southern Crushed Concrete, Inc.
Grantmaker type: Independent foundation.
Financial data (yr. ended 12/31/04): Assets, $5,538,762 (M); gifts received, $2,160,000; expenditures, $1,055,477; total giving, $1,038,546; qualifying distributions, $1,050,047; giving activities include $1,038,546 for 7 grants (high: $328,571; low: $5,000).
Purpose and activities: Giving primarily for health care, including to a cancer center, as well as for education.
Fields of interest: Elementary/secondary education; Hospitals (specialty); Health care; Cancer; Human services.
Type of support: Capital campaigns.
Limitations: Applications not accepted. Giving primarily in MI. No grants to individuals.
Application information: Contributes only to pre-selected organizations.
Directors: Joan Webber; Wayne Webber.
EIN: 383390733

1998
Weber Family Foundation
P.O. Box 7607
Flint, MI   48507

Established in 1997 in MI.
Donor: Donald H. Weber.
Grantmaker type: Independent foundation.
Financial data (yr. ended 12/31/05): Assets, $1,442,042 (M); gifts received, $980,754; expenditures, $58,570; total giving, $57,500; qualifying distributions, $57,500; giving activities include $57,500 for grants.
Purpose and activities: Support for the Church of the Nazarene in Michigan and Missouri.
Fields of interest: Christian agencies & churches.
Limitations: Applications not accepted. Giving primarily in MI and MO. No grants to individuals.
Application information: Contributes only to pre-selected organizations.
Officer: Donald H. Weber, Pres.
Directors: Beverly A. Weber; Donald D. Weber; Gary L. Weber; Julie A. Weber; Larry P. Weber.
EIN: 383325676

1999
Webster Family Foundation
1535 Lincolnshire Dr.
Lapeer, MI   48446
Contact: Sarah Webster, Tr.
Application address: c/o Freedman & Goldberg, C.P.A., 2444 E. Hill Rd., Grand Blanc, MI 48439, tel.: (810) 694-0336

Established in 1998 in MI.
Donor: Sarah Webster.
Grantmaker type: Independent foundation.
Financial data (yr. ended 12/31/04): Assets, $22,502 (M); gifts received, $11,000; expenditures, $8,520; total giving, $8,000; qualifying distributions, $8,000; giving activities include $8,000 for grants.
Fields of interest: Roman Catholic agencies & churches.
Limitations: Giving primarily in Lapeer, MI.
Application information:
  Initial approach: Proposal
  Deadline(s): None
Trustee: Sarah Webster.
EIN: 383416886

2000
Arthur H. Webster, Jr. Endowment Fund
c/o Citizens Bank Wealth Management, N.A.
328 S. Saginaw St., M/C 002702
Flint, MI   48502   (989) 776-7368
Application address: c/o Citizens Bank Wealth Management, N.A., Attn.: Helen James, 101 N. Washington Ave., Saginaw, MI 48607, tel.: (989) 776-7368

Established in 2004 in MI.
Donor: Lorraine Webster Residual Trust.
Grantmaker type: Independent foundation.
Financial data (yr. ended 8/31/05): Assets, $796,379 (M); gifts received, $729,909; expenditures, $12,638; total giving, $0; qualifying distributions, $8,848.
Purpose and activities: Giving primarily to Saginaw Community Foundation; some giving to organizations in Saginaw County, MI.
Fields of interest: Foundations (community).
Type of support: General/operating support.
Limitations: Giving primarily in Saginaw, MI.
Application information: Application form required.
  Deadline(s): None
Trustee: Citizens Bank Wealth Management, N.A.
EIN: 386635520

2001
Wege Foundation
P.O. Box 6388
Grand Rapids, MI   49516-6388   (616) 957-0480
Contact: Ellen Satterlee, Treas. and Exec. Dir.

Established on July 13, 1967 in MI.
Donor: Peter M. Wege.
Grantmaker type: Independent foundation.
Financial data (yr. ended 12/31/04): Assets, $161,051,374 (M); expenditures, $17,490,860; total giving, $16,098,666; qualifying distributions, $16,843,614; giving activities include $16,098,666 for 399 grants (high: $500,000; low: $400; average: $1,000–$50,000).

Purpose and activities: Giving primarily to museums, performing arts, health and human services, youth, Christian agencies, and education.
Fields of interest: Museums; Performing arts; Elementary/secondary education; Higher education; Environment, natural resources; Hospitals (general); Human services; Children/youth, services; Community development; Christian agencies & churches.
Type of support: Annual campaigns; Capital campaigns; Building/renovation; Equipment; Endowments; Program development; Curriculum development; Matching/challenge support.
Limitations: Giving primarily in greater Kent County, MI, with emphasis on the Grand Rapids area. No grants to individuals, or for operating budgets.
Publications: Application guidelines; Annual report.
Application information: Accepts CMF Common Grant Application Form. Application form not required.
  Initial approach: Proposal
  Copies of proposal: 1
  Deadline(s): Feb. 15 and Sept. 15
Officers and Directors: * Peter M. Wege,* Pres.; Terri McCarthy, V.P., Progs; Peter M. Wege II,* V.P.; W. Michael Van Haren,* Secy.; Ellen Satterlee, Treas. and Exec. Dir.; Mary Goodwillie Nelson; Christopher Wege; Diana Wege Sherogan; Jonathan C. Wege.
Number of staff: 3 full-time professional.
EIN: 386124363
Selected grants: The following grants were reported in 2004.
$2,000,000 to Saint Marys Mercy Medical Center, Grand Rapids, MI. 4 grants: $500,000 each
$1,325,770 to Grand Rapids Art Museum, Grand Rapids, MI. 3 grants: $437,885, $437,885, $450,000
$500,000 to Catholic Secondary Schools, Grand Rapids, MI. 2 grants: $250,000 each
$500,000 to Nature Conservancy, Arlington, VA.

2002
Wege Osman Foundation
111 Lyon St. N.W., Ste. 900
Grand Rapids, MI   49503-2487

Established in 1998 in MI.
Donor: Johanna Wege Osman.
Grantmaker type: Independent foundation.
Financial data (yr. ended 12/31/04): Assets, $1,397,034 (M); expenditures, $58,655; total giving, $50,000; qualifying distributions, $50,000; giving activities include $50,000 for grants.
Fields of interest: Neuroscience research; Islam.
Type of support: General/operating support.
Limitations: Applications not accepted. Giving primarily in FL. No grants to individuals.
Application information: Contributes only to pre-selected organizations.
Officers: Magdy Abdelazim Osman, Pres.; Johanna Wege Osman, Secy.-Treas.
EIN: 383420052

2003
Weigel Family Foundation
c/o First National Bank
5817 Maintee Ave. W.
Bradenton, FL   34209   (941) 794-6969

Established in 1997 in FL.

Donors: Raymond A. Weigel, Jr.; Wavelet M. Weigel.
Grantmaker type: Independent foundation.
Financial data (yr. ended 12/31/05): Assets, $646,850 (M); expenditures, $27,857; total giving, $23,200; qualifying distributions, $23,200; giving activities include $23,200 for grants.
Limitations: Giving primarily in FL and Cadillac, MI. No grants to individuals.
Application information:
  Initial approach: Proposal
  Deadline(s): None
Trustee: Wavelet M. Weigel.
EIN: 650741135

2004
Weikart Family Foundation
15141 Sheridan Rd.
Clinton, MI 49236-9605
Contact: Phyllis S. Weikart, Pres.

Established in 2004 in MI.
Donor: David Weikart†.
Grantmaker type: Independent foundation.
Financial data (yr. ended 12/31/05): Assets, $2,390,365 (M); expenditures, $263,190; total giving, $217,666; qualifying distributions, $239,415; giving activities include $217,666 for 6 grants (high: $68,176; low: $10,000).
Fields of interest: Education; Children/youth, services.
Type of support: Research.
Application information:
  Initial approach: Letter
  Deadline(s): Mar. 31
Officers: Phyllis S. Weikart, Pres.; Jennifer D. Danko, V.P.; Catherine L. Yeckel, Secy.; Cynthia W. Embry, Treas.
EIN: 200456632

2005
Max & Edith Weinberg Family Foundation
12928 Talbot Ln.
Huntington Woods, MI 48070

Grantmaker type: Independent foundation.
Financial data (yr. ended 12/31/05): Assets, $149,046 (M); expenditures, $19,171; total giving, $13,200; qualifying distributions, $13,200; giving activities include $13,200 for grants.
Fields of interest: Human services; Jewish agencies & temples.
Limitations: Applications not accepted. Giving primarily in MI and New York, NY. No grants to individuals.
Application information: Contributes only to pre-selected organizations.
Officers: Judith A. Weinberg, Pres.; Barbara Dechter, Secy.-Treas.
Director: Donald Lifton.
EIN: 386116736

2006
David and Effi Weinberg Foundation
95 Manorwood Dr.
Bloomfield Hills, MI 48304-2130

Established in 1999 in MI; funded in 2001.
Donor: American Montessori Center, Inc.
Grantmaker type: Independent foundation.

Financial data (yr. ended 12/31/04): Assets, $335,904 (M); expenditures, $95,433; total giving, $92,000; qualifying distributions, $92,000; giving activities include $92,000 for grants.
Fields of interest: Jewish agencies & temples.
Type of support: General/operating support.
Limitations: Applications not accepted. Giving primarily in Chicago, IL and New York, NY. No grants to individuals.
Application information: Contributes only to pre-selected organizations.
Officers: David R. Weinberg, Pres.; Effi Weinberg, V.P.; Walter D. Jaeger, Treas.
EIN: 383459139

2007
Weiner Family Foundation
P.O. Box 3005
Farmington Hills, MI 48333-3005
Contact: Sarah Weiner Keidan, Pres.

Established in 1999 in MI.
Donor: Josephine S. Weiner.
Grantmaker type: Independent foundation.
Financial data (yr. ended 12/31/04): Assets, $284,345 (M); expenditures, $14,599; total giving, $12,000; qualifying distributions, $12,721; giving activities include $12,000 for grants.
Fields of interest: Arts; Education, early childhood education; Human services; Family services.
Limitations: Giving primarily in the metropolitan Detroit, MI, area. No grants to individuals, or generally for ongoing expenses.
Application information:
  Initial approach: Letter
  Deadline(s): None
Officers: Sarah Weiner Keidan, Pres.; Laura Keidan Martin, V.P.; Mimi Keidan Seltzer, Secy.-Treas.
EIN: 383449750

2008
The Weiner Foundation
38500 N. Woodward Ave., Ste. 100
Bloomfield Hills, MI 48304

Established in 1987 in MI.
Donors: Ernest J. Weiner; Barbara Weiner.
Grantmaker type: Independent foundation.
Financial data (yr. ended 11/30/04): Assets, $6,996 (M); expenditures, $240; total giving, $0; qualifying distributions, $0.
Limitations: Applications not accepted. Giving primarily in MI. No grants to individuals.
Application information: Contributes only to pre-selected organizations.
Officers and Directors:* Ernest J. Weiner,* Chair., Pres. and Treas.; Barbara Weiner,* Secy.
EIN: 382784674

2009
Weingartz Family Foundation
P.O. Box 182008
Shelby Township, MI 48318

Established in 2004 in MI.
Donor: Power Equipment Distributors, Inc.
Grantmaker type: Independent foundation.
Financial data (yr. ended 12/31/04): Assets, $1,152,708 (M); gifts received, $1,060,000;

expenditures, $0; total giving, $0; qualifying distributions, $0.
Officers and Directors:* Raymond Weingartz,* Pres.; Marie Weingartz, V.P.; Edward Radtke, Secy.; Daniel Weingartz,* Treas.; Beverly Devrident; Catherine Radtke.
EIN: 201516609

2010
Bernard and Helen Weisberg Family Foundation
2075 E. Fourteen Mile Rd.
Birmingham, MI 48009

Established in 1985 in MI.
Donors: Bernard Weisberg; Helen Weisberg.
Grantmaker type: Independent foundation.
Financial data (yr. ended 10/31/04): Assets, $122,853 (M); expenditures, $14,590; total giving, $13,887; qualifying distributions, $13,887; giving activities include $13,887 for grants.
Limitations: Applications not accepted. No grants to individuals.
Application information: Contributes only to pre-selected organizations.
Officers: Bernard Weisberg, Pres.; Helen Weisberg, V.P.
EIN: 382639090

2011
Harvey & Lucille Weisberg Family Foundation
4795 Apple Grove Ct.
Bloomfield Hills, MI 48301

Established in 1985 in MI.
Grantmaker type: Independent foundation.
Financial data (yr. ended 10/31/04): Assets, $242,320 (M); expenditures, $15,071; total giving, $14,516; qualifying distributions, $14,516; giving activities include $14,516 for grants.
Fields of interest: Jewish agencies & temples.
Limitations: Applications not accepted. Giving primarily in MI. No grants to individuals.
Application information: Contributes only to pre-selected organizations.
Officers: Harvey Weisberg, Pres.; Lucille Weisberg, V.P.
EIN: 382637140

2012
Peter & Clara Weisberg Family Foundation
4795 Apple Grove Ct.
Bloomfield Hills, MI 48301

Established in 1985 in MI.
Grantmaker type: Independent foundation.
Financial data (yr. ended 10/31/04): Assets, $1 (M); expenditures, $9,316; total giving, $8,842; qualifying distributions, $8,842; giving activities include $8,842 for grants.
Fields of interest: Jewish agencies & temples.
Limitations: Applications not accepted. Giving primarily in MI and NY. No grants to individuals.
Application information: Contributes only to pre-selected organizations.
Officers and Directors:* Bernard Weisberg,* Pres.; Harvey Weisberg,* V.P.; Harold Weisberg,* Secy.; Alvin Weisberg,* Treas.
EIN: 386077328

2013
Alvin A. & Henrietta G. Weisberg Foundation

1166 Charrington Rd.
Bloomfield Hills, MI   48301-2112
Contact: Alvin A. Weisberg, Tr.

Established in 1993 in FL.
Donor: Alvin A. Weisberg.
Grantmaker type: Independent foundation.
Financial data (yr. ended 12/31/04): Assets, $176,580 (M); gifts received, $125,500; expenditures, $64,281; total giving, $64,281; qualifying distributions, $64,281; giving activities include $64,281 for grants.
Purpose and activities: Giving primarily for Jewish agencies and temples.
Fields of interest: Media, television; Museums (specialized); Performing arts, orchestra (symphony); Cystic fibrosis; Cancer, leukemia; Heart & circulatory diseases; Arthritis; Multiple sclerosis; Diabetes; Cancer research; Human services; Jewish federated giving programs; Jewish agencies & temples.
Type of support: General/operating support.
Limitations: Giving on a national basis.
Application information: Application form not required.
   Initial approach: Letter
   Deadline(s): None
Trustees: Alvin A. Weisberg; Henrietta G. Weisberg; Steven R. Weisberg.
EIN: 656135998

2014
The Weisblat Foundation, Inc.

834 King Hwy., Ste. 110
Kalamazoo, MI   49001   (269) 344-9236
Contact: G. Philip Dietrich, Secy.

Established in 1991 in MI.
Donor: Christine Weisblat.
Grantmaker type: Independent foundation.
Financial data (yr. ended 12/31/04): Assets, $439,779 (M); expenditures, $28,066; total giving, $6,500; qualifying distributions, $8,656; giving activities include $6,500 for grants.
Fields of interest: Arts; Education; Environment; Health care; Safety/disasters; Children/youth, services.
Type of support: General/operating support.
Limitations: Giving primarily in MI.
Application information: Application form not required.
   Initial approach: Letter
   Deadline(s): Oct. 31
Officers: Christine Weisblat, Pres.; Sara L. Schastok, V.P.; G. Philip Dietrich, Secy.; Ann M. Ford, Treas.
Trustee: David A. Weisblat.
EIN: 383014535

2015
Weitzenhoffer-Seminole Foundation

(formerly Seminole Foundation)
P.O. Box 1366
Columbus, MS   39703
Contact: Marjorie Robertson, Secy.

Established in 1985 in MS.
Grantmaker type: Independent foundation.

Financial data (yr. ended 12/31/05): Assets, $1,183,934 (M); expenditures, $56,613; total giving, $49,950; qualifying distributions, $49,950; giving activities include $49,950 for grants.
Purpose and activities: Giving to higher education and federated giving programs.
Fields of interest: Higher education; Education; Boy scouts; Children/youth, services; Federated giving programs; Government/public administration.
Limitations: Giving primarily in MI and MS.
Application information:
   Initial approach: Letter
   Deadline(s): Oct. 30
Officers: Max Weitzenhoffer, Pres.; William J. Threadgill, V.P.; Marjorie Robertson, Secy.
EIN: 640711566

2016
Anne and Martin Welch Charitable Foundation

3022 W. Ridge Ct.
Bloomfield Hills, MI   48302

Established in 1997 in MI.
Grantmaker type: Independent foundation.
Financial data (yr. ended 6/30/05): Assets, $108,518 (M); expenditures, $25,956; total giving, $25,930; qualifying distributions, $25,930; giving activities include $25,930 for grants.
Fields of interest: Elementary/secondary education; Higher education; Children, services.
Type of support: General/operating support.
Limitations: Applications not accepted. Giving primarily in MI. No grants to individuals.
Application information: Contributes only to pre-selected organizations.
Officers: Martin E. Welch III, Pres.; Anne M. Welch, V.P.
EIN: 383385005

2017
James & Jane Welch Foundation

c/o Fifth Third Bank
P.O. Box 3636
Grand Rapids, MI   49501-3636

Established in 1990 in MI.
Donor: James C. Welch.
Grantmaker type: Independent foundation.
Financial data (yr. ended 9/30/05): Assets, $4,361,574 (M); gifts received, $1,412; expenditures, $293,589; total giving, $286,500; qualifying distributions, $287,123; giving activities include $286,500 for 13 grants (high: $150,000; low: $2,000).
Fields of interest: Museums; Libraries (public); Children/youth, services; Federated giving programs; Christian agencies & churches; Protestant agencies & churches.
Limitations: Applications not accepted. Giving primarily in TX. No grants to individuals.
Application information: Contributes only to pre-selected organizations.
Officer: James C. Welch, Mgr.
Trustee: Fifth Third Bank.
EIN: 382927749

2018
James A. Welch Foundation

5206 Gateway Ctr., Ste. 100
Flint, MI   48507
Contact: Eugene Grice, Pres.

Established in 1960 in MI.
Grantmaker type: Independent foundation.
Financial data (yr. ended 6/30/05): Assets, $2,211,778 (M); expenditures, $121,879; total giving, $101,800; qualifying distributions, $101,800; giving activities include $101,800 for 15 grants (high: $15,000; low: $640; average: $640–$15,000).
Purpose and activities: Giving to organizations providing educational guidance and counseling for local gifted students, including museums, educational institutions, and performing arts groups.
Fields of interest: Performing arts, theater; Performing arts, music; Secondary school/education; Education; Recreation, camps; YM/YWCAs & YM/YWHAs; Children/youth, services; Science.
Type of support: General/operating support.
Limitations: Giving limited to Genesee County, MI. No grants to individuals.
Application information: Application form required.
   Initial approach: Proposal
   Copies of proposal: 6
   Deadline(s): Feb. 20, May 20, Aug. 20, and Nov. 20
   Board meeting date(s): Jan., Mar., June, and Sept.
Officers: Eugene Grice, Pres.; James Kettler, V.P.; John C. Briggs, Secy.-Treas.
Directors: Gail Ganakas; Patricia Gruener; Dennis Haley.
EIN: 381690381

2019
Weller Family Foundation

0-8335 Kenowa Ave. S.W.
Grand Rapids, MI   49544

Established in 2001 in MI.
Donors: Dorothy M. Weller; Harry M. Weller.
Grantmaker type: Independent foundation.
Financial data (yr. ended 12/31/05): Assets, $377,114 (M); expenditures, $33,721; total giving, $32,750; qualifying distributions, $32,750; giving activities include $32,750 for grants.
Fields of interest: Christian agencies & churches.
Limitations: Applications not accepted. No grants to individuals.
Application information: Contributes only to pre-selected organizations.
Officers: James A. Davidson, Pres.; Harry M. Weller, V.P.; Dorothy M. Weller, Secy.-Treas.
EIN: 383588896

2020
Leon Wells Trust

c/o Monroe Bank & Trust
102 E. Front St.
Monroe, MI   48161-2162

Established in MI.
Donor: Leon Wells†.
Grantmaker type: Independent foundation.
Financial data (yr. ended 5/31/05): Assets, $333,855 (M); expenditures, $38,451; total giving,

$34,104; qualifying distributions, $36,097; giving activities include $34,104 for grants to individuals.
Purpose and activities: Scholarships awards to graduates of Dundee Community and Summerfield Community high school, MI.
Type of support: Scholarships—to individuals.
Limitations: Giving limited to residents of Dundee and Summerfield, MI.
Application information: Application form required.
   Deadline(s): May 1
Trustee: Monroe Bank & Trust.
EIN: 386146348

2021
Thomas Welsh Foundation
P.O. Box 290
St. Clair Shores, MI   48080-0290
Application address: c/o Macomb Community College, Office of Resource Devel. or Office of Financial Aid, 14500 E. 12 Mile Rd., Warren, MI 48093-3896, tel.: (586) 445-7302

Grantmaker type: Independent foundation.
Financial data (yr. ended 11/30/04): Assets, $190,436 (M); gifts received, $1,900; expenditures, $8,933; total giving, $4,095; qualifying distributions, $4,095; giving activities include $4,095 for grants.
Fields of interest: Christian agencies & churches.
Type of support: Scholarship funds.
Limitations: Giving limited to Warren, MI.
Officers and Directors: Lorie Jo Welsh, Pres.; Thomas S. Welsh III,* Secy.; Michael D. Murray.
EIN: 383111330

2022
Henry E. and Consuelo S. Wenger Foundation, Inc.
8916 Gale Rd.
White Lake, MI   48386

Incorporated in 1959 in MI.
Donor: Consuelo S. Wenger.
Grantmaker type: Independent foundation.
Financial data (yr. ended 12/31/05): Assets, $14,586,816 (M); expenditures, $920,564; total giving, $884,805; qualifying distributions, $888,045; giving activities include $884,805 for 81 grants (high: $125,000; low: $100).
Purpose and activities: Support for the arts, secondary and higher education, environmental preservation, hospitals, and Christian churches.
Fields of interest: Arts; Elementary/secondary education; Higher education; Environment; Hospitals (general); Health care; Youth development, centers/clubs; Human services; Christian agencies & churches.
Limitations: Applications not accepted. Giving primarily in FL, IL, MA, MI, NH, NY, and RI. No grants to individuals.
Application information: Contributes only to pre-selected organizations.
Officer: Diane Wenger Wilson, Pres.
EIN: 386077419

2023
Charles R. & Marie Werner Foundation
1530 Blythe Ct. N.W.
Grand Rapids, MI   49504   (616) 453-9334
Contact: Marie Werner, Tr.

Established in 1966.
Grantmaker type: Independent foundation.
Financial data (yr. ended 6/30/05): Assets, $78,044 (M); expenditures, $146,346; total giving, $145,000; qualifying distributions, $145,733; giving activities include $145,000 for 23 grants (high: $35,000; low: $300).
Fields of interest: Education; Human services; Family services; Protestant agencies & churches.
Limitations: Giving on a national basis. No support for private foundations. No grants to individuals.
Application information:
   Initial approach: Letter or brochure
   Deadline(s): None
Trustees: Elizabeth Ann Paauw; William Spoelhof; Susan Steinbrecher; Marie Werner.
EIN: 386079502

2024
Wesselink Family Foundation
1133 Western Ave.
Northbrook, IL   60062

Established in 2000 in IL.
Donors: David D. Wesselink; Linda R. Wesselink.
Grantmaker type: Independent foundation.
Financial data (yr. ended 12/31/04): Assets, $1,636,641 (M); gifts received, $882,365; expenditures, $62,218; total giving, $61,000; qualifying distributions, $61,000; giving activities include $61,000 for grants.
Fields of interest: Higher education; Protestant agencies & churches.
Limitations: Applications not accepted. Giving on a national basis, with emphasis on IA, IL, and MI. No grants to individuals.
Application information: Contributes only to pre-selected organizations.
Officers and Directors: David D. Wesselink,* Pres.; William J. Wesselink,* V.P.; Linda R. Wesselink,* Secy.; Catherine E. Wesselink,* Treas.
EIN: 364405466

2025
Elton W. and Elsie M. West Trust
c/o Citizens Bank Wealth Mgmt., N.A.
328 S. Saginaw St., M/C 002072
Flint, MI   48502

Established in 1997 in MI.
Donors: Elton West; Elsie West.
Grantmaker type: Independent foundation.
Financial data (yr. ended 12/31/04): Assets, $243,486 (M); expenditures, $5,442; total giving, $724; qualifying distributions, $1,196; giving activities include $724 for grants.
Purpose and activities: Support only for the Court Street Methodist Church, MI.
Fields of interest: Protestant agencies & churches.
Type of support: General/operating support.
Limitations: Applications not accepted. Giving limited to Flint, MI. No grants to individuals.
Application information: Contributes only to a pre-selected organization.
Trustee: Citizens Bank, N.A.
EIN: 386690988

2026
Jack & Wynnita Joy Westerbeek Family Foundation
P.O. Drawer 427
Grosse Ile, MI   48138-0427

Established in 1996 in MI.
Donors: Jack Westerbeek; Wynnita Joy Westerbeek.
Grantmaker type: Independent foundation.
Financial data (yr. ended 12/31/05): Assets, $939,554 (M); gifts received, $110,000; expenditures, $108,963; total giving, $105,000; qualifying distributions, $105,000; giving activities include $105,000 for 16 grants (high: $17,500; low: $500).
Purpose and activities: Giving primarily to Presbyterian and other Christian organizations.
Fields of interest: Higher education; Education; Christian agencies & churches; Protestant agencies & churches.
Type of support: Endowments; Scholarship funds; General/operating support.
Limitations: Applications not accepted. Giving primarily in MI. No grants to individuals.
Application information: Contributes only to pre-selected organizations.
Officers and Directors: Wynnita Joy Westerbeek,* Pres.; Scot Westerbeek,* V.P.; D. James Barton,* Secy.; Gary Westerbeek,* Treas.; Valerie Burkhart.
EIN: 383324067

2027
Samuel L. Westerman Foundation
40700 N. Woodward Ave., Ste. A
Bloomfield Hills, MI   48304
Contact: Ruth R. LoPrete, Grant Off.
Application address: 2861 Masefield Dr., Bloomfield Hills, MI 48303, tel.: (248) 203-9343

Established in 1971 in MI.
Donor: Samuel L. Westerman†.
Grantmaker type: Independent foundation.
Financial data (yr. ended 12/31/04): Assets, $9,010,657 (M); expenditures, $459,759; total giving, $407,950; qualifying distributions, $407,950; giving activities include $407,950 for 145 grants (high: $15,000; low: $250).
Purpose and activities: Giving primarily for education, youth services and religious programs.
Fields of interest: Performing arts, music; Arts; Higher education; Education; Hospitals (general); Health care; Health organizations, association; Human services; Children/youth, services; Religion.
Type of support: General/operating support; Continuing support; Endowments; Program development; Scholarship funds; Research.
Limitations: Giving primarily in MI. No grants to individuals.
Publications: Grants list.
Application information: Very limited funds available for new grants. Application form not required.
   Initial approach: Letter
   Copies of proposal: 1
   Deadline(s): None
   Board meeting date(s): Quarterly
   Final notification: Via letter
Officers and Trustees: James H. LoPrete,* Pres.; Cameron K. Muir,* V.P. and Treas.; Ruth LoPrete, V.P. and Grant Off.; Kent G. LoPrete,* V.P., Investment Comm.; Gordon J. Muir, V.P., Investment

Comm.; Martha M. Muir,* V.P.; Mary M. Lyneus, Secy.
EIN: 237108795

2028
Robert B. Westfall Foundation
906 James St.
Adrian, MI 49221

Established in 1986 in MI.
Donor: Ruthmary Westfall.
Grantmaker type: Independent foundation.
Financial data (yr. ended 9/30/04): Assets, $705,835 (M); gifts received, $108,235; expenditures, $22,882; total giving, $20,000; qualifying distributions, $20,000; giving activities include $20,000 for grants.
Limitations: Applications not accepted. Giving primarily in Ann Arbor, MI. No grants to individuals.
Application information: Contributes only to pre-selected organizations.
Officers and Directors:* Ruthmary Westfall,* Pres.; Harley J. Westfall,* Secy.; Charles D. Dunham.
EIN: 382711284

2029
Warren Westrate Foundation
4037 Lakeridge Dr.
Holland, MI 49424-2263

Established in 1992 in MI.
Donor: Warren K. Westrate†.
Grantmaker type: Independent foundation.
Financial data (yr. ended 12/31/05): Assets, $156,211 (M); expenditures, $11,737; total giving, $10,480; qualifying distributions, $10,480; giving activities include $10,480 for grants.
Limitations: Applications not accepted. Giving primarily in Holland, MI. No grants to individuals.
Application information: Contributes only to pre-selected organizations.
Trustee: Marcia Westrate.
EIN: 383051181

2030
Wetmore Family Foundation
c/o Comerica Bank
P.O. Box 75000
Detroit, MI 48275-3302

Established in 1994 in DE.
Grantmaker type: Independent foundation.
Financial data (yr. ended 12/31/05): Assets, $100,761 (M); expenditures, $6,472; total giving, $4,265; qualifying distributions, $4,265; giving activities include $4,265 for grants.
Limitations: Applications not accepted. Giving on a national basis. No grants to individuals.
Application information: Contributes only to pre-selected organizations.
Trustee: Orville C. Wetmore.
EIN: 510350462

2031
The Wetsman Foundation
P.O. Box 3032, No. 282
Birmingham, MI 48012

Established in 1962 in MI.

Donors: Lillian R. Wetsman; William M. Wetsman.
Grantmaker type: Independent foundation.
Financial data (yr. ended 12/31/04): Assets, $3,009,324 (M); gifts received, $12,500; expenditures, $182,286; total giving, $169,030; qualifying distributions, $166,701; giving activities include $160,030 for 50 grants (high: $43,025; low: $100).
Purpose and activities: Support primarily for federated giving programs and Jewish organizations; giving also for the arts and health.
Fields of interest: Arts; Hospitals (general); Health care; Human services; Jewish federated giving programs; Jewish agencies & temples.
Type of support: General/operating support.
Limitations: Applications not accepted. Giving primarily in MI. No grants to individuals.
Application information: Contributes only to pre-selected organizations.
Officers: William M. Wetsman, Pres.; David J. Wetsman, V.P. and Secy.; Janis B. Wetsman, V.P. and Treas.; Adam F. Wetsman, V.P.
EIN: 386056692
Selected grants: The following grants were reported in 2004.
$43,025 to Detroit Institute of Arts, Detroit, MI.
$40,000 to Jewish Federation of Metropolitan Detroit, Bloomfield Hills, MI.
$25,000 to United Jewish Foundation, Bloomfield Hills, MI.
$10,000 to Childrens Hospital of Michigan, Detroit, MI.
$9,000 to Detroit Symphony Orchestra, Detroit, MI.
$6,000 to Huron Valley-Sinai Hospital, Commerce Township, MI.
$5,000 to Renbrook School, West Hartford, CT.
$4,000 to Cornerstone Schools Association, Detroit, MI.
$3,000 to United Jewish Fund of Greater Los Angeles, Los Angeles, CA.
$3,000 to University of Guam Foundation, Mangilao, GU.

2032
Louis F. and Florence H. Weyand 1977 Charitable Trust
P.O. Box 64713
St. Paul, MN 55164-0713
Application address: 800 Nicollet Mall, Minneapolis, MN 55101, tel.: (651) 466-8709

Established in 1977 in CA and MN.
Donors: Louis F. Weyand†; Florence H. Weyand.
Grantmaker type: Independent foundation.
Financial data (yr. ended 9/30/05): Assets, $3,565,145 (M); expenditures, $216,965; total giving, $166,931; qualifying distributions, $176,713; giving activities include $166,931 for 62 grants (high: $35,930; low: $25).
Fields of interest: Performing arts, orchestra (symphony); Arts; Education; Human services; Religion.
Type of support: General/operating support; Building/renovation.
Limitations: Giving generally limited to CA, FL, and MI. No grants to individuals.
Application information:
  Initial approach: Proposal
  Deadline(s): None
Trustees: Lois Bachman; Carolyn Yorston; U.S. Bank, N.A.
EIN: 942473421

2033
Weyand Charitable Trust
c/o U.S. Bank, N.A.
P.O. Box 64713
St. Paul, MN 55164-0713
Application address: c/o John T. Blodgett, 101 E. 5th St., St. Paul, MN 55164

Established in MN.
Grantmaker type: Independent foundation.
Financial data (yr. ended 12/31/05): Assets, $1,412,786 (M); expenditures, $86,390; total giving, $65,970; qualifying distributions, $65,970; giving activities include $65,970 for grants.
Purpose and activities: Giving for education and public service.
Fields of interest: Protestant agencies & churches.
Limitations: Giving limited to CA, FL, and MI.
Application information: Application form not required.
  Initial approach: Letter
  Deadline(s): None
Trustees: Lois V. Bachman; Susan F. Teal; U.S. Bank, N.A.
EIN: 416011494

2034
Weyerhaeuser/Day Foundation
30 E. 7th St., Ste. 2000
St. Paul, MN 55101-4930 (651) 228-0935
Contact: Vivian W. Day, Pres.

Established in 1995 in MN.
Donors: Lynn Weyerhaeuser Day†; Stanley R. Stanley.
Grantmaker type: Independent foundation.
Financial data (yr. ended 12/31/04): Assets, $9,961,899 (M); gifts received, $261,376; expenditures, $197,982; total giving, $160,000; qualifying distributions, $177,103; giving activities include $160,000 for 7 grants (high: $25,000; low: $10,000).
Fields of interest: Higher education; Environment, natural resources; Health care.
Type of support: Continuing support.
Limitations: Giving primarily in MI.
Application information: Application form not required.
  Initial approach: Proposal
  Deadline(s): None
Officers and Directors:* Vivian W. Day,* Pres.; Lincoln W. Day,* V.P.; Stanley R. Day, Jr.,* Secy.; Frederick W. Day,* Treas.; Stanley R. Day.
EIN: 411815686

2035
Wheeler Family Foundation, Inc.
c/o TMW Enterprises, Inc.
2120 Austin Ave., Ste. 100
Rochester Hills, MI 48309-3667

Established in 1997 in DE.
Donor: Thomas M. Wheeler.
Grantmaker type: Independent foundation.
Financial data (yr. ended 6/30/05): Assets, $10,268,558 (M); expenditures, $576,061; total giving, $432,500; qualifying distributions, $432,500; giving activities include $432,500 for 20 grants (high: $100,000; low: $400).
Purpose and activities: Giving primarily for elementary and secondary education, as well as for

a Roman Catholic church; funding also for youth and social services.
Fields of interest: Elementary/secondary education; Human services; Salvation Army; Youth, services; Roman Catholic agencies & churches.
Limitations: Applications not accepted. Giving primarily in CO, FL, and MI. No grants to individuals.
Application information: Contributes only to pre-selected organizations.
Officers and Directors: Michaleon A. Wright,* Pres.; Douglas S. Soifer,* Secy.; Paul Oster, Treas.; Lisa W. Huzella; Thomas M. Wheeler; Thomas R. Wheeler; Erin Wright; Morgan Wright.
EIN: 383392912

2036
The John and Chris Wheeler Family Foundation
5854 Chanterelle Ct.
Belmont, MI 49306

Established in 2004 in MI.
Donors: John J. Wheeler; Christine A. Wheeler.
Grantmaker type: Independent foundation.
Financial data (yr. ended 12/31/05): Assets, $391,090 (M); gifts received, $110,000; expenditures, $30,671; total giving, $28,500; qualifying distributions, $28,500; giving activities include $28,500 for grants.
Fields of interest: Education; Public health; Christian agencies & churches; Economically disadvantaged.
Limitations: Applications not accepted. Giving primarily in MI. No grants to individuals.
Application information: Contributes only to pre-selected organizations.
Officers: John J. Wheeler, Pres. and Treas.; Christine A. Wheeler, V.P. and Secy.
Directors: Jason J. Wheeler; Ryan K. Wheeler; Steven B. Wheeler.
EIN: 201963760

2037
Irving and Birdella White Foundation
900 Fifth Third Ctr.
111 Lyon St. N.W., Ste. 900
Grand Rapids, MI 49503

Established in 1999 in MI.
Donor: Irving E. White.
Grantmaker type: Independent foundation.
Financial data (yr. ended 12/31/05): Assets, $222,879 (M); expenditures, $15,492; total giving, $13,570; qualifying distributions, $13,570; giving activities include $13,570 for grants.
Limitations: Applications not accepted. No grants to individuals.
Application information: Contributes only to pre-selected organizations.
Officer: Roy A. White, Pres. and Secy.-Treas.
Trustee: Irving E. White.
EIN: 383493724

2038
The White Foundation
c/o Glenn E. White
5530 Crabtree Rd.
Bloomfield Hills, MI 48301-1200

Established in 1945 in MI.

Donors: Glenn E. White; Ruth E. White; David B. White; Nancy White; Charles E. White; Carol L. White.
Grantmaker type: Independent foundation.
Financial data (yr. ended 12/31/05): Assets, $3,934,000 (M); gifts received, $136,000; expenditures, $453,000; total giving, $428,000; qualifying distributions, $428,000; giving activities include $428,000 for 13 grants (high: $300,000; low: $500).
Purpose and activities: Grants primarily to organizations associated with the Free Methodist Church.
Fields of interest: Higher education; Christian agencies & churches.
Limitations: Applications not accepted. Giving primarily in MI. No grants to individuals.
Application information: Contributes only to pre-selected organizations.
Officers and Directors: Glenn E. White,* Pres. and Treas.; Ruth E. White,* V.P.; Nancy Bergsma,* Secy.; Verlyn Beardslee; Charles E. White; David B. White.
EIN: 386054883
Selected grants: The following grants were reported in 2004.
$52,000 to Spring Arbor University, Spring Arbor, MI. For scholarships.
$37,000 to Ferndale Free Methodist Church, Ferndale, MI. For general support.
$10,000 to International Institute for Christian Studies, Overland Park, KS.
$10,000 to Somerset Beach Campground, Somerset, MI. For bath house.
$7,500 to Free Methodist Foundation, Spring Arbor, MI. For Hope Africa University dormatory.
$7,500 to Praying for You, Midlothian, TX. For general support.
$5,300 to Southfield Christian School, Southfield, MI. For library media, art, and chapel programs.
$5,000 to Greenville College, Greenville, IL. For comprehensive campaign.
$3,500 to Free Methodist Church of North America, Winona Lake, IN. For Operation Hope.
$1,000 to Rincon Mountain Presbyterian Church, Tucson, AZ. For Carl Woodson Mission.

2039
The John and Elizabeth Whiteley Foundation
c/o Hubbard Law Firm
5801 W. Michigan Ave.
Lansing, MI 48908-0857 (517) 886-7176
Contact: Donald B. Lawrence, Jr., Secy.-Treas.
Application address: P.O. Box 80502, Lansing, MI 48908-0502

Incorporated in 1955 in MI.
Donor: Nellie M. Zimmerman†.
Grantmaker type: Independent foundation.
Financial data (yr. ended 12/31/05): Assets, $0 (M); expenditures, $107,304; total giving, $42,000; qualifying distributions, $63,723; giving activities include $26,000 for 5 grants, and $16,000 for 15 grants to individuals.
Purpose and activities: Giving primarily for human services and education, including business education scholarship awards to students whose parents reside in Ingham County, Michigan.
Fields of interest: Higher education; Salvation Army; Christian agencies & churches.
Type of support: General/operating support; Scholarships—to individuals.

Limitations: Giving limited to Ingham County, MI.
Application information: Application form required.
Deadline(s): May 1st for scholarships
Officers: Romayne E. Hicks, Pres.; John Smythe, V.P.; Donald B. Lawrence, Jr., Secy.-Treas.
Director: Stephen D. Plumb.
Trustee: Richard F. Burmeister.
EIN: 381558108

2040
James H. Whiting Auditorium Trust
c/o Citizens Bank
901 Citizens Bank Bldg.
Flint, MI 48502

Grantmaker type: Independent foundation.
Financial data (yr. ended 12/31/05): Assets, $3,809,218 (M); expenditures, $168,270; total giving, $150,000; qualifying distributions, $150,000; giving activities include $150,000 for grants.
Purpose and activities: Support only to the Flint Cultural Center Corp. for maintenance of the Whiting Auditorium.
Fields of interest: Arts; General charitable giving.
Limitations: Applications not accepted. Giving limited to Flint, MI. No grants to individuals.
Application information: Contributes only to a pre-selected organization.
Trustees: Donald E. Johnson, Jr.; Donald E. Johnson III; John T. Lindholm; Citizens Bank.
EIN: 386041292

2041
The Whiting Foundation
G-9460 S. Saginaw St., Ste. A
Grand Blanc, MI 48439
Application address: c/o Donald E. Johnson, Jr., Pres., 901 Citizens Bank Bldg., Flint, MI 48502, tel.: (810) 767-3600

Incorporated in 1940 in MI.
Donor: Members of the Johnson family.
Grantmaker type: Independent foundation.
Financial data (yr. ended 6/30/05): Assets, $22,525,196 (M); expenditures, $908,392; total giving, $840,000; qualifying distributions, $866,082; giving activities include $840,000 for 41 grants (high: $575,000; low: $500).
Purpose and activities: Giving primarily for cultural activities, and for basic needs for people who are underprivileged.
Fields of interest: Historic preservation/historical societies; Arts; Education; Cancer; Medical research, institute; Housing/shelter, development; Children/youth, services; Community development; Federated giving programs.
Type of support: General/operating support; Program development.
Limitations: Giving primarily in the Genesee County, MI, area, including the city of Flint.
Application information: Application form not required.
Initial approach: Concise proposal
Copies of proposal: 1
Deadline(s): Apr. 30
Officers: Donald E. Johnson, Jr., Pres.; John T. Lindholm, Secy.-Treas.; Marsha A. Kump, Exec. Dir.
Trustees: Mary Alice J. Heaton; Linda J. Lemieux.
EIN: 386056693

Selected grants: The following grants were reported in 2003.

$522,000 to Flint Cultural Center Corporation, Flint, MI.

$30,000 to Whaley Childrens Center, Flint, MI.

$21,000 to Genesee, County of, Flint, MI.

$18,000 to United Way of Genesee County, Flint, MI.

$10,000 to Cancer Research Institute, New York, NY.

$10,000 to Insight, Inc., Flint, MI.

$10,000 to Sloan Museum, Flint, MI.

$7,500 to Christ Episcopal Center, Flint, MI.

$5,000 to Daisys in Recovery, Holly, MI.

$5,000 to National Childhood Cancer Foundation, Arcadia, CA.

2042
Henry and Harriet Whiting Memorial Foundation

c/o Fifth Third Bank
P.O. Box 630858
Cincinnati, OH 45263
Application address: c/o Franklin H. Moore Jr., 200 S. Riverside Ave., St. Clair., MI 48079-5330

Established in 1950 in MI.
Donor: Harriet Clark Whiting‡.
Grantmaker type: Independent foundation.
Financial data (yr. ended 12/31/04): Assets, $2,820,485 (M); expenditures, $145,899; total giving, $127,200; qualifying distributions, $127,470; giving activities include $127,200 for 21 grants (high: $20,000; low: $500).
Purpose and activities: Giving for community foundations, health, religion, youth groups, community services, and federated giving programs.
Fields of interest: Health care; Health organizations, association; Recreation, parks/playgrounds; Youth development; Human services; YM/YWCAs & YM/YWHAs; Children/youth, services; Community development; Foundations (community); Federated giving programs; Christian agencies & churches.
Type of support: General/operating support; Building/renovation; Equipment; Endowments; Emergency funds.
Limitations: Giving primarily in St. Clair and Port Huron, MI. No grants to individuals.
Application information:
  Initial approach: Letter
  Deadline(s): None
Officers: Franklin H. Moore, Jr., Pres. and Treas.; Charles Staiger, Secy.
Trustee: Frederick S. Moore.
EIN: 386091633

2043
Lulu M. Pickard Whiting Trust

c/o Monroe Bank & Trust
102 E. Front St.
Monroe, MI 48161
Application address: Selection Committee, c/o Superintendent, Bedford High School, 1575 W. Tempance Rd., Temperance, MI 48182, tel.: (734) 847-6736

Donor: Lulu M. Pickard Whiting‡.
Grantmaker type: Independent foundation.
Financial data (yr. ended 6/30/03): Assets, $80,237 (M); expenditures, $5,347; total giving,

$3,865; qualifying distributions, $4,561; giving activities include $3,865 for 11 grants to individuals (high: $400; low: $293).
Purpose and activities: Scholarships only to graduates of Bedford High School, MI.
Fields of interest: Higher education, college.
Type of support: Scholarships—to individuals.
Limitations: Giving limited to residents of Bedford, MI.
Publications: Application guidelines.
Application information: Application form required.
  Deadline(s): May 1
Trustee: Monroe Bank & Trust.
EIN: 386433033

2044
Whitman Family Foundation

c/o Northpoint Financial
920 E. Lincoln St.
Birmingham, MI 48009-3608   (248) 644-1901

Established in 1994 in MI.
Donors: Marina V.N. Whitman; Robert F. Whitman.
Grantmaker type: Independent foundation.
Financial data (yr. ended 12/31/05): Assets, $1,929,839 (M); gifts received, $92,608; expenditures, $113,303; total giving, $104,000; qualifying distributions, $104,000; giving activities include $104,000 for 17 grants (high: $15,000; low: $1,000).
Fields of interest: Performing arts; Higher education; International relief; Social sciences; Economics; Public policy, research.
Limitations: Giving in the U.S., with emphasis on Ann Arbor, MI, and Washington, DC. No grants to individuals.
Application information:
  Initial approach: Letter
  Deadline(s): None
Officers and Directors:* Marina V.N. Whitman,* Pres.; Robert F. Whitman,* V.P. and Secy.-Treas.; David Downie; Laura Whitman Downie; Malcolm Whitman.
EIN: 383191221

2045
The Whitman-Carlyon Foundation

c/o Barbara Whitman
38 Grove Ave.
Larchmont, NY 10538

Established in 2002 in NY.
Donors: Barbara Whitman; David Carlyon.
Grantmaker type: Independent foundation.
Financial data (yr. ended 12/31/03): Assets, $995,079 (M); gifts received, $16,238; expenditures, $265,450; total giving, $262,500; qualifying distributions, $263,988; giving activities include $262,500 for 4 grants (high: $200,000; low: $2,500).
Fields of interest: Higher education; Human services.
Limitations: Applications not accepted. Giving primarily in NY and MI. No grants to individuals.
Application information: Contributes only to pre-selected organizations.
Trustees: David Carlyon; Barbara Whitman.
EIN: 571144326

2046
David & Barbara Whitwam Foundation, Inc.

c/o Northern Trust Co.
P.O. Box 803878
Chicago, IL 60680
Application address: c/o David R. Whitwam, 1408 Manley Ct., St. Joseph, MI 49085, tel.: (269) 923-3150

Established in 1986 in MI.
Donors: David R. Whitwam; Barbara Whitwam.
Grantmaker type: Independent foundation.
Financial data (yr. ended 12/31/05): Assets, $4,668,456 (M); expenditures, $392,943; total giving, $339,050; qualifying distributions, $339,050; giving activities include $339,050 for 23 grants (high: $200,000; low: $250).
Fields of interest: Education; Human services; Federated giving programs; Christian agencies & churches.
Limitations: Giving primarily in Benton Harbor, Stevensville, and St. Joseph, MI. No grants to individuals.
Application information: Application form not required.
  Deadline(s): None
Officer and Directors:* David R. Whitwam,* Pres.; Barbara Whitwam.
EIN: 382712616

2047
The Wicker's Foundation

6097 Otto Rd.
Charlotte, MI 48813

Established in 1993 in MI.
Donors: John Wicker; Joyce R. Wicker.
Grantmaker type: Independent foundation.
Financial data (yr. ended 12/31/05): Assets, $268,452 (M); expenditures, $12,921; total giving, $12,400; qualifying distributions, $12,400; giving activities include $12,400 for grants.
Limitations: Applications not accepted. No grants to individuals.
Application information: Contributes only to pre-selected organizations.
Officers: John Wicker, Pres. and Treas.; Joyce R. Wicker, V.P. and Secy.
EIN: 383114681

2048
Harvey Randall Wickes Foundation

Plaza N., Ste. 472
4800 Fashion Sq. Blvd.
Saginaw, MI 48604   (989) 799-1850
Contact: Hugo E. Braun, Jr., Pres.
FAX: (989) 799-3327;
E-mail: HRWickes@concentric.net

Incorporated in 1945 in MI.
Donors: Harvey Randall Wickes‡; members of the Wickes family.
Grantmaker type: Independent foundation.
Financial data (yr. ended 12/31/05): Assets, $43,166,791 (M); expenditures, $2,072,590; total giving, $1,750,003; qualifying distributions, $1,838,697; giving activities include $1,750,003 for 54 grants (high: $500,000; low: $400).
Purpose and activities: Giving primarily for civic affairs groups, parks and recreation agencies;

support also for a library, youth and social services, hospitals, and cultural programs, for the betterment of Saginaw County, MI.

Fields of interest: Arts; Libraries/library science; Education; Hospitals (general); Recreation; Human services; Children/youth, services.

Type of support: Annual campaigns; Building/renovation; Equipment; Seed money.

Limitations: Giving limited to the Saginaw, MI, area. No support for government where support is forth coming from tax dollars. No grants to individuals, or for endowments, travel, conferences, or film or video projects; no loans.

Publications: Application guidelines; Financial statement.

Application information: Application form not required.

  Initial approach: Letter followed by proposal
  Copies of proposal: 1
  Deadline(s): Submit proposal 2 weeks prior to meeting
  Board meeting date(s): Mar., June, Sept. and Dec.
  Final notification: 2 weeks following board meeting

Officers and Trustees:* Hugo E. Braun, Jr.,* Pres.; Craig W. Horn,* V.P.; Michele Pavlicek, Secy.; Lloyd J. Yeo,* Treas.; Mary Lou Case; Ellen Crane; Peter Ewend; William A. Hendrick; Richard Heuschele; Richard Katz.

Number of staff: 1 part-time professional; 1 part-time support.

EIN: 386061470

2049
Wickson-Link Memorial Foundation

3023 Davenport St.
P.O. Box 3275
Saginaw, MI   48605   (989) 793-9830
Contact: Lloyd J. Yeo, Pres.

Established in 1973 in MI.

Donors: James Wickson†; Meta Wickson†.

Grantmaker type: Independent foundation.

Financial data (yr. ended 12/31/05): Assets, $5,384,258 (M); expenditures, $339,802; total giving, $283,987; qualifying distributions, $303,648; giving activities include $283,987 for grants.

Purpose and activities: Support for community funds, social services and programs for the disadvantaged, youth and child welfare, cultural organizations, health, and education, including business and higher education, programs for minorities and early childhood education, and libraries.

Fields of interest: Arts; Education, early childhood education; Higher education; Business school/education; Libraries/library science; Health care; Health organizations, association; Human services; Children/youth, services; Federated giving programs; Minorities; Economically disadvantaged.

Type of support: General/operating support; Annual campaigns; Capital campaigns; Building/renovation; Equipment; Matching/challenge support.

Limitations: Giving primarily in Saginaw County, MI. No support for churches for building or operations. No grants to individuals.

Application information: Application form not required.

  Initial approach: Letter
  Copies of proposal: 7
  Deadline(s): None

Board meeting date(s): Quarterly
Final notification: 60 days

Officers: Lloyd J. Yeo, Pres. and Treas.; B.J. Humphreys, V.P. and Secy.

Directors: David Beyerlein; Louis Hanisho; John Humphreys; Charles Nichleso; Susan Piesko.

Number of staff: 1 part-time professional.

EIN: 386083931

Selected grants: The following grants were reported in 2004.

$25,000 to Mid-Michigan Childrens Museum, Saginaw, MI. For general support.

$11,000 to Boys and Girls Club of Saginaw County, Saginaw, MI. For general support.

$10,750 to Saginaw Art Museum, Saginaw, MI. For general support.

$10,000 to Saginaw Valley State University Foundation, University Center, MI. For general support.

$5,200 to HealthSource Saginaw, Saginaw, MI. For general support.

$3,500 to East Side Soup Kitchen, Saginaw, MI. For general support.

$3,000 to Junior Achievement of Northeast Michigan, Saginaw, MI. For general support.

$2,500 to Emmaus House of Saginaw, Saginaw, MI. For general support.

$1,250 to Saginaw Symphony Association, Saginaw, MI. For general support.

$500 to Hidden Harvest, Saginaw, MI. For general support.

2050
The Wieczorek Family Foundation

121 Belleview St.
Mount Clemens, MI   48043

Established in 2001 in MI.

Donor: Dale M. Wieczorek.

Grantmaker type: Independent foundation.

Financial data (yr. ended 12/31/05): Assets, $954,203 (M); expenditures, $114,919; total giving, $110,150; qualifying distributions, $110,889; giving activities include $110,150 for 13 grants (high: $25,000; low: $500).

Fields of interest: Education; Human services; Children/youth, services; Christian agencies & churches.

Limitations: Applications not accepted. Giving primarily in MI. No grants to individuals.

Application information: Contributes only to pre-selected organizations.

Officers: Dale M. Wieczorek, Chair.; Paulette Wieczorek, V.P.; Courtney Wieczorek, Secy.; Shannon Wieczorek, Treas.

EIN: 383625798

2051
The Wierenga Family Foundation, Inc.

P.O. Box 3805
Rancho Santa Fe, CA   92067   (858) 756-2045
Contact: Wendell Wierenga, Pres.

Established in 2000 in MI.

Donor: Wendell Wierenga.

Grantmaker type: Independent foundation.

Financial data (yr. ended 12/31/05): Assets, $862,986 (M); gifts received, $208,899; expenditures, $58,396; total giving, $53,000; qualifying distributions, $53,000; giving activities include $53,000 for grants.

Fields of interest: Christian agencies & churches.

Limitations: Giving primarily in MI.

Application information:

  Initial approach: Letter
  Deadline(s): None

Officer: Wendell Wierenga, Pres.

Directors: Melissa Bok; Janelle Wierenga; Pamela Wierenga.

EIN: 943374775

2052
Earl & Irene Wiese Foundation

c/o Citizens Bank Wealth Mgmt., N.A.
328 S. Saginaw St., M/C 002072
Flint, MI   48502

Established in 2000 in WI.

Donor: Earl A. Wiese.

Grantmaker type: Independent foundation.

Financial data (yr. ended 12/31/05): Assets, $187,982 (M); expenditures, $7,084; total giving, $4,086; qualifying distributions, $4,086; giving activities include $4,086 for grants.

Fields of interest: Christian agencies & churches.

Type of support: General/operating support.

Limitations: Applications not accepted. No grants to individuals.

Application information: Contributes only to pre-selected organizations.

Trustee: Citizens Bank.

EIN: 396737448

2053
Wigginton Educational Foundation

c/o Fifth Third Bank
233 Washington Ave.
Grand Haven, MI   49417
Contact: Lisa Danicek, Treas.
Application address: 1415 S. Beachtree St., Grand Haven, MI 49417, tel.: (616) 842-6760

Donor: Ruth Wigginton†.

Grantmaker type: Independent foundation.

Financial data (yr. ended 12/31/05): Assets, $445,582 (M); expenditures, $18,863; total giving, $13,771; qualifying distributions, $13,771; giving activities include $13,771 for grants to individuals.

Purpose and activities: Awards scholarships only to residents of the city of Grand Haven, or the counties of Ottawa and Muskegon, Michigan.

Type of support: Grants to individuals; Scholarships—to individuals.

Limitations: Giving limited to residents of the City of Grand Haven and Muskegon and Ottawa counties, MI.

Application information: Application form required.

  Deadline(s): 5 days prior to board meeting
  Board meeting date(s): 1st Wed. in Feb., Apr., June, Sept., Oct., and Dec.

Officers: James Bonner, Pres.; Anne Runschke, V.P.; Sandy Huber, Secy.; Lisa Danicek, Treas.

Trustees: Steve Avram; Barbara Schmitt; Linda Welsh; Tracy Wilson.

EIN: 382388277

2054
Wilcox Family Foundation
6377 Cardeno Dr.
La Jolla, CA   92037
Application address: c/o Win Schrader, 6260 Tower
Rd., Plymouth, MI 48170, tel.: (734) 455-6222
Scholarship address: Win Schrader, c/o Plymouth
Salem High School, 45181 Joy Rd., Canton, MI
48187

Established in 2002 in MI.
Donor: Daniel Herriman.
Grantmaker type: Independent foundation.
Financial data (yr. ended 12/31/04): Assets,
$3,468,411 (M); gifts received, $1,250;
expenditures, $250,838; total giving, $122,025;
qualifying distributions, $228,956; giving activities
include $120,628 for 18 grants (high: $33,997;
low: $500), $1,397 for 1 grant to an individual, and
$42,600 for 1 foundation-administered program.
Purpose and activities: Scholarship awarded to high
school seniors residing in the Plymouth/Canton
school district; grants to 501(c)(3) organizations.
Fields of interest: Education; Human services.
Type of support: General/operating support;
Building/renovation; Program development;
Scholarships—to individuals.
Limitations: Giving primarily in Plymouth, MI.
Application information: Scholarship applicants
must submit an essay or research paper based on
the history of one or more of Plymouth, Michigan's
longtime businesses or business districts.
Application form required.
  Initial approach: Completed application form for
    grants; completed application for scholarships
  Deadline(s): Apr. 1 and Oct. 1 for grants; Mar. 22
    for scholarships
Officers: Scott Dodge, Pres. and Treas.; Win
Schrader, V.P. and Secy.; John Gaffield, V.P.
EIN: 311804402

2055
J. Ernest and Almena Gray Wilde Foundation
500 Woodward Ave., Ste. 3500
Detroit, MI   48226   (313) 965-8288
Contact: David E. Nims, V.P.

Established in 1998 in MI.
Donor: J. Ernest Wilde.
Grantmaker type: Independent foundation.
Financial data (yr. ended 12/31/05): Assets,
$1,611,815 (M); gifts received, $1,729,136;
expenditures, $62,654; total giving, $50,000;
qualifying distributions, $50,000; giving activities
include $50,000 for grants.
Purpose and activities: Giving primarily for the
United Way and some giving to children's homes.
Fields of interest: Arts; Human services; Children/
youth, services; Residential/custodial care;
Federated giving programs; Protestant agencies &
churches.
Limitations: Applications not accepted. Giving
limited to southeastern MI.
Application information: Contributes only to
pre-selected organizations.
Officers: J. Ernest Wilde, Pres.; David E. Nims, V.P.
and Secy.; Leonard W. Smith, V.P. and Treas.
EIN: 383427843

2056
The Bill & Sally Wildner Foundation
1842 Lyster Ct.
Troy, MI   48085

Established in 2000 in MI.
Donor: William R. Wildner.
Grantmaker type: Independent foundation.
Financial data (yr. ended 12/31/04): Assets,
$244,814 (M); expenditures, $11,580; total giving,
$9,600; qualifying distributions, $9,600; giving
activities include $9,600 for grants.
Limitations: Applications not accepted. Giving
primarily in MI. No grants to individuals.
Application information: Contributes only to
pre-selected organizations.
Officers: William R. Wildner, Pres.; Sally Wildner,
Secy.; L.M. Jager, Treas.
Director: Jillian Cavellier.
EIN: 383513719

2057
Lawrence Scripps Wilkinson Foundation
25821 Jefferson Ave.
St. Clair Shores, MI   48081-2316

Established in 1997 in MI.
Grantmaker type: Independent foundation.
Financial data (yr. ended 12/31/04): Assets,
$539,645 (M); expenditures, $116,480; total
giving, $8,585; qualifying distributions, $40,850;
giving activities include $8,585 for grants.
Fields of interest: Museums; Performing arts;
Historical activities; Health care; Transportation.
Limitations: Applications not accepted. Giving on a
national basis, with some emphasis on MI and the
eastern states. No grants to individuals.
Application information: Contributes only to
pre-selected organizations.
Directors: Richard J. Godfrey; William A. Sankbeil;
Elizabeth Stark; Malcolm J. Sutherland; Lawrence S.
Wilkinson; Lawrence S. Wilkinson, Jr.; Suzanne H.
Wilkinson.
EIN: 382314365

2058
Ronald A. & Patricia M. Williams Charitable Foundation
1535 44th St. S.W., Ste. 400
Wyoming, MI   49509-4481
Contact: Ronald A. Williams, Pres.

Established in 1997 in MI.
Donor: Ronald A. Williams.
Grantmaker type: Independent foundation.
Financial data (yr. ended 12/31/05): Assets,
$1,061,242 (M); expenditures, $86,258; total
giving, $77,175; qualifying distributions, $77,175;
giving activities include $77,175 for grants.
Purpose and activities: Giving primarily for Catholic
institutions.
Fields of interest: Children, services; Roman
Catholic agencies & churches.
Limitations: Giving primarily in MI.
Application information:
  Initial approach: Proposal
  Deadline(s): None
Officers: Ronald A. Williams, Pres.; Patricia M.
Williams, Secy.-Treas.
EIN: 383382931

2059
Lillian J. Williams Charitable Trust
c/o Mellon Bank, N.A.
P.O. Box 185
Pittsburgh, PA   15230-9897

Established in 2001 in PA.
Donor: L.J. Williams.
Grantmaker type: Independent foundation.
Financial data (yr. ended 12/31/05): Assets,
$542,206 (M); expenditures, $33,818; total giving,
$26,855; qualifying distributions, $26,855; giving
activities include $26,855 for grants.
Fields of interest: Higher education, university.
Type of support: General/operating support.
Limitations: Applications not accepted. Giving
primarily in MI. No grants to individuals.
Application information: Contributes only to
pre-selected organizations.
Trustee: Mellon Bank, N.A.
EIN: 256595045

2060
Sam Williams Foundation
c/o Spieth, Bell, McCurdy & Nowell Co.
925 Euclid Ave., Ste. 2000
Cleveland, OH   44115-1496

Established in 1997 in MI.
Donors: Sam B. Williams; The Williams Family
Foundation.
Grantmaker type: Independent foundation.
Financial data (yr. ended 12/31/04): Assets,
$708,654 (M); expenditures, $134,539; total
giving, $120,000; qualifying distributions,
$120,000; giving activities include $120,000 for 1
grant.
Fields of interest: Medical research, institute.
Limitations: Applications not accepted. Giving on a
national basis, with emphasis on Detroit, MI, and
Louisville, KY. No grants to individuals.
Application information: Contributes only to
pre-selected organizations.
Trustee: Sam B. Williams.
EIN: 316565449

2061
The Jamison Williams Foundation
380 N. Old Woodward Ave., Ste. 300
Birmingham, MI   48009   (248) 642-0333
Contact: R. Jamison Williams, Jr., Pres.

Established in 1988 in MI.
Donors: R. Jamison Williams; Betty J. Williams.
Grantmaker type: Independent foundation.
Financial data (yr. ended 12/31/05): Assets,
$5,953,723 (M); expenditures, $373,572; total
giving, $294,000; qualifying distributions,
$294,000; giving activities include $294,000 for 11
grants (high: $125,000; low: $1,000).
Purpose and activities: Giving primarily for the arts.
Fields of interest: Museums; Performing arts;
Performing arts, orchestra (symphony); Arts;
Education.
Type of support: General/operating support.
Limitations: Giving primarily in the metropolitan
Detroit, MI, area. No grants to individuals.
Application information:
  Initial approach: Proposal
  Deadline(s): None
  Final notification: Within 2 months

Officer and Directors: * R. Jamison Williams, Jr.,* Pres.; Wendy J. Lynch.
EIN: 382837463
Selected grants: The following grants were reported in 2004.
$80,000 to Detroit Symphony Orchestra, Detroit, MI. For general support.
$25,000 to Henry Ford Health System, Henry Ford Heart and Vascular Institute, Detroit, MI. For general support.
$20,000 to Junior League of Birmingham, Birmingham, MI. For general support.
$10,000 to Child Abuse and Neglect Council of Oakland County, Pontiac, MI. For general support.
$10,000 to Cranbrook Academy of Art, Bloomfield Hills, MI. For general support.
$8,500 to American Academy in Rome, New York, NY. For general support.
$8,500 to Architectural League of New York, New York, NY. For general support.
$7,000 to Public Art Fund, New York, NY. For general support.
$5,000 to American Folk Art Museum, New York, NY. For general support.
$5,000 to Michigan State University, East Lansing, MI. For general support.

2062
Lewis E. Williams Trust
c/o Comerica Bank
P.O. Box 75000, MC 8280
Detroit, MI 48275

Established in 2000 in MI.
Grantmaker type: Independent foundation.
Financial data (yr. ended 12/31/05): Assets, $137,614 (M); expenditures, $12,953; total giving, $10,409; qualifying distributions, $10,409; giving activities include $10,409 for grants.
Purpose and activities: Support only for the Michigan Department of Public Health, Detroit.
Fields of interest: Public health.
Type of support: General/operating support.
Limitations: Applications not accepted. Giving limited to Detroit, MI. No grants to individuals.
Application information: Contributes only to a pre-selected organization.
Trustee: Comerica Bank.
EIN: 386043678

2063
Elizabeth Ruthruff Wilson Foundation
301 N. Union St.
Tecumseh, MI 49286
Application address: c/o Theresa Powers, P.O. Box 27, Tecumseh, MI 49286, tel.: (517) 423-4148

Established in 1997 in MI.
Donor: Mary Elizabeth Wilson†.
Grantmaker type: Independent foundation.
Financial data (yr. ended 12/31/04): Assets, $3,792,825 (M); gifts received, $3,100; expenditures, $242,427; total giving, $169,216; qualifying distributions, $194,209; giving activities include $169,216 for 28 grants (high: $31,920; low: $40).
Fields of interest: Performing arts; Performing arts, music.
Officers: Theresa Powers, Pres.; Marilyn Mason, V.P.; John Waltman, Secy.

Number of staff: 1 part-time support.
EIN: 383372941

2064
Ralph C. Wilson Foundation
99 Kercheval Ave.
Grosse Pointe Farms, MI 48236-3618

Established around 1954.
Donor: Ralph C. Wilson, Jr.
Grantmaker type: Independent foundation.
Financial data (yr. ended 10/31/05): Assets, $2,811,192 (M); gifts received, $50,000; expenditures, $970,963; total giving, $902,045; qualifying distributions, $970,963; giving activities include $902,045 for 48 grants (high: $200,000; low: $50).
Purpose and activities: Giving primarily for education, health associations, social services, and federated giving programs.
Fields of interest: Higher education; Law school/education; Education; Health organizations; Food banks; Human services; Children/youth, services; Residential/custodial care, hospices; Federated giving programs; Christian agencies & churches.
Type of support: General/operating support.
Limitations: Applications not accepted. Giving on a national basis, with emphasis on MI, NY, and OH. No grants to individuals.
Application information: Contributes only to pre-selected organizations.
Officers and Trustees: * Ralph C. Wilson, Jr.,* Pres.; Mary M. Owen, Secy.; Jeffrey C. Littmann,* Treas.; Eugene Driker; Mary M. Wilson.
EIN: 386091638

2065
Matilda R. Wilson Fund
1901 Saint Antoine St., 6th Fl.
Detroit, MI 48226 (313) 392-1040
Contact: David P. Larsen, Secy.
FAX: (313) 393-7579;
E-mail: roosterveen@bodmanllp.com

Incorporated in 1944 in MI.
Donors: Matilda R. Wilson†; Alfred G. Wilson†.
Grantmaker type: Independent foundation.
Financial data (yr. ended 12/31/04): Assets, $42,694,094 (M); expenditures, $2,497,823; total giving, $2,057,700; qualifying distributions, $2,210,375; giving activities include $2,057,700 for 36 grants (high: $500,000; low: $1,000; average: $10,000–$100,000).
Purpose and activities: Support for the arts, youth agencies, higher education, and social services.
Fields of interest: Arts; Higher education; Hospitals (general); Human services; Youth, services.
Type of support: General/operating support; Building/renovation; Equipment; Endowments; Program development; Scholarship funds; Research; Matching/challenge support.
Limitations: Giving primarily in southeast MI. No grants to individuals; no loans.
Application information: Application form not required.
Initial approach: Letter
Copies of proposal: 1
Deadline(s): None
Board meeting date(s): Apr., Aug., and Dec.

Officers and Trustees: * David M. Hempstead,* Pres.; David P. Larsen,* Secy.; David B. Stephens,* Treas.
EIN: 386087665
Selected grants: The following grants were reported in 2003.
$900,000 to Michigan State University, East Lansing, MI. 2 grants: $400,000 (For capital support), $500,000 (For capital support).
$350,000 to Detroit Symphony Orchestra, Detroit, MI. 2 grants: $250,000 to Detroit Symphony Orchestra Hall (For capital support), $100,000 (For operating support).
$200,000 to College for Creative Studies, Detroit, MI. 2 grants: $100,000 (For operating support), $100,000 (For capital support).
$150,000 to Oakland University, Rochester, MI. For capital and operating support.
$125,000 to Edison Institute, Dearborn, MI. For capital support.
$100,000 to New Detroit Science Center, Detroit, MI. For capital support.
$100,000 to Stratford Shakespearean Festival, Ontario, Canada. For capital support.

2066
Wilson Scholarship Fund
(formerly Rodney B. Wilson Scholarship Fund)
c/o Citizens Bank Wealth Management, N.A.
328 S. Saginaw St., M/C 002072
Flint, MI 48502
Application address: c/o St. John's Public High School, Attn.: Janet Thelen, P.O. Box 230, St. Johns, MI 48879

Established in 2004 in MI.
Donor: Rodney B. Wilson.
Grantmaker type: Independent foundation.
Financial data (yr. ended 12/31/05): Assets, $468,850 (M); expenditures, $16,221; total giving, $10,000; qualifying distributions, $13,077; giving activities include $10,000 for 10 grants to individuals (high: $1,000; low: $1,000).
Purpose and activities: Scholarship awards to graduating seniors at St. John's Public High School, MI, who are in the upper one-third of their class.
Fields of interest: Higher education.
Type of support: Scholarships—to individuals.
Limitations: Giving limited to St. John's, MI.
Application information: Application form required.
Deadline(s): Apr. 1 and Aug. 1
Trustee: Citizens Bank, N.A.
EIN: 386619088

2067
Lula C. Wilson Trust
c/o JPMorgan Chase Bank, N.A.
611 Woodward Ave., Ste. MI 1-8113
Detroit, MI 48226-3408 (313) 225-2549
Contact: Harry L. Hunter, Asst. V.P.
FAX: (313) 225-3948; E-mail:
harry_hunter@bankone.com

Trust established in 1963 in MI.
Donor: Lula C. Wilson†.
Grantmaker type: Independent foundation.
Financial data (yr. ended 12/31/05): Assets, $2,880,458 (M); expenditures, $158,951; total giving, $139,500; qualifying distributions, $144,507; giving activities include $139,500 for 23 grants (high: $10,000; low: $2,000).

Purpose and activities: Support primarily for community development; support also for family and social services, youth and child welfare, women, the handicapped, hospices, performing arts groups and other cultural programs, and higher and secondary education.
Fields of interest: Performing arts; Performing arts, theater; Arts; Child development, education; Secondary school/education; Higher education; Reproductive health, family planning; Substance abuse, services; Human services; Children/youth, services; Child development, services; Family services; Residential/custodial care, hospices; Women, centers/services; Community development; Disabilities, people with; Women; Economically disadvantaged.
Type of support: General/operating support; Continuing support; Annual campaigns; Capital campaigns; Building/renovation; Equipment; Emergency funds; Seed money; Program-related investments/loans; Matching/challenge support.
Limitations: Giving limited to Pontiac and Oakland County, MI. No grants to individuals, or for endowment funds, research, deficit financing, land acquisition, special projects, publications, conferences, scholarships, or fellowships.
Application information: Application form not required.
Initial approach: Letter
Copies of proposal: 1
Deadline(s): None
Board meeting date(s): As required
Final notification: 1 month
Trustee: JPMorgan Chase Bank, N.A.
EIN: 386058895

2068
The Ralph C. Wilson, Sr. and Ralph C. Wilson, Jr. Medical Research Foundation
c/o Jeffrey C. Littman
15400 E. Jefferson Ave.
Grosse Pointe Park, MI 48230-1329

Established in 2000 in MI.
Donor: Ralph C. Wilson, Jr.
Grantmaker type: Independent foundation.
Financial data (yr. ended 6/30/05): Assets, $1,301,400 (M); gifts received, $8,000; expenditures, $1,217,023; total giving, $1,190,890; qualifying distributions, $1,190,890; giving activities include $1,190,890 for grants.
Purpose and activities: Support only to the Miami Project, Florida, University of Michigan, Ann Arbor and Wayne State University, Detroit, Michigan, Mayo Foundation for Medical Education and Research, Rochester, Minnesota, Roswell Park Alliance Foundation Buffalo, New York, and Cleveland Clinic Foundation, Ohio.
Fields of interest: Medical research.
Type of support: General/operating support.
Limitations: Applications not accepted. Giving limited to Miami, FL, Ann Arbor and Detroit, MI, Rochester, MN, Buffalo, NY, and Cleveland, OH. No grants to individuals.
Application information: Contributes only to 6 pre-selected organizations.
Trustee: Jeffrey C. Littmann.
EIN: 383505430

2069
Mark and Carol Windemuller Charitable Foundation
2900 Rush Creek Dr. S.W.
Byron Center, MI 49315-9441
Contact: Mark Windemuller, Pres.

Established in 1998 in MI.
Donors: Mark Windemuller; Carol Windemuller.
Grantmaker type: Independent foundation.
Financial data (yr. ended 12/31/05): Assets, $1 (M); gifts received, $10; expenditures, $10; total giving, $0; qualifying distributions, $0.
Purpose and activities: Support for religious causes to assist meeting mission goals.
Fields of interest: Christian agencies & churches.
Limitations: Giving primarily in Bryon Center and Grand Rapids, MI.
Application information: Application form not required.
Initial approach: Letter
Deadline(s): None
Officers: Mark Windemuller, Pres. and Treas.; Carol Windemuller, Secy.
EIN: 383414824

2070
Isadore & Beryl Winkelman Foundation
2169 Colony Club Ct.
West Bloomfield, MI 48322-4344

Established in 1961.
Donor: Beryl Winkelman.
Grantmaker type: Independent foundation.
Financial data (yr. ended 12/31/05): Assets, $935,843 (M); expenditures, $53,937; total giving, $47,763; qualifying distributions, $47,763; giving activities include $47,763 for grants.
Purpose and activities: Giving primarily to education and Jewish agencies; support also for the arts, health, and human services.
Fields of interest: Arts; Higher education; Health care; Health organizations, association; Human services; Jewish agencies & temples; General charitable giving.
Type of support: General/operating support.
Limitations: Applications not accepted. Giving primarily in Detroit, Southfield, and West Bloomfield, MI. No grants to individuals.
Application information: Contributes only to pre-selected organizations.
Officers and Trustees:* Beryl Winkelman,* Pres.; Jan Z. Winkelman,* V.P.; Ned Z. Winkelman,* Treas.; Harriet Winkelman.
EIN: 386068511

2071
The Edith and Leslie Winkler Family Foundation
17515 W. Nine Mile Rd., Ste. 550
Southfield, MI 48075

Established in 1997 in MI.
Donor: Leslie Winkler.
Grantmaker type: Independent foundation.
Financial data (yr. ended 12/31/05): Assets, $105,647 (M); expenditures, $4,355; total giving, $4,355; qualifying distributions, $4,355; giving activities include $4,355 for grants.
Fields of interest: Jewish agencies & temples.
Type of support: General/operating support.

Limitations: Applications not accepted. Giving primarily in MI. No grants to individuals.
Application information: Contributes only to pre-selected organizations.
Trustees: Leslie Winkler; Richard Winkler.
EIN: 386628188

2072
Winkler Foundation
1700 Prestwick Rd.
Detroit, MI 48236-1992

Established in 1986 in MI.
Donors: Irving T. Winkler; Lois N. Winkler.
Grantmaker type: Independent foundation.
Financial data (yr. ended 11/30/03): Assets, $81,904 (M); expenditures, $2,413; total giving, $1,225; qualifying distributions, $2,345; giving activities include $1,225 for 3 grants.
Limitations: Applications not accepted. Giving primarily in Grosse Pointe, MI. No grants to individuals.
Application information: Contributes only to pre-selected organizations.
Officers and Directors:* Irving T. Winkler, Jr.,* Pres.; Lois N. Winkler,* V.P.
EIN: 382408198

2073
John J. Winkler Memorial Trust
c/o University of Michigan, English Dept.
3187 Angell Hall, 435 S. State St.
Ann Arbor, MI 48109-1003

Established in 1990 in CA.
Grantmaker type: Independent foundation.
Financial data (yr. ended 5/31/05): Assets, $30,413 (M); gifts received, $350; expenditures, $1,850; total giving, $1,500; qualifying distributions, $1,500; giving activities include $1,500 for grants.
Purpose and activities: Winkler Prize awarded to students in the classics.
Type of support: Grants to individuals.
Application information:
Initial approach: Essay on neglected or marginal topics in classical studies
Deadline(s): Apr. 1
Trustees: David A. Braaten; Lesley Dean-Jones; David M. Halperin; Kirk Ormand; Daniel L. Selden; Froma I. Zeitlin.
EIN: 776062330

2074
Bill and June Winn Foundation
9450 Cottage Pointe Dr.
Charlevoix, MI 49720
Contact: William H. Winn, Sr., Pres.
Application Address: P.O. Box 4219, Traverse City, MI 49685-4219

Established in 1988 in MI.
Donors: William H. Winn, Sr.; June C. Winn.
Grantmaker type: Independent foundation.
Financial data (yr. ended 12/31/04): Assets, $93,206 (M); gifts received, $6,250; expenditures, $34,497; total giving, $34,250; qualifying distributions, $34,250; giving activities include $34,250 for grants.

Fields of interest: Arts; Higher education; Human services.
Type of support: General/operating support.
Limitations: Giving on a national basis. No grants to individuals.
Application information: Application form not required.
 Initial approach: Letter
 Deadline(s): None
Officers: William H. Winn, Sr., Pres.; June C. Winn, Secy.-Treas.
EIN: 382786283

2075
John and Zita Winn Foundation
(formerly John and Mary Jo Winn Foundation)
125 Belvedere Ave.
Charlevoix, MI 49720
Contact: John A. Winn, Pres.

Established in 1988 in MI.
Donors: John A. Winn; Mary Jo Winn.
Grantmaker type: Independent foundation.
Financial data (yr. ended 12/31/04): Assets, $20,501 (M); expenditures, $11,001; total giving, $11,000; qualifying distributions, $11,000; giving activities include $11,000 for grants.
Fields of interest: Human services.
Limitations: Giving primarily in Charlevoix, MI.
Application information: Application form not required.
 Initial approach: Letter
 Deadline(s): None
Officer: John A. Winn, Pres. and Secy.-Treas.
Trustee: Dorenda R. Buisch.
EIN: 382792625

2076
Winship Memorial Scholarship Foundation
c/o Comerica Bank, Trust Div.
49 W. Michigan Ave.
Battle Creek, MI 49017-3603 (269) 966-6340
Contact: Lori A. Hill, Secy.

Established in 1961 in MI.
Donor: Virginia Winship‡.
Grantmaker type: Independent foundation.
Financial data (yr. ended 12/31/05): Assets, $3,653,930 (M); expenditures, $247,626; total giving, $183,650; qualifying distributions, $209,412; giving activities include $183,650 for 96 grants to individuals (high: $2,950; low: $1,000).
Purpose and activities: Scholarships only for graduates of Battle Creek, MI, area public high schools.
Type of support: Grants to individuals; Scholarships—to individuals.
Limitations: Giving limited to residents of the Battle Creek, MI, area.
Publications: Application guidelines; Annual report; Informational brochure.
Application information: Applications distributed and processed through the guidance counselors' offices of Battle Creek, MI, area, public high schools only. Application form required.
 Copies of proposal: 1
 Deadline(s): Nov. 15th
 Board meeting date(s): 3rd Wed. in Apr.
Officers and Trustees:* John Stetler,* Pres.; David P. Lucas,* V.P.; Lori A. Hill, Secy.; James Keating,* Treas.; Marcia A. Owen, Exec. Dir.; Charles

Coleman; Mike Cope; Donna Gray; Cindy Ruble; Bruce Shurtz; William S. Ticknor; Charles D. Walker; Chris Wigent.
Corporate Trustee: Comerica Bank.
EIN: 386092543

2077
Evelyn and Ronald Wirick Foundation
504 Maple Dr.
Morenci, MI 49256-1222 (517) 458-7189
Contact: Ralph R. Ferris, Pres.

Established in 1987 in MI.
Grantmaker type: Independent foundation.
Financial data (yr. ended 12/31/05): Assets, $1,190,192 (M); expenditures, $31,843; total giving, $13,200; qualifying distributions, $13,200; giving activities include $13,200 for grants to individuals.
Purpose and activities: Scholarships only to the graduates of the Morenci Public School District, MI.
Type of support: Scholarships—to individuals.
Limitations: Giving limited to residents of Morenci, MI.
Application information:
 Initial approach: Letter
 Deadline(s): None
Officers: Ralph R. Ferris, Pres.; Judy J. Randall, Secy.; Mary E. Ferris, Treas.
Trustees: Russell Beaverson; Roger Porter; Dale Storrer.
EIN: 382700421

2078
The Wirt Family Foundation
2301 Gysin Ct.
Bay City, MI 48708

Established in 1998 in WI.
Grantmaker type: Independent foundation.
Financial data (yr. ended 9/30/04): Assets, $1,397,774 (M); expenditures, $54,134; total giving, $51,783; qualifying distributions, $51,783; giving activities include $51,783 for grants (high: $10,000).
Purpose and activities: Giving primarily for education, human services, a women's center, Jewish giving, and the United Way.
Fields of interest: Higher education; Human services; Jewish federated giving programs; Jewish agencies & temples; Women.
Type of support: General/operating support; Building/renovation; Scholarship funds.
Limitations: Applications not accepted. Giving primarily in Bay City, MI. No grants to individuals.
Application information: Contributes only to pre-selected organizations.
Officer: Jack Wirt, Pres.
EIN: 383428534

2079
John W. and Wanda A. Wirtz Charitable Foundation
c/o John W. Wirtz
P.O. Box 610037
Port Huron, MI 48061

Established in 2001 in MI.
Donors: John W. Wirtz; Wanda A. Wirtz.
Grantmaker type: Independent foundation.

Financial data (yr. ended 12/31/04): Assets, $81,494 (M); gifts received, $20,036; expenditures, $27,861; total giving, $27,050; qualifying distributions, $27,050; giving activities include $27,050 for grants.
Fields of interest: YM/YWCAs & YM/YWHAs.
Type of support: General/operating support.
Application information: Application form not required.
 Initial approach: Letter
 Deadline(s): None
Trustees: John W. Wirtz; Wanda A. Wirtz.
EIN: 383640193

2080
Wirtz Family Foundation
1105 24th St.
P.O. Box 5006
Port Huron, MI 48061-5006

Established in 2000 in MI.
Grantmaker type: Independent foundation.
Financial data (yr. ended 12/31/04): Assets, $46,517 (M); gifts received, $928; expenditures, $485; total giving, $100; qualifying distributions, $100; giving activities include $100 for grants.
Application information: Application form not required.
 Initial approach: Letter
 Deadline(s): None
Trustee: John O. Wirtz.
EIN: 383572595

2081
Wise Fund
2026 Devonshire Rd.
Ann Arbor, MI 48104-4058

Donor: Manfred Kochen‡.
Grantmaker type: Independent foundation.
Financial data (yr. ended 12/31/04): Assets, $514 (M); expenditures, $81; total giving, $50; qualifying distributions, $81; giving activities include $50 for grants.
Officer: Paula Kochen, Pres.
EIN: 382441115

2082
Wisne Charitable Foundation
27145 Sheraton Dr.
Novi, MI 48377

Established in 1997 in MI.
Donor: Anthony E. Wisne.
Grantmaker type: Independent foundation.
Financial data (yr. ended 12/31/04): Assets, $936,968 (M); expenditures, $76,585; total giving, $71,500; qualifying distributions, $72,243; giving activities include $71,500 for 8 grants (high: $15,000; low: $2,500).
Fields of interest: Education; Health care, organ/tissue banks; Health organizations; Children/youth, services.
Limitations: Applications not accepted. Giving primarily in New York, NY; with some emphasis in MI. No grants to individuals.
Application information: Contributes only to pre-selected organizations.

Officers: Lawrence A. Wisne, Pres.; Alan L. Wisne, V.P.; Toni Wisne Young, V.P.; Joseph L. Wisne, Secy.-Treas.
EIN: 383269446

2083
WMY Fund
(formerly William R. & Madeleine Couzens Yaw Foundation)
c/o Miller, Canfield, Paddock & Stone
150 W. Jefferson Ave., Ste. 2500
Detroit, MI 48226-4415 (313) 963-6420
Contact: Stevan Uzelac

Established in 1987 in MI.
Donor: William Rumer Yaw†.
Grantmaker type: Independent foundation.
Financial data (yr. ended 12/31/05): Assets, $974,364 (M); expenditures, $85,127; total giving, $77,000; qualifying distributions, $77,000; giving activities include $77,000 for grants.
Purpose and activities: Giving for religion, education, and for children's services.
Fields of interest: Arts; Higher education; Health organizations, association; Human services; Children/youth, services; Christian agencies & churches.
Type of support: General/operating support.
Limitations: Giving primarily in MI and VA. No grants to individuals.
Application information:
   Initial approach: Letter
   Deadline(s): None
Officers: Margot Y. Burgwyn, Pres.; Madeleine Yaw Kirk, V.P.; James J. Yaw, V.P.; William Rumer Yaw, Jr., Secy.-Treas.
EIN: 382364686

2084
Henry W. Wohlgemuth Trust
c/o Citizens Bank Wealth Mgmt., N.A.
328 S. Saginaw St., M/C 002072
Flint, MI 48502

Established in MI.
Grantmaker type: Independent foundation.
Financial data (yr. ended 12/31/05): Assets, $93,420 (M); expenditures, $6,744; total giving, $4,332; qualifying distributions, $6,563; giving activities include $4,332 for 3 grants (high: $1,444; low: $1,444).
Limitations: Applications not accepted. Giving primarily in Jackson, MI. No grants to individuals.
Application information: Contributes only to pre-selected organizations.
Trustee: Citizens Bank, N.A.
EIN: 386310303

2085
Wolfe Family Foundation
(formerly Howard H. & Joan M. Wolfe Family Foundation)
909 Willow St.
Ann Arbor, MI 48103-3741
Contact: Howard H. Wolfe, Pres.

Established in 1984 in MI.
Donor: Howard H. Wolfe.
Grantmaker type: Independent foundation.

Financial data (yr. ended 4/30/05): Assets, $341,533 (M); expenditures, $12,292; total giving, $11,500; qualifying distributions, $11,500; giving activities include $11,500 for grants.
Fields of interest: Higher education, college; Protestant agencies & churches.
Limitations: Giving on a national basis. No grants to individuals.
Application information:
   Initial approach: Letter
   Deadline(s): None
Officers and Directors:* Howard H. Wolfe,* Pres.; C. Christopher Wolfe,* V.P.; Ann H. Doerfler; Victoria R. Mueller.
EIN: 382532527

2086
The Andrea L. and Lawrence A. Wolfe Family Foundation
8655 E. Eight Mile Rd.
Warren, MI 48089

Established in 1997 in MI.
Donors: Lawrence A. Wolfe; Andrea L. Wolfe.
Grantmaker type: Independent foundation.
Financial data (yr. ended 12/31/05): Assets, $76,360 (M); gifts received, $7,524; expenditures, $3,033; total giving, $1,050; qualifying distributions, $1,050; giving activities include $1,050 for grants.
Fields of interest: Arts; Civil rights, advocacy; Jewish agencies & temples.
Type of support: General/operating support.
Limitations: Applications not accepted. Giving primarily in MI and NY. No grants to individuals.
Application information: Contributes only to pre-selected organizations.
Officers and Trustees:* Andrea L. Wolfe,* Pres.; Lawrence A. Wolfe,* Secy.; Arthur A. Weiss.
EIN: 383323521

2087
Jean & Lewis Wolff Family Foundation
c/o Comerica Bank
P.O. Box 75000, MC 3302
Detroit, MI 48275-3302
Application address: c/o Keith Wolff, 11828 La Grange Ave., Ste. 200, Los Angeles, CA 90025-5200

Established in 1998 in CA.
Donors: Jean Wolff; Lewis Wolff.
Grantmaker type: Independent foundation.
Financial data (yr. ended 5/31/05): Assets, $2,032,381 (M); expenditures, $114,840; total giving, $100,305; qualifying distributions, $101,479; giving activities include $100,305 for grants.
Purpose and activities: Support primarily for museums.
Fields of interest: Museums (art); Education; Reproductive health, family planning; Health organizations, association; Human services; Children/youth, services; Jewish agencies & temples.
Limitations: Giving primarily in CA. No grants to individuals.
Application information: Application form not required.
   Initial approach: Letter
   Deadline(s): None

Officers: Lewis Wolff, Pres.; Jean Wolff, V.P.; Kevin Wolff, V.P.; Kari Wolff Goldstein, Secy.; Keith Wolff, C.F.O. and Treas.
EIN: 954679221

2088
The Drew and Colleen Wolford Foundation
46959 Elmsmere Dr.
Northville, MI 48167-3302

Established in 2003 in MI.
Donor: Paul H. Johnson.
Grantmaker type: Independent foundation.
Financial data (yr. ended 12/31/04): Assets, $825,611 (M); expenditures, $49,442; total giving, $45,413; qualifying distributions, $45,413; giving activities include $45,413 for grants.
Limitations: Applications not accepted. No grants to individuals.
Application information: Contributes only to pre-selected organizations.
Officers: Colleen M. Wolford, Pres.; Paul H. Johnson, V.P.; Drew M. Wolford, Secy.-Treas.
EIN: 200305451

2089
Wolohan Family Foundation
1705 Crosby Rd.
Wayzata, MN 55391

Established in 1986 in MI.
Donors: Richard V. Wolohan; Angela M. Wolohan; James L. Wolohan; Christine M. Wolohan.
Grantmaker type: Independent foundation.
Financial data (yr. ended 12/31/04): Assets, $15,281,028 (L); expenditures, $866,692; total giving, $647,250; qualifying distributions, $650,279; giving activities include $647,250 for 32 grants (high: $101,000; low: $100).
Purpose and activities: Giving primarily to Roman Catholic organizations for education and human services.
Fields of interest: Higher education; Residential/custodial care; International development; Foundations (community); Roman Catholic agencies & churches.
Limitations: Applications not accepted. Giving primarily in MI. No grants to individuals.
Application information: Contributes only to pre-selected organizations.
Officers: Christine M. Wolohan, Pres.; James L. Wolohan, V.P. and Treas.; Michael J. Wolohan, Secy.
Directors: Mary K. Ness; Richard P. Wolohan; Sharon L. Wolohan.
EIN: 382700797

2090
Kate & Richard Wolters Foundation
2260 Cascade Springs Dr. S.E.
Grand Rapids, MI 49546
Contact: Kate P. Wolters, Pres.

Established in 1997 in MI.
Donors: Kate Pew Wolters; Richard Wolters†.
Grantmaker type: Independent foundation.
Financial data (yr. ended 12/31/05): Assets, $9,394,424 (M); gifts received, $100,000; expenditures, $1,840,859; total giving, $1,762,500; qualifying distributions, $1,767,445;

giving activities include $1,762,500 for 42 grants (high: $270,000; low: $1,000).
Purpose and activities: Giving primarily for arts and culture, higher and other education, and human services.
Fields of interest: Museums (art); Performing arts, orchestra (symphony); Arts; Elementary/secondary education; Higher education; Human services; Children/youth, services; Christian agencies & churches.
Type of support: General/operating support; Capital campaigns; Program development.
Limitations: Giving primarily in Grand Rapids and Lansing, MI.
Application information:
  Initial approach: Letter
  Deadline(s): None
Officer and Trustee:* Kate Pew Wolters,* Pres. and Secy.-Treas.
EIN: 383384598

2091
Wolverine Foundation
c/o Daniel M. Helmholdt
5940 Tahoe Dr. S.E.
Grand Rapids, MI 49546-7121

Established in 1998 in MI.
Donors: Daniel M. Helmholdt; Edwin J. Timmer.
Grantmaker type: Independent foundation.
Financial data (yr. ended 12/31/04): Assets, $7,709 (M); gifts received, $1,010; expenditures, $13,510; total giving, $12,500; qualifying distributions, $13,015; giving activities include $12,500 for grants.
Fields of interest: Protestant agencies & churches.
Type of support: General/operating support.
Limitations: Applications not accepted. Giving primarily in Grand Rapids, MI. No grants to individuals.
Application information: Contributes only to pre-selected organizations.
Officers: Daniel M. Helmholdt, Pres.; David P. Breihof, Secy.; Edwin J. Timmer, Treas.
EIN: 383385447

2092
The Lawrence and Sylvia Wong Foundation
1501 Portage Ave.
Three Rivers, MI 49093
Contact: G. Philip Dietrich, Secy.
Application address: 834 King Hwy., Ste. 110, Kalamazoo, MI 49001, tel.: (269) 344-9236

Established in 1995 in MI.
Donors: Lawrence Wong; Sylvia Wong.
Grantmaker type: Independent foundation.
Financial data (yr. ended 12/31/05): Assets, $426,463 (M); expenditures, $27,875; total giving, $22,000; qualifying distributions, $22,000; giving activities include $22,000 for grants.
Purpose and activities: Giving to organizations which benefit southwestern Michigan children, including through the visual and performing arts; giving also for education about and the preservation of endangered species of plants and animals, medical research for the understanding of Sjogren's Syndrome and related diseases and their treatment, and the conservation of areas of significant biodiversity.

Fields of interest: Environment, natural resources; Animals/wildlife, endangered species; Health organizations; Youth development.
Limitations: Giving primarily in southwestern MI.
Application information: Application form not required.
  Deadline(s): June 1 and Sept. 30
Officers and Directors:* Lawrence Wong,* Pres.; Sylvia Wong,* V.P. and Treas.; G. Philip Dietrich, Secy.; Laura Bird; Michael Wong.
EIN: 383244488

2093
Wood Foundation, Inc.
c/o James F. Keenan
423 Sycamore St., Ste. 101
Niles, MI 49120

Established in 2003 in MI.
Donor: J. Edward French.
Grantmaker type: Independent foundation.
Financial data (yr. ended 12/31/05): Assets, $3,476,669 (M); expenditures, $187,242; total giving, $147,950; qualifying distributions, $166,922; giving activities include $147,950 for 7 grants (high: $45,300; low: $5,000).
Fields of interest: Education; Human services.
Limitations: Applications not accepted. No grants to individuals.
Application information: Contributes only to pre-selected organizations.
Officers: J. Edward French, Chair.; Jerry E. French, Pres.; James F. Keenan, V.P. and Secy.; Donald F. Walter, Treas.; Brian French, Mgr.
EIN: 331067481

2094
The Woodall Foundation
2525 Telegraph Rd., Ste. 102
Bloomfield Hills, MI 48302

Established in 1943 in MI.
Grantmaker type: Independent foundation.
Financial data (yr. ended 12/31/05): Assets, $370,023 (M); expenditures, $73,960; total giving, $50,000; qualifying distributions, $50,000; giving activities include $50,000 for grants.
Purpose and activities: Giving primarily for organizations which promote the understanding of Christian Science.
Fields of interest: Arts; Education; Animal welfare; Human services; Youth, services; Religion.
Type of support: General/operating support.
Limitations: Applications not accepted. Giving in the U.S., with emphasis on MI and VA. No grants to individuals.
Application information: Contributes only to pre-selected organizations.
Trustees: Harold C. McPike; Virginia W. McPike; Barbara J. Weaver.
EIN: 386070915
Selected grants: The following grants were reported in 2003.
$10,000 to Bluemont Concert Series, Leesburg, VA. For unrestricted support.
$9,000 to Principia Corporation, Saint Louis, MO. For unrestricted support.
$8,000 to Cheboygan Youth Council, Cheboygan, MI. For unrestricted support.
$7,000 to Community Memorial Hospital, Cheboygan, MI. For unrestricted support.

$6,000 to Humane Society, Cheboygan County, Cheboygan, MI. For unrestricted support.
$5,000 to Asher Student Foundation, Englewood, CO. For unrestricted support.
$5,000 to Womens Resource Center of Northern Michigan, Petoskey, MI. For unrestricted support.
$4,500 to Christian Science Society, Irvine, CA. For unrestricted support.
$4,000 to Leader Dogs for the Blind, Rochester, MI. For unrestricted support.
$3,500 to YMCA of Metropolitan Detroit, Detroit, MI. For unrestricted support.

2095
Woodworth Upjohn Foundation
c/o Parish Assocs.
244 N. Rose St., Ste. 100
Kalamazoo, MI 49007-3838

Established in 1986 in MI.
Donor: Nancy U. Woodworth.
Grantmaker type: Independent foundation.
Financial data (yr. ended 12/31/04): Assets, $20,582 (M); gifts received, $56,410; expenditures, $51,720; total giving, $48,000; qualifying distributions, $48,700; giving activities include $48,000 for grants.
Fields of interest: Education; Protestant agencies & churches.
Type of support: General/operating support.
Limitations: Giving primarily in FL, IL, and MI. No grants to individuals.
Application information:
  Initial approach: Letter
  Deadline(s): None
Officers and Trustees:* Thomas B. Woodworth,* Pres.; Nancy U. Woodworth,* Secy.-Treas.
EIN: 382708118

2096
Word Investments, Inc.
4079 Park East Ct. S.E., Ste. 102
Grand Rapids, MI 49546
Contact: Clare De Graaf, Pres.

Established in 1984 in MI.
Grantmaker type: Independent foundation.
Financial data (yr. ended 12/31/04): Assets, $9,719,624 (M); gifts received, $120,566; expenditures, $1,662,315; total giving, $315,777; qualifying distributions, $357,976; giving activities include $315,777 for 32 grants (high: $59,370; low: $292).
Purpose and activities: Emphasis on Christian missionary programs.
Fields of interest: Christian agencies & churches; Religion.
Limitations: Applications not accepted. Giving primarily in MI.
Application information: Funds fully committed through 2015. No new grants will be awarded.
Officers: Clare De Graaf, Pres. and Treas.; Susan De Graaf, Secy.
Number of staff: 1 full-time professional; 1 part-time professional.
EIN: 382470907
Selected grants: The following grants were reported in 2003.
$23,482 to Good Shepherd Orphanage and Schools Foundation, Grandville, MI.

$17,519 to Bethany Christian Services, Grand Rapids, MI.

$8,281 to Open Doors International, Santa Ana, CA.

$7,560 to Peace of the City Ministries, Buffalo, NY.

$5,000 to Church Planters Training International, Grand Rapids, MI.

$2,000 to LaGrave Avenue Christian Reformed Church, Grand Rapids, MI.

$2,000 to Young Life in Grand Rapids, Grand Rapids, MI.

$1,500 to Winning Cities for Jesus Christ, Grand Rapids, MI.

$750 to Morningstar Ministries International, Redondo Beach, CA.

$500 to Victory Campus Ministries, Torrance, CA.

2097
Word of Life Foundation
3510 Apache Ct.
Grandville, MI 49418

Established in 1994 in MI.
Donors: Steven Maas; Lisa Maas.
Grantmaker type: Independent foundation.
Financial data (yr. ended 12/31/05): Assets, $11,465 (M); gifts received, $29,727; expenditures, $20,442; total giving, $19,700; qualifying distributions, $19,700; giving activities include $19,700 for grants.
Fields of interest: Children, services; Christian agencies & churches.
Type of support: General/operating support.
Limitations: Applications not accepted. Giving primarily in Grandville, MI. No grants to individuals.
Application information: Contributes only to pre-selected organizations.
Officers: Steven Maas, Pres.; Lisa Maas, Secy.
EIN: 383167930

2098
The Workers Foundation
567 Purdy St.
Birmingham, MI 48009 (248) 642-0910
Contact: Edward F. Andrews, Jr., Pres.

Established in 1993 in MI.
Donor: General Motors Corp.
Grantmaker type: Independent foundation.
Financial data (yr. ended 12/31/05): Assets, $415,727 (M); expenditures, $18,216; total giving, $18,000; qualifying distributions, $18,000; giving activities include $18,000 for grants.
Fields of interest: Employment, services; Food services; Human services.
Limitations: Giving limited to MI.
Application information:
  Initial approach: Letter
  Deadline(s): None
  Final notification: Within 2 months
Officers: Edward F. Andrews, Jr., Pres. and Treas.; Robert C. Seger, V.P. and Secy.
EIN: 383112401

2099
World Heritage Foundation
2675 W. Jefferson Ave.
Trenton, MI 48183

Established in 1985 in MI.

Donors: Heinz C. Prechter†; Thomas Denomme; Heinz C. Prechter Charitable Lead Trust.
Grantmaker type: Independent foundation.
Financial data (yr. ended 12/31/04): Assets, $9,350,194 (M); gifts received, $1,498; expenditures, $717,350; total giving, $608,433; qualifying distributions, $655,615; giving activities include $608,433 for 33 grants (high: $333,333; low: $100).
Purpose and activities: Support primarily for a museum and for higher education.
Fields of interest: Museums; Arts; Higher education; Business school/education; Engineering school/education; Health care; Mental health, depression; Medical research; Human services; Economic development.
Type of support: Capital campaigns; General/operating support; Program development.
Limitations: Giving primarily in MI; some giving also in Washington, DC. No grants to individuals.
Publications: Informational brochure (including application guidelines).
Application information: Application form required.
  Initial approach: Letter
  Deadline(s): None
Officers: Mrs. Waltraud Prechter, Pres.; Lori Koenig, V.P. and Secy.-Treas.; Paul Prechter, V.P.; Stephanie Prechter, V.P.
EIN: 382640416
Selected grants: The following grants were reported in 2003.
$1,640,514 to Heinz C. Prechter Bipolar Research Fund, Southgate, MI.
$333,333 to Edison Institute, Dearborn, MI.
$50,000 to Detroit Symphony Orchestra, Detroit, MI.
$50,000 to University of Michigan, Department of Engineering, Dearborn, MI.
$25,000 to Michigan Opera Theater, Detroit, MI.
$10,000 to Center for Creative Studies: Institute of Music and Dance, Detroit, MI.
$10,000 to Michigan State University, East Lansing, MI.
$3,000 to Downriver Council for the Arts, Taylor, MI.
$2,000 to Wayne State University, Detroit, MI.
$100 to Hutzel Hospital, Detroit, MI.

2100
World Parish Foundation
c/o Eric A. Law
1864 Ellwood Ave.
Berkley, MI 48072-1091

Donors: Eric A. Law; Candace G. Law.
Grantmaker type: Independent foundation.
Financial data (yr. ended 12/31/05): Assets, $12,470 (M); gifts received, $5,642; expenditures, $30,213; total giving, $0; qualifying distributions, $0.
Limitations: Applications not accepted. No grants to individuals.
Application information: Contributes only to pre-selected organizations.
Officers: Eric A. Law, Pres.; Candace G. Law, V.P. and Secy.-Treas.
Directors: William K. Quick; Bruce E. Stanley.
EIN: 383504325

2101
Worthington Foods Foundation
430 E. Granville Rd.
Worthington, OH 43085 (614) 885-4426
Contact: Allan R. Buller, Tr.

Donors: Allan R. Buller; George T. Harding IV; Worthington Foods, Inc.
Grantmaker type: Independent foundation.
Financial data (yr. ended 6/30/05): Assets, $954,620 (M); gifts received, $9,000; expenditures, $49,117; total giving, $5,000; qualifying distributions, $5,000; giving activities include $5,000 for grants.
Purpose and activities: Grants limited to local community projects or to research and education in the fields of health and nutrition.
Fields of interest: Higher education; Scholarships/financial aid; Protestant agencies & churches.
Type of support: General/operating support; Scholarship funds.
Limitations: Giving primarily in Loma Linda, CA, Berrien Springs, MI, and Columbus, OH.
Application information:
  Initial approach: Letter
  Deadline(s): None
Trustees: Allan R. Buller; George T. Harding IV; Dale E. Twomley.
EIN: 311286538

2102
Esther Wright Trust
c/o Citizens Bank, Wealth Mgmt.
100 E. Michigan Ave.
Jackson, MI 49201

Established in MI.
Donor: Esther Wright†.
Grantmaker type: Independent foundation.
Financial data (yr. ended 3/31/05): Assets, $116,898 (M); expenditures, $5,891; total giving, $3,199; qualifying distributions, $3,199; giving activities include $3,199 for grants.
Purpose and activities: Support only for Parkinson's Disease Foundation, NY.
Fields of interest: Parkinson's disease research.
Type of support: General/operating support.
Limitations: Applications not accepted. Giving limited to New York, NY. No grants to individuals.
Application information: Contributes only to a pre-selected organization.
Trustee: Citizens Bank.
EIN: 386349418

2103
V. Ennis Wright Trust
c/o Citizens Bank, Wealth Mgmt.
328 Saginaw St., MC 002072
Flint, MI 48502
Contact: Richard D. Fauble
Application address: c/o Litchfield Community Schools, 210 Williams St., Litchfield, MI 49252

Established in 1998 in MI.
Donor: V. Ennis Wright†.
Grantmaker type: Independent foundation.
Financial data (yr. ended 12/31/05): Assets, $482,415 (M); expenditures, $54,046; total giving, $47,750; qualifying distributions, $47,750; giving activities include $47,750 for grants.
Fields of interest: Education.

Type of support: Scholarship funds.
Limitations: Giving limited to Litchfield, MI.
Application information: Application available in The Litchfield Counseling Office. Application form required.
Deadline(s): May 15
Trustee: Citizens Bank.
EIN: 386115132

2104
Leroy M. Wurst and Janice K. Wurst Charitable Foundation
9935 Sunset Blvd.
Pigeon, MI 48755

Established in 1995 in MI.
Donors: Leroy M. Wurst; Janice K. Wurst.
Grantmaker type: Independent foundation.
Financial data (yr. ended 7/31/05): Assets, $203,977 (M); expenditures, $19,952; total giving, $17,500; qualifying distributions, $17,500; giving activities include $17,500 for grants.
Type of support: Scholarship funds.
Limitations: Applications not accepted. Giving primarily in Pigeon, MI. No grants to individuals.
Application information: Contributes only to pre-selected organizations.
Officers and Directors:* Leroy M. Wurst,* Pres. and Treas.; Janice K. Wurst,* V.P. and Secy.
EIN: 383251294

2105
Marion and Robert Wyatt Foundation
2514 Endsleigh Dr.
Bloomfield Hills, MI 48301

Established in 1986 in MI.
Donors: Robert Wyatt; Marion Wyatt.
Grantmaker type: Independent foundation.
Financial data (yr. ended 11/30/05): Assets, $632,244 (M); expenditures, $29,512; total giving, $27,700; qualifying distributions, $27,700; giving activities include $27,700 for grants.
Limitations: Applications not accepted. Giving primarily in MI. No grants to individuals.
Application information: Contributes only to pre-selected organizations.
Officers and Trustees:* Robert Wyatt,* Pres.; Marion Wyatt,* Secy.-Treas.; Curtis J. Mann.
EIN: 382709482

2106
Robert & Patricia Wynalda Foundation
3395 Valley View N.E.
Rockford, MI 49341-8032
Application address: c/o Robert Wynalda, 8221 Graphic Dr., Rockford, MI 49341, tel.: (616) 866-1561

Established in 1989 in MI.
Donors: Wynalda Litho, Inc.; Robert Wynalda; Patricia Wynalda.
Grantmaker type: Independent foundation.
Financial data (yr. ended 12/31/05): Assets, $83,063 (M); gifts received, $57,596; expenditures, $248,465; total giving, $247,327; qualifying distributions, $248,172; giving activities include $247,327 for 6 grants (high: $217,911; low: $736).
Purpose and activities: Giving primarily to missions.

Fields of interest: Christian agencies & churches; Religion.
Type of support: General/operating support; Continuing support; Building/renovation; Land acquisition; Debt reduction; Emergency funds.
Limitations: Giving on a national basis, with some emphasis on PA. No grants to individuals.
Application information: Application form not required.
Initial approach: Letter
Copies of proposal: 3
Deadline(s): None
Officers: Robert Wynalda, Pres. and Treas.; Patricia Wynalda, V.P. and Secy.
Director: Robert Wynalda, Jr.
EIN: 382851989
Selected grants: The following grants were reported in 2004.
$29,800 to Resurrection Fellowship Church, Grand Rapids, MI.
$27,000 to United Servants Abroad, Wellington, FL.
$25,000 to Algoma Christian Academy, Rockford, MI.
$22,618 to BCM International, Akron, PA.
$20,000 to Biblical Counseling Center, Jenison, MI.
$15,000 to Pioneers, Inc., Orlando, FL.
$4,680 to SIM USA, Charlotte, NC.
$735 to Association of Baptists for World Evangelism, New Cumberland, PA.

2107
Frederick and Katherine Yaffe Foundation
(formerly Frederick S. Yaffe Foundation)
2000 Tiverton Rd.
Bloomfield Hills, MI 48304
Contact: Frederick Yaffe, Chair.
Application address: 26913 Northwestern Hwy., Ste. 500, Southfield, MI 48034

Established in 1995 in MI.
Donors: Frederick Yaffe; Katherine Yaffe; The Fung Foundation.
Grantmaker type: Independent foundation.
Financial data (yr. ended 12/31/04): Assets, $120,064 (M); gifts received, $20,000; expenditures, $101,926; total giving, $101,850; qualifying distributions, $101,850; giving activities include $101,850 for 8 grants (high: $79,000; low: $350).
Fields of interest: Higher education; Human services; Jewish agencies & temples.
Type of support: General/operating support.
Limitations: Giving primarily in MI.
Application information: Application form not required.
Deadline(s): None
Officers and Directors:* Frederick Yaffe,* Chair.; Katherine Yaffe,* Secy.; John Cassidy, Treas.
EIN: 383232086

2108
Yankama Feed the Children Charitable Foundation
601 S. Shore Dr.
Battle Creek, MI 49015

Established in 1994 in MI.
Donor: Andrew S. Yankama.
Grantmaker type: Independent foundation.
Financial data (yr. ended 12/31/04): Assets, $21,391 (M); expenditures, $22,628; total giving,

$20,683; qualifying distributions, $22,628; giving activities include $2,468 for 7 grants (high: $1,000; low: $20), and $18,215 for 26 grants to individuals (high: $10,000; low: $25).
Fields of interest: Food services; Christian agencies & churches; Economically disadvantaged.
Type of support: General/operating support; Grants to individuals.
Limitations: Giving in the U.S., primarily in Battle Creek, MI; some giving also in Canada and South America.
Officers: Andrew S. Yankama, Pres.; Rachel D. Yankama, Treas.
EIN: 383219667

2109
Charles F. Yeager Foundation, Inc.
3155 W. Big Beaver Rd., Ste. 103
Troy, MI 48084-3006 (248) 643-4965
Contact: Mark Zurek, Pres.

Established in 2001 in MI.
Donor: Charles F. Yeager Trust.
Grantmaker type: Independent foundation.
Financial data (yr. ended 12/31/04): Assets, $404,997 (M); expenditures, $39,082; total giving, $13,550; qualifying distributions, $21,615; giving activities include $13,550 for grants.
Purpose and activities: Giving primarily for human services.
Fields of interest: Human services; Children/youth, services; General charitable giving.
Limitations: Giving on a national basis, with some emphasis on MI.
Application information:
Initial approach: Letter
Deadline(s): None
Final notification: 2 months
Officers: Mark Zurek, Pres.; Wayne Stewart, Secy.-Treas.
EIN: 383530854

2110
S. K. Yee Foundation, Inc.
c/o The Bank of New York, Tax Dept.
1 Wall St., 28th Fl.
New York, NY 10286

Established in 1984 in NY.
Donor: S.K. Yee.
Grantmaker type: Independent foundation.
Financial data (yr. ended 6/30/05): Assets, $10,291,580 (M); expenditures, $561,506; total giving, $500,000; qualifying distributions, $500,000; giving activities include $500,000 for grants.
Purpose and activities: Support only for the University of Chicago, Stamford University, University of California, Columbia University, and University of Michigan.
Fields of interest: Law school/education; Scholarships/financial aid.
Type of support: Scholarship funds.
Limitations: Applications not accepted. Giving limited to CA, CT, IL, MI, and NY. No grants to individuals.
Application information: Contributes only to 5 pre-selected organizations.

Officers and Directors:* Robert Anthoine,* Pres.; Kevin Bannon,* V.P. and Treas.; Sutton Keany, Secy.; Herma Hill Kay; David Leebron.
EIN: 133202047

2111
Yeo Family Foundation
1169 Glendale St.
Saginaw, MI   48603-4722   (989) 792-7151
Contact: Lloyd J. Yeo, Tr.

Donors: Judith N. Yeo; Lloyd J. Yeo.
Grantmaker type: Independent foundation.
Financial data (yr. ended 12/31/05): Assets, $198,185 (M); gifts received, $7,419; expenditures, $10,313; total giving, $8,330; qualifying distributions, $8,330; giving activities include $8,330 for 19 grants (high: $2,520; low: $40).
Fields of interest: Human services; Community development.
Limitations: Giving primarily in Saginaw, MI. No grants to individuals.
Application information:
  Initial approach: Letter
  Deadline(s): None
Trustees: Barbara Haines; Judith N. Yeo; Lloyd J. Yeo; William E. Yeo.
EIN: 382426134

2112
Ykema Family Foundation
c/o Richard Vandebrake
1773 McCabe Ave. S.E.
Lowell, MI   49331-9771

Established in 1997 in MI.
Donor: Harriet Ykema.
Grantmaker type: Independent foundation.
Financial data (yr. ended 12/31/05): Assets, $442,163 (M); gifts received, $20,000; expenditures, $34,272; total giving, $25,000; qualifying distributions, $25,000; giving activities include $25,000 for grants.
Fields of interest: Education; Christian agencies & churches.
Type of support: General/operating support.
Limitations: Applications not accepted. Giving primarily in Visalia, CA. No grants to individuals.
Application information: Contributes only to pre-selected organizations.
Officers: Harriet Ykema, Pres.; Ruth Harmsen, V.P.; Glenda Vandebrake, Secy.; Alicia Ykema, Treas.
EIN: 383363198

2113
Jerome B. & Eilene M. York Foundation
950 Lake George Rd.
Oakland, MI   48363-1118
Application address: c/o Jerome B. York, 3700 Tremonte Cir. S., Rochester, MI 48306

Established in 1997 in MI.
Donors: Eilene M. York; Jerome B. York.
Grantmaker type: Independent foundation.
Financial data (yr. ended 12/31/05): Assets, $33,242 (M); expenditures, $28,520; total giving, $26,000; qualifying distributions, $27,270; giving activities include $26,000 for 4 grants (high: $10,000; low: $1,000).

Fields of interest: Education.
Type of support: General/operating support.
Limitations: Giving on a national basis.
Application information: Application form not required.
  Initial approach: Letter of inquiry
  Deadline(s): None
Trustees: Eilene M. York; Jerome B. York.
EIN: 383353431

2114
Young Charity Trust
c/o The Northern Trust Co.
P.O. Box 803878
Chicago, IL   60680

Established in 1988 in IL.
Grantmaker type: Independent foundation.
Financial data (yr. ended 4/30/05): Assets, $25,191,966 (M); expenditures, $900,374; total giving, $631,612; qualifying distributions, $829,975; giving activities include $631,612 for grants.
Purpose and activities: Support only for the George Young Recreational Complex, Gaastra.
Fields of interest: Recreation, centers.
Limitations: Applications not accepted. Giving limited to Gaastra, MI. No grants to individuals.
Application information: Contributes only to a pre-selected organization.
Trustees: Charles Hamacher; Ralph J. Schindler, Jr.; The Northern Trust Co.
EIN: 366897850

2115
Young Family Foundation
P.O. Box 5430
Plymouth, MI   48170

Established in 2001 in MI.
Donors: William P. Young‡; Plastipak Holdings, Inc.
Grantmaker type: Independent foundation.
Financial data (yr. ended 12/31/05): Assets, $2,803,721 (M); gifts received, $300,000; expenditures, $991,501; total giving, $965,465; qualifying distributions, $978,483; giving activities include $965,465 for 12 grants (high: $300,000; low: $5,000; average: $50,000–$125,000).
Purpose and activities: Giving primarily to a Roman Catholic university, as well as for other education; some funding also for human services.
Fields of interest: Secondary school/education; Higher education; Scholarships/financial aid; Environment, natural resources; Animals/wildlife; Human services; American Red Cross; Roman Catholic agencies & churches.
Type of support: Building/renovation; Scholarship funds; General/operating support.
Limitations: Applications not accepted. Giving primarily in MI, with emphasis on Ann Arbor and Detroit. No grants to individuals.
Application information: Contributes only to pre-selected organizations.
Officers and Directors:* William C. Young,* Pres.; William Patrick Young,* V.P.; Tracey L. Deal,* Secy.; Amy L. Morgan,* Treas.
EIN: 300003762

2116
Young Foundation
6372 Muirfield Ct.
Bloomfield Hills, MI   48301-1503
Contact: Donna H. Young, Secy.-Treas.

Established in 1994 in MI.
Donor: Walter R. Young, Jr.
Grantmaker type: Independent foundation.
Financial data (yr. ended 12/31/05): Assets, $2,986,409 (M); gifts received, $390,300; expenditures, $104,081; total giving, $75,100; qualifying distributions, $76,595; giving activities include $75,100 for grants.
Purpose and activities: Giving primarily for innovative, quality projects that will benefit at-risk children and families.
Fields of interest: Humanities; Education; Human services; Children, services; Family services.
Type of support: General/operating support; Program development.
Limitations: Giving primarily in Oakland County, MI. No support for political organizations. No grants to individuals (including scholarships), or for endowments.
Application information: Application form required.
  Initial approach: Letter
  Copies of proposal: 1
  Deadline(s): Nov. 1
Officers: Walter R. Young, Jr., Pres.; Donna H. Young, Secy.-Treas.
Directors: Mark Young; Michelle Young-Bueltel.
Number of staff: None.
EIN: 383193515

2117
Young Woman's Home Association
(formerly Young Woman's Home Association of Detroit)
32 Winthrop Pl.
Grosse Pointe Farms, MI   48236
Contact: Tish Colett
E-mail: ywha@inbox.com

Established in 1877 in MI.
Donor: Jessie Castle Roberts‡.
Grantmaker type: Independent foundation.
Financial data (yr. ended 3/31/05): Assets, $2,318,867 (M); gifts received, $7,355; expenditures, $134,954; total giving, $125,150; qualifying distributions, $125,173; giving activities include $125,150 for 46 grants (high: $6,000; low: $500).
Purpose and activities: Grants made to non-profit organizations that provide basic needs and educational programs for disadvantaged women and children in the Detroit, MI, metropolitan area.
Fields of interest: Child development, education; Children/youth, services; Disabilities, people with; Women; Economically disadvantaged.
Type of support: Continuing support; Equipment; Emergency funds; Program development; Curriculum development.
Limitations: Giving in the Detroit, MI, metropolitan area. No grants for general operating budgets, capital campaigns, salaries, start-up programs, or scholarships.
Application information: Application form required.
  Initial approach: Letter or E-mail requesting application
  Copies of proposal: 1
  Deadline(s): Sept. 1 and Mar. 1

Board meeting date(s): 3rd Tues. of Jan., Mar., Apr., Sept., Oct., and Dec.
Final notification: Apr. or Oct.
Officers and Trustees: Laura Huebner,* Pres.; Susan Durant, V.P.; Debby Smith,* Rec. Secy.; Anne Franco, Corr. Secy.; Ann Nicholson,* Treas.; and 14 additional trustees.
EIN: 381360595
Selected grants: The following grants were reported in 2004.
$5,000 to Assistance League of Southeastern Michigan, Rochester Hills, MI. For Operation School Bell.
$3,500 to Cass Corridor Youth Advocates, Detroit, MI. For field trip expenses.
$3,500 to Crossroads of Michigan, Detroit, MI. For funding for families headed by women.

2118
The Youth Foundation of America
P.O. Box 2068
Petoskey, MI 49770
Contact: Pamela Siena, Tr.
Application address: 1141 S. Fernandez Ave., Arlington Heights, IL 60005-3038

Incorporated in 1947 in MI.
Donor: Franklin C. Browne Trust.
Grantmaker type: Independent foundation.
Financial data (yr. ended 12/31/05): Assets, $54,386 (M); gifts received, $101,971; expenditures, $159,889; total giving, $82,000; qualifying distributions, $152,824; giving activities include $82,000 for grants.
Purpose and activities: Grants to Michigan organizations that provide outdoor, overnight camping experience for Michigan youth.
Fields of interest: Recreation, camps; Youth development, scouting agencies (general); YM/YWCAs & YM/YWHAs.
Type of support: General/operating support.
Limitations: Giving limited to MI. No grants to individuals.
Application information: Application form not required.
Initial approach: Letter
Copies of proposal: 1
Deadline(s): None
Board meeting date(s): Annually
Officer and Trustees: Kimberly Hines,* Secy.; Robert Bales, Jr.; Paul W. Brown; Pamela Siena.
EIN: 386090960

2119
Herbert T. Zacharias Trust
c/o Leonard Meleski
8090 Evergreen Park Dr.
Saginaw, MI 48609-4205

Grantmaker type: Independent foundation.
Financial data (yr. ended 12/31/05): Assets, $253,490 (M); expenditures, $15,101; total giving, $12,000; qualifying distributions, $12,000; giving activities include $12,000 for grants.
Purpose and activities: Support only for the Roman Catholic Church of the Diocese of Saginaw, MI and the Society for the Propagation of the Faith, NY.
Fields of interest: Roman Catholic agencies & churches.
Type of support: General/operating support.

Limitations: Applications not accepted. Giving limited to Saginaw, MI and New York, NY. No grants to individuals.
Application information: Contributes only to 2 pre-selected organizations.
Trustee: Leonard Meleski.
EIN: 386555107

2120
The Zahra Foundation
26300 Telegraph Rd., 2nd Fl.
Southfield, MI 48034 (248) 359-2300

Established in 1994 in MI.
Grantmaker type: Independent foundation.
Financial data (yr. ended 12/31/04): Assets, $18,420 (M); gifts received, $50,000; expenditures, $32,430; total giving, $30,000; qualifying distributions, $30,000; giving activities include $30,000 for grants.
Officer: Ali Fadel, Pres.
EIN: 383141079

2121
Santo, Maria, Frank & John Zanetti Foundation
67 W. Michigan Ave., Rm. 312
Battle Creek, MI 49017

Donor: Members of the Zanetti Family.
Grantmaker type: Independent foundation.
Financial data (yr. ended 12/31/05): Assets, $139,270 (M); gifts received, $55,000; expenditures, $7,894; total giving, $6,500; qualifying distributions, $6,500; giving activities include $6,500 for grants.
Fields of interest: Health care; Human services.
Limitations: Applications not accepted. Giving primarily in Battle Creek, MI. No grants to individuals.
Application information: Unsolicited requests for funds not accepted.
Officers: Santo L. Zanetti, Pres.; Maria L. Zanetti, V.P.; Frankie A. Zanetti, Secy.; John L. Zanetti, Treas.
EIN: 200489552

2122
The Louise Tumarkin Zazove Foundation, Inc.
2903 Craig Rd.
Ann Arbor, MI 48103
Contact: Philip Zazove, Pres.
E-mail: earl@ltzfoundation.org; *Mailing address:* 6858 N. Kenneth Ave., Chicago, IL 60712-4705; *URL:* http://www.ltzfoundation.org/

Established in 2002 in MI.
Donors: Philip Zazove; Earl Zazove.
Grantmaker type: Independent foundation.
Financial data (yr. ended 8/31/05): Assets, $51,366 (M); gifts received, $40,505; expenditures, $14,829; total giving, $7,500; qualifying distributions, $7,500; giving activities include $7,500 for grants.
Purpose and activities: The foundation provides scholarships and related assistance to people with hearing loss.
Fields of interest: Deaf/hearing impaired.
Type of support: Scholarships—to individuals.

Limitations: Giving limited to U.S. citizens or permanent residents.
Application information: See foundation Web site for full application guidelines and requirements, including downloadable application form. Application form required.
Deadline(s): May 31
Final notification: July 15; scholarship recipients will be notified by July 23
Officers and Directors: Philip Zazove,* Pres.; Karen Williamson,* V.P.; Earl Zazove,* Secy.-Treas.
EIN: 383658887

2123
Edwin L. & Marion Zehnder Foundation
101 N. Washington Ave.
Saginaw, MI 48607

Donors: Edwin L. Zehnder; Marion Zehnder.
Grantmaker type: Independent foundation.
Financial data (yr. ended 9/30/05): Assets, $283,708 (M); gifts received, $2,175; expenditures, $19,706; total giving, $14,000; qualifying distributions, $14,000; giving activities include $14,000 for grants.
Limitations: Applications not accepted. Giving primarily in CA and MI. No grants to individuals.
Application information: Contributes only to pre-selected organizations.
Director: Albert F. Zehnder.
EIN: 237336306

2124
William & Dorothy Zehnder Foundation
(formerly William Zehnder, Jr. & Dorothy Zehnder Foundation)
1055 S. Main St.
Frankenmuth, MI 48734-1684

Donors: William A. Zehnder, Jr.; Dorothy Zehnder; Frankenmuth Bavarian Inn.
Grantmaker type: Independent foundation.
Financial data (yr. ended 9/30/05): Assets, $2,001,621 (M); gifts received, $52,746; expenditures, $102,494; total giving, $42,498; qualifying distributions, $82,655; giving activities include $42,198 for 26 grants (high: $20,000; low: $10), and $300 for 2 grants to individuals (high: $200; low: $100).
Purpose and activities: Giving primarily for Lutheran churches, as well as for education, health, human services, religious purposes, and community development.
Fields of interest: Arts; Health organizations, association; Human services; Community development; Protestant agencies & churches.
Limitations: Applications not accepted. Giving in the U.S., with emphasis on MI. No grants to individuals; no loans or scholarships.
Application information: Contributes only to pre-selected organizations.
Officers: William A. Zehnder, Jr., Pres.; Dorothy Zehnder, V.P.; William A. Zehnder, Secy.; Donald Keller, Treas.
Trustees: Amie Grossi; Judy Keller; Karen Zehnder; Michael Zehnder.
EIN: 237321185

2125
Beverly A. Zelt Foundation
1465 Kilborn Dr.
Petoskey, MI 49770
Contact: Beverly A. Zelt, Pres.

Established in 2002 in MI.
Grantmaker type: Independent foundation.
Financial data (yr. ended 12/31/04): Assets, $4,732 (M); expenditures, $42; total giving, $0; qualifying distributions, $42; giving activities include $42 for foundation-administered programs.
Fields of interest: Protestant agencies & churches.
Application information:
  Initial approach: Letter
  Deadline(s): None
Officer: Beverly A. Zelt, Pres. and Secy.-Treas.
EIN: 371423013

2126
The George M. and Pearl A. Zeltzer Foundation
7106 Suncrest Rd.
West Bloomfield, MI 48322-4340

Established in 1996 in MI; funded in 2001.
Donors: George M. Zeltzer; Pearl A. Zeltzer.
Grantmaker type: Independent foundation.
Financial data (yr. ended 12/31/03): Assets, $0 (M); expenditures, $895; total giving, $895; qualifying distributions, $895; giving activities include $895 for grants.
Fields of interest: Jewish federated giving programs.
Type of support: General/operating support.
Limitations: Giving primarily in Detroit, MI. No grants to individuals.
Officers and Directors:* George M. Zeltzer, Pres.; Pearl A. Zeltzer, Secy.-Treas.
EIN: 383416505

2127
Zerbe Family Foundation
2228 Old Falls Dr.
Ann Arbor, MI 48103-8305

Established in 2002 in MI.
Donor: Robert L. Zerbe.
Grantmaker type: Independent foundation.
Financial data (yr. ended 12/31/05): Assets, $670,710 (M); gifts received, $40,853; expenditures, $64,613; total giving, $54,155; qualifying distributions, $54,155; giving activities include $54,155 for grants.
Fields of interest: Medical school/education.
Type of support: Scholarship funds.
Limitations: Applications not accepted. Giving primarily in Bloomington, IN. No grants to individuals.
Application information: Contributes only to pre-selected organizations.
Officers: Robert L. Zerbe, Pres.; Linda L. Zerbe, Secy.-Treas.
Directors: Anne E. Zerbe; Eric R. Zerbe; Sarah C. Zerbe.
EIN: 300119840

2128
Erwin C. and Isabelle Ziegelman Foundation
17117 W. 9 Mile Rd.
Southfield, MI 48075

Established in 1988 in MI.
Donor: Erwin C. Ziegelman.
Grantmaker type: Independent foundation.
Financial data (yr. ended 6/30/05): Assets, $968,210 (M); expenditures, $49,387; total giving, $41,107; qualifying distributions, $41,107; giving activities include $41,107 for grants.
Fields of interest: Performing arts, orchestra (symphony); Higher education, university; Hospitals (general); Jewish agencies & temples.
Limitations: Applications not accepted. Giving primarily in MI. No grants to individuals.
Application information: Contributes only to pre-selected organizations.
Officers: Isabelle Ziegelman, Pres.; Andrea Ziegelman, Secy.
EIN: 382831525

2129
Paul R. Ziegler & Colleen M. Ziegler Family Foundation
P.O. Box 250428
Franklin, MI 48025

Established in 1996 in MI.
Donors: Paul R. Ziegler; Colleen Ziegler.
Grantmaker type: Independent foundation.
Financial data (yr. ended 11/30/05): Assets, $48,737 (M); gifts received, $45,000; expenditures, $29,770; total giving, $29,750; qualifying distributions, $29,750; giving activities include $29,750 for grants.
Fields of interest: Children/youth, services.
Type of support: General/operating support.
Limitations: Applications not accepted. No grants to individuals.
Application information: Contributes only to pre-selected organizations.
Officers: Paul R. Ziegler, Pres.; Colleen Ziegler, V.P.
EIN: 383325793

2130
Mary and George Herbert Zimmerman Foundation
200 Maple Park Blvd., Rm. 201
St. Clair Shores, MI 48081-2211

Established in 1937 in MI.
Donors: Doris Z. Bato; Elaine Z. Peck; members of the Zimmerman family.
Grantmaker type: Independent foundation.
Financial data (yr. ended 12/31/05): Assets, $4,139,132 (M); expenditures, $238,420; total giving, $204,810; qualifying distributions, $204,810; giving activities include $204,810 for 52 grants (high: $15,000; low: $491).
Purpose and activities: Giving primarily for education, health care, and human services.
Fields of interest: Higher education, college; Education; Hospitals (general); Health care; Alzheimer's disease; Human services; Homeless, human services; Foundations (community); Roman Catholic agencies & churches.
Limitations: Applications not accepted. Giving on a national basis. No grants to individuals.

Application information: Contributes only to pre-selected organizations.
Officers: Georgia Z. Loftus, Pres.; Elaine Z. Peck, V.P. and Corres. Secy.; Doris Z. Bato, Recording Secy.; Martha Z. Harris, Treas.
EIN: 381685880
Selected grants: The following grants were reported in 2004.
$15,000 to San Isidro Catholic Church, San Francisco, CA.
$10,000 to Saint Vincent Hospital Foundation, Santa Fe, NM.
$10,000 to Santa Fe Community College Foundation, Santa Fe, NM.
$4,000 to Parkinsons Disease Foundation, New York, NY.
$3,500 to Childrens Hospital of Michigan, Detroit, MI.
$3,000 to Alzheimers Association, Chicago, IL.
$3,000 to Connecticut Childrens Medical Center Foundation, Hartford, CT.
$1,500 to Detroit Institute for Children, Detroit, MI.
$1,500 to Sacred Heart Rehabilitation Center, Detroit, MI.
$1,000 to Princeton University, Princeton, NJ.

2131
The Zionist Cultural Committee
6735 Telegram Rd.
Bloomfield Hills, MI 48301
Application address: c/o Lester Zeff, V.P., 4318 Bristol, Troy, MI 48098

Established in 1999.
Donor: Jewish Welfare Federation Metro Detroit.
Grantmaker type: Independent foundation.
Financial data (yr. ended 6/30/05): Assets, $274,978 (M); expenditures, $37,579; total giving, $35,000; qualifying distributions, $35,000; giving activities include $35,000 for grants.
Fields of interest: Religion.
Limitations: Giving primarily in Bloomfield Hills, MI.
Application information:
  Initial approach: Letter
  Deadline(s): None
Officers: George P. Mann, Pres.; Lester Zeff, V.P.; Leon Warshay, Secy.; Sidney Silverman, Treas.
EIN: 383473208

2132
Mr. & Ms. Zip Foundation
36480 Front St.
New Baltimore, MI 48047-2518

Established in 1983.
Donor: John J. Andary.
Grantmaker type: Independent foundation.
Financial data (yr. ended 12/31/05): Assets, $2,070 (M); expenditures, $573; total giving, $0; qualifying distributions, $0.
Limitations: Giving primarily in MI.
Officer: John J. Andary, Pres.
EIN: 382476785

2133
Zoller Family Foundation
26235 Pembroke Rd.
Huntington Woods, MI 48070-1624
Contact: Howard L. Zoller, V.P.

Application address: 25800 Northwestern Hwy., Ste. 950, Southfield, MI 48075

Established in 1990; funded in 1991.
Grantmaker type: Independent foundation.
Financial data (yr. ended 12/31/05): Assets, $34,628 (M); gifts received, $3,500; expenditures, $4,801; total giving, $4,500; qualifying distributions, $4,500; giving activities include $4,500 for grants.
Fields of interest: Higher education.
Type of support: Scholarship funds.
Limitations: Giving primarily in Gainesville, FL. No grants to individuals.
Application information:
   Initial approach: Letter
   Deadline(s): None
Officers: Lawrence C. Zoller, Pres.; Howard L. Zoller, V.P.; Walter F. Zoller, Secy.-Treas.
EIN: 382948781

2134
P. J. and Mary Zondervan Foundation
(also known as Zondervan Foundation)
2216 Edgewood Ave. S.E.
Grand Rapids, MI   49546-5702
Contact: Mary Beth Schouten, Secy.
Application address: 752 Brag Hill, Norwick, VT 05055

Established in 1981 in MI.
Donors: Peter J. Zondervan†; Mary Zondervan.
Grantmaker type: Independent foundation.
Financial data (yr. ended 12/31/04): Assets, $2,581,300 (M); expenditures, $141,799; total giving, $119,050; qualifying distributions, $123,660; giving activities include $119,050 for 13 grants (high: $91,700; low: $1,000).
Purpose and activities: To spread the gospel of Jesus Christ.
Fields of interest: Christian agencies & churches.
Type of support: Equipment; Program development; Conferences/seminars; Curriculum development; Scholarship funds; Research.
Limitations: Giving primarily in Grand Rapids, MI. No grants to individuals.
Application information:

Initial approach: Letter
Deadline(s): None
Final notification: Within 12 months
Officers and Directors:* Robert Lee Zondervan, M.D., Pres.; Norman Pulman,* V.P.; Mary Beth Schouten,* Secy.; Tom Kladder,* Treas.
EIN: 382411884
Selected grants: The following grants were reported in 2003.
$88,600 to Calvin Theological Seminary, Grand Rapids, MI. For college seminary PhD chair.
$2,500 to Bethany Christian Services, Grand Rapids, MI. To purchase educational materials.
$2,500 to Mission India, Grand Rapids, MI. For literacy program.
$2,500 to Redeemer Presbyterian Church, Ada, MI. For Haitian bible ministry.
$2,500 to Saint Justin Education Fund for Los Angeles, Los Angeles, CA.
$2,500 to Westminster Theological Seminary, Philadelphia, PA. For library resource development.
$2,000 to Young Life, Colorado Springs, CO.
$1,000 to New Horizons Youth Ministries, Marion, IN.
$1,000 to Rehoboth Christian School, Rehoboth, NM. For ministry.

2135
Melvin L. and Hilda J. Zuehlke Charitable Foundation
3023 Davenport Ave.
Saginaw, MI   48602-3652
Contact: Lloyd J. Yeo, Pres.
Application address: P.O. Box 3275, Saginaw, MI 48605

Established in 1994 in MI.
Donors: Melvin L. Zuehlke; Hilda J. Zuehlke.
Grantmaker type: Independent foundation.
Financial data (yr. ended 12/31/05): Assets, $1,584,143 (M); expenditures, $298,247; total giving, $274,907; qualifying distributions, $274,907; giving activities include $274,907 for grants.

Purpose and activities: Emphasis on higher education and human services, including alleviating hunger.
Fields of interest: Performing arts, orchestra (symphony); Secondary school/education; Higher education; Education; Health care; Food services; Human services; Federated giving programs.
Type of support: Scholarships—to individuals; Matching/challenge support; Building/renovation; Capital campaigns; General/operating support.
Limitations: Giving limited to MI, with some emphasis on Saginaw.
Publications: Application guidelines.
Application information: Application form not required.
   Initial approach: Letter
   Copies of proposal: 3
   Deadline(s): None
   Board meeting date(s): Quarterly
   Final notification: Post quarterly meetings
Trustees: B.J. Humphreys; Judy Weldy; Lloyd J. Yeo.
Number of staff: 1 part-time professional.
EIN: 383200771

2136
W. Tom Zurschmiede, Sr. Foundation
10 Stratton Pl.
Grosse Pointe Shores, MI   48236-1755
Contact: W. Thomas Zurschmiede, Jr., Chair.

Donors: W. Thomas Zurschmiede; W. Thomas Zurschmiede, Jr.
Grantmaker type: Independent foundation.
Financial data (yr. ended 12/31/05): Assets, $171,256 (M); gifts received, $14,900; expenditures, $18,997; total giving, $17,915; qualifying distributions, $17,915; giving activities include $17,915 for grants.
Fields of interest: Higher education; Christian agencies & churches; General charitable giving.
Limitations: Giving primarily in MI. No grants to individuals.
Application information:
   Initial approach: Letter
   Deadline(s): None
Officer: W. Thomas Zurschmiede, Jr., Chair.
EIN: 237423944

CORPORATE FUNDERS

2137
The Alro Steel Foundation
3100 E. High St.
Jackson, MI   49203

Established in 2004 in MI.
Donor: Alro Steel Corp.
Grantmaker type: Company-sponsored foundation.
Financial data (yr. ended 12/31/05): Assets, $1,306,358 (M); gifts received, $50,000; expenditures, $157,681; total giving, $150,903; qualifying distributions, $150,903; giving activities include $150,903 for grants.
Purpose and activities: The foundation supports history museums and organizations involved with arts and culture and health.
Fields of interest: Museums (history); Arts; Health care; Federated giving programs.
Type of support: General/operating support.
Limitations: Applications not accepted. Giving primarily in MI, with emphasis on Jackson. No grants to individuals.
Application information: Contributes only to pre-selected organizations.
Officers: Alvin L. Glick, Pres.; Barry J. Glick, V.P.; Carlton L. Glick, Secy.; Randal L. Glick, Treas.
EIN: 300254220

2138
Alticor Inc. Corporate Giving Program
(formerly Amway Corporation Contributions Program)
c/o Corp. Citizenship Dept.
7575 Fulton St. E., 49-2N
Ada, MI   49355-0001
Contact: Erin Rowe-Graves, Mgr., Corp. Citizenship
FAX: (616) 787-4764;
E-mail: contributions@alticor.com; URL: http:// www.alticor.com/communities/contributions.html

Grantmaker type: Corporate giving program.
Purpose and activities: Alticor makes charitable contributions to nonprofit organizations involved with children. Support is given on a national and international basis in areas of company operations.
Fields of interest: Arts; Education; Health care; Children, services; Human services; Children; Disabilities, people with; Economically disadvantaged.
Type of support: Donated products; Employee volunteer services; General/operating support; Sponsorships; In-kind gifts.
Limitations: Giving on a national and international basis in areas of company operations, with emphasis on western MI. No support for fraternal organizations or school athletic teams, bands, or choirs. No grants to individuals, or for travel or scholarships, school publications or advertising, social events, religious projects, or sports events; no loans.
Publications: Application guidelines; Informational brochure.
Application information: Proposals should be no longer than 1 page. Proposals should be submitted using organization letterhead. Organizations

receiving support are asked to provide a final report. Application form required.
Initial approach: Download application form and mail or fax proposal and application form to headquarters
Copies of proposal: 1
Deadline(s): None
Final notification: 2 months

2139
American Axle & Manufacturing Holdings, Inc. Corporate Giving Program
1 Dauch Dr.
Detroit, MI   48211-1198   (313) 758-4884
Contact: Dawn Uranis, Mgr., Corp. Rels.
FAX: (313) 974-3442; E-mail: uranisd@aam.com;
URL: http://www.aam.com/about/ about_community.html

Grantmaker type: Corporate giving program.
Purpose and activities: American Axle & Manufacturing makes charitable contributions to nonprofit organizations involved with education and youth development. Support is given primarily in areas of company operations.
Fields of interest: Education; Youth development.
Type of support: Employee volunteer services; Sponsorships.
Limitations: Giving primarily in areas of company operations.

2140
Amerisure Mutual Insurance Company Contributions Program
c/o Corp. Contribs.
26777 Halsted Rd.
Farmington Hills, MI   48331-3586
(248) 615-9000
Contact: Florence Woody, Admin. Asst.
FAX: (248) 615-8548;
E-mail: fwoody@amerisure.com; URL: http:// www.amerisure.com/au_1d_community.cfm

Grantmaker type: Corporate giving program.
Financial data (yr. ended 12/31/05): Total giving, $264,907, including $264,907 for grants.
Purpose and activities: Amerisure makes charitable contributions to nonprofit organizations involved with education and health. Support is given on a national basis.
Fields of interest: Education; Health care.
Type of support: General/operating support; Employee volunteer services; Sponsorships; Employee matching gifts.
Limitations: Giving on a national basis. No grants to individuals, or for tickets or individual pledge fulfillment; no indirect gifts.
Publications: Application guidelines.
Application information: The Human Resources Department handles giving. A contributions committee reviews all requests. Application form not required.

Initial approach: Proposal to headquarters or nearest company facility
Copies of proposal: 1
Deadline(s): Dec. 31
Committee meeting date(s): Jan.
Final notification: Following review
Number of staff: 5 full-time professional.

2141
ArvinMeritor Trust Foundation
(formerly Meritor Automotive, Inc. Trust)
c/o Community Rels.
2135 W. Maple Rd.
Troy, MI   48084-7186   (248) 435-7907
Contact: Jerry Rush, Sr. Dir., Govt. Rels.
FAX: (248) 435-1031;
E-mail: jerry.rush@arvinmeritor.com; URL: http:// www.arvinmeritor.com/community/community.asp

Established in 1997 in MI.
Donors: Meritor Automotive, Inc.; ArvinMeritor, Inc.
Grantmaker type: Company-sponsored foundation.
Financial data (yr. ended 10/2/05): Assets, $102,297 (M); gifts received, $1,565,272; expenditures, $1,508,610; total giving, $1,508,610; qualifying distributions, $1,508,610; giving activities include $1,405,277 for 236 grants (high: $200,000; low: $500), and $103,333 for 141 employee matching gifts.
Purpose and activities: The foundation supports organizations involved with arts and culture, education, health, medical research, safety, youth development, human services, community development, and civic affairs.
Fields of interest: Arts; Engineering school/ education; Education; Public health; Health care, cost containment; Health care; Medical research; Safety, education; Youth development; Human services; Community development; Science, formal/general education; Public affairs; Youth.
Type of support: Program development; Employee-related scholarships.
Limitations: Giving primarily in areas of company operations. No support for discriminatory organizations, religious or sectarian organizations not of direct benefit to the entire community, labor, political, or veterans' organizations, or fraternal, athletic, or social clubs. No grants to individuals (except for employee-related scholarships), or for general operating support for local United Way agencies, sponsorship of fundraising activities for individuals, debt reduction, or seminars, conferences, trips, or tours; no loans.
Publications: Informational brochure (including application guidelines).
Application information: Application form not required.
Initial approach: Proposal
Deadline(s): Aug.
Officers and Trustees:* Larry Yost, Chair. and C.E.O.; Terry O'Rourke, C.O.O. and Pres.; Vernon Baker, Sr. V.P., Secy., and General Counsel; Carl Soderstrom,* Sr. V.P. and C.F.O.; Lin Cummins,* Sr. V.P., Communications; Juan De La Riva,* Sr. V.P., Corp. Develop and Strategy; Ernie Whitus, Sr.

V.P., Human Resources; Diane Bullock, V.P. and Cont.
EIN: 522089611

2142
AT&T Michigan Corporate Giving Program
(formerly SBC Michigan Corporate Giving Program)
444 Michigan Ave., Rm. 1700
Detroit, MI 48226-2517 (313) 223-5747
Contact: Lisa M. Tepatti, Dir., Contribs. and Ext. Affairs
FAX: (313) 223-9008; E-mail: lh2151@sbc.com

Grantmaker type: Corporate giving program.
Purpose and activities: AT&T Michigan makes technology-focused charitable contributions to nonprofit organizations involved with education and community economic development.
Fields of interest: Education; Urban/community development.
Type of support: Program development; Technical assistance.
Limitations: Giving primarily in areas of company operations in MI. No grants for general operating support or capital campaigns.

2143
Autocam Corporation Contributions Program
4070 E. Paris Ave. S.E.
Kentwood, MI 49512-3909 (616) 698-0707
FAX: (616) 698-6876

Grantmaker type: Corporate giving program.
Purpose and activities: Autocam makes charitable contributions to nonprofit organizations on a case by case basis. Support is given primarily in Michigan.
Fields of interest: General charitable giving.
Type of support: General/operating support.
Limitations: Giving primarily in MI.

2144
Barton-Malow Company Foundation
c/o Barton-Malow Co.
26500 American Dr.
Southfield, MI 48034

Established in 1954 in MI.
Donors: Barton-Malow Enterprises, Inc.; Cloverdale Equipment Co.
Grantmaker type: Company-sponsored foundation.
Financial data (yr. ended 3/31/05): Assets, $224,707 (M); gifts received, $200,000; expenditures, $143,049; total giving, $141,150; qualifying distributions, $141,150; giving activities include $141,150 for 11 grants (high: $51,500; low: $150).
Purpose and activities: The foundation supports public charities, hospitals, and organizations involved with higher education, health, and community development.
Fields of interest: Higher education; Hospitals (general); Health care; YM/YWCAs & YM/YWHAs; Community development; Foundations (public); Federated giving programs.
Type of support: General/operating support.
Limitations: Giving primarily in MI. No grants to individuals.
Application information: Application form not required.

Initial approach: Letter of inquiry
Deadline(s): None
Trustees: Mark A. Bahr; Ben C. Maibach, Jr.; Ben C. Maibach III.
EIN: 386088176

2145
The John C. Bates Foundation
2401 Front St.
Toledo, OH 43605

Established in 1993 in OH.
Donors: Heidtman Steel Products, Inc.; Centaur, Inc.; HS Processing, LP.
Grantmaker type: Company-sponsored foundation.
Financial data (yr. ended 3/31/05): Assets, $1,282 (M); gifts received, $810,000; expenditures, $830,111; total giving, $829,492; qualifying distributions, $829,492; giving activities include $829,492 for 23 grants (high: $575,075; low: $250).
Purpose and activities: The foundation supports Christian agencies and churches and organizations involved with education, health, and human services.
Fields of interest: Elementary/secondary education; Higher education; Education; Zoos/zoological societies; Health care; Cancer; Family services; Human services; Foundations (community); Christian agencies & churches; Roman Catholic agencies & churches.
Type of support: Capital campaigns; Program development; Scholarship funds.
Limitations: Applications not accepted. Giving primarily in IN, MI, and OH. No grants to individuals.
Application information: Contributes only to pre-selected organizations.
Officers and Trustees: * Darlene B. Dotson,* Pres.; John M. Carey,* Secy.; Mark E. Ridenour,* Treas.; Sarah J. Bates; Debra A. Shinkle.
EIN: 341749094

2146
The Batts Foundation
3855 Sparks Dr. S.E., Ste. 222
Grand Rapids, MI 49546
Contact: Jane Sandtveit, Admin. Mgr.
E-mail: jsand@battsgroup.com

Established in 1988 in MI.
Donor: The Batts Group, Ltd.
Grantmaker type: Company-sponsored foundation.
Financial data (yr. ended 12/31/05): Assets, $2,331,949 (M); expenditures, $123,492; total giving, $96,000; qualifying distributions, $98,296.
Purpose and activities: The foundation supports organizations involved with arts and culture, K-12 and higher education, disease, and human services.
Fields of interest: Arts; Elementary/secondary education; Higher education; Health organizations; Children/youth, services; Human services.
Type of support: General/operating support; Continuing support; Annual campaigns; Capital campaigns; Building/renovation; Endowments; Program development; Scholarship funds; Matching/challenge support.
Limitations: Giving primarily in Holland, Zeeland, and the Grand Rapids, MI, area. No grants to individuals.
Publications: Annual report.

Application information: Application form not required.
Initial approach: Letter of inquiry
Copies of proposal: 1
Deadline(s): None
Board meeting date(s): Quarterly
Final notification: 1 to 3 months
Officer and Directors: * John H. Batts,* Pres.; James L. Batts; John T. Batts; Michael A. Batts; Robert H. Batts.
Number of staff: 1 part-time support.
EIN: 382782168

2147
The Berry Foundation
29100 Northwestern Hwy., Ste. 290
Southfield, MI 48034

Donors: Berry Investment Co.; Louis Berry‡; Harold Berry; Lawrence Berry; Louis Berry Marital Trust; Berry Ventures; Vivian Berry.
Grantmaker type: Company-sponsored foundation.
Financial data (yr. ended 12/31/05): Assets, $171,094 (M); gifts received, $105,570; expenditures, $97,810; total giving, $96,654; qualifying distributions, $97,174; giving activities include $96,654 for 169 grants (high: $26,250; low: $10).
Purpose and activities: The foundation supports organizations involved with education, health, and Judaism.
Fields of interest: Higher education; Education; Health care; Jewish agencies & temples.
Limitations: Applications not accepted. Giving on a national basis, with some emphasis on MI, New York, NY, and Washington, DC. No grants to individuals.
Application information: Contributes only to pre-selected organizations.
Officers and Trustees: Harold Berry, Pres. and Treas.; Lawrence Berry, V.P.; Peter C. Seagle, Secy.; Barbara Berry; Elliott B. Berry; Betsy Heuer; Selma B. Schwartz; Miriam Seagle.
EIN: 386064574

2148
Bierlein Companies Foundation
2000 Bay City Rd.
Midland, MI 48642

Established in 1985 in MI.
Donors: Bierlein Demolition Contractors, Inc.; Bierlein Environmental Services, Inc.; Bierlein Cos., Inc.
Grantmaker type: Company-sponsored foundation.
Financial data (yr. ended 12/31/04): Assets, $74,463 (M); gifts received, $80,000; expenditures, $90,145; total giving, $90,075; qualifying distributions, $90,093; giving activities include $90,075 for 45 grants (high: $6,650; low: $50).
Purpose and activities: The foundation supports Christian agencies and churches and organizations involved with arts and culture, education, health, children and youth, human services, and community development.
Fields of interest: Arts; Higher education; Education; Health care; Children/youth, services; Human services; Community development; Federated giving programs; Christian agencies & churches.

Type of support: General/operating support.
Limitations: Applications not accepted. Giving primarily in the Saginaw Valley, MI. No grants to individuals.
Application information: Contributes only to pre-selected organizations.
Officers: Michael D. Bierlein, Pres. and Treas.; Thomas L. Bierlein, V.P.; Kenneth W. LeCureux, Secy.
EIN: 382615341

2149
The Birds Eye Foods Foundation
(formerly Agrilink Foods/Pro-Fac Foundation)
P.O. Box 20670
Rochester, NY 14602-0670 (585) 264-3155
Contact: Susan C. Riker, Secy.
URL: http://www.birdseyefoods.com/corp/about/foundation.asp

Established in 1966 in NY.
Donors: Agrilink Foods, Inc.; Birds Eye Foods, Inc.
Grantmaker type: Company-sponsored foundation.
Financial data (yr. ended 6/25/05): Assets, $54,850 (M); gifts received, $75,000; expenditures, $131,950; total giving, $131,250; qualifying distributions, $131,800; giving activities include $113,480 for 36 grants (high: $15,000; low: $250), and $17,770 for employee matching gifts.
Purpose and activities: The foundation supports organizations involved with arts and culture, education, health, and human services.
Fields of interest: Arts; Education; Health care; Youth, services; Human services; Federated giving programs.
Type of support: General/operating support; Annual campaigns; Building/renovation; Program development; Scholarship funds; Sponsorships; Employee matching gifts.
Limitations: Giving primarily in areas of company operations in Watsonville, CA, Montezuma, GA, Fennville, MI, Waseca, MN, Bergen, Brockport, Fulton, Oakfield, and Rochester, NY, Berlin, PA, Algona and Tacoma, WA, and Darien, Fairwater, and Green Bay, WI. No support for religious or political organizations. No grants to individuals, or for land acquisition, start-up needs, internships, pilot projects, publications, conferences or seminars, or continuing support; no loans; no matching gifts.
Application information: Application form not required.
 Initial approach: Proposal
 Copies of proposal: 1
 Deadline(s): None
 Board meeting date(s): Usually in Jan., Mar., June, Aug., and Nov.
Officers and Trustees:* Paul Roe,* Chair.; Susan C. Riker,* Secy.; Thomas Facer; Virginia Ford; Dennis Mullen; William Rice.
Number of staff: 1 part-time support.
EIN: 166071142

2150
Blue Cross and Blue Shield of Michigan Foundation
(formerly Michigan Health Care Education and Research Foundation/MHCERF)
600 Lafayette E., X520
Detroit, MI 48226-2928 (313) 225-8706
Contact: Ira Strumwasser Ph.D., C.E.O. and Exec. Dir.
FAX: (313) 225-7730;
E-mail: foundation@bcbsm.com; Additional tel.: (313) 225-7560; URL: http://www.bcbsm.com/foundation/

Established in 1980 in MI.
Donor: Blue Cross Blue Shield of Michigan.
Grantmaker type: Company-sponsored foundation.
Financial data (yr. ended 12/31/04): Assets, $60,069,406 (M); expenditures, $3,224,278; total giving, $2,218,038; giving activities include $340,107 for 21 grants (high: $67,837; low: $450), and $1,877,931 for 53 grants to individuals (high: $175,648; low: $500).
Purpose and activities: The foundation supports projects that focus on enhancing the quality of health care and improving access to and containing the cost of health care. Grants are available to Michigan-based researchers, physicians licensed and practicing in Michigan, students enrolled in medical or doctoral programs at Michigan universities, and service delivery organizations initiating innovative projects. The foundation also maintains the Caring Program for Children, which provides preventive health care to lower-income, uninsured children throughout the state.
Fields of interest: Health care; Medical research, institute.
Type of support: Income development; Seed money; Program development; Fellowships; Research; Technical assistance; Grants to individuals; Matching/challenge support.
Limitations: Giving primarily in MI.
Publications: Application guidelines; Annual report (including application guidelines); Informational brochure (including application guidelines).
Application information: Application form required.
 Deadline(s): Jan. 1 for Excellence in Research Awards and Excellence in Research Awards for Students; Apr. 3 for Research Award for Improving Patient Safety and Research Award for Identification and Treatment of Depression; and Apr. 30 for Student Awards Program
 Board meeting date(s): May, Aug., and Nov.
 Final notification: Aug. for Student Awards Program; quarterly for Matching Grants Program
Officers and Directors:* Shauna Ryder Diggs, M.D.*, Chair.; Joel I. Ferguson,* Vice-Chair.; Ira Strumwasser, Ph.D., C.E.O. and Exec. Dir.; George F. Francis III,* Pres.; Marla Larkin, Secy.; Peter Ajluni, D.O.*, Treas.; Haifa Fakhouri, Ph.D.; Krishna K. Sawhney, M.D.; Willard S. Stawski, M.D.
Number of staff: 3 full-time professional; 2 full-time support.
EIN: 382338506

2151
Blue Cross Blue Shield of Michigan Corporate Giving Program
600 E. Lafayette Blvd.
Detroit, MI 48226
Application addresses: Caring for Children Angel Awards: Caring for Children Angel Awards, c/o Community Affairs, M.C. 0250, 600 E. Lafayette Blvd., Detroit, MI 48226-2998, tel.: (800) 733-2583, Domestic Violence and Abuse Prevention: Shoma Pal, c/o Social Mission Health Initiatives, B761, 27000 W. 11 Mile Rd., Southfield, MI 48034, tel.: (248) 448-5027, E-mail: spal@bcbsm.com, Physical Activity and Nutrition: Tyffany Shadd-Coleman, c/o Health Policy and Social Mission, M.C. B761, 27300 11 Mile Rd., Southfield, MI 48034, tel.: (248) 448-5045, E-mail: tshadd@bcbsm.com; Contact for Depression Awareness and Treatment: Carolyn Wiener, tel.: (248) 448-5026, E-mail: cwiener@bcbsm.com; URL: http://www.bcbsm.com/home/commitment/community_support.shtml

Grantmaker type: Corporate giving program.
Financial data (yr. ended 12/31/02): Total giving, $2,000,000, including $2,000,000 for grants (high: $100,000; low: $1,000; average: $1,000–$100,000).
Purpose and activities: As a complement to its foundation, Blue Cross Blue Shield of Michigan also makes charitable contributions to nonprofit organizations directly. Support is limited to Michigan.
Fields of interest: Health care; Mental health, depression; Crime/violence prevention, abuse prevention; Crime/violence prevention, sexual abuse; Nutrition; Recreation; Children, services; Children; Youth; Aging.
Type of support: General/operating support; Employee volunteer services.
Limitations: Giving limited to MI.
Application information: Proposals for Caring for Children Angel Awards should be no longer than 2 pages. Multi-year funding for Domestic Violence and Abuse Prevention is not automatic. Proposals for Domestic Violence and Abuse Prevention should be no longer than 11 pages. Proposals for Physical Activity and Nutrition should be no longer than 1,500 words. Organizations receiving Physical Activity and Nutrition grants are asked to provide periodic progress reports. An independent panel of judges reviews all requests for Caring for Children Angel Awards. A contributions committee reviews all requests for Domestic Violence and Abuse Prevention. Application form required.
 Initial approach: Download nomination form and mail proposal and nomination form to application address for Caring for Children Angel Awards; download application form and E-mail proposal and application form to program contact for Depression Awareness and Treatment
 Deadline(s): May 14 for Caring for Children Angel Awards; June 11 for Depression Awareness and Treatment; and May 3 for Domestic Violence and Abuse Prevention
Number of staff: 2 part-time professional; 2 part-time support.

2152
Bodman LLP
(formerly Bodman, Longley & Dahling LLP)
1901 St. Antoine St., 6th Fl., Ford Field
Detroit, MI 48226 (313) 259-7777
Contact: Christopher J. Dine, Partner
FAX: (313) 393-7579; E-mail:
cdine@bodmanllp.com; URL: http://
www.bodmanllp.com/about_bodman/giving_back/
index.html

Grantmaker type: Corporate giving program.
Purpose and activities: Bodman attorneys have a
long tradition of supporting worthy organizations
through donations, volunteerism and pro bono legal
services to charitable and community-based
organizations. Its public service commitment
extends to universities, professional associations
and governmental agencies.
Fields of interest: Legal services; Philanthropy/
voluntarism.

2153
**Borders Group, Inc. Corporate Giving
Program**
100 Phoenix Dr.
Ann Arbor, MI 48108
Contact: Sherry Pringle, Admin., Corp. Affairs
FAX: (734) 477-1517;
E-mail: springle@bordersgroupinc.com; URL: http://
www.bordersgroupinc.com/community/index.html

Grantmaker type: Corporate giving program.
Financial data (yr. ended 1/28/06): Total giving,
$600,000, including $350,000 for grants, and
$250,000 for in-kind gifts.
Purpose and activities: Borders makes charitable
contributions to nonprofit organizations involved
with arts and culture and literacy. Support is given
on a national and international basis in areas of
company operations.
Fields of interest: Performing arts, music; Arts;
Education, reading.
Type of support: Use of facilities; Capital
campaigns; In-kind gifts; Cause-related marketing;
Sponsorships; Donated products.
Limitations: Giving on a national and international
basis in areas of company operations, with some
emphasis on Ann Arbor, MI.
Application information: Proposals should be
submitted using organization letterhead. The
Corporate Affairs and Marketing Department
handles giving. Application form not required.
  Initial approach: Proposal to headquarters
  Copies of proposal: 1
Administrators: Sherry Pringle, Admin., Corp.
Affairs; Anne Roman, Dir., Public Affairs.

2154
The Budres Foundation
(formerly The George V. Budres and Anna Dean
Budres Charitable Foundation)
800 Calder Plz. Bldg.
Grand Rapids, MI 49503

Established in 1991 in MI.
Donor: Budres Lumber Co.
Grantmaker type: Company-sponsored foundation.
Financial data (yr. ended 10/31/05): Assets,
$831,195 (M); expenditures, $44,068; total giving,

$19,000; qualifying distributions, $19,000; giving
activities include $19,000 for grants.
Purpose and activities: The foundation supports
organizations involved with education.
Fields of interest: Arts education; Performing arts,
education; Higher education; Environmental
education.
Limitations: Applications not accepted. Giving
primarily in MI. No grants to individuals.
Application information: Contributes only to
pre-selected organizations.
Officers: Diane Lynn Budres, Pres.; Harold C.
Schmidt, V.P.; Michael J. Taylor, Secy.; John E.
Mack, Treas.
EIN: 382966979

2155
Buffalo Bills Youth Foundation, Inc.
99 Kercheval Ave.
Grosse Pointe, MI 48236
Contact: Michelle Roberts
Application address: 1 Bills Dr., Orchard Park, NY
14127, tel.: (716) 648-1800; URL: http://
www.buffalobills.com/community/
YouthFoundation.jsp

Established in 1987 in NY.
Donors: Buffalo Bills Inc.; The Boston Beer Co.
Grantmaker type: Company-sponsored foundation.
Financial data (yr. ended 12/31/04): Assets,
$555,266 (M); gifts received, $361,453;
expenditures, $268,740; total giving, $260,314;
qualifying distributions, $268,740; giving activities
include $260,314 for 92 grants (high: $45,000;
low: $135).
Purpose and activities: The foundation supports
organizations involved with education, children and
youth, and disabled people.
Fields of interest: Education; Children/youth,
services; Disabilities, people with.
Type of support: General/operating support;
Equipment; Program development; Research.
Limitations: Giving primarily in western NY. No
grants to individuals.
Application information: Application form required.
  Initial approach: Download application form and
    mail to foundation
  Copies of proposal: 4
  Deadline(s): Mar. 31
  Final notification: Within 3 months
Officers and Directors:* P. Jane Wright,* Secy.;
Jeffrey C. Littmann,* Treas.; Charles Mitschow;
William G. Munson II; Edward Rutkowski; Ralph C.
Wilson, Jr.
EIN: 161291355

2156
Butzel Long Charitable Trust
(formerly The Butzel Long Gust & Van Zile Charitable
Trust)
150 W. Jefferson Ave., Ste. 900
Detroit, MI 48226-4450 (313) 225-7000
Contact: Richard E. Rassel, Tr.

Established in 1983 in MI.
Donor: Butzel Long.
Grantmaker type: Company-sponsored foundation.
Financial data (yr. ended 12/31/04): Assets,
$6,612 (M); gifts received, $5,470; expenditures,
$19,396; total giving, $19,322; qualifying

distributions, $19,322; giving activities include
$19,322 for grants.
Purpose and activities: The foundation supports
organizations involved with education and legal
services. Special emphasis is directed toward legal
education.
Fields of interest: Law school/education;
Education; Legal services.
Application information: Application form not
required.
  Initial approach: Proposal
  Deadline(s): Dec. 31
Trustees: Keefe Brooks; Gordon Didier; Richard E.
Rassel.
EIN: 382510263

2157
Cadillac Products Inc. Foundation
5800 Crooks Rd.
Troy, MI 48098-2830 (248) 879-5000
Contact: Roger K. Williams, Treas.

Established in 1985 in MI.
Donors: Cadillac Products Inc.; Robert J. Williams,
Sr.
Grantmaker type: Company-sponsored foundation.
Financial data (yr. ended 7/31/05): Assets,
$773,315 (M); expenditures, $4,454; total giving,
$2,000; qualifying distributions, $2,000; giving
activities include $2,000 for 2 grants (high: $1,000;
low: $1,000).
Purpose and activities: The foundation supports
Roman Catholic agencies and churches and
organizations involved with education, children and
youth, and human services.
Fields of interest: Education, fund raising/fund
distribution; Higher education; Education; Children/
youth, services; Residential/custodial care; Human
services; Roman Catholic agencies & churches.
Type of support: General/operating support.
Limitations: Giving primarily in Phoenix, AZ, and MI.
Application information: Application form not
required.
  Initial approach: Letter of inquiry
  Deadline(s): None
Officers: Robert J. Williams, Sr., Pres.; Michael P.
Williams II, V.P.; Robert J. Williams, Jr., Secy.; Roger
K. Williams, Treas.
EIN: 382636705

2158
**Champion Enterprises, Inc. Corporate
Giving Program**
2701 Cambridge Ct., Ste. 300
Auburn Hills, MI 48326-2566 (248) 340-9090
Contact: Phyllis Knight, C.F.O.

Grantmaker type: Corporate giving program.
Purpose and activities: Champion makes charitable
contributions to nonprofit organizations on a case by
case basis. Support is given primarily in areas of
company operations.
Fields of interest: General charitable giving.
Type of support: General/operating support;
Employee volunteer services; In-kind gifts.
Limitations: Giving primarily in areas of company
operations.
Application information: Application form not
required.
  Initial approach: Proposal to headquarters
  Deadline(s): None

2159
The Charter One Foundation

c/o Citizens Bank
870 Westminster St.
Providence, RI   02903

Established in 2001 in OH.
Donors: Charter One Bank, F.S.B.; Charter One Bank, N.A.
Grantmaker type: Company-sponsored foundation.
Financial data (yr. ended 12/31/04): Assets, $21,598,270 (M); expenditures, $4,508,701; total giving, $4,461,725; qualifying distributions, $4,461,725; giving activities include $4,461,725 for 296 grants (high: $250,000; low: $200).
Purpose and activities: The foundation supports organizations involved with arts and culture, education, human services, civil rights, and community development.
Fields of interest: Arts; Higher education; Education; Human services; Civil rights; Community development; Federated giving programs; Jewish federated giving programs.
Type of support: General/operating support.
Limitations: Applications not accepted. Giving in the U.S., with emphasis on IL, IN, MI, and OH. No grants to individuals.
Application information: Contributes only to pre-selected organizations.
Trustees: Citizens Bank; Lawrence K. Fish.
EIN: 300005922

2160
Chemical Financial Corporation
Contributions Program

333 E. Main St.
Midland, MI   48640
FAX: (517) 839-5479

Grantmaker type: Corporate giving program.
Purpose and activities: Chemical makes charitable contributions to nonprofit organizations involved with community development. Support is given primarily in areas of company operations.
Fields of interest: Community development.
Type of support: General/operating support; Sponsorships; In-kind gifts.
Limitations: Giving primarily in areas of company operations, with emphasis on MI.

2161
Citizens Banking Corporation Charitable
Foundation

c/o Citizens Bank Wealth Management, N.A.
328 S. Saginaw St., M.C. 002072
Flint, MI   48502

Established in 1999 in MI.
Donor: Citizens Banking Corp.
Grantmaker type: Company-sponsored foundation.
Financial data (yr. ended 12/31/05): Assets, $508,152 (M); gifts received, $69,326; expenditures, $1,055,994; total giving, $1,038,951; qualifying distributions, $1,040,533; giving activities include $1,038,951 for 363 grants (high: $75,000; low: $250).
Purpose and activities: The foundation supports organizations involved with arts and culture, education, health, human services, and community development.

Fields of interest: Arts; Education; Hospitals (general); Health care; Youth, services; Human services; Community development; Federated giving programs.
Limitations: Applications not accepted. Giving primarily in IA, MI, and WI. No grants to individuals.
Application information: Contributes only to pre-selected organizations.
Trustee: Citizens Bank Wealth Management, N.A.
EIN: 386742630

2162
Citizens Banking Corporation
Contributions Program

328 S. Saginaw St.
Flint, MI   48502
Contact: David Albert, Asst. V.P.

Grantmaker type: Corporate giving program.
Purpose and activities: As a complement to its foundation, Citizens also makes charitable contributions to nonprofit organizations directly. Support is given primarily in the Genesee County area of Flint, Michigan.
Fields of interest: Youth development; Economic development; General charitable giving.
Type of support: General/operating support; Employee volunteer services.
Limitations: Giving primarily in the Genesee County area of Flint, MI. No grants for annual campaigns or building or renovation; no employee matching gifts.
Application information: Application form not required.
   Initial approach: Proposal to headquarters

2163
Citizens First Foundation, Inc.

(formerly Citizens First Savings Charitable Foundation, Inc.)
525 Water St.
Port Huron, MI   48060

Established in 1998 in MI.
Donor: Citizens First Savings Bank.
Grantmaker type: Company-sponsored foundation.
Financial data (yr. ended 12/31/04): Assets, $23,163,631 (M); expenditures, $1,048,810; total giving, $1,023,740; qualifying distributions, $1,035,284; giving activities include $1,023,740 for 118 grants (high: $473,860; low: $50).
Purpose and activities: The foundation supports hospitals, community foundations, and organizations involved with arts and culture, education, heart and circulatory diseases, and human services.
Fields of interest: Arts; Education; Hospitals (general); Heart & circulatory diseases; Human services; Foundations (community); Federated giving programs.
Type of support: General/operating support.
Limitations: Applications not accepted. Giving primarily in MI. No grants to individuals.
Application information: Contributes only to pre-selected organizations.
Officers and Directors: Marshall J. Campbell, Pres.; Timothy D. Regan, Secy.-Treas.; Ronald W. Cooley; David C. Devendorf; Christopher A. Kellerman.
EIN: 383401243

2164
The Cleveland-Cliffs Foundation

1100 Superior Ave.
Cleveland, OH   44114-2589
Contact: Dana W. Byrne, V.P.
URL: http://www.cleveland-cliffs.com/General/Community/foundation.asp

Established in 1962 in OH.
Donors: Cleveland-Cliffs Inc; Tilden Mining Co.; Empire Iron Mining Partnership; Hibbing Taconite Co.; Northshore Mining Co.
Grantmaker type: Company-sponsored foundation.
Financial data (yr. ended 12/31/04): Assets, $625,086 (M); gifts received, $700,000; expenditures, $242,487; total giving, $242,387; qualifying distributions, $242,487; giving activities include $205,961 for 40 grants (high: $50,000; low: $250), and $36,426 for 48 employee matching gifts.
Purpose and activities: The foundation supports museums and hospitals and organizations involved with education and human services.
Fields of interest: Museums; Higher education; Education; Hospitals (general); Children/youth, services; Human services; Federated giving programs.
Type of support: General/operating support; Annual campaigns; Capital campaigns; Building/renovation; Employee matching gifts.
Limitations: Giving primarily in areas of company operations, with emphasis on the upper MI peninsula, northeastern MN, and Cleveland, OH. No grants to individuals; no loans.
Publications: Application guidelines.
Application information: Application form not required.
   Initial approach: Proposal
   Copies of proposal: 1
   Deadline(s): None
Officers and Trustees:* John S. Brinzo,* Pres.; Dana W. Byrne, V.P.; William R. Calfee; Donald J. Gallagher; David H. Gunning.
EIN: 346525124

2165
CMS Energy Foundation

c/o Consumers Energy, Tax Dept.
1 Energy Plz., EP 10-228
Jackson, MI   49201-2276   (517) 788-0432
Contact: Carolyn A. Bloodworth, Secy.-Treas.

Established in 2001 in MI.
Donor: CMS Energy Corp.
Grantmaker type: Company-sponsored foundation.
Financial data (yr. ended 2/28/05): Assets, $111,536 (M); gifts received, $100,000; expenditures, $20; total giving, $0; qualifying distributions, $20.
Purpose and activities: The foundation supports organizations involved with arts and culture, education, health, and human services.
Fields of interest: Arts; Education; Children/youth, services; Human services; Economic development; Federated giving programs.
Type of support: General/operating support.
Limitations: Giving on a national basis, with some emphasis on MI, MO, and TX. No support for discriminatory organizations, United Way-supported organizations, political organizations, religious organizations not of direct benefit to the entire community, or labor, veterans', fraternal, or social organizations. No grants to individuals, or for

fundraising, debt reduction, sports tournaments, talent or beauty contests, or political campaigns; no loans for small business.

Application information: Proposals should be no longer than 2 pages in length. Additional information may be requested at a later date. Application form not required.

    Initial approach: Proposal

    Deadline(s): None

Officers and Directors:* Kenneth Whipple,* Chair.; David G. Mengebier, Pres.; Carolyn A. Bloodworth, Secy.-Treas.; Thomas W. Elward; David W. Joos; S. Kinnie Smith, Jr.; Thomas J. Webb.

EIN: 383575175

2166
Collins & Aikman Foundation

(formerly The Wickes Foundation)
250 Stephenson Hwy.
Troy, MI 48083

Established in 1987 in CA.

Donor: Collins & Aikman Corp.

Grantmaker type: Company-sponsored foundation.

Financial data (yr. ended 12/31/04): Assets, $2,250,978 (M); expenditures, $188,432; total giving, $183,127; qualifying distributions, $188,432; giving activities include $183,127 for 36 grants (high: $32,000; low: $50).

Purpose and activities: The foundation supports organizations involved with education, health, and children and youth.

Fields of interest: Higher education; Education; Health care; Boy scouts; Children/youth, services; Federated giving programs.

Type of support: General/operating support; Scholarship funds; Employee matching gifts.

Limitations: Applications not accepted. Giving primarily in MI. No grants to individuals.

Application information: Contributes only to pre-selected organizations.

Officers and Directors:* Bryce M. Koth,* Pres.; John A. Galante,* V.P. and Treas.; Jay B. Knoll,* Secy.

EIN: 954085655

Selected grants: The following grants were reported in 2003.

$75,000 to First Tee of Michigan Foundation, Huntington Woods, MI.

$52,500 to North American International Auto Show, Troy, MI.

$32,000 to March of Dimes Birth Defects Foundation, Southfield, MI.

$27,100 to National Merit Scholarship Corporation, Evanston, IL.

$10,000 to Boys and Girls Club.

$7,500 to Hospice of Michigan, Detroit, MI.

$5,000 to Detroit Science Center, Detroit, MI.

$3,500 to Childrens Charities Coalition, Pontiac, MI.

$2,500 to Boy Scouts of America.

$1,000 to Salvation Army.

2167
Comerica Bank Corporate Giving Program

P.O. Box 75000, M.C. 3390
Detroit, MI 48275 (313) 222-3571
Contact: Caroline Chambers, V.P.
FAX: (313) 222-5555;
E-mail: caroline_chambers@comerica.com;
URL: http://www.comerica.com/
vgn-ext-templating/v/index.jsp?

vgnextoid=25fa788635bd2010VgnVCM10000043 02a8c0RCRD

Grantmaker type: Corporate giving program.

Purpose and activities: As a complement to its foundation, Comerica also makes charitable contributions to nonprofit organizations directly. Support is given primarily in areas of company operations.

Fields of interest: Arts; Health care; Health organizations; Housing/shelter; Human services; Economic development; Community development; Public affairs.

Type of support: General/operating support; Technical assistance; Employee volunteer services; Sponsorships.

Limitations: Giving primarily in areas of company operations, with emphasis on CA, FL, MI, and TX.

2168
Comerica Foundation

c/o Comerica Inc.
P.O. Box 75000, M.C. 3390
Detroit, MI 48275-3390 (313) 222-7356
Contact: Caroline E. Chambers, Secy.
FAX: (313) 222-5555; Application address: 500 Woodward Ave., Detroit, MI 48226-3390;
URL: http://www.comerica.com/
vgn-ext-templating/v/index.jsp?
vgnextoid=374970d75d994010VgnVCM1000004 502a8c0RCRD

Established in 1997 in MI.

Donors: Comerica Bank; Comerica Inc.

Grantmaker type: Company-sponsored foundation.

Financial data (yr. ended 12/31/04): Assets, $5,456,570 (M); gifts received, $7,162,500; expenditures, $7,692,490; total giving, $7,687,140; qualifying distributions, $7,691,681; giving activities include $7,687,140 for 648 grants (high: $805,000; low: $25).

Purpose and activities: The foundation supports organizations involved with arts and culture, education, health, human services, and community development.

Fields of interest: Arts; Elementary/secondary education; Higher education; Education; Health care; Children/youth, services; Human services; Community development; Federated giving programs.

Limitations: Giving primarily in MI.

Publications: Application guidelines; Annual report.

Application information: Application form not required.

    Initial approach: Mail proposal to application address

    Deadline(s): None

Officers: Richard A. Collister, Pres.; Caroline E. Chambers, Secy.; Megan Burkhart, Treas.

Directors: Beth Acton; Frank DeAramas; Linda Forte; Mike Fulton; Jim Garavaglia; John Haggerty; Ron Marcinelli; Sharon McMurray; Albert Taylor; Mark Yonkman.

EIN: 383373052

Selected grants: The following grants were reported in 2004.

$971,000 to United Way for Southeastern Michigan, Detroit, MI. 2 grants: $805,000 (For Torch Drive Corporate Campaign), $166,000 (For New Detroit Fund).

$500,000 to Detroit Renaissance, Detroit, MI. For Downtown Development Initiative.

$250,000 to ACCION San Diego, San Diego, CA.

$250,000 to Community Financial Resource Center, Los Angeles, CA.

$200,000 to Greenlining Institute, Berkeley, CA. For capital campaign.

$187,500 to Local Initiatives Support Corporation (LISC), Detroit, MI.

$167,000 to Charles H. Wright Museum of African-American History, Detroit, MI.

$167,000 to Michigan Opera Theater, Detroit, MI. For New Century Fund Campaign.

$150,000 to Detroit Regional Chamber, Detroit, MI. For partnership.

2169
Consumers Energy Company Contributions Program

(formerly Consumers Power Company Contributions Program)
1 Energy Plz., Rm. EP8-210
Jackson, MI 49201 (517) 788-0432
Contact: Carolyn A. Bloodworth, Dir., Corp. Giving

Grantmaker type: Corporate giving program.

Financial data (yr. ended 12/31/02): Total giving, $293,300, including $293,300 for 133 grants (high: $25,000; low: $100).

Purpose and activities: As a complement to its foundation, Consumers Energy also makes charitable contributions to nonprofit organizations directly. Support is given primarily in areas of company operations.

Fields of interest: Museums; Performing arts; Performing arts, theater; Performing arts, music; Arts; Education, fund raising/fund distribution; Education; Environment; Animals/wildlife, preservation/protection; Health care; Mental health/crisis services; Health organizations; Youth, services; Family services; Human services; Urban/ community development; Community development; Government/public administration; Public affairs; General charitable giving; Minorities; Women.

Type of support: General/operating support; Annual campaigns; Capital campaigns; Building/ renovation; Equipment; Endowments; Program development; Conferences/seminars; Publication; Seed money; Employee matching gifts; In-kind gifts; Matching/challenge support.

Limitations: Giving primarily in areas of company operations, with emphasis on MI. No support for fraternal or veterans' organizations, churches, or K-12 schools. No grants to individuals.

Publications: Application guidelines.

Application information: The Government and Public Affairs Department handles giving. Application form not required.

    Initial approach: Proposal to headquarters

    Copies of proposal: 1

    Deadline(s): First quarter is preferred

    Final notification: 8 to 10 weeks

Number of staff: 1 full-time professional; 1 full-time support.

2170
Consumers Energy Foundation

(formerly Consumers Power Foundation)
1 Energy Plz., Rm. EP8-210
Jackson, MI 49201 (517) 788-0432
Contact: Carolyn A. Bloodworth, Secy.-Treas.
FAX: (517) 788-2281;
E-mail: foundation@consumersenergy.com;

Additional tel.: (877) 501-4952; URL: http://
www.consumersenergy.com/foundation

Established in 1990 in MI.
Donors: Consumers Power Co.; Consumers Energy
Co.
Grantmaker type: Company-sponsored foundation.
Financial data (yr. ended 12/31/04): Assets,
$2,520,448 (M); gifts received, $1,000,000;
expenditures, $587,945; total giving, $587,925;
qualifying distributions, $587,945; giving activities
include $587,925 for 327 grants (high: $25,000;
low: $50).
Purpose and activities: The foundation supports
organizations involved with arts and culture,
education, the environment, human services, and
community development.
Fields of interest: Arts; Higher education;
Education; Environment; Human services;
Community development.
Type of support: General/operating support; Capital
campaigns; Building/renovation; Employee
matching gifts.
Limitations: Giving primarily in MI; some giving also
on a national and international basis. No support for
religious organizations not of direct benefit to the
entire community, labor, political, or veterans'
organizations, fraternal or social clubs, or United
Way-supported organizations. No grants to
individuals, or for endowments, debt reduction,
sports tournaments, talent or beauty contests, or
tickets for fundraising events; no loans for small
businesses.
Publications: Application guidelines; Informational
brochure.
Application information: The CMF Common Grant
Application Form is required. Application form
required.
  Initial approach: Mail proposal and application
    form to foundation
  Copies of proposal: 1
  Deadline(s): None
  Board meeting date(s): Quarterly
  Final notification: 6 to 8 weeks
Officers and Directors:* Kenneth Whipple,* Chair.;
David Mengebier,* Pres.; Carolyn A. Bloodworth,
Secy.-Treas.; David W. Joos; John G. Russell; S.
Kinnie Smith, Jr.; Thomas T. Webb.
Number of staff: 2 full-time professional; 2 full-time
support.
EIN: 382935534
Selected grants: The following grants were reported
in 2003.
$99,500 to United Way of Jackson County, Jackson,
  MI.
$50,000 to Detroit Institute of Arts, Detroit, MI.
$18,000 to United Way, Greater Kalamazoo,
  Kalamazoo, MI.
$6,000 to Nature Conservancy, Lansing, MI.
$5,000 to Community Foundation for Muskegon
  County, Muskegon, MI.
$5,000 to Davenport University, Grand Rapids, MI.
$5,000 to Disability Connections, Jackson, MI.
$5,000 to Leila Arboretum Society, Battle Creek, MI.
$5,000 to Michigan Opera Theater, Detroit, MI.
$5,000 to Western Michigan University Foundation,
  Kalamazoo, MI.

2171
DaimlerChrysler Corporation Contributions Program
(formerly Chrysler Corporation Contributions
Program)
c/o 485-10-94
1000 Chrysler Dr.
Auburn Hills, MI 48326-2766 (248) 512-2502
Contact: Brian Glowiak, V.P. and Secy.,
DaimlerChrysler Corporation Fund

Grantmaker type: Corporate giving program.
Purpose and activities: As a complement to its
foundation, DaimlerChrysler also makes charitable
contributions to nonprofit organizations directly.
Support is given primarily in areas of company
operations.
Fields of interest: Business/industry; Public affairs;
General charitable giving.
Type of support: Cause-related marketing; Public
relations services; Sponsorships.
Limitations: Giving primarily in areas of company
operations.
Application information: Application form required.
  Initial approach: Complete online application form
  Copies of proposal: 1
  Deadline(s): None
  Final notification: 1 to 3 months

2172
DaimlerChrysler Corporation Fund
(formerly Chrysler Corporation Fund)
CIMS: 485-10-94
1000 Chrysler Dr.
Auburn Hills, MI 48326-2766 (248) 512-2502
Contact: Brian G. Glowiak, V.P. and Secy.
FAX: (248) 512-2503; E-mail: mek@dcx.com;
URL: http://www2.daimlerchrysler.com/dccfund/

Incorporated in 1953 in MI.
Donors: Chrysler Corp.; DaimlerChrysler Corp.
Grantmaker type: Company-sponsored foundation.
Financial data (yr. ended 12/31/05): Assets,
$37,859,586 (M); gifts received, $35,000,000;
expenditures, $27,102,579; total giving,
$25,954,013; qualifying distributions,
$27,081,543; giving activities include
$25,954,013 for 1,190 grants (high: $1,850,769).
Purpose and activities: The fund supports
organizations involved with arts and culture,
vocational, higher education, business, and
engineering education, the environment,
employment, highway safety, human services,
community development, science, and
transportation.
Fields of interest: Arts, cultural/ethnic awareness;
Arts; Vocational education; Higher education;
Business school/education; Engineering school/
education; Education; Environment, energy;
Environment; Employment, training; Safety,
automotive safety; Human services; Economic
development; Business/industry; Science; Public
policy, research; Transportation.
Type of support: General/operating support;
Continuing support; Annual campaigns; Emergency
funds; Program development; Curriculum
development; Employee matching gifts;
Employee-related scholarships.
Limitations: Giving primarily in areas of company
operations in Wittman, AZ, Irvine, CA, Englewood,
CO, Newark, DE, Washington, DC, Orlando, FL,
Belvidere and Lisle, IL, Indianapolis and Kokomo,

IN, Elkridge, MD, Detroit, MI, Fenton, MO, Syracuse
and Tappan, NY, Perrysburg, Toledo, and Twinsburg,
OH, and Addison, TX, Kenosha, WI; giving also to
regional and national organizations. No support for
discriminatory organizations or private or corporate
foundations. No grants to individuals (except for
employee-related scholarships), or for endowments,
general operating support for local United Way
agencies, direct health care delivery programs,
additions or renovations to real estate, fundraising
activities related to individual sponsorship, debt
reduction, religious or sectarian programs, athletic
programs involving individual teams; no loans; no
vehicle donations.
Publications: Application guidelines; Annual report
(including application guidelines).
Application information: Multi-year funding is not
automatic. Application form required.
  Initial approach: Complete online application form
  Deadline(s): Nov. 1
  Board meeting date(s): As required, usually
    quarterly
  Final notification: 4 months
Officers and Trustees:* W. Frank Fountain,* Pres.;
Brian G. Glowiak, V.P. and Secy.; Timothy P. Dykstra,
V.P. and Treas.; E.S. "Steve" Harris, Cont.; Joachim
W. Eberhardt; Frank J. Ewasyshyn; Frank O. Klegon;
Robert G. Liberatore; Nancy A. Rae; Thomas W.
Sidlik; Jason H. Vines; Jurgen Walker.
Number of staff: 2 full-time professional; 5 full-time
support; 1 part-time support.
EIN: 386087371
Selected grants: The following grants were reported
in 2004.
$2,444,700 to United Way for Southeastern
  Michigan, Detroit, MI. For Torch Drive pledge and
  Automotive Business Match.
$1,596,300 to Detroit Renaissance Foundation,
  Detroit, MI. For Directors Contributions.
$1,073,303 to Detroit Institute of Arts, Detroit, MI.
  For Century Campaign.
$685,300 to Scholarship America, Saint Peter, MN.
  For DCCF Scholarship Program Awards.
$500,000 to Focus: Hope, Detroit, MI. For Center
  for Advanced Technologies (CAT), educating
  students in manufacturing while they work toward
  bachelor and associate engineering degrees.
$67,000 to United Way of Summit County, Akron,
  OH. For corporate contribution.
$50,000 to Executive Service Corps of Detroit,
  Southfield, MI. For Management Assistance
  Program.
$31,960 to Pennsylvania State University,
  University Park, PA. For Aid to Higher Education
  Program: for Society of Black Engineers.
$25,000 to Hispanic Association of Colleges and
  Universities, San Antonio, TX. For Aid to Higher
  Education Program: Diversity grant.
$25,000 to Toledo Cultural Arts Center at Valentine
  Theater, Toledo, OH. For season sponsorship of
  productions.

2173
Dearborn Cable Communications Fund
22211 W. Warren St.
Dearborn Heights, MI 48127-2531
(313) 277-5800
Contact: Margaret Campbell

Established in 1984 in MI.
Donors: Group W Cable, Inc.; Cablevision of
Michigan, Inc.
Grantmaker type: Company-sponsored foundation.

Financial data (yr. ended 12/31/05): Assets, $1,039,986 (M); expenditures, $75,376; total giving, $42,894; qualifying distributions, $42,894; giving activities include $42,894 for grants.
Purpose and activities: The foundation supports programs designed to provide cable television programming of interest to the general community.
Fields of interest: Media/communications.
Type of support: General/operating support; Building/renovation; Equipment; Technical assistance.
Limitations: Giving primarily in the Dearborn, MI, area.
Application information: Application form not required.
   Initial approach: Proposal
   Copies of proposal: 9
   Deadline(s): None
   Board meeting date(s): Bimonthly
   Final notification: 60 days
Officers: Peggy Campbell, Pres.; Betsy Cushman, V.P.; Mark Campbell, Secy.; Nancy Daher, Treas.; Andy Fradkin, Compt.
Directors: Kurt Doelle; Bill Dunning; Russ Gibb; Mike Katona; Barb Parker.
EIN: 382571195

2174
Delphi Corporation Contributions Program
(formerly Delphi Automotive Systems Corporation Contributions Program)
c/o Corp. Affairs Dept.
5725 Delphi Dr., M.C. 483-400-501
Troy, MI 48098
Contact: Ronald L. Beeber, Corp. Dir., Govt. and Community Rels.
URL: http://delphi.com/about/social

Grantmaker type: Corporate giving program.
Purpose and activities: As a complement to its foundation, Delphi also makes charitable contributions to nonprofit organizations directly. Support is given on a national basis in areas of company operations.
Fields of interest: Education; Science; General charitable giving.
Type of support: Sponsorships.
Limitations: Applications not accepted. Giving on a national basis in areas of company operations. No support for political, legislative, lobbying, or fraternal organizations, private foundations, or hospitals or health care institutions. No grants to individuals, or for endowments, capital campaigns or construction, general operating support or debt reduction, or conferences, workshops, or seminars not directly related to Delphi's business interests.
Application information: Contributes only to pre-selected organizations. The Corporate Affairs Department handles giving. Contributions are currently very limited.
Number of staff: 4 part-time professional; 1 part-time support.

2175
Delphi Foundation, Inc.
5725 Delphi Dr., M.C. 483-400-501
Troy, MI 48098
URL: http://delphi.com/about/social/delphifoundation

Established in 1998 in MI.

Donors: General Motors Foundation, Inc.; Delphi Automotive Systems Corp.; Delphi Corp.
Grantmaker type: Company-sponsored foundation.
Financial data (yr. ended 12/31/04): Assets, $17,728,304 (M); expenditures, $1,034,308; total giving, $777,608; qualifying distributions, $770,513; giving activities include $777,608 for 192 grants (high: $65,000; low: $100).
Purpose and activities: The foundation supports organizations involved with science and technology education and other areas related to Delphi's business objectives.
Fields of interest: Education; General charitable giving.
Limitations: Applications not accepted. Giving on a national basis. No support for political, lobbying, or fraternal organizations, private foundations, hospitals, health care institutions, schools, or religious organizations. No grants to individuals, or for endowments, capital campaigns, general operating support, debt reduction, or conferences, workshops, or seminars not directly related to Delphi's business interests.
Publications: IRS Form 990-PF.
Application information: The foundation utilizes an invitation only Request For Proposal (RFP) process. Unsolicited requests are not accepted.
Officers and Trustees:* Karen L. Healy,* Chair.; Nancy Moss, Secy.; John Arle, Treas.; Ronald L. Beeber; Mary Beth Inaciak; James P. Whitson.
EIN: 383442971

2176
DENSO International America, Inc. Corporate Giving Program
24777 DENSO Dr.
P.O. Box 5047, M.C. 4600
Southfield, MI 48086-5047 (248) 372-8232
Contact: John Voorhorst, V.P., Ext. Affairs
FAX: (248) 213-2550;
E-mail: john_voorhorst@denso-diam.com;
URL: http://www.densocorp-na.com/corporate/community.html

Grantmaker type: Corporate giving program.
Financial data (yr. ended 3/31/05): Total giving, $535,928, including $512,865 for 65 grants (high: $60,000; low: $200), $2,585 for 18 employee matching gifts, and $20,478 for 8 in-kind gifts.
Purpose and activities: As a complement to its foundation, DENSO International also makes charitable contributions to nonprofit organizations directly. Support is given primarily in southeastern Michigan.
Fields of interest: Elementary/secondary education; Environment.
Type of support: Program development; Scholarship funds; Employee volunteer services; Sponsorships; Employee matching gifts; Donated equipment; Donated products.
Limitations: Giving primarily in southeastern MI. No support for discriminatory organizations, religious organizations, political organizations, or veterans' or labor organizations or social clubs. No grants to individuals, or for endowments, political initiatives, dinners or fundraisers, political campaigns, capital campaigns, conferences, trips, or similar events, or advertising.
Publications: Application guidelines.
Application information: The External Affairs Department handles giving. A contributions committee reviews all requests. Application form required.

   Initial approach: Complete online application form
   Copies of proposal: 1
   Deadline(s): None
   Committee meeting date(s): Aug. and Jan.
   Final notification: Following review
Contributions Committee: John Voorhorst, Chair.; Barbara Wertheimer, Prog. Coord.
Number of staff: 1 part-time professional.

2177
DENSO North America Foundation
24777 DENSO Dr.
Southfield, MI 48033 (248) 372-8233
Contact: John Voorhorst, Pres.
FAX: (248) 213-2550;
E-mail: densofoundation@denso-diam.com;
URL: http://www.densofoundation.org

Established in 2001 in MI.
Donor: DENSO International America, Inc.
Grantmaker type: Company-sponsored foundation.
Financial data (yr. ended 12/31/05): Assets, $7,570,508 (M); expenditures, $374,612; total giving, $373,500; qualifying distributions, $372,074; giving activities include $373,500 for grants.
Purpose and activities: The foundation supports organizations involved with engineering education and related business areas. Special emphasis is directed toward programs designed to advance automotive engineering and supply-side business practices.
Fields of interest: Business school/education; Engineering school/education.
International interests: Canada; Mexico.
Type of support: Building/renovation; Equipment; Program development.
Limitations: Applications not accepted. Giving on a national basis, with emphasis on CA, MI, and TN, and in Canada and Mexico. No grants to individuals.
Application information: The foundation utilizes an invitation only Request For Proposal (RFP) process. Unsolicited requests are not accepted.
   Board meeting date(s): May and Oct.
Officers and Directors: John Voorhorst, Pres.; Barbara Wertheimer, Secy.; Kim Madaj, Treas.; David Cole; Stanley Tooley; James Woroniecki.
Number of staff: 1 full-time professional.
EIN: 383547055
Selected grants: The following grants were reported in 2005.
$50,000 to Pellissippi State Technical Community College, Knoxville, TN. For equipment.
$50,000 to Robert B. Miller College, Battle Creek, MI. For equipment.
$50,000 to University of Michigan, Dearborn, MI. For building improvement.
$45,000 to Lawrence Technological University, Southfield, MI. For building improvement.
$41,000 to California State University, Long Beach, CA. For equipment.
$37,500 to Tennessee Technological University, Cookeville, TN. For building improvement.
$30,000 to Michigan Technological University, Houghton, MI. For program support.
$25,000 to American Red Cross, National Headquarters, DC. For disaster relief for Hurricane Katrina.
$25,000 to University of Tennessee, Knoxville, TN. For equipment.
$20,000 to Kettering University, Flint, MI. For building improvement.

2178
Detroit Diesel Scholarship Foundation, Inc.
c/o Detroit Diesel Corp.
13400 Outer Dr. W.
Detroit, MI 48239-4001
Contact: Ken Holman

Established in 1990 in MI.
Donor: Detroit Diesel Corp.
Grantmaker type: Company-sponsored foundation.
Financial data (yr. ended 12/31/05): Assets, $1,536 (M); gifts received, $6,000; expenditures, $6,039; total giving, $6,000; qualifying distributions, $6,000; giving activities include $6,000 for grants to individuals.
Purpose and activities: The foundation awards college scholarships to spouses, children, and grandchildren of employees of Detroit Diesel Corp.
Type of support: Employee-related scholarships.
Limitations: Applications not accepted. Giving limited to Detroit, MI.
Application information: Contributes only through employee-related scholarships.
   Board meeting date(s): Mar.
Officers and Directors: Philip Bezaire,* Pres.; Joseph M. Herrick, Secy.; Joshua W. Yacker, Secy.; Andrew M. Williamson, Treas.; Paul Ryznar; Joseph B. Street.
EIN: 382964503

2179
The Detroit Lions, Inc. Corporate Giving Program
222 Republic Dr.
Allen Park, MI 48101
URL: http://www.detroitlions.com/section_display.cfm?section_id=5&top=1&level=2

Grantmaker type: Corporate giving program.
Purpose and activities: The Detroit Lions make charitable contributions of memorabilia to nonprofit organizations on a case by case basis. Support is given primarily in Michigan.
Fields of interest: General charitable giving.
Type of support: In-kind gifts.
Limitations: Giving primarily in MI. No game ticket donations.
Application information: Proposals should be submitted using organization letterhead. Application form not required.
   Initial approach: Proposal to headquarters
   Copies of proposal: 1
   Deadline(s): 6 weeks prior to need

2180
Detroit Pistons Basketball Company Contributions Program
c/o Community Rels.
4 Championship Dr.
Auburn Hills, MI 48326-9906 (248) 377-8472
URL: http://www.nba.com/pistons/community

Grantmaker type: Corporate giving program.
Purpose and activities: The Detroit Pistons make charitable contributions of game tickets and memorabilia to nonprofit organizations involved with youth development and on a case by case basis. Support is given primarily in Michigan.
Fields of interest: Youth development; General charitable giving.

Type of support: In-kind gifts; Donated products.
Limitations: Giving primarily in MI. No support for political organizations or candidates. No grants to individuals, or for general operating support, political campaigns, trips or tours, or seminars; no in-kind gifts for prizes, recognition gifts, or giveaways.
Application information: Proposals should be submitted using organization letterhead. Proposals should be brief. Support is limited to 1 contribution per organization during any given year. Application form not required.
   Initial approach: Proposal to headquarters
   Copies of proposal: 1
   Deadline(s): 6 weeks prior to need
   Final notification: 1 to 2 weeks prior to need

2181
Detroit Red Wings, Inc. Corporate Giving Program
600 Civic Center Dr.
Detroit, MI 48226 (313) 396-7524
FAX: (313) 567-0296; *URL:* http://www.detroitredwings.com/community

Grantmaker type: Corporate giving program.
Purpose and activities: The Detroit Red Wings make charitable contributions of memorabilia to nonprofit organizations on a case by case basis. Support is given primarily in Michigan.
Fields of interest: General charitable giving.
Type of support: In-kind gifts.
Limitations: Giving primarily in MI. No game ticket donations.
Application information: Proposals should be submitted using organization letterhead. Application form not required.
   Initial approach: Proposal to headquarters
   Copies of proposal: 1

2182
Detroit Shock Corporate Giving Program
c/o Community Rels.
3 Championship Dr.
Auburn Hills, MI 48326-9906 (248) 377-8637
URL: http://www.wnba.com/shock/community

Grantmaker type: Corporate giving program.
Purpose and activities: The Detroit Shock make charitable contributions of game tickets and memorabilia to nonprofit organizations involved with youth development and on a case by case basis. Support is given primarily in Michigan.
Fields of interest: Youth development; General charitable giving.
Type of support: In-kind gifts; Donated products.
Limitations: Giving primarily in MI. No support for political organizations or candidates. No grants to individuals, or for general operating support, political campaigns, trips or tours, or seminars; no game ticket or memorabilia donations for prizes, volunteer recognition gifts, or giveaways.
Application information: Proposals should be submitted using organization letterhead. Proposals should be brief. Support is limited to 1 contribution per organization during any given year. Organizations receiving support are asked to provide a final report. Application form not required.
   Initial approach: Proposal to headquarters
   Copies of proposal: 1

   Deadline(s): 6 weeks prior to need
   Final notification: 1 to 2 weeks prior to need for memorabilia donations

2183
Dickinson Wright PLLC Corporate Giving Program
38525 Woodward Ave., Ste. 2000
Bloomfield Hills, MI 48304-2970
(248) 433-7200
Contact: Henry M. Grix, Partner
FAX: (248) 433-7274;
E-mail: hgrix@dickinson-wright.com

Grantmaker type: Corporate giving program.
Purpose and activities: Dickinson Wright makes charitable contributions to nonprofit organizations on a case by case basis. Support is given primarily in areas of company operations.
Fields of interest: General charitable giving.
Type of support: General/operating support.
Limitations: Giving primarily in areas of company operations.

2184
Domino's Pizza, Inc. Corporate Giving Program
c/o Community Rels.
30 Frank Lloyd Wright Dr., P.O. Box 997
Ann Arbor, MI 48106-0997
FAX: (734) 930-4346

Grantmaker type: Corporate giving program.
Purpose and activities: Domino's makes charitable contributions of pizza to nonprofit organizations on a case by case basis. Support is given primarily in areas of company operations.
Fields of interest: General charitable giving.
Type of support: Donated products.
Limitations: Giving primarily in areas of company operations, with emphasis on the Ann Arbor, Saline, and Ypsilanti, MI, areas; giving also to national organizations.
Application information: Application form not required.
   Initial approach: Proposal to nearest company store; mail or fax proposal to headquarters for organizations located in the Ann Arbor, Saline, or Ypsilanti, MI, areas

2185
The Dow Chemical Company Foundation
2030 Dow Ctr.
Midland, MI 48674
Contact: R.N. "Bo" Miller, Pres. and Exec. Dir.
URL: http://www.dow.com/about/corp/social/social.htm

Established in 1979 in MI.
Donor: The Dow Chemical Co.
Grantmaker type: Company-sponsored foundation.
Financial data (yr. ended 12/31/05): Assets, $115,244,709 (M); gifts received, $125,000,000; expenditures, $15,955,345; total giving, $15,953,729; qualifying distributions, $15,953,729; giving activities include $15,953,729 for 711 grants (high: $3,920,000; low: $25).
Purpose and activities: The foundation supports organizations involved with K-12 education, the

environment, community development, and chemistry.

Fields of interest: Elementary/secondary education; Environment; Community development; Chemistry.

Type of support: In-kind gifts; General/operating support; Program development; Employee matching gifts.

Limitations: Giving primarily in areas of company operations. No support for political or religious organizations. No grants to individuals (except through special relief funds), or for travel or administrative costs.

Publications: Informational brochure.

Application information: Application form not required.

   Initial approach: Letter of inquiry
   Copies of proposal: 1
   Deadline(s): None
   Board meeting date(s): Usually 4 times per year
   Final notification: 2 to 3 months

Officers and Trustees:* Andrew N. Liveris,* Chair.; R.N. "Bo" Miller,* Pres. and Exec. Dir.; Luciano R. Respini,* V.P.; V.A. Gilfeather, Secy.; G.J. McGuire, Treas.; P.H. Cook; J. McIlvenny; R.S. Myers; G.R. Veurink; O.U. Vignart; L.J. Washington.

Number of staff: 1 part-time professional; 1 part-time support.

EIN: 382314603

Selected grants: The following grants were reported in 2004.

$550,000 to University of Michigan, Business School, Ann Arbor, MI.

$500,000 to Brazosport College Foundation, Lake Jackson, TX.

$500,000 to Purdue University, West Lafayette, IN. For Chemical Engineering Capital Campaign Fund.

$354,020 to Kansas State University Foundation, Manhattan, KS.

$150,000 to Midland County Educational Service Agency, Midland, MI.

$139,081 to Texas A & M University Development Foundation, College Station, TX.

$100,000 to Clemson University, College of Engineering and Science, Clemson, SC.

$100,000 to University of Minnesota, Department of Chemistry, Minneapolis, MN.

$97,540 to Delta College, University Center, MI.

$95,000 to Northwestern University, Evanston, IL.

2186
Dow Corning Foundation

2200 W. Salzburg Rd., Mail No. C01252
Midland, MI 48686-0994 (989) 496-6290
Contact: Anne M. DeBoer, Exec. Dir.
E-mail: community@dowcorning.com; *URL:* http://www.dowcorning.com/content/about/aboutcomm/aboutcomm_globalgivingstrategy1.asp

Established in 1982 in MI.

Donor: Dow Corning Corp.

Grantmaker type: Company-sponsored foundation.

Financial data (yr. ended 12/31/04): Assets, $17,446,131 (M); gifts received, $2,500,000; expenditures, $1,721,245; total giving, $1,612,006; qualifying distributions, $1,714,994; giving activities include $1,324,967 for 74 grants (high: $235,000; low: $100), and $287,039 for 318 employee matching gifts.

Purpose and activities: The foundation supports organizations involved with K-12 education. Special emphasis is directed toward programs designed to

increase access to math, science, and technology education.

Fields of interest: Elementary/secondary education.

International interests: Belgium; Brazil; China; Germany; India; Japan; South Korea; Wales.

Type of support: Capital campaigns; Building/renovation; Equipment; Program development; Seed money; Curriculum development; Employee matching gifts.

Limitations: Giving on a national and international basis in areas of company operations, with emphasis on Noble and Switzerland counties, IN, Carroll and Hardin counties, KY, Bay, Midland, and Saginaw counties, MI, Guilford County, NC, Seneffe, Belgium, Campinas, Brazil, Songjiang, China, Wiesbaden, Germany, Pune, India, Chiba, Fukui, and Yamakita, Japan, Jincheon, South Korea, and Barry, Wales. No support for veterans', religious, or political organizations. No grants to individuals, or for general operating support, conferences, dinners, fundraising events, or public advertisements.

Publications: Application guidelines.

Application information: An application form will be sent following a telephone or personal interview. Application form required.

   Initial approach: E-mail or telephone foundation
   Deadline(s): None
   Board meeting date(s): Quarterly

Officers and Trustees:* Marie N. Eckstein,* Pres.; Thomas H. Lane, V.P.; Paul A. Marcela, Secy.; Brad E. Sauve, Treas.; Mohamed A. Ahmed; Scott E. Fuson; Kim R. Houston-Philpot; Feifei Lin; James W. White.

Number of staff: 1 part-time professional; 1 part-time support.

EIN: 382376485

2187
DTE Energy Company Contributions Program

c/o Corp. Contribs. and Community Involvement
2000 2nd Ave., Rm. 1046 WCB
Detroit, MI 48226
Contact: Karla Hall, Mgr., Corp. Contribs. and Community Involvement
URL: http://www.dteenergy.com/community

Grantmaker type: Corporate giving program.

Financial data (yr. ended 12/31/04): Total giving, $480,000, including $380,000 for 350 grants (high: $25,000; low: $100), and $100,000 for 400 in-kind gifts.

Purpose and activities: As a complement to its foundation, DTE also makes charitable contributions to nonprofit organizations directly. Support is given primarily in areas of company operations.

Fields of interest: Education; Environment; Civil rights, equal rights; Community development; Leadership development.

Type of support: Employee volunteer services; Annual campaigns; Cause-related marketing; Sponsorships; In-kind gifts.

Limitations: Giving primarily in areas of company operations in MI. No support for religious, fraternal, political, labor, or veterans' organizations. No grants to individuals, or for conferences, advertising, research, or general operating support for tax-supported organizations.

Publications: Application guidelines; Corporate giving report; Informational brochure (including application guidelines); Program policy statement.

Application information: The Corporate and Government Affairs Department handles giving. A contributions committee reviews all requests. Application form not required.

   Initial approach: Proposal to headquarters
   Copies of proposal: 1
   Deadline(s): Apr. 15, Aug. 15, and Dec. 15
   Committee meeting date(s): 3 times per year
   Final notification: 6 to 12 weeks

Number of staff: 3 full-time professional; 2 full-time support.

2188
DTE Energy Foundation

(formerly Detroit Edison Foundation)
2000 2nd Ave., Rm. 1046 WCB
Detroit, MI 48226-1279
Contact: Karla Hall, V.P. and Secy.
URL: http://www.dteenergy.com/about/community/foundation/foundationSupport.html

Established in 1986 in MI.

Donor: The Detroit Edison Co.

Grantmaker type: Company-sponsored foundation.

Financial data (yr. ended 12/31/04): Assets, $22,311,575 (M); expenditures, $6,641,424; total giving, $6,409,972; qualifying distributions, $6,543,066; giving activities include $6,096,623 for 443 grants (high: $502,632; low: $70), and $313,349 for 204 employee matching gifts.

Purpose and activities: The foundation supports organizations involved with education, the environment, diversity, community development, engineering, and leadership development.

Fields of interest: Elementary/secondary education; Higher education; Engineering school/education; Education; Environment, air pollution; Environment, water pollution; Environment, energy; Environmental education; Environment; Civil rights, equal rights; Urban/community development; Community development; Engineering; Leadership development.

Type of support: Employee volunteer services; General/operating support; Capital campaigns; Employee matching gifts.

Limitations: Giving limited to MI. No support for political organizations, religious organizations not of direct benefit to the entire community, or disease-specific health organizations. No grants to individuals, or for student group trips or capital campaigns or equipment for hospitals.

Publications: Informational brochure (including application guidelines); Program policy statement.

Application information: Application form required.

   Initial approach: Download application form and mail proposal and application form to foundation
   Copies of proposal: 1
   Deadline(s): Apr. 15, Aug. 15, and Dec. 15; Jan. 31 for Achieving Excellence
   Board meeting date(s): 3 times per year
   Final notification: 60 to 90 days

Officers and Directors:* Frederick E. Shell, Pres.; Karla Hall,* V.P. and Secy.; Naif A. Khouri,* Treas.; Chris Brown; Robert J. Buckler; Stephen E. Ewing; Joyce Hayes-Giles; Paul Hillegonds; Bruce Peterson; Michael C. Porter; Larry E. Steward.

Number of staff: 1 full-time professional; 2 full-time support.

EIN: 382708636

Selected grants: The following grants were reported in 2004.

$690,132 to United Way for Southeastern Michigan, Detroit, MI. 2 grants: $502,632, $187,500
$500,000 to Detroit Renaissance Foundation, Detroit, MI.
$255,000 to Detroit Symphony Orchestra, Detroit, MI.
$200,000 to New Detroit, Detroit, MI.
$150,000 to Wayne State University, Detroit, MI.
$45,000 to University Cultural Center Association, Detroit, MI.
$40,000 to Detroit Science Center, Detroit, MI.
$27,468 to Eastern Michigan University, Ypsilanti, MI.
$25,000 to Upper Peninsula Community Foundation, Gladstone, MI.

2189
Dura Automotive Systems, Inc. Charitable Foundation
(formerly Excel Industries, Inc. Charitable Foundation)
2791 Research Dr.
Rochester Hills, MI 48309

Established in 1988 in IN.
Donor: Excel Industries, Inc.
Grantmaker type: Company-sponsored foundation.
Financial data (yr. ended 12/31/05): Assets, $132,634 (M); expenditures, $37,837; total giving, $34,300; qualifying distributions, $34,300; giving activities include $34,300 for grants.
Purpose and activities: The foundation supports organizations involved with education, cancer, and human services.
Fields of interest: Education; Cancer; Boy scouts; Human services; Federated giving programs.
Type of support: General/operating support; Scholarship funds.
Limitations: Applications not accepted. Giving primarily in Elkhart, IN. No grants to individuals.
Application information: Contributes only to pre-selected organizations.
Trustee: KeyBank N.A.
EIN: 311243165

2190
Elder Foundation
4251 W. Industries Rd.
Richmond, IN 47374 (765) 966-7676

Established in 1994 in IN.
Donors: Elder Groups, Inc.; Vandor Corp.; Bruce E. Elder Trust.
Grantmaker type: Company-sponsored foundation.
Financial data (yr. ended 6/30/05): Assets, $0 (M); gifts received, $6,000; expenditures, $44,611; total giving, $42,734; qualifying distributions, $42,734; giving activities include $42,734 for 5 grants (high: $30,000; low: $1,000).
Purpose and activities: The foundation supports Christian agencies and churches and organizations involved with youth development.
Fields of interest: Youth development; Christian agencies & churches.
Limitations: Applications not accepted. Giving primarily in IN, MI. and PA.
Application information: Contributes only to pre-selected organizations.
Trustees: Alan Elder; Anjuli Elder; Jack E. Elder; Julie Elder; Karen Elder; Paul A. Elder.
EIN: 351944291

2191
Eliason Foundation
c/o Eliason Corp.
P.O. Box 2353
Kalamazoo, MI 49003-2353 (269) 327-7003
Contact: John Steffen, Treas.

Donors: Eliason Corp.; Wanda M. Eliason.
Grantmaker type: Company-sponsored foundation.
Financial data (yr. ended 11/30/05): Assets, $324,567 (M); expenditures, $24,231; total giving, $23,900; qualifying distributions, $23,958; giving activities include $23,900 for 66 grants (high: $1,400; low: $100).
Purpose and activities: The foundation supports botanical gardens and organizations involved with arts and culture, higher education, human services, and Christianity.
Fields of interest: Arts; Higher education; Botanical gardens; Children/youth, services; Human services; Federated giving programs; Christian agencies & churches.
Type of support: General/operating support.
Limitations: Giving primarily in MI. No grants to individuals.
Application information: Application form required.
  Initial approach: Contact foundation for application form
  Deadline(s): None
Officers: Edwanda M. Eliason, Pres.; David J. Eliason, V.P.; Diane Ogasian, Secy.; John Steffen, Treas.
EIN: 382364961

2192
The Engle Foundation
3850 Munson Hwy.
Hudson, MI 49247 (517) 448-8921
Contact: Edward Engle, Jr., Dir.

Established in 1988 in MI.
Donors: The Rima Manufacturing Co.; Edward J. Engle, Jr.
Grantmaker type: Company-sponsored foundation.
Financial data (yr. ended 8/31/05): Assets, $22,653 (M); gifts received, $2,325; expenditures, $7,864; total giving, $6,500; qualifying distributions, $6,500; giving activities include $6,500 for grants.
Purpose and activities: The foundation supports organizations involved with higher education, health, and religion.
Fields of interest: Higher education; Health care; Religion.
Limitations: Giving primarily in MI. No grants to individuals.
Application information: Application form not required.
  Initial approach: Proposal
  Deadline(s): None
Directors: Anne E. Engle; Edward J. Engle, Jr.; Jed Engle.
EIN: 382826866

2193
Fabiano Foundation
1219 N. Mission
Mount Pleasant, MI 48858

Established in 1997 in MI.
Donor: Fabiano Brothers, Inc.

Grantmaker type: Company-sponsored foundation.
Financial data (yr. ended 12/31/05): Assets, $1,230,146 (M); gifts received, $200,000; expenditures, $126,810; total giving, $124,500; qualifying distributions, $124,500; giving activities include $124,500 for 18 grants (high: $50,200; low: $100).
Purpose and activities: The foundation supports Roman Catholic agencies and churches and organizations involved with education and human services.
Fields of interest: Elementary/secondary education; Higher education; Education; Human services; Roman Catholic agencies & churches.
Type of support: Capital campaigns; General/operating support.
Limitations: Applications not accepted. No grants to individuals.
Application information: Contributes only to pre-selected organizations.
Officers: James C. Fabiano, Pres. and Treas.; James C. Fabiano II, V.P.; Joseph R. Fabiano II, V.P.; Evangeline L. Fabiano, Secy.
EIN: 383324462
Selected grants: The following grants were reported in 2003.
$76,100 to Sacred Heart Academy Foundation, Mount Pleasant, MI.
$25,000 to University of Notre Dame, Notre Dame, IN.
$10,000 to Nouvel Catholic Central High School, Saginaw, MI.
$1,100 to Little Traverse Conservancy, Harbor Springs, MI.
$1,000 to Blessed Sacrament Parish Community, Midland, MI.
$250 to Central Michigan University, Mount Pleasant, MI. For Pregnancy Services.
$100 to Saint Joseph Mercy Oakland, Alice Gustafson Center, Pontiac, MI.
$100 to Saint Josephs Church, MI.
$100 to Tip of the Mitt Watershed Council, Petoskey, MI.

2194
Fabri-Kal Foundation
c/o Fabri-Kal Corp.
Plastics Pl.
Kalamazoo, MI 49001 (269) 385-5050
Contact: Robert P. Kittredge, Pres.

Established in 1969 in MI.
Donor: Fabri-Kal Corp.
Grantmaker type: Company-sponsored foundation.
Financial data (yr. ended 12/31/05): Assets, $103 (M); gifts received, $466,470; expenditures, $466,564; total giving, $466,472; qualifying distributions, $466,564; giving activities include $152,277 for 20 grants (high: $35,789; low: $1,000), and $314,195 for 77 grants to individuals (high: $16,112; low: $40).
Purpose and activities: The foundation supports organizations involved with arts and culture, education, human services, and Christianity.
Fields of interest: Arts; Education; Human services; Federated giving programs; Christian agencies & churches.
Type of support: Capital campaigns; Building/renovation; Equipment; Employee-related scholarships.
Limitations: Giving limited to Kalamazoo, MI, Hazleton, PA, and Greenville, SC.

Application information: Application form not required.
- *Initial approach:* Proposal
- *Deadline(s):* None
- *Board meeting date(s):* May

Officers: Robert P. Kittredge, Pres.; R.L. Weyhing III, Secy.; Gary Galia, Treas.
EIN: 237003366

2195
Farbman Group Charitable Foundation
28400 Northwestern Hwy., 4th Fl.
Southfield, MI 48034-1839

Grantmaker type: Company-sponsored foundation.
Financial data (yr. ended 12/31/04): Assets, $515 (M); expenditures, $20; total giving, $0; qualifying distributions, $20.
Limitations: Applications not accepted.
Application information: Contributes only to pre-selected organizations.
Officers and Director:* Burton D. Farbman,* Chair.; David S. Farbman, Pres.; Andrew V. Farbman, Exec. V.P.
EIN: 383343675

2196
Farmer Jack Corporate Giving Program
18718 Borman St.
Detroit, MI 48228-1112
URL: http://www.farmerjack.com/donation_requests.asp

Grantmaker type: Corporate giving program.
Purpose and activities: Farmer Jack makes charitable contributions of store gift cards to nonprofit organizations involved with the education, health, and welfare of children. Support is given primarily in areas of company store operations.
Fields of interest: Education; Health care; Human services; Children.
Type of support: Donated products.
Limitations: Giving primarily in areas of company store operations. No support for political organizations or discriminatory organizations. No grants to individuals, or for advertising.
Application information: Support is limited to 1 contribution per organization during any given year. Proposals should be submitted using organization letterhead. Application form required.
- *Initial approach:* Download application form and deliver proposal and application form to nearest company store
- *Copies of proposal:* 1
- *Deadline(s):* 1 month prior to need
- *Final notification:* 1 month

2197
Farr Foundation, Inc.
200 Armstrong Ave.
Williamstown, WV 26187-1310

Established in 1989 in WV.
Donors: Farr Manufacturing & Engineering Co.; Douglas R. Farr.
Grantmaker type: Company-sponsored foundation.
Financial data (yr. ended 12/31/05): Assets, $2,003 (M); expenditures, $2,587; total giving, $2,475; qualifying distributions, $2,475; giving activities include $2,475 for grants.

Purpose and activities: The foundation supports organizations involved with choral music, education, and school athletics.
Fields of interest: Performing arts, music (choral); Education; Athletics/sports, school programs.
Type of support: General/operating support; Employee-related scholarships.
Limitations: Applications not accepted. Giving primarily in MI, OH, and WV.
Application information: Contributes only through employee-related scholarships and to pre-selected organizations.
Officers and Trustees:* Douglas R. Farr,* Pres.; Douglas R. Farr, Jr.,* V.P.; Marilyn E. Farr,* Secy.; Bradley E. Farr,* Treas.
EIN: 550694965

2198
Federal Screw Works Foundation, Inc.
20229 Nine Mile Rd.
St. Clair Shores, MI 48080-1775
(586) 443-4200
Contact: W.T. Zurschmiede, Jr., Tr.

Established in 1953 in MI.
Donor: Federal Screw Works.
Grantmaker type: Company-sponsored foundation.
Financial data (yr. ended 6/30/05): Assets, $95,406 (M); expenditures, $4,951; total giving, $4,500; qualifying distributions, $4,922; giving activities include $4,500 for 13 grants (high: $2,000; low: $100).
Purpose and activities: The foundation supports organizations involved with arts and culture, education, health, children and youth, and community development.
Fields of interest: Arts; Education; Health care; Children/youth, services; Community development.
Type of support: General/operating support.
Limitations: Giving primarily in Detroit, MI. No grants to individuals.
Application information: Application form not required.
- *Initial approach:* Proposal
- *Copies of proposal:* 1
- *Deadline(s):* None

Officer and Trustees: David C. Swerc, Treas.; Wade C. Plaskey; W. Thomas Zurschmiede, Jr.*; Thomas Zurschmiede.
EIN: 386088208

2199
Felpausch Foundation
127 S. Michigan Ave.
Hastings, MI 49058

Established in 1998 in MI.
Donors: G&R Felpausch Co.; T&D Parker Investments, LLC; Parker T. Feldpausch.
Grantmaker type: Company-sponsored foundation.
Financial data (yr. ended 12/31/04): Assets, $966,570 (M); gifts received, $535; expenditures, $70,830; total giving, $65,200; qualifying distributions, $67,982; giving activities include $65,200 for 16 grants (high: $50,000; low: $300).
Purpose and activities: The foundation supports hospitals, Christian agencies and churches, and organizations involved with arts and culture and human services.

Fields of interest: Arts; Hospitals (general); Human services; Federated giving programs; Christian agencies & churches.
Type of support: Annual campaigns.
Limitations: Applications not accepted. Giving primarily in MI. No grants to individuals.
Application information: Contributes only to pre-selected organizations.
Officers: Parker T. Feldpausch, Pres.; Mark S. Feldpausch, Secy.; Keith R. Tolger, Treas.; Kimberly A. Brubaker.
EIN: 383417534

2200
Fibre Converters Foundation, Inc.
1 Industrial Dr.
P.O. Box 248
Constantine, MI 49042
Contact: David Posey, Cont.

Incorporated in 1957 in MI.
Donor: Fibre Converters, Inc.
Grantmaker type: Company-sponsored foundation.
Financial data (yr. ended 3/31/05): Assets, $733,156 (M); expenditures, $50,341; total giving, $43,050; qualifying distributions, $43,070; giving activities include $43,050 for 30 grants (high: $25,000; low: $100).
Purpose and activities: The foundation supports Christian agencies and churches and organizations involved with education and health.
Fields of interest: Education; Health care; Health organizations, association; Christian agencies & churches; Disabilities, people with.
Limitations: Giving primarily in MI. No grants to individuals.
Application information: Application form not required.
- *Initial approach:* Proposal
- *Deadline(s):* None

Officer: David Posey, Cont.
Director: James D. Stuck.
EIN: 386081026

2201
First Federal Community Foundation
100 S. 2nd Ave.
Alpena, MI 49707   (989) 354-7319
Contact: Michael W. Mahler, Pres.
URL: http://www.first-federal.com/ffnm_foundation.htm

Established in 2005 in MI.
Donor: First Federal of Northern Michigan Bancorp, Inc.
Grantmaker type: Company-sponsored foundation.
Financial data (yr. ended 12/31/05): Assets, $679,940 (M); gifts received, $339,970; expenditures, $33,997; total giving, $33,997; giving activities include $33,997 for 32 grants (high: $6,000; low: $300).
Purpose and activities: The purpose of the foundation is to enhance the relationship between First Federal of Northern Michigan and the communities in which it operates and to enable its communities to share in its long-term growth. The foundation will be dedicated completely to community activities and the promotion of charitable causes.
Fields of interest: Community development.

Limitations: Giving limited to Alcona, Alpena, Antrim, Cheboygan, Charlevoix, Crawford, Emmet, Iosco, Kalkaska, Montmorency, Ogemaw, Oscoda, Otsego, and Presque Isle counties, MI. No support for religious organizations not of direct benefit to the entire community. No grants to individuals, or for general operating support or debt reduction.
Application information: Application form required.
  Initial approach: Download application form
  Deadline(s): 1st regular workday of the month
  Board meeting date(s): Monthly
Officers and Directors: Gary C. VanMassenhove,* Chair.; Michael W. Mahler,* Pres.; Amy E. Esex,* V.P. and Secy.-Treas.; Lora Greene.

2202
Ford Motor Company Contributions Program

1 American Rd.
P.O. Box 1899, Rm. 211
Dearborn, MI 48126-2798 (888) 313-0102
Contact: Sandra E. Ulsh, Pres., Ford Motor Co. Fund
FAX: (313) 594-7001; URL: http://www.ford.com/en/goodworks/default.htm

Grantmaker type: Corporate giving program.
Financial data (yr. ended 12/31/05): Total giving, $30,000,000, including $28,700,000 for grants, and $1,300,000 for in-kind gifts.
Purpose and activities: As a complement to its foundation, Ford also makes charitable contributions to nonprofit organizations directly. Support is given on a national and international basis in areas of company operations.
Fields of interest: Visual arts; Performing arts; Arts; Higher education; Business school/education; Education; Environment; Medical research; Youth, services; International affairs; Engineering/technology; Science; Minorities.
International interests: Asia; Australia; Canada; Europe; Mexico; South America.
Type of support: General/operating support; Building/renovation; Conferences/seminars; Scholarship funds; Research; Technical assistance; Employee volunteer services; Loaned talent; Use of facilities; Sponsorships; Donated equipment; Donated land; Donated products; In-kind gifts.
Limitations: Giving on a national and international basis in areas of company operations, including in Asia, Australia, Canada, Europe, Mexico, and South America. No grants to individuals, or for capital campaigns or endowments.
Publications: Application guidelines; Corporate giving report.
Application information: The company has a staff that only handles contributions. Application form not required.
  Initial approach: Letter of inquiry to headquarters
  Copies of proposal: 1
  Deadline(s): None
  Final notification: 6 Months

2203
Ford Motor Company Fund

1 American Rd.
P.O. Box 1899
Dearborn, MI 48126-2798 (313) 248-4745
Contact: Sandra E. Ulsh, Pres.
FAX: (313) 594-7001; E-mail: fordfund@ford.com; Additional tel.: (888) 313-0102; URL: http://www.ford.com/go/fordfund

Incorporated in 1949 in MI.
Donor: Ford Motor Co.
Grantmaker type: Company-sponsored foundation.
Financial data (yr. ended 12/31/04): Assets, $107,283,149 (M); gifts received, $81,500,000; expenditures, $40,236,667; total giving, $77,916,903; qualifying distributions, $77,946,735; giving activities include $77,916,903 for 1,546+ grants (high: $4,100,000).
Purpose and activities: The fund supports organizations involved with arts and culture, education, auto industry environmental issues, health, auto safety, youth development, human services, diversity, community development, public affairs, and minorities.
Fields of interest: Arts, cultural/ethnic awareness; Arts; Higher education; Business school/education; Engineering school/education; Education; Environment, air pollution; Environment; Hospitals (general); Health care; Safety, automotive safety; Youth development; Human services; Civil rights, equal rights; Community development; Mathematics; Engineering/technology; Science; Public affairs, alliance; Minorities.
Type of support: Continuing support; Annual campaigns; Capital campaigns; Equipment; Emergency funds; Program development; Conferences/seminars; Curriculum development; Scholarship funds; Research; Employee matching gifts; In-kind gifts; Matching/challenge support.
Limitations: Giving primarily in areas of company operations, with emphasis on southeastern MI. No support for religious organizations not of direct benefit to the entire community, political or fraternal organizations, animal rights organizations, labor groups, private schools, or species-specific organizations. No grants to individuals (except for employee-related scholarships), or for fellowships, endowments, debt reduction, general operating support, or beauty or talent contests; no loans or program-related investments; no vehicle donations.
Publications: Application guidelines; Annual report; Corporate giving report; Informational brochure.
Application information: Application form required.
  Initial approach: Download application form and mail, fax, or E-mail to foundation
  Copies of proposal: 1
  Deadline(s): None
  Board meeting date(s): Apr. and Oct.
  Final notification: Within 6 weeks
Officers and Trustees: James G. Vella,* Chair.; Sandra E. Ulsh, Pres.; Susan M. Cischke, V.P.; Peter Sherry, Jr., Secy.; Ann Marie Petach, Treas.; Alfred B. Ford; Sheila Ford Hamp; Timothy O'Brian; Ziad Ojakli.
Number of staff: 11 full-time professional; 10 full-time support.
EIN: 381459376
Selected grants: The following grants were reported in 2004.
$4,100,000 to Conservation International, DC.
$2,000,000 to Georgia Institute of Technology, Atlanta, GA.
$2,000,000 to Northwestern University, Evanston, IL.
$2,000,000 to Smith College, Northampton, MA.
$1,400,000 to Mount Vernon Ladies Association, Mount Vernon, VA.
$1,200,000 to Chicagos Environmental Fund, Chicago, IL.
$1,026,000 to Berry College, Mount Berry, GA.
$1,000,000 to Dearborn Community Fund, Dearborn, MI.

$1,000,000 to Detroit Renaissance Foundation, Detroit, MI.
$1,000,000 to Muhammad Ali Museum and Education Center, Louisville, KY.

2204
Futureation Foundation

c/o Eric Serr, MCPS
101 N. Main St., 7th Fl.
Ann Arbor, MI 48104

Established in 2001 in MI.
Donor: Ideation, Inc.
Grantmaker type: Company-sponsored foundation.
Financial data (yr. ended 12/31/04): Assets, $857 (M); expenditures, $12,152; total giving, $8,000; qualifying distributions, $8,000; giving activities include $8,000 for grants.
Purpose and activities: The foundation supports organizations involved with arts and culture.
Fields of interest: Arts.
Limitations: Applications not accepted. Giving primarily in MI. No grants to individuals.
Application information: Contributes only to pre-selected organizations.
Officers and Directors: William C. Ferguson,* Pres.; Virginia Lum,* Secy.; Erik Serr.
EIN: 383594238

2205
General Motors Cancer Research Foundation, Inc.

300 Renaissance Ctr., M.C. 482-C27-D76
Detroit, MI 48265-3000
Contact: Samuel A. Wells, Jr., M.D., Pres.
E-mail: gmcraward@mc.duke.edu; URL: http://www.gm.com/company/gmability/philanthropy/cancer_research/index.htm

Established in 1978 in MI.
Donors: General Motors Corp.; General Motors Foundation, Inc.
Grantmaker type: Company-sponsored foundation.
Financial data (yr. ended 12/31/04): Assets, $1,151,133 (M); gifts received, $2,830,000; expenditures, $2,926,130; total giving, $1,962,000; qualifying distributions, $2,926,167; giving activities include $1,212,000 for 11 grants (high: $216,000; low: $24,000), and $750,000 for 4 grants to individuals (high: $250,000; low: $125,000).
Purpose and activities: The foundation supports programs designed to promote scientific research into the diagnosis, treatment, and prevention of cancer in its various forms and awards grants to individuals recognized for seminal contributions in cancer research.
Fields of interest: Cancer research.
Type of support: Research; Grants to individuals.
Limitations: Applications not accepted. Giving on a national and international basis. No grants for scholarships or fellowships; no loans.
Application information: Contributes only to pre-selected organizations and through an invitation only request for nomination process for grants to individuals.
  Board meeting date(s): May
Officers and Trustees: Harry J. Pearce, Jr.,* Chair.; Phillip A. Sharp, Ph.D.*, Chair., Awards Assembly; Samuel A. Wells, Jr., M.D.*, Pres.; James C. Cubbin, V.P.; Christopher C. Green, M.D., Ph.D., V.P.;

Deborah I. Dingell, Secy.; Margreta D. Mobley, Treas.; Joseph G. Fortner, M.D.; Karen L. Katen; LaSalle D. Laffall, Jr., M.D.; John F. Smith, Jr.; Roger B. Smith; Louis W. Sullivan, M.D.
Number of staff: 1
EIN: 382219731
Selected grants: The following grants were reported in 2003.
$162,000 to Dartmouth College, Medical School, Hanover, NH. For cancer research scholars grant.
$108,000 to Johns Hopkins University, Baltimore, MD. For cancer research scholars grant.
$108,000 to University of Pittsburgh, Pittsburgh, PA. For cancer research scholars grant.
$54,000 to Dana-Farber Cancer Institute, Boston, MA. For cancer research scholars grant.
$54,000 to Memorial Sloan-Kettering Cancer Center, New York, NY. For cancer research scholars grant.
$54,000 to Northwestern University, Evanston, IL. For cancer research scholars grant.
$54,000 to Ohio State University, Columbus, OH. For cancer research scholars grant.
$54,000 to University of Alabama, Birmingham, AL. For cancer research scholars grant.
$54,000 to University of Pennsylvania Medical Center, Cancer Center, Philadelphia, PA. For research scholars grant.
$54,000 to University of Southern California, Cancer Center, Los Angeles, CA. For cancer research scholars grant.

2206
General Motors Foundation, Inc.
(also known as GM Foundation)
300 Renaissance Ctr., M.C. 482-C27-D76
Detroit, MI 48265-3000 (313) 665-0824
URL: http://www.gm.com/company/gmability/community/index.html

Incorporated in 1976 in MI.
Donor: General Motors Corp.
Grantmaker type: Company-sponsored foundation.
Financial data (yr. ended 12/31/04): Assets, $255,698,530 (M); expenditures, $35,642,725; total giving, $34,416,411; qualifying distributions, $34,434,762; giving activities include $34,416,411 for 1,329 grants (high: $2,647,640; low: $25).
Purpose and activities: The foundation supports organizations involved with arts and culture, education, the environment, health, cancer, cancer research, human services, community development, civic affairs, and minorities.
Fields of interest: Arts, public education; Arts, cultural/ethnic awareness; Arts education; Arts; Business school/education; Engineering school/education; Education; Environment, alliance; Environment, energy; Environment; Health care; Cancer; Cancer research; Human services; Community development, public education; Community development; Federated giving programs; Mathematics; Science; Public policy, research; Government/public administration; Public affairs; Minorities.
Type of support: General/operating support; Continuing support; Annual campaigns; Equipment; Emergency funds; Program development; Publication; Seed money; Research; Technical assistance; Employee matching gifts; Matching/challenge support.
Limitations: Giving primarily in areas of company operations; giving also to international

organizations. No support for special interest groups, hospitals, religious organizations, political parties or candidates, or United Way-supported organizations. No grants to individuals, or for debt reduction, capital campaigns, conferences, workshops, or seminars not directly related to GM's business interests, or endowments; no loans.
Publications: Annual report (including application guidelines); Informational brochure.
Application information: Application form required.
Initial approach: Complete online application form
Deadline(s): None
Board meeting date(s): Quarterly
Final notification: 4 to 8 weeks
Officers and Trustees:* Roderick D. Gillum,* Chair.; Deborah I. Dingell,* Vice-Chair.; Karen A. Merkle, Secy.; Paul W. Schmidt, C.F.O.; William Wimsatt, Treas.
Number of staff: 4 full-time professional; 2 full-time support.
EIN: 382132136
Selected grants: The following grants were reported in 2004.
$2,165,050 to United Way for Southeastern Michigan, Detroit, MI. 3 grants: $785,050, $380,000, $1,000,000
$1,000,000 to National Safety Council, Itasca, IL. 2 grants: $500,000 each
$730,000 to Focus: Hope, Detroit, MI. 2 grants: $350,000, $380,000
$300,000 to American Red Cross, National Headquarters, DC.
$250,000 to Detroit Symphony Orchestra, Detroit, MI.
$250,000 to Hispanic Scholarship Fund, San Francisco, CA.

2207
Generations Foundation
13919 S.W. Bay Shore Dr., Ste. G-01
Traverse City, MI 49684

Established in 2003 in MI.
Donors: Generations Management LLC; HIS Foundation.
Grantmaker type: Company-sponsored foundation.
Financial data (yr. ended 12/31/05): Assets, $259 (M); gifts received, $25,100; expenditures, $24,940; total giving, $24,850; qualifying distributions, $24,850; giving activities include $24,850 for grants.
Purpose and activities: The foundation supports organizations involved with right to life and civic affairs.
Fields of interest: Civil liberties, right to life; Public affairs.
Limitations: Applications not accepted. Giving primarily in Washington, DC, and MI. No grants to individuals.
Application information: Contributes only to pre-selected organizations.
Trustees: Jonathan Crosby; Cori Nielson; Keith Nielson.
EIN: 746524789

2208
Giddings & Lewis Foundation, Inc.
142 Doty St.
Fond du Lac, WI 54935 (920) 921-9400
Contact: Terri Groth

Incorporated in 1952 in WI.
Donors: Giddings & Lewis, Inc.; Giddings & Lewis, LLC.
Grantmaker type: Company-sponsored foundation.
Financial data (yr. ended 12/31/04): Assets, $1,834,309 (M); gifts received, $66,396; expenditures, $186,888; total giving, $177,060; qualifying distributions, $177,060; giving activities include $117,494 for 24 grants (high: $72,000; low: $20), $34,250 for 30 grants to individuals (high: $2,000; low: $250), and $25,316 for 53 employee matching gifts.
Purpose and activities: The foundation matches contributions made by employees of Giddings & Lewis and awards college scholarships to the family members of employees.
Type of support: Employee matching gifts; Employee-related scholarships.
Limitations: Applications not accepted. Giving primarily in CA, MI, OH, and WI. No grants to individuals (except for employee-related scholarships).
Application information: Contributes only through employee matching gifts and employee-related scholarships.
Officer: Stephen Peterson, Pres.
EIN: 396061306
Selected grants: The following grants were reported in 2003.
$72,000 to Fond du Lac School District, Fond du Lac, WI. For new performing arts center.
$37,007 to United Way. 5 grants: $6,912, $21,177, $1,060, $6,271, $1,587
$2,015 to United Way of Dayton, Dayton, WA.
$1,500 to Windhover Center for the Arts, Fond du Lac, WI.
$50 to United Way of Odessa, Odessa, TX.
$25 to United Way of Orange County.

2209
GM Corporate Giving Program
300 Renaissance Ctr., M.C. 482-C27-D76
Detroit, MI 48265-3000 (313) 665-0824
URL: http://www.gm.com/company/gmability/community

Grantmaker type: Corporate giving program.
Financial data (yr. ended 12/31/05): Total giving, $19,700,000, including $9,200,000 for grants, and $10,500,000 for in-kind gifts.
Purpose and activities: As a complement to its foundation, GM also makes charitable contributions to nonprofit organizations directly. Support is given primarily in areas of company operations.
Fields of interest: Arts; Education; Environment, energy; Environment; Health care; Human services; Civil rights, equal rights; Community development; Public policy, research; Public affairs.
Type of support: Continuing support; General/operating support; Technical assistance; Employee volunteer services; Sponsorships; Donated products; In-kind gifts.
Limitations: Giving primarily in areas of company operations. No support for discriminatory organizations, religious organizations, or political parties or candidates. No grants to individuals, or for general operating support for U.S. hospitals or health care institutions, capital campaigns, endowments, or conferences, workshops, or seminars not directly related to GM's business interests.
Publications: Application guidelines; Corporate giving report.

Application information: Multi-year funding is not automatic. Additional information may be requested at a later date. The Corporate Relations Department handles giving. A contributions committee reviews all requests. Application form required.

Initial approach: Complete online application form
Deadline(s): None
Number of staff: 3 full-time professional; 3 full-time support.

2210
Gordon Food Service, Inc. Corporate Giving Program

c/o Donation Comm.
P.O. Box 1787
Grand Rapids, MI   49501
Contact: Sharon Boersma, Contribs. Coord.
URL: http://www.gfs.com/content_us/about_gfs/aboutgfs_philanthropy.html

Grantmaker type: Corporate giving program.
Purpose and activities: Gordon Food Service makes charitable contributions to nonprofit organizations on a case by case basis. Support is given primarily in areas of company operations.
Fields of interest: General charitable giving.
Type of support: Sponsorships; Donated products.
Limitations: Giving primarily in areas of company operations, with emphasis on the Midwest.
Application information: Proposals should be submitted using organization letterhead. Faxes and E-mail messages are not encouraged. A contributions committee reviews all requests. Application form not required.

Initial approach: Proposal to headquarters
Copies of proposal: 1
Deadline(s): None
Final notification: 3 weeks

2211
Grand Rapids Label Foundation

2351 Oak Industrial Dr. N.E.
Grand Rapids, MI   49505-6073   (616) 459-8134
Contact: William M. Muir, Secy.

Established in 1979.
Donor: Grand Rapids Label Co.
Grantmaker type: Company-sponsored foundation.
Financial data (yr. ended 6/30/05): Assets, $239,075 (M); expenditures, $73,965; total giving, $73,945; qualifying distributions, $73,965; giving activities include $73,945 for 56 grants (high: $26,500; low: $100).
Purpose and activities: The foundation supports organizations involved with arts and culture, education, and children and youth.
Fields of interest: Arts; Education; Children/youth, services; Federated giving programs.
Type of support: General/operating support; Continuing support; Annual campaigns; Capital campaigns; Building/renovation; Program development; Scholarship funds.
Limitations: Giving primarily in Kent County, MI. No support for foundations or religious or political organizations. No grants to individuals, or for fundraising.
Application information: Application form required.
Initial approach: Contact foundation for application form

Copies of proposal: 1
Board meeting date(s): Sept., Dec., Mar., and June
Officers and Directors:* Elizabeth J. Crosby,* Pres.; Stephen J. Allen, V.P.; William M. Muir, Secy.; James S. Crosby, Treas.; Martin J. Allen; Susan J. Allen; Kathleen K. Muir; William W. Muir, Jr.
EIN: 382281916

2212
Grange Mutual Casualty Company Contributions Program

650 S. Front St.
Columbus, OH   43206   (614) 445-2900
Contact: Randall Montelone, V.P. and C.F.O.

Grantmaker type: Corporate giving program.
Purpose and activities: Grange makes charitable contributions to nonprofit organizations involved with arts and culture, education, and on a case by case basis. Support is given primarily in areas of company operations.
Fields of interest: Arts; Education; General charitable giving.
Type of support: General/operating support; Employee volunteer services; Employee matching gifts.
Limitations: Giving primarily in areas of company operations in GA, IL, IN, KY, MI, OH, and TN.

2213
Great Lakes Castings Corporation Foundation

800 N. Washington Ave.
Ludington, MI   49431   (231) 843-2501
Contact: Carol Henke

Donor: Great Lakes Castings Corp.
Grantmaker type: Company-sponsored foundation.
Financial data (yr. ended 12/31/05): Assets, $793,570 (M); gifts received, $2,767; expenditures, $27,400; total giving, $18,750; qualifying distributions, $18,750; giving activities include $18,750 for grants.
Purpose and activities: The foundation supports organizations involved with higher education and health and awards college scholarships to high school students in Ludington, Michigan, area school districts.
Fields of interest: Higher education; Health care; Federated giving programs.
Type of support: General/operating support; Scholarships—to individuals.
Limitations: Giving limited to the Ludington, MI, area.
Application information:
Initial approach: Contact foundation for application information
Deadline(s): Apr. 1 for scholarships
Officers: Rob Killips, Chair.; Frederick W. Clarke, Secy.; Paula Dudukovich, Treas.
EIN: 382250546

2214
Green Bay Packers, Inc. Corporate Giving Program

c/o Donations
P.O. Box 10628
Green Bay, WI   54307-0628   (920) 569-7500
FAX: (920) 569-7302; URL: http://www.packers.com/community

Grantmaker type: Corporate giving program.
Purpose and activities: The Green Bay Packers make charitable contributions of memorabilia to nonprofit organizations involved with arts and culture, education, the environment, animal welfare, health, hunger, athletics and fitness, human services, community development, civic affairs, religion, senior citizens, homeless people, and on a case by case basis. Support is given primarily in upper Michigan and Wisconsin.
Fields of interest: Arts; Education; Environment; Animal welfare; Health care; Food services; Recreation; Human services; Community development; Public affairs; Religion; General charitable giving; Aging; Homeless.
Type of support: In-kind gifts.
Limitations: Giving primarily in upper MI and WI. No game ticket donations.
Publications: Corporate giving report.
Application information: Proposals should be submitted using organization letterhead. The Community Relations Department handles giving. The company has a staff that only handles contributions. Application form not required.
Initial approach: Mail or fax proposal to headquarters
Copies of proposal: 1
Deadline(s): 6 to 8 weeks prior to need
Final notification: 2 to 4 weeks
Administrators: Julie Broeckel, Community Rels. Asst.; Cathy A. Dworak, Mgr., Community Rels.; Bobbi Jo Eisenreich, Coord., Corp. Donations.
Number of staff: 1 full-time professional; 1 full-time support; 1 part-time support.

2215
Guardian Industries Educational Foundation

2300 Harmon Rd.
Auburn Hills, MI   48326-1714

Established in 1986 in DE and MI.
Donor: Guardian Industries Corp.
Grantmaker type: Company-sponsored foundation.
Financial data (yr. ended 12/31/05): Assets, $36,862 (M); gifts received, $1,051,910; expenditures, $1,061,180; total giving, $1,011,123; qualifying distributions, $1,061,180; giving activities include $1,011,123 for 265 grants to individuals (high: $4,000; low: $1,000).
Purpose and activities: The foundation awards college scholarships to children of full-time employees of Guardian Industries and its subsidiaries. The scholarship program is administered by Educational Testing Service.
Type of support: Employee-related scholarships.
Limitations: Applications not accepted. Giving primarily in areas of company operations. No loans or program-related investments.
Application information: Contributes only through employee-related scholarships.

Officers and Directors:* William Davidson,* Pres.; Bruce Cummings, V.P.; Ralph J. Gerson,* V.P.; Robert H. Gorlin, Secy.; Jeffrey A. Knight, Treas.
EIN: 382707035

2216
Gygi and von Wyss Foundation

(formerly Hans Gygi Foundation)
P.O. Box 122
Dundee, MI 48131
Contact: Karen Dierks, Asst. Secy.
E-mail: karen.dierks@holcim.com; Application address: 6211 N. Ann Arbor Rd., Dundee, MI 48131-0122; URL: http://www.holcim.com/USA/EN/b/null/oid/57272/module/gnm50/jsp/templates/editorial/editorial.html

Incorporated in 1983 in MI.
Donors: Holnam Inc.; Holcim (US) Inc.
Grantmaker type: Company-sponsored foundation.
Financial data (yr. ended 12/31/05): Assets, $51,209 (M); gifts received, $120,206; expenditures, $128,563; total giving, $115,958; qualifying distributions, $115,958; giving activities include $115,958 for grants to individuals.
Purpose and activities: The foundation awards college scholarships to the children and step-children of full-time employees of Holcim (US) Inc. and Holcim Texas, LP.
Type of support: Employee-related scholarships.
Limitations: Applications not accepted. Giving on a national basis.
Application information: Contributes only through employee-related scholarships.
Board meeting date(s): Jan. 29
Officers: Brian Smith, V.P.; Scott Greenhouse, V.P.; Teresa Low, Secy.; Stephan Pott, Treas.
EIN: 382472472

2217
The Hammond Foundation

c/o Hammand Machinery, Inc.
1600 Douglas Ave.
Kalamazoo, MI 49007 (269) 345-7151
Contact: Michael A. Carl, Secy.

Established in 1952 in MI.
Donor: Hammond Machinery, Inc.
Grantmaker type: Company-sponsored foundation.
Financial data (yr. ended 12/31/05): Assets, $979,974 (M); expenditures, $81,452; total giving, $60,775; qualifying distributions, $60,775; giving activities include $60,775 for grants.
Purpose and activities: The foundation supports organizations involved with arts and culture, education, health, and children and youth.
Fields of interest: Arts; Higher education; Education; Health care; Children/youth, services; Federated giving programs.
Type of support: General/operating support.
Limitations: Applications not accepted. Giving primarily in Kalamazoo, MI. No grants to individuals; no loans.
Application information: Contributes only to pre-selected organizations.
Officer and Trustees: Michael A. Carl, Secy.; Christine A. Hammond; Robert E. Hammond.
EIN: 386061610

2218
The Hanover Insurance Group Foundation, Inc.

(formerly Allmerica Financial Charitable Foundation, Inc.)
440 Lincoln St.
Worcester, MA 01653 (508) 855-1000
URL: http://www.hanover.com/thg/about/community/grant.htm

Established in 1990 in MA.
Donors: First Allmerica Financial Life Insurance Co.; The Hanover Insurance Co.
Grantmaker type: Company-sponsored foundation.
Financial data (yr. ended 12/31/03): Assets, $3,962,483 (M); expenditures, $726,453; total giving, $725,995; qualifying distributions, $725,154; giving activities include $725,995 for 306 grants (high: $47,500; low: $50).
Purpose and activities: The foundation supports organizations involved with arts and culture, education, health, recreation, and human services.
Fields of interest: Arts; Elementary/secondary education; Higher education; Education; Health care; Health organizations, association; Recreation; Human services; Children/youth, services; Federated giving programs.
Type of support: Scholarship funds.
Limitations: Giving primarily in Worcester, MA, and MI. No grants to individuals.
Application information: Application form required.
Initial approach: Download application form
Deadline(s): None
Officers and Directors:* Cheryl M. Lapriore,* Pres.; K. David Nunley, V.P.; Laura Gobron, Treas.; Richard Lavey; Joseph W. MacDougall, Jr.*.
EIN: 043105650

2219
Haworth Inc. Corporate Giving Program

1 Haworth Ctr.
Holland, MI 49423-9576
Contact: Virginia Conklin, Coord., Corp. Contribs.

Grantmaker type: Corporate giving program.
Purpose and activities: Haworth makes charitable contributions to nonprofit organizations on a case by case basis. Support is given primarily in areas of company operations.
Fields of interest: General charitable giving.
Type of support: Employee matching gifts; Donated products.
Limitations: Giving primarily in areas of company operations.
Application information: The Executive Management Department handles giving. A contributions committee reviews all requests. Application form not required.
Initial approach: Proposal to headquarters
Copies of proposal: 1
Committee meeting date(s): Quarterly
Final notification: Following review

2220
The John Henry Company—Lou Brand Scholarship Foundation

5800 W. Grand River Ave.
Lansing, MI 48906-9111 (517) 886-2460
Contact: Shahriar Ghoddousi, Vice-Chair.

Established in 1995 in MI.

Donors: The John Henry Co.; Floral Innovations, Inc.
Grantmaker type: Company-sponsored foundation.
Financial data (yr. ended 6/30/05): Assets, $409,537 (M); gifts received, $15,423; expenditures, $21,608; total giving, $19,700; qualifying distributions, $21,510; giving activities include $19,700 for 40 grants to individuals (high: $2,000; low: $100).
Purpose and activities: The foundation awards college scholarships to children of employees of the John Henry Company.
Type of support: Employee-related scholarships.
Limitations: Applications not accepted. Giving primarily in areas of company operations.
Application information: Contributes only through employee-related scholarships.
Officer and Directors:* Louis J. Brand,* Chair.; Shahriar Ghoddousi,* Vice-Chair. and Pres.; Marta Palmer,* Secy.-Treas.
EIN: 383243055

2221
HFF Foundation

c/o Herman Frankel, Tr.
7214 Hidden Creek Ct.
West Bloomfield, MI 48322-5209

Established in 1993 in MI.
Donors: Simwood Co.; Herman Frankel; Suburban Communities, LLC.
Grantmaker type: Company-sponsored foundation.
Financial data (yr. ended 12/31/05): Assets, $3,588,700 (M); expenditures, $450,584; total giving, $448,686; qualifying distributions, $448,686; giving activities include $448,686 for 17 + grants (high: $214,500).
Purpose and activities: The foundation supports organizations involved with arts and culture, health, and Judaism.
Fields of interest: Performing arts; Performing arts, orchestra (symphony); Performing arts, opera; Arts; Health care; Jewish federated giving programs; Jewish agencies & temples.
Limitations: Applications not accepted. Giving primarily in MI, with emphasis on Detroit. No grants to individuals.
Application information: Contributes only to pre-selected organizations.
Trustee: Herman Frankel.
EIN: 383149105

2222
Holcim (US) Inc. Corporate Giving Program

(formerly Holnam Inc. Corporate Giving Program)
P.O. Box 122
Dundee, MI 48131
URL: http://www.holcim.com/USA/EN/b/null/oid/57129/channel_id/-8801/module/gnm50/jsp/templates/editorial/editorial.html

Grantmaker type: Corporate giving program.
Purpose and activities: Holcim (US) makes charitable contributions to nonprofit organizations involved with education and community development. Support is given primarily in areas of company operations.
Fields of interest: Education; Community development.

Type of support: General/operating support; Employee volunteer services; Loaned talent; Donated products.
Limitations: Giving primarily in areas of company operations.

2223
Isabella Bank and Trust Foundation
200 E. Broadway, P.O. Box 100
Mount Pleasant, MI 48858 (989) 772-9471

Established in 1997 in MI.
Donor: Isabella Bank and Trust.
Grantmaker type: Company-sponsored foundation.
Financial data (yr. ended 12/31/04): Assets, $1,744,450 (M); gifts received, $870,335; expenditures, $164,659; total giving, $158,155; qualifying distributions, $158,155; giving activities include $158,155 for 20 grants (high: $100,000; low: $500).
Purpose and activities: The foundation supports hospitals and organizations involved with arts and culture, education, human services, and community development.
Fields of interest: Arts; Education; Hospitals (general); American Red Cross; Residential/custodial care, hospices; Human services; Community development; Federated giving programs.
Type of support: General/operating support.
Limitations: Giving primarily in the Mount Pleasant, MI, area, including Isabella County. No grants to individuals.
Application information: Application form not required.
   Initial approach: Proposal
   Deadline(s): None
Officers and Directors: Ronald E. Schumacher,* Chair.; Richard J. Barz,* Pres.; Mary Ann Breuer,* Secy.; Steven D. Pung,* Treas.; Dennis P. Angner; David W. Hole.
EIN: 383348258

2224
Issa Foundation
341 E. Huron St.
Ann Arbor, MI 48104

Established in 1997 in MI.
Donor: Issa Properties.
Grantmaker type: Company-sponsored foundation.
Financial data (yr. ended 12/31/04): Assets, $2,804 (M); gifts received, $8,525; expenditures, $8,490; total giving, $7,900; qualifying distributions, $7,900; giving activities include $7,400 for 5 grants (high: $5,000; low: $400), and $500 for 1 grant to an individual.
Purpose and activities: The foundation supports Islamic agencies and mosques and organizations involved with arts and culture, health, and housing and awards grants to individuals for health care costs.
Fields of interest: Arts; Education; Hospitals (general); Health care; Housing/shelter; Islam.
Type of support: General/operating support; Grants to individuals.
Limitations: Applications not accepted.
Application information: Contributes only to pre-selected organizations and individuals.

Directors: Abdulaziz M. Issa; Anwar M. Issa; Mohamad M. Issa; Raed Issa; Said Issa.
EIN: 383379607

2225
Jackson National Life Insurance Company Contributions Program
c/o Human Resources, M.C. S12
1 Corporate Way
Lansing, MI 48951 (517) 367-3826
Contact: Denise Goron
E-mail: denise.gordon@jnli.com

Grantmaker type: Corporate giving program.
Purpose and activities: Jackson makes charitable contributions to nonprofit organizations involved with education, health, and children. Support is given primarily in areas of company operations.
Fields of interest: Education; Health care; Children, services.
Type of support: General/operating support; Program development; Sponsorships.
Limitations: Giving primarily in areas of company operations, with emphasis on Santa Monica, CA, Denver, CO, Chicago, IL, and Lansing, MI.
Application information: Application form not required.
   Initial approach: Proposal to headquarters
   Copies of proposal: 1
   Deadline(s): 2 months prior to need

2226
Johnson Corporation Scholarship Foundation
805 Wood St.
Three Rivers, MI 49093-1053
Contact: Tom O. Monroe, Chair.

Donor: The Johnson Corp.
Grantmaker type: Company-sponsored foundation.
Financial data (yr. ended 6/30/05): Assets, $10,345 (M); gifts received, $10,200; expenditures, $7,650; total giving, $7,650; qualifying distributions, $7,650; giving activities include $7,650 for grants to individuals.
Purpose and activities: The foundation awards college scholarships to graduates of Three Rivers High School in Michigan planning to attend a Michigan institution to pursue studies in engineering, dentistry, nursing, medicine, teaching, or science.
Type of support: Scholarships—to individuals.
Limitations: Giving limited to Three Rivers, MI.
Application information: Application form required.
   Initial approach: Contact foundation for application form
   Deadline(s): End of high school year
Officer and Advisory Committee:* Tom O. Monroe, Sr.,* Chair.; Andy Boyd; Chris Katsaros; Sally Middleton; Dan Snyder.
EIN: 386098327

2227
JPMorgan Chase Philanthropy - Michigan
611 Woodward Ave., MI1-8038
Detroit, MI 48226 (313) 225-2125
Contact: Christine Kageff, V.P., Philanthropy and Community Relations

FAX: (313) 225-3333;
E-mail: christine.kageff@chase.com; URL: http://www.jpmorganchase.com/giving

Donor: JPMorgan Chase & Co.
Grantmaker type: Company-sponsored foundation.
Purpose and activities: JPMorgan Chase provides support to Michigan not-for-profit organizations through grants and sponsorships whose missions are in alignment with its three focus areas of philanthropic giving: community asset development - to encourage, sustain and develop economic self-reliance through affordable housing, quality jobs, and business opportunities; youth education - to help young people succeed in life and in work through strong public schools, programs that support and enable educational excellence, and educational opportunities for all; and community life - to enrich communities with sponsorships and events focused on arts and culture, including quality of life through arts and culture, arts and civic programming that celebrates diversity, programs that help build arts and cultural capacity and sustainability, and environmental awareness.
Fields of interest: Arts, cultural/ethnic awareness; Arts education; Visual arts; Performing arts; Arts; Employment, training; Housing/shelter, development; Community development, neighborhood development; Economic development; Community development, small businesses; Community development; Economically disadvantaged.
Type of support: Program development; Technical assistance; Sponsorships.
Limitations: Giving limited to areas of company operations in MI. No support for fraternal organizations, athletic teams or social groups, public agencies, private schools, public schools (unless in partnership with a qualified not-for-profit organization), parent-teacher associations, volunteer-operated organizations, programs designed to promote religious or political doctrines, higher education (unless program is specifically within guidelines), health- or medical-related organizations (unless program fits within stated giving guidelines), or organizations that discriminate on the basis of race, sex, sexual orientation, age or religion. No grants to individuals, or for funds to pay down operating deficits, fundraising events, advertising (including ads in event, performance or athletic programs), scholarships or tuition assistance; generally no grants for endowments or capital campaigns (exceptions are made by invitation only).
Application information: The company has a staff that only handles contributions.
   Initial approach: Submit completed online application form
   Deadline(s): Generally application should be made in first quarter for payment during calendar year
   Final notification: By Nov. 1
Number of staff: 2 full-time professional.

2228
JSJ Foundation
700 Robbins Rd.
Grand Haven, MI 49417
Contact: Lynne Sherwood, Chair.

Established in 1983 in MI.
Donor: JSJ Corp.
Grantmaker type: Company-sponsored foundation.

Financial data (yr. ended 12/31/05): Assets, $276,787 (M); gifts received, $300,000; expenditures, $187,523; total giving, $186,135; qualifying distributions, $186,080; giving activities include $186,135 for 33 grants (high: $25,000; low: $300).

Purpose and activities: The foundation supports organizations involved with arts and culture, education, human services, and civic affairs.

Fields of interest: Humanities; Arts; Higher education; Education; Children/youth, services; Human services; Federated giving programs; Public affairs.

Type of support: General/operating support; Continuing support; Annual campaigns; Capital campaigns; Building/renovation.

Limitations: Giving primarily in areas of company operations in Ormond Beach, FL, Grand Haven and Grand Rapids, MI, Belton, TX, and La Crosse, WI. No grants to individuals, or for exchange programs, fellowships, internships, lectureships, or professorships; no loans.

Application information: Application form not required.

  Initial approach: Proposal
  Copies of proposal: 1
  Deadline(s): Oct. 31
  Board meeting date(s): Nov.
  Final notification: By year end

Officers and Trustees:* Lynne Sherwood,* Chair.; Nelson C. Jacobson, Secy.-Treas.; Erick P. Johnson; Robert J. Mesereau.

EIN: 382421508

Selected grants: The following grants were reported in 2004.

$26,020 to United Way, Greater Ottawa County, Holland, MI. For operating support.

$25,000 to YMCA, Tri-Cities Family, Grand Haven, MI. For capital campaign.

$15,000 to Center for Women in Transition, Holland, MI. For capital campaign.

$15,000 to Michigan Colleges Foundation, Southfield, MI. For scholarships.

$10,000 to Citizens Research Council of Michigan, Livonia, MI. For endowment.

$10,000 to Grand Rapids Symphony, Grand Rapids, MI. For operating support.

$6,000 to Tri-Cities Ministries, Grand Haven, MI. For operating support.

$4,000 to West Shore Symphony Orchestra, Muskegon, MI. For operating support.

$2,668 to United Way, Oceana County, Hart, MI. For operating support.

$1,000 to Opera Grand Rapids, Grand Rapids, MI. For operating support.

2229
The Jubilee Foundation

(formerly Herman Miller Design Foundation)
P.O. Box 94651
Cleveland, OH   44101

Established in 1994 in MI.

Donor: Herman Miller, Inc.

Grantmaker type: Company-sponsored foundation.

Financial data (yr. ended 5/31/05): Assets, $1,930,380 (M); gifts received, $2,063,721; expenditures, $2,861,142; total giving, $2,859,393; qualifying distributions, $2,860,728; giving activities include $2,859,393 for grants.

Purpose and activities: The foundation supports organizations involved with arts and culture,

education, health, human services, community development, and minorities.

Fields of interest: Performing arts, orchestra (symphony); Arts; Higher education; Education; Health care; Children/youth, services; Human services; Community development; Minorities.

Type of support: General/operating support; Scholarship funds.

Limitations: Applications not accepted. Giving primarily in IL, MD, and MI. No grants to individuals.

Application information: Contributes only to pre-selected organizations.

Officers and Directors: Michael A. Volkema, Pres.; James E. Christenson, Secy.; Elizabeth A. Nickels, Treas.; May Vermeer Andringa; Douglas D. French; Brian Griffiths; C. William Pollard.

EIN: 383003821

Selected grants: The following grants were reported in 2004.

$85,484 to Goshen College, Goshen, IN. For general support.

$65,000 to Fuller Theological Seminary, Pasadena, CA. For general support.

$65,000 to Western Theological Seminary, Holland, MI. For general support.

$62,400 to Scholarship America, Saint Peter, MN. For general support.

$50,000 to Cornerstone Schools, Detroit, MI. For general support.

$45,000 to Calvary Christian School of Byesville, Byesville, OH. For general support.

$45,000 to Wycliffe Bible Translators, Orlando, FL. For general support.

$40,000 to World Radio Missionary Fellowship, Colorado Springs, CO. For general support.

$37,500 to Reformed Bible College, Grand Rapids, MI. For general support.

$30,000 to Potters House, Grand Rapids, MI. For general support.

2230
Albert Kahn Associated Architects & Engineers Foundation

Albert Kahn Bldg.
7430 2nd Ave.
Detroit, MI   48202

Donor: Albert Kahn Associates, Inc.

Grantmaker type: Company-sponsored foundation.

Financial data (yr. ended 1/31/06): Assets, $1,050 (M); gifts received, $16,940; expenditures, $16,970; total giving, $16,940; qualifying distributions, $16,940; giving activities include $16,940 for 1 grant.

Purpose and activities: The foundation supports the United Way of Detroit, Michigan.

Fields of interest: Federated giving programs.

Type of support: Annual campaigns.

Limitations: Applications not accepted. Giving limited to Detroit, MI. No grants to individuals.

Application information: Contributes only to a pre-selected organization.

Officers: Stephen Q. Whitney, Pres.; Garabed Hoplamazian, Secy.; Charles T. Robinson, Treas.

EIN: 382144518

2231
Kalleward-Bergerson Charitable Foundation, Inc.

300 S. 8th St.
Kalamazoo, MI   49009   (269) 372-7300
Contact: James Kalleward, Pres.

Established in 1990 in MI.

Donors: Kalleward-Bergerson, Inc.; Kalleward Group, Inc.

Grantmaker type: Company-sponsored foundation.

Financial data (yr. ended 3/31/05): Assets, $160 (M); gifts received, $2,340; expenditures, $2,360; total giving, $1,800; qualifying distributions, $1,800; giving activities include $1,800 for 1 grant.

Purpose and activities: The foundation supports organizations involved with multiple sclerosis, medical research, and disabled people.

Fields of interest: Multiple sclerosis; Medical research; Disabilities, people with.

Type of support: General/operating support.

Limitations: Giving limited to the Kalamazoo, MI, area. No grants to individuals.

Application information: Application form not required.

  Initial approach: Proposal
  Deadline(s): None
  Board meeting date(s): 3rd Thurs. in May

Officers and Directors:* James Kalleward,* Pres.; Clyde W. Crawford,* V.P.

EIN: 382935399

2232
The Kasle Foundation

c/o Kasle Steel Corp.
4343 Wyoming Ave.
Dearborn, MI   48126-3724

Established in 1945 in MI.

Donors: Kasle Steel Corp.; Roger Kasle.

Grantmaker type: Company-sponsored foundation.

Financial data (yr. ended 12/31/04): Assets, $11,975 (M); gifts received, $25,000; expenditures, $25,770; total giving, $24,629; qualifying distributions, $24,629; giving activities include $24,629 for grants.

Purpose and activities: The foundation supports organizations involved with arts and culture, health, human services, and community development.

Fields of interest: Arts; Health organizations, association; Athletics/sports, Special Olympics; Human services; Community development; Federated giving programs.

Limitations: Applications not accepted. Giving primarily in FL and MI. No grants to individuals.

Application information: Contributes only to pre-selected organizations.

Officers and Trustees:* Roger Kasle,* Chair.; Matthew Kasle, Pres.; Keith Bailey, Secy.-Treas.

EIN: 386062714

2233
Kellogg Company 25-Year Employees Fund, Inc.

c/o Kellogg Co.
1 Kellogg Sq.
P.O. Box 3599
Battle Creek, MI   49016-3599   (269) 961-2000
Contact: Timothy S. Knowlton, Pres.
Application address: c/o Managing Decisions, 400 Orchard Ave., Battle Creek, MI 49017

Established in 1944 in MI.
Donor: W.K. Kellogg‡.
Grantmaker type: Company-sponsored foundation.
Financial data (yr. ended 12/31/04): Assets, $61,365,510 (M); expenditures, $1,267,200; total giving, $1,105,899; qualifying distributions, $1,246,443; giving activities include $1,105,899 for 166 grants to individuals (high: $35,500; low: $21).
Purpose and activities: The fund supports retiree associations and awards grants for living and medical expenses to current and former 25-year employees and the dependents of 25-year employees of Kellogg.
International interests: Canada; England; Mexico; South Africa.
Type of support: General/operating support; Grants to individuals.
Limitations: Giving primarily in areas of company operations, with emphasis on Battle Creek, MI; giving also in Canada, England, Mexico, and South Africa. Generally, no support for organizations. No grants to employees or dependents of employees not employed by Kellogg or a Kellogg subsidiary for at least 25 years or individuals with income greater than living expenses or liquid assets greater than $20,000 per couple or $15,000 per individual.
Application information: Application form not required.
Initial approach: Proposal
Board meeting date(s): Jan., Apr., July, and Oct.
Officers and Trustees: * Timothy S. Knowlton,* Pres.; J.W. Misner,* V.P.; D.M. Smith, Secy.; J. Wittenberg, Treas.; D.J. Banks; M.L. Bivens; C.A. Clark; G.A. Franklin; C.B. Hughes.
Number of staff: 1 full-time support.
EIN: 386039770

2234
Kellogg Company Contributions Program
1 Kellogg Sq.
P.O. Box 3599
Battle Creek, MI   49016-3599   (269) 961-2612
URL: http://www.kelloggcompany.com/social.aspx?id=57

Grantmaker type: Corporate giving program.
Purpose and activities: As a complement to its foundation, Kellogg also makes charitable contributions to nonprofit organizations directly. Support is given on a national and international basis.
Fields of interest: Health care; Agriculture/food; Children/youth, services; Human services; Community development.
Type of support: General/operating support; Employee volunteer services; Sponsorships; Donated equipment; Donated products.
Limitations: Giving on a national and international basis in areas of company operations.

2235
Kellogg's Corporate Citizenship Fund
1 Kellogg Sq.
Battle Creek, MI   49016-3599   (616) 961-2000
Contact: Dawn M. Smith, Secy.

Established in 1994 in MI.
Donor: Kellogg Co.
Grantmaker type: Company-sponsored foundation.

Financial data (yr. ended 12/31/04): Assets, $14,881,783 (M); gifts received, $8,700,000; expenditures, $4,277,240; total giving, $3,959,388; qualifying distributions, $4,260,148; giving activities include $3,557,810 for 102 grants (high: $971,459; low: $277), and $401,578 for 363 employee matching gifts.
Purpose and activities: The foundation supports organizations involved with arts and culture, education, wildlife preservation and protection, and human services.
Fields of interest: Arts; Elementary/secondary education; Higher education; Education; Animals/wildlife, preservation/protection; Human services; Federated giving programs.
Type of support: General/operating support; Employee matching gifts.
Limitations: Giving primarily in areas of company operations.
Application information: Application form not required.
Initial approach: Proposal
Deadline(s): None
Officers and Directors: * Celeste A. Clark,* Pres.; Gary Pilnick,* V.P.; Dawn M. Smith, Secy.; Janice L. Perkins,* Treas.; Timothy S. Knowlton,* Exec. Dir.; Carolee Deuel; Jeff Montle; Edward Moore.
EIN: 383167772
Selected grants: The following grants were reported in 2004.
$971,459 to United Way of Greater Battle Creek, Battle Creek, MI. For campaign support.
$250,000 to Heritage Center Foundation, Kelloggs Cereal City USA, Battle Creek, MI. For general support.
$250,000 to World of Children, Columbus, OH. For general support.
$151,257 to Baylor College of Medicine, Houston, TX. For program support.
$100,545 to United Way of the DuPage Area, Oak Brook, IL. For campaign support.
$99,750 to University of Kentucky, Lexington, KY. For program support.
$21,179 to United Way of the Central Savannah River Area, Augusta, GA. For campaign support.
$20,000 to Langston University National Alumni Association, Langston, OK. For program support.
$7,500 to Family Y Center of Battle Creek, Battle Creek, MI. For program support.
$3,070 to Music Center of South Central Michigan, Battle Creek, MI. For program support.

2236
The Kelly Services, Inc. Foundation
999 W. Big Beaver Rd.
Troy, MI   48084
Contact: Kim Flowers, Admin.
FAX: (248) 244-5497;
E-mail: kim_flowers@kellyservices.com

Established in 1994 in MI.
Donor: Kelly Services, Inc.
Grantmaker type: Company-sponsored foundation.
Financial data (yr. ended 1/2/05): Assets, $73,417 (M); gifts received, $250,000; expenditures, $544,770; total giving, $550,840; qualifying distributions, $544,762; giving activities include $550,840 for 456 grants (high: $200,000; low: $150).
Purpose and activities: The foundation supports organizations involved with arts and culture, education, health, employment, and children and youth.

Fields of interest: Arts; Higher education; Education; Hospitals (specialty); Health care; Employment; Children/youth, services; Federated giving programs.
Type of support: General/operating support; Continuing support; Annual campaigns; Emergency funds.
Limitations: Giving primarily in southeast MI. No grants to individuals.
Application information: Application form not required.
Initial approach: Proposal
Copies of proposal: 1
Deadline(s): None
Board meeting date(s): Semiannually
Final notification: Within 1 month
Officers and Directors: * Terence E. Adderley,* Pres.; Carl T. Camden, V.P.; Michael Durik, Secy.; William Gerber, Treas.
EIN: 383207679

2237
Kolene Corporation Contributions Program
12890 Westwood Ave.
Detroit, MI   48223   (313) 273-9220
FAX: (313) 273-5207

Grantmaker type: Corporate giving program.
Purpose and activities: Kolene makes charitable contributions to nonprofit organizations on a case by case basis. Support is given primarily in Detroit, Michigan.
Fields of interest: General charitable giving.
Type of support: General/operating support.
Limitations: Giving primarily in Detroit, MI.

2238
Kowalski Sausage Company Charitable Trust
c/o Bank One Trust Co., N.A.
P.O. Box 1308
Milwaukee, WI   53201
Application address: Bank One Trust Co., N.A., 611 Woodward Ave., Detroit, MI 48226, tel.: (313) 225-3454

Established in 1951 in MI.
Donor: Kowalski Sausage Co.
Grantmaker type: Company-sponsored foundation.
Financial data (yr. ended 12/31/05): Assets, $1,116,664 (M); expenditures, $41,275; total giving, $40,000; qualifying distributions, $40,000; giving activities include $40,000 for grants.
Purpose and activities: The foundation supports Roman Catholic agencies and churches and organizations involved with arts and culture, education, health, cancer, and youth development.
Fields of interest: Arts; Higher education; Education; Health care; Cancer; Youth development; Residential/custodial care, hospices; Roman Catholic agencies & churches.
Type of support: General/operating support; Continuing support; Annual campaigns; Building/renovation; Scholarship funds; Research.
Limitations: Giving primarily in FL, IN, and MI. No grants to individuals.
Application information: Application form required.
Initial approach: Contact foundation for application form
Copies of proposal: 1

Deadline(s): None
Board meeting date(s): Varies
Officers and Trustees: * Stephen Kowalski,* Chair.; Donald Kowalski, Pres.; Agnes Kowalski; Kenneth Kowalski; Bank One Trust Co., N.A.
EIN: 386046508

2239
La-Z-Boy Foundation
(formerly La-Z-Boy Chair Foundation)
1284 N. Telegraph Rd.
Monroe, MI 48162-3390 (734) 242-1444
Contact: Donald E. Blohm, Admin.

Incorporated in 1953 in MI.
Donors: La-Z-Boy Chair Co.; La-Z-Boy Inc.; E.M. Knabusch†; Edwin J. Shoemaker†; H.F. Gertz†.
Grantmaker type: Company-sponsored foundation.
Financial data (yr. ended 12/31/05): Assets, $22,078,876 (M); expenditures, $1,278,780; total giving, $1,179,350; qualifying distributions, $1,193,350; giving activities include $1,179,350 for 138 grants (high: $187,500; low: $500).
Purpose and activities: The foundation supports organizations involved with education, health, human services, and government and public administration.
Fields of interest: Education; Health care; Human services; Federated giving programs; Government/public administration.
Type of support: General/operating support; Building/renovation.
Limitations: Giving primarily in Siloam Springs, AR, Redlands, CA, Monroe, MI, Newton and Saltillo, MS, Neosho, MO, Greensboro, Hickory, Hudson, Lenoir, Lincolnton, North Wilkesboro, and Taylorsville, NC, Dayton and New Tazewell, TN, Tremonton, UT, and Bedford and Martinsville, VA. No support for religious or political organizations. No grants to individuals, or for travel or conferences or start-up needs; no loans.
Publications: Application guidelines; Annual report (including application guidelines).
Application information: Proposals should be brief. Additional information may be requested at a later date. Application form not required.
Initial approach: Proposal
Copies of proposal: 1
Deadline(s): Mar. 1, June 1, Sept. 1, and Dec. 1
Board meeting date(s): Mar., June, Sept., and Dec.
Final notification: 3 months
Officers and Directors: * P.H. Norton,* Chair.; K.L. Darrow,* C.E.O. and Pres.; David M. Risley,* Exec. V.P., Finance; J.H. Foss; D.K. Hehl; J.W. Johnston; H.G. Levy; R.E. Lipford; D.L. Mitchell; H.O. Petrauskas; J.L. Thompson.
Number of staff: 1 part-time support.
EIN: 386087673

2240
LaSalle Bank Midwest N.A. Corporate Giving Program
(formerly Standard Federal Bank N.A. Corporate Giving Program)
2600 W. Big Beaver Rd.
Troy, MI 48084 (248) 643-9600
URL: http://www.lasallebankmidwest.com/about/community.html

Grantmaker type: Corporate giving program.

Purpose and activities: LaSalle Bank Midwest makes charitable contributions to nonprofit organizations on a case by case basis. Support is given on a national basis.
Fields of interest: General charitable giving.
Type of support: General/operating support; In-kind gifts.
Limitations: Giving on a national basis.

2241
R. Dale Lausch Foundation
3425 Lake Eastbrook Blvd. S.E.
Grand Rapids, MI 49546

Established in 1985 in MI.
Donors: River City Food Co.; R. Dale Lausch.
Grantmaker type: Company-sponsored foundation.
Financial data (yr. ended 12/31/05): Assets, $35,830 (M); expenditures, $1,424; total giving, $1,400; qualifying distributions, $1,400; giving activities include $1,400 for grants.
Purpose and activities: The foundation supports organizations involved with education and health.
Fields of interest: Education; Health care.
Type of support: General/operating support; Annual campaigns; Scholarship funds.
Limitations: Applications not accepted. Giving limited to Grand Rapids, MI. No grants to individuals.
Application information: Contributes only to pre-selected organizations.
Officer and Directors: * R. Dale Lausch,* Pres.; Shirley Lausch.
EIN: 382641104

2242
Lear Corporation Charitable Foundation
21557 Telegraph Rd.
Southfield, MI 48034

Established in 2003 in MI.
Donor: Lear Corp.
Grantmaker type: Company-sponsored foundation.
Financial data (yr. ended 12/31/05): Assets, $107,363 (M); gifts received, $1,000,000; expenditures, $1,725,577; total giving, $1,724,000; qualifying distributions, $1,724,000; giving activities include $1,724,000 for 21 grants (high: $221,500; low: $20,000).
Purpose and activities: The foundation supports organizations involved with children and youth.
Fields of interest: Performing arts; Higher education; Children/youth, services; Federated giving programs.
Type of support: Capital campaigns.
Limitations: Applications not accepted. Giving primarily in MI, with emphasis on Detroit.
Application information: Contributes only to pre-selected organizations.
Trustees: Daniel A. Ninivaggi; Mel Stephens; James H. Vandenberghe.
EIN: 200302085

2243
Loomis Sayles
39533 Woodward Ave., Ste. 300
Bloomfield Hills, MI 48304-5106
(248) 646-2100
Contact: David G. Sowerby, V.P.
FAX: (248) 646-3235; *E-mail:* dsowerby@loomissayles.com; *URL:* http://

loomissayles.com/Internet/Internet.nsf/AboutUs_CharitableMission?OpenForm

Grantmaker type: Corporate giving program.
Financial data (yr. ended 12/31/05): Total giving, $660,000, including $615,000 for grants, and $45,000 for employee matching gifts.
Purpose and activities: The Loomis Sayles charitable giving mission is to support charities, particularly educational programs, which work with underprivileged children and families living in urban areas. Areas of interest include community development, the arts, education, social service and healthcare.
Fields of interest: Arts; Education; Health care; Human services; Children/youth, services; Family services; Urban/community development; Community development; Economically disadvantaged.
Limitations: Giving primarily in areas of company operations.

2244
Luhtanen-Howes Charitable Foundation, Inc.
17488 N. Laurel Park Dr.
Livonia, MI 48152-3981

Established in 1999 in MI.
Donor: Dynatek, Inc.
Grantmaker type: Company-sponsored foundation.
Financial data (yr. ended 12/31/05): Assets, $456,552 (M); gifts received, $25,000; expenditures, $25,217; total giving, $20,000; qualifying distributions, $20,000; giving activities include $20,000 for 8 grants (high: $6,000; low: $1,000).
Purpose and activities: The foundation supports organizations involved with youth development, human services, and Christianity.
Fields of interest: Youth development; Salvation Army; Children, services; Human services; Christian agencies & churches.
Limitations: Applications not accepted. Giving limited to MI.
Application information: Contributes only to pre-selected organizations.
Officers: Jack D. Luhtanen, Pres.; Todd A. Luhtanen, V.P.; Phillip J. McClain, V.P.; Linda L. Luhtanen, Secy.-Treas.
EIN: 383497266

2245
MAC Valves Foundation
P.O. Box 111
Wixom, MI 48393 (248) 624-7700
Contact: Martha Welch, Mgr.

Grantmaker type: Company-sponsored foundation.
Financial data (yr. ended 11/30/05): Assets, $968,707 (M); expenditures, $125,231; total giving, $122,031; qualifying distributions, $122,031; giving activities include $122,031 for grants.
Purpose and activities: The foundation primarily supports organizations involved with education and human services.
Fields of interest: Education; Human services; Federated giving programs.
Limitations: Giving limited to MI.

Application information: Application form not required.
Initial approach: Proposal
Deadline(s): None
Officer: Martha Welch, Mgr.
EIN: 382440953

2246
Magline Inc. Charitable Trust
503 S. Mercer St.
Pinconning, MI 48650-9309

Donor: Magline Inc.
Grantmaker type: Company-sponsored foundation.
Financial data (yr. ended 12/31/05): Assets, $120,497 (M); expenditures, $14,606; total giving, $13,800; qualifying distributions, $14,475; giving activities include $13,800 for 2 grants (high: $12,800; low: $1,000).
Purpose and activities: The foundation supports public libraries and organizations involved with ecomomic development.
Fields of interest: Libraries (public); Economic development.
Type of support: Capital campaigns; General/operating support.
Limitations: Applications not accepted. Giving limited to Bay City, MI. No grants to individuals.
Application information: Contributes only to pre-selected organizations.
Trustee: D. Brian Law.
EIN: 386082038

2247
The Manufacturing Academy
4909 W. Michigan Ave.
Jackson, MI 49201

Established in 2002 in MI.
Donor: C. Thorrez Industries, Inc.
Grantmaker type: Company-sponsored foundation.
Financial data (yr. ended 12/31/04): Assets, $46,078 (M); gifts received, $12,060; expenditures, $21,938; total giving, $0; qualifying distributions, $0.
Purpose and activities: The foundation supports Spring Arbor University.
Fields of interest: Business school/education.
Limitations: Applications not accepted. Giving primarily in MI.
Application information: Contributes only to pre-selected organizations.
Officers: Camiel Thorrez, Pres.; Steve Lazaroff, V.P.; Annette Norris, Secy. and Exec. Dir.
Directors: Tom Bartol; Scott Brockie; Jim Carpenter; Steve Lazaroff; Bill Wilson.
EIN: 383103954

2248
Masco Corporation Contributions Program
21001 Van Born Rd.
Taylor, MI 48180 (313) 792-6154
Contact: Melonie B. Colaianne, Dir., Corp. Affairs
URL: http://www.masco.com/corporate_information/citizenship/index.html

Grantmaker type: Corporate giving program.
Financial data (yr. ended 12/31/03): Total giving, $4,100,000, including $4,100,000 for grants.

Purpose and activities: As a complement to its foundation, Masco also makes charitable contributions to nonprofit organizations directly. The company supports organizations involved with arts and culture. Special emphasis is directed toward programs designed to promote decent housing environments for low-income families. Support is given primarily in areas of company operations.
Fields of interest: Arts; Housing/shelter.
Type of support: General/operating support; Capital campaigns; Employee volunteer services; Sponsorships; Employee matching gifts; Donated products; In-kind gifts; Matching/challenge support.
Limitations: Giving primarily in areas of company operations. No grants to individuals, or for endowments, research, or religious purposes; no loans.
Publications: Corporate giving report.
Application information: The Corporate Affairs Department handles giving. Application form not required.
Initial approach: Proposal to headquarters
Copies of proposal: 1
Deadline(s): None
Final notification: Following review
Number of staff: 3

2249
Masco Corporation Foundation
(formerly Masco Corporation Charitable Trust)
c/o Corp. Affairs
21001 Van Born Rd.
Taylor, MI 48180 (313) 274-7400
FAX: (313) 792-6262; *URL:* http://www.masco.com/corporate_information/citizenship/foundation/index.html

Trust established in 1952 in MI.
Donor: Masco Corp.
Grantmaker type: Company-sponsored foundation.
Financial data (yr. ended 12/31/05): Assets, $8,204,339 (M); gifts received, $2,000,000; expenditures, $5,687,612; total giving, $5,596,950; qualifying distributions, $5,599,327; giving activities include $5,596,950 for 128 grants (high: $980,000; low: $2,000).
Purpose and activities: The foundation supports organizations involved with arts and culture outreach for disadvantaged youth, human services, and civic affairs. Special emphasis is directed toward programs designed to promote decent housing environments for disadvantaged, low-income families.
Fields of interest: Arts; Housing/shelter; Human services; Public affairs; Youth.
Type of support: General/operating support; Annual campaigns; Capital campaigns; Building/renovation; Matching/challenge support.
Limitations: Giving primarily in areas of company operations, with emphasis on the greater Detroit, MI, area. No support for discriminatory organizations, political organizations or candidates or lobbying organizations, athletic clubs, religious organizations not of direct benefit to the entire community, or organizations benefiting few people. No grants to individuals, or for debt reduction, endowments, sports programs or events or school extracurricular activities, or conferences, travel, seminars, or film or video projects; no loans.
Publications: Application guidelines; Annual report; Corporate giving report.
Application information: Application form not required.

Initial approach: Letter of inquiry or telephone
Copies of proposal: 1
Deadline(s): None
Board meeting date(s): Spring and fall
Officers and Trustees: Sharon Rothwell, Chair.; Melonie B. Colaianne, Pres.; Eugene A. Gargaro, Jr., Secy.; Alan H. Barry; Richard A. Manoogian; Comerica Bank.
Number of staff: 2 full-time professional; 1 full-time support.
EIN: 386043605
Selected grants: The following grants were reported in 2003.
$400,000 to Detroit Renaissance Foundation, Detroit, MI. 2 grants: $200,000 each
$270,000 to Detroit Institute of Arts, Detroit, MI.
$160,000 to Detroit Science Center, Detroit, MI. 2 grants: $80,000 each
$123,000 to Detroit Educational Television Foundation-W T V S Channel 56, Detroit, MI.
$115,000 to Oakwood Healthcare System Foundation, Dearborn, MI.
$101,500 to Detroit Symphony Orchestra, Detroit, MI.
$70,000 to Charles H. Wright Museum of African-American History, Detroit, MI.
$50,000 to Jewish Federation of Metropolitan Detroit, Bloomfield Hills, MI.

2250
MEEMIC Foundation for the Future of Education
691 N. Squirrel Rd., Ste. 100
Auburn Hills, MI 48326 (248) 375-7535
Contact: Kristy Mitchell, Dir.
FAX: (248) 375-7549;
E-mail: foundation@meemic.com; *URL:* http://www.meemic.com/comfndoverCKR.htm

Established in 1992 in MI.
Donors: Michigan Educational Employees Mutual Insurance Co.; MEEMIC Insurance Co.
Grantmaker type: Company-sponsored foundation.
Financial data (yr. ended 12/31/05): Assets, $1,718,302 (M); gifts received, $8,710; expenditures, $73,406; total giving, $47,705; qualifying distributions, $47,705; giving activities include $47,705 for grants to individuals.
Purpose and activities: The foundation awards grants to educators at public, private, charter, and parochial schools in Michigan for programs designed to incorporate technology, science, literacy, mentoring, and the arts.
Type of support: Grants to individuals.
Limitations: Giving limited to MI. No grants for school supplies or equipment.
Application information: Application form required.
Initial approach: Complete online application form
Copies of proposal: 1
Deadline(s): Apr. 28
Final notification: The end of May
Directors: Douglas Goulait; Lynn Kalinowski; Kristy Mitchell; Mike Post; Christine Schmitt; Donald Weatherspoon.
Number of staff: 1 full-time professional; 1 part-time professional.
EIN: 383048526

2251
Meijer, Inc. Corporate Giving Program
c/o Public and Consumer Affairs Dept.
2929 Walker Ave. N.W.
Grand Rapids, MI   49544-9428
URL: http://www.meijer.com/pr

Grantmaker type: Corporate giving program.
Purpose and activities: Meijer makes charitable contributions to nonprofit organizations involved with arts and culture, K-12 education, parks and recreation, senior citizens, and to hospitals, police and fire departments, food banks, and churches. Support is given primarily in areas of company operations.
Fields of interest: Arts; Elementary/secondary education; Medical care, in-patient care; Crime/law enforcement, police agencies; Food banks; Disasters, fire prevention/control; Recreation, parks/playgrounds; Recreation; Christian agencies & churches; Aging.
Type of support: General/operating support; Employee volunteer services; Donated products.
Limitations: Giving primarily in areas of company operations.
Application information: The Public and Consumer Affairs Department handles giving.
Initial approach: Contact headquarters for application information

2252
MGM Mirage Corporate Giving Program
c/o Corp. Diversity and Community Affairs Dept.
3260 Industrial Rd.
Las Vegas, NV   89109
FAX: (702) 650-7401; *URL:* http://www.mgmmiragevoice.com/pages/voice.asp

Grantmaker type: Corporate giving program.
Purpose and activities: MGM Mirage makes charitable contributions to nonprofit organizations involved with childhood development, education, youth development, diversity, and community development. Support is given primarily in Michigan, Mississippi, and Nevada.
Fields of interest: Child development, education; Education; Youth development; Civil rights, equal rights; Community development.
Type of support: General/operating support.
Limitations: Giving primarily in MI, MS, and NV. No support for discriminatory organizations. No grants to individuals, or for athletic sponsorships; no gaming or casino items for children.
Application information: Application form not required.
Initial approach: Mail or fax proposal to headquarters
Copies of proposal: 1
Deadline(s): Oct. 1

2253
Michigan Automotive Compressor, Inc. Corporate Giving Program
c/o Community Rels.
2400 N. Dearing Rd.
Parma, MI   49269
Contact: Cheryl R. Norey, Community Rels. Coord.
FAX: (517) 531-1711;
E-mail: noreyc@michauto.com

Grantmaker type: Corporate giving program.

Purpose and activities: Michigan Automotive Compressor makes charitable contributions to nonprofit organizations involved with K-12 education and environmental education. Support is given primarily in the Parma, Michigan, area.
Fields of interest: Elementary/secondary education; Environmental education.
Type of support: General/operating support; Scholarship funds; In-kind gifts.
Limitations: Giving primarily in the Parma, MI, area. No support for social clubs, labor or veterans' organizations, or religious or fraternal organizations. No grants to individuals.
Application information: The Community Relations Department handles giving. A contributions committee reviews all requests. Application form not required.
Initial approach: Proposal to headquarters
Copies of proposal: 1
Committee meeting date(s): Monthly
Final notification: Following review

2254
Milacron Foundation
(formerly Cincinnati Milacron Foundation)
2090 Florence Ave.
Cincinnati, OH   45206   (513) 487-5912
Contact: John C. Francy, Secy.

Incorporated in 1951 in OH.
Donors: Cincinnati Milacron Inc.; Milacron Inc.
Grantmaker type: Company-sponsored foundation.
Financial data (yr. ended 12/31/04): Assets, $158,431 (M); gifts received, $300,000; expenditures, $351,164; total giving, $341,000; qualifying distributions, $340,763; giving activities include $341,000 for 3 grants (high: $290,000; low: $5,000).
Purpose and activities: The foundation supports organizations involved with arts and culture, education, human services, children and youth services, and community development.
Fields of interest: Arts; Higher education; Education; Children/youth, services; Human services; Community development; Federated giving programs.
Type of support: Continuing support; Annual campaigns; Capital campaigns; Building/renovation; Program development; Seed money; Scholarship funds; Research.
Limitations: Giving primarily in Cincinnati, OH; some giving also in MI. No support for United Way-supported agencies. No grants to individuals, or for endowments.
Publications: Application guidelines.
Application information: Application form not required.
Initial approach: Proposal
Copies of proposal: 1
Deadline(s): None
Board meeting date(s): Quarterly
Officer and Trustees:* R.D. Brown, Pres.; J.C. Francy, Secy.; R.A. Anderson, Treas.; R.D. Brown; J.A. Steger; C.F.C. Turner.
EIN: 316030682

2255
Miller, Canfield, Paddock and Stone, P.L.C. Corporate Giving Program
150 W. Jefferson St., Ste. 2500
Detroit, MI   48226
Contact: Amanda Van Dusen
FAX: (313) 496-8450

Grantmaker type: Corporate giving program.
Financial data (yr. ended 12/31/02): Total giving, $150,000, including $150,000 for grants.
Purpose and activities: Miller, Canfield, Paddock and Stone makes charitable contributions to nonprofit organizations involved with arts and culture and human services. Support is given primarily in areas of company operations.
Fields of interest: Arts; Human services.
Type of support: General/operating support; Annual campaigns; Capital campaigns; Building/renovation; Endowments; Consulting services; Employee volunteer services; Donated equipment.
Limitations: Giving primarily in areas of company operations, with emphasis on Detroit, MI.
Application information: Unsolicited requests are accepted but not encouraged. A contributions committee reviews some requests. Application form not required.
Initial approach: Proposal to nearest company office
Copies of proposal: 1
Final notification: Following review

2256
Herman Miller, Inc. Corporate Giving Program
855 E. Main Ave.
Zeeland, MI   49464-0302

Grantmaker type: Corporate giving program.
Purpose and activities: Herman Miller makes charitable contributions to nonprofit organizations on a case by case basis. Support is given on a national and international basis.
Fields of interest: General charitable giving.
Type of support: General/operating support.
Limitations: Giving on a national and international basis in areas of company operations.

2257
The Miller-Davis Foundation
1029 Portage St.
Kalamazoo, MI   49001

Established in 2001 in MI.
Donor: Miller-Davis Co.
Grantmaker type: Company-sponsored foundation.
Financial data (yr. ended 12/31/05): Assets, $298,082 (M); expenditures, $15,000; total giving, $15,000; qualifying distributions, $15,000; giving activities include $15,000 for grants.
Purpose and activities: The foundation supports organizations involved with K-12 education, the environment, and health.
Fields of interest: Elementary/secondary education; Environment, natural resources; Health care.
Type of support: General/operating support; Capital campaigns.
Limitations: Applications not accepted. Giving primarily in Kalamazoo, MI. No grants to individuals.

Application information: Contributes only to pre-selected organizations.
Officers and Directors: * Rex L. Bell,* Chair. and Pres.; Thomas Georgoff,* Secy.-Treas.; Alfred J. Gemrich.
EIN: 383607242

2258
Morgan Stanley Contributions Program - Michigan
7457 Franklin Rd., Ste. 200
Bloomfield Hills, MI 48301
Contact: Thomas Forbes, Investment Consultant
E-mail: thomas.forbes@morganstanley.com

Grantmaker type: Corporate giving program.
Purpose and activities: Morgan Stanley is committed to improving the quality of life in the communities where its employees live and work. In addition to providing extensive financial support to social services, cultural, educational and other charitable organizations, employees are encouraged to give something back to their communities.
Fields of interest: Arts; Education; Human services.

2259
Munder Capital Management Corporate Giving Program
480 Pierce St., Ste. 300
Birmingham, MI 48009-6063 (248) 647-9200
FAX: (248) 647-5931

Grantmaker type: Corporate giving program.
Purpose and activities: Munder makes charitable contributions to nonprofit organizations on a case by case basis. Support is given on a national basis.
Fields of interest: General charitable giving.
Type of support: General/operating support.
Limitations: Giving on a national basis, with emphasis on MI.

2260
National City Corporation Contributions Program
National City Ctr.
1900 E. 9th St., LOC-2157
Cleveland, OH 44114-3484 (216) 222-2000
Contact: Bruce A. McCrodden, Sr. V.P., Corp. Public Afffairs
URL: http://www.nationalcity.com/about/commurelations/default.asp

Grantmaker type: Corporate giving program.
Purpose and activities: As a complement to its foundation, National City also makes charitable contributions to nonprofit organizations directly. Support is given primarily in areas of company operations.
Fields of interest: Museums; Arts; Higher education; Education; Health care; Health organizations; Employment; Economic development; Urban/community development; Community development; Public affairs; Disabilities, people with; Minorities; Women.
Type of support: Annual campaigns; Capital campaigns; Building/renovation; Employee volunteer services; Loaned talent; Donated equipment.
Limitations: Giving primarily in areas of company operations in IL, IN, KY, MI, MO, OH, and western

PA; giving also to regional and national organizations.
Publications: Application guidelines; Corporate giving report; Program policy statement.
Application information: The Corporate Public Affairs Department handles giving. The company has a staff that only handles contributions. A contributions committee reviews all requests. Application form not required.
   Initial approach: Proposal to nearest company facility
   Copies of proposal: 1
   Deadline(s): None
   Committee meeting date(s): Quarterly
   Final notification: Following review
Number of staff: 2 full-time professional; 2 full-time support.

2261
National Starch and Chemical Foundation, Inc.
c/o ICI Tax Dept.
10 Finderne Ave.
Bridgewater, NJ 08807 (908) 685-5201
Contact: Carmen M. Ortiz

Incorporated in 1968 in NY.
Donor: National Starch and Chemical Co.
Grantmaker type: Company-sponsored foundation.
Financial data (yr. ended 12/31/03): Assets, $47,608 (M); gifts received, $1,864,660; expenditures, $1,877,600; total giving, $1,875,664; qualifying distributions, $1,877,600; giving activities include $1,875,664 for 900+ grants (high: $272,298).
Purpose and activities: The foundation supports hospitals and organizations involved with higher education and youth.
Fields of interest: Higher education; Hospitals (general); Youth, services; Federated giving programs.
Type of support: General/operating support; Continuing support; Employee matching gifts; Employee-related scholarships.
Limitations: Giving limited to areas of company operations in CA, IL, IN, MA, ME, MI, MN, MO, NC, NJ, PA, SC, TN, and VA.
Application information: Application form required.
   Initial approach: Telephone foundation for application form
   Copies of proposal: 1
   Deadline(s): Dec. 31
Officers and Directors: * M.J. Torbert,* Chair.; C.E. Montgomery,* Pres.; P.C. Maloff, Secy.; R.J. Forrest,* Treas.; L.J. Berlik; R.W. Buchan; C.F. Knott; W.H. Powell; P.A. Salit; W.F. Schlauch.
EIN: 237010264
Selected grants: The following grants were reported in 2003.
$272,298 to United Way of Somerset County, Bridgewater, NJ.
$80,000 to Somerset Medical Center, Somerville, NJ. 3 grants: $30,000, $20,000 (For Breaking New Ground), $30,000.
$67,192 to United Way of Central Indiana, Indianapolis, IN.
$60,207 to National Merit Scholarship Corporation, Evanston, IL.
$51,960 to United Way of the Piedmont, Spartanburg, SC.
$33,559 to United Way, Heart of America, Kansas City, MO.

$25,000 to State Theater Regional Arts Center at New Brunswick, New Brunswick, NJ.
$20,000 to Hunterdon Medical Center Foundation, Flemington, NJ.

2262
NCC Charitable Foundation
(formerly NCC Charitable Foundation II)
c/o National City Bank
1900 E. 9th St., LOC 2157
Cleveland, OH 44114 (216) 222-2994
Contact: Joanne Clark, V.P.
E-mail: joanne.clark@nationalcity.com; Additional
E-mail: bruce.mccrodden@nationalcity.com;
URL: http://www.nationalcity.com/about/commurelations/default.asp

Established in 1993.
Donors: National City Bank of Kentucky; National City Corp.
Grantmaker type: Company-sponsored foundation.
Financial data (yr. ended 6/30/05): Assets, $64,643,246 (M); expenditures, $22,748,790; total giving, $22,728,115; qualifying distributions, $22,728,915; giving activities include $22,728,115 for 2,817 grants (high: $440,000).
Purpose and activities: The foundation supports organizations involved with arts and culture, education, health, human services, and community development.
Fields of interest: Arts; Education; Health care; Human services; Community development; Federated giving programs.
Type of support: Continuing support; Annual campaigns; Capital campaigns; Program development; Employee matching gifts.
Limitations: Giving primarily in IL, IN, KY, MI, OH, and PA, with emphasis on OH. No grants to individuals.
Publications: Corporate giving report.
Application information: Application form not required.
   Initial approach: Proposal
   Deadline(s): None
   Board meeting date(s): Quarterly
Officers: Joanne Clark, V.P.; David A. Daberko, Off.; Bruce McCrodden, Off.; William E. McDonald, Off.
Trustee: National City Bank.
EIN: 347050989
Selected grants: The following grants were reported in 2004.
$400,000 to Cuyahoga Community College, Cleveland, OH. 2 grants: $200,000 each (For general support).
$400,000 to Western Michigan University, Kalamazoo, MI. 2 grants: $200,000 each (For general support).
$213,000 to Greater Louisville Fund for the Arts, Louisville, KY. For general support.
$150,000 to Detroit Symphony Orchestra, Detroit, MI. For general support.
$150,000 to Local Initiatives Support Corporation (LISC), Cleveland, OH. For general support.
$150,000 to Southwest Michigan First Corporation, Kalamazoo, MI. For general support.
$150,000 to University of Illinois Foundation, Champaign, IL. For general support.
$142,857 to Cleveland Clinic Foundation, Cleveland, OH. For general support.

2263
The Nissan Foundation
P.O. Box 191, M.S. N-3-A
Gardena, CA 90248-0191 (310) 771-3300
FAX: (310) 516-7967; URL: http://
www.nissanusa.com/about/corporate_info/
community_relations.html#TheNissanFoundation

Established in 1993 in CA.
Donors: Nissan Motor Corp. U.S.A.; Nissan North America, Inc.
Grantmaker type: Company-sponsored foundation.
Financial data (yr. ended 6/30/05): Assets, $8,390,363 (M); gifts received, $1,000,000; expenditures, $402,331; total giving, $383,000; qualifying distributions, $383,000; giving activities include $383,000 for 23 grants (high: $40,000; low: $5,000).
Purpose and activities: The foundation supports organizations involved with automobile industry vocational education and cultural diversity.
Fields of interest: Arts, cultural/ethnic awareness; Vocational education; Employment, services.
Type of support: General/operating support; Program development; Seed money.
Limitations: Giving limited to areas of company operations in southern CA, southeastern MI, south central MS, the New York, NY, metropolitan area, middle TN, and north central TX. No support for disease advocacy, research, or religious organizations. No grants to individuals, or for fundraising events, sponsorships, or political activities or capital campaigns.
Publications: Grants list; Informational brochure (including application guidelines).
Application information: Letters of inquiry should be no longer than 2 double-spaced pages. Application form not required.
    Initial approach: Mail or fax letter of inquiry to foundation
    Copies of proposal: 3
    Deadline(s): Nov. 23
    Final notification: Dec.
Officers and Directors:* Jim Morton,* Pres.; Kent Brawner, V.P.; Joy Crose, Secy.; Ralph Porter,* Treas.; John Calandro; Rita Ghosn; Greg Kelly; Lou Knierim; Tony Lucente; Galen Medlin; Michele Mottola; Chris O'Bannion; Mark Perry; Mario Polit; John Spoon; Mark Stout; George Vazquez.
EIN: 954413799
Selected grants: The following grants were reported in 2003.
$50,000 to Los Angeles Pierce College, Woodland Hills, CA.
$45,000 to Japanese American National Museum, Los Angeles, CA.
$39,000 to Art Center College of Design, Pasadena, CA.
$35,000 to Accelerated School, Los Angeles, CA.
$23,000 to Ford Theater Foundation, Los Angeles, CA.
$20,000 to 100 Black Men of Jackson, Jackson, MS.
$20,000 to Boys and Girls Club of Middle Tennessee, Nashville, TN.
$15,000 to Bayside Community Center, San Diego, CA.
$15,000 to Self Help Graphics and Art, Los Angeles, CA.
$10,000 to Mississippi School for Mathematics, Columbus, MS.

2264
Nissan North America, Inc. Corporate Giving Program
c/o Nissan Neighbors
P.O. Box 191, M.S. N-3-A
Gardena, CA 90248-0191 (310) 771-5594
FAX: (310) 516-7967; URL: http://
www.nissanusa.com/insideNissan/
CorporateOutreach/0,,,00.html

Grantmaker type: Corporate giving program.
Purpose and activities: As a complement to its foundation, Nissan also makes charitable contributions to nonprofit organizations directly. Support is given primarily in areas of company operations.
Fields of interest: Education; Environment; Disasters, preparedness/services; Youth development.
Type of support: General/operating support; Employee volunteer services; Employee matching gifts; In-kind gifts.
Limitations: Giving primarily in southern CA, metropolitan Detroit, MI, south central MS, middle TN, and Dallas and Fort Worth, TX.
Application information: Application form required.
    Initial approach: Complete online application form
    Copies of proposal: 1
    Deadline(s): None
    Final notification: 4 to 6 weeks

2265
The Northern Trust Company Charitable Trust
c/o The Northern Trust Co., Community Affairs Div.
50 S. LaSalle St., L7
Chicago, IL 60675 (312) 630-1762
Contact: Chastity Davis
E-mail: northern_trust_charitable_trust@ntrs.com;
URL: http://www.northerntrust.com/pws/jsp/
display2.jsp?XML=pages/nt/
0601/1137700254265_667.xml

Trust established in 1966 in IL.
Donor: The Northern Trust Co.
Grantmaker type: Company-sponsored foundation.
Financial data (yr. ended 12/31/05): Assets, $556,621 (M); gifts received, $4,449,617; expenditures, $4,319,503; total giving, $4,317,978; qualifying distributions, $4,318,337; giving activities include $3,583,107 for 209+ grants (high: $212,500; low: $25), and $734,871 for 928 employee matching gifts.
Purpose and activities: The trust supports organizations involved with arts and culture, education, and social welfare. Special emphasis is directed toward programs designed to advance the well being of disadvantaged women and children and people with disabilities.
Fields of interest: Arts; Education; Human services; Children; Disabilities, people with; Women; Economically disadvantaged.
Type of support: General/operating support; Continuing support; Annual campaigns; Capital campaigns; Building/renovation; Endowments; Program development; Employee volunteer services; Employee matching gifts; Matching/challenge support.
Limitations: Giving primarily in the Chicago, IL, neighborhoods of Chatham, Englewood, Humboldt Park, Logan Square, Loop, Washington Park, and West Town. No support for United Way-supported organizations (over 5 percent of budget), national health organizations or the local affiliates of national health organizations or research or disease advocacy organizations, political, labor, or fraternal organizations or social clubs, religious organizations not of direct benefit to the entire community, individual pre-K-12 schools, or organizations established less than 2 years ago. No grants to individuals, or for scholarships or fellowships, fundraising events, advertising or marketing, sports, athletic events, or athletic programs, travel-related events, book, film, video, or television development or production, memorial campaigns, or multi-year general operating support.
Publications: Corporate giving report (including application guidelines); Grants list.
Application information: Support is limited to 3 years. Application form required.
    Initial approach: Complete online letter of inquiry form; complete online application form for current grantees
    Deadline(s): Dec. 1 and June 30 for Social Welfare; Mar. 30 for Arts and Culture and Education; Jan. 12 and Aug. 10 for Social Welfare for current grantees; May 11 for Arts and Culture and Education for current grantees
    Board meeting date(s): Late Mar., July, and Oct.
    Final notification: 2 months
Trustee: The Northern Trust Co.
Number of staff: 2 full-time professional; 1 part-time professional; 1 full-time support; 1 part-time support.
EIN: 366147253
Selected grants: The following grants were reported in 2003.
$50,000 to Advocate Charitable Foundation, Park Ridge, IL. For capital support.
$50,000 to Northwestern University, Evanston, IL. To endow Freshman Urban Program.
$35,000 to Big Shoulders Fund, Chicago, IL. For support for inner-city schools.
$33,000 to Chicago Public Education Fund, Chicago, IL. For operating support.
$30,000 to Local Initiatives Support Corporation (LISC), Chicago, IL. For Campaign for Communities.
$30,000 to Museum of Science and Industry, Chicago, IL. For Science Club Network.
$25,000 to Childrens Memorial Foundation, Chicago, IL. For program support.
$25,000 to DePaul University, Chicago, IL. For financial assistance for needy undergraduate students.
$25,000 to Kohl Childrens Museum of Greater Chicago, Glenview, IL. For capital support.
$25,000 to Roosevelt University, Chicago, IL. For financial assistance for students in Renaissance II programs.

2266
Perrigo Company Charitable Foundation
515 Eastern Ave.
Allegan, MI 49010

Established in 2000 in MI.
Donor: L. Perrigo Co.
Grantmaker type: Company-sponsored foundation.
Financial data (yr. ended 6/30/05): Assets, $781,028 (M); gifts received, $600,000; expenditures, $994,557; total giving, $995,282; qualifying distributions, $995,282; giving activities include $995,282 for 129 grants (high: $200,000; low: $100).

Purpose and activities: The foundation supports organizations involved with arts and culture, education, health, medical research, youth development, and human services.
Fields of interest: Arts; Elementary/secondary education; Higher education; Education; Health care; Cancer research; Medical research; Youth development; Human services; Foundations (community); Federated giving programs.
Type of support: Building/renovation; Program development.
Limitations: Applications not accepted. Giving primarily in MI. No grants to individuals.
Application information: Contributes only to pre-selected organizations.
Officers: David T. Gibbons, Pres.; Douglas R. Schrank, Exec. V.P. and C.F.O.; John T. Hendrickson, Exec. V.P.; Todd W. Kingma, Secy.; James R. Ondersma, Treas.
EIN: 383553518
Selected grants: The following grants were reported in 2003.
$190,718 to United Way, Allegan County, Allegan, MI.
$57,000 to University of California, San Francisco, CA.
$28,000 to Saugatuck Center for the Arts, Saugatuck, MI.
$27,730 to United Way of Greenville County, Greenville, SC.
$25,000 to Citizens for a Sound Economy, DC.
$25,000 to Partnership for a Drug-Free America, New York, NY.
$25,000 to West Michigan Strategic Alliance, Holland, MI.
$15,000 to Davenport University Foundation, Grand Rapids, MI.
$13,600 to Allegan General Hospital Foundation, Allegan, MI.
$11,000 to Chamber of Commerce, Grand Rapids Area, Grand Rapids, MI.

2267
The Pistons-Palace Foundation
c/o Palace Sports & Entertainment, Inc.
4 Championship Dr.
Auburn Hills, MI   48326   (248) 377-0100
Contact: Dennis Sampier
URL: http://www.nba.com/pistons/community

Established in 1989 in MI.
Donors: Detroit Pistons Basketball Co.; The Palace of Auburn Hills; Guardian Industries Corp.; Bank One, N.A.; Palace Sports & Entertainment, Inc.; Ticketmaster Group, Inc.; Belle Tire.
Grantmaker type: Company-sponsored foundation.
Financial data (yr. ended 2/28/05): Assets, $301,766 (M); gifts received, $321,151; expenditures, $245,082; total giving, $153,280; qualifying distributions, $155,432; giving activities include $114,185 for 14 grants (high: $71,910; low: $450).
Purpose and activities: The foundation supports organizations involved with disaster relief, children and youth, human services, and community development.
Fields of interest: Safety/disasters, fund raising/fund distribution; Youth development; Children/youth, services; Human services; Community development.
Type of support: Research; Program development; General/operating support; Building/renovation; In-kind gifts.

Limitations: Giving primarily in the tri-county metropolitan Detroit area and southeastern MI. No grants to individuals.
Publications: Application guidelines.
Application information: Application form required.
Initial approach: Contact foundation for application form
Copies of proposal: 1
Deadline(s): Aug. 1
Officers and Trustees:* William Davidson,* Chair.; Oscar Feldman, Pres.; Ralph J. Gerson, V.P.; Herbert Tyner, V.P.; Thomas S. Wilson, V.P.; Ann Newman, Secy.; Ronald J. Campbell, Treas.; Eugene Mondry, Treas.; Ethan Davidson; Marla Davidson-Karimipour; Milton Dressner; Byron Gerson; Dorothy Gerson; Dan Hauser; Bill Laimbeer; William J. Robinson.
Number of staff: 3 full-time professional.
EIN: 382858649

2268
Plante & Moran, PLLC Corporate Giving Program
27400 Northwestern Hwy.
Southfield, MI   48034-4724

Grantmaker type: Corporate giving program.
Purpose and activities: Plante & Moran makes charitable contributions to nonprofit organizations on a case by case basis. Support is given primarily in areas of company operations.
Fields of interest: General charitable giving.
Type of support: General/operating support; In-kind gifts.
Limitations: Giving primarily in areas of company operations, with emphasis on MI.

2269
R. L. Polk & Co. Contributions Program
26955 Northwestern Hwy.
Southfield, MI   48034
Contact: Joseph Walker

Grantmaker type: Corporate giving program.
Purpose and activities: R.L. Polk makes charitable contributions to nonprofit organizations on a case by case basis. Support is given primarily in areas of company operations.
Fields of interest: General charitable giving.
Type of support: General/operating support; Sponsorships; In-kind gifts.
Limitations: Giving primarily in areas of company operations.
Application information: Application form not required.
Initial approach: Proposal to headquarters
Copies of proposal: 1
Deadline(s): None
Final notification: Varies

2270
ProQuest Company Contributions Program
(formerly Bell & Howell Company Contributions Program)
789 Eisenhower Pkwy.
P.O. Box 1346
Ann Arbor, MI   48106-1346   (734) 761-4700
Contact: Elliot Forsythe, V.P., Human Resources
URL: http://www.proquestcompany.com/about/community.shtml

Grantmaker type: Corporate giving program.
Purpose and activities: ProQuest makes charitable contributions to nonprofit organizations involved with arts and culture, education, health, human services, science, and government and public administration. Support is given on a national basis in areas of company operations.
Fields of interest: Humanities; Arts; Higher education; Education; Health care; Youth, services; Human services; Federated giving programs; Engineering/technology; Science; Government/public administration.
Type of support: General/operating support; Program development; Employee matching gifts; Matching/challenge support.
Limitations: Giving on a national basis in areas of company operations. No support for national organizations, political parties or candidates, religious organizations, or fraternal, veterans', or labor organizations. No grants to individuals.
Application information: Application form not required.
Initial approach: Proposal to headquarters

2271
Pulte Homes, Inc. Corporate Giving Program
(formerly Pulte Corporation Contributions Program)
c/o Charitable Giving Office
100 Bloomfield Hills Pkwy., Ste. 300
Bloomfield Hills, MI   48304   (248) 433-4534
URL: http://www.pulte.com/about_us/contributions_missionstatement.asp

Grantmaker type: Corporate giving program.
Purpose and activities: Pulte Homes makes charitable contributions to nonprofit organizations involved with higher education, the environment, health and human services, and housing. Support is given primarily in areas of company operations.
Fields of interest: Higher education; Environment; Health care; Housing/shelter; Human services.
Type of support: Capital campaigns; Professorships; Employee volunteer services; Scholarships—to individuals.
Limitations: Giving primarily in areas of company operations, with emphasis on the metropolitan Detroit, MI, area. No support for discriminatory organizations, religious, fraternal, or veterans' organizations not of direct benefit to the entire community, or pass-through organizations. No grants to individuals (except for scholarships), or for general operating support.
Application information: Proposals should be no longer than 5 pages. Housing contributions have been allocated through 2006. A contributions committee reviews all requests. Application form required.
Initial approach: Download application form and mail proposal and application form to headquarters; mail to nearest company facility for health and human services
Copies of proposal: 1
Deadline(s): None

2272
Quicksilver Resources Inc. Corporate Giving Program
c/o Corp. Contribs.
777 W. Rosedale, Ste. 300
Fort Worth, TX 76104
URL: http://www.qrinc.com/about/
community_involvement.shtml

Grantmaker type: Corporate giving program.
Purpose and activities: Quicksilver makes charitable contributions to nonprofit organizations involved with the environment and youth development. Support is given primarily in Gaylord, Michigan, Cut Bank, Montana, Fort Worth, Texas, and Casper, Wyoming.
Fields of interest: Environment; Youth development.
Type of support: General/operating support; Scholarship funds; Employee volunteer services; Use of facilities.
Limitations: Giving primarily in Gaylord, MI, Cut Bank, MT, Fort Worth, TX, and Casper, WY.
Application information: Application form not required.
Initial approach: Proposal to headquarters
Copies of proposal: 1
Final notification: Following review

2273
Edward F. Redies Foundation, Inc.
P.O. Box 411
Saline, MI 48176 (734) 429-9421
Application address: c/o R&B Machine Tool Co., 118 E. Michigan Ave., Saline, MI 48176

Incorporated in 1981 in MI.
Donor: R&B Machine Tool Co.
Grantmaker type: Company-sponsored foundation.
Financial data (yr. ended 12/31/04): Assets, $5,154,561 (M); expenditures, $271,846; total giving, $232,000; qualifying distributions, $235,750; giving activities include $232,000 for 26 grants (high: $50,000; low: $1,000).
Purpose and activities: The foundation supports hospitals, parks and playgrounds, and organizations involved with education, human services, and government and public administration.
Fields of interest: Elementary/secondary education; Higher education; Education; Hospitals (general); Recreation, parks/playgrounds; Children, services; Human services; Government/public administration.
Type of support: Capital campaigns; Building/renovation; Equipment; Scholarship funds.
Limitations: Giving primarily in the greater Washtenaw County, MI, area. No grants to individuals.
Application information: Application form not required.
Initial approach: Proposal
Deadline(s): Mar. 30
Officers and Directors: R. Edward Redies, Pres.; Robert D. Redies, V.P.; Karen Redies, Secy.-Treas.; Paul Bunten; Elizabeth J. Redies; Thomas D. Redies; William D. Redies; Milton Stemen; Dennis Valenti.
EIN: 382391326

2274
The Redlum Foundation
257 Norwood Dr.
Holland, MI 49424

Established in 1998 in MI.
Donor: Redlum, Ltd.
Grantmaker type: Company-sponsored foundation.
Financial data (yr. ended 12/31/05): Assets, $139,395 (M); gifts received, $62,000; expenditures, $74,873; total giving, $74,000; qualifying distributions, $74,000; giving activities include $74,000 for grants.
Purpose and activities: The foundation supports organizations involved with education, health, human services, and religion.
Fields of interest: Education; Health organizations; Recreation, camps; Human services; Religion.
Limitations: Applications not accepted. Giving primarily in Holland, MI. No grants to individuals.
Application information: Contributes only to pre-selected organizations.
Directors: Jeffrey Mulder; Jeri Mulder; Karen Mulder; Kimberly Mulder; Michael Mulder.
EIN: 383443698

2275
River City Food Company Foundation
3425 Lake Eastbrook Blvd. S.E.
Grand Rapids, MI 49546

Established in 1997 in MI.
Donor: River City Food Co.
Grantmaker type: Company-sponsored foundation.
Financial data (yr. ended 12/31/03): Assets, $52,762 (M); expenditures, $4,407; total giving, $3,000; qualifying distributions, $3,000; giving activities include $3,000 for 1 grant.
Purpose and activities: The foundation supports organizations involved with higher education and Christianity.
Fields of interest: Higher education, college (community/junior); Christian agencies & churches.
Type of support: General/operating support.
Limitations: Applications not accepted. Giving primarily in Grand Rapids, MI. No grants to individuals.
Application information: Contributes only to pre-selected organizations.
Officer and Director:* R. Dale Lausch,* Pres.
EIN: 383300379

2276
Roto Plastics Corporation Fund
c/o Roto Plastics Corp.
245 N. Winter St.
Adrian, MI 49221

Established in 1994 in MI.
Donors: Roto Plastics Corp.; C.W. Durst.
Grantmaker type: Company-sponsored foundation.
Financial data (yr. ended 12/31/05): Assets, $484,712 (M); gifts received, $50,000; expenditures, $16,544; total giving, $16,239; qualifying distributions, $16,239; giving activities include $16,239 for grants.
Purpose and activities: The foundation supports organizations involved with arts and culture, education, cancer, and human services.
Fields of interest: Performing arts, opera; Arts; Higher education; Education, services; Cancer; Athletics/sports, football; American Red Cross; Human services; Federated giving programs.
Type of support: General/operating support.
Limitations: Applications not accepted. Giving primarily in Adrian, MI. No grants to individuals.

Application information: Contributes only to pre-selected organizations.
Trustees: Clyne W. Durst, Jr.; Jennifer C. Durst; David C. Mulligan.
EIN: 386627275

2277
The Ryder System Charitable Foundation, Inc.
c/o Corp. Tax
11690 N.W. 105th St.
Miami, FL 33178 (305) 500-3031

Established in 1984 in FL.
Donor: Ryder System, Inc.
Grantmaker type: Company-sponsored foundation.
Financial data (yr. ended 12/31/04): Assets, $133,383 (M); gifts received, $1,167,962; expenditures, $1,287,089; total giving, $1,287,089; qualifying distributions, $1,287,089; giving activities include $1,261,714 for 130 grants (high: $100,000; low: $25), $25,275 for 44 grants to individuals (high: $1,850; low: $150), and $100 for 1 employee matching gift.
Purpose and activities: The foundation supports organizations involved with arts and culture, education, health, human services, community development, civic affairs, minorities, and economically disadvantaged people.
Fields of interest: Arts; Elementary school/education; Secondary school/education; Higher education; Education; Health care; Minorities/immigrants, centers/services; Human services; Community development; Federated giving programs; Government/public administration; Minorities; Economically disadvantaged.
Type of support: General/operating support; Annual campaigns; Employee matching gifts; Grants to individuals; In-kind gifts.
Limitations: Giving limited to Los Angeles, CA, southern FL, Atlanta, GA, Detroit, MI, St. Louis, MO, Cincinnati, OH, and Dallas, TX.
Publications: Corporate giving report.
Application information: Application form not required.
Initial approach: Proposal
Copies of proposal: 1
Deadline(s): None
Board meeting date(s): Annually and as needed
Final notification: Within 60 days
Officers and Directors:* Gregory T. Swienton,* Pres.; Robert D. Fatovic,* V.P. and Secy.; W. Daniel Susik, V.P. and Treas.; Tracy A. Leinbach,* V.P.; Vicki A. O'Meara, V.P. and Secy.; Richard H. Siegel, V.P.; R. Ray Goode,* C.A.O. and Exec. Dir.
Number of staff: 1 full-time professional; 1 full-time support.
EIN: 592462315

2278
SEMCO Energy Gas Company Contributions Program
c/o Corp. Contribs.
405 Water St.
Port Huron, MI 48060
Additional application addresses: central MI: David Allen, Mgr., Public Affairs, 55 Hamblin Ave., Battle Creek, MI 49017, tel.: (800) 624-2019, ext. 5560, FAX: (269) 966-0419,
E-mail: dave.allen@semcoenergy.com, northern MI: Karen Kimar-Johnson, Mgr., Public Affairs, 34 E.

U.S. Hwy. 41, Negaunee, MI 49866, tel.: (800) 624-2019, ext. 5904, FAX: (906) 475-6292, E-mail: karen.kimar@semcoenergy.com, western and southwestern MI: Amanda Price, Mgr., Public Affairs, 739 Paw Paw Dr., Holland, MI 49423, tel.: (800) 624-2019, ext. 5775, FAX: (616) 392-4566, E-mail: amanda.price@semcoenergy.com; URL: http://www.semcoenergygas.com/about/community.html

Grantmaker type: Corporate giving program.
Purpose and activities: SEMCO makes charitable contributions to nonprofit organizations involved with arts and culture, education, health and human services, and community development. Support is given primarily in Michigan.
Fields of interest: Arts; Education; Health care; Human services; Community development.
Type of support: General/operating support; Capital campaigns; Employee volunteer services.
Limitations: Giving primarily in MI.
Application information: Proposals should be submitted using organization letterhead. The Public Affairs Department handles giving. Application form not required.
  Initial approach: Proposal to nearest company facility
  Copies of proposal: 1
  Deadline(s): None
  Final notification: Following review

2279
Sky Foundation
221 S. Church St.
Bowling Green, OH   43402-0428
(419) 327-6300
Contact: Angie Hill, Asst. Secy. and Admin.

Established in 1998 in OH.
Donors: Sky Financial Group, Inc.; Sky Holdings, Inc.
Grantmaker type: Company-sponsored foundation.
Financial data (yr. ended 12/31/04): Assets, $2,557,964 (M); gifts received, $425,125; expenditures, $502,832; total giving, $481,787; qualifying distributions, $481,787; giving activities include $481,787 for 56 grants (high: $50,000; low: $2,000).
Purpose and activities: The foundation supports organizations involved with arts and culture, education, health, human services, and community development.
Fields of interest: Performing arts, orchestra (symphony); Arts; Elementary/secondary education; Higher education; Libraries (public); Education; Health care; YM/YWCAs & YM/YWHAs; Human services; Community development.
Limitations: Giving limited to northeast IN, southern MI, OH, western PA, and northern WV. No support for private foundations. No grants to individuals.
Application information: Application form required.
  Initial approach: Contact foundation for application form
  Deadline(s): None
Trustees: Marty E. Adams; Jennifer L. Iliff; Darlene Minnick; Rockette "Rocky" Richardson; Curtis E. Shepherd; C.J. Keller Smith; Eric C. Stachler; Kevin T. Thompson; Paul Tomko; D.J. Valentine.
EIN: 341886344
Selected grants: The following grants were reported in 2004.
$50,000 to Bowling Green State University, Bowling Green, OH.

$25,000 to Lucas County Educational Service Center, Toledo, OH.
$20,000 to Library Legacy Foundation, Toledo, OH.
$20,000 to YMCA of Youngstown, Youngstown, OH.
$20,000 to Youngstown Symphony Society, Youngstown, OH.
$15,000 to National Aviary in Pittsburgh, Pittsburgh, PA.
$15,000 to Toledo Museum of Art, Toledo, OH.
$12,500 to Mon Valley Education Consortium, McKeesport, PA.
$12,500 to West Liberty State College, West Liberty, WV.
$10,000 to Logan County Landmark Preservation, Bellefontaine, OH.

2280
Sommers, Schwartz, Silver & Schwartz Foundation
c/o Sommers, Schwartz, Silver & Schwartz Investment Co.
2000 Town Ctr., Ste. 900
Southfield, MI   48075

Donors: Sommers, Schwartz, Silver & Schwartz; Leonard Schwartz; Donald Epstein; Steve Schwartz; Paul Hines; James J. Vlasic.
Grantmaker type: Company-sponsored foundation.
Financial data (yr. ended 11/30/05): Assets, $29,750 (M); expenditures, $74,203; total giving, $74,141; qualifying distributions, $74,141; giving activities include $74,141 for grants.
Purpose and activities: The foundation supports hospitals and organizations involved with higher education, health, and youth development.
Fields of interest: Higher education; Hospitals (general); Health organizations, association; Youth development.
Limitations: Applications not accepted. Giving primarily in MI. No grants to individuals.
Application information: Contributes only to pre-selected organizations.
Officers: Paul Hines, Pres.; James J. Vlasic, Secy.; Steve Schwartz, Treas.
EIN: 382783183

2281
Steelcase Foundation
P.O. Box 1967, CH-4E
Grand Rapids, MI   49501-1967
Contact: Susan Broman, Exec. Dir.
FAX: (616) 475-2200;
E-mail: sbroman@steelcase.com; URL: http://www.steelcase.com/na/steelcase_foundation_ourcompany.aspx?f=18486

Established in 1951 in MI.
Donor: Steelcase Inc.
Grantmaker type: Company-sponsored foundation.
Financial data (yr. ended 11/30/05): Assets, $113,151,982 (M); gifts received, $336,862; expenditures, $7,930,027; total giving, $7,337,772; qualifying distributions, $7,674,634; giving activities include $6,892,139 for 360 grants (high: $700,000), and $445,633 for employee matching gifts.
Purpose and activities: The foundation supports organizations involved with arts and culture, education, the environment, health, human services, and community development. Special emphasis is directed toward programs designed to

assist youth, the elderly, disabled people, and economically disadvantaged people.
Fields of interest: Arts; Education; Environment; Health care; Human services; Economic development; Community development; Youth; Aging; Disabilities, people with; Economically disadvantaged.
International interests: Canada.
Type of support: Employee-related scholarships; General/operating support; Capital campaigns; Building/renovation; Equipment; Land acquisition; Program development; Seed money; Scholarship funds; Employee matching gifts; Matching/challenge support.
Limitations: Giving limited to areas of company operations, with emphasis on Athens, AL, City of Industry, CA, Grand Rapids, MI, and Markham, Canada. No support for churches or religious organizations not of direct benefit to the entire community or discriminatory organizations. No grants to individuals (except for employee-related scholarships), or for endowments or conferences or seminars.
Publications: Application guidelines; Annual report (including application guidelines).
Application information: Application form required.
  Initial approach: Download application form
  Copies of proposal: 1
  Deadline(s): Quarterly
  Board meeting date(s): Quarterly
  Final notification: At least 90 days
Officers and Trustees:* Kate Pew Wolters,* Chair.; Susan Broman, Exec. Dir.; James P. Hackett; Earl D. Holton; David D. Hunting, Jr.; Mary Goodwillie Nelson; Robert C. Pew III; Peter M. Wege II; James C. Welch; Fifth Third Bank.
Number of staff: 1 full-time professional; 1 full-time support.
EIN: 386050470
Selected grants: The following grants were reported in 2004.
$630,032 to Grand Rapids Art Museum, Grand Rapids, MI.
$545,000 to Child and Family Resource Council, Grand Rapids, MI.
$500,000 to YMCA of Greater Grand Rapids, Grand Rapids, MI.
$250,000 to Baxter Community College.
$250,000 to Hope Network, Grand Rapids, MI.
$200,000 to Asheville-Buncombe Community Christian Ministry, Asheville, NC.
$152,405 to Grand Rapids Symphony, Grand Rapids, MI.
$125,000 to Hospice of Henderson County, Hendersonville, NC.
$118,095 to Grand Valley State University, Allendale, MI.
$111,950 to Calvin College, Grand Rapids, MI.

2282
Steelcase Inc. Corporate Giving Program
c/o Corp. Rels. Dept.
P.O. Box 1967, CH-4E
Grand Rapids, MI   49501-1967   (616) 475-2009
URL: http://www.steelcase.com/na/in_the_community_ourcompany.aspx?f=18478

Grantmaker type: Corporate giving program.
Financial data (yr. ended 2/28/04): Total giving, $826,500, including $560,000 for 101 grants (high: $250,000; low: $100), and $266,500 for 63 in-kind gifts. The company also provided $35,000 for 2 company-administered programs.

Purpose and activities: As a complement to its foundation, Steelcase also makes charitable contributions to nonprofit organizations directly. Support is given primarily in the Athens, Alabama, City of Industry and Los Angeles County, California, Grand Rapids, Michigan, Toronto, Canada, and Tijuana, Mexico, areas.

Fields of interest: Arts; Higher education; Education; Environment, natural resources; Reproductive health, family planning; Health care; Substance abuse, services; Mental health/crisis services; AIDS; Alcoholism; Health organizations; AIDS research; Food services; Children/youth, services; Human services; Civil rights, equal rights; Community development; Public affairs, government agencies; Public affairs; Aging; Disabilities, people with; Minorities; Women; Economically disadvantaged; Homeless.

International interests: Canada; Mexico.

Type of support: General/operating support; Scholarship funds; Employee volunteer services; Use of facilities; Donated products; In-kind gifts.

Limitations: Giving primarily in the Athens, AL, City of Industry and Los Angeles County, CA, Grand Rapids, MI, Toronto, Canada, and Tijuana, Mexico, areas.

Publications: Informational brochure (including application guidelines).

Application information: The Corporate Relations Department handles giving. The company has a staff that only handles contributions. Application form required.

> *Initial approach:* Download application form and mail to nearest company facility
> *Copies of proposal:* 1
> *Deadline(s):* None
> *Final notification:* Following review

Number of staff: 1 full-time professional.

2283
Target Corporation Contributions Program

1000 Nicollet Mall, TPS-3080
Minneapolis, MN 55403   (612) 696-6098
Additional tel.: (800) 800-8800; URL: http://target.com/target_group/community_giving/index.jhtml

Grantmaker type: Corporate giving program.

Financial data (yr. ended 1/29/05): Total giving, $76,100,000, including $76,100,000 for 7,112 grants (high: $25,000; low: $1,000; average: $1,500–$5,000).

Purpose and activities: As a complement to its foundation, Target also makes charitable contributions to nonprofit organizations directly and awards college scholarships to high school seniors, high school graduates, and college undergraduate students. Support is given on a national and international basis in areas of company store operations.

Fields of interest: Arts; Education; Crime/violence prevention, domestic violence; Crime/violence prevention, child abuse; Family services, domestic violence.

International interests: Africa; Asia; Europe; India; Latin America; Middle East.

Type of support: Capital campaigns; Emergency funds; Program development; Scholarship funds; Cause-related marketing; Employee volunteer services; Sponsorships; Employee-related scholarships; Scholarships—to individuals; Donated products; In-kind gifts.

Limitations: Giving on a national and international basis in areas of company store operations, including in Africa, Asia, Europe, India, Latin America, and the Middle East; giving in the continental U.S. for Target All-Around Scholarships. No support for foundations, religious organizations not of direct benefit to the entire community, athletic teams, or advocacy or research organizations. No grants to individuals (except for scholarships), or for endowments, treatment programs, athletic events, or fundraising or gala events.

Publications: Informational brochure (including application guidelines).

Application information: The Community Relations Department handles giving. Application form required.

> *Initial approach:* Contact nearest company store for application form; complete online application form for Target All-Around Scholarships
> *Copies of proposal:* 1
> *Deadline(s):* Mar. 1 to May 31; Nov. 1 for Target All-Around Scholarships
> *Final notification:* By Sept. 30; after Feb. 15 for Target All-Around Scholarships

Number of staff: 19 full-time professional; 14 full-time support.

2284
Taubman Centers, Inc. Corporate Giving Program

200 E. Long Lake Rd., Ste. 300
Bloomfield Hills, MI 48303-0200
(734) 258-6800

Grantmaker type: Corporate giving program.

Purpose and activities: Taubman Centers makes charitable contributions to nonprofit organizations on a case by case basis. Support is given primarily in Detroit, Michigan.

Fields of interest: General charitable giving.

Type of support: General/operating support; Employee volunteer services; Employee matching gifts.

Limitations: Giving primarily in Detroit, MI.

Application information: Application form not required.

> *Initial approach:* Proposal to headquarters
> *Copies of proposal:* 1
> *Deadline(s):* None

2285
TCF Foundation

c/o Community Affairs Off.
200 Lake St. E., M.C. EXO-02-C
Wayzata, MN 55391-1693
Contact: Denise Peterson, Community Affairs Off.
FAX: (952) 745-2775; E-mail: dpete@tcfbank.com;
Additional application addresses: CO: TCF National Bank, CRA Off., 6400 S. Fiddler's Green Cir., Ste. 800, M.C. C00-00-0, Englewood, CO 80111, tel.: (720) 200-2469, IL, IN, and WI: TCF National Bank, V.P., Community Affairs, 800 Burr Ridge Pkwy., Burr Ridge, IL 60527, tel.: (630) 986-4920, MI: TCF National Bank, Dir., Community Affairs, 401 E. Liberty St., M.C. 604-05-E, Ann Arbor, MI 48104-2298, tel.: (800) 362-5555; URL: http://www.tcfbank.com/About/about_community_relations.jsp

Established in 1989 in MN.

Donors: TCF National Bank Minnesota; TCF National Bank.

Grantmaker type: Company-sponsored foundation.

Financial data (yr. ended 12/31/04): Assets, $37,210 (M); gifts received, $1,988,126; expenditures, $1,941,266; total giving, $1,941,241; qualifying distributions, $1,968,389; giving activities include $1,720,849 for 143 grants (high: $100,000; low: $50), and $220,392 for 704 employee matching gifts.

Purpose and activities: The foundation supports organizations involved with arts and culture, education, health, housing, youth development, financial literacy, human services, economic development, and community development.

Fields of interest: Performing arts; Arts; Education; Health care; Housing/shelter; Youth development; Human services, financial counseling; Human services; Economic development; Community development, small businesses; Community development; Disabilities, people with; Mentally disabled; Economically disadvantaged.

Type of support: General/operating support; Continuing support; Annual campaigns; Capital campaigns; Program development; Scholarship funds; Employee volunteer services; Loaned talent; Employee matching gifts; Employee-related scholarships.

Limitations: Giving primarily in areas of company operations in CO, MI, and MN, the greater Chicago, IL, area, northwest IN, and southeastern WI, including Kenosha, the greater Milwaukee area, and Racine; giving also to regional organizations. No support for political parties or candidates, religious organizations not of direct benefit to the entire community, lobbying organizations, or social organizations. No grants to individuals (except for employee-related scholarships), or for social events or advertising or publications.

Publications: Application guidelines; Annual report; Informational brochure.

Application information: The Minnesota Common Grant Application Form is recommended for organizations located in MN. Unsolicited requests from non-youth development arts and culture organizations located in IL, IN, and WI are not accepted. Unsolicited requests for capital campaign support from organizations located in IL, IN, and WI are not accepted. Support is limited to 3 years for organizations located in IL, IN, and WI. Multi-year funding is not automatic.

> *Initial approach:* Mail cover letter and application form to foundation for organizations located in MN; visit Web site for application information for organizations located in CO, IL, IN, and WI; proposal to application address for organizations located in MI
> *Copies of proposal:* 1
> *Deadline(s):* Telephone foundation for deadlines for organizations located in CO and MN; visit Web site for deadlines for organizations located in IL, IN, and WI
> *Board meeting date(s):* Telephone foundation for dates
> *Final notification:* At least 2 months for organizations located in MN; visit Web site for dates for organizations located in IL, IN, and WI

Officers and Directors:* William A. Cooper,* Chair.; Gregory S. Pulles, Secy.; Neil W. Brown, Treas.; Mark L. Jeter; Jason E. Korstange.

Number of staff: 1 full-time professional.

EIN: 411659826

2286
Tigers Care Program

2100 Woodward
Detroit, MI 48210 (313) 962-4000
Contact: Celia Bobrowsky, Dir., Community Rels.
FAX: (313) 471-2144;
E-mail: tigerscare@detroittigers.com; URL: http://
detroit.tigers.mlb.com/NASApp/mlb/det/
community/det_community_news.jsp

Grantmaker type: Corporate giving program.
Purpose and activities: The Detroit Tigers make
charitable contributions to nonprofit organizations
involved with recreation and youth development.
Support is given primarily in Michigan and northern
Ohio.
Fields of interest: Recreation; Youth development.
Type of support: Scholarship funds; Sponsorships.
Limitations: Giving primarily in MI and northern OH.
Application information: Application form not
required.
Initial approach: Proposal to headquarters
Copies of proposal: 1
Final notification: Following review

2287
A. M. Todd Company Foundation

c/o Fifth Third Bank
P.O. Box 3636
Grand Rapids, MI 49501-3636
Contact: Chris Czopek
Application address: 136 E. Michigan Ave.,
Kalamazoo, MI 49007, tel.: (269) 337-6768

Established in 1962 in MI.
Donors: A.M. Todd Co.; Zink & Triest Co.
Grantmaker type: Company-sponsored foundation.
Financial data (yr. ended 12/31/05): Assets,
$291,594 (M); expenditures, $115,492; total
giving, $112,750; qualifying distributions,
$113,000; giving activities include $112,750 for 45
grants (high: $23,500; low: $200).
Purpose and activities: The foundation supports
Christian agencies and churches and organizations
involved with arts and culture, education, the
environment, health, human services, and
community development.
Fields of interest: Arts; Education; Environment;
Hospitals (general); Health care; Human services;
Community development; Federated giving
programs; Christian agencies & churches.
Type of support: Continuing support; Annual
campaigns; Capital campaigns; Building/
renovation.
Limitations: Giving limited to Kalamazoo County, MI.
No grants to individuals.
Application information: Application form not
required.
Initial approach: Proposal
Deadline(s): None
Trustees: Ian D. Blair; A.J. Todd III; Fifth Third Bank.
EIN: 386055829

2288
Tyco Electronics Foundation

(formerly AMP Foundation)
c/o Tyco Electronics Corp.
P.O. Box 3608, M.S. 140-10
Harrisburg, PA 17105-3608 (717) 592-4869
Contact: Mary J. Rakoczy, Admin.

FAX: (717) 592-4022;
E-mail: mjrakocz@tycoelectronics.com; Application
address for overnight delivery: 2901 Fulling Mill Rd.,
M.S. 140-10, Middletown, PA 17057; URL: http://
www.tycoelectronics.com/aboutus/community/
foundation.asp

Established in 1977 in PA.
Donor: AMP Inc.
Grantmaker type: Company-sponsored foundation.
Financial data (yr. ended 12/31/05): Assets,
$15,356,741 (M); expenditures, $1,287,049; total
giving, $1,159,313; qualifying distributions,
$1,159,313; giving activities include $1,159,313
for 160 grants (high: $55,000; low: $20).
Purpose and activities: The foundation supports
organizations involved with secondary and higher
education and community development.
Fields of interest: Secondary school/education;
Higher education; Community development.
Type of support: Program development; In-kind gifts.
Limitations: Giving primarily in areas of company
operations, with emphasis on Menlo Park and
northern CA, Boston, MA, Detroit, MI, NC, Harrisburg
and central PA, SC, Austin, Dallas, and Houston, TX,
and Lynchburg, VA. No support for religious or
political organizations, private foundations, national
organizations, or fraternal, social, labor, or trade
organizations. No grants to individuals.
Publications: Application guidelines.
Application information: Application form not
required.
Initial approach: Proposal
Copies of proposal: 1
Deadline(s): Mar. 15, June 15, Sept. 15, and Dec.
15
Board meeting date(s): Jan., Apr., July, and Oct.
Final notification: 4 to 6 weeks following board
meetings
Trustee: M&T Investment Group.
Number of staff: 1 full-time professional.
EIN: 232022928

2289
The Bob Ufer Foundation

2349 E. Stadium Blvd.
Ann Arbor, MI 48104

Established in 1997 in MI.
Donor: Ufer Spirit, Inc.
Grantmaker type: Company-sponsored foundation.
Financial data (yr. ended 10/31/05): Assets,
$52,787 (M); gifts received, $28,900;
expenditures, $13,469; total giving, $12,000;
qualifying distributions, $12,000; giving activities
include $12,000 for grants.
Purpose and activities: The foundation supports
organizations involved with education and athletics.
Fields of interest: Elementary/secondary
education; Education; Athletics/sports, amateur
competition.
Type of support: Equipment; Curriculum
development; Scholarship funds.
Limitations: Applications not accepted. Giving
primarily in Ann Arbor, MI. No grants to individuals.
Application information: Contributes only to
pre-selected organizations.
Officers: Thomas W. Ufer, Pres.; David S. Ufer, V.P.;
Robert P. Ufer, V.P.; Pamela S. Wood, Secy.-Treas.
EIN: 383381600

2290
Universal Forest Products Education Foundation

(formerly Universal Companies, Inc. Education
Foundation)
2801 E. Beltline Ave. N.E.
Grand Rapids, MI 49525-9600 (616) 364-6161
Contact: Nancy DeGood

Established in 1990 in MI.
Donor: Universal Forest Products, Inc.
Grantmaker type: Company-sponsored foundation.
Financial data (yr. ended 12/31/05): Assets,
$557,736 (M); gifts received, $35,000;
expenditures, $25,401; total giving, $25,200;
qualifying distributions, $25,200; giving activities
include $25,200 for grants to individuals.
Purpose and activities: The foundation awards
college scholarships to children and adopted
children of full-time employees of Universal Forest
Products.
Type of support: Employee-related scholarships.
Limitations: Applications not accepted.
Application information: Contributes only through
employee-related scholarships.
Officer and Directors:* Michael R. Cole,* Pres.;
Nancy DeGood; Glenda Glenn; Ronald J. Schollaart.
EIN: 382945715

2291
Valassis Communications, Inc. Corporate Giving Program

c/o Valassis Giving Comm.
19975 Victor Pkwy.
Livonia, MI 48152 (734) 591-3000
Contact: Marcia L. Hyde, V.P., Human Resources
and Comms.

Grantmaker type: Corporate giving program.
Purpose and activities: Valassis makes charitable
contributions to nonprofit organizations involved
with arts and culture, education, health, civil rights,
and community development. Support is given
primarily in areas of company operations.
Fields of interest: Arts; Education; Health care; Civil
rights, equal rights; Civil rights; Community
development.
Type of support: General/operating support;
Employee volunteer services; Sponsorships;
Employee-related scholarships.
Limitations: Giving primarily in areas of company
operations.
Application information: Application form not
required.
Initial approach: Proposal to headquarters
Copies of proposal: 1
Deadline(s): Dec. 31
Final notification: Following review

2292
Van Wyk Risk & Financial Management Corporate Giving Program

5136 Cascade Rd. S.E.
Grand Rapids, MI 49546
URL: http://www.vanwykcorp.com/news/
stewardship.html

Grantmaker type: Corporate giving program.
Purpose and activities: Van Wyk makes charitable
contributions to nonprofit organizations involved
with education, civic affairs, and on a case by case

basis. Support is given primarily in areas of company operations.
Fields of interest: Education; Public affairs; General charitable giving.
Type of support: General/operating support; In-kind gifts.
Limitations: Giving primarily in areas of company operations.

2293
Varnum, Riddering, Schmidt & Howlett LLP Corporate Giving Program
333 Bridge St., N.W.
Grand Rapids, MI 49504 (616) 336-6000
Contact: Kathleen Maine, Chair., Corp. Contribs. Comm.
FAX: (616) 336-7000; URL: http://www.varnumlaw.com/about/community.php

Grantmaker type: Corporate giving program.
Purpose and activities: Varnum makes charitable contributions to nonprofit organizations involved with arts and culture, education, and business and industry. Support is given primarily in western Michigan.
Fields of interest: Arts; Education; Business/industry.
Type of support: General/operating support; Employee volunteer services.
Limitations: Giving primarily in western MI.
Application information: A contributions committee reviews all requests.
Corporate Contributions Committee: Kathleen Maine, Chair.; Randy Boileau; Dirk Hoffius; Pete Livingston; Larry Titley; Kent Vana.

2294
Velting Foundation
3060 Breton Rd. S.E.
Grand Rapids, MI 49512-1748

Established in 1980 in MI.
Donors: Velting Contractors, Inc.; James Velting; David L. Velting.
Grantmaker type: Company-sponsored foundation.
Financial data (yr. ended 11/30/05): Assets, $3,964 (M); expenditures, $2,821; total giving, $2,800; qualifying distributions, $2,800; giving activities include $2,800 for 6 grants (high: $800; low: $100).
Purpose and activities: The foundation supports organizations involved with health, human services, and Christianity.
Fields of interest: Health care; Human services; Christian agencies & churches.
Type of support: General/operating support.
Limitations: Applications not accepted. Giving primarily in Grand Rapids, MI. No grants to individuals.
Application information: Contributes only to pre-selected organizations.
Officers: Scott A. Velting, Pres.; Kevin Velting, V.P.; Abraham Moerland, Jr., Secy.-Treas.
EIN: 381859282

2295
Venturedyne, Ltd. Foundation
(formerly Wehr Corporation Foundation)
600 College Ave.
Pewaukee, WI 53072-3572
Contact: Brian L. Nahey, Pres.

Donor: Venturedyne, Ltd.
Grantmaker type: Company-sponsored foundation.
Financial data (yr. ended 12/31/05): Assets, $86,074 (M); expenditures, $10,611; total giving, $10,611; qualifying distributions, $10,611; giving activities include $10,611 for grants.
Purpose and activities: The foundation supports organizations involved with higher education and human services.
Fields of interest: Higher education; Human services; Federated giving programs.
Type of support: General/operating support; Scholarship funds.
Limitations: Giving primarily in MI and WI. No grants to individuals.
Application information: Application form not required.
> *Initial approach:* Proposal
> *Deadline(s):* None
Officers and Directors:* Brian L. Nahey,* Pres.; Nicole J. Daniels, V.P.; Nancy L. Johnson, Secy.-Treas.
EIN: 396096050

2296
The Visteon Fund
P.O. Box 850
Belleville, MI 48112-0850
URL: http://www.visteon.com/about/community.shtml

Established in 1999 in MI.
Donor: Visteon Corp.
Grantmaker type: Company-sponsored foundation.
Financial data (yr. ended 12/31/04): Assets, $2,009,718 (M); gifts received, $503,024; expenditures, $1,335,572; total giving, $1,328,918; qualifying distributions, $1,330,161; giving activities include $1,328,918 for 198 grants (high: $100,000; low: $500).
Purpose and activities: The fund supports museums and organizations involved with education, the environment, health, hunger, youth development, human services, and community development. Special emphasis is directed toward programs designed to enrich the lives of children; and improve the environment.
Fields of interest: Museums; Elementary/secondary education; Higher education; Education; Environment, natural resources; Environment; Hospitals (general); Health care; Food services; Youth development, scouting agencies (general); Youth development; Children/youth, services; Family services; Human services; Community development.
Type of support: General/operating support.
Limitations: Applications not accepted. Giving on a national basis in areas of company operations, with some emphasis on MI. No grants to individuals.
Application information: Contributes only to pre-selected organizations.
Officers and Trustees:* Peter J. Pestillo,* Pres.; Robert Marcin,* V.P.; Stacy L. Fox,* Secy.; Daniel R. Coulson,* Treas.; Peter Look,* Treas.; Michael Johnston.
EIN: 383566029

2297
Volkswagen of America Foundation
3800 Hamlin Rd.
Auburn Hills, MI 48326-2855

Established in 2001 in MI.
Donor: Volkswagen of America, Inc.
Grantmaker type: Company-sponsored foundation.
Financial data (yr. ended 12/31/05): Assets, $1,596,719 (M); gifts received, $505; expenditures, $562,500; total giving, $562,500; qualifying distributions, $562,500; giving activities include $500,000 for 1 grant, and $62,500 for 34 grants to individuals (high: $3,000; low: $500).
Purpose and activities: The foundation supports organizations involved with education and awards disaster relief grants to individuals.
Fields of interest: Education; American Red Cross.
Type of support: General/operating support; Grants to individuals.
Limitations: Applications not accepted. No grants to individuals (except for disaster relief grants).
Application information: Contributes only to pre-selected organizations and individuals.
Officers and Trustees:* Frank Witter,* Pres.; Joseph S. Folz,* Secy.-Treas.; Steve Keyes.
EIN: 383628606

2298
Volkswagen of America, Inc. Corporate Giving Program
3800 Hamlin Rd.
Auburn Hills, MI 48326 (248) 754-5000
Contact: Karla Waterhouse
E-mail: karla.waterhouse@vw.com

Grantmaker type: Corporate giving program.
Purpose and activities: As a complement to its foundation, Volkswagen also makes charitable contributions to nonprofit organizations directly. Support is given primarily in areas of company operations.
Fields of interest: Arts; Education; Health care.
Type of support: General/operating support; Sponsorships; Scholarships—to individuals.
Limitations: Giving primarily in areas of company operations. No grants to individuals (except for scholarships).
Application information: The Public Relations Department handles giving. A contributions committee reviews all requests. Application form not required.
> *Initial approach:* Proposal to headquarters
> *Deadline(s):* None

2299
Gary and Mary Vos Foundation
6160 E. Fulton St.
P.O. Box 189
Ada, MI 49301-0189

Established in 2001 in MI.
Donor: Dan Vos Construction Co.
Grantmaker type: Company-sponsored foundation.
Financial data (yr. ended 12/31/05): Assets, $76,701 (M); expenditures, $5,760; total giving, $5,000; qualifying distributions, $5,000; giving activities include $5,000 for 1 grant.
Purpose and activities: The foundation supports community centers and organizations involved with K-12 education.

Fields of interest: Elementary/secondary education; Youth development, centers/clubs.
Limitations: Applications not accepted. Giving primarily in Grand Rapids, MI. No grants to individuals.
Application information: Contributes only to pre-selected organizations.
Officers and Trustee: Gary Vos, Pres.; John Sellman, V.P.; Gordon De Young, Secy.; Everett Vander Tuin, Treas.; Mary Vos.
EIN: 383615658

2300
Whirlpool Corporation Contributions Program

c/o Community Rels. Dept.
2000 N. M-63, M.D. 2600
Benton Harbor, MI 49022
Contact: Karen L. Ackerman, Admin., Community Rels.
FAX: (269) 923-3442;
E-mail: karen_l_ackerman@whirlpool.com

Grantmaker type: Corporate giving program.
Financial data (yr. ended 12/31/02): Total giving, $175,000, including $175,000 for grants.
Purpose and activities: As a complement to its foundation, Whirlpool also makes charitable contributions to nonprofit organizations directly. Support is given primarily in Berrien County, Michigan.
Fields of interest: Community development.
Type of support: General/operating support; Employee volunteer services; Sponsorships; Donated products; In-kind gifts.
Limitations: Giving primarily in Berrien County, MI. No support for United Way-supported organizations, fraternal, social, political, labor, veterans', or lobbying organizations, or organizations posing a conflict of interest with Whirlpool. No grants to individuals.
Publications: Application guidelines.
Application information: Support is limited to 1 contribution per organization during any given year. The Corporate Community Relations Department handles giving. The company has a staff that only handles contributions. Application form not required.
Initial approach: Proposal to nearest company facility
Copies of proposal: 1
Deadline(s): 1 month prior to need
Final notification: Following review
Number of staff: 1 full-time support.

2301
Whirlpool Foundation

2000 N. M-63
Benton Harbor, MI 49022-2692
(269) 923-5580
Contact: Barbara Hall, Exec. Dir.
FAX: (269) 925-0154; URL: http://whirlpoolcorp.com/social_responsibility/whirlpoolfoundation/default.asp

Incorporated in 1951 in MI.
Donor: Whirlpool Corp.
Grantmaker type: Company-sponsored foundation.
Financial data (yr. ended 3/31/04): Assets, $257,343 (M); gifts received, $9,086,000; expenditures, $8,902,630; total giving,

$8,486,000; qualifying distributions, $8,907,069; giving activities include $5,875,032 for 351 grants (high: $1,000,000; low: $100), $747,736 for 211 grants to individuals (high: $14,500; low: $900), and $1,863,232 for 668 employee matching gifts.
Purpose and activities: The foundation supports organizations involved with arts and culture, education, health, domestic violence, employment, human services, intergroup and race relations, and community development. Special emphasis is directed toward programs designed to promote lifelong learning, quality family life, and cultural diversity.
Fields of interest: Arts, cultural/ethnic awareness; Arts; Child development, education; Higher education; Adult/continuing education; Adult education—literacy, basic skills & GED; Education; Health care; Crime/violence prevention, domestic violence; Employment, services; Children, day care; Family services; Human services; Civil rights, race/intergroup relations; Community development.
International interests: Asia.
Type of support: General/operating support; Continuing support; Program development; Scholarship funds; Research; Employee matching gifts; Employee-related scholarships; Matching/challenge support.
Limitations: Giving limited to Fort Smith, AR, Evansville and La Porte, IN, Benton Harbor, MI, Oxford, MS, Clyde, Findlay, Greenville, and Marion, OH, OK, and Knoxville and Lavergne, TN. No support for religious, theological, or other religion-related organizations training individuals for religious professions, social, labor, veterans', alumni, or fraternal organizations, athletic associations, or national organizations with local chapters already supported by Whirlpool. No grants to individuals (except for employee-related scholarships), or for conferences or seminars, political causes, capital campaigns or endowments, sporting events, goodwill advertisements for fundraising benefits or program books or tickets for testimonials or similar benefit events, or general operating support for United Way agencies.
Publications: Annual report (including application guidelines).
Application information: Application form required.
Initial approach: Contact foundation for application form
Copies of proposal: 1
Deadline(s): Jan. 1, Apr. 1, July 1, and Oct. 1
Board meeting date(s): Quarterly
Final notification: 2 months
Officers and Trustees:* Daniel F. Hopp,* Chair. and Pres.; Frank J. Luongo, Secy.-Treas.; Barbara A. Hall, Exec. Dir.; John E. Alexander; Robert T. Kenagy; Kathryn L. Nelson; David Shellito; Thomas Welke.
Number of staff: 1 full-time professional; 1 full-time support.
EIN: 386077342
Selected grants: The following grants were reported in 2004.
$205,000 to Lake Michigan College Foundation, Benton Harbor, MI. For lifelong learning programs.
$150,000 to University of Notre Dame, Notre Dame, IN. For MBA Program's lifelong learning programs.
$50,000 to Boys and Girls Club of Benton Harbor, Benton Harbor, MI. For lifelong learning programs.
$50,000 to Montessori House of Children, Benton Harbor, MI. For lifelong learning programs.

$50,000 to University of Michigan, School of Business Administration, Ann Arbor, MI. For quality family life programs.
$44,350 to Michigan Tech Fund, Houghton, MI. For lifelong learning programs.
$44,200 to Matej Bel University, Banska Bystrica, Slovakia. For lifelong learning programs.
$31,300 to Inroads/Southwest Michigan, Grand Rapids, MI. For cultural diversity programs.
$30,000 to Benton Harbor Area Schools, Benton Harbor, MI. For lifelong learning programs.
$25,000 to Partners in Education, Marion Area, Marion, OH. For lifelong learning programs.

2302
Wisconsin Energy Corporation Foundation, Inc.

(formerly Wisconsin Electric System Foundation, Inc.)
231 W. Michigan St., Rm. P423
Milwaukee, WI 53203-0001 (414) 221-2107
Contact: Patricia L. McNew, Admin.
FAX: (414) 221-2412;
E-mail: patti.mcnew@we-energies.com; URL: http://www.wec-foundation.com/

Incorporated in 1982 in WI.
Donor: Wisconsin Energy Corp.
Grantmaker type: Company-sponsored foundation.
Financial data (yr. ended 12/31/05): Assets, $25,830,489 (M); gifts received, $5,000,000; expenditures, $6,036,625; total giving, $5,848,211; qualifying distributions, $6,013,903; giving activities include $5,848,211 for 1,351 grants (high: $435,000).
Purpose and activities: The foundation supports organizations involved with arts and culture, education, the environment, emergency services, and human services.
Fields of interest: Arts; Education; Environment; Disasters, preparedness/services; Human services; Federated giving programs.
Type of support: General/operating support; Capital campaigns; Equipment; Endowments; Scholarship funds; Sponsorships; Employee matching gifts; In-kind gifts.
Limitations: Giving limited to areas of company operations in the Upper Peninsula, MI, area and WI. No support for political action or legislative advocacy organizations or veterans' or fraternal organizations. No grants to individuals, or for trips, tours, pageants, team or extra-curricular school events, or student exchange programs, programs whose primary purpose is the promotion of religious doctrine or tenets, or programs whose purpose is solely athletic in nature.
Application information: Additional information may be requested at a later date. Application form required.
Initial approach: Complete online application form or download application form and mail to foundation
Deadline(s): At least three months before funds are needed
Board meeting date(s): As required
Final notification: 90 days
Directors: Charles R. Cole; Gale E. Klappa; Rick Kuester; Allen Leverett; Kristine A. Rappe; Thelma A. Sias.
EIN: 391433726

2303
Wolverine World Wide Foundation
(formerly Wolverine Charitable Foundation)
9341 Courtland Dr. N.E.
Rockford, MI 49351 (616) 866-5500
Contact: Robert J. Sedrowski, Tr.
URL: http://www.wolverineworldwide.com/
main_foundation.asp

Trust established in 1959 in MI.
Donor: Wolverine World Wide, Inc.
Grantmaker type: Company-sponsored foundation.
Financial data (yr. ended 12/31/04): Assets, $2,263,581 (M); gifts received, $830,000; expenditures, $650,792; total giving, $636,790; qualifying distributions, $636,790; giving activities include $636,790 for 240 grants (high: $150,000; low: $20).
Purpose and activities: The foundation supports organizations involved with arts and culture, higher education, health, children and youth, and minorities.
Fields of interest: Performing arts, music; Arts; Higher education; Health care; Children/youth, services; Federated giving programs; Minorities.
Type of support: General/operating support; Employee matching gifts.
Limitations: Giving primarily in Big Rapids, Grand Rapids, and Rockford, MI. No grants to individuals.
Application information: Application form not required.
Initial approach: Proposal
Copies of proposal: 1
Deadline(s): None
Trustees: Robert J. Sedrowski; UBS Financial Services Inc.
Officer: Christi Cowdin, V.P.
EIN: 383056939

2304
Wolverine World Wide, Inc. Corporate Giving Program
9341 Courtland Dr.
Rockford, MI 49351 (616) 866-5521

Grantmaker type: Corporate giving program.
Financial data (yr. ended 12/31/03): Total giving, $420,775, including $414,165 for 247 grants (high: $27,500; low: $50; average: $50–$27,500), and $6,610 for 36 employee matching gifts.
Purpose and activities: As a complement to its foundation, Wolverine also makes charitable contributions to nonprofit organizations directly. Support is given primarily in areas of company operations.
Fields of interest: Arts; Education; Health care.
Type of support: General/operating support; Employee matching gifts; Donated products.
Limitations: Giving primarily in areas of company operations, with emphasis on the Big Rapids and Grand Rapids, MI, areas.
Application information: The Human Resources Department handles giving.

2305
WPS Foundation, Inc.
(formerly Wisconsin Public Service Foundation, Inc.)
700 N. Adams St.
Green Bay, WI 54301
Contact: P.J. Reinhard
Application address: P.O. Box 19001, Green Bay, WI 54307-9001; URL: http://www.wpsr.com/community/solarwise.asp
Scholarship application address: c/o Scholarship Prog., Scholarship Assessment Svc., P.O. Box 5189, Appleton, WI 54912-5189

Incorporated in 1964 in WI.
Donor: Wisconsin Public Service Corp.
Grantmaker type: Company-sponsored foundation.
Financial data (yr. ended 12/31/04): Assets, $19,161,797 (M); gifts received, $500,000; expenditures, $1,034,328; total giving, $1,017,726; qualifying distributions, $1,021,593; giving activities include $846,026 for grants, and $171,700 for grants to individuals.
Purpose and activities: The foundation supports organizations involved with arts and culture, education, health, and human services and awards college scholarships.
Fields of interest: Museums; Performing arts; Historic preservation/historical societies; Arts; Higher education; Education; Environment, natural resources; Hospitals (general); Health care; Health organizations, association; Family services; Human services.

Type of support: General/operating support; Continuing support; Annual campaigns; Capital campaigns; Building/renovation; Equipment; Program development; Scholarship funds; Research; Employee matching gifts; Scholarships—to individuals.
Limitations: Giving generally limited to upper MI and northeastern WI. Generally, no grants for endowments.
Publications: Application guidelines; Informational brochure.
Application information: Application form required.
Initial approach: Download application form
Copies of proposal: 1
Deadline(s): Dec. 15 for scholarships
Board meeting date(s): May and as required
Final notification: Feb.
Officers: L.L. Weyers, Pres.; T.P. Meinz, V.P.; B.J. Wolf, Secy.; J.P. O'Leary, Treas.
EIN: 396075016

2306
Zatkoff Family Foundation
23230 Industrial Park Dr.
Farmington Hills, MI 48335-2850

Established in 2000 in MI.
Donor: Roger Zatkoff Co.
Grantmaker type: Company-sponsored foundation.
Financial data (yr. ended 12/31/05): Assets, $2,163,215 (M); expenditures, $106,133; total giving, $103,933; qualifying distributions, $103,933; giving activities include $103,933 for 40 grants (high: $80,258; low: $50).
Purpose and activities: The foundation supports organizations involved with education, health, and Christianity.
Fields of interest: Higher education; Education; Health care; Federated giving programs; Christian agencies & churches.
Limitations: Applications not accepted. Giving limited to MI. No grants to individuals.
Application information: Contributes only to pre-selected organizations.
Officer: Gary Zatkoff, Pres.
EIN: 383574982

COMMUNITY FOUNDATIONS

2307
Albion Community Foundation
(formerly Albion Civic Foundation)
203 S. Superior St.
P.O. Box 156
Albion, MI 49224   (517) 629-3349
Contact: David C. Farley, Exec. Dir.
FAX: (517) 629-8027;
E-mail: director@albionfoundation.org; URL: http://
www.albionfoundation.org

Established in 1968 in MI.
Donor: Thomas T. Lloyd†.
Grantmaker type: Community foundation.
Financial data (yr. ended 12/31/04): Assets,
$3,997,866 (M); gifts received, $141,449;
expenditures, $323,362; total giving, $216,385;
giving activities include $216,385 for 24+ grants
(high: $24,570; low: $1,000).
Purpose and activities: The mission of the
foundation is to enhance the quality of life in the
Greater Albion area, now and for generations to
come, by promoting philanthropy, building a
permanent community endowment, addressing
community needs through grantmaking, and
providing leadership on key community issues.
Fields of interest: Arts; Education; Environment;
Children/youth, services; Economic development;
Community development.
Type of support: Scholarship funds; Program
evaluation; Management development/capacity
building; Land acquisition; Building/renovation;
Equipment; Program development; Conferences/
seminars; Publication; Seed money; Curriculum
development; Consulting services; Matching/
challenge support.
Limitations: Giving limited to the greater Albion, MI,
area. No support for religious, fraternal, or service
organizations (except for proposed grants that meet
a general community need in a non-sectarian,
non-exclusive manner). No grants to individuals, or
for general operating support, endowments, or
annual fundraising campaigns.
Publications: Application guidelines; Annual report;
Annual report (including application guidelines);
Grants list; Informational brochure; Informational
brochure (including application guidelines);
Newsletter.
Application information: Visit foundation Web site
for application form and guidelines. Application form
required.
  Initial approach: Submit application form
  Copies of proposal: 1
  Deadline(s): Jan. 10, Apr. 10, and Sept. 10
  Board meeting date(s): 12 times per year
  Final notification: Within 90 days
Officers and Trustees:* Karen Dobbins,* Pres.; Jeff
Bell,* V.P.; Susan Ferguson,* Secy.; Donald
Hawkins,* Treas.; David C. Farley,* Exec. Dir.;
Morris Arvoy; David Habicht; Bernie Konkle, Jr.;
Mandy Konkle; Andrew Kooi; Dan Ohmer; Joyce
Spicer; Paulene Story; William Wheaton; Karen
Yankie.
Number of staff: 1 full-time professional; 1 part-time
support.
EIN: 237019029

2308
The Alger Regional Community Foundation, Inc.
411 Elm Ave., 2nd Fl.
Munising, MI 49862-0039   (906) 387-3900
Contact: Thomas Luckey, Pres.
FAX: (906) 387-2988;
E-mail: foundation@algercounty.com; Application
address.: P.O. Box 39, Munising, MI 49862;
URL: http://www.algercounty.com/
communityfoundation

Established in 1992 in MI; in 2003 became a
geographic affiliate of the Community Foundation of
the Upper Peninsula.
Grantmaker type: Community foundation.
Purpose and activities: The purpose of the
foundation is to enhance the quality of life in Alger
County, Michigan, in the areas of education, culture,
environment, youth, health, social welfare, and
recreation.
Fields of interest: Arts; Education; Environment;
Health care; Recreation; Youth development;
Human services.
Limitations: Giving limited to Alger County, MI. No
support for sectarian religious purposes. No grants
to individuals (except for scholarships), or for capital
campaigns, fundraising events, budget deficits,
routine operating expenses, or endowments.
Application information: ARCF grant application
form available on foundation's Web site. Grants are
generally given 1-time only for specific purposes.
Application form required.
  Initial approach: Maximum 5 typed pages
  Copies of proposal: 5
  Deadline(s): Apr. 1 and Oct. 1
  Board meeting date(s): Quarterly
  Final notification: Within 1 week following board
    of directors' meeting
Officers and Directors:* Thomas Luckey,* Pres.;
Mary Bowerman, Treas.; Elaine M. LeVeque, Exec.
Dir.; Thomas Adams; Richard Bowerman; Audrey
Des Armo; D. Robb Ferguson; Betty Goewey; Judy
Hendricksen; Mark Luoma; Stephen Norman;
Steven Peffers.
EIN: 383056051

2309
Allegan County Community Foundation
(formerly Allegan County Foundation)
524 Marshall St.
Allegan, MI 49010   (269) 673-8344
Contact: Theresa Bray, Exec. Dir.
FAX: (269) 673-8745;
E-mail: info@alleganfoundation.org; URL: http://
www.alleganfoundation.org

Established in 1965 in MI.
Donors: Earl Delano†; Chester Ray†; Ethol Stone†.
Grantmaker type: Community foundation.
Financial data (yr. ended 12/31/05): Assets,
$11,351,519 (M); gifts received, $633,021;
expenditures, $547,758; total giving, $261,026;
giving activities include $261,026 for grants.

Purpose and activities: The mission of the
foundation is to provide the means for donors to
make a lasting impact on Allegan County through the
establishment and growth of endowed funds. Giving
primarily for education, health and human services.
Fields of interest: Arts; Education; Health care;
Recreation; Children/youth, services; Human
services; Community development, neighborhood
development.
Type of support: Continuing support; Building/
renovation; Equipment; Land acquisition;
Emergency funds; Program development; Seed
money; Curriculum development; Matching/
challenge support.
Limitations: Giving in Allegan County, MI, only. No
grants to individuals.
Publications: Application guidelines; Annual report;
Financial statement; Grants list; Informational
brochure (including application guidelines).
Application information: Visit foundation Web site
for application information. Application form
required.
  Initial approach: Meeting with foundation staff;
    application available at that time
  Copies of proposal: 1
  Deadline(s): Nov. 1 for TAG grants; Dec. 15 for
    Unrestricted grants
  Board meeting date(s): Bi-monthly
  Final notification: Apr.
Officers and Trustees:* Paula Baker,* Pres.; Pam
Tanis,* Secy.; Nancy Fifelski, Treas.; Theresa Bray,
Exec. Dir.; Steve Angle; David Balas; Bob Brenner;
Sara Kubanek; John Mahan; Rob Marciniak; Mary
Ann Moeller; Todd Oyler.
Number of staff: 2 full-time professional.
EIN: 386189947

2310
Allendale Community Foundation
P.O. Box 365
Allendale, MI 49401   (616) 895-4777
URL: http://www.allendale-twp.org/foundation.html

Established in 2001 in MI as an affiliate of Grand
Haven Area Community Foundation.
Grantmaker type: Community foundation.
Purpose and activities: The foundation serves as a
catalyst and resource for philanthropy in Allendale,
leveraging resources to meet the community's
needs, and providing a cost effective way for donors
to give back to their community. Areas of priority
include youth and recreation, arts and culture, start
up projects, matching grants, heath and human
services, and problem prevention.
Fields of interest: Arts; Health care; Recreation;
Youth development; Human services.
Type of support: Matching/challenge support; Seed
money.
Limitations: Giving limited to the Allendale Charter
Township area in northeast Ottawa County, MI. No
support for religious programs. No grants to
individuals, or for general operating expenses, debt
reduction, or fundraising events.
Application information: See foundation Web site
for application form. Application form required.

Copies of proposal: 11
Deadline(s): Feb. 1 nd Aug. 1
Final notification: Grants are reviewed in Mar. and Sept.
Officers and Trustees: Dave Degenhardt,* Chair. and Pres.; Harley Sietsema,* V.P.; Candy Kraker,* Secy.; James VanderVoord,* Treas.; Doug Becker; Gary Gemmen; Aaron Haight; Carl Jesser; Bart Merkle; David VanderWall; Randy Weener.

2311
Anchor Bay Community Foundation
c/o Citizens State Bank
51066 Washington St.
New Baltimore, MI 48047 (586) 949-5316
Contact: Lynne Hoover Musilli, Vice-Chair., Community Rels.; For grants: Max J. Plante, Secy.
E-mail: abcfoundation@comcast.net; URL: http://www.abcommunityfoundation.org

Established in 1997 in MI.
Grantmaker type: Community foundation.
Financial data (yr. ended 12/31/04): Assets, $225,424 (M); gifts received, $29,590; expenditures, $30,496; total giving, $26,730; giving activities include $26,730 for grants.
Purpose and activities: The foundation has been organized to raise and distribute financial and other resources; to promote lifelong learning for children and families; to enhance and strengthen cultural, social and educational opportunities for the Anchor Bay community, including the greater New Baltimore and Chesterfield, MI areas.
Fields of interest: Arts; Education; Environment; Health care; Recreation; Youth, services; Human services; Community development.
Type of support: General/operating support; Scholarship funds.
Limitations: Giving primarily in greater New Baltimore and Chesterfield, MI.
Application information: Visit foundation Web site for application form for grants up to $500. The foundation's Board meets monthly to review applications. Application form required.
Initial approach: Submit application form
Copies of proposal: 1
Deadline(s): None
Board meeting date(s): Monthly
Officers and Directors: Mary R. Socia,* Chair.; Lynne Hoover Musilli,* Vice-Chair., Community Rels.; Joseph D. Stabile,* Vice-Chair.; Max J. Plante,* Secy.; Oscar F. Socia,* Treas.; Roger Facione, Dir. Emeritus; Robert Miller III, Dir. Emeritus; Greg Bayer; Mary Ann Bayer; Patricia L. Gendernalik; Marion A. Lusardi; Denise Mello; Barbara Richards; Juliana Texley, Ph.D.; Steven B. Whittlesey; Leonard Woodside.
EIN: 383255728

2312
Ann Arbor Area Community Foundation
(formerly Ann Arbor Area Foundation)
201 S. Main St., Ste. 501
Ann Arbor, MI 48104-2113 (734) 663-0401
Contact: Cheryl W. Elliott, C.E.O.; For grants: Martha L. Bloom, V.P., Prog.
FAX: (734) 663-3514; E-mail: info@aaacf.org; Additional tel.: (734) 663-2173; Additional E-mail: mbloom@aaacf.org; URL: http://www.aaacf.org

Incorporated in 1963 in MI.

Grantmaker type: Community foundation.
Financial data (yr. ended 12/31/05): Assets, $40,146,458 (M); expenditures, $2,143,548; total giving, $1,229,398; giving activities include $1,229,398 for grants.
Purpose and activities: The mission of the foundation is to enrich the quality of life in the greater Ann Arbor, MI, area through building a permanent endowment, providing a flexible vehicle for donors, and acting as a leader for the philanthropic community.
Fields of interest: Visual arts; Performing arts; Performing arts, theater; Arts; Higher education; Education; Environment, natural resources; Environment; Health care; Health organizations, association; Crime/violence prevention, domestic violence; Disasters, Hurricane Katrina; Children/youth, services; Family services; Aging, centers/services; Homeless, human services; Human services; Economic development; Community development; Aging; Homeless.
Type of support: Income development; Management development/capacity building; Emergency funds; Program development; Conferences/seminars; Publication; Seed money; Scholarship funds; Research; Matching/challenge support.
Limitations: Giving limited to Washtenaw County, MI. No support for religious or sectarian purposes. No grants to individuals (except from designated funds), or for normal operating expenses (except for start-up purposes), construction projects, computer hardware equipment, annual campaigns, or capital campaigns; no loans.
Publications: Application guidelines; Annual report (including application guidelines); Informational brochure (including application guidelines); Newsletter; Program policy statement.
Application information: Visit foundation Web site for application guidelines and specific deadlines. Applicants must log on to http://www.communitygrants.org to create an online agency profile and complete the Short Outcome Funding Application. Application form required.
Initial approach: Create an online agency profile
Deadline(s): 2nd Wed. of Feb. and 1st Wed. of Oct. for grants; Sept. for youth projects
Board meeting date(s): Jan., Mar., May, July, Sept., and Nov.
Final notification: May and Dec. for grants
Officers and Trustees: Bill Kinley,* Chair.; Deborah Beuche,* Vice-Chair.; Cheryl W. Elliot, C.E.O. and Pres.; Martha L. Bloom, V.P., Prog.; Kevin McDonald,* Secy.; Doug Weber, C.F.O.; Hugh Morgan,* Treas.; Sue Sharra, Cont.; D.J. Boehm; Cal Fette; Jyoti Gupta; Gary Hahn; Hon. John Kirkendall; John Martin; Betsy McCallister; John W. Reed; Timothy Wadhams; Marc Weiser; Sandra L. White; Roy Wilbanks.
Number of staff: 1 full-time professional; 2 part-time professional; 1 full-time support; 1 part-time support.
EIN: 386087967

2313
Baraga County Community Foundation
P.O. Box 338
L'Anse, MI 49946 (906) 353-7898
Contact: Gordette M. Cote, Exec. Dir.

Established in 1995 in MI.
Grantmaker type: Community foundation.
Financial data (yr. ended 12/31/03): Assets, $772,764 (M); gifts received, $92,308;

expenditures, $79,086; total giving, $20,900; giving activities include $17,500 for 16 grants (high: $4,930; low: $250), and $3,400 for 7 grants to individuals (high: $1,000; low: $200).
Purpose and activities: Giving for programs that address immediate or emerging community needs, arts and the humanities, community services, education, conservation and the environment, health, and human and social services.
Fields of interest: Arts; Education; Environment; Health care; Children/youth, services; Human services; Community development.
Limitations: Giving limited to Baraga County, MI. No support for sectarian religious purposes. No grants for endowments, or for budget deficits, or routine operating expenses of existing organizations.
Application information: Application form not required.
Initial approach: Letter, no more than 2 typed pages
Copies of proposal: 4
Deadline(s): Apr. for spring/summer cycle, Oct. for fall/winter cycle
Officers and Trustees: Kent Thomas,* Pres.; Michael Ostermeyer,* V.P.; Denise Marth,* Secy.; Jeff Howe,* Treas.; Gordette Marie Cote, Exec. Dir.; Susan Berutti; Patrick Brennan; Leann Davis; Gale Eilola; John Jacobson; Karen Jacobson; Michael Jensen; William Menge; Vern Miron; David Morehouse; Joseph O'Leary; Tony Selkey.
EIN: 383198122

2314
Barry Community Foundation
629 W. State St., Ste. 201
Hastings, MI 49058-0644 (269) 945-0526
Contact: Bonnie Hildreth, Pres.
FAX: (269) 945-0826; E-mail: bonnie@barrycf.org; Additional E-mail: grants@barrycf.org; URL: http://www.barrycf.org

Established in 1996 in MI.
Grantmaker type: Community foundation.
Financial data (yr. ended 6/30/05): Assets, $8,257,821 (M); gifts received, $1,148,648; expenditures, $598,870; total giving, $427,253; giving activities include $427,253 for grants.
Purpose and activities: The mission of the foundation is to develop and manage endowed funds for helping and involving the people of Barry County, MI, to make a positive difference in their lives.
Fields of interest: Arts; Education; Environment, natural resources; Hospitals (general); Children/youth, services; Human services; Community development, neighborhood development; Community development.
Type of support: General/operating support; Annual campaigns; Capital campaigns; Building/renovation; Equipment; Endowments; Program development; Conferences/seminars; Seed money; Curriculum development; Scholarship funds; Research; Technical assistance; Consulting services; Program evaluation; Matching/challenge support.
Limitations: Giving limited to Barry County, MI. No support for private organizations, including churches. No grants to individuals (except for scholarships), or for operating expenses or regularly upgrading equipment.
Publications: Application guidelines; Annual report; Informational brochure; Newsletter.

Application information: Visit foundation Web site for application form and guidelines. Number of copies vary per grant type. Application form required.

> *Initial approach:* Telephone
> *Copies of proposal:* 15
> *Deadline(s):* Oct. 15; Jan. 15, Apr. 15, and July 15 for interim grants up to $3,000
> *Board meeting date(s):* 3rd Thurs. monthly
> *Final notification:* Within 8 weeks

Officers and Directors:* Fred Jacobs, Chair.; Bonnie Hildreth,* Pres.; Jennifer Richards,* V.P.; Kathy Johnson,* Secy.; Jim Toburen,* Treas.; Bob Byington; Maggie Coleman; Don Drummond; Jan Hartough; Karen Heath; Pat Markle; Deb McKeown; Kim Norris; Jon Simpson.

Number of staff: 1 full-time professional; 1 full-time support; 1 part-time support.

EIN: 383246131

2315

Battle Creek Community Foundation

(formerly Greater Battle Creek Foundation)
1 Riverwalk Ctr.
34 W. Jackson St.
Battle Creek, MI   49017-3505   (269) 962-2181
Contact: Brenda L. Hunt, C.E.O.; For grants: Kelly Boles Chapman, V.P., Progs.
FAX: (269) 962-2182;
E-mail: bccf@bccfoundation.org; Grant inquiry E-mail: kelly@bccfoundation.org; URL: http://www.bccfoundation.org

Established in 1974 in MI.

Grantmaker type: Community foundation.

Financial data (yr. ended 3/31/05): Assets, $82,360,581 (M); gifts received, $19,960,388; expenditures, $5,203,743; total giving, $2,700,511; giving activities include $2,498,459 for grants, and $202,052 for grants to individuals.

Purpose and activities: The foundation seeks to promote giving, build endowment, and provide leadership to improve quality of life. Grantmaking for programming in the Battle Creek, MI, area serves the citizens of the community through education, health, human services, arts, public affairs, and community development; scholarships are also available to students residing in the greater Battle Creek area.

Fields of interest: Arts; Child development, education; Adult education—literacy, basic skills & GED; Education, reading; Education; Animal welfare; Hospitals (general); Health care; Health organizations, association; Children/youth, services; Child development, services; Minorities/immigrants, centers/services; Human services; Community development; Public affairs; Youth; Minorities.

Type of support: Building/renovation; Equipment; Land acquisition; Emergency funds; Program development; Conferences/seminars; Publication; Seed money; Curriculum development; Scholarship funds; Technical assistance; Program evaluation; Program-related investments/loans; Scholarships —to individuals; Matching/challenge support.

Limitations: Giving limited to the greater Battle Creek, MI, area. No grants for operating budgets, deficit financing, endowments, or research; no loans (except for program-related investments).

Publications: Application guidelines; Annual report; Biennial report (including application guidelines); Financial statement; Grants list; Informational brochure; Newsletter; Program policy statement.

Application information: Visit foundation Web site for grant application packets, guidelines per grant type, and specific deadlines. Contact high school counselors for scholarship applications and guidelines. Application form required.

> *Initial approach:* Letter or telephone
> *Copies of proposal:* 20
> *Deadline(s):* Mar., June, Sept., and Dec.
> *Board meeting date(s):* Monthly
> *Final notification:* Within 2 months

Officers and Trustees:* David L. Schweitzer,* Chair.; Betsy L. Briere,* Vice-Chair.; Brenda Jackson,* 2nd Vice-Chair.; Brenda L. Hunt, C.E.O. and Pres.; Kelly Boles Chapman, V.P., Progs.; Kimberly L. Holley, V.P., Mktg. and Comms.; Shelly Miller, V.P., Finance; Mahesh Karamchandani, M.D.*, Secy.; Robert G. Byelich, Treas.; Carolyn Ballard; John R. Bromley; Charles A. Cooper, Jr.; B. Scott Durham; David H. Eddy; Tim Kool; Denise Little; David P. Lucas; Victor R. Sanchez; James K. Sholl; Colleen Starring; Morgan Steely; Terris Eugene Todd.

Number of staff: 12 full-time professional; 2 part-time professional; 3 full-time support; 1 part-time support.

EIN: 382045459

Selected grants: The following grants were reported in 2004.

$500,000 to Battle Creek Health System, Battle Creek, MI. For facility project grant.

$90,000 to Kingman Museum, Battle Creek, MI. 2 grants: $50,000 (For Disgistor I Planetarium), $40,000 (For heating-ventilation-air conditioning system).

$45,000 to Calhoun County Department of Public Health, Battle Creek, MI. For School-Based Health Center Program.

$25,625 to Volunteer Center of Battle Creek, Battle Creek, MI.

$25,000 to Family Health Center of Battle Creek, Battle Creek, MI. For dental care at Family Health Center of Albion.

$20,000 to Urban League, Southwestern Michigan, Battle Creek, MI.

$19,000 to Albion Health Care Alliance, Albion, MI. For Health and Wellness Promotion Education Program.

$15,000 to Calhoun Intermediate School District, Marshall, MI. For network for young children.

$15,000 to Council of Michigan Foundations, Grand Haven, MI. For challenge grant for Learning to Give Program.

2316

Bay Area Community Foundation

703 Washington Ave.
Bay City, MI   48708-5732   (989) 893-4438
Contact: Roger Merrifield, C.E.O.; For grants: Ashley Morse, Prog. Off.
FAX: (989) 893-4448;
E-mail: bacfnd@bayfoundation.org; Additional tel.: (800) 926-3217; Addition E-mail: ashleym@bayfoundation.org; URL: http://www.bayfoundation.org

Established in 1982 in MI.

Grantmaker type: Community foundation.

Financial data (yr. ended 12/31/05): Assets, $27,868,887 (M); gifts received, $2,182,084; expenditures, $1,753,645; total giving, $1,253,218; giving activities include $1,253,218 for grants.

Purpose and activities: To fulfill a wide array of donors' charitable wishes by building permanent endowment funds and serving as a leader for community improvement through effective grantmaking and collaboration. Priority will be given to projects that focus on the following areas: charitable; cultural; educational; and environmental for Michigan's Bay and Arenac counties.

Fields of interest: Visual arts; Performing arts; Arts; Education; Environment, energy; Environment; Health care; Housing/shelter; Recreation; Human services; Community development; Science; Youth.

Type of support: Building/renovation; Program development; Seed money; Curriculum development; Internship funds; Scholarship funds; Research; Technical assistance; Matching/challenge support.

Limitations: Giving limited to Bay and Arenac counties, MI. No grants to individuals (excluding scholarships), or for capital campaigns, existing obligations, endowments, or fundraising events.

Publications: Annual report; Financial statement; Grants list; Informational brochure.

Application information: Visit foundation Web site for application form and guidelines. Applications sent by fax will not be accepted. Application form required.

> *Initial approach:* Telephone
> *Deadline(s):* Varies
> *Board meeting date(s):* Monthly, except in June, Aug., and Dec.

Officers and Trustees:* Gary Labadie,* Chair.; Diane Demers,* Vice-Chair.; Roger Merrifield, C.E.O. and Pres.; Michael Stoner,* Secy.; Mike Hanisko,* Treas.; Gary Bosco; Charles B. Curtiss; Mike Dewey; Kevin Dykema; Jane Hagen; Robert Hetzler; Lucy Horak; Ruth Jaffe; Michael Kasperski; Mike Kelly; Steve Kessler; John Lore; Gary Manthey; Pamela Monastiere; Robert Monroe; Abel Torres; Carolyn Wierda; Jerome Yantz.

Number of staff: 3 full-time professional; 2 part-time support.

EIN: 382418086

2317

The Bay Harbor Foundation

750 Bay Harbor Dr.
Bay Harbor, MI   49770   (231) 439-2700
Contact: Lisa McComb, Interim Exec. Dir.
FAX: (231) 439-2701;
E-mail: info@bayharborfoundation.org; Additional E-mail: lisa@bayharborfoundation.org; URL: http://www.bayharborfoundation.org

Established in 2004 in MI.

Grantmaker type: Community foundation.

Financial data (yr. ended 12/31/04): Assets, $29,408 (M); gifts received, $186,911; expenditures, $213,553; total giving, $187,000; giving activities include $187,000 for 7 grants (high: $47,500; low: $22,500).

Purpose and activities: The foundation is a charitable, nonprofit organization established to provide a structure for receiving donations and distributing grants in northern, lower Michigan for programs in the arts, education, the environment, and health and human services.

Fields of interest: Arts; Education; Environment; Health care; Human services.

Limitations: Giving in northern lower MI.

Application information: Visit foundation Web site for application information. The foundation will invite selected organizations to submit a full grant application based on letters of intent. Application form required.

Initial approach: Submit letter of intent
Deadline(s): Feb. 15 for letter of intent; Mar. 30 for full grant application
Final notification: Mar. 1 for letter of intent determination; May for grants

Officers and Directors:* Joseph T. Nachtrab, Chair.; Judy Phillips, Vice-Chair.; Candace Fitzsimons, Secy.; William U. Parfet, Treas.; Lisa McComb, Interim Exec. Dir.; Sen. Jason Allen, Hon. Dir.; Kim Aikens, M.D.; Lori Coates-Hay; William Cobb; James Crofford; Elizabeth Dickinson; Christine Etienne; William Fair; Tina Frescoln; Dale S. Hanson; David V. Johnson; Pamela Johnson; Scot Morrison; Linda Parker; Robert Roskam; Stephen Schott; James Singleton; Judy Singleton; Barb Spencer; Chuck Spencer; Joe Sproles; Jaime Rae Turnbull.
EIN: 371491024

2318
Bedford Community Foundation
(formerly Bedford Foundation)
P.O. Box 103
Lambertville, MI   48144   (734) 854-1722
Contact: Ms. Mary Ann McBee, V.P.
E-mail: mary.a.mcbee.b0zz@statefarm.com

Established in MI as an affiliate of the Community Foundation of Monroe County; became an independent community foundation in 2004.
Grantmaker type: Community foundation.
Financial data (yr. ended 3/31/05): Assets, $125,300 (M); gifts received, $188,840; expenditures, $136,704; total giving, $134,026; giving activities include $134,026 for 18 grants (high: $52,000; low: $110).
Purpose and activities: The foundation adminsters funds from donors to build permanent endowments for the charitable needs of Bedford Township in the areas of health, arts, the environment, education, and youth activities.
Fields of interest: Arts; Education; Environment; Health care; Youth development; Community development.
Limitations: Giving limited to Bedford Township, MI.
Officers: Steven Elzinga, Pres.; Mary Ann McBee, V.P.; LaMar Frederick, Secy.; Norbert C. Abel, Treas.
Trustees: Arlene Bates; W. Thomas Graham; Michael Heller; Margaret Smith; Sharon Throm; Walt Wilburn.
EIN: 383544941

2319
Berrien Community Foundation, Inc.
2900 S. State St., Ste. 2E
St. Joseph, MI   49085   (269) 983-3486
Contact: For grants: Anne McCausland, Prog. Dir.
FAX: (269) 983-4939;
E-mail: bcf@BerrienCommunity.org; Grant application tel.: (269) 983-3304, ext. 2; Additional E-mail: AnneMcCausland@BerrienCommunity.org; Grant application E-mail: NanetteKeiser@BerrienCommunity.org; URL: http://www.berriencommunity.org

Incorporated in 1952 in MI.
Grantmaker type: Community foundation.
Financial data (yr. ended 12/31/05): Assets, $17,419,418 (M); gifts received, $1,300,795; expenditures, $876,810; total giving, $599,889;

giving activities include $599,889 for 289 grants (high: $20,000; low: $100).
Purpose and activities: The mission of the foundation is to promote philanthropy, to build a spirit of community, and to enhance the quality of life in Berrien County through its stewardship of permanently endowed and other funds. The foundation shall accomplish this mission by: building permanent endowments and other funds providing a broad range of flexible and cost-effective donor services; investing and managing funds prudently and professionally; making grants to support a broad range of projects and programs that address community needs, with a focus on building a spirit of community/arts and culture, nurturing children, and youth leadership and development; and serving as a facilitative leader, catalyst, and resource for local communities.
Fields of interest: Historic preservation/historical societies; Arts; Education; Health care; Substance abuse, prevention; Housing/shelter; Youth development; Children, day care; Youth, pregnancy prevention; Family services; Human services; Community development; Youth; Aging.
Type of support: Program development; Seed money; Curriculum development; Scholarship funds; Program evaluation; Matching/challenge support.
Limitations: Giving primarily in Berrien County, MI for Undesignated and Field-of-Interest funds; giving in the U.S. for Advised funds. No support for sectarian religious purposes. No grants to individuals (except for scholarships), or for consulting services for grant writing, ongoing operating funds, deficit financing, national fundraising efforts, annual fund drives, or program-related investments.
Publications: Biennial report; Financial statement; Informational brochure (including application guidelines).
Application information: Visit foundation Web site for application information; guidelines and forms are available on request. 20 copies of application required for youth-oriented projects only. Application form required.
Initial approach: Telephone (ext. 2) or e-mail
Copies of proposal: 15
Deadline(s): Sept. 1
Board meeting date(s): Oct.
Final notification: 10 to 14 weeks
Officers and Trustees:* Joanne Sims,* Chair.; Gregory C. Vaughn,* Vice-Chair.; Dr. Nanette Keiser, Pres.; Robert D. Gottlieb,* Secy.; Sharon Vargo,* Treas.; Hillary Bubb; Rev. James Childs; Patricia Forbes; Nadra Kissman; Brenda Layne; Jane Marohn; Tim Passaro; Gladys Peeples-Burks, Ph.D.; Allan J. Westmaas.
Number of staff: 2.5 full-time professional.
EIN: 386057160

2320
Branch County Community Foundation
2 W. Chicago St., Ste. E-1
Coldwater, MI   49036-1602   (517) 278-4517
Contact: Colleen Knight, Exec. Dir.
FAX: (517) 279-2319;
E-mail: info@brcofoundation.org; Additional E-mail: colleen@brcofoundation.org; URL: http://www.brcofoundation.org

Established in 1991 in MI.
Grantmaker type: Community foundation.
Financial data (yr. ended 9/30/05): Assets, $4,057,246 (M); gifts received, $2,714,104; expenditures, $2,912,569; total giving,

$2,728,581; giving activities include $2,728,581 for grants.
Purpose and activities: The foundation seeks to build a permanent endowment by attracting funds from and providing services to a wide range of donors, and to grant the income from those funds to serve the community.
Fields of interest: Humanities; Arts; Education; Environment; Health care; Housing/shelter, homeless; Human services; Community development.
Type of support: General/operating support; Equipment; Endowments; Conferences/seminars; Scholarship funds; Technical assistance; In-kind gifts; Matching/challenge support.
Limitations: Giving limited to Branch County and Branson, Coldwater, Colon, Quincy, and Union City, MI. No support for sectarian religious programs. No grants to individuals (except for scholarships); no loans or program-related investments.
Publications: Application guidelines; Annual report; Financial statement; Informational brochure; Newsletter; Occasional report.
Application information: Visit foundation Web site for grant application information. Before submitting a proposal, applicants may attend a funding workshop that is held a few weeks before each grant cycle; contact foundation for more information and specific deadlines. Application form required.
Initial approach: Telephone, fax, or e-mail foundation for application packets
Deadline(s): Varies
Board meeting date(s): Monthly
Final notification: May 1 and Nov. 1
Officers and Directors:* M. Joe Ganger,* Pres.; Bruce Bloom,* V.P.; Hillary Eley,* Secy.; Edward Callahan,* Treas.; Colleen Knight, Exec. Dir.; Susan Sparrow, Cont.; Patricia Klein-Shoemaker, Dir. Emeritus; Bob Mayer, Dir. Emeritus; Ray Bregger; Paul Creal; Sandra Davis; Klaudia Fisher; Nancy Hutchins; Sandra Jackson; Mary Jo Kranz; Remus Rigg; Dave Wright; Bruce Young.
Number of staff: 1 full-time professional; 1 full-time support.
EIN: 383021071

2321
Cadillac Area Community Foundation
201 N. Mitchell St., Ste. 101
P.O. Box 102
Cadillac, MI   49601   (231) 775-9911
Contact: Linda L. Kimbel, Exec. Dir.
FAX: (231) 775-8126;
E-mail: cacf@cadillacfoundation.org; URL: http://www.cadillacfoundation.org

Established in 1988 in MI.
Grantmaker type: Community foundation.
Financial data (yr. ended 12/31/05): Assets, $5,395,867 (M); gifts received, $343,586; expenditures, $196,964; total giving, $60,582; giving activities include $56,332 for 22 grants (high: $10,000; low: $250), $4,250 for grants to individuals, and $7,676 for 1 foundation-administered program.
Purpose and activities: The foundation seeks to develop a community-wide vehicle for permanent endowments to enhance the quality of life in the area and to establish and manage worthwhile endowed funds for the betterment of the community.
Fields of interest: Arts; Education, early childhood education; Elementary school/education; Education; Environment, natural resources;

Environment; Reproductive health, OBGYN/Birthing centers; Health care; Substance abuse, services; Mental health, smoking; Health organizations, association; Recreation; Youth development; Youth, services; Residential/custodial care, hospices; Aging, centers/services; Homeless, human services; Human services; Economic development; Community development; Federated giving programs; Economics; Aging; Homeless.
Type of support: Building/renovation; Equipment; Emergency funds; Program development; Publication; Seed money; Curriculum development; Research; Technical assistance; Program evaluation; Scholarships—to individuals; Matching/challenge support; Student loans—to individuals.
Limitations: Giving limited to the greater Cadillac, MI, area as defined by the Wexford-Missaukee ISD, or CAPS (depends on specific grant program limitations). No support for sectarian programs. No grants to individuals (except as allowed by specific law or funds so designated), or for general operating support, endowments, fundraising campaigns, or conferences.
Publications: Application guidelines; Annual report; Annual report (including application guidelines); Grants list; Informational brochure; Occasional report; Program policy statement.
Application information: Visit foundation Web site for application forms and specific guidelines per grant type. Application form required.
  Initial approach: Contact foundation
  Copies of proposal: 11
  Deadline(s): Mar. 31 and Aug. 31 for trustee grant program (unrestricted grants); varies for others
  Board meeting date(s): Varies
  Final notification: Within 3 months for trustee grant program; varies for others
Officers and Trustees: Lee J. Brown,* Pres.; Frederick O. Sprague,* V.P.; John H. Bishop,* Secy.-Treas.; Linda L. Kimbel, Exec. Dir.; Richard Heydenberk; Chris Huckle; Melissa Sjogren; Robert J. Van Dellen.
Number of staff: 1 part-time professional; 1 full-time support.
EIN: 382848513

2322
Canton Community Foundation
50430 School House Rd., Ste. 200
Canton, MI 48187 (734) 495-1200
Contact: Joan Noricks, Pres.
FAX: (734) 495-1212;
E-mail: info@cantonfoundation.org; Additional E-mail: jnoricks@cantonfoundation.org; URL: http://www.cantonfoundation.org

Established in 1990 in MI.
Grantmaker type: Community foundation.
Financial data (yr. ended 6/30/05): Assets, $1,760,767 (M); gifts received, $275,493; expenditures, $318,480; total giving, $87,878; giving activities include $52,287 for 20+ grants, and $35,591 for 30 grants to individuals.
Purpose and activities: The foundation's mission is to enhance the quality of life in Canton, MI and surrounding areas by identifying and directing resources that address current and evolving community needs through grants from permanent endowments entrusted to the foundation for the common good.
Fields of interest: Visual arts, sculpture; Performing arts; Student services/organizations; Education;

Environment; Health care; Human services; Community development.
Type of support: General/operating support; Program development; Scholarships—to individuals.
Limitations: Giving limited to the greater Canton, MI, area.
Publications: Annual report; Grants list; Informational brochure (including application guidelines).
Application information: Application form required.
  Initial approach: Letter or telephone
  Copies of proposal: 5
  Deadline(s): None for grants; Mar. 3 for scholarships
Officers and Directors: H. Kristene Rautio,* Chair.; Robert Zulker,* Vice-Chair.; Joan Noricks, Pres.; Paul Denski, Jr.,* Secy.; Deborah Krone, Treas.; Sally Bailey; Terry Bennett; Shahnaz Broucek; Jack Demmer; Dan Durack; Michael Gerou; Jean LaJoy; Gurbachan Mann; Carla O'Malley; Greg Schupra; Herb Scott; Maria Stante; Ron Thompson; Joe Van Esley; Lynn Weaver; Rev. Alexander Whitfield.
Number of staff: 1 full-time professional; 1 part-time support.
EIN: 382898615

2323
Capital Region Community Foundation
6035 Executive Dr., Ste. 104
Lansing, MI 48911 (517) 272-2870
Contact: Dennis W. Fliehman, Pres.
FAX: (517) 272-2871;
E-mail: dfliehman@crcfoundation.org; URL: http://www.crcfoundation.org

Established in 1987 in MI.
Grantmaker type: Community foundation.
Financial data (yr. ended 12/31/04): Assets, $49,361,717 (M); gifts received, $7,001,301; expenditures, $2,484,522; total giving, $1,905,979; giving activities include $1,905,979 for 504 grants (high: $657,860; low: $37).
Purpose and activities: The purpose of the foundation is to build the number and size of permanent endowment funds, income from which is used for grants that meet the charitable needs of Clinton, Eaton, and Ingham counties, MI. The foundation provides support for humanities, education, environment, health care, human services, and public benefit.
Fields of interest: Humanities; Education; Environment; Health care; Children/youth, services; Human services; Community development; Public affairs.
Type of support: General/operating support; Capital campaigns; Building/renovation; Equipment; Program development; Seed money; Technical assistance; Matching/challenge support.
Limitations: Giving limited to Clinton, Eaton, and Ingham counties, MI. No support for international organizations, religious programs, or sectarian purposes. No grants to individuals (except for scholarships), or for endowment funds, administrative costs of fundraising campaigns, annual meetings, routine operating expenses, or for existing obligations, debts, or liabilities.
Publications: Application guidelines; Annual report; Financial statement; Newsletter.
Application information: Visit foundation Web site for application form and guidelines. Faxed or

e-mailed applications are not accepted. Application form required.
  Initial approach: Telephone
  Copies of proposal: 18
  Deadline(s): Apr. 1; Jan. 30 for Youth Fund
  Board meeting date(s): Bimonthly
Officers and Trustees: David Donovan,* Chair.; Chris Laverty,* Chair.-Elect; Dennis W. Fliehman,* Pres.; Julia Oliver, V.P., Finance; Charles Blockett, Jr.,* Secy.; Gregg Cornell,* Treas.; Diana Rodriguez Algra; Mark Alley; John Arehart; Joan Bauer; Rolland Bethards, M.D.; Michael Clark, M.D.; Sam L. Davis; Hon. R. George Economy; Nancy A. Elwood; Eugenio Fernandez; Vincent J. Ferris; Mark Hooper; Nancy L. Little; Dorothy E. Maxwell; Douglas A. Mielock; Suzanne B. Mills; Rachelle Neal; Debra Pozega Osburn, Ph.D.; Mary J. Schafer; Mary Ellen Sheets; Sherry Solomon.
Number of staff: 4 full-time professional; 1 full-time support.
EIN: 382776652

2324
Central Montcalm Community Foundation
1631 S. Nevins
Sidney, MI 48885 (517) 328-1230
Contact: Marilyn Thomsen

Established in 1999 in MI.
Grantmaker type: Community foundation.
Financial data (yr. ended 12/31/02): Assets, $187,083 (M); gifts received, $24,216; expenditures, $14,132; total giving, $12,576; giving activities include $12,576 for 9 grants (high: $6,862; low: $500).
Purpose and activities: Interest primarily in educational support through programs, equipment, and scholarships.
Fields of interest: Education; Health care; Children/youth, services; Aging, centers/services; Community development.
Limitations: Giving limited to Central Montcalm County, MI.
Publications: Informational brochure.
Application information: Application form required.
  Initial approach: Letter or telephone
  Copies of proposal: 2
  Deadline(s): Apr. 30
  Board meeting date(s): Monthly
  Final notification: 60 days
Officer: Connie McKwein, Pres.
Number of staff: 1 part-time professional.
EIN: 383068773

2325
Charlevoix County Community Foundation
507 Water St.
P.O. Box 718
East Jordan, MI 49727 (231) 536-2440
Contact: Robert G. Tambellini, C.E.O.
FAX: (231) 536-2640; E-mail: info@c3f.org;
URL: http://www.c3f.org

Established in 1992 in MI.
Grantmaker type: Community foundation.
Financial data (yr. ended 12/31/05): Assets, $18,113,170 (M); gifts received, $2,044,365; expenditures, $1,384,316; total giving, $1,051,556; giving activities include $1,045,910 for 156 grants (high: $204,402; low: $50), and

$5,646 for 3 grants to individuals (high: $4,000; low: $95).

Purpose and activities: The foundation seeks to enhance the quality of life in Charlevoix County, MI, now and for generations to come, by building a permanent charitable endowment from a wide range of donors, addressing needs through grantmaking, and providing leadership on matters of community concern. The foundation provides support for worthwhile programs and projects focusing on the arts, education, environmental preservation, human services, wellness, civic improvement, and economic development.

Fields of interest: Arts; Higher education; Education; Environment; Health care; Recreation; Children/youth, services; Human services; Economic development; Community development; Government/public administration.

Type of support: Scholarships—to individuals; Endowments; Emergency funds; Program development; Seed money; Scholarship funds; Technical assistance; Consulting services.

Limitations: Giving limited to Charlevoix County, MI. No support for sectarian purposes. No grants to individuals (except for scholarships), or for ongoing operations, deficit spending, office equipment, or fundraising projects; no loans.

Publications: Application guidelines.

Application information: Visit foundation Web site for grant application cover sheet and guidelines. Application form required.

Initial approach: Telephone
Copies of proposal: 21
Deadline(s): Apr. 1 and Oct. 1
Board meeting date(s): 4th Mon. of the month, 5 times per year
Final notification: June and Dec.

Officers and Trustees: * Jim Howell,* Chair.; Don Spencer,* Vice-Chair.; Robert G. Tambellini, C.E.O. and Pres.; Bill Lorne,* Corp. Secy.; Kirk Jabara,* Treas.; Rhea Dow; Sally Fogg; Tom Hanna; Kay Heise; Bruce Herbert; Tom Irwin; Pat Poineau; Barbara Pritchard; Jeff Rogers; Nancy Wright.

Number of staff: 2 full-time professional; 1 full-time support.

EIN: 383033739

2326
Chippewa County Community Foundation
(formerly Sault Area Community Foundation)
206 Greenough St.
P.O. Box 1979
Sault Sainte Marie, MI   49783   (906) 635-1046
Contact: Ms. Sue Atkins-Wagner, Exec. Dir.
FAX: (775) 417-7368; E-mail: cccf@lighthouse.net

Established in MI; rejoined the Community Foundation of the Upper Peninsula as a geographic affiliate in 2005.

Grantmaker type: Community foundation.

Purpose and activities: The mission of the Chippewa County Community Foundation is to be a vehicle for receiving monies from a variety of sources to establish permanent endowment funds for charitable, educational, cultural, recreational, environmental, and social welfare purposes in a manner which promotes the spirit of philanthropy, utilizes the abilities of its youth, and meets the needs of the citizens of Chippewa County.

Fields of interest: Environment; Health care; Recreation; Youth development.

Type of support: Endowments; Program development; Scholarship funds.

Limitations: Giving limited to Chippewa County, MI.

Application information: Application form required.
Initial approach: Telephone or e-mail
Copies of proposal: 5
Deadline(s): Jan. 15, Apr. 15, July 15, and Oct. 15

Officer: Kerry O'Connor, Chair.

Number of staff: 1 part-time professional.

2327
Clare County Community Foundation
c/o Midland Area Community Foundation
109 E. Main St.
P.O. Box 289
Midland, MI   48640-0289   (800) 906-9661
Contact: Brian Jackson, Prog. Off.
E-mail: bjackson@midlandfoundation.com

Established in 1997 in MI; a geographic affiliate of MIdland Area Community Foundation.

Grantmaker type: Community foundation.

Purpose and activities: Support for a wide variety of community programs, such as arts and culture, civic improvement, education, environment, health, human services, recreation and youth.

Fields of interest: Arts; Education; Environment; Recreation; Youth development; Community development.

Limitations: Giving limited to benefit Clare County, MI. No support for sectarian religious programs. No grants for operating budgets, annual fund raising, normal office equipment, endowment campaigns, debt reduction, or travel.

Application information: Application form required.
Deadline(s): Jan. 15, Apr. 15, July 15, and Oct. 15
Final notification: Within 2 months

2328
Clio Area Community Fund
c/o Community Foundation of Greater Flint
502 Church St.
Flint, MI   48502-1206

Established in 1991 in MI as a geographic component fund of Community Foundation of Greater Flint.

Grantmaker type: Community foundation.

Purpose and activities: The fund is an endowment created to enhance the quality of life in the Clio area by awarding grants to eligible tax exempt organizations to benefit its residents in the areas of education, arts and recreation, community development, and health.

Fields of interest: Arts; Education; Health care; Recreation; Community development.

Limitations: Giving limited to the Clio, MI, area.

2329
Community Foundation for Delta County, Michigan, Inc.
2500 7th Ave. S., Ste. 103, Box 5
Escanaba, MI   49829   (906) 786-6654
Contact: Gary LaPlant, Exec. Dir.
FAX: (906) 786-9124; E-mail: cffdc@chartermi.net

Established in 1989 in MI; a geographic affiliate of the Community Foundation of the Upper Peninsula.

Grantmaker type: Community foundation.

Purpose and activities: The foundation seeks to enhance the quality of life in the Delta County, Michigan, area by improving the educational,

cultural, recreational, environmental and social welfare resources of the area, and developing youth for community leadership.

Fields of interest: Performing arts; Environment; Health care; Health organizations; Recreation; Human services; Family services; Residential/ custodial care, hospices; Voluntarism promotion; Government/public administration.

Type of support: General/operating support; Emergency funds; Seed money; Scholarship funds; In-kind gifts; Matching/challenge support.

Limitations: Giving limited to Delta County, MI. No grants for fundraising, exhibits, religious or sectarian purposes, or operational funding.

Publications: Application guidelines; Annual report; Informational brochure.

Application information: Call or write for complete guidelines. Application form required.
Initial approach: Letter or telephone
Copies of proposal: 11
Deadline(s): Feb. 1, May 1, Aug. 1 and Nov. 1
Board meeting date(s): Monthly
Final notification: Feb. 28, May 31, Aug. 31 and Nov. 30

Officers and Trustees: * Willard Carne, Sr.,* Chair.; William A. LeMire III,* 1st Vice-Chair.; Bonnie Wenick-Kutz,* 2nd Vice-Chair.; Matt Smith, Jr.,* Pres.; Sally Bittner,* Secy.; Alice Butch,* Treas.; Gary LaPlant, Exec. Dir.; John Beaumier; James Boes; Mary Cretens; Vicky Giguere; Barbara Hammerberg; Dennis Harrison; Rev. Richard Hutton; Carol Krieg, M.D.; Emily Krieg; William Lake; Mark Lukacs; Brian Pahnke; David Schaaf; Erin Thomas; Robert Van Damme; David Williams.

EIN: 382907795

2330
Community Foundation for Livingston County
P.O. Box 200
Brighton, MI   48116-0200
URL: http://www.cfsem.org/grants/affiliates/ livingston.html

Established in 1991 in MI as a geographic affiliate of the Community Foundation for Southeastern Michigan.

Grantmaker type: Community foundation.

Purpose and activities: To support and improve the public well-being and quality of life in Livingston County, Michigan. Areas of interest include but are not limited to arts and culture, civic affairs, education, environment and land use, health, human services, neighborhood and regional economic development, and workforce development.

Fields of interest: Arts; Education; Environment, land resources; Environment; Health care; Employment, services; Human services; Community development, neighborhood development; Economic development; Government/public administration.

Limitations: Giving limited to Livingston County, MI. No support for organizations lacking 501(c)(3) status or for sectarian religious programs. No grants to individuals, or for buildings or equipment, general operating support, endowments, fundraising campaigns, conferences and annual meetings, or computers or computer systems.

Application information: Application form not required.

Initial approach: The foundation strongly encourages potential applicants to telephone prior to preparing a full grant proposal
Deadline(s): Mar. 1, June 1, Sept. 1, and Dec. 1
Final notification: Generally 4 months after deadline: June, Sept., Dec. and June
Officer: Lee Reeves, Mgr., Philanthropic Svcs.

2331
Community Foundation for Mason County
317 N. Park St.
Ludington, MI   49431-1641   (231) 845-0326
Contact: Michael Oakes, Coord.
E-mail: moakes@yahoo.com

Established in 1988 in MI as the Ludington Area Foundation; in 1996 became an affiliate of Community Foundation for Muskegon County.
Donors: West Shore Family YMCA; Mason County Central Senior Center; City of Scottville.
Grantmaker type: Community foundation.
Purpose and activities: The foundation was established to promote philanthropy in Mason County, and to serve as a grantmaker to the region's nonprofit community organizations. The foundation administers donor-advised, scholarship, field of interest, and organization endowment funds. During 2004 $258,812 in grants were awarded to Mason County non-profits.
Fields of interest: Community development; Philanthropy/voluntarism.
Type of support: Capital campaigns; Building/renovation; Equipment; Program development.
Limitations: Giving limited to Mason County, MI.

2332
Community Foundation for Muskegon County
(formerly Muskegon County Community Foundation, Inc.)
425 W. Western Ave., Ste. 200
Muskegon, MI   49440   (231) 722-4538
Contact: Chris Ann McGuigan, C.E.O.; For grants: Arnold "Arn" Boezaart, V.P., Grant Progs.
FAX: (231) 722-4616; *E-mail:* info@cffmc.org; Grant application *E-mail:* aboezaart@cffmc.org;
URL: http://www.cffmc.org

Incorporated in 1961 in MI.
Donors: Alta Daetz†; Harold Frauenthal†; Charles Goodnow†; George Hilt; Jack Hilt; John Hilt; Paul C. Johnson†; Henry Klooster†; Ernest Settle†.
Grantmaker type: Community foundation.
Financial data (yr. ended 12/31/04): Assets, $88,320,829 (M); gifts received, $3,449,419; expenditures, $4,879,031; total giving, $2,726,558; giving activities include $2,726,558 for 1,148 grants (high: $85,000; low: $4).
Purpose and activities: The foundation seeks to assist worthwhile projects, with emphasis on health and human services, arts and culture, education, community development, and youth. Of particular interest are pilot programs and collaborative projects.
Fields of interest: Arts education; Performing arts, theater; Arts; Scholarships/financial aid; Education; Environment, air pollution; Environment, water pollution; Environment, land resources; Environment; Health care; Health organizations, association; Youth development; Youth, pregnancy prevention; Human services; Economic

development; Urban/community development; Community development; Infants/toddlers; Children.
Type of support: Continuing support; Building/renovation; Equipment; Emergency funds; Program development; Conferences/seminars; Professorships; Publication; Seed money; Internship funds; Scholarship funds; Research; Consulting services; Program-related investments/loans; Scholarships—to individuals; Exchange programs; Matching/challenge support.
Limitations: Giving limited to Muskegon County, MI. No support for sectarian religious programs, or individual schools or districts. No grants to individuals (except for scholarships), or for deficit financing, routine operating expenses, capital equipment, endowment campaigns, special fundraising events, conferences, camps, publications, videos, films, television or radio programs, or for advertising.
Publications: Application guidelines; Annual report (including application guidelines); Financial statement; Grants list; Informational brochure (including application guidelines); Newsletter; Program policy statement.
Application information: Visit foundation Web site for grant information; call the foundation for proposal guidelines and specific deadlines.
Initial approach: Telephone
Deadline(s): Varies
Board meeting date(s): Feb., Apr., June, Aug., Oct., and Dec.
Final notification: 3 months
Officers and Trustees:* Michael Bozym, Ph.D.*, Chair.; Patricia B. Johnson,* Vice-Chair. and Pres. Emeritus; Peter M. Turner,* Vice-Chair.; Chris Ann McGuigan,* C.E.O., Pres., and Secy.; Arnold "Arn" Boezaart, V.P., Grant Progs.; Robert Chapla, V.P., Devel.; Ann Van Tassel, V.P., Finance; Scott Musselman,* Treas.; Tim Achterhoft; B. Dennis Albrechtsen; Nancy L. Crandall; Lowell B. Dana; Barbara L. DeBruyn; Holly J. Hughes; Dr. John L. Mixer; Stephen G. Olsen; Michael A. Pepper; Hon. Greg C. Pittman; Rev. Charles Poole; Bruce C. Rice; Arthur V. Scott; John W. Swanson II; Sue Wierengo; Judith L. Wilcox; John Workman.
Trustee Banks: Comerica Bank; Fifth Third Bank; The Huntington National Bank; National City Bank.
Number of staff: 7 full-time professional; 5 full-time support.
EIN: 386114135
Selected grants: The following grants were reported in 2004.
$110,000 to Frauenthal Center for the Performing Arts, Muskegon, MI. For operating subsidy for theater which is operated as service to community.
$100,000 to Muskegon Area First, Muskegon, MI. For re-development of downtown.
$50,000 to MGH Family Health Center, Muskegon Family Care, Muskegon, MI. For construction of new health care facility.
$40,000 to Downtown Muskegon Development Corporation, Muskegon, MI. For consulting work for former Muskegon Mall property.
$30,000 to Hospice of Muskegon-Oceana, Muskegon, MI. For Poppen Hospice Residence.
$30,000 to Senior Resources of West Michigan, Muskegon Heights, MI. For development of Mukegon County 2-1-1.
$25,000 to Hackley Hospital, Muskegon, MI. For Hackley Emergency Center.
$20,000 to Hackley Public Library, Friends of, Muskegon, MI. For Stained Glass Window Repair.

$17,500 to Muskegon, City of, Muskegon, MI. For matching funds for Michigan Economic Development Corporation.
$11,000 to Salvation Army, Muskegon, MI. For shelter and utility assistance to City of Muskegon residents.

2333
Community Foundation for Northeast Michigan
(doing business as North Central Michigan Community Foundation)
(formerly Northeast Michigan Community Foundation)
111 Water St.
P.O. Box 495
Alpena, MI   49707   (989) 354-6881
Contact: Barbara A. Willyard, Exec. Dir.
FAX: (989) 356-3319; *E-mail:* bwillyard@cfnem.org; Additional tel.: (877) 354-6881; *URL:* http://www.cfnem.org

Incorporated in 1974 in MI.
Grantmaker type: Community foundation.
Financial data (yr. ended 9/30/05): Assets, $22,968,969 (M); gifts received, $4,927,192; expenditures, $999,172; total giving, $716,392; giving activities include $716,392 for 540 grants (high: $200,000; low: $100).
Purpose and activities: The foundation seeks to serve the community and to preserve the charitable goals of a wide range of donors now and for generations to come.
Fields of interest: Humanities; Arts; Libraries/library science; Education; Environment; Health care; Health organizations, association; Children/youth, services; Human services; Government/public administration.
Type of support: Building/renovation; Equipment; Program development; Conferences/seminars; Seed money; Scholarship funds; Technical assistance.
Limitations: Giving limited to Alcona, Alpena, Montmorency, and Presque Isle counties, and through affiliates: Crawford, Cheboygan, Iosco, Ogemaw, and Oscoda counties, MI. No support for religious or sectarian purposes. No grants to individuals (except for scholarships), or for annual giving campaigns or capital campaigns, normal operating expenses, or multi-year or sustained funding; no loans.
Publications: Application guidelines; Annual report; Financial statement; Grants list; Informational brochure; Newsletter; Program policy statement.
Application information: Visit foundation Web site for application forms and guidelines. For grants of $300 or less, organizations should use the 2-page mini-grant application and follow its specific guidelines. Application form required.
Initial approach: Submit application forms and attachments
Copies of proposal: 1
Deadline(s): Feb. 1, Aug. 1, and Nov. 1
Board meeting date(s): Quarterly
Final notification: Within 6 weeks
Officers and Trustees:* Steve Lappan,* Pres.; Nancy Coombs,* V.P.; Bill Morford,* Secy.; Georgene Hildebrand,* Treas.; Barbara A. Willyard, Exec. Dir.; Marcia Aten; Benjamin Bolser; Carolyn Brummund; Larry Bruski; Ann Burton; Hugo Burzlaff; George "Ted" Cavin; Beach Hall; Carl Huebner; Sue Keller; Jennie Kerr; Chuck Manning; Damone Sorenson; Bill Speer.

Number of staff: 4 full-time professional.
EIN: 237384822

2334
Community Foundation for Oceana County

563 S. 88th Ave
Shelby, MI 49455-9605 (231) 861-6887
Contact: Tammy Carey, Prog. Coord.
FAX: (231) 861-6396; E-mail: carey@oceana.net

Established in 1989 in MI as an affiliate of
Community Foundation for Muskegon County.
Grantmaker type: Community foundation.
Purpose and activities: The Community Foundation
for Oceana County was the first affiliate in the state
of Michigan. In 2003 it distributed over $92,000 in
grants to local communities.
Fields of interest: Community development.
Limitations: Giving limited to Oceana County, MI.

2335
Community Foundation for Southeastern Michigan

333 W. Fort St., Ste. 2010
Detroit, MI 48226 (313) 961-6675
Contact: Mariam C. Noland, Pres.
FAX: (313) 961-2886; E-mail: cfsem@cfsem.org;
URL: http://www.cfsem.org

Established in 1984 in MI.
Grantmaker type: Community foundation.
Financial data (yr. ended 12/31/05): Assets,
$454,103,157 (M); gifts received, $47,470,217;
expenditures, $33,870,694; total giving,
$27,473,684; giving activities include
$27,473,684 for grants.
Purpose and activities: The foundation strengthens
the region's quality of life by: 1) building "community
capital"; 2) enhancing the region's quality of life; 3)
engaging people and organizations in philanthropy;
4) convening, planning and working for positive
change; and 5) supporting and launching new
initiatives. Supports projects in the areas of civic
affairs, social services, arts and culture, health,
education, environment and land use, neighborhood
and regional economic development and workforce
development.
Fields of interest: Arts; Education; Environment;
Health care; Health organizations, association;
Youth development, services; Youth, services;
Human services; Civil rights, race/intergroup
relations; Economic development; Community
development; Government/public administration;
Leadership development; Public affairs;
Economically disadvantaged.
Type of support: Program development; Seed
money; Scholarship funds; Technical assistance;
Scholarships—to individuals.
Limitations: Giving limited to southeast MI. No
support for sectarian religious programs. No grants
to individuals (from unrestricted funds), or for capital
projects, endowments, annual campaigns, general
operating support, conferences, computers and
computer systems, fundraising, annual meetings,
buildings, or equipment.
Publications: Application guidelines; Annual report
(including application guidelines); Grants list;
Informational brochure (including application
guidelines); Newsletter.
Application information: There are separate
grantmaking guidelines for several special

grantmaking projects. These guidelines and special
application forms are available by contacting the
foundation or consulting the foundation's
Guidelines for Grantmaking. Visit foundation Web
site for general grant application guidelines.
Application form not required.
  Initial approach: Telephone
  Copies of proposal: 1
  Deadline(s): Mar. 1, June 1, Sept. 1, and Dec. 1
  Board meeting date(s): Mar., June, Sept., and
  Dec.
  Final notification: 3 months after submission of
  proposal
Officers and Trustees:* Allan D. Gilmour,* Chair.;
Alfred R. Glancy III,* Vice-Chair.; Alan E. Schwartz,*
Vice-Chair.; Mariam C. Noland, Pres.; Robin D.
Ferriby, V.P., Philanthropy Svcs.; Cassandra Joubert,
Sc.D., V.P., Community Investment; Karen L.
Leppanen, V.P., Finance and Admin.; Anne S.
Weekley, V.P., Comms.; Hon. Anna Diggs Taylor,*
Secy.; Michael T. Monahan,* Treas.; Penny B.
Blumenstein,* Chair., Prog. and Distrib.; Frederick
M. Adams, Jr.; Margaret Acheson Allesee; Hon.
Dennis W. Archer; Norma C. Barfield; Albert M.
Berriz; Andrew L. Camden; Julie Fisher Cummings;
Tarik S. Daoud; Paul R. Dimond; Deborah I. Dingell;
Anthony F. Earley, Jr.; Irma B. Elder; David T. Fischer;
Phillip W. Fischer; W. Frank Fountain; Steven K.
Hamp; David M. Hempstead; William M. Hermann;
William K. Howenstein; Joseph L. Hudson, Jr.; John
D. Lewis; Dana M. Locniskar; Ben C. Maibach III;
Florine Mark; Jack Martin; Kathleen McCree-Lewis;
Edward J. Miller; Eugene A. Miller; James B.
Nicholson; Bruce E. Nyberg; David K. Page; Cynthia
J. Pasky; William F. Pickard; Sandra E. Pierce; John
Rakolta, Jr.; Jack A. Robinson; Pamela Rodgers;
Howard F. Sims; Vivian Day Stroh; Gary Torgow;
Reginald M. Turner; Barbara C. Van Dusen; Ken
Whipple; Tom Wilson.
Number of staff: 16 full-time professional; 1
part-time professional; 9 full-time support; 2
part-time support.
EIN: 382530980
Selected grants: The following grants were reported
in 2004.
$1,000,000 to Detroit Riverfront Conservancy,
  Detroit, MI. For construction of Detroit RiverWalk.
$1,000,000 to Princeton University, Princeton, NJ.
  For program support.
$500,000 to Detroit Symphony Orchestra, Detroit,
  MI. For capital campaign.
$348,761 to Archdiocese of Detroit, Detroit, MI. For
  program support.
$100,000 to American Red Cross, Washtenaw
  County Chapter, Ann Arbor, MI. For program
  support.
$96,000 to Preserve Our Parks, Hamtramck, MI. For
  planning and design of trail connecting Veterans
  Memorial Park in Hamtramck to Dequindre Cut.
$25,000 to American Indian College Fund, Denver,
  CO. For program support.
$20,000 to Edison Institute, Dearborn, MI. For
  annual campaign.
$20,000 to First Presbyterian Church of Colorado
  Springs, Colorado Springs, CO. For program
  support.
$20,000 to Gangaji Foundation, Ashland, OR. For
  general operating support.

2336
Community Foundation of Greater Flint

502 Church St.
Flint, MI 48502-1206 (810) 767-8270
Contact: Kathi Horton, Pres.
FAX: (810) 767-0496; E-mail: cfgf@cfgf.org;
Additional E-mail: khorton@cfgf.org; URL: http://
www.cfgf.org

Established in 1988 in MI.
Grantmaker type: Community foundation.
Financial data (yr. ended 12/31/05): Assets,
$117,794,673 (M); gifts received, $3,762,963;
expenditures, $7,753,362; total giving,
$5,369,711; giving activities include $5,369,711
for 648 grants (high: $403,331), and $347,382 for
24 foundation-administered programs.
Purpose and activities: The foundation serves the
common good in Genesee County, building a strong
community by engaging people in philanthropy and
developing the community's permanent
endowment, now and for generations to come. The
foundation seeks to respond to current or emerging
needs in the local area in conservation and the
environment, arts and humanities, education,
health and human services, and leadership
development.
Fields of interest: Humanities; Arts; Education;
Environment, natural resources; Environment;
Health care; Youth development, services;
Children/youth, services; Human services;
Leadership development; Children/youth;
Economically disadvantaged.
Type of support: General/operating support;
Management development/capacity building;
Program development; Seed money; Scholarship
funds; Technical assistance; Program evaluation;
Matching/challenge support.
Limitations: Giving primarily in Genesee County, MI.
No support for sectarian religious purposes
(generally). No grants to individuals (except for
scholarships), or for deficit reduction, routine
operating expenses of existing organizations, or
endowments.
Publications: Application guidelines; Annual report;
Financial statement; Grants list; Informational
brochure; Occasional report; Program policy
statement.
Application information: Visit foundation Web site
for application guidelines. There are separate
grantmaking guidelines for several special
grantmaking projects. These guidelines and special
application forms are available by contacting the
foundation. Application form required.
  Initial approach: Telephone or personal contact
  Copies of proposal: 4
  Deadline(s): Varies
  Board meeting date(s): Feb., Apr., June, Aug.,
  Oct., and Dec.
Officers and Trustees:* Lawrence E. Moon,* Chair.;
Sherri E. Stephens,* Vice-Chair.; Kathi Horton,
Pres.; Mary Ittigson, V.P., Finance and Admin.;
Tanya Jefferson, V.P., Community Impact; AnnMarie
VanDuyne, V.P., Philanthropic Svcs.; Jo Anne G.
Mondowney,* Secy.; Daniel Coffield,* Treas.; Rudy
V. Collins; Samuel Cox; F. James Cummins;
Shannon M. Easter; Cheryl A. Gifford; Nancy Hanflik;
Nina M. Jones; Timothy H. Knecht; Stanley Liberty;
Juan Mestas; William Morgan; Bobby Mukkamala;
Clarence Sevillian II; Susan Tippett.
Number of staff: 9 full-time professional; 3 full-time
support.
EIN: 382190667

2337
Community Foundation of Greater Rochester

(formerly Greater Rochester Area Community Foundation)
P.O. Box 80431
Rochester, MI 48308-0431 (248) 608-2804
Contact: Peggy Hamilton, Exec. Dir.
FAX: (248) 608-2826; E-mail: cfound@cfound.org;
URL: http://www.cfound.org
Scholarship application address for hand delivery:
Community Fdn. Office, 127 W. University Dr.,
Rochester, MI 48307

Incorporated in 1983 in MI.
Grantmaker type: Community foundation.
Financial data (yr. ended 12/31/04): Assets, $0 (M); gifts received, $930,288; expenditures, $845,111; total giving, $660,469; giving activities include $518,882 for 82 grants (high: $57,637; low: $50), and $141,587 for 98 grants to individuals (high: $4,000; low: $63).
Purpose and activities: The foundation seeks to enhance the quality of life for community residents within the following funding categories: arts and culture, education, youth, civic beautification, health, recreation, human services, and community development.
Fields of interest: Museums; Performing arts; Performing arts, music; Arts; Elementary school/education; Education; Environment, natural resources; Environment; Health care; Recreation; Youth, services; Family services; Human services; Economic development; Community development; Youth; Disabilities, people with.
Type of support: General/operating support; Annual campaigns; Building/renovation; Equipment; Endowments; Emergency funds; Seed money; Scholarship funds; Scholarships—to individuals; Matching/challenge support.
Limitations: Giving limited to the greater Rochester, MI, area. No grants to individuals (except for designated scholarship funds), or for operating budgets.
Publications: Annual report (including application guidelines); Financial statement; Informational brochure; Newsletter.
Application information: Visit the foundation Web site for application forms and specific guidelines per grant type. Application form required.
  Initial approach: Letter of Intent or telephone
  Copies of proposal: 7
  Deadline(s): Mar. 31 and Sept. 30 for grant application forms; Mar. 18 for scholarships
  Board meeting date(s): Quarterly
Officers and Trustees:* Edward A. Golick,* Chair.; David de Steiger, Vice-Chair., Devel.; Linda Preede,* Vice-Chair., Investment; George Seifert,* Vice-Chair., Pro Tem; Patricia Botkin,* Secy.; Mary Ann Reidinger,* Treas.; Peggy Hamilton, Exec. Dir.; Kenneth D. Bilodeau; Joseph Champagne; Jack DiFranco; Gail Duncan; Michael Glass; Brian Hunter; Vern Pixley; Dave Shellenbarger.
Members: Johanna Allen; Corey Bordine; Frank Cardimen; Gerald Carvey; Jerry Collins; Penny Crissman; Kathy Dziurman; Tom Finnerty; Lois Haack; Robert Justin; Bruce Kresge; Richard Maibauer; Patrick McKay; Ed McKibbon; Sid Mittra; Pamela Mitzelfeld; John Modetz; Don Pixley; Katy Plummer; John Schultz; Russ Shelton; Marty Sibert; Mary Beth Snyder; Lawrence Ternan; Brad Upton.
Number of staff: 1 full-time professional; 1 part-time support.
EIN: 382476777

2338
Community Foundation of Monroe County

P.O. Box 627
Monroe, MI 48161 (734) 242-1976
Contact: Kristyn Theisen, Exec. Dir.
FAX: (734) 242-1234; E-mail: info@cfmonroe.org;
URL: http://www.cfmonroe.org

Established in 1978 in MI.
Grantmaker type: Community foundation.
Financial data (yr. ended 3/31/05): Assets, $3,799,971 (M); gifts received, $334,495; expenditures, $412,713; total giving, $173,463; giving activities include $121,438 for 71 grants (high: $34,800; low: $16), $52,025 for 68 grants to individuals (high: $4,245; low: $200), and $178,769 for 5 foundation-administered programs.
Purpose and activities: The foundation's mission is to encourage and facilitate philanthropy in Monroe County, MI.
Fields of interest: Performing arts; Performing arts, theater; Performing arts, music; History/archaeology; Historic preservation/historical societies; Arts; Elementary school/education; Higher education; Adult education—literacy, basic skills & GED; Education, reading; Education; Environment, natural resources; Environment; Health care; Substance abuse, services; Health organizations, association; Food services; Housing/shelter, development; Children/youth, services; Aging, centers/services; Minorities/immigrants, centers/services; Homeless, human services; Human services; Community development; Voluntarism promotion; Public affairs; Aging; Disabilities, people with; Minorities; Economically disadvantaged.
Type of support: Capital campaigns; Building/renovation; Equipment; Program development; Seed money; Curriculum development; Scholarship funds; Research; Technical assistance; Scholarships—to individuals; Exchange programs; In-kind gifts; Matching/challenge support.
Limitations: Giving limited to MI, with emphasis on Monroe County. No support for sectarian religious purposes. No grants to individuals (except through designated scholarship funds), or for annual fundraising drives, endowment campaigns, operational phases of established programs, conferences, travel, scholarly research, or for multi-year grant commitments; no loans.
Publications: Application guidelines; Annual report; Financial statement; Grants list; Informational brochure; Newsletter.
Application information: Visit foundation Web site for application information. Application form required.
  Initial approach: Letter or telephone
  Copies of proposal: 15
  Deadline(s): Jan. 15, Apr. 15, July 15, and Oct. 15
  Board meeting date(s): 4th Wed. of each month, except Dec.
  Final notification: One month
Officers and Trustees:* Robert L. Yeo,* Pres.; Christine Gakenheimer,* V.P.; Jeff Pezzano,* Secy.; Daniel Maletich,* Treas.; Kristyn Theisen, Exec. Dir.; Dale Brunt; James M. DuBay; Nicole Ernst; Gail Hauser-Hurley; Danny Johnson; John Kauffman, Jr.; Mike McCormick; Jeanne Micka; Randy Richardville; Susan Westerdale.
Number of staff: 1 full-time professional; 1 part-time professional; 1 full-time support; 2 part-time support.
EIN: 382236628

2339
Community Foundation of St. Clair County

516 McMorran Blvd.
Port Huron, MI 48060 (810) 984-4761
Contact: Randy D. Maiers, C.E.O.
FAX: (810) 984-3394;
E-mail: info@stclairfoundation.org; Grant application
E-mail: grants@stclairfoundation.org; Additional
E-mail: randy@stclairfoundation.org (for Randy Maiers); URL: http://www.stclairfoundation.org

Established in 1944 in MI.
Grantmaker type: Community foundation.
Financial data (yr. ended 12/31/04): Assets, $27,914,951 (M); gifts received, $3,887,213; expenditures, $1,617,994; total giving, $1,095,716; giving activities include $1,095,716 for 79 grants (high: $236,748; low: $100).
Purpose and activities: The foundation seeks to serve the charitable needs and enhance the quality of life of the community by: providing a flexible and convenient vehicle for donors having a variety of charitable goals and needs; receiving and investing contributions to build permanent endowments; responding to changing and emerging community needs; serving as a steward for individuals, families, foundations, and organizations entrusting assets to its care; and providing grants to philanthropic organizations, social services, civic concerns, education, arts and culture, recreation and youth.
Fields of interest: Arts; Education; Recreation; Family services; Human services; Economic development; Community development; Youth.
Type of support: Building/renovation; Equipment; Program development; Publication; Seed money; Scholarship funds; Scholarships—to individuals; Matching/challenge support.
Limitations: Giving limited to St. Clair County, MI. No support for religious activities. No grants to individuals directly, or for endowments, equipment, annual meetings, conferences, travel expenses, venture capital funds, or film, video, or TV projects, deficit reduction, annual fundraising, capital campaigns, marketing or public relations, general operating expenses, or land use.
Publications: Application guidelines; Annual report; Financial statement; Grants list; Informational brochure.
Application information: Visit foundation Web site for application form and guidelines. Application form required.
  Initial approach: Contact foundation
  Copies of proposal: 1
  Deadline(s): Jan. 1, Apr. 1, July 1, and Oct. 1
  Board meeting date(s): Quarterly
  Final notification: Mar., June, Sept., and Dec.
Officers and Board Members:* Frederick S. Moore,* Chair.; Charles G. Kelly,* Vice-Chair.; Randy D. Maiers, C.E.O. and Pres.; Marshall J. Campbell,* Secy.; Don C. Fletcher,* Treas.; Karen Lee, Cont.; Douglas R. Austin; Beth Belanger; Rose B. Bellanca; Heather Bokram; Ronald W. Cooley; Gary Fletcher; Lee C. Hanson; Steve Hill; Thomas A. Hunter; Roy W. Kelcha; Gerald J. Kramer; John R. Monahan; Franklin H. Moore; Donna M. Niester; David P. O'Connor; Will Oldford; Bill Robinson; Lynne M. Secory; John W. Shier; Douglas S. Touma; Joseph A. Vito; Martin E. Weiss; Cathy Wilkinson.
Number of staff: 4 full-time professional; 3 part-time support.
EIN: 381872132

2340

The Community Foundation of the Holland/Zeeland Area

(formerly Holland Community Foundation, Inc.)
70 W. 8th St., Ste. 100
Holland, MI 49423 (616) 396-6590
Contact: Janet DeYoung, Exec. Dir.
FAX: (616) 396-3573; E-mail: info@cfhz.org;
Additional E-mail: janet@cfhz.org; URL: http://www.cfhz.org

Incorporated in 1951 in MI.
Grantmaker type: Community foundation.
Financial data (yr. ended 12/31/04): Assets, $22,308,089 (M); gifts received, $1,601,833; expenditures, $2,916,521; total giving, $2,579,111; giving activities include $2,579,111 for 274 grants (high: $520,143; low: $100).
Purpose and activities: The foundation seeks to make the greater Holland/Zeeland area a better place in which to live and work by enhancing the quality of life for all its citizens through the use of permanent endowments built from a wide variety of donors.
Fields of interest: Visual arts, art conservation; Historic preservation/historical societies; Arts; Education; Environment; Health care; Housing/shelter; Recreation; Children/youth, services; Human services; Economic development; Community development; Youth; Aging.
Type of support: Capital campaigns; Building/renovation; Equipment; Program development; Seed money; Curriculum development; Scholarship funds; Technical assistance; Program evaluation; Employee-related scholarships; In-kind gifts.
Limitations: Giving limited to the Holland/Zeeland, MI, area and surrounding townships. No support for sectarian religious programs. No grants for endowment funds, operating budgets, expenses for established programs, fundraising drives, capital equipment, conference attendance, salaries, stipends, sabbatical leaves, debt reduction, research, fellowships, matching gifts, travel, or computers, video equipment, or vehicles; no loans.
Publications: Application guidelines; Annual report; Informational brochure (including application guidelines); Newsletter.
Application information: Visit foundation Web site for application guidelines. Letter of intent is mandatory for invitation of full proposal from foundation (10 copies required). 35 copies of the application are required if the project is of primary benefit of youth programming for people under 21 years of age. Application form required.
  Initial approach: Telephone
  Copies of proposal: 15
  Deadline(s): Oct. 26 for letter of intent; Jan. 18 for grant application
  Board meeting date(s): Feb., Apr., Aug., and Oct.
  Final notification: Within 1 month for letter of intent determination; Apr. for grant determination
Officers and Trustees:* Thun Champassak,* Chair., Investment Comm.; Melissa Kamara,* Chair., Devel.; Peter Neydon,* Pres.; John R. Marquis,* 1st V.P.; Donna Vanlwaarden,* 2nd V.P.; Carla Masselink,* Secy.; Janet De Young, Exec. Dir.; Char Amante; Kenneth Bing; Susan Den Herder; Frank Garcia; Jeff Helder; Jim Jurries; Matthew Lepard; Hannes Meyers, Jr.; Grace Van Haitsma.
Number of staff: 3 full-time professional; 2 part-time professional.
EIN: 386095283

2341

Community Foundation of the Upper Peninsula

(formerly Upper Peninsula Community Foundation Alliance)
2500 7th Ave. S., Ste. 103
Escanaba, MI 49829-1176 (906) 789-5972
Contact: Gary LaPlant, Exec. Dir.
FAX: (906) 786-9124; E-mail: cfup@chartermi.net;
URL: http://cfup.org/about_CFUP.htm

Established in 1994 in MI.
Grantmaker type: Community foundation.
Financial data (yr. ended 12/31/04): Assets, $8,356,884 (M); gifts received, $990,513; expenditures, $1,192,119; total giving, $886,119; giving activities include $846,019 for 209 grants (high: $200,000; low: $62), and $40,100 for 29 grants to individuals (high: $9,250; low: $200).
Purpose and activities: The foundation seeks to enhance the quality of life in the Upper Peninsula of MI. The foundation will provide its own U.P.-wide philanthropy and that of its geographic affiliate members through growth of permanent endowment funds from a wide range of donors. The CFUP also provides financial, administrative, communication, and other support services to its affiliate members and to other U.P. community foundations.
Fields of interest: Historic preservation/historical societies; Environment; Health care; Human services; Economic development; Youth.
Type of support: Capital campaigns; Scholarship funds; Technical assistance; Scholarships—to individuals.
Limitations: Giving limited to the Upper Peninsula, MI, area, including Chippewa County, Schoolcraft County, Gogebic County, Alger, Cedarville, Delta, Ontonagon, Paradise, St. Ignace, Watersmeet County areas. No support for religious or sectarian purposes. No grants to individuals (except for scholarships), or for memberships, memorials, endowments, fundraising, social events, exhibits, or deficits in operating budgets or normal operating expenses, construction of buildings, or maintenance.
Publications: Application guidelines; Annual report; Financial statement; Informational brochure; Informational brochure (including application guidelines).
Application information: Visit foundation Web site for application Cover Sheet and guidelines. Application form required.
  Initial approach: Submit Cover Sheet and attachments
  Copies of proposal: 8
  Deadline(s): Spring
  Board meeting date(s): Feb., Apr., July, and Oct.
  Final notification: By mail
Officers and Trustees:* William LeMire III, M.D.*, Co-Pres.; Dr. K. Gerald Marsden,* Co-Pres.; Dr. Kenneth Drenth,* V.P.; William W. Lake,* V.P.; Mary Bowerman,* Secy.; Tom Luckey,* Treas.; Gary LaPlant, Exec. Dir.; Elio Argentati; Margaret LaPonsie; John MacFarlane III; Keith Neve; Walter North; Kerry O'Connor; Francis E. Paoli; Matt Smith, Jr.; Bonnie Wenick-Kutz.
Number of staff: 2 full-time professional; 1 part-time professional; 1 part-time support.
EIN: 383227080

2342

Community Foundation of Troy

(formerly Troy Community Foundation)
1120 E. Long Lake Rd., Ste. 250
Troy, MI 48085-4960 (248) 740-7600
Contact: For grants: Jim Cyrulewski, Dir.
E-mail: jcyrulewski@itctransco.org; Additional E-mail: drondo@communityfoundationoftroy.org; Grant inquiry tel.: (248) 374-7130; URL: http://www.communityfoundationoftroy.org

Established in 1998 in MI.
Grantmaker type: Community foundation.
Financial data (yr. ended 12/31/04): Assets, $198,296 (M); gifts received, $54,777; expenditures, $57,965; total giving, $21,516; giving activities include $21,516 for 4+ grants (high: $8,121).
Purpose and activities: The foundation is a philanthropic organization dedicated to investing in and enhancing the quality of life in Troy and the surrounding communities by awarding grants to support outstanding organizations and projects. Giving primarily in the areas of the arts, education at all levels, human services, including senior self-sufficiency skills building, family counseling programs, transportation programs and parenting skills building, and economic vitality of the community, including economic development, business retention, technology innovation programs, environmental programs and crime prevention, with an emphasis on education and business partnerships.
Fields of interest: Museums; Performing arts; Arts; Higher education; Libraries (public); Education; Environment, public education; Environment; Dental care; Public health; Health care; Substance abuse, services; Mental health, smoking; Crime/violence prevention; Recreation; Family services; Aging, centers/services; Human services; Economic development; Community development, business promotion; Youth; Aging.
Limitations: Giving limited to the greater Troy, MI, area. No support for religious organizations for religious (denominational) purposes, or for single purpose health organizations, or national or international organizations, unless they are providing benefits directly in service-area residents. No grants to individuals, or for general operating support, student group trips, conferences, or hospitals (for building or equipment needs).
Application information: Visit foundation Web site for application Cover Sheet and guidelines. Requests initiated by telephone will not be acted upon until a written request is received; requests initiated by fax are discouraged. Application form required.
  Initial approach: Submit application Cover Sheet and attachments
  Copies of proposal: 4
  Deadline(s): Mar. 31, June 30, Sept. 30, and Dec. 31
  Board meeting date(s): Quarterly
Officers and Directors:* Gregory Merritt,* Chair.; Thomas Kaszubski,* Pres.; Cheryl A. Whitton,* V.P.; Marc Kaszubski,* Secy.; Anthony Iaquinto,* Treas.; Denise Rondo, Exec. Dir.; Jim Cyrulewski; Cele Dilley; David Hanley; Michael A. Kaszubski; David Nelson; David Robertson; Deborah Schneider; Cynthia Stewart.
Number of staff: 1 full-time professional.
EIN: 383390605

2343
Coopersville Area Community Foundation

P.O. Box 205
Coopersville, MI 49404
URL: http://www.ghacf.org/affiliates/
coopersville.htm

Established in 1993 in MI as an affiliate of Grand Haven Area Community Foundation.
Grantmaker type: Community foundation.
Limitations: Giving limited for the benefit the northeast Ottawa County region of Coopersville and Polkton, Wright, Tallmadge, and Chester townships, MI.
Publications: Occasional report.
Application information: Application form required.
    Copies of proposal: 12
    Board meeting date(s): Monthly
Officers and Trustees: Ward Verseput,* Pres.; Howard Dykhouse,* V.P.; Denise Busman,* Secy.; Paul Spoelman,* Treas.; William Adema; Sherman J. Hecksel, Jr.; Karen Lemmen; Lori Lieffers; Barbara Throop; Ron Veldman.

2344
Crystal Falls/Forest Park Area Community Fund

104 Elm Grove Ln.
Crystal Falls, MI 49920-1025 (906) 875-4289

Established in MI; in 2001 became an affiliate of Dickinson Area Community Foundation.
Grantmaker type: Community foundation.
Fields of interest: Arts; Education; Environment; Health care; Human services; Economic development; Community development.
Limitations: Giving for the benefit of the Crystal Falls/Forest Park, MI, area.
Officers: Gene Dziubinski, Pres.; Roger Stoor, Treas.
Trustees: Charlene Anderson; Susan Flood-Dziubinski; Frank Groeneveld; Patricia Kosiba; Harold Payne; Pearl Ross; Don Schmidt; Doug Wagner; Beverly Wilcox.

2345
Dickinson Area Community Foundation

(formerly Dickinson County Area Community Foundation)
427 S. Stephenson, Ste. 207
Iron Mountain, MI 49801-0648 (906) 774-3131
Contact: Debra J. Flannery, Exec. Dir.
FAX: (906) 774-7640; E-mail: dcacf@uplogon.com;
URL: http://www.dcacf.org

Established in 1995 in MI.
Grantmaker type: Community foundation.
Financial data (yr. ended 4/30/05): Assets, $4,755,081 (M); gifts received, $74,388; expenditures, $201,528; total giving, $107,142; giving activities include $18,251 for 25+ grants, and $88,891 for 106 grants to individuals (high: $1,500; low: $45).
Purpose and activities: The foundation seeks to enhance the quality of life in local communities by meeting the changing needs with endowments for good and forever. To that end, the foundation makes grants in broad program areas of education, health and human services, arts and culture, environment, community and economic development.
Fields of interest: Arts; Education; Environment; Health care; Recreation; Children, services; Human services; Economic development; Community development; Social sciences; Children/youth; Aging.
Type of support: Seed money.
Limitations: Giving limited to the Dickinson County, MI, area and surrounding MI and WI communities, including Crystal Falls and Forest Park, MI, and Florence and Niagara, WI. No support for religious or sectarian purposes, or fraternal organizations serving a limited constituency. No grants to individuals (except for scholarships), or for endowments, fundraising, travel, deficit reduction, capital expenditures, memberships, or memorials.
Publications: Application guidelines; Annual report; Financial statement; Grants list.
Application information: Visit foundation Web site for application form and guidelines. Application form required.
    Initial approach: Telephone
    Deadline(s): Mid-Sept.
    Board meeting date(s): 1st Tues. of Jan., Mar., Aug., Oct., and Dec.
    Final notification: Nov.
Officers and Trustees: Steve Faust,* Chair.; Al Filizetti,* Secy.; Mary Kay Paul,* Treas.; Debra J. Flannery, Exec. Dir.; Richard J. Debelak; Eugene Dziubinski; Carolee Dodge Francis; Christine Hanley; Bob Hansen; Julie LaCost; Chris Momont; David Ostwald; Debbie Recla; Don Schmidt; Karen Thekan.
Number of staff: 1 part-time professional; 1 part-time support.
EIN: 383218990

2346
The Eaton County Community Fund

Eaton County MSU Ext. Office
551 Courthouse Dr., Ste. 1
Charlotte, MI 48813 (517) 372-5594
Contact: Thomas S. Eveland, Chair.
E-mail: c56@voyager.net; URL: http://www.crcfoundation.org/eccfindex.html

Established in 1996 in MI as an affiliate of Capitol Region Community Foundation.
Grantmaker type: Community foundation.
Purpose and activities: The foundation grants funds to benefit youth, family service, education, community welfare, art and culture throughout Eaton County.
Fields of interest: Arts; Education; Youth development; Family services; Community development.
Limitations: Giving limited to Eaton County, MI.
Application information: See foundation Web site for downloadable application form. Applications submitted by facsimile or e-mail will not be accepted. Application form required.
    Copies of proposal: 18
    Deadline(s): Mar. 1
Advisory Board: Hon. Thomas Eveland, Chair.; Susan Steiner Bolhouse; Michael DeGrow; Peter Dunlap; Mona J. Ellard; Kathleen Fear; Vince Ferris; David Gray; Gene Carolan; Tricia Johnson; Jon Kaufmann; Joe E. Pray; Dan Templin; Gary Wichman.

2347
Farmington Hills/Farmington Community Foundation

(formerly Farmington Hills Community Foundation for Children, Youth and Families)
36520 W. 12 Mile Rd.
Farmington Hills, MI 48331 (248) 345-9090
Contact: Barabra G. Yuhas, Exec. Dir.
FAX: (248) 478-7461;
E-mail: help@fhfcfoundation.org; URL: http://www.fhfcfoundation.org/

Established in 1996 in MI.
Grantmaker type: Community foundation.
Financial data (yr. ended 12/31/04): Assets, $233,856 (M); gifts received, $215,074; expenditures, $97,968; total giving, $54,500; giving activities include $54,500 for 3 grants (high: $50,000; low: $2,000).
Purpose and activities: The foundation's purpose is to provide financial support to endeavors that enrich the lives of children, youth and families within the Farmington Hills and Farmington communities. It does this by soliciting contributions, establishing endowments and making grants to support various community activities and organizations.
Fields of interest: Boys & girls clubs; Community development, neighborhood development.
Limitations: Giving limited to Farmington and Farmington Hills, MI. No grants to individuals.
Application information: Visit foundation Web site for application information. Application form required.
    Initial approach: Telephone or e-mail for application form
    Deadline(s): Apr. 15 and Oct. 15
Officers and Trustees: Paul Blizman, Pres.; David L. Steinberg, V.P.; Hon. Marla Parker, Secy.; Robin Sessel,* Treas.; Barbara G. Yuhas, Exec. Dir.; Edward Cleland; William Dwyer; Dennis Fitzgerald; Kimberly Riley Fouts; Robert Heinrich; Albert Ludwig; William Luse; William T. McCarthy; Richard Miller; Theresa Rich; Sam Slaughter; Joanne Smith; Susan Zurvalec.
EIN: 383254708

2348
Four County Community Foundation

(formerly Four County Foundation)
231 E. Saint Clair St.
P.O. Box 539
Almont, MI 48003-0539 (810) 798-0909
Contact: Janet Bauer, Exec. Dir.
FAX: (810) 798-0908; E-mail: info@4ccf.org;
Additional E-mail: janet@4ccf.org; URL: http://www.4ccf.org

Established in 1987 in MI; originally converted from Community Hospital Foundation and sold to Saint Joseph Mercy of Macomb North.
Grantmaker type: Community foundation.
Financial data (yr. ended 12/31/05): Assets, $9,563,324 (M); gifts received, $179,310; expenditures, $492,273; total giving, $329,983; giving activities include $329,983 for 99 grants (high: $19,000; low: $100).
Purpose and activities: The foundation is dedicated to bringing together human and financial resources to support progressive ideas in education, health, community, youth and adult programs.

Fields of interest: Education; Environment; Health care; Health organizations, association; Recreation; Children/youth, services; Community development.
Type of support: Continuing support; Equipment; Program development; Conferences/seminars; Scholarship funds; Matching/challenge support.
Limitations: Giving limited to northwest Oakland, northwest Macomb, southeast Lapeer, and southwest St. Clair counties, MI. No support for sectarian religious programs. No grants to individuals, or for operating expenses or basic educational or municipal functions (generally).
Publications: Application guidelines; Annual report; Newsletter; Program policy statement.
Application information: Visit foundation Web site for application forms and additional guidelines per grant type. Faxed applications are not accepted. Application form required.
　Initial approach: Submit application form
　Copies of proposal: 9
　Deadline(s): Jan. 1, Apr. 1, July 1, and Oct. 1
　Board meeting date(s): 6 meetings per year
　Final notification: Within 1 month
Officers and Trustees:* Charles Schiedegger,* Pres.; Joseph Salas,* V.P.; Kim Jorgensen,* Secy.; Barbara Quain,* Treas.; Janet Bauer, Exec. Dir.; Judy Czerepowicz; William R. Duggan, Jr.; Timothy Edwards; Katherine Eschenburg; Schaeffer Greene; Henry Malburg; Hank Nichols; Sean O'Bryan; Brenda K. Pinskey; Laura Schapman; Barbara Stremler; Al Verlinde.
Number of staff: 1 full-time professional; 2 part-time support.
EIN: 382736601

2349
Greater Frankenmuth Area Community Foundation

7450 Junction Rd.
Frankenmuth, MI　48734　(989) 652-8074
Contact: Ron Bell, Chair.
E-mail: ronaldbell6497@sbcglobal.net

Established in 1977 in MI.
Grantmaker type: Community foundation.
Financial data (yr. ended 12/31/04): Assets, $2,133,048 (M); gifts received, $289,690; expenditures, $300,421; total giving, $276,140; giving activities include $276,140 for 8 grants (high: $204,360).
Purpose and activities: The foundation seeks to support the public, educational, recreational, charitable, and benevolent organizations of the greater Frankenmuth, MI, community.
Fields of interest: Community development; Federated giving programs.
Type of support: Building/renovation; Emergency funds; Program development; Scholarship funds; Scholarships—to individuals.
Limitations: Giving limited to the Frankenmuth, MI, area.
Officers and Board Members:* Ron Bell,* Chair.; Ann Frank,* Secy.; Thomas D. Zuellig, Treas.; Miriam Ehlert; Alan Knoll; Bill Speer; Bill Varney; Karen Zehnder.
Trustee: National City Bank of the Midwest.
EIN: 382140032

2350
Fremont Area Community Foundation

(formerly The Fremont Area Foundation)
4424 W. 48th St.
P.O. Box B
Fremont, MI　49412　(231) 924-5350
Contact: Elizabeth Cherin, C.E.O.
FAX: (231) 924-5391; E-mail: info@tfacf.org;
Additional FAX: (231) 924-7637; Additional E-mails: echerin@tfacf.org and gzerlaut@tfacf.org;
URL: http://www.tfacf.org

Incorporated in 1951 in MI.
Grantmaker type: Community foundation.
Financial data (yr. ended 12/31/05): Assets, $194,738,922 (M); gifts received, $3,086,579; expenditures, $11,557,038; total giving, $9,386,427; giving activities include $9,386,427 for 825 grants (high: $1,100,000; low: $500), and $80,000 for 1 loan/program-related investment.
Purpose and activities: The foundation has established six broad funding categories: 1) Newaygo County Community Services: to sustain operations of this autonomous agency established for the delivery of general social welfare services and educational programs; 2) Community Development: to strengthen the municipal activities of villages, cities, governmental units, and other related organizations; 3) Education: to augment and promote the special projects of schools, libraries, and other organizations for instruction and training, and for scholarships to promote higher education and learning in specialized programs; 4) Arts and Culture: to support activities that promote appreciation of and participation in artistic expression such as music, theater, dance, sculpture, and painting; 5) Human Services: to foster the delivery of services and the operation of programs to help meet basic human needs and to support the provision of rehabilitative services; and 6) Health Care: made to health care providers and other related organizations for activities designed to promote optimal well-being and to provide health-related education. The foundation is also interested in supporting programs that address the particular needs of youth and older (aged) adults.
Fields of interest: Visual arts; Performing arts; Arts; Libraries/library science; Education; Environment; Medical care, rehabilitation; Health care; Substance abuse, services; Health organizations, association; Recreation; Children/youth, services; Family services; Aging, centers/services; Human services; Community development; Government/public administration; Youth; Aging; Economically disadvantaged.
Type of support: General/operating support; Continuing support; Management development/capacity building; Capital campaigns; Building/renovation; Equipment; Endowments; Emergency funds; Program development; Conferences/seminars; Seed money; Curriculum development; Scholarship funds; Technical assistance; Consulting services; Program evaluation; Program-related investments/loans; Employee matching gifts; Scholarships—to individuals; Matching/challenge support.
Limitations: Giving primarily in Newaygo County, MI. No support for religious organizations for specific religions. No grants to individuals (except for scholarships), or for contingencies, reserves, services which are considered general government or school obligations, or deficit financing.
Publications: Application guidelines; Annual report; Financial statement; Grants list; Informational brochure; Newsletter.
Application information: Visit foundation Web site for application Cover Sheet and guidelines. Application form required.
　Initial approach: Letter or telephone to arrange interview
　Copies of proposal: 1
　Deadline(s): Feb. 15, May 15, and Sept. 15 for grants; Mar. 15 for scholarships
　Board meeting date(s): Bimonthly
　Final notification: Within 3 months
Officers and Trustees:* Mary Schafer,* Chair.; Robert Johnson,* Vice-Chair.; Elizabeth Cherin, C.E.O. and Pres.; Gregory Zerlaut, C.O.O. and C.F.O.; Jack Hendon,* Treas.; Carl Dekuiper; Peggy Gunnell; Duane Jones; Hendrick Jones; Sheryl Meyer; Lynne Robinson; Terry Sharp; Robert Wood; Kirk Wyers; Robert Zeldenrust.
Number of staff: 8 full-time professional; 7 full-time support.
EIN: 381443367
Selected grants: The following grants were reported in 2003.
$1,000,586 to Newaygo County Community Services, Fremont, MI. 3 grants: $143,529 (For matching grant for new building), $732,057 (For general operating support and program support), $125,000 (For matching grant for general operating support and program support).
$463,547 to Newaygo County General Hospital Association, Newaygo, MI. For matching grant for medical equipment for expansion and renovation project.
$356,532 to Newaygo Public Schools, Newaygo, MI. 2 grants: $206,532 (For Newaygo County Even Start Family Literacy program), $150,000 (For Newaygo County Parents as Teachers program).
$250,000 to Newaygo County Commission on Aging, White Cloud, MI. For senior programs and services.
$180,000 to Arts Center for Newaygo County, Fremont, MI. For Dogwood Center for the Performing Arts general operating support.
$159,450 to Fremont, City of, Fremont, MI. For non-motorized recreation and nature path.
$128,758 to Grant Public Schools, Grant, MI. For After-School Academic Enrichment program.

2351
Grand Haven Area Community Foundation, Inc.

1 S. Harbor Dr.
Grand Haven, MI　49417　(616) 842-6378
Contact: Ann Irish Tabor, Pres.; For grants: Carol Bedient, Dir., Grants and Progs.
FAX: (616) 842-9518; E-mail: info@ghacf.org; Grant application E-mail: cbedient@ghacf.org;
URL: http://www.ghacf.org

Incorporated in 1971 in MI.
Grantmaker type: Community foundation.
Financial data (yr. ended 3/31/04): Assets, $37,641,101 (M); gifts received, $1,928,451; expenditures, $2,763,806; total giving, $2,385,118; giving activities include $2,385,118 for grants.
Purpose and activities: Primary areas of interest include: education (including technical training, mathematics, and business and accounting education), the environment, health, crime prevention, and community collaboration.

Scholarship awards are limited to students of Grand Haven, Spring Lake, Holland Christian, Catholic Central, West Michigan Christian, West Ottawa, and Fruitport high schools, in MI.

Fields of interest: Vocational education, post-secondary; Business school/education; Environment; Health care; Crime/law enforcement; Community development; Mathematics.

Type of support: Land acquisition; Capital campaigns; Equipment; Program development; Seed money; Scholarship funds; Scholarships—to individuals; Matching/challenge support.

Limitations: Giving primarily in the MI Tri-Cities area. No support for profit-making organizations or religious programs that serve, or appear to serve, specific religious denominations. No grants to individuals (except for scholarships), or for annual campaigns, emergency or deficit financing, operating costs or ongoing operating support, fundraising events, or endowments.

Publications: Application guidelines; Annual report (including application guidelines); Financial statement; Informational brochure (including application guidelines); Newsletter; Program policy statement.

Application information: Visit foundation Web site for full application form and guidelines. Application form required.

  Initial approach: Submit application form and attachments
  Copies of proposal: 12
  Deadline(s): Jan. 5, Apr. 2, and Sept. 29
  Board meeting date(s): Distribution committee meets quarterly: Jan., Apr., July, and Oct.; board meetings are usually 2 weeks following the distribution committee meeting
  Final notification: 1 week after board meeting

Officers and Trustees:* Jim MacLachlan,* Chair.; Don Anderson,* Vice-Chair.; Ann Irish Tabor, Pres.; Holly Johnson,* Secy.; Dennis Dornbush,* Treas.; Jeffrey Beswick; Melinda Brink; Mary Eagin; Mike McKeough; Darell Moreland; Shirley Poulton; L.J. Verplank.

Number of staff: 4 full-time professional.

EIN: 237108776

2352
Grand Rapids Community Foundation
(formerly The Grand Rapids Foundation)
161 Ottawa Ave. N.W., Ste. 209-C
Grand Rapids, MI   49503-2757   (616) 454-1751
Contact: Diana R. Sieger, Pres.; For grant inquiries: Ann Puckett, Admin. Asst.
FAX: (616) 454-6455;
E-mail: grfound@grfoundation.org; Grant inquiry tel.: (616) 454-1751, ext. 123, and E-mail: apuckett@grfoundation.org; URL: http://www.grfoundation.org

Established in 1922 in MI by resolution and declaration of trust; Incorporated 1989.

Grantmaker type: Community foundation.

Financial data (yr. ended 6/30/05): Assets, $194,189,277 (M); gifts received, $8,515,770; expenditures, $10,829,473; total giving, $7,824,644; giving activities include $7,824,644 for grants.

Purpose and activities: The foundation seeks to provide support for projects or causes designed to benefit the people and the quality of life in Grand Rapids, MI, and its surrounding communities through grants for social needs, youth agencies, cultural programs, health, recreation, neighborhood

development, the environment, and education, including scholarships for Kent County residents to attend selected colleges. Grant decisions are made according to a project's fit with the following guiding principles: Accountability, Collaboration, Diversity, Justice, Prevention, Social Capital and Systems Approach.

Fields of interest: Museums; Performing arts; Performing arts, theater; Humanities; Arts; Higher education; Education, reading; Education; Environment; Health organizations, association; AIDS; Alcoholism; Employment; Nutrition; Housing/shelter, development; Recreation; Youth development, services; Children/youth, services; Family services; Aging, centers/services; Women, centers/services; Minorities/immigrants, centers/services; Human services; Civil rights, immigrants; Civil rights, minorities; Civil rights, disabled; Civil rights, women; Civil rights, aging; Civil rights, gays/lesbians; Civil rights, race/intergroup relations; Civil liberties, reproductive rights; Community development, neighborhood development; Community development; Voluntarism promotion; Leadership development; Aging; Disabilities, people with; Minorities; Asians/Pacific Islanders; African Americans/Blacks; Native Americans/American Indians; Women; LGBTQ; Immigrants/refugees; Economically disadvantaged; Homeless.

Type of support: Capital campaigns; Building/renovation; Land acquisition; Program development; Seed money; Scholarship funds; Technical assistance; Program-related investments/loans; Employee matching gifts; Employee-related scholarships; Scholarships—to individuals; Matching/challenge support.

Limitations: Giving limited to Kent County, MI. No support for religious programs, hospitals, child care centers, or nursing homes/retirement facilities. No grants to individuals (except for scholarships), or for continued operating support, annual campaigns, travel expenses, medical or scholarly research, deficit financing, endowment funds, computers, vehicles, films, videos, or conferences; no student loans; no venture capital for competitive profit-making activities.

Publications: Application guidelines; Annual report; Informational brochure; Newsletter.

Application information: Visit foundation Web site for letter of inquiry application, guidelines, and specific geographic fund deadlines. Faxed or e-mailed letters of inquiry are not accepted. The foundation will request a full proposal based on letter of inquiry. Application form required.

  Initial approach: Submit online letter of inquiry (reviewed every 2 weeks)
  Copies of proposal: 9
  Deadline(s): Jan. 1 and Apr. 1
  Board meeting date(s): 6 times a year (bimonthly)
  Final notification: Within 30 days for letter of inquiry; June 16 for scholarships

Officers and Trustees:* Margaret Sellers-Walker,* Chair.; Marilyn A. Lankfer,* Vice-Chair.; Diana R. Sieger, Pres.; Lynne Black, V.P., Finance and Admin.; Roberta F. King, V.P., Public Rels. and Mktg.; Marcia Rapp, V.P., Progs.; Marilyn Zack, V.P., Devel.; Samuel M. Cummings; Paul Doyle; Cecile C. Fehsenfeld; Richard P. Haslinger; Joseph A. Medcalf; Mark Meijer; Bonnie K. Miller; Juan R. Olivarez; Thomas L. Stevens; Michelle Van Dyke.

Number of staff: 11 full-time professional; 1 part-time professional; 8 full-time support.

EIN: 382877959

Selected grants: The following grants were reported in 2005.

$1,000,000 to Grand Rapids Art Museum, Grand Rapids, MI.

$200,000 to Community Media Center, Grand Rapids, MI. To acquire Wealthy Theatre properties, equip with technology, and establish programs.

$183,000 to Grand Valley State University, Grand Rapids, MI. To operate and expand Community Research Institute capacity.

$150,000 to Dwelling Place of Grand Rapids, Grand Rapids, MI. To renovate buildings which currently comprise Dwelling Place Inn and construct new addition to increase both size of residential units and to increase number of units.

$150,000 to YMCA of Greater Grand Rapids, Grand Rapids, MI.

$145,000 to Lighthouse Communities, Grand Rapids, MI. For Healthy Neighborhoods model of neighborhood revitalization in central Grand Rapids neighborhoods.

$124,500 to Family Outreach Center, Grand Rapids, MI. To divert traditional foster care placements, by placing children at-risk of abuse and neglect with relatives.

$81,827 to Lowell Area Schools, Lowell, MI. To assure all children have opportunity to begin school healthy and ready to learn.

$75,000 to Alano Club of Kent County, Grand Rapids, MI. To renovate and expand current facility to meet needs of community.

$75,000 to Kent County Literacy Council, Grand Rapids, MI. To expand adult tutoring program and development and implementation of family literacy program.

2353
Grand Traverse Regional Community Foundation
250 E. Front St., Ste. 310
Traverse City, MI   49684   (231) 935-4066
Contact: Jeanne Snow, Exec. Dir.
FAX: (231) 941-0021; E-mail: info@gtrcf.org;
URL: http://www.gtrcf.org

Established in 1992 in MI.

Grantmaker type: Community foundation.

Financial data (yr. ended 12/31/05): Assets, $24,244,902 (M); gifts received, $3,087,392; expenditures, $1,868,231; total giving, $1,472,738; giving activities include $1,472,738 for grants.

Purpose and activities: The foundation seeks to enhance the quality of life and facilitate philanthropy in Antrim, Benzie, Grand Traverse, Kalkaska, and Leelanau counties, MI.

Fields of interest: Arts; Education; Environment; Community development; Youth.

Type of support: Building/renovation; Equipment; Endowments; Program development; Seed money; Curriculum development; Scholarship funds; Technical assistance; Scholarships—to individuals; Matching/challenge support.

Limitations: Giving limited to the counties of Antrim, Benzie, Grand Traverse, Kalkaska, and Leelanau, MI. No grants for routine training or professional conferences, annual events, budget shortfalls, or payroll or other general operating expenses.

Publications: Annual report; Informational brochure; Newsletter.

Application information: Visit foundation Web site for application form and guidelines. Applications can not be submitted without first setting an appointment with the foundation's Executive

Director to discuss program in depth. Application form required.
- *Initial approach:* Letter or telephone
- *Copies of proposal:* 1
- *Deadline(s):* Dec. 31 for MOD fund grants
- *Board meeting date(s):* Quarterly

Officers and Directors:* Sydney McManus,* Chair.; Alan Olson,* Treas.; Jeanne Snow, Exec. Dir.; Truman Bicum; Gus Bishop; Lawrence Burks; Jerry Cannon; Bud Cline; Gail Dall'Olmo; Preston Dilts, Jr.; Gary Drew; Charlie Gilbert; John Hoagland; Stan Holzhauer; Dick Kennedy; Brenda Miller; Larry Miller; Jim Modrall; Joseph Muha; Clarine Olson; Peter Phinny; Al Potts; Bob Robbins; Louis H. Sanford; Donna Sowers; Toby Tull; Rob Turney; Suzanne Voltz; John Yeager.

Number of staff: 4 full-time professional; 1 part-time support.

EIN: 383056434

2354
Gratiot County Community Foundation
1131 E. Center St.
P.O. Box 310
Ithaca, MI 48847-0310 (989) 875-4222
Contact: Tina M. Travis, Exec. Dir.
FAX: (989) 875-2858; E-mail: gccf@edzone.net;
Additional tel.: (989) 875-5101, ext. 248

Incorporated in 1992 in MI; operations began in late 1994.

Grantmaker type: Community foundation.

Financial data (yr. ended 9/30/05): Assets, $4,480,738 (M); gifts received, $393,524; expenditures, $156,957; total giving, $78,449; giving activities include $78,449 for grants.

Purpose and activities: The foundation seeks to enhance the lives of Gratiot County citizens by identifying and addressing needs within the county, by building permanent endowments, and distributing grants in the fields of the arts, education, environment, health, youth development, human services and community development.

Fields of interest: Arts; Education; Environment; Health care; Youth development; Human services; Community development.

Type of support: Program development; Seed money; Internship funds; Research; Scholarships—to individuals.

Limitations: Giving limited to Gratiot County, MI.

Publications: Application guidelines; Annual report; Informational brochure; Newsletter.

Application information: Application form required.
- *Initial approach:* Letter or telephone
- *Copies of proposal:* 10
- *Deadline(s):* Mar. 1 and Sept. 1
- *Board meeting date(s):* 1st Tues. of each month
- *Final notification:* Apr. and Oct.

Officers and Directors:* Pam Munderloh,* Pres.; James Wheeler,* V.P. and Chair., Finance; Sheila Rummer,* Secy.; Patrick Duffy,* Treas. and Chair., Distribution; Marlene Miller,* Chair., Special Events; Linda Williams,* Chair., Devel.; Tina M. Travis, Exec. Dir.; Ginna Holmes,* YAC Advisor; Richard Abbott; Steve Bakker; Kevin Collison; Robert Crist; Penny Daniels; Sharon Fenton; Charles Fortino; Cheryl Grueneberg; Roger Keck; Barbara McKenzie; Josh Merchant; Dr. James Seals; Scott Showers; Brad Vibber; Craig Zeese.

Number of staff: 2 full-time professional.

EIN: 383087756

2355
Greenville Area Community Foundation
(formerly Greenville Area Foundation)
101 N. Lafayette St.
Greenville, MI 48838-1853 (616) 754-2640
Contact: Alison Barberi, C.E.O.
FAX: (616) 754-3174; E-mail: alison@gacfmi.org;
URL: http://www.gacfmi.org

Established in 1989 in MI.

Grantmaker type: Community foundation.

Financial data (yr. ended 12/31/05): Assets, $11,579,845 (M); gifts received, $965,175; expenditures, $595,874; total giving, $379,573; giving activities include $379,573 for grants.

Purpose and activities: The foundation seeks to enhance the quality of life in the Greenville area. Giving for education, health, the arts, the environment, recreation, youth services, and community development.

Fields of interest: Arts; Adult education—literacy, basic skills & GED; Education; Environment; Health care; Recreation; Children/youth, services; Community development; Government/public administration.

Type of support: Building/renovation; Capital campaigns; Equipment; Program development; Publication; Seed money; Scholarship funds; Matching/challenge support.

Limitations: Giving limited to Montcalm County, MI. No support for sectarian religious programs. No grants for general operating support, annual fundraising, or endowments (outside the foundation).

Publications: Application guidelines; Annual report; Financial statement; Grants list; Informational brochure; Informational brochure (including application guidelines); Newsletter.

Application information: Visit foundation Web site for grant information. Application forms are available at the foundation's office. Applicants are encouraged to call and set-up a visit to discuss proposal. Application form required.
- *Initial approach:* Telephone
- *Copies of proposal:* 16
- *Deadline(s):* Late summer; Educational request, early spring
- *Board meeting date(s):* Jan., Apr., June, Sept., Oct., and Nov.
- *Final notification:* Dec. 1

Officers and Directors:* Peter Blinkilde,* Chair.; Charlotte Lothian,* Vice-Chair.; Alison Barberi, C.E.O. and Pres.; Christine Kohn,* Secy.-Treas.; Byron Cook,* Chair. Emeritus; Lemont Renterghem,* Chair. Emeritus; Jon Aylsworth; Bill Braman; Mike Devereaux; Dan Eagles; Richard Ellafrits; Jae Evans; Jelane Hamper; Eric Januzelli; John O'Donald, D.D.S.

Number of staff: 1 full-time professional; 2 part-time professional.

EIN: 382899657

2356
Hillsdale County Community Foundation
2 S. Howell St.
P.O. Box 276
Hillsdale, MI 49242-0276 (517) 439-5101
Contact: Sharon E. Bisher, Exec. Dir.
FAX: (517) 439-5109; E-mail: info@abouthccf.org;
URL: http://www.abouthccf.org

Established in 1991 in MI.

Grantmaker type: Community foundation.

Financial data (yr. ended 9/30/04): Assets, $8,103,365 (M); gifts received, $574,017; expenditures, $463,436; total giving, $217,080; giving activities include $217,080 for 21 grants, and $23,267 for 1 foundation-administered program.

Purpose and activities: The foundation gives to support community organizations and services in Hillsdale County, MI. The foundation also administers a scholarship program for area students.

Fields of interest: Visual arts; Performing arts; Performing arts, theater; Arts; Education, association; Education, early childhood education; Child development, education; Elementary school/education; Higher education; Libraries/library science; Education; Environment, natural resources; Environment; Animal welfare; Hospitals (general); Health care; Health organizations, association; Crime/violence prevention, youth; Crime/law enforcement; Employment; Food services; Recreation; Youth development, services; Children/youth, services; Child development, services; Family services; Residential/custodial care, hospices; Aging, centers/services; Human services; Community development; Voluntarism promotion; Biological sciences; Economics; Leadership development; Public affairs; Aging; Economically disadvantaged.

Type of support: Conferences/seminars; Publication; Seed money; Scholarship funds; In-kind gifts; Matching/challenge support.

Limitations: Giving limited to Hillsdale County, MI. No support for religious or sectarian purposes. No grants to individuals (except for scholarships), or for new building campaigns, routine maintenance, remodeling, or capital campaigns; no loans.

Publications: Application guidelines; Annual report; Financial statement; Informational brochure (including application guidelines); Newsletter.

Application information: Visit foundation Web site for application form and guidelines. Application form required.
- *Initial approach:* Telephone or in person
- *Copies of proposal:* 1
- *Deadline(s):* May 1 and Nov. 1 for general grants; Mar. 1, July 1, and Nov. 1 for Kellogg YOUTH grants; and Apr. 1 for scholarships
- *Board meeting date(s):* 1st Tues. of the month
- *Final notification:* Within 2 months

Officers and Trustees:* Muriel Alexandrowski,* Pres.; Michael Nye,* V.P.; Barry Hill,* Secy.; Eric Leutheuser,* Treas.; Sharon Bisher, Exec. Dir.; Penny Arnn; Alyssa Bernklau; Michelle Bianchi; Brett Boyd; Diane Clow; Robert Henthorne; Harold March; James B. Parker; David Pope; Bill Smith; Stanley Smith; Bambi Somerlott; Mollie Wolf.

Number of staff: 1 full-time professional; 2 part-time professional; 1 part-time support.

EIN: 383001297

2357
Huron County Community Foundation
1160 S. Van Dyke Rd.
Bad Axe, MI 48413-9615 (989) 269-2850

Established in 1996 in MI.

Grantmaker type: Community foundation.

Financial data (yr. ended 12/31/04): Assets, $1,146,580 (M); gifts received, $83,876; expenditures, $136,032; total giving, $47,568; giving activities include $32,568 for 26 grants (high: $5,000; low: $200), and $14,672 for 24 grants to individuals (high: $1,222; low: $250).

Purpose and activities: Grant awards to charitable organizations in Huron County, MI, to improve the community through arts and culture, education, community development, health and human services, and youth services.
Fields of interest: Arts; Education; Health care; Recreation; Youth development, centers/clubs; Children/youth, services; Human services; Community development.
Limitations: Giving limited to Huron County, MI.
Application information:
  Initial approach: Letter or telephone
  Deadline(s): None
Officer and Trustees: * Debbie Oglenski,* Exec. Dir.; Mary Babcock; Christopher Bachman; David Batzer; Thomas Dibble; Steve Harmon; Joyce Kiehl; Marvin Kociba; Tom Kreh; Karen Mayes; William Mayes; Lowell McDonald; John Moore; Carl Osentoski; Martha Thuemmel.
EIN: 383160009

2358
Ionia County Community Foundation
c/o Grand Rapids Community Foundation
161 Ottawa Ave., N.W., Ste. 209-C
Grand Rapids, MI 49503 (616) 527-5820
Contact: Brian Talbot, Grant Comm. Chair.
Application address for general grants: 230 W. Main St., Ionia, MI 48846;
E-mail: brtalbot@grfoundation.org; URL: http://www.grfoundation.org/ionia/

Established in 1995 in MI as a regional affiliate of Grand Rapids Community Foundation.
Grantmaker type: Community foundation.
Purpose and activities: The foundation gives priority to projects that address the areas of art and culture, community development, education, environment, health, or social needs.
Fields of interest: Arts; Education; Environment; Health care; Youth development; Human services; Community development; Aging.
Type of support: Capital campaigns; Building/renovation; Equipment.
Limitations: Giving limited for the benefit of Ionia County, MI. No support for organizations lacking 501(c)(3) status, or for religious organizations for religious purposes. No grants to individuals, or for annual fundraising drives, ongoing operating expenses of established institutions, endowments or debt reduction, conferences, medical research, venture capital for competitive profit-making activities, sabbatical leaves, scholarly research, travel, tours or trips, or for films, videos or television projects.
Application information: See foundation Web site for complete guidelines and requirements. The foundation uses CMF Common Grant Application Form. Application form required.
  Copies of proposal: 7
  Deadline(s): Dec. 30
  Final notification: Mar. 31

2359
Iosco County Community Foundation
c/o Community Foundation for Northeast Michigan
P.O. Box 495
Alpena, MI 49707 (877) 354-6881
Contact: Christine Hitch
FAX: (989) 356-3319; E-mail: chitch@cfnem.org;
URL: http://www.iccf-online.org/

Established in 2000 in MI as an affiliate of the Community Foundation for Northeast Michigan.
Grantmaker type: Community foundation.
Purpose and activities: The foundation seeks to serve Iosco County and to preserve the charitable goals of a wide range of donors now and for generations to come by supporting 501(c)(3) organizations, churches for non-religious purposes, and government agencies.
Fields of interest: Community development.
Type of support: Technical assistance; Seed money; Scholarships—to individuals; Publication; Program development; Equipment; Conferences/seminars; Building/renovation.
Limitations: Giving limited to Iosco County, MI. No grants to individuals (except for scholarships), or for routine operating needs or budget deficits.
Publications: Application guidelines; Annual report; Financial statement; Grants list; Informational brochure; Newsletter.
Application information: See foundation Web site for Common Grant Application Form and requirements. Application form required.
  Deadline(s): Contact foundation for current deadline
  Final notification: Within 6 weeks of deadline dates
Officers and Trustees: * Susan Elliott,* Chair.; Carl Huebner,* Vice-Chair.; David Wentworth,* Treas.; John Alexander; Joann Hintz; Clarissa Hoffman; Ed Nagy; Jane Peters.

2360
Greater Ishpeming Area Community Fund
205 S. Main
Ishpeming, MI 49849-2018 (906) 485-6311
Contact: Jim Steward, Chair.
FAX: (906) 485-1929; E-mail: jsteward@stewardsheridan.com; URL: http://www.mqt-cf.org/GIACF.htm

Established in 1994 in MI with matching funds from the Kellogg Foundation as an affiliate of the Marquette Community Foundation.
Grantmaker type: Community foundation.
Fields of interest: Education; Youth development; Community development.
Limitations: Giving limited to western Marquette County, MI, including the City of Ishpeming, Ishpeming Township, Ely Township, Tilden Township, Champion, Michigamme and Republic.
Officers and Board Members: * Jim Steward,* Chair.; Terri Smith,* Vice-Chair.; Glenn Adams; Dennis Bell; Patrizia Benstrom; Shannon Edmark; James T. Prophet.

2361
The Jackson County Community Foundation
(formerly The Jackson Community Foundation)
1 Jackson Sq., Ste. 110A
Jackson, MI 49201-1406 (517) 787-1321
Contact: Shelly Saines, C.E.O.; For grants: Jan Maino, V.P., Progs.
FAX: (517) 787-4333; E-mail: info@jacksoncf.org;
Additional E-mail: ssaines@jacksoncf.org;
URL: http://www.jacksoncf.org

Incorporated in 1948 in MI.
Grantmaker type: Community foundation.

Financial data (yr. ended 12/31/05): Assets, $18,768,103 (M); gifts received, $1,459,057; expenditures, $1,470,533; total giving, $913,909; giving activities include $777,909 for grants, and $136,000 for grants to individuals.
Purpose and activities: The foundation seeks to improve the quality of life for the residents of Jackson County, MI.
Fields of interest: Humanities; Historic preservation/historical societies; Arts; Adult education—literacy, basic skills & GED; Education, reading; Education; Environment; Health care; Substance abuse, services; Recreation; Children/youth, services; Human services; Economic development; Community development.
Type of support: Scholarships—to individuals; Capital campaigns; Building/renovation; Equipment; Land acquisition; Program development; Seed money; Technical assistance; Consulting services; Program evaluation; Program-related investments/loans; Matching/challenge support.
Limitations: Giving limited to Jackson County, MI. No support for religious purposes. No grants to individuals (except for scholarships), or for endowment funds, debt retirement, fellowships, publications, or conferences.
Publications: Application guidelines; Annual report (including application guidelines); Newsletter.
Application information: Visit foundation Web site for application forms, guidelines, and specific deadlines. Grants over $5,000 require an approval based on letter of intent prior to full application submission. Application form required.
  Initial approach: Submit Community Partner grant application for grants less than $5,000; Letter of Intent for grants over $5,000
  Copies of proposal: 15
  Deadline(s): Varies
  Board meeting date(s): Jan., Mar., May, July, Sept., and Nov.
  Final notification: Within 14 days for Letter of Intent; 10 days after board meeting for grant determination
Officers and Trustees: * James S. Grace,* Chair.; Kevin T. Lavery, M.D.*, Incoming Chair.; Shelly Saines, C.E.O. and Pres.; Jan Maino, V.P., Progs.; Karen A. Brant; Anne E. Campau; Deborah Ann Craft; Carrie Glick; Dennis A. Hill; Miles E. Jones; Lt. Aaron B. Kantor; Carlene Walz Lefere, M.D.; Dennis E. Means, M.D.; R. Dale Moretz; Katherine Patrick; Dr. Daniel J. Phelan; John G. Russell; Ric Walton.
Number of staff: 4 full-time professional; 1 part-time professional.
EIN: 386070739

2362
Kalamazoo Community Foundation
(formerly Kalamazoo Foundation)
151 S. Rose St., Ste. 332
Kalamazoo, MI 49007-4775 (269) 381-4416
Contact: David D. Gardiner, V.P., Community Investment
FAX: (269) 381-3146; E-mail: info@kalfound.org;
Additional E-mails: dgardiner@kalfound.org and sspringgate@kalfound.org; URL: http://www.kalfound.org

Established in 1925; incorporated in 1930 in MI.
Grantmaker type: Community foundation.
Financial data (yr. ended 12/31/05): Assets, $265,355,347 (M); gifts received, $9,842,141; expenditures, $17,903,599; total giving,

$14,156,832; giving activities include $14,156,832 for 84+ grants.
Purpose and activities: The foundation is dedicated to enhancing the spirit of the community and quality of life in the greater Kalamazoo area through its stewardship of permanently endowed funds. Primary areas of giving include: 1) economic development; 2) early childhood learning and school readiness; 3) community engagement and youth development; and 4) individuals and families. Grants largely for capital purposes and innovative programs.
Fields of interest: Education; Environment; Health care; Housing/shelter, development; Youth development; Family services; Economic development; Community development.
Type of support: General/operating support; Capital campaigns; Building/renovation; Equipment; Emergency funds; Program development; Seed money; Scholarship funds; Technical assistance; Program-related investments/loans; Employee matching gifts; Scholarships—to individuals; Matching/challenge support.
Limitations: Giving generally limited to Kalamazoo County, MI. No grants to individuals (except for scholarships), or for endowment funds.
Publications: Application guidelines; Annual report; Financial statement; Informational brochure; Informational brochure (including application guidelines); Newsletter; Quarterly report.
Application information: Visit foundation Web site for application information. Application form required.
Initial approach: Telephone
Copies of proposal: 1
Deadline(s): Jan. and July for individuals and families, and economic development; Apr. and Oct. for early childhood learning and school readiness, and community engagement and youth development
Board meeting date(s): Jan., Mar., June. Sept., Oct., Nov., and Dec.
Final notification: 10 weeks
Officers and Distribution Committee:* Jeffrey L. DeNooyer,* Chair.; Marilyn J. Schlack,* Vice-Chair.; John E. "Jack" Hopkins, C.E.O., Pres. and Secy.-Treas.; Wesley Freeland, V.P., Donor Rels.; David D. Gardiner, V.P., Community Investment; Gloria Z. Royal, V.P., Mktg. Comms.; Susan Springgate, V.P., Finance and Admin.; Karen Racette, Cont.; J. Louis Felton; Barbara L. James; Judith L. Maze; Ronda E. Stryker; Donald J. Vander Kooy.
Custodian Bank: National City Bank.
Number of staff: 16 full-time professional; 3 part-time professional; 5 full-time support; 2 part-time support.
EIN: 383333202
Selected grants: The following grants were reported in 2005.
$200,000 to Southwest Michigan First Corporation, Kalamazoo, MI. For operational support.
$153,493 to Goodwill Industries of Southwestern Michigan, Kalamazoo, MI. For Literacy Together, intensive integration of literacy activities to promote school readiness and family literacy.
$150,000 to Family Health Center, Kalamazoo, MI. For capital campaign to construct larger, state-of-the-art medical facility to increase access to health care for uninsured and underinsured Kalamazoo area residents.
$150,000 to United Way, Greater Kalamazoo, Emergency Financial Assistance Network, Kalamazoo, MI. To ease individuals' or families'

immediate emergency needs for housing, prescriptions, and utilities.
$100,000 to Big Brothers/Big Sisters of Greater Kalamazoo, Kalamazoo, MI. To assist with renovation of A Community of Caring, new Big Brothers Big Sisters Mentoring Center, with enough space to double number of children served.
$90,000 to Kalamazoo Area Housing Corporation, Kalamazoo, MI. To construct single-family homes for low- to moderate-income families in Rosewood Development.
$80,000 to Gull Lake Community Schools, Richland, MI. To continue Making Connections program, helping parents work with their children to ensure school readiness.
$40,000 to Edison Neighborhood Association, Kalamazoo, MI. To continue Edison Weed and Seed program after federal funding ends.
$35,000 to Kalamazoo Junior Girls, Kalamazoo, MI. To build organizational capacity.
$29,290 to Covenant Senior Day Program, Portage, MI. For kitchen and bathroom renovations.

2363
Keweenaw Community Foundation
326 Sheldon Ave., Upper Level
P.O. Box 101
Houghton, MI 49931-2146 (906) 482-9673
Contact: Barbara Rose, Exec. Dir.
FAX: (906) 482-9679;
E-mail: kcf@charterinternet.com; URL: http://www.keweenaw-community-foundation.org
Alternate URL: http://www.k-c-f.org

Established in 1994 in MI.
Grantmaker type: Community foundation.
Financial data (yr. ended 3/31/05): Assets, $2,463,492 (M); gifts received, $83,729; expenditures, $96,265; total giving, $28,086; giving activities include $28,086 for 5+ grants (high: $4,000; low: $100).
Purpose and activities: The foundation is committed to serving the residents of Houghton and Keweenaw counties, MI, by developing a permanent endowment to provide stable local funding sources for grants to vital local programs; by increasing charitable giving to a broad range of non-profit organizations; by providing a flexible philanthropic vehicle capable of adapting to changing community needs; and by serving as a catalyst to nurture community leadership.
Fields of interest: Arts; Education; Environment; Health care; Athletics/sports, winter sports; Human services; Community development.
Type of support: Annual campaigns; Endowments; Program development; Scholarship funds; In-kind gifts; Matching/challenge support.
Limitations: Giving primarily in Houghton and Keweenaw counties, MI. No grants to individuals, or for membership drives, fundraising events, multi-year funding, construction projects, or normal operating expenses.
Publications: Annual report; Informational brochure; Occasional report.
Application information: Visit foundation Web site for application form and guidelines. Proposals submitted by fax not accepted. Application form required.
Initial approach: Telephone
Copies of proposal: 1
Deadline(s): Varies

Board meeting date(s): 3rd Wed., bimonthly beginning in Jan.
Final notification: Varies
Officers and Trustees:* James Bogan,* Chair.; John Sullivan,* Vice-Chair.; Paul Ollila,* Secy.; Karen Van Dyke, Corp. Secy.; Joseph Daavettila,* Corp. Treas.; Barbara Rose, Exec. Dir.; Joseph Evans; Paul Freshwater; Ronald P. Helman; Jim Lahti; William W. Predebon; Doug Sherk; Richard E. Taylor; Joel Tuoriniemi; Steve Zutter.
Number of staff: 2 part-time professional; 2 part-time support.
EIN: 383223079

2364
Lake County Community Foundation
P.O. Box 995
Baldwin, MI 49304 (231) 745-2732
Contact: Connie Theunick-Perley, Pres.
E-mail: lake@msue.msu.edu; URL: http://www.tfaf.org/foundpart/lake.html

Established in 1992 in MI as an affiliate of Fremont Area Community Foundation.
Grantmaker type: Community foundation.
Purpose and activities: Grants for projects that have a lasting effect on the Lake County community and fulfill the purpose of the foundation to enhance the quality of life for Lake County citizens and visitors.
Type of support: Scholarship funds; Program development; General/operating support; Continuing support; Building/renovation.
Limitations: Giving limited to the Lake County, MI, area.
Publications: Application guidelines; Annual report; Informational brochure; Newsletter.
Application information: Application form required.
Initial approach: Telephone
Copies of proposal: 1
Deadline(s): Contact foundation for current deadline dates
Final notification: 90 days
Officers and Trustees:* Connie Theunick-Perley,* Pres.; Bob Fisher,* Secy.; Mike Verdun,* Treas.; Jim Clark; Larry Doorn; Vedra Grant; Randy Howes; Ellen Kerans; Jane Larson; Ken Moore; Dave Randall; Cinda Rock.
Number of staff: None.

2365
Lapeer County Community Foundation
(formerly Lapeer County Community Fund)
220 W. Nepessing St., Ste. 202
Lapeer, MI 48446 (810) 664-0691
Contact: Janet Manning, Exec. Dir.
FAX: (810) 664-0691;
E-mail: lccf@charterinternet.com; URL: http://www.lapeercountycommunityfoundation.org/

Established in 1996 in MI as an affiliate of the Community Foundation of Greater Flint; became an independent community foundation in 2005.
Grantmaker type: Community foundation.
Financial data (yr. ended 12/31/05): Assets, $6,487,314 (M); gifts received, $118,913; expenditures, $176,989; total giving, $59,194; giving activities include $9,894 for grants, and $49,300 for grants to individuals.
Purpose and activities: The Lapeer County Community Foundation builds and manages permanent endowment funds from a wide variety of

donors to provide grants that enhance the quality of life in Lapeer County , now and for future generations. Grants from unrestricted funds are made in the areas of education, arts and culture, the environment, health care, human services, recreation and other project topics.

Fields of interest: Arts; Education; Environment; Health care; Recreation; Human services.

Type of support: Annual campaigns; Endowments; Scholarship funds; In-kind gifts; Matching/challenge support.

Limitations: Giving limited to Lapeer County, MI. No support for religious or sectarian purposes, or for legislative or political purposes. No grants to individuals (except for scholarships), or for re-granting purposes, routine maintenance, or administrative costs for maintaining the operation of an organization.

Publications: Application guidelines; Annual report; Grants list; Informational brochure; Newsletter; Program policy statement.

Application information: The foundation encourages contacting the executive director to discuss the proposal prior to submiting an application. Full application guidelines and requirements are available at foundation Web site, including downloadable application forms. Application form required.

   Initial approach: Letter, telephone, office visit, or online
   Copies of proposal: 4
   Deadline(s): None
   Board meeting date(s): 2nd Wed. of each month
   Final notification: 8 weeks

Officers and Trustees: Nick O. Holowka,* Chair.; Don H. Poniatowski,* Vice-Chair.; Janet L. Watz,* Secy.; Kim R. Brown, C.P.A.*, Treas.; Janet Manning, Exec. Dir.; Thomas K. Butterfield; Curt Carter; Ralph Deshetsky; Pamela Duke; Della Hammond; Patricia Lamoreaux; Kathryn L. Lawter; Thomas Neuhard; Hon. Clayton Preisel.

Number of staff: 1 part-time professional.

EIN: 201271563

2366
Leelanau Township Community Foundation, Inc.

104 Wing St.
P.O. Box 818
Northport, MI   49670   (231) 386-9000
Contact: Sue Bolde, Exec. Dir.; Merry C. Hawley, Executive Asst.
FAX: (231) 386-9000; E-mail: ltcf@localnet.com

Incorporated in 1945 in MI.

Donor: F.H. Haserot†.

Grantmaker type: Community foundation.

Financial data (yr. ended 12/31/04): Assets, $2,251,363 (M); gifts received, $38,545; expenditures, $156,777; total giving, $78,320; giving activities include $78,320 for 27 grants (high: $19,000; low: $300).

Purpose and activities: The foundation supports public charities in Leelanau Township, MI area.

Fields of interest: Arts; Education, early childhood education; Education; Environment, natural resources; Hospitals (general); Health care; Recreation.

Type of support: Capital campaigns; Building/renovation; Equipment; Endowments; Seed money; Scholarships—to individuals.

Limitations: Giving limited to Leelanau Township, MI.

Publications: Annual report; Newsletter.

Application information: Application form required.
   Initial approach: Telephone
   Copies of proposal: 2
   Deadline(s): 2 weeks prior to board meeting
   Board meeting date(s): Quarterly

Officers and Trustees:* Basil Antenucci,* Chair.; Joan Kalchik-Tenbrock,* Vice-Chair.; Sue Bolde, Exec. Dir.; Cory Connolly; Mary Crowgey; Alison Heiser; Charles Kalchik; Richard Lang; Susan O'Connor; Tara Stoffel; Eugene Scott Van Holt.

Number of staff: 2 part-time professional; 2 part-time support.

EIN: 386060138

2367
Lenawee Community Foundation

(formerly Tecumseh Community Fund Foundation)
603 N. Evans St.
P.O. Box 142
Tecumseh, MI   49286   (517) 423-1729
Contact: Suann Hammersmith, Exec. Dir.
FAX: (517) 424-6579; E-mail: info@lenaweecf.com;
Grant request E-mail: shammersmith@ubat.com;
URL: http://www.lenaweecf.com

Established in 1961 in MI.

Grantmaker type: Community foundation.

Financial data (yr. ended 9/30/05): Assets, $5,557,456 (M); gifts received, $998,797; expenditures, $628,358; total giving, $458,989; giving activities include $370,113 for 248 grants (high: $16,000; low: $250; average: $250–$16,000), and $88,876 for 89 grants to individuals (high: $2,000; low: $250; average: $250–$2,000).

Purpose and activities: The mission of the foundation is to enhance the quality of life of the citizens of Lenawee County, Michigan by: 1) identifying and addressing current and anticipated community needs; and 2) raising, managing, and distributing funds for charitable purposes in the areas of civic, cultural, health, education, and social services with an emphasis on permanent endowments.

Fields of interest: Arts; Education; Health organizations, association; Human services; Community development; Youth.

Type of support: Capital campaigns; Building/renovation.

Limitations: Giving limited for the benefit of Lenawee County, MI. No support for religious purposes. No grants to individuals (except for scholarships), or for general operating expenses, fundraising, or construction or renovation of buildings.

Publications: Application guidelines; Annual report (including application guidelines); Grants list; Informational brochure.

Application information: Visit foundation Web site for application guidelines. Application form not required.
   Initial approach: Inquiry by telephone or e-mail
   Copies of proposal: 1
   Deadline(s): Mar. 15, June 15, Sept. 15, and Dec. 15
   Board meeting date(s): Quarterly, 4th Wed. of the month
   Final notification: Feb. 28, May 30, Aug. 30, and Nov. 30

Officers and Directors:* David S. Hickman,* Pres. and Treas.; David E. Maxwell,* V.P.; Charles H.

Gross,* Secy.; Suann D. Hammersmith,* Exec. Dir.; Merlyn H. Downing, Dir. Emeritus; Dr. Carlton Cook; Frank Dick; Christina Frost; Sue Goldsen; Scott Hill; Jim Kapnick; Kathryn Mohr; Breinne Reeder; Claude Rowley; W. Brett Shelton.

Number of staff: 1 full-time professional.

EIN: 386095474

2368
Livonia Community Foundation, Inc.

33300 Five Mile Rd., Ste. 105
Livonia, MI   48154   (734) 522-2285
Contact: Hon. Robert Bennett, Pres.
FAX: (734) 421-5591; E-mail: wcfried@wcfried.com;
URL: http://livoniacommunityfoundation.org

Established in 1994 in MI.

Grantmaker type: Community foundation.

Financial data (yr. ended 12/31/05): Assets, $670,000 (M); gifts received, $59,000; expenditures, $30,100; total giving, $16,200; giving activities include $16,200 for 12 grants (high: $5,000; low: $300).

Purpose and activities: The foundation supports the promotion and development of community resources including historic edifices, public interest and support in the arts and culture, and charitable programs for the welfare of the community.

Fields of interest: Historic preservation/historical societies; Arts; Education; Human services; Community development.

Type of support: General/operating support; Continuing support; Annual campaigns; Building/renovation; Equipment; Land acquisition; Endowments; Emergency funds; Publication; Seed money; Employee matching gifts.

Limitations: Giving limited to Livonia, MI. No support for religious purposes.

Publications: Application guidelines; Annual report; Financial statement; Grants list; Informational brochure (including application guidelines).

Application information: Application form required.
   Initial approach: Request application form
   Copies of proposal: 2
   Deadline(s): Bimonthly, on the 3rd Thurs. of that month
   Board meeting date(s): 3rd Thurs., bi-monthly
   Final notification: 30 days

Officers and Directors:* Hon. Robert Bennett,* Pres.; Gerald A. Bagazinski,* Secy.; William C. Fried,* Treas.; Hon. Jack R. Engebretson; Carole Goodfellow; Henry D. "Bud" Kimple; Hon. Jack Kirksey; Thomas J. Martin; Michael P. McGee; Brian Meakin; Patrick D. Nalley; Tom O'Meara; Dan Putman; Susan Rosiek.

Number of staff: 1 part-time support.

EIN: 383104141

2369
M & M Area Community Foundation

1101 11th Ave., Ste. 2
P.O. Box 846
Menominee, MI   49858-0846   (906) 864-3599
Contact: Richard O'Farrell, Exec. Dir.
FAX: (906) 864-3657;
E-mail: mmfoundation@czwireless.net; Additional E-mail: ricko@menominee.net; URL: http://www.mmcommunityfoundation.org

Established in 1994 in MI.

Grantmaker type: Community foundation.

Financial data (yr. ended 12/31/04): Assets, $4,085,254 (M); gifts received, $212,974; expenditures, $267,278; total giving, $85,783; giving activities include $46,065 for 48 grants (high: $5,810; low: $100), and $39,718 for 16 grants to individuals (high: $27,500; low: $68).
Purpose and activities: The foundation's mission is to receive and administer funds and property in the form of permanent endowments from a wide range of donors for educational, environmental, cultural, recreational, and charitable purposes in a manner that promotes the spirit of philanthropy and meets the needs of the people of Menominee County, MI and Marinette County, WI.
Fields of interest: Arts; Higher education; Education; Environment; Health care; Recreation; Youth development; Human services; Community development; Youth.
Type of support: Continuing support; Equipment; Program development; Seed money; Technical assistance; Employee matching gifts; Scholarships—to individuals; Matching/challenge support.
Limitations: Giving limited to Menominee County, MI, and Marinette County, WI. No support for sectarian religious purposes. No grants to individuals (except for scholarships), or for routine operating expenses, endowments, annual campaigns, debt retirement, or for-profit enterprises.
Publications: Annual report; Financial statement; Grants list; Informational brochure; Newsletter.
Application information: Visit foundation Web site for online Letter of Intent form, full grant application form, and guidelines. Full grant applications are accepted only after the project is deemed eligible based on Letter of Intent. Application form required.
  Initial approach: Complete online Letter of Intent
  Copies of proposal: 1
  Deadline(s): 1 month prior to full application deadline for Letter of Intent; Apr. 21 for youth grants and Apr. 28 for senior grants
  Board meeting date(s): Quarterly; grants committee meets in Sept.
  Final notification: May for youth grants
Officers and Trustees:* Wesley Hoffman,* Pres.; Katherine Holewinski,* V.P.; Ken Jones,* Secy.-Treas.; Richard O'Farrell, Exec. Dir.; Cindy Bailey; Stephen Caselton; Sharon Danielson; Gene Davenport; Barb Killen; Frank Lauerman; John MacIntyre; Robert Martin; Larry Melgary; Roger Peters; Greg Salmen; North Shetter; Jennifer "Jenny" Short; Mary Staudenmaier; Laurie Stupak; Robin West; Gail Wright.
Number of staff: 1 full-time professional; 3 part-time professional.
EIN: 383264725

2370
Mackinac Island Community Foundation
Twilight Inn
P.O. Box 1933
Mackinac Island, MI 49757-1933
(906) 847-3701
Contact: Jennifer Bloswick, Exec. Dir.
FAX: (906) 847-3893; E-mail: info@micf.org; Additional E-mail: jbloswick@micf.org; URL: http://www.micf.org

Established in 1995 in MI.
Grantmaker type: Community foundation.
Financial data (yr. ended 12/31/04): Assets, $4,426,241 (M); gifts received, $296,124; expenditures, $278,944; total giving, $96,599;

giving activities include $96,599 for 47 grants (high: $10,293), and $182,345 for 22 foundation-administered programs.
Purpose and activities: Recognizing the dignity and beauty of Mackinac Island, the Mackinac Island Community Foundation serves the general well-being of Island residents and visitors. The foundation is most interested in projects that focus on arts and humanities, social service, education, community enrichment, youth, environmental awareness and protection, health and wellness, or the horse tradition on Mackinac Island.
Fields of interest: Humanities; History/archaeology; Arts; Higher education; Education; Environment, natural resources; Environment; Health care; Housing/shelter, development; Athletics/sports, equestrianism; Recreation; Youth development; Children/youth, services; Human services; Community development; Youth.
Type of support: General/operating support; Continuing support; Emergency funds; Program development; Seed money; Scholarship funds.
Limitations: Giving limited to the Mackinac Island area, MI. No support for organizations lacking 501(c)(3) status or for sectarian purposes. No grants to individuals, or generally for deficit financing, operating expenses, or annual fundraising campaigns; no loans.
Publications: Application guidelines; Annual report (including application guidelines); Financial statement; Grants list; Informational brochure (including application guidelines); Newsletter.
Application information: Visit foundation Web site for application form and guidelines. Application form required.
  Initial approach: Letter, e-mail, or telephone
  Copies of proposal: 10
  Deadline(s): Apr. 1 and Nov. 1
  Board meeting date(s): Mar., May, June, July, Aug., Sept., and Dec.
  Final notification: June and Dec.
Officers and Trustees:* Wesley H. Maurer, Jr.,* Chair.; R. Daniel Musser III,* Vice-Chair.; Bradley T. Chambers,* Pres.; Margaret M. Doud,* Secy.; Michael Young,* Treas.; Jennifer Bloswick, Exec. Dir.; Penny Barr; Jack E. Dehring; Charles F. Kleber; Kimberly Kolatski; Kathleen S. Lewand; John S. Lore; Mary K. McIntire; Walter North; Carole Rearick; Lorna Puttkammer Straus.
Number of staff: 1 full-time professional.
EIN: 383179612

2371
Manistee County Community Foundation
77 Spruce St.
Manistee, MI 49660 (231) 723-7269
Contact: Karen Bruchan, Exec. Dir.
FAX: (231) 723-4983;
E-mail: manisteefoundation@net-port.com; Additional E-mail: mccf@manisteefoundation.org; URL: http://www.manisteefoundation.org

Established in 1987 in MI.
Grantmaker type: Community foundation.
Financial data (yr. ended 12/31/05): Assets, $1,145,466 (M); gifts received, $195,383; expenditures, $123,328; total giving, $72,189; giving activities include $71,189 for 15+ grants, and $1,000 for 1 grant to an individual.
Purpose and activities: The foundation seeks to enhance the quality of life in Manistee County for now and forever. This includes managing

endowment funds, making grants and acting as a neutral convenor for the community at large.
Fields of interest: Arts; Education; Environment; Recreation; Human services; Community development; Youth.
Type of support: Annual campaigns; Endowments; Seed money; Scholarship funds.
Limitations: Giving limited to the Manistee County, MI, area.
Publications: Application guidelines; Annual report; Financial statement; Grants list; Informational brochure.
Application information: Grant (RFP) information is available each Feb. through the foundation's Web site or by calling the foundation. Application form required.
  Initial approach: Letter or telephone
  Copies of proposal: 7
  Deadline(s): Mid-Oct.
  Board meeting date(s): Monthly
  Final notification: 6 weeks
Officers and Directors:* Tim Ervin,* Pres.; Charlene Myers,* V.P.; Clara Vargo,* Secy.; Michael Thompson,* Treas.; Karen Bruchan, Exec. Dir.; Ted Arens; Jim Goodwin; Rosalind Jaffe; By Lyon; Beth McCarthy; Steve Paine.
Number of staff: 1 full-time professional; 1 part-time professional.
EIN: 382741723

2372
Marquette Community Foundation
401 E. Fair Ave.
P.O. Box 37
Marquette, MI 49855 (906) 226-7666
Contact: Cathy Nardi, Exec. Dir.
FAX: (906) 226-2104; E-mail: mcf@chartermi.net; URL: http://www.mqt-cf.org

Established in 1988 in MI.
Grantmaker type: Community foundation.
Financial data (yr. ended 12/31/04): Assets, $7,055,237 (M); gifts received, $501,489; expenditures, $369,682; total giving, $206,806; giving activities include $180,306 for 79 grants (high: $30,000; low: $38), and $26,500 for 44 grants to individuals (high: $2,000; low: $500).
Purpose and activities: The foundation supports organizations involved with the arts, education, health, and human services.
Fields of interest: Arts; Education; Health care; Health organizations, association; Children/youth, services; Human services.
Type of support: Capital campaigns; Building/renovation; Equipment; Program development; Seed money; Scholarship funds; Scholarships—to individuals.
Limitations: Giving limited to Marquette County, MI. No support for religious programs that promote their particular religion.
Publications: Application guidelines; Annual report; Financial statement; Informational brochure; Newsletter; Program policy statement.
Application information: Visit foundation Web site for application form and guidelines. Application form required.
  Initial approach: Telephone
  Copies of proposal: 6
  Deadline(s): Apr. 1 and Oct. 1
  Board meeting date(s): Once per month
  Final notification: Within one week of board meeting

Officers and Trustees: * Kellie Holmstrom,* Pres.; Chris Vanabel,* V.P.; Don Mourand,* Treas.; Cathy Nardi, Exec. Dir.; Patti Benstrom; Mark Cande; Martha Conley; Robert Cowell; Lynne Hammerstrom; John Marshall; Dan Mazzuchi; Alan Nelson; Pat Ryan O'Day; Michael Prokopowicz; Mike Roy; Terri Smith; Craig Stien, M.D.; Mary Tavernini; Roger Zappa.
Number of staff: 2 part-time professional.
EIN: 382826563

2373
Marshall Community Foundation

(formerly Marshall Civic Foundation)
126 W. Michigan Ave., Ste. 202
Marshall, MI   49068   (269) 781-2273
Contact: Sherry Anderson, Exec. Dir.
FAX: (269) 781-9747;
E-mail: marshallcomfdn@aol.com; URL: http://www.marshallcf.org

Established in 1970 in MI.
Grantmaker type: Community foundation.
Financial data (yr. ended 9/30/05): Assets, $8,600,689 (M); gifts received, $284,817; expenditures, $308,340; total giving, $204,378; giving activities include $137,973 for 59 grants (high: $31,446; low: $68), and $66,405 for 50 grants to individuals (high: $11,000; low: $100).
Purpose and activities: The foundation's mission is to help make the Marshall area an even better place to live, work, and raise a family. This is done by attracting permanently endowed funds from a wide range of donors serving as a conduit for special projects and distributing of grants in support of innovative programs, while always being mindful to carry out the intention of the donors.
Fields of interest: Arts; Education; Health care; Health organizations, association; Youth, services; Human services; Community development.
Type of support: General/operating support; Building/renovation; Equipment; Program development; Conferences/seminars; Seed money; Curriculum development; Scholarship funds; Technical assistance; Scholarships—to individuals; Matching/challenge support.
Limitations: Giving limited to Calhoun County, MI. No support for religious or sectarian purposes. No grants to individuals (except for scholarships), or for annual fundraising drives or capital campaigns, endowments or debt reductions, or normal operating expenses (except for start-up purposes and/or special needs).
Publications: Annual report; Informational brochure.
Application information: Visit foundation Web site for application forms and guidelines. Application form required.
Initial approach: Letter or telephone
Copies of proposal: 20
Deadline(s): Jan.1 , Apr. 1, July 1, and Oct. 1
Board meeting date(s): Quarterly
Final notification: Within 2 months
Officers and Trustees: * Charles B. Cook,* Pres.; Sandra J. Dobbins, V.P.; Mark F. Stuart,* Secy.; Frank E. Boley,* Treas.; Sherry Anderson, Exec. Dir.; Mary Jo Byrne; Thomas F. Franke; Pastor Richard Gerten; Matthew Glazer; Lynne M. Haley; Michael E. Kinter; Dr. Jay Larson; Darlene Neidlinger; James A. Pardoe; Dr. Joyce Phillips; Ron Smith; Morris Stulberg; Kathy Tarr.
Number of staff: 1 part-time professional; 1 part-time support.
EIN: 237011281

2374
Mecosta County Community Foundation

P.O. Box 1012C
Big Rapids, MI   49307   (231) 796-3065
URL: http://www.mccf.us

Established in 1991 in MI as an affiliate of Fremont Area Community Foundation.
Grantmaker type: Community foundation.
Purpose and activities: The mission of the foundation is to enhance the quality of life for all citizens in Mecosta County in the areas of art and culture, education, health, nature conservation and the environment, community development, historical resources, and social services.
Fields of interest: Historical activities; Arts; Education; Environment, natural resources; Health care; Human services; Community development.
Type of support: Seed money; Scholarships—to individuals; Scholarship funds; Program development; General/operating support; Equipment; Building/renovation.
Limitations: Giving limited to Mecosta County, MI. No support for organizations lacking 501(c)(3) status, or for religious organizations for solely religious purposes. No grants for general operating support.
Publications: Application guidelines; Annual report; Newsletter.
Application information: See foundation Web site for application guidelines and requirements. Application form required.
Copies of proposal: 5
Deadline(s): Apr. 1 and Oct. 1 for grants; Apr. 1 for scholarships
Officers and Trustees: * Isabel Kempton,* Pres.; John Norton,* 1st V.P.; Gary Trimarco,* 2nd V.P.; Glen Pepper,* Treas.; Yo Bellingar; Pete Chesebrough; Rita Conrad; Bob Hampson; Robert Horan; Karl Linebaugh; Mike Mohnke; Debbie Patterson; Bill Scheible; Debra Szot; Judy Tressler.
Number of staff: None.

2375
Michigan Gateway Community Foundation

(formerly Buchanan Area Foundation)
111 Days Ave.
Buchanan, MI   49107-1609   (269) 695-3521
Contact: Robert N. Habicht, C.E.O.
FAX: (269) 695-4250; E-mail: mgcf@mgcf.org;
URL: http://www.mgcf.org

Established in 1978 in MI.
Grantmaker type: Community foundation.
Financial data (yr. ended 3/31/05): Assets, $4,761,078 (M); gifts received, $159,908; expenditures, $362,838; total giving, $135,554; giving activities include $135,554 for grants.
Purpose and activities: The foundation provides support for the arts, education, and social services. Scholarships are for local-area high school seniors for study in any field.
Fields of interest: Arts; Education; Health care; Human services.
Type of support: General/operating support; Income development; Equipment; Program development; Conferences/seminars; Seed money; Curriculum development; Program evaluation; Scholarships—to individuals; Matching/challenge support.
Limitations: Giving limited to Cass County and southern Berrien County, MI.

Publications: Application guidelines; Annual report; Financial statement; Informational brochure; Newsletter.
Application information: Visit foundation Web site for application information. Use of the Common Grant Application of the Council of Michigan Foundations is encouraged. Application form required.
Initial approach: Telephone
Copies of proposal: 1
Deadline(s): Feb. 1, May 1, Aug. 1, and Nov. 1 for grants; May for scholarships
Board meeting date(s): Mar., May, July, Aug., and Nov.
Final notification: Within 1 month
Officers and Trustees: * Louis A. Desenberg,* Chair.; Robert N. Habicht,* C.E.O. and Pres.; Taylor "Tim" Tyler,* Treas.; Pete Brandstatter; Nancy O. Butler; David Casey; Robert Cochrane; Karin Falkenstein; John Gore; Don Stibbs; Judy Truesdell; Stephen K. Woods.
Number of staff: 1 full-time professional; 1 part-time support.
EIN: 382180730

2376
Midland Area Community Foundation

(formerly Midland Foundation)
109 E. Main St.
P.O. Box 289
Midland, MI   48640-0289   (989) 839-9661
Contact: Nicole Charles, V.P. and C.F.O.
FAX: (989) 839-9907;
E-mail: info@midlandfoundation.com; Additional tel: (800) 906-9661; URL: http://www.midlandfoundation.com

Established in 1973 in MI.
Grantmaker type: Community foundation.
Financial data (yr. ended 12/31/05): Assets, $55,817,605 (M); gifts received, $2,990,152; expenditures, $3,861,367; total giving, $1,467,133; giving activities include $1,275,201 for 260 grants (high: $50,000; low: $100), and $191,932 for 105 grants to individuals (high: $5,000; low: $500).
Purpose and activities: The foundation seeks to promote and enable philanthropic giving to improve the quality of life for the people in the community.
Fields of interest: Humanities; Arts; Adult/continuing education; Education; Environment, energy; Environment; Health care; Recreation; Youth, services; Human services; Economic development; Community development.
Type of support: Building/renovation; Equipment; Seed money; Scholarship funds; Technical assistance; Consulting services; Matching/challenge support.
Limitations: Giving primarily in full support services to Midland and Gladwin counties, MI, and also Clare County through affiliate. No support for sectarian religious programs or basic governmental services. No grants to individuals (except for scholarships), or for operating budgets, continuing support, annual campaigns, deficit financing, endowment funds, or travel for groups such as school classes, clubs, or sports teams.
Publications: Application guidelines; Annual report; Grants list; Informational brochure; Newsletter.
Application information: Visit foundation Web site for application guidelines. Application form required.
Initial approach: Telephone Prog. Off. to discuss project

Copies of proposal: 3
Deadline(s): Jan. 15, Apr. 15, July 15, and Oct. 15
Board meeting date(s): 4th Mon. of every month
Final notification: Early in Mar., June, Sept., and
Dec.
Officers and Trustees:* Brian Rodgers,* Chair.;
Maureen Donker,* Vice-Chair.; Elyse Rogers, Interim
Pres. and C.E.O.; Nicole Charles, V.P. and C.F.O.;
Marty McGuire,* Secy.; Chris Velasquez,* Treas.;
Linda Cline; Carole Dennings; Richard Dolinski;
Thomas Erickson; L. Scott Govitz; Bridgette
Gransden; Kevin Guigou; Jim Hop; Cindy Newman;
Linda Owen; Donna Rapp.
Number of staff: 4 full-time professional; 1 part-time
professional; 2 full-time support; 1 part-time
support.
EIN: 382023395

2377
Missaukee County Community Foundation
P.O. Box 749
Lake City, MI   49651-0749
Contact: James Hinkamp, Pres.
E-mail: jhinkamp@i2k.com; URL: http://
www.cadillacfoundation.org/missaukee.php

Established in 1999 in MI as a geographic
component fund of the Cadillac Area Community
Foundation.
Grantmaker type: Community foundation.
Purpose and activities: The primary purpose of the
Missaukee Area Community Foundation is to
develop a community-wide vehicle for permanent
endowments to enhance the quality of life in the
area (County of Missaukee, Michigan), and to
establish and manage worthwhile funds for the
benefit of our community. Support for youth
activities, education, and community improvement
projects.
Fields of interest: Education; Youth development;
Community development.
Type of support: Continuing support; Annual
campaigns; Seed money; Consulting services;
Matching/challenge support.
Limitations: Giving limited to Missaukee County, MI.
No support for sectarian programs. No grants to
individuals, or generally for general operating
support, fundraising campaigns, endowments, or
conferences.
Publications: Application guidelines; Occasional
report; Program policy statement.
Application information: See foundation Web site
for application requirements, including
downloadable application form. Application form
required.
Initial approach: Letter or telephone
Copies of proposal: 8
Deadline(s): See foundation Web site for current
deadline information. Applications are only
considered during specific award cycles (at
least 1 per year)
Board meeting date(s): As needed

2378
Mount Pleasant Area Community Foundation
(formerly Mount Pleasant Community Foundation)
113 W. Broadway
P.O. Box 1283
Mount Pleasant, MI   48804-1283
(989) 773-7322
FAX: (989) 773-1517; E-mail: info@mpacf.org;
Additional E-mail: srathbun@mpacf.org;
URL: http://www.mpacf.org

Established in 1990 in MI.
Grantmaker type: Community foundation.
Financial data (yr. ended 12/31/04): Assets,
$4,572,440 (M); gifts received, $267,234;
expenditures, $232,395; total giving, $74,450;
giving activities include $74,450 for grants.
Purpose and activities: The foundation seeks to
enhance the quality of life for all citizens of Isabella
County, both current and future generations, by
holding and attracting permanent, endowed funds
from a wide range of donors, addressing needs
through grant making, and providing leadership on
key community issues. The foundation currently
grants money to organizations in the community for
healthy senior programs, after school programs,
homelessness prevention, diversity education,
environmental needs, health & safety programs, the
arts & humanities, emergency health care, as well
as operating expenses, capital needs, and
educational scholarships.
Fields of interest: Education, research; Education;
Environment; Health care; Youth development;
Human services; Community development,
neighborhood development.
Type of support: Capital campaigns; Building/
renovation; Equipment; Land acquisition;
Endowments; Emergency funds; Program
development; Conferences/seminars; Publication;
Seed money; Scholarship funds; Research;
Technical assistance; Scholarships—to individuals;
Matching/challenge support; Student loans—to
individuals.
Limitations: Giving limited to Isabella County, MI. No
support for the promotion of religious teaching of
any kind. No grants to individuals (except for
scholarships), or for annual operating expenses.
Publications: Application guidelines; Annual report;
Financial statement; Grants list; Informational
brochure; Newsletter.
Application information: Visit foundation Web site
for application Cover Sheet and guidelines. Faxed or
e-mailed applications are not accepted. Application
form required.
Initial approach: Submit application Cover Sheet
and attachments
Copies of proposal: 15
Deadline(s): Apr. 1, June 3, Sept. 30, or Nov. 30
for general grants; Mar. 1 for scholarships
Board meeting date(s): Bimonthly
Final notification: Within 2 weeks of board
meeting
Officers and Trustees:* Shirley Martin Decker,*
Pres.; Robert L. Wheeler,* V.P.; Kay A. Smith,*
Secy.; Nancy Ridley,* Treas.; Stan Rathbun, Exec.
Dir.; Dan Boge; Mary Ellen Brandell; Mary Ann
Breuer; Doug Dodge; George W. Dunn; Jim Goodrich;
Doug Heinze; Chuck Hubscher; Eric R. Janes; Robert
A. Janson; Dave Keilitz; Steve Martineau; Diane
Morey; Susan K. Murray; Donald Schuster; W.
Sidney Smith; Naomi Stark; Jan Strickler; Thomas
Sullivan.

Number of staff: 1 full-time professional; 1 part-time
support.
EIN: 382951873

2379
Negaunee Area Community Fund
1036 Maas St.
Negaunee, MI   49866-1504   (906) 226-7666
Contact: Alan Nelson, Tr.
FAX: (906) 226-2104; E-mail: alnelson@up.net

Established in MI as an affiliate of Marquette
Community Foundation.
Grantmaker type: Community foundation.
Fields of interest: Community development.
Limitations: Giving primarily in western Marquette
County, MI.

2380
North Central Michigan Community Foundation
c/o Community Foundation for Northeast Michigan
P.O. Box 495
Alpena, MI   49707   (877) 354-6881
Contact: Christine Hitch
FAX: (989) 356-3319; E-mail: chitch@cfnem.org;
URL: http://www.ncmcf.org/

Established in 1998 in MI as an affiliate of the
Community Foundation for Northeast Michigan.
Grantmaker type: Community foundation.
Purpose and activities: The foundation seeks to
serve Crawford, Ogemaw, and Oscoda counties and
to preserve the charitable goals of a wide range of
donors now and for generations to come by
supporting 501(c)(3) organizations, churches for
non-religious purposes, and government agencies.
Type of support: Technical assistance; Seed money;
Scholarships—to individuals; Publication; Program
development; Equipment; Conferences/seminars;
Building/renovation.
Limitations: Giving limited to Crawford, Ogemaw and
Oscoda counties, MI. No grants to individuals
(except for scholarships), or for routine operating
needs or budget deficits.
Publications: Application guidelines; Annual report;
Financial statement; Grants list; Informational
brochure; Newsletter.
Application information: See foundation Web site
for Common Grant Application Form and
requirements. Application form required.
Deadline(s): Sept. 30 for grants; 1st regular
workday of Feb., Aug., or Nov. for mini-grants;
Mar. 31 for tobacco grants
Final notification: Within 6 weeks of grant
deadlines
Officers and Trustees:* Bernard Bak,* Chair.; Hugo
Burzlaff,* Vice-Chair.; Bill Gascoigne, Secy.-Treas.;
Bob Carpenter; Mark Clements; Carolyn DiPonio; Jim
Howard; Joe Porter; David Waltz.

2381
Northville Community Foundation
18600 Northville Rd. Ste. 275
Northville, MI   48168   (248) 374-0200
Contact: Shari Peters, Pres.
FAX: (248) 374-0403;
E-mail: nvillefoundation@aol.com; URL: http://
www.northvillecommunityfoundation.com

Established in 1997 in MI.
Grantmaker type: Community foundation.
Financial data (yr. ended 12/31/05): Assets, $543,270 (M); gifts received, $371,138; expenditures, $467,971; total giving, $8,579; giving activities include $7,079 for 5 grants (high: $4,500; low: $259), $1,500 for 3 grants to individuals (high: $500; low: $500), and $441,073 for foundation-administered programs.
Purpose and activities: The foundation seeks to benefit the Northville community through promotion of education, arts, music, and cultural events; support also for environmental conservation.
Fields of interest: Performing arts, music; Arts; Education; Environment, natural resources.
Limitations: Giving limited to Northville, MI.
Application information: Application form required.
  Initial approach: Telephone
Officers and Directors: * Shari Peters,* Pres. and Exec. Dir.; Audrey Mistor,* Treas.; Chris Belcher; Eric Colthurst; Tom Denome; Andrea Marlow; Paul Olexa; Chris Willerer.
EIN: 383361844

2382
Norway Area Community Fund
NorthPointe
715 Pyle Dr.
Kingsford, MI   49802-4456   (906) 779-0637
Contact: Bill Reid, Vice-Chair.
FAX: (906) 779-0645; E-mail: breid@nbhs.org

Established in MI; a geographic affiliate of Dickinson Area Community Foundation.
Grantmaker type: Community foundation.
Purpose and activities: Grants are made in the areas of advancing philanthropy, arts and the humanities, community services, education, conservation and the environment, health, and human and social services.
Fields of interest: Humanities; Arts; Education; Environment; Health care; Human services; Community development; Philanthropy/voluntarism.
Limitations: Giving limited to Norway, MI, and its surrounding townships. No support for sectarian religious purposes. No grants to individuals, or for budget deficits, routine operating expenses of existing organizations, or endowments.
Application information: Contact foundation for deadline and decision dates.
Officer: Bill Reid, Vice-Chair.
Trustees: Ray Anderson; Judy Carlsen; Tim Mattson; Sara Sleik; Allyn Thornberry; Randall Van Gasse; Pastor Dave Wallis; Robert Wurzer.

2383
Osceola County Community Foundation
P.O. Box 37
Reed City, MI   49677   (231) 832-6139
URL: http://www.occf.info/

Established in MI as an affiliate of Fremont Area Community Foundation.
Grantmaker type: Community foundation.
Purpose and activities: The mission of the foundation is to make Osceola County a better place in which to live and work by enhancing the quality of life and building a strong community spirit through support of programs in the areas of human services, arts and culture, environment, health care, and education.

Fields of interest: Arts; Education; Environment; Health care; Human services; Community development.
Limitations: Giving limited to Osceola County, MI. No support for religious organizations, except for services provided on a secular basis. No grants to individuals (except for scholarships adminstered through schools),.
Application information: See foundation Web site for application guidelines, including downloadable application form. Application form required.
  Copies of proposal: 9
  Deadline(s): Jan. 10, Apr. 10, adn Oct. 10
  Board meeting date(s): Feb., May, and Nov.
  Final notification: Apr., July, and Dec.
Officers and Trustees: * Jerry Lindquist,* Pres.; Joe Curtin,* V.P.; Deb Ahlich-Remus,* Secy.; Chuck Holmquist,* Treas.; Ron Babb; Alan Bengry; Larry Emig; Hon. Susan Grant; Judy Hays; Howard Hyde; Amy Keller; Larry Neiderheide; Theresa Rasor; Marie Wilkerson.

2384
Otsego County Community Foundation
P.O. Box 344
Gaylord, MI   49734-0344   (989) 731-0597
Contact: William Dawson, Exec. Dir.
FAX: (989) 731-0597;
E-mail: otsegofoundation@mysgo.com; URL: http://www.otsegofoundation.org

Established in 1995 in MI as a regional affiliate of Grand Traverse Regional Community Foundation; became an independent community foundation in 2002.
Grantmaker type: Community foundation.
Financial data (yr. ended 12/31/04): Assets, $1,752,898 (M); gifts received, $89,169; expenditures, $172,731; total giving, $88,992; giving activities include $88,992 for 9 grants (high: $50,000; low: $400).
Purpose and activities: The foundation's mission is to enhance the quality of life for all citizens of the Otsego County, Michigan area now and for future generations by building community endowment, awarding grants to address community needs, and convening leadership on key issues.
Fields of interest: Arts; Education; Environment; Health organizations, association; Cancer; Recreation; Children/youth, services; Community development.
Limitations: Giving limited to Otsego County, MI.
Officers and Directors: * Peter Amar,* Chair.; Carol Nelson-Snyder,* Vice-Chair.; Maureen Derenzy,* Secy.; Kevin Reynolds,* Treas.; William "Bill" Dawson, Exec. Dir.; Carlee Allen; Dan Bebble; Mason Buckingham; Charles "Chad" Dutcher; David Gast; Tim Granahan; Rick Marshall; Jill Miner; Matt Rooyakker; Susan Hlywa Topp.
EIN: 383216235

2385
Petoskey-Harbor Springs Area Community Foundation
616 Petoskey St., Ste. 100
Petoskey, MI   49770   (231) 348-5820
Contact: Maureen M. Nicholson, Exec. Dir.
FAX: (231) 348-5883; E-mail: info@phsacf.org;
Additional E-mails: mnicholson@phsacf.org and lwendland@phsacf.org; URL: http://www.petoskey-harborspringsfoundation.org

Established in 1991 in MI.
Grantmaker type: Community foundation.
Financial data (yr. ended 3/31/05): Assets, $10,166,572 (M); gifts received, $1,090,124; expenditures, $745,296; total giving, $441,144; giving activities include $409,144 for 103+ grants (high: $28,224; average: $50–$15,000), and $32,000 for 18 grants to individuals (high: $10,000; low: $500).
Purpose and activities: The foundation awards grants to nonprofit organizations, schools or municipalities in Emmet County, MI or to those that serve a significant number of Emmet County residents.
Fields of interest: Historic preservation/historical societies; Arts; Higher education; Education; Environment; Health care; Recreation; Youth development; Human services; Economic development; Community development.
Type of support: Scholarships—to individuals; Building/renovation; Equipment; Program development; Seed money; Scholarship funds; Technical assistance; Matching/challenge support.
Limitations: Giving limited to Emmet County, MI. No support for sectarian religious purposes. No grants to individuals (except for scholarships), or for endowments, debt reduction, annual fundraising drives, operational phases of established programs, conferences, travel, or scholarly research; no loans.
Publications: Application guidelines; Annual report; Financial statement; Informational brochure.
Application information: Potential applicants must contact the foundation prior to submitting an application to discuss their project. Visit foundation Web site for application information. Application form required.
  Initial approach: Telephone
  Copies of proposal: 25
  Deadline(s): Early Apr. and early Oct.
  Board meeting date(s): Monthly
  Final notification: Approx. 2 months
Officers and Directors: * James T. Ramer,* Pres.; Louise T. Graham,* V.P.; David T. Buzzelli,* Secy.; Maureen M. Nicholson, Exec. Dir.; Sandra T. Baker; Lisa G. Blanchard; Kristin Clark; Jane T. Damschroder; Michael FitzSimons; Charles H. Gano; Charles W. Johnson; Kate Marshall; Virginia B. McCoy; Philip H. Millard; Kyle Ronquist; Todd Winnell.
Number of staff: 2 full-time professional; 1 full-time support.
EIN: 383032185

2386
Roscommon County Community Foundation
701 Lake St.
P.O. Box 824
Roscommon, MI   48653-0824   (989) 275-3112
Contact: Mary Fry, Exec Dir.
FAX: (989) 275-3112; E-mail: rccf@kirtland.edu

Established in 1997 as an affiliate of NCMCF; recognized as an independent community foundation in 2001.
Donors: Rex Gillen†; Arlene Gillen†.
Grantmaker type: Community foundation.
Financial data (yr. ended 12/31/05): Assets, $5,437,067 (M); gifts received, $176,511; expenditures, $219,935; total giving, $116,722; giving activities include $116,722 for 33 grants (high: $25,000; low: $50).

Purpose and activities: The foundation seeks to improve the quality of life for all present and future residents of Roscommon County by providing stewardship and leadership, by attracting and holding permanent endowment funds from a wide range of donors, and by making grants of the income from its permanent endowment funds. The foundation is committed to protecting the personal investments that all residents have made, demonstrating concern for youth and many issues affecting their future; recognizing the value and importance of the natural environment now and for the future; and improving and building the future for families.
Fields of interest: Education; Environment; Health care; Safety/disasters; Recreation.
Type of support: Endowments; Scholarship funds.
Limitations: Giving limited to Roscommon County, MI. No support for religious or for-profit organizations.
Publications: Application guidelines; Annual report; Annual report (including application guidelines); Financial statement; Grants list; Informational brochure; Newsletter.
Application information: Application form required.
  Initial approach: Open
  Copies of proposal: 7
  Deadline(s): Jan. 31, Apr. 30, and Oct. 31
  Board meeting date(s): Varies
  Final notification: 2 months
Officers and Trustees:* Robert Pacella,* Pres.; Randall Seymour,* V.P.; Roland Eno,* Secy.; Barb Mick,* Treas.; Mary Fry,* Exec. Dir.; James Anderson; Richard Brown; Louise Bucco; Thomas Hamp; Henri Junod, Jr.; Rev. James Kent; Darcia Little; Thomas Morleau; Carol Silverman; P.J. Steeby.
Number of staff: 1 full-time professional; 1 part-time support.
EIN: 383612480

2387
Saginaw Community Foundation
100 S. Jefferson Ave., Ste. 201
Saginaw, MI 48607 (989) 755-0545
Contact: Renee S. Johnston, Pres.; For grants: Ken Horn, V.P., Progs. and Donor Svcs.
FAX: (989) 755-6524;
E-mail: info@saginawfoundation.org; Additional E-mail: Ken@saginawfoundation.org; URL: http://www.saginawfoundation.org

Incorporated in 1984 in MI.
Grantmaker type: Community foundation.
Financial data (yr. ended 12/31/05): Assets, $33,429,153 (M); gifts received, $4,989,493; expenditures, $1,934,559; total giving, $680,194; giving activities include $680,194 for 195 grants (high: $67,481; low: $84).
Purpose and activities: Support for projects not currently being served by existing community resources and for projects providing leverage for generating other funds and community resources.
Fields of interest: Arts; Education; Environment; Health care; Recreation; Family services; Human services; Community development; General charitable giving; Youth; Aging.
Type of support: Building/renovation; Equipment; Emergency funds; Program development; Publication; Seed money; Scholarship funds; Technical assistance; Scholarships—to individuals; Matching/challenge support.

Limitations: Giving limited to Saginaw County, MI. No support for churches or sectarian religious programs. No grants to individuals (except for designated scholarship funds), or for operating budgets, endowment campaigns, debt reduction, travel, or basic municipal or educational services; generally no multi-year grants.
Publications: Application guidelines; Annual report (including application guidelines); Occasional report.
Application information: Visit foundation Web site for application cover form and guidelines. Application form required.
  Initial approach: Telephone
  Copies of proposal: 3
  Deadline(s): Feb. 1, May 1, Aug. 1, and Nov. 1
  Board meeting date(s): Monthly
  Final notification: 2 months after deadline
Officers and Directors:* Richard T. Watson,* Chair.; Joseph W. Madison,* Vice-Chair.; Renee S. Johnston, C.E.O. and Pres.; Ken Horn, V.P., Progs. and Donor Svcs.; Mark S. Flegenheimer,* Secy.; David J. Abbs,* Treas.; Raana Akbar, M.D.; Heidi A. Bolger; David R. Butts; David Carbajal; Bishop Robert J. Carlson; Paul Chaffee; Morrall M. Claramunt; Rev. Hurley J. Coleman, Jr.; Ellen E. Crane; JoAnn Crary; Desmon Daniel, Ph.D.; Craig C. Douglas, Ph.D.; James Fabiano II; Andrea L. Fisher; Frederick C. Gardner; Smallwood Holoman, Jr.; Deborah G. Kimble; Richard D. Lane; Timothy M. MacKay; Susan A. Pumford; Kala Kuru Ramasamy, M.D.; Ricardo Resio; Jerry L. Seese; Sam Shaheen, M.D.; James J. Shinners; Linda L. Sims; Martin H. Stark; Julie Case Swieczkowski; Mamie Thorns, Ph.D.; Jerry Ulrey.
Number of staff: 4 full-time professional.
EIN: 382474297

2388
Sanilac County Community Foundation
47 Austin St.
P.O. Box 307
Sandusky, MI 48471-0307 (810) 648-3634
Contact: Joan Nagelkirk, Exec. Dir.
FAX: (810) 648-4418;
E-mail: director@sanilaccountycommunityfoundation.org; Additional E-mail: joan@clearideas.biz; URL: http://www.sanilaccountycommunityfoundation.org

Established in 1994 in MI.
Grantmaker type: Community foundation.
Financial data (yr. ended 12/31/05): Assets, $2,993,521 (M); gifts received, $725,711; expenditures, $161,022; total giving, $129,953; giving activities include $129,953 for 34 grants.
Purpose and activities: The foundation holds a collection of endowed funds, contributed by many individuals, corporations, private foundations and government agencies to benefit the Sanilac County, MI, area.
Fields of interest: Arts; Education; Environment; Health care; Recreation; Youth development; Children/youth, services; Community development; Federated giving programs.
Limitations: Giving limited to Sanilac County, MI. No support for religious or sectarian purposes. No support for loans.
Application information: Visit foundation Web site for application information. An application form for grants of $5,000 or less is available online. Application form required.
  Initial approach: Telephone

Copies of proposal: 12
Deadline(s): May 1 and Nov. 1
Board meeting date(s): 3rd Tues. of every month
Final notification: May 30 or Nov. 30
Officers and Board Members:* I. Lee Cork,* Co-Chair.; Bill Sarkella,* Co-Chair.; Ed Gamache,* Vice-Chair.; Susan Dreyer,* Secy.; Joe Nartker,* Treas.; Joan Nagelkirk,* Exec. Dir.; Judy Albrecht; Bob Armstrong; Curt Backus; Robert Barnes; Louise Blasius; Henry Buxton; Dick Carncross; Paul Cowley; Bill Coyne; Sharon Danek; Roger Dean; John Espinoza; Judy Ferguson; David Hearsch; Linda Kelke; David Kirkbride; Duane Lange; Frank Merriman; Ed McGraw; Paul Muxlow; Gail Nartker; Mark Ruggles; Dave Tubbs; Jane Walls.
EIN: 383204484

2389
Schoolcraft Area Community Foundation
(formerly Schoolcraft County Community Foundation)
221 S. Maple St.
P.O. Box 452
Manistique, MI 49854-0452 (906) 341-2834
Contact: John E. MacFarlane III, Advisory Board Pres. and Dir.
FAX: (906) 341-2834; E-mail: robpan@up.net

Established in 1995 in MI; in 2001 became a geographic affiliate of the Community Foundation of the Upper Peninsula.
Grantmaker type: Community foundation.
Purpose and activities: Primarily awards scholarships to local area youth; support also to organizations in the areas of arts and culture, education, health, human services, community development, and the environment.
Fields of interest: Arts; Education; Environment; Health care; Human services; Community development.
Type of support: Equipment; Scholarships—to individuals.
Limitations: Giving limited to Manistique, MI.
Officers: Bob Panek, Pres.; Marilyn Pitts-Johnson, V.P.; Jeff Himes, Secy.; John MacFarlene, Treas. and Exec. Dir.
Trustees: Marty Fuller; Rev. Pam Fulton; Rev. David Hueter; Christina Keener; Fr. Peter Menelli; Rick Wodzinski.
EIN: 383181869

2390
Shelby Community Foundation
P.O. Box 183181
Shelby Township, MI 48318 (586) 731-5400
Contact: Linda Stout, Chair.
URL: http://shelbyhistory.tripod.com/id59.html

Established in 1996 in MI.
Grantmaker type: Community foundation.
Financial data (yr. ended 12/31/04): Assets, $247,157 (M); gifts received, $53,487; expenditures, $29,672; total giving, $21,900; giving activities include $21,900 for grants.
Purpose and activities: The foundation supports projects which offer innovative and practical approaches to community needs. Its major goals are to promote activities and programs that provide residents of the township with the following opportunities: cultural enrichment, historic preservation, recreational activities, life-long

education, community beautification, and support for the township library.

Fields of interest: Historic preservation/historical societies; Arts; Education, continuing education; Libraries (public); Education; Environment, beautification programs; Recreation; Community development.

Limitations: Giving limited to Shelby Township, MI.

Officers and Directors:* Linda Maccarone,* Chair.; Nancy Bates,* Vice-Chair.; Thomas J. Dearlove,* Secy.; Linda Stout,* Treas.; Mark R. Beck; Joe Dindo; Linda O'Keefe; Richard E. Pearson; Robert E. Pechur; Theresa Toia; Kathleen Vallis; Rick Young.

EIN: 383341102

2391
Shiawassee Community Foundation

(formerly Shiawassee Foundation)
100 E. Main St., 2nd Fl.
P.O. Box 753
Owosso, MI   48867   (989) 725-1093
FAX: (989) 729-1358;
E-mail: shiafdn@michonline.net

Established in 1974 in MI.

Donor: John Northway.

Grantmaker type: Community foundation.

Financial data (yr. ended 9/30/05): Assets, $3,136,526 (M); gifts received, $262,616; expenditures, $190,398; total giving, $105,123; giving activities include $105,123 for 53 grants (high: $18,750; low: $28).

Purpose and activities: The foundation primarily supports organizations involved with higher education, health, and human services.

Fields of interest: Arts; Higher education; Education; Environment; Health care; Human services; Community development.

Type of support: Continuing support; Endowments; Program development; Conferences/seminars; Curriculum development; Scholarship funds.

Limitations: Giving limited to Shiawassee County, MI. No support for religious programs serving specific religious denominations. No grants to individuals (except for designated funds), or for routine operating expenses or expenses for established programs, fundraising drives, capital equipment, computers, video equipment, or vehicles, conference attendance, speakers, salaries, or projects that are primarily cause-related.

Publications: Annual report; Newsletter.

Application information: Upon review of letter of intent, organizations meeting the foundation's funding and priority guidelines will be invited to submit a full grant application. Application form required.

Initial approach: Telephone
Copies of proposal: 2
Deadline(s): Feb. 28 for letter of intent; Mar. 30 for full grant application
Board meeting date(s): Varies
Final notification: Annually, prior to Sept.

Officers and Trustees:* Donald D. Levi,* Pres.; Mary Slingerland,* V.P. and Secy.; Bryan J. Gross,* Treas.; Carol Soule, Exec. Dir.; Richard Batchelor; Ann Bentley; Jacqueline Flynn; Jessica Janego; Glen Merkel; Dr. Mark E. Miller; Christine Mitchell; Mary Plowman; Paul Schluckebier; Stacey Schluckebier; Dr. Marie Jean Brinkman Sloan; Catherine Stevenson; Barbara Williamson.

EIN: 383285624

2392
South Haven Community Foundation

228 Broadway
South Haven, MI   49090-1472   (269) 639-1631
URL: http://www.kalfound.org/page20372.cfm

Established in MI a geographic affiliate of Kalamazoo Community Foundation.

Grantmaker type: Community foundation.

Purpose and activities: The foundation makes grants to help improve the quality of life in the greater South Haven, Michigan, area.

Fields of interest: Performing arts; Elementary/secondary education; Housing/shelter; Youth development; Community development.

Type of support: Equipment; Program development; Scholarship funds.

Limitations: Giving limited to the greater South Haven, MI, area. No support for organizations lacking 501(c)(3) status.

Application information: Grant awards are made quarterly.

Advisory Board: Dick Averill; Bruce Barker; Tyler Dotson; Gwen DeBruyn; Dorann Fleming; Ann Habicht; Don Hixson; Jim Marcoux; Glenn Pientenpol; Bill Rockhold; Gordon D. Smith; Pamela Utke; Janice Varney; Karen Willming.

2393
Southeast Ottawa Community Foundation

(formerly Hudsonville Community Fund)
c/o Grand Rapids Community Foundation
161 Ottawa Ave. N.W., Ste. 209-C
Grand Rapids, MI   49503-2757
Contact: Kate Luckert, Prog. Dir.
Tel.: (616) 454-1751, ext. 117;
E-mail: kluckert@grfoundation.org; URL: http://www.grfoundation.org/ottawa/

Established in 1990 in MI; an affiliate of Grand Rapids Community Foundation.

Grantmaker type: Community foundation.

Purpose and activities: The foundation gives priority to projects that address the areas of art and culture, community development, education, environment, health, or social needs.

Fields of interest: Arts; Education; Environment; Health care; Human services; Community development.

Limitations: Giving limited to Georgetown Township, Hudsonville, and Jamestown Township, MI. No support for religious organizations for religious purposes, or organizations lacking 501(c)(3) status. No grants to individuals, or for annual fundraising drives, endowments or debt reduction, capital projects without site control, medical research, ongoing operating expenses of established institutions, sabbatical leaves, scholarly research, travel, tours or trips, underwriting of conferences, films, videos or television projects, or venture capital for competitive profit-making activities.

Application information: Accepts CMF Common Grant Application Form. See foundation Web site for full guidelines and requirements. Application form required.

Copies of proposal: 14

2394
Southfield Community Foundation

25630 Evergreen Rd.
Southfield, MI   48075   (248) 796-4190
Contact: Warren E. Goodell, Exec. Dir.
E-mail: info@scfmi.org; URL: http://www.scfmi.org

Established in 1989 in MI.

Grantmaker type: Community foundation.

Financial data (yr. ended 6/30/04): Assets, $1,802,367 (M); gifts received, $60,379; expenditures, $170,500; total giving, $30,247; giving activities include $27,997 for 10 grants (high: $5,000; low: $400), and $2,250 for 4 grants to individuals (high: $750; low: $500).

Purpose and activities: The foundation seeks to connect people who care with causes that matter in the local community. The foundation focuses on systematic change, enabling philanthropy and empowering collaborative efforts.

Fields of interest: Arts, cultural/ethnic awareness; Arts; Education, public education; Higher education; Education; Youth development; Civil rights, race/intergroup relations; Community development; Aging.

Type of support: Emergency funds; Program development; Seed money; Curriculum development; Scholarships—to individuals.

Limitations: Giving limited to the Southfield and Lathrup Village, MI, area. No support for sectarian or religious purposes or programs/projects that duplicate existing services. No grants to individuals (except for scholarships), or for endowments, debt reduction, or operational, maintenance, or ongoing program expenses, fundraising events, or advertising.

Publications: Financial statement; Grants list.

Application information: Accepts CMF Common Grant Application Form. Applicants are encouraged to call the foundation to review the scope and appropriateness of their proposals before submitting a formal application. Visit foundation Web site for application guidelines. Application form not required.

Initial approach: Telephone
Copies of proposal: 1
Deadline(s): None
Board meeting date(s): Approximately 6 times annually
Final notification: Varies

Officers and Directors:* Michael Balloch,* Interim Chair.; Louise Beller,* Secy.; Tracey Ewing,* Treas.; Warren E. Goodell, Exec. Dir.; and 21 additional directors.

Number of staff: 1 full-time professional; 1 part-time professional.

EIN: 382918048

2395
Sparta Community Foundation

c/o Grand Rapids Community Foundation
161 Ottawa Ave., N.W., Ste. 209-C
Grand Rapids, MI   49503
Contact: Kate Luckert, Prog. Dir.; Cris Kooyer, Youth Prog. Assoc.
Tel.: (616) 454-1751, ext. 117;
E-mail: kluckert@grfoundation.org; URL: http://www.grfoundation.org/sparta/

Established in 1996 in MI as a regional affiliate of Grand Rapids Community Foundation.

Grantmaker type: Community foundation.

Purpose and activities: The foundation gives priority to projects that address the areas of art and culture, community development, education, environment, health, or social needs.
Fields of interest: Arts; Education; Health care; Human services; Community development.
Type of support: Equipment; Seed money; Building/renovation; Capital campaigns.
Limitations: Giving limited to the greater Sparta, MI, area. No support for religious organizations for religious purposes, or organizations lacking 501(c)(3) status. No grants to individuals, or for annual fundraising drives, endowments or debt reduction, capital projects without site control, medical research, ongoing operating expenses of established institutions, sabbatical leaves, scholarly research, travel, tours or trips, underwriting of conferences, films, videos or television projects, or venture capital for competitive profit-making activities.
Application information: See foundation Web site for information on RFP process.
Number of staff: None.

2396
Sterling Heights Community Foundation
P.O. Box 7023
Sterling Heights, MI 48311-7023
URL: http://www.ci.sterling-heights.mi.us

Established in 1991 in MI.
Grantmaker type: Community foundation.
Financial data (yr. ended 12/31/04): Assets, $390,303 (M); gifts received, $75,884; expenditures, $90,836; total giving, $10,000; giving activities include $10,000 for 10 grants to individuals (high: $1,000; low: $1,000), and $76,670 for 7 foundation-administered programs.
Purpose and activities: The goals of the foundation are to: 1) initiate and coordinate functions and activities within Sterling Heights, MI to enhance the quality of life of its citizens; 2) award grants and/or support projects that are in accordance with the foundation's purpose; 3) acquire, improve and preserve historical areas, public facilities, and parks and recreational areas of Sterling Heights; 4) offer tax benefits to the foundation's contributors; and 5) develop civic leadership and initiate civic action.
Fields of interest: Arts; Education; Recreation.
Type of support: Scholarships—to individuals.
Limitations: Giving primarily in Sterling Heights, MI.
Application information: Visit foundation Web site for scholarship application information.
  Initial approach: Contact foundation
  Deadline(s): Nov. 17 for scholarships
Board Members: Karl G. Oskoian, Pres.; Michael Lazzara, Treas.; Ken Lampar, Exec. Dir.; Frank E. Henke, Legal Counsel; Lil Adams; John Bozymowski; Dr. Martin Brown; Larry Calcaterra; Ron Chriss; Wallace Doebler; Brian Glowiak; Randy Happel; Herb Harbaugh; Mark Hurst; Alexandria Maciag; Michael McCurry; Phil Ruggeri.
EIN: 383004613

2397
Straits Area Community Foundation
c/o Community Foundation for Northeast Michigan
P.O. Box 495
Alpena, MI 49707 (877) 354-6881
Contact: Christine Hitch

FAX: (989) 356-3319; E-mail: cbruske@cfnem.org; URL: http://www.sacf.net/

Established in 1998 in MI as an affiliate of the Community Foundation for Northeast Michigan.
Grantmaker type: Community foundation.
Purpose and activities: The foundation seeks to serve Cheboygan County and Mackinaw City and to preserve the charitable goals of a wide range of donors now and for generations to come by supporting 501(c)(3) organizations, schools, churches for non-religious purposes, and government agencies.
Type of support: Building/renovation; Equipment; Program development; Conferences/seminars; Publication; Seed money; Technical assistance; Scholarships—to individuals.
Limitations: Giving limited to Cheboygan County or Mackinaw City, MI. No grants to individuals (except for scholarships), or routine operating needs or budget deficits.
Publications: Application guidelines; Annual report; Financial statement; Grants list; Informational brochure; Newsletter.
Application information: See foundation Web site for Common Grant Application Form and requirements. Application form required.
  Final notification: Within 6 weeks of the grant deadlines
Officers and Trustees:* Katie Darrow,* Pres.; Dean Scheerens,* V.P.; Jenifer Lee; Joann Leal; Marilyn McFarland; Alex McVey; Kathy Scoon; Lawton Smith.

2398
Sturgis Area Community Foundation
(formerly Sturgis Foundation)
310 N. Franks Ave.
Sturgis, MI 49091
FAX: (269) 659-8508; E-mail: stfound@i2k.com

Established in 1962 in MI.
Grantmaker type: Community foundation.
Financial data (yr. ended 3/31/05): Assets, $9,848,117 (M); gifts received, $700,681; expenditures, $596,844; total giving, $410,045; giving activities include $410,045 for 30 grants (high: $169,500).
Purpose and activities: The foundation seeks to provide benefits to area community charitable organizations.
Fields of interest: Human services.
Type of support: General/operating support; Capital campaigns; Building/renovation; Equipment; Program development; Scholarship funds; Consulting services; Scholarships—to individuals; Matching/challenge support; Student loans—to individuals.
Limitations: Giving limited to the Sturgis, MI, area. No support for religious organizations. No grants for new business loans.
Publications: Application guidelines; Annual report; Financial statement; Grants list; Informational brochure; Informational brochure (including application guidelines).
Application information: Application form required.
  Copies of proposal: 10
  Deadline(s): May 1 and Nov. 1
  Board meeting date(s): Monthly
  Final notification: June 30 and Dec. 31
Officers and Trustees:* James Goethals,* Chair.; Laura Brothers,* Vice-Chair.; Mary Dresser, Co-Dir.; John Wiedlea, Co-Dir.; Tom Kool; LeeAnn McConnell;

Kelly Murphy; Sheila Riley; John Svendsen; Philip Ward.
Number of staff: 1 full-time professional; 1 part-time support.
EIN: 383649922

2399
Three Rivers Area Community Foundation
(formerly Three Rivers Community Foundation)
P.O. Box 453
Three Rivers, MI 49093 (269) 279-7402
Contact: James Stuck, Pres.

Established in 1974 in MI.
Grantmaker type: Community foundation.
Financial data (yr. ended 12/31/04): Assets, $1,413,862 (M); gifts received, $58,725; expenditures, $75,526; total giving, $44,142; giving activities include $35,392 for 13 grants, and $8,750 for 7 grants to individuals (high: $1,000; low: $500).
Purpose and activities: The Three Rivers Area Community Foundation, serving three rivers and surrounding townships, is dedicated to the growth and stewardship of donor funds, while improving the quality of life in the community through pro-active problem solving, partnerships with others of similar goals, and responsible grantmaking.
Fields of interest: Performing arts, theater; Performing arts, music; Historic preservation/historical societies; Arts; Libraries/library science; Scholarships/financial aid; Education; Hospitals (general); Health care; Health organizations; Crime/violence prevention, domestic violence; Housing/shelter, development; Recreation; Family services; Residential/custodial care, hospices; Community development.
Type of support: Capital campaigns; Building/renovation; Equipment; Seed money; Scholarship funds; Scholarships—to individuals.
Limitations: Giving limited to the city of Three Rivers and surrounding townships in MI. No support for religious purposes, or special interest groups that appeal only to a narrow band of citizens. No grants to individuals (except for scholarships), or for profit ventures.
Publications: Annual report; Informational brochure.
Application information: Application form required.
  Initial approach: Letter or telephone
  Copies of proposal: 8
  Deadline(s): Apr. 1 and Nov. 1
  Board meeting date(s): Feb., May, Aug., and Nov. 1
  Final notification: After board meeting
Officers and Trustees:* James Stuck,* Pres.; Patricia S. Burke,* Secy.-Treas.; Carolyn Roberts, Exec. Dir.; Joe Bippus; Sally Carpenter; John Carton; Richard Dyer; Richard Gatton; Phil Hoffine; Carl Howe; Thomas Meyer; David T. Stuck.
EIN: 382051672
Selected grants: The following grants were reported in 2005.
$6,300 to Keystone Place, Centreville, MI. For furnace.
$5,000 to Three Rivers Area Mentoring, Three Rivers, MI. For mentoring program elementary students.
$4,450 to Three Rivers, City of, Three Rivers, MI. 2 grants: $2,000 (For harmony fest), $2,450 (For nature programs in park).
$3,500 to Silliman House Museum. For building restoration.
$3,000 to Domestic Assault Shelter Coalition, Three Rivers, MI. For operating support.

$2,500 to Carnegie Center Council for the Arts, Three Rivers, MI. For equipment.

$2,000 to Fontana Chamber Arts, Kalamazoo, MI. For concerts.

$2,000 to Glen Oaks Community College, Centreville, MI. For program support.

$2,000 to Kalamazoo Symphony Society, Kalamazoo, MI. For concert.

2400
Tuscola County Community Foundation

P.O. Box 534
Caro, MI 48723 (989) 673-8223
Contact: Ken Micklash, Exec. Dir.
E-mail: tccf534@yahoo.com

Established in 1997 in MI.
Grantmaker type: Community foundation.
Financial data (yr. ended 12/31/04): Assets, $4,029,874 (M); gifts received, $219,908; expenditures, $191,693; total giving, $102,817; giving activities include $102,817 for grants.
Purpose and activities: Support in the areas of human services, recreation, education, youth, and seniors.
Fields of interest: Education; Recreation; Youth development; Human services; Aging.
Type of support: Program development; Building/renovation; Equipment; Endowments; Emergency funds; Seed money; Curriculum development; Scholarship funds; Matching/challenge support.
Limitations: Giving limited to Tuscola County, MI.
Publications: Application guidelines; Annual report; Financial statement; Grants list; Informational brochure; Newsletter.
Application information: Application form required.
Initial approach: Letter or telephone
Copies of proposal: 5
Deadline(s): Mar. 15 and Sept. 15

Board meeting date(s): 4th Thurs., quarterly
Final notification: 3 months
Officers and Board Members:* Susan Andrus,* Pres.; Steve Cook,* V.P.; Dorothy Scollon,* Secy.; Sherri Diegel,* Treas.; Ken Micklash, Exec. Dir.; Sara Dost; Richard F. Kern; Richards B. Randsford; Sue Ransford; James E. Reehl; Cheryl Seeley; Randy Stee; Jill White; Dale Wingert.
Number of staff: 1 part-time professional; 1 part-time support.
EIN: 383351315

2401
Wyoming Community Foundation

c/o Grand Rapids Community Foundation
161 Ottawa Ave. N.W., Ste. 209-C
Grand Rapids, MI 49503
Contact: Kate Luckert, Prog. Dir.
Tel.: (616) 454-1751, ext. 117;
E-mail: kluckert@grfoundation.org; URL: http://www.grfoundation.org/wyoming/

Established in 1992 in MI as an affiliate of the Grand Rapids Community Foundation.
Grantmaker type: Community foundation.
Purpose and activities: The foundation gives priority to projects that address the areas of art and culture, community development, education, environment, health, or social needs.
Fields of interest: Arts; Education; Environment; Health care; Human services; Community development.
Type of support: Seed money; Equipment; Building/renovation; Capital campaigns.
Limitations: Giving limited to the Wyoming, MI, area. No support for religious organizations for religious purposes, or for organizations lacking 501(c)(3) status. No grants to individuals, or for annual fundraising drives, endowments or debt reduction,

capital projects without site control, medical research, ongoing operating expenses of established institutions, sabbatical leaves, scholarly research, travel, tours or trips, underwriting of conferences, films, videos or television projects, or venture capital for competitive profit-making activities.
Publications: Application guidelines; Informational brochure.
Application information: See foundation Web site for RFP information. Application form required.
Number of staff: None.

2402
Ypsilanti Area Community Fund

c/o Ann Arbor Area Community Foundation
201 S. Main St., Ste. 501
Ann Arbor, MI 48104 (734) 663-2173
Contact: Martha Bloom, AAACF V.P.
E-mail: info@aaacf.org; E-mail: mbloom@aaacf.org; URL: http://aaacf.org/yacf.asp

Established in 2001 in MI as a regional affiliate fund of the Ann Arbor Area Community Foundation.
Grantmaker type: Community foundation.
Purpose and activities: The fund is a geographic affiliate fund of the Ann Arbor Area Community Foundation to serve residents of the Ypsilanti area. The fund is a permanent endowment established to support programs, events and projects in the greater Ypsilanti area.
Fields of interest: Community development.
Limitations: Giving limited to the greater Ypsilanti, MI, area.
Application information:
Initial approach: Pre-application discussion of proposal is required to help determine if project is eligible for consideration
Deadline(s): Oct. 6 for letter of intent

PUBLIC CHARITIES

2403
Adrian Kiwanis Foundation, Inc.
121 N. Main St.
Adrian, MI 49221-2711   (517) 265-6154
Contact: Dave Wagley, Pres.

Established in 1985 in MI.
Grantmaker type: Public charity.
Financial data (yr. ended 12/31/04): Revenue, $687,286; assets, $3,759,836 (M); gifts received, $310,717; expenditures, $198,790; total giving, $183,495; program services expenses, $183,495; giving activities include $183,495 for 15 grants (high: $35,000; low: $2,000).
Purpose and activities: The foundation supports education, including scholarship funds, the performing arts, youth, and community development.
Fields of interest: Performing arts; Education; Youth development; Community development.
Type of support: Scholarship funds.
Limitations: Giving limited to Adrian, MI.
Officers and Directors:* Dave Wagley,* Pres.; John Koselka,* V.P.; Linda Arnett; Garry Clift; David Dennis; Patt Hayes; Edward Leahy; Don McCarthy; Dave Mitzell; Paul Mueller; Jeeri Righter; Larry Stephen; Jerry Van Buren.
EIN: 382563747

2404
Albion-Homer United Way
P.O. Box 447
Albion, MI 49224

Established in MI.
Grantmaker type: Public charity.
Financial data (yr. ended 12/31/04): Revenue, $60,577; assets, $63,020 (M); gifts received, $60,003; expenditures, $97,229; total giving, $68,925; program services expenses, $68,925; giving activities include $68,925 for 24 grants (high: $13,500; low: $275).
Fields of interest: Community development.
Officers: M. Sue Klepper, Pres.; Sharon Ponds, V.P.; Pauline Story, Secy.; Melissa Hoath, Treas.; Terry Langston, Exec. Dir.
Directors: Martin P. Blashfield; Miriam Daly; Barbara Frederick; Sharon Harris; Diana Holdridge; Gerry Nelson; Walter Nichols; Juanita Solis-Kidder; Scott Stephen.
EIN: 381841180

2405
Allegan County United Way
650 Grand St.
Allegan, MI 49010

Established in MI.
Grantmaker type: Public charity.
Financial data (yr. ended 6/30/05): Revenue, $631,410; assets, $764,143 (M); gifts received, $623,876; expenditures, $595,890; total giving, $329,425; program services expenses, $508,884;

giving activities include $293,858 for 22+ grants (high: $19,550), and $35,567 for in-kind gifts.
Purpose and activities: The organization seeks to increase the impact of people's caring in Allegan County and further those efforts by connecting and supporting volunteers and groups for the betterment of the community.
Fields of interest: Community development.
Type of support: In-kind gifts.
Limitations: Giving primarily in Allegan County, MI.
Officers and Directors:* John Mellein,* Pres.; Mary Howard,* V.P.; Pam Reed,* Secy.; Rebecca Lamper,* Treas.; Cindy Bezaury; Barb Boot; Cathy Burton-Snell; Timothy Dickinson, M.D.; Larry Johnson; Brian Kilbane; and 5 additional directors.
EIN: 386063214

2406
Altrusa International, Inc. of Saginaw, Michigan Foundation
405 N. Center Rd.
Saginaw, MI 48603   (989) 799-2441
Contact: Jan Barber, Pres.
Additional tel.: (989) 868-4077; URL: http://www.altrusaofsaginawmi.bravehost.com/Foundation.html

Established in 2004 in MI as an affiliate of Altrusa International, Inc. Foundation.
Grantmaker type: Public charity.
Purpose and activities: The foundation focuses on contributions and support of the charitable and service projects of Altrusa Interntional, Inc. of Saginaw, Michigan.
Fields of interest: Adult education—literacy, basic skills & GED; Education; Children/youth, services; Family services; Community development; Women.
Limitations: Applications not accepted. Giving limited generally to the greater Saginaw County, MI, area; also some international giving.
Officers: Beth Bauer, Pres.; Patty Shaheen, V.P.; Carolyn Otto, Secy.; Sylvia Reimus, Treas.
Director: Jan Barber.
EIN: 383684913

2407
American Autoimmune Related Diseases Association
22100 Gratiot Ave.
East Detroit, MI 48021   (586) 776-3900
Contact: Virginia T. Ladd, Pres. and Exec. Dir.
E-mail: aarda@aol.com; URL: http://www.aarda.org

Grantmaker type: Public charity.
Financial data (yr. ended 9/30/05): Revenue, $482,072; assets, $476,146 (M); gifts received, $478,478; expenditures, $480,759; total giving, $97,750; program services expenses, $438,618; giving activities include $97,750 for 19 grants (high: $20,000; low: $250).
Purpose and activities: The organization is dedicated to the eradication of autoimmune diseases and the alleviation of suffering and the

socioeconomic impact of autoimmunity through fostering and facilitating collaboration in the areas of education, public awareness, research, and patient services in an effective, ethical, and efficient manner.
Fields of interest: Immunology research.
Type of support: Research.
Limitations: Applications not accepted. Giving on a national basis.
Publications: Annual report; Financial statement; Informational brochure; Newsletter.
Application information: Contributes only to pre-selected organizations.
  Board meeting date(s): 3 times per year
Officers and Directors:* Stanley M. Finger, Ph.D.*, Chair.; Virginia T. Ladd, RT*, Pres. and Exec. Dir.; Michelle Ouellet,* Secy.; Robert Meyer, C.P.A.*, Treas.; T. Stephen Balch, M.D.; John McCarthy; and 6 additional directors.
Number of staff: 1 full-time professional; 3 part-time professional; 1 part-time support.
EIN: 383027574

2408
American Dysautonomia Institute
28879 Willow Creek
Farmington Hills, MI 48331   (248) 470-3992
Contact: Gil Chinitz, Grant/Fdn. Librarian
FAX: (248) 553-4529;
E-mail: librarian@adiwebsite.org; Additional addresses: California office: 1399 9th Ave., No. 718, San Diego, CA 92101, tel.: (248) 470-3992, Florida office: 2760 Night Hawk Ct., Longwood, FL 32779, tel.: (248) 470-3992, Illinois office: 1411 W. Ohio St., No. 1R, Chicago, IL 60622, tel.: (248) 470-3992, South Carolina office: 1578 Dowden Ct., Charleston, SC 29407, tel: (248) 470-3992; URL: http://www.adiwebsite.org/

Established in 2004 in MI.
Grantmaker type: Public charity.
Purpose and activities: The institute funds non-familial dysautonomia research, a disease of the autonomic nervous system. The institute also advocates for increased research funding and disease awareness.
Fields of interest: Health care, public policy; Medicine/medical care, public education; Medical research.
Type of support: Research.
Limitations: Giving on a national basis.
Application information: Applicant institution must be headed by a medical doctor, osteopathic physician, or an individual with an with an appropriately related earned Ph.D., and must have a track record of research regarding or treatment of non-familial dysautonomia. Application form not required.
  Initial approach: Letter

2409
American Federation of Ramallah Education Fund
27484 Ann Arbor Trail
Westland, MI 48185 (734) 425-1600
Contact: Roy Watts

Grantmaker type: Public charity.
Financial data (yr. ended 5/31/05): Revenue, $110,237; assets, $2,289,073 (M); gifts received, $27,530; expenditures, $122,698; total giving, $15,000; program services expenses, $76,457; giving activities include $15,000 for grants to individuals.
Purpose and activities: The fund fosters cooperation in the Ramallah community to perpetuate and enhance closer ties to Ramallah people and to enhance appreciation of the culture and history of the Ramallah community.
Fields of interest: Arts, cultural/ethnic awareness.
Application information: Application form required.
   Deadline(s): May 31
Officers and Directors:* David Batch,* Pres.; Terry Ahwal-Morris,* Secy.; Hanna Faris,* Treas.; Salem Abdelnour; Karim Ajloni; Sonya Kassis; George N. Khoury; Michael Mufarreh; Hala Taweel.
EIN: 386096449

2410
American Israel Education Fund
2301 W. Big Beaver Rd., Ste. 900
Troy, MI 48084

Supporting organization of First Traditional School of Jerusalem and the University of Michigan at Ann Arbor.
Grantmaker type: Public charity.
Financial data (yr. ended 6/30/05): Assets, $368,454 (M); gifts received, $298,550; expenditures, $588,198; total giving, $554,530; giving activities include $554,530 for 2 grants (high: $287,030; low: $267,500).
Fields of interest: Higher education; Education.
International interests: Israel.
Limitations: Giving limited to Jerusalem, Israel, and Ann Arbor, MI. No grants to individuals.
Application information: Contributes only to pre-selected organizations; unsolicited requests for funds not considered or acknowledged.
Officers and Directors:* Samuel Frankel,* Pres.; Barbara Levin,* Exec. V.P.; William Davidson,* V.P.; Stanley Frankel,* Secy.-Treas.; Robert Aronsovo; Mandell Berman; Sol Drachler; and 6 additional directors.
EIN: 382232754

2411
The Anderson Fund
c/o Comm. Fdn. for Southeastern Michigan
333 W. Fort St., Ste. 2010
Detroit, MI 48226 (313) 961-6675
Contact: Mariam C. Noland, Secy.-Treas.

Incorporated in 1952 in MI; became an affiliate of the Community Foundation for Southeastern Michigan in 1991.
Grantmaker type: Public charity.
Financial data (yr. ended 12/31/04): Revenue, $147,927; assets, $3,848,717 (M); expenditures, $238,891; total giving, $149,000; program services expenses, $209,095; giving activities

include $149,000 for 11 grants (high: $25,000; low: $500).
Purpose and activities: The organization provides support to certain nonprofit organizations.
Fields of interest: Arts; Education; Community development.
Type of support: General/operating support.
Limitations: Giving primarily in MI. No support for organizations currently receiving funds from other organizations which the foundation supports. No grants to individuals.
Application information: Require ID of applicant's charitable status and outline of the intended charitable purpose of the funds required. Application form not required.
   Board meeting date(s): As required
Officers and Directors:* Wendell W. Anderson, Jr.,* Pres.; John W. Anderson II,* V.P.; Mariam C. Noland,* Secy.-Treas.; William K. Howenstein; Joseph L. Hudson, Jr.
EIN: 386053694

2412
Andersons Fund Supporting Organization
c/o Toledo Community Foundation, Inc.
608 Madison Ave., Ste. 1540
Toledo, OH 43604-1151
Contact: Keith Burwell, Secy.-Treas.

Established in OH; supporting organization of Toledo Community Foundation, Inc.
Grantmaker type: Public charity.
Financial data (yr. ended 12/31/04): Revenue, $117,324; assets, $4,511,044 (M); expenditures, $441,816; total giving, $416,042; program services expenses, $416,042; giving activities include $416,042 for 17 grants (high: $100,000; low: $5,000).
Purpose and activities: Support for organizations with programs in the areas of education, social services, physical and mental health, neighborhood and urban affairs, natural resources and the arts.
Fields of interest: Arts; Education; Environment, natural resources; Health care; Mental health/crisis services; Human services; Urban/community development; Community development.
Type of support: Capital campaigns.
Limitations: Giving primarily in southeast MI and northwest OH, with emphasis on the greater Toledo area. No support for organizations lacking 501(c)(3) status; generally no support for sectarian activities of religious organizations. No grants to individuals, or generally for endowment campaigns, annual or ongoing operating costs, or for new, untested programs.
Application information:
   Initial approach: Narrative proposal, no more than 5 or 6 pages
   Deadline(s): Apr. 15
   Final notification: By late July
Officers and Trustees:* Joel Levine,* Pres.; Keith Burwell,* Secy.-Treas.; Thomas H. Anderson; Dale Fallat; Donald Saunders.
EIN: 341817757

2413
Ann Arbor Film Festival
203 E. Ann St.
Ann Arbor, MI 48104 (734) 995-5356
Contact: Christen McArdle, Exec. Dir.

FAX: (734) 995-5396; E-mail: info@aafilmfest.org; URL: http://aafilmfest.org

Established in 1963 in MI.
Grantmaker type: Public charity.
Financial data (yr. ended 10/31/04): Revenue, $177,230; assets, $47,095 (M); gifts received, $57,330; expenditures, $174,113; program services expenses, $124,539.
Purpose and activities: The festival seeks to encourage (through awards and prizes) the work of the independent and experimental filmmaker; to promote the concept of film as art; and to organize and present an annual film festival of 16mm independent and experimental film.
Fields of interest: Media, film/video.
Limitations: Giving limited to Ann Arbor, MI.
Publications: Informational brochure (including application guidelines); Newsletter.
Application information: An entry form must be completed for each film entered, accompanied by a $35 entry fee for each film. Application procedures available on festival's Web site. Application form required.
   Initial approach: Letter or telephone for guidelines
   Deadline(s): Dec. 1
   Final notification: Feb. 20
Officer: Christen McArdle, Exec. Dir.
Directors: Steve Bergman; Tom Bray; Heidi Kumao; Tara McComb; Ed McDonald; Jay Nelson; Bryan Rogers; Joe Tiboni.
Number of staff: 2 part-time professional.
EIN: 382379836

2414
Applebaum Family Support Foundation
P.O. Box 2030
6735 Telegraph Rd.
Bloomfield Hills, MI 48301

Established in 1989; a supporting organization of the Jewish Federation of Metropolitan Detroit.
Grantmaker type: Public charity.
Financial data (yr. ended 5/31/05): Revenue, $293,584; assets, $1,651,578 (M); gifts received, $120,000; expenditures, $563,857; total giving, $532,005; program services expenses, $532,005; giving activities include $532,005 for 2 grants (high: $332,005; low: $200,000).
Purpose and activities: The foundation is a supporting organization of the Jewish Federation of Metropolitan Detroit, for medical research, education, the arts, and Jewish programs.
Fields of interest: Arts; Higher education; Medical research; Jewish federated giving programs; Jewish agencies & temples.
Type of support: General/operating support; Research.
Limitations: Giving limited to Detroit, MI.
Officers and Directors:* Eugene Applebaum,* Pres.; Marcia Applebaum,* V.P.; Robert R. Aronson,* Secy.; Dorothy Benyas,* Treas.; Lisa Applebaum; Pamela Applebaum; Robert R. Aronson; Penny Blumenstein; Mark Hauser; Doreen Hermelin; Lawrence S. Jackier.
EIN: 382870708

2415
Arts Council of Greater Kalamazoo
359 S. Kalamazoo Mall
Kalamazoo, MI 49007 (269) 342-5059
FAX: (269) 342-6531;
E-mail: info@kalamazooarts.com; URL: http://
www.kalamazooarts.com

Established in 1966 in MI.
Grantmaker type: Public charity.
Financial data (yr. ended 9/30/05): Revenue,
$947,273; assets, $400,599 (M); gifts received,
$890,124; expenditures, $868,848; total giving,
$310,216; program services expenses, $590,400;
giving activities include $310,216 for grants.
Purpose and activities: The council funds,
promotes, and supports the arts and culture of
Kalamazoo County, Michigan, through its
involvement in many activities for individual artists
and member arts and cultural organizations, such as
arts management, audience development, cultural
tourism, and educational programs. As a regional
re-granting program, the council re-grants funds from
the Michigan Council of Arts and Cultural Affairs, as
well as funds from private local foundations.
Fields of interest: Arts, artist's services; Arts.
Type of support: General/operating support;
Continuing support; Equipment; Program
development; Conferences/seminars; Publication;
Internship funds; Scholarship funds; Technical
assistance; Consulting services; Program
evaluation; Grants to individuals.
Limitations: Giving limited to residents of
Kalamazoo County, MI, for most programs and to
Barry, Berrien, Cass, Kalamazoo, St. Joseph, and
Van Buren counties, MI, for State Regional minigrant
(decentralized) program. No grants for capital
improvements, endowment, consulting services,
publication, fundraising, or for existing deficits of
more than two years.
Publications: Application guidelines; Annual report;
Biennial report; Grants list; Informational brochure;
Informational brochure (including application
guidelines); Multi-year report; Newsletter; Program
policy statement.
Application information: First-time applicants for
Arts Council grants, and repeat applicants whose
prior applications were not funded, must schedule
an appointment to discuss application criteria and
procedures. See Web site for additional application
guidelines. Application form required.
Initial approach: Telephone or e-mail
Deadline(s): Jan. 10, Apr. 1, July 1, and Oct. 1 for
Gilmore Emerging Artist Grant; Feb. 1 and July
1 for MCACA Region Mini-grants; Mar. 1 for Arts
Outreach Fund; June 1 for Capacity Building
Grant; Dec. 1 for Arts Fund
Board meeting date(s): 2nd Thurs. of each month
Final notification: Varies
Officers and Directors:* Anne Fassler,* Pres.;
James M. Marquardt,* V.P.; Norman L. Hamann, Jr.,
Secy.; Gail Shuster Morton, Treas.; Kathleen M.
Tosco, Exec. Dir.; Robert Beam; Robert S. Doud;
Brooks Godfrey; Carole Spight Greene; and 14
additional directors.
Number of staff: 4 full-time professional; 1 full-time
support; 1 part-time support.
EIN: 386121183

2416
Arts Midwest
2908 Hennepin Ave., Ste. 200
Minneapolis, MN 55408-1987 (612) 341-0755
Contact: David J. Fraher, Exec. Dir.
FAX: (612) 341-0902;
E-mail: general@artsmidwest.org; Additional tel. (for
Performing Arts Fund): (816) 421-1388; TDD: (612)
822-2956; URL: http://www.artsmidwest.org

Established in 1985 in MN.
Grantmaker type: Public charity.
Financial data (yr. ended 6/30/04): Revenue,
$4,775,487; assets, $3,921,907 (M); gifts
received, $4,285,598; expenditures, $5,127,010;
total giving, $1,531,485; program services
expenses, $4,709,209; giving activities include
$1,531,485 for 160 grants (high: $55,000; low:
$500).
Purpose and activities: The organization enables
individuals and families throughout America's
heartland to share in and enjoy the art and culture
of their region and the world. Giving is primarily to
performing arts presenters.
Fields of interest: Performing arts.
Type of support: Matching/challenge support.
Limitations: Giving limited to IA, IL, IN, MI, MN, ND,
OH, SD, and WI.
Publications: Application guidelines.
Application information: Applications will be
reviewed on a first-come, first-served basis. Early
application may increase the likelihood of funding.
Application form required.
Initial approach: Download application form
Deadline(s): May 2 for Performing Arts Fund
Board meeting date(s): May and Nov.
Officer and Directors:* David J. Fraher,* Exec. Dir.;
Tom Benson; Peter Capell; Loann Crane; Ken
Fischer; Dennis Holub; William H. Jackson; Sylvia C.
Kaufman; Leonard Pas; Rhoda A. Pierce; Barbara
Robinson; Anita Walker; Pam Perri Weaver; Jan
Webb; Woodie T. White.
Number of staff: 9 full-time professional; 3 full-time
support.
EIN: 411000424

2417
ArtServe Michigan
17515 W. Nine Mile Rd., Ste. 1025
Southfield, MI 48075 (248) 557-8288
Contact: Barbara Kratchman, Pres.
FAX: (248) 557-8581;
E-mail: bkratchman@artservemichigan.org;
URL: http://www.artservemichigan.org

Established in 1997 in MI through a merger of Arts
Fdn. of Michigan, Business Volunteers for the Arts,
Concerned Citizens for the Arts in Michigan, and
Michigan Alliance for Arts Education.
Grantmaker type: Public charity.
Financial data (yr. ended 9/30/04): Revenue,
$697,984; assets, $837,039 (M); gifts received,
$285,492; expenditures, $946,464; total giving,
$6,988; program services expenses, $627,810;
giving activities include $6,988 for grants.
Purpose and activities: The organization serves,
supports, and advocates for an enriched cultural
environment, and promotes the arts as a valuable
state and community resource. It assists and
informs individuals and organizations in the state of
Michigan through education, professional services,
networking, support of artists and cultural

organizations, volunteer assistance, and
collaborations.
Fields of interest: Arts education; Arts.
Type of support: Conferences/seminars; Grants to
individuals.
Limitations: Giving limited to MI.
Publications: Financial statement; Informational
brochure; Newsletter.
Application information: See Web site for
application forms and guidelines. Application form
required.
Initial approach: Telephone or e-mail
Copies of proposal: 6
Board meeting date(s): Quarterly
Officers and Directors:* Karen Mulvahill,* Chair.;
Nancy Barker,* Vice-Chair., Nominating; Barbara
Kratchman,* Pres.; David Mix,* Secy.; Randy
Paschke,* Treas.; Steven Antoniotti; Bruce Ashley;
Lillian Bauder; Leon Cohan; and 32 additional
directors.
Number of staff: 6 full-time professional.
EIN: 382537585

2418
Assistance League to the Northeast Guidance Center
20303 Kelly Rd.
Detroit, MI 48225 (313) 245-7012
E-mail: administrator@alnegc.org; URL: http://
www.alnegc.org

Established in 1964 in MI; supporting organization
of the Northeast Guidance Center.
Grantmaker type: Public charity.
Financial data (yr. ended 8/31/05): Revenue,
$345,400; assets, $19,757 (M); expenditures,
$344,337; total giving, $338,528; program
services expenses, $338,528; giving activities
include $338,528 for grants.
Purpose and activities: The league supports and
enhances related healthcare services that impact
high-risk children and adults on Detroit's Eastside.
Fields of interest: Health care; Human services.
Limitations: Giving limited to Detroit, MI.
Publications: Newsletter.
Officers and Directors:* Mary Wolking,* Pres.;
Debbie Dubay,* Pres.-Elect; Geraldine Lacombe,*
1st V.P., Projects; Nancy Dloski,* 2nd V.P.,
Membership; Susan Allison,* 3rd V.P., Service;
Karen Horn,* Treas.; Allison Kuhnlein; Sue Martin.
EIN: 237012010

2419
Asthma & Allergy Foundation of America - Michigan Chapter
17520 W. 12 Mile Rd., Ste. 102
Southfield, MI 48076 (248) 557-8050
Contact: Mary Hagen R.N., Exec. Dir.
FAX: (248) 557-8768;
E-mail: aafamich@sbcglobal.net; Toll-free tel.: (888)
444-0333; URL: http://www.aafamich.org

Established in 1985 in MI.
Grantmaker type: Public charity.
Financial data (yr. ended 12/31/05): Revenue,
$93,420; assets, $73,751 (M); gifts received,
$62,856; expenditures, $108,241; total giving,
$4,713; program services expenses, $88,112;
giving activities include $4,713 for 1 grant.
Purpose and activities: The foundation seeks to
improve the quality of life for individuals affected by

asthma and allergic diseases and to promote awareness of these disorders.

Fields of interest: Education; Environment; Public health; Allergies; Asthma.

Type of support: Annual campaigns; Scholarships—to individuals.

Limitations: Giving limited to MI.

Publications: Application guidelines; Informational brochure; Newsletter.

Application information: Application form required.
Initial approach: Download application form
Deadline(s): Mar. 10 for Camp Michi-MAC; and Sept. 1 for Jean Mullins Yonke Asthma Scholarship
Board meeting date(s): Quarterly
Final notification: Apr. 1 for Camp Michi-MAC; and Sept. 15 for Scholarship

Officers and Directors:* Lawrence Pasik, M.D.*, Pres.; Linda Brunetto, R.N.*, V.P., Progs.; Clyde Flory, M.D.*, V.P., Comms./Legislative Affairs; Irving Miller, M.D.*, V.P., Devel.; Jacqueline Moore, M.D.*, V.P., Medical Affairs; Susan Stridiron, R.N., B.S.N.*, Secy.; Matthew Hunter,* Treas.; Mary Hagen, R.N., Exec. Dir.; Carol Finkelstein; Lana Hardin; Melissa Peura; Allen Sosin, M.D.; and 7 additional directors.

Number of staff: 1 full-time professional.

EIN: 382534175

2420
Atanas Ilitch Osteosarcoma Foundation

2211 Woodward Ave.
Detroit, MI 48201-3460 (313) 983-6070

Grantmaker type: Public charity.

Financial data (yr. ended 12/31/04): Revenue, $3,868; assets, $342,788 (M); expenditures, $82,771; total giving, $82,728; program services expenses, $82,728; giving activities include $60,000 for 2 grants (high: $50,000; low: $10,000), and $22,728 for grants to individuals.

Purpose and activities: The foundation provides assistance to individuals and organizations dedicated to research and treatment of people diagnosed with osteosarcoma.

Fields of interest: Cancer, leukemia.

Type of support: Grants to individuals; Research.

Limitations: Giving primarily in MI.

Officers: Atanas Ilitch, Pres.; Robert Carr, V.P.; Christopher Ilitch, V.P.; Denise Ilitch, V.P.

EIN: 383514195

2421
Barry County United Way

450 Meadow Run
P.O. Box 644
Hastings, MI 49058 (269) 945-4010
FAX: (269) 945-4536; E-mail: bcuw@sbcglobal.net;
URL: http://www.bcunitedway.org/

Grantmaker type: Public charity.

Financial data (yr. ended 3/31/05): Revenue, $481,572; assets, $440,572 (M); gifts received, $479,555; expenditures, $404,030; total giving, $269,844; program services expenses, $338,490; giving activities include $269,844 for grants.

Purpose and activities: The mission of the Barry County United Way is to improve lives by mobilizing the caring power of Barry County communities through five funding areas: preparing youth to become accountable adults, supporting families to

achieve well-being and success, helping senior adults find support and maintain independence, impacting people through positive change, and addressing urgent needs in Barry County.

Fields of interest: Youth development; Family services; Human services, emergency aid; Aging, centers/services; Community development.

Limitations: Giving limited to Barry County, MI.

Application information: See Web site for downloadable allocation application form. Application form required.

Officers and Directors:* Matt Thompson,* Pres.; Jan Hartough,* V.P.; Dana Walters,* Secy.; Chris Fluke,* Treas.; Lani Forbes, Exec. Dir.; Rick Arnett; Joe Babiak; Deb Button; Cort Collison; and 27 additional directors.

EIN: 386062803

2422
Charles F. Barth Trust

c/o Standard Federal Bank N.A.
135 S. LaSalle St., Ste. 2060
Chicago, IL 60603

Established in 1972; supporting organization of St. Paul's Episcopal Church, Flint, MI.

Grantmaker type: Public charity.

Financial data (yr. ended 6/30/05): Revenue, $83,969; assets, $1,822,315 (M); expenditures, $71,457; total giving, $60,612; program services expenses, $60,612; giving activities include $60,612 for 1 grant.

Fields of interest: Protestant agencies & churches.

Limitations: Applications not accepted. Giving limited to Flint, MI.

Application information: Contributes only to a pre-selected organization; unsolicited requests for funds not considered or acknowledged.

Trustee: Standard Federal Bank N.A.

EIN: 386063158

2423
Basilica of St. Adalbert Foundation

701 4th St., N.W.
Grand Rapids, MI 49504-5104

Grantmaker type: Public charity.

Financial data (yr. ended 6/30/05): Revenue, $25,162; assets, $418,637 (M); gifts received, $823; expenditures, $18,200; total giving, $18,160; program services expenses, $18,200; giving activities include $12,480 for grants, and $5,680 for grants to individuals.

Purpose and activities: Support for education through grants and educational scholarships to parishioners of Basilica of St. Adalbert for attendance at Catholic elementary or Catholic high schools.

Fields of interest: Roman Catholic agencies & churches.

Type of support: Scholarships—to individuals.

Limitations: Giving primarily in Grand Rapids, MI.

Officers: Rev. Thomas DeYoung, Pres.; Bernard Prawozik, V.P.; Joan Jung, Secy.; Donald G. Karpinski, Treas.

Directors: Margaret Downer; Raymond Nowak.

EIN: 382685451

2424
Hugh Michael Beahan Foundation

302 Sheldon Blvd. S.E.
Grand Rapids, MI 49503-4516

Established in 1984; supporting organization of St. Andrews School.

Grantmaker type: Public charity.

Financial data (yr. ended 8/31/05): Revenue, $252,227; assets, $896,420 (M); gifts received, $109,269; expenditures, $298,019; total giving, $226,414; program services expenses, $226,414; giving activities include $226,414 for 1 grant.

Fields of interest: Elementary/secondary education; Christian agencies & churches.

Limitations: Applications not accepted. Giving limited to Grand Rapids, MI.

Application information: Contributes only to a pre-selected organization; unsolicited requests for funds not considered or acknowledged.

Officers and Directors:* Lisa McManus,* Pres.; Elizabeth Welch Lykins,* V.P.; Mary Swanson,* Treas.; Margaret Gagen, Exec. Dir.; Rob Beahan; Stan Greene; Margaret Howard; Carol Karr; Ted Vecchio; Marilyn Zack.

Number of staff: 1 full-time professional; 1 part-time support.

EIN: 382500720

2425
Madeleine and Mandell L. Berman Support Foundation

6735 Telegraph Rd.
Bloomfield Hills, MI 48301

Supporting organization of the Jewish Federation of Metropolitan Detroit.

Grantmaker type: Public charity.

Financial data (yr. ended 5/31/05): Revenue, $849,269; assets, $9,045,347 (M); expenditures, $751,171; total giving, $740,500; program services expenses, $740,500; giving activities include $740,500 for 15+ grants (high: $334,000).

Purpose and activities: Support primarily for Jewish agencies, including education; support also for other education and the arts.

Fields of interest: Arts; Education; Jewish federated giving programs; Jewish agencies & temples.

Limitations: Giving on a national basis, with some emphasis on MI and New York City, NY.

Officers: Mandell L. Berman, Pres.; Madeleine H. Berman, V.P.; Robert P. Aronson, Secy.; Dorothy Benyas, Treas.

Directors: Ann Berman; Jonathan Berman, M.D.; David Handleman; Alan E. Schwartz; Joel D. Tauber; Arthur Weiss.

EIN: 382582289

2426
Bethany Ministry Foundation

2930 Holbrook St.
Hamtramck, MI 48212

Grantmaker type: Public charity.

Financial data (yr. ended 12/31/04): Revenue, $29,270; assets, $252; gifts received, $29,270; expenditures, $33,441; total giving, $32,974; program services expenses, $32,974; giving activities include $32,974 for 6 grants (high: $16,274; low: $500).

Fields of interest: Christian agencies & churches.

Limitations: Giving in MI, primarily in Detroit.
Officers: Joseph Ciaramitaro, Pres.; Jerome
Ciaramitaro, Secy.; Robert Kaczmarek, Treas.
EIN: 383592943

2427
The Jerome Bettis "BSH Foundation"
P.O. Box 211089
Detroit, MI 48221 (248) 827-4837
Contact: Gloria Bettis, Dir.
E-mail: foundation@thebus36.com; URL: http://
www.thebus36.com

Established in 1996 in MI.
Grantmaker type: Public charity.
Financial data (yr. ended 12/31/04): Revenue,
$175,570; assets, $42,272 (M); gifts received,
$175,570; expenditures, $224,015; total giving,
$175,570; program services expenses, $213,215;
giving activities include $175,570 for grants.
Purpose and activities: The foundation provides
programs, activities, and services that continue to
help youngsters reach their goals and improve the
quality of life.
Fields of interest: Education; Recreation, centers;
Athletics/sports, academies.
Type of support: Scholarship funds.
Limitations: Giving limited to Detroit, MI.
Officers and Directors:* Gladys Bettis,* Pres.;
Jerome Bettis,* V.P.; Lasundres Davis,* Secy.;
Gloria Bettis.
EIN: 383378049

2428
Birmingham-Bloomfield Symphony Orchestra
1592 Buckingham
Birmingham, MI 48009 (248) 645-2276
Contact: Carla D. Lamphere, Exec. Dir.
Application address: c/o Millicent Berry, 25435
Wareham, Huntington Woods, MI 48070;
URL: http://www.bbso.org/

Established in 1975 in MI.
Grantmaker type: Public charity.
Financial data (yr. ended 6/30/04): Revenue,
$107,684; assets, $28,770 (M); gifts received,
$52,934; expenditures, $114,321; program
services expenses, $79,486.
Purpose and activities: The orchestra maintains a
high quality professional orchestra in the
Birmingham-Bloomfield community and surrounding
areas, and provides the opportunity to experience
quality performances featuring distinguished artists.
Fields of interest: Performing arts, orchestra
(symphony).
Limitations: Giving primarily in MI.
Publications: Informational brochure; Informational
brochure (including application guidelines).
Application information: Applicant must reside in
Michigan and be in the 12th grade and younger.
Application form required only for Young Artist
Competition. Application form required.
  Deadline(s): Dec.
  Board meeting date(s): 3rd Wed. of every month
  Final notification: Varies
Officers and Directors:* Rich Tropea,* Chair.; Carla
Lamphere,* Pres. and Exec. Dir.; Ward Lamphere,*
V.P.; Michael A. Lochricchio, J.D.*, Treas.; Millicent
R. Berry; June McGregor; Kent Shafer; Joan Stern;
Mary Synk; Lucius Theus.

Number of staff: 2
EIN: 382088537

2429
Blissfield First Presbyterian Church Trust
c/o Comerica Bank
P.O. Box 75000, MC 3302
Detroit, MI 48275-3302

Established in 2001 in MI; supporting organization
of First Presbyterian Church of Blissfield, MI.
Grantmaker type: Public charity.
Financial data (yr. ended 12/31/05): Revenue,
$13,377; assets, $300,060 (M); expenditures,
$53,199; total giving, $49,370; program services
expenses, $49,370; giving activities include
$49,370 for 1 grant.
Fields of interest: Protestant agencies & churches.
Type of support: Building/renovation.
Limitations: Applications not accepted. Giving
limited to Blissfield, MI. No grants to individuals.
Application information: Contributes only to a
pre-selected organization; unsolicited requests for
funds not considered or acknowledged.
Trustee: Comerica Bank.
EIN: 386314379

2430
Borders Group Foundation
100 Phoenix Dr.
Ann Arbor, MI 48108 (734) 477-1100
E-mail: bgf@bordersgroupinc.com; URL: http://
www.bordersgroupinc.com/community/
foundation.htm

Donor: Borders Group, Inc.
Grantmaker type: Public charity.
Financial data (yr. ended 12/31/04): Revenue,
$982,169; assets, $2,878,749; gifts received,
$824,045; expenditures, $422,495; total giving,
$396,717; program services expenses, $408,514;
giving activities include $396,717 for grants to
individuals.
Purpose and activities: The foundation provides
assistance to employees of Borders Group, Inc. and
their immediate families who have demonstrated
financial need in times of hardship or emergency
and also provides scholarships to employees.
Type of support: Employee-related scholarships;
Grants to individuals.
Limitations: Applications not accepted. Giving on a
national basis.
Application information: Unsolicited requests for
funds not accepted.
Officers and Board Members:* George Mrkonic,*
Pres.; Jim Lathrop,* V.P.; Lauren Comai,* Secy.;
Dawn Maracle,* Treas.; Thom Bales; Thomas
Borders; Charlotte Decker; Judey Henretty; Cathie
Lashinsky; and 4 additional board members.
EIN: 383279018

2431
Branch County United Way, Inc.
P.O. Box 312
Coldwater, MI 49036

Established in MI.
Grantmaker type: Public charity.
Financial data (yr. ended 12/31/04): Revenue,
$294,359; assets, $222,508 (M); gifts received,

$291,800; expenditures, $320,147; total giving,
$258,719; program services expenses, $258,719;
giving activities include $258,719 for 53+ grants
(high: $28,000).
Fields of interest: Health care; Community
development.
Limitations: Giving primarily in Branch County, MI.
Officers: Teri Cohen, Pres.; Linda George, V.P.; Jill
Smoker, Treas.
Board Members: Keith Baker; Cathy Gordon;
Melissa Lafferty; Mark Ludlow; David O'Rourke;
Sara Roper; Bill Stewart; Eric Zuzga; and 4 additional
board members.
EIN: 381554662

2432
Bray Charitable Trust
c/o JPMorgan Chase Bank, N.A.
P.O. Box 1308
Milwaukee, WI 53201

Established in 1975; supporting organization of the
Flint Institute of Arts.
Grantmaker type: Public charity.
Financial data (yr. ended 8/31/05): Revenue,
$12,133; assets, $1,438,828 (M); expenditures,
$10,167.
Fields of interest: Museums.
Limitations: Applications not accepted. Giving
limited to Flint, MI. No grants to individuals.
Application information: Contributes only to a
pre-selected organization; unsolicited requests for
funds not considered or acknowledged.
Trustees: Flint Board of Education; Flint Institute of
Arts; JPMorgan Chase Bank, N.A.
EIN: 386317991

2433
Bronson Health Foundation
1 Healthcare Plz.
Kalamazoo, MI 49007 (269) 341-8100
Contact: Frank J. Sardone, Pres. and C.E.O.
URL: http://bronsonhealth.com/content_serv.asp?
menu=A8

Established in 1983 in MI.
Grantmaker type: Public charity.
Financial data (yr. ended 12/31/04): Revenue,
$1,037,553; assets, $8,858,809 (M); gifts
received, $646,044; expenditures, $662,534; total
giving, $528,964; program services expenses,
$548,802; giving activities include $528,964 for
grants.
Purpose and activities: The organization awards
grants to Bronson staff or community organizations
to support new or improved health services.
Fields of interest: Public health; Health care.
Limitations: Giving in MI.
Officers and Directors:* Randall W. Eberts III,*
Chair.; Barbara L. James,* Vice-Chair.; Frank J.
Sardone,* Pres. and C.E.O.; Kenneth L. Taft,*
C.O.O. and Exec. V.P.; Scott Larson, M.D.*, Sr. V.P.,
Medical Affairs; James B. Falahee, Jr.,* Sr. V.P.,
Legal; Susan M. Ulshafer,* Sr. V.P., Human
Resources; Geoffrey A. Wardell,* Secy.; Floyd L.
Parks,* Treas.; Gordon Brown; and 13 additional
directors.
EIN: 382415081

2434
Constance R. Brown Trust
c/o National City Bank
108 E. Michigan Ave.
Kalamazoo, MI 49007

Established in 1942; a supporting organization of the Kalamazoo Community Foundation.
Grantmaker type: Public charity.
Financial data (yr. ended 12/31/04): Revenue, $20,749; assets, $605,358 (M); expenditures, $38,075; total giving, $36,242; program services expenses, $36,242; giving activities include $36,242 for 1 grant.
Fields of interest: Foundations (community).
Limitations: Applications not accepted. Giving limited to Kalamazoo, MI.
Application information: Contributes only to a pre-selected organization; unsolicited requests for funds not considered or acknowledged.
Trustee: National City Bank.
EIN: 386041534

2435
Byron Center Fine Arts Foundation
P.O. Box 13
Byron Center, MI 49315-0013 (616) 878-6818
Contact: Jonathan Bower, Pres.

Established in 1999 in MI.
Grantmaker type: Public charity.
Financial data (yr. ended 12/31/04): Revenue, $24,404; assets, $77,671 (M); gifts received, $9,896; expenditures, $18,284; total giving, $7,000; giving activities include $5,000 for 1 grant, and $2,000 for 2 grants to individuals (high: $1,000; low: $1,000).
Purpose and activities: The foundation provides funds for scholarships and grants, and promotes education, training, and performing in the performing and visual arts.
Fields of interest: Visual arts; Performing arts.
Type of support: General/operating support; Program-related investments/loans; Scholarships —to individuals.
Limitations: Giving primarily in Kent County, MI.
Application information: Application form required.
Initial approach: Letter or telephone requesting application
Deadline(s): Early Mar. for Scholarships
Board meeting date(s): 3rd Wed. of each month
Final notification: End of Apr. for Scholarships
Officers and Board Members:* Jonathan Bower,* Pres.; Joyce Winchester,* V.P.; David Hart,* Secy.; Leon De Lange,* Treas.; Ed Elderkin; Hank Haan; Tim Hitson; Tim Newhouse.
Number of staff: 1 part-time professional.
EIN: 383498857

2436
Cable Communications Public Benefit Corporation
(also known as Public Benefit Corporation)
2111 Woodward Ave.
Palms Bldg., Ste. 1006
Detroit, MI 48201 (313) 965-3565
Contact: Latitia McCree, Dir., Progs.
FAX: (313) 965-3165;
E-mail: lmccreepbc@earthlink.net; URL: http://www.pbcdetroit.org/

Established in 1985 in MI in a franchise agreement between the City of Detroit and Barden Cablevision.
Grantmaker type: Public charity.
Purpose and activities: The organization seeks to provide citizens of Detroit, Michigan with financial support, educational services, and other assistance to promote and encourage greater citizen interest, communication, and involvement in the development of community-produced programming by way of cable television (Comcast Cablevision).
Fields of interest: Media/communications.
Type of support: General/operating support; Continuing support; Equipment; Endowments; Program development; Curriculum development; Technical assistance; Consulting services; Grants to individuals; In-kind gifts.
Limitations: Giving primarily in the Detroit, MI, area.
Publications: Application guidelines; Annual report; Biennial report; Financial statement; Grants list; Informational brochure (including application guidelines); Newsletter.
Application information: Applications are reviewed annually in Apr., Aug., and Dec. See Web site to download RFP. Application form required.
Initial approach: Telephone
Copies of proposal: 1
Deadline(s): Mar., July, and Nov.
Board meeting date(s): 3rd Wed. of each month
Officers and Directors:* Robert Scott,* Pres.; Ann E. Eskridge,* V.P.; Rebie R. Kingston, Ph.D.*, Secy.; Ted Talbert,* Treas.; Harriet Berg.
Number of staff: 2 full-time professional; 3 full-time support; 1 part-time support.
EIN: 382705978

2437
Capital Area United Way
1111 Michigan Ave., Ste. 300
East Lansing, MI 48823 (517) 203-5000
FAX: (517) 203-5001; URL: http://www.capitalareaunitedway.org

Grantmaker type: Public charity.
Financial data (yr. ended 6/30/05): Revenue, $5,810,176; assets, $5,445,964 (M); gifts received, $5,097,555; expenditures, $5,489,258; total giving, $4,002,342; program services expenses, $4,816,108; giving activities include $4,002,342 for 35 grants (high: $309,540; low: $1,160).
Purpose and activities: The mission of the Capital Area United Way is to unite people and resources to solve defined problems and improve the quality of life for individuals and families in need. Current program goals include: meeting short-term emergency needs, youth development, strengthening families by strengthening parenting, domestic violence prevention, job retention, and enable adults and seniors to maintain their self-sufficiency and independence.
Fields of interest: Crime/violence prevention, domestic violence; Employment, services; Youth development; Human services; Family services; Family services, parent education; Aging, centers/services.
Limitations: Giving limited to the greater Lansing, MI, area.
Publications: Annual report.
Officers and Directors:* Jerry King,* Chair.; Michael Brown, Pres.; Janet Gibbons, C.E.O., Internal Opers.; Sharon Granger, V.P., Community Impact; Teresa Kmetz, V.P., Campaign & Comms.; Jerry

Ambrose; Joan Bauer; Ken Beall; Angela Brown; James Butler; and 40 additional directors.
EIN: 381363572

2438
Caravan Youth Center
3504 Ridgefield Rd.
Lansing, MI 48906-3547

Grantmaker type: Public charity.
Financial data (yr. ended 8/31/05): Revenue, $45,014; assets, $292,042 (M); expenditures, $30,435; total giving, $10,362; program services expenses, $10,462; giving activities include $10,262 for 8 grants (high: $1,807; low: $913), and $100 for 1 in-kind gift.
Purpose and activities: The organization aims to improve the lives of youth.
Fields of interest: Youth, services.
Type of support: In-kind gifts.
Limitations: Giving primarily in MI.
Directors: Wayne Caruss; Lester Florida; W. Monte Ream; Robert R. Smith; William Turney; Francis E. Walker.
EIN: 386099677

2439
Caring Athletes Team for Children's and Henry Ford Hospitals
223 Fisher Bldg.
3011 W. Grand Blvd.
Detroit, MI 48202 (313) 876-9399
Contact: Jim Hughes, Exec. Dir.
FAX: (313) 876-9241;
E-mail: jhughes@catchcharity.org; Additional E-mail: info@catchcharity.org; URL: http://www.catchcharity.org

Established in 1987 in MI.
Grantmaker type: Public charity.
Financial data (yr. ended 12/31/04): Revenue, $825,997; assets, $5,959,564 (M); gifts received, $670,682; expenditures, $692,034; total giving, $337,597; program services expenses, $337,597; giving activities include $314,597 for 4 grants (high: $200,000; low: $10,000), and $23,000 for grants to individuals.
Purpose and activities: The organization is dedicated to improving the quality of life of pediatric patients at Children's Hospital and Henry Ford Hospital and through the development of a board-designated endowment fund, the organization will provide needy pediatric patients with assistance which is not otherwise available.
Fields of interest: Hospitals (specialty); Pediatrics.
Limitations: Giving limited to MI.
Officers and Trustees:* Edsel B. Ford II,* Chair.; John Ginopolis,* Vice-Chair.; David Levy,* Vice-Chair.; Peter A. Schweitzer,* Vice-Chair.; Thomas F. McNulty,* Treas.; James F. Hughes, Exec. Dir.; Rod Alberts; Dennis W. Archer; David B. Bergman; Brian Coughlin; and 48 additional trustees.
EIN: 382746810

2440
Cash for Kids
2939 S. Rochester Rd., Ste. 190
Rochester Hills, MI 48307
Contact: Donyale Martin

E-mail: dmartin@swincash.com; URL: http://swincash.com/cashforkids/cfkmission.html

Grantmaker type: Public charity.

Purpose and activities: The mission of Cash for Kids is to provide the essential tools for kids to "get in the game" educationally and on the court. With a focus on helping children develop their skills inside and outside of the classroom, Cash for Kids provides financial support to the arts while focusing on culture, literacy, athletics and youth development initiatives.

Fields of interest: Arts; Education; Athletics/sports, basketball; Youth development.

Limitations: Giving primarily in the Detroit, MI, area and McKeesport, PA.

Application information:
Initial approach: Proposal

2441
Cass County United Way, Inc.
205 S. Front St.
Dowagiac, MI   49047

Established in MI.

Grantmaker type: Public charity.

Financial data (yr. ended 9/30/04): Revenue, $109,260; assets, $105,168 (M); gifts received, $108,857; expenditures, $88,500; total giving, $66,406; program services expenses, $66,406; giving activities include $66,406 for grants.

Fields of interest: Community development.

Limitations: Giving primarily in Cass County, MI.

Officers and Directors:* Joy Decker, Chair.; Eileen Crouse, Vice-Chair.; Mary Jane Visingardi,* Secy.; Norma Thompson, Treas.; Dale Blunier; Dawn Conner; Mary Cooper; Hal Davis; Kelli Fiala; Sue McCormick; and 8 additional directors.

EIN: 382410856

2442
Cedar Springs Educational Foundation
204 E. Muskegon St.
Cedar Springs, MI   49319

Established in 1991 in MI; supporting organization of Cedar Springs public schools.

Grantmaker type: Public charity.

Financial data (yr. ended 12/31/04): Revenue, $23,308; assets, $214,417 (M); gifts received, $9,364; expenditures, $53,617; total giving, $53,018; program services expenses, $53,018; giving activities include $53,018 for 4 grants (high: $41,076; low: $1,000).

Fields of interest: Elementary/secondary education.

Limitations: Applications not accepted. Giving limited to Cedar Springs, MI.

Application information: Contributes only to a pre-selected organization; unsolicited requests for funds not considered or acknowledged.

Officers and Trustees:* George Waite,* Pres.; Carolyn Zank,* V.P.; Debbie McIntyre,* Secy.; Kathy Anderson,* Treas.; Lisa Caron; Russell Cole; Russell Durst; Carol Hordyk; June Mabie; Elizabeth Marckini; Ellen Moore; Ron Shelden.

EIN: 382722498

2443
Char-Em United Way
103 Bridge St.
P.O. Box 22
Charlevoix, MI   49720

Established in MI.

Grantmaker type: Public charity.

Financial data (yr. ended 6/30/05): Revenue, $118,578; assets, $90,283 (M); gifts received, $118,068; expenditures, $124,225; total giving, $64,259; program services expenses, $64,259; giving activities include $64,259 for grants.

Fields of interest: Community development.

Limitations: Giving primarily in Charlevoix and Emmet counties, MI.

Officers: Mike Atchison, Pres.; Tim Petrosky, V.P.; Jennifer Archamba, Secy.; Sam Clark, Treas.

Directors: Steve Andreae; Dave Atkins; Dianne Clifford; Sabra Hayden; Laura Kemp; Brynne Klawuhn.

EIN: 237049778

2444
Charity for All Foundation
26300 Telegraph Rd., 2nd Fl.
Southfield, MI   48034

Established in 2000 in MI.

Grantmaker type: Public charity.

Financial data (yr. ended 12/31/04): Revenue, $122,573; assets, $617,077 (M); gifts received, $118,322; expenditures, $30,875; total giving, $14,888; program services expenses, $15,833; giving activities include $14,888 for 3 grants (high: $8,900; low: $2,988).

Fields of interest: Philanthropy/voluntarism.

Officer: Ahmad Hadied, Pres.

EIN: 383520607

2445
Cheboygan County United Way
224 N. Main St.
Cheboygan, MI   49721   (231) 627-2288
FAX: (231) 627-2062; *E-mail:* ccuw@hotmail.com

Grantmaker type: Public charity.

Financial data (yr. ended 1/31/05): Revenue, $69,664; assets, $7,218 (M); gifts received, $50,663; expenditures, $69,235; total giving, $69,235; program services expenses, $69,235; giving activities include $69,235 for grants.

Purpose and activities: The Cheboygan County United Way activates community resources to assist various local charitable organizations to help children and youth succeed, strengthen families, and support vulnerable and aging populations.

Fields of interest: Youth development; Human services; Children/youth, services; Family services; Aging, centers/services; Developmentally disabled, centers & services.

Limitations: Giving limited to Cheboygan County, MI.

Officers and Directors:* Twyla Brooks,* Pres.; Jean Boucher,* V.P.; Lynn Cavitt,* Secy.; Susan Caswell,* Treas.; Michelle Bidigare, Exec. Dir.; Candace Mosher; Carol Northcott.

EIN: 386094846

2446
Chelsea Education Foundation, Inc.
P.O. Box 295
Chelsea, MI   48118-0295
URL: http://chelseaeducationfoundation.org/

Established in 1990 in MI.

Grantmaker type: Public charity.

Financial data (yr. ended 6/30/04): Revenue, $117,153; assets, $559,028; gifts received, $74,448; expenditures, $70,868; total giving, $58,730; program services expenses, $58,730; giving activities include $21,230 for 6 grants (high: $17,285; low: $200), and $37,500 for 42 grants to individuals (high: $1,500; low: $500).

Purpose and activities: The foundation provides funding for a wide spectrum of educational activities to benefit the residents of Chelsea, Michigan, including scholarships to individuals, innovative school programs, community forums, building projects, and extra-curricular classes and experiences.

Fields of interest: Education.

Type of support: Program development; Scholarships—to individuals.

Limitations: Giving limited for the benefit of Chelsea, MI, citizens and organizations.

Application information: Application forms may be downloaded from foundation Web site. See Web site for scholarship application guidelines for specific requirements for eligibility. Application form required.
Initial approach: Completed application form plus 7 copies (for grants) or 8 copies (for scholarships)
Deadline(s): Check foundation Web site for current deadline information

Officers and Board Members:* Owen Ballow,* Pres.; Anne Merkel,* V.P.; Julie Hermann,* Secy.; Bill Wells,* Treas.; Stacie Battaglia; Charna Boquette; Jami Camburn; Matt Cole; and 7 additional members.

EIN: 382953926

2447
Chelsea United Way
P.O. Box 176
Chelsea, MI   48118

Established in MI.

Grantmaker type: Public charity.

Financial data (yr. ended 12/31/05): Revenue, $144,722; assets, $54,760 (M); gifts received, $143,959; expenditures, $132,203; total giving, $120,854; program services expenses, $120,854; giving activities include $120,584 for 18 grants (high: $43,000; low: $25).

Purpose and activities: The organization seeks to raise and disburse funds to qualified nonprofit and volunteer organizations in the community.

Fields of interest: Human services; Community development.

Limitations: Giving primarily in MI.

Officers: Mary Underwood, Secy.; Robert Stephens, Treas.

Directors: Celeste Balogh; Doug Beaumont; Bob Frayer; Dave Herman; Annette Houle; Wanda Killips; Scott Moore; George Olson; and 10 additional directors.

EIN: 237128098

2448
Children's Charities at Adios
30435 Groesbeck Hwy.
Roseville, MI 48066 (586) 779-8010
Contact: John Bertakis, Pres.

Established in 1991.
Grantmaker type: Public charity.
Financial data (yr. ended 12/31/04): Revenue, $82,799; assets, $12,441 (M); gifts received, $70,963; expenditures, $76,000; total giving, $76,000; program services expenses, $76,000; giving activities include $76,000 for 16 grants (high: $9,200; low: $1,000).
Purpose and activities: The organization raises funds to support children's charities.
Fields of interest: Children, services.
Limitations: Giving on a national basis.
Officers: John Bertakis, Pres.; Michael Pannuto, V.P.; Onorio Moscone, Secy.; William I. Minoletti, Treas.
EIN: 382924503

2449
Children's Leukemia Foundation of Michigan
29777 Telegraph Rd., Ste. 1651
Southfield, MI 48034 (248) 353-8222
Contact: Glen R. Trevisian, Pres. and C.E.O.
FAX: (248) 353-0157;
E-mail: info@leukemiamichigan.org; URL: http://www.leukemiamichigan.org

Established in 1952 in MI.
Grantmaker type: Public charity.
Financial data (yr. ended 6/30/05): Revenue, $1,427,978; assets, $732,005 (M); gifts received, $1,442,782; expenditures, $1,381,589; total giving, $305,434; program services expenses, $1,077,826; giving activities include $47,500 for grants, and $257,934 for grants to individuals.
Purpose and activities: The foundation seeks to provide and promote compassionate, personalized support to people in Michigan affected by leukemia and other related disorders.
Fields of interest: Cancer, leukemia.
Type of support: Grants to individuals; Research.
Limitations: Giving limited to MI.
Publications: Annual report.
Officers and Directors:* Kathryn A. Pothier,* Chair.; Anne McAlpine,* Vice-Chair.; Glen R. Trevisian, Pres. and C.E.O.; Denise Glassmeyer,* Secy.; William Erfourth,* Treas.; Benjamin Brown; Kay Carolin; Pearlie Matthews; Greg Snider; and 4 additional directors.
EIN: 381682300

2450
Henry Clark Stroke Foundation
(formerly Henry O. Clark, Jr. Foundation)
3430 E. Jefferson
P.O. Box 531
Detroit, MI 48207 (313) 531-9098
Contact: Barbara Lewis-Clark, Pres.
FAX: (313) 541-2494;
E-mail: info@hcstrokefoundation.org; Additional address: P.O. Box 35284, Detroit, MI 48235; Toll-free tel.: (800) 531-9242; URL: http://www.hcstrokefoundation.org

Established in 2002 in MI.

Donors: Henry O. Clark, Jr.†; Barbara Lewis-Clark.
Grantmaker type: Public charity.
Financial data (yr. ended 3/31/04): Revenue, $17,196; assets, $905 (M); gifts received, $16,992; expenditures, $22,910; total giving, $2,100; program services expenses, $12,142; giving activities include $2,100 for grants.
Purpose and activities: The foundation seeks to increase the knowledge of stroke among those people who are at the greatest risk of suffering a stroke and the least likely to obtain immediate medical attention by working with organizations that contribute to the better health of the community. Programs supported by foundation funds include stroke support groups, providing transportation to individuals under a physician's care, providing meals to the elderly through Meals on Wheels, and the Boys and Girls Club.
Fields of interest: Heart & circulatory diseases; Heart & circulatory research; Food distribution, meals on wheels; Boys & girls clubs; Human services, transportation; Aging.
Limitations: Applications not accepted. Giving primarily in the metropolitan Detroit, MI, area. No grants to individuals.
Publications: Informational brochure; Newsletter.
Application information: Unsolicited requests for funds not considered at this time.
 Board meeting date(s): 3rd Sun. of each month
Officer: Barbara Lewis-Clark, Pres.
Directors: Clarence Carpenter III; Chandra Clark-Young; Jeffrey Harris, M.D.; Matt Laver; Nonearl McClinton-Jones; Shawn Young.
EIN: 743043339

2451
Community Foundation Alliance of Calhoun County
104 S. Hillsdale St.
P.O. Box 101
Homer, MI 49245 (517) 568-5222
Contact: Carol Petredean-DiSalvio, Admin.
FAX: (517) 568-5433; E-mail: cfa@cc.org;
URL: http://www.cfa-cc.org/

Established in 1998 in MI as a supporting organization of Calhoun County; now a supporting organization of Battle Creek Community Foundation, Albion Community Foundation, Athens Area Community Foundation, Homer Area Community Foundation, and Marshall Community Foundation.
Grantmaker type: Public charity.
Financial data (yr. ended 3/31/05): Revenue, $558,551; assets, $490,580 (M); gifts received, $542,712; expenditures, $749,497; total giving, $623,985; program services expenses, $687,542; giving activities include $623,985 for 40 grants (high: $75,000; low: $85).
Purpose and activities: To improve the quality of life and access to opportunity in Calhoun County, with an emphasis on youth.
Fields of interest: Elementary/secondary education; Mental health, smoking; Athletics/sports, school programs; Recreation; Youth development; Community development; Foundations (community); Youth.
Type of support: Program development; Scholarship funds.
Limitations: Giving limited to Calhoun County, MI.
Application information: See foundation Web site for grant and scholarship application guidelines and requirements.

Officer and Directors:* Rachel Maksimchuk,* Pres.; Sherry Anderson; Holly Blashfield; Betsy Briere; David Farley; Paul Frederick; Lynn Haley; Carol Sybesma; Karen Yankie.
EIN: 043597340

2452
Concrete Research & Education Foundation
38800 Country Club Dr.
Farmington Hills, MI 48333
E-mail: scholarships@concrete.org; URL: http://www.concrete.org/about/ab_conref.htm

Supporting organization of American Concrete Institute.
Grantmaker type: Public charity.
Financial data (yr. ended 12/31/04): Revenue, $476,345; assets, $872,883 (M); gifts received, $324,543; expenditures, $326,981; total giving, $14,000; program services expenses, $125,368; giving activities include $11,000 for 6 grants (high: $3,000; low: $1,000), and $3,000 for 2 grants to individuals (high: $2,000; low: $1,000).
Purpose and activities: The foundation supports educational, research, scientific, and charitable purposes; building knowledge for improvements in concrete design and construction.
Fields of interest: Higher education; Engineering school/education; Business/industry.
Type of support: Fellowships; Scholarship funds; Research; Scholarships—to individuals.
Limitations: Giving on a national basis.
Application information: Only students nominated by faculty members who are also ACI members will be eligible to receive applications for the ACI Student Fellowship Program. After a student is formally nominated, the foundation will convey an official application directly to the nominated student. Application form required.
Officers and Trustees:* James O. Jirsa,* Chair.; H.S. Lew,* Vice-Chair.; Philip T. Seabrook,* Treas.; Paul D. Carter; James R. Cagley; Richard F. Heitzmann; Charles K. Nmai; William R. Tolley; and 3 additional trustees.
EIN: 382986800

2453
Conrad Charitable Foundation
504 W. Dunlap St.
Northville, MI 48167-1409

Established in 2001 in MI.
Grantmaker type: Public charity.
Financial data (yr. ended 12/31/04): Revenue, $264,135; assets, $131,815 (M); gifts received, $258,000; expenditures, $282,547; total giving, $280,276; program services expenses, $282,547; giving activities include $265,311 for 32 grants (high: $100,000; low: $100), and $14,965 for 5 in-kind gifts.
Purpose and activities: The foundation supports education, youth, human services and Christian agencies; awards are primarily but not exclusively targeted to assist single parents and their children and women returning to work.
Fields of interest: Secondary school/education; Higher education; Youth development; Human services; Family services, single parents; Christian agencies & churches; Single parents.
Type of support: In-kind gifts.

Limitations: Giving in the U.S., primarily in Northville and Wayne County, MI.
Director: Beth Beson.
EIN: 383607715

2454
Copper Country United Way
604 Shelden Ave.
P.O. Box 104
Houghton, MI 49931-0104 (906) 482-3276

Grantmaker type: Public charity.
Financial data (yr. ended 2/28/05): Revenue, $142,902; assets, $211,553 (M); gifts received, $140,548; expenditures, $141,165; total giving, $115,739; program services expenses, $115,739; giving activities include $115,739 for grants.
Purpose and activities: The Copper Country United Way allocates funds to charitable agencies in the Keweenaw Peninsula, Michigan.
Fields of interest: Human services; Community development.
Limitations: Giving limited to Keweenaw Peninsula, the northwestern end of the Upper Peninsula of MI.
Officers and Directors:* Frank J. Stipech,* Pres.; Nancy Archambeau,* V.P.; Jan Woodbeck,* Secy.; Rick West,* Treas.; Lois Gemignani; Mark Jalkannen; Chen Raasio; Brian Rimpela; Virginia Schaller; and 12 additional directors.
EIN: 386030235

2455
Coville-Triest Family Foundation
6735 Telegraph Rd.
P.O. Box 2030
Bloomfield Hills, MI 48301

Established in 1984.
Grantmaker type: Public charity.
Financial data (yr. ended 5/31/05): Assets, $0 (M); expenditures, $168; total giving, $168; program services expenses, $168; giving activities include $168 for 1 grant.
Purpose and activities: The foundation provides grants and awards to other charitable organizations.
Fields of interest: Jewish federated giving programs.
Limitations: Giving limited to MI.
Officers and Directors:* Warren J. Coville,* Pres.; Margot Coville,* V.P.; Robert P. Aronson,* Secy.; Mark Davidoff,* Treas.; Dorothy Benyas; and 5 additional directors.
EIN: 382548695

2456
Crawford County United Way
P.O. Box 171
Grayling, MI 49738

Established in MI.
Grantmaker type: Public charity.
Financial data (yr. ended 12/31/04): Revenue, $56,140; assets, $30,070 (M); gifts received, $52,976; expenditures, $69,815; total giving, $51,475; giving activities include $51,475 for 18 grants (high: $6,000; low: $625).
Fields of interest: Human services; Community development.
Limitations: Giving primarily in MI.

Officers: Linda Golnick, Pres. and Treas.; Nancy Hunt, V.P.; Kathi Moss, Secy.; April Brunger, Exec. Dir.
Directors: Kay Cosgray; Kathy Laudenslager; Kim Millikin; Don Schanz; Joe Smock; Joe Swain; Kirk Wakefield; Cathy Wiley.
EIN: 382777940

2457
Edward Davis Education Foundation
585 E. Larned St., Ste. 100
Detroit, MI 48226 (313) 963-2209
Contact: Randi Payton, Pres. and C.E.O.
FAX: (313) 963-7778; URL: http://www.onwheelsinc.com/EDEFoundation/

Established in 1998 in MI.
Grantmaker type: Public charity.
Financial data (yr. ended 12/31/05): Revenue, $55,076; assets, $28,678 (M); gifts received, $55,000; expenditures, $89,757; total giving, $7,500; program services expenses, $7,500; giving activities include $7,500 for 4 grants to individuals (high: $2,000; low: $1,500).
Purpose and activities: The foundation's mission is to increase diversity within the automotive industry, increase seatbelt safety awareness among African Americans and Latinos, and promote career opportunities for ethnic minorities through scholarship, internship, and mentoring programs.
Fields of interest: Education; Safety, automotive safety; Business/industry; Minorities; African Americans/Blacks; Hispanics/Latinos.
Type of support: Internship funds; Scholarships—to individuals.
Limitations: Giving on a national basis.
Publications: Application guidelines.
Application information: Scholarship applicants must attach offical transcript of the most recent academic work, typed resume, two letters of recommendation, and typed essay to application. Application form required.
  Initial approach: Download application form
  Deadline(s): Aug. 1
  Final notification: Nov. 7
Officer: Randi Payton, Pres. and C.E.O.
Directors: Katherine J. Adams; V. Diane Freeman; Ronald Goldsberry, Ph.D.; Eric Peterson; Cecil Ward; Ronald Wilson.
EIN: 383431880

2458
Costantino Del Signore Foundation
39000 Schoolcraft
Livonia, MI 48150

Grantmaker type: Public charity.
Financial data (yr. ended 12/31/05): Revenue, $93,581; assets, $20,372 (M); expenditures, $105,956; total giving, $31,225; program services expenses, $105,956; giving activities include $31,225 for 5 grants (high: $10,000; low: $225).
Fields of interest: Hospitals (general); Cancer.
Limitations: Giving primarily in MI.
Officers: Costantino Del Signore, Pres.; Angelo Colone, Secy.; Jim Carver, Treas.
EIN: 383331000

2459
Delta Dental Foundation
(formerly Delta Dental Fund)
P.O. Box 293
Okemos, MI 48805 (517) 347-5333
Contact: Lawrence D. Crawford D.D.S., Vice-Chair.
FAX: (517) 347-5320; E-mail: ddfund@ddpmi.com;
URL: http://www.deltadentalmi.com/ddf/index.htm

Established in 1980 in MI.
Grantmaker type: Public charity.
Financial data (yr. ended 12/31/04): Revenue, $580,397; assets, $15,963,915 (M); expenditures, $725,371; total giving, $344,016; program services expenses, $654,927; giving activities include $344,016 for grants.
Purpose and activities: The fund supports education and research for the advancement of dental science and promotes the oral health of the public through education and service activities, particularly for those with special needs.
Fields of interest: Dental school/education; Dental care; Economically disadvantaged.
Type of support: Conferences/seminars; Scholarship funds; Research; Scholarships—to individuals.
Limitations: Giving limited to IN, MI, and OH.
Publications: Application guidelines; Biennial report (including application guidelines).
Application information: Application form required.
  Initial approach: Download application form
  Deadline(s): Apr. 15 and Oct. 15 for Research Grants
  Final notification: June and Dec.
Officers and Trustees:* Jack W. Gottschalk, D.D.S.*, Chair.; Lawrence D. Crawford, D.D.S.*, Vice-Chair.; Penelope K. Majeske, Ph.D.*, Secy.; James P. Hallan,* Treas.; Stephen A. Eklund, D.D.S.; Lonny E. Zietz; and 6 additional trustees.
EIN: 382337000

2460
Detroit Lions Charities
222 Republic Dr.
Allen Park, MI 48101-3650 (313) 216-4050
Contact: William Clay Ford, Pres.
URL: http://www.detroitlions.com/document_display.cfm?document_id=3588

Established in 1990 in MI.
Grantmaker type: Public charity.
Financial data (yr. ended 2/28/05): Revenue, $597,980; assets, $905,275 (M); gifts received, $619,775; expenditures, $525,527; total giving, $490,979; program services expenses, $497,166; giving activities include $490,979 for grants.
Purpose and activities: The organization assists charitable and worthwhile causes in Michigan. It supports activities and programs that benefit all age groups in education, civic affairs, and health and human services.
Fields of interest: Education; Health care; Human services; Community development.
Limitations: Giving limited to MI. No support for political campaigns and activities. No grants to individuals (including loans and scholarships), or for building, raffles, banquets, advertising, equipment, or endowments.
Application information:
  Initial approach: Letter (no more than 2 pages)
  Deadline(s): Between Oct. 1 and Dec. 31
  Board meeting date(s): Feb.
  Final notification: Mar.

Officers: William Clay Ford, Pres.; William Clay Ford, Jr., V.P.; J. Thomas Lesnau, Treas.
Trustee: Timothy A. Pendell.
EIN: 382945709

2461
Detroit Youth Foundation

7375 Woodward Ave., Ste. 2800
Detroit, MI   48202   (313) 875-3400
FAX: (313) 875-3401;
E-mail: gsmith@detroityouth.org; Additional tel.:
(313) 309-1400; URL: http://www.detroityouth.org

Established in 1999 in MI.
Donor: W.K. Kellogg Foundation.
Grantmaker type: Public charity.
Financial data (yr. ended 6/30/04): Revenue, $5,542,841; assets, $16,661,318 (M); gifts received, $5,425,418; expenditures, $2,601,147; total giving, $717,210; program services expenses, $2,117,874; giving activities include $717,210 for grants.
Purpose and activities: The foundation supports programs and activities at the community level that support children and guide youth development.
Fields of interest: Youth development.
Type of support: General/operating support; Equipment; Consulting services; Matching/challenge support.
Limitations: Giving limited to Detroit, MI, particularly in the Northern High School area.
Publications: Annual report; Financial statement; Grants list; Informational brochure; Newsletter.
Application information: The format and instructions to the grant application are currently under review. See Web site for updated information on application forms.
Officers and Directors:* Hon. Freddie G. Burton, Jr.,* Chair.; Linda D. Forte,* Vice-Chair.; Gerald K. Smith, Ed.D.*, Pres. and C.E.O.; Judith J. Jackson,* C.O.O. and V.P.; Ed Howbert, Secy.; George A. Nicholson III, C.P.A.*, Treas.; Rev. Edward L. Branch; Donna Burke; Dawna Edwards; and 15 additional directors.
Number of staff: 3 full-time professional; 3 full-time support.
EIN: 383461153

2462
Kenneth B. Detwiler, Jr. Free Spirit Memorial Foundation, Inc.

51180 Country Rd. 652
Mattawan, MI   49071-0000
Contact: Linda L. Millek, Exec. Dir.

Established in 1996 in MI.
Grantmaker type: Public charity.
Purpose and activities: The foundation focuses its giving around educational pursuits.
Fields of interest: Teacher school/education; Education, continuing education; Education; Family services.
Type of support: Building/renovation; Program development; Seed money; Curriculum development; Scholarship funds; Research; Grants to individuals; Scholarships—to individuals.
Limitations: Giving primarily in Van Buren County, MI, and surrounding area.
Publications: Application guidelines; Occasional report; Program policy statement.
Application information: Application form required.

Initial approach: Letter or telephone
Deadline(s): May 25
Board meeting date(s): 2nd Mon. of each month
Officers and Directors:* Linda L. Millek,* Pres. and Exec. Dir.; Sandy Stoll,* V.P.; Tony Millek,* Treas.; Dan Hoff; Richard Stoll.
EIN: 383179584

2463
Domino's Pizza Partners Foundation

30 Frank Lloyd Wright Dr.
Ann Arbor, MI   48106-0977

Grantmaker type: Public charity.
Financial data (yr. ended 12/31/05): Revenue, $1,704,357; assets, $2,928,215 (M); gifts received, $1,600,279; expenditures, $1,494,297; total giving, $1,145,887; program services expenses, $1,270,873; giving activities include $1,145,887 for grants to individuals.
Purpose and activities: The foundation was established to assist Domino's Pizza team members in time of special need or tragedy as a result of natural disaster, unexpected afflictions, on-the-job accidents, and other emergencies.
Type of support: Grants to individuals.
Limitations: Applications not accepted.
Application information: Contributes only through employee-related emergency grants.
Officers and Trustees:* Jim Stansik,* Chair.; Dana Stearns, Exec. Dir.; Aisha Brown; Mike Brown; Francisca Fernandez; Jim Garner; Danny Malamis; Dave Melton; Anthony Osani; Ken Peebles; George Ralph; Phil Rands.
EIN: 581703733

2464
Eastpointe Community Chest/Networking Forum

P.O. Box 442
Eastpointe, MI   48021

Grantmaker type: Public charity.
Financial data (yr. ended 12/31/04): Revenue, $11,759; assets, $102,553; gifts received, $5,132; expenditures, $16,598; total giving, $16,183; program services expenses, $16,183; giving activities include $16,183 for grants.
Purpose and activities: To enhance the lives of local residents by meeting community needs.
Fields of interest: Education; Recreation, parks/playgrounds; Community development.
Limitations: Giving primarily in Eastpointe and East Detroit, MI.
Officers: Michael Lauretti, Pres.; Margaret Torp, V.P.; Karen Arondoski, Corresponding Secy.; Maria Miller, Recording Secy.; Robert Kern, Treas.
EIN: 383203070

2465
Eaton County United Way

111 W. 1st St.
P.O. Box 14
Charlotte, MI   48813   (517) 543-5402
FAX: (517) 543-5651; E-mail: ecuw@ecuw.org;
URL: http://www.eatoncountyunitedway.org

Established in MI.
Grantmaker type: Public charity.

Financial data (yr. ended 6/30/05): Revenue, $408,851; assets, $449,854 (M); gifts received, $402,380; expenditures, $351,086; total giving, $251,570; program services expenses, $297,993; giving activities include $251,570 for 30 grants (high: $37,016; low: $449).
Purpose and activities: The organization's mission is to focus community resources to meet community needs.
Fields of interest: Health care; Human services; Community development.
Limitations: Giving primarily in Eaton County, MI.
Publications: Annual report.
Application information: Application form required.
Deadline(s): Apr. 21 for Health and Human Service Grants
Officers and Directors:* Janine Nierenberger,* Pres.; Joni Risner, Exec. Dir.; Ronald Byerly; Wayne Buletza; Sean Cotter; Tim Daiaa; Mary M. Douma; Tracy Freeman; David Harwood; and 5 additional directors.
EIN: 383483965

2466
Fischer Family Fund

1795 Maplelawn
Troy, MI   48084   (248) 553-3900
Contact: David T. Fischer, Pres.

Established in 2003 in MI.
Grantmaker type: Public charity.
Financial data (yr. ended 12/31/04): Revenue, $65,988; assets, $2,148,764 (M); expenditures, $47,949; total giving, $47,807; program services expenses, $47,807; giving activities include $47,807 for 2 grants (high: $25,000; low: $22,807).
Purpose and activities: The foundation receives and administers funds for charitable, scientific and educational purposes.
Fields of interest: Medical research, institute.
Limitations: Giving primarily in MI and MN.
Officers and Directors:* David T. Fischer,* Pres.; William M. Fischer,* V.P.; Richard A. Fischer, Jr.,* Secy.; Calvin E. Mackey,* Treas.; Edward C. Dawda; Timothy Leroy.
EIN: 370056435

2467
Max M. & Marjorie S. Fisher Support Foundation

6735 Telegraph Rd.
P.O. Box 2030
Bloomfield Hills, MI   48303

Established in 1984; supporting organization of the Jewish Federation of Metropolitan Detroit.
Grantmaker type: Public charity.
Financial data (yr. ended 5/31/05): Revenue, $8,746,780; assets, $20,405,630 (M); gifts received, $7,657,367; expenditures, $5,030,278; total giving, $4,998,326; program services expenses, $4,998,326; giving activities include $4,998,326 for 20 grants (high: $3,104,897; low: $1,000).
Fields of interest: Jewish federated giving programs; Jewish agencies & temples.
Limitations: Applications not accepted. Giving limited to Detroit, MI.

Application information: Contributes only to pre-selected organizations; unsolicited requests for funds not considered or acknowledged.
Officers: Marjorie S. Fisher, Pres.; Phillip M. Fisher, V.P.; Robert P. Aronson, Secy.; Robert Naftaly, Treas.
Directors: Penny Blumenstein; Julie F. Cummings.
EIN: 382490338

2468
Floriculture Industry Research and Scholarship Trust
(formerly Bedding Plants Foundation)
P.O. Box 280
East Lansing, MI 48826-0280 (517) 333-4617
Contact: William T. Willbrandt, Exec. Dir.
FAX: (517) 333-4494;
E-mail: first@firstinfloriculture.org; URL: http://www.firstinfloriculture.org

Established in 2001 through the merger of Bedding Plants Foundation and Ohio Floriculture Foundation.
Grantmaker type: Public charity.
Financial data (yr. ended 3/31/05): Revenue, $178,187; assets, $1,754,704 (M); gifts received, $76,856; expenditures, $286,688; total giving, $101,510; program services expenses, $188,931; giving activities include $42,500 for 2 grants (high: $30,000; low: $12,500), and $59,010 for 29 grants to individuals (high: $12,000; low: $500).
Purpose and activities: The trust funds research and education in floriculture to improve the production and marketability of plants.
Fields of interest: Environment, plant conservation; Horticulture/garden clubs; Environmental education; Botany.
Type of support: Research; Scholarships—to individuals.
Limitations: Giving on a national and international basis, with emphasis on U.S. and Canadian residents and organizations. No grants for overhead or travel expenses.
Publications: Application guidelines; Grants list.
Application information: Scholarship applicants may apply for up to 5 scholarships each year (only one application is needed). Application form required.
Initial approach: Download application form for research grants; Online application for scholarships
Deadline(s): Jan. 1 - May 1 for scholarships; Sept. 1 for research grants
Officer: William T. Willbrandt, Exec. Dir.
Directors: Ken Altman; Doug Cole; Jim Corfield; Chad Corso; Robyn Dill; Bill Foster; Royal Heins; Delilah Onofrey; Paul A. Thomas; Lloyd Traven.
EIN: 591975717

2469
L. H. Foley & M. H. Frischkorn Nature Conservancy Fund I
c/o Comerica Bank
P.O. Box 75000, MC 3302
Detroit, MI 48275

Supporting organization of the Nature Conservancy, Inc.
Grantmaker type: Public charity.
Financial data (yr. ended 9/30/05): Revenue, $26,539; assets, $655,028 (M); expenditures, $27,595; total giving, $12,025; program services

expenses, $12,025; giving activities include $12,025 for 1 grant.
Fields of interest: Animals/wildlife, single organization support; Animals/wildlife, preservation/protection; Animals/wildlife, sanctuaries; Animals/wildlife.
Limitations: Applications not accepted. Giving limited to Arlington, VA.
Application information: Contributes only to a pre-selected organization; unsolicited requests for funds not considered or acknowledged.
Trustees: George Stege III, Ph.D; Comerica Bank.
EIN: 386646186

2470
L. H. Foley & M. H. Frischkorn Wildlife & Conservation Fund II
c/o Comerica Bank
P.O. Box 75000, MC 3302
Detroit, MI 48275

Supporting organization of the North American Wildlife Foundation.
Grantmaker type: Public charity.
Financial data (yr. ended 9/30/05): Revenue, $23,157; assets, $655,817 (M); expenditures, $28,622; total giving, $13,269; program services expenses, $13,269; giving activities include $13,269 for 1 grant.
Fields of interest: Environment, natural resources; Animals/wildlife, preservation/protection; Animals/wildlife.
Limitations: Applications not accepted. Giving limited to Deerfield, IL. No grants to individuals.
Application information: Contributes only to a pre-selected organization; unsolicited requests for funds not considered or acknowledged.
Trustees: George Stege III, Ph.D.; Comerica Bank.
EIN: 386646185

2471
Gerald R. Ford Foundation
303 Pearl St., N.W.
Grand Rapids, MI 49504-5353
Contact: Diane Van Allsburg, Admin. Asst.
E-mail: geraldfordfoundation@nara.gov; URL: http://www.geraldrfordfoundation.org
Additional tel.: (616) 254-0373, e-mail address: barbara.packer@nara.gov (Prizes); Contact Helmi Raaska, c/o Gerald R. Ford Presidential Library, 1000 Beal Ave., Ann Arbor, MI 48109-2114, tel.: (734) 205-0555, e-mail address: helmi.raaska@nara.gov (Travel).

Established in 1981 in MI.
Grantmaker type: Public charity.
Financial data (yr. ended 12/31/05): Revenue, $1,250,872; assets, $18,832,070 (M); gifts received, $542,415; expenditures, $696,495; total giving, $35,325; program services expenses, $466,683; giving activities include $35,325 for 6 grants to individuals (high: $5,000; low: $1,050).
Purpose and activities: The foundation supports the Gerald R. Ford Library and Museum, through historical exhibits, educational programs, conferences, research grants and awards.
Fields of interest: Media/communications; Museums (history); Elementary/secondary education; Higher education; Libraries (academic/research).

Type of support: Grants to individuals; Research; Scholarships—to individuals.
Publications: Informational brochure.
Application information: See Web site for additional application information. Application form required.
Copies of proposal: 7
Deadline(s): Mar. 3 for Gerald R. Ford Journalism Prizes, Mar. 15 and Sept. 15 for Research Travel Grants
Officers and Trustees:* John G. Ford,* Chair.; Hank Meijer,* Vice-Chair.; Gregory D. Willard,* Secy.; David G. Frey,* Treas.; Susan Ford Bales; Robert E. Barrett; Benton L. Becker; and 45 additional trustees.
Number of staff: 1 part-time support.
EIN: 382368003

2472
Foundation for Mentally Ill Children, Inc.
P.O. Box 80184
Rochester, MI 48308-0184

Established in 1958 in MI.
Grantmaker type: Public charity.
Financial data (yr. ended 8/31/04): Revenue, $3,887; assets, $10,762 (M); gifts received, $3,339; expenditures, $10,849; total giving, $10,000; program services expenses, $10,000; giving activities include $10,000 for 1 grant.
Purpose and activities: The foundation seeks to assist emotionally disturbed children.
Fields of interest: Children; Disabilities, people with.
Officers: Lee Uhlig, Pres.; Martha Toree, Treas.
EIN: 386089417

2473
Foundation for Saline Area Schools
P.O. Box 5
Saline, MI 48176 (734) 429-7378
Contact: Dan Ouellette, Pres.
E-mail: americandano@cs.com; URL: http://www.saline.lib.mi.us/fsas

Established in 1987 in MI.
Grantmaker type: Public charity.
Financial data (yr. ended 12/31/05): Revenue, $37,598; assets, $275,555 (M); gifts received, $32,844; expenditures, $33,184; total giving, $32,916; program services expenses, $32,916; giving activities include $32,916 for 28 grants to individuals (high: $9,990; low: $150).
Purpose and activities: The foundation enhances the quality of education and educational opportunities to Saline area schools through enrichment programs and other projects which promote student learning opportunities, encourage excellence and growth of all staff, and facilitate community/school partnerships.
Fields of interest: Education.
Type of support: Seed money; Grants to individuals.
Limitations: Giving limited to Saline, MI. No support for religious programs.
Publications: Application guidelines.
Application information: See Web site for application information. Application form required.
Initial approach: Proposal
Copies of proposal: 5
Deadline(s): 2nd Tues. of Apr. and Oct.
Officers and Trustees:* Daniel J. Ouellette,* Pres.; Nancy T. Byers,* V.P.; Abha Wiersba,* Treas.; Scott

E. Fosdick; Elaine T. Heiserman; Beth Henschen; Thomas S. Kirvan; Mary Laidlaw; Bernice "Woodie" Merchant; Cathy Redies; Kenneth H. Rogers, Jr.; Nancy Schmerberg; Norma M. Smith; Terry Walters.
EIN: 382733854

2474
Foundation of Michigan Association of Physicians of Indian Origin
P.O. Box 531840
Livonia, MI   48153

Grantmaker type: Public charity.
Financial data (yr. ended 12/31/04): Revenue, $109,955; assets, $87,709 (M); gifts received, $40,000; expenditures, $50,803; total giving, $49,800; program services expenses, $49,800; giving activities include $49,800 for grants.
Purpose and activities: Support given to free medical clinics and other charitable causes in India and Michigan.
Fields of interest: Health care, clinics/centers.
Limitations: Giving limited to MI and India.
Officer: Kirit Shah, M.D., Pres.
EIN: 383032459

2475
Samuel and Jean Frankel Support Foundation
6735 Telegraph Rd.
P.O. Box 2030
Bloomfield Hills, MI   48301   (248) 642-4260
Contact: Samuel Frankel, Pres.

Established in 1985; supporting organization of the Jewish Federation of Metropolitan Detroit.
Grantmaker type: Public charity.
Financial data (yr. ended 5/31/05): Revenue, $1,868,043; assets, $9,304,918 (M); gifts received, $1,190,000; expenditures, $5,076,787; total giving, $5,029,460; program services expenses, $5,029,460; giving activities include $5,029,460 for 21 grants (high: $1,387,200; low: $10,000).
Purpose and activities: The foundation supports organizations that further the mission of the Jewish Federation of Metropolitan Detroit.
Fields of interest: Jewish federated giving programs.
Limitations: Giving primarily in MI.
Officers and Directors:* Samuel Frankel,* Pres.; Stanley D. Frankel, V.P.; Robert P. Aronson, Secy.; Dorothy Benyas, Treas.; Jean Frankel; Lawrence S. Jackier; Arthur A. Weiss.
EIN: 382582299

2476
Fraser Area Educational Foundation
33466 Garfield Rd.
Fraser, MI   48026-1892

Grantmaker type: Public charity.
Financial data (yr. ended 6/30/05): Revenue, $12,335; assets, $227,674 (M); gifts received, $10,183; expenditures, $14,446; total giving, $11,218; program services expenses, $11,218; giving activities include $2,066 for 2+ grants (high: $1,360; low: $706), and $9,152 for 10 grants to individuals (high: $1,000; low: $204).
Purpose and activities: The foundation provides mini-grants for enrichment to the student curriculum

above regular funding source, and awards scholarships to outstanding students.
Fields of interest: Secondary school/education.
Type of support: Scholarships—to individuals; Scholarship funds.
Limitations: Giving limited to Fraser, MI.
Application information: The applicant must attach a minimum of three recommendation letters from employers, teachers, sponsors, coaches, etc. Application form required.
   Initial approach: Application
   Deadline(s): Mar.
   Board meeting date(s): Annually
Officers and Trustees:* James Walsh,* Pres.; Sharron Henderson,* Treas.; Joanne Hartzel; Deuane Martin; Gerald McCaffrey; Carol Nine; Gary Westby; Doreen Winnega.
EIN: 382785496

2477
Free Press Charities, Inc.
600 W. Fort St.
Detroit, MI   48226-3138   (313) 222-6595

Established in 1933 in MI.
Grantmaker type: Public charity.
Financial data (yr. ended 12/31/04): Revenue, $1,521,435; assets, $219,853 (M); gifts received, $1,519,270; expenditures, $1,525,509; total giving, $1,482,951; program services expenses, $1,520,997; giving activities include $1,482,951 for grants.
Purpose and activities: The organization supports youth welfare and development through Children First Summer Dreams, Gift of Reading, Ruth Alden Children's Clothing Fund Drive, the Manny Crisostomo Scholarship Fund, and the High School Journalism Fund.
Fields of interest: Youth development; Children/youth, services.
Type of support: Scholarships—to individuals.
Limitations: Giving on a national basis.
Officers and Directors:* Carole Leigh Hutton,* Pres.; Ronald Dzwonkowski,* V.P.; Thomas Fladung, V.P.; Polk Laffoon, Secy.; J Gerard Teagan,* Treas.; Carlos Abaunza; Gary Effren; Lynda Hauswirth; Adrienne Lilly; Sharon Orlando; Alice Wang; Gordan Yamate.
EIN: 381437917

2478
Genesee Area Focus Fund, Inc.
503 S. Saginaw St., Ste. 810
Flint, MI   48502   (810) 232-6420
Contact: Timothy Herman, Pres.

Established in 1989; supporting organization of the Genessee Area Focus Council, Inc.
Grantmaker type: Public charity.
Financial data (yr. ended 8/31/04): Revenue, $199,497; assets, $198,589 (M); gifts received, $196,812; expenditures, $395,693; total giving, $5,000; program services expenses, $395,693; giving activities include $5,000 for 1 grant.
Fields of interest: Community development.
Limitations: Giving limited to the Genesee County, MI, area.
Officers and Directors:* Bill Winiarski,* Chair.; Robert Fuller,* Vice-Chair.; Timothy Herman,* Pres.; Rhetta Hunyady,* V.P.; Julius Spears,* Secy.; Robert Bellairs,* Treas.; Velma Allen, Ph.D.; Greg

Beckman; Bruce Colansanti; and 40 additional directors.
EIN: 382771641

2479
Genevieve U. Gilmore Endowment for the Arts
c/o National City Bank
K-B01-2A
Kalamazoo, MI   49007

Established in 1984; supporting organization of Kalamazoo College.
Grantmaker type: Public charity.
Financial data (yr. ended 6/30/05): Revenue, $69,577; assets, $1,350,010 (M); expenditures, $58,766; total giving, $49,063; program services expenses, $49,063; giving activities include $49,063 for 1 grant.
Fields of interest: Higher education, college.
Limitations: Applications not accepted. Giving limited to Kalamazoo, MI.
Application information: Contributes only to a pre-selected organization; unsolicited requests for funds not considered or acknowledged.
Trustee: National City Bank.
EIN: 386470228

2480
Irving S. Gilmore International Keyboard Festival
359 S. Kalamazoo Mall, Ste. 101
Kalamazoo, MI   49007-4843   (269) 342-1166
Contact: Thomas W. Lambert, Pres.
FAX: (269) 342-0968; Toll-free tel.: (800) 347-4266; URL: http://www.gilmore.org/gilmore_festival/festival_2006.asp

Grantmaker type: Public charity.
Financial data (yr. ended 8/31/05): Revenue, $1,632,732; assets, $1,782,089 (M); gifts received, $1,544,057; expenditures, $1,671,233; total giving, $79,738; program services expenses, $1,108,683; giving activities include $79,738 for grants to individuals.
Purpose and activities: The festival promotes and develops world-class keyboard musical experiences that inspire present and future artists and audiences.
Fields of interest: Performing arts, music.
Type of support: Grants to individuals.
Limitations: Applications not accepted.
Publications: Newsletter.
Application information: Awards by nomination only; unsolicited requests for funds not considered or acknowledged.
Officers and Trustees:* Thomas W. Lambert,* Pres.; Judith K. Jolliffe, Pres.-Elect; Barbara J. Parish,* Secy.; Jerry L. Miller,* Treas.; Rosemary K. Brown; Russell Gabier; Charles Hall; George T. Nguyen; Donald R. Parfet; and 16 additional trustees.
EIN: 382868071

2481
The Gilmour Fund
c/o Community Fdn. for Southeastern Michigan
333 W. Fort St., Rm. 2010
Detroit, MI   48226

Established in 1995 in MI; supporting organization of the Community Foundation for Southeastern Michigan.

Grantmaker type: Public charity.

Financial data (yr. ended 12/31/04): Assets, $4,232,837 (M); expenditures, $284,549; total giving, $265,150; program services expenses, $265,150; giving activities include $265,150 for 51 grants (high: $52,500; low: $250).

Purpose and activities: The fund is an affiliate of the Community Foundation for Southeastern Michigan to support education, arts and culture, human services, health care, and other charitable activities.

Fields of interest: Arts; Higher education; Education; Health care; Human services; Civil rights; Foundations (community); Federated giving programs; LGBTQ.

Type of support: Program development; General/operating support.

Limitations: Applications not accepted. Giving primarily in the seven counties of southeastern MI.

Application information: Contributes only to pre-selected organizations.

Officers and Directors:* Allan D. Gilmour,* Pres.; Mariam C. Noland, Secy.-Treas.; David Adamany; Eric C. Jirgens; Christopher Nern.

EIN: 383251051

2482
Glen Arbor Art Association

P.O. Box 305
Glen Arbor, MI 49636 (231) 334-6112
Contact: Shirley Hoagland, Pres.
E-mail: info@glenarborart.org; *URL:* http://www.glenarborart.org

Established in MI.

Grantmaker type: Public charity.

Financial data (yr. ended 12/31/04): Revenue, $120,993; assets, $336,033 (M); gifts received, $18,606; expenditures, $124,963; total giving, $150; program services expenses, $74,931; giving activities include $150 for grants to individuals.

Purpose and activities: The association is dedicated to furthering the arts in the Glen Lake, Michigan, area, by providing residencies, in which no monetary support is given.

Fields of interest: Visual arts, photography; Visual arts, sculpture; Visual arts, painting; Visual arts, ceramic arts; Performing arts, music; Philosophy/ethics.

Type of support: Use of facilities.

Limitations: Giving on a national basis.

Publications: Application guidelines.

Application information: Application form required.
Initial approach: Letter of intent
Deadline(s): Mar. 15 for Artists in Residence

Officers: Shirley Hoagland, Pres.; Jane Batteiger, V.P.; David Early, Secy.; Bill Alldredge, Treas.

Board Members: Beth Bricker; Bobbie Collins; Renie Cutler; T.J. Ewing; Harvey Gordon; Lous Heiser; Ted Peterson; Lois Saltsman; Ann Wettlaufer.

EIN: 382886660

2483
Gogebic Range United Way

P.O. Box 248
Ironwood, MI 49938

Grantmaker type: Public charity.

Financial data (yr. ended 12/31/05): Revenue, $45,502; assets, $18,897 (M); gifts received, $45,502; expenditures, $29,653; total giving, $24,183; program services expenses, $24,183; giving activities include $24,183 for 23+ grants (high: $2,187).

Fields of interest: Community development.

Limitations: Giving primarily in MI.

Officers: Anneito Grosso, Pres.; Carolyn Carlson, V.P.; Cindy Simmons, Secy.-Treas.

Directors: Julie Ahnen; Margaret Celeski; Robert Hautala; Gina Kretschmar; Karl Kretschmar; Randy Mezzano; Marge Mickelson; Robert Mickelson.

EIN: 381940876

2484
Gordon Christian Trust

3333 Evergreen Dr. N.E., Ste. 201
Grand Rapids, MI 49525 (616) 363-9209
Contact: Ronald Williams, Exec. Dir.

Established in 1985.

Grantmaker type: Public charity.

Financial data (yr. ended 12/31/04): Revenue, $2,161,119; assets, $16,623,750 (M); gifts received, $1,200,000; expenditures, $2,872,675; total giving, $2,482,491; program services expenses, $2,482,491; giving activities include $2,482,491 for grants.

Fields of interest: Christian agencies & churches.

Officers and Trustees:* John M. Gordon, Jr.,* Chair.; Ronald Williams, Exec. Dir.; Paul Deal; James Dekruyter; James D. Gordon; Max Smith.

EIN: 382596725

2485
Paul B. and Dorothy D. Gordon Family Christian Trust

3333 Evergreen Dr. N.E., Ste. 201
Grand Rapids, MI 49525

Established in 1981; supporting organization of Gull Lake Bible and Missionary Conference.

Grantmaker type: Public charity.

Financial data (yr. ended 12/31/05): Revenue, $92,855; assets, $1,929,395 (M); expenditures, $79,085; total giving, $78,936; program services expenses, $78,936; giving activities include $78,936 for 10 grants (high: $51,911; low: $700).

Fields of interest: Protestant agencies & churches.

Limitations: Applications not accepted. Giving primarily in Hickory Corners, MI.

Application information: Contributes only to pre-selected organizations; unsolicited requests for funds not considered or acknowledged.

Trustees: Paul B. Gordon; Max E. Smith.

EIN: 386426709

2486
Grace Episcopal Youth Ministry Trust

c/o A.G. Edwards Trust Co.
P.O. Box 66734
St. Louis, MO 63166

Established in 1998 in MO.

Grantmaker type: Public charity.

Financial data (yr. ended 12/31/03): Assets, $601,940 (M); expenditures, $36,244; total giving, $29,385; program services expenses, $29,385; giving activities include $29,385 for 1 grant.

Purpose and activities: The trust exists for the sole benefit of Grace Episcopal Church Youth Ministry in Port Huron, Michigan.

Fields of interest: Christian agencies & churches.

Limitations: Applications not accepted. Giving limited to Port Huron, MI. No grants to individuals.

Application information: Contributes only to a pre-selected organization; unsolicited requests for funds not considered or acknowledged.

Trustee: A.G. Edwards Trust Co.

EIN: 436812820

2487
Grand Rapids E.C. Foundation, Inc.

0-2800 Buchanan St.
Marne, MI 49435

Established in 1997 in MI.

Grantmaker type: Public charity.

Financial data (yr. ended 8/31/05): Revenue, $14,529; assets, $9,217 (M); gifts received, $12,820; expenditures, $21,522; total giving, $19,319; program services expenses, $19,319; giving activities include $500 for 1 grant, and $18,819 for grants to individuals.

Fields of interest: Performing arts, music; Human services, gift distribution; Human services, emergency aid.

Officers: Jeffrey B. Carpenter, Pres.; Lawrence D. Bos, V.P.; John Laninga, Secy.; Rusty S. Snyder, Treas.

EIN: 383110178

2488
Grand Rapids Jaycees Foundation

2774 Birchcrest Dr. S.E.
Grand Rapids, MI 49506 (616) 954-9409
FAX: (616) 949-8742; *URL:* http://www.grjayceesfoundation.org

Grantmaker type: Public charity.

Financial data (yr. ended 12/31/04): Revenue, $2,766,526; assets, $1,625,105 (M); gifts received, $14,663; expenditures, $2,719,030; total giving, $167,904; program services expenses, $183,914; giving activities include $167,904 for 6 + grants (high: $61,967).

Purpose and activities: The foundation provides assistance to promote community involvement in community affairs and to promote the community's welfare; support primarily for cancer services, housing and shelter, youth development, and children's services.

Fields of interest: Cancer; Housing/shelter; Youth development; Children/youth, services.

Type of support: Capital campaigns.

Limitations: Giving limited to western MI.

Publications: Newsletter.

Application information: See foundation Web site for application form and additional application information. Application form required.
Initial approach: Application
Board meeting date(s): Monthly

Officers and Directors:* Cathy Prein,* Chair.; John Mousel,* Pres.; Amanda Schelling,* Secy.; John Greko,* Treas.; Ryan Bruce; Martin Hillard; Mark Hills; David Klein; David Morgenstern; Kris Nylaan; Fay Poissant.

EIN: 382425009

2489
Grand Rapids Student Advancement Foundation
118 Commerce S.W.
Grand Rapids, MI 49503   (616) 632-1005
FAX: (616) 459-8460;
E-mail: saf@unitedwaycares.com; URL: http://www.grsaf.org

Established in 1993 in MI.
Grantmaker type: Public charity.
Financial data (yr. ended 6/30/05): Revenue, $1,345,973; assets, $1,613,082 (M); gifts received, $1,359,000; expenditures, $1,109,934; total giving, $993,834; program services expenses, $1,014,738; giving activities include $993,834 for 54 grants (high: $543,982; low: $6).
Purpose and activities: The organization aims to acquire and distribute resources that support Grand Rapids Public Schools' programs and projects aimed at enhancing, enriching and supplementing learning opportunities for students, staff and community.
Fields of interest: Elementary/secondary education.
Limitations: Applications not accepted. Giving limited to Grand Rapids, MI.
Application information: Contributes only to pre-selected organizations; unsolicited requests for funds not considered or acknowledged.
Board meeting date(s): 4th Tues. of each month
Officers and Directors:* Lynn Afendoulis,* Pres.; Phil Biggs,* V.P., Fund Devel.; Jon Marsh,* V.P., Projects and Progs.; Karen O'Donovan, Secy.; Kiki Lown,* Treas.; Susan Heartwell, Exec. Dir.; Roger Martin; Joan Secchia; and 15 additional directors.
Number of staff: 1 full-time professional.
EIN: 383137984

2490
Great Lakes Center for Youth Development
(also known as GLCYD)
(formerly Marquette-Alger Youth Foundation)
307 S. Front St.
Marquette, MI 49855   (906) 228-8919
Contact: Judy Watson Olson, Pres.
FAX: (906) 228-7712; E-mail: jwatson@glcyd.org; Toll-free tel.: (877) 33YOUTH; URL: http://www.glcyd.org/

Established in 2000 in MI as a part of the Kellogg Youth Initiative Partnerships through the W.K. Kellogg Foundation.
Grantmaker type: Public charity.
Financial data (yr. ended 6/30/05): Revenue, $1,191,607; assets, $3,983,681 (M); gifts received, $1,074,909; expenditures, $725,382; total giving, $89,500; program services expenses, $577,123; giving activities include $89,500 for 15 grants (high: $26,000; low: $1,000).
Purpose and activities: The organization is committed to helping rural communities build healthy youth environments by strengthening organizations that serve youth.
Fields of interest: Youth development.
Type of support: Scholarship funds.
Limitations: Giving limited to the Upper Peninsula region in MI.
Application information:
Initial approach: Telephone

Officers and Directors:* Mike Prokopowicz,* Chair.; Connie Koutouzos,* Vice-Chair.; Judy Watson Olson,* Pres.; Gary Murrell,* Secy.; Jesse Bell,* Treas.; Angela Balbierz; William Bernard; Rochelle Cotey; Amy Hill; Whitney Johnson; Pete Kelto; June Schaefer, Ph.D.
EIN: 383522344

2491
Great Lakes Chapter of Links, Inc.
18615 E. Chelton Dr.
Beverly Hills, MI 48025-5220   (248) 644-2434

Grantmaker type: Public charity.
Financial data (yr. ended 12/31/04): Revenue, $74,939; assets, $84,848 (M); gifts received, $65,794; expenditures, $55,293; total giving, $28,264; program services expenses, $55,293; giving activities include $28,264 for 4+ grants (high: $25,000).
Purpose and activities: The chapter promotes service and friendship in the community.
Fields of interest: Community development, service clubs.
Limitations: Giving primarily in MI.
Officers: Judith Caliman, Pres.; Rose Marie Nance, V.P.; Pauline J. Givens, Treas.
EIN: 382922101

2492
Great Lakes Energy People Fund
1323 Boyne Ave.
P.O. Box 70
Boyne City, MI 49712
Contact: Terry Distel, Pres.
FAX: (231) 582-6213;
E-mail: glenergy@glenergy.com; Toll-free tel.: (888) 485-2537; URL: http://www.gtlakes.com/commprog/peoplefund/

Established in 1996 in MI.
Donor: Customers of Great Lakes Energy.
Grantmaker type: Public charity.
Financial data (yr. ended 12/31/05): Revenue, $135,468; assets, $293,642 (M); gifts received, $130,144; expenditures, $130,844; total giving, $130,844; program services expenses, $130,844; giving activities include $130,844 for grants.
Purpose and activities: The fund is part of Operation RoundUp, a voluntary charitable contribution program sponsored by Great Lakes Energy customers. Grants are awarded to nonprofit organizations and charitable activities within the geographical area served by Great Lakes Energy.
Fields of interest: Community development.
Limitations: Giving limited to Great Lakes Energy's service area in the 26 counties in western and northern MI, from the Mackinac Straits to Kalamazoo. No support for religious activities or for continuing school projects. No grants to individuals, or generally for normal operating expenses of established programs, annual fundraising campaigns, endowment funds, or deficit spending; no loans.
Publications: Annual report.
Application information: See Web site for additional application information. Application form required.
Officers and Directors:* Terry Distel,* Pres.; David Wagner,* V.P.; Sharon Templar, Secy.; Mike Stowe,* Treas.; Kathleen Andersen; Laura Beyer; Wayne Bumstead; Beverly Cassidy; Yolanda

Estrada; Shirley Farrier; Carol Holtrop; Shelley Myers; Edmund Rybicki; Pat Stapp; Tom Walenta.
EIN: 383220304

2493
Great Lakes Fishery Trust
c/o Public Sector Consultants
600 W. St. Joseph, Ste. 10
Lansing, MI 48933-2265   (517) 371-7468
Contact: Holly Madill, Asst. Mgr.
FAX: (517) 484-6549; E-mail: glft@glft.org; URL: http://www.glft.org/

Established in 1996 in MI.
Grantmaker type: Public charity.
Financial data (yr. ended 12/31/05): Revenue, $2,000,000; assets, $21,600,000 (M); expenditures, $2,200,000; total giving, $2,900,000; program services expenses, $2,900,000; giving activities include $2,900,000 for 14 grants (high: $583,212; low: $32,000).
Purpose and activities: The trust provides funding to enhance, protect, and rehabilitate Great Lakes fishery resources and to mitigate for lost use and enjoyment of the Lake Michigan fishery resulting from the operation of the Ludington Pumped Storage Plant.
Fields of interest: Environment, research; Environment, public education; Environment, water resources; Animals/wildlife, preservation/protection; Animals/wildlife, fisheries.
Type of support: Scholarship funds; Technical assistance; Publication; Program evaluation; Internship funds; Fellowships; Building/renovation; Continuing support; Equipment; Land acquisition; Program development; Conferences/seminars; Seed money; Curriculum development; Research; Matching/challenge support.
Limitations: Giving limited to MI, with Lake Michigan and its tributaries the primary geographic target for projects; secondary consideration given to projects that primarily benefit fisheries or fishing access outside the Lake Michigan watershed. No support for lobbying. No grants to individuals.
Publications: Application guidelines; Annual report; Financial statement; Grants list; Informational brochure; Occasional report.
Application information: Proposal is accepted by e-mail; see Web site for additional application information. Application form required.
Initial approach: Letter or telephone
Copies of proposal: 1
Deadline(s): Sept. for Fishing Access, and Apr. for Research
Board meeting date(s): Feb., May, Aug., and Nov.
Final notification: Aug. for Research and Nov. for Fishing Access
Officer and Trustees:* Rebecca A. Humphries,* Chair.; Andy Buchsbaum; James Ekdahl; Suzanne McSawby; Jim Riley; Sam Washington; Charles Wooley.
Number of staff: 1 full-time professional; 4 part-time professional.
EIN: 383331471

2494
Irwin and Bethea Green Support Foundation
6735 Telegraph Rd.
P.O. Box 2030
Bloomfield Hills, MI 48301-3141
(248) 642-4260
Contact: Bethea Green, Pres.

Established in 1984.
Grantmaker type: Public charity.
Financial data (yr. ended 5/31/05): Revenue, $1,347,870; assets, $3,694,032 (M); gifts received, $675,000; expenditures, $1,681,279; total giving, $1,629,000; program services expenses, $1,629,000; giving activities include $1,629,000 for 15 grants (high: $500,000; low: $3,000).
Purpose and activities: The foundation supports a wide range of Jewish organizations, schools, and federated giving programs.
Fields of interest: Jewish federated giving programs; Jewish agencies & temples.
Limitations: Giving primarily in MI and NY.
Officers and Directors:* Bethea Green,* Pres.; Irwin Green,* V.P.; Robert P. Arnson,* Secy.; Dorothy Benyas, Treas.; Mandell Berman; Don Green; Margo Green; Richard Green; and 3 additional directors.
EIN: 382490337

2495
Grosse Pointe Park Foundation
15115 E. Jefferson Ave.
Grosse Pointe Park, MI 48230

Supporting organization for community recreation center.
Grantmaker type: Public charity.
Financial data (yr. ended 12/31/04): Revenue, $279,499; assets, $129,946; gifts received, $279,119; expenditures, $263,747; total giving, $260,000; program services expenses, $260,000; giving activities include $260,000 for 1 grant.
Fields of interest: Recreation, community facilities; Recreation, centers.
Limitations: Giving limited to Grosse Pointe Park, MI.
Officers and Board Members:* Dinesh J. Telang,* Pres.; Robert Denner,* V.P.; Lou Perrone,* Secy.; John B. Kretzschmar,* Treas.; and 15 additional board members.
EIN: 382558941

2496
Gus & Dorothy Gutmueller Foundation
c/o Fifth Third Bank
P.O. Box 3636
Grand Rapids, MI 49501-3636

Supporting organization of Aquinas College.
Grantmaker type: Public charity.
Financial data (yr. ended 12/31/05): Revenue, $37,480; assets, $805,382 (M); expenditures, $20,181; total giving, $14,417; program services expenses, $14,417; giving activities include $14,417 for 1 grant.
Purpose and activities: Support only for Aquinas College for its use in granting scholarships.
Fields of interest: Higher education, college.
Type of support: Scholarship funds.

Limitations: Applications not accepted. Giving limited to Grand Rapids, MI. No grants to individuals.
Application information: Contributes only to a pre-selected organization; unsolicited requests for funds not considered or acknowledged.
Trustee: Fifth Third Bank.
EIN: 386050826

2497
Hackley Trust
c/o Fifth Third Bank
P.O. Box 3636
Grand Rapids, MI 49501-3636

Supporting organization of Hackley Public Library, Muskegon, MI.
Grantmaker type: Public charity.
Financial data (yr. ended 6/30/05): Revenue, $13,286; assets, $197,711 (M); expenditures, $18,767; total giving, $15,006; program services expenses, $15,006; giving activities include $15,006 for 1 grant.
Fields of interest: Libraries (public).
Limitations: Applications not accepted. Giving limited to Muskegon, MI. No grants to individuals.
Application information: Contributes only to a pre-selected organization; unsolicited requests for funds not considered or acknowledged.
Trustee: Fifth Third Bank.
EIN: 386051395

2498
Rita C. and John M. Haddow Family Support Foundation
6735 Telegraph Rd.
P.O. Box 2030
Bloomfield Hills, MI 48301-3141

Established in 1988; supporting organization of the Jewish Federation of Metropolitan Detroit.
Grantmaker type: Public charity.
Financial data (yr. ended 5/31/05): Revenue, $188,187; assets, $1,687,210 (M); gifts received, $43,800; expenditures, $153,222; total giving, $121,370; program services expenses, $121,370; giving activities include $121,370 for 26 grants (high: $50,000; low: $250).
Fields of interest: Jewish federated giving programs; Jewish agencies & temples.
Limitations: Applications not accepted. Giving in the U.S., primarily in Detroit and Bloomfield Hills, MI.
Application information: Contributes only to pre-selected organizations; unsolicited requests for funds not considered or acknowledged.
Officers and Directors:* John M. Haddow,* Pres.; Rita C. Haddow,* V.P.; Robert P. Aronson,* Secy.; Dorothy Benyas, Treas.; Amy C. Coyer; and 6 additional directors.
EIN: 382824409

2499
Constance Parks Hagelshaw & June Hagelshaw Scholarship Fund
c/o Comerica Bank
P.O. Box 75000, MC 330
Detroit, MI 48275-3302 (734) 930-2416

Established in 1997 in FL; supporting organization of Michigan State University.
Donor: Alice Hagelshaw‡.

Grantmaker type: Public charity.
Financial data (yr. ended 2/28/05): Revenue, $19,965; assets, $591,945 (M); expenditures, $8,258.
Purpose and activities: The fund provides scholarship funds for the Department of Food Science and Human Nutrition, and the College of Human Ecology of Michigan State University.
Fields of interest: Higher education, university; Nutrition.
Type of support: Scholarship funds.
Limitations: Applications not accepted. Giving limited to Lansing, MI.
Application information: Contributes only to a pre-selected organization; unsolicited requests for funds not considered or acknowledged.
Trustee: Comerica Bank.
EIN: 656231899

2500
The Jim Harbaugh Foundation
2038 Winsted Ct.
Ann Arbor, MI 48103 (734) 994-1049
Contact: Peter J. Savarino, V.P. and Secy.

Grantmaker type: Public charity.
Financial data (yr. ended 12/31/04): Revenue, $4,286; assets, $271,619 (M); expenditures, $16,590; total giving, $16,000; program services expenses, $16,000; giving activities include $16,000 for 5 grants (high: $10,000; low: $500).
Purpose and activities: The foundation aids youth primarily in southeastern Michigan by providing leadership, support and financial backing to organizations who promote and provide aid to them.
Fields of interest: Youth development.
Limitations: Giving limited to southeastern MI.
Officers and Directors:* James J. Harbaugh,* Pres.; Peter J. Savarino,* V.P. and Secy.; Robert N. Pollock, Jr.,* Treas.; John Berry.
EIN: 363891987

2501
Harbor Springs Educational Foundation
P.O. Box 844
Harbor Springs, MI 49740

Grantmaker type: Public charity.
Financial data (yr. ended 12/31/05): Revenue, $706,717; assets, $340,748 (M); gifts received, $688,777; expenditures, $399,743; total giving, $387,110; program services expenses, $387,110; giving activities include $324,619 for 2 grants, $7,500 for 5 grants to individuals (high: $4,000; low: $500), and $54,991 for in-kind gifts.
Fields of interest: Education.
Type of support: In-kind gifts; Scholarships—to individuals.
Limitations: Giving primarily in MI.
Officers: Fred Hoffmann, Pres.; Susan Clarke, Secy.; Kathie Breighner, Treas.
Directors: Linda Heminger; Lee Kramer; Lynn Koss; Gary Morse; Danielle Ottimer; Frank Shumway; Peter Wallin.
EIN: 383458936

2502
Del Harder Rehabilitation Fund
261 Mack Blvd.
Detroit, MI 48201

Established in 1974; supporting organization of the Rehabilitation Institute, Inc.
Grantmaker type: Public charity.
Financial data (yr. ended 12/31/04): Revenue, $113,049; assets, $3,512,763 (M); total giving, $27,373; giving activities include $27,373 for 1 grant.
Fields of interest: Medical care, rehabilitation.
Limitations: Applications not accepted. Giving limited to Detroit, MI.
Application information: Contributes only to a pre-selected organization; unsolicited requests for funds not considered or acknowledged.
Officers and Trustees: * David Viano, Ph.D., M.D.*, Pres.; Marilyn Wayland, Ph.D., Secy.; Ernest C. Fackler,* Treas.; Duane L. Block, M.D.; Steven Hinderer, M.D.; Albert King, Ph.D.; Robert Mathog, M.D.; Jay Meythaler, M.D.; Terry A. Reiley; Beverly J. Schmoll, Ph.D.
EIN: 237390927

2503
Haven Hill Foundation
P.O. Box 1741
Ann Arbor, MI 48106-1741

Grantmaker type: Public charity.
Financial data (yr. ended 12/31/04): Revenue, $82,512; assets, $135,416 (M); gifts received, $80,238; expenditures, $120,974; total giving, $9,107; program services expenses, $47,791; giving activities include $9,107 for 3 grants (high: $6,607; low: $1,000).
Purpose and activities: The foundation supports various Christian faith-based organizations.
Fields of interest: Christian agencies & churches.
Type of support: General/operating support; Continuing support; Consulting services.
Limitations: Applications not accepted.
Application information: Unsolicited requests for funds not considered.
 Board meeting date(s): Dec.
Officers and Trustees: * Kenneth Roesler,* Pres.; Dennis Michalak,* Secy.; R. Deane Melvin,* Treas.; William E. Bullard,* Exec. Dir.; Alan Borg; Chester Browne; Murray Jones.
Number of staff: 1 full-time professional; 1 part-time professional; 1 full-time support; 1 part-time support.
EIN: 237032661

2504
Heart of West Michigan United Way
118 Commerce Ave., S.W.
Grand Rapids, MI 49503-4106 (616) 459-6281
FAX: (616) 459-8460; URL: http://www.unitedwaycares.com/

Established in 1961 in MI.
Grantmaker type: Public charity.
Financial data (yr. ended 6/30/05): Revenue, $15,901,188; assets, $24,593,386 (M); gifts received, $15,028,774; expenditures, $15,549,668; total giving, $12,087,410; program services expenses, $14,114,609; giving activities include $12,087,410 for grants.
Purpose and activities: United Way partners with local human service providers and volunteers to identify community needs and implement effective solutions. Resources are focused on the most important needs in the community and specifically

targets the five issue areas that include: 1) ensure the healthy development and school readiness of children; 2) prepare youth to become accountable adults; 3) equip adults with skills for independence and changing life stages; 4) helps senior adults find support and maintain independence; and 5) support families to achieve well being and success.
Fields of interest: Education; Health care; Youth development; Children/youth, services; Family services; Aging, centers/services.
Limitations: Giving limited to west MI.
Officers and Directors: * Mary Ellen Rodgers,* Chair.; Robert G. Haight, Pres.; Tanya Berg, V.P. Marketing; Tony Campbell, V.P., Community Investment; Susan Stoddard, V.P., Finance; Kathy White, V.P., Resource Development; Sharon Caldwell-Newton; Michael David; James E. Dunlap; Patricia D. Gardner; Kim Gilpin; Martha Gonzalez-Cortes; Susan Levy; Mark A. Michon; Mark T. Mossing; Daniel Oglesby; Penny Pestle; Lori A. Portfleet; David Spieker.
EIN: 381360923

2505
Hemophilia Foundation of Michigan
1921 W. Michigan Ave.
Ypsilanti, MI 48197 (734) 544-0015
Contact: Ivan C. Harner FACHE, Exec. Dir.
FAX: (734) 544-0095; E-mail: hfm@hfmich.org; Toll-free tel.: (800) 482-3041; URL: http://www.hfmich.org

Established in 1997 in MI.
Grantmaker type: Public charity.
Financial data (yr. ended 12/31/04): Revenue, $2,230,311; assets, $1,774,308 (M); gifts received, $1,760,466; expenditures, $2,020,396; total giving, $1,062,281; program services expenses, $1,863,980; giving activities include $1,057,281 for 19 grants (high: $202,551; low: $15,946), and $5,000 for grants to individuals.
Purpose and activities: The organization is dedicated to improving the quality of life for all those affected by hemophilia and hereditary bleeding disorders and related complications including HIV infection and AIDS, through the support of individual, family and community services, education, health care, advocacy and research with the ultimate goal of finding a cure.
Fields of interest: Hemophilia; AIDS; Hemophilia research.
Type of support: Grants to individuals; Research.
Limitations: Giving limited to MI.
Publications: Annual report.
Application information: See Web site to download application form. Application form required.
 Initial approach: Application
 Deadline(s): Mar. 3 for scholarships
Officers and Directors: * Shelley Gerson, MEd., LLPC*, Pres.; Lauren Shellenberger,* 1st V.P.; Dave Meuleman,* 2nd V.P.; Angie Guadagnini,* Secy.; James Meretta,* Treas.; Ivan C. Harner, Exec. Dir.; Jeff Burgoon; Michael Dempsey; and 10 additional directors.
EIN: 381905673

2506
Virginia Henry Charitable Trust
c/o Comerica Bank
P.O. Box 75000, M/C 3302
Detroit, MI 48275-3302 (602) 606-5791

Established in 1997 in AZ; supporting organization of YMCA and YWCA, Marshalltown, IA.
Grantmaker type: Public charity.
Financial data (yr. ended 12/31/05): Revenue, $1,984,516; assets, $276,378,400 (M); expenditures, $1,608,035; total giving, $1,472,633; program services expenses, $1,472,633; giving activities include $1,472,633 for 2 grants (high: $736,317; low: $736,316).
Fields of interest: YM/YWCAs & YM/YWHAs.
Limitations: Applications not accepted. Giving limited to Marshalltown, IA. No grants to individuals.
Application information: Contributes only to pre-selected organizations.
Trustee: Comerica Bank.
EIN: 860942459

2507
Florence E. Herman Charitable Trust
c/o Fifth Third Bank
P.O. Box 3636
Grand Rapids, MI 49501-3636

Established in 1991; supporting organization of the Kalamazoo County Humane Society.
Grantmaker type: Public charity.
Financial data (yr. ended 6/30/05): Revenue, $249,352; assets, $1,878,461 (M); expenditures, $65,715; total giving, $52,716; program services expenses, $52,716; giving activities include $52,716 for 1 grant.
Fields of interest: Animal welfare.
Limitations: Applications not accepted. Giving limited to Kalamazoo, MI.
Application information: Contributes only to a pre-selected organization; unsolicited requests for funds not considered or acknowledged.
Trustee: Fifth Third Bank.
EIN: 386567414

2508
Hermelin Family Support Foundation
(formerly Hermelin Family Foundation)
6735 Telegraph Rd.
P.O. Box 2030
Bloomfield Hills, MI 48301

Established in 1985 in MI; supporting organization of the Jewish Federation of Metropolitan Detroit.
Donor: David B. Hermelin.
Grantmaker type: Public charity.
Financial data (yr. ended 5/31/05): Revenue, $356,786; assets, $4,284,148 (M); expenditures, $478,868; total giving, $446,916; program services expenses, $446,916; giving activities include $446,916 for 36 grants (high: $25,000; low: $500).
Purpose and activities: The foundation supports Orthodox and Conservative Judaism through grants for education, temples, and federated giving programs; giving also for the arts and health care.
Fields of interest: History/archaeology; Arts; Education; Health care; Medical research; Jewish federated giving programs; Jewish agencies & temples.
Limitations: Giving primarily in New York, NY, and MI. No grants to individuals.
Application information: Application form not required.
 Deadline(s): None

Officers and Directors:* Doreen Hermelin,* Pres.; Brian Hermelin,* V.P.; Francine G. Hermelin, Secy.; Julie C. Hermelin, Treas.; Eugene Applebaum; Penny Blumenstein; Karen Hermelin Borman; Marcie Hermelin Orley; Arthur Weiss.
EIN: 382574834

2509
F. W. & Elsie Heyl Science Scholarship Fund
c/o National City Bank
171 Monroe Ave., N.W., KC17-63
Grand Rapids, MI 49503
Contact: For Kalamazoo College applicants: Dr. Diane R. Kiino, Exec. Dir.; For WMU Bronson School of Nursing applicants: Dr. Marie Gates
URL: http://www.kzoo.edu/heyl/

A supporting organization of Kalamazoo College, Western Michigan University Bronson School of Nursing, and Yale University.
Donors: Frederick W. Heyl‡; Mrs. Frederick W. Heyl‡.
Grantmaker type: Public charity.
Financial data (yr. ended 12/31/04): Revenue, $2,574,589; assets, $33,015,189 (M); gifts received, $1,784; expenditures, $2,374,203; total giving, $2,191,619; program services expenses, $2,213,804; giving activities include $2,191,619 for grants to individuals.
Purpose and activities: Scholarships for tuition, fees, college housing and a book allowance are available for study in the natural sciences, mathematics, computer science or health sciences at Kalamazoo College and for nursing at Western Michigan University Bronson School of Nursing. The fund also provides fellowships (renewable for a maximum of four years) for graduate study in certain (usually chemistry-related) disciplines at Yale University. These are available to any graduate of Kalamazoo College majoring in one of the exact sciences.
Fields of interest: Nursing school/education; Health sciences school/education; Science; Chemistry; Mathematics; Computer science.
Type of support: Fellowships; Scholarships—to individuals.
Limitations: Giving primarily for the benefit of residents of Kalamazoo, MI.
Application information: See fund Web site for application requirements. Application form required.
Officers: Eileen Wilson-Oyelaran, Pres.; Larry Lueth, V.P.; Scott Campbell, Secy.-Treas.; Diane Kiino, Exec. Dir.
Directors: Henry Holland; Marian Klein; Cindy Kole; Jon Streeter; James Walter.
Trustee: National City Bank.
EIN: 386194019

2510
Hillsdale County United Way
30 N. Howell St., Ste. 21
P.O. Box 203
Hillsdale, MI 49242 (517) 439-5050
FAX: (517) 439-5058; E-mail: hcuw@frontiernet.net; URL: http://www.hillsdalecountyunitedway.org/

Grantmaker type: Public charity.
Financial data (yr. ended 3/31/05): Revenue, $162,566; assets, $370,575 (M); gifts received, $154,073; expenditures, $140,695; total giving, $54,072; program services expenses, $107,347; giving activities include $54,072 for grants.
Purpose and activities: Hillsdale County United Way provides funding for programs and services that address critical community needs to human service agencies in Hillsdale County.
Fields of interest: Health care; Human services; Community development.
Limitations: Giving limited to Hillsdale County, MI.
Officers and Directors:* Bill VanArsdalen,* Pres.; Julie Gaier,* V.P.; Sandra Grimm,* Secy.; Jill Pulley,* Treas.; Pia Seebach-York, Exec. Dir.; Jill Carey; Ron Hayes; Eric Moore; Debbie Treiber; and 15 additional directors.
EIN: 237218311

2511
William & Sarah E. Hinman Endowment Fund Corporation
c/o National City Bank of Michigan/Illinois
171 Monroe Ave. N.W., KC17-63
Grand Rapids, MI 49503

Supporting organization of Lansing Community College, Lansing Public School District, and Michigan State University.
Donor: Charles Hinman.
Grantmaker type: Public charity.
Financial data (yr. ended 12/31/05): Revenue, $248,403; assets, $1,941,233 (M); expenditures, $106,970; total giving, $100,610; program services expenses, $100,610; giving activities include $100,610 for 3 grants (high: $40,244; low: $30,183).
Fields of interest: Higher education, college; Higher education, university; Scholarships/financial aid; Education.
Type of support: Scholarship funds.
Limitations: Applications not accepted. Giving limited to Lansing and East Lansing, MI.
Application information: Contributes only to pre-selected organizations; unsolicited requests for funds not considered or acknowledged.
Officers and Directors:* Lee June, Ph.D.*, Pres.; E. Sharon Banks, Ph.D.*, V.P.; Scott Campbell,* Secy.-Treas.; Sue Fisher; Scott Freeman; National City Bank.
EIN: 386069372

2512
Holland Christian Education Foundation
956 Ottawa Ave.
Holland, MI 49423-4628

Established in 1989; supporting organization of the Holland Christian Education Society.
Grantmaker type: Public charity.
Financial data (yr. ended 8/31/05): Revenue, $467,099; assets, $6,641,590 (M); gifts received, $292,021; expenditures, $361,449; total giving, $278,909; program services expenses, $278,909; giving activities include $278,909 for 1 grant.
Purpose and activities: The foundation provides financial support for the education for kindergarten through 12th grade students at Holland Christian Schools.
Fields of interest: Education, early childhood education; Elementary school/education; Secondary school/education.
Limitations: Applications not accepted. Giving limited to Holland, MI.

Application information: Contributes only to a pre-selected organization; unsolicited requests for funds not considered or acknowledged.
Officers: James Schippers, Pres.; Troy Dokter, V.P.; Mary Westrate, Secy.; Bruce Johnson, Treas.
Board Members: Willa Beckman; Peter Hoekstra; Leon Koops; Glenn Meyaard; Dale Scholten; Jonathan Steiner.
EIN: 382885151

2513
Home Builders Association of Livingston County Foundation, Inc.
(also known as HBALC Foundation)
132 E. Grand River Ave.
Brighton, MI 48116
Contact: Jeff Doyle, Pres.
URL: http://www.hbalc.com/charitablefound.cfm

Established in 1998 in MI.
Grantmaker type: Public charity.
Financial data (yr. ended 12/31/04): Assets, $4,118; gifts received, $26,105; expenditures, $35,733; total giving, $31,118; giving activities include $28,118 for 1 grant, and $3,000 for 3 grants to individuals (high: $1,000; low: $1,000).
Purpose and activities: Provides training and education for students pursuing a career in the building industry, as well as assisting in community service programs focusing on special housing needs.
Fields of interest: Housing/shelter, development.
Type of support: Scholarships—to individuals; General/operating support.
Limitations: Giving limited to Livingston, County, MI.
Application information: See foundation Web site for application guidelines and downloadable application form. Application form required.
Deadline(s): Mar. 25
Officers and Directors:* Jeff Doyle,* Pres.; Joan Humphrey,* Secy.; Linda Hanba,* Treas.; Tom Boyle; Dale Brewer; Jim Coe; Marie Karas; Dennis Korenchuk.
EIN: 383466735

2514
Hope Network Foundation
(formerly Hope Foundation, Inc.)
P.O. Box 890
Grand Rapids, MI 49518-0890

Established in 1987; supporting organization of Hope Network and its affiliates.
Grantmaker type: Public charity.
Financial data (yr. ended 9/30/05): Revenue, $1,382,737; assets, $2,560,522 (M); gifts received, $1,180,170; expenditures, $1,342,913; total giving, $1,048,667; program services expenses, $1,093,658; giving activities include $1,048,667 for grants.
Fields of interest: Disabilities, people with.
Limitations: Applications not accepted. Giving limited to MI.
Application information: Contributes only to pre-selected organizations; unsolicited requests for funds not considered or acknowledged.
Officers: Bill Lettinga, Pres.; Dan Devos, V.P.; Kathy Dunlap, Secy.; Larry Fredericks, Treas.
Directors: John Canepa; Sam Cummings; Lou Ann Gaydou; Ken Hoexum; Jeffrey Hughes; Mike

Jandernoa; Jim McKay; Tom Van Laan; John Vander Ploeg; Russ Warner.
EIN: 382731395

2515
Huckle Family Fund
503 N. Harris Trail
Cadillac, MI   49601-8945   (231) 775-4773
Contact: Thomas C. Huckle, Chair.
E-mail: thuckle@cadillacnews.com

Established in 1995 in MI as a donor-advised fund of the Cadillac Area Community Foundation.
Grantmaker type: Public charity.
Fields of interest: Children/youth, services; Family services.
Limitations: Applications not accepted. Giving limited to the greater Cadillac, MI area.
Officer: Thomas C. Huckle, Chair.
Number of staff: None.

2516
Ilitch Charities for Children, Inc.
2211 Woodward Ave.
Detroit, MI 48201-3400   (313) 983-6340
Contact: Anne Marie Krappmann, V.P.
URL: http://www.ilitchcharitiesforchildren.com

Grantmaker type: Public charity.
Financial data (yr. ended 12/31/03): Revenue, $198,140; assets, $222,933 (M); gifts received, $134,542; expenditures, $175,155; total giving, $172,790; program services expenses, $172,790; giving activities include $154,790 for 6 grants (high: $110,790; low: $1,000), and $18,000 for 6 grants to individuals (high: $4,000; low: $2,000).
Purpose and activities: The organization is dedicated to improving the lives of children in the areas of health, education, and recreation.
Fields of interest: Arts, association; Education; Health care; Recreation.
Type of support: Scholarships—to individuals.
Limitations: Giving primarily in the metropolitan Detroit, MI, area.
Officers and Directors:* Christopher Ilitch,* Chair.; David Agius,* Pres. and Treas.; Michael Healy,* V.P.; Anne Marie Krappmann,* V.P.; Stan Berenbaum,* Secy.; Rick Fenton; Jordan Field; and 6 additional directors.
EIN: 383548144

2517
Ironwood Area Scholarship Foundation
650 E. Ayer St.
Ironwood, MI   49938
Contact: Tim Kolesar, Pres.

Grantmaker type: Public charity.
Financial data (yr. ended 6/30/05): Revenue, $68,274; assets, $595,252 (M); gifts received, $3,146; expenditures, $21,256; total giving, $17,000; program services expenses, $17,000; giving activities include $17,000 for grants to individuals.
Purpose and activities: The foundation provides scholarships to high school graduates based on their performances, grades, and achievements.
Fields of interest: Education.
Type of support: Scholarships—to individuals.
Application information: Application form required.

Officers: Tim Kolesar, Pres.; Darlene Dugan, V.P.; Wendy Stolt, Secy.; Sue Murphy, Treas.
Directors: James Anderson; Dan Corullo; John Garske; Dan Hannigan; Shirley Pertile; and 5 additional directors.
EIN: 382822183

2518
Italian American Delegates, Inc.
15985 Canal Rd., Ste. 5
Clinton Township, MI   48038-5021
(586) 228-5800
Contact: Vito Tocco, Pres.

Established in 1989.
Grantmaker type: Public charity.
Financial data (yr. ended 10/31/05): Revenue, $53,584; assets, $15,462 (M); gifts received, $17,800; expenditures, $57,244; total giving, $55,850; program services expenses, $55,850; giving activities include $51,350 for 17 grants (high: $10,000; low: $1,000), and $4,500 for 4 grants to individuals (high: $2,000; low: $500).
Purpose and activities: The organization supports cultural and educational programs and provides assistance to the disadvantaged, especially to those of Italian American heritage, children and senior citizens.
Fields of interest: Arts, cultural/ethnic awareness; Disabilities, people with; Economically disadvantaged.
International interests: Italy.
Type of support: Endowments; Grants to individuals.
Limitations: Giving limited to the Detroit metropolitan area, MI.
Officers: Vito Tocco, Pres.; Daniel Patrona, Sr., V.P.; Ted Barrie, Secy.; Frank Coppola, Treas.
EIN: 382840038

2519
Thomas S. Jerome Lecture Fund
c/o Comerica Bank
P.O. Box 75000, MC 3302
Detroit, MI   48275

Supporting organization of the University of Michigan and the Academy of Rome.
Grantmaker type: Public charity.
Financial data (yr. ended 12/31/05): Revenue, $28,138; assets, $258,090 (M); expenditures, $7,378; total giving, $3,000; program services expenses, $3,000; giving activities include $3,000 for 1 grant.
Fields of interest: Higher education, university.
Type of support: Conferences/seminars.
Limitations: Applications not accepted. Giving limited to MI and Rome, NY. No grants to individuals.
Application information: Contributes only to pre-selected organizations; unsolicited requests for funds not considered or acknowledged.
Trustee: Comerica Bank.
EIN: 386042485

2520
Jewish Federation of Grand Rapids
4127 Embassy S.E.
Grand Rapids, MI   49546   (616) 942-5553
Contact: Mike Presant, Chair.
FAX: (616) 942-5780; URL: http://www.jewishgrandrapids.org/

Established in 1947 in MI.
Grantmaker type: Public charity.
Financial data (yr. ended 6/30/05): Revenue, $701,945; assets, $2,944,195 (M); gifts received, $554,916; expenditures, $595,798; total giving, $304,049; program services expenses, $457,418; giving activities include $304,049 for 18 grants (high: $242,872; low: $200).
Purpose and activities: The federation seeks to strengthen and unify the Jewish community and function as an umbrella organization to provide for the cultural, social and financial needs of its community, world Jewry and the State of Israel. Areas of focus include social services, senior assistance, immigrant assistance, singles involvement, youth and family activities, and summer camp for younger children.
Fields of interest: Youth development; Human services; Family services; Jewish agencies & temples; Aging; Immigrants/refugees.
Limitations: Giving in the U.S., with some emphasis on Grand Rapids, MI, and in Israel.
Officers and Trustees:* Mike Presant,* Chair.; Karen Padnos,* 1st Vice-Chair.; Dan Hurwitz,* Vice-Chair.; Judith Joseph,* Vice-Chair.; Greg Kaufman,* Vice-Chair.; Claude Titche III,* Treas.; and 14 additional trustees.
EIN: 386099686

2521
Jewish Federation of Metropolitan Detroit
6735 Telegraph Rd.
P.O. Box 2030
Bloomfield Hills, MI   48303-2030
(248) 642-4260
Contact: Howard Neistein
FAX: (248) 642-4941; URL: http://www.thisisfederation.org

Established in 1926 in MI.
Grantmaker type: Public charity.
Financial data (yr. ended 5/31/05): Revenue, $41,638,161; assets, $39,265,086 (M); gifts received, $37,534,126; expenditures, $37,162,571; total giving, $28,483,496; program services expenses, $33,282,107; giving activities include $28,483,496 for grants.
Purpose and activities: The foundation, in partnership with its agencies, plays the leadership role in identifying needs within the Jewish community and in mobilizing human and financial resources, engaging in communal planning, and allocating and advocating to meet those needs.
Fields of interest: Philanthropy/voluntarism; Jewish federated giving programs; Jewish agencies & temples.
International interests: Israel.
Type of support: Annual campaigns; Capital campaigns; Program development.
Limitations: Giving on a national and international basis.
Publications: Annual report; Financial statement.
Officers: Robert P. Aronson, C.E.O.; Dorothy Benyas, C.F.O.
Directors: Peter M. Alter; Penny B. Blumenstein; Diane Klein; Linda Z. Klein; Richard Krugel; Norman A. Pappas; Jerome Schostak; Saul A. Weingarden; Lawrence A. Wolfe; Neal F. Zalenko; and 146 additional directors.
EIN: 381359214

2522
The Jewish Fund

6735 Telegraph Rd.
Bloomfield Hills, MI   48303-2030
(248) 203-1487
Contact: Howard Neistein

Established in 1997 in MI.
Grantmaker type: Public charity.
Financial data (yr. ended 5/31/05): Revenue, $1,728,017; assets, $60,183,614 (M); expenditures, $3,755,171; total giving, $3,537,620; program services expenses, $3,537,620; giving activities include $3,537,620 for 37 grants (high: $627,625; low: $15,000).
Purpose and activities: Affiliated with the Jewish Federation of Metropolitan Detroit, the fund provides support for health-related programs and the promotion of community relations between the Jewish and general communities.
Fields of interest: Health care; Family services; Aging, centers/services; Human services; Jewish agencies & temples; Aging.
Type of support: Program development; Seed money; Curriculum development; Technical assistance; Program evaluation; Matching/challenge support.
Limitations: Giving limited to southeastern MI, primarily metropolitan Detroit. No support for religious activities, sectarian education, or overseas projects. No grants to individuals, or for annual campaigns, capital campaigns, equipment, endowments, or debt reduction; no loans.
Publications: Application guidelines; Annual report.
Application information: Follow Jewish Fund guidelines; first step in application process is letter of intent. Application form required.
   Initial approach: Letter of intent
   Copies of proposal: 2
   Deadline(s): Mar. and Sept.
   Board meeting date(s): Jan., May, Aug., Nov., and Dec.
   Final notification: Jan. and Aug.
Officers and Board Members:* Robert Naftaly, Chair.; Michael Maddin,* Vice-Chair.; David Aronow; Selwyn Isakow; Mark Schlussel; Jerry Schostak; Gary Torgow.
Number of staff: None.
EIN: 383323875

2523
Jewish Women's Foundation of
Metropolitan Detroit

6735 Telegraph Rd.
P.O. Box 2030
Bloomfield Hills, MI   48303-2030
(248) 642-4260
Contact: Helen Katz, Dir.
FAX: (248) 645-7857; E-mail: katz@jfmd.org;
URL: http://www.jfmd.org/JWF/

Established in 1999 in MI; a component fund of Jewish Federation of Metropolitan Detroit.
Grantmaker type: Public charity.
Financial data (yr. ended 5/31/05): Total giving, $76,250 Giving activities include $76,250 for 8 grants (high: $13,750; low: $3,000).
Purpose and activities: The Jewish Women's Foundation of Metropolitan Detroit, a special grantmaking fund within the United Jewish Foundation of Metropolitan Detroit, seeks to expand and improve opportunities and choices in all

aspects of Jewish women's and girls' lives through strategic and effective grantmaking. The foundation endeavors to empower women as funders, decision makers, and agents for change through projects and programs that promote change among, and address the unmet needs of, Jewish women and girls, such as domestic abuse, health concerns, employment, resettlement, aging, poverty, and single-parent support.
Fields of interest: Health care; Crime/violence prevention, domestic violence; Employment; Family services, single parents; Aging; Women; Immigrants/refugees; Economically disadvantaged.
Type of support: Continuing support; Program development; Conferences/seminars; Seed money; Curriculum development; Research; Technical assistance.
Limitations: Giving currently limited to programs, projects or initiatives in MI. No support for political campaigns or organizations. No grants to individuals, or for scholarships or tuition reimbursement, sponsorships for special events, or purchase of tickets or tables for events; no loans.
Publications: Application guidelines; Informational brochure (including application guidelines); Program policy statement.
Application information: See foundation Web site for full application guidelines and requirements, including Letter of Intent. Application form required.
   Initial approach: Letter of Intent (available on foundation Web site); full grant application should be submitted only upon invitation.
   Copies of proposal: 1
   Deadline(s): See foundation Web site for current deadline for Letter of Intent
   Final notification: Mid-Mar. for Letter of Intent
Officers and Trustees:* Sharon Hart,* Chair.; Lisa Lis,* Assoc. Chair.; Helen Katz,* Dir.; and 117 additional trustees.
Number of staff: 1 part-time professional; 1 full-time support.

2524
Paul C. Johnson Foundation

425 W. Western Ave., Ste. 200
Muskegon, MI   49440
URL: http://www.cffmc.org/paulcjohnson.htm

Established in 1989 in MI as a supporting foundation of the Community Foundation for Muskegon County.
Grantmaker type: Public charity.
Financial data (yr. ended 12/31/04): Revenue, $170,019; assets, $3,763,593 (M); expenditures, $115,133; total giving, $86,100; program services expenses, $86,100; giving activities include $86,100 for 4 grants (high: $50,000; low: $1,100).
Purpose and activities: The foundation complements the mission of the community foundation to support the Muskegon community's most urgent needs through innovative proposals and diverse grantmaking.
Fields of interest: Arts; Education; Community development.
Limitations: Applications not accepted. Giving primarily in Muskegon County, MI.
Publications: Grants list.
Application information: Contributes only to pre-selected organizations.
Officer and Directors:* Charles E. Johnson II,* Pres.; Lowell B. Dana; Larry W. Hines; Charles E. Johnson III; Patricia B. Johnson; Peter C. Johnson;

Wendy Kersman; Chris Ann McGuigan; James M. Sheridan.
EIN: 382919769

2525
Junior League of Lansing, Michigan

271 Woodland Pass Centre, Ste. 115
East Lansing, MI   48823   (517) 324-3734
FAX: (517) 324-3735; URL: http://www.jllansing.org/

Established in 1970 in MI.
Grantmaker type: Public charity.
Financial data (yr. ended 6/30/04): Revenue, $172,965; assets, $758,955; gifts received, $6,466; expenditures, $122,792; total giving, $49,589; program services expenses, $74,160; giving activities include $46,589 for grants, and $3,000 for grants to individuals.
Purpose and activities: The Junior League of Lansing, Michigan is a non-profit organization of women committed to promoting volunteerism, developing the potential of women, and improving the community through the effective action and leadership of trained volunteers. Its purpose is exclusively educational and charitable.
Fields of interest: Community development; Philanthropy/voluntarism; Women.
Type of support: Scholarships—to individuals.
Limitations: Giving limited to a 25-mile radius of the Lansing, MI, area.
Officers: Amy Uecker, Pres.; Cheryl Bartholic, Pres.-Elect; Michelle Ballein, V.P., Education; DeAnna Fenech, V.P., Membership; Brigit Pendred, V.P., Communication; Barb Wirtz, V.P., Community; Sandy Grettenberg, Secy.; Tracy Jelneck, Treas.
Sustaining Advisors: Janet Freund; Kim Hartman.

2526
Kalamazoo Public Education Foundation

714 S. Westnedge Ave., Ste. 214
Kalamazoo, MI   49007-5094   (269) 337-0498
Contact: Pamela Kingery, Exec. Dir.
FAX: (269) 337-0496; E-mail: kpefcec@aol.com;
URL: http://www.geocities.com/kpef_2000/

Established in 1991.
Grantmaker type: Public charity.
Financial data (yr. ended 12/31/05): Revenue, $2,054,500; assets, $2,693,959 (M); gifts received, $1,883,588; expenditures, $2,091,893; total giving, $59,631; program services expenses, $1,995,678; giving activities include $59,631 for grants.
Purpose and activities: The foundation supports programs to benefit students in Kalamazoo public schools.
Fields of interest: Elementary/secondary education.
Type of support: Program development; Scholarships—to individuals.
Limitations: Giving limited to Kalamazoo, MI.
Publications: Application guidelines; Grants list.
Application information: See Web site for additional application information. Application form required.
   Deadline(s): Varies
Officers and Directors:* Larry Lueth,* Chair.; Jim Harrington,* Vice-Chair.; Rebekah Fennell,* Secy.-Treas.; Pamela Kingery, Exec. Dir.; Janice

Brown; Kevin Campbell; Stephen Denenfeld; James A. Harrington; and 25 additional directors.
EIN: 382873188

2527
Kalamazoo Regional Catholic Schools Foundation

1000 W. Kilgore Rd.
Kalamazoo, MI 49008-3616 (269) 381-2646
Contact: Rendel Stasik, Pres.

Supporting organization of Kalamazoo area Catholic elementary schools and Hackett Catholic Central High School, MI.
Grantmaker type: Public charity.
Financial data (yr. ended 6/30/05): Revenue, $193,743; assets, $1,674,101 (M); gifts received, $148,599; expenditures, $100,452; total giving, $100,437; program services expenses, $100,437; giving activities include $100,437 for grants.
Fields of interest: Elementary/secondary education; Roman Catholic agencies & churches.
Limitations: Giving limited to the Kalamazoo, MI, area.
Officers: Randal Stasik, Pres.; Daniel DeMent, Secy.-Treas.
EIN: 382476783

2528
Kalamazoo Rotary Club Charities

P.O. Box 50251
Kalamazoo, MI 49005-0251

Grantmaker type: Public charity.
Financial data (yr. ended 6/30/05): Revenue, $57,132; assets, $63,395 (M); gifts received, $56,773; expenditures, $26,589; total giving, $26,048; program services expenses, $26,048; giving activities include $26,048 for 11 grants (high: $5,000; low: $674).
Fields of interest: Community development.
Type of support: Seed money.
Limitations: Giving primarily in Kalamazoo, MI.
Officers: Timothy L. Brown, Pres.; Randall Eberts, V.P.; James Bridenstine, Secy.; Robert Kent, Treas.
Directors: Rex Bell; J. Joseph Brogger II; Drew Elliott; Blake Hart; Rachel Packer; Keith Roe.
EIN: 386089188

2529
Greater Kalamazoo United Way

709 S. Westnedge Ave.
Kalamazoo, MI 49007 (269) 343-2524
FAX: (269) 344-7250;
E-mail: information@KalamazooUnitedWay.org;
URL: http://www.kalamazoounitedway.org/

Established in 1945 in MI.
Grantmaker type: Public charity.
Financial data (yr. ended 12/31/04): Revenue, $8,231,521; assets, $14,423,741 (M); gifts received, $8,121,979; expenditures, $7,659,345; total giving, $5,353,805; program services expenses, $6,293,225; giving activities include $5,353,805 for grants.
Purpose and activities: The GKUW makes an impact by investing time and resources in initiatives, collaborations and programs in seven target areas: health care, healthy families, addressing basic

needs, coping with crisis, increasing self-sufficiency, youth development, and community building.
Fields of interest: Health care; Youth development; Human services; Family services; Community development.
Limitations: Giving limited to the greater Kalamazoo, MI, area.
Application information: See Web site for application guidelines and requirements, including downloadable application form. Application form required.
  Deadline(s): See Web site for current deadlines for grants for permanent supportive housing, addressing grief and loss for children, early childhood systems change, and cultural understanding.
Officers: Carolyn Williams, Chair.; Frank Sardone, Vice-Chair.; Eric Dewey, Pres.; Sanford Tolchin, M.D., Secy.; David Furgason, Treas.
EIN: 381359193

2530
Kensington Academy Foundation, Inc.

32605 Bellvine Trail
Beverly Hills, MI 48025 (248) 647-8060

Supporting organization of Kensington Academy.
Grantmaker type: Public charity.
Financial data (yr. ended 6/30/05): Revenue, $466,392; assets, $2,151,521 (M); gifts received, $165,744; expenditures, $254,816; total giving, $3,000; program services expenses, $3,000; giving activities include $3,000 for 2 grants to individuals (high: $2,000; low: $1,000).
Fields of interest: Education.
Type of support: Scholarships—to individuals; General/operating support.
Limitations: Applications not accepted. Giving primarily to residents of MI.
Application information: Contributes only to a pre-selected organization; unsolicited requests for funds not considered or acknowledged.
Officers and Directors:* Gary Tadian,* Pres.; Thomas Herbst,* Secy.; Thomas Larabell,* Treas.; Charles Hess; Buddy Stoddard.
EIN: 381874886

2531
Kiwanis Foundation of Harbor Springs

P.O. Box 485
Harbor Springs, MI 49740

Grantmaker type: Public charity.
Financial data (yr. ended 9/30/05): Revenue, $30,493; assets, $294,494 (M); gifts received, $12,980; expenditures, $42,166; total giving, $39,880; program services expenses, $39,880; giving activities include $30,880 for 7 grants (high: $20,000; low: $500), and $9,000 for 9 grants to individuals (high: $1,000; low: $1,000).
Purpose and activities: Support for education, including scholarships to high school graduates for college.
Fields of interest: Education.
Type of support: Program development; Scholarships—to individuals.
Limitations: Giving primarily in Harbor Springs, MI.
Officers and Directors:* Bob Kickel,* Pres.; Matthew Keene,* V.P.; Hal Dorf,* Secy.; Gary Kent,* Treas.; Steve Hoffman.
EIN: 382577262

2532
Kolo Charities, Inc.

2410 Correll Dr.
Lake Orion, MI 48360
Contact: Robert Kowalkowski, Pres.

Grantmaker type: Public charity.
Financial data (yr. ended 12/31/04): Revenue, $86,006; assets, $121,913 (M); gifts received, $80,418; expenditures, $74,181; total giving, $54,450; program services expenses, $54,450; giving activities include $54,450 for grants.
Purpose and activities: The organization provides funds for charitable and educational purposes.
Fields of interest: Education.
Officers and Directors:* Robert Kowalkowski,* Pres.; Scott Kowalkowski,* V.P.; Matt Didio,* Secy.; J. Thomas Lesnau,* Treas.; Daniel Jaroshewich.
EIN: 382999444

2533
Lakeland Health Foundation, Niles

(formerly Pawating Health Foundation)
1234 Napier Ave.
St. Joseph, MI 49085
Contact: Chickie Landgraf, Chair.

Established in 1992 in MI; converted from Pawating Hospital.
Grantmaker type: Public charity.
Financial data (yr. ended 9/30/05): Revenue, $128,628; assets, $859,334 (M); gifts received, $61,661; expenditures, $660,950; total giving, $602,364; program services expenses, $648,061; giving activities include $585,941 for 1 grant, and $16,423 for grants to individuals.
Purpose and activities: The foundation seeks to promote and assist in providing health care services.
Fields of interest: Health care.
Type of support: Equipment; Scholarships—to individuals.
Limitations: Giving limited to southwestern MI.
Application information: Application form required.
  Deadline(s): Apr. 1 for scholarships
Officers and Directors:* Anita Chickie Landgraf,* Chair.; Tim Childs,* Vice-Chair.; Leo Soorus,* Pres.; Pat McCullough,* Secy.-Treas.; Michele Boyd; Nancy Butler; Robert Feldman; and 24 additional directors.
EIN: 383130558

2534
Lansing Art Gallery

113 S. Washington Sq.
Lansing, MI 48933 (517) 374-6400
Contact: Catherine A. Babcock, Exec. Dir.
E-mail: lansingartgallery@yahoo.com; URL: http://www.lansingartgallery.org

Established in 1964 in MI.
Grantmaker type: Public charity.
Financial data (yr. ended 6/30/05): Revenue, $230,429; assets, $73,984 (M); gifts received, $89,579; expenditures, $223,281; program services expenses, $171,944.
Purpose and activities: The gallery promotes public awareness, enjoyment and education of the visual arts through the support of Michigan artists.
Fields of interest: Visual arts.
Type of support: Scholarships—to individuals.

Limitations: Giving limited to Lansing, MI.
Application information: See Web site for additional application information.
  Initial approach: Submit portfolio for Art Scholarship
Officers and Directors: * Daniel Warmels,* Pres.; Anne E. Hodgins,* Treas.; Catherine Allswede-Babcock, Exec. Dir.; Connie Christy; Gary McRay; and 15 additional directors.
EIN: 381889973

2535
Latvian Foundation, Inc.
16776 White Haven Dr.
Northville, MI 48167
Contact: Ugis Sprudzs, V.P.

Established in 1976.
Grantmaker type: Public charity.
Financial data (yr. ended 4/30/03): Revenue, $69,089; assets, $778,956 (M); gifts received, $33,911; expenditures, $61,343; total giving, $46,110; program services expenses, $48,808; giving activities include $46,110 for 18+ grants (high: $6,600).
Purpose and activities: The foundation seeks to preserve Latvian culture.
International interests: Latvia.
Limitations: Giving limited to Latvia.
Officers and Trustees: * Sandra Milevska,* Pres.; Aivars Celmins, V.P.; Elisa Freimane, V.P.; Ugis Sprudz,* V.P.; Aija Abene,* Secy.; Sandra Robeznieks-Inka,* Treas.; Janis Kukainis; Peteris Muizniecks; Juris Rungis.
EIN: 237089477

2536
Lenawee Christian Ministries
(formerly Christian Family Foundation)
1800 W. U.S. Hwy. 223
Adrian, MI 49221

Established in 1986; supporting organization of the Christian Family Centre and Lenawee Christian School.
Grantmaker type: Public charity.
Financial data (yr. ended 6/30/05): Revenue, $2,635,002; assets, $19,157,551 (M); gifts received, $2,633,000; expenditures, $3,329,005; total giving, $2,063,474; program services expenses, $2,063,474; giving activities include $2,063,474 for grants.
Fields of interest: Education; Christian agencies & churches.
Type of support: General/operating support.
Limitations: Applications not accepted. Giving limited to the Adrian, MI area.
Application information: Contributes only to pre-selected organizations; unsolicited requests for funds not considered or acknowledged.
Officers and Trustees: * James A. McClellan, Jr., Co-Pres.; Richard D. Merillat,* Co-Pres.; Cliff Miller,* V.P.; Ruth A. Merillat,* Secy.-Treas.; Dick Anderson; Mark Buzzetta; Ed Cannon; G. Blair Dowden, Ph.D.
EIN: 382602775

2537
Lenawee United Way
1354 N. Main St.
Adrian, MI 49221

Established in MI.
Grantmaker type: Public charity.
Financial data (yr. ended 12/31/05): Revenue, $1,117,166; assets, $1,585,550 (M); gifts received, $1,082,830; expenditures, $1,091,017; total giving, $693,672; program services expenses, $940,318; giving activities include $693,672 for 76 grants.
Fields of interest: Community development.
Limitations: Giving primarily in Lenawee County, MI.
Officers and Directors: * Jan Parson,* Pres.; Dennis Wright,* 1st V.P.; Michael Wade,* 2nd V.P.; John Wanke,* Treas.; Kathleen Schanz, Exec. Dir.; Jeff Adams; Judy Billington; Louise Brown; John Clark; Gary Clift; Rick DeVries; and 29 additional directors.
EIN: 381598949

2538
Library of Michigan Foundation
702 W. Kalamazoo St.
P.O. Box 30159
Lansing, MI 48909-7507   (517) 373-1297
Contact: Judith K. Moore, Exec. Dir.
FAX: (517) 241-9048;
E-mail: lmfoundation@michigan.gov; URL: http://www.michigan.gov/hal/0,1607,7-160-17445_19270_19410—,00.html

Established in 1985 in MI.
Grantmaker type: Public charity.
Financial data (yr. ended 9/30/05): Revenue, $312,320; assets, $2,078,934 (M); gifts received, $267,616; expenditures, $298,526; total giving, $8,244; program services expenses, $154,197; giving activities include $8,244 for 1+ grant (high: $5,000).
Purpose and activities: The foundation's interests include libraries and literacy projects. External grantmaking is made through the program Read Indeed, and occasionally through donor-designated funds. Currently, the foundation is raising funds for literacy, rare book preservation, and collections and technology enhancements.
Fields of interest: Adult education—literacy, basic skills & GED; Libraries (public).
Type of support: General/operating support; Annual campaigns; Equipment; Program development; Curriculum development; Technical assistance; Matching/challenge support.
Limitations: Giving limited to MI.
Publications: Application guidelines; Annual report; Financial statement; Grants list; Informational brochure; Newsletter.
Application information: See Web site for guidelines. Application form required.
  Initial approach: Letter or telephone
  Deadline(s): Jan. 1 and Sept. 1 for ALA and PLA Awards; Mar. 23, June 21, and Oct. 24 for Scholarships; June 15 for Read Indeed
  Board meeting date(s): Quarterly
  Final notification: Apr. 1, Aug. 1, and Dec. 1 for Scholarships; Aug. for Read Indeed
Officers and Board Members: * Robert T. Wilson,* Chair.; Anne E. Harcus,* Secy.; George Borel,* Treas.; Judith K. Moore, Exec. Dir.; Mark Hoffman; J. Lawrence Lipton; Albert F. Zehnder; and 7 additional board members.

Number of staff: 2 full-time professional.
EIN: 382611742

2539
Richard U. Light Foundation
244 N. Rose St., Ste. 100
Kalamazoo, MI 49007-3824

Donor: Richard Upjohn Light†.
Grantmaker type: Public charity.
Financial data (yr. ended 12/31/04): Revenue, $3,321,392; assets, $64,231,610 (M); expenditures, $2,544,298; total giving, $2,210,930; program services expenses, $2,267,488; giving activities include $2,210,930 for 3 grants (high: $1,210,930; low: $500,000).
Purpose and activities: Support only for Culver Education Foundation, Culver City, CA, Wells College, Aurora, NY, and Yale University, New Haven, CT.
Fields of interest: Elementary/secondary education; Higher education.
Type of support: Fellowships; Scholarship funds.
Limitations: Applications not accepted. Giving limited to Culver City, CA, New Haven, CT, and Aurora, NY. No grants to individuals.
Application information: Contributes only to 3 pre-selected organizations.
Officers: Timothy Light, Pres.; Barbara J. Parish, V.P. and Treas.; Richard D. Reed, Secy.
EIN: 382456949

2540
Kenneth Lindsay Foundation
c/o Comerica Bank
P.O. Box 75000, M/C 3302
Detroit, MI 48275-3302

Established in 2002 in OH; supporting organization of Shriners Hospital for Children, Mercy Hospital, Washington Street United Methodist Church, and Community Hospice Care.
Donor: Kenneth Lindsay†.
Grantmaker type: Public charity.
Financial data (yr. ended 12/31/04): Revenue, $290,941; assets, $1,924,557 (M); expenditures, $196,811; total giving, $160,346; program services expenses, $160,346; giving activities include $160,346 for 7 grants.
Fields of interest: Animal welfare; Hospitals (general); Hospitals (specialty); End of life care; Human services; Salvation Army; Protestant agencies & churches.
Limitations: Applications not accepted. Giving limited to Tiffin, OH, and Tampa, FL. No grants to individuals.
Application information: Contributes only to pre-selected organizations; unsolicited requests for funds not considered or acknowledged.
Trustee: Comerica Bank.
EIN: 016209149

2541
Lions of Michigan Service Foundation, Inc.
5730 Executive Dr.
Lansing, MI 48911   (517) 887-6640
Contact: Chad McCann, Exec. Dir.
FAX: (517) 887-6642; E-mail: lmsf@acd.net;
URL: http://www.lmsf.net

Grantmaker type: Public charity.
Financial data (yr. ended 6/30/05): Revenue, $266,193; assets, $1,225,252 (M); gifts received, $103,615; expenditures, $276,374; total giving, $88,844; program services expenses, $88,844; giving activities include $28,551 for 2 grants (high: $28,451; low: $100), and $60,293 for 36 grants to individuals (high: $5,000; low: $40).
Purpose and activities: The foundation works in partnership with Lions Clubs in Michigan to address needs beyond the scope and capabilities of a single Lions Club to provide assistance to deserving individuals and organizations in the areas of sight and hearing conservation, medical care and expenses, activities for the disabled, emergency disaster relief, community development, and youth activities and services.
Fields of interest: Health care; Disasters, preparedness/services; Community development; Disabilities, people with; Blind/visually impaired; Deaf/hearing impaired.
Type of support: Grants to individuals.
Limitations: Giving limited to MI.
Officers and Trustees:* Tom Doyle,* Pres.; Robert Jenkins,* V.P.; Harvey Holm,* Secy.; Gary Babcock, Treas.; Chad McCann, Exec. Dir.; and 19 additional trustees.
EIN: 382537921

2542
Livingston County United Way
2980 Dorr Rd.
Brighton, MI 48116 (810) 494-3000
FAX: (810) 494-3004; Additional tel.: (810) 494-3003 (Helpline); URL: http://lcunitedway.org/

Established in 1977 in MI.
Grantmaker type: Public charity.
Financial data (yr. ended 6/30/05): Revenue, $1,434,634; assets, $2,841,447 (M); gifts received, $1,401,213; expenditures, $1,253,954; total giving, $885,483; program services expenses, $980,417; giving activities include $885,483 for 30 grants (high: $136,970).
Purpose and activities: The mission of the Livingston County United Way is to represent and serve the overall interests of the citizens of Livingston County in matters concerning individual and community health and well being. Current areas of focus include funding programs in the need areas of community wellness and healthy aging, assisting the disabled, emergency services, strengthening families, and youth services.
Fields of interest: Medical care, community health systems; Health care, clinics/centers; Public health; Health care; Children/youth, services; Family services; Human services, emergency aid; Aging, centers/services.
Limitations: Giving limited to Livingston County, MI.
Officers and Directors:* Chuck Breiner,* Pres.; Becky Best,* V.P.; Greg Clum,* Secy.-Treas.; Nancy A. Rosso, Exec. Dir.; Gladys Bottum; Patricia Claffey; Greg Earl; Dennis Gehringer; Lauraine Hoensheid; Tom Lawrence; and 11 additional directors.
EIN: 382174453

2543
Lovelight Foundation
111 Mack Ave.
Detroit, MI 48201 (313) 874-2100
Contact: Julie F. Cummings, Pres.

FAX: (313) 874-4001; E-mail: crj8870@aol.com

Incorporated in 1992 in MI.
Grantmaker type: Public charity.
Financial data (yr. ended 12/31/05): Revenue, $774; assets, $48,842 (M); expenditures, $740.
Purpose and activities: The foundation provides grants to other charitable organizations within the metro Detroit area that provides support to impoverished women and children through programs focusing on health, nutrition, and education.
Fields of interest: Children/youth, services; Women, centers/services; Economically disadvantaged.
Limitations: Giving primarily in the metropolitan Detroit, MI, area. No grants to individuals.
Application information:
  Initial approach: Letter of intent
  Board meeting date(s): Quarterly
Officers and Director:* Julie F. Cummings,* Pres.; Susan Kleinpell,* Secy.-Treas.; Denise Ilitch-Lites.
Number of staff: 1 full-time professional.
EIN: 383092224

2544
Lowell Area Community Fund
c/o Grand Rapids Community Foundation
161 Ottawa Ave. N.W., Ste. 209-C
Grand Rapids, MI 49503
Contact: Kate Luckert, Prog. Dir.
Tel.: (616) 454-1751, ext. 117;
E-mail: kluckert@grfoundation.org; URL: http://www.grfoundation.org/lowell/

Established in 1997 in MI as a fund adminstered by Grand Rapids Community Foundation.
Grantmaker type: Public charity.
Purpose and activities: The fund's mission is to assure community cooperation and participation that supports a healthy, dynamic community. It places an emphasis on broad educational initiatives, but also supports initiatives in the areas of arts and culture, community development, environment, health, human services, and recreation.
Fields of interest: Arts; Education; Environment; Health care; Recreation; Human services; Community development.
Limitations: Giving limited to the Lowell, MI, area. No support for religious organizations for religious purposes, or for organizations lacking 501(c)(3) status. No grants to individuals.
Publications: Application guidelines.
Application information: See foundation Web site for downloadable application form. Application form required.
  Initial approach: Completed application form
  Copies of proposal: 10
  Deadline(s): 3rd Fri. in Apr., Aug., and Dec.
  Final notification: 2 months

2545
Ludington Area Catholic Education Foundation
702 E. Bryant Rd.
Ludington, MI 49431

Established in 1990 in MI; supporting organization of Ludington Area Catholic School.
Grantmaker type: Public charity.

Financial data (yr. ended 12/31/05): Revenue, $102,557; assets, $1,450,304 (M); gifts received, $51,752; expenditures, $69,171; total giving, $69,151; program services expenses, $69,151; giving activities include $66,151 for 2 grants (high: $55,000; low: $11,151), and $3,000 for 3 grants to individuals (high: $1,000; low: $1,000).
Purpose and activities: Support limited to Ludington Area Catholic School for operations and tuition waivers; also awards scholarships to graduates of Ludington Area Catholic School.
Fields of interest: Elementary school/education; Roman Catholic agencies & churches.
Type of support: General/operating support; Scholarship funds; Scholarships—to individuals.
Limitations: Applications not accepted. Giving limited to Ludington, MI.
Application information: Unsolicited requests for funds not considered or acknowledged.
Officers: James R. Jensen, Pres.; John Fellows, V.P.; John R. Bulger, Secy.; John W. Claire, Treas.
Directors: Richard Boes; Geralyn C. Claire; Rick Deering; Greg Knudsen; Marc Lenz; Mike O'Brien; Lorraine Oseland; Fr. Ken Schichtel; Robert Seidel; Collin Thompson.
EIN: 382932594

2546
Jeanne McMurchy Luyckx Trust
41800 W. Eleven Mile Rd., Ste. 115
Novi, MI 48375-2572
Contact: David M. Fried, Tr.

Established in 2000; supporting organization of Michigan Humane Society and Michigan Anti-Cruelty Society.
Donor: Jeanne McMurchy Luyckx‡.
Grantmaker type: Public charity.
Financial data (yr. ended 12/31/04): Revenue, $52,271; assets, $2,238,995 (M); expenditures, $52,271; total giving, $50,419; program services expenses, $50,419; giving activities include $50,419 for 2 grants (high: $25,210; low: $25,209).
Fields of interest: Animal welfare.
Limitations: Applications not accepted. Giving limited to Detroit, MI.
Application information: Contributes only to pre-selected organizations; unsolicited requests for funds not considered or acknowledged.
Trustee: David M. Fried.
EIN: 386679502

2547
The Macomb Lutheran Charitable Foundation
12900 Hall Rd., Ste. 350
Sterling Heights, MI 48313

Established in 2002 in MI.
Grantmaker type: Public charity.
Financial data (yr. ended 12/31/04): Revenue, $42,792; assets, $37,128 (M); gifts received, $12,805; expenditures, $89,829; total giving, $89,025; program services expenses, $89,829; giving activities include $89,025 for grants (high: $44,250).
Purpose and activities: Support for Lutheran schools and churches.
Fields of interest: Protestant agencies & churches.

Officers: Robert Grozenski, Pres.; Terry Olson, V.P.; John A. Nitz, Secy.; Nicky Robinson, Treas.
EIN: 383618892

2548
Marquette Area Public Schools Education Foundation
1201 W. Fair Ave.
Marquette, MI 49855

Grantmaker type: Public charity.
Financial data (yr. ended 6/30/05): Revenue, $41,358; assets, $606,084 (M); gifts received, $25,163; expenditures, $33,752; total giving, $23,130; program services expenses, $24,903; giving activities include $8,930 for 7 grants (high: $2,447; low: $488), and $14,200 for 23 grants to individuals (high: $1,000; low: $200).
Purpose and activities: The foundation acquires and distributes financial and other resources to the Marquette Public Schools for unique programs and activities which supplement and enhance the quality of education and provide students with extended learning opportunities.
Fields of interest: Education.
Type of support: Scholarships—to individuals.
Limitations: Giving limited to the Marquette, MI, area.
Application information:
  Board meeting date(s): Quarterly
Officers and Trustees:* Linda Winslow,* Pres.; Laura Goodney,* V.P.; Barbara Kelly,* Secy.; Mike Morgan,* Treas.; Michael Anderegg; Bruce Anderson; Thomas L. Baldini; and 6 additional trustees.
EIN: 382972673

2549
Marshall United Way
124 W. Michigan Ave.
P.O. Box 190
Marshall, MI 49068-0190 (616) 781-3325
E-mail: marshalluway@aol.com

Grantmaker type: Public charity.
Financial data (yr. ended 8/31/05): Revenue, $227,958; assets, $200,151 (M); gifts received, $219,865; expenditures, $228,880; total giving, $209,302; program services expenses, $209,302; giving activities include $209,302 for grants (high: $20,000).
Purpose and activities: Marshall United Way provides funding to various charities in Calhoun County, Michigan and the surrounding areas.
Fields of interest: Health care; Legal services; Youth development; Human services; Family services.
Limitations: Giving limited to Calhoun County, MI, and surrounding areas.
Officers and Directors:* Mindy Deno,* Pres.; Nancy Stulberg,* Pres.-Elect; Kevin Giannunzio,* V.P.; Jean Rogers,* Exec. Dir.; Sherry Anderson; Linda Bennick; Rick Boyer; Peggy Day; David DeGraw; and 8 additional directors.
EIN: 237161104

2550
Mason Area United Way
P.O. Box 13
Mason, MI 48854

Grantmaker type: Public charity.
Financial data (yr. ended 1/31/05): Revenue, $81,215; assets, $120,303 (M); gifts received, $80,518; expenditures, $48,996; total giving, $48,686; program services expenses, $48,686; giving activities include $48,686 for 10 grants (high: $11,000; low: $486).
Fields of interest: Crime/violence prevention, abuse prevention; Recreation; Youth development; Human services; Family services; Aging, centers/services; Christian agencies & churches.
Limitations: Giving limited to the greater Mason, MI, area.
Officers: Robert L. Smith, Jr., Chair.; Tim Tuthill, Vice-Chair.; Linda Burkhelder, Secy.; Tom Peterson, Treas.
EIN: 382844122

2551
Masonic Foundation of Michigan, Inc.
233 E. Fulton St., Ste. 20
Grand Rapids, MI 49503-3270 (616) 459-2451
Contact: Richard I. Williams, Pres.
FAX: (616) 459-3912;
E-mail: mmhcf@masonichome.com

Established in 1980.
Grantmaker type: Public charity.
Financial data (yr. ended 3/31/05): Revenue, $435,948; assets, $2,348,809 (M); gifts received, $194,790; expenditures, $288,035; total giving, $96,086; program services expenses, $163,278; giving activities include $28,661 for 92 grants, and $67,425 for 221 grants to individuals (high: $750).
Purpose and activities: The foundation supports and maintains a library and museum, and provides funds for educational scholarships.
Fields of interest: Museums; Libraries/library science.
Type of support: Scholarship funds; Scholarships—to individuals.
Limitations: Giving primarily in MI.
Officers: David Neff, Pres.; W. Johnson, V.P.; Robert Stevens, Secy.; T. Hamlin, Treas.
Trustees: W. Keith Bankwitz; Robert Helmic; A. Meyer; R. Ruhland; I. Slaven; B. Valentine; R. Watts; W. Wheeler; D. Williamson.
EIN: 382284259

2552
McCarty Cancer Foundation
27387 Woodward Ave.
Berkley, MI 48072 (800) 746-0355
FAX: (248) 336-2330;
E-mail: mccartycf@comcast.net; URL: http://www.cancerfoundation.org

Established in 1997.
Grantmaker type: Public charity.
Financial data (yr. ended 6/30/04): Revenue, $555,709; assets, $769,673 (M); gifts received, $680,208; expenditures, $460,016; total giving, $305,250; program services expenses, $305,250; giving activities include $305,250 for 6 grants (high: $275,000; low: $50).
Purpose and activities: The foundation is dedicated to raising awareness of multiple myeloma and improving the quality of life of myeloma cancer patients while working toward prevention and a cure.
Fields of interest: Cancer; Cancer research.
Type of support: Research.

Limitations: Giving on a national basis.
Officer and Directors:* Roberta McCarty,* Pres.; Edsel Ford II; Mariam Ilitch; Linda K. Jacob; Donald Keeble; Patrick Kelly; Darren McCarty; Edwin Pump; Joseph Vicari; Donald Weaver.
EIN: 383359447

2553
McKinley Foundation
P.O. Box 8649
Ann Arbor, MI 48107-8649 (734) 769-8520
Contact: Eileen Lappin Weiser, Exec. Dir.

Established in 1985 in MI.
Grantmaker type: Public charity.
Financial data (yr. ended 5/31/05): Revenue, $100,051; assets, $999,056 (M); gifts received, $21,941; expenditures, $73,934; total giving, $57,429; program services expenses, $57,429; giving activities include $53,545 for 8 grants, and $3,884 for in-kind gifts.
Purpose and activities: The foundation acts as a catalyst for innovative community projects, and assists nonprofits in becoming self-sufficient.
Fields of interest: Arts; Environment; Women, centers/services; Community development.
Type of support: Program development; Seed money; Technical assistance; In-kind gifts.
Limitations: Giving primarily in Washtenaw County, MI. No grants to individuals.
Publications: Application guidelines; Program policy statement.
Application information: Application form required.
  Initial approach: Telephone requesting application guidelines and mission statement
  Copies of proposal: 1
  Deadline(s): None
  Board meeting date(s): Annually
Officers and Trustees:* Paul Dimond,* Pres.; Karen Andrews,* Secy.; C. Wendell Dunbar,* Treas.; Eileen Lappin Weiser, Exec. Dir.; Albert Berriz; Ann Black; Martha Darling; Molly Dobson; Otto Gago, M.D.; Carol A. Goss; Jane Lieberthal; Theodore St. Antoine; Eileen Lappin Weiser; Marc Weiser; Cynthia Wilbanks.
Number of staff: 1 part-time professional; 1 part-time support.
EIN: 382642551

2554
Mecosta-Osceola United Way, Inc.
315 Ives Ave.
P.O. Box 311
Big Rapids, MI 49307 (231) 592-4144
FAX: (231) 592-1138;
E-mail: unitedway@tucker-usa.com; URL: http://www.uwmich.org/public/luw/main.asp?uworgid=50

Grantmaker type: Public charity.
Financial data (yr. ended 9/30/05): Revenue, $308,704; assets, $235,284 (M); gifts received, $308,580; expenditures, $308,111; total giving, $224,761; program services expenses, $239,761; giving activities include $224,761 for grants.
Purpose and activities: The organization seeks to increase the organized capacity of people to care for one another.
Fields of interest: Community development.
Officers and Directors:* Jeremy Mishler,* Pres.; Duane Shafer,* V.P.; Margaret Taylor,* Secy.; Jean

Misenar,* Treas.; Jim Becker; John Calabrese; Gerald Flessland; Hon. Susan H. Grant; Susan Haut; Bob Hodge; Tom Hogenson; Steven Petersmark.
EIN: 382489813

2555
Mercy Memorial Hospital Foundation
718 N. Macomb St.
Monroe, MI 48162 (734) 240-4520
Contact: Catherine Ciha, Dir., Fund Devel.
FAX: (734) 384-5640;
E-mail: catherine.ciha@mercymemorial.org;
URL: http://www.mercymemorial.org

Established in 1986 in MI; converted from a voluntary merger between Mercy Hospital and Memorial Hospital, creating Mercy Memorial Hospital Corp., which became Mercy Memorial Hospital Foundation.
Grantmaker type: Public charity.
Financial data (yr. ended 6/30/04): Revenue, $1,248,640; assets, $13,871,822 (M); gifts received, $570,356; expenditures, $966,828; total giving, $375,010; program services expenses, $661,010; giving activities include $367,300 for 1 grant, and $7,710 for in-kind gifts.
Fields of interest: Hospitals (general); Health care.
Type of support: In-kind gifts.
Limitations: Applications not accepted. Giving limited to Monroe County, MI.
Application information: Contributes only to a pre-selected organization; unsolicited requests for funds not considered or acknowledged.
Officers and Directors:* Richard J. Tangeman,* Chair.; Lois M. Yaeger,* Vice-Chair.; Richard S. Hiltz,* Pres. and C.E.O.; Mark J. Rossman,* V.P. and C.F.O.; Robert B. Wells,* Secy.; Peter H. Carlton, CPA*, Treas.; S. Raim Nair, M.D.; Thomas D. Ready, Esq.; Douglas E. Robinson; Patricia E. Sprenger; Gerald Welch.
Number of staff: 1 full-time professional; 1 full-time support.
EIN: 382704263

2556
MGM Mirage Voice Foundation
3260 Industrial Rd.
Las Vegas, NV 89109 (702) 650-7400
Contact: Christina Roth, Dir., Corp. Philanthropy
Application address for southern MS: c/o Sara Miller, P.O. Box 7777, Biloxi, MS 39540; URL: http://www.mgmmiragevoice.com/pages/eg_foundation.asp

Established in 2002.
Donor: MGM Mirage.
Grantmaker type: Public charity.
Financial data (yr. ended 4/30/04): Revenue, $1,840,716; assets, $158,866; gifts received, $1,840,070; expenditures, $1,718,933; total giving, $1,717,569; program services expenses, $1,718,933; giving activities include $1,717,569 for 532 grants (high: $305,000; low: $4).
Purpose and activities: The foundation supports charitable organizations in the communities where MGM Mirage employees live, work, and care for their families.
Fields of interest: Education; Safety/disasters; Human services; Community development; Foundations (community).

Limitations: Giving limited to Detroit, MI, southern MS, and southern NV. No support for individual public or private schools or governmental entities. No grants for sponsorship of fundraising events, capital campaigns, or endowments.
Application information: See foundation Web site for downloadable application form. For Nevada or the Detroit, Michigan area, submit original application plus 10 copies; for Mississippi, submit original applications plus 8 copies. Application form required.
Initial approach: Completed application form
Copies of proposal: 10
Deadline(s): May 5
Officer: J. Terrence Lanni, Chair. and C.E.O.
EIN: 010640027

2557
Michigan Accountancy Foundation
5480 Corporate Dr., Ste. 200
P.O. Box 5068
Troy, MI 48007-5068 (248) 267-3700
FAX: (248) 267-3737; E-mail: macpa@michcpa.org;
URL: http://www.michcpa.org/maf/s_criteria.asp

Established in 1961 in MI.
Grantmaker type: Public charity.
Financial data (yr. ended 6/30/05): Revenue, $80,955; assets, $59,540 (M); gifts received, $80,339; expenditures, $58,691; total giving, $40,785; program services expenses, $40,785; giving activities include $40,785 for 16 grants to individuals.
Purpose and activities: The foundation gives out awards through its scholarship program to assist current college accounting majors in funding their fifth/graduate year.
Fields of interest: Business school/education.
Type of support: Scholarships—to individuals.
Limitations: Giving limited to U.S. citizens enrolled in an accredited MI college or university.
Publications: Application guidelines.
Application information: Application form required.
Initial approach: Download application form
Deadline(s): Jan. 15
Final notification: Mar. 15
Officers and Trustees:* Stephen H. Epstein, C.P.A.*, Pres.; Peggy A. Dzierzawski,* Secy.; Gadis J. Dillon, C.P.A.*, Treas.; Robert A. Bogan, Jr.; S. Thomas A. Cianciolo, CPA; Richard E. Czarnecki; and 19 additional trustees.
EIN: 386090334

2558
Michigan AIDS Fund
21700 Northwestern Hwy., Ste. 1150
Southfield, MI 48075-4906 (248) 395-3244
Contact: Stacey Barbas, Interim Exec. Dir.
FAX: (248) 395-3215;
E-mail: info@michaidsfund.org; URL: http://www.michaidsfund.org/

Established in 1989 in MI.
Grantmaker type: Public charity.
Financial data (yr. ended 3/31/05): Revenue, $935,724; assets, $1,116,155 (M); gifts received, $928,557; expenditures, $1,251,610; total giving, $671,532; program services expenses, $1,129,957; giving activities include $671,532 for 30 grants (high: $50,000; low: $1,480).

Purpose and activities: The fund awards grants to nonprofit, community-based organizations in Michigan with AIDS-related programs, with emphasis on collaborative projects; provides networking and conference opportunities for grantees and others; offers foundations a pooled fund for AIDS-related grantmakers; and encourages public policy responses on AIDS issues.
Fields of interest: AIDS; AIDS, people with.
Type of support: General/operating support; Program development; Seed money; Technical assistance; Matching/challenge support.
Limitations: Giving limited to MI. No support for non-AIDS related projects or political lobbying. No grants to individuals, or for endowments, annual fund drives, events, basic research, or operating deficits.
Publications: Application guidelines; Informational brochure.
Application information: Application form available from Web site. Application form required.
Initial approach: Letter of intent
Copies of proposal: 1
Deadline(s): Varies
Final notification: Early May
Officers and Trustees:* Elizabeth Sullivan,* Chair.; Terri D. Wright,* Vice-Chair.; Eric Jirgens,* Secy.; Susan K. Broman,* Treas.; Stacey Barbas, Interim Exec. Dir.; Carol Goss; Wendy Lawson; Judith D. Rumelhart; Geneva J. Williams; and 5 additional trustees.
Number of staff: 2 full-time professional; 2 part-time professional.
EIN: 383151591

2559
Michigan Council on Economic Education
c/o Walsh College
41500 Gardenbrook Rd.
Novi, MI 48375-1313 (248) 596-9560
Contact: David A. Dieterle Ph.D., Pres.
FAX: (248) 596-9562;
E-mail: david@mceeonline.org; URL: http://www.mceeonline.org

Established in 1978 in MI.
Grantmaker type: Public charity.
Financial data (yr. ended 12/31/04): Revenue, $349,511; assets, $123,043 (M); gifts received, $281,058; expenditures, $398,311; program services expenses, $240,387.
Purpose and activities: The council provides leadership promoting and strengthening economic education in the state of Michigan.
Fields of interest: Education; Economics.
Limitations: Giving primarily in MI.
Officers and Directors:* Thomas E. Hoeg,* Chair.; Robert E. Hoisington,* Vice-Chair., Admin.; Mark B. Williams,* Vice-Chair., Progs.; David A. Dieterle, Ph.D.*, Pres.; Jon Sudduth,* Secy.; Richard J. Francis,* Treas.; Chuck Anderson; and 53 additional directors.
EIN: 382183524

2560
Michigan Dental Association Relief Fund
230 N. Washington Ave., Ste. 208
Lansing, MI 48933-1302 (517) 372-9070
Contact: Gerri Cherney C.A.E., Exec. Dir.
E-mail: deason@michigandental.org

Established in 1966; supporting organization of Michigan Dental Association.
Grantmaker type: Public charity.
Financial data (yr. ended 12/31/05): Revenue, $18,209; assets, $313,983 (M); gifts received, $2,229; expenditures, $15,290; total giving, $2,858; program services expenses, $2,858; giving activities include $2,858 for grants to individuals.
Purpose and activities: The fund provides assistance to dentists, and their dependents who, because of injury, medical condition or advanced age, are not self-supporting.
Fields of interest: Human services; Economically disadvantaged.
Type of support: Grants to individuals.
Limitations: Giving limited to MI.
Application information: Applicant must be a Michigan resident. Application form required.
 Initial approach: Telephone
 Copies of proposal: 1
 Deadline(s): None
 Board meeting date(s): Varies
 Final notification: Immediately for qualified applicants
Officers and Trustees:* Joseph Kolling, D.D.S.*, Pres.; Edwin Secord, D.D.S., M.S.*, Pres.-Elect; Steven Dater, D.D.S.*, V.P.; Joanne Dawley, D.D.S.*, Secy.; William Wright, D.D.S.*, Treas.; Gerri Cherney, C.A.E., Exec. Dir.; Sherill Behnke, D.D.S.; Todd Christy, D.D.S.; and 12 additional trustees.
Number of staff: 1 part-time professional; 1 part-time support.
EIN: 386112478

2561
Michigan Education Association Scholarship Fund
1216 Kendale Blvd.
East Lansing, MI 48826
URL: http://www.mea.org/awards/meascholarship.html

Established in MI; a supporting organization of Michigan Education Association.
Grantmaker type: Public charity.
Financial data (yr. ended 8/31/05): Revenue, $76,293; assets, $871,026 (M); gifts received, $9,496; expenditures, $28,565; total giving, $20,200; program services expenses, $20,200; giving activities include $20,200 for 16 grants to individuals.
Purpose and activities: Scholarships awarded to students attending public, post-K through 12 educational institutions in Michigan. Those attending the following private institutions are also eligible: Baker College-Flint/Owosso; University of Detroit-Mercy; Davenport University-Eastern Region Campus; Adrian College; Finlandia University; Albion College; and Kendall College of Art and Design of Ferris State University.
Type of support: Scholarships—to individuals.
Limitations: Giving limited to MI.
Application information: Applications are available from local affiliates of the MEA, Uniserv offices or high school counseling offices. Application form required.
 Deadline(s): Feb. 11
Officers and Trustees:* Mary Christian,* Chair.; Linda Carter,* Vice-Chair.; Pattie Bayless; Cathy King; E. Craig Lesley; Lillian McFadden; Leo Sell.
EIN: 383285500

2562
Michigan Friends of Education
P.O. Box 183
Gregory, MI 48137-0183 (734) 498-3003

Established in 1984 in MI.
Grantmaker type: Public charity.
Financial data (yr. ended 9/30/05): Revenue, $2,689,663; assets $7,524,857 (M); gifts received, $2,685,692; expenditures, $3,400,567; total giving, $3,221,422; program services expenses, $3,400,567; giving activities include $3,221,422 for in-kind gifts.
Purpose and activities: The organization seeks to stimulate interest in reading and is intended to motivate children and adults to broaden their horizons, creating interest and a sense of anticipation in the selection of books that they may keep. Books are distributed to educational programs and to nursing/rest homes and agencies that care for the ill and underprivileged. Michigan Friends of Education does not award cash grants.
Fields of interest: Education, reading.
Type of support: In-kind gifts.
Limitations: Giving limited to MI. No grants to individuals directly.
Publications: Annual report; Newsletter.
Application information:
 Initial approach: Submit completed Request for Materials Form
 Board meeting date(s): Dec.
Officers and Directors:* Mike Burtch,* Pres.; Kristen McDonald Stone,* V.P.; Joe Lentine,* Secy.-Treas.; Donald H. Porter, Exec. Dir.
Number of staff: 4 full-time professional; 2 part-time professional.
EIN: 382547207

2563
Michigan Humanities Council
119 Pere Marquette Dr., Ste. 3B
Lansing, MI 48912-1270 (517) 372-7770
Contact: Jan Fedewa, Exec. Dir.
FAX: (517) 372-0027;
E-mail: contact@mihumanities.org; URL: http://michiganhumanities.org

Established in 1975 in MI.
Grantmaker type: Public charity.
Financial data (yr. ended 10/31/05): Revenue, $1,122,690; assets, $742,654 (M); gifts received, $1,104,670; expenditures, $1,103,190; total giving, $519,008; program services expenses, $831,636; giving activities include $519,008 for 27 + grants (high: $25,000).
Purpose and activities: The council supports humanities projects based in Michigan, particularly those which enhance humanities education in schools and in the community.
Fields of interest: Humanities; Education.
Type of support: Program development.
Limitations: Giving limited to MI. No support for advocacy or action programs, or for travel. No grants to individuals, or for equipment, or capital purchases.
Publications: Application guidelines; Annual report; Newsletter.
Application information: Applicants must use grant applications available for download from Council Web site. Application form required.
 Initial approach: Letter, telephone, or e-mail
 Deadline(s): Jan. 15 and Sept. 15 for Grants Program and We the People grants; Aug.

25-Sept. 10 and Feb. 25-Mar. 10 for Touring Program grants
 Board meeting date(s): 3 times per year
 Final notification: Mar. 15 and Nov. 15 for Grants Program and We the People grants; Apr. 15 and Oct. 15 for Touring Program grants
Officers and Trustees:* Judy Rapanos,* Chair.; Timothy Chester,* Vice-Chair.; Elizabeth Brooks,* Secy.; Sarah Deson-Fried,* Treas.; Jan Fedewa, Exec. Dir.; Christine Albertini; Anan Ameri; Marlee Brown; Ana Luisa Cardona; Marguerite Cotto; Gloria Fikes; Patrick LeBeau; Michael Margolin; Sue Ann Martin; James McConnell; Craig McDonald; John X. Miller; Shaun Nethercott; Erik Nordberg; Dominic Pangborn; Kelvin Smyth.
Number of staff: 5 full-time professional; 1 part-time professional; 1 part-time support.
EIN: 510164775

2564
Michigan Minority Business Development Council, Inc.
3011 W. Grand Blvd., Ste. 230
Detroit, MI 48202 (313) 873-3200
FAX: (313) 873-4783; E-mail: mail@mmbdc.com; URL: http://www.mmbdc.com

Grantmaker type: Public charity.
Financial data (yr. ended 12/31/04): Revenue, $2,919,620; assets, $4,428,011 (M); gifts received, $1,015,870; expenditures, $2,710,318; total giving, $20,000; program services expenses, $1,777,000; giving activities include $20,000 for 10 grants to individuals (high: $2,000; low: $2,000).
Purpose and activities: The organization aims to enhance business opportunities and professional development.
Fields of interest: Economic development; Community development, small businesses; Minorities.
Limitations: Giving limited to MI.
Publications: Newsletter.
Officers and Directors:* Tony Brown,* Chair.; Keith E. Wandell,* Vice-Chair.; Charles R. Scales, Jr.,* Secy.; Don Alessi,* Treas.; Mary Brown,* Interim Pres. and C.E.O.; Robert Fisher; V. Diane Freeman; E. Delbert Gray, Ph.D.; Ronald E. Hall; and 5 additional directors.
EIN: 382292187

2565
Michigan Parkinson Foundation
30400 Telegraph Rd., Ste. 150
Bingham Farms, MI 48025 (248) 433-1011
FAX: (248) 433-1150; E-mail: mpfdir@yahoo.com; Toll-free tel.: (800) 852-9781; URL: http://www.parkinsonsmi.org

Grantmaker type: Public charity.
Financial data (yr. ended 12/31/04): Revenue, $562,837; assets, $573,536 (M); gifts received, $557,985; expenditures, $403,236; total giving, $22,835; program services expenses, $257,023; giving activities include $22,835 for grants to individuals.
Purpose and activities: The foundation's mission is to educate and provide support to people with Parkinson's and related disorders, their loved ones and care partners, and the physicians and other allied health professionals who diagnose and treat

those affected by the illness; to support research into the mechanisms underlying the disease and therapeutic strategies aimed at reducing the burden of illness; and to engage and enlist the support of institutions and individuals whose activities impact the needs of people with Parkinson's and related disorders.

Fields of interest: Parkinson's disease; Parkinson's disease research.

Type of support: Fellowships; Grants to individuals.

Limitations: Giving primarily in MI.

Officers and Directors: * Leonard S. Borman,* Chair.; Carol A. Britton,* Vice-Chair.; Paul A. Cullis, M.D.*, Vice-Chair.; Peter A. LeWitt, M.D.*, Pres.; Hon. Gail McKnight,* Secy.; Lawrene Millman,* Treas.; David Bartczak; Robert Berlow, J.D.; Peter Hasbrook; and 4 additional directors.

EIN: 382494280

2566
Michigan State Bar Foundation

306 Townsend St.
Lansing, MI 48933 (517) 346-6400
Contact: Linda K. Rexer, Exec. Dir.
FAX: (517) 371-3325; E-mail: msbf@msbf.org;
Toll-free tel.: (800) 968-6723; URL: http://www.msbf.org

Established in 1947 in MI.

Grantmaker type: Public charity.

Financial data (yr. ended 9/30/05): Revenue, $2,317,458; assets, $5,182,606 (M); gifts received, $679,998; expenditures, $2,252,872; total giving, $1,724,377; program services expenses, $2,229,935; giving activities include $1,724,377 for 70 grants (high: $150,000; low: $26).

Purpose and activities: The foundation promotes improvements in the administration of justice; makes advancements in the science of jurisprudence; promotes improvements in the uniformity of judicial proceedings and decisions; elevates judicial standards; advances professional ethics; improves relations between members of the bar, the judiciary, and the public; preserves the American constitutional form of government through education, scientific research, and publicity; and furthers the delivery of legal services to the poor.

Fields of interest: Legal services.

Limitations: Giving limited to MI. No grants to individuals, or for endowments or capital expenses.

Publications: Application guidelines; Annual report.

Application information: See Web site for application information; application available on Web site. Application form required.

Deadline(s): Varies
Board meeting date(s): Monthly

Officers and Trustees: * Margaret J. Nichols,* Pres.; Hon. Alfred M. Butzbaugh,* V.P.; Stefani A. Carter,* Secy.; Lamont E. Buffington,* Treas.; Linda K. Rexer, Exec. Dir.; Peter H. Ellsworth; Julie I. Fershtman; Michael G. Harrison; R. Stuart Hoffius; Hon. Harold Hood; Jon H. Kingsepp; Hon. William B. Murphy; Jon R. Muth; Richard K. Rappleye; Hon. Victoria A. Roberts; Richard A. Soble.

Number of staff: 4
EIN: 381459016

2567
Michigan Women's Foundation

17177 N. Laurel Park Dr., Ste. 161
Livonia, MI 48152-3997 (734) 542-3946
Contact: Barbara A. Hill, Pres. and C.E.O.
FAX: (734) 542-3952; E-mail: info@miwf.org;
Toll-free tel.: (800) 404-4372; Additional address: 118 Commerce S.W., Grand Rapids, MI 49503; URL: http://www.miwf.org

Established in 1986 in MI.

Grantmaker type: Public charity.

Financial data (yr. ended 9/30/05): Revenue, $638,700; assets, $1,738,150 (M); gifts received, $414,592; expenditures, $845,091; total giving, $175,000; program services expenses, $466,432; giving activities include $175,000 for 46 grants (high: $9,700; low: $1,500).

Purpose and activities: The foundation focuses solely on the economic barriers that prevent MI women and girls from becoming self-sufficient. The foundation develops emerging women leaders and provides financial and technical assistance to non-profits, creating skills and leadership opportunities.

Fields of interest: Health care; Employment, training; Women, centers/services; Leadership development.

Type of support: General/operating support; Program development; Technical assistance; Consulting services.

Limitations: Giving limited to MI. No support for projects that require religious participation as a condition for receiving services. No grants to individuals, or for building funds, capital campaigns, or endowments.

Publications: Application guidelines; Annual report; Grants list; Informational brochure; Newsletter; Occasional report.

Application information: Application form required.
Initial approach: Submit proposal; telephone inquiries encouraged
Copies of proposal: 3
Deadline(s): July 31 for Mini-grants
Board meeting date(s): Apr., June, Sept., and Nov.

Officers and Trustees: * Beverly Hall Burns,* Chair.; Barbara A. Hill,* Pres. and C.E.O.; Betty R. Anderson; Jan Danford; Deborah I. Dingell; Kathy Fore; Linda D. Forte; Delores Clark Givens; Toni M. Hoover; and 21 additional trustees.

Number of staff: 3 full-time professional; 1 full-time support.

EIN: 382689979

2568
Midland Christian School Association

503 Crescent Dr.
Midland, MI 48640-3432

Established in 1974; supporting organization of Midland Christian School.

Grantmaker type: Public charity.

Financial data (yr. ended 6/30/05): Revenue, $235,551; assets, $4,491,134 (M); gifts received, $153,839; expenditures, $250,748; total giving, $194,000; program services expenses, $250,748; giving activities include $194,000 for 1 grant.

Fields of interest: Education.

Type of support: Continuing support.

Limitations: Applications not accepted. Giving limited to Midland, MI.

Application information: Contributes only to a pre-selected organization; unsolicited requests for funds not considered or acknowledged.

Officers: Joe Grant, Chair.; Greg Stewart, Vice-Chair.; Tim Keppel, Secy.; William Vanderkooi, Treas.

EIN: 386036106

2569
Morenci Education Foundation

500 Page St.
Morenci, MI 49256
Contact: Bill Van Valkenburg, Pres.

Established in 2004 in MI.

Grantmaker type: Public charity.

Financial data (yr. ended 12/31/05): Revenue, $31,120; assets, $38,136 (M); gifts received, $30,450; expenditures, $19,528; total giving, $10,520; program services expenses, $10,520; giving activities include $10,520 for grants.

Purpose and activities: The foundation provides scholarships to Morenci area school graduates and mini-grants for teachers of the Morenci area school district.

Type of support: Grants to individuals; Scholarships —to individuals.

Limitations: Giving limited to Morenci, MI.

Application information: Application form not required.
Initial approach: Letter
Deadline(s): None

Officers: Bill Van Valkenburg, Pres.; Rosemary Dickerson, V.P.; Neal Singles, Secy.; Philip R. Burley, Treas.

EIN: 043721858

2570
Ms. Molly Foundation

c/o Molly Maid, Inc.
3948 Ranchero Dr.
Ann Arbor, MI 48108
URL: http://www.mollymaid.com/MainMsMollyFoundation.aspx

Established in 1996 in MI.

Grantmaker type: Public charity.

Financial data (yr. ended 12/31/04): Revenue, $55,342; assets, $3,471 (M); gifts received, $55,342; expenditures, $52,330; total giving, $47,011; program services expenses, $47,011; giving activities include $47,011 for grants.

Purpose and activities: The foundation is dedicated to assisting victims and families affected by domestic violence through its support of hundreds of local shelters and safe houses across America providing refuge and personal care items to victims of domestic violence.

Fields of interest: Crime/violence prevention, domestic violence.

Limitations: Giving on a national basis.

Officers and Directors: * David Dickinson,* Co-Chair.; Stephanie Zikakis,* Co-Chair.; David McKinnon, V.P.; Lynn Butler; Mary Dickinson.

EIN: 383290026

2571
National Kidney Foundation of Michigan, Inc.
1169 Oak Valley Dr.
Ann Arbor, MI   48108   (734) 222-9800
Contact: Daniel M. Carney, Pres. and C.E.O.
FAX: (734) 222-9801; E-mail: mgerlach@nkfm.org;
Toll-free tel.(in MI): (800) 482-1455; URL: http://
www.nkfm.org

Grantmaker type: Public charity.
Financial data (yr. ended 6/30/05): Revenue,
$3,576,930; assets, $5,713,195 (M); gifts
received, $1,917,781; expenditures, $3,440,343;
total giving, $228,847; program services expenses,
$2,415,824; giving activities include $228,847 for
grants to individuals.
Purpose and activities: The foundation seeks to
prevent kidney disease and improve the quality of
life for those living with it.
Fields of interest: Kidney diseases; Kidney
research.
Type of support: Research; Grants to individuals.
Limitations: Giving primarily in MI.
Officers and Trustees:* Hon. Kurtis Wilder,* Chair.;
Robert Provenzano, M.D.*, 1st Vice-Chair.; M. David
Campbell,* 2nd Vice-Chair.; Daniel M. Carney,*
Pres. and C.E.O.; Joseph M. Maiuri,* Treas.; Larry
D. Alexander; Mark E. Behm; Charles L. Blanchard;
Jack Roettenberger; and 7 additional trustees.
EIN: 381559941

2572
National Multiple Sclerosis Society Michigan Chapter, Inc.
21311 Civic Center Dr.
Southfield, MI   48076-3911   (248) 350-0020
FAX: (248) 350-0029; E-mail: info@mig.nmss.org;
Toll-free tel.: (800) 243-5767; URL: http://
www.nmssmi.org

Established in 1948 in MI.
Grantmaker type: Public charity.
Financial data (yr. ended 9/30/05): Revenue,
$4,069,462; assets, $1,855,925 (M); gifts
received, $4,138,085; expenditures, $4,026,546;
total giving, $751,538; program services expenses,
$3,024,105; giving activities include $745,384 for
grants (high: $708,164; low: $4,070), and $6,154
for grants to individuals.
Purpose and activities: The society is organized to
end the devastating effects of multiple sclerosis by
supporting the national organization and its
research into the cause and cure of the disease; as
well as supporting those afflicted with multiple
sclerosis.
Fields of interest: Multiple sclerosis; Multiple
sclerosis research.
Type of support: Grants to individuals; Research.
Limitations: Giving limited to MI.
Publications: Annual report; Newsletter.
Application information: Accepts applications from
hospitals and clinics. Application form required.
  Initial approach: Telephone
  Deadline(s): None
  Board meeting date(s): Quarterly
Officers and Board Members:* Jeff A. Bell,* Chair.;
Peter Burton,* 1st Vice-Chair.; Jim Gismondi,*
Secy.; Steven A. Micsowicz,* Treas.; Eugene
Applebaum; David Arney; Tim Blett; Thomas W.
Cunnington; and 28 additional board members.
EIN: 381410476

2573
New Detroit, Inc.
3011 W. Grand Blvd., Ste. 1200
Detroit, MI   48202   (313) 664-2000
FAX: (313) 664-2071;
E-mail: sstancato@newdetroit.org; URL: http://
www.newdetroit.org

Established in 1967 in MI.
Grantmaker type: Public charity.
Financial data (yr. ended 12/31/04): Revenue,
$3,458,971; assets, $4,971,721 (M); gifts
received, $3,227,446; expenditures, $3,012,747;
total giving, $416,345; program services expenses,
$2,348,046; giving activities include $416,345 for
99 grants (high: $182,600; low: $100).
Purpose and activities: The organization works as
the coalition of Detroit area leadership to address
the issue of race relations by positively impacting
issues and policies that ensure economic and social
equality.
Fields of interest: Community development,
neighborhood development.
Limitations: Giving limited to Detroit, MI.
Publications: Application guidelines.
Application information: Application form required.
  Initial approach: Download application
  Deadline(s): Nov. 14
Officers: Shirley R. Stancato, Pres. and C.E.O.;
Leatrice W. Eagleson, V.P., Admin.; Daniel
Piepszowski, V.P., Progs.; Susan Urban, V.P., Fund
Devel.
EIN: 386159215

2574
Newaygo County Community Services
6308 S. Warner Ave.
P.O. Box 149
Fremont, MI   49412   (231) 924-0641
Contact: Beverly Cassidy, Exec. Dir.
FAX: (231) 924-5594; E-mail: info@nccsweb.org;
URL: http://www.nccsweb.org

Established in 1968.
Grantmaker type: Public charity.
Financial data (yr. ended 12/31/04): Revenue,
$5,429,138; assets, $5,322,346 (M); gifts
received, $5,001,276; expenditures, $3,801,572;
total giving, $2,401,798; program services
expenses, $3,617,155; giving activities include
$54,122 for grants, and $2,347,676 for grants to
individuals.
Purpose and activities: The organization seeks to
serve the positive development of individuals and
their communities.
Fields of interest: Human services; Economically
disadvantaged.
Type of support: Grants to individuals.
Limitations: Giving primarily in Newaygo County, MI.
Publications: Annual report.
Officers and Directors:* Scott Rumsey,* Pres.; Pam
Semlow,* V.P.; Mary Lantz,* Secy.; John Cooper,*
Treas.; Beverly Cassidy, Exec. Dir.; Jelanie Bush;
Bob Clark; Chris Haynor; Mike Paige; Andy Paris;
Sharla Schipper; Suzanne VanWieren.
EIN: 386158533

2575
Nichols & Chruch Trust
c/o JPMorgan Chase Bank, N.A.
P.O. Box 1308
Milwaukee, WI   53201

Established in 1957; supporting organization of the
Episcopal Student Foundation.
Grantmaker type: Public charity.
Financial data (yr. ended 12/31/04): Revenue,
$22,751; assets, $712,735 (M); expenditures,
$37,917; total giving, $36,000; program services
expenses, $36,000; giving activities include
$36,000 for 1 grant.
Fields of interest: Education, single organization
support; Christian agencies & churches.
Limitations: Applications not accepted. Giving
limited to Ann Arbor, MI.
Application information: Contributes only to a
pre-selected organization; unsolicited requests for
funds not considered or acknowledged.
Officers and Trustees:* Rev. Wendell Gibb, Jr.,*
Pres.; George Watson,* V.P.; Karen Thomas,*
Secy.; Chandler Matthews,* Treas.; JPMorgan
Chase Bank, N.A.
EIN: 386046831

2576
Nonprofit Finance Fund
(formerly Nonprofit Facilities Fund)
70 W. 36th St., 11th Fl.
New York, NY   10018   (212) 868-6710
FAX: (212) 868-8653; E-mail: ny@nffusa.org;
URL: http://www.nonprofitfinancefund.org

Established in 1980 in NY.
Grantmaker type: Public charity.
Financial data (yr. ended 12/31/05): Revenue,
$9,539,000; assets, $70,900,000 (M);
expenditures, $9,350,000; total giving,
$6,027,000; program services expenses,
$7,845,000; giving activities include $6,027,000
for grants.
Purpose and activities: The fund provides loans,
advice, small pre-project planning grants and capital
grants to nonprofit organizations.
Fields of interest: Arts; Education; Health care;
Employment; Recreation; Youth development;
Human services; Community development;
Population studies; Religion.
Type of support: Building/renovation; Equipment;
Land acquisition; Technical assistance; Consulting
services; Program-related investments/loans;
Matching/challenge support.
Limitations: Giving in the U.S., primarily in the San
Francisco Bay Area, CA, Washington, DC, Detroit,
MI, New England, New York City, NY metropolitan
area, NJ, and the greater Philadelphia, PA area.
Publications: Application guidelines; Annual report;
Financial statement; Grants list; Informational
brochure; Multi-year report; Occasional report.
Application information: Application form required.
  Initial approach: Telephone
  Board meeting date(s): Quarterly
  Final notification: 6 to 8 weeks
Officers and Directors:* Elizabeth C. Sullivan,*
Chair.; Clara Miller,* Pres. and C.E.O.; Elizabeth Hall
Ortiz,* C.O.O.; Anita Feiger, V.P., Western Region;
Chris Jenkins, V.P., Program and Product Devel.;
Norah McVeigh, V.P., Financial Services; Andrew
Ditton,* Secy.; Robert S. Robbin,* Treas.; Daniel
Ben Horin; Ellen Lazar; Alvertha Bratton Penny; Ruth

M. Salzman; William E. Strickland, Jr.; David Vollmayer; and 4 additional directors.
Number of staff: 41 full-time professional; 1 part-time professional; 8 full-time support.
EIN: 133238657

2577
Northville Educational Foundation
501 W. Main St.
Northville, MI 48167
URL: http://www.northville.k12.mi.us/district/educational-foundation.asp

Established in 2000 in MI.
Grantmaker type: Public charity.
Purpose and activities: NEF is a community-based organization managed by a board of trustees comprised of parents and community leaders. It works in partnership with the Northville Public Schools to support special programs that enhance the classroom experience, including technology integration, innovative grants for classroom initiatives, teacher leadership programs, and student and staff scholarhips.
Fields of interest: Education.
Type of support: Scholarship funds; Scholarships—to individuals.
Limitations: Giving limited to Northville, MI.
Trustees: Gregory Boll; Richard H. Brown, Jr.; Joseph Dunkerley; Laurie Marrs; Robert O. McMahon; Michael Mnich; Karen Paciorek; Michael Poterala; Leonard Rezmierski.
EIN: 383503644

2578
Novi Educational Foundation
25345 Taft Rd.
Novi, MI 48374 (248) 449-1205
Contact: Bob Schram, Exec. Dir.

Grantmaker type: Public charity.
Financial data (yr. ended 6/30/05): Revenue, $73,374; assets, $55,304 (M); gifts received, $12,650; expenditures, $51,228; total giving, $38,050; program services expenses, $11,644; giving activities include $38,050 for 13 grants to individuals (high: $3,500; low: $175).
Purpose and activities: The foundation awards scholarships to Novi, Michigan students and provides grant opportunities to the teaching and administrative staff of the Novi community schools.
Fields of interest: Education.
Type of support: Scholarships—to individuals.
Limitations: Applications not accepted. Giving limited to Novi, MI.
Publications: Informational brochure.
Officers and Trustees: * John Sholar,* Chair.; Mary Alice Brunnar,* Vice-Chair.; Geoffrey Scott,* Secy.; John Lokar,* Treas.; and 13 additional trustees.
EIN: 382665305

2579
Novi Parks Foundation
P.O. Box 1169
Novi, MI 48376-1169 (888) 288-1199
FAX: (248) 474-6659; E-mail: info@noviparks.org; URL: http://www.noviparks.org/

Established in 2004 in MI.
Grantmaker type: Public charity.

Financial data (yr. ended 12/31/04): Assets, $5,714 (M); gifts received, $6,475; expenditures, $761.
Purpose and activities: It is the mission of the foundation to maximize non-tax financial support of the facilities and programs of the Parks, Recreation & Forestry Department of the City of Novi by developing and promoting a broad program for private donations and public grants.
Fields of interest: Recreation, parks/playgrounds.
Type of support: Scholarships—to individuals; Equipment.
Limitations: Giving limited to Novi, MI.
Officers and Directors: * Charles Staab,* Chair. and Pres.; Dave Staudt,* Vice-Chair. and V.P.; Kathy Cosentino,* Secy.; Sue Engebretson,* Treas.; Kelly Adams; Linda Blair; Brian Cartwright; Robert Churella, Sr.; Bruce Lys; Mark Merlanti; David Paul; Pam Superfisky.
EIN: 200902251

2580
Oakland County Community Trust
c/o Comerica Bank
P.O. Box 75000, MC 3302
Detroit, MI 48275-3317

Established in 1965 in MI.
Grantmaker type: Public charity.
Financial data (yr. ended 12/31/04): Revenue, $12,936; assets, $408,378 (M); expenditures, $15,213; total giving, $8,000; program services expenses, $8,000; giving activities include $8,000 for 2 grants (high: $4,000; low: $4,000).
Fields of interest: Education.
Type of support: Scholarships—to individuals.
Limitations: Giving limited to Oakland County, MI.
Trustee: Comerica Bank.
Number of staff: 1 part-time support.
EIN: 386102697

2581
Oakland Township United Fund
575 Letts Rd.
Oakland, MI 48363

Established in MI.
Grantmaker type: Public charity.
Financial data (yr. ended 4/30/05): Revenue, $149,126; assets, $141,243 (M); gifts received, $148,944; expenditures, $193,460; total giving, $190,275; program services expenses, $190,275; giving activities include $190,275 for 25 grants (high: $55,600; low: $275).
Fields of interest: Community development.
Officers and Directors: * Dan Eller,* Pres.; Joan Fogler,* V.P.; Carlotta Aurelia,* Secy.; Bill Kroger,* Treas.; Amy Chamberlain; Greg Clay; Sharon Creps; Don Sherman; Karen Sweeney; Michael Sweeney; Maureen Thalmann.
EIN: 386101090

2582
Oceana County United Way
P.O. Box 603
Hart, MI 49420

Established in MI.
Grantmaker type: Public charity.

Financial data (yr. ended 12/31/02): Revenue, $131,159; assets, $78,241 (M); gifts received, $129,235; expenditures, $139,180; total giving, $110,144; program services expenses, $110,144; giving activities include $110,144 for grants.
Fields of interest: Community development.
Officers and Board Members: * Tom Pellon,* Chair.; Doug Fessenden,* Vice-Chair.; Paul Frendo,* Secy.-Treas.; Paul Inglis; Bob Moritz.
EIN: 382497072

2583
Ogemaw County United Way
P.O. Box 588
West Branch, MI 48661

Established in MI.
Grantmaker type: Public charity.
Financial data (yr. ended 12/31/04): Revenue, $20,982; assets, $20,472 (M); gifts received, $20,887; expenditures, $21,121; total giving, $13,750; program services expenses, $13,750; giving activities include $13,750 for 19 grants (high: $2,000; low: $200).
Fields of interest: Community development.
Limitations: Giving primarily in Ogemaw County, MI.
Officers: Scott Williams, Chair.; Clarice Spetty, Secy.; Trina Edwards, Treas.; Erma Lurvey-Nimeth, Exec. Dir.
EIN: 383020652

2584
The Ontonagon Area Scholarship Foundation
P.O. Box 92
Ontonagon, MI 49953

Grantmaker type: Public charity.
Financial data (yr. ended 5/31/05): Revenue, $52,121; assets, $451,089 (M); gifts received, $43,837; expenditures, $12,296; total giving, $9,000; program services expenses, $9,000; giving activities include $9,000 for grants to individuals.
Purpose and activities: Awards scholarships for higher education to graduates of Ontonagon Area High School.
Type of support: Scholarships—to individuals.
Limitations: Giving limited to residents of Ontonagon, MI.
Officers: Janet Wolfe, Pres.; James Morin, V.P.; Marilyn Anderson, Secy.; Gerald Domitrovich, Treas.
EIN: 383525614

2585
The Optimist Club Foundation
P.O. Box 891
Clarkston, MI 48347

Grantmaker type: Public charity.
Financial data (yr. ended 9/30/05): Revenue, $61,506; assets, $68,114 (M); expenditures, $48,922; total giving, $4,721; program services expenses, $24,254; giving activities include $2,615 for grants, and $2,106 for grants to individuals.
Fields of interest: Youth development.
Type of support: Scholarships—to individuals.
Officers: Michael Page, Pres.; James Ward, V.P.; Nancy Knitter, Secy.; Joe Barger, Treas.
EIN: 383373756

2586
Oscoda Area United Way
5671 Skeel Ave., Ste. 32
Oscoda, MI 48750

Established in MI.
Grantmaker type: Public charity.
Financial data (yr. ended 12/31/04): Revenue, $35,200; assets, $41,245 (M); gifts received, $34,809; expenditures, $31,701; total giving, $29,184; program services expenses, $29,184; giving activities include $29,184 for 19 grants (high: $4,525; low: $62).
Fields of interest: Community development.
Limitations: Giving primarily in the Oscoda, MI, area.
Officers: Carolyn Brummond, Pres.; Daryl Hansen, 1st V.P.; Thom Grant, 2nd V.P.; Dale Ewart, Secy.; Jane Meyer, Treas.
Directors: Matt Buresh; Mary Donovan; Julie Dyer; Edna Ferber; Ed Reeder.
EIN: 237134135

2587
Oswald Supporting Organization
c/o Toledo Community Foundation, Inc.
608 Madison Ave., Ste. 1540
Toledo, OH 43604-1151
Contact: Virginia Keller, Prog. Assoc.

Established in OH as a supporting organization of the Toledo Community Foundation, Inc.
Grantmaker type: Public charity.
Financial data (yr. ended 12/31/04): Revenue, $879,373; assets, $2,226,611 (M); gifts received, $823,824; expenditures, $91,594; total giving, $79,208; program services expenses, $79,208; giving activities include $79,208 for 8 grants (high: $28,732; low: $100).
Purpose and activities: Support primarily for projects or programs that: 1) enable families (both traditional and non-traditional) to develop the skills/resources needed to nurture each member, and 2) promote the advancement, self-sufficiency and intellectual, social, emotional and cultural growth of women and children of all ages.
Fields of interest: Children/youth, services; Family services; Children/youth; Women.
Limitations: Applications not accepted. Giving primarily in southeast MI and northwest OH, with emphasis on Toledo. No support for sectarian activities of religious organizations. No grants to individuals, or for annual campaigns or to reduce or eliminate budget deficits for established programs.
Application information: Unsolicited grant applications or proposals not considered.
Officer: Keith Burwell, Secy.-Treas.
Trustees: Bonnie Oswald; Jennifer Oswald; Charles Stocking; Stephen Stranahan; David K. Welles, Jr.
EIN: 341952405

2588
Otsego County United Way, Inc.
116 E. 5th St.
Gaylord, MI 49735

Grantmaker type: Public charity.
Financial data (yr. ended 12/31/04): Revenue, $271,321; assets, $205,040 (M); gifts received, $261,830; expenditures, $232,230; total giving, $109,620; program services expenses, $190,565; giving activities include $91,903 for 16 grants (high:

$13,250; low: $750), $13,117 for grants to individuals, and $4,600 for in-kind gifts.
Purpose and activities: The organization seeks to provide support to organizations serving the social welfare of Otsego County, Michigan.
Fields of interest: Human services.
Type of support: Grants to individuals; In-kind gifts.
Limitations: Giving primarily in Otsego County, MI.
Officers: Mary Sanders, Pres.; Sheri Quay, 1st V.P.; Bruce Brown, 2nd V.P.; Cindy Pushman, Secy.; Bill O'Neill, Treas.; Natalie Davis, Exec. Dir.
Directors: Bill Blaker; Ron Chavey; Kevin Drummond; Kellie Galer; Julie Kucharek; Bill McKay; Lori Reichard; Dave Taylor.
EIN: 237156104

2589
Greater Ottawa County United Way
115 Clover St. Ste. 300
Holland, MI 49423 (616) 396-7811
FAX: (616) 396-5140; E-mail: info@gouwvc.org; Mailing address: P.O. Box 1349, Holland, MI 49422-1349; URL: http://www.gouwvc.org

Grantmaker type: Public charity.
Financial data (yr. ended 3/31/05): Revenue, $2,413,862; assets, $3,731,889 (M); gifts received, $2,332,313; expenditures, $2,269,825; total giving, $1,170,108; program services expenses, $1,817,415; giving activities include $1,170,108 for grants.
Purpose and activities: The Greater Ottawa County United Way seeks to improve lives by mobilizing communities to create sustained changes in community conditions, focusing on solutions in the areas of Thriving Kids, Strong Families, and Healthy Communities.
Fields of interest: Public health; Youth development; Human services; Children/youth, services; Family services; Community development.
Limitations: Giving limited to the greater Ottawa County, MI, area.
Application information: See Web site for application requirements, including downloadable forms. Applications submitted by fax or electronically not accepted. Application form required.
Officers and Trustees:* George Smart,* Chair.; Don Auch,* Vice-Chair.; Tom Vander Hulst,* Secy.; Tim Parker,* Treas.; Rob Betts; Thomas J. Bos; John Carter; Margaret DeBruyn; Roxanne DeWeerd; and 10 additional trustees.
EIN: 383522782

2590
Palestine Aid Society of America
c/o Rabia Shafie
3325 Bluett Dr.
Ann Arbor, MI 48105-1556

Grantmaker type: Public charity.
Financial data (yr. ended 12/31/05): Revenue, $92,376; assets, $36,477 (M); gifts received, $92,063; expenditures, $88,197; total giving, $87,446; program services expenses, $87,446; giving activities include $87,446 for grants.
Purpose and activities: The society provides education and health support to third-world children who have lost parents in the War.
Fields of interest: Human services; International affairs.

International interests: West Bank/Gaza.
Type of support: Grants to individuals.
Limitations: Applications not accepted. Giving on an international basis.
Application information: Unsolicited requests for funds not considered or acknowledged.
Director: Rabia Shafie.
EIN: 382381291

2591
Estes Palmer Foundation
c/o National City Bank
171 Monroe Ave. N.W.
Grand Rapids, MI 49503

Established in 1973; supporting organization of Adrian College and Asbury Theological Seminar.
Grantmaker type: Public charity.
Financial data (yr. ended 12/31/04): Revenue, $726,661; assets, $5,959,057 (M); expenditures, $293,134; total giving, $182,000; program services expenses, $182,000; giving activities include $182,000 for 2 grants (high: $91,000; low: $91,000).
Fields of interest: Higher education, college; Theological school/education.
Limitations: Applications not accepted. Giving limited to Adrian, MI, and Wilmore, KY.
Application information: Contributes only to pre-selected organizations; unsolicited requests for funds not considered or acknowledged.
Directors: Richard F. Burmeister; Richard J. Halik, Ph.D.; Lance R. Lynch; Neil McLean; Frank W. Perrin.
Trustee: National City Bank.
EIN: 386258410

2592
Norman A. & Susan L. Pappas Family Foundation
6735 Telegraph Rd.
P.O. Box 2030
Bloomfield Hills, MI 48301

Established in 1985; supporting organization of the Jewish Federation of Metropolitan Detroit.
Grantmaker type: Public charity.
Financial data (yr. ended 5/31/05): Revenue, $208,723; assets, $1,556,338 (M); expenditures, $161,102; total giving, $129,250; program services expenses, $129,250; giving activities include $129,250 for 11 grants (high: $90,000; low: $500).
Fields of interest: Jewish federated giving programs.
Limitations: Applications not accepted. Giving limited to Detroit, MI.
Application information: Contributes only to a pre-selected organization; unsolicited requests for funds not considered or acknowledged.
Officers: Norman A. Pappas, Pres.; Susan L. Pappas, V.P.; Robert P. Aronson, Secy.; Dorothy Benyas, Treas.
Direcotrs: Lawrence Jackier; Howard Neistein; Edward H. Pappas.
EIN: 382582300

2593
Pennock Foundation
1009 W. Green St.
Hastings, MI 49058-1790 (269) 948-3122
Contact: Matthew J. Thompson

FAX: (269) 945-4130; URL: http://
www.pennockhealth.com/pennock_foundation/

Established in 1987.
Grantmaker type: Public charity.
Financial data (yr. ended 9/30/05): Revenue,
$1,378,522; assets, $4,276,141 (M); gifts
received, $1,213,829; expenditures, $153,871;
total giving, $73,716; program services expenses,
$104,286; giving activities include $19,740 for 8+
grants (high: $6,807), and $53,972 for grants to
individuals.
Purpose and activities: The foundation seeks to
improve and promote medical care and health care
in the community of Hastings, Michigan.
Fields of interest: Health care.
Type of support: Scholarships—to individuals.
Limitations: Giving limited to Hastings, MI.
Application information: Application form required.
Initial approach: Download application form
Officer and Directors:* James Wiswell,* Chair.;
David Baum; Bill Wallace; John Walker.
EIN: 382713275

2594
Pewabic Society, Inc.
10125 E. Jefferson Ave.
Detroit, MI 48214 (313) 822-0954
Contact: Terese Ireland, Exec. Dir.
FAX: (313) 822-6266;
E-mail: pewabic1@pewabic.com; URL: http://
www.pewabic.com

Grantmaker type: Public charity.
Financial data (yr. ended 9/30/04): Revenue,
$2,053,141; assets, $1,776,782 (M); gifts
received, $512,163; expenditures, $1,901,528;
program services expenses, $1,401,362.
Purpose and activities: The society is dedicated to
the preservation of the arts and crafts curriculum of
educational programs, support of individual artists,
outreach to various communities and leadership in
the exhibition of contemporary and historic
collections and archiving of scholarly research.
Fields of interest: Visual arts, sculpture; Visual arts,
ceramic arts.
Type of support: Grants to individuals.
Limitations: Giving on a national basis.
Application information: Contact society for
application deadlines.
Initial approach: E-mail
Board meeting date(s): Annually
Officers and Trustees:* Cameron Duncan,* Pres.;
James Sansoterra,* Sr. V.P.; Barbara Bierbusse,
V.P.; Joseph Vassallo,* V.P.; Terese Ireland, Exec.
Dir.; Theresita Dietrich; Sandra Fleming; Sharon
Snodgrass; and 17 additional trustees.
EIN: 382277840

2595
Eleanor S. Pitkin Trust
c/o Kalamazoo Community Foundation
151 S. Rose St., Ste. 332
Kalamazoo, MI 49007

Established in 1951; supporting organization of the
Kalamazoo Community Foundation.
Grantmaker type: Public charity.
Financial data (yr. ended 12/31/04): Revenue,
$18,138; assets, $520,972 (M); expenditures,
$13,638; total giving, $11,989; program services

expenses, $11,989; giving activities include
$11,989 for 1 grant.
Fields of interest: Foundations (community).
Limitations: Applications not accepted. Giving
limited to Kalamazoo, MI.
Application information: Contributes only to a
pre-selected organization; unsolicited requests for
funds not considered or acknowledged.
Trustee: National City Bank.
EIN: 386041533

2596
Plumbers and Pipefitters Local No. 333
Scholarship Plan
3101 Allied Dr., Ste. B
Jackson, MI 49201 (517) 784-7500

Grantmaker type: Public charity.
Financial data (yr. ended 6/30/05): Revenue,
$61,636; assets, $64,195 (M); gifts received,
$59,435; expenditures, $64,075; total giving,
$62,075; program services expenses, $64,075;
giving activities include $62,075 for 97 grants to
individuals (high: $650; low: $325).
Type of support: Scholarships—to individuals.
Trustees: Todd Carve; Jim Davis; Larry Gunthorpe;
David Knapp; Charles Osborne; Terry Potts;
Abraham Rahar; Russ Smith.
EIN: 386191955

2597
Plymouth Christian Schools Foundation
P.O. Box 150032
Grand Rapids, MI 49515-0032

Established in 1995 in MI.
Grantmaker type: Public charity.
Financial data (yr. ended 12/31/04): Revenue,
$138,176; assets, $1,085,434 (M); gifts received,
$93,733; expenditures, $39,168; total giving,
$38,209; program services expenses, $38,209;
giving activities include $38,209 for 1 grant.
Fields of interest: Elementary/secondary
education; Christian agencies & churches.
Limitations: Giving primarily in Grand Rapids, MI.
Officers and Trustees:* Gary R. Bleeker,* Pres.;
Daniel Parmeter, Jr.,* Secy.; James D. Bleeker,*
Treas.; John Bazen, Jr.; Fred Kegel; Ken Lugthart;
Orie VanderBoon; Richard Westrate, Jr.
EIN: 383271783

2598
Plymouth Community United Way
960 W. Ann Arbor Trail, Ste. 2
Plymouth, MI 48170 (734) 453-6879
E-mail: plymouthunitedway@ameritech.net;
URL: http://plymouthunitedway.org

Established in 1944 in MI.
Grantmaker type: Public charity.
Financial data (yr. ended 12/31/04): Revenue,
$1,082,413; assets, $2,911,455 (M); gifts
received, $874,221; expenditures, $999,623; total
giving, $665,601; program services expenses,
$755,977; giving activities include $665,601 for 13
+ grants (high: $133,782).
Purpose and activities: Plymouth Community United
Way's mission is to reach out and serve human
needs which go beyond the reach of government or

private service groups, through various nonprofit
health and welfare organizations.
Fields of interest: Health care; Human services;
Community development.
Limitations: Giving primarily in Plymouth, MI.
Publications: Newsletter.
Officers and Directors:* Howard Behr,* Chair.;
Harry Crespy,* Vice-Chair.; Marie Morrow, Pres.;
Jerry Schoenle, Secy.; George Atsalis, D.D.S.; Roger
Ballard; Rick Debruyne; Gregory Foster; Paul Haver;
Don Johnson; Martha Logan.
EIN: 237327248

2599
Plymouth Rotary Foundation, Inc.
1095 S. Main St.
P.O. Box 701308
Plymouth, MI 48170 (734) 453-6280
Contact: Tim Joy, Dir.

Established in 1965.
Grantmaker type: Public charity.
Financial data (yr. ended 6/30/05): Revenue,
$103,266; assets, $235,816 (M); gifts received,
$99,057; expenditures, $88,203; total giving,
$81,593; program services expenses, $81,593;
giving activities include $81,593 for grants.
Purpose and activities: The foundation supports
charitable, religious, scientific, literary, or
educational purposes.
Fields of interest: Literature; Education; Science;
Religion.
Officers and Directors:* Marie Morrow,* Pres.;
Charles Bares, V.P.; John Warner,* Secy.; Robert
Carrigan,* Treas.; Art Gulick; Jeff Horton; Tim Joy;
Thomas Kennedy; Dave Willett; Habib Zuberi.
EIN: 386107391

2600
Portland Community Fund Association
P.O. Box 524
Portland, MI 48875

Established in MI.
Grantmaker type: Public charity.
Financial data (yr. ended 6/30/05): Revenue,
$31,735; assets, $40,137 (M); gifts received,
$31,093; expenditures, $30,383; total giving,
$26,900; program services expenses, $26,502;
giving activities include $26,900 for 13 grants (high:
$7,500; low: $100).
Purpose and activities: The association seeks to
support charitable activities for residents of the
Portland School District.
Fields of interest: Human services; Community
development.
Limitations: Giving primarily in MI.
Officers: Julie Hughes, Pres.; Sandy Olsen, V.P.;
Wayne Brown, Treas.
EIN: 237168046

2601
Hughes L. and Sheila M. Potiker Support
Foundation
6735 Telegraph Rd.
Bloomfield Hills, MI 48301-3141
Contact: Hughes L. Potiker, Pres.

Established in 1988.
Grantmaker type: Public charity.

Purpose and activities: The foundation supports Jewish education and human services.
Fields of interest: Education; Human services; Jewish agencies & temples.
Limitations: Giving limited to CA, MI, and NY.
Officers and Directors:* Sheila M. Potiker,* V.P.; Robert P. Aronson,* Secy.; Joseph Imberman,* Treas.; Dorothy Benyas; Mark Davidoff.
EIN: 382805116

2602
Prentis Family Support Foundation
(formerly Prentis-Morris Family Support Foundation)
6735 Telegraph Rd.
P.O. Box 2030
Bloomfield Hills, MI 48301-3141
(248) 642-4260

Established in 1988; supporting organization of the Jewish Federation of Metropolitan Detroit.
Grantmaker type: Public charity.
Financial data (yr. ended 5/31/05): Revenue, $580,332; assets, $7,182,109 (M); expenditures, $229,449; total giving, $197,497; program services expenses, $197,497; giving activities include $197,497 for 31 grants (high: $76,250; low: $500).
Purpose and activities: Giving primarily to Jewish agencies, including federated giving programs, and for higher education and the arts.
Fields of interest: Museums; Performing arts; Higher education; Education; Jewish federated giving programs; Jewish agencies & temples.
Type of support: Research.
Limitations: Giving primarily in MI.
Officers and Directors:* Patrice M. Phillips,* Pres.; Jeffrey P. Strauss, V.P.; Robert P. Aronson,* Secy.; Dorothy Benyas, Treas.; Michael W. Maddin; Robert P. Morris; and 4 additional directors.
EIN: 382805115

2603
Purtan Family Ovarian Cancer Research Foundation
6208 Rue Du Lac
West Bloomfield, MI 48323

Established in 1999 in MI as a private foundation; status changed to a public charity.
Grantmaker type: Public charity.
Financial data (yr. ended 12/31/04): Revenue, $8,995; assets, $244,807 (M); gifts received, $7,500; expenditures, $30,150; total giving, $30,000; program services expenses, $30,000; giving activities include $30,000 for 1 grant.
Purpose and activities: The foundation supports organizations that conduct cancer research.
Fields of interest: Cancer research.
Type of support: Research.
Officers and Directors:* Paul R. Purtan,* Pres. and Treas.; Gail Purtan,* Secy.; Jennifer Purtan Goldstein; Joanne Purtan Gudeman; Jessica Purtan Harrell; Jacqueline Purtan Levenson; Julie Nicole Purtan; Jill Purtan Swoish.
EIN: 383498771

2604
Rebuilding Together - Saginaw
(formerly Saginaw Christmas in July, Inc.)
120 N. Michigan Ave., Ste. 301
Saginaw, MI 48602
Contact: Jim Stone, Pres.

Established in 1992; status changed to a public charity in 2002.
Grantmaker type: Public charity.
Financial data (yr. ended 12/31/04): Revenue, $44,941; assets, $16,047; gifts received, $44,324; expenditures, $92,942; program services expenses, $92,942.
Purpose and activities: The organization paints and repairs homes of low-income senior citizens and handicapped people.
Fields of interest: Housing/shelter, aging; Housing/shelter, repairs; Aging; Disabilities, people with; Economically disadvantaged.
Type of support: In-kind gifts.
Limitations: Giving limited to Saginaw County, MI.
Publications: Application guidelines; Newsletter.
Officers and Board Members:* Jim Stone,* Pres.; Don Kropp,* 1st V.P.; Amos O'Neal,* 2nd V.P.; Marge Paron,* Secy.; Paul Schaub,* Treas.; Adrienne Lewis, Exec. Dir.; Jodi McFarland; Larry Riley; Joe Spleet; Robert Stroebel.
EIN: 383069399

2605
Walter and May Reuther Memorial Fund
c/o Comerica Bank
P.O. Box 75000, MC 3462
Detroit, MI 48275-3462 (313) 222-4085

Established in 1970.
Grantmaker type: Public charity.
Financial data (yr. ended 12/31/05): Revenue, $92,883; assets, $809,382 (M); gifts received, $20,054; expenditures, $60,391; total giving, $56,150; program services expenses, $56,150; giving activities include $42,550 for 2 grants (high: $25,000; low: $17,550), and $13,600 for 18 grants to individuals (high: $1,500; low: $500).
Purpose and activities: The fund provides scholarships and grants to individuals and institutions for the study or provider of educational services in the fields of labor, human relations, and betterment of mankind.
Fields of interest: Education; Labor studies; Social sciences.
Type of support: Scholarships—to individuals.
Application information: Scholarship applicants must be a member or dependent of a member of the UAW or another labor organization, or be a student in an accredited educational institution.
Officers and Trustees:* Ron Gettelfinger,* Pres.; Elizabeth Bunn,* Secy.-Treas.; Douglas A. Fraser; Carly Murdy; Elizabeth Reuther; Linda Reuther; Victor G. Reuther; Comerica Bank.
EIN: 237067164

2606
Ridge Adrian College Foundation
c/o P.O. Box 960
1919 Douglas, MACN8000-027
Omaha, NE 68102

Established in 1957; supporting organization of Adrian College, MI.

Grantmaker type: Public charity.
Financial data (yr. ended 12/31/04): Revenue, $103,018; assets, $1,764,710 (M); expenditures, $74,602; total giving, $59,859; program services expenses, $63,521; giving activities include $59,859 for 1 grant.
Fields of interest: Higher education, college.
Limitations: Applications not accepted. Giving limited to Adrian, MI.
Application information: Contributes only to a pre-selected organization; unsolicited requests for funds not considered or acknowledged.
Trustee: Wells Fargo Bank Indiana, N.A.
EIN: 356013001

2607
H. M. Riley Trust for Watch Tower Bible and Tract Society
c/o Comerica Bank
P.O. Box 75000, MC 3302
Detroit, MI 48275

Supporting organization of the Watch Tower Bible and Tract Society, Brooklyn, NY.
Donor: H.M. Riley†.
Grantmaker type: Public charity.
Financial data (yr. ended 4/30/05): Revenue, $1,613,009; assets, $2,028,215 (M); expenditures, $1,774,331; total giving, $1,771,732; program services expenses, $1,771,732; giving activities include $1,771,732 for 1 grant.
Fields of interest: Religion.
Limitations: Applications not accepted. Giving limited to Brooklyn, NY.
Application information: Contributes only to a pre-selected organization; unsolicited requests for funds not considered or acknowledged.
Trustee: Comerica Bank.
EIN: 386043103

2608
Roscommon County United Way
P.O. Box 324
Roscommon, MI 48653

Grantmaker type: Public charity.
Financial data (yr. ended 12/31/05): Revenue, $68,779; assets, $18,192 (M); gifts received, $68,639; expenditures, $81,628; total giving, $66,092; giving activities include $66,092 for grants.
Fields of interest: Community development.
Officers: Bill Curnilia, Pres.; Charles Darocy, V.P.; James Beinke, Secy.; Gregory Bush, Treas.
EIN: 382977871

2609
Rotary Charities of Traverse City
250 E. Front St., Ste. 320
Traverse City, MI 49684-2510 (231) 941-4010
Contact: Marsha J. Smith, Exec. Dir.
FAX: (231) 941-4066;
E-mail: msmith@rotarycharities.org; URL: http://www.rotarycharities.org

Established in 1976.
Donor: Rotary Club of Traverse City.
Grantmaker type: Public charity.

Financial data (yr. ended 6/30/05): Revenue, $2,568,261; assets, $40,058,863 (M); expenditures, $1,413,889; total giving, $943,486; program services expenses, $1,051,648; giving activities include $943,486 for 32+ grants (high: $130,000).
Purpose and activities: The charity focuses on managing growth and the environment, education, affordable housing, cultural recreation, and strengthening families.
Fields of interest: Arts; Education; Environment, management/technical aid; Housing/shelter, search services; Recreation; Family services.
Type of support: Capital campaigns; Building/renovation; Equipment; Seed money; Technical assistance; Matching/challenge support.
Limitations: Giving limited to Antrim, Benzie, Grand Traverse, Kalkaska, and Leelanau counties, MI. No support for religious activities or programs. No grants to individuals, or for endowment funds or ongoing support; no loans to individuals.
Publications: Application guidelines; Annual report (including application guidelines); Financial statement; Grants list.
Application information: Accepts CMF Common Grant Application Form; pre-application telephone conversations are strongly encouraged; see Web site for additional guidelines. Application form required.
Initial approach: Online application
Copies of proposal: 1
Deadline(s): Mar. 1 for Program and Capital Grants requests of $100,000 or less; Sept. 1 for Program and Capital Grant request of $100,000 or more; June 1 and Dec 1 for Implementation Capacity Grants; First of each month for Readiness Capacity Grants
Board meeting date(s): Monthly
Officers and Trustees:* Dick Ford,* Chair.; Henry Zuilhof,* Secy.-Treas.; Marsha J. Smith, Exec. Dir.; George Bearup; Ed Downing; Don Fraser; Don Harmer; Homer Nye; Bob Portenga; George Powell; Gregg Smith.
Number of staff: 1 full-time professional; 1 part-time professional; 1 full-time support.
EIN: 382170564

2610
Rotary Club of Lowell Community Foundation
P.O. Box 223
Lowell, MI 49331

Grantmaker type: Public charity.
Financial data (yr. ended 12/31/05): Revenue, $37,144; assets, $78,845 (M); gifts received, $3,355; expenditures, $7,233; total giving, $6,500; program services expenses, $6,500; giving activities include $6,500 for grants to individuals.
Purpose and activities: The foundation awards individual scholarships and makes charitable contributions to organizations.
Fields of interest: Community development.
Type of support: Scholarships—to individuals.
Officers: Gregory Flick, Pres.; R. Tony Asselta, V.P.; Roger Chapman, Secy.; Betty Morlock, Treas.
EIN: 383563288

2611
Rotary Club of Novi Foundation, Inc.
P.O. Box 159
Novi, MI 48376-0159

Grantmaker type: Public charity.
Financial data (yr. ended 6/30/05): Revenue, $33,453; assets, $37,575 (M); gifts received, $13,724; expenditures, $33,927; total giving, $33,529; program services expenses, $33,529; giving activities include $28,529 for grants, and $5,000 for grants to individuals.
Purpose and activities: Support for community development; also awards scholarships to Novi, Michigan high school graduates.
Fields of interest: International development; Community development, service clubs; Community development.
Type of support: Scholarships—to individuals.
Limitations: Giving primarily in the U.S.; scholarships limited to residents of Novi, MI.
Officers and Trustees:* Robert Limbright,* Chair.; Robert Button,* Treas.; Maryanne Cornelius; Victor Merritt; Anthony Musu; Albert Ponkey; Keith Tappan.
EIN: 383218968

2612
Rotary District 6360 Foundation
12248 Southgate Dr.
Plainwell, MI 49080-9052
E-mail: district6360@cablespeed.com; URL: http://www.district6360.com/district_foundation/index.htm

Established in 1992 in MI.
Grantmaker type: Public charity.
Financial data (yr. ended 6/30/05): Revenue, $105,406; assets, $93,294 (M); gifts received, $80,750; expenditures, $105,954; total giving, $95,856; program services expenses, $95,856; giving activities include $95,856 for grants.
Purpose and activities: The foundation supports local area literacy programs and other community service projects, and provides aid for educational and capital improvements in Nicaragua and Mexico.
Fields of interest: Adult education—literacy, basic skills & GED; Education.
International interests: Mexico; Nicaragua.
Type of support: Capital campaigns; Equipment; Program development; Seed money; Matching/challenge support.
Limitations: Giving primarily in Kalamazoo, MI; giving also in Nicaragua and Mexico. No grants to District 6360 Rotarians, a Rotary employee or a parent, grandparent, child, grandchild of a Rotarian, or their spouses, or for individual travel expenses, salaries, personnel costs, research consultant fees, operating administrative expenses, or pre-project planning costs.
Publications: Annual report (including application guidelines); Informational brochure; Program policy statement.
Application information: Grant applications can be requested in writing or downloaded from Web site. Application form required.
Initial approach: Letter
Copies of proposal: 1
Deadline(s): None
Board meeting date(s): Apr. 25, June 10, Aug. 10, Oct. 24, and Dec. 12
Final notification: Within 30 to 60 days
Officers: Marguerite Alden, Pres.; Chuck Kendal, Secy.; Lee Seguin, Treas.

Number of staff: 1 part-time support.
EIN: 383002325

2613
Wade E. & Viola Sackner Foundation
c/o Michael J. Taylor
250 Monroe Ave. N.W., Ste. 800
P.O. Box 306
Grand Rapids, MI 49501

Established in 1954; supporting organization of the Mary Free Bed Fund, American Cancer Society Michigan Division, American Red Cross of West Central Michigan, Saladin Shrine for Children, Heart of West Michigan United Way, and the George Slykhouse Scholarship.
Grantmaker type: Public charity.
Financial data (yr. ended 11/30/05): Revenue, $545,358; assets, $8,241,693 (M); expenditures, $503,551; total giving, $446,084; program services expenses, $446,084; giving activities include $446,084 for 6 grants (high: $146,964; low: $5,200).
Fields of interest: Education; Health care; Federated giving programs.
Limitations: Applications not accepted. Giving limited to Grand Rapids and Lansing, MI.
Application information: Contributes only to pre-selected organizations; unsolicited requests for funds not considered or acknowledged.
Officers and Trustees:* Sarah Jackoboice,* Pres.; Robert Haight,* V.P.; Michael J. Taylor,* Secy.; Richard T. Higgins, Treas.; Kenneth Helbling; Lisa Marks; Richard A. Orrell.
EIN: 386092077

2614
Saint Mary's Doran Foundation
c/o St. Mary's Health Care
200 Jefferson St. S.E.
Grand Rapids, MI 49503 (616) 752-6762
Contact: Michelle Rabideau, Exec. Dir.
E-mail: rabideaa@trinity-health.org; URL: http://www.smmmc.org/about/foundation/philanthropic.shtml

Grantmaker type: Public charity.
Financial data (yr. ended 6/30/05): Revenue, $13,014,654; assets, $22,456,255 (M); gifts received, $12,302,682; expenditures, $6,647,590; total giving, $6,335,292; program services expenses, $6,335,292; giving activities include $6,335,292 for 2 grants (high: $6,333,792; low: $1,500).
Purpose and activities: The organization receives and administers funds in order to promote and support the health care mission and philosophy of Saint Mary's Health Care.
Fields of interest: Health care.
Limitations: Giving primarily in MI.
Publications: Annual report.
Officers and Directors:* William J. Passinault, M.D.*, Chair.; David D. Baumgartner, M.D.*, Vice-Chair.; Lawrence P. Burns,* Secy.; Lisa Wurst,* Treas.; Michelle Rabideau, Exec. Dir.; Micki Benz; Harold E. Bowman, M.D.; Ellamae Braun; Robert D. Burton, M.D.; Steven A. Crane, M.D.; and 21 additional directors.
EIN: 381779602

2615
Henry M. Seldon Charitable Trust
c/o Comerica Bank
P.O. Box 75000
Detroit, MI 48275-3462

Established in 1975; supporting organization of Adrian College, Boys and Girls Club of Southeast Michigan, Central United Methodist Church, Salvation Army, and Wayne State University.
Grantmaker type: Public charity.
Financial data (yr. ended 12/31/04): Revenue, $579,406; assets, $7,702,478 (M); expenditures, $231,679; total giving, $172,530; program services expenses, $172,530; giving activities include $172,530 for 5 grants (high: $34,506; low: $34,506).
Fields of interest: Higher education, college; Higher education, university; Boys & girls clubs; Salvation Army; Protestant agencies & churches.
Limitations: Applications not accepted.
Application information: Contributes only to pre-selected organizations; unsolicited requests for funds not considered or acknowledged.
Officers and Directors:* Richard Strowger,* Chair.; Andrew Strong,* Vice-Chair.; Lewis A. Rockwell,* Secy.; Jane K. Nugent,* Treas.; William H. Francis; Daniel Lis; Charles H. Nicholl; Thomas E. O'Hara.
EIN: 386323073

2616
Shaevsky Family Foundation
(formerly Shaevsky Family Support Foundation)
6735 Telegraph Rd.
P.O. Box 2030
Bloomfield Hills, MI 48301

Established in 1998 in MI; a supporting organization of Jewish Federation of Metropolitan Detroit.
Grantmaker type: Public charity.
Financial data (yr. ended 5/31/05): Revenue, $581,253; assets, $1,043,255 (M); gifts received, $513,437; expenditures, $121,752; total giving, $89,900; program services expenses, $89,900; giving activities include $89,900 for 11 grants (high: $42,000; low: $800).
Purpose and activities: Support primarily for Jewish federated programs; giving also for the arts and human services.
Fields of interest: Performing arts; Arts; Human services; Jewish federated giving programs; Jewish agencies & temples.
Type of support: General/operating support; Annual campaigns.
Limitations: Giving primarily in Bloomfield Hills and Detroit, MI.
Officers: Lois L. Shaevsky, Pres.; Robert P. Aronson, V.P.; Jonathan Lowe, Secy.; Dorothy Benyas, Treas.
Directors: Penny Blumenstein; Mark Hauser; Lawrence Jackier; Lawrence K. Shaevsky; Mark Shaevsky; Thomas L. Shaevsky.
EIN: 383423716

2617
Joel H. and Loraine Shapiro Family Foundation
6735 Telegraph Rd.
P.O. Box 2030
Bloomfield Hills, MI 48301
Contact: Loraine Shapiro, Pres.

Established in 1989; supporting organization of the Jewish Federation of Metropolitan Detroit.
Grantmaker type: Public charity.
Financial data (yr. ended 5/31/05): Revenue, $40,339; assets $484,495 (M); expenditures, $63,352; total giving, $31,500; program services expenses, $31,500; giving activities include $31,500 for 12 grants (high: $6,500; low: $500).
Fields of interest: Jewish federated giving programs.
Limitations: Giving primarily in MI.
Officers and Directors:* Loraine Shapiro,* Pres.; Aaron L. Shapiro,* V.P.; Bonnie L. Shapiro,* V.P.; Phyllis A. Shapiro Siegal,* V.P.; Robert P. Aronson,* Secy.; Dorothy Benyas,* Treas.; Penny Blumenstein; Mark R. Hauser; Michael W. Maddin; Joel Shapiro.
EIN: 382870707

2618
Shiawassee United Way
1302 W. Main St.
P.O. Box 664
Owosso, MI 48867

Established in MI.
Grantmaker type: Public charity.
Financial data (yr. ended 12/31/04): Revenue, $366,384; assets, $384,306 (M); gifts received, $317,116; expenditures, $405,613; total giving, $257,270; program services expenses, $349,229; giving activities include $257,270 for 16 grants (high: $46,607; low: $200).
Fields of interest: Community development.
Limitations: Giving primarily in Owosso, MI.
Officers: Joane Ford, Pres.; Ed Brush, V.P.; Charles Dahl, Treas.; Renita Mikolajczyk, Exec. Dir.
Directors: Tom Bridges; Laurie Cook; Mark Erickson; Steve Grinnell; Mary Kay Kenney; James Kruger; Joy Welty; Ron Zimmerman; and 7 additional directors.
EIN: 386006199

2619
Smoke on the Grill, Inc.
c/o Kevin T. O'Brien
1234 Linden St.
Dearborn, MI 48124-4006

Grantmaker type: Public charity.
Financial data (yr. ended 12/31/05): Revenue, $18,334; assets, $1,993 (M); gifts received, $26,126; expenditures, $20,000; total giving, $20,000; program services expenses, $20,000; giving activities include $20,000 for grants.
Fields of interest: Education; Human services.
Limitations: Giving primarily in Dearborn, MI.
Officers and Directors:* Kevin T. O'Brien,* Chair.; John W. Tanner III,* Pres.; Gary Jefferson,* Secy.-Treas.; Robert Leinen.
EIN: 383533453

2620
Society of Manufacturing Engineers Education Foundation
(also known as SME Education Foundation)
1 SME Dr.
P.O. Box 930
Dearborn, MI 48121-0930 (313) 425-3300
Contact: Sherril K. West, Pres.
FAX: (313) 425-3411; E-mail: foundation@sme.org;
URL: http://www.sme.org/foundation

Established in 1979 in MI.
Donor: Society of Manufacturing Engineers.
Grantmaker type: Public charity.
Financial data (yr. ended 12/31/04): Revenue, $1,634,070; assets, $23,309,005 (M); gifts received, $907,358; expenditures, $1,651,514; total giving, $729,302; program services expenses, $1,146,428; giving activities include $510,972 for 15 grants (high: $207,536; low: $1,500), and $218,330 for grants to individuals.
Purpose and activities: The foundation serves the manufacturing profession by providing support for the advancement of education for manufacturing engineering and technology programs in North America.
Fields of interest: Engineering school/education.
Type of support: Annual campaigns; Capital campaigns; Equipment; Program development; Seed money; Curriculum development; Fellowships; Scholarship funds; Research; Scholarships—to individuals.
Limitations: Giving limited to the U.S. and Canada.
Publications: Application guidelines; Annual report; Grants list; Program policy statement.
Application information: Consult Web site for further details of scholarship programs. Application form required.
  Initial approach: Telephone
  Deadline(s): Feb.
  Board meeting date(s): May and Oct.
  Final notification: May
Officers and Directors:* Sherril K. West,* Pres.; Glen H. Pearson,* V.P.; Sandra L. Bouckley,* Secy.; Peter F. Mackie,* Treas.; John D. Belzer; Lesia Crumpton-Young, Ph.D.; Gregg O. Ekberg; Cecil W. Schneider; and 10 additional directors.
Number of staff: 4 full-time professional; 1 part-time professional; 3 full-time support.
EIN: 382746841

2621
Sojourner Foundation
25940 Grand River Ave.
Detroit, MI 48240-1485 (313) 538-5892
Contact: Onnie Barnes Jacque, Pres.

Established in 1985 in MI.
Grantmaker type: Public charity.
Financial data (yr. ended 12/31/04): Revenue, $30,714; assets, $41,528 (M); gifts received, $35,182; expenditures, $36,969; total giving, $21,000; program services expenses, $21,842; giving activities include $21,000 for 13 grants (high: $3,800; low: $50).
Purpose and activities: The foundation provides funds to worthwhile organizations serving women and girls that encounter difficulty in raising adequate support from traditional sources. Grants are awarded to organizations which seek to eliminate the barriers preventing women and girls from exercising their full human rights.
Fields of interest: Health care, infants; Reproductive health; Crime/violence prevention, domestic violence; Crime/violence prevention, child abuse; Civil rights, women; Women.
Type of support: Continuing support; Annual campaigns; Program development; Conferences/seminars; Technical assistance; In-kind gifts.
Limitations: Giving limited to Wayne, Oakland, Livingston, Washtenaw, St. Clair, Monroe, and Macomb counties, MI. No support for programs and services that do not serve population groups made up of a majority of women and girls.

Publications: Application guidelines; Grants list; Informational brochure; Newsletter.
Application information: Application form required.
Initial approach: Letter
Deadline(s): Sept. 15
Board meeting date(s): 3rd Wed. of each month
Final notification: Dec. 31
Officers and Trustees:* Onnie Barnes Jacque,* Pres.; Helen Kozlowski-Hicks,* V.P.; Brenda Scoggins,* Secy.; Sandra McClennen,* Treas.; Holly Billiter; Esther Gargalino; Ann Sullivan Smith.
Number of staff: 1 part-time professional; 1 part-time support.
EIN: 382477123

2622
Southfield Kappa Foundation
P.O. Box 446
Southfield, MI   48037
E-mail: info@southfieldkappafoundation.org;
URL: http://www.southfieldkappafoundation.org

Established in 1993 in MI.
Donor: Members of the Southfield Alumni Chapter of Kappa Alpha Psi Frate.
Grantmaker type: Public charity.
Financial data (yr. ended 12/31/03): Revenue, $21,213; assets, $47,091; gifts received, $3,920; expenditures, $25,000; total giving, $25,000; program services expenses, $25,000; giving activities include $25,000 for 25 grants to individuals (high: $1,000; low: $1,000).
Purpose and activities: Awards scholarships to African-American male and female students attending public or private high schools in the Detroit, Michigan, metropolitan area to attend a four-year accredited college or university in the school year following the award.
Fields of interest: African Americans/Blacks.
Type of support: Scholarships—to individuals.
Limitations: Giving limited to the Detroit metropolitan area: Wayne and Oakland counties, MI.
Application information: Application form available after Oct. 1 and may be downloaded from the foundation's Web site. Application form required.
Deadline(s): Mar. 7
Final notification: May 1
Officers and Directors:* Chris Carswell,* Chair.; Niko Dawson,* Vice-Chair.; Darryl Dixon, Pres.; Tony Zeringue, V.P.; Carlton Powell, Secy.; Douglas Sanders, Treas.; Garrett Ford; Harry Franklin; Ralph Jefferson; David Joseph; Harry Porter; Cliff Stovall.
EIN: 383050851

2623
Spaulding for Children
16250 Northland Dr., Ste. 100
Southfield, MI   48075   (248) 443-7080
FAX: (248) 443-7099; URL: http://www.spaulding.org

Established in 1968.
Grantmaker type: Public charity.
Financial data (yr. ended 9/30/04): Revenue, $6,087,594; assets, $3,290,363 (M); gifts received, $2,860,515; expenditures, $6,010,942; total giving, $54,661; program services expenses, $5,233,231; giving activities include $54,661 for grants to individuals.

Purpose and activities: Spaulding for Children finds permanent homes for children that have been in the foster care and adoption system the longest.
Fields of interest: Children, adoption.
Type of support: Scholarships—to individuals.
Officers: Addie Williams, Pres. and C.E.O.; Kay E. Brown, V.P., Finance; Kris Henneman, V.P., Spaulding Institute; Drenda S. Lakin, V.P., NRC; Charles Stults, V.P., Child and Family Svcs.
EIN: 381871660

2624
William and Sarah Speck Trust
c/o Comerica Bank
P.O. Box 75000
Detroit, MI   48275

Established in 1991 in MI; supporting organization of the American Cancer Society, Lansing, MI, Moslem Temple Association, Detroit, MI, and Mercy Hospital, Detroit, MI.
Grantmaker type: Public charity.
Financial data (yr. ended 6/30/05): Revenue, $62,911; assets, $1,328,231 (M); expenditures, $50,845; total giving, $36,440; program services expenses, $36,440; giving activities include $36,440 for 3 grants (high: $12,147; low: $12,146).
Fields of interest: Hospitals (general); Cancer; Cancer research; Islam.
Limitations: Applications not accepted. Giving limited to Detroit and Lansing, MI.
Application information: Contributes only to pre-selected organizations; unsolicited requests for funds not considered or acknowledged.
Trustee: Comerica Bank.
EIN: 386162140

2625
Spectrum Health Foundation
(formerly Blodgett Butterworth Health Care Foundation)
100 Michigan Ave. N.E.
Grand Rapids, MI   49503-2560
URL: http://blodgett.spectrum-health.org/

Established in 1987 in MI.
Grantmaker type: Public charity.
Financial data (yr. ended 6/30/05): Revenue, $16,728,776; assets, $67,299,673 (M); gifts received, $12,514,750; expenditures, $20,163,918; total giving, $17,559,569; program services expenses, $18,390,529; giving activities include $17,559,569 for grants.
Purpose and activities: To advance, through philanthropy, the health of the western Michigan community by supporting excellence in health care. Funding includes support for families of patients hospitalized at Spectrum Health and DeVos Children's Hospital, research and equipment, and educaitonal scholarships for health professionals.
Fields of interest: Medical school/education; Nursing school/education; Health care, patient services; Health care, counseling/pastoral care; Health care; Medical research.
Type of support: Scholarships—to individuals; Student loans—to individuals; Equipment; Scholarship funds; Research.
Limitations: Applications not accepted. Giving limited for the benefit of the western MI region.

Application information: Contributes only to pre-selected organizations; unsolicited requests for funds not considered or acknowledged.
Officers: Dick DeVos, Chair.; Richard Antonini, Vice-Chair.; Vicki Weaver, Pres.; Kristin Duryee, Secy.; Wilbur Lettinga, Treas.
Trustees: Richard Breon; Jack Carter; Edward Clark; Peter Cook; David Custer; James Delavan, M.D.; Donnalee Holton; Robert Hooker; Carl Kelly, Jr.; Thomas Kyros; and 13 additional trustees.
EIN: 382752328

2626
The Sphinx Organization
(formerly Concert Competitions & Musical Development, Inc.)
400 Renaissance Ctr., Ste. 2550
Detroit, MI   48243   (313) 877-9100
Contact: Aaron Dworkin, Pres.
FAX: (313) 877-0164;
E-mail: info@sphinxmusic.org; URL: http://www.sphinxmusic.org

Established in 1996.
Grantmaker type: Public charity.
Financial data (yr. ended 12/31/04): Revenue, $1,072,096; assets, $1,006,269 (M); gifts received, $1,014,996; expenditures, $1,248,900; total giving, $64,479; program services expenses, $1,019,548; giving activities include $64,479 for grants to individuals.
Purpose and activities: The foundation develops and encourages classical musical talent in the Black and Latinos communities and among all youth.
Fields of interest: Performing arts, orchestra (symphony); African Americans/Blacks; Hispanics/Latinos.
Type of support: Scholarships—to individuals.
Limitations: Giving on a national basis.
Publications: Application guidelines.
Application information: Each applicant must submit with their application a preliminary audition tape or CD which includes all of the required preliminaries repertoire for their instrument category. A $35 application fee must also be enclosed. Application form required.
Initial approach: Download application
Deadline(s): Nov. 15
Final notification: Dec. 15
Officers and Directors:* Betty W. Brooks,* Chair.; Jenice C. Mitchell,* Vice-Chair.; Aaron P. Dworkin, Pres.; Hon. Kurtis T. Wilder, Secy.; Al McDonough,* Treas.; Ruben Acosta; Phil Cole; and 9 additional directors.
EIN: 383283759

2627
St. John Vianney Educational Foundation
4101 Clyde Park Ave. S.W.
Wyoming, MI   49509

Established in 1987.
Grantmaker type: Public charity.
Financial data (yr. ended 9/30/05): Revenue, $61,032; assets, $905,546 (M); gifts received, $29,006; expenditures, $49,188; total giving, $33,120; program services expenses, $33,120; giving activities include $26,920 for 13 grants (high: $10,000; low: $225), and $6,200 for grants to individuals.
Fields of interest: Education.

Type of support: Scholarships—to individuals.
Limitations: Applications not accepted.
Application information: Contributes only to pre-selected organizations; unsolicited requests for funds not considered or acknowledged.
Officers: Tim Kernosky, Pres.; Susan Rysdyk, Secy.-Treas.
Trustees: Robert Cercek; Karen Kriscunas; Dan Lennon; Sandy Maxim; Rev. Loc Trinh; Tom Truskowski.
EIN: 382700546

2628
St. Joseph County United Way
132 W. Main St.
P.O. Box 577
Centreville, MI 49032

Established in MI.
Grantmaker type: Public charity.
Financial data (yr. ended 12/31/04): Revenue, $475,488; assets, $711,519 (M); gifts received, $468,658; expenditures, $542,096; total giving, $380,194; program services expenses, $380,194; giving activities include $380,194 for 44 grants (high: $25,869; low: $500).
Purpose and activities: The organization seeks to promote the social welfare of St. Joseph County, Michigan.
Fields of interest: Human services.
Limitations: Giving primarily in St. Joseph County, MI.
Officers: Tracey Nielson-Trine, Pres.; Skip Sisson, 1st V.P.; Brian Ringle, 2nd V.P.; Rick Strawser, Treas.; Kelly Hostetler, Exec. Dir.
Trustees: Pattie Bender; Scott Boland; Mark Brown; David Franks; Marcus Gleaton; Robert Labarge; Bill Miller; Scott Mitchell; Laura Perry; Ivin Riddle; and 9 additional trustees.
EIN: 386095409

2629
St. Joseph/Benton Harbor Rotary Foundation, Inc.
P.O. Box 335
St. Joseph, MI 49085
URL: http://www.sjbhrotary.org/foundation/foundation.html

Established in 1980 in MI.
Grantmaker type: Public charity.
Financial data (yr. ended 6/30/05): Revenue, $67,468; assets, $597,594 (M); gifts received, $38,665; expenditures, $40,018; total giving, $38,237; program services expenses, $38,237; giving activities include $38,237 for grants.
Purpose and activities: The mission of the foundation is to improve the quality of life, primarily in the greater St. Joseph/Benton Harbor community, through human development projects that focus on promoting the health, education and self-development of people in the community, and community development projects that focus on activities that improve and enhance physical aspects of the community.
Fields of interest: Education; Health care; Human services; Community development.
Limitations: Giving primarily in the greater St. Joseph and Benton Harbor, MI, area.
Officers and Trustees:* Kurt Marzke,* Chair.; John Proos,* Vice-Chair.; Steve Banyon, Exec. Dir.; Randy

Bettich; Charles Jespersen; Nanette Kaiser; Jim Marohn; Christine Vanlandingham; Chuck Wells; Char Wenham.
EIN: 382336366

2630
St. Lawrence Educational Foundation, Inc.
44633 Utica Rd.
Utica, MI 48317-5470

Established in 1973; supporting organization of St. Lawrence Parish.
Grantmaker type: Public charity.
Financial data (yr. ended 12/31/05): Revenue, $45,369; assets, $1,329,906 (M); gifts received, $2,110; expenditures, $52,046; total giving, $36,713; program services expenses, $36,713; giving activities include $36,713 for 1 grant.
Fields of interest: Education; Religion.
Type of support: General/operating support.
Limitations: Applications not accepted. Giving limited to Utica, MI.
Application information: Contributes only to a pre-selected organization; unsolicited requests for funds not considered or acknowledged.
    Board meeting date(s): Quarterly
Officers and Trustees:* Rev. Robert Fisher,* Pres.; Antonio Cavaliere,* V.P.; Connie McKee,* Secy.; Douglas L. McKay,* Treas.; Pam Cottone; Thomas Dixon; Robert Kulka; Tom Naborczyk; Mary Paonessa; Sam Serra; Patrick Sporka.
EIN: 237350121

2631
Tahquamenon Education Foundation
P.O. Box 482
Newberry, MI 49868
E-mail: teflil@lighthouse.net

Established in 1987 in MI.
Grantmaker type: Public charity.
Financial data (yr. ended 6/30/05): Revenue, $50,830; assets, $551,764 (M); gifts received, $38,905; expenditures, $86,453; total giving, $42,500; program services expenses, $62,815; giving activities include $42,500 for 42 grants to individuals (high: $2,000; low: $500).
Purpose and activities: The foundation provides support to the Tahquamenon Area School District through scholarships, special grants, and teacher mini-grants.
Fields of interest: Elementary/secondary education.
Type of support: Equipment; Program development; Scholarships—to individuals.
Limitations: Giving limited to the Tahquamenon Area School District, including Newberry, Hulbert, Seney, Curtis, Germfask, McMillan, Lakefield, and Deer Park, MI.
Officers and Trustees:* Steven Derusha,* Pres.; Michael Slaght,* V.P.; Cheryl Bowler, Secy.-Treas.; Christopher Beaulieu; Chad Peltier; Scott Pillion; Donald Stephenson.
EIN: 382744932

2632
Robert H. Tannahill Foundation
333 W. Fort St., Ste. 2010
Detroit, MI 48226

Established in 1962 in MI; supporting organization of Christ Church Grosse Point, College for Creative Studies, Detroits Artist Market, Detroit Institute of Arts Founders Society, Detroit Symphony Orchestra, Episcopal Diocese of Michigan, Grosse Pointe War Memorial, and Wayne State University.
Grantmaker type: Public charity.
Financial data (yr. ended 12/31/04): Revenue, $3,494,754; assets, $56,940,225 (M); expenditures, $2,812,175; total giving, $2,412,758; program services expenses, $2,412,758; giving activities include $2,412,758 for 8 grants (high: $1,212,758; low: $60,000).
Fields of interest: Arts, formal/general education; Performing arts, orchestra (symphony); Historical activities, war memorials; Arts, artist's services; Higher education, university; Protestant agencies & churches.
Limitations: Applications not accepted. Giving limited to Detroit and Grosse Pointe, MI.
Application information: Contributes only to pre-selected organizations; unsolicited requests for funds not considered or acknowledged.
Trustees: David M. Hempstead; Gilbert Hudson; J.L. Hudson, Jr.; Harvey B. Wallace II; Comerica Bank.
EIN: 386054453

2633
Tauber Family Support Foundation
(formerly Joel D. Tauber Support Foundation)
6735 Telegraph Rd.
P.O. Box 2030
Bloomfield Hills, MI 48301-3141
Contact: Joel D. Tauber, Pres.

Established in 1985; supporting organization of the Jewish Federation of Metropolitan Detroit.
Grantmaker type: Public charity.
Financial data (yr. ended 5/31/05): Revenue, $57,492; assets, $22,142 (M); gifts received, $56,629; expenditures, $151,852; total giving, $120,000; program services expenses, $120,000; giving activities include $120,000 for 4 grants (high: $50,000; low: $10,000).
Purpose and activities: Giving primarily to Jewish organizations.
Fields of interest: Business school/education; Jewish federated giving programs.
Officers and Directors:* Joel D. Tauber,* Pres.; David Handleman,* V.P.; Robert P. Aronson,* V.P.; Dorothy Benyas,* Secy.; Michael W. Maddin,* Treas.; Mandell Berman; and 6 additional directors.
EIN: 382581585

2634
Tawas-Whittemore-Hale Area United Fund
P.O. Box 28
East Tawas, MI 48730-0028

Grantmaker type: Public charity.
Financial data (yr. ended 3/31/05): Revenue, $20,621; assets, $17,068 (M); gifts received, $20,472; expenditures, $23,091; total giving, $21,638; program services expenses, $21,638; giving activities include $21,638 for 16 grants (high: $2,131; low: $800).
Fields of interest: Education; Health care; Youth development; Human services; Family services.
Limitations: Giving in Iosco County, MI, primarily in the Tawas, Whittemore, and Hale areas.

Officers: John Lorenz, Chair.; Peter Stoll, Vice-Chair.; John Morris, Secy.; Blinda Baker, Treas.
EIN: 237149665

2635
Thornapple Kellogg Education Foundation
P.O. Box 164
MIddleville, MI   49333-0164

Established in 2002 in MI.
Grantmaker type: Public charity.
Financial data (yr. ended 6/30/05): Revenue, $54,446; assets, $135,149 (M); gifts received, $48,626; expenditures, $7,726; total giving, $4,750; program services expenses, $4,750; giving activities include $500 for grants, and $4,250 for grants to individuals (average: $250–$1,500).
Purpose and activities: Support primarily through student scholarships to promote education in Barry County, Michigan.
Fields of interest: Scholarships/financial aid; Education.
Type of support: Scholarship funds.
Limitations: Giving limited to Barry County, MI.
Officers and Directors:* Donald Williamson,* Pres.; Diane Weatherhead,* V.P.; Cheryl Peters,* Secy.; Charles Wolverton,* Treas.; Bob Bender; Joanne Dipp; Barb Dykstra; Bob Evans; Marilyn Finkbeiner; Robert Wlliams.
EIN: 383051928

2636
Travelers Aid Society of Metropolitan Detroit
1800 David Scott Bldg.
1150 Griswold St.
Detroit, MI   48226   (313) 926-6740
E-mail: info@travelersaiddetroit.org; URL: http://www.travelersaiddetroit.org

Grantmaker type: Public charity.
Financial data (yr. ended 6/30/05): Revenue, $3,146,540; assets, $360,251 (M); gifts received, $3,146,786; expenditures, $3,093,527; total giving, $1,687,335; program services expenses, $2,886,545; giving activities include $1,687,335 for grants to individuals.
Purpose and activities: The society provides permanent housing and supportive services to socially-economically challenged individuals and/or disconnected families and travelers by returning them to point of origin, advancing the well-being of the community and empowering them to become self-sufficient contributing members of society.
Fields of interest: Housing/shelter; International migration/refugee issues; Economically disadvantaged.
Type of support: Grants to individuals.
Publications: Annual report.
Officers and Directors:* Eric Foster,* Pres.; Nathaniel Warshay,* V.P.; Alfred J. Gittleman,* Secy.; Wendy L. Smith,* Treas.; Harriet Cosby; Monica Davie; John L. Davis II; Lamar Richardson; and 7 additional directors.
EIN: 381358052

2637
Trinity Community Services & Educational Foundation
1050 Porter St.
Detroit, MI   48224   (313) 965-4450
Contact: Fr. Russell Kohler, Pres.

Established in 1994; status changed to a public charity.
Grantmaker type: Public charity.
Financial data (yr. ended 12/31/04): Revenue, $427,958; assets, $966,387 (M); gifts received, $367,595; expenditures, $167,243; total giving, $126,229; program services expenses, $167,243; giving activities include $91,954 for grants, and $34,275 for grants to individuals.
Purpose and activities: The foundation provides scholarships, based on established criteria, to elementary, primary and secondary school students living in the Corktown District of Detroit, Michigan. The foundation also subsidizes the operations of the Sister Frances Cabrini Health Clinic in the Corktown District of Detroit, Michigan.
Fields of interest: Elementary/secondary education; Health care, clinics/centers; Roman Catholic agencies & churches.
Type of support: Scholarship funds; Grants to individuals; Scholarships—to individuals.
Limitations: Giving limited to Detroit, MI.
Application information: Scholarship applications may be submitted by the student's family or school. Scholarship awards are paid directly to the school.
Officers: Gerald Coyne, Chair.; Fr. Russell Kohler, Pres.; Paul Manion, Secy.
EIN: 383129349

2638
United Jewish Foundation
6735 Telegraph Rd.
Bloomfield Hills, MI   48301   (248) 642-4260
Contact: Howard Neistein

Grantmaker type: Public charity.
Financial data (yr. ended 5/31/05): Revenue, $39,843,386; assets, $325,988,143 (M); gifts received, $31,266,587; expenditures, $36,601,395; total giving, $29,479,339; program services expenses, $33,460,818; giving activities include $29,479,339 for 780 grants (high: $8,364,160; low: $250).
Purpose and activities: A partner with the Jewish Federation of Metropolitan Detroit, the foundation provides support for organizations serving the Jewish community.
Fields of interest: Jewish federated giving programs; Jewish agencies & temples.
Limitations: Giving limited to the metropolitan Detroit, MI, area. No grants to individuals.
Publications: Annual report; Financial statement.
Officers and Directors:* Allan Nachman,* Pres.; Robert P. Aronson, C.E.O.; Dorothy Benyas, C.F.O.; Mark Davidoff, Exec. Dir.; Douglas Etkin; Phillip Fisher; Margot Halperin; Terran Leemis; Norman Pappas; and 81 additional directors.
EIN: 381360585

2639
United Way for Southeastern Michigan
1212 Griswold
Detroit, MI   48226   (313) 226-9200
URL: http://www.uwsem.org/

Established in 2005 in MI as a result of the consolidation of operations of United Way Community Services and United Way of Oakland County.
Grantmaker type: Public charity.
Purpose and activities: The mission of United Way for Southeastern Michigan is to mobilize the caring power of Detroit and southeastern Michigan to improve communities and individual lives in measurable and lasting ways.
Limitations: Giving limited to Wayne, Oakland and Macomb counties, MI, except Plymouth.
Officers and Directors:* Anthony F. Earley, Jr.,* Chair.; Reginald Turner,* Vice-Chair.; Michael J. Brennan, Pres. and C.E.O.; Deb Macon,* Secy.; Mike Hanley,* Treas.; and 26 additional directors.

2640
United Way of Bay County
909 Washington Ave.
P.O. Box 602
Bay City, MI   48707   (989) 893-7508
FAX: (989) 893-0087; URL: http://www.unitedwaybaycounty.org

Established in MI.
Grantmaker type: Public charity.
Financial data (yr. ended 12/31/04): Revenue, $1,551,769; assets, $2,345,607 (M); gifts received, $1,491,929; expenditures, $1,651,286; total giving, $1,091,929; program services expenses, $1,387,915; giving activities include $1,091,929 for 22 grants (high: $125,174; low: $3,510).
Purpose and activities: The organization's mission is to build the community's financial and human ability to effectively and efficiently meet its human care needs and to create increased awareness in the community.
Fields of interest: Human services; Community development.
Limitations: Giving primarily in Bay County, MI.
Officers: Harvey Schneider, Pres.; Judi Klawinski, V.P.; Linda Mathewson, Secy.; Bob Hagen, Treas.; Jennifer L. Carroll, Exec. Dir.
Directors: Judy Adair; Judy Bagley; Laurie Bush; George Charles; Kim Coonan; Tony Dearing; Mike Dewey; Mike Hanisko; Matt Jeffery; Eric Jylha; and 20 additional directors.
EIN: 381360524

2641
United Way of Chippewa County
138 Ridge St.
P.O. Box 451
Sault Sainte Marie, MI   49783-0451
(906) 632-3700
Contact: Molly Paquin, Exec. Dir.
FAX: (906) 632-3190;
E-mail: unitedwaycc@30below.com; URL: http://www.uwmich.org/public/luw/luwdefault.asp?uworgid=19

Established in MI.
Grantmaker type: Public charity.
Financial data (yr. ended 6/30/05): Revenue, $312,881; assets, $235,860 (M); gifts received, $264,340; expenditures, $304,136; total giving, $174,348; program services expenses, $213,996; giving activities include $174,348 for grants.

Purpose and activities: The organization strives to increase the organized capacity of people to care for one another.
Fields of interest: Youth development; Human services.
Limitations: Giving limited to Chippewa County, MI.
Officers: Phil Becker, Pres.; William Munsell, Treas.; Molly Paquin, Exec. Dir.
Directors: Lee Baatz; Tony Bosbous; Paul Brewster; Barry Davis; Betsy Demaray; Don Gerrie; and 9 additional directors.
EIN: 381678240

2642
United Way of Clare County
c/o 106 W. 7th St.
P.O. Box 116
Clare, MI   48617-0116   (989) 386-6015
FAX: (989) 386-6548;
E-mail: info@unitedwayclare.org; URL: http://www.unitedwayclare.org/

Established in 1993 in MI.
Grantmaker type: Public charity.
Financial data (yr. ended 6/30/05): Revenue, $224,114; assets, $268,978 (M); gifts received, $217,805; expenditures, $231,885; total giving, $117,502; program services expenses, $179,451; giving activities include $116,000 for grants, and $1,502 for grants to individuals.
Purpose and activities: Through its network of member agencies, volunteers, and community leaders, the United Way of Clare County take a leadership role in addressing health and human service issues that face Clare County.
Fields of interest: Health care; Human services; Community development.
Limitations: Giving limited to Clare County, MI.
Officers and Directors:* Tom Jared,* Pres.; Jeff Poet,* V.P.; Don Richards,* Secy.-Treas.; Sandina Hages, Exec. Dir.; Jeff Goyt; Dennis LaFleur; Thomas House; Joseph Manifold; Jeanie Mishler; and 6 additional directors.
EIN: 383013356

2643
United Way of Delta County
1100 Ludington St., Ste. 300
Escanaba, MI   49829-3500

Grantmaker type: Public charity.
Financial data (yr. ended 12/31/04): Revenue, $327,820; assets, $300,035 (M); gifts received, $325,039; expenditures, $344,402; total giving, $249,209; program services expenses, $290,129; giving activities include $249,209 for 14 grants (high: $48,000; low: $2,209).
Fields of interest: Health care; Youth development; Human services.
Limitations: Giving limited to Delta County, MI, primarily in Escanaba and Marquette.
Officers: Will Carne, Pres.; Todd Salo, V.P.; Paddy Fitch, Secy.; Jim Wayne, Treas.; Jodi Olsen, Exec. Dir.
EIN: 381740320

2644
United Way of Dickinson County, Inc.
N3307 Woodland Dr.
Iron Mountain, MI   49801

Established in MI.
Grantmaker type: Public charity.
Financial data (yr. ended 12/31/04): Revenue, $94,205; assets, $98,785 (M); gifts received, $93,989; expenditures, $109,533; total giving, $93,903; program services expenses $93,903; giving activities include $93,903 for 12 grants (high: $21,502; low: $1,077).
Fields of interest: Human services; Community development.
Limitations: Giving primarily in MI.
Officers: Susie Tracy, Pres.; Sharon Hagberg, Pres.-Elect; Martee Trepanier, V.P.; Bruce Le Blanc, Secy.-Treas.; Barb Messer, Exec. Dir.
EIN: 237112824

2645
United Way of Genesee County
P.O. Box 949
Flint, MI   48501   (810) 232-8121
FAX: (810) 232-9370; URL: http://www.unitedwaygenesee.org/

Established in 1950 in MI.
Grantmaker type: Public charity.
Financial data (yr. ended 6/30/05): Revenue, $7,829,056; assets, $7,741,478 (M); gifts received, $7,703,088; expenditures, $8,527,669; total giving, $3,697,121; program services expenses $7,646,166; giving activities include $3,697,121 for grants.
Purpose and activities: Support for philanthropic, health, social, educational, and community organizations within Genesee, Lapeer, and all participating Michigan counties. Areas of focus include 1) Basic Needs: to provide a safety net for individuals and families whose circumstances put them at risk and who need assistance for essential services in the areas of shelter, food, transportation and clothing; 2) Child/Youth Development: to create safe environments to ensure healthy development, positive values and skills for life; 3) Older Adults: to provide opportunities for independent living and ensure the safety and physical and emotional well being of older adults, including support for caregivers; and 4) Strengthening Families: to develop a pathway to self-sufficiency through support of programs that promote physical and emotional health and opportunities for personal growth.
Fields of interest: Education; Health care; Youth development; Human services; Family services; Aging, centers/services; Community development; Philanthropy/voluntarism; Children/youth; Aging.
Limitations: Giving limited to Genesee, Lapeer, and other participating counties, MI.
Officers: Hannah Goodstein, C.O.O.; Ted Yockey, C.F.O.; Ron Butler, Exec. Dir.
EIN: 381359516

2646
United Way of Gladwin County
P.O. Box 620
Gladwin, MI   48624

Grantmaker type: Public charity.
Financial data (yr. ended 12/31/04): Revenue, $118,935; assets, $293,910 (M); gifts received, $110,190; expenditures, $116,463; total giving, $70,652; program services expenses, $100,202; giving activities include $70,652 for grants.

Purpose and activities: The organization seeks to represent and serve the overall interests of the citizens of Gladwin County in matters concerning community health and social well-being.
Fields of interest: Human services; Community development.
Limitations: Giving primarily in Gladwin County, MI.
Officer: Tamara Jenkinson, Exec. Dir.
Board Members: Sherry Augustine; Connie Buswell; JoAnne Cameron; Mike Drey; Sue Landenberger; Deb Lechner; Liz Looker; Kara Pahl; Cathy Roehrs; Georgann Schuster; and 7 additional board members.
EIN: 382476861

2647
United Way of Gratiot County
110 W. Superior St.
Alma, MI   48801   (989) 463-6245
Contact: Sharon Fenton, Exec. Dir.
FAX: (989) 463-6588;
E-mail: unitedway@gratiot.com; URL: http://www.gratiotunitedway.com

Grantmaker type: Public charity.
Financial data (yr. ended 12/31/05): Revenue, $333,671; assets, $419,166 (M); gifts received, $328,899; expenditures, $317,824; total giving, $245,542; program services expenses, $270,285; giving activities include $219,379 for 20 grants (high: $33,469; low: $59), and $26,163 for grants to individuals.
Purpose and activities: The organization seeks to raise and distribute funds to local health and human service organizations; financially support programs that produce measurable success and help those at risk of becoming disconnected from society; monitor effective human service programs that benefit the needs of Gratiot County; foster the opportunity for people to care for one another by giving their time, talents, and/or money; empower volunteers to become personally involved in meeting health and human service needs; recognize the rights of donors to direct their gifts; and research and identify grants and other funding opportunities.
Fields of interest: Health care; Human services; Community development; Federated giving programs.
Type of support: Grants to individuals; Research.
Limitations: Giving primarily in Gratiot County, MI.
Officers: Patti Johnston, Pres.; Zachary Everitt, V.P.; Janet Hunter, Secy.; Rich Rice, Treas.; Sharon Fenton, Exec. Dir.
Directors: Martha Barnfield; Rich Barratt; Larry Butterworth; Sue Gay; Nate Harris; Richard Henry; Jack Koester; Sonia Lark; and 16 additional directors.
EIN: 386093791

2648
United Way of Greater Battle Creek
34 W. Jackson St., Ste. 4B
P.O. Box 137
Battle Creek, MI   49017-0137   (269) 962-9538
Contact: Michael J. Larson, Pres.
FAX: (269) 962-0074; E-mail: info@uwgbc.org; URL: http://www.uwgbc.org

Established in MI.
Grantmaker type: Public charity.

Financial data (yr. ended 6/30/05): Revenue, $3,656,819; assets, $4,672,931 (M); gifts received, $3,268,366; expenditures, $3,404,822; total giving, $2,480,533; program services expenses, $2,856,352; giving activities include $2,480,533 for 35 grants (high: $268,685; low: $5,330).
Purpose and activities: The organization's mission is to address some of the community's most pressing problems and improve the lives of individuals in need.
Fields of interest: Human services; Community development.
Limitations: Giving primarily in the greater Battle Creek, MI, area.
Officers and Directors:* Brian Schneider,* Chair.; Michelle Reen,* Chair.-Elect; Dale Kimball,* 1st Vice-Chair.; Michael J. Larson, Pres. and C.P.O.; Dennis Bietsch,* Treas.; Jeffrey Arnold; Lauren Blaine; Teresa Durham; Kathy Griffey; Jeff Herrington; Jonice Hinds; Bill Knapp; and 16 additional directors.
EIN: 381846794

2649
United Way of Greater Niles, Inc.
210 E. Main St.
P.O. Box 375
Niles, MI 49120

Grantmaker type: Public charity.
Financial data (yr. ended 3/31/04): Revenue, $244,010; assets, $259,367 (M); gifts received, $234,310; expenditures, $241,188; total giving, $159,042; program services expenses, $168,364; giving activities include $159,042 for grants.
Fields of interest: Community development.
Limitations: Giving primarily in MI.
Officers: Melissa Tharp, Pres.; Elizabeth Watson, V.P.; Ellwin Coulston, Treas.; John Stauffer, Exec. Dir.
Directors: Tim Bagby; Nancy Campbell; Jennen Conway; Richard Devos; Mickey Hutchison; Wyvonne Johnson; Larry Pickles; Colette Pointer; Dale Rector; Ken Waggoner; Jim Zaker.
EIN: 386065024

2650
United Way of Ionia County
P.O. Box 95
Ionia, MI 48846

Grantmaker type: Public charity.
Financial data (yr. ended 3/31/05): Revenue, $145,651; assets, $31,031 (M); gifts received, $145,161; expenditures, $152,602; total giving, $110,079; program services expenses, $121,539; giving activities include $110,079 for grants.
Purpose and activities: The United Way of Ionia County makes allocations to 501(c)(3) organizations that benefit its community by promoting self-sufficiency, strengthening and supporting families, supporting vulnerable and aging populations, helping children and youth succeed, and builidng vital and safe neighborhoods.
Fields of interest: Crime/violence prevention; Youth development; Human services; Children/youth, services; Family services; Community development, neighborhood development; Community development; Aging; Economically disadvantaged.
Limitations: Giving limited to Ionia County, MI.

Officers and Directors:* Greg Patera, O.D.*, Pres.; Norene Peterman,* V.P.; Karen Hubbard,* Secy.; Kevin Meade,* Treas.; Sheila Ransom,* Exec. Dir.; Dan Avery; Charles Barker; Aaron Baylis; Marvin Beauchamp; and 19 additional directors.
EIN: 237136978

2651
United Way of Isabella County
402 S. University
Mount Pleasant, MI 48858 (989) 773-9863
FAX: (989) 772-8152; URL: http://www.unitedwayisaco.org/

Grantmaker type: Public charity.
Financial data (yr. ended 6/30/05): Revenue, $436,743; assets, $462,396 (M); gifts received, $398,537; expenditures, $395,622; total giving, $211,720; program services expenses, $296,269; giving activities include $211,720 for grants.
Purpose and activities: The United Way of Isabella County exists to enhance community needs by supporting agencies that bring forth programs that educate, provide basic needs, strengthen families, care for the elderly, prevent substance abuse and violence, care for our childen and reach out to those that needs support through effective human service programs.
Fields of interest: Substance abuse, prevention; Crime/violence prevention; Human services; Children/youth, services; Family services; Human services, victim aid; Aging, centers/services; Economically disadvantaged.
Limitations: Giving limited to Isabella County, MI.
Officers and Directors:* Maxine Kent,* Pres.; Tim Snellenberger,* V.P.; Phyllis Heinze,* Secy.; Tina Powell,* Treas. and Finance/Facilities Chair.; Nichole Bliss, Exec. Dir.; Carolyn Bennett; Becky Bolles; Chris Bundy; John Boley; and 14 additional directors.
EIN: 381957175

2652
United Way of Jackson County
729 W. Michigan Ave.
Jackson, MI 49204-1345 (517) 784-0511
FAX: (517) 784-2430; URL: http://www.uwjackson.org

Grantmaker type: Public charity.
Financial data (yr. ended 6/30/05): Revenue, $2,944,432; assets, $4,333,750 (M); expenditures, $3,084,578; total giving, $1,782,906; program services expenses, $2,107,723; giving activities include $1,782,906 for grants (high: $234,233).
Purpose and activities: To improve people's lives by mobilizing the caring power of Jackson County.
Limitations: Giving lmiited for the benefit of Jackson County, MI.
Officers: Ric Walton, Pres.; Mike Shore, 1st V.P.; Kathy Schmaltz, 2nd V.P.; Ruben Marquez, Secy.; Scott McIntosh, Treas.; Ken Toll, Exec. Dir.
EIN: 381368341

2653
United Way of Lapeer County
220 W. Nepessing St., Ste. 201
Lapeer, MI 48446 (810) 667-3114
FAX: (810) 664-2016; URL: http://unitedwaylapeer.org/

Established in 1927 in MI.
Grantmaker type: Public charity.
Financial data (yr. ended 6/30/05): Revenue, $554,246; assets, $574,835 (M); gifts received, $541,828; expenditures, $331,873; total giving, $159,081; program services expenses, $267,816; giving activities include $159,081 for grants (high: $18,750).
Purpose and activities: United Way of Lapeer County is a community solutions leader, uniting its community to measurably improve people's lives and build the most vital caring community in America. Current areas of priority are helping children succeed, supporting older adults, providing basic needs, and building strong families.
Fields of interest: Human services; Children/youth, services; Family services; Aging, centers/services.
Application information: See Web site for full application requirements and guidelines, including downloadable forms. Application form required.
EIN: 383509445

2654
United Way of Manistee County
30 Jones St.
Manistee, MI 49660 (231) 723-2331
E-mail: info@uwmanistee.org; URL: http://www.uwmanistee.org/

Established in 1942 in MI.
Grantmaker type: Public charity.
Financial data (yr. ended 3/31/05): Revenue, $149,322; assets, $194,859 (M); gifts received, $145,826; expenditures, $135,316; total giving, $95,074; program services expenses, $101,708; giving activities include $95,074 for grants.
Purpose and activities: Allocations are made to various nonprofit organizations in the Manistee community to improve lives and build stronger communities.
Fields of interest: Youth development; Human services; Community development.
Limitations: Giving limited to Manistee County, MI.
Officers and Directors:* Nick Jaskiw,* Pres.; Mary Hurley,* V.P.; Candace Owens,* Secy.; Wayne Birkmeier,* Treas.; Sharron Lemmer,* Exec. Dir.; David Bachman; Holly Davis; Jim Engstrom; Tracy Gavin; and 4 additional directors.
EIN: 386032839

2655
United Way of Marquette County
401 E. Fair Ave.
P.O. Box 73
Marquette, MI 49855 (906) 226-8171
FAX: (906) 226-7050;
E-mail: unitedway@uwmqt.org; URL: http://www.uwmqt.org/

Established in 1943 in MI.
Grantmaker type: Public charity.
Financial data (yr. ended 6/30/05): Revenue, $505,598; assets, $739,655 (M); gifts received, $470,307; expenditures, $508,557; total giving,

$369,476; program services expenses, $436,989; giving activities include $369,476 for grants.

Purpose and activities: The mission of the United Way of Marquette County is to improve lives by focusing community resources to meet community needs. Current areas of focus include: unemployment and underemployment, domestic violence and substance abuse, positive youth development, health education, and elderly and adults with disabilities.

Fields of interest: Public health; Substance abuse, services; Crime/violence prevention, domestic violence; Employment, services; Youth development; Aging; Disabilities, people with; Economically disadvantaged.

Limitations: Giving limited to Marquette County, MI.

Officers and Board Members: * Glenn Hametta, * Pres.; Donna Day, * V.P.; Diane Giddens, * Secy.; Ward Rantala, * Treas.; Jeff Bero; Joe Burdick; Bruce Miller; Ed Sloan; Bob Toutant; and 12 additional members.

EIN: 381358204

2656
United Way of Mason County
5868 West U.S. 10
Ludington, MI 49431 (231) 843-8593
Contact: Lynne Russell, Exec. Dir.
E-mail: lynner@uwmasoncounty.org; URL: http://www.uwmasoncounty.org/

Grantmaker type: Public charity.

Financial data (yr. ended 3/31/05): Revenue, $370,034; assets, $539,189 (M); gifts received, $342,603; expenditures, $417,017; total giving, $267,782; program services expenses, $296,635; giving activities include $267,782 for 18 grants (high: $46,688; low: $435).

Purpose and activities: The mission of the United Way of Mason County is to improve the lives of the people of Mason County by funding programs for: basic needs and self-sufficiency, nurturing environments for children and youth, self-sufficiency for older adults, and behavioral and physical health services.

Fields of interest: Public health; Health care; Housing/shelter, development; Youth development; Human services; Children/youth, services; Aging, centers/services; Developmentally disabled, centers & services.

Limitations: Giving limited to Mason County, MI.

Officers and Directors: * Jeff Evans, * Pres.; Barbara Costanzo, * V.P.; Russ Carroll, * Treas.; Lynne Russell, Exec. Dir.; Herb Cross; Doug Damkoehler; Nancy Houk; Debra Kinnaird; Jeanne Oakes; Bill Schoenlein; Dan Sleeman.

EIN: 382943115

2657
United Way of Midland County
220 W. Main St., Ste. 100
Midland, MI 48640 (989) 631-3670
FAX: (989) 832-5524;
E-mail: answers@unitedwaymidland.org;
URL: http://www.unitedwaymidland.org/

Grantmaker type: Public charity.

Financial data (yr. ended 12/31/05): Revenue, $5,157,115; assets, $10,299,628 (M); gifts received, $4,854,283; expenditures, $4,826,827; total giving, $3,601,892; program services

expenses, $4,368,235; giving activities include $3,580,342 for 29 grants (high: $605,000; low: $981), and $21,550 for grants to individuals.

Purpose and activities: To mobilize the caring resources of the Midland, Michigan community through leadership, collaboration, and charitable fundraising. Priority areas include strengthening families, nurturing children and youth, promoting health and healing, increasing self-sufficiency, and maximizing community impact.

Fields of interest: Youth development; Neighborhood centers; Children/youth, services; Family services; Aging, centers/services; Voluntarism promotion.

Type of support: Grants to individuals.

Limitations: Giving limited to Midland County, MI.

Officers and Directors: * Terrie Allemang, * Pres.; Jim St. Louis, * V.P.; Linda Allen, * Secy.; Brent McCumons, * Treas.; John Zimmerman, Exec. Dir.; and 17 additional directors.

EIN: 381434224

2658
United Way of Monroe County, Inc.
216 N. Monroe St.
Monroe, MI 48162-2620 (734) 242-1331
FAX: (734) 337-3378;
E-mail: uwmhoydic@monroeuw.org; Additional tel.: (734) 242-4357 (First Call for Help); URL: http://www.monroeuw.org/

Grantmaker type: Public charity.

Financial data (yr. ended 6/30/05): Revenue, $1,297,390; assets, $1,768,416 (M); gifts received, $1,211,622; expenditures, $1,417,868; total giving, $866,923; program services expenses, $1,129,961; giving activities include $851,211 for grants, and $35,712 for in-kind gifts.

Purpose and activities: The mission of the United Way of Monroe County is to provide finanical and related management support to human service organizations providing needed community services.

Fields of interest: Human services; Community development.

Limitations: Giving limited to Monroe County, MI.

Officers and Directors: * Matt Hehl, * Pres.; Jim DuBay, * 1st V.P.; Don Spencer, * 2nd V.P.; Dave Abalos, * 3rd V.P.; Tom Myers, * Treas.; Michael D. Hoydic, Exec. Dir.; Jeanine Bragg; Bob Cebina; Jeff Hensley; and 14 additional directors.

EIN: 381437937

2659
United Way of Montcalm County
P.O. Box 128
Greenville, MI 48838

Established in MI.

Grantmaker type: Public charity.

Financial data (yr. ended 3/31/04): Revenue, $235,812; assets, $194,692 (M); gifts received, $230,705; expenditures, $220,276; total giving, $131,774; program services expenses, $199,530; giving activities include $131,774 for 35 grants (high: $14,600; low: $5).

Purpose and activities: The organization seeks to provide resources that address health and human service needs in Montcalm County.

Fields of interest: Health care; Human services; Community development.

Limitations: Giving primarily in Montcalm County, MI.

Officers: Don Halst, Pres.; Lisa Lund, V.P.; Sharon McInnis, Secy.; Tom Breen, Treas.; Denise Hubbard, Exec. Dir.

EIN: 382387149

2660
United Way of Muskegon County
P.O. Box 207
Muskegon, MI 49443

Established in MI.

Grantmaker type: Public charity.

Financial data (yr. ended 12/31/04): Revenue, $2,282,467; assets, $2,886,295 (M); gifts received, $2,231,064; expenditures, $2,267,184; total giving, $1,673,780; program services expenses, $1,888,659; giving activities include $1,673,780 for grants.

Purpose and activities: The organization seeks to improve lives and change community conditions.

Fields of interest: Community development.

Limitations: Giving primarily in Muskegon County, MI.

Officers and Board Members: * Bob Scolnik, * Chair.; Mary Lou Achterhoff, * Vice-Chair.; John De Wolf, * Secy.; Dana Bryant, * Treas.; James Anthony; Mike Bozym; Vicki Broge; Laura Carpenter; Earl Geiger; Judith Hayner; and 13 additional board members.

EIN: 381426895

2661
United Way of Northeast Michigan
3022 U.S. Hwy. 23 S.
Alpena, MI 49707

Grantmaker type: Public charity.

Financial data (yr. ended 12/31/04): Revenue, $320,435; assets, $356,729 (M); gifts received, $309,890; expenditures, $323,006; total giving, $188,960; program services expenses, $260,322; giving activities include $188,960 for 21+ grants (high: $28,000).

Fields of interest: Community development.

Limitations: Giving primarily in northeastern MI.

Officers: Barbara Wilmot, Pres.; Mike Mahler, Pres.-Elect; Cindi Bauer, Secy.; Thomas Peters, Treas.

Directors: Bob Budnik; Tim Buse; Pam Dyess; William Ellingboe; Ed Klimczak; Tom Lanway; Ken Lauer; Joey Plowman; Bill Speer; Kathy Stepaniak.

EIN: 381608840

2662
United Way of Northwest Michigan
521 S. Union
Traverse City, MI 49685-0694 (231) 947-3200
Contact: Sandy Holliday, Exec. Asst.
FAX: (231) 947-3201; Application mailing address: P.O. Box 694, Traverse City, MI 49685-0694; E-mail: sandy@unitedway.tcnet.org; URL: http://www.unitedway.tcnet.org/

Grantmaker type: Public charity.

Financial data (yr. ended 3/31/05): Revenue, $1,175,410; assets, $1,326,069 (M); gifts received, $1,147,904; expenditures, $1,238,874; total giving, $626,116; program services expenses,

$1,041,965; giving activities include $626,116 for grants (high: $104,718).
Purpose and activities: To improve the lives of community members by making value-added grants in the areas of youth development, human services, and health.
Fields of interest: Elementary/secondary education; Public health; Health care; Youth development; Human services; Homeless, human services.
Limitations: Giving limited to Antrim, Kalkaska, Grand Traverse and Leelanau counties, MI.
Application information: Requests for proposals are issued each fall and can be downloaded from Web site. Application form required.
   Deadline(s): Mid-Jan.
   Final notification: Late Mar.
Officers and Directors:* Mary Marois,* Pres.; Chet Janik,* V.P.; Bruce Reavely,* Secy.; Jim Lievense,* Treas.; Becky Beauchamp, Exec. Dir.; Mike Hill; Amy Johnson; Doug Luciani; Peter Marinoff; Patty Maxbauer; Jayne Mohr; Jim Pavelka; Pamela Prairie.
EIN: 381679060

2663
United Way of Saginaw County
100 S. Jefferson Ave.
Saginaw, MI   48607   (989) 755-0505
E-mail: info@unitedwaysaginaw.org; URL: http://www.unitedwaysaginaw.org

Grantmaker type: Public charity.
Financial data (yr. ended 12/31/03): Revenue, $2,577,143; assets, $4,941,126 (M); gifts received, $2,487,490; expenditures, $2,955,760; total giving, $2,000,115; program services expenses, $2,532,443; giving activities include $2,000,115 for 28 grants (high: $240,674; low: $3,469).
Purpose and activities: The organization seeks to promote volunteerism and raise funds to address important health and human service issues.
Fields of interest: Health care; Human services; Voluntarism promotion.
Limitations: Giving primarily in Saginaw County, MI.
Officer: Cherrie Benchley, Interim Pres. and C.E.O.
EIN: 381358215

2664
United Way of Sanilac County, Inc.
P.O. Box 245
Lexington, MI   48450

Grantmaker type: Public charity.
Financial data (yr. ended 12/31/04): Revenue, $179,568; assets, $129,148 (M); gifts received, $179,933; expenditures, $176,505; total giving, $122,211; program services expenses, $145,231; giving activities include $122,211 for grants.
Fields of interest: Community development.
Officers and Directors:* Virgil Strickler,* Pres.; Tony Parker,* V.P.; Julie Crowell,* Secy.; Jean Morgan,* Treas.; Stuart Armstead; Wayne Bank; Arthur Birdsall; Jim Beyer; Dennis Cargill; and 16 additional directors.
EIN: 237123395

2665
United Way of Southwest Michigan
185 E. Main St., Ste. 601
P.O. Box 807
Benton Harbor, MI   49023   (269) 925-7772
FAX: (269) 925-1590; E-mail: info@uwsm.org; URL: http://www.uwsm.org

Established in MI.
Grantmaker type: Public charity.
Financial data (yr. ended 12/31/04): Revenue, $2,760,495; assets, $3,591,890 (M); gifts received, $2,719,840; expenditures, $2,588,297; total giving, $1,900,333; program services expenses, $2,204,097; giving activities include $1,900,333 for 22 grants (high: $462,527; low: $3,667).
Purpose and activities: The organization seeks to improve lives and build stronger communities.
Fields of interest: Community development.
Limitations: Giving primarily in southwestern MI.
Application information: Application form required.
   Initial approach: Download application form
   Deadline(s): Mar. 15 for Community Investment Grants; July 24 for Flexi-Fund Grants
Officers and Directors:* Emil Gallay,* Chair.; Martin Golob, Exec. Dir.; Robert Harrison; John Holmes; Tim Mackay; Deb Milkowski; Rev. Dan Miller; Don Raddler; Ken Rollins; and 24 additional directors.
EIN: 381358411

2666
United Way of St. Clair County
1723 Military St.
Port Huron, MI   48060   (810) 985-8169
FAX: (810) 982-7202; URL: http://www.uwsccmi.org

Grantmaker type: Public charity.
Financial data (yr. ended 3/31/05): Revenue, $1,846,492; assets, $2,912,705 (M); gifts received, $1,815,890; expenditures, $1,584,409; total giving, $1,087,579; program services expenses, $1,323,536; giving activities include $1,087,579 for grants (high: $168,493).
Purpose and activities: The mission of the United Way of St. Clair County is to mobilize the community and to raise funds and/or resources to meet identified human service needs with the highest level of accountability and community involvement.
Fields of interest: Health care; Crime/violence prevention, abuse prevention; Employment; Youth development; Human services; Human services, emergency aid; Community development; Disabilities, people with; Economically disadvantaged; Homeless.
Limitations: Giving limited to St. Clair County, MI.
Officers and Directors:* Dennis Guiser,* Pres.; Chuck Wanninger,* V.P.; Cynthia Lane,* Secy.; Steve Warsinske,* Treas.; Roy Klecha,* Vice-Treas.; Lonnie Stevens, Exec. Dir.; Rose Bellanca; Mary Berckley; Dan DeGrow; and 15 additional directors.
EIN: 381357996

2667
United Way of Tuscola County
P.O. Box 505
Caro, MI   48723

Established in MI.

Grantmaker type: Public charity.
Financial data (yr. ended 12/31/04): Revenue, $68,774; assets, $29,669 (M); gifts received, $68,647; expenditures, $80,478; total giving, $71,363; program services expenses, $71,363; giving activities include $71,363 for 30 grants (high: $5,000; low: $65).
Fields of interest: Community development.
Limitations: Giving primarily in Tuscola County, MI.
Officers: Raymond Bates, Pres.; Jim Heiser, V.P.; Michele Hill, Secy.; Jim Walker, Treas.
EIN: 383004648

2668
United Way of Wexford County
117 W. Cass St.
P.O. Box 177
Cadillac, MI   49601   (231) 775-3753
FAX: (231) 775-0169;
E-mail: info@unitedwaywexford.org; URL: http://www.unitedwaywexford.org/

Grantmaker type: Public charity.
Financial data (yr. ended 3/31/05): Revenue, $298,675; assets, $364,251 (M); gifts received, $291,996; expenditures, $307,279; total giving, $223,700; program services expenses, $264,386; giving activities include $223,700 for 17 grants (high: $47,000; low: $3,000).
Purpose and activities: The United Way of Wexford County is committed to building a better community by meeting critical needs, and working to achieve community solutions. It supports over 26 direct local health and human service programs, and a variety of emerging needs through Community Response Grants.
Fields of interest: Public health; Health care; Housing/shelter; Youth development; Children/youth, services; Family services.
Limitations: Giving limited to Wexford County, MI.
Application information: See Web site for application guidelines and requirements, including downloadable forms and checklists. Application form required.
Officers and Directors:* John MacLeod,* Pres.; Paul Liabenow,* 1st V.P.; Van Eldridge,* 2nd V.P.; Melody Hurley,* Secy.; Tim McNalley,* Treas.; Diane Dykstra,* Exec. Dir.; Todd Bennington; Mary Jo Binkley; Jim Blackburn; and 11 additional directors.
EIN: 237112549

2669
Millie K. Upjohn & Mary S. Kirby Memorial Trust
c/o National City Bank
108 E. Michigan Ave.
Kalamazoo, MI   49007-3931

Established in 1945; supporting organization of Kalamazoo Community Foundation, MI.
Grantmaker type: Public charity.
Financial data (yr. ended 12/31/04): Revenue, $15,234; assets, $449,195 (M); expenditures, $11,720; total giving, $10,501; program services expenses, $10,501; giving activities include $10,501 for 1 grant.
Fields of interest: Foundations (community).
Limitations: Applications not accepted. Giving limited to Kalamazoo, MI.

Application information: Contributes only to a pre-selected organization; unsolicited requests for funds not considered or acknowledged.
Trustee: National City Bank.
EIN: 386065409

2670
W. E. Upjohn Unemployment Trustee Corporation
300 S. Westnedge Ave.
Kalamazoo, MI 49007 (269) 343-5541
FAX: (269) 343-3308;
E-mail: webmaster@upjohninstitute.org;
URL: http://www.upjohninstitute.org

Incorporated in 1932 in MI.
Donor: W.E. Upjohn†.
Grantmaker type: Public charity.
Financial data (yr. ended 12/31/05): Revenue, $16,460,232; assets, $145,941,868 (M); gifts received, $6,392,496; expenditures, $11,863,958; total giving, $5,958,079; program services expenses, $10,233,618; giving activities include $112,541 for grants, and $5,845,538 for grants to individuals.
Purpose and activities: The organization supports research into the causes, effects, prevention, and alleviation of unemployment, and provides funding to support W.E. Upjohn Institute for Employment Research.
Fields of interest: Employment; Economics.
Type of support: Research; Grants to individuals.
Limitations: Giving on a national basis. No grants for building/renovation, endowment funds, operating budgets, scholarships, or matching gifts; no loans.
Publications: Application guidelines; Program policy statement.
Application information: Submissions via fax or e-mail are not accepted; See Web site for additional application information. Application form not required.
Initial approach: Proposal
Copies of proposal: 8
Deadline(s): July 7 for Dissertation Awards
Board meeting date(s): May, Oct. and Dec.
Final notification: 90 days
Officers and Trustees:* Preston Parish,* Chair.; Donald R. Parfet,* Vice-Chair.; Marilyn J. Schlack,* Secy.-Treas.; Randall W. Eberts, Exec. Dir.; James F. Jones, Jr.; Thomas W. Lambert; William C. Richardson; Paul H. Todd; Amanda Van Dusen; B. Joseph White.
Number of staff: 24 full-time professional; 6 part-time professional; 12 full-time support; 14 part-time support.
EIN: 381360419

2671
Van Buren County United Way
181 W. Michigan Ave., Ste. 4
Paw Paw, MI 49079

Established in MI.
Grantmaker type: Public charity.
Financial data (yr. ended 12/31/04): Revenue, $445,143; assets, $190,340 (M); gifts received, $444,033; expenditures, $386,157; total giving, $320,233; program services expenses, $320,315; giving activities include $320,233 for grants.

Fields of interest: Human services; Community development.
Limitations: Giving primarily in Van Buren, MI.
Board Members: Jalayne Bennett; Cathy Cowles; Laura Crouse; Maria Diaz; Leanne Fader; Douglas Fuller; Jeffrey Johnson; Steve Owens; Char Tomczak; Susan Woodruff.
EIN: 237113927

2672
Peter Van Haften Charitable Trust
c/o Comerica Bank
151 S. Rose St.
Kalamazoo, MI 49007

Established in MI; a supporting organization of American Cancer Society, Michigan Division and American Diabetes Association, Michigan Affilate.
Grantmaker type: Public charity.
Financial data (yr. ended 5/31/05): Revenue, $22,242; assets, $323,000 (M); expenditures, $11,789; total giving, $6,406; program services expenses, $6,406; giving activities include $6,406 for 2 grants (high: $3,203; low: $3,203).
Purpose and activities: Giving limited to American Cancer Society and American Diabetes Association.
Fields of interest: Cancer; Diabetes.
Limitations: Giving limited to MI.
Trustee: Comerica Bank.
EIN: 386527243

2673
Peter Van Haften Trust
c/o Comerica Bank
151 S. Rose St.
Kalamazoo, MI 49007

Established in 1989; supporting organization of the Kalamazoo Community Foundation, MI.
Grantmaker type: Public charity.
Financial data (yr. ended 5/31/05): Revenue, $26,358; assets, $410,036 (M); expenditures, $9,312; total giving, $4,686; program services expenses, $4,686; giving activities include $4,686 for 1 grant.
Fields of interest: Foundations (community).
Limitations: Applications not accepted. Giving limited to Kalamazoo, MI. No grants to individuals.
Application information: Contributes only to a pre-selected organization; unsolicited requests for funds not considered or acknowledged.
Trustee: Comerica Bank.
EIN: 382870344

2674
The Village Woman's Club Foundation
190 E. Long Lake Rd.
Bloomfield Hills, MI 48304-2325
(248) 644-3450
Contact: Joan Keller, Pres.
FAX: (248) 644-7308; URL: http://www.thevillageclub.org/foundation.htm

Established in 1956.
Donor: Members of the Village Club.
Grantmaker type: Public charity.
Financial data (yr. ended 4/30/05): Revenue, $130,432; assets, $1,694,971 (M); gifts received, $78,250; expenditures, $93,859; total giving, $75,000; program services expenses, $75,000;

giving activities include $75,000 for 43 grants (high: $4,000; low: $300).
Purpose and activities: The foundation promotes philanthropic projects in the form of grants which further educational, cultural and human services in Oakland, Wayne and Macomb counties, MI.
Fields of interest: Children/youth, services; Family services; Human services; Women; Economically disadvantaged.
Type of support: General/operating support; Equipment; Program development.
Limitations: Giving limited to Oakland, Wayne, and Macomb counties, MI. No support for private foundations. No grants to individuals, or for medical research, scholarship funds, or emergency appeals.
Application information: See Web site for additional application guidelines. Application form required.
Initial approach: Letter requesting application and guidelines
Copies of proposal: 2
Deadline(s): Aug. 1
Final notification: Apr.
Officers and Trustees:* Joan Keller,* Pres.; Karen Heiwig,* V.P.; Patricia Wasson,* Secy.; Jayne M. Zellers,* Treas.; Mary Callam*; Sarah Kerr; Catherine White Meyer; Martha Torre; Linda Wilson.
EIN: 381690100

2675
John D. Voelker Foundation
P.O. Box 15222
Lansing, MI 48901-5222 (616) 897-4036
E-mail: rvanderveen@voelkerfdn.org; URL: http://www.voelkerfdn.org

Established in 1999 in MI.
Grantmaker type: Public charity.
Financial data (yr. ended 12/31/04): Revenue, $8,189; assets, $31,377 (M); gifts received, $6,167; expenditures, $12,295; total giving, $10,000; giving activities include $10,000 for 5 grants to individuals (high: $4,000; low: $1,000).
Fields of interest: Law school/education; Athletics/sports, fishing/hunting; Native Americans/American Indians.
Type of support: Grants to individuals; Scholarships —to individuals.
Limitations: Giving limited to Native American members of a federally recognized MI or WI tribe.
Application information: Letters of reference from teachers or employers, transcripts, and documentation confirming tribal membership are encouraged for scholarship applications. See Web site for additional application information.
Initial approach: Letter
Officers and Directors:* Richard F. Vander Veen III, Pres.; James F. Graves,* V.P.; Frederick M. Baker, Jr.,* Secy.-Treas.; Walter Abbott; Nick Lyons Adam; John W. Cummiskey; John Frey; Anthony Gagliardi; George Hyde III; John Voelker Overturf; Adam John Tsaloff; Grace Voelker Wood.
EIN: 382913091

2676
VSA arts of Michigan
100 W. Alexandrine
P.O. Box 02805
Detroit, MI 48202-2805 (313) 832-3303
FAX: (313) 832-3387; E-mail: info@vsami.org;
URL: http://www.vsami.org

Established in 1977 in MI.

Grantmaker type: Public charity.

Financial data (yr. ended 6/30/05): Revenue, $410,661; assets, $77,080 (M); gifts received, $407,284; expenditures, $389,241; program services expenses, $348,187.

Purpose and activities: The organization assists in the promotion and advancement of training and education in the arts for disabled individuals.

Fields of interest: Arts; Disabilities, people with.

Limitations: Giving primarily in MI.

Publications: Newsletter.

Officers: Diane L. McCall, Pres.; Christine M. Clinton-Cali, Pres.-Elect; Kathyrn Travnikar, Secy.; Randy McNeil, Treas.; Lora Frankel, Exec. Dir.

Board Members: Paul Batty; Ed Cheeney; Jan Cheeney; Diane Conklin; Jim Edwards; Dale Hull; Marie Louise Lannen; Marcia Lowe; Terry Monkaba; Judy Purdy; Larry Simpson.

Advisory Council: Julie A. Avery, Ph.D.; John T. Baron, C.P.A.; Sesta Peekstok, Ph.D.

EIN: 382690117

2677
Walther Cancer Institute and Foundation, Inc.

3202 N. Meridian St.
Indianapolis, IN   46208-4646   (317) 921-2040
Contact: Fred Haslam, Exec. V.P.
FAX: (317) 924-4688; E-mail: fhaslam@walther.org;
URL: http://www.walther.org
For fellowships: Peggy Weber, Dir. of Prog. Devel., Tel.: (317) 274-7563, E-mail: bcog@walther.org

Established in 1985 in IN.

Grantmaker type: Public charity.

Financial data (yr. ended 6/30/05): Revenue, $5,454,443; assets, $54,754,154 (M); gifts received, $1,514,959; expenditures, $4,946,422; total giving, $3,179,147; program services expenses, $3,227,906; giving activities include $3,015,097 for 1 grant, and $164,050 for 16 grants to individuals (high: $30,000; low: $750).

Purpose and activities: The foundation primarily supports the Walther Cancer Institute, Inc. in addition to providing scholarships and awards to individuals. The institute conducts basic laboratory, clinical and behavioral cancer research at affiliated academic institutions: Indiana University, Purdue University, University of Notre Dame, University of Michigan, Michigan State University, Ohio State University, Duke University, and University of California, San Diego.

Fields of interest: Cancer research.

Type of support: Program development; Seed money; Research; Scholarships—to individuals.

Limitations: Applications not accepted. Giving limited to affiliated institutions in IN, MI, OH, NC, and CA. No grants for building, renovation and research.

Publications: Annual report; Newsletter; Program policy statement.

Application information:
  Board meeting date(s): Feb. 1, May 26, and Aug. 2

Officers and Directors: * Donald C. Danielson,* Chair.; Leonard Betley,* Pres. and C.E.O.; Fred Haslam,* Exec. V.P.; Mary Beth Gradus,* V.P.; Sara Slipher,* V.P.; Stephen C. Gaerte, C.P.A.*, Secy.-Treas.; and 2 additional directors.

EIN: 351650570

2678
Washtenaw United Way

2305 Platt Rd.
Ann Arbor, MI   48104   (734) 971-8200
FAX: (734) 971-6230; URL: http://www.wuway.org/

Established in 1971 in MI.

Grantmaker type: Public charity.

Financial data (yr. ended 6/30/05): Revenue, $8,045,302; assets, $11,235,452 (M); gifts received, $7,773,155; expenditures, $7,789,058; total giving, $6,157,366; program services expenses, $6,633,741; giving activities include $6,157,366 for grants.

Purpose and activities: The mission of Washtenaw United Way is to generate and allocate resources to help individuals and families build better lives and stronger communities.

Fields of interest: Health care; Human services; Community development.

Limitations: Giving limited to Washtenaw County, MI.

Officers and Directors: * Daniel Foss,* Chair.; Robert Chapman,* Chair.-Elect; John Eman,* Interim Pres.; Carl Martin,* Secy.; Brian Miller,* Treas.; and 24 additional directors.

EIN: 381951024

2679
Waterford Foundation for Public Education

P.O. Box 300681
Waterford, MI   48330-0681
Contact: Mary Lou Simmons, Pres.
URL: http://www.waterford.k12.mi.us/foundation/

Established in 1984.

Grantmaker type: Public charity.

Financial data (yr. ended 6/30/05): Revenue, $203,951; assets, $1,001,858 (M); gifts received, $11,250; expenditures, $125,359; total giving, $55,613; program services expenses, $117,752; giving activities include $48,113 for grants, and $7,500 for 3 grants to individuals (high: $2,500; low: $2,500).

Purpose and activities: The foundation seeks to support schools and education programs within the local school district.

Fields of interest: Elementary/secondary education.

Type of support: Program development; Annual campaigns; Curriculum development; Grants to individuals; Scholarships—to individuals.

Limitations: Applications not accepted. Giving limited to the Waterford, MI, area. No support for salaries.

Publications: Annual report; Financial statement.

Application information:
  Board meeting date(s): Monthly

Officers and Directors: * Mary Lou Simmons,* Pres.; Richard Anderson,* V.P.; Ruth Schluchter,* Rec. Secy.; Heather Coats,* Corresp. Secy.; Margie Gobler,* Treas.; Lynn Anselmi; Ron Arnold; Donald Arsen; Paul Coughlin; Kim Erznoznik; Henry George; Kris Kuhn; Tim Patterson.

EIN: 382528009

2680
Waverly Education Foundation

1018 Powderhorn Dr.
Lansing, MI   48917   (517) 886-4265
Contact: Janice Cunningham, Tr.

Application address: c/o Grant Comm., P.O. Box 80353, Lansing, MI 48908-0353, tel.: (517) 482-0222

Established in 1993 in MI.

Grantmaker type: Public charity.

Financial data (yr. ended 6/30/05): Revenue, $45,880; assets, $240,775 (M); gifts received, $24,891; expenditures, $37,952; total giving, $25,186; program services expenses, $25,808; giving activities include $25,186 for 1 grant.

Purpose and activities: Support for school programs within the Waverly school district.

Fields of interest: Elementary/secondary education.

Limitations: Giving limited to the Waverly School District, MI.

Application information: Application form required.
  Deadline(s): Last Fri. in Feb. and Sept.
  Board meeting date(s): 8 times annually; board meets on grant funding Apr. and Nov.

Officers and Trustees: * Steve Slater,* Pres.; Randall Roost,* V.P.; Cindy Bowen,* Secy.; Arnold Weinfeld,* Treas.; Susan Steiner Bolhouse; Cheval Breggins; Janice Cunningham; Mike Curley; Robert Forgrave; Calvin Jones; Tom Klein; Holly LaPratt; Will Mahoney; and 5 additional trustees.

EIN: 383190405

2681
Wayne County Medical Society Foundation

(formerly Metropolitan Detroit Foundation for Health Education)
3031 W. Grand Blvd., Ste. 645
Detroit, MI   48202   (313) 874-1360
FAX: (313) 874-1366; E-mail: wcms1@msms.org;
URL: http://www.wcmssm.org//p_foundation.htm

Established in 1987 in MI; supporting organization of Wayne County Medical Society.

Grantmaker type: Public charity.

Financial data (yr. ended 12/31/04): Revenue, $130,698; assets, $248,382 (M); gifts received, $124,202; expenditures, $78,333; total giving, $24,000; program services expenses, $60,527; giving activities include $24,000 for 1 grant.

Fields of interest: Health organizations, single organization support.

Limitations: Applications not accepted. Giving limited to Detroit, MI.

Application information: Contributes only to a pre-selected organization; unsolicited requests for funds not considered or acknowledged.

Officers and Directors: * Joseph M. Beals, M.D.*, Chair.; James P. Gallagher, M.D.*, Vice-Chair.; Janet T. Bush,* Secy.; Lourdes V. Andaya, M.D.*, Treas.; Adam R. Jablonowski, M.P.A., Exec. Dir.; Rosemary Bannon; Edward C. Bush, M.D.; Ned I. Chalat, M.D.; Ronald M. Davis, M.D.; and 5 additional directors.

EIN: 382768088

2682
Wayne Rotary Foundation

3024 S. Wayne Rd.
Wayne, MI   48184

Grantmaker type: Public charity.

Financial data (yr. ended 6/30/05): Revenue, $47,484; assets, $761,158 (M); gifts received, $31,654; expenditures, $37,396; total giving,

$31,633; giving activities include $31,633 for 20 grants (high: $7,000; low: $100).
Fields of interest: Youth development; Community development.
Limitations: Giving primarily in the Wayne, MI, area.
Officers and Trustees:* John Van Stipoonk,* Chair.; G. Steinhauer, Secy.; David Carpenter, Treas.; Robert McLellan; Patricia Rice; Lois Van Stipoonk; David Willett.
EIN: 386091615

2683
Chris Webber Foundation, Inc.
(doing business as The Chris Webber Foundation Southeast Michigan)
16250 Northland Dr., Ste. 239
Southfield, MI 48075   (248) 423-3970

Established in 1994.
Donor: Chris Webber.
Grantmaker type: Public charity.
Financial data (yr. ended 6/30/05): Revenue, $56,742; assets, $11,408 (M); gifts received, $56,705; expenditures, $51,244; total giving, $47,699; program services expenses, $47,699; giving activities include $47,699 for grants.
Purpose and activities: To provide positive educational and recreational opportunities to youth, particularly those who are disadvantaged. Funds are used to purchase: tickets to Sacramento Kings home games for youth, community groups and individuals in need; books for disadvantaged children to encourage literacy; and toys, clothing, books, educational materials and food for youth, individuals in need, and church and community groups.
Fields of interest: Education, reading; Athletics/sports, basketball; Children/youth, services; Family services; Children/youth; Economically disadvantaged.
Limitations: Giving on a national basis.
Officers and Directors:* Mayce Webber, Sr.,* Pres.; Marquita Davis,* V.P.; Doris Webber,* Secy.; Rebecca Davis; Kurt Keener; Dennis Talbert; Amyre Porter-Makupson; Mayce Webber.
EIN: 383122548

2684
Nathan Weidner Memorial Foundation
1392 S. Valley Center Dr.
Bay City, MI 48706

Grantmaker type: Public charity.
Financial data (yr. ended 12/31/04): Revenue, $105,190; assets, $28,005 (M); gifts received, $72,787; expenditures, $28,631; total giving, $28,005; program services expenses, $28,005; giving activities include $6,000 for 1 grant, and $22,005 for 13 grants to individuals (high: $3,084; low: $587).
Purpose and activities: The foundation aids and assists in charitable and educational activities for the mental, moral, intellectual, and physical development of young men and women of Bay County.
Fields of interest: Education.
Type of support: Scholarships—to individuals.
Limitations: Giving limited to Bay County, MI.
Officers and Board Members:* Gavin Goetz,* Pres.; Pat Hubert,* V.P.; Ann Weidner,* Secy.; Jack Weidner,* Treas.; Glenn Eyre; JoAnn Kuhn; Sandy

Meyer; Barbara Powers; Hon. Ken Schmidt; Mark Weidner; Matt Weidner.
EIN: 383262641

2685
Robert J. Whaley Trust
c/o The Rector St. Paul's Episcopal Church
711 S. Saginaw St.
Flint, MI 48502

Established in 1999 in MI; status changed to a public charity in 2003; supporting organization of Donald Whaley Children's Center.
Grantmaker type: Public charity.
Financial data (yr. ended 6/30/05): Revenue, $91,620; assets, $1,121,434 (M); gifts received, $7,376; expenditures, $47,334; total giving, $36,378; program services expenses, $36,378; giving activities include $36,378 for 1 grant.
Fields of interest: Children/youth, services.
Limitations: Applications not accepted. Giving limited to Flint, MI. No grants to individuals.
Application information: Contributes only to a pre-selected organization specified in the governing instrument.
Trustees: John Anderson; Melinda Bass; G. Andrew Dill; Danny C. Grier; Ferrell Katzenberger; Marsha Kump; David A. Michael; Ann Marie Van Duyne; and 4 additional trustees.
EIN: 386758742

2686
Whitney Fund
(formerly Grayling Fund)
333 W. Fort St., Rm. 2010
Detroit, MI 48226
Contact: Peter P. Thurber, Pres.
Additional address: 150 W. Jefferson, Ste. 2500, Detroit, MI 48226-4415

Incorporated in 1935 in MI; supporting organization of the Community Foundation for Southeastern Michigan.
Donors: Katherine Tuck†; The David M. Whitney Fund.
Grantmaker type: Public charity.
Financial data (yr. ended 12/31/04): Revenue, $3,968,090; assets, $49,277,850 (M); expenditures, $1,800,319; total giving, $1,393,000; program services expenses, $1,610,983; giving activities include $1,393,000 for 30 grants (high: $250,000; low: $5,000).
Purpose and activities: The organization is an affiliated foundation of the Community Foundation for Southeastern Michigan that supports arts and cultural organizations, including the fine and performing arts, museums, libraries, zoos, parks, and recreational organizations; educational programs and projects; and projects that serve children and youth, including programs that focus on early childhood development and family life.
Fields of interest: Visual arts; Museums; Performing arts; Performing arts, theater; Performing arts, music; Arts; Libraries (public); Education; Zoos/zoological societies; Human services; Youth, services; Child development, services.
Type of support: Technical assistance; Seed money; Program development; General/operating support.
Limitations: Giving limited for the benefit of southeast MI: Wayne, Oakland, Macomb, Monroe, Washtenaw, St. Clair, and Livingston counties. No

support for sectarian religious programs. No grants to individuals, or for general operating support, buildings and equipment, fundraising campaigns, conferences, or endowments.
Application information: Applicants are encouraged to contact the fund before preparing an application. Application form not required.
  Initial approach: Proposal
  Copies of proposal: 1
  Deadline(s): Mar. 1, June 1, and Sept. 1
  Board meeting date(s): 3 times a year
  Final notification: Grant decisions announced in June, Sept., and Dec.
Officers and Trustees:* Peter P. Thurber,* Pres.; Joseph L. Hudson, Jr.,* V.P.; Mariam C. Noland, Secy.-Treas.; Richard B. Gushee; William K. Howenstein; Michael A. Indenbaum; Barbara C. Van Dusen; Jonathan T. Walton.
EIN: 386040079

2687
George & Emily Harris Willard Trust
3 W. Vanburen St.
Battle Creek, MI 49017-3009

Established in 1939.
Grantmaker type: Public charity.
Financial data (yr. ended 6/30/05): Revenue, $24,431; assets, $918,090 (M); expenditures, $39,225; total giving, $39,225; program services expenses, $39,225; giving activities include $39,225 for grants to individuals.
Purpose and activities: The trust seeks to provide care for under-privileged children residing within the city of Battle Creek attending the public schools therein.
Fields of interest: Education.
Type of support: Grants to individuals; Scholarships—to individuals.
Limitations: Giving limited to residents of Battle Creek, MI.
Trustee: School District/City of Battle Creek.
EIN: 386053144

2688
Women's Initiative
c/o Community Foundation of St. Clair County
516 McMorran Blvd.
Port Huron, MI 48060   (810) 984-4761
FAX: (810) 984-3394;
E-mail: info@stclairfoundation.org; URL: http://www.stclairfoundation.org/cgi-bin/content/content.cgi?db=funds&uid=default&ww=on&id=105&view_records=1

Component fund of the Community Foundation of St. Clair County.
Grantmaker type: Public charity.
Financial data (yr. ended 12/31/05): Gifts received, $60,966; total giving, $17,928; giving activities include $17,928 for grants to individuals.
Purpose and activities: The initiative seeks to provide women an excellent opportunity to pool their resources and help others on a larger scale by creating a bridge between those who want to help and those that need help.
Fields of interest: Dental care; Women.
Type of support: Grants to individuals.
Limitations: Giving primarily in St. Clair County, MI.

2689
Worldwide Christian Schools
1009 44th St. S.W., Ste. A2
Grand Rapids, MI 49509-4480 (616) 531-9102
Contact: Scott Vander Kooy, Pres.
FAX: (616) 531-0602; E-mail: info@wwcs.org;
Toll-free tel.: (800) 886-9000; URL: http://
www.wwcs.org

Established in 1987 in MI.
Grantmaker type: Public charity.
Financial data (yr. ended 6/30/05): Revenue,
$1,733,360; assets, $1,745,282 (M); gifts
received, $1,529,104; expenditures, $1,936,081;
total giving, $1,264,066; program services
expenses, $1,527,386; giving activities include
$1,264,066 for grants.
Purpose and activities: The organization provides
funding to churches and other stable, accountable
nonprofits to build schools in developing countries.
Support is provided only for Christian
education-related projects and programs. The
organization is primarily focused on economically
disadvantaged children who have limited opportunity
for education.
Fields of interest: Teacher school/education;
Education; Children, services; Christian agencies &
churches.
International interests: Developing countries.
Type of support: Building/renovation; Equipment;
Program development; Conferences/seminars;
Curriculum development; Scholarship funds;
Consulting services; Program evaluation.
Limitations: Giving on an international basis. No
support for political organizations.
Publications: Application guidelines; Informational
brochure (including application guidelines);
Newsletter; Occasional report; Program policy
statement.
Application information: Application form required.
  Initial approach: Letter
  Copies of proposal: 1
  Deadline(s): None
  Board meeting date(s): 4th Thurs. of every other
  month
Officers and Directors:* Gloria Stronks, Ph.D.*,
Chair.; Melvin Busscher,* Vice-Chair.; Scott
VanderKooy,* Pres.; Ken Van Den Bosch,* Treas.;
Russell Bloem; Jeni Hoekstra; Robert Jonker.
Number of staff: 8 full-time professional; 1 part-time
professional; 1 full-time support.
EIN: 382693388

2690
Coleman A. Young Foundation
2111 Woodward Ave., Ste. 600
Detroit, MI 48201 (313) 962-2200
Contact: Claudette Y. Smith Ph.D., Exec. Dir.

FAX: (313) 962-2208;
E-mail: claudettesmith@cayf.org; URL: http://
www.cayf.org

Established in 1986.
Donor: National City Bank.
Grantmaker type: Public charity.
Financial data (yr. ended 12/31/04): Revenue,
$581,434; assets, $2,201,719 (M); gifts received,
$414,242; expenditures, $614,738; total giving,
$174,274; program services expenses, $531,895;
giving activities include $174,274 for 38 grants to
individuals (high: $5,000; low: $4,000).
Purpose and activities: The foundation provides
scholarships to high school students for higher
education.
Fields of interest: Higher education.
Type of support: Scholarships—to individuals.
Limitations: Giving primarily in Detroit, MI.
Publications: Application guidelines; Annual report;
Financial statement; Informational brochure
(including application guidelines); Newsletter.
Application information: See Web site for further
application information. Application form required.
  Deadline(s): Apr. 1
  Board meeting date(s): Quarterly
Officers and Trustees:* David Baker Lewis,* Pres.;
Garry G. Carley,* V.P.; Fred Martin,* Secy.; Darrell
Burks,* Treas.; Claudette Y. Smith, Ph.D., Exec.
Dir.; Don Barden; Patti Bell; and 15 additional
trustees.
Number of staff: 3 full-time professional; 1 part-time
professional.
EIN: 382400801

OPERATING FOUNDATIONS

2691
A.I.R. Foundation
3181 Packard Rd.
Ann Arbor, MI   48108

Established in MI.
Donors: George H. Muller; Brigitte D. Muller.
Grantmaker type: Operating foundation.
Financial data (yr. ended 12/31/05): Assets,
$229,186 (M); gifts received, $12,211;
expenditures, $15,173; total giving, $0; qualifying
distributions, $0.
Officers: George H. Muller, Pres.; Frank G. Muller,
V.P. and Treas.; Brigitte D. Muller, V.P.
Trustees: Christine B. Ballard; Phillip G. Muller,
Ph.D.
EIN: 386120750

2692
Accelerated Learning Foundation
5353 Red Fox Run
Ann Arbor, MI   48105   (734) 764-9339
Contact: Layman E. Allen, Pres.
E-mail: msq@alf-learning.org; URL: http://
www.alf-learning.org/

Established in 1998 in MI.
Donors: Layman E. Allen; Detroit Mercy University.
Grantmaker type: Operating foundation.
Financial data (yr. ended 12/31/04): Assets,
$437,231 (M); gifts received, $36,700;
expenditures, $55,508; total giving, $11,550;
qualifying distributions, $32,199; giving activities
include $5,000 for 1 grant, and $6,550 for 4 grants
to individuals (high: $6,000; low: $50).
Purpose and activities: Giving primarily for
scholarship awards to high school seniors who are
both eligible for the National Academic Games and
are recommended by their coaches as outstanding.
Fields of interest: Higher education.
Type of support: Scholarships—to individuals.
Application information: Application form not
required.
   Deadline(s): Prior to annual tournament
Officers: Layman E. Allen, Pres.; Patricia R. Allen,
Secy.; Layman G. Allen, Treas.
EIN: 383423350

2693
The AFR Foundation
26300 Telegraph Rd., 2nd Fl.
Southfield, MI   48034

Established in 1994 in MI.
Grantmaker type: Operating foundation.
Financial data (yr. ended 12/31/04): Assets,
$97,811 (M); gifts received, $220,000;
expenditures, $200,321; total giving, $197,775;
qualifying distributions, $197,775; giving activities
include $197,775 for 6+ grants (high: $60,000).
Fields of interest: Higher education; Federated
giving programs; Islam.
Limitations: Giving primarily in MI. No grants to
individuals.

Officers: Mostafa M. Afr, Pres.; Zeinab Afr, V.P.;
Tamer Afr, Treas.
EIN: 383123848

2694
Akbar Waqf Foundation, Inc.
(formerly Aye-You Charitable Foundation, Inc.)
4701 Towne Centre, Ste. 303
Saginaw, MI   48604
Contact: Waheed Akbar, Dir.
Application address: 580 Golf View, Saginaw, MI
48603, tel.: (989) 790-6719

Established in 1994 in MI.
Donor: Waheed Akbar.
Grantmaker type: Operating foundation.
Financial data (yr. ended 12/31/05): Assets, $0
(M); gifts received, $62,500; expenditures,
$55,587; total giving, $54,340; qualifying
distributions, $54,340; giving activities include
$54,340 for grants.
Purpose and activities: Giving primarily to an
affiliated foundation in Pakistan; also gives for
Islamic organizations and human rights.
Fields of interest: Education; International human
rights; Community development; Islam.
International interests: Pakistan.
Limitations: Giving on a national and international
basis.
Application information: Application form not
required.
   Initial approach: Letter
   Deadline(s): None
Directors: Raana Akbar, M.D.; Waheed Akbar.
EIN: 363917606

2695
Jerome S. Amber Foundation, Inc.
1610 Hanley Ct.
Birmingham, MI   48009

Established in 2004.
Grantmaker type: Operating foundation.
Financial data (yr. ended 12/31/04): Assets,
$5,000 (M); gifts received, $5,000; expenditures,
$0; total giving, $0; qualifying distributions, $0.
Officer: Jerome S. Amber, Pres.
EIN: 200809177

2696
Amway Environmental Foundation
2905 Lucerne Dr. S.E.
Grand Rapids, MI   49546

Established as a company-sponsored operating
foundation in 1989 in MI.
Donors: Amway Corp.; Alticor Inc.
Grantmaker type: Operating foundation.
Financial data (yr. ended 8/31/04): Assets,
$1,914 (M); gifts received, $36,000; expenditures,
$156,427; total giving, $150,000; qualifying
distributions, $154,666; giving activities include

$150,000 for 1 grant, and $4,666 for
foundation-administered programs.
Purpose and activities: The foundation supports the
Grand Action Convention Center.
Fields of interest: Arts.
Limitations: Applications not accepted. Giving
limited to Grand Rapids, MI. No grants to individuals.
Application information: Contributes only to
pre-selected organizations.
Officers and Directors:* Mark O. Bain,* Pres.;
William G. Roth,* V.P. and Treas.; Kim S. Mitchell,
Secy.; William J. Viveen, Jr.
EIN: 382929328

2697
Angels in Motion Foundation
1800 W. Big Beaver Rd., Ste. 100
Troy, MI   48084-3531

Established in 2003 in MI.
Grantmaker type: Operating foundation.
Financial data (yr. ended 12/31/03): Assets,
$1,304 (M); gifts received, $375; expenditures,
$71; total giving, $0; qualifying distributions, $0.
Officers: Anita Krebs, Pres.; Stephen A. Metzler,
Secy.-Treas.
EIN: 200068383

2698
Annapurna Foundation
26329 Northpointe
Farmington Hills, MI   48331-4264

Established in 2003 in MI.
Donor: B.L. Narasimha Raju.
Grantmaker type: Operating foundation.
Financial data (yr. ended 6/30/04): Assets,
$21,759 (M); gifts received, $40,000;
expenditures, $18,241; total giving, $16,356;
qualifying distributions, $1,885; giving activities
include $16,356 for grants.
Fields of interest: Food services.
Type of support: General/operating support.
Limitations: Applications not accepted. No grants to
individuals.
Application information: Contributes only to
pre-selected organizations.
Director: B.L. Narasimha Raju.
EIN: 200190770

2699
Arjuna Institute
1507 Brooklyn Ave.
Ann Arbor, MI   48104-4416

Established around 1982 in MI.
Grantmaker type: Operating foundation.
Financial data (yr. ended 12/31/05): Assets,
$4,882 (M); gifts received, $10,551; expenditures,
$10,551; total giving, $0; qualifying distributions,
$10,551; giving activities include $10,551 for
foundation-administered programs.

Officer: Richard D. Mann, Pres.
Director: Edward Mann.
EIN: 382110752

2700
Armenian Children's Relief Fund

c/o John Kchikian
31800 W. 8 Mile Rd.
Farmington Hills, MI   48336

Established in 1992 in MI.
Donors: John Kchikian; K.P. Sogoigan.
Grantmaker type: Operating foundation.
Financial data (yr. ended 12/31/05): Assets, $35,912 (M); gifts received, $53,940; expenditures, $43,166; total giving, $42,248; qualifying distributions, $42,248; giving activities include $42,248 for grants.
Purpose and activities: Giving primarily to aid needy Armenian individuals by distributing food and medical care.
International interests: Armenia.
Limitations: Applications not accepted. Giving for the benefit of residents of Armenia and Artsakh. No grants to individuals.
Application information: Contributes only to pre-selected organizations.
Officers: John Kchikian, Pres.; Hovagim Manoogian, Treas.
EIN: 383024766

2701
Edmund Armstrong Foundation

(formerly Edmund Armstrong Educational Corporation)
1011 Glenhurst Dr.
Birmingham, MI   48009   (248) 258-4977
Contact: Jack Burket, Dir.

Grantmaker type: Operating foundation.
Financial data (yr. ended 7/31/04): Assets, $118,526 (M); expenditures, $14,713; total giving, $6,000; qualifying distributions, $5,994; giving activities include $6,000 for grants to individuals.
Purpose and activities: Scholarship awards to music majors and colleges with music departments.
Fields of interest: Performing arts, education.
Type of support: Scholarships—to individuals.
Application information:
   Initial approach: Proposal including letter of reference
   Deadline(s): None
Directors: Jack Burket; Herbert Couf.
EIN: 351603618

2702
The Aronoff Foundation, Inc.

38500 N. Woodward Ave., Ste. 310
Bloomfield Hills, MI   48304

Established in 1977 in MI.
Donors: Arnold Y. Aronoff; Edward C. Levy, Sr.†.
Grantmaker type: Operating foundation.
Financial data (yr. ended 5/31/03): Assets, $1,968 (M); gifts received, $59,000; expenditures, $57,928; total giving, $56,975; qualifying distributions, $56,975; giving activities include $56,975 for 24 grants (high: $20,000; low: $100).

Purpose and activities: Giving primarily to Jewish agencies, think tanks, and community service organizations.
Fields of interest: Higher education; Hospitals (general); Jewish agencies & temples.
Type of support: General/operating support.
Limitations: Applications not accepted. Giving primarily in MI. No grants to individuals.
Application information: Contributes only to pre-selected organizations.
Officers: Janet Aronoff, Pres.; Arnold Y. Aronoff, Secy.
Trustees: Daniel J. Aronoff; Jane Schulak.
EIN: 591865316

2703
James D. Azzar Foundation, Inc.

P.O. Box 1182
Grand Rapids, MI   49501

Established in 2001 in MI.
Donors: Azzar Industries, Inc.; Patty Processing, Inc.; Patty Paper, Inc.
Grantmaker type: Operating foundation.
Financial data (yr. ended 12/31/04): Assets, $225,228 (M); gifts received, $600,098; expenditures, $475,000; total giving, $475,000; qualifying distributions, $475,000; giving activities include $475,000 for 1 grant.
Purpose and activities: Support only for the Mackenzies Animal Sanctuary, Inc., MI.
Fields of interest: Animal welfare.
Type of support: General/operating support.
Limitations: Applications not accepted. Giving limited to Grand Rapids, MI. No grants to individuals.
Application information: Contributes only to a pre-selected organization.
Director: James D. Azzar.
EIN: 383533254

2704
W. S. Ballenger Trust f/b/o Ballenger Park

c/o Citizens Bank Wealth Mgmt., N.A.
328 S. Saginaw St., M/C 00272
Flint, MI   48502-2412

Classified as a private operating foundation in 1978.
Grantmaker type: Operating foundation.
Financial data (yr. ended 9/30/03): Assets, $1,533,262 (M); expenditures, $104,867; total giving, $0; qualifying distributions, $101,583.
Trustee: Citizens Bank.
EIN: 381408046

2705
W. S. Ballenger Trust f/b/o Memorial Park

c/o Citizens Bank Wealth Mgmt., N.A.
328 S. Saginaw St., M/C 00272
Flint, MI   48502-2412

Classified as a private operating foundation in 1978.
Grantmaker type: Operating foundation.
Financial data (yr. ended 9/30/03): Assets, $864,463 (M); expenditures, $11,133; total giving, $0; qualifying distributions, $9,118.
Trustee: Citizens Bank.
EIN: 381408160

2706
Ekrem Bardha Foundation, Inc.

3300 Lone Pine Rd.
West Bloomfield, MI   48323   (248) 851-7310
Contact: Ekrem Bardha, Pres.

Established in 1995 in MI.
Grantmaker type: Operating foundation.
Financial data (yr. ended 12/31/04): Assets, $90,139 (M); gifts received, $110,000; expenditures, $20,143; total giving, $20,000; qualifying distributions, $20,143; giving activities include $20,000 for 2 grants (high: $10,000; low: $10,000).
Fields of interest: Roman Catholic agencies & churches.
Limitations: Giving primarily in Albania. No grants to individuals.
Application information:
   Initial approach: Letter or telephone call
   Deadline(s): None
Officers: Ekrem Bardha, Pres.; Lumteri Bardha, Secy.
EIN: 383212623

2707
Barros Research Foundation

2430 College Rd.
Holt, MI   48842-9704

Classified as a private operating foundation in 1981.
Donors: Barnett Rosenberg; Tina Rosenberg.
Grantmaker type: Operating foundation.
Financial data (yr. ended 12/31/04): Assets, $402,708 (M); gifts received, $1,051,314; expenditures, $725,185; total giving, $0; qualifying distributions, $697,729.
Officers: Barnett Rosenberg, Pres.; Rita Rosenberg, Secy.-Treas.
Directors: Paul A. Rosenberg; Tina Rosenberg.
EIN: 382380724

2708
The Baskin Foundation

322 N. Old Woodward Ave.
Birmingham, MI   48009

Established in 2002 in MI.
Donor: Henry Baskin.
Grantmaker type: Operating foundation.
Financial data (yr. ended 12/31/04): Assets, $461,783 (M); expenditures, $22,300; total giving, $22,000; qualifying distributions, $22,000; giving activities include $22,000 for 2 grants (high: $20,000; low: $2,000).
Limitations: Applications not accepted. Giving primarily in MI. No grants to individuals.
Application information: Contributes only to pre-selected organizations.
Officer: Henry Baskin, Pres.
EIN: 320027399

2709
Donald and Ethel Baughey Foundation

7620 W. U.S. 223
Adrian, MI   49221

Established in 2001.
Donors: Donald Baughey†; Ethel Baughey†.

Grantmaker type: Operating foundation.
Financial data (yr. ended 12/31/05): Assets, $293,449 (M); expenditures, $25,826; total giving, $4,000; qualifying distributions, $19,459; giving activities include $4,000 for grants.
Officers: Donald Baughey, Jr., Pres.; Dorcas Baughey, Secy.
Director: Daniel Wright.
EIN: 383562947

2710
Beacon of Hope Foundation
8762 Sleeping Bear Rd.
Glen Arbor, MI   49636

Established in 2000 in OK. Classified as a private operating foundation in 2001.
Donors: Raymond G. Sobieck; Gayle Sobieck; Raymond M. Sobieck; Mary C. Sobieck; Charles W. Sobieck; Elizabeth A. Sobieck; Thomas A. Sobieck.
Grantmaker type: Operating foundation.
Financial data (yr. ended 12/31/05): Assets, $864,249 (M); gifts received, $100,249; expenditures, $86,233; total giving, $72,927; qualifying distributions, $84,053; giving activities include $72,927 for 15 grants (high: $18,004; low: $447).
Fields of interest: Education; Human services; Aging; Disabilities, people with; Economically disadvantaged.
Limitations: Applications not accepted. Giving on a national and international basis. No grants to individuals.
Application information: Contributes only to pre-selected organizations.
Officers: Raymond G. Sobieck, Pres.; Elizabeth A. Sobieck, Secy.; Gayle M. Sobieck, Treas.
Directors: Charles W. Sobieck; Raymond M. Sobieck; Thomas A. Sobieck; Mary Claire Sobieck-Howe.
EIN: 731598929

2711
Rudolf B. Becker Foundation
977 W. Harsdale Rd.
Bloomfield Hills, MI   48302

Established in 2000 in MI.
Donor: Rudolf B. Becker.
Grantmaker type: Operating foundation.
Financial data (yr. ended 12/31/04): Assets, $17,847 (M); gifts received, $10; expenditures, $1,510; total giving, $1,500; qualifying distributions, $1,500; giving activities include $1,500 for 2 grants (high: $1,000; low: $500).
Limitations: Applications not accepted. No grants to individuals.
Application information: Contributes only to pre-selected organizations.
Officer: Rudolf B. Becker, Pres.
EIN: 383520554

2712
Anu Bedi Charitable Society
c/o Parkash Bedi
2551 Rhodes Dr.
Troy, MI   48083-2440

Established in 1999 in MI.
Donor: Parkash Bedi.

Grantmaker type: Operating foundation.
Financial data (yr. ended 2/28/06): Assets, $0 (M); gifts received, $4,950; expenditures, $5,000; total giving, $4,950; qualifying distributions, $5,000; giving activities include $4,950 for foundation-administered programs.
Limitations: Applications not accepted. No grants to individuals.
Application information: Contributes only to pre-selected organizations.
Directors: Aruna Bedi; Parkash Bedi; Lawrence E. Jones.
EIN: 383475472

2713
Bellwether Foundation
P.O. Box 475
Fremont, MI   49412-0170

Established in 1994 in MI.
Donor: Danielle M. Rengo.
Grantmaker type: Operating foundation.
Financial data (yr. ended 12/31/04): Assets, $500,531 (M); gifts received, $95,796; expenditures, $275,048; total giving, $0; qualifying distributions, $246,470; giving activities include $275,048 for foundation-administered programs.
Fields of interest: Veterinary medicine, hospital.
Limitations: Applications not accepted. Giving primarily in Fremont, MI. No grants to individuals.
Application information: Contributes only to pre-selected organizations.
Officers: Danielle S. Merrill, Pres.; John M. Martin, Secy.; Catherine Obits, Treas.
EIN: 383182232

2714
Jesse Besser Museum
491 Johnson St.
Alpena, MI   49707-1496

Classified as a private operating foundation in 1972.
Donor: Besser Foundation.
Grantmaker type: Operating foundation.
Financial data (yr. ended 6/30/05): Assets, $6,529,112 (M); gifts received, $359,455; expenditures, $583,119; total giving, $0; qualifying distributions, $0.
Purpose and activities: Support only for a museum and planetarium.
Officers: Jon Hopkins, Pres.; Leona Wisniewski, V.P.; Joanne Brandt, Secy.; Lucas Pfeiffenberger, Treas.
EIN: 386111671

2715
The Les and Anne Biederman Foundation, Inc.
P.O. Box 564
Traverse City, MI   49685-0564
Contact: Chris Warren, Secy.

Established in 1986 in MI.
Donors: Lester M. Biederman†; Anna R. Biederman; Anne Biederman Trust.
Grantmaker type: Operating foundation.
Financial data (yr. ended 12/31/05): Assets, $4,181,241 (M); gifts received, $165,431; expenditures, $200,087; total giving, $180,552;

qualifying distributions, $180,552; giving activities include $180,552 for 26 grants (high: $35,000; low: $1,000).
Purpose and activities: Support for education, civic improvement, fine arts, health and human services, and recreation and youth services.
Fields of interest: Arts; Higher education; Education; Recreation; Human services; Youth, services; Federated giving programs; Government/public administration.
Type of support: General/operating support; Continuing support; Building/renovation; Equipment; Land acquisition; Endowments; Program development; Scholarship funds.
Limitations: Giving primarily in northern MI. No support for fraternal organizations, societies, or orders, political organizations or campaigns, or for religious organizations for sectarian purposes. No grants to individuals (except selected scholarships), or for deficit financing or debt retirement, endowment funds, travel or conferences, normal operating expenses, scientific research, or writing, publication or production of articles, books or films.
Publications: Application guidelines.
Application information: Application form required.
   Initial approach: Letter
   Copies of proposal: 7
   Deadline(s): 1 month prior to board meetings
   Board meeting date(s): 4 to 5 times annually
Officers and Trustees:* Ross Biederman,* Pres.; Lawrence E. Gorton, V.P.; Chris Warren, Secy.; Vojin Baic; Paul M. Biederman; Lee Russell.
Number of staff: None.
EIN: 382449838
Selected grants: The following grants were reported in 2004.
$50,000 to Grand Traverse Regional Land Conservancy, Traverse City, MI.
$25,000 to Northwestern Michigan College, Traverse City, MI.
$10,000 to Con Foster Museum, Friends of, Traverse City, MI.
$10,000 to Grand Traverse Soil and Water Conservation District, Traverse City, MI.
$10,000 to Inland Seas Education Association, Suttons Bay, MI.
$10,000 to Munson Healthcare Regional Foundation, Traverse City, MI.
$5,000 to City Opera House Heritage Association, Traverse City, MI.
$2,500 to Traverse Symphony Orchestra, Traverse City, MI.
$2,000 to Boy Scouts of America, Scenic Trails Council, Traverse City, MI.
$2,000 to Father Fred Foundation, Traverse City, MI.

2716
Karen Blackman Charitable Foundation
c/o Sidney D. Blackman
6230 Orchard Lake Rd., Ste. 100
West Bloomfield, MI   48322

Classified as a private operating foundation in 1998 in MI.
Grantmaker type: Operating foundation.
Financial data (yr. ended 12/31/02): Assets, $4,854 (M); expenditures, $50; total giving, $0; qualifying distributions, $0.
Limitations: Giving primarily in MI.
Officers: Sidney D. Blackman, Pres.; Debra R. Blackman, V.P.; Marc S. Blackman, Secy.; Jeffrey S. Blackman, Treas.
EIN: 383381251

2717
Blue Sky Foundation
430 N. Old Woodward Ave., Ste. 100
Birmingham, MI 48009

Established in 1997 in MI.
Donors: Jeffrey Sloan; Richard Sloan.
Grantmaker type: Operating foundation.
Financial data (yr. ended 12/31/04): Assets, $109 (M); expenditures, $0; total giving, $0; qualifying distributions, $0.
Officers: Jeffrey Sloan, Pres.; Richard Sloan, V.P.
EIN: 383320396

2718
Bryan Christian Services, Inc.
c/o Albert H. Bryan
3784 Fawn Dr.
Rochester, MI 48306-1029

Donors: Lillian P. Bryan; Albert Bryan.
Grantmaker type: Operating foundation.
Financial data (yr. ended 12/31/05): Assets, $83,019 (M); gifts received, $20,000; expenditures, $20,283; total giving, $20,010; qualifying distributions, $20,010; giving activities include $20,010 for grants.
Purpose and activities: Giving to religious churches for their missionary work; giving also for cancer research and some giving for tuition assistance at Rochester College.
Fields of interest: Higher education, college; Cancer research; Religion, association.
Type of support: Scholarship funds; General/ operating support.
Limitations: Applications not accepted. Giving primarily in MI. No grants to individuals.
Application information: Contributes only to pre-selected organizations.
Officers: Albert H. Bryan III, Pres.; Ann F. Bryan, V.P.; Albert H. Bryan IV, Secy.
EIN: 753089155

2719
Buist Foundation
8650 Byron Center Ave. S.W.
Byron Center, MI 49315 (616) 878-3315

Established as a company-sponsored operating foundation in 1998.
Donor: Buist Electric, Inc.
Grantmaker type: Operating foundation.
Financial data (yr. ended 12/31/05): Assets, $47,903 (M); gifts received, $233,819; expenditures, $172,293; total giving, $160,832; qualifying distributions, $172,293; giving activities include $62,759 for 42 grants (high: $7,000; low: $150), and $98,073 for grants to individuals.
Purpose and activities: The foundation supports organizations involved with education, human services, and Christianity and awards grants to needy families.
Fields of interest: Education; Human services; Christian agencies & churches.
Type of support: Scholarship funds; General/ operating support; Grants to individuals.
Limitations: Giving primarily in Grand Rapids, MI.
Application information: Application form not required.
Initial approach: Proposal
Deadline(s): None

Officer and Directors: Brent Brinks, Pres.; Lance Brinks; Kathy Burgess; Aaron Cooper; Matt Devries; Leo Harkema; Al Hubach; Cindy Meengs.
EIN: 383314509

2720
John R. & Mildred B. Burt Charitable Foundation
525 Morley Dr.
Saginaw, MI 48601

Established in 2002 in MI.
Grantmaker type: Operating foundation.
Financial data (yr. ended 12/31/05): Assets, $660,005 (M); gifts received, $228,672; expenditures, $27,858; total giving, $27,800; qualifying distributions, $27,800; giving activities include $27,800 for 2 grants (high: $25,000; low: $2,800).
Fields of interest: Higher education, university.
Limitations: Giving primarily in MI.
Officers: Jason Tunney, Pres.; Matthew Moeller, V.P.; Shawn Sny, Secy.
EIN: 300081622

2721
Cascade Hemophilia Consortium
210 E. Huron St., Ste. D
Ann Arbor, MI 48104
Contact: William T. Sparrow, Exec. Dir.

Established in 1996 in MI.
Grantmaker type: Operating foundation.
Financial data (yr. ended 12/31/04): Assets, $0 (M); gifts received, $550; expenditures, $1,449,529; total giving, $999,225; qualifying distributions, $999,225; giving activities include $999,225 for 33 grants (high: $276,016; low: $48).
Purpose and activities: Support limited to the medical care and research of hemophilia.
Fields of interest: Hemophilia; Hemophilia research.
Limitations: Applications not accepted. Giving primarily in MI and OH. No grants to individuals.
Application information: Foundation sends out Requests for Proposals and does not accept unsolicited requests for funds.
Officers: William Berk, M.D., Pres.; Stephen Pokoj, J.D., V.P.; Stephen Munk, Ph.D., Secy.; Carrie Voegtle, Treas.; William T. Sparrow, Exec. Dir.
Directors: Judith Andersen, M.D.; Tom Bills; Jane Dinnen, R.N.; Anne Eccles; Shelley Gerson; Ivan Harner; Phil Kucab; Caterine McClure, J.D.; Andy Muir; James Munn, R.N.; Linda Wacha, R.N.
EIN: 383199649
Selected grants: The following grants were reported in 2004.
$70,956 to Hemophilia Foundation of Michigan, Ann Arbor, MI. For camp rental, travel, administrative fees, Labtracker support and other regional services.
$48,500 to Indiana Hemophilia and Thrombosis Center, Indianapolis, IN. For nursing, physical therapy and social work.
$42,500 to Harper Hospital, Detroit, MI. For nursing, physical therapy, social work, genetic counseling, and dietician.
$35,500 to Ohio State University Medical Center, Columbus, OH. For Adult Hemophilia Treatment Center.

$34,000 to Munson Medical Center, Traverse City, MI. For social work, dietician, dental services and phlebotomist.
$33,000 to University Hospitals of Cleveland, Cleveland, OH. For nursing and social work.
$32,750 to University of Michigan Hospitals, Ann Arbor, MI. For Hemophilia Treatment Center.
$32,000 to Childrens Hospital Medical Center of Akron, Akron, OH. For nursing and social work.
$28,500 to Hurley Medical Center, Flint, MI.
$23,187 to Childrens Hospital of Michigan, Detroit, MI. For nursing and project assistant.

2722
Cavaliere Family Foundation
30078 Schoenherr Rd., Ste. 300
Warren, MI 48088

Donors: John Cavaliere; Fara Cavaliere.
Grantmaker type: Operating foundation.
Financial data (yr. ended 12/31/03): Assets, $20,734 (M); gifts received, $4,600; expenditures, $4,211; total giving, $1,800; qualifying distributions, $4,211; giving activities include $1,800 for 4 grants to individuals (high: $700; low: $300).
Purpose and activities: Scholarship awards are restricted to students enrolled in schools in Pignataro Interamna, Italy.
Type of support: Scholarships—to individuals.
Limitations: Applications not accepted.
Application information: Unsolicited requests for funds not accepted.
Officers: John Cavaliere, Pres.; Lorenzo J. Cavaliere, Secy.
Director: Anthony Cavaliere.
EIN: 383471566

2723
Centennial Mission Foundation, Inc.
15302 Club Course Dr.
Bath, MI 48808-8797

Established in 2002 in MI.
Donor: Suk J. Chang.
Grantmaker type: Operating foundation.
Financial data (yr. ended 12/31/05): Assets, $12,618 (M); gifts received, $10,304; expenditures, $5,377; total giving, $5,340; qualifying distributions, $5,377; giving activities include $5,340 for 1 grant to an individual.
Limitations: Applications not accepted.
Application information: Unsolicited requests for funds not accepted.
Directors: Suk J. Chang; Karen Cronk; John Song; William Vanderwall.
EIN: 300052982

2724
William J. Center Irrevocable Trust
c/o TD Banknorth, N.A. Investment Mgmt. Group.
P.O. Box 595
Williston, VT 05495-0595

Established in 1991 in VT.
Grantmaker type: Operating foundation.
Financial data (yr. ended 9/30/05): Assets, $189,204 (M); expenditures, $13,988; total giving, $10,648; qualifying distributions, $11,647; giving activities include $10,648 for grants.

Purpose and activities: Support only for a scholarship fund for a Sudbury graduate attending college or a technical school, the Town of Sudbury for an annual Christmas party, and to the Veterans of Foreign Wars National Home, MI.
Fields of interest: Historical activities, war memorials; Elementary/secondary education; Recreation.
Type of support: General/operating support; Scholarship funds.
Limitations: Applications not accepted. Giving limited to MI and VT. No grants to individuals.
Application information: Contributes only to 3 pre-selected organizations.
Trustee: TD Banknorth, N.A.
EIN: 036052220

2725
Central Care Management Organization
(formerly Network Community Services)
28303 Joy Rd.
Westland, MI 48185
Contact: Michelle Y. Scott, Exec. Dir.
Application address: 18100 Meyers Rd., Detroit, MI 48235, tel.: (313) 862-2800

Established in MI.
Donor: Wayne County Department of Child and Family Services.
Grantmaker type: Operating foundation.
Financial data (yr. ended 9/30/03): Assets, $5,723,182 (M); expenditures, $15,943,732; total giving, $42,362; qualifying distributions, $16,045,132; giving activities include $42,362 for grants, $15,901,370 for foundation-administered programs and $100,000 for loans/program-related investments.
Purpose and activities: Provides services to delinquent youth in Wayne County, MI.
Limitations: Giving limited to the central Detroit, Highland Park, and Hamtramck, MI, area.
Application information:
Initial approach: Letter or telephone
Deadline(s): Mar. 31
Officers: Charles D. Small, Chair.; Robert E. Ennis III, Vice-Chair.; Roger I. Swaninger, Secy.-Treas.; Michelle Y. Scott, Exec. Dir.
EIN: 383050521

2726
Cherlayne, Inc.
14531 Vaughn St.
Detroit, MI 48223-2130

Established in MI.
Grantmaker type: Operating foundation.
Financial data (yr. ended 12/31/04): Assets, $52,712 (M); expenditures, $292,107; total giving, $0; qualifying distributions, $284,956; giving activities include $284,956 for foundation-administered programs.
Officer: Cedell Murff, Pres.
EIN: 382838861

2727
Chiasson Family Foundation, Inc.
13631 Cantaberry Ct.
South Lyon, MI 48178

Established in MI.

Grantmaker type: Operating foundation.
Financial data (yr. ended 12/31/05): Assets, $2,550 (M); expenditures, $345; total giving, $0; qualifying distributions, $0.
Director: Laurette C. Walsh.
EIN: 383584565

2728
Children Need Both Parents
c/o Ronald Smith
629 Diamond Ave. N.E.
Grand Rapids, MI 49503-1845 (616) 301-1515
FAX: (616) 301-1616; URL: http://www.cnbp.org

Established in 1993 in MI.
Grantmaker type: Operating foundation.
Financial data (yr. ended 3/31/05): Assets, $0 (M); expenditures, $4,000; total giving, $0; qualifying distributions, $0.
Purpose and activities: The organization's goals include counseling to both parents, supervision of visitation, assistance with child support issues, services to domestic violence cases and workplace support, operating in Illinois, Wisconsin and Michigan.
Officers: Ronald E. Smith, C.E.O.; Beaetta Petty, Pres.; Deborah Sprinkle, Secy.; Naquetta Foster, Treas.; Scherry Shabazz, Exec. Dir.
EIN: 363884424

2729
Children's Ministries, Inc.
(formerly Fielstra Foundation)
288 Garfield Rd. N.
Traverse City, MI 49686

Established in 2002 in MI.
Donor: Gerald Fielstra.
Grantmaker type: Operating foundation.
Financial data (yr. ended 12/31/04): Assets, $33,842 (M); gifts received, $58,596; expenditures, $42,978; total giving, $0; qualifying distributions, $0.
Officers: Gerald Fielstra, Pres.; Don VanWingerden, V.P.; Marilyn Oom, Secy.; Sally Dykhuis, Treas.
Director: Thomas Dame; John Dyksterhouse.
EIN: 043641750

2730
Chisbetts Foundation
505 E. Huron St., Ste. 307
Ann Arbor, MI 48108

Established in 2002 in MI.
Donors: Betty Chisholm; Donald Chisholm.
Grantmaker type: Operating foundation.
Financial data (yr. ended 6/30/03): Assets, $328,369 (M); gifts received, $320,581; expenditures, $13,651; total giving, $12,000; qualifying distributions, $12,000; giving activities include $12,000 for grants.
Purpose and activities: Giving to the University of Michigan Music School, Ann Arbor.
Type of support: General/operating support.
Limitations: Applications not accepted. Giving primarily in Ann Arbor, MI. No grants to individuals.
Application information: Contributes only to pre-selected organizations.

Officer and Directors:* Donald Chisholm,* Pres.; Betty Chisholm.
EIN: 611437291

2731
Clinton Community Foundation
316 W. Michigan Ave.
Clinton, MI 49236

Established in 2002 in MI.
Donor: Kathleen Dee Thomas.
Grantmaker type: Operating foundation.
Financial data (yr. ended 12/31/03): Assets, $2,745 (M); gifts received, $5,500; expenditures, $6,649; total giving, $6,290; qualifying distributions, $6,479; giving activities include $6,290 for grants.
Limitations: Giving primarily in Clinton, MI.
Application information: Application form not required.
Deadline(s): None
Directors: Marge Green; Kathy Dee Thomas; Donna Service; Kevin Wilhelm.
EIN: 371441978

2732
Community Home Health and Hospice
2360 Stone Bridge Dr.
Flint, MI 48532

Established in MI.
Grantmaker type: Operating foundation.
Financial data (yr. ended 12/31/04): Assets, $7,533,487 (M); gifts received, $84,940; expenditures, $4,143,917; total giving, $0; qualifying distributions, $1,012,177; giving activities include $3,895,684 for foundation-administered programs.
Limitations: Applications not accepted. No grants to individuals.
Application information: Contributes only to pre-selected organizations.
Officers: Donald Lada, Chair.; Mary Periard, Vice-Chair.; Penny Murphy, C.E.O. and Pres.; Isabel Rook, Secy.; Barbara Scharich, Treas.; Patrick Miller, Exec. Dir.
Directors: Elizabeth Davis; Inez Boyd; Betty Harrison; Ernest Hawley; George Mansour; Anthony G. Michael; Barbara Scharich; Charles Snooks.
EIN: 382381728

2733
The Coville Photographic Art Foundation
29100 Northwestern Hwy., Ste. 290
Southfield, MI 48034

Established in 1993 in MI.
Donors: Warren J. Coville; Margot E. Coville.
Grantmaker type: Operating foundation.
Financial data (yr. ended 6/30/05): Assets, $498,248 (M); gifts received, $181,200; expenditures, $95,720; total giving, $31,040; qualifying distributions, $95,450; giving activities include $31,040 for 4+ grants (high: $20,000), and $64,410 for foundation-administered programs.
Fields of interest: Visual arts; Visual arts, photography.
Limitations: Applications not accepted. Giving on a national basis, with some emphasis in MI. No grants to individuals.

Application information: Contributes only to pre-selected organizations.
Officers: Warren J. Coville, Pres. and Treas.; Margot E. Coville, V.P.; Brent S. Triest, Secy.
EIN: 383153863

2734
Creative Health Institute
918 Union City Rd.
Union City, MI   49094-9753

Grantmaker type: Operating foundation.
Financial data (yr. ended 12/31/05): Assets, $43,010 (M); gifts received, $3,652; expenditures, $217,669; total giving, $1,286; qualifying distributions, $1,286; giving activities include $1,286 for grants.
Purpose and activities: Support only for programs that promote a healthy alternative lifestyle and diet.
Fields of interest: Health care.
Trustees: Joe Basset; Hiawatha Cromer; William Cromer; Mary J. Haughey.
EIN: 382557714

2735
Richard E. & Sandra J. Dauch Family Foundation
223 Bridge St.
P.O. Box 227
Charlevoix, MI   49720   (231) 547-4602
Contact: Thomas G. Bickersteth, Secy.

Established in 2002 in MI.
Donors: Richard E. Dauch; Sandra J. Dauch; Helen R. Dauch Trust.
Grantmaker type: Operating foundation.
Financial data (yr. ended 4/30/05): Assets, $11,863,229 (M); gifts received, $284,000; expenditures, $1,633,246; total giving, $1,520,620; qualifying distributions, $1,551,567; giving activities include $1,520,620 for 13 grants (high: $963,968; low: $2,000).
Fields of interest: Higher education; Medical care, rehabilitation; Diabetes research; Recreation, fairs/festivals; Boys & girls clubs; Civil rights; Protestant agencies & churches.
Limitations: Giving primarily in MI and OH.
Application information:
   Initial approach: Letter
   Deadline(s): None
Officers: Richard E. Dauch, Pres.; Sandra J. Dauch, V.P. and Treas.; Thomas G. Bickersteth, Secy.
EIN: 300074517
Selected grants: The following grants were reported in 2004.
$1,973,621 to Ashland University, Ashland, OH. 2 grants: $1,000,000 to College of Economics, $973,621 to College of Economics
$50,000 to Boys and Girls Clubs of Southeastern Michigan, Farmington Hills, MI. For program support.
$50,000 to Focus: Hope, Detroit, MI. For Machinist Training Project.
$25,000 to Trinity Lutheran Church, Ashland, OH. For program support.
$3,000 to Charlevoix Venetian Festival, Charlevoix, MI. For operating support.
$2,000 to Bloomfield Hills School District, Bloomfield Hills, MI. For Booster Club.
$1,000 to Ashland County Community Foundation, Ashland, OH. For program support.

2736
DeKock Family Foundation
861 Barkentine Dr.
Holland, MI   49424

Established in 2000 in MI.
Donors: Douglas DeKock; Sandra DeKock.
Grantmaker type: Operating foundation.
Financial data (yr. ended 12/31/04): Assets, $722,503 (M); gifts received, $85,000; expenditures, $30,338; total giving, $26,500; qualifying distributions, $26,500; giving activities include $26,500 for 6 grants (high: $10,000; low: $2,000).
Fields of interest: Elementary/secondary education; Higher education; Christian agencies & churches.
Limitations: Giving primarily in Grand Rapids and Holland, MI.
Officers: Douglas DeKock, Pres. and Treas.; Sandra DeKock, Secy.
EIN: 383534244

2737
DeShano Community Foundation
P.O. Box 539
Gladwin, MI   48624
Contact: Florence G. DeShano, Secy.
Application address: 4339 Round Lake Rd., Gladwin, MI 48624, tel.: (989) 426-0670

Established in 2001 in MI.
Donors: Florence G. DeShano; Gary L. DeShano.
Grantmaker type: Operating foundation.
Financial data (yr. ended 12/31/05): Assets, $68,152 (M); gifts received, $40,020; expenditures, $43,625; total giving, $43,438; qualifying distributions, $43,500; giving activities include $43,438 for grants.
Fields of interest: Education; Human services; Community development; Christian agencies & churches.
Limitations: Giving limited to the mid-MI region. No grants to individuals.
Application information:
   Initial approach: Letter
   Deadline(s): None
Officers: Gary L. DeShano, Pres.; Florence G. DeShano, Secy.
Trustees: Scott G. DeShano; Douglas A. Jacobson; Douglas F. Larner.
EIN: 382902743

2738
Detroit Christadelphian Bible Explorers, Inc.
14676 Berwick St.
Livonia, MI   48154-3550

Grantmaker type: Operating foundation.
Financial data (yr. ended 12/31/04): Assets, $0 (M); gifts received, $4,626; expenditures, $4,177; total giving, $0; qualifying distributions, $4,177; giving activities include $3,502 for foundation-administered programs.
Officers: William A. Robinson, Pres.; Jared Keyes, V.P.; Pam Styles, Secy.; Ruth Robinson, Treas.
Director: Jonathon Brinkerhoff.
EIN: 383497401

2739
Detroit Neurosurgical Foundation
3333 E. Jefferson Ave., Ste. 1117
Detroit, MI   48207   (313) 259-0391
Contact: Amy Berke, Exec. Dir.

Classified as a private operating foundation in 1977.
Donor: Joseph J. Berke, M.D., Ph.D.
Grantmaker type: Operating foundation.
Financial data (yr. ended 11/30/05): Assets, $1,103,883 (M); expenditures, $36,182; total giving, $1,650; qualifying distributions, $27,241; giving activities include $1,650 for grants, and $25,591 for foundation-administered programs.
Fields of interest: Medical research; Community development, neighborhood development.
Type of support: Annual campaigns; Capital campaigns; Program development; Conferences/seminars; Research; Program evaluation; Matching/challenge support.
Limitations: Giving limited to the metropolitan Detroit, MI, area.
Publications: Informational brochure.
Application information: Application form not required.
   Initial approach: Letter
   Copies of proposal: 1
   Board meeting date(s): As needed
Officers and Directors:* Joseph J. Berke, M.D., Ph.D.*, Pres.; Amy Berke, Exec. Dir.; Irving F. Keene; Herman Moehlman.
EIN: 382127946

2740
Detroit Workforce Development Board
707 W. Milwaukee St.
Detroit, MI   48202

Established in 2003 in MI.
Grantmaker type: Operating foundation.
Financial data (yr. ended 6/29/05): Assets, $327,000 (M); gifts received, $327,000; expenditures, $0; total giving, $0; qualifying distributions, $0.
Officers: Calvin Sharp, Chair.; John Hayden, Vice-Chair.; Veronica Madrigal, Secy.
EIN: 383353746

2741
The Diem Foundation
c/o Mark Diem
4345 Oak Grove
Bloomfield Hills, MI   48302

Established in 2002 in MI.
Donor: Mark Diem.
Grantmaker type: Operating foundation.
Financial data (yr. ended 9/30/03): Assets, $104,552 (M); gifts received, $100,000; expenditures, $5,060; total giving, $5,059; qualifying distributions, $5,059; giving activities include $5,059 for grants.
Limitations: Giving primarily in MI.
Officer: Mark Diem, Pres.
EIN: 383636684

2742
John D. & Jean E. Dinan Foundation
28815 8 Mile Rd., Ste. 101
Livonia, MI 48152-2042

Established in 1999 in MI.
Donors: Jean E. Dinan; John D. Dinan Irrevocable Trust.
Grantmaker type: Operating foundation.
Financial data (yr. ended 12/31/05): Assets, $882,561 (M); gifts received, $351,998; expenditures, $20,378; total giving, $12,325; qualifying distributions, $12,325; giving activities include $12,325 for 2 grants (high: $7,325; low: $5,000).
Fields of interest: Secondary school/education; American Red Cross; Roman Catholic agencies & churches.
Type of support: General/operating support; Scholarship funds.
Limitations: Applications not accepted. Giving primarily in MI. No grants to individuals.
Application information: Contributes only to pre-selected organizations.
Officers: John P. Dinan, Secy.; Catherine A. Dillon, Treas.
EIN: 383419348

2743
Alden B. and Vada B. Dow Creativity Foundation
315 Post St.
Midland, MI 48640 (989) 837-4478

Established in 1989 in MI; funded in 1991.
Donor: Vada B. Dow†.
Grantmaker type: Operating foundation.
Financial data (yr. ended 12/31/05): Assets, $1,746,308 (M); gifts received, $802,824; expenditures, $719,288; total giving, $0; qualifying distributions, $682,682; giving activities include $705,051 for foundation-administered programs.
Officers and Trustees:* Michael Lloyd Dow,* Pres.; Steven Carras,* Secy.; Mary Lloyd Dow Mills,* Treas.; Barbara D. Carras; Diane Hullet; Chris Mills.
EIN: 382852321

2744
The Elkes Foundation
12 Trails End
Rye, NY 10580 (914) 381-5350

Established in 1989 in NY.
Grantmaker type: Operating foundation.
Financial data (yr. ended 11/30/04): Assets, $6,045,928 (M); expenditures, $526,194; total giving, $511,450; qualifying distributions, $510,709; giving activities include $511,450 for 27 grants (high: $250,000; low: $100).
Purpose and activities: Giving primarily for higher education, with emphasis on a law school; some funding also to Jewish organizations and education.
Fields of interest: Arts; Higher education; Law school/education; Education; Medical care, in-patient care; Human services; Jewish agencies & temples.
Limitations: Applications not accepted. Giving primarily in Ann Arbor, MI and NY. No grants to individuals.
Application information: Contributes only to pre-selected organizations.

Trustees: Ruth F. Elkes; Terrence A. Elkes.
EIN: 133497016
Selected grants: The following grants were reported in 2003.
$250,000 to University of Michigan, Law School, Ann Arbor, MI.
$105,000 to Jewish Outreach Institute, Center for Jewish Studies, New York, NY.
$5,000 to American Ireland Fund, Boston, MA.
$5,000 to Jewish Educational Ventures, DC.
$5,000 to Middle East Forum, Philadelphia, PA.
$3,000 to Connecticut College, Development Office, New London, CT.
$2,500 to Grinnell College, Grinnell, IA.
$2,000 to Philharmonic-Symphony Society of New York, New York, NY.
$1,000 to Emelin Theater, Mamaroneck, NY.
$1,000 to Horace Mann School, Riverdale, NY.

2745
Elsona Foster Care, Inc.
1402 Jackson Ave.
Flint, MI 48504

Established around 1986.
Grantmaker type: Operating foundation.
Financial data (yr. ended 12/31/05): Assets, $500 (M); expenditures, $56,026; total giving, $0; qualifying distributions, $0.
Officer: Sonia Cassanda Walker, Pres.
EIN: 382661888

2746
The Eppert Family Foundation
31490 E. Bellvine Trail
Franklin, MI 48025-3703

Established in 2001 in MI.
Donors: Verlin R. Eppert, Jr.; Rosalie A. Eppert.
Grantmaker type: Operating foundation.
Financial data (yr. ended 12/31/04): Assets, $2,608,162 (M); expenditures, $147,159; total giving, $114,900; qualifying distributions, $114,920; giving activities include $114,900 for 19 grants (high: $15,000; low: $200).
Fields of interest: Elementary/secondary education; Human services; American Red Cross; Salvation Army; Children/youth, services; Family services.
Limitations: Applications not accepted. No grants to individuals.
Application information: Contributes only to pre-selected organizations.
Officers: Verlin R. Eppert, Jr., Pres.; Rosalie A. Eppert, Secy.-Treas.
EIN: 383536682

2747
Evergreene Foundation
19459 Thompson Ln.
Three Rivers, MI 49093-9039
Contact: Blaine A. Rabbers, Dir.

Grantmaker type: Operating foundation.
Financial data (yr. ended 12/31/05): Assets, $671,251 (M); expenditures, $26,473; total giving, $26,000; qualifying distributions, $26,000; giving activities include $26,000 for grants.

Purpose and activities: Giving primarily for human services, health care, education, and community development.
Fields of interest: Education; Health care; Human services; Community development; Protestant agencies & churches.
Type of support: General/operating support.
Limitations: Giving limited to MI. No grants to individuals.
Application information:
Initial approach: Letter or proposal
Deadline(s): July 1
Director: Blaine A. Rabbers.
EIN: 382737257

2748
Fahd Foundation
15113 S. Dixie Hwy.
Monroe, MI 48161

Established in 2000 in MI.
Donor: Tanvir I. Quershi.
Grantmaker type: Operating foundation.
Financial data (yr. ended 12/31/05): Assets, $775 (M); gifts received, $25,000; expenditures, $28,100; total giving, $28,100; qualifying distributions, $28,100; giving activities include $28,100 for 5 grants (high: $20,000; low: $100).
Purpose and activities: Giving for the benefit of Pakistan.
Limitations: Giving primarily in Pakistan.
Officers: Tanvir I. Quershi, Pres. and Treas.; Amber T. Quershi, Secy.
Directors: Riaz Ahmad; Shala Riaz Ahmad; Muzzamil Malik.
EIN: 383229397

2749
John E. Fetzer Institute, Inc.
(formerly John E. Fetzer Foundation, Inc.)
9292 West KL Ave.
Kalamazoo, MI 49009-9398
Contact: Thomas F. Beech, C.E.O. and Pres.
FAX: (269) 372-2163; E-mail: info@fetzer.org;
URL: http://www.fetzer.org

Established in 1956.
Donors: John E. Fetzer†; John E. Fetzer Memorial Trust; Institute for Research on Unlimited Love; Shinnyo-En Foundation.
Grantmaker type: Operating foundation.
Financial data (yr. ended 7/31/05): Assets, $374,178,286 (M); gifts received, $3,208,720; expenditures, $14,140,624; total giving, $751,945; qualifying distributions, $12,596,966; giving activities include $751,945 for 24 grants (high: $210,000), and $2,987,174 for 4 foundation-administered programs.
Purpose and activities: The institute is a nonprofit, private operating foundation with an interest in exploring the relationship between the inner life of mind and spirit and action and service in the world. The institute's mission is to foster awareness of the power of love and forgiveness in the emerging global community through research, education, and service programs.
Fields of interest: Education; Health care; Children/youth, services; Philanthropy/voluntarism; Social sciences, research; Law/international law; Social sciences.

Type of support: General/operating support; Program development; Conferences/seminars; Research; Program evaluation; Grants to individuals; Matching/challenge support.
Limitations: Applications not accepted. Giving on a national basis.
Publications: Informational brochure; Newsletter; Occasional report; Program policy statement.
Application information: Contributes only to pre-selected organizations.
  Board meeting date(s): Mar., June, Oct., and Dec.
Officers and Trustees: * Robert F. Lehman,* Chair.; Janis A. Claflin,* Vice-Chair.; Thomas F. Beech, Ed.D., C.E.O. and Pres.; Christina M. Adams, V.P., Finance and Admin.; Timothy J. Jones, V.P., Opers.; Shirley H. Showalter, Ph.D., V.P., Progs.; Kathleen M. Cavanaugh, Secy.; Bruce F. Fetzer,* Treas.; Angeles Arrien, Ph.D.; Carolyn Thompson Brown, Ph.D.; Bruce M. Carlson, M.D., Ph.D.; Lawrence E. Sullivan, Ph.D.; Lynn W. Twist; Frances E. Vaughan.
Number of staff: 24 full-time professional; 4 part-time professional; 17 full-time support; 6 part-time support.
EIN: 386052788

2750
Fieler Family Foundation
48759 Beaver Creek Dr.
Plymouth, MI 48170

Established in 2004 in MI.
Donors: Anthony Fielek; Carole Fielek.
Grantmaker type: Operating foundation.
Financial data (yr. ended 12/31/04): Assets, $10,000 (M); gifts received, $10,000; expenditures, $0; total giving, $0; qualifying distributions, $0.
Application information: Application form not required.
  Initial approach: Letter
  Deadline(s): None
Directors: Anthony Fielek; Carole Fielek.
EIN: 421642850

2751
Carrie Filer Board, Inc.
315 Lighthouse Way S.
Manistee, MI 49660

Established in MI.
Grantmaker type: Operating foundation.
Financial data (yr. ended 12/31/05): Assets, $286 (M); gifts received, $6,390; expenditures, $6,225; total giving, $5,900; qualifying distributions, $6,225; giving activities include $5,900 for grants.
Purpose and activities: Support only for West Shore Hospital and Manistee Medical Care Facility, MI, to help defray operating expenses in the care of elderly women.
Fields of interest: Hospitals (general); Aging; Women.
Type of support: General/operating support.
Limitations: Applications not accepted. Giving limited to Manistee, MI. No grants to individuals.
Application information: Contributes only to 2 pre-selected organizations.
Officers: Burton Parks, Pres.; Betty Noteware, V.P.; William L. Chapman, Secy.-Treas.
Trustees: Marijane Daneils; Rosie Solberg.
EIN: 381367303

2752
E. Root Fitch Foundation
107 Pennsylvania Ave.
Dowagiac, MI 49047

Established in MI.
Grantmaker type: Operating foundation.
Financial data (yr. ended 12/31/04): Assets, $909,630 (M); gifts received, $1,352; expenditures, $116,612; total giving, $0; qualifying distributions, $101,476; giving activities include $101,467 for foundation-administered programs.
Officers: Paul Bakeman, Pres.; Denise Wierman, Secy.; John Magyar, Treas.
EIN: 386009605

2753
Edsel & Eleanor Ford House
1100 Lake Shore Dr.
Grosse Pointe Shores, MI 48236-4106
URL: http://www.fordhouse.org/

Classified as a private operating foundation in 1981.
Grantmaker type: Operating foundation.
Financial data (yr. ended 6/30/05): Assets, $101,477,187 (M); expenditures, $4,825,406; total giving, $15,721; qualifying distributions, $3,915,378; giving activities include $15,721 for 7 grants (high: $12,169; low: $50), and $3,654,247 for 4 foundation-administered programs.
Purpose and activities: Support primarily for the Village of Grosse Pointe Shores, MI.
Fields of interest: Community development; Government/public administration.
Type of support: General/operating support.
Limitations: Applications not accepted. Giving limited to MI, with emphasis on Grosse Pointe Shores. No grants to individuals.
Application information: Contributes only to pre-selected organizations.
Officers and Trustees: * Edsel B. Ford II,* Chair.; John Franklin Miller, Pres.; Ann Fitzpatrick, V.P.; David Janssen, V.P.; David Hempstead,* Secy.; Margit A. Jackson, Treas.; Lynn F. Alandt; Lindsey Ford Buhl; Benson Ford, Jr.; Josephine F. Ford; Martha F. Ford; William Clay Ford; Walter Buhl Ford III.
EIN: 382218274

2754
Maxine and Stuart Frankel Foundation for Art
2301 W. Big Beaver Rd., Ste. 510
Troy, MI 48084

Established in 1996 in MI. Classified as a private operating foundation in 1997; funded in 1998.
Donors: Maxine Frankel; Stuart Frankel.
Grantmaker type: Operating foundation.
Financial data (yr. ended 12/31/04): Assets, $26,978,812 (M); gifts received, $5,278,633; expenditures, $217,445; total giving, $0; qualifying distributions, $0.
Officers: Maxine Frankel, Pres.; Stuart Frankel, Secy.-Treas.
EIN: 383357965

2755
Galesburg-Augusta Education Foundation
(formerly Galesburg-Augusta Community Foundation)
1076 N. 37th St.
Galesburg, MI 49053   (269) 484-2000

Established in 1991 in MI.
Grantmaker type: Operating foundation.
Financial data (yr. ended 6/30/05): Assets, $42,667 (M); gifts received, $9,500; expenditures, $6,858; total giving, $4,000; qualifying distributions, $6,858; giving activities include $4,000 for 8 grants to individuals (high: $500; low: $500).
Purpose and activities: Scholarship awards to graduates of Galesburg-Augusta High School who are in financial need, including one annual award to the student attending MSU for the study of forestry.
Fields of interest: Higher education; Environment, forests.
Type of support: Scholarships—to individuals.
Limitations: Giving limited to graduates of Galesburg-Augusta High School, MI.
Publications: Informational brochure.
Application information:
  Initial approach: Letter
  Deadline(s): None
Officers: Miriam Shannon, Pres.; Eric Palma, Secy.; Wanda Hartman, Treas.
Number of staff: None.
EIN: 383082334

2756
Lloyd Ganton Auto Museum Foundation, Inc.
7925 Spring Arbor Rd.
Spring Arbor, MI 49283

Classified as a private operating foundation in 1989 in MI.
Donors: Lloyd G. Ganton; Joyce Ganton; Kevin J. Ganton; Scott Ganton.
Grantmaker type: Operating foundation.
Financial data (yr. ended 6/30/05): Assets, $1,366,488 (M); gifts received, $89,573; expenditures, $28,401; total giving, $0; qualifying distributions, $0.
Purpose and activities: Support only for a museum.
Fields of interest: Museums.
Type of support: General/operating support.
Officers and Directors: * Lloyd G. Ganton,* Pres.; Troy L. Ganton,* V.P. and Exec. Dir.; Kevin J. Ganton,* V.P.; Scott Ganton,* V.P.; Judith L. Ganton,* Secy.-Treas.
EIN: 382837086

2757
Harold and Ruth Garber Family Foundation
4402 Ramsgate Ln.
Bloomfield Hills, MI 48302-1642
Contact: Stanley Garber, V.P.

Donor: Ruth Garber.
Grantmaker type: Operating foundation.
Financial data (yr. ended 12/31/05): Assets, $92,847 (M); expenditures, $2,911; total giving, $1,205; qualifying distributions, $1,205; giving activities include $1,205 for 2 grants (high: $955; low: $250).
Fields of interest: Jewish agencies & temples.

Limitations: Giving primarily in MI. No grants to individuals.
Application information:
  Initial approach: Letter
  Deadline(s): Dec. 1
Officers: Ruth Garber, Pres. and Treas.; Stanley Garber, V.P. and Secy.; Judith Freund, V.P.; Marjory Santacreu, V.P.
EIN: 383324811

2758
Genesis Program, Inc.
c/o Daniel R. Slate
P.O. Box 9
Fremont, MI 49412
Contact: Kenneth Wallace

Donor: The Cummings Fund.
Grantmaker type: Operating foundation.
Financial data (yr. ended 12/31/05): Assets, $129,463 (M); gifts received, $27,300; expenditures, $31,611; total giving, $0; qualifying distributions, $0.
Purpose and activities: Awards interest-free loans to qualified persons to aid in mortgage financing.
Limitations: Giving limited to residents of Fremont, MI.
Application information:
  Initial approach: Letter
  Deadline(s): None
Trustees: Andrew M. Cummings; Gay Gerber Cummings; Harrington M. Cummings; Samuel M. Cummings; Michael Flaherty.
EIN: 383305718

2759
Genevieve and Donald Gilmore Foundation
6865 W. Hickory Rd.
Hickory Corners, MI 49060

Classified as a private operating foundation in 1981.
Donors: William U. Parfet; MPI Research; Cole Gilmore; Off Brothers; Michael J. Welsh; William C. Holland; Patricia Ann Casey; Carol B. Coggan; Donald & Ann Parfet Family Foundation; William D. Johnston.
Grantmaker type: Operating foundation.
Financial data (yr. ended 12/31/04): Assets, $8,650,330 (M); gifts received, $275,923; expenditures, $842,124; total giving, $0; qualifying distributions, $719,571; giving activities include $643,095 for foundation-administered programs.
Fields of interest: Museums.
Officers and Trustees:* William U. Parfet,* Pres.; Carol B. Coggan, V.P.; Martha B. Vandermolen,* V.P.; Sydney Waldorf,* Secy.; Donald R. Parfet, Jr.,* Treas.; Michael J. Spezia, Exec. Dir.; Peter Coggan; Steven H. Maloney; and 8 additional trustees.
Board Members: Sherwood M. Boudeman*; Martha G. Parfet; Ray T. Parfet, Jr.; Jenn Gudebski; Daniel G. Maloney; Jon G. Vandermolen; Courtney Vandermolen.
EIN: 386154163

2760
Gleaner Life Insurance Society Scholarship Foundation
5200 W. U.S. Hwy. 223
P.O. Box 1894
Adrian, MI 49221   (800) 992-1894
FAX: (517) 265-7745;
E-mail: gleaner@gleanerlife.com; URL: http://www.gleanerlife.com/memben.htm

Established as a company-sponsored operating foundation in 1992 in MI.
Donors: Gleaner Life Insurance Society; Laura Viers.
Grantmaker type: Operating foundation.
Financial data (yr. ended 6/30/04): Assets, $100,528 (M); gifts received, $110,742; expenditures, $115,641; total giving, $113,400; qualifying distributions, $115,550; giving activities include $113,400 for 117 grants to individuals (high: $1,000; low: $400).
Purpose and activities: The foundation awards college scholarships to high school seniors or graduates who are members of Gleaner Life Insurance Society.
Type of support: Scholarships—to individuals.
Limitations: Giving on a national basis.
Application information: Application form required.
  Initial approach: Contact foundation for application form
  Deadline(s): Apr. 15
Officers and Directors:* Richard Bennett,* Chair.; Michael J. Wade,* Secy.; Frank Dick; Dudley L. Douterman; Suann D. Hammersmith; David E. Sutton; Bill B. Warner; Mark A. Willis.
EIN: 383006741

2761
Leo and Betty Goldstein Family Foundation
28421 Eastbrook Ct.
Farmington, MI 48334

Established in 1997 in MI.
Donors: Betty Goldstein; Leo Goldstein.
Grantmaker type: Operating foundation.
Financial data (yr. ended 12/31/05): Assets, $618,195 (M); gifts received, $46,857; expenditures, $29,133; total giving, $27,100; qualifying distributions, $27,100; giving activities include $27,100 for grants (high: $10,000).
Fields of interest: Education; Human services; Jewish federated giving programs; Jewish agencies & temples.
Type of support: General/operating support.
Limitations: Applications not accepted. Giving primarily in MI. No grants to individuals.
Application information: Contributes only to pre-selected organizations.
Officers: Leo Goldstein, Pres.; Betty Goldstein, V.P.; Lisa Goldstein, Secy.-Treas.
EIN: 383347294

2762
Gratiot Physicians Foundation
300 Warwick Dr.
Alma, MI 48801-1014   (989) 681-3232
Contact: William Thiemkey, Secy.-Treas.

Established in 2001 in MI.
Grantmaker type: Operating foundation.

Financial data (yr. ended 12/31/04): Assets, $142,333 (M); gifts received, $25,975; expenditures, $6,016; total giving, $5,000; qualifying distributions, $5,000; giving activities include $5,000 for 8 grants to individuals (high: $1,000; low: $400).
Purpose and activities: Scholarship awards to residents of Gratiot County who live within the Gratiot Hospital's service area and who have been accepted at a professional school for training in one of the various branches of health care, such as medical or nursing school, podiatry, physical therapy, X-ray or ultrasound technolgy.
Fields of interest: Medical school/education; Nursing school/education; Public health school/education; Health sciences school/education.
Type of support: Scholarships—to individuals.
Limitations: Giving limited to residents of the Gratiot County, MI, area.
Application information: Application form required.
  Deadline(s): None
Officers: David K. Austin, Pres.; Gregg Stefanek, V.P.; William Thiemkey, Secy.-Treas.
EIN: 383571320

2763
Great Lakes Capital Fund Nonprofit Housing Corporation
(formerly Michigan Capital Fund for Non-Profit Housing Corporation)
1000 S. Washington Ave., Ste. 200
Lansing, MI 48910-1647

Grantmaker type: Operating foundation.
Financial data (yr. ended 12/31/04): Assets, $32,325,190 (M); expenditures, $8,306,644; total giving, $1,199,813; qualifying distributions, $10,890,139; giving activities include $1,199,813 for 160 grants (high: $150,000; low: $50), $7,106,831 for foundation-administered programs and $2,639,766 for loans/program-related investments.
Purpose and activities: Giving primarily to the delivery of quality, affordable housing to the poor and underprivileged, the promotion of efforts to facilitate self-sufficiency and upward mobility of very-low and low-income households, and the preservation of social welfare through efforts to facilitate the construction and development of housing for very low-, low- and moderate-income households in a manner directed to eliminate prejudice and discrimination, lessen neighborhood tensions, and combat the deterioration of communities throughout MI.
Fields of interest: Housing/shelter; Economically disadvantaged.
Limitations: Applications not accepted. Giving primarily in MI.
Application information: Unsolicited requests for funds not accepted.
Officers: Mark McDaniel, C.E.O. and Pres.; Thomas Edmiston, C.O.O. and Sr. V.P.; Christopher Cox, C.F.O. and Sr. V.P.
Directors: Barbara Anderson; James Bernacki; Sally Harrison; Marsha Kreucher.
EIN: 383126310

2764
Greenwood Foundation
c/o George H. Jury
P.O. Box 190
Wolverine, MI 49799-0190

Classified as a private operating foundation in 1979.
Donors: George H. Jury; Jo-Ann Jury.
Grantmaker type: Operating foundation.
Financial data (yr. ended 5/31/05): Assets, $1,653,644 (M); gifts received, $77,967; expenditures, $91,456; total giving, $0; qualifying distributions, $0.
Purpose and activities: Support only for the protection and feeding of wildlife.
Officers and Trustees:* George H. Jury,* Pres. and Treas.; John R. Findlay,* V.P. and Secy.; Claire A. Findlay; Michelle Forton; E. James Gamble; David McCauley; Harriet McGraw; Mark W. Paddock.
EIN: 381775875

2765
Guppy Lake Restoration Foundation
916 Patricia Ave.
Ann Arbor, MI 48103

Established in 1999 in MI.
Donor: Nathaniel Borenstein.
Grantmaker type: Operating foundation.
Financial data (yr. ended 12/31/04): Assets, $188,210 (M); expenditures, $1,128; total giving, $0; qualifying distributions, $1,066; giving activities include $1,066 for foundation-administered programs.
Officer: Nathaniel Borenstein, Pres.
Directors: Trina R. Borenstein; Ernest Kurtz.
EIN: 383490163

2766
Rose Hamlin Tennis National Honor Society Scholarship Trust
7677 W. Sharpe Rd.
Fowlerville, MI 48836-8748
Contact: Ann Glover, Tr.

Classified as a private operating foundation in 1988 in MI.
Grantmaker type: Operating foundation.
Financial data (yr. ended 12/31/05): Assets, $9,949 (M); expenditures, $1,035; total giving, $1,000; qualifying distributions, $1,035; giving activities include $1,000 for 2 grants to individuals (high: $500; low: $500).
Purpose and activities: Scholarship awards to students in the Fowlerville School District who are members of the National Honor Society.
Fields of interest: Higher education.
Type of support: Scholarships—to individuals.
Limitations: Giving limited to the Fowlerville, MI, area.
Application information: Application form available at Fowlerville High School. Application form required.
Deadline(s): Varies
Trustees: Edward Alverson; Ann Glover.
EIN: 382777453

2767
Hanflik Family Foundation
1301 Woodlawn Park Dr.
Flint, MI 48503

Grantmaker type: Operating foundation.
Financial data (yr. ended 12/31/05): Assets, $15,658 (M); expenditures, $1,000; total giving, $1,000; qualifying distributions, $1,000; giving activities include $1,000 for grants.
Fields of interest: Jewish agencies & temples.
Limitations: Applications not accepted. Giving primarily in MI. No grants to individuals.
Application information: Contributes only to pre-selected organizations.
Officers: Henry Hanflik, Pres.; Nancy Hanflik, Secy.-Treas.
EIN: 043730227

2768
Luella Hannan Memorial Foundation
(formerly Luella Hannan Memorial Home)
4750 Woodward Ave.
Detroit, MI 48201
URL: http://www.hannan.org/

Established in 1935 in MI; classified as a private operating foundation in 1997.
Donors: William Hannan†; Luella Hannan†.
Grantmaker type: Operating foundation.
Financial data (yr. ended 11/30/04): Assets, $19,175,618 (M); expenditures, $1,542,837; total giving, $0; qualifying distributions, $1,241,546; giving activities include $1,241,546 for foundation-administered programs.
Officers and Trustees:* Brenda L. Ball,* Pres.; Joel D. Steinberg, M.D.*, V.P.; Ruth Dunkle, Ph.D., Secy.; N. Charles Anderson,* Treas.; Timothy Wintermute, Exec. Dir.; Marcia Baum; Zena Baum; Sandra Bulger; Hon. Freddie G. Burton, Jr.; Michael A. Indenbaum; Ruth Ray; Ben Robinson; Brent S. Triest.
EIN: 381358386

2769
Andrew William Hartke Memorial Education Foundation
6060 Dixie Hwy., Ste. H
Clarkston, MI 48346-3476

Grantmaker type: Operating foundation.
Financial data (yr. ended 12/31/05): Assets, $8,861 (M); expenditures, $0; total giving, $0; qualifying distributions, $0.
Officer: Rockwood W. Bullard III, Pres.
Directors: Edward S. Hartke; Margaret W. Hartke.
EIN: 383472247

2770
Health Education Activities, Ltd.
178 E. Harmony Rd.
Spring Arbor, MI 49283-9703

Classified as a private operating foundation in 1988.
Grantmaker type: Operating foundation.
Financial data (yr. ended 11/30/04): Assets, $47,154 (M); expenditures, $554; total giving, $200; qualifying distributions, $200; giving activities include $200 for grants.

Trustees: Beth A. Kuntzleman; Ronald L. Markowski.
EIN: 382287791

2771
Edith D. and E. William Heinrich Mineralogical Research Foundation Trust
43805 Paradise Rd.
Chassell, MI 49916-9200 (906) 523-6364
Contact: Beverly Salotti, Tr.

Established in 1992.
Grantmaker type: Operating foundation.
Financial data (yr. ended 12/31/04): Assets, $448,152 (M); gifts received, $144; expenditures, $33,729; total giving, $28,717; qualifying distributions, $33,729; giving activities include $28,717 for 1 grant.
Fields of interest: Museums.
Limitations: Giving primarily in MI.
Application information:
Initial approach: Letter
Deadline(s): None
Trustee: Beverly Salotti.
EIN: 386585026

2772
Patricia Hickey Scholarship Fund
22563 Gill Rd.
Farmington Hills, MI 48335-4037
(248) 471-3048
Contact: Mary O. Hickey, Secy.

Donor: Philip J. Hickey, Jr.
Grantmaker type: Operating foundation.
Financial data (yr. ended 6/30/03): Assets, $17,383 (M); gifts received, $16,515; expenditures, $10,608; total giving, $10,500; qualifying distributions, $10,608; giving activities include $10,500 for 3 grants to individuals (high: $3,500; low: $3,500).
Purpose and activities: Award scholarships only to St. Agatha High School students whose parents belong to the parish.
Type of support: Scholarships—to individuals.
Limitations: Giving limited to residents of Redford, MI.
Application information: Application form required.
Deadline(s): Apr. 1
Officers: Amy Roemer, Pres.; Mary O. Hickey, Secy.
EIN: 382927699

2773
Hillier Scholarship Fund of Evart
142 N. Main St.
Evart, MI 49631 (231) 734-5563
Contact: Lynn Salinas, Tr.
Application address: P.O. Box 608, Evart, MI 49631

Established in 1996 in MI.
Donor: Hillier Family Foundation.
Grantmaker type: Operating foundation.
Financial data (yr. ended 12/31/04): Assets, $153,941 (M); gifts received, $6,338; expenditures, $7,420; total giving, $7,383; qualifying distributions, $7,383; giving activities include $7,383 for grants to individuals.

Purpose and activities: Scholarship awards to graduates from Evart High School, MI, attending an accredited undergraduate institution.
Type of support: Scholarships—to individuals.
Limitations: Giving limited to residents of Evart, MI.
Application information: Application form required.
 Deadline(s): Mar. 15
Trustees: Alan Bengry; Carolyn Curtin; Charles Flachs; Lynn Salinas; Marie Wilkerson.
EIN: 383299844

2774
Historic Warbird Foundation
8190 Fernwood Dr.
Augusta, MI   49012

Established in 2004 in MI.
Donor: Timothy J. Brutsche.
Grantmaker type: Operating foundation.
Financial data (yr. ended 12/31/05): Assets, $580,253 (M); gifts received, $66,827; expenditures, $54,132; total giving, $0; qualifying distributions, $64,331; giving activities include $51,801 for foundation-administered programs.
Officers: Timothy J. Brutsche, Pres.; Katherine I. Brutsche, V.P.
Director: David M. Mills.
EIN: 201773413

2775
Howard & Ivah Hoffmeyer Charitable Trust
c/o Chemical Bank & Trust Co., Trust Dept.
P.O. Box 2049
Midland, MI   48640
Contact: Cheryl L. Whitman, Trust Off.

Established in 1992 in MI.
Donors: Ivah Hoffmeyer†; Howard Hoffmeyer†.
Grantmaker type: Operating foundation.
Financial data (yr. ended 12/31/05): Assets, $2,058,794 (M); expenditures, $118,305; total giving, $103,000; qualifying distributions, $103,000; giving activities include $103,000 for 8 grants (high: $33,000; low: $250).
Purpose and activities: Giving for education, religion and public services in the Breckenridge, MI and St. Louis, MI areas.
Fields of interest: Elementary school/education; Secondary school/education; Higher education; Education; Hospitals (general); Government/public administration; Protestant agencies & churches.
Type of support: Equipment; Program development; Scholarship funds.
Limitations: Giving limited to Breckenridge and St. Louis, MI.
Application information: Application form not required.
 Initial approach: Letter
 Deadline(s): Jan. 5
 Board meeting date(s): Jan.
Advisory Committee: Brian Cross; George Kubin; James Laurenz; Andrew Root, Jr.; Charles Seeley.
Trustee: Chemical Bank & Trust Co.
Number of staff: None.
EIN: 383026124

2776
The Hogue Family Foundation
5342 Corunna Rd., Ste. C
Flint, MI   48505

Established in 2000 in MI.
Donors: John H. Hogue; Larry J. Hogue.
Grantmaker type: Operating foundation.
Financial data (yr. ended 12/31/05): Assets, $164,361 (M); gifts received, $128,400; expenditures, $95,264; total giving, $7,840; qualifying distributions, $7,840; giving activities include $7,840 for grants.
Fields of interest: Community development, alliance.
Limitations: Applications not accepted. Giving primarily in Flint, MI. No grants to individuals.
Application information: Contributes only to pre-selected organizations.
Officers and Directors:* Larry J. Hogue,* Pres.; John H. Hogue,* Secy.-Treas.
EIN: 383511320

2777
Charles & Alda Horgan Charitable Trust
c/o Citizens Bank Wealth Mgmt., N.A.
328 S. Saginaw St., N/C 002027
Flint, MI   48502
Application address: c/o Helen James, Trust Off., Citizens Bank Wealth Mgmt., N.A.,101 N. Washington St., Saginaw, MI 48607, tel.: (989) 776-7368

Established in 1996 in MI.
Grantmaker type: Operating foundation.
Financial data (yr. ended 9/30/04): Assets, $1,089,939 (M); expenditures, $67,037; total giving, $50,196; qualifying distributions, $55,023; giving activities include $31,728 for grants, and $18,468 for 27 grants to individuals (high: $684; low: $684).
Purpose and activities: Giving primarily for Christian churches and for human services; some giving for art scholarships to residents of Saginaw, MI.
Fields of interest: Historic preservation/historical societies; Arts; Scholarships/financial aid; Cancer; Human services; Federated giving programs; Roman Catholic agencies & churches.
Type of support: General/operating support; Grants to individuals; Scholarships—to individuals.
Limitations: Giving limited to Saginaw, MI.
Application information: Applicants must have a 2.5 GPA or better, display ambition and leadership skills. Application form required.
 Initial approach: Letter requesting application
 Deadline(s): July 1
Trustee: Citizens Bank.
EIN: 386661683

2778
Hubbard Memorial Museum Foundation
317 Hanover St.
P.O. Box 463
Concord, MI   49237

Classified as a private operating foundation in 1992.
Donor: Bruce Lindsay Co.
Grantmaker type: Operating foundation.
Financial data (yr. ended 12/31/04): Assets, $1,664,756 (M); gifts received, $5,254; expenditures, $40,691; total giving, $0; qualifying distributions, $37,050.
Officers: Earl Schultz, Chair.; Elizabeth Schultz, Vice-Chair.; Joan Ropp, Secy.; Don Haughey, Treas.

Trustee: John Kinney.
EIN: 656084788

2779
Institute for Religious Research
(formerly Gospel Truths Ministries)
1340 Monroe Ave. N.W.
Grand Rapids, MI   49505   (616) 451-4562
Contact: Luke P. Wilson, Exec. Dir.

Classified as a private operating foundation in 1986.
Donor: Roger P. Hansen.
Grantmaker type: Operating foundation.
Financial data (yr. ended 2/29/04): Assets, $324,914 (M); gifts received, $204,649; expenditures, $209,136; total giving, $6,400; qualifying distributions, $152,786; giving activities include $6,400 for grants, and $35,466 for foundation-administered programs.
Fields of interest: Christian agencies & churches.
International interests: Brazil.
Limitations: Giving primarily in San Juan Capistrano, CA.
Application information:
 Initial approach: Letter
 Deadline(s): None
Officers and Directors:* Roger P. Hansen,* Pres.; John H. Wilson,* Secy.-Treas.; Luke P. Wilson,* Exec. Dir.; James M. Grier; Ronald V. Huggins; Rev. Louis J. Konopka; Ruth A. Tucker.
EIN: 382678172

2780
International Centre for Healing and the Law
9292 W. KL Ave.
Kalamazoo, MI   49009
E-mail: info@healingandthelaw.org; URL: http://www.healingandthelaw.org/

Established in 2002 in MI.
Grantmaker type: Operating foundation.
Financial data (yr. ended 7/31/03): Assets, $251,658 (M); expenditures, $385,505; total giving, $4,000; qualifying distributions, $385,505; giving activities include $4,000 for 1 grant.
Purpose and activities: The center is dedicated to the restoration of the legal profession's calling to serve in the spirit of the public good.
Fields of interest: Legal services.
Limitations: Applications not accepted. Giving on a national basis. No grants to individuals.
Application information: Contributes only to pre-selected organizations.
Officers and Trustees:* David T. Link,* C.E.O. and Pres.; Michael C. Gergely,* V.P.; Richard L. Halpert; Robert F. Lehman; Hon. William G. Schma.
EIN: 611426645

2781
International Wildlife Preservation Society
322 N. Old Woodward Ave.
Birmingham, MI   48009-5318

Classified as a private operating foundation in 1993.
Grantmaker type: Operating foundation.
Financial data (yr. ended 12/31/05): Assets, $6,877 (M); gifts received, $5,048; expenditures,

$5,048; total giving, $0; qualifying distributions, $5,048; giving activities include $5,048 for foundation-administered programs.
Officers: William Gordon Hipp, Pres.; J. Leonard Hyman, V.P.; Jane Cambel, Secy.; David Rybicki, Treas.
EIN: 383113596

2782
Investment Education Institute
100 Renaissance Ctr., 34th Fl.
Detroit, MI 48243-1001

Established in 1998 in MI.
Grantmaker type: Operating foundation.
Financial data (yr. ended 9/30/05): Assets, $83,595 (M); gifts received, $950; expenditures, $674; total giving, $0; qualifying distributions, $0.
Fields of interest: Libraries (public).
Type of support: General/operating support.
Directors: Herbert K. Barnett; Donald E. Danko; Robert W. Hague; Richard A. Holthaus; Donald J. Houtakker; Kenneth S. Janke, Sr.; Kenneth S. Janke, Jr.; Robert A. O'Hara; Thomas E. O'Hara; Lewis A. Rockwell.
EIN: 383162028

2783
Jackson Literary & Art Association
1709 Probert Rd.
Jackson, MI 49203
Contact: Mary Lou Blanchard, Pres.
Application address: 3530 Maidstone Rd., Jackson, MI 49203

Classified as a private operating foundation in 1984.
Grantmaker type: Operating foundation.
Financial data (yr. ended 12/31/05): Assets, $250,316 (M); expenditures, $9,902; total giving, $9,200; qualifying distributions, $9,701; giving activities include $9,200 for 9 grants (high: $2,500; low: $250).
Fields of interest: Literature; Arts.
Limitations: Giving primarily in the Jackson, MI, area.
Application information:
Initial approach: Letter
Deadline(s): None
Officers: Mary Lou Blanchard, Pres.; Dorothy Kobs, Secy.; Joyce Grace, Treas.
Trustees: LeeAnn Kendall; Helen Greene; Kay Marcoux; Sue Schaffer; Nan Sparks; Beverly Walters; Comerica Bank.
EIN: 386089640

2784
June 8th Foundation, Inc.
12142 Peninsula Dr.
Traverse City, MI 49686

Established in 2002 in MI.
Donor: John W. Matz, Jr.
Grantmaker type: Operating foundation.
Financial data (yr. ended 12/31/05): Assets, $274,423 (M); expenditures, $31,367; total giving, $22,200; qualifying distributions, $22,200; giving activities include $22,200 for grants.

Limitations: Applications not accepted. Giving primarily in MI, with some emphasis on Traverse City. No grants to individuals.
Application information: Contributes only to pre-selected organizations.
Officers and Directors:* John W. Matz, Jr.,* Pres.; Jane Matz,* V.P.; Barbara Matz,* Secy.; Terry Griffin; John C. Matz.
EIN: 383637092

2785
The Kadry Foundation
26300 Telegraph Rd., 2nd Fl.
Southfield, MI 48034

Established in 2001 in MI.
Grantmaker type: Operating foundation.
Financial data (yr. ended 12/31/04): Assets, $439,127 (M); gifts received, $300,000; expenditures, $10,037; total giving, $8,262; qualifying distributions, $8,262; giving activities include $8,262 for 5 grants (high: $5,200; low: $200).
Limitations: Giving primarily in MI.
Officer: Othman Kadry, Pres.
EIN: 383593641

2786
Kaiser Family Charitable Trust
c/o First National Bank
88 N. Main St.
Three Rivers, MI 49093-1560

Established in 1997 in MI.
Grantmaker type: Operating foundation.
Financial data (yr. ended 12/31/05): Assets, $92,462 (M); expenditures, $7,161; total giving, $5,218; qualifying distributions, $7,161; giving activities include $5,218 for grants.
Limitations: Applications not accepted. Giving limited to Three Rivers, MI. No grants to individuals.
Application information: Contributes only to pre-selected organizations.
Trustee: First National Bank.
EIN: 386685615

2787
The Kalamazoo Aviation History Museum
6151 Portage Rd.
Portage, MI 49002

Classified as a private operating foundation in 1977.
Donors: Preston S. Parish; Suzanne D. Parish; Bowers Manufacturing Company; Diane Patriacca; George Polla; Albert Schiffer; Anna Schiffer; Mrs. Michael Schiffer; Michael Schiffer; Preston Parish; Vlado Lenoch; Arnold Herskovic; Ronda E. Stryker; William D. Johnson; Ley Smith; Lois Smith; Dorothy U. Dalton Foundation.
Grantmaker type: Operating foundation.
Financial data (yr. ended 12/31/04): Assets, $28,927,785 (M); gifts received, $4,242,780; expenditures, $5,883,990; total giving, $0; qualifying distributions, $9,696,746; giving activities include $4,261,954 for foundation-administered programs.
Officers and Directors:* Preston S. Parish,* Chair.; Suzanne D. Parish,* Pres.; John M. Ellis III,* V.P.; Ronald N. Kilgore, Secy.-Treas.; Robert E. Ellis,

Exec. Dir.; James Bridenstine; David Hatfield; Donald Parfet; William Parish; Barry Smith; Ley Smith; Dale Snodgrass; Wes Stricker.
EIN: 382144402

2788
Keep Coming Back
33 N. Broadway St.
Lake Orion, MI 48362-3101

Established in 2004 in MI.
Grantmaker type: Operating foundation.
Financial data (yr. ended 12/31/05): Assets, $16,513 (M); gifts received, $9,885; expenditures, $25,212; total giving, $0; qualifying distributions, $25,212; giving activities include $35,700 for 4 foundation-administered programs.
Officers: Kenneth S. Novack, Chair.; Chris Cumming, Vice-Chair.; David Rich, Secy.; Kenneth Campbell, Treas.
EIN: 383238477

2789
Albert F. Kessel Foundation
900 Fifth Third Ctr.
111 Lyon St. N.W.
Grand Rapids, MI 49503-2487
Contact: Albert F. Kessel, Pres. and Treas.

Newly funded in 2001 in MI by the Bette V. Kessel Charitable Trust.
Donor: Bette V. Kessel Charitable Trust.
Grantmaker type: Operating foundation.
Financial data (yr. ended 12/31/05): Assets, $28,121 (M); expenditures, $758; total giving, $0; qualifying distributions, $0.
Limitations: Applications not accepted. No grants to individuals.
Application information: Unsolicited requests for funds not considered.
Officers and Trustee:* Albert F. Kessel,* Pres. and Treas.; James A. Kessel, V.P.; Jeffrey B. Power, Secy.
EIN: 383545901

2790
Kiamba Medical Foundation, Inc.
P.O. Box 130
Niles, MI 49120-0130
Contact: Luzviminda N. Aquino, Dir.

Donor: Florentino A. Aquino, M.D.
Grantmaker type: Operating foundation.
Financial data (yr. ended 12/31/04): Assets, $26,081 (M); gifts received, $32,100; expenditures, $8,992; total giving, $8,000; qualifying distributions, $8,000; giving activities include $8,000 for foundation-administered programs.
Purpose and activities: Giving to provide medical training and support to physicians in the Sarangami Providence of the Philippines.
International interests: Philippines.
Type of support: General/operating support.
Limitations: Giving primarily in the Philippines. No grants to individuals.
Application information:
Initial approach: Letter
Deadline(s): None
Officer: Florentino A. Aquino, M.D., Pres.

Directors: Luzviminda N. Aquino; Kim Choong-Man, M.D.; Noemi Faustino, M.D.; Bart Saucelo, M.D.; Antonio Soledad; Hai Soonlee, M.D.
EIN: 383225516

2791
The Knowlton Foundation
1655 Yeager St.
Port Huron, MI 48060

Established in 1999 in MI.
Donors: Norman F. Knowlton; Agnes Knowlton.
Grantmaker type: Operating foundation.
Financial data (yr. ended 12/31/05): Assets, $561,777 (M); gifts received, $25,063; expenditures, $59,412; total giving, $0; qualifying distributions, $0.
Limitations: Applications not accepted. No grants to individuals.
Application information: Contributes only to pre-selected organizations.
Officers and Directors:* Suzanne A. Knowlton,* Secy.; Judith A. Campbell,* Treas.; Agnes J. Knowlton; Charles J. Knowlton; Norman F. Knowlton.
EIN: 383506105

2792
Koinonia Foundation
1939 Talamore Ct. S.E.
Grand Rapids, MI 49546

Established in 2004 in MI.
Donors: United Methodist Church; Dale L. Williams, M.D.
Grantmaker type: Operating foundation.
Financial data (yr. ended 12/31/04): Assets, $17,135 (M); gifts received, $133,000; expenditures, $129,898; total giving, $31,000; qualifying distributions, $129,898; giving activities include $31,000 for grants, and $93,303 for foundation-administered programs.
Purpose and activities: Giving primarily for medical and educational supplies for Rwanda.
Fields of interest: International development; International relief.
International interests: Rwanda.
Limitations: Applications not accepted. Giving primarily for the benefit of Rwanda. No grants to individuals.
Application information: Contributes only to pre-selected organizations.
Officers: Dale L. Williams, Chair.; Andrew K. Williams, Pres.; Christel G. Williams, Secy.-Treas.
Directors: Dale F. Williams; Susan B. Williams.
EIN: 201025162

2793
Douglas L. and Kathy J. Kool Charitable Foundation
2440 Glen Echo Dr. S.E.
Grand Rapids, MI 49546-5525

Established in 1993 in MI.
Donor: Douglas L. Kool.
Grantmaker type: Operating foundation.
Financial data (yr. ended 12/31/04): Assets, $200,355 (M); expenditures, $53,389; total giving, $51,832; qualifying distributions, $51,832; giving activities include $51,832 for 4 grants (high: $20,000; low: $6,666).

Fields of interest: Secondary school/education; Theological school/education; Protestant agencies & churches.
Type of support: Program development; Scholarship funds; Building/renovation.
Limitations: Applications not accepted. Giving primarily in Grand Rapids, MI. No grants to individuals.
Application information: Contributes only to pre-selected organizations.
Officers: Douglas L. Kool, Pres.; Harry DeJung, Secy.-Treas.
EIN: 383072060

2794
L & L Educational Foundation
160 McLean Dr.
Romeo, MI 48065 (586) 336-1608
Contact: Margaret Domenick-Muscat, Pres.
FAX: (586) 336-1635;
E-mail: peggy_domenick@llproducts.com
Application address: c/o Patti Lange, 160 McLean Dr., Romeo, MI 48065; tel.: (586) 336-3501; E-mail: patti_lange@llproducts.com

Established in 1987 in MI.
Donors: W. Eugene Lane; Robert M. Ligon; Lane Texas Partners; Lesle E. Cole; Susan Lane Mulka.
Grantmaker type: Operating foundation.
Financial data (yr. ended 12/31/05): Assets, $5,985,141 (M); gifts received, $501,750; expenditures, $248,220; total giving, $223,727; qualifying distributions, $225,727; giving activities include $223,727 for 97 grants to individuals (high: $6,656; low: $52).
Purpose and activities: Scholarships only to employees and their spouses and children of L & L Products, Inc.
Fields of interest: Higher education.
Type of support: Employee-related scholarships.
Limitations: Giving limited to residents of MI.
Application information: Application form required.
    Deadline(s): Apr. 1
Officers: Margaret Domenick-Muscat, Pres.; Shelly Lewallen, V.P.; Shelley Semren, V.P.; Susan Deeb, Secy.; Kara Wawrowski, Treas.
Trustees: Lesle E. Cole; Claude Z. Demby; Robert M. Ligon; Susan Lane Mulka.
EIN: 382785121

2795
Lahser Interspecies Research Foundation
3770 Lahser Rd.
Bloomfield, MI 48302-1535

Established in 2003 in MI.
Donors: Kevin J. Gaffney, M.D.; Scott B. Karlene, M.D.
Grantmaker type: Operating foundation.
Financial data (yr. ended 12/31/04): Assets, $36,366 (L); gifts received, $258,006; expenditures, $256,698; total giving, $0; qualifying distributions, $256,698.
Officers: Scott B. Karlene, M.D., Pres. and Secy.; Kevin J. Gaffney, M.D., V.P. and Treas.
EIN: 384542343

2796
Let These Animals Live, Inc.
c/o Gerald J. Jenkins
13990 Fairmont Dr.
Rapid City, MI 49676

Grantmaker type: Operating foundation.
Financial data (yr. ended 5/31/05): Assets, $204,175 (M); gifts received, $116,559; expenditures, $14,655; total giving, $0; qualifying distributions, $0.
Officers: Gerald J. Jenkins, Pres.; Mary Ann Bingham, Secy.-Treas.
Directors: Daniel Jenkins; Elizabeth Jenkins; Lerlie White.
EIN: 383301656

2797
Light Action Foundation
564 S. Main St.
Ann Arbor, MI 48104-2921

Grantmaker type: Operating foundation.
Financial data (yr. ended 6/30/03): Assets, $64,672 (L); gifts received, $5,700; expenditures, $3,859; total giving, $3,500; qualifying distributions, $3,500; giving activities include $3,500 for 4 grants (high: $1,000; low: $250).
Limitations: Applications not accepted. Giving primarily in Santa Monica, CA. No grants to individuals.
Application information: Contributes only to pre-selected organizations.
Officer: Henry J. Bednarz, Pres.
EIN: 382477755

2798
Living Free Foundation
(formerly Living Free Fellowship)
330 E. Maple Rd., No. 444
Birmingham, MI 48009
FAX: (248) 723-6640;
E-mail: livingfree@comcast.net; URL: http://www.livingfreefdn.org/

Established in 2000 in MI.
Donor: Lesli R. Cohen.
Grantmaker type: Operating foundation.
Financial data (yr. ended 12/31/04): Assets, $162,919 (M); gifts received, $90,570; expenditures, $140,894; total giving, $124,517; qualifying distributions, $136,417; giving activities include $124,517 for 13 grants (high: $25,000; low: $50), and $7,310 for foundation-administered programs.
Fields of interest: Public health; Health care.
Limitations: Applications not accepted. Giving on a national basis, with emphasis on MI. No grants to individuals.
Application information: Contributes only to pre-selected organizations.
Officer and Director:* Lesli R. Cohen,* Pres. and Treas.
Trustee: Margo V. Cohen.
EIN: 383538880

2799
Loiselle Foundation, Inc.
865 S. Main St., Ste. 2
Plymouth, MI 48170-2085
Contact: Jason R. Loiselle, Pres.

Established in 2004 in FL.
Grantmaker type: Operating foundation.
Financial data (yr. ended 12/31/04): Assets, $100
(M); gifts received, $100; expenditures, $0; total
giving, $0; qualifying distributions, $0.
Officers: Jason R. Lioselle, Pres. and Treas.;
Lawrence K. Loiselle, V.P. and Secy.
Director: Ronald G. Loiselle.
EIN: 200707679

2800
The Edward Lowe Foundation
58220 Decatur Rd.
P.O. Box 8
Cassopolis, MI 49031-0008 (800) 232-5693
Contact: Mark Lange, Exec. Dir.
FAX: (269) 445-2648; E-mail: info@lowe.org;
URL: http://www.EdwardLowe.org/

Established in 1985 in MI.
Donor: Edward Lowe†.
Grantmaker type: Operating foundation.
Financial data (yr. ended 12/31/04): Assets,
$116,564,708 (M); gifts received, $60,000;
expenditures, $5,743,155; total giving, $30,030;
qualifying distributions, $5,098,745; giving
activities include $30,030 for grants, and
$4,355,786 for 3 foundation-administered
programs.
Purpose and activities: Giving to champion the
entrepreneurial spirit by providing information,
research and education experiences which support
second stage entrepreneurs and the free enterprise
system.
Fields of interest: Business school/education;
Business/industry.
Type of support: Program development;
Conferences/seminars; Publication; Research;
Technical assistance; Program-related
investments/loans; In-kind gifts.
Limitations: Applications not accepted. Giving on a
national basis. No grants to individuals.
Publications: Informational brochure.
Application information: Contributes only to
pre-selected organizations.
Officers and Trustees:* Darlene B. Lowe,* Chair.
and C.E.O.; Daniel J. Wyant,* Pres. and C.O.O.;
Kathy J. Browning, Secy.; Donald R. Bauters, Treas.;
Mark S. Lange, Exec. Dir.; Thomas F. Meagher; Peter
L. Pairitz; John M. Pycik; Murray J. Swindell.
Number of staff: 22 full-time professional; 18
full-time support; 15 part-time support.
EIN: 382679673

2801
Lowell Area Housing, Inc.
P.O. Box 186
Lowell, MI 49331-0186

Classified as a private operating foundation in
1991.
Grantmaker type: Operating foundation.
Financial data (yr. ended 12/31/05): Assets,
$1,668,988 (M); gifts received, $102,690;
expenditures, $388,119; total giving, $601;

qualifying distributions, $601; giving activities
include $601 for grants.
Officers: Phillip H. Schneider, Jr., Pres.; Jody
Haybarker, Secy.
Director: Lillian J. Crout.
EIN: 381945437

2802
Dr. Faite R-P. Mack Family Conservancy Foundation
c/o Faite R-P. Mack
466 Fountain St. N.E., Ste. 1
Grand Rapids, MI 49503-3335

Established in 2001 in MI.
Grantmaker type: Operating foundation.
Financial data (yr. ended 12/31/05): Assets,
$26,326 (M); gifts received, $28,575;
expenditures, $27,248; total giving, $1,350;
qualifying distributions, $27,248; giving activities
include $1,350 for 26 grants to individuals (high:
$100; low: $50).
Type of support: Grants to individuals.
Limitations: Applications not accepted. Giving
primarily in Thailand.
Application information: Unsolicited requests for
funds not accepted.
Officers: Faite R-P. Mack, Pres.; Vou Many Norasing,
V.P.; Katie Mack, Treas.
Trustee: Seau Mack.
EIN: 383523916

2803
Mackenzie's Animal Sanctuary, Inc.
(formerly Mackensie's Shelter, Inc.)
8665 Thompson Rd.
Lake Odessa, MI 48849
URL: http://www.mackenzies.info/

Established in 2000 in MI.
Donor: James D. Azzar Foundation.
Grantmaker type: Operating foundation.
Financial data (yr. ended 12/31/04): Assets,
$241,429 (M); gifts received, $496,375;
expenditures, $434,034; total giving, $0; qualifying
distributions, $393,410.
Director: James D. Azzar.
EIN: 383533253

2804
The Masri Foundation
26300 Telegraph Rd., 2nd Fl.
Southfield, MI 48034

Established in 1994 in MI.
Grantmaker type: Operating foundation.
Financial data (yr. ended 12/31/04): Assets,
$512,671 (M); expenditures, $460; total giving, $0;
qualifying distributions, $0.
Officer: Haitham Masri, Pres.
EIN: 383188054

2805
Mayim Foundation
c/o Century Bank and Trust
100 W. Chicago St.
Coldwater, MI 49036

Established in 1996 in MI.

Donor: More About Jesus Ministries.
Grantmaker type: Operating foundation.
Financial data (yr. ended 5/31/05): Assets,
$277,621 (M); expenditures, $45,917; total giving,
$150; qualifying distributions, $150; giving
activities include $150 for grants.
Purpose and activities: The foundation's purpose is
to spread the gospel by the teachings of Paul
Sorko-Ram.
Limitations: Applications not accepted. No grants to
individuals.
Application information: Contributes only to
pre-selected organizations.
Officers: Peggy White, Pres.; Scott Connely, V.P.;
Alicia Rissman, V.P.; Sharon Wickey, Secy.; Nancy
Watreas, Treas.
EIN: 383262768

2806
Stanley and Homeira McDonald Charitable Foundation
c/o Stanley C. McDonald
910 N. Riverside
St. Clair, MI 48079

Grantmaker type: Operating foundation.
Financial data (yr. ended 12/31/05): Assets,
$3,438 (M); expenditures, $2,419; total giving,
$2,000; qualifying distributions, $2,000; giving
activities include $2,000 for 2 grants (high: $1,500;
low: $500).
Limitations: Giving primarily in MI.
Officers: Stanley C. McDonald, Pres. and Treas.;
Homeira M. McDonald, Secy.
EIN: 383539523

2807
McDonald's Historic Automobile Foundation
3126 Davenport Ave.
Saginaw, MI 48602-3656
Contact: Thomas W. McDonald Sr., Pres.
Application address: 1520 S. Thomas Rd., Saginaw,
MI 48609-9701

Donors: Thomas W. McDonald, Sr.; Ruth B.
McDonald.
Grantmaker type: Operating foundation.
Financial data (yr. ended 12/31/04): Assets,
$897,665 (M); gifts received, $46,000;
expenditures, $70,589; total giving, $2,000;
qualifying distributions, $2,000; giving activities
include $2,000 for 2 grants (high: $1,000; low:
$1,000).
Fields of interest: Historical activities.
Limitations: Giving primarily in Saginaw, MI.
Application information:
  Initial approach: Letter
  Deadline(s): None
Officers: Thomas W. McDonald, Sr., Pres.; Ruth B.
McDonald, V.P.; Thomas W. McDonald, Jr., Secy.;
William McDonald, Treas.
EIN: 382489799

2808
McFarlan Home
700 E. Kearsley St.
Flint, MI 48503 (810) 235-3077

Established in 1926 in MI; classified as a private operating foundation in 1974.
Grantmaker type: Operating foundation.
Financial data (yr. ended 12/31/04): Assets, $26,084,274 (M); expenditures, $1,146,705; total giving, $119,076; qualifying distributions, $953,726; giving activities include $119,076 for 6 grants (high: $29,076; low: $5,000), and $963,754 for foundation-administered programs.
Fields of interest: Historical activities; Arts; Higher education; Health care; Human services; Residential/custodial care, senior continuing care.
Limitations: Applications not accepted. Giving primarily in Flint, MI. No grants to individuals.
Application information: Grants made at discretion of board of directors.
Officers and Trustees:* Robert Bessert,* Pres.; Louise McAra, V.P.; Ellajane S. Rundles,* Secy.; David J. Millhouse, Treas.; Eleanor Brownell; Robert A. Burchfield; Bob Carpenter; Charlene Farella; Barbara Hayes; Kathleen Kelly; Perry Lemelin; Mary Snell.
EIN: 381390531

2809
The Mark C. and Carolyn A. McQuiggan Foundation
29653 Club House Ln.
Farmington Hills, MI   48334-2015

Established in 1998 in MI.
Donors: Mark C. McQuiggan; Carolyn A. McQuiggan.
Grantmaker type: Operating foundation.
Financial data (yr. ended 6/30/03): Assets, $380 (M); gifts received, $4,200; expenditures, $4,635; total giving, $3,350; qualifying distributions, $3,350; giving activities include $3,350 for 5 grants.
Type of support: General/operating support.
Limitations: Applications not accepted. Giving limited to MI. No grants to individuals.
Application information: Contributes only to pre-selected organizations.
Directors: Carolyn A. McQuiggan; Mark C. McQuiggan.
EIN: 383435181

2810
Medical Society Foundation
4438 Oakbridge Dr., Ste. B
Flint, MI   48532   (810) 733-6260
Contact: Peter Levine, Exec. Dir.

Reorganized into a private foundation in 2005 in MI.
Grantmaker type: Operating foundation.
Financial data (yr. ended 10/31/05): Assets, $478,998 (M); gifts received, $7,750; expenditures, $157,071; total giving, $1,700; qualifying distributions, $159,655; giving activities include $1,700 for grants.
Purpose and activities: The foundation acquires, provides, uses, develops and finances methods, means and facilities for post graduate, general and lay medical education and research.
Fields of interest: Medical school/education.
Type of support: Research.
Limitations: Applications not accepted.
Application information: Contributes only to pre-selected organizations.

Officers: Allen Turcke, M.D., Pres.; Walter Griffin, V.P.; Peter Levine, Exec. Dir.; M. Nagaraju, M.D.; Robert Soderstrom, M.D.
EIN: 382872664

2811
Memorial Nature Preserve
124 W. Allegan St., Ste. 1000
Lansing, MI   48933

Established in 1979; classified as a private operating foundation in 1985.
Grantmaker type: Operating foundation.
Financial data (yr. ended 12/31/05): Assets, $232,067 (M); gifts received, $7,969; expenditures, $5,581; total giving, $0; qualifying distributions, $1,852; giving activities include $1,852 for foundation-administered programs.
Officers and Directors:* Joan Ryan,* Pres.; Garry McKeen,* V.P.; Jane Thompson,* Secy.; J. Paul Thompson, Jr.,* Treas.; Gary Hoffman; Bruce Turnbull; Ron Kuykendall.
EIN: 382221489

2812
Meridian Foundation
c/o Mark D. Wahl
2204 Bollman
Lansing, MI   48917

Established in 2000 in MI. Classified as an operating foundation in March 2001.
Donors: Roger W. Imeson; Mark D. Wahl; David L. Gingery.
Grantmaker type: Operating foundation.
Financial data (yr. ended 6/30/03): Assets, $200,075 (M); gifts received, $4,800; expenditures, $5,075; total giving, $4,800; qualifying distributions, $5,075; giving activities include $4,800 for 3 grants (high: $3,700; low: $500).
Limitations: Applications not accepted. No grants to individuals.
Application information: Contributes only to pre-selected organizations.
Officer: Roger W. Imeson, Pres.
EIN: 383572442

2813
Michigan Association of the Blind and Visually Impaired, Inc.
c/o John McMahon
517 S. 13th St.
Escanaba, MI   49829

Classified as a private operating foundation in 1991.
Grantmaker type: Operating foundation.
Financial data (yr. ended 12/31/04): Assets, $63,250 (M); gifts received, $11,720; expenditures, $7,180; total giving, $0; qualifying distributions, $7,163.
Fields of interest: Blind/visually impaired.
Limitations: Giving limited to MI.
Officers: Michael Geno, Pres.; James Moore, V.P.; Donna Rose, V.P.; Deb Wild, Secy.; John McMahon, Treas.
EIN: 237365823

2814
Michigan Railroad Historic Preservation Foundation, Inc.
1225 10th St.
Port Huron, MI   48060

Classified as a private operating foundation in 1983.
Donor: Alexander G. Ruthven II, M.D.
Grantmaker type: Operating foundation.
Financial data (yr. ended 6/30/05): Assets, $367,486 (M); expenditures, $20; total giving, $0; qualifying distributions, $0.
Officer: Alexander G. Ruthven II, M.D., Pres.
EIN: 382477844

2815
Michigan Wildlife & Forest Preservation Foundation
1939 Briarcliff Blvd.
Owosso, MI   48867

Classified as a private operating foundation in 1992.
Donors: Fred Van Alstine; Kathleen Van Alstine.
Grantmaker type: Operating foundation.
Financial data (yr. ended 12/31/05): Assets, $367,085 (M); gifts received, $18,565; expenditures, $21,460; total giving, $0; qualifying distributions, $0.
Officers: Fred J. Van Alstine, Pres.; Kathleen Van Alstine, Secy.
EIN: 383005117

2816
Mid-Michigan Railway Historical Society
P.O. Box 79
Flint, MI   48501

Established in 1998 in MI.
Grantmaker type: Operating foundation.
Financial data (yr. ended 12/31/03): Assets, $10,675 (M); gifts received, $2,612; expenditures, $2,116; total giving, $200; qualifying distributions, $2,116; giving activities include $200 for grants, and $2,116 for foundation-administered programs.
Fields of interest: Historic preservation/historical societies.
Limitations: Applications not accepted. Giving limited to MI. No grants to individuals.
Application information: Contributes only to pre-selected organizations.
Officers: Don Westcott, Pres.; Richard Lawrence, V.P.; Terry Sweet, Secy.; David Friddell, Treas.
Directors: Jan Gormanda; Don Harban; Dan Mitchell.
EIN: 382484876

2817
Mid-Michigan Society for Animal Protection
P.O. Box 14264
Lansing, MI   48901-4264

Established in MI.
Grantmaker type: Operating foundation.
Financial data (yr. ended 3/31/05): Assets, $728 (M); gifts received, $7,819; expenditures, $8,138; total giving, $0; qualifying distributions, $8,073;

giving activities include $8,138 for foundation-administered programs.
Purpose and activities: Giving primarily to programs aimed to reducing pet over population.
Fields of interest: Animal welfare; Animals/wildlife.
Dircetors: Naney Bischot; Lisa Diehl.
Board Members: Charles Ogar; Michele Pursley.
EIN: 382920947

2818
Moholy-Nagy Foundation, Inc.
1204 Gardner Ave.
Ann Arbor, MI   48104-4321   (734) 996-4469
Contact: Hattula Moholy-Nagy, Treas.
URL: http://www.moholy-nagy.org

Established in 2003 in IL.
Donor: Hattula Maholy-Nagy.
Grantmaker type: Operating foundation.
Financial data (yr. ended 12/31/05): Assets, $152,382 (M); gifts received, $4,000; expenditures, $18,379; total giving, $15,500; qualifying distributions, $15,500; giving activities include $15,500 for 1 grant to an individual.
Purpose and activities: Giving for research on the works of artist Laszlo Moholy-Nagy.
Fields of interest: Arts, research.
Type of support: General/operating support; Grants to individuals.
Application information:
   Initial approach: Proposal
   Deadline(s): None
Officers: Andreas L. Hug, Pres.; Daniel C. Hug, Secy.; Hattula Moholy-Nagy, Treas.
EIN: 770612896

2819
Murff Manor, Inc.
1574 Cadillac Blvd.
P.O. Box 32539
Detroit, MI   48232

Established in MI.
Grantmaker type: Operating foundation.
Financial data (yr. ended 12/31/04): Assets, $51,879 (M); expenditures, $278,612; total giving, $0; qualifying distributions, $272,954; giving activities include $272,954 for 1 foundation-administered program.
Officers: James Talbert, Pres.; Errol Talbert, V.P.
EIN: 382838860

2820
Nakadar Foundation
3707 Durham Ct.
Bloomfield Hills, MI   48302   (248) 478-1100
Contact: Abdul Rahman Nakadar, Pres.

Donor: Abdul Rahman Nakadar.
Grantmaker type: Operating foundation.
Financial data (yr. ended 12/31/04): Assets, $727,803 (M); gifts received, $381,538; expenditures, $346,098; total giving, $302,471; qualifying distributions, $302,471; giving activities include $34,625 for 41 grants (high: $10,401; low: $50), and $267,846 for 1 foundation-administered program.
Fields of interest: Health care; Islam.
Limitations: Giving primarily in MI. No grants to individuals.

Application information: Application form not required.
   Deadline(s): None
Officers: Abdul Rahman Nakadar, Pres.; Najma Nakadar, V.P.
EIN: 382541935

2821
Navigations, Inc.
4820 Wayne Rd.
Battle Creek, MI   49015-1024

Grantmaker type: Operating foundation.
Financial data (yr. ended 12/31/04): Assets, $62,591 (M); expenditures, $350,482; total giving, $43,000; qualifying distributions, $43,000; giving activities include $43,000 for 1 grant, and $309,682 for foundation-administered programs.
Fields of interest: Goodwill Industries.
Type of support: General/operating support.
Limitations: Applications not accepted. Giving in Battle Creek, MI. No grants to individuals.
Application information: Contributes only to pre-selected organizations.
Officers and Directors:* Larry Keiser,* Chair.; Floyd Gates,* Vice-Chair.; Paul Smith,* Vice-Chair.; Robert S. Holderbaum, C.E.O. and Pres.; Trish Kern,* Secy.; James Galardi,* Treas.; Phil Anderson; James Baldwin; Robert Byelich; Cassandra Carter; Christine Gregory; Bonnie Hogoboom; Tina Kyger; James Lewis; Tracy Loza; John Nash; Rhonda Ostrander; Arnold Siegert; Cathy Winer.
EIN: 383029800

2822
Neff Family Foundation
3890 E. 79th St.
Indianapolis, IN   46240   (317) 577-3733
Contact: Virginia M. Neff, Secy.

Established in 1997 in IN.
Donors: Neff Engineering Co., Inc.; Harry M. Neff.
Grantmaker type: Operating foundation.
Financial data (yr. ended 12/31/04): Assets, $152,529 (M); gifts received, $28,145; expenditures, $7,000; total giving, $6,000; qualifying distributions, $6,000; giving activities include $6,000 for 17 grants (high: $900; low: $125).
Purpose and activities: The foundation supports hospitals and organizations involved with education, youth development, Down syndrome, cancer, and human services.
Fields of interest: Education; Hospitals (general); Down syndrome; Cancer; Youth development; Human services.
Limitations: Giving primarily in IN, MI, and WI.
Application information: Application form required.
   Initial approach: Contact foundation for application form
   Deadline(s): Sept. 30
Officers: Betty M. Neff, Pres. and Mgr.; Elizabeth W. Neff, V.P.; Julia D. Neff, V.P.; Virginia M. Neff, Secy.; I. Marie Neff, Treas.
EIN: 352008774

2823
Nehru-Lincoln Human Services
c/o Jitendra M. Mishra
1400 Michigan N.E.
Grand Rapids, MI   49503

Established in 1991 in MI.
Donors: Jitendra Mishra; Mithilesh Mishra.
Grantmaker type: Operating foundation.
Financial data (yr. ended 12/31/05): Assets, $16,608 (M); gifts received, $12,337; expenditures, $13,174; total giving, $0; qualifying distributions, $0.
Officers: Jitendra Mishra, Pres.; Mithilesh Mishra, V.P.
EIN: 382968976

2824
Sara L. Nieman Scholarship Fund
c/o Argus Corp.
12540 Beech Daly
Redford, MI   48239
Contact: Sandra K. Nieman, Pres.
Application address: 1012 Kensington, Grosse Pointe Park, MI 48230-1403, tel.: (313) 937-2900

Established in 2000 in MI.
Donor: Divine Child High School Scholarship Fund.
Grantmaker type: Operating foundation.
Financial data (yr. ended 12/31/05): Assets, $48,677 (M); gifts received, $10,810; expenditures, $4,759; total giving, $4,000; qualifying distributions, $4,000; giving activities include $4,000 for 4 grants to individuals.
Type of support: Scholarships—to individuals.
Limitations: Giving primarily to residents of MI.
Application information: Application form required.
   Initial approach: Letter or telephone
   Deadline(s): May 1
Officers: Sandra K. Neiman, Pres. and Treas.; Fred J. Ransford, Secy.
EIN: 383570934

2825
Greater Niles Economic Development Full Employment Corporation
1105 N. Front St.
Niles, MI   49120-1673

Classified as a private operating foundation in 1983.
Grantmaker type: Operating foundation.
Financial data (yr. ended 12/31/05): Assets, $955,143 (M); gifts received, $40,000; expenditures, $130,589; total giving, $42,500; qualifying distributions, $130,589; giving activities include $42,500 for grants, and $130,589 for foundation-administered programs.
Limitations: Applications not accepted. No grants to individuals.
Application information: Contributes only to pre-selected organizations.
Officers: Michael Dreber, Pres.; Michael Welch, V.P.; Tim Tyler, Secy.; Dominick Saratore, Treas.
Directors: Jerry French; Ted L. Halbritter III.
EIN: 382477818

2826
North Woodward Empowerment Center
17600 John Rd.
Detroit, MI 48203-2283 (313) 867-8348
Contact: Charles Tull, Pres.

Established in 1998 in MI.
Grantmaker type: Operating foundation.
Financial data (yr. ended 12/31/03): Assets, $795,278 (M); expenditures, $5,859; total giving, $0; qualifying distributions, $0; giving activities include $60,818 for foundation-administered programs.
Application information:
Initial approach: Letter
Deadline(s): None
Officers: Charles Tull, Pres.; John Gruchala, V.P.; John S. White, Secy.
EIN: 383354331

2827
Northern Michigan Foundation
P.O. Box 932
Elk Rapids, MI 49629 (800) 652-4326
Contact: Robert Kozak

Established in 1996 in MI.
Donor: Stephen L. Ranzini.
Grantmaker type: Operating foundation.
Financial data (yr. ended 12/31/04): Assets, $1,317,016 (M); gifts received, $54,036; expenditures, $101,687; total giving, $2,965; qualifying distributions, $90,186; giving activities include $2,965 for 3 grants (high: $1,280; low: $500), and $87,221 for loans/program-related investments.
Purpose and activities: The foundation makes loans to businesses in economically distressed counties in the eastern upper and northern lower peninsula of MI. Applicants to be considered for loan purposes must have been denied credit by traditional lending institutions such as commercial banks and credit unions.
Fields of interest: Community development, business promotion; Community development, small businesses.
Type of support: Program-related investments/ loans.
Limitations: Giving limited to MI.
Application information: Application form required.
Initial approach: Letter
Deadline(s): None
Officers: Stephen L. Ranzini, Pres. and Treas.; Charles S. McDowell, V.P. and Secy.
Directors: Andrew Johnson; Stuart Merillat; James Trumbull.
EIN: 383136089

2828
The David O'Hare Foundation, Inc.
2701 Blackberry Ln. N.E.
Grand Rapids, MI 49525-9760 (616) 363-1441
Contact: Maria O'Hare, Exec. Dir.

Established in 1997 in MI.
Donors: Patrick O'Hare; Maria O'Hare.
Grantmaker type: Operating foundation.
Financial data (yr. ended 12/31/05): Assets, $33,227 (M); gifts received, $945; expenditures, $1,519; total giving, $1,000; qualifying distributions, $1,060; giving activities include

$1,000 for 1 grant, and $1,060 for foundation-administered programs.
Limitations: Giving primarily in MI.
Application information:
Initial approach: Letter or telephone
Deadline(s): None
Officers: Lisa Squires, Chair.; Patrick O'Hare, Treas.; Maria O'Hare, Exec. Dir.
EIN: 383338582

2829
The O'Neill Foundation
30801 Barrington Ave., Ste. 125
Madison Heights, MI 48071-5105
(248) 524-4119
Contact: John O'Neill, Pres.

Established in 2003 in MI.
Donors: John O'Neill; Madeline S. O'Neill.
Grantmaker type: Operating foundation.
Financial data (yr. ended 12/31/05): Assets, $626,843 (M); gifts received, $1,500; expenditures, $28,535; total giving, $23,300; qualifying distributions, $24,280; giving activities include $23,300 for grants.
Application information:
Initial approach: Proposal
Officers: John O'Neill, Pres.; Madeline S. O'Neill, Secy.
EIN: 223887218

2830
Ohana Research Foundation
3207 River Dr.
Wallace, MI 49893-9612

Established in IL.
Donor: Alfred M. Tenny.
Grantmaker type: Operating foundation.
Financial data (yr. ended 12/31/04): Assets, $1,856,064 (M); expenditures, $49,411; total giving, $0; qualifying distributions, $48,006; giving activities include $35,200 for 4 foundation-administered programs.
Officers and Director: Alfred M. Tenny,* Pres.; Karen S. Tenny, Exec. Dir.; Dorothy Tolliver.
EIN: 943240747

2831
Paraklesis Ministries
642 Broadview St. S.E.
Grand Rapids, MI 49507-3537
Contact: James H. DeVries, Pres.
Application address: 205 Taos Ave. N.E., Ada, MI 49301

Classified as a private operating foundation in 1988.
Donors: DLP, Inc.; James H. DeVries; Judith L. DeVries; James H. and Judith L. DeVries Charitable Foundation.
Grantmaker type: Operating foundation.
Financial data (yr. ended 12/31/05): Assets, $4,155 (M); gifts received, $33,000; expenditures, $32,990; total giving, $10,000; qualifying distributions, $32,659; giving activities include $10,000 for grants, and $22,659 for foundation-administered programs.
Application information:

Initial approach: Letter
Deadline(s): None
Officers: James H. DeVries, Pres.; Judith L. DeVries, Secy.-Treas.
EIN: 382805132

2832
Pardee Cancer Treatment Fund of Bay County
P.O. Box 541
Bay City, MI 48707 (989) 891-8815
Contact: Vicki Place, Mgr.

Classified as a private operating foundation in 1991.
Donor: Elsa U. Pardee Foundation.
Grantmaker type: Operating foundation.
Financial data (yr. ended 9/30/05): Assets, $0 (M); gifts received, $144,800; expenditures, $145,386; total giving, $134,027; qualifying distributions, $134,027; giving activities include $134,027 for grants to individuals.
Purpose and activities: Financial assistance provided to help pay medical bills of cancer patients who are residents of Bay County, MI.
Fields of interest: Cancer.
Type of support: Grants to individuals.
Limitations: Giving limited to residents of Bay County, MI.
Application information: Application form required.
Initial approach: Letter
Deadline(s): None
Officer: Dominic Monastiere, Pres.
Directors: David Foster; Elizabeth Gresch; George R. Heron; Walter L. Howland; Gay McGee; Robert Sarow; Richard Steele; Andreas Teich.
EIN: 382877951

2833
Pardee Cancer Treatment Fund of Gratiot County
c/o Gratiot Community Hospital
300 E. Warwick Dr.
Alma, MI 48801 (989) 466-7411
Contact: Lala Threloff

Donor: Elsa U. Pardee Foundation.
Grantmaker type: Operating foundation.
Financial data (yr. ended 9/30/05): Assets, $0 (M); gifts received, $128,817; expenditures, $160,257; total giving, $143,570; qualifying distributions, $143,570; giving activities include $143,570 for grants.
Fields of interest: Cancer; Health organizations; Medical research.
Application information:
Deadline(s): None
Officers: Chuck Fortino, Vice-Chair.; Janet Sherwood, Secy.; Vicki Root, Treas.; Lala Threloff, Client Coord.
Directors: Kathleen Crumbaugh; Nancy Fenn; Carol Goffnett; Roger Keck; Don Pavlik; Jamey Seals; Gregg Stefanek; Bernard Siler; Brad Vibber; Robin Whitmore.
EIN: 383532130

2834
William Lyon Phelps Foundation
178 Lothrop St.
Grosse Pointe Farms, MI 48236
(313) 640-0123
Contact: Charles A. Parcells, Jr., Chair.
FAX: (313) 640-0011; E-mail: kparcells@aol.com;
URL: http://www.wlpf.org

Established in 1947 in MI.
Donors: David S. Arms; Charles A. Parcells, Jr.;
Frank H. Parcells†; Frances H. Parcells†; Charles S.
Arms; Mariana P. Wagoner; Anne Leete Parcells;
Charles A. Parcells Foundation.
Grantmaker type: Operating foundation.
Financial data (yr. ended 12/31/04): Assets,
$1,272,793 (M); gifts received, $30,496;
expenditures, $126,199; total giving, $0; qualifying
distributions, $117,248; giving activities include
$117,565 for foundation-administered programs.
Purpose and activities: Operates historical
buildings and museums in Huron City, MI.
Fields of interest: Museums.
Type of support: General/operating support; Annual
campaigns; Endowments; In-kind gifts.
Limitations: Applications not accepted. Giving
primarily in MI. No grants to individuals.
Publications: Financial statement.
Application information: Contributes only to
pre-selected organizations.
Officers and Trustees:* Charles A. Parcells, Jr.,*
Chair.; Kathryn Parcells,* Pres. and Treas.; Frances
Ann Benoit,* V.P. and Secy.
Number of staff: 2 part-time professional; 3
part-time support.
EIN: 386006236

2835
The Willard G. & Jessie M. Pierce Foundation
701 W. Cloverdale Rd.
Hastings, MI 49058 (269) 721-4470
Contact: Michelle Skedgell, Secy.

Established in 1989 in MI.
Donors: Willard G. Pierce†; Jessie M. Pierce†;
Flexfab Horizons International.
Grantmaker type: Operating foundation.
Financial data (yr. ended 12/31/05): Assets,
$34,014,247 (M); gifts received, $44,196;
expenditures, $1,569,890; total giving, $52,078;
qualifying distributions, $868,164; giving activities
include $52,078 for grants.
Purpose and activities: Giving to programs that
improve the quality of life for residents in Barry
County, MI. The foundation has a strong interest in
environmental education.
Fields of interest: Education; Environmental
education.
Type of support: Internship funds; Scholarship
funds; Research.
Limitations: Giving limited to Barry County, MI. No
support for No support generally for health care
institutions or programs. No grants to individuals.
Publications: Application guidelines; Informational
brochure; Newsletter.
Application information: Application form required.
Initial approach: Telephone
Copies of proposal: 1
Deadline(s): Oct.
Board meeting date(s): Oct.
Final notification: Dec.

Officers and Trustees:* Hilary F. Snell,* Pres.; Carl
Schoessel,* V.P.; Michelle Skedgell,* Secy.; James
R. Toburen,* Treas.; Christopher L. Cooley; Jeff
Garrison; Willard L. Pierce; Gary J. Pierce.
Number of staff: 6 full-time professional; 1 part-time
professional; 2 part-time support.
EIN: 382820095

2836
Project Freedom
c/o Detroit Commandery No. 1 K.T.
500 Temple Ave.
Detroit, MI 48201

Established in 2001 in MI.
Donor: Hospitalers Committee.
Grantmaker type: Operating foundation.
Financial data (yr. ended 12/31/05): Assets,
$1,133 (M); gifts received, $42,608; expenditures,
$11,096; total giving, $0; qualifying distributions,
$0.
Limitations: Applications not accepted. No grants to
individuals.
Application information: Contributes only to
pre-selected organizations.
Directors: George Loesch; Robert Legrand; Gil Rice.
EIN: 383610029

2837
Redeemer U.S. Foundation
2647 Cedar Grove S.
Jenison, MI 49428

Classified as a private operating foundation in
1995.
Grantmaker type: Operating foundation.
Financial data (yr. ended 12/31/05): Assets,
$2,485 (M); gifts received, $23,847; expenditures,
$24,016; total giving, $23,814; qualifying
distributions, $24,016; giving activities include
$23,814 for grants.
Purpose and activities: Support only for Redeemer
University College, Ontario, Canada for the benefit
of U.S. citizens enrolled or doing research work at
the university.
Fields of interest: Higher education.
Limitations: Applications not accepted. Giving
limited to Ontario, Canada. No grants to individuals.
Application information: Contributes only to a
pre-selected organization specified in the governing
instrument.
Officers and Trustees:* John Bolt,* Pres.; Jeffrey
A.D. Weiman,* Treas.; Rev. Dirk Hart.
EIN: 382944475

2838
The Redman Foundation
P.O. Box 630
Indian River, MI 49749

Established in 1999 in MI.
Donors: Robert Redman; Cynthia Redman.
Grantmaker type: Operating foundation.
Financial data (yr. ended 12/31/05): Assets,
$3,034,796 (M); gifts received, $4,000;
expenditures, $3,315; total giving, $0; qualifying
distributions, $0.
Purpose and activities: Support only for refuge land
in AR.
Type of support: General/operating support.

Limitations: Giving primarily in AR. No grants to
individuals.
Officers: Robert Redman, Pres.; Cynthia Redman,
V.P. and Secy.; Andrew Hoover, Treas.
EIN: 383517998

2839
The Reid Family Foundation
2600 Auburn Ct.
Auburn Hills, MI 48326

Established in 2000 in MI.
Donors: Glenn J. Reid; Flexible Products, Inc.
Grantmaker type: Operating foundation.
Financial data (yr. ended 12/31/05): Assets,
$2,769,838 (M); gifts received, $1,855,828;
expenditures, $31,275; total giving, $16,250;
qualifying distributions, $55,205; giving activities
include $16,250 for grants, and $15,025 for
foundation-administered programs.
Fields of interest: General charitable giving.
Type of support: General/operating support.
Limitations: Applications not accepted. Giving
primarily in MI. No grants to individuals.
Application information: Contributes only to
pre-selected organizations.
Directors: Sharon R. Grant; David J. Reid; Douglas
L. Reid; Glenn J. Reid; James G. Reid.
EIN: 912082304

2840
The Robey Charitable Trust
(formerly The Edmund W. Robey Charitable Trust)
2986 Meadow Hill Dr.
Clearwater, FL 33761-2825
Contact: Leon J. Robey, Tr.
Application address: 9 Brisbane Ct., Savannah, GA
31411, tel.: (912) 598-8202

Established in 1990 in FL. Classified as a private
operating foundation in 1995.
Donors: E.W. Robey; Leon J. Robey.
Grantmaker type: Operating foundation.
Financial data (yr. ended 12/31/02): Assets,
$189,409 (M); gifts received, $57,000;
expenditures, $69,977; total giving, $62,000;
qualifying distributions, $69,977; giving activities
include $62,000 for grants.
Purpose and activities: Giving primarily to
educational institutions maintaining Better
Effectiveness programs.
Fields of interest: Higher education.
Type of support: Program development; Scholarship
funds.
Limitations: Giving primarily in DE, MI, and NH. No
grants to individuals.
Application information:
Initial approach: Letter or telephone
Deadline(s): None
Trustees: A.M. Robey; Edmund W. Robey; Leon J.
Robey.
EIN: 596961615

2841
Michael Ross Memorial Foundation
c/o Jerrold Gottlieb
4501 College Blvd., Ste. 160
Leawood, KS 66211

Established in 1990 in KS.

Donors: Anthony Ross; Tony Stewart Motorsports, Inc.; Jim Head; Tom Kampeter; Vernon Massey; Ron Ditzfield; Gary Byers; Alan Ross; J.D. Byrder.
Grantmaker type: Operating foundation.
Financial data (yr. ended 12/31/03): Assets, $264,515 (M); gifts received, $178,404; expenditures, $114,385; total giving, $100,000; qualifying distributions, $99,929; giving activities include $100,000 for grants.
Purpose and activities: Support only for Bay Cliff Health Camp, MI.
Fields of interest: Youth development.
Limitations: Applications not accepted. Giving limited to Marquette, MI. No grants to individuals.
Application information: Contributes only to a pre-selected organization.
Trustee: Anthony Ross.
EIN: 481091978

2842
Nelson D. Rupp Foundation
P.O. Box 771
Marquette, MI 49855

Established in 2000 in MI.
Grantmaker type: Operating foundation.
Financial data (yr. ended 12/31/04): Assets, $162,241 (M); expenditures, $9,145; total giving, $8,897; qualifying distributions, $8,897; giving activities include $8,897 for 2 grants (high: $6,897; low: $2,000).
Limitations: Applications not accepted. No grants to individuals.
Application information: Contributes only to pre-selected organizations.
Trustee: Nelson D. Rupp.
EIN: 383563211

2843
Ghassan and Manal Saab Foundation
(formerly Ghassan M. Saab Foundation)
3407 Torrey Rd.
Flint, MI 48507-0718

Established in 1998 in MI.
Donor: Ghassan M. Saab.
Grantmaker type: Operating foundation.
Financial data (yr. ended 12/31/05): Assets, $3,106,716 (M); expenditures, $176,019; total giving, $156,900; qualifying distributions, $157,333; giving activities include $156,900 for 18 grants (high: $7,000; low: $200).
Fields of interest: Arts; Scholarships/financial aid; Education; Hospitals (general); Children/youth, services.
International interests: Lebanon; Middle East.
Limitations: Applications not accepted. Giving primarily in the U.S.; some giving in Lebanon. No grants to individuals.
Application information: Contributes only to pre-selected organizations.
Directors: Ghassan M. Saab; Khalil Saab; Nadim Saab.
EIN: 383416517

2844
The Seligman Medical Institute
1 Towne Sq., Ste. 1913
Southfield, MI 48076

Established in 2003 in NV.
Donor: Kiss Investment Co.
Grantmaker type: Operating foundation.
Financial data (yr. ended 12/31/05): Assets, $36,821 (M); gifts received, $91,050; expenditures, $84,814; total giving, $0; qualifying distributions, $0.
Officers: Scott J. Seligman, Pres.; Tammy Wong, Secy.-Treas.
Trustees: Erwin A. Rubenstein; Irving R. Seligman; Sandra Seligman.
EIN: 010792167

2845
The SEMP Foundation
(also known as Southeast Michigan Physicians)
17000 Hubbard Dr., Ste. 400
Dearborn, MI 48126   (313) 593-3915
FAX: (313) 593-3810;
E-mail: foundation@sempdocs.com; URL: http://www.sempdocs.com

Established in 2004 in MI.
Donors: Southeast Michigan Physicians, PC; Visionary Enterprises, Inc.; Kheder Davis & Associates.
Grantmaker type: Operating foundation.
Financial data (yr. ended 12/31/04): Assets, $54,426 (M); gifts received, $35,000; expenditures, $30,574; total giving, $15,780; qualifying distributions, $15,780; giving activities include $15,780 for grants.
Purpose and activities: The foundation will enable SEMP to support various community endeavors by giving charitable, scientific and educational grants and scholarships.
Fields of interest: Cancer research.
Limitations: Giving primarily in Dearborn, MI. No grants to individuals.
Application information: Application form not required.
    Deadline(s): None
Officers and Directors:* Robert C. Schwyn, M.D.*, Pres.; Steven Pickard, M.D.*, V.P.; Chilakapati Kumer, M.D.*, Treas.; Sunil Bhatia, M.D.; Sanganur Mahadevan, M.D.; Thomas S. Siegel, M.D.
EIN: 200747612

2846
The Nawal & Jalal Shallal Foundation
21711 W. 10 Mile, Ste. 227
Southfield, MI 48075

Donors: Jalal Shallal; Nawal Shallal.
Grantmaker type: Operating foundation.
Financial data (yr. ended 12/31/05): Assets, $21,693 (M); expenditures, $1,450; total giving, $1,200; qualifying distributions, $1,450; giving activities include $1,200 for 4 grants (high: $500; low: $100).
Fields of interest: Christian agencies & churches.
Limitations: Applications not accepted. Giving primarily in MI. No grants to individuals.
Application information: Contributes only to pre-selected organizations.
Trustees: Jalal Shallal; Nawal Shallal.
EIN: 383352933

2847
Share with the World Foundation
1417 Joliet Pl.
Detroit, MI 48207-2802

Established in 1997 in MI.
Grantmaker type: Operating foundation.
Financial data (yr. ended 12/31/04): Assets, $1,440 (M); gifts received, $30,324; expenditures, $29,300; total giving, $29,200; qualifying distributions, $29,200; giving activities include $29,200 for grants.
Fields of interest: Human services; Human services, personal services.
Type of support: General/operating support.
Limitations: Giving primarily in India.
Officers: Kanji Khatana, Pres.; Shanta Khatana, Secy.
Trustees: Dinesh Mehta; Kirit Pandya; Marcella Silva; Yvan Silva; Nalin Vaidya.
EIN: 383277120

2848
Jay & Susan Shayevitz Family Foundation
14240 Vernon St.
Oak Park, MI 48237-1388

Established in 2002.
Grantmaker type: Operating foundation.
Financial data (yr. ended 12/30/02): Assets, $22,058 (M); gifts received, $26,918; expenditures, $5,202; total giving, $5,202; qualifying distributions, $5,202; giving activities include $5,202 for grants.
Directors: Jay Shayevitz; Susan Shayevitz.
EIN: 912159549

2849
Sigma Gamma Foundation
P.O. Box 290
St. Clair Shores, MI 48080-0290

Grantmaker type: Operating foundation.
Financial data (yr. ended 12/31/05): Assets, $1,669,498 (M); gifts received, $404,461; expenditures, $81,392; total giving, $65,000; qualifying distributions, $65,000; giving activities include $65,000 for grants.
Purpose and activities: Support only for the Detroit Institute for Children, Detroit, MI.
Fields of interest: Medical care, rehabilitation; Children/youth; Disabilities, people with.
Type of support: General/operating support.
Limitations: Applications not accepted. Giving limited to Detroit, MI. No grants to individuals.
Application information: Contributes only to a pre-selected organization.
Officers and Directors:* Anna D. Warren,* Pres.; Anna W. Birgbauer,* V.P.; Jean M. Hull,* Secy.; Cynthia T. Semple, Treas.; Mary M. Begg; Marjorie S. Campbell; Lyn G. Carpenter; Mary K.S. Crain; Nancy M. Donnelly; Georgiann Henritzy; Didi T. Hughes; Eleanor F. Mecke; Dorothy Mooney; Nancy N. Nicholson; Nancy R. Smith.
EIN: 386074066

2850
Gilbert & Lila Silverman Fluxus Collection Foundation
4054 Cranbrook Ct.
Bloomfield Hills, MI 48301

Classified as a private operating foundation in 1990 in MI.
Donors: Gilbert B. Silverman; Lila Silverman.
Grantmaker type: Operating foundation.
Financial data (yr. ended 12/31/04): Assets, $4,286,791 (M); gifts received, $170,000; expenditures, $183,656; total giving, $1,900; qualifying distributions, $243,103; giving activities include $1,900 for grants, and $181,756 for foundation-administered programs.
Purpose and activities: Giving primarily for an art museum.
Fields of interest: Museums (art).
Limitations: Applications not accepted. No grants to individuals.
Application information: Contributes only to pre-selected organizations.
Officers: Gilbert B. Silverman, Pres.; Jon Hendricks, V.P.; Lila Silverman, Secy.-Treas.
EIN: 382839549

2851
Melvyn Maxwell & Sara Smith Foundation
32710 Franklin Rd.
Franklin, MI 48025-1135

Established in 1997 in MI.
Donor: Robert N. Smith.
Grantmaker type: Operating foundation.
Financial data (yr. ended 12/31/04): Assets, $1,654,539 (M); gifts received, $94,357; expenditures, $76,743; total giving, $0; qualifying distributions, $60,899; giving activities include $76,743 for foundation-administered programs.
Fields of interest: Museums.
Limitations: Applications not accepted. No grants to individuals.
Application information: Contributes only to pre-selected organizations.
Officer: Marvin S. Shwedel, Mgr.
EIN: 383335149

2852
Drs. Enrico and Esther Sobong Fundation
1442 Middlebrook Ave. S.E.
Grand Rapids, MI 49546-9724

Established in 2001 in MI.
Grantmaker type: Operating foundation.
Financial data (yr. ended 12/31/04): Assets, $148,879 (M); gifts received, $100,000; expenditures, $16,522; total giving, $15,700; qualifying distributions, $15,700; giving activities include $15,700 for 4 grants (high: $15,300; low: $100).
Fields of interest: Nursing school/education; Homeless.
Limitations: Giving primarily in MI.
Officers: Enrico Sobong, Pres.; Esther Sobong, V.P. and Secy.-Treas.
EIN: 383552149

2853
Society of the Brethren
P.O. Box 472
Leslie, MI 49251-0472

Established in 2002 in MI.
Donor: Diane Detore.
Grantmaker type: Operating foundation.
Financial data (yr. ended 12/31/05): Assets, $92 (M); gifts received, $11,678; expenditures, $12,023; total giving, $8,512; qualifying distributions, $9,183; giving activities include $8,512 for 1 grant.
Fields of interest: Elementary/secondary education.
Limitations: Giving primarily in Leslie, MI.
Officer: Diane Detore, Admin.
EIN: 382840350

2854
The Sonkin Family Foundation
3145 Bloomfield Shore Dr.
West Bloomfield, MI 48323-3505
Contact: Sheldon L. Sonkin, Pres.

Established in 1996 in MI.
Grantmaker type: Operating foundation.
Financial data (yr. ended 12/31/04): Assets, $1,046,391 (M); expenditures, $44,509; total giving, $41,626; qualifying distributions, $41,626; giving activities include $41,626 for 76 grants (high: $9,500; low: $20).
Purpose and activities: Giving primarily to Jewish federated giving programs and organizations, including schools, human services, and community centers; giving also for the fine and performing arts and education.
Fields of interest: Visual arts; Performing arts; Education; Human services; Jewish federated giving programs; Jewish agencies & temples.
Limitations: Giving primarily in MI.
Application information: Application form not required.
Initial approach: Letter
Deadline(s): None
Officer: Sheldon L. Sonkin, Pres.
EIN: 383322771

2855
Southeast Asia Art Foundation
71 Stone House Rd., Ste. 965
Hill, NH 03243-3258

Donors: John A. Thierry; Ann Gray.
Grantmaker type: Operating foundation.
Financial data (yr. ended 12/31/02): Assets, $43,223 (M); gifts received, $7,675; expenditures, $2,457; total giving, $1,822; qualifying distributions, $2,657; giving activities include $1,822 for grants, and $585 for foundation-administered programs.
Purpose and activities: Giving for research in the field of Southeast Asian art and archaeology.
Fields of interest: History/archaeology; Social sciences, research.
International interests: Southeast Asia.
Limitations: Applications not accepted. Giving on a national basis, with emphasis on MD, MI, and NH. No grants to individuals.
Application information: Contributes only to pre-selected organizations.

Officer and Trustees:* John A. Thierry,* Mgr.; Hiram W. Woodward, Jr.
EIN: 391285590

2856
Stepping Stones Foundation
203 S. Bridge St.
Dewitt, MI 48820

Established in 2004 in MI.
Donors: Abide Ministries; Dewitt Community Church; Block Imaging International.
Grantmaker type: Operating foundation.
Financial data (yr. ended 12/31/05): Assets, $4,369 (M); gifts received, $28,350; expenditures, $23,981; total giving, $2,735; qualifying distributions, $17,067; giving activities include $2,735 for grants.
Director: Bruce Block.
EIN: 201183305

2857
George Stines Family Foundation
2131 Itsell Rd.
Howell, MI 48843

Established in 2002.
Donor: Alfred Stines.
Grantmaker type: Operating foundation.
Financial data (yr. ended 12/31/05): Assets, $77,320 (M); gifts received, $147,990; expenditures, $55,015; total giving, $1,000; qualifying distributions, $1,000; giving activities include $1,000 for grants.
Trustee: Alfred Stines.
EIN: 300106874

2858
Lynn Stubberfield Foundation
126 E. Church St.
Adrian, MI 49221
Contact: Dan E. Bruggeman, Dir.

Grantmaker type: Operating foundation.
Financial data (yr. ended 12/31/05): Assets, $577,131 (M); expenditures, $45,950; total giving, $35,372; qualifying distributions, $35,372; giving activities include $35,372 for grants.
Application information: Application form not required.
Deadline(s): None
Director: Dan E. Bruggeman.
EIN: 383571515

2859
The Thomas Taylor & Charlotte Valentine Taylor Educational Foundation
c/o Tyler & Reynolds, PC
77 Summer St.
Boston, MA 02110

Established in 1984 in MA.
Donor: James L. Smithson.
Grantmaker type: Operating foundation.
Financial data (yr. ended 12/31/02): Assets, $6,053,908 (M); expenditures, $480,045; total giving, $440,765; qualifying distributions, $436,630; giving activities include $440,765 for grants.

Fields of interest: Higher education.
Limitations: Applications not accepted. Giving limited to Hartford, CT, Grinnell, IA, and Hillsdale, MI. No grants to individuals.
Application information: Contributes only to pre-selected organizations specified in the governing instrument.
Trustees: Sumner R. Andrews; Gordon E. Cadwgan; Gerald B. O'Grady III; James L. Smithson.
EIN: 222571261

2860
The Steve and Elizabeth Tengler Educational Fund
(also known as S.E.T. Educational Fund)
P.O. Box 36656
Grosse Pointe Farms, MI 48236
E-mail: contact@setfund.org; URL: http://www.setfund.org/

Established in 1999 in MI.
Donors: Steve Tengler; Elizabeth Tengler; Jeff Cornell; Catherine Cornell; Joe Johnston; Susan Johnston.
Grantmaker type: Operating foundation.
Financial data (yr. ended 12/31/04): Assets, $52,815 (M); gifts received, $17,042; expenditures, $5,576; total giving, $2,100; qualifying distributions, $5,576; giving activities include $2,100 for 1 grant to an individual.
Purpose and activities: Scholarship awards to MI residents, who are attending a public university in MI, and who are not related to the trustees or a previous scholarship winner.
Type of support: Scholarships—to individuals.
Limitations: Giving limited to residents of MI.
Application information: See fund Web site for full application requirements and guidelines, including downloadable application form. Application form required.
Initial approach: Letter
Deadline(s): June 1
Trustees: Catherine Cornell; Jeff Cornell; Elizabeth Tengler.
EIN: 383432884

2861
Torgow Family Foundation
220 W. Congress St., Ste. 500
Detroit, MI 48226-3289
Application address: P.O. Box 31-0737, Detroit, Mi 48231

Established in 2000 in MI.
Donors: Gary Torgow; Maika Torgow.
Grantmaker type: Operating foundation.
Financial data (yr. ended 12/31/04): Assets, $50,636 (M); gifts received, $50,000; expenditures, $62,672; total giving, $56,800; qualifying distributions, $62,671; giving activities include $56,800 for grants.
Purpose and activities: Giving primarily for Yeshivas.
Fields of interest: Jewish federated giving programs; Jewish agencies & temples.
Type of support: General/operating support.
Limitations: Giving primarily in NY and MI. No grants to individuals.
Application information:
Initial approach: Letter
Deadline(s): None

Officers and Trustees:* Gary Torgow,* Pres.; Maika Torgow, Secy.; Eliezer Torgow; Yonah Torgow.
EIN: 383560590

2862
Troy Internal Medicine Foundation
4600 Investment Dr., Ste. 300
Troy, MI 48098

Established in 2001 in MI.
Grantmaker type: Operating foundation.
Financial data (yr. ended 12/31/05): Assets, $8,814 (M); expenditures, $590; total giving, $0; qualifying distributions, $0.
Directors: James Henderson; Robert Martel; Mark Wilson.
EIN: 383563184

2863
University Renal Research and Education Association
(doing business as Arbor Research Collaborative for Health)
c/o Friedrich Port, M.D., Pres.
315 W. Huron St., Ste. 260
Ann Arbor, MI 48103-4262
URL: http://www.arborresearch.org/

Established in 1996 in MI. Classified as a private operating foundation in 1997.
Grantmaker type: Operating foundation.
Financial data (yr. ended 12/31/04): Assets, $17,653,492 (M); gifts received, $8,127,641; expenditures, $7,465,820; total giving, $0; qualifying distributions, $7,572,355.
Officers: Friedrich Port, M.D., M.S., Pres.; Amy Goode, Secy.; Trinh Pifer, Treas.
Directors: Mark Barr; David Dickenson; Lee Henderson; Maureen Michael; John Nemann; Peter De Oreo.
EIN: 383289521

2864
Lyle and Diane Victor Foundation
6130 Wing Lake Rd.
Bloomfield Hills, MI 48301

Established in 2000 in MI.
Donor: Lyle D. Victor.
Grantmaker type: Operating foundation.
Financial data (yr. ended 7/31/03): Assets, $33,021 (M); gifts received, $9,016; expenditures, $2,669; total giving, $2,660; qualifying distributions, $2,655; giving activities include $2,660 for 3 grants.
Limitations: Giving primarily in MI.
Application information:
Initial approach: Letter
Deadline(s): None
Directors: Diane A. Victor; Lyle D. Victor; Nadine E. Victor; Natalie N. Victor.
EIN: 383497934

2865
Irene M. & Milton R. Weed Foundation
1009 Audubon Rd.
Grosse Pointe Park, MI 48230
Contact: Bruno F. Domzalski, Dir.

Established in 2004 in MI.
Grantmaker type: Operating foundation.
Financial data (yr. ended 12/31/05): Assets, $1,865,128 (M); gifts received, $1,761,630; expenditures, $42,915; total giving, $39,500; qualifying distributions, $39,500; giving activities include $39,500 for grants.
Fields of interest: Education; Human services.
Limitations: Giving limited to the U.S.
Application information: Application form not required.
Initial approach: Letterhead
Deadline(s): None
Director: Bruno F. Domzalski.
EIN: 300241901

2866
Weinlander, Fitzhugh & Schairer Foundation, Inc.
P.O. Box 775
Bay City, MI 48707
Contact: Michael L. Hanisko, Pres.

Established in 1997 in MI. Classified as a private operating foundation in 1999.
Grantmaker type: Operating foundation.
Financial data (yr. ended 9/30/03): Assets, $10,190 (M); gifts received, $11,035; expenditures, $8,933; total giving, $8,933; qualifying distributions, $8,933; giving activities include $8,933 for 16 grants (high: $1,666; low: $50).
Limitations: Giving primarily in Bay City, MI.
Application information:
Initial approach: Letter
Deadline(s): None
Officers: Michael L. Hanisko, Pres.; Robert J. Duyck, Secy.
EIN: 383383676

2867
Evelyn & Fredrick Weissman Education and Charitable Foundation
30238 Spring River Dr.
Southfield, MI 48076-1047 (248) 203-9270
Contact: Rebecca Weissman, Dir.

Established in 1994 in MI.
Donor: Fredrick & Evelyn Weissman Charitable Lead Trust.
Grantmaker type: Operating foundation.
Financial data (yr. ended 12/31/04): Assets, $114,974 (M); gifts received, $10,000; expenditures, $55,037; total giving, $52,162; qualifying distributions, $52,162; giving activities include $43,662 for 8 grants (high: $20,000; low: $30), and $8,500 for 4 grants to individuals (high: $2,800; low: $1,700).
Fields of interest: Performing arts, dance; Arts; Education.
Type of support: Scholarships—to individuals.
Limitations: Giving on a national basis, with some emphasis on CO.
Application information: Application form required.
Deadline(s): None
Directors: Margaret Futernick; Patricia Weissman; Rebecca Weissman.
EIN: 383196147

2868
Lorna A. Welch Charitable Foundation
P.O. Box 390
Flushing, MI 48433

Established in 2001 in MI.
Donor: James L. Orr.
Grantmaker type: Operating foundation.
Financial data (yr. ended 12/31/04): Assets, $360,387 (M); expenditures, $17,253; total giving, $17,000; qualifying distributions, $17,000; giving activities include $17,000 for grants to individuals.
Fields of interest: Higher education.
Type of support: Scholarships—to individuals.
Limitations: Giving primarily to residents of Flushing, MI.
Trustee: James L. Orr.
EIN: 383553903

2869
Welter Foundation, Inc.
66480 High Meadow Ct.
Edwardsburg, MI 49112
Contact: Jill Ford
Application IN tel.: (574) 596-2543 (Jill Ford)

Established in 1997 in IN.
Donors: Edward P. Welter; Wilhelmina J. Welter.
Grantmaker type: Operating foundation.
Financial data (yr. ended 12/31/04): Assets, $5,476,927 (M); expenditures, $300,679; total giving, $248,150; qualifying distributions, $246,278; giving activities include $248,150 for 25 grants (high: $100,000; low: $200).
Fields of interest: Higher education, university; Diabetes research; Crime/violence prevention, child abuse; Human services; Salvation Army; Foundations (community); Federated giving programs; Christian agencies & churches.
Limitations: Giving primarily in Elkhart, IN.
Application information:
Initial approach: Letter
Deadline(s): None
Officers and Directors:* Edward P. Welter,* Pres.; Cynthia S. Gilard,* Secy.; Wilhelmina J. Welter,* Treas.
EIN: 352023590
Selected grants: The following grants were reported in 2004.
$100,000 to Charlevoix County Community Foundation, East Jordan, MI.
$40,000 to Beaver Island Rural Health Center, Beaver Island, MI.
$20,000 to Ball State University Foundation, Muncie, IN.
$15,000 to Child Abuse Prevention Services, Elkhart, IN.
$10,000 to Juvenile Diabetes Research Foundation International, South Bend, IN.
$10,000 to Salvation Army of Elkhart, Elkhart, IN.
$10,000 to United Way of Elkhart County, Elkhart, IN.
$5,000 to Loveway, Inc., Middlebury, IN.
$3,500 to Oaklawn Foundation for Mental Health, Goshen, IN.
$1,500 to Martin Memorial Foundation, Stuart, FL.

2870
The Widow's Mite Foundation
5657 Glasgow Dr.
Troy, MI 48098-3156 (248) 879-7970
Contact: Executive Board

Established in 1994 in MI.
Donors: Stephen Marr; Mary Marr.
Grantmaker type: Operating foundation.
Financial data (yr. ended 12/31/05): Assets, $59,718 (M); gifts received, $279,557; expenditures, $225,696; total giving, $0; qualifying distributions, $0.
Purpose and activities: Giving limited to Christian clergy and lay ministries.
Fields of interest: Christian agencies & churches.
Application information: Application form required.
Deadline(s): None
Officers: Stephen Marr, Pres.; Mary Marr, V.P. and Treas.; Merlynn Hanson, Secy.
Director: Steven Wright.
EIN: 383190906

2871
The Gerard I. and Beverly L. Winkle Foundation
7116 W. Lake Dr.
Lake City, MI 49651-8795
Contact: Gerard I. Winkle, Tr.

Established in MI.
Donors: Gerard I. Winkle; Beverly L. Winkle.
Grantmaker type: Operating foundation.
Financial data (yr. ended 12/31/05): Assets, $578,537 (M); expenditures, $27,210; total giving, $24,905; qualifying distributions, $24,905; giving activities include $24,905 for grants.
Purpose and activities: Giving primarily for Christian schools and churches.
Fields of interest: Education; Protestant agencies & churches.
Limitations: Giving primarily in western MI. No grants to individuals.
Application information: Application form not required.
Initial approach: Letter
Deadline(s): None
Trustees: Beverly L. Winkle; Gerard I. Winkle.
EIN: 383212032

2872
J. A. Woollam Foundation
c/o D.R. Stogsdill
233 S. 13th St., Ste. 1900
Lincoln, NE 68508-2095

Established in 2001 in NE.
Donors: John A. Woollam; John A. Woollam Co., Inc.
Grantmaker type: Operating foundation.
Financial data (yr. ended 12/31/04): Assets, $4,908,418 (M); gifts received, $3,623,242; expenditures, $517,367; total giving, $499,000; qualifying distributions, $508,388; giving activities include $499,000 for 17 grants (high: $210,000; low: $1,000).
Fields of interest: Environment, natural resources.
Limitations: Applications not accepted. Giving primarily in MI and NE; some funding also in CA. No grants to individuals.
Application information: Contributes only to pre-selected organizations.

Trustee: John A. Woollam.
EIN: 470812219

2873
World Outreach International
c/o Adalberto Vallejo
P.O. Box 10027
Detroit, MI 48210-0027

Established in 1999 in MI.
Grantmaker type: Operating foundation.
Financial data (yr. ended 12/31/02): Assets, $14,923 (M); gifts received, $4,590; expenditures, $2,575; total giving, $0; qualifying distributions, $1,575; giving activities include $1,575 for foundation-administered programs.
Officers: Adalberto Vallejo, Pres.; Osvaldo Lasacunte, Secy.
Director: Pastor Luz Vallejo.
EIN: 383090684

2874
Francis L. Wright and Bernice Harroff Wright Charitable Trust
c/o Terry L. Dalrymple
16728 Cleveland Ave.
Galien, MI 49113

Established in MI.
Grantmaker type: Operating foundation.
Financial data (yr. ended 12/31/05): Assets, $358,435 (M); expenditures, $24,529; total giving, $9,985; qualifying distributions, $19,209; giving activities include $9,985 for 27 grants (high: $1,700; low: $10).
Fields of interest: Human services.
Limitations: Applications not accepted. Giving primarily in the Galien and Buchanan, MI, areas. No grants to individuals.
Application information: Contributes only to pre-selected organizations.
Trustees: Carol L. Dalrymple; Terry L. Dalrymple.
EIN: 383081792

2875
Orlo H. Wright Scholarship Foundation
10225 Whittaker Rd.
Ypsilanti, MI 48197-8915
Contact: Sharon Wenzel, Tr.

Grantmaker type: Operating foundation.
Financial data (yr. ended 3/31/03): Assets, $34,140 (L); gifts received, $50; expenditures, $1,000; total giving, $1,000; qualifying distributions, $1,000; giving activities include $1,000 for grants to individuals.
Purpose and activities: Scholarships only to graduates of Lincoln High School, MI.
Type of support: Scholarships—to individuals.
Limitations: Giving limited to residents of Ypsilanti, MI.
Application information: Application form required.
Deadline(s): Apr. 10
Trustees: Sharon Wenzel; Sidney Wright.
EIN: 386432958

424   **THE MICHIGAN FOUNDATION DIRECTORY**

2876
Wyandotte Public Schools Scholarship Foundation

(also known as WPS Scholarship Foundation)
(formerly Wyandotte Public Schools Foundation)
P.O. Box 412
Wyandotte, MI   48192-0012   (734) 246-1008
E-mail: wpsf@wyandotte.org; URL: http://
www.wyandotte.org/wpsf.html
Application address: c/o Wyandotte Regional High
School, Principal, 540 Eureka Rd., Wyandotte, MI
48192-5709, tel.: (734) 246-1000

Established in 1989 in MI.
Grantmaker type: Operating foundation.
Financial data (yr. ended 6/30/03): Assets,
$414,674 (M); gifts received, $53,969;
expenditures, $54,185; total giving, $51,316;
qualifying distributions, $54,185; giving activities
include $300 for 1 grant, and $51,016 for 62 grants
to individuals (high: $1,246; low: $100).
Purpose and activities: College scholarships to
seniors at Wyandotte Regional High School in
Wyandotte, MI.
Type of support: Scholarships—to individuals.
Limitations: Giving limited to residents of
Wyandotte, MI.
Application information: Application forms available
in high school office. Application form required.
  Deadline(s): Apr. 28

Officers and Directors:* Ron Gulyas,* Pres.; James
Candela,* V.P.; Patricia Cole,* Secy.; Jeff Kreger,*
Treas.; Marcia Aller; Bob Deters; John Engfehr; Lisa
Kaiser; William E. Kreger; Christine Mathews; Mary
McFarlane; Kenneth Prygoski; James Sexton; Robert
Sharon, M.D.; Al Sliwinski; Patrick Sutka; James
Wagner.
EIN: 382898957

2877
Zemke Scholarship Fund
4396 Coats Grove Rd.
Hastings, MI   49058-8425
Application address: c/o Maple Valley Schools,
Attn.: Dawn Yager, Guidance Dept., 11090
Nashiville Hwy., Vermontville, MI 49096

Donor: Martha Zemke.
Grantmaker type: Operating foundation.
Financial data (yr. ended 12/31/05): Assets,
$13,366 (M); gifts received, $311; expenditures,
$504; total giving, $500; qualifying distributions,
$504; giving activities include $500 for 1 grant to
an individual.
Purpose and activities: Scholarship awards to a
graduating senior at Maple Valley High School, MI
intending to study agriculture, health, education,
mathematics or science.

Type of support: Scholarships—to individuals.
Limitations: Giving limited to the residents of
Vermontville, MI, area.
Application information: Scholarships are for 1 year
only. Application form required.
  Deadline(s): Apr. 1
Trustees: Jeanne Bocher; Margaret Cook; Edith
Grashuis; Martha Zemke; Mary Zemke.
EIN: 386515402

2878
Zimmer Foundation
350 Corrie Rd.
Ann Arbor, MI   48105-1033

Classified as a private operating foundation in
1982.
Donors: Edward F. Zimmer; Kathryn M. Straith.
Grantmaker type: Operating foundation.
Financial data (yr. ended 9/30/03): Assets,
$1,550,274 (M); gifts received, $127,212;
expenditures, $205,461; total giving, $0; qualifying
distributions, $178,272; giving activities include
$89,759 for foundation-administered programs.
Officers: Edward F. Zimmer, Pres. and Treas.;
Kathryn Zimmer, Secy.
Director: Amy Zimmer.
EIN: 382335996

INDEX TO DONORS, OFFICERS, TRUSTEES

Hodgkins, Charles D., 850
Hodgkins, Charles D., III, 850
Hodgkins, Shelby S., 850
Hodgkins, Whitney S., 850
Hodgman, William, 1212
Hoeg, Thomas E., 2559
Hoekstra, Jeni, 2689
Hoekstra, Peter, 2512
Hoensheid, Lauraine, 2542
Hoexum, Ken, 2514
Hof, Ellen, 851
Hof, Helmut, 851
Hofbauer, Gregory J., 791
Hoff, Dan, 2462
Hoff, Rackeline, 603
Hoffer, Marilyn, 1131
Hoffine, Phil, 2399
Hoffius, Dirk, 2293
Hoffius, R. Stuart, 2566
Hoffman, Clarissa, 2359
Hoffman, Gary, 2811
Hoffman, Mark, 2538
Hoffman, Stanley, 16
Hoffman, Steve, 2531
Hoffman, Wesley, 2369
Hoffmann, Fred, 2501
Hoffmeyer, Howard, 2775
Hoffmeyer, Ivah, 2775
Hofman, Thomas D., 723
Hogenson, Tom, 2554
Hogoboom, Bonnie, 2821
Hogue, John H., 2776
Hogue, Larry J., 2776
Hoisington, Robert E., 2559
Hoke, Karen M., 1335
Holbrook, Deborah, 662
Holcim (US) Inc., 2216
Holcomb, Keith A., 852
Holcomb, Steven J., 852
Holden, James S., 853
Holden, Lynelle A., 853
Holden, Patricia, 151
Holderbaum, Robert S., 2821
Holdridge, Diana, 2404
Hole, David W., 2223
Holewinski, Katherine, 2369
Holik, Heather, 1644
Holik, Jan, 1644
Holkeboer, Jim, 351
Holl, Dale S., 854
Holl, Patricia M., 854
Holland, Henry, 2509
Holland, Hudson, Jr., 876
Holland, William C., 2759
Hollenbeck, Laura L., 855
Hollenbeck, Martyn T., 855
Holley, Cheri T., 1866
Holley, George M., 856
Holley, George M., III, Rev., 856
Holley, Guadalupe M., 502
Holley, John C., Sr., 856
Holley, Kimberly L., 2315
Holley, Lisa C., 1058
Holley, Margaret E., 856
Holley, Mark, 502
Holley, Stephen, 856
Holloway, Deborah S., 1673
Holloway, Nancy, 1785
Holly, Julie A.Rodecker, 430
Holm, Harvey, 2541
Holm, Herbert W., 274
Holmes, Andrea L., 270, 490
Holmes, Carl, 1360
Holmes, Christine, 1962
Holmes, Christine M., 490, 1962
Holmes, Ginna, 2354
Holmes, Howard S., 490, 1529
Holmes, Howard S. "Howdy", 1619
Holmes, John, 2665
Holmes, Kathryn W., 490, 1619
Holmes, Mary B., 490
Holmes, Robert, Jr., 769
Holmes, Wendy B., 1470
Holmes, William B., 1470

Holmquist, Chuck, 2383
Holmstrom, Kellie, 2372
Holnam Inc., 2216
Holoman, Smallwood, Jr., 2387
Holowka, Nick O., 2365
Holthaus, Richard A., 2782
Holton, Donnalee, 2625
Holton, Earl D., 2281
Holtrop, Carol, 2492
Holtsford, Jeanine, 1464
Holtvluwer, Clutch, 857
Holub, Dennis, 2416
Holvick, Gary C., 793
Holwerda, Joann, 1892
Holzhauer, Stan, 58, 2353
Honasoge, Mahalakshmi, 1635
Honasoge, Nataraj, 1635
Honigman, Daniel M., 859
Honigman, David M., 859
Honigman, Edith, 859
Honigman, Jason L., 859
Honigman-Singer, Kay, 859
Hood, Darlene, 1766
Hood, Harold, Hon., 2566
Hood, Joseph W., 860
Hood, Kevin, 860
Hood, Nancy, 860
Hoogeboom, Marjorie G., 1523
Hoogeboom, Sarah, 1944
Hoogeboom, Thomas J., 1523
Hoogendoorn, Case, 684
Hoogerwerf, Bryan, 861
Hoogerwerf, Dave, 861
Hoogerwerf, Lynn, 861
Hoogewind, Cheryl L., 1523
Hoogland, Charles E., 862
Hoogland, Charles R., 862
Hoogland, Kathleen, 862
Hoogland, Keith A., 862
Hooker, David S., 863, 864
Hooker, Joseph J., 864
Hooker, Judith S., 864
Hooker, Leslie A., 863
Hooker, Robert, 2625
Hooker, Robert L., 864
Hooker, Robert L., Jr., 864
Hooper, Mark, 2323
Hoover, Andrew, 2838
Hoover, Toni M., 2567
Hop, Jim, 2376
Hopkins, John E. "Jack", 2362
Hopkins, Jon, 2714
Hoplamazian, Garabed, 2230
Hopp, Daniel F., 2301
Hopp, Karyn A., 1222
Horak, Lucy, 2316
Horan, Robert, 2374
Horder-Koop, Robin, 779
Hordyk, Carol, 2442
Horin, Daniel Ben, 2576
Horing, Ellen T., 1861
Horn, Craig W., 2048
Horn, Karen, 2418
Horn, Ken, 2387
Horonzy, Joseph G., 1882, 1884
Horowitz, Ellen Levy, 1104
Horowitz, Gregg M., 1102
Horton, Gerald L., 1024
Horton, Jeff, 2599
Horton, Kathi, 2336
Horvitz, David W., 1049
Hosey, Mary Ann, 338
Hosking, John, 167
Hoskins, Lynn, 934
Hospitalers Committee, 2836
Hostetler, Kelly, 2628
Houck, Gary, 1604
Hougen, Bradley, 868
Hougen, Douglas S., 868
Hougen, Everett D., 868
Hougen, Randall B., 868
Hougen, Therese Y., 868
Hougen, Victor L., 868
Houghtaling, Thomas, 1766

Houghton, Ralph H., Jr., 455
Houk, Nancy, 2656
Houle, Annette, 2447
House, David, 869
House, Karla, 869
House, Robert, 869
House, Thomas, 2642
Houseman, Cathy, 415
Houston-Philpot, Kim R., 2186
Houtakker, Donald J., 2782
Hovinga Charitable Foundation, James P. and Debra K., The, 1
Hovinga, Debra K., 1
Hovinga, James P., 1
Howard, Andrew T., 872
Howard, Jim, 2380
Howard, Margaret, 2424
Howard, Mary, 2405
Howard, Mary Jane, 872
Howard, Michael J., 2
Howard, Winship C., 872
Howbert, Ed, 2461
Howe, Brian V., 383
Howe, Carl, 2399
Howe, Gordy, 721
Howe, Jeff, 2313
Howe, John J., 87
Howell, Don N., 789
Howell, Jim, 2325
Howenstein, William K., 2335, 2411, 2686
Howes, Randy, 2364
Howland, Walter L., 2832
Hoydic, Michael D., 2658
Hoyt, Anne, 1604
HS Processing, LP, 2145
Hsieh, Doug, 1928
HTC Global Svcs., Inc., 1061
Hubach, Al, 2719
Hubbard, Denise, 2659
Hubbard, Karen, 2650
Hubbell Steel, 630
Huber, Sandy, 2053
Hubert, Pat, 2684
Hubinger, Carl, 286
Hubscher, Chuck, 2378
Huck, Nancy E., 1065
Huck, Thomas B., 1065
Huckle, Chris, 2321
Huckle, Thomas C., 2515
Hudsek, Phillis, 1393
Hudson Co., J.L., The, 876
Hudson, Gilbert, 876, 2632
Hudson, J. Clifford, 590
Hudson, J.L., Jr., 2632
Hudson, Joseph L., IV, 876
Hudson, Joseph L., Jr., 876, 2335, 2411, 2686
Huebner, Carl, 2333, 2359
Huebner, Cynthia K., 877
Huebner, Julius J., 877
Huebner, Laura, 2117
Huebner, Peter F., 877
Hueter, David, Rev., 2389
Hug, Andreas L., 2818
Hug, Daniel C., 2818
Huggins, Ronald V., 2779
Huggler, Tom, 688
Hughes, C.B., 2233
Hughes, David T., 1126
Hughes, Didi T., 2849
Hughes, Holly J., 2332
Hughes, James F., 2439
Hughes, Jeffrey, 2514
Hughes, Julie, 2600
Hughes, Robert, 1339
Hughey, Richard M., Jr., 683
Hughey, Richard M., Sr., 683
Huizenga Foundation, E.I., 954
Huizenga Foundation, Elizabeth I., 322
Huizenga, Elizabeth I., 49
Huizenga, Heidi A., 878
Huizenga, J.C., 1090
Huizenga, John C., 322

Huizenga, Laura B., 322
Huizenga, P.J., 878
Huizenga, Peter H., 878
Huizenga, Tim, 878
Huling, Lori S., 65
Hull, Dale, 2676
Hull, Jean M., 2849
Hull, Norm, 1852
Hullet, Diane, 479, 2743
Hullet, Diane Dow, 478
Humbarger, Robert, 1772
Humbert, Ines M., 881
Humphrey, Glenn E., 882
Humphrey, Joan, 2513
Humphrey, Malvina S., 882
Humphreys, B.J., 253, 1923, 2049, 2135
Humphreys, John, 1923, 2049
Humphries, Rebecca A., 2493
Hunia, Edward M., 1049
Hunt, Ann M., 1249
Hunt, Brenda L., 2315
Hunt, John, 721
Hunt, Nancy, 2456
Hunter, Brian, 2337
Hunter, David H., 883
Hunter, Doug, 764
Hunter, Edward, 884
Hunter, Harriette E., 883
Hunter, Irma, 884
Hunter, Janet, 2647
Hunter, Matthew, 2419
Hunter, Rip, 1852
Hunter, Stephen K., 883
Hunter, Thomas A., 2339
Hunting, Allen I., 885
Hunting, Allen I., Jr., 885
Hunting, Anne, 885
Hunting, David D., Jr., 2281
Hunting, Helen J., 885
Hunting, John R., 499, 885
Huntington National Bank, The, 416, 2332
Huntington-Kriska, Anna, 632
Hunyady, Rhetta, 2478
Hurley, Mary, 2654
Hurley, Melody, 2668
Hurst, Anthony P., 886
Hurst, Elizabeth S., 886
Hurst, Mark, 2396
Hurst, Mary Ann, 887
Hurst, Peter F., 886
Hurst, Richard, 887
Hurst, Todd, 887
Hurwitz, Dan, 2520
Hurwitz, Shirley B., 147
Husband, Timothy, 1264
Huston, Barbara T., 1084
Hutchcroft, Alan C., 889
Hutchcroft, Elizabeth B., 889
Hutcheson, Mary Ellen, 274
Hutchins, Nancy, 2320
Hutchinson, Dolores Rock, 1360
Hutchison, Mickey, 2649
Huth, Samuel Paul, 425
Hutton, Carole Leigh, 2477
Hutton, Richard, Rev., 2329
Huzella, Lisa W., 2035
Hyde, George, III, 2675
Hyde, Howard, 2383
Hyman, J. Leonard, 2781

Iacobelli, Celia J., 892
Iacobelli, Mario F., 892
Iaquinto, Anthony, 2342
Ideation, Inc., 2204
Idema, Beatrice A., 894
Idema, William M., 894, 926
Idziak, Eileen L., 362
Ihrke, Jill M., 483
Ikram, Farhat S., 1618
Ikram, Khawaja H., 1618
Ikram, Khawaja M., 1618

Lampar, Ken, 2396
Lamper, Rebecca, 2405
Lamphere, Carla, 2428
Lamphere, Ward, 2428
Lancione, John G., 905
Landau, Arlene, 186
Landau, Graham, 186
Lande, Nelson P., 1506
Landenberger, Sue, 2646
Landers, Maurice B., III, 1109
Landers, Stephen D., 1109
Landgraf, Anita Chickie, 2533
Landsberg, Carol P., 1071
Landsberg, Kent H., 1071
Lane Texas Partners, 2794
Lane, Cynthia, 2666
Lane, Richard D., 2387
Lane, Thomas H., 2186
Lane, W. Eugene, 2794
Lang, Jeanne, 1198
Lang, Richard, 2366
Langbo, Arnold G., 1073
Langbo, Martha M., 1073
Langbo, Maureen, 1073
Lange, Ann H., 1074
Lange, Duane, 2388
Lange, Mark S., 2800
Lange, Robert, 1074
Langholz, David E., M.D., 1475
Langhorne, Susan, 110
Langlois, Paul, 1582
Langston, Terry, 2404
Laninga, John, 2487
Lankard, Dune, 632
Lankfer, Marilyn A., 2352
Lannen, Marie Louise, 2676
Lanni, J. Terrence, 2556
Lanphear, Gail E., 37, 668, 1428
Lansdell, Lyle T., 1300
Lanser, Janet L., 1549
Lanser, Peter L., 1549
Lanting, Arlyn, 1076
Lanting, Marcia, 1076
Lantz, Mary, 2574
Lanway, Tom, 2661
Lapham, Charles P., 1077
Lapinski, Nancy, 915
LaPlant, Gary, 2329, 2341
LaPonsie, Margaret, 2341
Lappan, Steve, 2333
LaPratt, Holly, 2680
Lapriore, Cheryl M., 2218
Larabell, Thomas, 2530
Larisch, Linda C. Goad, 694
Lark, Sonia, 2647
Larkin, Marla, 2150
Larner, Douglas F., 2737
Larsen, David P., 2065
Larsen, Lawrence W., 1078
Larson, Bonnie Ann, 1080
Larson, Claudia K., 766
Larson, Eric B., 1079
Larson, Jane, 2364
Larson, Jay, Dr., 2373
Larson, Jonathan B., 766
Larson, Kathryn W., 1079
Larson, Mark C., 728
Larson, Michael J., 2648
Larson, Robert C., 1049, 1079, 1080
Larson, Scott, 2433
Larson, Scott T., 766
Larson, Susan, 915
Larson, Thomas R., 766
Larvick, Jeanne, 394
Larzelere, Annabel S., 1082
Larzelere, Henry E., 1082
Larzelere, John H., 1082
Lasacunte, Osvaldo, 2873
LaSalle Bank, N.A., 1124
Lashinsky, Cathie, 2430
Lasko, Gary, 1084
Lasko, John C., 1084
Lathrop, Jim, 2430
Latimer, Barbara, 1085

Latimer, Darryl, 363
Latimer, Jaira, 1085
Latimer, Thomas, 1085
Latour, Christine, 1151
Laub, Carol N., 373
Laudenslager, Kathy, 2456
Lauderbach, William, 37
Lauer, Ken, 2661
Lauerman, Frank, 2369
Laughlin, David, 329
Laughlin, David W., 1922
Laur, Kimber Persia, 1462
Laurenz, James, 2775
Lauretti, Michael, 2464
Lausch, R. Dale, 2241, 2275
Lausch, Shirley, 2241
LaValley, Daniel J., 1298
Laver, Matt, 2450
Laverty, Chris, 2323
Lavery, Kevin T., 2361
Lavey, Richard, 2218
Lavictoire Trust, Daisy Harder, 1087
Lavins, Dolores, 1088
Lavins, Paul N., 1088
Law, Bruce, 1089
Law, Candace G., 2100
Law, D. Brian, 966, 2246
Law, Eric A., 2100
Law, Jacquelyn D., 1089
Lawler, Paul J., 988
Lawrence, Charles, 1475
Lawrence, David L., 884
Lawrence, Dee M., 1412
Lawrence, Donald B., Jr., 2039
Lawrence, Philip S., 1412
Lawrence, Richard, 2816
Lawrence, Richard H., 1412
Lawrence, Tom, 2542
Lawrence, Warren, 1968
Lawrie, Henry DeVos, Jr., 1598
Lawrsile, Zachari, 314
Lawson, Wendy, 2558
Lawter, Kathryn L., 2365
Lawton, Bill, 352
Lawton, Doreen A., 352
Layne, Brenda, 2319
Lazar, Ellen, 2576
Lazaro, Florencia M., 1520
Lazaroff, Steve, 2247
Lazzara, Michael, 2396
Lazzara, Michael J., 401
Le Blanc, Bruce, 2644
Leach, Gwen, 979
Leach, Lloyd, 496
Leaders, Rance L., 1284
Leahy, Edward, 2403
Leal, Joann, 2397
Lear Corp., 2242
LeBeau, Patrick, 2563
Lechner, Deb, 2646
LeCureux, Janet M., 1838
LeCureux, Kenneth W., 1838, 2148
Lecznar, John F., 588
Lecznar, Mary R., 588
Ledy, Sharon, 1461
Ledyard, Allen, 585
Ledyard, William H., Mrs., 1888
Lee, Carl E., 1091
Lee, E. Winifred, 1091
Lee, Jenifer, 2397
Lee, Karen, 2339
Lee, Leslie, 830
Lee, Simon, 347
Lee, Whilma B., 1092
Leebron, David, 2110
Leeburg, Louis, 564
Leemis, Terran, 2638
LeFeber, Marilyn S., 1332
Lefere, Carlene Walz, 2361
Legg, Louis E., Jr., 1878
Legrand, Robert, 2836
Lehman, Alan, 1094
Lehman, Ari, 1094
Lehman, John, 1094

Lehman, Robert, 564
Lehman, Robert F., 2749, 2780
Leinbach, Tracy A., 2277
Leinen, Robert, 2619
Leith, Shirley, 419
Lemelin, Perry, 2808
Lemen, Margaret K., 1452
Lemieux, Linda J., 2041
Lemieux, Mariette, 684
LeMire, William A., III, 2329
LeMire, William, III, 2341
Lemmen, Helene, 1096
Lemmen, Karen, 2343
Lemmen, Wayne E., 1096
Lemmer, Sharron, 2654
Lennon, Dan, 2627
Lennon, George, 684, 1957
Lenoch, Vlado, 2787
Lentine, Joe, 2562
Lenz, Marc, 2545
Leonard, Janice F., 1097
Leonard, Jerry F., Jr., 1097
Leonard, John C., 121
Leonard, Kathryn R., 121
Leonard, Patricia A., 121
Leonard, Scot A., 1464
Leonard, Theodore, 121
Leonard, Timothy J., 121
Leonard-Licari, Michelle R., 1097
Lepard, Matthew, 2340
Leppanen, Karen L., 2335
Leppien, Cleo M., 1098
Leppien, John C., 1098
Leroy, Timothy, 2466
Lesley, E. Craig, 2561
Leslie Metal Arts Co., Inc., The, 1860
Lesnau, J. Thomas, 2460, 2532
Lethorn, Larry J., 1369
Lettinga, Al, 1090
Lettinga, Bill, 2514
Lettinga, Wilbur, 2625
Leutheuser, Eric, 2356
Levanovich, Kimberly Aikens, 19
Leven, Marilyn, 1100
Leven, Myron P., 1101
Leven, Norman J., 1100
Levenson, Jacqueline Purtan, 2603
LeVeque, Elaine M., 2308
Leverett, Allen, 2302
Levey, Richard H., 1707
Levi, Aaron, 294
Levi, Boaz, 294
Levi, Catherine B., 294
Levi, Donald D., 2391
Levi, Ethan, 294
Levi, Shaul, 294
Levin, Arthur D., 485
Levin, Barbara, 2410
Levin, Charles L., 485, 1581
Levin, Joseph, 1581
Levin, Nancy, 44
Levin, Robert M., 1136
Levine, David M., 146
Levine, Joel, 20, 2412
Levine, Peter, 2810
Levy Co., Edward C., 1104
Levy, Carol, 1104
Levy, Carol Anne, 1103
Levy, David, 2439
Levy, Edward C., Jr., 1104
Levy, Edward C., Sr., 2702
Levy, Ellen, 1102, 1103, 1104
Levy, H.G., 2239
Levy, Stanley, 1422
Levy, Susan, 2504
Lew, H.S., 2452
Lewallen, Shelly, 2794
Lewand, Kathleen S., 2370
Lewis, A. Bart, 243
Lewis, Adrienne, 2604
Lewis, Clara M., Rev., 748
Lewis, David Baker, 1739, 2690
Lewis, James, 2821
Lewis, John, 1105

Lewis, John D., 2335
Lewis, Pam, 1105
Lewis, Susan, 243
Lewis-Clark, Barbara, 2450
LeWitt, Peter A., 2565
Li, Min-Duo, 1928
Liabenow, Paul, 2668
Liberatore, Robert G., 2172
Liberty, Stanley, 2336
Lieberthal, Jane, 2553
Liebler, Arthur C., 1106
Liebler, Nancy C., 1106
Liebler, Patrick, 1106
Liechty, Ron, 161
Lieffers, Lori, 2343
Lievense, Jim, 2662
Lifton, Donald, 2005
Liggett, Robert G., Jr., 1540
Light, Richard Upjohn, 2539
Light, Timothy, 1934, 2539
Ligon, Robert M., 2794
Lileikis, Frank, 1107
Lileikis, Thomas, 1107
Lilly, Adrienne, 2477
Limbright, Robert, 2611
Lin, Feifei, 2186
Lincoln, Barbara, 50
Lincy Foundation, 627
Lindbeck, Kathleen M., 228
Linden, Allan J., 1110
Linden, Hanna, 1110
Linden, J. Stewart, 1110
Linden, Sanford J., 1110
Lindholm, John T., 2040, 2041
Lindquist, Jerry, 2383
Lindsay Co., Bruce, 2778
Lindsay, Kenneth, 2540
Lindsey, Troy, 1610
Linebaugh, Karl, 2374
Lingenfelter, Kenneth J., 1340
Lingfelter, Kenneth J., 1340
Link, David T., 2780
Lioselle, Jason R., 2799
Lipford, R.E., 2239
Lipford, Rocque E., 1229, 1711
Lipford, Rocque L., 1227, 1228
Lipman, Lynn B., 1859
Lipsitz, Lori, 816
Lipton, J. Lawrence, 2538
Lis, Daniel, 2615
Lis, Daniel T., 853
Lis, Lisa, 2523
Lishman, Ruth, 1603
Little Caesar Enterprises, Inc., 268
Little, Darcia, 2386
Little, Denise, 2315
Little, Elsie, 1114
Little, Fran, 645
Little, Frances A., 1113
Little, Nancy L., 2323
Little, Virginia S., 1113
Little, William T., 645
Little, William Tedrow, 1113
Littleton, Barbara C., 302
Littmann, Jeffrey C., 2064, 2068, 2155
Liu, Hanmin, 988
Liveris, Andrew N., 478, 2185
Liveris, Paula A., 668
Livingston, David, 1116
Livingston, Pete, 2293
Livingston, Sheryl, 1116
Llewellyn, Rebecca, 619
Lloyd, Thomas T., 2307
Lochricchio, Michael A., 2428
Locniskar, Dana M., 2335
Loeb, Frederick, 1118
Loerup, Richard, 1352
Loesch, George, 2836
Loesel, George F., 465
Loesel, Robert A., 166
Loesel, Susan D., 465
Loftus, Georgia Z., 2130
Logan, John M., 598
Logan, Kelley C., 598

McMurray, Sharon, 2168
McNalley, Tim, 2668
McNally, Brian, 1240
McNally, Dwight, 1240
McNally, William, 50
McNally, William F., 1240
McNealy, Scott, 261
McNealy, Susan, 261
McNeil, Randy, 2676
McNish, Carol A., 1242
McNish, Christine, 1242
McNish, Colleen, 1242
McNish, Elizabeth, 1242
McNulty, Thomas F., 2439
McPherson, Mary Ann Smith, 534
McPherson, R. Duncan, 534
McPike, Harold C., 2094
McPike, Virginia W., 2094
McQuiggan, Carolyn A., 2809
McQuiggan, Mark C., 2809
McRay, Gary, 2534
McRee, Edward B., 1398
McSawby, Suzanne, 2493
McVeigh, Norah, 2576
McVey, Alex, 2397
McVicar, Mary, 1244
McWilliams, Jim, 1784
Meade, Kevin, 2650
Meader, Edwin, 1934
Meader, Mary, 1934
Meader, Mary U., 1934
Meadlock, Concetta, 1245
Meadlock, William A., 1245
Meadowbrook Investment Advisors, 1532
Meagher, Thomas F., 2800
Meakin, Brian, 2368
Means, Dennis E., 2361
Mecke, Eleanor F., 2849
Meconi, Nancy, 1561
Medcalf, Joseph A., 2352
Medlin, Galen, 2263
Meehan, C. Edward, 326
Meek, Phillip J., 1486
Meeks, Andrew, 1246
Meeks, Berneda, 1743
Meeks, Debra, 1246
Meeks, Jenny Lynn, 1246
Meeks, Robert, 1246
MEEMIC Insurance Co., 2250
Meengs, Cindy, 2719
Meer, Brian, 1248
Meer, Lisa, 1248
Meer, Robert D., 1247
Meer, Sondra, 1247
Meerman, Sharon C., 1503
Mehaffie, Amy W., 1312
Mehaffie, Constance Monroe, 1312
Mehaffie, Hugh, 1312
Mehney, David P., 1250
Mehney, Linda M., 1250
Mehra, Anita, 1251
Mehra, Santosh, 1251
Mehta, Dinesh, 2847
Meijer, Frederik G.H., 1252
Meijer, Hank, 2471
Meijer, Inc., 1252
Meijer, Lena, 1252
Meijer, Mark, 2352
Meinberg, Fred, 1604
Meinz, T.P., 2305
Mekjan, Kathy, 535
Melby, Karen, 939
Melby, Scott A., 939
Meleski, Leonard, 2119
Melgary, Larry, 2369
Mellein, John, 2405
Mello, Denise, 2311
Mellon Bank, N.A., 2059
Melton, Dave, 2463
Melvin, Diana H., 797
Melvin, James C., 230, 263, 294, 353, 845, 895, 1011, 1502
Melvin, R. Deane, 2503

Mendenhall, M. Karen, 881
Mendoza, Amelia, 1632
Mendoza, Guido, 1632
Mendoza, Pablo, 1632
Menelli, Peter, Fr., 2389
Menge, William, 2313
Mengebier, David, 2170
Mengebier, David G., 2165
Meninga, Dorothy, 64
Menko, Susan B., 1720
Menor, Minda, 1786
Ment, Bernadine, 1254
Meny, Edward E., 1785
Merchant, Bernice "Woodie", 2473
Merchant, Josh, 2354
Meredith, James H., 818
Meretta, James, 2505
Meriggi-Gibbons, Marina, 854
Merillat, Lynette S., 1256
Merillat, Orville D., 1255
Merillat, Richard D., 1255, 1256, 2536
Merillat, Ruth A., 1255, 2536
Merillat, Stuart, 2827
Meritor Automotive, Inc., 2141
Merkel, Anne, 2446
Merkel, Glen, 2391
Merkle, Bart, 2310
Merkle, Karen A., 2206
Merkle, Mark, 838
Merkley, Martha K., 1257
Merlanti, Mark, 2579
Merrifield, Roger, 2316
Merrill Charitable Lead Unitrust, Dorothy Scott, 463
Merrill Lynch Trust Co., 319
Merrill, Danielle, 463
Merrill, Danielle S., 2713
Merrill, Dorothy Scott, 463
Merrill, Frank G., 463
Merrill, Holly S., 463
Merriman, Frank, 2388
Merritt, Gregory, 2342
Merritt, James, 159
Merritt, Victor, 2611
Mertz, Alyssa, 961
Mervenne, A. John, 1258
Mervenne, Kathryn D., 1258
Mesereau, Robert J., 2228
Messer, Barb, 2644
Mestas, Juan, 2336
Mestdagh, Kristine B., 192
Metcalf, Samuel C., 910
Metcalf, Samuel H., 910
Mette, Norman H., 1262
Mettler, Constance, 556
Metz, Douglas, 933
Metzler, Stephen A., 2697
Meuleman, Dave, 2505
Meusey, Joseph K., 905
Meyaard, Glenn, 2512
Meyer, A., 2551
Meyer, Adolph H., 47
Meyer, Catherine White, 2674
Meyer, David L., 1015
Meyer, G. Darryl, 1641
Meyer, Ida M., 47
Meyer, Jane, 2586
Meyer, Olga Sutaruk, 1845
Meyer, Robert, 2407
Meyer, Rosalind, 1263
Meyer, Sandy, 2684
Meyer, Sheryl, 2350
Meyer, Thomas, 2399
Meyer, Tom, 1845
Meyer, Wendell, 1015
Meyer, William, 1263
Meyers, Hannes, Jr., 2340
Meyers, Nydia, 1264
Meyers, Susan, 916
Meythaler, Jay, 2502
Mezzano, Randy, 2483
MGM Grand Casino, 1359
MGM Mirage, 2556
Michael & Associates, Inc., 900

Michael, Anthony G., 2732
Michael, David A., 2685
Michael, Maureen, 2863
Michaels, Robert S., 1730
Michaels, Ronald F., 87
Michalak, Dennis, 2503
Michell, Roy G., 1265
Michell, Roy G., Jr., 1265
Michell, William, 1265
Michigan Boating Industries Assn., 1540
Michigan Educational Employees Mutual Insurance Co., 2250
Michigan Elks Assn., 1267
Michlash, Kenneth, 348
Michner, Walter J., 1269
Michon, Mark A., 2504
Mick, Barb, 2386
Micka, Jeanne, 2338
Mickelson, Marge, 2483
Mickelson, Robert, 2483
Micklash, Ken, 2400
Micklow, Patricia L., 1551
Micsowicz, Steven A., 2572
Mida, Richard E., 1976
Middleton, Sally, 2226
Mieitinen, Richard M., 1761
Mielock, Douglas A., 2323
Mika, Ernest A., 1947
Mika, Harry, 857
Mikolajczyk, Renita, 2618
Milacron Inc., 2254
Milan, Charles, 1272
Milan, David M., 1273
Milan, E. Ronald, 1273
Milan, Estelle M., 1273
Milan, Florence, 1272
Milan, Henry, 1272
Milan, Ruth M., 1273
Milan-Houser, Susan V., 1273
Milbeck, Steve, 1527
Milberger, Moniek, 312
Miles, Patrick, Jr., 956
Milevska, Sandra, 2535
Milewski, Stanley, Msgr., 1036
Milkowski, Deb, 2665
Millard, Philip H., 2385
Millek, Linda L., 2462
Millek, Tony, 2462
Miller Clock Co., Howard, 1281
Miller Energy, Inc., 1275
Miller Trust, Rhea E., 1285
Miller, Allen B., 1284
Miller, Anna, 936
Miller, Betty E., 1277
Miller, Bill, 2628
Miller, Bonnie K., 2352
Miller, Brenda, 2353
Miller, Brian, 2678
Miller, Bruce, 2655
Miller, C. John, 1275
Miller, C.E., 1277
Miller, Catherine M., 1478
Miller, Clara, 2576
Miller, Clem, Jr., 161
Miller, Cliff, 2536
Miller, Dan, Rev., 2665
Miller, Daniel, 936
Miller, Daniel R., 1277
Miller, Donald J., 853
Miller, Donna M., 1283
Miller, Edward J., 856, 2335
Miller, Elaine, 1629
Miller, Eugene A., 1226, 2335
Miller, George D., Jr., 978
Miller, Glen, 688
Miller, Herman, Inc., 2229
Miller, Howard J., 1281
Miller, Irving, 2419
Miller, J. William, 1279
Miller, Jack H., 1281
Miller, Jean, 161
Miller, Jerry L., 809, 2480
Miller, Joan R., 1551
Miller, John Franklin, 2753

Miller, John X., 2563
Miller, Katharine P., 1431
Miller, Katherine S., 1659
Miller, Kelly E., 1277
Miller, Kenneth V., 809
Miller, Larry, 2353
Miller, Linda, 818
Miller, Lloyd, 1264
Miller, Lorraine M., 1279
Miller, Louise B., 1284
Miller, Louise Tuller, 1286
Miller, Margaret, 984, 1278
Miller, Maria, 2464
Miller, Mark E., Dr., 2391
Miller, Marlene, 2354
Miller, Michael, 1278
Miller, Michael J., 1275
Miller, Milton J., 1280
Miller, Nancy J., 1282
Miller, Patrick, 2732
Miller, Patrick D., 1478
Miller, Philip D., 1281, 1282
Miller, Phillip D., 730
Miller, Phyllis, 1276
Miller, R.N. "Bo", 2185
Miller, Reva A., 1275
Miller, Richard, 2347
Miller, Rita L., 982
Miller, Robert B., 1284
Miller, Robert B., Jr., 1284
Miller, Robert, III, 2311
Miller, Roger D., 1283
Miller, Shelly, 2315
Miller, Stanley O., 1276
Miller, Timothy P., 503
Miller, Winston, 1917
Miller-Davis Co., 2257
Millhouse, David J., 2808
Milligan, Cynthia H., 988
Milligan, David, 1482
Millikin, Kim, 2456
Millman, Ellin R., 1287
Millman, Jode, 1287
Millman, Lawrene, 2565
Mills, Bob, 721
Mills, Chris, 479, 2743
Mills, David M., 2774
Mills, Frances Goll, 1288
Mills, Lloyd, 479
Mills, Mary Lloyd Dow, 2743
Mills, Suzanne B., 2323
Millsport, 1920
Millward, Christopher, 1289
Millward, Daniel, 1289
Millward, Laura, 1289
Milos, Janet, 255
Milos, Wayne, 255
Mindlin, Alan M., 1268
Miner, Jill, 2384
Mingerink, Marv, 351
Minkin, Edna, 1292
Minkin, Jerold R., 1292
Minkin, Philip S., 1292
Minkin, Richard A., 1292
Minnick, Darlene, 2279
Minoletti, William I., 2448
Mirafzali, Hamid, 1293
Mirafzali, Shadan, 1293
Miro, Jeffrey H., 1294, 1862, 1863, 1864
Miro, Marsha, 1294
Miron, Vern, 2313
Misenar, Jean, 2554
Miserendino, Cathy M., 65
Miserlian, Lisa, 546
Mishler, Jeanie, 2642
Mishler, Jeremy, 2554
Mishra, Jitendra, 2823
Mishra, Mithilesh, 2823
Misner, J.W., 2233
Missad, John E., 1295
Missad, Matthew J., 388, 1295
Missad, Scott N., 1295
Mistele, Elisabeth M., 321

Myler, Thomas J., Sr., 1384

Naborczyk, Tom, 2630
Nachazel, Anne M., 1268
Nachman, Allan, 2638
Nachtrab, Joseph T., 2317
Nadolski, Lesli D., 1897
Naftaly, Robert, 2467, 2522
Nagaraju, M., 2810
Nagaraju, Marigowda, 1354
Nagaraju, Pradeep, 1354
Nagaraju, Renuka, 1354
Nagelkirk, Joan, 2388
Nagy Family Foundation, 40
Nagy, Ed, 2359
Nagy, Kathy S., 40, 1355
Nahey, Brian L., 2295
Nair, S. Raim, 2555
Naish, Donald R., 1468
Nakadar, Abdul Rahman, 2820
Nakadar, Najma, 2820
Nalley, Patrick D., 2368
Nance, Rose Marie, 2491
Nardi, Cathy, 2372
Narens, Edward, 1356
Narens, Judith, 1356
Nartelski, Evelyn, 1357
Nartker, Gail, 2388
Nartker, Joe, 2388
Nascimbeni, Teresa, 1380
Nash, John, 2821
Nass, Joel M., 1770
National City Bank, 54, 125, 165, 231,
    330, 423, 453, 670, 757, 1029,
    1064, 1075, 1095, 1149, 1152,
    1209, 1285, 1311, 1390, 1500,
    1543, 1650, 1700, 1885, 1960,
    1982, 2262, 2332, 2362, 2434,
    2479, 2509, 2511, 2591, 2595,
    2669, 2690
National City Bank of Kentucky, 2262
National City Bank of the Midwest, 124,
    1312, 2349
National City Corp., 2262
National Starch and Chemical Co., 2261
Nawrocki, Michael, 720
Naz, Mary D., 791
Neal, Eleanor, 1360
Neal, Rachelle, 2323
Neckers, Bruce W., 1361
Nedd, Khan J., M.D., 1475
Nedeau, Mike, 1413
Needham, Charles, 726
Neef, Allan, 1517, 1666
Neely, Lisa Heeler, 1232
Neely, Mary M., 1428
Neff Engineering Co., Inc., 2822
Neff, Betty M., 2822
Neff, David, 2551
Neff, Elizabeth W., 2822
Neff, Harry M., 2822
Neff, I. Marie, 2822
Neff, Julia D., 2822
Neff, Virginia M., 2822
Neiderheide, Larry, 2383
Neidlinger, Darlene, 2373
Neilson, Jeffrey T., 1569
Neiman, Sandra K., 2824
Neistein, Howard, 2592
Neithercut, Edward J., 1440
Neithercut, Elizabeth M., 1440
Nelson, Alan, 2372
Nelson, Allen J., 1366
Nelson, Bonnie S., 1364
Nelson, Chad M., 1363
Nelson, Constance M., 1363
Nelson, David, 2342
Nelson, David N., 1364
Nelson, Donald J., 1366
Nelson, Gerald R., 1363
Nelson, Gerald R., Jr., 1363
Nelson, Gerry, 2404
Nelson, Gordon E., 748

Nelson, Harry, 1365
Nelson, Irving T., 1366
Nelson, James B., 879
Nelson, James E., 1012
Nelson, Jay, 2413
Nelson, Jay N., 1364
Nelson, Jerry, 1264
Nelson, John R., 1640
Nelson, Kathryn L., 2301
Nelson, Kenneth, 1475
Nelson, Linden David, 1365
Nelson, Lois, 1365
Nelson, Marilyn K., 1367
Nelson, Marilyn S., 1364
Nelson, Mary Goodwillie, 1012, 2001,
    2281
Nelson, Merlin A., 1366
Nelson, Robin N., 1364
Nelson, Rod, 552
Nelson, Roger L., 1367
Nelson, Todd J., 1363
Nelson-Snyder, Carol, 2384
Nemann, John, 2863
Nern, Christopher, 2481
Nervo, Paolo, 1380
Ness, Mary K., 2089
Nethercott, Shaun, 2563
Neu, Cheryl, 379
Neu, Richard, 379
Neuhard, Thomas, 2365
Neve, Keith, 2341
Nevin-Folino, Nancy, 661
Newberry, Joan, 533
Newby, Barbara Hill, 840
Newhof, Garretta, 13
Newhof, Thomas, 13
Newhouse, Tim, 2435
Newman, Ann, 2267
Newman, Cindy, 2376
Newman, Donald L., 1370
Newman, Frank, 64
Newman, Max K., 1370
Newman, Max Karl, 1370
Newman, Ruth A., 431
Newman, Sandra, 64
Newman, Steven E., 1370
Newton, Alex, 530
Newton, Coco, 530
Newton, Keri, 530
Newton, Roger S., 530
Newton, Russell, 530
Neydon, Peter, 2340
Nguyen, George T., 2480
Nichleso, Charles, 2049
Nicholl, Charles H., 2615
Nichols, Hank, 2348
Nichols, John R., 1338
Nichols, Margaret J., 2566
Nichols, Walter, 2404
Nicholson, Ann, 2117
Nicholson, George A., III, 2461
Nicholson, James B., 1226, 2335
Nicholson, Maureen M., 2385
Nicholson, Nancy N., 2849
Nicholson, Raymond J., 1526
Nickels, Elizabeth A., 2229
Nickless, Allen E., 1372
Nickless, Arthur H., 1371
Nickless, Charles, 1372
Nickless, Marie A., 1372
Nicola, Nick, 857
Nicolay, Ernest L., III, 1373
Nicolay, Ernest L., Jr., 1373
Nicolay, JoAnn, 1373
Nicolay, Joanne, 1374
Nidhiry, Rosamma S., 1197
Nielsen, Cheryl, 351
Nielson Enterprises Corp., 749
Nielson, Barbara A., 749
Nielson, Cori, 2207
Nielson, Dale M., 289, 749, 1572
Nielson, Keith, 2207
Nielson, Kirstin, 58
Nielson, Melvin K., 749

Nielson, Ruth E., 749
Nielson-Trine, Tracey, 2628
Niemiec, Brian G., 1375
Niemiec, Valerie J., 1375
Nierenberger, Janine, 2465
Nierenberger, Janine L., 1775
Niester, Donna M., 10, 2339
Nike, Inc., 1920
Nill Trust, Mabel E., 1376
Nimmo, Sally J., 49
Nims, David E., 585, 2055
Nine, Carol, 2476
Ninivaggi, Daniel A., 2242
Ninomiya, Chris, 451
Nirenberg, Henry M., 1771
Nissan Motor Corp. U.S.A., 2263
Nissan North America, Inc., 2263
Nitz, John A., 2547
Nixon, Barbara P., 588
Nixon, William R., Jr., 588
Nmai, Charles K., 2452
Nock, Lela M., 1379
Nock, Walter Ronald, 1379
Noland, Mariam C., 2335, 2411, 2481,
    2686
Nolf, Patricia A., 1366
Norasing, Vou Many, 2802
Nordberg, Erik, 2563
Noricks, Joan, 2322
Norman, Marilyn, 446
Norman, Stephen, 2308
Norman, Thomas, 446
Normandine, Casey, 764
Norris, Annette, 2247
Norris, Kim, 2314
North Central Trust Co., 1854
North, Walter, 2341, 2370
Northcott, Carol, 2445
Northern Michigan Bank & Trust Co.,
    331, 772, 1108, 1147
Northern Trust Co., The, 251, 405,
    1421, 1673, 2114, 2265
Northshore Mining Co., 2164
Northway, John, 2391
Norton, John, 2374
Norton, P.H., 2239
Noteware, Betty, 2751
Novack, Kenneth S., 2788
Nowak, Catherine A., 258
Nowak, John M., 1385
Nowak, Maureen K., 1385
Nowak, Raymond, 2423
Nowak, Tom, 1641
Nugent, Jane K., 2615
Nunley, K. David, 2218
Nurmi, Lila E., 95
Nusbaum, Anna, 1389
Nusbaum, Barbara, 1388
Nusbaum, Irving, 1388
Nusbaum, Joseph, 1389
Nyberg, Bruce E., 2335
Nye, Homer, 2609
Nye, Homer E., 290
Nye, Michael, 2356
Nylaan, Kris, 2488
Nyman, Joelyn, 613

O'Bannion, Chris, 2263
O'Brian, Timothy, 2203
O'Brien, Kay, 1718
O'Brien, Kevin T., 2619
O'Brien, Martha A., 738
O'Brien, Michael, 424
O'Brien, Mike, 2545
O'Bryan, Sean, 2089
O'Connell, Christine, 415
O'Connell, Kathleen M., 362
O'Connell, Mary S., 1350
O'Conner, Thomas J., 995
O'Connor, David P., 2339
O'Connor, Elizabeth F., 623
O'Connor, Elizabeth Friedman, 115
O'Connor, Kerry, 2326, 2341

O'Connor, Maureen A., 3
O'Connor, N. James, 1391
O'Connor, Norman J., Fr., 1391
O'Connor, Patrick D., 1391
O'Connor, Stella Matutina, 1391
O'Connor, Susan, 2366
O'Day, Pat Ryan, 2372
O'Donald, John, 2355
O'Donovan, Karen, 2489
O'Donovan, Karen J., 1392
O'Donovan, Timothy J., 1392
O'Farrell, Richard, 2369
O'Grady, Gerald B., III, 2859
O'Grady, John B., 137
O'Hara, Robert A., 2782
O'Hara, Thomas E., 2615, 2782
O'Hare, Maria, 2828
O'Hare, Patrick, 2828
O'Keefe, Brian D., 555
O'Keefe, Linda, 2390
O'Kennedy, Patrick, 906
O'Leary, J.P., 2305
O'Leary, Joseph, 2313
O'Malley, Carla, 2322
O'Meara, Tom, 2368
O'Meara, Vicki A., 2277
O'Neal, Amos, 2604
O'Neill, Bill, 2588
O'Neill, John, 2829
O'Neill, Madeline S., 2829
O'Rourke, David, 2431
O'Rourke, Terry, 2141
O'Wright, O'Neal, 87
Oakes, Jeanne, 2656
Oakland Mall Ltd., 1034
Oberman, William, 875
Obermiller, James J., 1002
Obits, Catherine, 2713
Obloy, Bernice, 1393
Obloy, Leo A., 1393
Obloy, Michael H., 1393
Obrec, Linda J., 1554
Ochoa, Greg, 1342
Odahowski, David A., 274
Oehmke, Harold W., 425
Oetting, Martin C., 1570
Oetting, Roger H., 803
Off Brothers, 2759
Offield, Chase, 1394
Offield, Dorothy Wrigley, 1394
Offield, James S., 1394
Offield, Meighan, 1394
Offield, Paxson H., 1394
Ogar, Charles, 2817
Ogasian, Diane, 2191
Oglenski, Debbie, 2357
Oglesby, Daniel, 2504
Ogne, Patricia M., 1395
Ogne, Wayne L., 1395
Ohm, Paul R., 1284
Ohmer, Dan, 2307
Ojakli, Ziad, 2203
Okonski, Raymond N., 1747
Okulski, Clark J., 1396
Okun, Marvin, 1397
Okun, Rosalie, 1397
Olah, Henry, 1382
Oldford, Will, 2339
Olds, Ransom E., 1398
Oldt, Patricia, 1381
Oleson, Donald W., 1399
Oleson, Frances M., 1399
Oleson, Gerald E., 1399
Oleson, Gerald W., 1399
Olexa, Paul, 2381
Olinger, Allen, 589
Olinger, Deborah, 589
Olivarez, Juan R., 2352
Oliver, Julia, 2323
Ollila, Paul, 2363
Olsen, Gary, 1616
Olsen, Jodi, 2643
Olsen, Robert, 869
Olsen, Sandy, 2600

Olsen, Stephen G., 2332
Olson, Alan, 2353
Olson, Clarine, 2353
Olson, George, 2447
Olson, Judy Watson, 2490
Olson, M. Richard, 1807
Olson, Michael, 1608
Olson, Ronald, 1400
Olson, Terry, 2547
Omdusa, Inc., 1920
OmniCare Health Plan, 1359
Ondersma, James R., 2266
Onofrey, Delilah, 2468
Oom, Marilyn, 2729
Oosterhouse, Mary, 1718
Opperman, Jim, 721
Oreffice, Franca G., 1402
Oreffice, Paul F., 668, 1402
Oren, Newell, 1701
Oriel, Pat, 37
Oriel, Patrick J., 1428
Orlando, Sharon, 2477
Orley, Graham A., 1405
Orley, Gregg C., 1403
Orley, Harriet, 1403
Orley, Joseph H., 1404
Orley, Marcie Hermelin, 2508
Orley, Sally A., 1405
Orley, Suzanne E., 1404
Ormand, Kirk, 2073
Orosz, Caroline E., 1933
Orosz, Florence U., 1933
Orosz, Florence Upjohn, 1934
Orosz, Joel, 167
Orosz, Joel E., 1933
Orosz, Joel J., 1381
Orr, James L., 2868
Orrell, Richard A., 2613
Orris, Albert J., 1406
Ortiz, Armando, 1408
Ortiz, Elizabeth Hall, 2576
Ortiz, Joan, 1408
Osani, Anthony, 2463
Osborne, Charles, 2596
Osborne, Kathy Polk, 1492
Osburn, Debra Pozega, 2323
Oseland, Lorraine, 2545
Osentoski, Carl, 2357
Oskoian, Karl G., 2396
Osman, Johanna Wege, 2002
Osman, Magdy Abdelazim, 2002
Ostahowski, Mark, 37
Oster, Paul, 2035
Osterink, Bruce, 806
Osterling, Howard, 337
Ostermeyer, Michael, 2313
Ostrander, Rhonda, 2821
Ostwald, David, 2345
Ostwald, Johana, 451
Oswald, Bonnie, 2587
Oswald, Jennifer, 2587
Oswalt, William, 1968
Ott, Alan W., 668, 1428
Ott, Richard E., 1409
Ott, Richard E., Jr., 1409
Otterlei, John, 827
Ottimer, Danielle, 2501
Otto, Barbara, 1410
Otto, Carolyn, 2406
Otto, Fred, 1410
Ouellet, Michelle, 2407
Ouellette, Daniel J., 2473
Oumedian, Dan, 759
Oumedian, Daniel, 90
Overturf, John Voelker, 2675
Owen, Calvin, 910
Owen, Linda, 2376
Owen, Marcia A., 2076
Owen, Mary M., 2064
Owens, Anna E., 358
Owens, Candace, 2654
Owens, Ralph L., 1414
Owens, Steve, 2671
Oyler, Todd, 2309

Ozinga, Charles J., 932
Ozinga, Judith A., 932
Ozinga, Kenneth J., 932

Paauw, Elizabeth Ann, 2023
Pacella, Robert, 2386
Pacella, Roman, 400
Paciorek, Karen, 2577
Packer Family Foundation, The, 1920
Packer, Rachel, 2528
Paddock, Mark W., 2764
Padnos Foundation, Louis & Helen, 1416
Padnos Iron and Metal Co., Louis, 1416
Padnos, Barbara, 1417
Padnos, Cynthia B., 1416
Padnos, Daniel P., 1416
Padnos, Douglas B., 1416
Padnos, Esther, 1415
Padnos, Jeffrey S., 1416
Padnos, Karen, 2520
Padnos, Mitchell W., 1416
Padnos, Seymour, 1415
Padnos, Shelley L., 1416
Padnos, Stuart, 1417
Padnos, William R., 1416
Page, Arlene, 1418
Page, David K., 2335
Page, Forrest, 1418
Page, Michael, 2585
Pahl, Kara, 2646
Pahnke, Brian, 2329
Pahssen, Wayne A., 553
Paige, Mike, 2574
Paine, G. William, 1420
Paine, Martha L., 1420
Paine, Steve, 2371
Paine-McGovern, Carol, 1420
Pairitz, Peter L., 2800
Paisley, Beverly, 122
Paisley, Bonnie, 122
Paisley, Charles, 122
Paisley, Martha, 122
Paisley, Peter, 122
Paisley, Peter, Jr., 122
Palace of Auburn Hills, The, 2267
Palace Sports & Entertainment, Inc., 2267
Palazzolo, Lauri A., 1052
Palchaudhuri, Raj, 1896
Palchaudhuri, Sunil, 1896
Palchaudhuri, Titir, 1896
Palermino, Lenny, 1014
Palma, Eric, 2755
Palman, Irving, 1422
Palmer, Maria F., 1424
Palmer, Marta, 2220
Palmer, Michael, 1852
Palmer, Ronald, 1423
Palmer, Shirley, 645
Palmer, Walter E., 1424
Palms, Deborah Holley, 874
Palms, Jeffrey, 874
Pandya, Kirit, 2847
Panek, Bob, 2389
Pangborn, Dominic, 2563
Pannuto, Michael, 2448
Paoli, Francis E., 2341
Paonessa, Mary, 2630
Papa, Carl, 1014
Pappas, Charles N., 1425
Pappas, Edward H., 2592
Pappas, Norman, 2638
Pappas, Norman A., 1425, 2521, 2592
Pappas, Susan L., 1425, 2592
Paquette, Russell M., 907
Paquin, Molly, 2641
Paragon Die & Engineering Co., 986
Parcells Foundation, Charles A., 2834
Parcells, Anne Leete, 2834
Parcells, Charles A., Jr., 1427, 2834
Parcells, Frances H., 2834
Parcells, Frank H., 2834

Parcells, Kathryn, 2834
Parcells, Kathryn H., 1427
Pardee Foundation, Elsa U., 2832, 2833
Pardee, Elsa U., 1428
Pardoe, James A., 2373
Parekh, Deepika K., 1429
Parekh, Kamlesh K., 1429
Parfet Family Foundation, Donald & Ann, 2759
Parfet, Ann V., 1430
Parfet, Donald, 2787
Parfet, Donald R., 1430, 2480, 2670
Parfet, Donald R., Jr., 2759
Parfet, Martha G., 2759
Parfet, Ray T., Jr., 2759
Parfet, William U., 2317, 2759
Paris, Andy, 2574
Paris, Linda Susan, 466
Paris, Roger L., 875
Parish, Barbara E., 1432
Parish, Barbara J., 1433, 2480, 2539
Parish, Preston, 2670, 2787
Parish, Preston L., 1431
Parish, Preston S., 1433, 2787
Parish, Suzanne D., 398, 2787
Parish, Suzanne U.D., 1431
Parish, William, 2787
Park, James C., 155
Parke, Jennifer Hudson, 876
Parker Investments, T&D, LLC, 2199
Parker, Andrew D., 1435
Parker, Barb, 2173
Parker, James B., 2356
Parker, Linda, 2317
Parker, Lynne, 1690
Parker, Marla, Hon., 2347
Parker, Mary Webber, 876
Parker, Robert W., 1435
Parker, T. Gilbert, 1435
Parker, Tim, 2589
Parker, Tony, 2664
Parks, Burton, 2751
Parks, Edward M., 1437, 1882, 1884
Parks, Floyd L., 683, 1934, 2433
Parks, Hugh, 1770
Parks, Tracy Schwartz, 1668
Parmeter, Daniel, Jr., 2597
Paron, Julie M., 849
Paron, Marge, 2604
Parson, Jan, 2537
Partnership for a Drug-Free America, 1920
Pas, Leonard, 2416
Pasant, David A., 1438
Pasant, Shirley K., 1438
Paschke, Randy, 2417
Pasik, Lawrence, 2419
Pasky, Cynthia J., 2335
Passaro, Tim, 2319
Passinault, William J., 2614
Passino, Jacque H., Jr., 1120
Passino, Pamela A., 1120
Patel, Maheshkumar, 1474
Patel, Prameela, 1354
Patel, Vrajesh, 924
Pater, Jason, 1090
Patera, Greg, 2650
Paterson, John, 348
Patino, Douglas X., 1332
Patnaude, Jude T., 1482
Patriacca, Diane, 2787
Patrias, Rebecca, 40
Patrick, Katherine, 2361
Patrona, Daniel, Sr., 2518
Patterson, Debbie, 2374
Patterson, James W., 1752
Patterson, Linda B., 499
Patterson, Tim, 2679
Patterson, William R., 792
Patty Paper, Inc., 2703
Patty Processing, Inc., 2703
Patzer, Shane A., 8
Patzer, Tiffany L., 8
Paul, Beatrice, 1439

Paul, David, 2579
Paul, John, 682
Paul, Mary Kay, 2345
Pauling, Delayne H., Rev., 290
Paulsen, Eugene M., 396
Pavelka, Jim, 2662
Pavlicek, Michele, 2048
Pavlick, John, 1352
Pavlik, Don, 2833
Pawlanta, George, 605
Pawlanta, Joseph E., 605
Pawlanta, Marilyn, 605
Payne, Brenda, 545
Payne, Harold, 2344
Payne, Larry L., 545
Payne, Thomas W., 617, 831, 1051, 1527
Payton, Randi, 2457
Pearce, Harry J., Jr., 2205
Pearlman, Joseph H., 1447
Pearlman, Maxine, 1447
Pearson, Elaine A., 1448
Pearson, Glen H., 2620
Pearson, Heidi, 528
Pearson, James T., 528
Pearson, John E., 528
Pearson, Richard E., 1448, 2390
Pearson, Susan R., 528
Pechur, Robert E., 2390
Peck Family Foundation, 1362
Peck, Elaine, 1362
Peck, Elaine Z., 1449, 2130
Peck, George R., 1449
Peck, Lee P., 1450
Peck, Rankin, 1449
Pederson, Suzanne H., 1268
Peebles, Ken, 2463
Peekstok, Sesta, 2676
Peeples-Burks, Gladys, 2319
Peffer, Steve, 120
Peffers, Steven, 2308
Pellerito, Coleen O., 1451
Pellerito, Frank A., 1451
Pellon, Tom, 2582
Peltier, Chad, 2631
Peltz, Charles, 548
Pemberton, Rosemary, 984
Pendell, Timothy A., 2460
Pendred, Brigit, 2525
Penner, Jonathan, 1454
Penner, Ruth M., 1454
Penner, Terri, 1454
Penniman Revocable Trust, Lucille, 1455
Penny, Alvertha Bratton, 2576
Penny, Dale A., 938
Penoyar, Richard E., Jr., 1766
Penta, Anita, 1458
Penta, Anthony C., III, 1458
Penta, Thia A., 1458
Pentecost, Joe D., 1457
Pepper, Glen, 2374
Pepper, Michael A., 2332
Pepsi Cola Company, 1920
Peracchio, Lisa A., 373
Perez-Cruet, Mick, 1368
Periard, Mary, 2732
Perkins, Janice L., 2235
Perlos, Lisa A., 1557
Perniciaro Trust, Katherine, 1458
Perrigo Co., L., 2266
Perrin, Frank W., 688, 2591
Perrone, Dianne C., 1459
Perrone, John, 1459
Perrone, Lou, 2495
Perry, Beverly, 1482
Perry, Laura, 2628
Perry, Mark, 2263
Perry, Sara W., 1994
Persia, Raymond J., 1462
Persia, Sonya K., 1462
Pertile, Shirley, 2517
Peslar, Drew, 1463
Peslar, Karen, 1463

Pestillo, Peter J., 2296
Pestle, Penny, 2504
Petach, Ann Marie, 2203
Peterman, Jerry, 981
Peterman, Norene, 2650
Peters Trust, Katherine, 1464
Peters, Cheryl, 2635
Peters, Daniel S., 1465
Peters, Jane, 2359
Peters, Jennifer McDonald, 1221
Peters, Katherine, 1464
Peters, Lovett C., 1465
Peters, Phillip H., 1332
Peters, Roger, 2369
Peters, Ruth Stott, 1465
Peters, Shari, 2381
Peters, Thomas, 2661
Petersen, Ray, 1466
Petersmark, Steven, 2554
Peterson, Bruce, 2188
Peterson, Dan A., 451
Peterson, Eric, 2457
Peterson, Harry S., Jr., 1468
Peterson, Kevin, 1468
Peterson, Mark R., 1467
Peterson, Robert, 1467
Peterson, Stephen, 2208
Peterson, Ted, 2482
Peterson, Tom, 2550
Petinga, Christina, 521
Petinga, Thomas, 1474
Petinga, Thomas J., Jr., 521
Petinga, Thomas J., Jr., Mrs., 521
Petitpren, Dean, 1469
Petitpren, Diane, 1469
Petrauskas, H.O., 2239
Petredean, Thomas, 858
Petri, Dennis J., 265
Petrie, Jennifer Margaret, 378
Petrosky, Tim, 2443
Pettee, Sheila, 1449
Petty, Beaetta, 2728
Peura, Melissa, 2419
Pew, Margaret E., 1175
Pew, Robert C., III, 2281
Pew, Ronald K., 1175
Pezzano, Jeff, 2338
Pfeiffenberger, Lucas, 2714
Pfeiffer, Daniel B., 503
Pfeiffer, Eugene K., 503
Pfizer Inc., 1920
Pharmacia & Upjohn, Inc., 1920
Phelan, Daniel J., Dr., 2361
Phelps Foundation, William Lyon, 1427
Phillips, Joyce K., 381
Phillips, Joyce, Dr., 2373
Phillips, Judy, 2317
Phillips, Mark, 1709
Phillips, Patrice M., 2602
Phillips, Renee, 1709
Phinny, Peter, 2353
Phinny, Robert H., 1473
Phinny, Sally G., 1473
Phinny, Stephen D., 1473
Phipps, Robert J., 1457
Physician's Organization of Western
    Michigan, 1475
Pickard, Steven, 2845
Pickard, William F., 2335
Pickett, Jason, 1215
Pickett, Kiatra, 1215
Pickett, Sherry, 1215
Pickford, Marcia, 1724
Pickles, Larry, 2649
Pido, Antonio J.A., 1520
Pido, Teresa G., 1520
Pieczynski, Bernie A., 1167
Pientenpol, Glenn, 2392
Piepszowski, Daniel, 2573
Pierce, Barbara, 1777
Pierce, Brigid S., 1833
Pierce, Elsie, 404
Pierce, Gary J., 2835
Pierce, Jessie M., 2835

Pierce, Milton J., 1476
Pierce, Rhoda A., 2416
Pierce, Sandra E., 2335
Pierce, Sylvia, 1476
Pierce, Watson, 404
Pierce, Willard G., 2835
Pierce, Willard L., 2835
Pierson, Carol C., 1477
Piesko, Susan, 2049
Pifer, Richard L., 1969
Pifer, Trinh, 2863
Piggott, Cameron H., 1969
Pillion, Scott, 2631
Pilnick, Gary, 2235
Pincus, Bernard E., 1480
Pincus, Irwin Jack, 1481
Pincus, Lena, 1481
Pincus, Marilyn, 1480
Pincus, Robert, 1481
Pinderski, Louis A., 1785
Pindiak, John, 1514
Pink, Joel E., 905
Pinnah, Helen Byrd, 1085
Pinney Irrevocable Trust, Lottie W., 1482
Pinney, Annette L., 1482
Pinskey, Brenda K., 2348
Piotrowski, Lawrence D., 1773
Piotrowski, Nancy, 1773
Piper, William H., 1332
Pitt, Doris, 1484
Pitt, Ina C., 1483
Pitt, Jeffery S., 1483
Pitt, Michael L., 1484
Pitt, Murray C., 1483
Pitt, Peggy, 1484
Pittman, Greg C., Hon., 2332
Pitts-Johnson, Marilyn, 2389
Pivarnik, Michael, 608
Pivnick, Ben, 1485
Pivnick, Lorraine, 1485
Pixley, Don, 2337
Pixley, Vern, 2337
Plachta, Brian J., 1647
Plante, Max J., 2311
Plaskey, Wade C., 2198
Plastipak Holdings, Inc., 2115
Platt, Harry, 748
Plowman, Joey, 2661
Plowman, Mary, 2391
Plumb, Stephen D., 2039
Plummer, Katy, 2337
Plunkett, Steve, 1212
Plym, Andrew J., 1488
Plym, Francis J., Mrs., 1488
Plym, J. Eric, 1488
Plym, John E., Jr., 1488
PNC Bank, N.A., 1694
Poddar, Devesh Darshan, 901
Poddar, Mayurika, 901
Poddar, Shrikumar, 901
Poet, Jeff, 2642
Pohl, Judy C., 1842
Pohl, Ronald R., 1842
Poineau, Pat, 2325
Pointer, Arthur J., 421
Pointer, Colette, 2649
Pointer, Demark, 421
Pointer, Lillian Joan, 421
Pointer, P.J., 421
Poissant, Fay, 2488
Pokoj, Stephen, 2721
Polan, Jesse N., 1490
Polasky, Frank, 1041
Polasky, Frank M., 1491
Polasky, Frumeth Hirsh, 1491
Polit, Mario, 2263
Polk, Albert F., Sr., 1442
Polk, Julie A., 1492
Polk, Patricia, 1442
Polk, Ralph L., 1492
Polk, Richard, 685
Polk, Richard A., 1581
Polk, Stephen R., 1492
Polk, Susan E., 1492

Polk, Winifred E., 1492
Polla, George, 2787
Pollack, Henry N., 1493
Pollack, Lana B., 1493
Pollack, Mary Catherine, 1647
Pollard, C. William, 2229
Pollock, Robert N., Jr., 2500
Ponds, Sharon, 2404
Poniatowski, Don H., 2365
Ponicall, Kay, 658
Ponicall, Michael, 658
Ponkey, Albert, 2611
Pontiac, Joseph, Inc., 860
Ponting Trust, William Fitzherbert, The,
    1494
Pool, Robert M., 1221
Pool, Susan S., 1333
Poole, Charles, Rev., 2332
Poole, Steven W., 661
Pope, David, 2356
Pope, Janet DeVlieg, 437
Popielarz, Don, 1991
Port, Friedrich, 2863
Portenga, Bob, 2609
Porter Machinery Co., Burke E., 955,
    1496
Porter Trust, Burke, 1496
Porter, A.J., 421
Porter, Donald H., 2562
Porter, Harry, 2622
Porter, Jack, 1517
Porter, Joe, 2380
Porter, John W., 1332
Porter, Michael C., 2188
Porter, Ralph, 2263
Porter, Roger, 552, 2077
Porter, Thomas S., 1495
Porter, Warren, 215
Porter-Makupson, Amyre, 2683
Portfleet, Lori A., 2504
Portnoy, Harold D., 1368
Posey, David, 2200
Posey, Jill M., 1497
Posey, Lee, 1497
Posey, Sally, 1497
Post, Arden R., 1498
Post, John W., Jr., 1498
Post, Martha, 1559
Post, Mike, 2250
Postema, Miles J., 956
Postema, Richard R., 1499
Postema, Ruth E., 1499
Poteat-Flores, Jennifer R., 1901
Poterala, Michael, 2577
Pothier, Kathryn A., 2449
Potiker, Sheila M., 2601
Pott, Stephan, 2216
Potter, Daniel, 1917
Potter, Sharon L., 907
Potts Trust, Norine, 1500
Potts, Al, 2353
Potts, Terry, 2596
Poulton, Shirley, 2351
Powell, B.F., 1501
Powell, Bernard F., 1501
Powell, Carlton, 2622
Powell, Dick, 1352
Powell, George, 2609
Powell, Mary Ann, 1501
Powell, Mavis C., 1366
Powell, Tina, 2651
Powell, W.H., 2261
Power Equipment Distributors, Inc.,
    2009
Power, Eugene B., 1502
Power, Jeffery, 1323
Power, Jeffrey B., 234, 469, 1808, 2789
Power, Kathleen K., 1502
Power, Philip H., 1502
Power, Sadye H., 1502
Powers, Barbara, 2684
Powers, Carol A., 1503
Powers, Linda A., 1503
Powers, Robert J., 1503

Powers, Theresa, 2063
Prabhaker, Bangalore S., 89
Prabhaker, Indira, 89
Prairie, Pamela, 2662
Pratt, Carolyn M., 1724
Praveen Soni, 1296
Prawozik, Bernard, 2423
Pray, Joe E., 2346
Prechter Charitable Lead Trust, Heinz C.,
    2099
Prechter, Heinz C., 2099
Prechter, Paul, 2099
Prechter, Stephanie, 2099
Prechter, Waltraud, Mrs., 2099
Predebon, William W., 2363
Predhomme, Michael J., 1176
Preede, Linda, 2337
Preede, Linda C., 1504
Preede, Phillip D., 1504
Preede, Roger B., 1504
Preede, Stephen R., 1504
Prein, Barbara J., 1505
Prein, Cathy, 2488
Prein, Ed, 1505
Prein, H. Edward, 1505
Prein, June, 1505
Preisel, Clayton, Hon., 2365
Presant, Mike, 2520
Preston, James E., 1507
Preston, L.A., 1279
Preston, Larry L., 1622
Preston, Marie C., 1507
Prevo's Family Markets, Inc., 1508
Prevo, Aaron P., 1508
Prevo, Dan R., 1508
Prevo, Pamela M., 1508
Pribil Trust, Maxwell, 1510, 1511
Price, Anne Sage, 1621
Price, Henry J., 905
Price, Robert E., 1512
PricewaterhouseCoopers, LLC, 1920
Pridnia, John, 981
Prince Corp., 1513
Prince Foundation, 439
Prince Holding Corp., 505, 620, 940,
    1780
Prince, Edgar, 940
Prince, Edgar D., 620, 1513
Prince, Elsa, 940
Prince, Elsa D., 620, 1513
Prince, Erik D., 620, 1513
Prince, Joan, 620
Pringle, Sherry, 2153
Pritchard, Barbara, 2325
Productions, D&M, 481
Prokopowicz, Michael, 2372
Prokopowicz, Mike, 2490
Promotions Network, The, 1920
Proos, John, 2629
Prophet, James T., 2360
Prost, Lucinda, 434
Provenzano, Robert, 2571
Providence Energy, Inc., 1275
Prus, A. Michael, 706
Prus, Jeffrey G., 706
Prus, Judith G., 706
Prus, Michael G., 706
Prygoski, Kenneth, 2876
Pryor, Daniel A., 1516
Pryor, Esther A., 1516
Pryor, Frederic L., 1516
Pryor, Mary S., 1516
Pryor, Millard H., 1516
Psarouthakis, John, 1419
Puerner, Michael W., 806
Puff, Eric, 880
Puff, Randy A., 661
Pugh, Edgar W., Jr., 425
Pulles, Gregory S., 2285
Pulley, Jill, 2510
Pulman, Norman, 2134
Pumford, Susan A., 2387
Pump, Edwin, 2552
Pung, Steven D., 2223

Purdy, Judy, 2676
Pursley, Michele, 2817
Purtan, Gail, 2603
Purtan, Julie Nicole, 2603
Purtan, Paul R., 2603
Puryear & Associates, 900
Puryear, Michelle, 79
Pushman, Cindy, 2588
Putman, Dan, 2368
Puuri, Lorraine, 1009
Puuri, Lorraine K., 865
Pycik, John M., 2800
Pyle, Margaret, 1518
Pyle, Owen, Jr., 1518
Pynnonen, Linda, 416
Pynnonen, Linda A., 1112
Pynnonen, Wayne E., 1112
Pyper, Sally, 648

Qazi, Mohammad, 1519
Quain, Barbara, 2348
Quaker Oates Co., 1920
Quay, Sheri, 2588
Queller, Robert L., 506
Quershi, Amber T., 2748
Quershi, Tanvir I., 2748
Quiachon, Ernesto B., 1520
Quiachon, Rose S., 1520
Quiachon, Vincent Louis, 1520
Quick, William K., 2100
Quinn, Bert, 1790

R&B Machine Tool Co., 2273
Raab, John, 1087
Raasio, Chen, 2454
Rabahy, David, 1521
Rabahy, Donald L., 1521
Rabahy, Rosemary, 1521
Rabbers, Blaine A., 2747
Rabbitt, Kenneth, 1443
Rabbitt, Patricia, 1443
Rabideau, Michelle, 2614
Rabideau, Theresa, 1482
Racette, Karen, 2362
Rachor, James Michael, 1522
Rachor, Michael Garry, 1522
Rachor-Beste, Terese Marie, 1522
Racine, William, 884
Raddler, Don, 2665
Radocy, Robert, 1377
Radom, Steve, 1969
Radtke, Catherine, 2009
Radtke, Edward, 2009
Radtke, Gerald W., 228
Radtke, Janelle M., 228
Rae, Nancy A., 2172
Raese, Robert, 1454
Raese, Shirley, 1454
Raggio, Michael, 1924
Ragin, Luther M., Jr., 827
Rahar, Abraham, 2596
Rahilly, John, 100
Rains, Doris, 1754
Raj, Ethiraj G., 654
Raj, Geetha, 654
Raj, Kumar, 654
Raj, Padma, 654
Raj, Shanthi, 654
Rajput, Hemant, 1525
Rajput, Minoti H., 1525
Raju, B.L. Narasimha, 2698
Rakolta, John, Jr., 2335
Ralph, George, 2463
Ramasamy, Kala Kuru, 2387
Ramer, James T., 2385
Ran, Gary L., 1528
Ran, Rhonda S., 1528
Randall, Dave, 2364
Randall, Judy J., 2077
Randolph, Jeff, 83
Rands, Dale, 98
Rands, Dale C., 1530

Rands, Dale G., 898, 1530
Rands, Phil, 2463
Randsford, Richards B., 2400
Ranger, Thomas F., 47
Ranney, Joan E., 422
Ransford, Fred J., 2824
Ransford, Sue, 2400
Ransom, Sheila, 2650
Rantala, Ward, 2655
Ranusch, Robert, 400
Ranzini, Stephen L., 2827
Rao, Guthinkonda, 1474
Rapanos, Judy, 2563
Rapinchuk, Grace, 1531
Rapinchuk, James, 1531
Rapinchuk, Jane, 1531
Rapinchuk, John, 1531
Rapp, Donna, 2376
Rapp, Marcia, 2352
Rappe, Kristine A., 2302
Rappleye, Richard K., 2566
Rapson, Richard "Rip", 1049
Rasmussen, Douglas J., 674
Rasor, Theresa, 2383
Rassel, Richard E., 1138, 2156
Rathbun, Stan, 2378
Ratner, Milton M., 1532
Rattner, Ruth, 1533
Rautio, H. Kristene, 2322
Raval, Tejas H., 1534
Ravitz Revocable Living Trust, Edward,
   The, 1535
Rawal, Harish, 1534
Rawal, Sudha, 1534
Rawson, Delbert E., 1536
Ray, Chester, 2309
Ray, Ruth, 2768
Rayes, Ayman, 1537
Raymond, John J., Jr., 1434
Rayna, Jose L., 499
RBC Centura Bank, 989, 1811
RBS Foundation, 1745
Read, Janet P., 1492
Ready, Thomas D., 2555
Reagen-Rosales, Christine, 1378
Ream, W. Monte, 2438
Rearick, Carole, 2370
Reavely, Bruce, 2662
Recla, Debbie, 2345
Rector, Dale, 2649
Redding, Brenda, 1065
Reddy, Madhava, 1061
Reddy, Madhava G., 1061
Reddy, Sobha, 1061
Redies, Cathy, 2473
Redies, Elizabeth J., 2273
Redies, Karen, 2273
Redies, R. Edward, 2273
Redies, Robert D., 2273
Redies, Thomas D., 2273
Redies, William D., 2273
Redjicker, Arnie, 151
Redlawski, Marvin, 1396
Redlum, Ltd., 2274
Redman, Cynthia, 2838
Redman, Robert, 2838
Reed, John W., 905, 2312
Reed, Lawrence, 1574
Reed, Pam, 2405
Reed, Rhoda Newberry, 1562
Reed, Richard D., 2539
Reed, Robin, 1218
Reeder, Breinne, 2367
Reeder, Ed, 2586
Reehl, James E., 2400
Reen, Michelle, 2648
Reese, Caleb F., 1542
Reese, David E., 1542
Reese, Everett, 1542
Reese, Everett D., 1542
Reese, Everett D., II, 1542
Reese, Louise R., 1542
Reese-Pumford, Mary, 1369
Reeves, Lee, 2330

Regan, Amy, 485
Regan, Julie W., 926
Regan, Timothy D., 2163
Regotti, Doris J., 608
Reichard, Lori, 2588
Reichenbach, G. Robert, 384
Reid, Alex, 1546
Reid, Alex A., 1545
Reid, Alice Serra, 1690
Reid, Bill, 2382
Reid, Colleen, 1547
Reid, Cristin, 1547
Reid, David J., 2839
Reid, Douglas L., 2839
Reid, Glenn J., 2839
Reid, James G., 2839
Reid, Jerry, 1547
Reid, Joseph D., 1547
Reid, Joseph D., III, 1547
Reidinger, Mary Ann, 2337
Reiley, Terry A., 2502
Reilly, Karen Dermidoff, 581
Reimus, Sylvia, 2406
Reinke, John, 561
Reitz, Carl E., 155
Remes, Norton P., 1100
Remien, Mary, 910
Rengo, Danielle M., 2713
Reniger, Douglas A., 323
Reniger, Jerilyn J., 323
Renner, Rick, 187
Renstrom, Stig, 1910
Renterghem, Lemont, 2355
Rentrop, Gary, 47
Republic Die and Tool Co., 1084
Resio, Ricardo, 2387
Respini, Luciano R., 2185
Reuter Estate Trust, Loraine, 1550
Reuther, Elizabeth, 2605
Reuther, Linda, 2605
Reuther, Victor G., 2605
Revenaugh, Elsie B., 203
Rexer, Linda K., 2566
Reynolds, Alice M., 1551
Reynolds, Kevin, 2384
Reynolds, Phyllis M., 1551
Reynolds, Richard M., 1821
Rezmierski, Leonard, 2577
Rhee, Chi Sun, 1552
Rhee, Robert, 1552
Rhee, Stephan, 1552
Rhee, Sung Hi, 1552
Rhoders, Paul F., 1948
Rice, Bruce C., 2332
Rice, Gil, 2836
Rice, Gilbert A., 867
Rice, Patricia, 2682
Rice, Rich, 2647
Rice, Susan J., 339
Rice, William, 2149
Rich, David, 2788
Rich, Theresa, 2347
Richard, Margaret A., 715
Richard, Robert C., 1001
Richards, Barbara, 2311
Richards, Don, 2483
Richards, Don, Rev., 399
Richards, Jennifer, 2314
Richards, Risa L., 271
Richards, Vincent William, Jr., 111
Richardson, Evelyn K., 1655
Richardson, Faye, 1381
Richardson, Lamar, 2636
Richardson, Rockette "Rocky", 2279
Richardson, Suzy A., 730
Richardson, William C., 2670
Richardville, Randy, 2338
Richelsen, Karen M., 945
Richter, Kerry, 1554
Richter, Nancy D., 1554
Richter, O. Frank, 1554
Ricker, Sally Richards, 220
Ricker, William L., 220
Rickert, Donna J., 1555

Rickert, Herbert E., 1555
Rickert, Ray, 338
Riddle, Ivin, 2628
Ridenour, Mark E., 2145
Ridgeway, Lisa M., 858
Ridley, Nancy, 2378
Riecker, John, 1573
Riecker, John E., 1901
Riecker, Margaret Ann, 478, 1901
Riecker, Steven Towsley, 1901
Riekse, Nan Jean, 1556
Rifai, Samir, 781
Rigg, Remus, 2320
Rigger, Roberta M., 1148
Riggs, Gail, 1815
Righter, Jeeri, 2403
Rigsby, David C., 895
Riker, Bernard, 423
Riker, Susan C., 2149
Riley, Anne E., 513
Riley, Bruce A., 513
Riley, Bruce P., 513
Riley, Daniel G., 1558
Riley, Dolores, 1558
Riley, George, 1558
Riley, George K., 1558
Riley, H.M., 2607
Riley, Jim, 2493
Riley, Joane, 1557
Riley, Larry, 2604
Riley, Linda E., 513
Riley, Michael J., 1558
Riley, Philip A., Jr., 1557
Riley, Sheila, 2398
Riley, William D., 1558
Rima Manufacturing Co., The, 2192
Rimpela, Brian, 2454
Ring, Eunice, 1038
Ringle, Brian, 2628
Ringwelski, Mark, 1745
Ringwelski, Susan, 1745
Risley, David M., 2239
Risner, Joni, 2465
Rissman, Alicia, 2805
Ritchie, Carol A., 1007
Ritchie, Marilyn, 786
Ritchie, Robert J., 1007
Ritter, Robert F., 905
Rittmueller, Franklin, 1424
River City Food Co., 2241, 2275
Robb, Barbara, 879
Robbin, Robert S., 2576
Robbins, Bob, 2353
Robbins, Charlotte R., 119
Robbins, Edith M., 1565
Robbins, J. Marshall, 1564
Robbins, Joy, 306
Robbins, Lori, 658
Robbins, Michael, 658
Robert Flint Trust, 586
Roberts, Carolyn, 2399
Roberts, Jessie Castle, 2117
Roberts, Kathleen Ann, 1487
Roberts, Pam, 1590
Roberts, Ralph, 1487
Roberts, Susan E., 483
Roberts, Victoria A., Hon., 2566
Robertson, David, 1461, 2342
Robertson, Gloria J., 1284
Robertson, Marjorie, 2015
Robey, A.M., 2840
Robey, E.W., 2840
Robey, Edmund W., 2840
Robey, Leon J., 2840
Robeznieks-Inka, Sandra, 2535
Robideau, Gladys E., 1567
Robideau, James J., 1567
Robideau, Jeffrey T., 1567
Robinson, Barbara, 2416
Robinson, Ben, 2768
Robinson, Bill, 2339
Robinson, Charles T., 2230
Robinson, Douglas E., 2555
Robinson, Fannie, 582

Sarow, Robert, 2832
Sarow, Robert D., 966, 1752
Sasiela, Joseph, 966
Satterlee, Ellen, 2001
Saucelo, Bart, 2790
Sauer, Fran, 1413
Sauer, Jonathan B., 1785
Saugatuck-Douglas Lions Club, 1641
Saulson, Marjorie Shuman, 1642
Saunders, Cheryl A., 181
Saunders, Donald, 2412
Sauter, Lawrence J., 791
Sauve, Brad E., 2186
Savage, James M., 1643
Savage, Margaret, 994
Savage, Mary T., 1643
Savarino, Peter J., 2500
Savas, Sue Ann, 1559
Savas, Zachary, 1559
Sawhney, Krishna K., 2150
Sayer, James, 151
Sayre, James D., 1143
Sazima, Sue, 1701
Scales, Charles R., Jr., 2564
Scamardella, Lino, 1380
Scears, Gweneth M., 1644
Schaaf, David, 2329
Schad, Vernis, 602
Schaefer, June, 2490
Schafer, Hal, 1014
Schafer, Mary, 2350
Schafer, Mary J., 2323
Schaffer, Sue, 2783
Schaible, David, 316
Schaller, Albert, 83
Schaller, Marilyn, 83
Schaller, Virginia, 2454
Schalon, Edward I., 1646
Schalon, Marcella, 647
Schalon, Marcella J., 647, 1646
Schalon, Scott, 1646
Schalon, Susan, 1646
Schalter, Richard J., 1775
Schanz, Don, 2456
Schanz, Donald C., 1647
Schanz, Donald K., 1647
Schanz, Kathleen, 2537
Schapman, Laura, 2348
Scharich, Barbara, 2732
Schastok, Sara L., 2014
Schaub, Paul, 2604
Schaubman, Debbi, 1378
Schaver, Emma, 1648
Schaver, Isaac, 1648
Scheerens, Dean, 2397
Scheible, Bill, 2374
Schelling, Amanda, 2488
Schichtel, Ken, Fr., 2545
Schiedegger, Charles, 2348
Schierbeek, Robert H., 439, 441, 1956
Schiffer, Albert, 2787
Schiffer, Anna, 2787
Schiffer, Michael, 2787
Schiffer, Michael, Mrs., 2787
Schindler, Ralph J., Jr., 2114
Schipper, Alyce J., 1793
Schipper, Earl J., 1793
Schipper, Sharla, 2574
Schippers, James, 2512
Schlachtenhaufen, Harold, 1339
Schlachtenhaufen, Kari, 1339
Schlack, Marilyn J., 2362, 2670
Schlafer Trust, Shirley K., 1651
Schlafer, Shirley K., 1651
Schlauch, W.F., 2261
Schlichting, Nancy M., 1049
Schluchter, Ruth, 2679
Schluckebier, Paul, 2391
Schluckebier, Stacey, 2391
Schlussel, Mark, 98, 898, 2522
Schma, William G., Hon., 2780
Schmaltz, Kathy, 2652
Schmerberg, Nancy, 2473
Schmerin, David, 522

Schmerin, Denise, 522
Schmid, Frederick E., 1653
Schmidt, Buzz, 827
Schmidt, Carol D., 219
Schmidt, Don, 2344, 2345
Schmidt, Harold C., 2154
Schmidt, Ken, Hon., 2684
Schmidt, Paul W., 2206
Schmiege, Phil, 1266
Schmier, Regene, 1654
Schmitt, Barbara, 2053
Schmitt, Christine, 2250
Schmitt, Dana L., 658
Schmitt, Eric, 1137
Schmitt, Heidi L., 1137
Schmoll, Beverly J., 2502
Schmuckal Land Co., 1655
Schmuckal, Arthur M., 1655
Schmuckal, Donald A., 1655
Schmuckal, Paul M., 1655
Schneider, Anna B., 1657
Schneider, Brian, 2648
Schneider, Cecil W., 2620
Schneider, Deborah, 2342
Schneider, Harvey, 2640
Schneider, John P., 1002
Schneider, Phillip H., Jr., 2801
Schoenle, Jerry, 2598
Schoenlein, Bill, 2656
Schoessel, Carl, 2835
Schollaart, Ronald J., 2290
Scholten, Alice, 158
Scholten, Dale, 2512
Scholten, Herm, 351
School District/City of Battle Creek,
   2687
Schooley, Susan, 1226
Schoonbeck, Caroline P., 1659
Schoonbeck, Fredrick, 1659
Schornberg, Albert, 28
Schornberg, Cindy, 28
Schostak, Jerome, 2521
Schostak, Jerry, 2522
Schott, Stephen, 2317
Schouten, Mary Beth, 2134
Schrader, Win, 2054
Schrank, Douglas R., 2266
Schregardus, Ralph, 1660
Schregardus, Randall, 1660
Schreiber, Cece, 1661
Schreiber, Herbert L., 1661
Schreibman, Jay, 1128
Schriber, Ann S., 1662, 1762
Schriber, John C., 1662
Schriber, Maria A., 1662
Schriber, Sarah E., 1662
Schriber, Thomas J., 1662
Schroeder, David, 499
Schroeder, Fred D., 1663
Schuette, William D., 668, 1428
Schuetz, Ingeborg, 1038
Schuitmaker, Harold, 151
Schulak, Jane, 2702
Schuler, Dana D., 477
Schulte, John, 551
Schultz, Earl, 2778
Schultz, Elizabeth, 2778
Schultz, John, 2337
Schultze, Brian D., 1066
Schulz, Bobbie F., 1665
Schulz, Donald J., 1665
Schulz, Joseph A., 1665
Schulz, Kelly M., 1665
Schumacher, George T., 645
Schumacher, Ronald E., 2223
Schupra, Greg, 2322
Schuster, Donald, 2378
Schuster, Georgann, 2646
Schut, D. Maxine, 642
Schut, Dorothy, 642
Schut, Mark A., 1676
Schut, Warren H., 642
Schwab, Paul, 1768
Schwach, Ronald B., 1262

Schwartz, A.E., 1695
Schwartz, Alan E., 1667, 2335, 2425
Schwartz, Caroline, 1668
Schwartz, Daniel, 70
Schwartz, Leonard, 2280
Schwartz, Marc A., 1667, 1695
Schwartz, Marianne S., 1667, 1695
Schwartz, Robert, 1128
Schwartz, Robert G., 1668
Schwartz, Robert G., Jr., 1668
Schwartz, Selma B., 2147
Schwartz, Steve, 2280
Schwarz, Frank W., III, 1669
Schwarz, Frank W., Jr., 1669
Schwarz, Patricia D., 1669
Schwedler, John, 1761
Schweitzer, David L., 2315
Schweitzer, Peter A., 2439
Schwendener, Benjamin O., Jr., 1878
Schwyn, Robert C., 2845
Scofield, Emily, 1670
Scoggins, Brenda, 2621
Scolatti, Norma T., 1366
Scollon, Dorothy, 2400
Scolnik, Bob, 2660
Scoon, Kathy, 2397
Scott, Arthur V., 2332
Scott, Geoffrey, 2578
Scott, Herb, 2322
Scott, Michelle Y., 2725
Scott, Robert, 2436
Scully, John, 1671
Seabrook, Philip T., 2452
Seabury, Charles Ward, 1673
Seabury, Louise Lovett, 1673
Seagle, Miriam, 2147
Seagle, Peter C., 2147
Seagram, Laura, 1346
Seals, James, Dr., 2354
Seals, Jamey, 2833
Seavoy, Kenneth, 974
Sebastian, Audrey M., 1675
Sebastian, David S., 1675
Sebastian, James R., 1675
Sebastian, John O., 1675
Secchia, Joan, 2489
Secchia, Peter F., 1676
Seckendorf, Bruce, 1196
Secontine, Vincent C., 73
Secord, Edwin, 2560
Secory, Lynne M., 2339
Sedrowski, Robert J., 2303
Seebach-York, Pia, 2510
Seeley, Charles, 2775
Seeley, Cheryl, 2400
Seelye, Lindsey M., 1679
Seelye, Mauri L., 1679
Seelye, Michael N., 1679
Seelye, Michael T., 1679
Seelye, Michelle N., 1679
Seelye, Sharon K., 1679
Seese, Jerry L., 2387
Seevers, Gary L., 1680
Seevers, Gary L., Jr., 1680
Seevers, Sharon, 1680
Seger, Martha R., 1681
Seger, Robert C., 2098
Seger, Susan I., 1681
Seguin, Lee, 2612
Sehn, Francis J., 1682
Sehn, James T., 1682
Seidel, Robert, 2545
Seidman, B. Thomas, 1683
Seidman, Esther L., 1683
Seidman, Frank E., 1683
Seidman, L. William, 1683
Seidman, Nancy C., 1683
Seidman, Sarah B., 1683
Seidman, Sarah L., 1683
Seifert, Elizabeth J., 1684
Seifert, George, 2337
Seifert, George H., 1684
Seifert, George K., 1684
Seitl, Wayne, 1828

Seizert, Candace C., 1685
Seizert, Gerald L., 1685
Sekerke, Linda S., 285
Sekkarie, Mohamed A., 1686
Selby, Carol, 1623
Selden, Daniel L., 2073
Seligman, Irving, 1687
Seligman, Irving R., 2844
Seligman, Mary K., 1687
Seligman, Sandra, 2844
Seligman, Scott J., 2844
Selkey, Tony, 2313
Sell, Leo, 2561
Sellers-Walker, Margaret, 2352
Sellman, John, 2299
Seltzer, Mimi Keidan, 2007
Seman, Jean, 1991
Semeyn, Peter, 58
Semizian, John, 535
Semlow, Pam, 2574
Semmes, Prewitt, Jr., 1688
Semple, Cynthia T., 2849
Semren, Shelley, 2794
Sequin Lumber Corp., 1689
Sequin, Denise A., 1689
Sequin, Peter A., 1689
Sequin, Thomas E., Jr., 1689
Serendipity Books, 992
Serr, Erik, 2204
Serr, Erik H., 1619
Serra, Albert, 1690
Serra, Lois, 1690
Serra, Sam, 2630
Service, Donna, 2731
Sessel, Robin, 2347
Sessions, Mary E., 1788
Settle, Ernest, 2332
Sevillian, Clarence, II, 2336
Sewell, Beverly D., 121
Sexton, James, 2876
Seyburn, Bruce H., 1388
Seydel, Catherine, 805
Seydel, Laura Turner, 1922
Seydlitz, Orval, 933
Seyferth, Anna Jane, 1691
Seyferth, Donald F., 803
Seyferth, Eric, 1691
Seyferth, James R., 1691
Seyferth, Thomas, 803
Seymour, B.A., III, 1692
Seymour, B.A., Jr., 1692
Seymour, Marcy Carolyn, 1570
Seymour, Randall, 2386
Seymour, William P., 1692
Shabazz, Scherry, 2728
Shaevsky, Lawrence K., 2616
Shaevsky, Lois L., 2616
Shaevsky, Mark, 2616
Shaevsky, Thomas L., 2616
Shafer, Duane, 2554
Shafer, Kent, 2428
Shaffer Administration Trust, Ula G.,
   1821
Shaffer, Barbara Broomfield, 241
Shafie, Rabia, 2590
Shah, Akshay, 924
Shah, Arvind, 924
Shah, Jayshree, 924
Shah, Kaushik, 901
Shah, Kirit, 2474
Shaheen, Patty, 2406
Shaheen, Sam, 2387
Shaheen, Shaheen A., 1693
Shaheen, Shouky A., 1693
Shallal, Jalal, 2846
Shallal, Nawal, 2846
Shan, Kirit, 1474
Shander, Josephine, 1694
Shannon, Miriam, 2755
Shapero, Jean E., 1695
Shapero, Nate S., 1695
Shapiro, Aaron L., 2617
Shapiro, Bonnie L., 2617
Shapiro, Jennifer, 947

Shapiro, Joel, 2617
Shapiro, Loraine, 2617
Shapiro, Mickey, 1696
Sharfman, Donald, 1041
Sharon, Robert, 2876
Sharp, Barton W., 1697
Sharp, Calvin, 2740
Sharp, Margaret B., 1697
Sharp, Marilyn, 1772
Sharp, Phillip A., 2205
Sharp, Terry, 2350
Sharp, William K., 1697
Sharra, Sue, 2312
Shaw, Jim, 1968
Shaw, Shirley, 1461
Shaw, Tim, 1769
Shayevitz, Jay, 2848
Shayevitz, Susan, 2848
Sheehan, Georgette, 344
Sheets, Mary Ellen, 2323
Shelby, Carole, 1698
Shelby, Christian, 1698
Shelby, David, 1698
Shelby, David T., 1698
Shelby, Justin, 1698
Shelby, Kaylynn, 1698
Shelby, Paige, 1698
Shelby, Sarah, 1698
Shelden, Allan, III, 1699
Shelden, Elizabeth Warren, 1699
Shelden, Ron, 2442
Shelden, W. Warren, 1699
Shelden, William W., Jr., 1226, 1699
Sheldon, Brenda, 881
Sheldon, Mark, 1973
Shell, Frederick E., 2188
Shell, Hilary F., 1860
Shellenbarger, Dave, 2337
Shellenberger, Lauren, 2505
Shelley, Charles, 286
Shellito, David, 2301
Shelton, Royce, 1515
Shelton, Russ, 2337
Shelton, W. Brett, 2367
Shemtov, Beryl, 1648
Shepard, Holley R., 1058
Shepherd, Curtis E., 2279
Sherbow, Mark D., 268
Sherbow, Susan S., 268
Shereda, Martin, 1703
Sheridan, James M., 189, 2524
Sherk, Doug, 2363
Sherman, D. Larry, 1704
Sherman, David F., 1704
Sherman, Don, 2581
Sherman, Emily Sharon, 919
Sherman, Jane, 1704
Sherman, Jane Ellen, 577
Sherman, Jane F., 1704
Sherman, Scott R., 1704
Sherogan, Diana Wege, 2001
Sherr, Rose Lynn, 1606
Sherriff, Horst, 1540
Sherry, Peter, Jr., 2203
Sherwood, B.P., 1705
Sherwood, Janet, 2833
Sherwood, Lynne, 1706, 2228
Sherwood, Marilyn W., 1705
Sherwood, Peter K., 1706
Shetter, North, 2369
Shier, John W., 2339
Shiffman, Abraham, 1707
Shiffman, Douglas, 156
Shifman, Burton R., 1535
Shin, Chae S., 1708
Shingleton, Barbara, 825
Shinkle, Debra A., 2145
Shinners, James J., 2387
Shinnyo-En Foundation, 2749
Shively, Thomas, 1218
Shockley, Stuart, 100
Shoemaker Marital Trust, Ruth M., 1710
Shoemaker, Dale, 1711
Shoemaker, Dale A., 1711

Shoemaker, Edwin J., 1711, 2239
Shoemaker, Erich C., 1711
Shoemaker, Jacob, 1382
Shoemaker, Robert L., 1711
Sholar, John, 2578
Sholl, James K., 2315
Shore, Mike, 2652
Short, Jennifer "Jenny", 2369
Shoushanian, Diana, 1714
Shoushanian, Martin, 1714
Showalter, Daron C., 1587
Showalter, H.D. Hollins, 1587
Showalter, Shirley H., 2749
Showers, Scott, 2354
Shreve, Keith, 1373
Shrikian, Movses J., 425
Shubeck, Michael B., 1715
Shufro, Arthur S., 1716
Shufro, Norma, 1716
Shugart, Robert, 1151
Shukairy, Fayez, 1541
Shukairy, Khaled, 1717
Shulman, Joel, 1164
Shulz, Bobbie F., 1665
Shumsky, Matilda, 1718
Shumway, Frank, 2501
Shunsky, Vincent, 1520
Shurlow, Wanda, 1719
Shurlow, William, 1719
Shurtz, Bruce, 2076
Shwedel, Marvin S., 2851
Sias, Thelma A., 2302
Sibert, Charles M., 1720
Sibert, Marty, 2337
Siddiqui, Athar, 1721
Sidlik, Thomas W., 1722, 2172
Siebelink, Annette, 1892
Siebenthaler, Elizabeth C., 1723
Siebenthaler, William A., 1723
Siegal, Phyllis A. Shapiro, 2617
Siegel, Alan, 1475
Siegel, Bobbette Smith, 609
Siegel, Richard H., 2277
Siegel, Thomas S., 2845
Sieger, Diana R., 2352
Siegert, Arnold, 2821
Sielaff, Dale L., 182
Siena, Pamela, 2118
Sietsema, Harley, 2310
Sigman, Kathryn Smith, 1224
Sigmund Trust, Violet S., 1724
Sigmund Trust, W.A., 1724
Sigmund, William A., 1724
Sikora, Tammy Sue V., 963
Siler, Bernard, 2833
Silk, Dorothy, 1878
Silky, Charles E., Jr., 415, 1382
Sills, Arthur M., 1725
Sills, Claudia, 1725
Sills, Douglas, 1725
Sills, Rhoda, 1725
Sills, Susan, 1725
Silva, Marcella, 2847
Silva, Veronica, 1632
Silva, Yvan, 2847
Silverman, Carol, 2386
Silverman, Gilbert B., 1727, 2850
Silverman, Lila, 1727, 2850
Silverman, Sidney, 2131
Simasko, Patrick M., 1217
Simmons, Carroll B., 1728
Simmons, Cindy, 2483
Simmons, Constance M., 1729
Simmons, David T., 1729
Simmons, Mary Lou, 2679
Simmons, Michael S., 1728
Simmons, Steve M., 1729
Simmons, Timothy P., 1728
Simmons, Valerie L., 1001
Simmons, Walter P., 1728
Simon, Ronald A., 7
Simon, Theresa, 7
Simone, Christine M., 1173
Simone, David, 1173

Simone, Louise M., 1173
Simone, Mark, 1173
Simpson, Jon, 2314
Simpson, Larry, 2676
Simpson, Sharon, 1359
Sims, Howard F., 988, 2335
Sims, Joanne, 2319
Sims, Linda L., 1622, 2387
Sims, Mark A., 567
Simwood Co., 2221
Singel, Suzanne, 301
Singles, Neal, 2569
Singleton, James, 2317
Singleton, Judy, 2317
Sirchio, John Kristin, 1731
Sirhal, John M., 317
Sisson, Garry, 1785
Sisson, Harry A., 1732
Sisson, Skip, 2628
Sitler, Scott, 1352
Sjaarda, Harvey, 1733
Sjaarda, Russell, 1733
Sjaarda, Verdi, 1733
Sjogren, Melissa, 2321
Skandalaris, Robert J., 1734
Skau, Elizabeth, 1839
Skau, Gregory, 1839
Skedgell, Michelle, 2835
Skendzel, Jean, 1736
Skendzel, Laurence, 1736
Skilling Trust, Hugh H., 1738
Skilling, Hazel D., 1738
Skillman, Rose P., 1739
Skrzypczak, Jill S., 1740
Skrzypczak, Michael S., 1740
Skulsky, Craig S., 1370
Sky Financial Group, Inc., 2279
Sky Holdings, Inc., 2279
Slack, D. Jerome, 1741
Slack, Margery C., 1741
Sladen, Frank J., Jr., 802
Slaght, Michael, 2631
Slater, Steve, 2680
Slaughter, Sam, 2347
Slaven, I., 2551
Slavik, Edna, 1743
Slavik, Joseph F., 1743
Slavik, Mary E., 1742
Slavik, Richard, 1742
Slavik, Stephan F., Sr., 1742
Sledge, Thomas W., 435
Sleeman, Dan, 2656
Sleik, Sara, 2382
Slemons Trust, Elmer & Mabel, 1744
Slezak, Mark, 1136
Slikkers, Barbara, 1539
Slikkers, David A., 1745, 1746
Slikkers, Dolores E., 1057, 1745
Slikkers, Lee, 1746
Slikkers, Leon R., 1057, 1745
Slikkers, Mary B., 1745, 1746
Slikkers, Robert, 1539
Slikkers, Robert L., 1539, 1745
Slikkers, Steve, 1746
Slikkers, Thomas B., 1745
Slikkers-Ringwelski, Susan K., 1745
Slingerland, Mary, 2391
Slipher, Sara, 2677
Sliwinski, Al, 2876
Sloan, Anne J. Griffin, 737
Sloan, Ed, 2655
Sloan, Jeffrey, 2717
Sloan, Marie Jean Brinkman, Dr., 2391
Sloan, Richard, 2717
Sloat, Suzanne M., 1747
Slocum, Elizabeth, 1748
Slocum, Jody, 1748
Slocum, Mabel H., 1748
Slocum, William W., Jr., 1748
Small, Charles D., 2725
Small, Christi Cracchiolo, 372
Small, Faith F., 1749
Small, R.V., 1750

Smallegan Charitable Remainder
  Unitrust, Florence J., 1751
Smallegan, Judith, 1751
Smallegan, Karen, 1751
Smallegan, Kenneth D., 1751
Smallegan, Kevin, 1751
Smallegan, Lisa, 1751
Smart, George, 2589
Smies, David J., 576
Smies, Deborah, 576
Smith, Alilah, 1461
Smith, Ann Sullivan, 2621
Smith, April L., 49
Smith, Arthur L., 1755
Smith, Barry, 2787
Smith, Benedict J., 603
Smith, Bill, 2356
Smith, Billy W., 1756
Smith, Brian, 2216
Smith, C.J. Keller, 2279
Smith, Carl H., Jr., 1285
Smith, Carra J., 1755
Smith, Claudette Y., 2690
Smith, D.M., 2233
Smith, Dariel S., 1759
Smith, David L., 315
Smith, David R., 409
Smith, Dawn M., 2235
Smith, Debby, 2117
Smith, Diane C., 1285
Smith, Dolly, 1757
Smith, Earla B., 1754
Smith, Gerald K., 2461
Smith, Gordon D., 2392
Smith, Gregg, 2609
Smith, H. Warren, 557
Smith, Hugh M., 1758
Smith, Isabel F., 1758
Smith, J. Peter, 585
Smith, Jan, 1757, 1772
Smith, Jay C., 1759
Smith, Jean M.R., 1761
Smith, Jim, 552
Smith, Joanne, 2347
Smith, John F., Jr., 2205
Smith, Karen L., 1755
Smith, Karla M., 662
Smith, Kay A., 2378
Smith, Kendall A., 1760
Smith, Lawton, 2397
Smith, Leonard W., 585, 2055
Smith, Levi, 609
Smith, Ley, 2787
Smith, Lillie Mae, 363
Smith, Lois, 1756, 2787
Smith, Margaret, 2318
Smith, Mark L., 1758
Smith, Marsha J., 2609
Smith, Mary Beth, 1224
Smith, Matt N., Jr., 1616
Smith, Matt, Jr., 2329, 2341
Smith, Max, 2484
Smith, Max E., 2485
Smith, Maxine E., 1752
Smith, Michael J., 1332
Smith, Nancy Fehsenfeld, 557
Smith, Nancy R., 2849
Smith, Norma M., 2473
Smith, Patricia M., 1760
Smith, Paul, 2821
Smith, Ralph L., 1758
Smith, Robert C., 609
Smith, Robert L., Jr., 2550
Smith, Robert N., 2851
Smith, Robert R., 2438
Smith, Roger B., 2205
Smith, Roger D., 1757
Smith, Ron, 2373
Smith, Ronald E., 2728
Smith, Russ, 2596
Smith, S. Kinnie, Jr., 2165, 2170
Smith, S.W., 436
Smith, Scott D., 1760
Smith, Sidney W., Jr., 436, 532

Smith, Stanley, 2356
Smith, Stanton K., 1224
Smith, Staton E., Sr., 1224
Smith, Terri, 2360, 2372
Smith, Tim, 1497
Smith, Valerie, 551
Smith, W. Sidney, 2378
Smith, Wendy L., 2636
Smith, Wesley H., 1756
Smith, William H., 1760
Smith-Hornung, Isabel Claire, 1758
Smithers Foundation, Christopher D., 1920
Smithers-Fornaci, Adele, 1920
Smithson, James L., 2859
Smits, James, 446
Smits, Kerri Sue, 446
Smock, Joe, 2456
Smoker, Jill, 2431
Smokler Trust, Toba, 1020
Smokler, Carol S., 1020
Smokler, Irving A., 1020
Smolenski, J. Robert, Hon., 1955
Smyth, Betty, 948
Smyth, Kelvin, 2563
Smyth, Maureen H., 1332
Smyth, Roy G., 948
Smythe, John, 2039
Sneden Foundation, Robert W. and Margaret D., 404
Sneden, Kathleen, 404
Sneden, Kathleen M., 404
Sneden, Marcia A., 404
Sneed, Cornelia L., 1762
Sneed, Jacquelyn, 1085
Sneed, James, 1762
Sneed, Jane B., 1762
Sneed, Robert E., 1762
Sneideraitis, Marianne, 77
Snell, Hilary, 823
Snell, Hilary F., 2835
Snell, Hillary F., 1975
Snell, Mary, 2808
Snellenberger, Tim, 2651
Snide, Donald A., 929
Snide, Donald W., 929
Snider, Greg, 2449
Snider, Ira, 1763
Snider, Joan, 1763
Snider, Van W., Jr., 1540
Snoap, Dana L., 1835
Snodgrass, Dale, 2787
Snodgrass, Sharon, 2594
Snooks, Charles, 2732
Snow, Angela, 762
Snow, Jeanne, 2353
Sny, Shawn, 2720
Snyder, Arthur H., 1765
Snyder, Clarence A., 1765
Snyder, Clarence A., Mrs., 1765
Snyder, Dan, 2226
Snyder, Harold F., 1765
Snyder, Harold Z., 1764
Snyder, James A., 1764
Snyder, John S., 1262
Snyder, John S., Mrs., 1888
Snyder, Mary Beth, 2337
Snyder, Michelle A., 1869
Snyder, Rusty S., 2487
Snyder, Steve, 1764
Soave, Anthony, 1866
Sobieck, Charles W., 2710
Sobieck, Elizabeth A., 2710
Sobieck, Gayle, 2710
Sobieck, Gayle M., 2710
Sobieck, Mary C., 2710
Sobieck, Raymond G., 2710
Sobieck, Raymond M., 2710
Sobieck, Thomas A., 2710
Sobieck-Howe, Mary Claire, 2710
Soble, Jerome, 751
Soble, Kenneth, 751
Soble, Richard, 751
Soble, Richard A., 2566

Sobong, Enrico, 2852
Sobong, Esther, 2852
Socia, Mary R., 2311
Socia, Oscar F., 2311
Society of Manufacturing Engineers, 2620
Sockarmoen, Didik, 1968
Soderstrom, Carl, 2141
Soderstrom, Robert, 2810
Sogoigan, K.P., 2700
Soifer, Douglas S., 2035
Sokolof, Phil, 923
Solberg, Rosie, 2751
Soledad, Antonio, 2790
Soley, Jill, 1989
Soley, John, 1989
Soley, Judy, 1989
Soley, Robert L., 1989
Solis-Kidder, Juanita, 2404
Solomon, Daniel B., 336
Solomon, Sherry, 2323
Somerlott, Bambi, 2356
Sommer, Anthony G., 1977
Sommerfield, David W., 1782
Sommers, Dana E., 1001
Sommers, Schwartz, Silver & Schwartz, 2280
Song, John, 2723
Sonkin, Sheldon L., 2854
Sonneveldt, Carol A., 1767
Sonneveldt, Lance C., 1767
Sonneveldt, Robyn J., 1767
Soonlee, Hai, 2790
Soorus, Leo, 2533
Sorensen, Paul T., 956
Sorenson, Damone, 2333
Sosin, Allen, 2419
Sosnowski, Julie, 423
Souder, Jr. Charitable Lead Trust, William F., 1768
Souder, Susanna J., 1768
Souder, William F., Jr., 1768
Soule, Carol, 2391
Southeast Michigan Physicians, PC, 2845
Southern Crushed Concrete, Inc., 1997
Southern Michigan Bank & Trust, 952, 1627, 1735
Southwest Regional Rehabilitation Center, 1772
Southwicke, Sara J., 1275
Southwood, Susan, 323
Sovel, Susan, 961
Sowers, Donna, 2353
Spanos, George, 267
Sparks, Nan, 2783
Sparks, Pamela Rowan, 1601
Sparrow, Susan, 2320
Sparrow, William T., 2721
Spartan Motors, Inc., 1775
Spears, Julius, 2478
Speer, Bill, 2333, 2349, 2661
Speirn, Sterling, 988
Spencer, Barb, 2317
Spencer, Carol, 1778
Spencer, Chuck, 2317
Spencer, Don, 2325, 2658
Spencer, Hildreth, 1824
Spencer, John R., 1399
Spencer, Kenneth, 1778
Spetty, Clarice, 2583
Spezia, Michael J., 2759
Spica, Amanda, 1383
Spica, Beth J., 1383
Spica, Frederick P., 66
Spica, Joseph P., 66
Spica, Julaine M., 66
Spica, Robert, 1383
Spicer, Gary, 488, 1757
Spicer, Joyce, 2307
Spicer, S. Gary, 196, 1105, 1236, 1374, 1779, 1795
Spieker, David, 2504
Spilman, Jeffrey D., 99

Spleet, Joe, 2604
Spoelhof, John, 1780
Spoelhof, Judith, 1780
Spoelhof, Judy, 1780
Spoelhof, Scott, 1780
Spoelhof, William, 2023
Spoelman, Paul, 2343
Spoon, John, 2263
Sporka, Patrick, 2630
Sport Fun, Inc., 1920
Spotts, Connie, 915
Sprague, Frederick O., 2321
Sprenger, Patricia E., 2555
Sprik, Harlan J., 813
Spring, Mary Ellen, 204
Springer, Bruce C., 1001
Springgate, Susan, 2362
Springsteen, Bruce, 339
Sprinkle, Deborah, 2728
Sproles, Joe, 2317
Sprudz, Ugis, 2535
Squires, Lisa, 2828
St. Antoine, Theodore, 2553
St. Louis, Jim, 2657
Staab, Charles, 2579
Stabile, Joseph D., 2311
Stachler, Eric C., 2279
Staffaroni, Paul J., 1554
Staiger, Charles, 2042
Staiger, Charles W., 1319
Stancato, Shirley R., 2573
Standard Federal Bank N.A., 229, 363, 376, 985, 1125, 1359, 1471, 2422
Stange Trust, Mary G., 1787
Stanhope, Marylyn, 1384
Stankey, Charles, 1764
Stanley, Bruce E., 2100
Stanley, Iola, 979
Stanley, Mandel, 979
Stanley, Stanley R., 2034
Stansik, Jim, 2463
Stante, Maria, 2322
Stanton, David J., 1789
Stanton, Dorothy, 1788
Stanton, Dorothy M., 1788
Stanton, James B., 1788
Stanton, Laura M., 1789
Stanton, Michael J., 1788
Stanton, Paul A., 1788
Stapp, Pat, 2492
Stark, Elizabeth, 2057
Stark, Harry S., 1286
Stark, Martin H., 2387
Stark, Naomi, 2378
Stark, R. Keith, 1213
Starring, Colleen, 2315
Stasa, Mark J., 380
Stasevich, Nicolas, 1961
Stasik, Randal, 2527
Staudenmaier, Mary, 2369
Staudt, Dave, 2579
Stauffer & Co., 1791
Stauffer, Donald R., 1791
Stauffer, Elizabeth, 1791
Stauffer, John, 2649
Stavropoulos, William S., 668
Stawski, Willard S., 1001, 2150
Stearns, Dana, 2463
Stee, Randy, 2400
Steeby, P.J., 2386
Steelcase Inc., 2281
Steele, Betty, 501
Steele, Esther L., 1792
Steele, Harold E., 1792
Steele, John O., 501
Steele, Richard, 2832
Steely, Morgan, 2315
Stefanek, Gregg, 2762, 2833
Stefani, Andrew, 1474
Steffen, John, 2191
Stege, Evelyn, 1918
Stege, George, III, 2469, 2470
Steger, J.A., 2254
Stehouwer, William H., 1793

Steimle, John, 339
Steinberg, David L., 2347
Steinberg, Joel D., 2768
Steinbrecher, Susan, 2023
Steiner Sports Memorabilia, 1920
Steiner, Jonathan, 2512
Steinhauer, Bruce W., 1226
Steinhauer, G., 2682
Steinmann, Diane J., 1794
Steinmann, Karl, 1794
Steinmann, Karl M., 1794
Stella, Frank, 1961
Stemen, Milton, 2273
Stepaniak, Kathy, 2661
Stephen, Larry, 2403
Stephen, Scott, 2404
Stephens, David B., 2065
Stephens, Deborah, 1398
Stephens, Evelyn G., 432
Stephens, Mel, 2242
Stephens, Robert, 2447
Stephens, Sherri E., 2336
Stephenson, Donald, 2631
Sterban, Donna L., 1795
Sterban, Richard A., 1795
Sterk, Marlene, 1796
Sterk, Marlene J., 1796
Sterk, William, 1796
Stern, Elaine, 45
Stern, Helmut F., 1797
Stern, Joan, 2428
Sternberg, Leslie D., 1798
Sternberg, Mervyn H., 1798
Stetler, Gary, 437
Stetler, Gerald, 437
Stetler, John, 2076
Stevens, Derek, 342
Stevens, Elizabeth, 342
Stevens, Gregory, 342
Stevens, Jan, 1279
Stevens, Lonnie, 2666
Stevens, Robert, 2551
Stevens, Theresa J., 1891
Stevens, Thomas L., 2352
Stevenson, Bobby G., 457
Stevenson, Catherine, 2391
Stevenson, Delaine, 457
Steward, Hyun A. Rhee, 1552
Steward, Jim, 2360
Steward, Larry E., 2188
Stewart Motorsports, Tony, Inc., 2841
Stewart, Alexander, 1801
Stewart, Bill, 2431
Stewart, Cynthia, 2342
Stewart, Gordon L., 1802
Stewart, Greg, 2568
Stewart, Joseph M., 988
Stewart, Linda A., 1802
Stewart, Marise M.M., 1332
Stewart, Philip, 1801
Stewart, Robert, 1801
Stewart, Samuel S., III, 269
Stewart, Wayne, 1018, 1376, 1890, 2109
Stewatt, C. Allan, 688
Stibbs, Don, 2375
Stieg, Annette D., 1803
Stieg, Edward C., 290, 1803
Stieg, Elizabeth A., 290, 1803
Stieg, Harold E., 290, 1803
Stieg, William H., 1803
Stien, Craig, 2372
Stillman, Judith S., 175
Stines, Alfred, 2857
Stipech, Frank J., 2454
Stirling, David, 1931
Stockbridge Enterprise Inc., 1804
Stocking, Charles, 2587
Stockton, Florence, 1805
Stoddard, Alice A., 1809
Stoddard, Buddy, 2530
Stoddard, Charles C., 1806, 1808
Stoddard, Janet O., 1808
Stoddard, Jennie C., 1806

TYPE OF SUPPORT INDEX

List of terms: Terms for the major types of support used in this index are listed below with definitions.

Index: In the index itself, grantmaker entries are arranged under each term by state location, abbreviated name, and sequence number. Grantmakers in boldface type make grants on a national, regional, or international basis. The others generally limit giving to the state or city in which they are located.

Annual campaigns: any organized effort by a nonprofit to secure gifts on an annual basis; also called annual appeals.

Building/renovation: money raised for construction, renovation, remodeling, or rehabilitation of buildings; may be part of an organization's capital campaign.

Capital campaigns: a campaign, usually extending over a period of years, to raise substantial funds for enduring purposes, such as building or endowment funds.

Cause-related marketing: linking gifts to charity with marketing promotions. This may involve donating products which will then be auctioned or given away in a drawing with the proceeds benefiting a charity. The advertising campaign for the product will be combined with the promotion for the charity. In other cases it will be advertised that when a customer buys the product a certain amount of the proceeds will be donated to charity. Often gifts made to charities stemming from cause-related marketing are not called charitable donations and may be assigned as expenses to the department in charge of the program. Public affairs and marketing are the departments usually involved.

Conferences/seminars: a grant to cover the expenses of holding a conference or seminar.

Consulting services: professional staff support provided by the foundation to a nonprofit to consult on a project of mutual interest or to evaluate services (not a cash grant).

Continuing support: a grant that is renewed on a regular basis.

Curriculum development: grants to schools, colleges, universities, and educational support organizations to develop general or discipline-specific curricula.

Debt reduction: also known as deficit financing. A grant to reduce the recipient organization's indebtedness; frequently refers to mortgage payments.

Donated equipment: surplus furniture, office machines, paper, appliances, laboratory apparatus, or other items that may be given to charities, schools, or hospitals.

Donated land: land or developed property. Institutions of higher education often receive gifts of real estate; land has also been given to community groups for housing development or for parks or recreational facilities.

Donated products: companies giving away what they make or produce. Product donations can include periodic clothing donations to a shelter for the homeless or regular donations of pharmaceuticals to a health clinic resulting in a reliable supply.

Emergency funds: a one-time grant to cover immediate short-term funding needs on an emergency basis.

Employee matching gifts: a contribution to a charitable organization by a corporate employee which is matched by a similar contribution from the employer. Many corporations support employee matching gift programs in higher education to stimulate their employees to give to the college or university of their choice. In addition, many foundations support matching gift programs for their officers and directors.

Employee volunteer services: an ongoing coordinated effort through which the company promotes involvement with nonprofits on the part of employees. The involvement may be during work time or after hours. (Employees may also volunteer on their own initiative; however, that is not described as corporate volunteerism). Many companies honor their employees with awards for outstanding volunteer efforts. In making cash donations, many favor the organizations with which their employees have worked as volunteers. Employee volunteerism runs the gamut from school tutoring programs to sales on work premises of employee-made crafts or baked goods to benefit nonprofits. Management of the programs can range from fully-staffed offices of corporate volunteerism to a part-time coordinating responsibility on the part of one employee.

Employee-related scholarships: a scholarship program funded by a company-sponsored foundation usually for children of employees; programs are frequently administered by the National Merit Scholarship Corporation which is responsible for selection of scholars.

Endowments: a bequest or gift intended to be kept permanently and invested to provide income for continued support of an organization.

Equipment: a grant to purchase equipment, furnishings, or other materials.

Exchange programs: usually refers to funds for educational exchange programs for foreign students.

Fellowships: usually indicates funds awarded to educational institutions to support fellowship programs. A few foundations award fellowships directly to individuals.

Film/video/radio: grants to fund a specific film, video, or radio production.

General/operating support: a grant made to further the general purpose or work of an organization, rather than for a specific purpose or project; also called unrestricted grants.

Grants to individuals: awards made directly by the foundation to individuals rather than to nonprofit organizations; includes aid to the needy. (See also "Fellowships," "Scholarships—to individuals," and "Student loans—to individuals.")

In-kind gifts: a contribution of equipment, supplies, or other property as distinct from a monetary grant. Some organizations may also donate space or staff time as an in-kind contribution.

Income development: grants for fundraising, marketing, and to expand audience base.

Internship funds: usually indicates funds awarded to an institution or organization to support an internship program rather than a grant to an individual.

Land acquisition: a grant to purchase real estate property.

Lectureships: see "Curriculum development."

Loaned talent: an aspect of employee volunteerism. It differs from the usual definition of such in that it usually involves loaned professionals and executive staff who are helping a nonprofit in an area involving their particular skills. Loaned talents can assist a nonprofit in strategic planning, dispute resolution or negotiation services, office administration, real estate technical assistance, personnel policies, lobbying, consulting, fundraising, and legal and tax advice.

Loans: see "Program-related investments/ loans" and "Student loans—to individuals.")

Loans—to individuals: assistance distributed directly to individuals in the form of loans.

Management development/capacity building: grants for salaries, staff support, staff training, strategic and long-term planning, capacity building, budgeting and accounting.

Matching/challenge support: a grant which is made to match funds provided by another donor. (See also "Employee matching gifts.")

Operating budgets: see "General/operating support."

Professorships: a grant to an educational institution to endow a professorship or chair.

Program development: grants to support specific projects or programs as opposed to general purpose grants.

Program evaluation: grants to evaluate a specific project or program; includes awards both to agencies to pay for evaluation costs and to research institutes and other program evaluators.

Program-related investments/loans: a loan is any temporary award of funds that must be repaid. A program-related investment is a loan or other investment (as distinguished from a grant) made by a foundation to another organization for a project related to the foundation's stated charitable purpose and interests.

Public relations services: may include printing and duplicating, audio-visual and graphic arts services, helping to plan special events such as festivals, piggyback advertising (advertisements that mention a company while also promoting a nonprofit), and public service advertising.

Publication: a grant to fund reports or other publications issued by a nonprofit resulting from research or projects of interest to the foundation.

Renovation projects: see "Building/renovation."

Research: usually indicates funds awarded to institutions to cover costs of investigations and clinical trials. Research grants for individuals are usually referred to as fellowships.

Scholarship funds: a grant to an educational institution or organization to support a scholarship program, mainly for students at the undergraduate level. (See also "Employee-related scholarships.")

Scholarships—to individuals: assistance awarded directly to individuals in the form of educational grants or scholarships. (See also "Employee-related scholarships.")

Seed money: a grant or contribution used to start a new project or organization. Seed grants may cover salaries and other operating expenses of a new project. Also known as "start-up funds."

Special projects: see "Program development."

Sponsorships: endorsements of charities by corporations; or corporate contributions to all or part of a charitable event.

Student aid: see "Fellowships," "Scholarships— to individuals," and "Student loans—to individuals."

Student loans—to individuals: assistance awarded directly to individuals in the form of educational loans.

Technical assistance: operational or management assistance given to nonprofit organizations; may include fundraising assistance, budgeting and financial planning, program planning, legal advice, marketing, and other aids to management. Assistance may be offered directly by a foundation staff member or in the form of a grant to pay for the services of an outside consultant.

Use of facilities: this may include rent free office space for temporary periods, dining and meeting facilities, telecommunications services, mailing services, transportation services, or computer services.

Annual campaigns

Florida: Ludy 1130, Ryder 2277
Illinois: Northern 2265, Souder 1768
Michigan: **Arcus 70**, Asthma 2419, Baldwin 90, Bargman 98, Barry 2314, Barstow 109, **Bath 118**, Batts 2146, Borman's 199, Brauer 219, Bregi 222, Burdick 263, Burroughs 269, Camp 285, Clannad 329, Community 2337, Consumers 2169, Cook 358, **DaimlerChrysler 2172**, Davis 408, Detroit 2739, DeVos 438, DeVos 439, DeVos 440, DeVos 441, DeWitt 448, Doan 459, Dow 479, DTE 2187, Ervin 528, Farver 547, Felpausch 2199, Ford 2203, General 2206, Gerstacker 668, Gilmore 683, Gornick 715, Grand Rapids 2211, Granger 722, **H.I.S. 749**, Harding 788, Herrick 829, Hudson 876, Hunter 884, Imerman 898, **Isabel 909, Jewish 2521**, Johnson 937, JSJ 2228, Kahn 2230, Kaufman 974, Kelly 2236, Keweenaw 2363, Kinney 1011, Lansing 1075, Lapeer 2365, Lausch 2241, Library 2538, Liebler 1106, Livonia 2368, Manistee 2371, Marsilje 1181, Masco 2249, Michigan 1268, Miller 1284, Miller 1286, Miller 2255, Missaukee 2377, Monroe 1313, Moore 1316, Morley 1325, **National 1359**, Olds 1398, Oleson 1399, Parfet 1430, Parish 1432, Parish 1433, Phelps 2834, Power 1502, **Sage 1621**, Shaevsky 2616, Shelden 1699, Sisson 1732, **Society 2620**, Sojourner 2621, **Teitel 1870**, Todd 2287, Towsley 1901, **Triford 1906, Tubergen 1913**, Upton 1935,

Vanderweide 1956, Vicksburg 1968, Walker 1979, Warchol 1986, Waterford 2679, Weatherwax 1996, Wege 2001, Wickes 2048, Wickson 2049, Wilson 2067
Minnesota: TCF 2285
New Mexico: Seidman 1683
New York: Birds 2149, Millman 1287
Ohio: Anderson 52, Cleveland 2164, Hildreth 838, Milacron 2254, National 2260, NCC 2262, St. Clair 1783
Pennsylvania: Pryor 1516
Washington: Fehsenfeld 557
Wisconsin: Beauchamp 129, Bishop 172, Bray 220, Hess 831, Kowalski 2238, WPS 2305

Building/renovation

California: Landsberg 1071, Wilcox 2054
Florida: Bush 274
Illinois: Loutit 1124, Northern 2265, Souder 1768
Michigan: **Africa 16**, Albion 2307, Alldredge 34, Allegan 2309, Americana 47, Andersen 50, Annis 62, **Arcus 70**, Baldwin 90, Bargman 98, Barry 2314, Barth 110, Baske 115, Battle Creek 2315, Batts 2146, Bauervic 121, Bauervic 122, Bay 2316, Besser 155, Biederman 2715, Blissfield 183, Blissfield 2429, Blodgett 184, Blume 187, Bonisteel 193, Brauer 219, Buhr 259, Burdick 263, Burroughs

269, Cadillac 2321, Capital 2323, Community 2331, Community 2332, Community 2333, Community 2337, Community 2338, Community 2339, Community 2340, Consumers 2169, Consumers 2170, Cook 358, Cronin 381, Dagenais 397, Dalton 398, Daoud 401, Dart 403, Davenport 404, Davis 408, Dearborn 2173, Deffenbaugh 417, **DeKorne 422**, Delano 423, **DENSO 2177**, Detwiler 2462, DeVos 438, DeVos 440, DeVos 441, DiPonio 455, **Dow 2186**, Dow 477, Dow 478, Drake 480, Fabri 2194, Farver 547, Fike 568, Ford 593, **Ford 2202**, Foundation 603, Frankenmuth 2349, Fremont 2350, Gary 644, Gast 647, Gerstacker 668, Gilmore 683, Grand Rapids 2352, Grand Rapids 2211, Grand 2353, Great 2493, Greenville 2355, **H.I.S. 749**, Hall 768, Hancock 778, **Heron 828**, Herrick 829, Holden 853, Holl 854, Home 857, Hudson 876, Hunter 884, Hurst 886, Idema 894, Imerman 898, Ionia 2358, Iosco 2359, Irwin 907, Jackson 2361, Jonathan 942, JSJ 2228, Kahn 960, **Kakarala 962**, Kalamazoo 2362, Kantzler 966, Kaufman 977, Keller 986, Kennedy 996, Kinney 1011, Knight 1026, Kool 2793, **Kresge 1049**, La-Z-Boy 2239, Lake 2364, Lansing 1075, Leelanau 2366, Lenawee 2367, Liebler 1106, Livonia 2368, Malpass 1163, Manoogian 1171, Marquette 2372, Marshall 2373, Masco 2249, McCormick 1216, McGregor 1226, Mecosta 2374, Merillat 1255, Midland 2376, Miller 1277, Miller 1284, Miller 2255, Mills 1288, Mitchell

1299, Monroe 1313, Moore 1316, Morley 1325, Mount Pleasant 2378, Mt. Zion 1339, Murphy 1349, North 2380, Olds 1398, Oleson 1399, Palmer 1424, Parfet 1430, Pearson 1448, Pentecost 1457, Perrigo 2266, Petoskey 2385, Pinney 1482, Pistons 2267, Plym 1488, Power 1502, Ratner 1532, Rattner 1533, Redies 2273, Robell 1566, Robison 1570, Rotary 2609, **Sage 1621**, Saginaw 2387, Schalon 1646, **Secchia 1676**, Shelden 1699, Shiffman 1707, Slemons 1744, Sparta 2395, Spoelhof 1780, Steelcase 2281, Stolaruk 1812, Straits 2397, Strosacker 1821, Stubnitz 1824, Sturgis 2398, Tauber 1861, **Teitel 1870**, Three 2399, Tiscornia 1897, Todd 2287, Towsley 1901, Tuscola 2400, Upton 1935, Vanderweide 1956, Vicksburg 1968, Walters 1983, Warchol 1986, Weatherwax 1996, Wege 2001, Wickes 2048, Wickson 2049, Wilson 2065, Wilson 2067, Wirt 2078, **Worldwide 2689, Wynalda 2106**, Wyoming 2401, Young 2115, Zuehlke 2135
Minnesota: Weyand 2032
New Mexico: Seidman 1683
New York: Birds 2149, **Nonprofit 2576**
Ohio: Anderson 52, Cleveland 2164, Milacron 2254, National 2260, Steele 1792, Whiting 2042
Washington: Fehsenfeld 557
Wisconsin: Bishop 172, Bray 220, Hess 831, Kowalski 2238, WPS 2305

Capital campaigns
Florida: Bush 274
Illinois: Loutit 1124, Northern 2265
Michigan: Alldredge 34, Andersen 50, **Arcus 70**, Baldwin 90, Barry 2314, Barth 110, **Bath 118**, Batts 2146, Besser 155, Bonisteel 193, **Borders 2153**, Borman's 199, Brauer 219, Buhr 259, Burdick 263, Burroughs 269, Camp 285, Capital 2323, Carls 290, Combs 349, Community 2331, Community 2338, Community 2340, Community 2341, Consumers 2169, Consumers 2170, Cook 358, **Cummings 386**, Dalton 398, Daoud 401, Davenport 404, Davis 408, Detroit 2739, DeVos 438, DeVos 439, DeVos 440, DeVos 441, Dole 464, Doornink 469, **Dow 2186**, Dow 477, Dow 479, Drake 480, DTE 2188, Fabiano 2193, Fabri 2194, Farver 547, Ford 2203, Fremont 2350, Frey 621, Gershenson 667, Gerstacker 668, Gilmore 683, Grand Haven 2351, Grand Rapids 2352, Grand Rapids 2488, Grand Rapids 2211, Granger 722, Greenville 2355, **H.I.S. 749**, Herrick 829, Hickman 835, Hudson 876, Idema 894, Ionia 2358, Jackson 2361, **Jewish 2521**, JSJ 2228, Jurries 954, Kalamazoo 2362, Kantzler 966, Keller 986, Kinney 1011, Knight 1026, **Kresge 1049**, Lansing 1075, Lear 2242, Leelanau 2366, Lenawee 2367, Lincoln 1109, Magline 2246, Marquette 2372, Marsilje 1181, Martin 1186, Masco 2248, Masco 2249, McGregor 1226, Miller 1277, Miller 1284, Miller 1286, Miller 2255, Miller 2257, Monroe 1313, Moore 1316, Morley 1325, Mount Pleasant 2378, Nelson 1364, Olds 1398, Oleson 1399, Parfet 1430, Parish 1432, Parish 1433, Polk 1492, Power 1502, Pulte 2271, Redies 2273, Robison 1570, Rotary 2609, Rotary 2612, **Sage 1621**, SEMCO 2278, Shelden 1699, Shepherd 1702, Slemons 1744, Smith 1756, **Society 2620**, Sparta 2395, Steelcase 2281, Sturgis 2398, Sundquist 1841, **Teitel 1870**, Three 2399, Tiscornia 1897, Todd 2287, Towsley 1901, **Tubergen 1913**, Upton 1935, Vanderweide 1956, Vicksburg 1968, Weatherwax 1996, Webber 1997, Wege 2001, Wickson 2049, Wilson 2067, Wolters 2090, World 2099, Wyoming 2401, Zuehlke 2135
Minnesota: **Target 2283**, TCF 2285
New Mexico: Seidman 1683
Ohio: Anderson 52, Andersons 2412, Bates 2145, Cleveland 2164, Milacron 2254, National 2260, NCC 2262
Pennsylvania: Pryor 1516
Wisconsin: Wisconsin 2302, WPS 2305

Cause-related marketing
Michigan: **Borders 2153**, DaimlerChrysler 2171, DTE 2187
Minnesota: **Target 2283**

Conferences/seminars
California: Landsberg 1071
Florida: **Hagen 758**
Michigan: Albion 2307, Americana 47, Ann Arbor 2312, **Arcus 70**, Arts 2415, ArtServe 2417, Barry 2314, Battle Creek 2315, Branch 2320, Colina 347, Community 2332, Community 2333, Consumers 2169, Dart 403, Delta 2459, Detroit 2739, Dow 479, **Earhart 506, Fetzer 2749, Ford 2202**, Ford 2203, Four 2348, Fremont 2350, Gilmore 683, Great 2493, Henley 820, Hillsdale 2356, India 901, Iosco 2359, Jerome 2519, Jewish 2523, Lansing 1075, **Lowe 2800**, Marshall 2373, Michigan 2375, **Mott 1332**, Mount Pleasant 2378, North 2380, Olds 1398, Shiawassee 2391, Shiffman 1707, Sojourner 2621, Straits 2397, Thompson 1888, Vicksburg 1968, Weatherwax 1996, **Worldwide 2689**, Zondervan 2134
New York: **Ford 590**
Ohio: Anderson 52
Wisconsin: Bradshaw 215

Consulting services
Florida: Bush 274
Michigan: Albion 2307, **Arcus 70**, Arts 2415, Barry 2314, Blodgett 184, Cable 2436, Charlevoix 2325, Community 2332, Detroit 2461, Dyer 499, Fremont 2350, Gilmore 683, Haven 2503, Hudson 876, Jackson 2361, Lansing 1075, Michigan 2567, Midland 2376, Miller 1284, Miller 2255, Mills 1288, Missaukee 2377, Sturgis 2398, Weatherwax 1996, **Worldwide 2689**
New York: **Ford 590, Nonprofit 2576**
Pennsylvania: Pryor 1516

Continuing support
Florida: Church 326
Illinois: Crane 376, Northern 2265
Massachusetts: Cowan 369
Michigan: Allegan 2309, **Arcus 70**, Arts 2415, Bargman 98, Batts 2146, Besser 155, Biederman 2715, Braude 218, Brauer 219, Burdick 263, Burroughs 269, Cable 2436, Clannad 329, Community 2332, **DaimlerChrysler 2172**, Dalton 398, Dart 403, Davis 408, Delano 423, Detroit 431, DeVos 438, DeVos 439, DeVos 440, DeVos 441, Doan 459, Dole 464, Doll 465, Dow 477, Dow 479, Drake 480, Ervin 528, Farver 547, Ford 2203, Four 2348, Fremont 2350, General 2206, Gerstacker 668, Gilmore 683, GM 2209, Grand Rapids 2211, Great 2493, **H.I.S. 749**, Harding 788, Haven 2503, Henley 820, Henry 823, Herrick 829, Holden 853, Hudson 876, Imerman 898, **Isabel 909**, Jewish 2523, Johnson 937, JSJ 2228, Keller 986, Kelly 2236, KT 1052, Lake 2364, Livonia 2368, M & M 2369, Mackinac 2370, Manoogian 1171, McGregor 1226, Merkley 1257, Midland 2568, Miller 1286, Mills 1288, Missaukee 2377, Molloy 1307, Moore 1316, Morley 1325, **Mott 1332**, Mott 1333, Oleson 1399, Parfet 1430, Power 1502, Ratner 1532, Robison 1570, **Sage 1621**, Shelden 1699, Shiawassee 2391, Shiffman 1707, Smith 1756, Sojourner 2621, Strosacker 1821, **Teitel 1870**, Thoman 1878, Thompson 1888, Tiscornia 1897, Todd 2287, Towsley 1901, Vanderweide 1956, Vicksburg 1968, Vollbrecht 1976, Walker 1979, Warchol 1986, Westerman 2027, Whirlpool 2301, Wilson 2067, **Wynalda 2106**, Young 2117
Minnesota: TCF 2285, Weyerhaeuser 2034
New Jersey: National 2261
New York: **Ford 590**, Greenspan 735, **Heron 827**
Ohio: Milacron 2254, NCC 2262

Wisconsin: Beauchamp 129, Bishop 172, Bray 220, Kowalski 2238, McIntyre 1227, WPS 2305

Curriculum development
California: Landsberg 1071
Florida: **Hagen 758**
Michigan: Albion 2307, Allegan 2309, **Arcus 70**, AtWater 81, Barry 2314, Battle Creek 2315, Bay 2316, Berrien 2319, Binda 167, Blodgett 184, Cable 2436, Cadillac 2321, Camp 285, Community 2338, Community 2340, **DaimlerChrysler 2172**, Dart 403, Davenport 404, Delano 423, Detwiler 2462, **Dow 2186**, Dyer 499, **Earhart 506**, Flinn 585, Ford 2203, Fremont 2350, Grand 2353, Great 2493, Herrick 829, Jewish 2522, Jewish 2523, Keller 986, Library 2538, Marshall 2373, Michigan 2375, Miller 1286, Oleson 1399, Shiawassee 2391, **Society 2620**, Southfield 2394, Tuscola 2400, Ufer 2289, Vicksburg 1968, Warchol 1986, Waterford 2679, Weatherwax 1996, Wege 2001, **Worldwide 2689**, Young 2117, Zondervan 2134
New York: **Ford 590**
Wisconsin: Bradshaw 215

Debt reduction
Michigan: Camp 285, Dalton 398, Gilmore 683, Jury 955, Knight 1026, **Wynalda 2106**
Wisconsin: Bishop 172

Donated equipment
Michigan: DENSO 2176, **Ford 2202, Kellogg 2234**, Miller 2255
Ohio: National 2260

Donated land
Michigan: **Ford 2202**

Donated products
Michigan: **Alticor 2138, Borders 2153**, DENSO 2176, Detroit 2180, Detroit 2182, Domino's 2184, Farmer 2196, **Ford 2202**, GM 2209, Gordon 2210, Haworth 2219, Holcim 2222, **Kellogg 2234**, Masco 2248, Meijer 2251, **Steelcase 2282**, Whirlpool 2300, Wolverine 2304
Minnesota: **Target 2283**

Emergency funds
Florida: Bush 274
Michigan: Allegan 2309, Ann Arbor 2312, Barstow 109, Battle Creek 2315, Cadillac 2321, Charlevoix 2325, Clannad 329, Community 2325, Community 2332, Community 2337, **DaimlerChrysler 2172**, Dalton 398, Drake 480, Ervin 528, Farver 547, Ford 2203, Frankenmuth 2349, Fremont 2350, General 2206, Gerstacker 668, Gilmore 683, Henley 820, Herrick 829, Hunter 884, Kalamazoo 2362, Kelly 2236, KT 1052, Lansing 1075, Livonia 2368, Mackinac 2370, Manoogian 1171, Michigan 1268, Miller 1284, Mills 1288, Moore 1316, Morley 1325, Mount Pleasant 2378, Olds 1398, Parfet 1430, Pellerito 1451, Perry 1461, Saginaw 2387, Southfield 2394, Stubnitz 1824, **Teitel 1870**, Tiscornia 1897, Tuscola 2400, Warchol 1986, Weatherwax 1996, Wilson 2067, **Wynalda 2106**, Young 2117
Minnesota: **Target 2283**
Ohio: Anderson 52, Whiting 2042
Pennsylvania: Pryor 1516
Wisconsin: Bishop 172, Bradshaw 215, Bray 220

Employee matching gifts
California: Nissan 2264

Florida: Bush 274, Ryder 2277
Illinois: Northern 2265
Michigan: **Amerisure 2140, Arcus 70**, Collins 2166, Consumers 2169, Consumers 2170, **DaimlerChrysler 2172**, DENSO 2176, Dow 2185, **Dow 2186**, DTE 2188, Ford 2203, Fremont 2350, Frey 621, General 2206, Gilmore 683, Grand Rapids 2352, Haworth 2219, Hudson 876, Kalamazoo 2362, **Kellogg 988**, Kellogg's 2235, **Kresge 1049**, Livonia 2368, M & M 2369, Masco 2248, McGregor 1226, Morley 1325, **Mott 1332**, Parfet 1430, **ProQuest 2270**, Skillman 1739, Steelcase 2281, Taubman 2284, Towsley 1901, Whirlpool 2301, Wolverine 2303, Wolverine 2304
Minnesota: TCF 2285
New Jersey: National 2261
New York: Birds 2149, **Ford 590, Heron 827**
Ohio: Cleveland 2164, Grange 2212, NCC 2262
Washington: UNOVA 1932
Wisconsin: Giddings 2208, Wisconsin 2302, WPS 2305

Employee volunteer services

California: Nissan 2264
Illinois: Northern 2265
Michigan: **Alticor 2138**, American 2139, **Amerisure 2140**, Blue 2151, Champion 2158, Citizens 2162, Comerica 2167, DENSO 2176, DTE 2187, DTE 2188, **Ford 2202**, GM 2209, Holcim 2222, **Kellogg 2234**, Masco 2248, Meijer 2251, Miller 2255, Pulte 2271, SEMCO 2278, **Steelcase 2282**, Taubman 2284, Valassis 2291, Varnum 2293, Whirlpool 2300
Minnesota: **Target 2283**, TCF 2285
Ohio: Grange 2212, National 2260
Texas: Quicksilver 2272

Employee-related scholarships

Michigan: **ArvinMeritor 2141, Borders 2430**, Community 2340, **DaimlerChrysler 2172**, Detroit 2178, Fabri 2194, Grand Rapids 2352, Guardian 2215, **Gygi 2216**, Henry 2220, Kohn 1035, L & L 2794, Steelcase 2281, Universal 2290, Valassis 2291, Whirlpool 2301
Minnesota: **Target 2283**, TCF 2285
New Jersey: National 2261
West Virginia: Farr 2197
Wisconsin: Giddings 2208

Endowments

Florida: Church 326, Ludy 1130
Illinois: Lurie 1136, Northern 2265
Michigan: Adray 14, Annis 62, **Arcus 70**, Barry 2314, Barstow 109, Batts 2146, Biederman 2715, Branch 2320, Brauer 219, Burroughs 269, Cable 2436, Charlevoix 2325, Chippewa 2326, Community 2337, Consumers 2169, Dow 477, Dow 478, Dow 479, Drake 480, Fremont 2350, Gerstacker 668, Grand 2353, Henry 823, Herrick 829, Hickman 835, Holley 856, Imerman 897, Italian 2518, Jurries 954, Keweenaw 2363, Lapeer 2365, Leelanau 2366, Livonia 2368, Manistee 2371, Manoogian 1171, Marsilje 1181, McCardell 1211, Miller 1286, Miller 2255, Mount Pleasant 2378, Olds 1398, Paine 1420, Parfet 1430, Pennock 1456, Pentecost 1457, Phelps 2834, Ratner 1532, **Riley 1557**, Roscommon 2386, **Sage 1621**, Shelden 1699, Shiawassee 2391, Strosacker 1821, Sundquist 1841, **Teitel 1870**, Towsley 1901, Tuscola 2400, Vicksburg 1968, Wege 2001, Westerbeek 2026, Westerman 2027, Wilson 2065
New Mexico: Seidman 1683
New York: **Ford 590**
Ohio: Whiting 2042
Wisconsin: Hess 831, Wisconsin 2302

Equipment

California: Landsberg 1071
Florida: Bush 274
Illinois: Loutit 1124, Seabury 1673
Massachusetts: Cowan 369
Michigan: Adray 14, Albion 2307, Allegan 2309, Andersen 50, Annis 62, Arts 2415, Baldwin 90, Barry 2314, Barstow 109, Battle Creek 2315, Bauervic 121, Bauervic 122, Biederman 2715, Blodgett 184, Bonisteel 193, Boutell 210, Branch 2320, Buffalo 2155, Cable 2436, Cadillac 2321, Capital 2323, Clannad 329, Community 2331, Community 2332, Community 2333, Community 2337, Community 2338, Community 2339, Community 2340, Consumers 2169, Cronin 381, Dagenais 397, Dalton 398, Daoud 401, Dearborn 2173, Delano 423, **DENSO 2177**, Detroit 431, Detroit 2461, Doll 465, **Dow 2186**, Dow 478, Dow 479, Eddy 508, Fabri 2194, Farley 545, Farver 547, Ford 2203, Four 2348, Fremont 2350, General 2206, Gerstacker 668, Gilmore 683, Grand Haven 2351, Grand 2353, Great 2493, Greenville 2355, **H.I.S. 749**, Herrick 829, Hoffmeyer 2775, Holden 853, Hunter 884, Hurst 886, Ionia 2358, Iosco 2359, Irwin 907, **Isabel 909**, Jackson 2361, Jennings 929, Kalamazoo 2362, Kantzler 966, **Kresge 1049**, Kutz 1055, Lakeland 2533, Lansing 1075, Leelanau 2366, Library 2538, Livonia 2368, M & M 2369, Malpass 1163, Manoogian 1171, Marquette 2372, Marshall 2373, McGregor 1226, McNally 1241, Mecosta 2374, Merillat 1255, Metro 1261, Michigan 2375, Michigan 1268, Midland 2376, Miller 1284, Mills 1288, Mitchell 1299, Moore 1316, Morley 1325, Mount Pleasant 2378, North 2380, Novi 2579, Olds 1398, Oleson 1399, Parker 1435, Pellerito 1451, Petoskey 2385, Pinney 1482, Ponting 1494, Ratner 1532, Redies 2273, Robison 1570, Rotary 2609, Rotary 2612, Royal 1603, **Sage 1621**, Saginaw 2387, Schoolcraft 2389, **Secchia 1676**, Shelden 1699, Simmons 1729, **Society 2620**, South 2392, Southwest 1772, Sparta 2395, Spectrum 2625, Steelcase 2281, Straits 2397, Strosacker 1821, Stubnitz 1824, Sturgis 2398, Tahquamenon 2631, Thompson 1883, Thompson 1888, Three 2399, Tiscornia 1897, Tuscola 2400, Ufer 2289, Upton 1935, Vicksburg 1968, Village 2674, Weatherwax 1996, Wege 2001, Wickes 2048, Wickson 2049, Wilson 2065, Wilson 2067, **Worldwide 2689**, Wyoming 2401, Young 2117, Zondervan 2134
New Mexico: Seidman 1683
New York: Millman 1287, **Nonprofit 2576**
Ohio: St. Clair 1783, Whiting 2042
Wisconsin: Beauchamp 129, Bishop 172, Bradshaw 215, Bray 220, Wisconsin 2302, WPS 2305

Exchange programs

Michigan: Community 2332, Community 2338, Henley 820, Warchol 1986

Fellowships

Florida: Church 326
Michigan: Baldwin 90, Blue 2150, Cejka 302, **Concrete 2452, Earhart 506**, Great 2493, **H.I.S. 749**, Henley 820, Heyl 2509, Irwin 907, Light 2539, Manoogian 1171, Marzke 1192, Michigan 2565, **Society 2620**, Stern 1797
New York: **Ford 590**

Film/video/radio

New York: **Ford 590**

General/operating support

Arizona: Loichle 1119
Arkansas: Sulieman 1832

California: Nissan 2263, Nissan 2264, Shook 1713, Wilcox 2054
Florida: Corr 364, Dexter 449, Fisher 578, Frank 610, Friedman 623, Garrison 643, Hasey 805, Hibbert 834, Ryder 2277, Slocum 1748
Georgia: Shaheen 1693
Illinois: Barron 107, Crane 376, Denniston 428, Hutchcroft 889, Meeks 1246, Northern 2265, Pajeau 1421, Seabury 1673, Souder 1768, Stulberg 1826, Vineyard 1971
Iowa: Cole 346
Louisiana: Behl 134
Maryland: Broomfield 241
Massachusetts: Cowan 369
Michigan: Abbarah 2, Adray 14, Agley 17, Akers 20, Akers 21, Akl 22, Al-Ameri 23, Al-Hadidi 25, Alacin 28, Aljabban 32, Alldredge 34, Alro 2137, **Alticor 2138**, Americana 47, **Amerisure 2140**, Anchor 2311, Anderson 2411, **Animal 60**, Annapurna 2698, Annis 62, Anton 65, Applebaum 2414, **Arcus 70**, Aronoff 2702, Arts 2415, Attwood 80, Autocam 2143, Azzar 2703, Baker 87, Baker 88, Balk 91, Bandstra 94, Bar 96, Bargman 98, Barnett 102, Barnett 104, Barnett 105, Barry 2314, Barstow 109, Barth 110, Barton 2144, Baske 115, Bates 116, Batts 2146, Bauervic 122, Beals 126, Beard 128, Beck 131, Bernstein 150, Beson 154, Besser 155, **Betty 159**, Beyler 161, BFK 162, Biederman 2715, Bierlein 2148, Birtwistle 170, Bittker 173, Blake 178, Blue 2151, Boersma 191, Boll 192, Bonisteel 193, Bonner 195, Bonsall 196, Borovoy 202, Bradstrum 216, Branch 2320, Brauer 219, Bregi 222, Brems 223, Brinkerhoff-Sample 232, Broadleaf 234, Bronner 237, Brooks 239, Brunkow 253, Bryan 2718, Bryan 255, Buffalo 2155, Buist 2719, Burdick 263, Burns 266, Burns 267, Busch 273, Byron 2435, Cable 2436, Cadillac 2157, Cady 279, Camp 285, Camp 286, Campbell 288, Canaan 289, Canton 2322, Capital 2323, Carlson 292, Causley 300, Cejka 302, Chamberlain 305, Chamberlin 306, Champion 2158, Charlupski 312, Chemical 2160, Cherney 317, Chisbetts 2730, Christian 321, Christian 322, Citizens 2162, Citizens 2163, Clannad 329, Clark 332, Clason 333, Claus 334, Clearbrook 335, **CMS 2165**, Cochrane 340, **Cohen 341**, Cold 342, Collins 2166, Combs 349, Comerica 2167, Community 2329, Community 2336, Community 2337, Conrad 354, Consumers 2169, Consumers 2170, **Conway 355**, Cook 357, Cook 358, Coon 360, Cooper 361, Cortright 365, Cracchiolo 371, Cracchiolo 372, Cracchiolo 373, Croskey 382, **Cummings 386**, Dagenais 397, **DaimlerChrysler 2172**, Dalton 398, Daoud 401, Dart 403, Dearborn 2173, Deffenbaugh 417, Delano 423, Detroit 431, Detroit 2461, Devereaux 436, DeVlieg 437, DeVos 438, DeVos 439, DeVos 440, DeVos 441, DeVries 442, DeVries 443, Dewey 445, Dickinson 2183, DiClemente 452, Diebolt 454, Dinan 2742, Doan 459, Doan 460, Doctor 461, Dole 464, Donahey 466, Donlin 467, Doornink 469, **Dorfman 471**, Dorris 473, **Doud 475**, Dow 2185, Dow 477, Dow 478, Dow 479, Drake 480, **Dryden 483**, DTE 2188, Dura 2189, Duzyj 498, Eagle 505, Egger 515, Eliason 2191, Elson 519, Erb 526, Ervin 528, Esser 531, Evergreene 2747, Ewald 536, Fabiano 2193, Faigle 538, Farrehi 542, Farver 547, Federal 2198, **Fetzer 2749**, Fetzer 564, Field 566, Filer 2751, Fink 570, Fish 576, **Ford 589**, Ford 593, Ford 2753, **Ford 2202**, Foundation 606, Frankel 614, Freedom 618, Freeman 619, Fremont 2350, Fuller 631, Galencher 635, Ganton 2756, Gantos 640, Gardner 641, Gast 647, Gegax 655, Geist 656, General 2206, George 660, Gershenson 663, Gershenson 664, Gerstacker 668, Gibbs 672, Giddey 675, Gilmore 683, Gilmour 2481, Glenn 689, GM 2209, Goldstein 2761, Good 704, **Gordon 710**, Gordon 713, Grand Rapids 719, Grand Rapids 2211, Great 2213, Greenberg 731, Greene 732, Greene 733, **Greeney 734**, Hadied 756, Haggard 760, Hall 768, Hammond 2217, Hampson 774, Hamzavi 776, Harding 788, Harper 795, Hartmann

Matching/challenge support

Florida: Bush 274, **Hagen 758**

Illinois: Northern 2265, Seabury 1673

Massachusetts: Cowan 369

Michigan: Albion 2307, Allegan 2309, Allendale 2310, Americana 47, Ann Arbor 2312, **Arcus 70**, Barry 2314, Barstow 109, Barth 110, Battle Creek 2315, Batts 2146, Bay 2316, Berrien 2319, Besser 155, Blodgett 184, Blue 2150, Branch 2320, Cadillac 2321, Capital 2323, Colina 347, Community 2329, Community 2332, Community 2336, Community 2337, Community 2338, Community 2339, Consumers 2169, Dalton 398, Dart 403, Detroit 431, Detroit 2739, Detroit 2461, DeVos 438, DeVos 440, DeVos 441, Dow 478, **Fetzer 2749**, Ford 2203, Four 2348, Fremont 2350, General 2206, **Gerber 661**, Gerstacker 668, Gilmore 683, Grand Haven 2351, Grand Rapids 2352, Grand 2353, Great 2493, Greenville 2355, **H.I.S. 749**, Hancock 778, Herrick 829, Hillsdale 2356, Holden 853, Hudson 876, Hunter 884, India 901, Jackson 2361, Jewish 2522, Kalamazoo 2362, Kantzler 966, Keller 986, **Kellogg 988**, Keweenaw 2363, **Kresge 1049**, Lansing 1075, Lapeer 2365, Library 2538, M & M 2369, Manoogian 1171, Marshall 2373, Masco 2248, Masco 2249, Metro 1261, Michigan 2558, Michigan 2375, Michigan 1268, Midland 2376, Miller 1284, Mills 1288, Missaukee 2377, Monroe 1313, Moore 1316, Morley 1325, **Mott 1332**, Mott 1333, Mount Pleasant 2378, Olds 1398, Oleson 1399, Pellerito 1451, Petoskey 2385, Plym 1488, Porter 1496, **ProQuest 2270**, Ratner 1532, Rotary 2609, Rotary 2612, **Sage 1621**, Saginaw 2387, Shapero 1695, Steelcase 2281, Sturgis 2398, **Teitel 1870**, Thoman 1878, Towsley 1901, Tuscola 2400, Vanderweide 1956, Vicksburg 1968, Warchol 1986, Weatherwax 1996, Wege 2001, Whirlpool 2301, Wickson 2049, Wilson 2065, Wilson 2067, Zuehlke 2135

Minnesota: Arts 2416

New York: **Ford 590, Heron 827**, Millman 1287, **Nonprofit 2576**

Ohio: Anderson 52

Wisconsin: Bray 220

Professorships

Michigan: Baldwin 90, Community 2332, DeVlieg 437, Farrehi 546, Herrick 829, Pulte 2271, Towsley 1901

Program development

California: Landsberg 1071, Nissan 2263, Wilcox 2054

Florida: Bush 274, **Hagen 758**, Ludy 1130, Robey 2840

Illinois: Burnett 264, Loutit 1124, Northern 2265, Seabury 1673

Indiana: Walther 2677

Massachusetts: Cowan 369

Michigan: Abrams 8, Albion 2307, Allegan 2309, Americana 47, Ann Arbor 2312, **Arcus 70**, Arts 2415, **ArvinMeritor 2141**, AT&T 2142, Ave 83, Barry 2314, Barstow 109, Barth 110, Battle Creek 2315, Batts 2146, Bauervic 121, Bauervic 122, Bay 2316, Berrien 2319, Biederman 2715, Binda 167, Blodgett 184, Blue 2150, Boutell 210, Buffalo 2155, Burroughs 269, Cable 2436, Cadillac 2321, Canton 2322, Capital 2323, Cejka 302, Charlevoix 2325, Chelsea 2446, Chippewa 2326, Cipa 328, Colina 347, Community 2451, Community 2331, Community 2332, Community 2333, Community 2335, Community 2336, Community 2338, Community 2339, Community 2340, Consumers 2169, Cook 358, Cronin 381, Dagenais 397, **DaimlerChrysler 2172**, Dalton 398, Dart 403, Davenport 404, Delano 423, DENSO 2176, **DENSO 2177**, DeRoy 430, Detroit 2739, Detwiler 2462, DeVos 438, DeVos 440, DeVos 441, DeVries 443, Doornink 469, Dow 2185, **Dow 2186**, Dow 477, Dow 478, Dyer 499, Eddy 508, Ervin 528, **Fetzer**

2749, Flinn 585, Ford 2203, Four 2348, Frankenmuth 2349, Fremont 2350, Frey 621, General 2206, Gilmore 683, Gilmour 2481, Grand Haven 2351, Grand Rapids 2352, Grand Rapids 2211, Grand 2353, Gratiot 2354, Great 2493, **Greeney 734**, Greenville 2355, Hancock 778, **Heron 828**, Herrick 829, Hoffmeyer 2775, Holley 856, Home 857, Hudson 876, Hurst 886, Idema 894, Iosco 2359, Jackson 2361, Jackson 2225, **Jewish 2521**, Jewish 2522, Jewish 2523, Johnson 937, JPMorgan 2227, Jury 955, Justice 956, Kalamazoo 2362, Kalamazoo 2526, Kantzler 966, Kaufman 974, Kaufman 977, Keller 986, **Kellogg 988**, Kennedy 996, Keweenaw 2363, Kiwanis 2531, Knight 1026, Kool 2793, Kutz 1055, Lake 2364, Lansing 1075, Leven 1101, Library 2538, Lincoln 1109, Loeb 1118, **Lowe 2800**, M & M 2369, Mackinac 2370, Marcks 1176, Marquette 2372, Marshall 2373, McGregor 1226, McKinley 2553, Mecosta 2374, Meer 1247, Merkley 1257, Metro 1261, Michigan 2558, Michigan 2375, Michigan 2563, Michigan 1268, Michigan 2567, Miller 1284, Miller 1286, Mitchell 1299, Monroe 1313, Morley 1325, **Mott 1332**, Mott 1333, Mount Pleasant 2378, Mt. Zion 1339, **Nine 1378**, Nokomis 1381, North 2380, Palmer 1424, Parfet 1430, Perrigo 2266, Petoskey 2385, Pistons 2267, Plym 1488, Ponting 1494, **ProQuest 2270**, Ratner 1532, Rotary 2612, **Sage 1621**, Saginaw 2387, Shiawassee 2391, Shumsky 1718, Skillman 1739, Slemons 1744, **Society 2620**, Sojourner 2621, South 2392, Southfield 2394, Speckhard 1776, St. Deny's 1784, Steelcase 2281, **Stoddard 1807**, Straits 2397, Strosacker 1821, Stubnitz 1824, Sturgis 2398, Summers 1839, Tahquamenon 2631, **Teitel 1870**, Thoman 1878, Thompson 1884, Thompson 1888, Towsley 1901, Tuscola 2400, Upjohn 1934, Upton 1935, Valenti 1938, Vanderweide 1956, Vicksburg 1968, Village 2674, Waterford 2679, Wege 2001, Westerman 2027, Whirlpool 2301, Whiting 2041, Whitney 2686, Wilson 2065, Wolters 2090, World 2099, **Worldwide 2689**, Young 2116, Young 2117, Zondervan 2134

Minnesota: **Target 2283**, TCF 2285

New York: Birds 2149, **Ford 590, Heron 827**, Millman 1287

Ohio: Anderson 52, Bates 2145, Milacron 2254, Moore 1319, NCC 2262

Pennsylvania: Tyco 2288

Wisconsin: Beauchamp 129, Bradshaw 215, Hess 831, WPS 2305

Program evaluation

Michigan: Albion 2307, **Arcus 70**, Arts 2415, Barry 2314, Battle Creek 2315, Berrien 2319, Blodgett 184, Cadillac 2321, Community 2336, Community 2340, Detroit 2739, **Fetzer 2749**, Flinn 585, Fremont 2350, Gilmore 683, Great 2493, Hudson 876, Jackson 2361, Jewish 2522, **Kellogg 988**, Michigan 2375, **Mott 1332**, Mott 1333, Nokomis 1381, Weatherwax 1996, **Worldwide 2689**

New York: **Ford 590, Heron 827**

Program-related investments/loans

Florida: Bush 274

Michigan: **Arcus 70**, Battle Creek 2315, Byron 2435, Community 2332, Fremont 2350, Grand Rapids 2352, Jackson 2361, Kalamazoo 2362, **Lowe 2800**, Miller 1284, Moore 1316, Northern 2827, Shiffman 1707, Thoman 1878, Wilson 2067

New York: **Ford 590, Heron 827, Nonprofit 2576**

Public relations services

Michigan: DaimlerChrysler 2171

Publication

Michigan: Albion 2307, Americana 47, Ann Arbor 2312, **Arcus 70**, Arts 2415, Battle Creek 2315, Cadillac 2321, Community 2332, Community 2339, Consumers 2169, Dart 403, Detroit 431, Dyer 499, General 2206, Gilmore 683, Great 2493, Greenville 2355, Hillsdale 2356, Holden 853, Iosco 2359, Lansing 1075, Livonia 2368, **Lowe 2800**, Michigan 1268, Mount Pleasant 2378, Mt. Zion 1339, North 2380, Saginaw 2387, Straits 2397

New York: **Ford 590**

Ohio: Anderson 52

Research

California: Landsberg 1071

Indiana: Walther 2677

Michigan: Abrams 8, Adopt 13, **American 2407, American 2408**, Ann Arbor 2312, Applebaum 2414, Ash 76, Atanas 2420, Barry 2314, Bay 2316, Blue 2150, Buffalo 2155, Cadillac 2321, Campbell 287, Children's 2449, Cipa 328, Cochrane 340, Community 2332, Community 2338, **Concrete 2452**, Dalton 398, Dart 403, Davis 408, Delta 2459, Detroit 2739, Detwiler 2462, Dow 477, Dow 478, **Earhart 506, Fetzer 2749**, Fetzer 564, Flinn 585, **Floriculture 2468**, Ford 2471, **Ford 2202**, Ford 2203, Frey 621, **General 2205**, General 2206, **Gerber 661**, Gerstacker 668, Gratiot 2354, Great 2493, **Greeney 734**, Hemophilia 2505, Henley 820, Herrick 829, Hill 841, Holden 853, Jewish 2523, Kaufman 977, Kinney 1011, Lansing 1075, Lincoln 1109, Manoogian 1171, **McCarty 2552**, Meadlock 1245, Medical 2810, Morley 1325, Mount Pleasant 2378, Murphy 1349, National 2571, National 2572, Nill 1376, **Pardee 1428**, Pellerito 1451, Pierce 2835, Pistons 2267, Power 1502, Prentis 2602, Purtan 2603, Ratner 1532, Robison 1570, Royal 1603, **Sage 1621**, Shelden 1699, **Society 2620**, Spectrum 2625, Stonisch 1815, Strosacker 1821, Towsley 1901, United 2647, Upjohn 1934, **Upjohn 2670**, Upton 1935, Walker 1979, Weikart 2004, Westerman 2027, Whirlpool 2301, Wilson 2065, Zondervan 2134

New York: **Ford 590**, Greenspan 735, Rudel 1606

Ohio: Anderson 52, Milacron 2254

Virginia: Freiheit 620

Wisconsin: Bishop 172, Bradshaw 215, Kowalski 2238, WPS 2305

Scholarship funds

California: J.C. 914, Landsberg 1071

Florida: Church 326, **Hagen 758**, Hibbert 834, Robey 2840, Watson 1993

Illinois: Burnett 264, Crane 376, Meeks 1246, Seabury 1673, Tucker 1914

Iowa: Cole 346

Massachusetts: Hanover 2218

Michigan: Abrams 8, Adrian 2403, **Africa 16**, Albion 2307, Alexandrowski 30, Alpert 45, Anchor 2311, Andersen 50, Ann Arbor 2312, Annis 62, Arts 2415, Ash 76, Attwood 80, Baker 87, Barnett 101, Barry 2314, Battle Creek 2315, Batts 2146, Bay 2316, Bentley 143, Berkery 145, Berrien 2319, Bettis 2427, Biederman 2715, Binda 167, Bonner 195, Branch 2320, **Bretzlaff 228**, Bronner 237, Bryan 2718, Buist 2719, Cejka 302, Chamberlain 305, **Chang 308**, Chapman 309, Charlevoix 2325, Chippewa 2326, Collins 2166, Combs 349, Community 2451, Community 2329, Community 2332, Community 2333, Community 2335, Community 2336, Community 2337, Community 2338, Community 2339, Community 2340, Community 2341, **Concrete 2452**, Cook 358, Dagenais 397, Dancey 399, Daoud 401, Debower 415, Deffenbaugh 417, Delta 2459, Delta 425, DENSO 2176, Detwiler 2462, DeVlieg 437, Dewey

445, Dinan 2742, Doran 470, **Doud 475**, Dow 477, Dura 2189, Ellias 518, Favor 551, Ford 593, **Ford 2202**, Ford 2203, Foss 599, Four 2348, Frankenmuth 2349, Fraser 2476, Fremont 2350**, Gagliardi 634**, Gast 647, Gershenson 667, Gilmore 683, Graham 718, Grand Haven 2351, Grand Rapids 2352, Grand Rapids 2211, Grand 2353, Great 2490, Great 2493, Greenville 2355, Grimaldi 739, Gutmueller 2496, **H.I.S. 749**, Hagelshaw 2499, Harding 788, Harper 795, Henry 823, Herrick 829, Hillsdale 2356, Hinman 2511, Hoffmeyer 2775, Holden 853, Hudson 875, Idema 894, Irwin 907, Jaffe 918**, Johnson 936**, Jury 955, Kahn 960, Kalamazoo 2362, Kantzler 966, Kaufman 974, Keller 986, Keweenaw 2363, Kool 2793, Kutz 1055, Lake 2364, Lansing 1075, Lapeer 2365, Lausch 2241, Leven 1101, Light 2539, Lincoln 1109, Ludington 2545, M & S 1143, Mackinac 2370, Manistee 2371, Manoogian 1171, Marquette 2372, Marshall 2373, Martin 1183, Martin 1186, Martin 1187, Marzke 1192, Masonic 2551, McCormick 1216, McNish 1242, Mecosta 2374, Metro 1261, Mette 1262, Michigan 2253, Midland 2376, Miller 1277, Miller 1286, Mims 1290, Morey 1323, Mott 1333, Mount Pleasant 2378, Muntwyler 1347, Nelson 1364, Nordman 1382, Northville 2577, Olds 1398, Owen 1413, Page 1418, Paine 1420, Parfet 1430, Pearson 1448, Petersen 1466, Petoskey 2385, Phelps 1472, Pierce 2835, Ponting 1494, **Rachor 1522**, Ratner 1532, Rattner 1533, Rawson 1536, Robison 1570, Roscommon 2386, Royal 1603**, Sage 1621**, Saginaw 2387, **San 1632**, Schael 1645, Schmid 1653, Schuyler 1666, **Secchia 1676**, Sharp 1697, Shiawassee 2391, Shumsky 1718, Simmons 1729, Sisson 1732, Skillman 1739, Slack 1741, Smith 1754, **Snyder 1765, Society 2620**, South 2392, Southeastern 1769, Spectrum 2625, St. Deny's 1784, Steelcase 2281, **Steelcase 2282**, Stern 1797, Stoddard 1809, Stubnitz 1824, Sturgis 2398, Sullivan 1835, Suter 1846, Tamer 1855, Tauber 1861, **Teitel 1870**, Thoman 1878, Thompson 1884, Thornapple 2635, Three 2399, Tigers 2286, Tiscornia 1897, Trinity 2637, Trudell 1911, Tuscola 2400, Ufer 2289, University 1929, Upjohn 1934, **Uyham 1936**, Valenti 1938, Vicksburg 1968, Vincent 1970, Vollbrecht 1976, Walker 1979, Walters 1983, Wanczyk 1985, Warchol 1986, Weatherwax 1996, Welsh 2021, Westerbeek 2026, Westerman 2027, Whirlpool 2301, Wilson 2065, Wirt 2078, **Worldwide 2689**, Wright 2103, Wurst 2104, Young 2115, Zerbe 2127, Zoller 2133, Zondervan 2134

Minnesota: **Target 2283**, TCF 2285
Nevada: Christian 324
New York: Adelman 12, Birds 2149, Yee 2110
Ohio: Anderson 52, Bates 2145, Dubois 487, Dumesnil 493, Gilbert 679, Hafer 757, Jubilee 2229, Milacron 2254, Miller 1285, Monroe 1311, O'Brien 1390, St. Clair 1783, Worthington 2101
Rhode Island: Buster 275, Robbins 1565
Texas: Quicksilver 2272
Vermont: Center 2724
Virginia: Bell 137
Wisconsin: Fernstrum 561, Hess 831, Kowalski 2238, McIntyre 1227, Venturedyne 2295, Wisconsin 2302, WPS 2305

Scholarships—to individuals

California: Wilcox 2054
Florida: Baese 84, Skandalaris 1734
Illinois: Brewer 229, Peters 1464
Indiana: Walther 2677
Michigan: Abbott 4, Accelerated 2692, Allen 38, Anderson 51, Anderson 54, Arden 71, Armstrong 2701, Ash 76, Asthma 2419, Barr 106, Basilica 2423, Battle Creek 2315, Beal 125, Bees 133, Bellinger 140, Bemis 141, Birtwistle 170, Blaske 180, Bonn 194, Brackett 214, Brenske 225,

Bucknell 256, Burrier 268, Busch 273, Byron 2435, Cadillac 2321, Canton 2322, Cavaliere 2722, Charfoos 310, Charlevoix 2325, Chelsea 2446, Clinton 337, Clupper 339, Cole 345, Coller 348, Community 352, Community 2332, Community 2335, Community 2337, Community 2338, Community 2339, Community 2341, **Concrete 2452**, Culver 385, Cunningham 387, Czado 394, D.U. 395, Danieleski 400, **Davis 2457**, Davis 407, Davis 409, Delta 2459, Detroit 433, Detwiler 2462, Dickinson 451, **Earhart 506**, Evereg 535, Ewald 536, Fedewa 556, Flemington 583, **Floriculture 2468**, Foran 588, Ford 2471, Foster 602, Frankenmuth 2349, Fraser 2476, **Free 2477**, Fremont 2350, Galesburg 2755, **Gerber 661**, Gibbs 672, Gilles 681, **Gleaner 2760**, Goldman 698, Goodrich 707, Goss 717, Grand Haven 2351, Grand Rapids 2352, Grand 2353, Gratiot 2354, Gratiot 2762, Great 2213, Grimaldi 739, Gumaer 746, Haas 754, Haines 764, Hamar 770, Hamlin 2766, Hammel 772, Harbor 2501, Harding 791, Hecht 812, Heeringa 813, Henley 820, Hess 833, Heyl 2509, Hickey 2772, Hickman 835, Hillier 2773, Home 857, Home 2513, Horgan 2777, Hovarter 870, Howe 873, Hudson 875, Humane 880, Humbert 881, Huss 888, Hutchings 890, I Have 891, Ilitch 2516, Iosco 2359, Ironwood 2517, Jackson 2361, Jackson 916, Jaffe 918, Johnson 2226, Johnson 938, Juhl 952, Junior 2525, Kalamazoo 2362, Kalamazoo 2526, Kay 979, Kensington 2530, Kent 1001, Kiwanis 2531, Kling 1017, Knabusch 1023, Koch 1028, Kondur 1036, Krause 1045, Laflin 1062, Laidlaw 1065, Lakeland 2533, Lansing 2534, Las 1083, Latimer 1085, LaVictoire 1087, Lee 1092, Leelanau 2366, **Legion 1093**, Little 1114, Ludington 2545, M & M 2369, MacDonald 1147, Marquette 2548, Marquette 2372, Marshall 2373, Martin 1190, Masonic 2551, Matson 1198, Mayhew 1206, McCabe 1209, McCurdy 1218, McKeen 1231, Mecosta 2374, MEG 1249, Meyers 1264, Michigan 2557, Michigan 1266, Michigan 2561, Michigan 1267, Michigan 2375, Michner 1269, Miller 1279, Miller 1281, Morenci 2569, Morrill 1327, Mount Pleasant 2378, **National 1359**, Nelson 1366, Newaygo 1369, Nieman 2824, Nill 1376, Nordman 1382, North 2380, Northville 2577, Novi 2578, Novi 2579, Oakland 2580, Olson 1400, Ontonagon 2584, Optimist 2585, Orris 1406, Owen 1413, Parker 1436, Paulsen 1441, Peacock 1445, Pennock 2592, Petoskey 2385, Plumbers 2596, Polakovic 1489, Prince 1514, Pulte 2271, **Rachor 1522**, Recreational 1540, Reuther 2605, Richter 1554, **Rislov 1559**, Roethke 1575, Rolka 1582, Rotary 2610, **Rotary 2611**, Ruf 1608, Rusch 1611, Saginaw 2387, Sallness 1628, Samuels 1631, Saugatuck 1641, Schemm 1649, Schleider 1652, Scholarship 1658, Schoolcraft 2389, Scofield 1670, Shepard 1700, Smith 1761, **Society 2620**, Southfield 2394, Southfield 2622, Spaulding 2623, Spectrum 2625, Speerstra 1777, **Sphinx 2626**, St. John 2627, St. Joseph 1785, Stanton 1790, Sterling 2396, Stewart 1802, Stokes 1811, Straits 2397, Sturgis 2398, Tahquamenon 2631, Tamer 1855, Tassell 1860, Taylor 1867, TDR 1869, Temple 1871, Tengler 2860, Thiemkey 1876, Thom 1877, Thomas 1880, Three 2399, Tiscornia 1897, Trinity 2637, Trinklein 1908, Trone 1910, University 1930, **Van Curler 1941**, Van Hollenbeck 1948, VanKley 1958, Vetowich 1967, Voelker 2675, Volkswagen 2298, Vomberg 1977, Waterford 2679, Watson 1991, Watson 1992, Weidner 2684, **Weissman 2867**, Welch 2868, Wells 2020, Whiteley 2039, Whiting 2043, Wigginton 2053, Willard 2687, Wilson 2066, Winship 2076, Wirick 2077, Wright 2875, Wyandotte 2876, Young 2690, **Zazove 2122**, Zemke 2877, Zuehlke 2135

Minnesota: **Target 2283**
New Jersey: Gruenberg 743
New Mexico: Peninsula 1452
Ohio: Mackey 1149, Myers 1352, O'Brien 1390, Potts 1500, Turner 1924
Pennsylvania: Sunal 1840

Wisconsin: Brege 221, Carpenter 293, WPS 2305

Seed money

California: Landsberg 1071, Nissan 2263
Florida: **Hagen 758**
Illinois: Loutit 1124, Seabury 1673
Indiana: Walther 2677
Massachusetts: Cowan 369
Michigan: Albion 2307, Allegan 2309, Allendale 2310, Ann Arbor 2312, Barry 2314, Barstow 109, Battle Creek 2315, Bay 2316, Berrien 2319, Binda 167, Blue 2150, Cadillac 2321, Capital 2323, Carls 290, Charlevoix 2325, Colina 347, Community 2329, Community 2332, Community 2333, Community 2335, Community 2336, Community 2337, Community 2338, Community 2339, Community 2340, Consumers 2169, **Cummings 386**, Dalton 398, Davenport 404, Detwiler 2462, DeVos 438, DeVos 441, DeVries 442, Dickinson 2345, **Dow 2186**, Dow 478, Dyer 499, Foundation 2473, Fremont 2350, Frey 621, General 2206, **Gerber 661**, Gerstacker 668, Gilmore 683, Grand Haven 2351, Grand Rapids 2352, Grand 2353, Gratiot 2354, Great 2493, Greenville 2355, **H.I.S. 749**, Hancock 778, Henley 820, Hillsdale 2356, Holley 856, Hudson 876, Hurst 886, Idema 894, India 901, Iosco 2359, Jackson 2361, Jewish 2522, Jewish 2523, Justice 956, Kalamazoo 2362, Kalamazoo 2528, Kantzler 966, Kaufman 977, Keller 986, **Kellogg 988**, Lansing 1075, Leelanau 2366, Livonia 2368, M & M 2369, Mackinac 2370, Manistee 2371, Manoogian 1171, Marquette 2372, Marshall 2373, McGregor 1226, McKinley 2553, Mecosta 2374, Michigan 2558, Michigan 2375, Michigan 1268, Midland 2376, Miller 1284, Mills 1288, Missaukee 2377, Morley 1325, **Mott 1332**, Mount Pleasant 2378, Mt. Zion 1339, Nokomis 1381, North 2380, Pellerito 1451, Petoskey 2385, Rotary 2609, Rotary 2612, Saginaw 2387, Shiffman 1707, Skillman 1739**, Society 2620**, Southfield 2394, Sparta 2395, Steelcase 2281, Straits 2397, Strosacker 1821, Stubnitz 1824, **Teitel 1870**, Thoman 1878, Three 2399, Tiscornia 1897, Towsley 1901, Tuscola 2400, Upjohn 1934, Valenti 1938, Vicksburg 1968, Whitney 2686, Wickes 2048, Wilson 2067, Wyoming 2401
New Mexico: Seidman 1683
New York: **Ford 590**
Ohio: Anderson 52, Milacron 2254
Wisconsin: Bishop 172, Bradshaw 215, Bray 220

Sponsorships

Michigan: **Alticor 2138**, American 2139, **Amerisure 2140, Borders 2153**, Chemical 2160, Comerica 2167, DaimlerChrysler 2171, **Delphi 2174**, DENSO 2176, DTE 2187, **Ford 2202**, GM 2209, Gordon 2210, Jackson 2225, JPMorgan 2227, **Kellogg 2234**, Masco 2248, Polk 2269, Tigers 2286, Valassis 2291, Volkswagen 2298, Whirlpool 2300
Minnesota: **Target 2283**
New York: Birds 2149
Wisconsin: Wisconsin 2302

Student loans—to individuals

Michigan: Abele 6, Brenske 226, Cadillac 2321, Clapp 330, Eddy 508, Glick 693, Harbor 786, Jeffers 927, Kelly 989, Kent 1001, Mount Pleasant 2378, Parker 1434, Peacock 1445, Reid 1546, Salisbury 1627, Sallness 1628, Spectrum 2625, Sturgis 2398, Tuohy 1918
Mississippi: Bancroft 93

Technical assistance

Florida: Bush 274, **Hagen 758**
Illinois: Seabury 1673

Michigan: Americana 47**, Arcus 70**, Arts 2415, AT&T 2142, Barry 2314, Barstow 109, Battle Creek 2315, Bay 2316, Blue 2150, Branch 2320, Cable 2436, Cadillac 2321, Capital 2323, Charlevoix 2325, Comerica 2167, Community 2333, Community 2335, Community 2336, Community 2338, Community 2340, Community 2341, Dearborn 2173, Dyer 499**, Ford 2202**, Fremont 2350, Frey 621, General 2206, Gilmore 683, GM 2209, Grand Rapids 2352, Grand 2353, Great 2493, India 901, Iosco 2359, Jackson 2361, Jewish 2522, Jewish 2523, JPMorgan 2227, Kalamazoo 2362, Library 2538, **Lowe 2800**, M & M 2369, Marshall 2373, McKinley 2553, Michigan 2558, Michigan 1268, Michigan 2567, Midland 2376, **Mott 1332**, Mott 1333, Mount Pleasant 2378, Nokomis 1381, North 2380, Petoskey 2385, Rotary 2609, Saginaw 2387, Shiffman 1707, Sojourner 2621, Straits 2397, Weatherwax 1996, Whitney 2686

New York: **Ford 590, Heron 827, Nonprofit 2576**

Use of facilities

Michigan: **Borders 2153, Ford 2202, Glen Arbor 2482, Steelcase 2282**

Texas: Quicksilver 2272

SUBJECT INDEX

List of terms: Terms used in this index conform to the Foundation Center's Grants Classification System's comprehensive subject area coding scheme. The alphabetical list below represents the complete list of subject terms found in this edition. "See also" references to related subject areas are also provided as an additional aid in accessing the giving interests of grantmakers in this volume.

Index: In the index itself, grantmaker entries are arranged under each term by state location, abbreviated name, and sequence number. Grantmakers in boldface type make grants on a national, regional, or international basis. The others generally limit giving to the state or city in which they are located.

Adult education—literacy, basic skills & GED
Adult/continuing education
Africa
African Americans/Blacks
Aging
Aging, centers/services
Agriculture
Agriculture, farm cooperatives
Agriculture/food
AIDS
see also People with AIDS (PWAs)
AIDS research
AIDS, people with
Alcoholism
Allergies
ALS research
Alzheimer's disease
Alzheimer's disease research
American Red Cross
Animal welfare
Animals/wildlife
Animals/wildlife, endangered species
Animals/wildlife, fisheries
Animals/wildlife, preservation/protection
Animals/wildlife, sanctuaries
Animals/wildlife, single organization support
Animals/wildlife, special services
Aquariums
Armenia
Arthritis
Arthritis research
Arts
see also dance; film/video; museums; music;
    performing arts; theater; visual arts
Arts councils
Arts education
Arts, artist's services
Arts, association
Arts, cultural/ethnic awareness
Arts, folk arts
Arts, formal/general education
Arts, public education
Arts, research
Asia
Asians/Pacific Islanders
Asthma
Athletics/sports, academies

Athletics/sports, amateur competition
Athletics/sports, baseball
Athletics/sports, basketball
Athletics/sports, equestrianism
Athletics/sports, fishing/hunting
Athletics/sports, football
Athletics/sports, golf
Athletics/sports, school programs
Athletics/sports, soccer
Athletics/sports, Special Olympics
Athletics/sports, training
Athletics/sports, winter sports
Australia
Bahai
Belgium
Big Brothers/Big Sisters
Biological sciences
Biomedicine
Blind/visually impaired
Botanical gardens
Botanical/horticulture/landscape services
Botany
Botswana
Boy scouts
Boys
Boys & girls clubs
Boys clubs
Brain research
Brazil
Breast cancer
Buddhism
Business school/education
Business/industry
Canada
Cancer
Cancer research
Cancer, leukemia
Cancer, leukemia research
Caribbean
Cerebral palsy
Chemistry
Child development, education
Child development, services
Children
Children, adoption
Children, day care
Children, foster care

Children, services
Children/youth
Children/youth, services
China
Christian agencies & churches
Civil liberties, advocacy
Civil liberties, reproductive rights
Civil liberties, right to life
Civil rights
Civil rights, advocacy
Civil rights, aging
Civil rights, disabled
Civil rights, equal rights
Civil rights, gays/lesbians
Civil rights, immigrants
Civil rights, minorities
Civil rights, race/intergroup relations
see also civil rights
Civil rights, women
Community development
Community development, alliance
Community development, business promotion
Community development, citizen coalitions
Community development, civic centers
Community development, neighborhood
    associations
Community development, neighborhood
    development
Community development, public education
Community development, public/private
    ventures
Community development, service clubs
Community development, small businesses
Community development, volunteer services
Community development, women's clubs
Computer science
Courts/judicial administration
Crime/law enforcement
Crime/law enforcement, administration/
    regulation
Crime/law enforcement, police agencies
Crime/violence prevention
see also domestic violence; gun control
Crime/violence prevention, abuse prevention
see also child abuse; domestic violence
Crime/violence prevention, child abuse
Crime/violence prevention, domestic violence

Mental health, disorders
Mental health, residential care
Mental health, smoking
Mental health, treatment
Mental health/crisis services
Mentally disabled
Mexico
Middle East
Military/veterans' organizations
Minorities
  see also African Americans/Blacks; Asians/Pacific
    Islanders; civil rights, minorities; Hispanics/
    Latinos; Native Americans/American Indians
Minorities/immigrants, centers/services
Mozambique
Multiple sclerosis
Multiple sclerosis research
Muscular dystrophy
Museums
Museums (art)
Museums (children's)
Museums (ethnic/folk arts)
Museums (history)
Museums (marine/maritime)
Museums (natural history)
Museums (science/technology)
Museums (specialized)
Native Americans/American Indians
Neighborhood centers
Netherlands
Neuroscience
Neuroscience research
Nicaragua
Nonprofit management
Nursing care
Nursing home/convalescent facility
Nursing school/education
Nutrition
Orthodox Catholic agencies & churches
Pakistan
Parkinson's disease
Parkinson's disease research
Pediatrics
Pediatrics research
Performing arts
Performing arts centers
Performing arts, ballet
Performing arts, dance
Performing arts, education
Performing arts, music
Performing arts, music (choral)
Performing arts, music composition
Performing arts, music ensembles/groups
Performing arts, opera
Performing arts, orchestra (symphony)
Performing arts, theater
Performing arts, theater (musical)
Peru
Pharmacy/prescriptions
Philanthropy/voluntarism

Philanthropy/voluntarism, association
Philanthropy/voluntarism, single organization
  support
Philippines
Philosophy/ethics
Physical therapy
Political science
Population studies
Pregnancy centers
Prostate cancer
Protestant agencies & churches
Psychology/behavioral science
Public affairs
Public affairs, alliance
Public affairs, citizen participation
Public affairs, government agencies
Public health
Public health school/education
Public health, STDs
Public policy, research
Recreation
Recreation, camps
Recreation, centers
Recreation, community facilities
Recreation, fairs/festivals
Recreation, government agencies
Recreation, parks/playgrounds
Religion
  see also Jewish agencies & temples; Protestant
    agencies & churches; Roman Catholic agencies &
    churches
Religion, association
Religion, interfaith issues
Religious federated giving programs
Reproductive health
Reproductive health, family planning
Reproductive health, OBGYN/Birthing centers
Reproductive health, sexuality education
Residential/custodial care
Residential/custodial care, hospices
Residential/custodial care, senior continuing
  care
Residential/custodial care, special day care
Roman Catholic agencies & churches
Roman Catholic federated giving programs
Rural development
Russia
Rwanda
Safety, automotive safety
Safety, education
Safety/disasters
Safety/disasters, fund raising/fund distribution
Salvation Army
Scholarships/financial aid
Science
  see also biological sciences; chemistry; computer
    science; engineering/technology; marine science;
    physical/earth sciences
Science, formal/general education
Secondary school/education

  see also elementary/secondary education
Single parents
Social sciences
  see also anthropology/sociology; economics; political
    science; psychology/behavioral science
Social sciences, public policy
Social sciences, research
South Africa
South America
South Korea
Southeast Asia
Southern Africa
Space/aviation
Speech/hearing centers
Spine disorders research
Spirituality
Student services/organizations
Substance abuse, prevention
Substance abuse, services
Substance abuse, treatment
Swaziland
Taiwan
Teacher school/education
Theological school/education
Theology
Transportation
Turks & Caicos Islands
Urban/community development
Veterinary medicine
Veterinary medicine, hospital
Vietnam
Visual arts
Visual arts, architecture
Visual arts, art conservation
Visual arts, ceramic arts
Visual arts, painting
Visual arts, photography
Visual arts, sculpture
Vocational education
Vocational education, post-secondary
Voluntarism promotion
Volunteers of America
Wales
West Bank/Gaza
Women
  see also civil rights, women; reproductive rights
Women, centers/services
YM/YWCAs & YM/YWHAs
Youth
Youth development
Youth development, business
Youth development, centers/clubs
Youth development, religion
Youth development, scouting agencies (general)
Youth development, services
Youth, pregnancy prevention
Youth, services
Zimbabwe
Zoos/zoological societies

Adult education—literacy, basic skills & GED

Michigan: Abrams 8, Altrusa 2406, Battle Creek 2315,
  Binda 167, Community 2338, Greenville 2355,
  Jackson 2361, Knight 1026, Library 2538, Rotary
  2612, Thoman 1878, Whirlpool 2301
Texas: Tapestry 1857

Adult/continuing education

Michigan: Buhr 259, **Kellogg 988**, Midland 2376, Miller
  1284, Whirlpool 2301

Africa

Michigan: Gayar 651, **Snyder 1765**
Minnesota: **Target 2283**
New York: **Ford 590**

African Americans/Blacks

Michigan: **Davis 2457**, Grand Rapids 2352, **Kellogg
  988**, Metro 1261, **National 1359**, Southfield 2622,
  Sphinx 2626

Aging

Florida: Bush 274
Illinois: Keith 985

Massachusetts: Cowan 369
Michigan: Ann Arbor 2312, **Beacon 2710**, Berrien 2319, Beyler 161, Blue 2151, Cadillac 2321, Clark 2450, Community 2338, Community 2340, Community 2342, Dickinson 2345, Duffy 490, Ervin 528, Filer 2751, Foundation 603, Fremont 2350, Gerstacker 668, Gilmore 682, Grand Rapids 2352, Hillsdale 2356, Ionia 2358, Isabella 910, **Jewish 2520**, Jewish 2522, Jewish 2523, Meijer 2251, Merkley 1257, Metro 1261, Prince 1513, Rebuilding 2604, Saginaw 2387, Southfield 2394, Steelcase 2281, **Steelcase 2282**, Thompson 1888, Tuscola 2400, United 2645, United 2650, United 2655
Wisconsin: Green Bay 2214

Aging, centers/services

Florida: Bush 274
Illinois: Keith 985
Michigan: Ann Arbor 2312, Barry 2421, Blodgett 184, Buhr 259, Burt 270, Cadillac 2321, Capital 2437, Central 2324, Cheboygan 2445, Community 2338, Community 2342, Donlin 467, Ervin 528, Fremont 2350, George 660, Gerstacker 668, Gilmore 682, Grand Rapids 2352, Heart 2504, Herrick 829, Hillsdale 2356, Isabella 910, Jewish 2522, Livingston 2542, Main 1157, Mason 2550, Metro 1261, Prince 1513, Spartan 1775, **Teitel 1870**, Thompson 1888, United 2645, United 2651, United 2653, United 2656, United 2657, Upjohn 1934
Ohio: McCalla 1210

Agriculture

Michigan: Americana 47, **Kellogg 988**, Victor 1969
New York: Ford 590
Ohio: Anderson 52

Agriculture, farm cooperatives

Michigan: Flint 586

Agriculture/food

Michigan: **Kellogg 2234**, **Kellogg 988**

AIDS

Massachusetts: Cowan 369
Michigan: Grand Rapids 2352, Hemophilia 2505, Levy 1103, Metro 1261, Michigan 2558, **Steelcase 2282**
New York: **Ford 590**

AIDS research

Michigan: Levy 1103, **Steelcase 2282**

AIDS, people with

Massachusetts: Cowan 369
Michigan: Levy 1102, Michigan 2558

Alcoholism

Michigan: Grand Rapids 2352, **Steelcase 2282**
Wisconsin: Hess 831

Allergies

Michigan: Asthma 2419

ALS research

Michigan: Hiller 842

Alzheimer's disease

Michigan: Bugas 258, Gershenson 664, May 1204, McCoy 1217, **Nartel 1357**, Shufro 1716, Sloat 1747, Smith 1759, **Zimmerman 2130**
Wisconsin: Stockton 1805

Alzheimer's disease research

Michigan: Dart 403, Dow 477, **Johnson 936**

American Red Cross

Michigan: Acheson 10, Borovoy 202, Buhr 259, Chase 313, **Cresswell 378**, Detroit 434, Dinan 2742, Dow 479, Eppert 2746, Havirmill 809, Howard 872, Isabella 2223, **Johnson 936**, Kravitz 1047, Lowell 1126, Lubin 1128, Marstrand 1182, **May 1205**, **Nelson 1367**, Roto 2276, Shufro 1716, Simmons 1728, Slavik 1742, Smith 1755, Thompson 1886, Trapp 1904, **Vattikuti 1961**, Vaughan 1962, Volkswagen 2297, Young 2115
Ohio: Beach 124, Thompson 1885
Wisconsin: Bray 220, Vellmure 1963

Animal welfare

Florida: Cook 359
Illinois: Pajeau 1421
Michigan: **Animal 60**, Azzar 2703, Bashur 114, Battle Creek 2315, **Berman 149**, Bonsall 196, Burroughs 269, Burt 270, Camp 285, Clason 333, **Dryden 483**, Duffy 490, Flint 586, Haveman 808, Herman 2507, Hillsdale 2356, Humane 880, Kierstead 1009, Lange 1074, Lindsay 2540, Lugers 1131, Lundstrom 1133, Luyckx 2546, Main 1157, Maldonado 1159, Malloure 1160, Marcks 1176, Mid-Michigan 2817, Muntwyler 1347, Semmes 1688, St. Deny's 1784, Vaughan 1962, Woodall 2094
Wisconsin: Green Bay 2214, Ross 1595

Animals/wildlife

Michigan: Caesar 280, **Conway 355**, Foley 2469, Foley 2470, Lewis 1105, Marstrand 1182, Mauser 1201, Mid-Michigan 2817, Mosaic 1329, MPS 1337, **Nine 1378**, **Robinson 1569**, Young 2115
Wisconsin: Beauchamp 129

Animals/wildlife, endangered species

Michigan: **Arcus 70**, Wong 2092

Animals/wildlife, fisheries

Michigan: Frey 621, Great 2493

Animals/wildlife, preservation/protection

California: Rothschild 1598
Illinois: Huizenga 878, Pajeau 1421
Michigan: Adopt 13, Burt 270, Consumers 2169, **Conway 355**, Devereaux 436, Foley 2469, Foley 2470, Frey 621, Great 2493, Kellogg's 2235, Maldonado 1159, Peterson 1468, Saddle 1619, **Turner 1921**, Turner 1922
Wisconsin: Green 728

Animals/wildlife, sanctuaries

Michigan: **Arcus 70**, Burt 270, Foley 2469

Animals/wildlife, single organization support

Michigan: Foley 2469

Animals/wildlife, special services

Michigan: **Arcus 70**, Duffy 490, Jospey 950, McLeod 1236

Aquariums

Illinois: Souder 1768

Armenia

Michigan: **Armenian 2700**, **Friends 627**, Manoogian 1173

Arthritis

Michigan: Borovoy 202, Hougen 868, **Weisberg 2013**
Missouri: Penniman 1455

Arthritis research

Illinois: Delta 424
Michigan: Puschelberg 1517

Arts

Arizona: Dawson 410, Estes 532, Reese 1542
California: Brooke 238, Bunker 261, Rothschild 1598
Florida: Bush 274, Friedman 623, Mondry 1310, Ryder 2277
Illinois: Borwell 203, Ceres 304, Daverman 405, Huizenga 878, Jentes 931, Northern 2265, Offield 1394, Seabury 1673
Indiana: Ball 92
Massachusetts: Hanover 2218
Michigan: Agley 17, Albion 2307, Alger 2308, Alldredge 34, Allegan 2309, Allendale 2310, Allesee 39, Alpern 44, Alro 2137, **Alticor 2138**, Amway 2696, Anchor 2311, Anderson 2411, Ann Arbor 2312, Applebaum 67, Applebaum 2414, Arts 2415, ArtServe 2417, **ArvinMeritor 2141**, AtWater 81, Baldwin 90, Balk 91, Baraga 2313, Barron 108, Barry 2314, Barth 110, Battle Creek 2315, Battle 119, Batts 2146, Bauervic 120, Bauervic 121, Bay 2316, Bay Harbor 2317, Bedford 2318, **Berman 149**, **Berman 2425**, Berrien 2319, Besser 155, Biederman 2715, Bierlein 2148, Binda 167, Blakely 179, Blatt 181, Blodgett 184, Blumenstein 188, Boll 192, Bonisteel 193, Bonsall 196, **Borders 2153**, Borman's 199, Branch 2320, Brandon 217, Broadleaf 234, Brown 245, Busby 272, Cadillac 2321, Camp 285, Cash 2440, Castaing 298, Charlevoix 2325, Charlupski 312, Citizens 2161, Citizens 2163, Clare 2327, Clio 2328, **CMS 2165**, Comerica 2167, Comerica 2168, Community 2330, Community 2332, Community 2333, Community 2335, Community 2336, Community 2337, Community 2338, Community 2339, Community 2340, Community 2342, Connable 353, Consumers 2169, Consumers 2170, Cook 357, Courtney 368, Crystal 2344, **DaimlerChrysler 2172**, Dalton 398, Delano 423, DeRoy 430, DeVlieg 437, DeVos 438, DeVos 439, DeVos 441, DeVries 442, Dickinson 2345, Doan 459, Doan 460, **Dogwood 463**, Doll 465, Donlin 467, Doornink 469, Dow 477, Dow 478, Dow 479, Drake 480, Duffey 489, Duffy 490, Dyer 499, Eaton 2346, Eliason 2191, Erb 526, Ervin 528, Fabri 2194, Farwell 548, Federal 2198, Felpausch 2199, Fisher 577, Ford 592, Ford 593, Ford 594, Ford 595, Ford 596, **Ford 2202**, Ford 2203, Frankel 612, Fremont 2350, Frey 621, Futureation 2204, **Gast 646**, General 2206, Gilmore 683, Gilmour 2481, Glancy 687, Glick 693, GM 2209, Goad 694, Goldman 699, Gordon 711, Gornick 715, Grand Rapids 2352, Grand Rapids 2211, Grand 2353, Gratiot 2354, Greenville 2355, Griffith 738, Hamilton 771, Hammond 2217, Hancock 778, Harding 788, Harlan 792, Hartmann 801, Hartwick 802, Hermelin 2508, Herrington 830, HFF 2221, Hickman 835, Hillsdale 2356, Himmel 844, Holden 853, Holl 854, Holley 856, Hooker 864, Horgan 2777, Hudson

876, Huebner 877, Hunting 885, Huron 2357, Hurst 886, Imerman 897, Ionia 2358, Isabella 2223, Issa 2224, Jackson 2361, Jackson 2783, Johnson 2524, Jones 946, JPMorgan 2227, JSJ 2228, Kahan 958, Kantzler 966, Kanzler 967, Kasle 2232, Katzman 973, Kaufman 975, Kaufman 977, Keeler 982, Kellogg's 2235, Kelly 2236, Keweenaw 2363, Klopcic 1019, Knight 1026, Korff 1037, **Kresge 1049**, L & H 1058, Lahti 1063, Lansing 1075, Lapeer 2365, Lavins 1088, Leelanau 2366, Lenawee 2367, Leven 1101, Lewis 1105, Liebler 1106, Livonia 2368, Loeb 1118, Loomis 2243, Lowell 2544, M & M 2369, Mackinac 2370, Manistee 2371, Manoogian 1171, Manoogian 1172, Manoogian 1173, Marcks 1176, Mardigian 1177, Marquette 2372, Marshall 2373, Marsilje 1181, Masco 2248, Masco 2249, McFarlan 2808, McGregor 1226, McKibben 1232, McKinley 2553, McLeod 1236, Mecosta 2374, Meer 1248, Meijer 2251, Michigan 2375, Midland 2376, Miller 1281, Miller 1286, Miller 2255, Mills 1288, Miro 1294, Monroe 1313, Morgan 2258, Morley 1325, Morrison 1328, Mosaic 1329, Mott 1333, Narens 1356, Nelson 1364, **Nine 1378**, Northville 2381, Norway 2382, Olds 1398, Orley 1405, Osceola 2383, Otsego 2384, **Padnos 1415**, Padnos 1416, Parfet 1430, Parish 1433, Paulina 1440, Perrigo 2266, Peslar 1463, Petitpren 1469, Petoskey 2385, Pincus 1480, Pitt 1483, Pivnick 1485, Plym 1488, Polasky 1491, Polk 1492, Porter 1496, Power 1502, Prentis 1506, Pribil 1509, **ProQuest 2270**, Pyle 1518, Reynolds 1551, Robideau 1567, Rogers 1579, Rosenthal 1591, Rotary 2609, Roto 2276, Rowan 1601, **Saab 2843**, **Sage 1621**, Saginaw 2387, Samaritan 1630, Sanilac 2388, Schalon 1646, Schaver 1648, Schlafer 1651, Schmier 1654, Schoolcraft 2389, Schwartz 1667, Sebastian 1675, Seifert 1684, Seligman 1687, SEMCO 2278, Semmes 1688, Shaevsky 2616, Shapero 1695, Shelby 2390, Shelden 1699, Sherman 1704, Shiawassee 2391, Shiffman 1707, Shubeck 1715, Shufro 1716, Silverman 1727, Simmons 1728, Skillman 1739, Slavik 1743, Slikkers 1745, Smith 1760, Southeast 2393, Southfield 2394, Sparta 2395, St. Clair 1782, Steelcase 2281, **Steelcase 2282**, Sterling 2396, Stern 1797, **Stoddard 1807**, Stollman 1813, Stryker 1823, Stulberg 1827, Sundquist 1841, Taubman 1862, Thoman 1878, Thompson 1883, Three 2399, Tiscornia 1897, Todd 2287, Towsley 1901, Trico 1905, Turner 1922, Upjohn 1934, Valassis 2291, Van Andel 1939, Varnum 2293, Vaughan 1962, Vlasic 1974, Volkswagen 2298, VSA 2676, Warchol 1986, Weatherwax 1996, Weiner 2007, Weisblat 2014, **Weissman 2867**, Wenger 2022, Westerman 2027, Wetsman 2031, Whirlpool 2301, Whiting 2040, Whiting 2041, Whitney 2686, Wickes 2048, Wickson 2049, Wilde 2055, Williams 2061, Wilson 2065, Wilson 2067, Winkelman 2070, **Winn 2074**, WMY 2083, Wolfe 2086, Wolters 2090, Wolverine 2303, Wolverine 2304, Woodall 2094, World 2099, Wyoming 2401, Zehnder 2124
Minnesota: **Target 2283**, TCF 2285, Weyand 2032
New Mexico: Seidman 1683
New York: Birds 2149, Elkes 2744, **Ford 590**, Millman 1287, **Nonprofit 2576**, Wasserman 1989
Ohio: Anderson 52, Andersons 2412, Grange 2212, Jubilee 2229, Milacron 2254, Mitchell 1298, National 2260, NCC 2262, PAV 1442, Sky 2279, St. Clair 1783
Oklahoma: Sneed 1762
Pennsylvania: Pryor 1516
Rhode Island: Charter 2159
Washington: Fehsenfeld 557
Wisconsin: Bishop 172, Green Bay 2214, Hess 832, Kowalski 2238, McIntyre 1227, McIntyre 1228, Miner 1291, Summerfield 1837, Wisconsin 2302, WPS 2305

Arts councils
Michigan: Burdick 263, Meyer 1263

Wisconsin: Vellmure 1963

Arts education
California: Brooke 238
Florida: Bush 274
Georgia: Blackney 177
Illinois: Borwell 203
Michigan: ArtServe 2417, Budres 2154, Community 2332, DeRoy 430, Frey 621, General 2206, Hartmann 801, JPMorgan 2227, Marstrand 1182, McLauchlin 1233, Ortiz 1408, Pollack 1493, Reuter 1550, Stoddard 1806

Arts, artist's services
Michigan: Arts 2415, Tannahill 2632

Arts, association
Michigan: Castaing 298, Hahn 763, Hartwick 802, Ilitch 2516, May 1204

Arts, cultural/ethnic awareness
California: Nissan 2263
Michigan: American 2409, **DaimlerChrysler 2172**, Ford 2203, Frey 621, General 2206, Italian 2518, JPMorgan 2227, Mott 1333, Southfield 2394, **U.S. 1928**, Whirlpool 2301

Arts, folk arts
Michigan: Frey 621, Marstrand 1182

Arts, formal/general education
Michigan: Tannahill 2632

Arts, public education
Michigan: General 2206

Arts, research
Michigan: Moholy-Nagy 2818

Asia
Michigan: **Ford 2202**, Whirlpool 2301
Minnesota: **Target 2283**
New York: **Ford 590**

Asians/Pacific Islanders
Michigan: Grand Rapids 2352, India 901, **National 1359**

Asthma
Michigan: Asthma 2419

Athletics/sports, academies
Michigan: Bettis 2427

Athletics/sports, amateur competition
Michigan: Ufer 2289

Athletics/sports, baseball
Michigan: Dow 479, Farver 547

Athletics/sports, basketball
Michigan: Cash 2440, **Webber 2683**

Athletics/sports, equestrianism
Michigan: Mackinac 2370, McCardell 1211, **Oreffice 1402**

Athletics/sports, fishing/hunting
Michigan: Glassen 688, Voelker 2675

Athletics/sports, football
Michigan: Roto 2276

Athletics/sports, golf
Michigan: Gary 645

Athletics/sports, school programs
Michigan: Community 2451, TDR 1869
West Virginia: Farr 2197

Athletics/sports, soccer
Michigan: Cronin 381, Foran 588

Athletics/sports, Special Olympics
Michigan: Kasle 2232, Thormann 1890

Athletics/sports, training
Michigan: Crowther 383, McNish 1242

Athletics/sports, winter sports
Michigan: Adray 14, Keweenaw 2363

Australia
Michigan: **Ford 2202**

Bahai
Michigan: Mirafzali 1293

Belgium
Michigan: **Dow 2186**

Big Brothers/Big Sisters
Michigan: Gabooney 633, Little 1113, Mill 1274
Wisconsin: Green 728

Biological sciences
Michigan: Camp 285, Hillsdale 2356

Biomedicine
Michigan: Bauervic 120, Newman 1370

Blind/visually impaired
Louisiana: Orten 1407
Michigan: Javitch 923, Jospey 950, Lions 2541, McNally 1241, Michigan 2813, Molinello 1305, Ratner 1532

Botanical gardens
Michigan: Balk 91, Bouwer 211, Eliason 2191, Frey 621, Meijer 1252

Botanical/horticulture/landscape services
Louisiana: Orten 1407
Michigan: Keller 986

Botany
Michigan: **Floriculture 2468**

Botswana
Michigan: **Kellogg 988**

Boy scouts
Michigan: Camp 286, Collins 2166, Dura 2189, Gabooney 633, Harlan 792, MacCrone 1146, Mills 1288, Parker 1435, Slavik 1742, Sloat 1747
Mississippi: Weitzenhoffer 2015
Washington: UNOVA 1932

Boys
Michigan: Green 727

Boys & girls clubs
California: House 869
Michigan: Barstow 109, Clark 2450, Crowther 383, Dart 403, Dauch 2735, Eddy 508, Farmington 2347, Ford 595, Hickman 835, Jeffers 928, Jones 945, Jurries 954, Mackey 1150, Padnos 1416, Ravitz 1535, Sheldon 2615, Thomas 1879, Tracy 1903
New York: Turn 1920
Ohio: Thompson 1885

Boys clubs
Michigan: Law 1089

Brain research
Michigan: Nill 1376

Brazil
Michigan: **Dow 2186**, Institute 2779

Breast cancer
Michigan: **Nartel 1357**

Buddhism
Michigan: Ford 591

Business school/education
California: Kanitz 965
Michigan: Camp 285, **DaimlerChrysler 2172**, **DENSO 2177**, **Ford 2202**, Ford 2203, General 2206, Grand Haven 2351, Harding 791, **Lowe 2800**, Manufacturing 2247, Michigan 2557, Morley 1325, Ponting 1494, Tauber 2633, Wickson 2049, World 2099

Business/industry
Michigan: **Concrete 2452**, DaimlerChrysler 2171, **DaimlerChrysler 2172**, **Davis 2457**, **H.I.S. 749**, **Lowe 2800**, Varnum 2293

Canada
Michigan: **DENSO 2177**, **Ford 2202**, **Kellogg 2233**, Steelcase 2281, **Steelcase 2282**

Cancer
Delaware: Warner 1987
Florida: Kent 998, Powell 1501
Indiana: Neff 2822
Louisiana: Orten 1407
Michigan: Agley 17, Alix 31, Beson 154, Borovoy 202, Bronner 237, Bugas 258, Cochrane 340, Deibel 420, Del Signore 2458, DiPonio 455, Dura 2189, Faigle 538, General 2206, Grand Rapids 2488, Greenberg 731, Gurwin 747, Horgan 2777, Inman 903, Korman 1038, Little 1113, Mahon 1155, Maldonado 1159, **McCarty 2552**, **Oreffice 1402**, Otsego 2384, Padnos 1416, Pardee 2832, Pardee 2833, **Pardee 1428**, Ramser 1527, Ravitz 1535, Rordor 1588, Roto 2276, Royal 1603, Schwartz 1667, Silverman 1727, Skeen 1735, Sloat 1747, Spartan 1775, Speck 2624, Stolaruk 1812, Stone 1814, Stonisch 1815, Taylor 1868, Thompson 1883, Van Haften 2672, Vlasic 1974, Webber 1997, Whiting 2041
Missouri: Penniman 1455
Ohio: Bates 2145, Hildreth 838
Pennsylvania: Higginson 837
Wisconsin: Kowalski 2238

Cancer research
Colorado: Munn 1346
Indiana: Walther 2677
Michigan: **Ambrosiani 46**, Bittker 173, Bordelove 197, Bryan 2718, Caldwell 282, **Degroot 419**, Devereaux 436, Donahey 466, Dow 477, Frisch 628, **General 2205**, General 2206, Gershenson 663, **Gofrank 696**, Hartmann 801, Hickman 835, Levy 1104, Manat 1164, **McCarty 2552**, McDole 1220, Meadlock 1245, Nill 1376, **Pardee 1428**, Perrigo 2266, Pitt 1483, Price 1512, Purtan 2603, Puschelberg 1517, Rais 1524, Rattner 1533, Rogers 1579, Schlafer 1651, SEMP 2845, Slavik 1742, Speck 2624, Stevenson 1799, Stonisch 1815, Thompson 1883, **Weisberg 2013**

Cancer, leukemia
Michigan: Atanas 2420, Children's 2449, **Weisberg 2013**

Cancer, leukemia research
Michigan: Shurlow 1719

Caribbean
Michigan: **Kellogg 988**

Cerebral palsy
Michigan: Hill 840

Chemistry
Michigan: Doan 459, Dow 2185, Heyl 2509

Child development, education
Michigan: Battle Creek 2315, Ervin 528, Frey 621, Hillsdale 2356, Nusbaum 1388, Skillman 1739, Vollbrecht 1976, Whirlpool 2301, Wilson 2067, Young 2117
Nevada: MGM 2252
Wisconsin: Hess 831

Child development, services
Michigan: Battle Creek 2315, Delano 423, Ervin 528, Frey 621, Hillsdale 2356, **Mott 1332**, Our 1411, Skillman 1739, Vollbrecht 1976, Whitney 2686, Wilson 2067
Wisconsin: Hess 831

Children
Illinois: Northern 2265
Michigan: **Alticor 2138**, Blue 2151, Community 2332, Farmer 2196, Foundation 2472

Children, adoption
Michigan: Bittker 173, Spaulding 2623, Speckhard 1776

Children, day care
Michigan: Berrien 2319, Frey 621, Whirlpool 2301
New York: **Heron 827**

Children, foster care
Michigan: Speckhard 1776

Children, services
Colorado: Munn 1346
Illinois: Delta 424
Michigan: **Alticor 2138**, Blue 2151, **Children's 2448**, Christian 322, Dickinson 2345, Federov 555, Fink 570, Flint 586, Ford 591, Frey 621, Gershenson 666, Helppie 817, Imoberstag 899, Jackson 2225, Katzman 971, Luhtanen 2244, Main 1157, **McDonald 1221**, Meyer 1263, Mojo 1303, **Mott 1332**, **Mousigian 1334**, Paradise 1426, Redies 2273, Seger 1681, Thormann 1890, Tzedukah 1926, Van Dalson 1942, Welch 2016, Williams 2058, Word 2097, **Worldwide 2689**, Young 2116
New Mexico: Seidman 1683
Ohio: Steele 1792
Pennsylvania: Higginson 837
Wisconsin: Green 728

Children/youth
Michigan: Alliance 40, Berrien 151, Community 2336, Dickinson 2345, **Hands 779**, Javitch 923, McPherson 1243, Sigma 2849, TLC 1899, United 2645, **Webber 2683**
Ohio: Oswald 2587

Children/youth, services
Arizona: Jasam 922
California: Eagle 504, House 869
Florida: Bush 274, Friedman 623, Moore 1317, Slocum 1748
Georgia: Shaheen 1693
Illinois: Ceres 304, Lurie 1136, Regal 1544, Sagan 1620, Seabury 1673, Souder 1768
Indiana: Ball 92
Louisiana: Orten 1407
Massachusetts: Cowan 369, Hanover 2218
Michigan: Albion 2307, Allegan 2309, Alon 42, Altrusa 2406, Ann Arbor 2312, Baldwin 90, Baraga 2313, Barry 2314, Barstow 109, Bash 112, Baske 115, Battle Creek 2315, Batts 2146, Beaman 127, Berkowitz 147, Besser 155, Bierlein 2148, Blatt 181, Blodgett 184, Boutell 210, Brown 245, Buffalo 2155, Buhr 259, Burroughs 266, Cadillac 2157, Caldwell 282, Camp 285, Capital 2323, Carls 290, Central 2324, Charlevoix 2325, Cheboygan 2445, Clannad 329, **CMS 2165**, Colina 347, Collins 2166, Comerica 2168, Community 2333, Community 2336, Community 2338, Community 2340, Conrad 354, Conway 356, Cook 358, Cracchiolo 372, Cracchiolo 373, Currie 388, Dart 403, Davis 408, **Day 411**, **Degroot 419**, DeRoy 430, DeVos 438, DeVos 439, DeVries 444, Doornink 469, Dow 477, Dow 479, Duffy 490, E-B 502, Eddy 508, Eliason 2191, Eppert 2746, Erb 526, Ervin 528, Ever 534, Farwell 548, Federal 2198, Ferber 559, **Fetzer 2749**, Ford 592, Ford 594, Ford 596, Four 2348, Frankel 612, **Free 2477**, Fremont 2350, Frey 621, Galencher 635,

Gary 645, General 658, Gerstacker 668, Glick 693, Gornick 715, Grand Rapids 719, Grand Rapids 2352, Grand Rapids 2488, Grand Rapids 2211, Greene 733, Greenville 2355, Hahn 763, Hammond 2217, Heart 2504, Henley 820, Herrick 829, Hickman 835, Hillsdale 2356, Himmel 844, Holden 853, Holley 856, Hooker 863, Hospitalers 867, Huckle 2515, Huron 2357, Idema 894, Ivkov 913, Jackson 2361, Joie 940, JSJ 2228, Jury 955, Kahn 960, Kaufman 974, Keller 986, **Kellogg 2234**, Kelly 2236, KidRelief 1008, Kiwanis 1015, Knabusch 1021, **Koster 1042**, Kutz 1055, Lahti 1063, Lear 2242, Leppien 1098, Lewis 1105, Litvak 1115, Livingston 2542, Loeb 1118, Loomis 2243, Lovelight 2543, Lugers 1131, Lynch 1138, Maas 1145, Mackinac 2370, Mahon 1155, Maisel 1158, Manat 1164, Manoogian 1172, Mardigian 1177, Marquette 2372, McLoughlin 1237, Messer 1260, Metro 1261, Michell 1265, Miller 1284, Miller 1286, **Molitor 1306**, Morley 1325, Mott 1333, Nelson 1365, Otsego 2384, Ottawa 2589, **Padnos 1415**, Pellerito 1451, Pennell 1453, Pistons 2267, Polk 1492, **Quiachon 1520**, Reynolds 1551, Rogers 1579, Rosso 1596, **Saab 2843**, **Sage 1621**, Samaritan 1630, Sanilac 2388, **Secchia 1676**, Shelden 1699, Skillman 1739, Slavik 1743, Small 1749, Smith 1753, Spoelhof 1780, Springview 1781, **Steelcase 2282**, Stoddard 1808, Stonisch 1815, Stucki 1825, Summers 1839, Superior 1844, Thomas 1879, Thompson 1883, Timmis 1894, Turner 1922, United 2650, United 2651, United 2653, United 2656, United 2657, United 2668, Upjohn 1933, Valenti 1938, Vanderwaals 1955, Vandomelen 1957, Village 2674, **Visteon 2296**, Vollbrecht 1976, Watson 1991, **Webber 2683**, Wege 2001, Weikart 2004, Weisblat 2014, Welch 2017, Welch 2018, Westerman 2027, Whaley 2685, Whiting 2041, Wickes 2048, Wickson 2049, Wieczorek 2050, Wilde 2055, Wilson 2064, Wilson 2067, Wisne 2082, WMY 2083, Wolff 2087, Wolters 2090, Wolverine 2303, **Yeager 2109**, Young 2117, Ziegler 2129
Mississippi: Bancroft 93, Weitzenhoffer 2015
New York: Turn 1920
Ohio: Anderson 52, Cleveland 2164, Jubilee 2229, Mariel 1178, Milacron 2254, Moore 1319, Oswald 2587, Whiting 2042
Washington: Fehsenfeld 557
Wisconsin: Bishop 172, Bray 220, Gless 690, Keeney 983, Schregardus 1660, Summerfield 1837

China

Michigan: **Dow 2186**, **H.I.S. 749**, **U.S. 1928**, Uyham **1936**

Christian agencies & churches

Arizona: Estes 532, Jasam 922, Loichle 1119
Arkansas: Sulieman 1832
California: Wierenga 2051
Colorado: Dunagan 494, Mol 1304, VanderArk 1954
Florida: Dexter 449, Hasey 805, Hibbert 834
Illinois: Delta 424, Hill 839, Huizenga 878, Peters 1464, Sagan 1620, Van Dyke 1945, Whitwam 2046
Indiana: Elder 2190
Michigan: 41 1, **Africa 16**, **Aikens 19**, Alldredge 34, **Amy 48**, **Anchor 49**, Anton 65, Aparche 66, Aprill 68, Ash 76, AtWater 81, Baldwin 90, Balk 91, Bandstra 94, Beahan 2424, Beals 126, Beck 131, Behrenwald 136, Benson 142, Bethany 2426, Betten 158, **Betty 159**, Bierlein 2148, BJB 176, Blume 187, Boll 192, Bouma 208, Bouma 209, Bouwer 211, Brauer 219, Bronner 237, Brooks 239, Brown 245, Bryan 255, Buhr 259, Buist 2719, Butts 277, Caesar 280, **Calling 283**, **Cassel 296**, Cebelak 301, Chamberlin 306, Cherney 317, Christian 321, Christian 322, Christian 323, Cimmarrusti 327, Cipa 328, Claus 334, Clearbrook 335, Cochrane 340, Conrad 2453, Cook 357, Coon 360, Courtney 368, Croskey 382, Cutler 392,

Czado 394, DeBruyn 416, Deffenbaugh 417, DeKock 2736, **DeKorne 422**, Deradoorian 429, DeShano 2737, Detroit 432, DeVos 438, DeVos 439, DeVos 440, DeVries 442, DeVries 444, **DeWitt 446**, DeWitt 448, DiClemente 452, DiPonio 455, Disselkoen 456, DJD 458, Dow 477, **Dryden 483**, **Dykstra 500**, Edwards 513, Eliason 2191, Erb 526, Fabri 2194, **Falk 539**, Farago 541, Farwell 548, Felpausch 2199, Fibre 2200, Field 566, Fish 576, Folkert 587, Foster 600, Gardner 641, Garland 642, Geenen 653, Gerberding 662, Gertz 669, **GII 678**, Glenn 689, **God's 695**, Good 702, Good 703, Gordon 2484, Grand Rapids 719, Granger 722, Granger 723, Greene 733, **Griffin 737**, Griffith 738, Grimaldi 739, **H.I.S. 749**, Hager 759, Halcyon 766, Harding 790, Harmony 794, Haveman 808, Haven 2503, Havirmill 809, Hendry 819, **Heritage 825**, **His 848**, Holl 854, Hoogerwerf 861, Hooker 864, **Hope 865**, Howard 872, ICN 893, Idema 894, In 900, Institute 2779, **Isabel 909**, **Johnson 936**, Johnson 937, **Johnson 939**, Joie 940, **Jonathan 941**, Jonathan 942, Joy 951, Jurries 954, Kaczperski 957, Keeler 982, Kemler 994, Kerkstra 1004, Key 1005, Kierstead 1009, **Kniff 1024**, Knight 1025, Koetje 1033, Kosch 1040, **Koster 1042**, Kreilick 1048, L & D 1057, Laker 1067, Lanting 1076, Larsen 1078, Lasko 1084, Latzer 1086, **Leaven 1090**, **Legion 1093**, Lemmen 1096, Lenawee 2536, Leppien 1098, Livingston 1116, Loeb 1118, Lot 1122, Luhtanen 2244, Maas 1144, Mackey 1150, Maibach 1156, **Manthei 1174**, **Maranatha 1175**, Mardigian 1177, Marsilje 1181, Martin 1189, Mason 2550, Mast 1195, **May 1205**, McCormick 1216, McDole 1220, **McDonald 1221**, Meijer 2251, Merkley 1257, Michell 1265, Miller 1275, Miller 1277, Miller 1281, Miller 1282, Miller 1283, Missad 1295, Mojo 1303, Molinello 1305, Monroe 1312, MPS 1336, Muller 1345, Nickless 1372, Oleson 1399, Olson 1400, Our 1411, Parish 1433, Parker 1435, Paulina 1440, Peck 1449, Peslar 1463, **Pilgrim 1479**, Plymouth 2597, Polk 1492, Powers 1503, Prince 1513, Providence 1515, **Quiachon 1520**, Rainbow 1523, RBS 1539, Resnal 1549, Rickert 1555, River 2275, Robell 1566, Robideau 1567, Roche 1571, **Rock 1572**, Roney 1584, Rordor 1588, Rost 1597, Russell 1612, Sackerson 1616, Sacred 1617, Saginaw 1622, Sanders 1633, Schalon 1646, Schanz 1647, Schmid 1653, Schulz 1665, **Secchia 1676**, Seger 1681, Serra 1690, Shallal 2846, Shepherd 1702, Shin 1708, Shoemaker 1711, Slack 1741, Slavik 1743, Smith 1756, **Snyder 1765**, **Sonneveldt 1767**, **Spencer 1778**, Spoelhof 1780, Springview 1781, St. Clair 1782, Stange 1787, Stauffer 1791, Stonisch 1815, Tamer 1855, Timothy 1895, Todd 2287, Trumbull 1912, **Tubergen 1913**, Tuinstra 1915, Upjohn 1934, Valenti 1938, Van Andel 1939, **Van Curler 1941**, Van Den Bosch 1944, Vanderweide 1956, Vanwingen 1959, Velting 2294, Verwys 1966, Victor 1969, Walters 1983, Warchol 1986, Weber 1998, Wege 2001, Welch 2017, Weller 2019, Welsh 2021, Welter 2869, Wenger 2022, Westerbeek 2026, Wheeler 2036, White 2038, Whiteley 2039, Widow's 2870, Wieczorek 2050, Wiese 2052, Wilson 2064, Windemuller 2069, WMY 2083, Wolters 2090, Word 2096, Word 2097, **Worldwide 2689**, **Wynalda 2106**, Yankama 2108, Ykema 2112, Zatkoff 2306, Zondervan 2134, Zurschmiede 2136
Missouri: Grace 2486, Hale 767
Nevada: Christian 324
New Jersey: Hamstra 775, Merillat 1256
Ohio: Bates 2145, Gorski 716, Guiding 744, Moore 1319, Whiting 2042
Pennsylvania: Shander 1694
Rhode Island: Cossin 366
Texas: Brucker 252, Guy 748
Virginia: Freiheit 620
Wisconsin: Firestone 573, JKO 932, McIntyre 1227, McIntyre 1228, Nichols 2575, VandenBelt 1951, Vogt 1975

Civil liberties, advocacy

Michigan: Pitt 1484, Swiss 1851

Civil liberties, reproductive rights

Michigan: Grand Rapids 2352

Civil liberties, right to life

Michigan: Generations 2207, **H.I.S. 749**, KidRelief 1008, Shoemaker 1711

Civil rights

Michigan: **Arcus 70**, Dauch 2735, DeVries 442, Gilmour 2481, Pitt 1483, Valassis 2291
New York: **Ford 590**
Rhode Island: Charter 2159

Civil rights, advocacy

Michigan: Levy 1103, Nokomis 1381, Wolfe 2086

Civil rights, aging

Michigan: Grand Rapids 2352

Civil rights, disabled

Michigan: Grand Rapids 2352

Civil rights, equal rights

Michigan: DTE 2187, DTE 2188, Ford 2203, GM 2209, **Steelcase 2282**, Valassis 2291
Nevada: MGM 2252

Civil rights, gays/lesbians

Michigan: **Arcus 70**, Grand Rapids 2352

Civil rights, immigrants

Michigan: Grand Rapids 2352

Civil rights, minorities

Michigan: Grand Rapids 2352

Civil rights, race/intergroup relations

Michigan: Community 2335, Grand Rapids 2352, **Mott 1332**, Shiffman 1707, Southfield 2394, Whirlpool 2301
New York: **Ford 590**

Civil rights, women

Michigan: Grand Rapids 2352, Sherwood 1705, Sojourner 2621

Community development

Arizona: Dawson 410
Florida: Ryder 2277
Illinois: Crane 376, Daverman 405, Delta 424, Loutit 1124, Seabury 1673
Michigan: Acheson 10, Adrian 2403, **Akbar 2694**, Albion 2307, Albion-Homer 2404, Allegan 2405, Altrusa 2406, Anchor 2311, Anderson 51, Anderson 2411, Ann Arbor 2312, Annis 62, **ArvinMeritor 2141**, Baraga 2313, Barry 2314, Barry 2421, Barton 2144, **Bath 118**, Battle Creek 2315, Bay 2316, Bedford 2318, Berrien 2319, Bierlein 2148, Binda 167, Birtwistle 170, Boersma 191, Borman's 199, Boutell 210, Branch 2320, Branch 2431, Brown 244, Brown 245, Cadillac 2321, Camp 285, Canton 2322, Capital 2323,

Carlson 291, Cass 2441, Central 2324, Char-Em 2443, Charlevoix 2325, Chelsea 2447, Chemical 2160, Citizens 2161, Clare 2327, Clio 2328, Comerica 2167, Comerica 2168, Community 2451, Community 2331, Community 2332, Community 2334, Community 2335, Community 2337, Community 2338, Community 2339, Community 2340, Consumers 2169, Consumers 2170, Copper 2454, Crawford 2456, Cronin 381, Crystal 2344, Dalton 398, **Day 411**, Delano 423, DeShano 2737, Detroit 2460, Dickinson 2345, Dow 2185, Dow 478, DTE 2187, DTE 2188, Eastpointe 2464, Eaton 2346, Eaton 2465, Evergreene 2747, Farver 547, Federal 2198, First 2201, Ford 2753, Ford 2203, Four 2348, Frankenmuth 2349, Fremont 2350, Garland 642, Gary 644, General 2206, Genesee 2478, Gertz 2484, Gilmore 683, GM 2209, Gogebic 2483, Grand Haven 2351, Grand Rapids 719, Grand Rapids 2352, Grand 2353, Gratiot 2354, Great 2492, Greenville 2355, Harlan 792, Hartwick 802, Helppie 817, Hillsdale 2356, Hillsdale 2510, Hilt 843, Holcim 2222, Hudson 875, Hunter 884, Huron 2357, Hurst 886, Ionia 2358, Iosco 2359, Isabella 2223, Ishpeming 2360, Jackson 2361, Janes 920, Jeffers 928, Johnson 2524, Johnson 938, JPMorgan 2227, Junior 2525, Kalamazoo 2362, Kalamazoo 2528, Kalamazoo 2529, Kantzler 966, Kasle 2232, Kaufman 974, **Kellogg 2234**, **Kellogg 988**, Keweenaw 2363, Klopcic 1019, Lavins 1088, Lenawee 2367, Lenawee 2537, Lions 2541, Livonia 2368, Loomis 2243, Loosemore 1121, Lowell 2544, M & M 2369, Mackinac 2370, Malpass 1163, Manistee 2371, Manoogian 1172, Marshall 2373, McKinley 2553, Mecosta 2374, Mecosta-Osceola 2554, Michigan 1268, Midland 2376, Missaukee 2377, Morley 1325, **Mott 1332**, Mott 1333, Negaunee 2379, Norway 2382, Oakland 2581, Oceana 2583, Ogemaw 2583, Olds 1398, Osceola 2383, Oscoda 2586, Otsego 2384, Ottawa 2589, Palmer 1424, Parfet 1430, Parish 1433, Petoskey 2385, Pistons 2267, Plymouth 2598, Portland 2600, Power 1502, Riley 1558, Roscommon 2608, Rosso 1596, Rotary 2610, **Rotary 2611**, Ruffner 1609, **Rukibai 1610**, Sackerson 1616, Saginaw 2387, Sanilac 2388, Schmuckal 1655, Schoolcraft 2389, Schwartz 1667, Seifert 1684, SEMCO 2278, Shelby 2390, Shiawassee 2391, Shiawassee 2618, Shiffman 1707, Shurlow 1719, Slemons 1744, South 2392, Southeast 2393, Southfield 2394, Sparta 2395, St. Joseph 2629, Steelcase 2281, **Steelcase 2282**, Stryker 1823, Stubnitz 1824, Superior 1844, Tassell 1860, Thompson 1887, Three 2399, Todd 2287, Turner 1923, United 2640, United 2642, United 2644, United 2645, United 2646, United 2647, United 2648, United 2649, United 2650, United 2654, United 2658, United 2659, United 2660, United 2661, United 2664, United 2665, United 2666, United 2667, Valassis 2291, Van Buren 2671, Vanderweide 1956, Vicksburg 1968, **Visteon 2296**, Washtenaw 2678, Wayne 2682, Wege 2001, Whirlpool 2300, Whirlpool 2301, Whiting 2041, Wilson 2067, Wyoming 2401, Yeo 2111, Ypsilanti 2402, Zehnder 2124
Minnesota: Inter 904, TCF 2285
Nevada: MGM 2252, MGM 2556
New York: **Ford 590**, **Nonprofit 2576**
Ohio: Anderson 52, Andersons 2412, DSLT 486, Jubilee 2229, Milacron 2254, Moore 1319, National 2260, NCC 2262, Sky 2279, St. Clair 1783, Whiting 2042
Pennsylvania: Tyco 2288
Rhode Island: Charter 2159
Wisconsin: Curtis 390, Green Bay 2214

Community development, alliance
Michigan: Hogue 2776

Community development, business promotion
Michigan: Community 2342, Home 857, Northern 2827, **Stoddard 1807**

Community development, citizen coalitions
New York: **Heron 827**

Community development, civic centers
Michigan: Frey 621

Community development, neighborhood associations
Michigan: Dyer 499

Community development, neighborhood development
Michigan: Allegan 2309, Alnour 41, Barry 2314, Community 2330, Detroit 2739, Dyer 499, Farmington 2347, Frey 621, Grand Rapids 2352, JPMorgan 2227, **Kellogg 988**, Michell 1265, Miller 1284, Mount Pleasant 2378, New 2573, Prince 1513, United 2650, Upjohn 1934
New York: **Heron 827**

Community development, public education
Michigan: General 2206, Morgan 1324

Community development, public/private ventures
Michigan: Frey 621

Community development, service clubs
Michigan: Great 2491, **Rotary 2611**

Community development, small businesses
Michigan: JPMorgan 2227, Michigan 2564, Northern 2827
Minnesota: TCF 2285

Community development, volunteer services
Michigan: Slikkers 1746

Community development, women's clubs
Michigan: Nokomis 1381

Computer science
Michigan: Heyl 2509

Courts/judicial administration
Michigan: Justice 956

Crime/law enforcement
Michigan: DeVries 442, Grand Haven 2351, Halpin 769, Hillsdale 2356

Crime/law enforcement, administration/ regulation
Michigan: Mitchell 1299

Crime/law enforcement, police agencies
Michigan: Gabooney 633, Meijer 2251

Crime/violence prevention
Michigan: Community 2342, Hudson 876, United 2650, United 2651

Crime/violence prevention, abuse prevention
Michigan: Blue 2151, Klopcic 1019, Mason 2550, **Molitor 1306**, United 2666
New York: **Ford 590**

Crime/violence prevention, child abuse
Michigan: Hahn 763, Sojourner 2621, Welter 2869
Minnesota: **Target 2283**
Wisconsin: Beauchamp 129

Crime/violence prevention, domestic violence
Florida: Bush 274
Michigan: Ann Arbor 2312, Capital 2437, Conway 356, **Dogwood 463**, Duffy 490, India 901, Jewish 2523, Mitchell 1299, **Ms. 2570**, Sojourner 2621, Three 2399, United 2655, Whirlpool 2301
Minnesota: **Target 2283**

Crime/violence prevention, sexual abuse
Michigan: Blue 2151

Crime/violence prevention, youth
Michigan: Ervin 528, Hillsdale 2356, Skillman 1739

Cystic fibrosis
Michigan: **Weisberg 2013**

Deaf/hearing impaired
Michigan: Lions 2541, **Zazove 2122**

Dental care
Michigan: Community 2342, Delta 2459, Women's 2688

Dental school/education
Michigan: Delta 2459, Mette 1262, Ravitz 1535

Developing countries
Michigan: **Worldwide 2689**

Developmentally disabled, centers & services
Louisiana: Orten 1407
Michigan: Cheboygan 2445, Main 1157, United 2656

Diabetes
Michigan: Borovoy 202, Bugas 258, Ford 596, Gurwin 747, Ogne 1395, Rogers 1576, Van Haften 2672, **Weisberg 2013**

Diabetes research
Michigan: Cipa 328, Dauch 2735, Thomas 1879, Welter 2869

Digestive disorders research
Michigan: Henley 820

Disabilities, people with
Florida: Bush 274
Illinois: Northern 2265
Massachusetts: Cowan 369
Michigan: **Alticor 2138**, **Beacon 2710**, **Berman 149**, Buffalo 2155, Community 2337, Community 2338, Farago 541, Fibre 2200, Foundation 2472, Gilmore

682, Grand Rapids 2352, Grand Rapids 721, Hope 2514, Italian 2518, Kalleward 2231, Lansing 1075, Lions 2541, Main 1157, McCardell 1211, McPherson 1243, Metro 1261, Pennell 1453, Rebuilding 2604, **Sage 1621**, Sigma 2849, Southwest 1772, Steelcase 2281, **Steelcase 2282**, United 2655, United 2666, Vollbrecht 1976, VSA 2676, Wilson 2067, Young 2117
Minnesota: TCF 2285
Missouri: Gieseking 676
Ohio: National 2260
Wisconsin: Keeney 983

Disasters, fire prevention/control

Louisiana: Orten 1407
Michigan: Gabooney 633, Jennings 929, Meijer 2251

Disasters, Hurricane Katrina

Michigan: Ann Arbor 2312, Causley 300

Disasters, preparedness/services

California: Nissan 2264
Michigan: Lions 2541
Wisconsin: Wisconsin 2302

Down syndrome

Indiana: Neff 2822
Michigan: Butts 277, Thompson 1886

Ear & throat diseases

Michigan: Rontal 1585, Smith 1759

Eastern Europe

Michigan: **Mott 1332**

Economic development

Michigan: Albion 2307, Ann Arbor 2312, Annis 62, Brown 245, Cadillac 2321, Charlevoix 2325, Citizens 2162, **CMS 2165**, Comerica 2167, Community 2330, Community 2332, Community 2335, Community 2337, Community 2339, Community 2340, Community 2341, Community 2342, Crystal 2344, **DaimlerChrysler 2172**, Dickinson 2345, Jackson 2361, JPMorgan 2227, Kalamazoo 2362, Magline 2246, Michigan 2564, Midland 2376, Miller 1284, **Mott 1332**, Petoskey 2385, Steelcase 2281, Strosacker 1821, World 2099
Minnesota: TCF 2285
New York: **Heron 827**
Ohio: National 2260

Economically disadvantaged

Florida: Bush 274, Ryder 2277
Illinois: Northern 2265
Massachusetts: Cowan 369
Michigan: **Alticor 2138**, **Beacon 2710**, Berkery 145, Binda 167, Clannad 329, Community 351, Community 2335, Community 2336, Community 2338, Delta 2459, Fremont 2350, Gilmore 682, Grand Rapids 2352, Great 2763, Haveman 808, Hillsdale 2356, Home 857, I Have 891, India 901, Italian 2518, Jewish 2523, JPMorgan 2227, Lansing 1075, Loomis 2243, Lovelight 2543, Mackey 1150, Metro 1261, Michigan 2560, Molinello 1305, **Mott 1332**, Newaygo 2574, Peach 1444, Perry 1461, **Pilgrim 1479**, Rebuilding 2604, Rockwell 1573, Samaritan 1630, Shelden 1699, Shiffman 1707, Skillman 1739, Steelcase 2281, **Steelcase 2282**, Thoman 1878, Travelers 2636, United 2650, United 2651, United 2655, United 2666, Village 2674, Wallace 1980, **Webber 2683**,

Wheeler 2036, Wickson 2049, Wilson 2067, Yankama 2108, Young 2117
Minnesota: TCF 2285
New York: **Ford 590**

Economics

Michigan: Cadillac 2321, **Earhart 506**, Harding 791, **Heritage 825**, Hillsdale 2356, Michigan 2559, Ten 1872, **Upjohn 2670**, Whitman 2044
New York: **Ford 590**

Education

Arizona: Dawson 410, Reese 1542
California: Bunker 261, Enberg 524, House 869, J.C. 914, Kanitz 965, Nissan 2264, Rothschild 1598, Wilcox 2054
Colorado: Fox 608, Skillin 1737
Delaware: Warner 1987
Florida: Bush 274, Church 326, Crawford 377, **Hagen 758**, Hasey 805, KMD 1020, Mondry 1310, Moore 1317, Powell 1501, Ryder 2277, Slocum 1748
Georgia: Shaheen 1693
Illinois: Barron 107, Brewer 229, Ceres 304, Crane 376, Daverman 405, Delta 424, Meeks 1246, Northern 2265, Offield 1394, Regal 1544, Seabury 1673, Souder 1768, Whitwam 2046
Indiana: Ball 92, Neff 2822
Iowa: Cole 346
Massachusetts: Hanover 2218
Michigan: Adrian 2403, Agley 17, **Aikens 19**, **Akbar 2694**, Albion 2307, Alexandrowski 30, Alger 2308, Allegan 2309, Allen 35, Allesee 39, Alon 42, Alpern 43, Alpern 44, Alpern 44, **Alticor 2138**, Altrusa 2406, American 2139, **American 2410**, **Amerisure 2140**, Anchor 2311, Andersen 50, Anderson 2411, Ann Arbor 2312, Anton 65, Applebaum 67, **ArvinMeritor 2141**, Ash 76, Asthma 2419, AT&T 2142, Ave 83, Baiardi 86, Balk 91, Bandstra 94, Bar 96, Baraga 2313, Barry 2314, Bash 112, **Bath 118**, Battle Creek 2315, Bauervic 120, Bay 2316, Bay Harbor 2317, **Beacon 2710**, Becharas 130, Beck 131, Bedford 2318, Bell 139, Berger 144, **Berman 2425**, Berrien 2319, **Berry 2147**, Besser 155, Betmar 156, Betten 158, Bettis 2427, Biederman 2715, Bierlein 2148, Binda 167, Birtwistle 170, Blumenstein 188, Borman's 199, Borovoy 202, Bouma 209, Branch 2320, Brodsky 235, Brown 245, Brown 249, Buffalo 2155, Buhr 259, Buist 2719, Burns 267, Butzel 2156, Cadillac 2321, Cadillac 2157, Camp 285, Canton 2322, Capital 2323, Carls 290, Cash 2440, Causley 300, Cebelak 301, Cejka 302, Central 2324, Chamberlain 305, Chamberlin 306, Charlevoix 2325, Charlupski 312, Chelsea 2446, Christian 322, Cipa 328, Citizens 2161, Citizens 2163, Clare 2327, Clark 331, Clearbrook 335, Clio 2328, **CMS 2165**, **Cohen 341**, Collins 2166, Comerica 2168, Community 2330, Community 2332, Community 2333, Community 2335, Community 2336, Community 2337, Community 2338, Community 2339, Community 2340, Community 2342, Consumers 2169, Consumers 2170, Cooper 361, Courtney 368, Cracchiolo 371, Cracchiolo 373, Cronin 381, Crystal 2344, Currie 388, **DaimlerChrysler 2172**, Dart 2431, **Davis 2457**, **Day 411**, Deibel 420, **Delphi 2174**, **Delphi 2175**, DeRoy 430, DeShano 2737, Detroit 2460, Detwiler 2462, DeVos 438, DeVos 439, DeVries 444, **DeWitt 446**, Dickinson 2345, DiClemente 452, Doan 460, **Dogwood 463**, Doll 465, Donlin 467, Doornink 469, Dow 478, Dow 479, **Dryden 483**, DTE 2187, DTE 2188, Duffey 489, Dura 2189, Duzyj 498, Dyer 499, E-B 502, Eastpointe 2464, Eaton 2346, Eddy 508, Ellias 518, Emerman 522, Evergreene 2747, Ewald 536, Fabiano 2193, Fabri 2194, Farago 541, Farbman 543, Farmer 2196, Farrehi 546, Farver 547, Farwell 548, Federal 2198, **Fetzer 2749**, Fibre 2200, Fink 570, Fisher 577, Ford 591, Ford 592, Ford 594, Ford 596, Ford 597, **Ford 2202**, Ford 2203, Foster 602, **Foundation 604**, Foundation

2473, Four 2348, Frankel 611, Frankel 612, Fremont 2350, Garland 642, Gary 645, **Gast 646**, General 2206, Gerberding 662, Gibson 673, Gilmore 683, Gilmour 2481, Glancy 687, Glassen 688, Glenn 689, GM 2209, Goad 694, Goldstein 2761, Goodale 705, Goodrich 707, Gordon 711, Grand Rapids 2352, Grand Rapids 2211, Grand 2353, Gratiot 2354, Greenville 2355, **H.I.S. 749**, Hager 759, Haggard 760, Halpin 769, Hamilton 771, Hammond 2217, Hampson 774, Hamzavi 776, Hancock 778, Harbor 2501, Harlan 792, Harris 798, Hartmann 801, Hartwick 802, Haveman 808, Heart 2504, Heeringa 813, Helppie 817, Hermelin 2508, **Heron 828**, Herrington 830, Hickman 835, Hillsdale 2356, Himmel 844, Hinman 2511, Hoffmeyer 2775, Holcim 2222, Holley 856, Homer 858, Hooker 863, Hospitalers 867, Howard 872, Hunting 885, Huron 2357, I Have 891, Idema 894, IDM 895, Ilitch 2516, Imerman 897, India 901, Ionia 2358, Ironwood 2517, Irwin 907, Isabella 2223, Isakow 911, Ishpeming 2360, Issa 2224, Jackson 2361, Jackson 2225, Jacob 917, Janes 920, **Johnson 936**, Johnson 2524, Johnson 938, **Johnson 939**, Joie 940, Jones 945, Jones 946, Joslin 949, JSJ 2228, Jurries 954, Kahn 960, Kalamazoo 2362, Kantzler 966, Kanzler 967, Kaufman 974, Kaufman 977, Keller 986, **Kellogg 988**, Kellogg's 2235, Kelly 989, **Kelly 990**, Kelly 2236, Kemp 995, Kensington 2530, Kent 1000, Kerkstra 1004, Keweenaw 2363, KidRelief 1008, Kiwanis 2531, Klopcic 1019, Knight 1025, Knight 1026, Kocurek 1030, Kolo 2532, Korff 1037, **Koster 1042**, Krause 1044, Kreilick 1048, **Krishnamurti 1050**, Kutz 1055, L & H 1058, La-Z-Boy 2239, LaMothe 1070, Lansing 1075, Lanting 1076, Lapeer 2365, Larsen 1078, Lausch 2241, Lavins 1088, Law 1089, Leelanau 2366, **Legion 1093**, Lemmen 1096, Lenawee 2536, Lenawee 2367, Lewis 1105, Liebler 1106, Litvak 1115, Livonia 2368, Loeb 1118, Loomis 2243, Lowell 2544, Lowenstein 1127, Lugers 1131, Lyon 1139, Lyon 1140, M & M 2369, Maas 1144, MAC 2245, Mackinac 2370, Maisel 1158, Malpass 1163, Manistee 2371, Manoogian 1172, Manoogian 1173, **Manthei 1174**, **Maranatha 1175**, Marcks 1176, Marquette 2548, Marquette 2372, Marshall 2373, Marzke 1192, May 1203, McBain 1207, McGregor 1226, McVicar 1244, Mecosta 2374, Mehney 1250, Merkley 1257, Michell 1265, Michigan 2559, Michigan 2375, Michigan 2563, Midland 2376, Midland 2568, Miller 1275, Miller 1281, Miller 1286, Mills 1288, Miro 1294, Missad 1295, Missaukee 2377, **Molitor 1306**, Molloy 1307, Monroe 1312, Monroe 1313, Morey 1323, Morgan 2258, Morley 1325, **Mott 1332**, Mott 1333, Mount Pleasant 2378, **Mousigian 1334**, MPS 1336, Muller 1345, Nelson 1364, Nickless 1372, Nicolay 1374, Northville 2381, Northville 2577, Norway 2382, Novi 2578, Nusbaum 1389, Oakland 2580, Obloy 1393, Okulski 1396, Olds 1398, Olson 1401, Orley 1404, Orley 1405, Ortiz 1408, Osceola 2383, Otsego 2384, Padnos 1416, Page 1418, Paine 1420, Palmer 1423, Paradise 1426, **Parekh 1429**, Parfet 1430, Paulina 1440, Peck 1449, Pellerito 1451, Perrigo 2266, Perrone 1459, Petitpren 1469, Petoskey 2385, Pierce 2835, Pitt 1483, Plym 1488, Plymouth 2599, Polk 1492, Ponting 1494, Porter 1496, Potiker 2601, Power 1502, Powers 1503, Prein 1505, Prentis 1506, Prentis 2602, Prevo 1508, Pribil 1509, **ProQuest 2270**, Pyle 1518, **Quiachon 1520**, Rainbow 1523, RBS 1539, Redies 2273, Redlum 2274, Reid 1547, Reuther 2605, Reynolds 1551, **Riley 1557**, RNR 1562, Robideau 1567, **Robinson 1569**, Robison 1570, Roche 1571, **Rock 1572**, **Rodney 1574**, Rogers 1577, Rogers 1579, Roon 1586, Rordor 1588, Roscommon 2386, Rosso 1596, Rotary 2609, Rotary 2612, Ruch 1605, **Saab 2843**, Sackner 2613, Saginaw 2387, Samaritan 1630, **San 1632**, Sanilac 2388, Saranac 1637, Schalon 1646, Schaver 1648, Schlafer 1651, Schmid 1653, Schoolcraft 2389, Schwartz 1667, Sebastian

DTE 2188, Ford 2203, General 2206, **Society 2620**, World 2099
Virginia: Bell 137

Engineering/technology

Michigan: Dart 403, DeVlieg 437, Doan 459, Dow 478, **Ford 2202**, Ford 2203, **ProQuest 2270**, Strosacker 1821

England

Michigan: **Kellogg 2233**

Environment

Arizona: Reese 1542
California: Nissan 2264, Rothschild 1598
Florida: Slocum 1748
Illinois: Huizenga 878, Seabury 1673
Michigan: Acheson 10, Adopt 13, Albion 2307, Alger 2308, Alldredge 34, Americana 47, Anchor 2311, Ann Arbor 2312, Asthma 2419, Baraga 2313, Barstow 109, Bay 2316, Bay Harbor 2317, Bedford 2318, Beers 132, Binda 167, Branch 2320, Burt 270, Cadillac 2321, Canton 2322, Capital 2323, Charlevoix 2325, Chippewa 2326, Clare 2327, Clark 331, Community 2329, Community 2330, Community 2332, Community 2333, Community 2335, Community 2336, Community 2337, Community 2338, Community 2340, Community 2341, Community 2342, Consumers 2169, Consumers 2170, Cronin 381, Crystal 2344, **DaimlerChrysler 2172**, Dalton 398, DENSO 2176, DeVlieg 437, Dickinson 2345, Dole 464, Dow 2185, Dow 479, DTE 2187, DTE 2188, Dyer 499, **Ford 2202**, Ford 2203, Four 2348, Fremont 2350, Frey 621, General 2206, Glassen 688, GM 2209, Grand Haven 2351, Grand Rapids 2352, Grand 2353, Gratiot 2354, Green 730, Greenville 2355, **Heron 828**, Herrington 830, Hickman 835, Hillsdale 2356, Ionia 2358, Jackson 2361, Kalamazoo 2362, **Keeler 982**, Keweenaw 2363, **Kresge 1049**, Lapeer 2365, Lewis 1105, Lowell 2544, Lutjens 1137, M & M 2369, Mackinac 2370, Manistee 2371, McKinley 2553, Midland 2376, Mosaic 1329, Mount Pleasant 2378, Norway 2382, Oleson 1399, Osceola 2383, Otsego 2384, Petoskey 2385, Pulte 2271, Roscommon 2386, Saginaw 2387, Sanilac 2388, Schoolcraft 2389, Shiawassee 2391, Southeast 2393, Speckhard 1776, Spicer 1779, St. Deny's 1784, Steelcase 2281, Swift 1850, Todd 2287, Upjohn 1934, **Visteon 2296**, Weisblat 2014, Wenger 2022, Wyoming 2401
New York: **Ford 590**
Texas: Quicksilver 2272
Wisconsin: Bradshaw 215, Green Bay 2214, Lamberson 1069, Wisconsin 2302

Environment, air pollution

Michigan: Community 2332, DTE 2188, Ford 2203

Environment, alliance

Michigan: General 2206

Environment, beautification programs

Michigan: Frey 621, Shelby 2390

Environment, energy

Michigan: Bay 2316, **DaimlerChrysler 2172**, DTE 2188, General 2206, GM 2209, Midland 2376

Environment, ethics

Wisconsin: Bradshaw 215

Environment, forests

Michigan: Galesburg 2755

Environment, land resources

Arizona: Reese 1542
Connecticut: PJM 1486
Illinois: Borwell 203
Michigan: Community 2330, Community 2332, Ford 591, Frey 621, Herrington 830, Larson 1081, Schulz 1665, Stieg 1803

Environment, management/technical aid

Michigan: Rotary 2609

Environment, natural resources

Arizona: Estes 532
Florida: Slocum 1748
Illinois: Harris 797, Lurie 1136
Michigan: Ann Arbor 2312, Barry 2314, BFK 162, Borovoy 202, Briarwood 230, Broadleaf 234, Burdick 263, Cadillac 2321, Carls 290, Clannad 329, Community 2336, Community 2337, Community 2338, Connable 353, DeVlieg 437, Dow 477, Dow 478, Duffy 490, Evenson 533, Ever 534, Foley 2470, Frey 621, Fund 632, Gary 645, Glancy 687, Griffith 738, Herrington 830, Hillsdale 2356, IDM 895, Jackson 915, Jury 955, Kantzler 966, Knight 1026, Kreilick 1048, LaMothe 1070, Larson 1081, Leelanau 2366, Mackinac 2370, Mahogany 1154, Marcks 1176, Martin 1186, Mecosta 2374, Miller 2257, **Mott 1332**, MPS 1337, **Nine 1378**, Northville 2381, Olds 1398, Parish 1433, Polk 1492, Pyle 1518, Saddle 1619, Serra 1690, **Skilling 1738**, **Steelcase 2282**, Stern 1797, Turner 1922, **Visteon 2296**, Wege 2001, Wong 2092, Young 2115
Minnesota: Weyerhaeuser 2034
Nebraska: Woollam 2872
New York: **Ford 590**, Seevers 1680
Ohio: Andersons 2412, Hildreth 838
Washington: Fehsenfeld 557
Wisconsin: Bradshaw 215, Green 728, WPS 2305

Environment, plant conservation

Michigan: **Floriculture 2468**

Environment, pollution control

Michigan: Hunting 885, **Mott 1332**

Environment, public education

Michigan: Community 2342, Great 2493

Environment, recycling

Michigan: Mahogany 1154

Environment, research

Illinois: Lurie 1136
Michigan: Great 2493

Environment, water pollution

Michigan: Community 2332, DTE 2188, Frey 621

Environment, water resources

Florida: Kent 998
Michigan: Frey 621, Great 2493

Environmental education

Florida: Fisher 578

Illinois: Peters 1464
Michigan: Budres 2154, Cook 358, DTE 2188, **Floriculture 2468**, Michigan 2253, Pierce 2835

Europe

Michigan: **Ford 2202**
Minnesota: **Target 2283**

Eye diseases

Michigan: Cooper 361, Dryer 484, Faigle 538, Lundy 1134, Perri 1458, Royal 1603
Wisconsin: Stockton 1805

Eye research

Michigan: **Johnson 936**, Perri 1458, Royal 1603, Shapiro 1696

Family services

Florida: Slocum 1748
Illinois: Huizenga 878, Seabury 1673, Sidlik 1722
Massachusetts: Cowan 369
Michigan: Alabaster 27, Altrusa 2406, **Anchor 49**, Ann Arbor 2312, Barry 2421, Beers 132, Berrien 2319, Capital 2437, Cheboygan 2445, Christian 322, Community 2329, Community 2337, Community 2339, Community 2342, Consumers 2169, Consumers 2170, Cooper 361, Dagenais 397, Detwiler 2462, DeVos 439, DeVos 440, **DeWitt 446**, DeWitt 448, DiPonio 455, Dow 477, Dow 479, Eagle 505, Eaton 2346, Eppert 2746, Fausell 549, Ferber 559, Frankel 612, Fremont 2350, Frey 621, George 660, Grand Rapids 2352, Hahn 763, Harris 798, Harvey 804, Heart 2504, Hillsdale 2356, Huckle 2515, **Jewish 2520**, Jewish 2522, Joie 940, Jones 945, Kalamazoo 2362, Kalamazoo 2529, Kaufman 974, Kaufman 977, Knight 1026, KT 1052, Livingston 2542, Loomis 2243, Malloure 1160, **Maranatha 1175**, Marshall 2549, Mason 2550, McLoughlin 1237, Miller 1275, Monroe 1312, Ottawa 2589, Prince 1513, Rotary 2609, Saginaw 2387, Skillman 1739, Springview 1781, Tawas 2634, Three 2399, United 2645, United 2650, United 2651, United 2653, United 2657, United 2668, Upjohn 1933, Upjohn 1934, Van Dalson 1942, Vander Laan 1953, Vandomelen 1957, Village 2674, **Visteon 2296**, **Webber 2683**, Weiner 2007, **Werner 2023**, Whirlpool 2301, Wilson 2067, Young 2116
New Jersey: Merillat 1256
Ohio: Bates 2145, CRN 379, Oswald 2587
Texas: Tapestry 1857
Wisconsin: WPS 2305

Family services, domestic violence

Michigan: Cutting 393, DiPonio 455, Gerberding 662
Minnesota: **Target 2283**

Family services, parent education

Michigan: Capital 2437, Colina 347, Frey 621, **Mott 1332**

Family services, single parents

Michigan: Conrad 2453, Jewish 2523

Federated giving programs

Florida: Crawford 377, Friedman 623, Moore 1317, Ryder 2277
Illinois: Ceres 304, Loutit 1124, Sidlik 1722, Whitwam 2046
Massachusetts: Hanover 2218
Michigan: Abrams 8, Acheson 10, AFR 2693, Alro 2137, Baiardi 86, Balk 91, Barth 110, Barton 2144, Beers

Food banks

Food distribution, meals on wheels

Food services

Food services, congregate meals

Foundations (community)

Foundations (private grantmaking)

Foundations (private independent)

Foundations (public)

Genetics/birth defects research

Geriatrics

Germany

Girl scouts

Global programs

Goodwill Industries

Government/public administration

Graduate/professional education

Greece

Haiti

Health care

1334, **Nagaraju 1354**, Nakadar 2820, Norway 2382, Obloy 1393, Oleson 1399, Osceola 2383, Parfet 1430, Peck 1449, Pennock 2593, Perrigo 2266, Petoskey 2385, Plymouth 2598, Prentis 1506, **ProQuest 2270**, Pulte 2271, Ravitz 1535, Razzak 1538, RNR 1562, Roche 1571, Roscommon 2386, Rosso 1596, Sackner 2613, Saginaw 2387, Saint 2614, Sanders 1633, Sanilac 2388, Schlafer 1651, Schoolcraft 2389, Schwartz 1667, Seizert 1685, SEMCO 2278, Semmes 1688, Serra 1690, Shelden 1699, Shiawassee 2391, Simmons 1728, Sinai 1730, Skillman 1739, Slavik 1743, **Snyder 1765**, Southeast 2393, Sparta 2395, Speckhard 1776, Spectrum 2625, St. Joseph 2629, Stange 1787, Stauffer 1791, Steelcase 2281, **Steelcase 2282**, Stulberg 1827, Superior 1844, Tassell 1860, Tawas 2634, Thompson 1883, Thompson 1886, Three 2399, Tiscornia 1897, Todd 2287, **Triford 1906**, Turner 1923, United 2642, United 2643, United 2645, United 2647, United 2656, United 2659, United 2662, United 2663, United 2666, United 2668, Upjohn 1933, Valassis 2291, Vandomelen 1957, Velting 2294, **Visteon 2296**, Vlasic 1974, Volkswagen 2298, Vollbrecht 1976, Washtenaw 2678, Weatherwax 1996, Webber 1997, Weisblat 2014, Wenger 2022, Westerman 2027, Wetsman 2031, Whirlpool 2301, Wickson 2049, **Wilkinson 2057**, Winkelman 2070, Wolverine 2303, Wolverine 2304, World 2099, Wyoming 2401, Zanetti 2121, Zatkoff 2306, **Zimmerman 2130**, Zuehlke 2135
Minnesota: TCF 2285, Weyerhaeuser 2034
Missouri: Hale 767
New York: Birds 2149, **Nonprofit 2576**, Schwartz 1668
Ohio: Andersons 2412, Bates 2145, Hire 846, Jubilee 2229, Moore 1319, National 2260, NCC 2262, Sky 2279, Whiting 2042
Wisconsin: Bishop 172, Green Bay 2214, Hess 832, Kowalski 2238, Miner 1291, WPS 2305

Health care, blood supply
Michigan: Idema 894

Health care, clinics/centers
Michigan: **Foundation 2474**, Jensen 930, Livingston 2542, Trinity 2637

Health care, cost containment
Michigan: **ArvinMeritor 2141**

Health care, counseling/pastoral care
Michigan: Spectrum 2625

Health care, EMS
Michigan: Emergency 521, RNR 1562

Health care, infants
Michigan: Alacin 28, **Gerber 661**, Sojourner 2621

Health care, organ/tissue banks
Michigan: Wisne 2082

Health care, patient services
Michigan: Spectrum 2625

Health care, public policy
Michigan: **American 2408**

Health care, reform
Michigan: **Kellogg 988**

Health care, research
Illinois: Shelby 1698
Michigan: Brunkow 253, Gau 649

Health care, single organization support
Michigan: **Heritage 825**, **Linse 1111**, Parish 1432

Health organizations
Michigan: Akers 20, Annis 62, Baiardi 86, Batts 2146, Bauervic 121, Beson 154, Betten 158, Brandon 217, Comerica 2167, Community 2329, Consumers 2169, Conway 356, Delano 423, Devereaux 436, DSL 485, Farwell 548, Fenkell 558, Fisher 577, Frankel 613, Hooker 864, Howard 872, Lincoln 1109, Livingston 1116, Loosemore 1121, Miller 1275, **Mousigian 1334**, **Niemiec 1375**, Olds 1398, **Padnos 1415**, Padnos 1416, Pardee 2833, Pitt 1483, Polasky 1491, Price 1512, Pyle 1518, Redlum 2274, Roche 1571, Rordor 1588, Spicer 1779, **Steelcase 2282**, Thomas 1879, Three 2399, Tiscornia 1897, Trillium 1907, Tzedukah 1926, Wasserman 1988, Wilson 2064, Wisne 2082, Wong 2092
New York: Gits 686
North Carolina: Comloquoy 350
Ohio: National 2260
Virginia: JCM 925
Wisconsin: Hess 832, McIntyre 1227

Health organizations, association
Arizona: Dawson 410
California: Bunker 261, Rothschild 1598
Delaware: Bartsch 111
Florida: Hibbert 834, Moore 1317, Slocum 1748
Illinois: Borwell 203, Ceres 304, Lurie 1136
Maryland: Broomfield 241
Massachusetts: Hanover 2218
Michigan: Allesee 39, Ann Arbor 2312, Ash 76, Battle Creek 2315, Betmar 156, Blatt 181, Blumenstein 188, Bronner 237, Brown 245, Brunkow 253, Cadillac 2321, Caldwell 282, Canaan 289, Cold 342, Community 2332, Community 2333, Community 2335, Community 2338, Connable 353, Cook 357, Cracchiolo 371, Cracchiolo 373, Dart 403, Detroit 431, Edwards 513, Fibre 2200, Ford 594, Four 2348, Frankel 612, Fremont 2350, Gallo 637, **Gerber 661**, Gerstacker 668, Gornick 715, Grand Rapids 2352, Grooters 741, Hampson 774, Hillsdale 2356, Himmel 844, Honigman 859, Hudson 875, Imerman 897, Kasle 2232, Katzman 971, Katzman 973, Kaufman 977, Keeler 982, **Kellogg 988**, **Kelly 990**, Knight 1025, Kraft 1043, LaMothe 1070, Lansing 1075, Larsen 1078, Lenawee 2367, Levy 1104, Lowell 1126, Lowenstein 1127, Maas 1145, Maibach 1156, Malloure 1160, Manat 1164, Manoogian 1172, Mardigian 1177, Marquette 2372, Marshall 2373, Mauser 1201, McGregor 1226, McKibben 1232, Metro 1261, Minkin 1292, Morley 1325, Newman 1370, **Oreffice 1402**, Otsego 2384, Parish 1433, Perrone 1459, Pincus 1480, Preston 1507, Prince 1513, Ratner 1532, **Rock 1572**, Rogers 1579, Rosen 1590, Rosenthal 1591, Schwartz 1667, **Secchia 1676**, Seligman 1687, Sills 1725, Silverman 1727, Slemons 1744, Smith 1753, Sommers 2280, Spartan 1775, Strosacker 1821, Superior 1844, Tamer 1855, Thompson 1883, Turner 1922, Westerman 2027, Wickson 2049, Winkelman 2070, WMY 2083, Wolff 2087, Zehnder 2124
Ohio: DSLT 486, Whiting 2042
Wisconsin: WPS 2305

Health organizations, research
Michigan: Schmier 1654

Health organizations, single organization support
Michigan: Wayne 2681

Health sciences school/education
Michigan: Gratiot 2762, Heyl 2509, Laidlaw 1065

Heart & circulatory diseases
Michigan: Citizens 2163, Clark 2450, Dagenais 397, Detroit 431, Gegax 655, Gordon 713, **Nartel 1357**, Perri 1458, Phelps 1471, Royal 1603, Skeen 1735, Stevenson 1799, **Weisberg 2013**

Heart & circulatory research
Michigan: Clark 2450, Detroit 431, Hill 841, Perri 1458, Ratner 1532

Hemophilia
Michigan: Cascade 2721, Hemophilia 2505

Hemophilia research
Michigan: Cascade 2721, Hemophilia 2505

Higher education
Arizona: Estes 532, Loichle 1119, Reese 1542
California: Eagle 504, Enberg 524, J.C. 914, Kanitz 965, Moh 1300, Shook 1713
Colorado: Munn 1346, VanderArk 1954
Florida: Dexter 449, Fisher 578, Friedman 623, Hibbert 834, Kent 998, KMD 1020, Lounsberry 1123, Powell 1501, Robey 2840, Ryder 2277, Slocum 1748
Georgia: Blackney 177
Illinois: Delta 424, Denniston 428, Hill 839, Hoogland 862, Huizenga 878, Hutchcroft 889, Jentes 931, Loutit 1124, Loutit 1125, Lurie 1136, Peters 1464, Seabury 1673, Sidlik 1722, Souder 1768, Wesselink 2024
Iowa: Cole 346
Louisiana: Behl 134, Orten 1407
Massachusetts: Hanover 2218, Taylor 2859
Michigan: Abbarah 2, Abrams 8, Accelerated 2692, AFR 2693, Akers 20, Al-Hadidi 25, Alix 31, **Allen 37**, Alpert 45, **American 2410**, Andersen 50, Anderson 55, Ann Arbor 2312, Annis 62, Applebaum 67, Applebaum 2414, Aronoff 2702, Ash 76, Attwood 80, **Bahadur 85**, Baldwin 90, Balk 91, Bar 96, Bargman 98, Barnett 101, Barron 108, Barth 110, Barton 2144, Baske 115, Batts 2146, Bauervic 121, Bauervic 122, Bell 139, Bentley 143, **Berkowitz 146**, Berkowitz 147, **Berry 2147**, Beson 154, Biederman 2715, Bierlein 165, Bierlein 2148, Binda 167, Bittker 173, Blodgett 184, Boersma 191, Boll 192, Bonisteel 193, Bonner 195, Borovoy 202, Bouma 208, Bouwer 211, Bradstrum 216, Brandon 217, Brauer 219, Bregi 222, Briarwood 230, Bronner 237, Brown 245, Browne 250, Bucknell 256, Budres 2154, Bugas 258, Buhr 259, Burch 262, Burdick 263, Burns 267, Busby 272, Busch 273, Cadillac 2157, Caesar 280, Cairn 281, Caldwell 282, Camp 285, Cejka 302, Celani 303, Chapman 309, Charlevoix 2325, Christian 322, Clapp 330, Claus 334, Clearbrook 335, Cline 336, Cold 342, Cole 345, Collins 2166, Combs 349, Comerica 2168, Community 2338, Community 2342, **Concrete 2452**, Connable 353, Conrad 2453, Consumers 2170, Cook 358, **Cresswell 378**, Czado 394, **DaimlerChrysler 2172**, Danieleski 400, Daoud 401, Dart 403, Dauch 2735, Davenport 404, Davis 408, Debower 415, DeBruyn 416,

Baldwin 90, Barry 2314, Barth 110, Barton 2144, Battle Creek 2315, Bauervic 122, **Berkowitz 146**, Blatt 181, Blumberg 186, Brandon 217, Brunkow 253, Bugas 258, Buhr 259, Caldwell 282, Carls 290, Catt 299, Charlupski 312, Citizens 2161, Citizens 2163, Cline 336, Cracchiolo 371, Cracchiolo 373, Cronin 381, Dagenais 397, Dalton 398, Dart 403, Davis 408, Deffenbaugh 417, Del Signore 2458, DeRoy 430, Detroit 431, DeVries 443, **Dorfman 471**, Duffy 490, Dykstra 501, Ervin 528, Felpausch 2199, Ferrantino 562, Filer 2751, Ford 592, Ford 594, Ford 595, Ford 596, Ford 2203, Foster 600, Gershenson 667, Gerstacker 668, Gertz 669, Gornick 715, Grosfeld 742, Herrick 829, Hillsdale 2356, Hoffmeyer 2775, Hooker 863, Isabella 2223, Issa 2224, Jeffers 928, Jones 946, Kennedy 996, Kiwanis 1015, Knooihuizen 1027, Kocurek 1030, Kraft 1043, Kutsche 1054, Leelanau 2366, Lincoln 1109, Lindsay 2540, Lubin 1128, Lyons 1141, MacCrone 1148, Mahon 1155, Malloure 1160, Manat 1164, McCormick 1216, McNally 1240, Mercy 2555, Messer 1259, Messer 1260, Miller 1281, Minkin 1292, Morley 1325, **Mukkamala 1344**, Nickless 1371, **Niemiec 1375**, Olds 1398, **Oreffice 1402**, Padnos 1416, Paine 1420, **Parekh 1429**, Parker 1435, Peck 1449, Pennock 1456, Perri 1458, Physician 1474, Polasky 1491, Prein 1505, Prentis 1506, Puschelberg 1517, Ratner 1532, Redies 2273, Robideau 1567, Robison 1570, Roney 1584, Rordor 1588, Rosen 1590, Royal 1603, **Saab 2843**, **Sage 1621**, Sekkarie 1686, Shelden 1699, Slavik 1742, Smith 1753, **Snyder 1765**, Sommers 2280, Spartan 1775, Speck 2624, Stern 1797, Tamer 1855, Taylor 1866, TDR 1869, Three 2399, Todd 2287, Toth 1900, **Tracy 1902**, Tracy 1903, **Triford 1906**, Turner 1922, **Visteon 2296**, Wege 2001, Wenger 2022, Westerman 2027, Wetsman 2031, Wickes 2048, Wilson 2065, Ziegelman 2128, **Zimmerman 2130**
Missouri: Gieseking 676
New Jersey: National 2261
New York: Seevers 1680
North Carolina: Comloquoy 350
Ohio: Beach 124, Cleveland 2164, McCalla 1210, Thompson 1885
Wisconsin: Bishop 172, Hess 831, Keeney 983, Talen 1854, Vellmure 1963, WPS 2305

Hospitals (specialty)

Florida: Frank 610
Michigan: Bargman 98, Caring 2439, Dow 477, Frankel 612, **Griffin 737**, Holden 853, Hood 860, Kay 978, Kelly 2236, Lindsay 2540, Maas 1145, **Robinson 1569**, Webber 1997
Ohio: Nowak 1385

Housing/shelter

Illinois: Vineyard 1971
Michigan: Allen 35, **Bahadur 85**, Bauervic 122, Bay 2316, Berrien 2319, Canaan 289, Comerica 2167, Community 2340, Drake 480, Dyer 499, Fausell 549, Frazier 616, Grand Rapids 2488, Great 2763, Issa 2224, Masco 2248, Masco 2249, **Molitor 1306**, Pulte 2271, South 2392, Superior 1844, Travelers 2636, United 2668
Minnesota: TCF 2285

Housing/shelter, aging

Michigan: Braude 218, Rebuilding 2604

Housing/shelter, alliance

Michigan: Key 1005

Housing/shelter, development

Michigan: Community 2338, Dalton 398, Grand Rapids 2352, Home 857, Home 2513, JPMorgan 2227, Kalamazoo 2362, Knight 1026, Mackinac 2370, Marstrand 1182, Schalon 1646, Stubnitz 1824, Three 2399, Trumbull 1912, United 2656, Whiting 2041
New York: **Ford 590**
Wisconsin: McIntyre 1228

Housing/shelter, home owners

New York: **Heron 827**

Housing/shelter, homeless

Michigan: Branch 2320, **Degroot 419**, Home 857, Kantzler 966, Mackey 1150

Housing/shelter, rehabilitation

Michigan: **Cummings 386**, Home 857

Housing/shelter, repairs

Michigan: Home 857, Rebuilding 2604

Housing/shelter, search services

Michigan: Rotary 2609

Housing/shelter, services

Michigan: Shepherd 1702

Housing/shelter, temporary shelter

Michigan: Home 857

Human services

Arizona: Estes 532, Jasam 922, Reese 1542
California: Bunker 261, House 869, Rothschild 1598, Wilcox 2054
Delaware: Bartsch 111
Florida: Bush 274, Dexter 449, Friedman 623, KMD 1020, Powell 1501, Ryder 2277
Georgia: Shaheen 1693
Illinois: Borwell 203, Ceres 304, Crane 376, Delta 424, Huizenga 878, Loutit 1124, Northern 2265, Regal 1544, Seabury 1673, Sidlik 1722, Souder 1768, Van Dyke 1945, Whitwam 2046
Indiana: Neff 2822
Louisiana: Orten 1407
Maryland: Broomfield 241
Massachusetts: Hanover 2218
Michigan: Acheson 10, Akers 20, Al-Ameri 23, Alger 2308, Alix 31, Alldredge 34, Allegan 2309, Allendale 2310, Allesee 39, Alon 42, Alpern 43, Alpern 44, **Alticor 2138**, Anchor 2311, Andersen 50, Anderson 55, Ann Arbor 2312, Annis 62, Anton 65, Aprill 68, Arman 74, **ArvinMeritor 2141**, Assistance 2418, Attwood 80, Ave 83, Baiardi 86, Baker 87, Baldwin 90, Balk 91, Baraga 2313, Barber 97, Bargman 98, Barron 108, Barry 2314, Barstow 109, Barth 110, Baske 115, Bates 116, **Bath 118**, Battle Creek 2315, Batts 2146, Bauervic 120, Bauervic 122, Baum 123, Bay 2316, Bay Harbor 2317, **Beacon 2710**, Beers 132, Bentley 143, Berger 144, **Berkowitz 146**, Bernstein 150, Berrien 2319, Beson 154, Besser 155, Betmar 156, Betten 158, **Betty 159**, BFK 162, Biederman 2715, Bierlein 165, Bierlein 2148, Binda 167, Birtwistle 170, Bittker 174, Blakely 179, Blatt 181, Blodgett 184, Boll 192, Borman 198, Borman's 199, Bouma 208, Bouma 209, Boutell 210, Bowie 212, Branch 2320, Brandon 217, Brauer 219, Bregi 222, Bronner 237, Brown 245, Brown 249, Bugas 258, Buhr 259, Buist 2719, Burdick 263, Burroughs 269, Burt 270, Cadillac 2321, Cadillac

2157, Caldwell 282, Canaan 289, Canton 2322, Capital 2437, Capital 2323, Carlson 292, Castaing 298, Charlevoix 2325, Charlupski 312, Cheboygan 2445, Chelsea 2447, Cherney 317, Christian 322, Cipa 328, Citizens 2161, Citizens 2163, Clannad 329, Clark 332, Claus 334, Clearbrook 335, **CMS 2165**, Comerica 2167, Comerica 2168, Community 351, Community 2329, Community 2330, Community 2332, Community 2333, Community 2335, Community 2336, Community 2337, Community 2338, Community 2339, Community 2340, Community 2341, Community 2342, Connable 353, Conrad 2453, Consumers 2169, Consumers 2170, Cook 357, Cooper 361, Copper 2454, Coyne 370, Cracchiolo 371, Cracchiolo 372, Crawford 2456, **Cresswell 378**, Cronin 381, Crystal 2344, **Cummings 386**, Currie 388, **DaimlerChrysler 2172**, Dalton 398, Daoud 401, Dart 403, Davis 408, DeBruyn 416, Deffenbaugh 417, Delano 423, DeRoy 430, DeShano 2737, Detroit 431, Detroit 432, Detroit 434, Detroit 2460, Devereaux 436, DeVos 438, DeVos 440, DeVries 442, DeVries 444, DeWitt 448, DHL 450, Dickinson 2345, DiPonio 455, Doan 460, **Dogwood 463**, Doll 465, Donahey 466, Doornink 469, Dow 477, Dow 478, Dow 479, Drake 480, **Dryden 483**, Dura 2189, Dyer 499, E-B 502, Eaton 2465, Eddy 508, Edwards 513, Eliason 2191, Emerman 522, Eppert 2746, Erb 526, Evergreene 2747, Ewald 536, Fabiano 2193, Fabri 2194, Faigle 538, Farago 541, Farber 542, Farley 545, Farmer 2196, Farver 547, Farwell 548, Felpausch 2199, Ferber 559, Ferrantino 562, Fink 570, Fisher 577, Flint 586, Ford 591, Ford 594, Ford 595, Ford 596, Ford 597, Ford 2203, Frankel 612, Frankel 613, Frazier 616, Fremont 2350, Gallo 637, Gary 645, **Gast 646**, Gast 647, General 2206, George 660, Gershenson 665, Gerstacker 668, Gertz 669, Gilmore 683, Gilmour 2481, Glancy 687, Glenn 689, Glick 693, GM 2209, Goldman 699, Goldstein 2761, Goodale 705, Gornick 715, Grand Rapids 2352, Granger 723, Gratiot 2354, Green 730, Greenstein 736, Grooters 741, Grosfeld 742, Gurwin 747, Haas 753, Hager 759, Hahn 763, Hamilton 771, Hampson 774, Hamzeh 777, Hancock 778, Hannan 781, Harden 787, Harding 788, Harris 798, Harris 799, Hartwick 802, Harvey 804, Hauenstein 807, Haveman 808, Havirmill 809, Hees 814, Hendry 819, Henry 823, **Heritage 825**, Herrick 829, Hickman 835, Hillsdale 2356, Hillsdale 2510, Hilt 843, Himmel 844, Hirvonen 847, Hitchens 849, Hollenbeck 855, Holley 856, Honigman 859, Hoogerwerf 861, Hooker 864, **Hope 865**, Horgan 2777, Hospitalers 867, Howard 872, Hudson 875, Hunter 884, Hunting 885, Huron 2357, Hurst 886, Idema 894, Imerman 898, Ionia 2358, Isabella 2223, Isabella 910, Isakow 911, Jackson 2361, Jacob 917, Jennings 929, **Jewish 2520**, Jewish 2522, Johnson 937, Johnson 938, **Johnson 939**, Joie 940, Jones 945, JSJ 2228, Julius 953, Jury 955, Kaczperski 957, Kahan 958, Kahn 960, Kalamazoo 2529, Kantzler 966, Kasle 2232, Katzman 971, Kaufman 974, Kaufman 977, Kay 978, Keeler 982, Keller 985, **Kellogg 2234**, Kellogg's 2235, **Kelly 990**, Kelly 991, Kemp 995, Kent 1000, Keweenaw 2363, Kinney 1011, Knight 1025, Knight 1026, Knooihuizen 1027, Kocurek 1030, Koetje 1033, Kogan 1034, Korff 1037, Kosch 1040, Kravitz 1047, **Kresge 1049**, KT 1052, L & H 1058, La-Z-Boy 2239, Lahti 1063, LaMothe 1070, Langbo 1073, Lapeer 2365, Larsen 1078, Lenawee 2367, Levy 1102, Lewis 1105, Linden 1110, Lindsay 2540, Litvak 1115, Livonia 2368, Loeb 1118, Loomis 2243, Loosemore 1121, Lowell 2544, Lowenstein 1127, Lugers 1131, Luhtanen 2244, Lutjens 1137, Lynch 1138, Lyon 1139, Lyon 1140, Lyons 1141, M & M 2369, Maas 1144, Maas 1145, MAC 2245, Mackey 1148, Mackey 1150, Mackinac 2370, Mahon 1155, Maisel 1158, Maldonado 1159, Malloure 1160, Mally 1161, Manat 1164, Manistee 2371, Manoogian 1171, Manoogian 1172, **Maranatha 1175**, Mardigian 1177, Marquette 2372, Marshall 2373, Marshall 2549, Marzke 1192, Masco 2249, Mason 2550,

Human services, emergency aid

Michigan: Barry 2421, Clannad 329, Grand Rapids 2487, Livingston 2542, United 2666

Human services, financial counseling

Minnesota: TCF 2285

Human services, gift distribution

Michigan: Grand Rapids 2487

Human services, mind/body enrichment

Michigan: Cochrane 340, Cook 357, Fetzer 564, Lachimi 1061

Human services, personal services

Michigan: **Share 2847**

Human services, transportation

Michigan: Clark 2450

Human services, victim aid

Michigan: United 2651

Humanities

Michigan: Branch 2320, Capital 2323, Clannad 329, Community 2333, Community 2336, Dyer 499, Ervin 528, Grand Rapids 2352, Jackson 2361, JSJ 2228, **Kresge 1049**, Mackinac 2370, Michigan 2563, Midland 2376, Norway 2382, **ProQuest 2270**, Shapero 1695, Young 2116

Immigrants/refugees

Michigan: Grand Rapids 2352, **Jewish 2520**, Jewish 2523
New York: **Ford 590**

Immunology research

Michigan: **American 2407**

India

Michigan: **Bahadur 85**, **Balaji 89**, **DeKorne 422**, DeVries 442, **Dow 2186**, **Griffin 737**, **His 848**, India 901, **Kakarala 962**, **Kniff 1024**, **Krishnamurti 1050**, **Mukkamala 1344**, **Nagaraju 1354**, **Parekh 1429**, **Rukibai 1610**, **TIR 1896**, **Vattikuti 1961**
Minnesota: **Target 2283**

Indigenous people

Michigan: Fund 632

Infants/toddlers

Michigan: Community 2332

International affairs

Michigan: **Ford 2202**, Grand Rapids 719, **Palestine 2590**, Siddiqui 1721, Timmis 1894
New York: **Ford 590**

International affairs, arms control

New York: **Ford 590**

International affairs, foreign policy

Michigan: Siddiqui 1721
New York: **Ford 590**

International development

Florida: Ludy 1130
Michigan: Berkowitz 147, DeBruyn 416, **His 848**, **Koinonia 2792**, Levy 1103, **Pilgrim 1479**, **Rotary 2611**, **Vattikuti 1961**
Minnesota: Wolohan 2089

International economic development

New York: **Ford 590**

International exchange, students

Michigan: Temple 1871

International human rights

Michigan: **Akbar 2694**, Levy 1103, Shiffman 1707, **U.S. 1928**
New York: **Ford 590**

International migration/refugee issues

Michigan: Travelers 2636

International relief

Michigan: **DeKorne 422**, Gayar 651, **Hands 779**, Haveman 808, Henley 820, KidRelief 1008, **Koinonia 2792**, **May 1205**, **Molitor 1306**, **Pilgrim 1479**, Rayes 1537, Theuerkorn 1875, Whitman 2044

International relief, 2004 tsunami

Michigan: **Vattikuti 1961**

International studies

Michigan: Earhart 506
New York: **Ford 590**

Islam
Michigan: AFR 2693, **Akbar 2694**, Akl 22, Aljabban 32, Alnour 41, Gayar 651, Hadied 756, Hamzavi 776, Issa 2224, Jondy 943, Mahmud 1153, Nakadar 2820, Qazi 1519, Rayes 1537, Razzak 1538, Sadaqa 1618, Shukairy 1717, Speck 2624, Stockbridge 1804, Wege 2002

Israel
Michigan: **American 2410**, Bargman 98, **Berman 149**, Borman's 199, **Jewish 2521**, Stollman 1813, **Teitel 1870**

Italy
Michigan: Italian 2518, **Secchia 1676**

Japan
Michigan: **Dow 2186**

Jewish agencies & temples
California: Rothschild 1598
Florida: KMD 1020, Mondry 1310
Illinois: Barron 107
Michigan: Akers 20, Alix 31, Allan 33, Alon 42, Alpern 43, Alpern 44, Applebaum 67, Applebaum 2414, Aronoff 2702, Bar 96, Bargman 98, Barron 108, Berger 144, **Berkowitz 146**, Berlin 148, **Berman 149**, **Berman 2425**, Bernstein 150, **Berry 2147**, Betmar 156, BFK 162, Bittker 174, Bizer 175, Bloom 185, Blumberg 186, Blumenstein 188, Borovoy 202, Braude 218, Brodsky 235, Brown 243, Brown 249, Chandler 307, Charlupski 312, **Cohen 341**, DeRoy 430, Doan 460, **Dorfman 471**, DSL 485, Epstein 525, Farbman 543, Fenkell 558, Ferber 559, **Ferber 560**, Fisher 577, Fisher 2467, Fleischman 582, Ford 592, Frankel 612, Frankel 613, Frankel 614, Friedman 622, Fruman 630, Garber 2757, Geist 656, Gershenson 663, Gershenson 665, Gershenson 667, Glick 691, Glick 693, Goldman 699, Goldman 700, Goldstein 2761, Gordon 711, Green 2494, Greenberg 731, Greenstein 736, Grosfeld 742, Gurwin 747, **H.S. 751**, Haddow 2498, Hanflik 2767, Hermelin 2508, HFF 2221, Himmel 844, Honigman 859, Imerman 897, Imerman 898, Isakow 911, Jacob 917, Jampel 919, **Jas 921**, Javitch 923, **Jewish 2520**, **Jewish 2521**, Jewish 2522, Kahan 958, Kahn 960, Kahn 961, Katz 969, Katzman 971, Katzman 972, Katzman 973, Kaufman 975, Kaufman 976, Kemp 995, Kogan 1034, Korman 1038, Kraft 1043, Kravitz 1047, Leven 1100, Levy 1104, Linden 1110, Litvak 1115, Loeb 1118, Lowenstein 1127, Lubin 1128, Maas 1145, Maisel 1158, Manat 1164, Mandelbaum 1165, May 1204, McCabe 1209, Meer 1247, Meer 1248, Milan 1272, Milan 1273, Mill 1274, Miller 1280, Minkin 1292, Miro 1294, Narens 1356, **Nartel 1357**, Nelson 1365, Newman 1370, Nusbaum 1388, Nusbaum 1389, Okun 1397, Orley 1404, Orley 1405, **Padnos 1415**, Padnos 1416, Palman 1422, Pappas 1425, Pierce 1476, Pincus 1480, Pitt 1483, Pivnick 1485, Polasky 1491, Potiker 2601, Prentis 1506, Prentis 2602, Ran 1528, Ravitz 1535, Rogers 1579, Rohlik 1581, Rontal 1585, Rosen 1590, Rosenthal 1591, **Rosenzweig 1592**, Saltsman 1629, Sandy 1634, **Saulson 1642**, Schmier 1654, Schreiber 1661, Schwartz 1667, Seligman 1687, Shaevsky 2616, Shapero 1695, Shapiro 1696, Sherman 1704, Shufro 1716, Sills 1725, Silverman 1727, Snider 1763, Sonkin 2854, Southeastern 1770, Stevenson 1799, Stoddard 1808, Stollman 1813, Stulberg 1827, Subar 1829, Swiss 1851, Tauber 1861, **Teitel 1870**, Torgow 2861, Trico 1905, Tzedukah 1926, United 2638, Wasserman 1988, Weinberg 2005, Weinberg 2006, Weisberg 2011, Weisberg 2012, **Weisberg 2013**, Wetsman 2031, Winkelman 2070, Winkler 2071, Wirt 2078, Wolfe 2086, Wolff 2087, Yaffe 2107, Ziegelman 2128
New York: Elkes 2744
Wisconsin: Frank 609

Jewish federated giving programs
Florida: KMD 1020, Mondry 1310
Illinois: Barron 107
Michigan: Akers 20, Alon 42, Applebaum 67, Applebaum 2414, Bar 96, Bargman 98, Barron 108, **Berman 2425**, Bernstein 150, Betmar 156, Birtwistle 170, Blumberg 186, Blumenstein 188, Borman 198, Borman's 199, Brodsky 235, Brown 243, Brown 249, Charlupski 312, Coville-Triest 2455, DeRoy 430, Emerman 522, Farber 542, Farbman 543, Fenkell 558, Ferber 559, **Ferber 560**, Finkelstein 572, Fisher 577, Fisher 2467, Fleischman 582, Frankel 611, Frankel 612, Frankel 613, Frankel 614, Frankel 2475, Friedman 622, Fruman 630, Geist 656, Gershenson 665, Glick 693, Goldman 699, Goldman 700, Goldstein 2761, Gordon 711, Green 2494, Greenberg 731, Greenstein 736, Grosfeld 742, **H.S. 751**, Haddow 2498, Harris 798, Hermelin 2508, HFF 2221, Honigman 859, Imerman 898, Isakow 911, Jacob 917, Jampel 919, **Jewish 2521**, Kahn 959, Kahn 960, Katz 969, Katzman 971, Katzman 973, Kaufman 975, Kaufman 977, Kemp 995, Kogan 1034, Korman 1038, Kravitz 1047, Leven 1100, Leven 1101, Levy 1104, Litvak 1115, Lowenstein 1127, Lubin 1128, Maas 1145, Manat 1164, Mandelbaum 1165, Matthews 1200, May 1204, Meer 1247, Milan 1272, Mill 1274, Miller 1280, Minkin 1292, Miro 1294, Mondry 1309, Narens 1356, **Nartel 1357**, Newman 1370, Nusbaum 1388, Nusbaum 1389, Orley 1405, Padnos 1416, Pappas 2592, Pincus 1480, Pitt 1483, Pitt 1484, Pivnick 1485, Polasky 1491, Prentis 1506, Prentis 2602, Rohlik 1581, Rosen 1590, Rosenthal 1591, **Rosenzweig 1592**, Sandy 1634, Schreiber 1661, Seligman 1687, Shaevsky 2616, Shapero 1695, Shapiro 2617, Sherman 1704, Shufro 1716, Sills 1725, Silverman 1727, Snider 1763, Sonkin 2854, Stewart 1801, Stollman 1813, Stulberg 1827, Subar 1829, Tauber 1861, Tauber 2633, Taubman 1863, **Teitel 1870**, Torgow 2861, Trico 1905, United 2638, **Weisberg 2013**, Wetsman 2031, Wirt 2078, Zeltzer 2126
New York: Greenspan 735
Rhode Island: Charter 2159
Wisconsin: Frank 609

Kidney diseases
Michigan: National 2571

Kidney research
Michigan: National 2571

Labor studies
Michigan: Reuther 2605

Language/linguistics
Texas: Posey 1497

Latin America
Michigan: **Kellogg 988**, **Leaven 1090**, **Mott 1332**
Minnesota: **Target 2283**
New York: **Ford 590**

Latvia
Michigan: **Latvian 2535**

Law school/education
Michigan: Butzel 2156, Imerman 898, **International 905**, Kemp 995, Maas 1145, Ponting 1494, **Rachor 1522**, Voelker 2675, Wilson 2064
New York: Elkes 2744, Yee 2110

Law/international law
Michigan: Fetzer 2749
New York: **Ford 590**

Leadership development
Michigan: Community 2335, Community 2336, DTE 2187, DTE 2188, Grand Rapids 2352, Hillsdale 2356, **Kellogg 988**, Michigan 2567, **Mott 1332**
New York: **Ford 590**

Lebanon
Michigan: **Abiragi 7**, **Saab 2843**

Legal services
Massachusetts: Cowan 369
Michigan: Bodman 2152, Butzel 2156, **International 2780**, **International 905**, Levy 1102, Marshall 2549, Michigan 2566
New York: **Ford 590**

Lesotho
Michigan: **Kellogg 988**

LGBTQ
Michigan: **Arcus 70**, Gilmour 2481, Grand Rapids 2352

Libraries (academic/research)
Michigan: Ford 2471, Valenti 1938

Libraries (public)
Florida: Cook 359
Michigan: Barnett 102, Battle 119, Burns 267, Community 2342, Delano 423, Frey 621, Friends 626, Gary 645, Hackley 2497, Hall 768, Hartwick 802, Investment 2782, Kantzler 966, Keeler 982, Library 2538, Magline 2246, McCabe 1209, Mott 1333, Pinney 1482, Pribil 1510, Reid 1547, Richardson 1553, Rosso 1596, Saginaw 1623, Shelby 2390, Slemons 1744, Smith 1752, Titche 1898, Welch 2017, Whitney 2686
New York: Seevers 1680
Ohio: Hildreth 838, Refke 1543, Sky 2279
Wisconsin: Talen 1854

Libraries (school)
Michigan: Seger 1681

Libraries/library science
Michigan: Abrams 8, Caesar 280, Camp 285, Community 2333, DeVos 438, **Dogwood 463**, Dow 478, Earle 507, Fremont 2350, Hillsdale 2356, Mahon 1155, Masonic 2551, Mills 1288, Parker 1435, Ruffner 1609, Thompson 1887, Three 2399, Trixie 1909, Tzedukah 1926, Vicksburg 1968, Wickes 2048, Wickson 2049
Ohio: Lahti 1064
Wisconsin: Neal 1360

Literature
Michigan: Hemingway 818, Jackson 2783, Plymouth 2599

Lung diseases
Michigan: Thompson 1886
Ohio: Beach 124

Malawi
Michigan: **Kellogg 988**

Mathematics
Michigan: Ford 2203, General 2206, Grand Haven 2351, Heyl 2509

Media, film/video
Michigan: Ann Arbor 2413, Levy 1102
New York: **Ford 590**

Media, journalism/publishing
Michigan: Arden 71

Media, radio
Michigan: Foster 600, Maldonado 1159, Mosaic 1329

Media, television
Michigan: Devereaux 436, Harding 788, Kantzler 966, Maldonado 1159, Riley 1558, Thompson 1886, **Weisberg 2013**

Media/communications
Michigan: Cable 2436, Dearborn 2173, Deibel 420, Ford 2471
New York: **Ford 590**

Medical care, community health systems
Michigan: Livingston 2542

Medical care, in-patient care
California: Shook 1713
Florida: Friedman 623
Michigan: Emergency 521, Ford 593, Gordon 713, McGregor 1226, Meijer 2251
New York: Elkes 2744

Medical care, outpatient care
Michigan: Ferrantino 562

Medical care, rehabilitation
Michigan: Cronin 381, Dauch 2735, Fremont 2350, Harder 2502, Pennell 1453, Sigma 2849, **Tubergen 1913**
Ohio: Hildreth 838

Medical research
California: Marsh 1180
Florida: Hasey 805
Michigan: **American 2408**, Applebaum 2414, **ArvinMeritor 2141**, Bashur 114, Berkowitz 147, Beson 154, Brown 249, Butts 277, Detroit 2739, Diebolt 454, Dow 477, **Ford 2202**, Glenn 689, Havirmill 809, Henley 820, Hermelin 2508, Kalleward 2231, Kinney 1011, **Molitor 1306**, **Mousigian 1334**, **Nelson 1367**, Orley 1404, Orley 1405, Pardee 2833, Perrigo 2266, Polasky 1491, Ravitz 1535, Shufro 1716, Shurlow 1719, Spectrum 2625, Stonisch 1815, Sutaruk 1845, Wilson 2068, World 2099
New York: Millman 1287
Wisconsin: McIntyre 1227

Medical research, association
Michigan: Ram 1526

Medical research, institute
Michigan: Bauervic 120, Blue 2150, Brown 245, Cebelak 301, Davis 408, Fischer 2466, Ford 594, **Gerber 661**, **Gofrank 696**, Holden 853, Hunting 885, Katzman 972, Molinello 1305, Newman 1370, **Pardee 1428**, Ratner 1532, Schlafer 1651, Semmes 1688, Silverman 1727, Sinai 1730, Slavik 1743, Taubman 1863, Thomas 1879, Thormann 1890, Towsley 1901, **Tracy 1902**, Whiting 2041
New Mexico: Seidman 1683
North Carolina: Blystone 189
Ohio: Jobst 933, Williams 2060

Medical school/education
California: Kanitz 965, Shook 1713
Illinois: Souder 1768
Louisiana: Orten 1407
Michigan: Camp 285, Cochrane 340, **Gagliardi 634**, Giddey 675, Gratiot 2762, Hammel 772, Irwin 907, Laidlaw 1065, Latimer 1085, Lincoln 1109, Medical 2810, Mette 1262, **Mukkamala 1344**, **Nagaraju 1354**, **National 1359**, Nill 1376, Okulski 1396, Puschelberg 1517, **Rachor 1522**, Rontal 1585, Semmes 1688, **Snyder 1765**, Spectrum 2625, Stern 1797, Stoddard 1809, Tauber 1861, Thomas 1879, Towsley 1901, Zerbe 2127

Medical specialty research
Michigan: Law 1089, Stoddard 1809

Medicine/medical care, public education
Michigan: **American 2408**

Mental health, addictions
Michigan: Carlson 291

Mental health, counseling/support groups
Michigan: Alliance 40, Doornink 469

Mental health, depression
Michigan: Blue 2151, World 2099

Mental health, disorders
Michigan: Flinn 585, Swiat 1849

Mental health, residential care
Michigan: **Griffin 737**, MacCrone 1146

Mental health, smoking
Michigan: Cadillac 2321, Community 2451, Community 2342

Mental health, treatment
Michigan: Fink 570, Flinn 585, Ravitz 1535

Mental health/crisis services
Michigan: Acheson 10, Consumers 2169, Dalton 398, Gerstacker 668, Kinney 1011, Miller 1281, Pitt 1483, Power 1502, **Steelcase 2282**
Ohio: Andersons 2412

Mentally disabled
Minnesota: TCF 2285

Mexico
Michigan: **DENSO 2177**, **Ford 2202**, **H.I.S. 749**, **Kellogg 2233**, **Morath 1321**, Rotary 2612, **Steelcase 2282**

Middle East
Michigan: **Saab 2843**
Minnesota: **Target 2283**
New York: **Ford 590**

Military/veterans' organizations
Michigan: Blissfield 183, Parker 1435, Ramser 1527

Minorities
Florida: Ryder 2277
Illinois: Regal 1544
Michigan: Battle Creek 2315, Binda 167, Community 2338, Consumers 2169, **Davis 2457**, **Ford 2202**, Ford 2203, General 2206, **Gerber 661**, Grand Rapids 2352, I Have 891, **Kellogg 988**, Manoogian 1171, Mardigian 1177, Michigan 2564, **Mott 1332**, **National 1359**, Shiffman 1707, **Steelcase 2282**, Wickson 2049, Wolverine 2303
New York: **Ford 590**
Ohio: Jubilee 2229, National 2260

Minorities/immigrants, centers/services
Florida: Ryder 2277
Michigan: Battle Creek 2315, Community 2338, Grand Rapids 2352, **Kellogg 988**, Manoogian 1171
New York: **Ford 590**

Mozambique
Michigan: **Kellogg 988**

Multiple sclerosis
Michigan: Borovoy 202, Kalleward 2231, National 2572, Shufro 1716, Sloat 1747, **Weisberg 2013**

Multiple sclerosis research
Michigan: National 2572

Muscular dystrophy
Michigan: Little 1113

Museums
Illinois: Loutit 1124
Michigan: Acheson 10, Allesee 39, Besser 155, Blakely 179, Community 2337, Community 2342, Conrad 354, Consumers 2169, Deibel 420, DeVos 438, DeVries 443, Edelweiss 509, Evenson 533, Fisher 577, Ford 591, Ford 593, Ford 595, Frankel 613, Frey 621, Ganton 2756, Gilmore 2759, Glancy 687, Grand Rapids 2352, Hancock 778, Hansen 783, Harris 799, Hauenstein 807, Heinrich 2771, Huebner 877, Hurst 886, **Johnson 936**, Jury 955, Kaufman 975, Korff 1037, Leven 1101, Loosemore 1121, Lyons 1141, Manoogian 1172, Marstrand 1182, Masonic 2551, Morley 1325, Mosaic 1329, Murdock 1348, **Padnos 1415**, Padnos 1416, Peslar 1463, Phelps 2834, Prentis 2602, Saddle 1619, Shapero 1695, Slemons 1744, Smith 1760, Smith 2851, Stern 1797, **Stoddard 1807**, Stryker 1823, Taubman 1862, Thompson 1883, Tzedukah 1926, **U.S. 1928**, Van Andel 1939, Vanderwaals 1955, **Visteon 2296**, Weatherwax 1996, Wege 2001,

Welch 2017, Whitney 2686, **Wilkinson 2057**, Williams 2061, World 2099
New York: **Ford 590**, Gits 686, Seevers 1680
Ohio: Cleveland 2164, Hildreth 838, Mariel 1178, National 2260
Wisconsin: Bray 2432, Frank 609, Lamberson 1069, WPS 2305

Museums (art)
California: Eagle 504
Michigan: Doornink 469, Dow 477, Frankel 612, Frey 621, Keeler 982, MacCrone 1146, McNally 1240, Meijer 1252, Porter 1496, RNR 1562, Ryan 1615, Sargent 1638, Schlafer 1651, Silverman 2850, Small 1749, Wolff 2087, Wolters 2090
Wisconsin: Bray 220, Pierson 1477

Museums (children's)
Illinois: Souder 1768
Michigan: Baske 115, Eddy 508, Frazier 616, Frey 621

Museums (ethnic/folk arts)
Michigan: Frey 621, Schlafer 1651, Silverman 1727

Museums (history)
Illinois: Loutit 1124, Loutit 1125
Michigan: Alro 2137, Americana 47, Cady 279, Ford 2471, Frey 621, Harding 790, Hudson 875, **Nartel 1357**, Parish 1431, Rosso 1596

Museums (marine/maritime)
Michigan: Frey 621, Mills 1288

Museums (natural history)
Michigan: Frey 621

Museums (science/technology)
Michigan: Castaing 298, Frey 621
Wisconsin: Leslie 1099

Museums (specialized)
California: House 869
Michigan: **Dogwood 463**, Frey 621, Gordy 714, Levy 1102, Olds 1398, Shapiro 1696, **Weisberg 2013**

Native Americans/American Indians
Michigan: Grand Rapids 2352, **National 1359**, Voelker 2675

Neighborhood centers
Michigan: Doll 465, Knight 1026, United 2657

Netherlands
Michigan: **Ackermans 11**

Neuroscience
Michigan: Campbell 287, Levy 1104, Toth 1900

Neuroscience research
Michigan: Campbell 287, Dow 477, Laboratory 1060, Wege 2002
New York: Rudel 1606

Nicaragua
Michigan: Rotary 2612

Nonprofit management
Florida: Bush 274
Michigan: Knight 1026

Nursing care
Michigan: Bellinger 140, Dow 477

Nursing home/convalescent facility
Michigan: Broadleaf 234, Frankel 614, Knabusch 1021, Thompson 1888, Vanwingen 1959

Nursing school/education
Michigan: Gratiot 2762, Heyl 2509, Jaffe 918, Laidlaw 1065, Latimer 1085, Metro 1261, **National 1359**, Sobong 2852, Spectrum 2625

Nutrition
Michigan: **Allen 37**, Bauervic 121, Blue 2151, **Gerber 661**, Grand Rapids 2352, Hagelshaw 2499

Orthodox Catholic agencies & churches
Michigan: Manoogian 1173, **Mousigian 1334**, **Perry 1460**

Pakistan
Michigan: **Akbar 2694**

Parkinson's disease
Michigan: Alon 42, Michigan 2565, **Oreffice 1402**

Parkinson's disease research
Michigan: Michigan 2565, Wright 2102

Pediatrics
Michigan: Caring 2439, **Degroot 419**, **Gerber 661**

Pediatrics research
Michigan: **Gerber 661**
Oklahoma: Sneed 1762

Performing arts
Florida: Dexter 449
Michigan: Adrian 2403, Alldredge 34, Allesee 39, Andersen 50, Ann Arbor 2312, Barnett 105, Bay 2316, Bell 139, Boutell 210, Burdick 263, Byron 2435, Canton 2322, Celani 303, Combs 349, Community 2329, Community 2337, Community 2338, Community 2342, Consumers 2169, Dalton 398, Deffenbaugh 417, Evenson 533, Fausell 549, Fisher 577, **Ford 589**, Ford 593, **Ford 2202**, Frankel 611, Frankel 613, Fremont 2350, Frey 621, Gabooney 633, Geist 656, Gilmore 683, Grand Rapids 2352, Hancock 778, Hartwick 802, Havirmill 809, Henry 823, HFF 2221, Hillsdale 2356, Huebner 877, Idema 894, Jospey 950, JPMorgan 2227, Jury 955, Katzman 972, Kaufman 977, Keeler 982, Keller 986, KINSHIP 1012, Lear 2242, Leven 1101, Loosemore 1121, Maas 1145, Manoogian 1172, Morley 1325, Mosaic 1329, Orley 1404, Pincus 1480, Prentis 1506, Prentis 2602, Rattner 1533, Saddle 1619, Schlafer 1651, Shaevsky 2616, Shapero 1695, Skillman 1739, Smith 1760, Sonkin 2854, South 2392, Strosacker

1821, Tracy 1903, Valenti 1938, Wege 2001, Whitman 2044, Whitney 2686, **Wilkinson 2057**, Williams 2061, Wilson 2063, Wilson 2067
Minnesota: Arts 2416, TCF 2285
New York: **Ford 590**
Ohio: Lahti 1064, Mariel 1178
Wisconsin: WPS 2305

Performing arts centers
Michigan: DeVos 438, Frey 621, **Heritage 825**, Knabusch 1022
Washington: UNOVA 1932

Performing arts, ballet
Michigan: Frey 621
Ohio: Hire 846

Performing arts, dance
Michigan: **Dorfman 471**, Frey 621, Kaufman 977, **Weissman 2867**
New York: **Ford 590**

Performing arts, education
Delaware: Esperance 530
Michigan: Armstrong 2701, Budres 2154, Frey 621, **Rislov 1559**

Performing arts, music
Delaware: Esperance 530
Michigan: **Borders 2153**, Burdick 263, Community 2337, Community 2338, Consumers 2169, Dalton 398, Dow 479, **Ford 589**, Frey 621, Gilmore 2480, **Glen Arbor 2482**, Gordy 714, Grand Rapids 2487, Green 730, **Greeney 734**, Harding 788, Hinson 845, Lane 1072, Marstrand 1182, Miller 1280, Mondry 1309, Northville 2381, Pollack 1493, Pribil 1511, Reuter 1550, **Rislov 1559**, Shapero 1695, Shelden 1699, Three 2399, **U.S. 1928**, Welch 2018, Westerman 2027, Whitney 2686, Wilson 2063, Wolverine 2303
New York: **Ford 590**
Ohio: Dumesnil 493, Gilbert 679, Lahti 1064, Miller 1285
Texas: Guy 748
Wisconsin: Summerfield 1836

Performing arts, music (choral)
Michigan: Frey 621
West Virginia: Farr 2197

Performing arts, music composition
Michigan: **Rislov 1559**

Performing arts, music ensembles/groups
Michigan: Frey 621

Performing arts, opera
Illinois: Jentes 931
Michigan: Bowie 212, Eschbach 529, Frankel 614, Frey 621, Gabooney 633, HFF 2221, Parcells 1427, Roto 2276, Sandy 1634, Schalon 1646, Wasserman 1988
New York: Seevers 1680
Texas: Posey 1497

Performing arts, orchestra (symphony)
Florida: Ludy 1130
Illinois: Borwell 203, Stulberg 1826

Michigan: Bowie 212, **Cassel 296**, Chamberlin 306, Gates 648, Grand Rapids 719, **Isabel 909**, Jonathan 942, Redlum 2274, Sundquist 1841, Welch 2018, Youth 2118
Mississippi: Bancroft 93

Recreation, centers
Illinois: Young 2114
Michigan: Bettis 2427, Grosse 2495, TLC 1899

Recreation, community facilities
Michigan: Grosse 2495, Schalon 1646

Recreation, fairs/festivals
Michigan: Dauch 2735, Dow 479

Recreation, government agencies
Michigan: Strong 1820

Recreation, parks/playgrounds
Michigan: Cronin 381, Dalton 398, Eastpointe 2464, Mehney 1250, Meijer 2251, Novi 2579, Pinney 1482, Redies 2273
New York: Turn 1920
Ohio: Whiting 2042

Religion
Illinois: Daverman 405
Michigan: Attanasio 78, Ave 83, Currie 388, Daystar 412, DeVos 441, Donlin 467, Engle 2192, Fike 568, Ford 594, Hancock 778, India 901, **Jonathan 941**, Kymal 1056, Lavins 1088, Manoogian 1171, Maust 1202, Merillat 1255, Meyer 1263, Mirafzali 1293, Mohindra 1301, **Mousigian 1334**, **Myers 1353**, **Parekh 1429**, Plymouth 2599, Redlum 2274, Riley 2607, Roon 1586, Ruch 1605, Seizert 1685, Sjaarda 1733, Sloat 1747, Smith 1756, **Snyder 1765**, St. Lawrence 2630, Summerland 1838, Thavarajah 1873, **V Care 1937**, Vander Laan 1953, Westerman 2027, Woodall 2094, Word 2096, **Wynalda 2106**, Zionist 2131
Minnesota: Weyand 2032
New York: **Nonprofit 2576**
Ohio: Anderson 52
Wisconsin: Beauchamp 129, Green Bay 2214, Hess 831, Schregardus 1660, Talen 1854

Religion, association
Florida: Crawford 377
Michigan: Bryan 2718

Religion, interfaith issues
New York: **Ford 590**, Hunter 883
Wisconsin: Firestone 574

Religious federated giving programs
Michigan: Bronner 237, Jondy 943, **McDonald 1221**, Merillat 1255, **Morath 1321**, **Snyder 1765**

Reproductive health
Michigan: Sojourner 2621
New York: **Ford 590**

Reproductive health, family planning
Florida: Slocum 1748
Michigan: Delano 423, Dole 464, Hill 840, Hinson 845, Kaufman 977, Padnos 1416, Sherwood 1705,

Steelcase 2282, Stucki 1825, Tiscornia 1897, Wilson 2067, Wolff 2087
Wisconsin: Bray 220

Reproductive health, OBGYN/Birthing centers
Michigan: Cadillac 2321

Reproductive health, sexuality education
New York: **Ford 590**

Residential/custodial care
Michigan: Cadillac 2157, Green 727, Martin 1184, Messer 1259, Nicolay 1374, Schneider 1656, Sparling 1774, Wilde 2055
Minnesota: Wolohan 2089

Residential/custodial care, hospices
Florida: Powell 1501, Slocum 1748
Michigan: Bauervic 122, Beson 154, Cadillac 2321, Camp 285, Canaan 289, Community 2329, Frisch 628, **H.I.S. 749**, Hillsdale 2356, Isabella 2223, Little 1113, Lugers 1131, Nusbaum 1388, Olds 1398, Padnos 1416, Price 1512, Ravitz 1535, Schmuckal 1655, Shapiro 1696, Stone 1814, Three 2399, Wilson 2064, Wilson 2067
Ohio: Hire 846
Wisconsin: Kowalski 2238

Residential/custodial care, senior continuing care
Florida: Frank 610
Michigan: Beyler 161, McFarlan 2808, Prentis 1506, Stevenson 1799

Residential/custodial care, special day care
Wisconsin: Neal 1360

Roman Catholic agencies & churches
Arkansas: Sulieman 1832
California: Hannan 780, Kanitz 965
Florida: Friedman 623, Hasey 805, Powell 1501
Georgia: Shaheen 1693
Michigan: Abele 6, **Abiragi 7**, **Ambrosiani 46**, Ave 83, Barber 97, **Bardha 2706**, Basilica 2423, Berkery 145, Brems 223, Buer 257, Burns 266, Busch 273, Cadillac 2157, Causley 300, Cebelak 301, Cold 342, Conrad 354, Coyne 370, Cracchiolo 371, Cracchiolo 372, Cracchiolo 373, Croskey 382, Daoud 401, Dinan 2742, Drake 480, Duchene 488, Duffey 489, Duffy 491, Ehmer 516, Fabiano 2193, Fruman 630, Goggins 697, Green 727, Grimaldi 739, Haas 753, Hancock 778, Horgan 2777, Jones 945, Julius 953, Kalamazoo 2527, Kennedy 996, Kinney 1011, Kocurek 1030, Korff 1037, LaMothe 1070, Langbo 1073, Ludington 2545, Lutjens 1137, Lynch 1138, Main 1157, Marzke 1192, Mathew 1197, McManus 1238, McNish 1242, Molloy 1307, Moore 1320, **Morath 1321**, Murphy 1349, Northern 1383, Okulski 1396, Olds 1398, Palmer 1424, Pearson 1448, Pellerito 1451, Persia 1462, **Quiachon 1520**, Reid 1547, Riley 1558, **Sage 1621**, Savage 1643, Sehn 1682, Seymour 1692, Shumsky 1718, **St. Joseph 1786**, Stolaruk 1812, Timmis 1894, **Tracy 1902**, Tracy 1903, Trinity 2637, Van Dam 1943, Van Elslander 1946, Van Gessel 1947, Vandomelen 1957, Vlasic 1974, Watson 1991, Webster 1999, Wheeler 2035, Williams 2058, Young 2115, Zacharias 2119, **Zimmerman 2130**
Minnesota: Wolohan 2089
Missouri: Mohler 1302
New Jersey: Manhardt 1166
North Carolina: Blystone 189

Ohio: Bates 2145, Monroe 1311, Nowak 1385, O'Brien 1390
Wisconsin: Hess 831, Kowalski 2238, McIntyre 1229, Stockton 1805

Roman Catholic federated giving programs
Michigan: Hancock 778, MSJ 1338, **Sage 1621**
North Carolina: Blystone 189
Wisconsin: Hess 831

Rural development
Michigan: **Kellogg 988**, **Mott 1332**
New York: **Ford 590**

Russia
Michigan: **Mott 1332**
New York: **Ford 590**

Rwanda
Michigan: **Koinonia 2792**

Safety, automotive safety
Michigan: **DaimlerChrysler 2172**, **Davis 2457**, Ford 2203

Safety, education
Michigan: **ArvinMeritor 2141**

Safety/disasters
Michigan: Roscommon 2386, Weisblat 2014
Nevada: MGM 2556

Safety/disasters, fund raising/fund distribution
Michigan: Pistons 2267

Salvation Army
Florida: Powell 1501
Michigan: **Ambrosiani 46**, Attwood 80, Barnett 104, Beard 128, Bugas 258, Deibel 420, Detroit 432, Eppert 2746, Esser 531, Fausell 549, Field 566, Kaczperski 957, Kay 978, Lindsay 2540, Lowell 1126, Luhtanen 2244, Maldonado 1159, Melgaard 1253, Mervenne 1258, Mills 1288, Nicolay 1373, Pearson 1448, Sheldon 2615, Simmons 1728, Slavik 1742, Thompson 1886, Vanderwaals 1955, Welter 2869, Wheeler 2035, Whiteley 2039
Ohio: Hire 846, Thompson 1885
Wisconsin: Tantlinger 1856, Vellmure 1963

Scholarships/financial aid
California: Kanitz 965, Moh 1300
Florida: Baese 84
Michigan: Binda 167, Boll 192, Brandon 217, **Bretzlaff 228**, Community 2332, Doran 470, **Dorfman 471**, Federov 555, Gibbs 672, Gilles 681, Hendry 819, Hinman 2511, Horgan 2777, Jaffe 918, Lowell 1126, Martin 1183, Martin 1187, Midgett 1271, Mims 1290, Newman 1370, Owen 1413, Ratner 1532, **Saab 2843**, **Sonneveldt 1767**, Stewart 1802, Stokes 1811, Sullivan 1835, Taylor 1866, Thomas 1880, Thornapple 2635, Three 2399, Walker 1979, Young 2115
New York: Yee 2110
Ohio: Worthington 2101
Virginia: Bell 137

Science
Florida: **Hagen 758**

Michigan: Bay 2316, **DaimlerChrysler 2172**, **Delphi 2174**, DeVlieg 437, Doan 459, Dow 478, **Ford 2202**, Ford 2203, General 2206, Heyl 2509, **Kresge 1049**, **Nine 1378**, Plymouth 2599, **ProQuest 2270**, Strosacker 1821, Warchol 1986, Welch 2018
New York: Hunter 883

Science, formal/general education
Michigan: **ArvinMeritor 2141**

Secondary school/education
California: Hannan 780
Delaware: Bartsch 111
Florida: Kegel 984, Ryder 2277, Watson 1993
Illinois: Seabury 1673, Sidlik 1722
Michigan: Attwood 80, Bemis 141, Binda 167, Brems 223, Cebelak 301, Conrad 2453, Croskey 382, DeBruyn 416, Dinan 2742, Fraser 2476, Grimaldi 739, Herrick 829, Hoffmeyer 2775, Holland 2512, Hurst 886, Idema 894, Inman 903, Kaufman 974, Keeler 982, **Kellogg 988**, Koch 1029, Kool 2793, Lutjens 1137, Manoogian 1171, Martin 1187, Morley 1325, Morrill 1327, MSJ 1338, **Perry 1460**, Peslar 1463, Ponting 1494, Rogers 1580, **Sage 1621**, Sarnowski 1640, **Skilling 1738**, Stonisch 1815, Tracy 1903, **Uyham 1936**, Van Andel 1939, Welch 2018, Wilson 2067, Young 2115, Zuehlke 2135
New York: **Ford 590**, Turn 1920
Ohio: Anderson 52, Monroe 1311, St. Clair 1783
Pennsylvania: Tyco 2288

Single parents
Michigan: Conrad 2453

Social sciences
Michigan: DeVos 441, Dickinson 2345, **Fetzer 2749**, Reuther 2605, **Rodney 1574**, Whitman 2044
New York: **Ford 590**

Social sciences, public policy
Michigan: **H.I.S. 749**

Social sciences, research
Illinois: Shelby 1698
Michigan: **Fetzer 2749**
New Hampshire: Southeast 2855

South Africa
Michigan: **Africa 16**, **Kellogg 2233**, **Kellogg 988**, **Mott 1332**

South America
Michigan: **Ford 2202**

South Korea
Michigan: **Dow 2186**

Southeast Asia
New Hampshire: Southeast 2855
New York: **Ford 590**

Southern Africa
Michigan: **Africa 16**

Space/aviation
Michigan: Parish 1431

Speech/hearing centers
Michigan: Abbarah 2, Carls 290

Spine disorders research
Michigan: Gau 649, Shereda 1703

Spirituality
Michigan: Lachimi 1061

Student services/organizations
Florida: Hibbert 834
Michigan: Canton 2322, **Stoddard 1807**

Substance abuse, prevention
Michigan: Berrien 2319, United 2651
New York: Turn 1920

Substance abuse, services
Michigan: Binda 167, Cadillac 2321, Community 2338, Community 2342, Ervin 528, Ford 595, Fremont 2350, Jackson 2361, Skillman 1739, **Steelcase 2282**, Sullivan 1834, United 2655, Wilson 2067

Substance abuse, treatment
New York: Turn 1920

Swaziland
Michigan: **Kellogg 988**

Taiwan
Michigan: **Morath 1321**

Teacher school/education
Michigan: Detwiler 2462, **Worldwide 2689**

Theological school/education
Illinois: Huizenga 878
Michigan: **Abiragi 7**, **Anchor 49**, **Bath 118**, Butts 277, Dancey 399, **DeWitt 446**, Fish 576, Glenn 689, Granger 723, Greenstein 736, **Griffin 737**, Grimaldi 739, Hart 800, Jurries 954, Koch 1029, Kool 2793, **McDonald 1221**, McNally 1240, Minkin 1292, **Myers 1353**, Neckers 1361, Palmer 2591, Schmid 1653, Schmuckal 1655, Scully 1671, Shepherd 1702, Shoemaker 1710, **Sonneveldt 1767**, Spoelhof 1780, Springview 1781
Nevada: Christian 324
New Jersey: Hamstra 775
Rhode Island: Cossin 366
Wisconsin: VandenBelt 1951

Theology
Michigan: Borovoy 202

Transportation
Michigan: Cassel 295, **Cassel 296**, DaimlerChrysler 2172, **Wilkinson 2057**

Turks & Caicos Islands
Michigan: **Foundation 604**

Urban/community development
Illinois: Borwell 203
Michigan: AT&T 2142, Community 2332, Consumers 2169, DTE 2188, Frey 621, Hudson 876, Loomis 2243, Monroe 1313, **Mott 1332**, Pinney 1482, Shiffman 1707
New York: **Ford 590**
Ohio: Andersons 2412, National 2260

Veterinary medicine
Michigan: Davis 409, Humane 880, Irwin 907, Muntwyler 1347

Veterinary medicine, hospital
Michigan: Bellwether 2713

Vietnam
Michigan: Henley 820

Visual arts
Michigan: Ann Arbor 2312, Bay 2316, Byron 2435, **Coville 2733**, **Ford 2202**, Fremont 2350, Frey 621, Hancock 778, Hillsdale 2356, JPMorgan 2227, Kaufman 977, **KINSHIP 1012**, Lansing 2534, Schlafer 1651, Shapero 1695, Skillman 1739, Sonkin 2854, Whitney 2686

Visual arts, architecture
Michigan: Binda 167, Clannad 329

Visual arts, art conservation
Michigan: Community 2340

Visual arts, ceramic arts
Michigan: **Glen Arbor 2482**, Hartwick 802, **Pewabic 2594**

Visual arts, painting
Michigan: Glen Arbor 2482

Visual arts, photography
Michigan: **Coville 2733**, **Glen Arbor 2482**

Visual arts, sculpture
Michigan: Canton 2322, Fredericks 617, **Glen Arbor 2482**, **Pewabic 2594**

Vocational education
California: Nissan 2263
Michigan: **DaimlerChrysler 2172**, Muer 1342

Vocational education, post-secondary
Michigan: Grand Haven 2351

Voluntarism promotion
Michigan: Community 2329, Community 2338, Fetzer 564, Grand Rapids 2352, Hillsdale 2356, **Kellogg 988**, Michigan 1268, **Mott 1332**, Nickless 1372, United 2657, United 2663

Volunteers of America
Michigan: Imerman 897

GRANTMAKER NAME INDEX

Numbers following the grantmaker names refer to the entry
sequence numbers in the Descriptive Directory.

Cadillac Products Inc. Foundation, MI, 2157
Cady Trust, Mary Ida, MI, 279
Caesar Puff Foundation, MI, 280
Cairn Foundation, The, MI, 281
Caldwell Foundation, Will & Jeanne, MI, 282
Calliea Family Foundation, The, MI, see 1899
Calling God's Tower Ministries, Inc., MI, 283
Cameron Foundation, The, MI, 284
Camp Foundation, Samuel Higby, MI, 285
Camp Rotary Foundation, MI, 286
Campbell Foundation for Neurological Research, Kenneth H., MI, 287
Campbell Fund, The, MI, 288
Canaan Foundation, MI, 289
Cancer Foundation of India, MI, see 1301
Canton Community Foundation, MI, 2322
Capital Area United Way, MI, 2437
Capital Region Community Foundation, MI, 2323
Caravan Youth Center, MI, 2438
Caring Athletes Team for Children's and Henry Ford Hospitals, MI, 2439
Carls Foundation, The, MI, 290
Carlson Foundation, Inc., Dwight, MI, 291
Carlson Foundation, The, MI, 292
Carpenter Scholarship Trust, Norman & Ardis, WI, 293
Cascade Hemophilia Consortium, MI, 2721
Cascadia Foundation, MI, 294
Cash for Kids, MI, 2440
Cass County United Way, Inc., MI, 2441
Cassel Charitable Foundation, Thomas and Jane, MI, 295
Cassel Family Foundation, Scott and Laura, MI, 296
Cassie, Jr. Foundation, James C., MI, 297
Castaing Family Foundation, MI, 298
Catt Foundation, C. Glen and Barbara A., MI, 299
Causley, Jr. Family Foundation, James F., MI, 300
Cavaliere Family Foundation, MI, 2722
Cavaliere Foundation, Inc., WI, see 215
Cebelak Foundation, Bernard J. & Camille, MI, 301
Cedar Springs Educational Foundation, MI, 2442
Cejka Foundation, Inc., Joseph B. Cejka and Florence V., MI, 302
Celani Charitable Foundation, Inc, MI, 303
Centennial Mission Foundation, Inc., MI, 2723
Center Irrevocable Trust, William J., VT, 2724
Central Care Management Organization, MI, 2725
Central Montcalm Community Foundation, MI, 2324
Ceres Foundation, IL, 304
Chamberlain Foundation, The, MI, 305
Chamberlin Foundation, Inc., Gerald W., MI, 306
Champion Enterprises, Inc. Corporate Giving Program, MI, 2158
Chandler Family Foundation, The, MI, 307
Chang Foundation, MI, 308
Chapman Scholarship Trust, MI, 309
Char-Em United Way, MI, 2443
Charfoos Charitable Foundation, Lawrence S., MI, 310
Charis Foundation II, MI, 311
Charity for All Foundation, MI, 2444
Charlevoix County Community Foundation, MI, 2325
Charlupski Foundation, Allen and Franka, MI, 312
Charter One Foundation, The, RI, 2159
Chase Foundation, Alfred W., MI, 313
Chatmon Scholarship Fund, Inc., Hattie & Floyd, The, MI, 314
Cheboygan County United Way, MI, 2445
Cheff Foundation, Stanley W., MI, 315
Chelsea Education Foundation, Inc., MI, 2446
Chelsea Kiwanis Club Foundation, MI, 316
Chelsea United Way, MI, 2447
Chemical Financial Corporation Contributions Program, MI, 2160
Cherlayne, Inc., MI, 2726
Cherney Irrevocable Charitable Living Trust dated 12/26/86, Edward, MI, 317
Cherri Foundation, Lila, MI, 318
Chiasson Family Foundation, Inc., MI, 2727
Children Need Both Parents, MI, 2728
Children's Charities at Adios, MI, 2448
Children's Leukemia Foundation of Michigan, MI, 2449
Children's Ministries, Inc., MI, 2729
Chippewa County Community Foundation, MI, 2326
Chisbetts Foundation, MI, 2730
Chormann Family Foundation, NJ, 319

Chortkiv Foundation, Inc., MI, 320
Christian Advancement, Inc., MI, 321
Christian Evangelical Foundation, MI, 322
Christian Family Foundation, MI, see 2536
Christian Foundation, MI, 323
Christian Heritage Communication Foundation, MI, see 323
Christian Missionary Scholarship Foundation, NV, 324
Christopher Foundation, The, MI, 325
Chrysler Corporation Contributions Program, MI, see 2171
Chrysler Corporation Fund, MI, see 2172
Church Educational Foundation, Inc., Lou, The, FL, 326
Cimmarrusti/Gray Family Foundation, The, MI, 327
Cincinnati Milacron Foundation, OH, see 2254
Cipa Foundation, The, MI, 328
Citizens Banking Corporation Charitable Foundation, MI, 2161
Citizens Banking Corporation Contributions Program, MI, 2162
Citizens First Foundation, Inc., MI, 2163
Citizens First Savings Charitable Foundation, Inc., MI, see 2163
Clannad Foundation, MI, 329
Clapp Scholarship Fund, Charles I. and Emma J., MI, 330
Clare County Community Foundation, MI, 2327
Clark Charitable Trust, Robert & Lottie, MI, 331
Clark Fund, MI, 332
Clark Stroke Foundation, Henry, MI, 2450
Clark, Jr. Foundation, Henry O., MI, see 2450
Clason Charitable Trust, Sonja, MI, 333
Claus Charitable Foundation, Thomas H. and Nancy J., MI, 334
Clearbrook Charitable Foundation, Inc., MI, 335
Cleveland-Cliffs Foundation, The, OH, 2164
Cline Foundation, The, MI, 336
Clinton Community Foundation, MI, 2731
Clinton Rotary Scholarship Foundation, MI, 337
Clinton Township-Yasu City Cultural Exchange Board, Inc., MI, 338
Clio Area Community Fund, MI, 2328
Clupper Scholarship Trust, John H., MI, 339
CMS Energy Foundation, MI, 2165
Cochrane M.D. and Agnes L. Cochrane Foundation, Edgar G., MI, 340
Cohen Foundation, Jerry, MI, 341
Cold Heading Foundation, The, MI, 342
Cole and Connie Belin Charitable Foundation, Marlin, IA, see 346
Cole Family Foundation, Jack, Evelyn, and Richard, MI, 344
Cole Family Foundation, MI, 343
Cole Trust, Bradford, MI, 345
Cole-Belin Education Foundation, IA, 346
Colina Foundation, MI, 347
Coller Foundation, MI, 348
Collins & Aikman Foundation, MI, 2166
Columbine Foundation, MI, see 1012
Combs Foundation, Julius V. & Alice G., MI, 349
Comerica Bank Corporate Giving Program, MI, 2167
Comerica Foundation, MI, 2168
Comloquoy Charitable Foundation, Robert & Sara S., NC, 350
Community Christian Ministries, MI, 351
Community Federal Credit Union Scholarship Fund, MI, see 352
Community Financial Scholarship Fund, MI, 352
Community Foundation Alliance of Calhoun County, MI, 2451
Community Foundation for Delta County, Michigan, Inc., MI, 2329
Community Foundation for Livingston County, MI, 2330
Community Foundation for Mason County, MI, 2331
Community Foundation for Muskegon County, MI, 2332
Community Foundation for Northeast Michigan, MI, 2333
Community Foundation for Oceana County, MI, 2334
Community Foundation for Southeastern Michigan, MI, 2335
Community Foundation of Greater Flint, MI, 2336
Community Foundation of Greater Rochester, MI, 2337
Community Foundation of Monroe County, MI, 2338
Community Foundation of St. Clair County, MI, 2339
Community Foundation of the Holland/Zeeland Area, The, MI, 2340
Community Foundation of the Upper Peninsula, MI, 2341
Community Foundation of Troy, MI, 2342

Community Home Health and Hospice, MI, 2732
Concert Competitions & Musical Development, Inc., MI, see 2626
Concrete Research & Education Foundation, MI, 2452
Connable Fund, H. P. and Genevieve, The, MI, 353
Conrad Charitable Foundation, MI, 2453
Conrad-Johnston Foundation, The, MI, 354
Consumers Energy Company Contributions Program, MI, 2169
Consumers Energy Foundation, MI, 2170
Consumers Power Company Contributions Program, MI, see 2169
Consumers Power Foundation, MI, see 2170
Conway Charitable Trust, Nadalynn, MI, 355
Conway Family Foundation, MI, 356
Cook Charitable Foundation, MI, 357
Cook Family Foundation, MI, 358
Cook Foundation, Brenton & Susan, FL, 359
Coon Foundation, Joanne Cross, MI, 360
Cooper Foundation, MI, 361
Coopersville Area Community Foundation, MI, 2343
Copley Charitable Foundation, Allan B., MI, 362
Copper Country United Way, MI, 2454
Corinthian Developments, Inc., MI, 363
Corr Family Foundation, FL, 364
Cortright Marshall Education Foundation, Max and Lucille, MI, 365
Cossin Trust, Evelyn, RI, 366
Cott Charitable Trust, Virginia A. Cott & Richard S., MI, 367
Courtney Family Foundation, William, MI, 368
Coville Photographic Art Foundation, The, MI, 2733
Coville-Triest Family Foundation, MI, 2455
Cowan Foundation Corporation, Lillian L. and Harry A., The, MA, see 369
Cowan Slavin Foundation, MA, 369
Coyne Foundation, MI, 370
Cracchiolo Foundation, Peter J. & Constance M., MI, 371
Cracchiolo Foundation, Raymond M. & Jane E., MI, 372
Cracchiolo Foundation, Thomas and Carol, MI, 373
Craig, Jr. Foundation, Wilson H., MI, 374
Crain Family Foundation, MI, 375
Crane Foundation, Matilda & Harold, IL, 376
Crawford County United Way, MI, 2456
Crawford Family Foundation, FL, 377
Creative Health Institute, MI, 2734
Cresswell Family Foundation, Inc., The, MI, 378
CRN Foundation, OH, 379
Cromarty Foundation, Inc., The, MI, 380
Cronin Foundation, MI, 381
Croskey Foundation, Inc., Carl and Lee, The, MI, 382
Crowther Foundation, The, MI, 383
Crystal Falls/Forest Park Area Community Fund, MI, 2344
CSO, Inc., MI, 384
Culver American Legion Scholarship Trust, William Alexander Fleet, MI, 385
Cummings Fund, The, MI, 386
Cunningham Scholarship Foundation, Louis, The, MI, 387
Currie Foundation, William G., MI, 388
Curtis Charitable Foundation, Robbie, MI, 389
Curtis Edmore Trust, Glenn D., WI, 390
Cutler Foundation, Cecelia B. and Kenneth B., The, NY, 391
Cutler Foundation, Robert and Elizabeth, The, MI, 392
Cutting Foundation, Allen B., The, MI, 393
Czado Catholic Education Fund, Mary, MI, 394

D. R. T. Fund, MI, see 632
D.U. Memorial Foundation, MI, 395
Dabney Foundation, Paul & Marjorie, MI, 396
Dagenais Foundation, Robert & Jeanine, MI, 397
DaimlerChrysler Corporation Contributions Program, MI, 2171
DaimlerChrysler Corporation Fund, MI, 2172
Dalton Foundation, Inc., Dorothy U., MI, 398
Dancey Memorial Foundation, Opal, MI, 399
Danieleski Scholarship Fund, Jack, MI, 400
Daoud Foundation, The, MI, 401
Darch Ministries, Inc., Carolyn, MI, 402
Dart Foundation, The, MI, 403
Dauch Family Foundation, Richard E. & Sandra J., MI, 2735
Davenport Foundation, M. E., MI, 404
Daverman Foundation, Robert J., IL, 405
Davidson Foundation, William, MI, 406
Davis Education Foundation, Edward, MI, 2457

Davis Family Reunion, Inc., Isaac and Dora, MI, 407
Davis Foundation, John R. & M. Margrite, The, MI, 408
Davis Trust, Jean M., MI, 409
Dawson Foundation, John and Jeanine, AZ, 410
Day Foundation, Joseph C., MI, 411
Daystar Foundation, MI, 412
de Irala Foundation, The, MI, 413
Dean Family Foundation, The, MI, 414
Dearborn Cable Communications Fund, MI, 2173
Debower Foundation Charitable Trust, MI, 415
DeBruyn Foundation, The, MI, 416
Deffenbaugh Foundation, George S. and Helen G., MI, 417
Defoe Family Foundation, MI, 418
Degroot Family Foundation, MI, 419
Deibel and Tim Allen Foundation, Laura, The, MI, 420
Dejard P. Foundation, Inc., The, MI, 421
DeKock Family Foundation, MI, 2736
DeKorne Family Foundation, MI, 422
Del Signore Foundation, Costantino, MI, 2458
Delano Foundation, Mignon Sherwood, The, MI, 423
DeLapa Family Foundation, MI, see 1630
Delphi Automotive Systems Corporation Contributions Program, MI, see 2174
Delphi Corporation Contributions Program, MI, 2174
Delphi Foundation, Inc., MI, 2175
Delta Dental Foundation, MI, 2459
Delta Dental Fund, MI, see 2459
Delta Foundation, IL, 424
Delta Theta Phi Metropolitan Detroit Alumni Senate Foundation, MI, 425
Demashkieh Foundation, The, MI, 426
Dennard Foundation, The, MI, 427
Denniston Family Foundation, The, IL, 428
DENSO International America, Inc. Corporate Giving Program, MI, 2176
DENSO North America Foundation, MI, 2177
Deradoorian Family Foundation, John O. Deradoorian & Margaret C., The, MI, 429
DeRoy Testamentary Foundation, MI, 430
DeSeranno Educational Foundation, Inc., MI, see 342
DeShano Community Foundation, MI, 2737
Detroit Armory Corporation, MI, 431
Detroit Chapter of the International Order of the King's Daughters & Sons, MI, 432
Detroit Christadelphian Bible Explorers, Inc., MI, 2738
Detroit Diesel Scholarship Foundation, Inc., MI, 2178
Detroit Edison Foundation, MI, see 2188
Detroit Foundation for Health Education, Metropolitan, MI, see 2681
Detroit Golf Club Caddie Scholarship Foundation, MI, 433
Detroit Industrial School, MI, 434
Detroit Lions Charities, MI, 2460
Detroit Lions, Inc. Corporate Giving Program, The, MI, 2179
Detroit Neurosurgical Foundation, MI, 2739
Detroit Pistons Basketball Company Contributions Program, MI, 2180
Detroit Red Wings, Inc. Corporate Giving Program, MI, 2181
Detroit Shock Corporate Giving Program, MI, 2182
Detroit Track and Field Old Timers, MI, 435
Detroit Workforce Development Board, MI, 2740
Detroit Youth Foundation, MI, 2461
Detwiler, Jr. Free Spirit Memorial Foundation, Inc., Kenneth B., MI, 2462
Devereaux Foundation, Richard C., The, MI, 436
DeVlieg Foundation, Charles, The, MI, see 437
DeVlieg Foundation, The, MI, 437
DeVos Foundation, Daniel and Pamella, MI, 438
DeVos Foundation, Dick & Betsy, MI, 439
DeVos Foundation, Douglas & Maria, MI, 440
DeVos Foundation, Richard and Helen, The, MI, 441
DeVries Charitable Foundation, James H. and Judith L., MI, 442
DeVries Family Foundation, Eileen and Brian G., MI, 443
DeVries Foundation, Milo & Abby, MI, 444
Dewey Educational Trust, Howard, MI, 445
DeWitt Families Conduit Foundation, MI, 446
DeWitt Family Foundation, Jack and Mary, MI, 448
DeWitt Family Foundation, Marvin G. and Jerene L., MI, 447
Dexter Memorial Foundation, Inc., Louis M., FL, 449
DHL Charitable Foundation, The, MI, see 450
DHL Private Charitable Foundation, The, MI, 450
Diamond Crystal Foundation, The, OH, see 486
Dickinson Area Community Foundation, MI, 2345

Dickinson County Area Community Foundation, MI, see 2345
Dickinson County War Veterans Scholarship Association, MI, 451
Dickinson Wright PLLC Corporate Giving Program, MI, 2183
DiClemente Foundation, Gino and Luciana, MI, 452
Diebel Charitable Trust, Lucile K., OH, 453
Diebolt Foundation, MI, 454
Diem Foundation, The, MI, 2741
Dinan Foundation, John D. & Jean E., MI, 2742
DiPonio Foundation, Angelo & Margaret, The, MI, 455
Disselkoen Foundation, Randy & Terri, MI, 456
Dixie Foundation, MI, 457
DJD Foundation, MI, 458
Doan Family Foundation, The, MI, 459
Doan Foundation, Herbert & Junia, The, MI, see 459
Doan Foundation, Herbert and Junia, The, MI, 460
Doctor Family Charitable Trust, Umakant S. and Shreedevi U., The, MI, 461
Doezema Charitable Trust, MI, 462
Dogwood Foundation, The, MI, 463
Dole Family Foundation, MI, 464
Doll-Loesel Foundation, MI, 465
Domino's Pizza Partners Foundation, MI, 2463
Domino's Pizza, Inc. Corporate Giving Program, MI, 2184
Donahey Foundation, Inc., Patricia A. and Richard M., MI, 466
Donlin Charitable Corporation, Mildred Mary, MI, 467
Door to Door Medical Supply Foundation, The, MI, 468
Doornink Foundation, The, MI, 469
Doran Foundation, The, MI, 470
Dorfman Foundation, Henry S. & Mala, MI, 471
Dorrell Farms Foundation, MI, 472
Dorris Charitable Trust, Albert, MI, 473
Dorris Trust, Albert W., MI, see 473
Doshi Family Foundation, MI, 474
Doud Scholarship Foundation, Howard R. and Margaret Bellows, MI, 475
Doud Scholarship Foundation, MI, see 475
Doulos Foundation, Inc., MI, 476
Dow Chemical Company Foundation, The, MI, 2185
Dow Corning Foundation, MI, 2186
Dow Creativity Foundation, Alden B. and Vada B., MI, 2743
Dow Foundation, Herbert H. and Barbara C., MI, 477
Dow Foundation, Herbert H. and Grace A., The, MI, 478
Dow Fund, Alden & Vada, MI, 479
Drake Quinn Family Foundation, The, MI, 480
Drew & Mike Charitable Private Foundation, MI, 481
Drew Family Foundation, MI, 482
Dryden Family Foundation, MI, 483
Dryer Family Foundation, MI, 484
DSL Foundation, MI, 485
DSLT Foundation, OH, 486
DTE Energy Company Contributions Program, MI, 2187
DTE Energy Foundation, MI, 2188
Dubois Scholarship Fund, Ruth, OH, 487
Duchene Foundation, Doris J. & Donald L., MI, 488
Duffey Foundation, Robert J., The, MI, 489
Duffy Foundation, The, MI, 490
Duffy Memorial Trust, Hubert and Marie, MI, 491
Dul Foundation, Inc., MI, 492
Dumesnil Trust, Evangeline L., OH, 493
Dunagan Family Foundation, CO, 494
Dunn-Mason Foundation, The, MI, 495
Dunning Foundation, Margaret, MI, 496
Dunnings Foundation, Inc., MI, 497
Dura Automotive Systems, Inc. Charitable Foundation, MI, 2189
Duzyj Charitable Foundation, MI, 498
Dyer-Ives Foundation, MI, 499
Dykstra Charitable Foundation, Robert T. and Marthene Vandyke, MI, 500
Dykstra Foundation, MI, 501

E-B Foundation, MI, 502
E.D.P. Foundation, MI, 503
Eagle Family Foundation, The, CA, 504
Eagle Foundation, MI, 505
Earhart Foundation, MI, 506
Earle Charitable Trust, Eva, MI, 507
Eastpointe Community Chest/Networking Forum, MI, 2464
Eaton County Community Fund, The, MI, 2346
Eaton County United Way, MI, 2465

Eddy Family Memorial Fund, C. K., MI, 508
Edelweiss Foundation, MI, 509
Edison Family Foundation, John and Penny, MI, 510
Edrington Charitable Foundation, Ruth, MI, 511
Edwards Foundation, Eddie K. & Mary D., MI, 512
Edwards Foundation, William J. and Julia M., MI, 513
Effendi Foundation, The, MI, 514
Egger Private Foundation, Inc., The, MI, 515
Ehmer Foundation, Arnulf F., MI, 516
Eldean Family Foundation, Pat & Herb, MI, 517
Elder Foundation, IN, 2190
Eliason Foundation, MI, 2191
Elkes Foundation, The, NY, 2744
Ellens Foundation, Dennis & Eileen, MI, see 940
Ellias Scholarship Foundation, Phillip G., MI, 518
Elson Family Charitable Trust, The, MI, 519
Elsona Foster Care, Inc., MI, 2745
Elzinga Foundation, Alvin and Marty, MI, 520
Emergency Medicine Education and Research Foundation, MI, 521
Emerman Foundation, Inc., David & Edith, MI, 522
En Gedi Foundation, MI, 523
Enberg Family Charitable Foundation, CA, 524
Engle Foundation, The, MI, 2192
Eppert Family Foundation, The, MI, 2746
Epstein Family Charitable Foundation, Marjory and Donald, MI, 525
Erb Foundation, MI, 526
Erlich Foundation, Joseph & Linda, The, MI, 527
Ervin Foundation, J. F., MI, 528
Eschbach Family Foundation, Rudolf & Ruth, The, MI, 529
Esperance Family Foundation, The, DE, 530
Esser Charitable Trust, Eliesabeth, MI, 531
Estes Foundation, Elliott M. & Constance L., AZ, 532
Evenson Foundation, Charles Robert, MI, 533
Ever Young and Green Foundation Trust, MI, 534
Evereg-Fenesse Mesrobian-Roupinian Educational Society, Inc., MI, 535
Evergreene Foundation, MI, 2747
Ewald Foundation, H. T., MI, 536
Excel Industries, Inc. Charitable Foundation, MI, see 2189
Eyster Charitable Family Foundation, MI, 537

F.I.R.E., MI, see 632
Fabiano Foundation, MI, 2193
Fabri-Kal Foundation, MI, 2194
Fahd Foundation, MI, 2748
Faigle Charitable Foundation, Ida M., MI, 538
Falk Family Foundation, The, MI, 539
Family Christian Stores Foundation, MI, 540
Farago Foundation Trust, Paul, The, MI, 541
Farber Family Foundation, William and Audrey, MI, 542
Farbman Family Foundation, The, MI, 543
Farbman Foundation, The, MI, see 543
Farbman Group Charitable Foundation, MI, 2195
Farhan Foundation, The, MI, 544
Farley Memorial Foundation, Marcus Martin Farley and Mable Stone, MI, 545
Farmer Jack Corporate Giving Program, MI, 2196
Farmington Hills Community Foundation for Children, Youth and Families, MI, see 2347
Farmington Hills/Farmington Community Foundation, MI, 2347
Farr Foundation, Inc., WV, 2197
Farrehi Family Foundation, Inc., MI, 546
Farver Foundation, The, MI, 547
Farwell Foundation, Drusilla, MI, 548
Fausell Charitable Trust, Gaynel L., MI, 549
Faust Charitable Foundation, Charles and Audrey, The, MI, 550
Favor Educational Trust, Charles E., MI, 551
Fay Foundation, Charles, The, MI, 552
Feather Foundation, MI, 553
Febbo Family Foundation, Albert J. and Helen E., MI, 554
Federal Screw Works Foundation, Inc., MI, 2198
Federov Foundation, Sergei, The, MI, 555
Fedewa Foundation, C. Scott, MI, 556
Fehsenfeld Charitable Foundation, Frank B. and Virginia V., WA, 557
Felpausch Foundation, MI, 2199
Fenkell Foundation, Sybil and Morris, MI, 558
Ferber Foundation, Miriam & Fred, The, MI, 560
Ferber Foundation, Ronda and Ron, The, MI, 559

Fernstrum Scholarship Foundation Trust, Robert W. & Caroline A., WI, 561
Ferrantino Charitable Foundation, Inc., MI, 562
Ferries Family Foundation, MI, 563
Fetzer Foundation, Inc., John E., MI, see 2749
Fetzer Institute, Inc., John E., MI, 2749
Fetzer Memorial Trust Fund, John E., MI, 564
Feuer Foundation, Seymour S. & Diana M., MI, 565
Fibre Converters Foundation, Inc., MI, 2200
Field Foundation, Malcolm & Lois, The, MI, 566
Fieldman Sims Foundation, MI, 567
Fieler Family Foundation, MI, 2750
Fielstra Foundation, MI, see 2729
Fike Family Foundation, MI, 568
Filer Board, Inc., Carrie, MI, 2751
Fill Foundation, Dr. Leon, MI, 569
Fink Foundation, George R. and Elise M., MI, 570
Finkel Family Foundation, MI, 571
Finkelstein Family Charitable Foundation, Morton M., MI, 572
Firestone, Jr. No. 2 Fund B, Harvey S., WI, 573
Firestone, Jr. No. 2 Fund C, Harvey S., WI, 574
First Federal Community Foundation, MI, 2201
First Fruits Foundation, MI, 575
Fischer Family Fund, MI, 2466
Fish Foundation, MI, 576
Fisher Foundation, Inc., Max M. and Marjorie S., MI, 577
Fisher Support Foundation, Max M. & Marjorie S., MI, 2467
Fisher Trust, Francenia, FL, 578
Fisher-Insley Foundation, The, MI, 579
Fishman Charitable Foundation, David and Deena, MI, 580
Fitch Foundation, E. Root, MI, 2752
Fitzgibbon Dermidoff Foundation, MI, 581
Fleischman Foundation, Edward I., MI, 582
Flemington Scholarship Trust, Nora, MI, 583
Fletcher Foundation, Edward J., The, MI, 584
Flinn Family Foundation, Ethel and James, MI, see 585
Flinn Foundation, Ethel and James, MI, 585
Flint Foundation, Mary G. & Robert H., MI, 586
Floriculture Industry Research and Scholarship Trust, MI, 2468
Foley & M. H. Frischkorn Nature Conservancy Fund I, L. H., MI, 2469
Foley & M. H. Frischkorn Wildlife & Conservation Fund II, L. H., MI, 2470
Folkert Family Foundation, MI, 587
Foran Charitable Trust, Jeff, MI, 588
Ford Foundation, Gerald R., MI, 2471
Ford Foundation, Geraldine C. and Emory M., MI, 589
Ford Foundation, The, NY, 590
Ford Foundation, William & Lisa, MI, 591
Ford Fund, Benson and Edith, MI, 592
Ford Fund, Eleanor and Edsel, MI, 593
Ford Fund, Walter and Josephine, MI, 594
Ford Fund, William and Martha, MI, 595
Ford House, Edsel & Eleanor, MI, 2753
Ford II Fund, Edsel B., MI, 596
Ford II Fund, Henry, The, MI, 597
Ford Motor Company Contributions Program, MI, 2202
Ford Motor Company Fund, MI, 2203
Forevergreen Foundation, MI, 598
Foss Family Foundation, MI, 599
Foster Family Foundation, MI, 600, 601
Foster Foundation, MI, 602
Foster Welfare Foundation, MI, see 602
Foundation for Birmingham Senior Residents, MI, 603
Foundation for Educational Advancement, The, MI, 604
Foundation for Mentally Ill Children, Inc., MI, 2472
Foundation for Saline Area Schools, MI, 2473
Foundation for the Glory of God, MI, 605
Foundation for Washington & Lee University, MI, 606
Foundation of Michigan Association of Physicians of Indian Origin, MI, 2474
Four County Community Foundation, MI, 2348
Four County Foundation, MI, see 2348
Fox Charitable Foundation, Henry A. Fox, Jr. and Kathleen O'Brien, MI, 607
Fox Charitable Foundation, Richard E., CO, 608
Frank Charitable Foundation, William Henry and Ruth Lambert, The, MI, see 1533
Frank Memorial Corporation, Leon & Rena, WI, 609
Frank Trust, William C., FL, 610
Frankel Family Foundation, Stanley and Judith, MI, 611

Frankel Foundation for Art, Maxine and Stuart, MI, 2754
Frankel Foundation, Barbara, The, MI, 614
Frankel Foundation, Maxine and Stuart, MI, 612
Frankel Foundation, Samuel & Jean, MI, 613
Frankel Jewish Heritage Foundation, Samuel and Jean, The, MI, 615
Frankel Support Foundation, Samuel and Jean, MI, 2475
Frankenmuth Area Community Foundation, Greater, MI, 2349
Fraser Area Educational Foundation, MI, 2476
Frazier Fund, Inc., MI, 616
Fredericks Foundation, Marshall M., MI, 617
Free Press Charities, Inc., MI, 2477
Freedom Educational Foundation, MI, 618
Freeman Foundation, The, MI, 619
Freiheit Foundation, VA, 620
Fremont Area Community Foundation, MI, 2350
Fremont Area Foundation, The, MI, see 2350
Frey Foundation, MI, 621
Friedman Family Foundation, Inc., The, MI, 622
Friedman Foundation, Robert G., FL, 623
Friedman Foundation, Steven Paul, The, MI, 624
Friend Foundation, MI, 625
Friends of Spring Lake District Library, MI, 626
Friends of the Warner Baird Library, MI, see 626
Friends of Yerevan State University, MI, 627
Frisch Family Foundation, Kurt C. & Sally S., The, MI, 628
Fromm Family Foundation, David & Barbara, MI, 629
Fruman Foundation, Albert & Dorothy, MI, 630
Fuller Charitable Trust, Golden & Lillian M., MI, 631
Fund for Indigenous Rights and the Environment, MI, 632
Futureation Foundation, MI, 2204

Gabooney Foundation, MI, 633
Gagliardi Foundation, Carmela, MI, 634
Galencher Nagy Foundation, MI, 635
Galesburg-Augusta Community Foundation, MI, see 2755
Galesburg-Augusta Education Foundation, MI, 2755
Gallant Foundation, Jon A., MI, 636
Gallo Irrevocable Trust, Frederick, MI, 637
Gandhi Foundation, The, MI, 638
Ganton Auto Museum Foundation, Inc., Lloyd, MI, 2756
Gantos Charitable Foundation, Richard L. and Claire A., NM, 639
Gantos Family Foundation, L. Douglas, MI, 640
Garber Family Foundation, Harold and Ruth, MI, 2757
Gardner Charitable Enterprises, MI, 641
Garland-Schut Foundation, MI, 642
Garrison Fund f/b/o University of Michigan, William Albright, FL, 643
Garrison Memorial Fund, William Albright, FL, see 643
Gary Family Foundation, The, MI, 644
Gary Sisters Foundation, MI, 645
Gast Charitable Foundation, Warren E. & D. Lou, MI, 646
Gast Foundation, MI, 647
Gates Foundation, The, MI, 648
Gau Foundation, Paul E., MI, 649
Gavin Family Foundation, IL, 650
Gayar Foundation, The, MI, 651
Geenen Family Foundation, MI, 652
Geenen Foundation, Richard and Sylvia, MI, 653
Geetha and Govindaraj Foundation, The, MI, 654
Gegax Family Foundation, MI, 655
Geist Foundation of Michigan, The, MI, 656
Gelman Educational Foundation, MI, 657
General Motors Cancer Research Foundation, Inc., MI, 2205
General Motors Foundation, Inc., MI, 2206
General Sports Foundation, MI, 658
Generation IV Charitable Trust, MI, 659
Generations Foundation, MI, 2207
Genesee Area Focus Fund, Inc., MI, 2478
Genesis Program, Inc., MI, 2758
George Fund, MI, 660
Gerber Companies Foundation, The, MI, see 661
Gerber Foundation, The, MI, 661
Gerberding/Fackler Family Foundation, Inc., The, MI, 662
Gershenson Family Foundation, Bruce and Suzy, The, MI, 663
Gershenson Family Foundation, Dennis and Nancy, The, MI, 664
Gershenson Family Foundation, Joel and Linda, The, MI, 665
Gershenson Family Foundation, Richard and Sherry, The, MI, 666

Gershenson Foundation, Charles H., MI, 667
Gerstacker Foundation, Rollin M., The, MI, 668
Gertz Foundation, Herman & Irene, MI, 669
Geyer Charitable Foundation, Inc., Wilmar, MI, 670
Ghitalla Foundation, MI, 671
Gibbs Charitable Trust, Ruby L., MI, 672
Gibson Foundation, Kirk, MI, 673
Giddey Charitable Fund, Irma, The, WI, 674
Giddey Trust, Doris J., MI, 675
Giddings & Lewis Foundation, Inc., WI, 2208
Gieseking Perpetual Trust, Henry, MO, 676
Giesy Foundation, John P. & Susan E., MI, 677
GII Charities, MI, 678
Gilbert Memorial Scholarship Fund, Muriel, OH, 679
Gilhooly & Rowan Gilhooly Sanford Educational Foundation, Karen L., MI, 680
Gilles Scholarship Trust, Herbert & Florence, MI, 681
Gilmore Endowment for the Arts, Genevieve U., MI, 2479
Gilmore Foundation, Genevieve and Donald, MI, 2759
Gilmore Foundation, Irving S., MI, 683
Gilmore Foundation, MI, 682
Gilmore International Keyboard Festival, Irving S., MI, 2480
Gilmore, Jr. Foundation, Jim, MI, 684
Gilmour Fund, The, MI, 2481
Ginsberg Foundation, Aaron & Anne, The, MI, 685
Gits Foundation, Norbert and Paula, NY, 686
Glancy Foundation, Inc., The, MI, 687
Glassen Memorial Foundation, Hal & Jean, MI, 688
GLCYD, see 2490
Gleaner Life Insurance Society Scholarship Foundation, MI, 2760
Glen Arbor Art Association, MI, 2482
Glenn Family Foundation, MI, 689
Gless Foundation, Joseph, WI, 690
Glick Charitable Foundation, Robert and Rose, The, MI, 691
Glick Foundation, Alvin L., The, MI, 692
Glick Memorial & Charitable Trust, Louis, MI, 693
GM Corporate Giving Program, MI, 2209
GM Foundation, MI, see 2206
Goad Foundation, Louis C., The, MI, see 694
Goad Foundation, The, MI, 694
God's Gift Foundation, MI, 695
Gofrank Foundation, Frank L. & Helen, MI, 696
Gogebic Range United Way, MI, 2483
Goggins Family Foundation, John & Sally, MI, 697
Goldman Foundation, Harry & Bertha A., MI, 698
Goldman Foundation, Irving & Doris Lee, MI, 699
Goldman Foundation, Marvin H. & Nola, MI, 700
Goldstein Family Foundation, Leo and Betty, MI, 2761
Goldstein Foundation, Sydney, MN, 701
Good News! Foundation, MI, 702
Good Part Foundation, The, MI, 703
Good Trust, Mary V., MI, 704
Goodale Fund, The, MI, 705
Goodnow/Prus Foundation, MI, 706
Goodrich College Education Fund, David, MI, 707
Goodrich Foundation, Inc., The, NY, 708
Googasian Family Foundation, The, MI, 709
Gordon Christian Foundation, MI, 710
Gordon Christian Trust, MI, 2484
Gordon Family Christian Trust, Paul B. and Dorothy D., MI, 2485
Gordon Family Foundation, Harold and Marion, The, MI, 711
Gordon Family Foundation, The, MI, see 711
Gordon Food Service, Inc. Corporate Giving Program, MI, 2210
Gordon Foundation, Frank & Doris, The, MI, 712
Gordon Foundation, Seymour & Marilynn, The, MI, 713
Gordy Foundation, Inc., MI, 714
Gornick Fund, The, MI, 715
Gorski Trust, Joseph, OH, 716
Gospel Truths Ministries, MI, see 2779
Goss Educational Testamentary Trust, Beatrice I., MI, 717
Grace Episcopal Youth Ministry Trust, MO, 2486
Graham Educational Fund, Inc., Meda, MI, 718
Grand Haven Area Community Foundation, Inc., MI, 2351
Grand Rapids Bar Foundation, MI, see 956
Grand Rapids Christian Foundation, MI, 719
Grand Rapids Community Foundation, MI, 2352
Grand Rapids E.C. Foundation, Inc., MI, 2487
Grand Rapids Elks Philanthropy Fund, MI, 720
Grand Rapids Foundation, The, MI, see 2352

Hospitalers Committee of Detroit Commandery No. 1
 Knights Templar, MI, 867
Hougen Foundation, MI, 868
House Family Foundation, CA, 869
House Family Foundation, Dave, CA, see 869
Hovarter Scholarship Fund Trust, Leon & Audrey, MI, 870
Howard City Action Center for Senior Citizens, MI, 871
Howard Foundation, John C. and Mary Jane, MI, 872
Howe Scholarship Trust, Marjorie W. Howe & Howard C., MI,
 873
HP Foundation, MI, 874
Hubbard Memorial Museum Foundation, MI, 2778
Huckle Family Fund, MI, 2515
Hudson Foundation, Inc., Robert P. & Ella B., MI, 875
Hudson-Webber Foundation, MI, 876
Hudsonville Community Fund, MI, see 2393
Huebner Foundation, Julius and Cynthia, MI, 877
Huizenga Foundation, IL, 878
Hull Memorial Foundation, George M., MI, 879
Humane Society of Macomb Foundation, Inc., MI, 880
Humbert Scholarship Trust, Paul A., MI, 881
Humphrey Foundation, Inc., Glenn E. & Malvina S., MI, see
 882
Humphrey-Admore Foundation, Inc., MI, 882
Hunter Charitable Trust, NY, 883
Hunter Foundation, Edward and Irma, MI, 884
Hunting Foundation, MI, 885
Huron County Community Foundation, MI, 2357
Hurst Foundation, Dick and Mary Ann, The, MI, 887
Hurst Foundation, The, MI, 886
Huss Memorial Fund, Theodore Huss, Sr. and Elsie Endert,
 MI, 888
Hutchcroft Perpetual Charitable Trust, IL, 889
Hutchings Fund Irrevocable Charitable Trust, Ruahmah J.,
 MI, 890

I Have a Dream Foundation - Port Huron, MI, 891
Iacobelli Family Foundation, MI, 892
ICN Foundation, MI, 893
Idema Foundation, Bill and Bea, MI, 894
IDM Foundation, MI, 895
Ikhlas Foundation, The, MI, 896
Ilitch Charities for Children, Inc., MI, 2516
Imerman Foundation, John & Ella, MI, 897
Imerman Memorial Foundation, Stanley, MI, 898
Imoberstag Charitable Foundation, Frances B., MI, 899
In His Love Foundation, MI, 900
India Foundation, MI, 901
Ingraham Foundation, Barton J. & Gail G., The, MI, 902
Inman Family Foundation, The, MI, 903
Institute for Religious Research, MI, 2779
Inter City Oil Foundation, MN, 904
International Centre for Healing and the Law, MI, 2780
International Society of Barristers Foundation, MI, 905
International Wildlife Preservation Society, MI, 2781
Investment Education Institute, MI, 2782
Ionia County Community Foundation, MI, 2358
Iosco County Community Foundation, MI, 2359
Irish American Information Service, MI, 906
Ironwood Area Scholarship Foundation, MI, 2517
Irwin Foundation, The, MI, 907
Isaac 880130 Foundation, MI, 908
Isabel Foundation, The, MI, 909
Isabella Bank and Trust Foundation, MI, 2223
Isabella Foundation, Inc., MI, 910
Isakow Foundation, MI, 911
Ishpeming Area Community Fund, Greater, MI, 2360
Issa Foundation, MI, 2224
Italian American Delegates, Inc., MI, 2518
Iverson Foundation, Keith A., MI, 912
Ivkov Foundation, John, MI, 913

J.C. Charitable Trust Fund, CA, 914
Jackson Audubon Society, Inc., MI, 915
Jackson Community Foundation, The, MI, see 2361
Jackson County Community Foundation, The, MI, 2361
Jackson Foundation, Corwill and Margie, MI, 916
Jackson Literary & Art Association, MI, 2783
Jackson National Life Insurance Company Contributions
 Program, MI, 2225
Jacob Family Foundation Corporation, The, MI, 917
Jaffe Charitable Trust f/b/o Colon High School, MI, see 918

Jaffe Scholarship Fund f/b/o Colon High School, Fredrica,
 Neva & Abraham, MI, 918
Jampel Family Foundation, The, MI, 919
Janes Family Foundation, The, MI, 920
Jas Foundation, The, MI, 921
Jasam Foundation Fund B, AZ, 922
Javitch Charitable Foundation, Karen Sokolof, MI, 923
Jaya Charitable Foundation, MI, 924
JCM Foundation, The, VA, 925
JCT Foundation, MI, 926
Jeffers Memorial Education Fund, Michael, MI, 927
Jeffers Memorial Fund, John Michael, MI, 928
Jennings Memorial Foundation, MI, 929
Jensen Foundation, MI, 930
Jentes Family Foundation, The, IL, 931
Jerome Lecture Fund, Thomas S., MI, 2519
Jewish Federation of Grand Rapids, MI, 2520
Jewish Federation of Metropolitan Detroit, MI, 2521
Jewish Fund, The, MI, 2522
Jewish Women's Foundation of Metropolitan Detroit, MI,
 2523
JKO Foundation Charitable Trust, The, WI, 932
Jobst Foundation, Conrad & Caroline, OH, 933
Johns Family Foundation, Donald L., MI, 934
Johnson Corporation Scholarship Foundation, MI, 2226
Johnson Family Foundation, Wilburn L. & Barbara J., MI, 935
Johnson Foundation, Lloyd and Mabel, The, MI, 936
Johnson Foundation, Paul A., MI, 937
Johnson Foundation, Paul C., MI, 2524
Johnson Foundation, Paul T. and Frances B., The, MI, 938
Johnson Foundation, The, MI, 939
Joie de Vivre Foundation, MI, 940
Jonathan & David Foundation, MI, 941
Jonathan Foundation, The, MI, 942
Jondy Foundation, The, MI, 943
Jones Family Foundation, Calvin and Deborah A., MI, 944
Jones Foundation, Mary Bartush, MI, 946
Jones Foundation, MI, 945
Jones Foundation, Sherrie L., MI, 947
Joseph Foundation, MI, 948
Joslin Foundation, Inc., The, MI, 949
Jospey Foundation, Marjorie and Maxwell, MI, 950
Joy Foundation, MI, 951
JPMorgan Chase Philanthropy - Michigan, MI, 2227
JSJ Foundation, MI, 2228
Jubilee Foundation, The, OH, 2229
Juhl Scholarship Fund, George W. & Sadie Marie, MI, 952
Julius Family Foundation, The, MI, 953
June 8th Foundation, Inc., MI, 2784
Junior League of Lansing, Michigan, MI, 2525
Jurries Family Foundation, Jim and Ginger, MI, 954
Jury Foundation, The, MI, 955
Justice Foundation of West Michigan, MI, 956

Kaczperski Foundation, Thomas E., MI, 957
Kadry Foundation, The, MI, 2785
Kahan Charitable Foundation, Leo A. Kahan and Emelie O.,
 MI, 958
Kahn Associated Architects & Engineers Foundation, Albert,
 MI, 2230
Kahn Family Foundation, Mark & Gayle, The, MI, 959
Kahn Family Foundation, Mark S., The, MI, see 959
Kahn Family Foundation, MI, see 960
Kahn Foundation, D. Dan and Betty, The, MI, 960
Kahn Sovel Mertz Fund, MI, 961
Kaiser Family Charitable Trust, MI, 2786
Kakarala Foundation, MI, 962
Kalamazoo Aviation History Museum, The, MI, 2787
Kalamazoo Community Foundation, MI, 2362
Kalamazoo Foundation, MI, see 2362
Kalamazoo Public Education Foundation, MI, 2526
Kalamazoo Regional Catholic Schools Foundation, MI, 2527
Kalamazoo Rotary Club Charities, MI, 2528
Kalamazoo United Way, Greater, MI, 2529
Kaleidoscope Foundation, MI, 963
Kalleward-Bergerson Charitable Foundation, Inc., MI, 2231
Kanaan Family Foundation, MI, 964
Kane Foundation, Inc., Beverly A., MI, see 476
Kanitz Scholarship Memorial Fund, Louis J. & Golda I., CA,
 965
Kantzler Foundation, The, MI, 966
Kanzler Foundation, Ernest and Rosemarie, MI, 967
Kashlan Foundation, The, MI, 968

Kasle Foundation, The, MI, 2232
Katz Foundation, Inc., Samuel P. & Martha L., MI, 970
Katz Foundation, Joseph & Ann, The, MI, 969
Katzman Foundation, Barney, MI, 972
Katzman Foundation, Paul & Lois, The, MI, 971
Katzman Foundation, Sidney and Robert, MI, 973
Katzman Foundation, Sidney, MI, see 973
Kaufman Endowment Fund, Louis G., MI, 974
Kaufman Foundation, Alan Jay & Sue, MI, 976
Kaufman Foundation, MI, 975
Kaufman Memorial Trust, Chaim, Fanny, Louis, Benjamin
 and Anne Florence, The, MI, 977
Kay Charitable Trust, Helen L., MI, 978
Kay Foundation, Helen L., MI, see 978
Kay Scholarship Foundation, Ryan Michael, MI, 979
Kebok Foundation, MI, 980
Kee Foundation, MI, 981
Keeler Foundation, The, MI, 982
Keeler Fund, Miner S. & Mary Ann, The, MI, see 982
Keeney Trust, Hattie Hannah, WI, 983
Keep Coming Back, MI, 2788
Kegel Family Foundation, FL, 984
Keith Charitable Trust, Lenna M., IL, 985
Keller Foundation, MI, 986
Kellogg Company 25-Year Employees Fund, Inc., MI, 2233
Kellogg Company Contributions Program, MI, 2234
Kellogg Foundation, Inc., Edward and June, MI, 987
Kellogg Foundation, W. K., MI, 988
Kellogg's Corporate Citizenship Fund, MI, 2235
Kelly Charitable Trust, C. L., MI, 989
Kelly Family Foundation, Joseph D. and Suzanne G., The, MI,
 990
Kelly Foundation, Charles, MI, 992
Kelly Foundation, Larry and Doris, The, MI, 991
Kelly Services, Inc. Foundation, The, MI, 2236
Kelter Foundation, Inc., MI, 993
Kemler Foundation, W. J. and Lillian, MI, 994
Kemp, Klein, Umphrey & Endelman Foundation, MI, see 995
Kemp, Klein, Umphrey, Endelman & May Foundation, MI,
 995
Kennedy Family Foundation, John C. & Nancy G., MI, 996
Kensington Academy Foundation, Inc., MI, 2530
Kent Charitable Trust, MI, 997
Kent Family Charitable Foundation, FL, 998
Kent Foundation, Floyd, MI, 1000
Kent Foundation, The, MI, 999
Kent Medical Foundation, MI, 1001
Kentwood Foundation, MI, 1002
Keough Family Foundation, MI, 1003
Kerkstra Family Charitable Foundation, MI, 1004
Kessel Foundation, Albert F., MI, 2789
Keweenaw Community Foundation, MI, 2363
Key-Hope Foundation, MI, 1005
Khilanani Foundation, Prem & Urmilla, The, MI, 1006
Kiamba Medical Foundation, Inc., MI, 2790
Kid Rock Foundation, MI, 1007
KidRelief Foundation, MI, 1008
Kierstead Foundation, MI, 1009
Kindred Spirit, MI, 1010
Kings Point Richmond Foundation, Inc., MI, see 1025
Kinney Foundation, Inc., Ronald F., MI, 1011
KINSHIP Foundation, MI, 1012
Kirt Foundation, The, MI, 1013
Kiwanis Club of Shorewood Foundation, MI, 1014
Kiwanis Foundation of Harbor Springs, MI, 2531
Kiwanis of Michigan Foundation, MI, 1015
Kleiman Family Foundation, Harvey and Aileen, The, MI,
 1016
Kling Scholarship Fund, Verne O. & Dorothy M., MI, 1017
Klingenmeyer Foundation, Ralph and Maggie, The, MI, see
 1111
Klobucar and Joseph D. Klobucher Foundation, John E., MI,
 1018
Klopcic Family Foundation, MI, 1019
KMD Foundation, FL, 1020
Knabusch Charitable Trust No. 1, Edward M. and Henrietta
 M., MI, 1021
Knabusch Charitable Trust No. 2, Edward M. and Henrietta
 M., MI, 1022
Knabusch Scholarship Foundation, Edward M. and Henrietta
 M., MI, 1023
Kniff Family Foundation, Inc., Stewart and Lenore, MI, 1024

Pivnick Family Foundation, MI, 1485
PJM Charitable Foundation, Inc., CT, 1486
Plante & Moran, PLLC Corporate Giving Program, MI, 2268
Platinum Charitable Foundation, MI, 1487
Pleasant Lake Park, Inc., MI, see 159
Plumbers and Pipefitters Local No. 333 Scholarship Plan, MI, 2596
Plym Foundation, MI, 1488
Plymouth Christian Schools Foundation, MI, 2597
Plymouth Community United Way, MI, 2598
Plymouth Rotary Foundation, Inc., MI, 2599
Polakovic Charitable Trust, John, MI, 1489
Polan Foundation, Jennifer Gordon, MI, 1490
Polasky Family Foundation, MI, 1491
Polk & Co. Contributions Program, R. L., MI, 2269
Polk Foundation, Ralph L. and Winifred E., MI, 1492
Pollack Educational Trust, Sara, MI, 1493
Ponting Foundation, Herbert and Elsa, MI, 1494
Porter Family Foundation, The, MI, 1495
Porter Foundation, MI, 1496
Portland Community Fund Association, MI, 2600
Posey Family Foundation, TX, 1497
Post Family Foundation, John W. Post, Jr. and Arden R., MI, 1498
Postema Family Foundation, Richard & Ruth, MI, 1499
Potiker Support Foundation, Hughes L. and Sheila M., MI, 2601
Potts Scholarship Trust, Norine E., OH, 1500
Powell Foundation, Inc., Bernard F. & Mary Ann, FL, 1501
Power Foundation, The, MI, 1502
Powers Family Foundation, The, MI, 1503
Preede Foundation, The, MI, 1504
Prein Foundation, Ed & June, MI, 1505
Prentis Family Foundation, Inc., Meyer and Anna, The, MI, 1506
Prentis Family Support Foundation, MI, 2602
Prentis-Morris Family Support Foundation, MI, see 2602
Preston Foundation, The, MI, 1507
Prevo Foundation, Dan R. and Pamela M., MI, 1508
Pribil Memorial Trust, Maxwell, MI, 1509
Pribil Trust f/b/o Hoyt Library, Maxwell, MI, 1510
Pribil Trust f/b/o Saginaw Symphony, Maxwell, MI, 1511
Price Foundation, Inc., Robert E., The, MI, 1512
Prince Foundation, Edgar and Elsa, MI, 1513
Prince Foundation, MI, see 1513
Prince Memorial Scholarship Fund, Leslie, MI, 1514
Project Freedom, MI, 2836
ProQuest Company Contributions Program, MI, 2270
Providence Foundation, MI, 1515
Pryor Foundation, The, PA, 1516
Public Benefit Corporation, MI, see 2436
Pulte Corporation Contributions Program, MI, see 2271
Pulte Homes, Inc. Corporate Giving Program, MI, 2271
Purtan Family Ovarian Cancer Research Foundation, MI, 2603
Puschelberg Foundation, George, MI, 1517
Pyle Foundation, The, MI, 1518

Qazi Foundation, The, MI, 1519
Quiachon, M.D. Foundation, Mary Anne S. Quiachon Memorial & Ernesto, MI, 1520
Quicksilver Resources Inc. Corporate Giving Program, TX, 2272

Rabahy Foundation, The, MI, 1521
Rachor Family Foundation, Ltd., MI, 1522
Rachor Professional School Scholarship Fund, Ltd., Michael Garry, MI, see 1522
Rainbow Foundation, MI, 1523
Rais Charitable Trust Foundation, Walter J. and Natalie M., MI, 1524
Rajput-Dasgupta Family Charitable Foundation, MI, 1525
Ram Foundation, Ltd., MI, 1526
Ramser-Morgan Foundation, MI, 1527
Ran Family Foundation, MI, 1528
Ranger Foundation, MI, 1529
Rankauf Foundation, The, MI, 1530
Ransom Fidelity Company, MI, see 1398
Rapinchuk Charitable Foundation, Inc., Grace, MI, 1531
Ratner Foundation, Milton M., MI, 1532
Rattner and the Ann F. and Norman D. Katz Charitable Foundation, Ruth F., The, MI, 1533
Raval Education Foundation, Inc., The, MI, 1534

Ravitz Foundation, The, MI, 1535
Rawson Foundation, Inc., MI, 1536
Rayes Foundation, The, MI, 1537
Razzak Foundation, The, MI, 1538
RBS Foundation, MI, 1539
Rebuilding Together - Saginaw, MI, 2604
Recreational Boating Industries Educational Foundation, MI, 1540
Redeemer U.S. Foundation, MI, 2837
Redies Foundation, Inc., Edward F., MI, 2273
Redlum Foundation, The, MI, 2274
Redman Foundation, The, MI, 2838
Reem Foundation, The, MI, 1541
Reese Family Foundation, David E., AZ, 1542
Refke Trust, Wallace O., OH, 1543
Regal Dean Family Foundation, The, IL, 1544
Reid Charitable Trust, C. & A., MI, 1545
Reid Educational Trust, M. C. & A. A., MI, 1546
Reid Family Charitable Foundation, Joseph D., The, MI, 1547
Reid Family Foundation, The, MI, 2839
Reid Trust, Carrie M. & Alex A., MI, see 1545
Rennie Scholarship Trust, Florence M., MI, 1548
Resnal Foundation, MI, 1549
Reuter Foundation, Loraine & Melinese, MI, 1550
Reuther Memorial Fund, Walter and May, MI, 2605
Reynolds Foundation, Phyllis and Max, MI, 1551
Rhee Foundation, Chi Sun, MI, 1552
Richardson Trust, James B., MI, 1553
Richter Foundation, Inc., R. Gene and Nancy D., MI, 1554
Rickert Family Foundation, MI, 1555
Ridge Adrian College Foundation, NE, 2606
Riekse Foundation, Nan Jean, The, MI, 1556
Riley Foundation, Philip and Joane, MI, 1557
Riley Foundation, The, MI, 1558
Riley Trust for Watch Tower Bible and Tract Society, H. M., MI, 2607
Rislov Foundation, Sigurd & Jarmila, MI, 1559
River City Food Company Foundation, MI, 2275
River City Foundation, MI, 1560
RJK Foundation, MI, 1561
RNR Foundation, Inc., MI, 1562
Roan Universal Foundation, MI, 1563
Robbins Foundation, J. Marshall, The, MI, 1564
Robbins Memorial Scholarship Fund, Frank E., RI, 1565
Robell Foundation, MI, 1566
Robey Charitable Trust, Edmund W., The, FL, see 2840
Robey Charitable Trust, The, FL, 2840
Robideau Foundation, Inc., The, MI, 1567
Robinson Family Foundation, MI, 1568
Robinson Foundation, Hattie, Anna and Harley, MI, 1569
Robison Foundation, Harold & Carolyn, MI, 1570
Roche Foundation, James M. and Louise C., MI, 1571
Rochester Area Community Foundation, Greater, MI, see 2337
Rock Foundation, MI, 1572
Rockwell Trust, George, MI, 1573
Rodney Fund, The, MI, 1574
Roethke Scholarship Fund, Otto & Helen, MI, 1575
Rogers Charitable Foundation, Wendell & Doris, MI, 1576
Rogers Family Foundation, Edward and Elyse, MI, 1578
Rogers Family Foundation, Inc., Robert G. Rogers and Jane E., The, MI, 1577
Rogers Foundation Corporation, S. Dennis and Leslie L., MI, 1579
Rogers Testamentary Trust, Charles A., MI, 1580
Rohlik Foundation, Sigmund and Sophie, MI, 1581
Rolka Scholarship Foundation, MI, 1582
Romence Family Foundation, Jack and Lija, MI, 1583
Roney Foundation, The, MI, 1584
Rontal Foundation, Joseph and Rose, The, MI, 1585
Roon Family Foundation, Pierson J., MI, 1586
Ropp Foundation, MI, 1587
Rordor Foundation, The, MI, 1588
Roscommon County Community Foundation, MI, 2386
Roscommon County United Way, MI, 2608
Rose Family Foundation, Carl F. & Donna M., MI, 1589
Rosen Family Foundation, Bruce H. and Rosalie N., The, MI, 1590
Rosenthal Family Foundation, Ann & Mike, MI, 1591
Rosenthal Family Foundation, MI, see 1591
Rosenzweig Coopersmith Foundation, The, MI, 1592
Roshak Foundation, Arthur & Honoria, MI, 1593
Ross Family Foundation, Sydney and Elizabeth, MI, 1594

Ross Foundation, Grace P., WI, 1595
Ross Memorial Foundation, Michael, KS, 2841
Rosso Family Foundation, MI, 1596
Rost Foundation, Ltd., Thomas and Nancy, MI, 1597
Rotary Charities of Traverse City, MI, 2609
Rotary Club of Lowell Community Foundation, MI, 2610
Rotary Club of Novi Foundation, Inc., MI, 2611
Rotary District 6360 Foundation, MI, 2612
Rothschild Fund, A. Frank and Dorothy B., CA, 1598
Roto Plastics Corporation Fund, MI, 2276
Rotter Family Foundation, MI, 1599
Rottman Charitable Foundation, Fritz and Carol, MI, see 1600
Rottman Family Charitable Foundation, MI, 1600
Rowan Foundation, MI, 1601
Rowan Foundation, Robert D., The, MI, 1602
Royal Foundation, May Mitchell, MI, 1603
Royal Oak Foundation for Public Education, MI, 1604
Ruch Family Foundation, MI, 1605
Rudel Foundation, Rita G., The, NY, 1606
Rudlaff Family Foundation, MI, 1607
Ruf Scholarship Trust, Clara A., MI, 1608
Ruffner Foundation, The, MI, 1609
Rukibai & Rijhumal Foundation, MI, 1610
Rupp Foundation, Nelson D., MI, 2842
Rusch Family Scholarship, John, The, MI, 1611
Russell Foundation, Herman, MI, 1612
Russell Medical Education Fund, Dorothy M., MI, 1613
Ryals Foundation, MI, 1614
Ryan Family Foundation, James R., MI, 1615
Ryder System Charitable Foundation, Inc., The, FL, 2277

S.E.T. Educational Fund, MI, see 2860
Saab Foundation, Ghassan and Manal, MI, 2843
Saab Foundation, Ghassan M., MI, see 2843
Sackerson Charitable Foundation, Edward J., MI, 1616
Sackner Foundation, Wade E. & Viola, MI, 2613
Sacred Family Causes Foundation, MI, 1617
Sadaqa Foundation, MI, 1618
Saddle Foundation, MI, 1619
Sagan Foundation, John & Margaret, IL, 1620
Sage Foundation, MI, 1621
Saginaw Christmas in July, Inc., MI, see 2604
Saginaw Community Foundation Depository, Inc., MI, 1622
Saginaw Community Foundation, MI, 2387
Saginaw Public Libraries Foundation, MI, 1623
Saini Memorial Foundation, Dr. Shanti Swarup & Mrs. Chawli Devi, MI, 1624
Saint Mary's Doran Foundation, MI, 2614
Salahi Foundation, The, MI, 1625
Saleh Foundation, The, MI, 1626
Salisbury Memorial Scholarship Fund, Burl E., MI, 1627
Sallness Memorial Scholarship Fund, Fritchof T. Sallness and Marian M., MI, 1628
Saltsman Family Foundation, Alex, MI, 1629
Samaritan Foundation, The, MI, 1630
Samuels, M.D. and Clarence E. Thompson Scholarship Fund, Inc., Joseph W., MI, 1631
San Pablo Foundation, Inc., MI, 1632
Sanders Memorial Fund, Jack & Marguerite, MI, 1633
Sandy Family Foundation, Inc., MI, 1634
Sanilac County Community Foundation, MI, 2388
Sankrithi Foundation, MI, 1635
Santa Maria Charitable Foundation, MI, 1636
Saranac Education Foundation, MI, 1637
Sargent Endowment Fund, Glenn and Elizabeth, MI, 1638
Sarin Family Foundation, MI, 1639
Sarnowski Foundation, Jerome & Caecilia, MI, 1640
Saugatuck-Douglas Lions Club Charitable Foundation, The, MI, 1641
Saulson Foundation, Marjorie Shuman, MI, 1642
Sault Area Community Foundation, MI, see 2326
Savage Foundation, MI, 1643
SBC Michigan Corporate Giving Program, MI, see 2142
Scears Foundation of Akron Michigan, MI, 1644
Schael Trust Fund, George E. and Agnes M., MI, 1645
Schalon Foundation, The, MI, 1646
Schanz Family Memorial Trust, Conrad Schanz and Nellie Grant, MI, 1647
Schaver Foundation, Inc., Morris and Emma, The, MI, 1648
Schemm Scholarship Trust, Maude Ripley, MI, 1649
Schiefer Charitable Trust, Olga, OH, 1650
Schlafer Foundation, Shirley K., The, MI, 1651

Schleider Education Fund, John, MI, 1652
Schmid Charitable Foundation, Inc., Frederick E., The, MI, 1653
Schmier Foundation, Leslie & Regene, MI, 1654
Schmuckal Family Foundation, Art and Mary, The, MI, 1655
Schneider Trust for Village of Lowell, Philip H., MI, 1656
Schneider-Engstrom Foundation, MI, 1657
Scholarship Fund of Flint Plumbing and Pipefitting Industry, MI, 1658
Schoolcraft Area Community Foundation, MI, 2389
Schoolcraft County Community Foundation, MI, see 2389
Schoonbeck Family Foundation, MI, 1659
Schregardus Family Foundation, Inc., The, WI, 1660
Schreiber Foundation, Herb & Cece, MI, 1661
Schriber Family Foundation, MI, 1662
Schroeder Foundation, Fred D. & Evelyn A., MI, 1663
Schultz Memorial Fund, E., MI, 1664
Schulz Family Foundation, MI, 1665
Schuyler Estate Trust, Carrie E. Smith, MI, 1666
Schwartz Family Foundation, MI, 1667
Schwartz Foundation, Robert and Caroline, NY, 1668
Schwarz Family Foundation, The, MI, 1669
Scofield Trust, Emily, MI, 1670
Scully Foundation, John, MI, 1671
Sea Dog Foundation, MI, 1672
Seabury Foundation, The, IL, 1673
Sears Scholarship Fund, Fred and Lizzie, MI, 1674
Sebastian Foundation, MI, 1675
Secchia Family Foundation, MI, 1676
Secchia Foundation, Peter F., MI, see 1676
Seed the World, Inc., MI, 1677
SEED Thompson Family Foundation, MI, 1678
Seelye Family Foundation, Mike and Sharon, The, MI, 1679
Seevers Family Foundation, NY, 1680
Seger Foundation, Martha R. and Susan I., MI, 1681
Sehn Foundation, The, MI, 1682
Seidman Family Foundation, NM, 1683
Seidman Foundation, Thomas Erler, The, NM, see 1683
Seifert Foundation, George & Elizabeth, The, MI, 1684
Seizert Family Foundation, MI, 1685
Sekkarie Foundation, The, MI, 1686
Seldon Charitable Trust, Henry M., MI, 2615
Seligman Family Foundation, The, MI, 1687
Seligman Medical Institute, The, MI, 2844
SEMCO Energy Gas Company Contributions Program, MI, 2278
Seminole Foundation, MS, see 2015
Semmes Foundation, Prewitt & Valerie D., MI, 1688
SEMP Foundation, The, MI, 2845
Sequin, Jr. Family Foundation, Thomas E., MI, 1689
Serra Family Foundation, MI, 1690
Seyferth Trust, Otto & Alma, MI, 1691
Seymour and Troester Foundation, MI, 1692
Shaevsky Family Foundation, MI, 2616
Shaevsky Family Support Foundation, MI, see 2616
Shaheen Charitable Trust, Azeez, GA, 1693
Shallal Foundation, Nawal & Jalal, The, MI, 2846
Shander Trust f/b/o St. Cyril & Methodius Seminary, Charles M., PA, 1694
Shapero Foundation, Nate S. and Ruth B., The, MI, 1695
Shapiro Charitable Trust, Mickey, MI, 1696
Shapiro Family Foundation, Joel H. and Loraine, MI, 2617
Share with the World Foundation, MI, 2847
Sharp Family Foundation, Inc., The, MI, 1697
Shayevitz Family Foundation, Jay & Susan, MI, 2848
Shelby Community Foundation, MI, 2390
Shelby Family Foundation, IL, 1698
Shelden Fund, Elizabeth, Allan and Warren, MI, 1699
Shepard Scholarship Fund Foundation, Inc., Leon and Josephine Wade, MI, 1700
Shepherd Area Historical Society, MI, 1701
Shepherd Foundation, The, MI, 1702
Shereda Foundation, Inc., Keith, The, MI, 1703
Sherman Family Foundation, The, MI, 1704
Sherwood Family Foundation, MI, 1705
Sherwood Foundation, Lynne, MI, 1706
Shiawassee Community Foundation, MI, 2391
Shiawassee Foundation, MI, see 2391
Shiawassee United Way, MI, 2618
Shiffman Foundation, The, MI, 1707
Shin Foundation for Medical Research and Betterment of Mankind, MI, 1708
Shir Chadash Foundation, MI, 1709

Shoemaker Charitable Trust, Ruth M., MI, 1710
Shoemaker Foundation, Edwin J. & Ruth M., MI, 1711
Shofnitz Charitable Trust, John R., MI, 1712
Shook Trust, Francis M., CA, 1713
Shoushanian Foundation, Martin and Diana, The, MI, 1714
Shubeck Monsour Foundation, MI, 1715
Shufro Family Foundation, Arthur S. and Norma J., MI, 1716
Shukairy Foundation, The, MI, 1717
Shumsky Foundation, John and Matilda, The, MI, 1718
Shurlow Foundation, Bill and Wanda, The, MI, 1719
Sibert & Virginia D. Aemisegger Charitable Trust, Charles J. Sibert, Clarissa B., MI, 1720
Sibert Trust, Charles J. & Clarissa B., MI, see 1720
Siddiqui Charitable Foundation, Qamar Tawakul, The, MI, 1721
Sidlik & Rebecca Boylan Foundation, Thomas, IL, 1722
Siebenthaler Foundation, MI, 1723
Sigma Gamma Foundation, MI, 2849
Sigmund Foundation, Bill & Vi, MI, 1724
Sills Foundation, Inc., MI, 1725
Silver Lining Foundation, The, MI, 1726
Silverman Fluxus Collection Foundation, Gilbert & Lila, MI, 2850
Silverman Foundation, Gilbert B. & Lila, MI, 1727
Simmons Family Foundation, Walter P. and Carroll B., MI, 1728
Simmons Foundation, MI, 1729
Simone Foundation, Louise Manoogian, MI, see 1173
Sinai Medical Staff Foundation, MI, 1730
Sirchio Foundation, Kris, MI, 1731
Sisson Charitable Trust, Harry A., MI, 1732
Sjaarda Family, Harvey and Verdi, MI, 1733
Skandalaris Family Foundation, FL, 1734
Skeen French Trust, Velma M., MI, 1735
Skendzel Family Foundation, MI, 1736
Skillin Charitable Foundation, Lloyd, CO, 1737
Skilling and Andrews Foundation, MI, 1738
Skillman Foundation, The, MI, 1739
Skrzypczak Foundation, Michael S. and Jill S., MI, 1740
Sky Foundation, OH, 2279
Slack Foundation, D. Jerome and Margery C., The, MI, 1741
Slavik Foundation Charitable Trust, Stephan F. & Mary E., MI, 1742
Slavik Foundation, Joseph F. & Edna, MI, 1743
Slemons Foundation, MI, 1744
Slikkers Foundation, David and Mary, The, MI, 1746
Slikkers Foundation, MI, 1745
Sloat and Ray Okonski Foundation, Suzanne, MI, 1747
Slocum Foundation, George M. & Mabel H., FL, 1748
Small Foundation, Faith F., MI, 1749
Small Trust f/b/o Cascades Humane Society, R. V., MI, 1750
Smallegan Family Foundation, Florence J., The, MI, 1751
SME Education Foundation, MI, see 2620
Smith Charitable Foundation, Russell H. & Maxine E., MI, 1752
Smith Charitable Trust, Jason L. and Carrie M., MI, 1753
Smith Educational Foundation, Earla B., MI, 1754
Smith Family Foundation, Arthur L. & Carra J., MI, 1755
Smith Family Foundation, Bill & Lois, MI, 1756
Smith Foundation, Don & Dolly, MI, 1757
Smith Foundation, Inc., Jay C. and Dariel S., MI, 1759
Smith Foundation, Isabel Francis Smith and Ralph Lawrence, MI, 1758
Smith Foundation, Jean M. R., MI, 1761
Smith Foundation, Melvyn Maxwell & Sara, MI, 2851
Smith Foundation, William H. and Patricia M., MI, 1760
Smoke on the Grill, Inc., MI, 2619
Sneed Foundation, Inc., OK, 1762
Snider Family Foundation, Joanie and Ira, The, MI, 1763
Snyder Christian Environmental Preservation Foundation, MI, 1764
Snyder Foundation, Inc., The, MI, 1765
Sobong Foundation, Drs. Enrico and Esther, MI, 2852
Society of Manufacturing Engineers Education Foundation, MI, 2620
Society of the Brethren, MI, 2853
Sojourner Foundation, MI, 2621
Solid Waste Management Foundation, MI, see 403
Solomon Foundation, Peter & Dorothy, MI, 1766
Solomon Foundation, Peter, MI, see 1766
Sommers, Schwartz, Silver & Schwartz Foundation, MI, 2280

Sonkin Family Foundation, The, MI, 2854
Sonneveldt Foundation, The, MI, 1767
Souder Family Foundation, IL, 1768
South Haven Community Foundation, MI, 2392
Southeast Asia Art Foundation, NH, 2855
Southeast Michigan Physicians, MI, see 2845
Southeast Ottawa Community Foundation, MI, 2393
Southeastern Michigan Chapter NECA Educational and Research Foundation, MI, 1769
Southeastern Michigan Tarbut Foundation, The, MI, 1770
Southfield Community Foundation, MI, 2394
Southfield Kappa Foundation, MI, 2622
Southfield Radiology Association Foundation, MI, 1771
Southwest Michigan Rehab Foundation, MI, 1772
Spark Foundation, The, MI, 1773
Sparling Trust, William F., MI, 1774
Sparta Community Foundation, MI, 2395
Spartan Motors Private Foundation, The, MI, 1775
Spaulding for Children, MI, 2623
Speck Trust, William and Sarah, MI, 2624
Speckhard-Knight Charitable Foundation, MI, 1776
Spectrum Health Foundation, MI, 2625
Speerstra Scholarship Fund Trust, Peter and Evelyn, MI, 1777
Spencer Family Foundation, MI, 1778
Sphinx Organization, The, MI, 2626
Spicer, Sr. Foundation, S. Gary, MI, 1779
Spoelhof Foundation, John and Judy, MI, 1780
Springview Foundation, MI, 1781
St. Clair Charitable Trust, MI, 1782
St. Clair Foundation, OH, 1783
St. Deny's Foundation, Inc., MI, 1784
St. John Vianney Educational Foundation, MI, 2627
St. Joseph County United Way, MI, 2628
St. Joseph Kiwanis Foundation, MI, 1785
St. Joseph the Worker Foundation, MI, 1786
St. Joseph/Benton Harbor Rotary Foundation, Inc., MI, 2629
St. Lawrence Educational Foundation, Inc., MI, 2630
Standard Federal Bank N.A. Corporate Giving Program, MI, see 2240
Stange Charitable Trust, Mary G., MI, 1787
Stanton Foundation, James and Dorothy, The, MI, 1788
Stanton Foundation, The, MI, 1789
Stanton Memorial Scholarship Foundation, Clarence Elbert, MI, 1790
Stauffer Foundation, The, MI, 1791
Stauffer Kentwood Foundation, MI, see 1002
Steelcase Foundation, MI, 2281
Steelcase Inc. Corporate Giving Program, MI, 2282
Steele Foundation, The, OH, 1792
Stehouwer Family Foundation, William & Marie, MI, 1793
Steinmann Family Foundation, The, MI, 1794
Stepping Stones Foundation, MI, 2856
Sterban Foundation, Richard A. and Donna L., MI, 1795
Sterk Family Foundation, MI, 1796
Sterling Heights Community Foundation, MI, 2396
Stern Foundation, Helmut, The, MI, 1797
Sternberg Foundation, Inc., Mervyn H. and Leslie D., MI, 1798
Stevenson Foundation, Walter H. and Ella, MI, 1799
Stewardship Foundation, The, MI, 1800
Stewart Family Foundation, Robert A., MI, 1801
Stewart Management Group Charitable Foundation, MI, 1802
Stieg Family Foundation, MI, 1803
Stines Family Foundation, George, MI, 2857
Stockbridge Foundation, MI, 1804
Stockton Charitable Foundation, North J. and Florence, WI, 1805
Stoddard Charitable Foundation, Jennie C., MI, 1806
Stoddard Family Foundation, Inc., MI, 1807
Stoddard Foundation, Charles and Janet, MI, 1808
Stoddard Trust, Alice A., MI, 1809
Stoker Charitable Trust, Margaret Jane, MI, 1810
Stokes Scholarship Trust, Olive A., MI, 1811
Stolaruk Foundation, Vivian Vivio Stolaruk and Steve, The, MI, 1812
Stollman Foundation, The, MI, 1813
Stone Trust, John Franklin, MI, 1814
Stonisch Foundation, MI, 1815
Stowe Trust, Emma, MI, 1816
Straits Area Community Foundation, MI, 2397
Stratton Foundation, The, MI, 1817

Stricof Family Foundation, The, MI, 1818
Strobel Foundation, Wally and Jo, The, MI, 1819
Strong Trust, Chester A., MI, 1820
Strosacker Foundation, Charles J., The, MI, 1821
Strunk Foundation, MI, 1822
Stryker and William D. Johnston Foundation, Ronda E., The, MI, 1823
Stryker Foundation, Jon L., MI, see 70
Stubberfield Foundation, Lynn, MI, 2858
Stubnitz Foundation, Maurice & Dorothy, MI, 1824
Stucki Family Foundation, Inc., The, MI, 1825
Stulberg Family Foundation, IL, 1826
Stulberg Foundation, David & Lois, MI, 1827
Sturdevant Charitable Trust, W. & H., MI, 1828
Sturgis Area Community Foundation, MI, 2398
Sturgis Foundation, MI, see 2398
Subar Foundation, Jerome P., MI, 1829
Sud Family Foundation, Anup and Parul, MI, 1830
Suleiman Foundation, MI, 1831
Sulieman Charitable Foundation, J. Samir, AR, 1832
Sullivan and Taylor Family Foundation, NV, 1833
Sullivan Foundation, Ann Ludington, The, MI, 1834
Sullivan Scholarship Fund Trust, MI, see 1835
Sullivan Scholarship Fund Trust, Robert and Timothy, MI, 1835
Summerfield Family Foundation, WI, 1836
Summerfield-MacArthur Foundation, WI, 1837
Summerland Foundation, MI, 1838
Summers Foundation, Inc., The, MI, 1839
Sunal Scholarship Foundation, Bernice B. Mayes, PA, 1840
Sundquist Charitable & Educational Trust, Ralph & Elaine, MI, 1841
Sunrise Community Foundation, MI, 1842
Sunshine Foundation, MI, 1843
Superior Consultant Charitable Foundation, MI, 1844
Sutaruk Foundation, MI, 1845
Suter Foundation, H. W., MI, 1846
Swanson Foundation, MI, 1847
Swets Family Foundation, William & Sally, MI, 1848
Swiat Foundation, Richard J. and Frances B., The, MI, 1849
Swift Foundation, William and Mary, MI, 1850
Swiss Foundation, Sol & Doris, MI, 1851
SYTA Youth Foundation, Inc., MI, 1852

Tahquamenon Education Foundation, MI, 2631
Take Time Out, MI, 1853
Talen Foundation, Anne, WI, 1854
Tamer Foundation, MI, 1855
Tannahill Foundation, Robert H., MI, 2632
Tantlinger Foundation, Keith W., The, WI, 1856
Tapestry Foundation, The, TX, 1857
Tarakji Foundation, MI, 1858
Target Corporation Contributions Program, MN, 2283
Tarnoff Family Foundation, MI, 1859
Tassell Foundation, Leslie E., The, MI, 1860
Tauber Family Foundation, MI, 1861
Tauber Family Support Foundation, MI, 2633
Tauber Support Foundation, Joel D., MI, see 2633
Taubman Centers, Inc. Corporate Giving Program, MI, 2284
Taubman Endowment for the Arts, The, MI, 1862
Taubman Foundation, A. Alfred, MI, 1863
Taubman Foundation, The, MI, 1864
Taunt Foundation, The, MI, 1865
Tawas-Whittemore-Hale Area United Fund, MI, 2634
Taylor Educational Foundation, Thomas Taylor & Charlotte Valentine, The, MA, 2859
Taylor Foundation, Maurice and Michelle, MI, 1866
Taylor Scholarship Trust, P. & H., MI, 1867
Taylor Trust f/b/o American Cancer Society, H., MI, 1868
TCF Foundation, MN, 2285
TDR, Inc., MI, 1869
Tecumseh Community Fund Foundation, MI, see 2367
Teitel Charitable Trust, Ben N., MI, 1870
Temple-Krick YFU Scholarship Fund, Inc., MI, 1871
Ten Talents Foundation, Ltd., The, MI, 1872
Tengler Educational Fund, Steve and Elizabeth, The, MI, 2860
Thavarajah and Puvaneswary Thavarajah Family Foundation, Krishnapilla, The, MI, 1873
Thawani Foundation, Bhagwani, MI, 1874
Theuerkorn Foundation, The, MI, 1875
Thiemkey Scholarship Foundation, Jean and Stewart, MI, 1876

Thom Charitable Foundation, Carl and Elinor Glyn, The, MI, 1877
Thoman Foundation, W. B. & Candace, MI, 1878
Thomas Foundation, The, MI, 1879
Thomas Scholarship Fund, Russ, MI, 1880
Thompson Community Charitable Trust, Jack W., MI, 1881
Thompson Educational Foundation, MI, 1882
Thompson Family Foundation, Lucille S., MI, 1883
Thompson Foundation, Margaret C., OH, 1885
Thompson Foundation, Mary, MI, 1888
Thompson Foundation, MI, 1884
Thompson Foundation, Richard K., The, MI, 1886
Thompson Foundation, William G., MI, 1887
Thompson Visiting Professorship Foundation, Jack W., MI, 1889
Thompson-McCully Foundation, MI, see 1884
Thormann Foundation, Inc., Floyd B. & Helen M., MI, 1890
Thornapple Kellogg Education Foundation, MI, 2635
Thorrez Foundation, MI, 1891
Three Rivers Area Community Foundation, MI, 2399
Three Rivers Community Foundation, MI, see 2399
Thy Kingdom Come Foundation, MI, 1892
Tigers Care Program, MI, 2286
Timmis Family Foundation No. 2, MI, see 327
Timmis Foundation, Gerald C. Timmis & Dorothy S., MI, 1893
Timmis Foundation, Michael T. & Nancy E., MI, 1894
Timothy Foundation, The, MI, 1895
TIR Foundation, MI, 1896
Tiscornia Foundation, Inc., The, MI, 1897
Titche Family Foundation, MI, 1898
TLC Foundation, MI, 1899
Todd Company Foundation, A. M., MI, 2287
Torgow Family Foundation, MI, 2861
Toth, Jr. Family Foundation, Steve, The, MI, 1900
Towsley Foundation, Harry A. and Margaret D., The, MI, 1901
Tracy Family Foundation, Thomas J., The, MI, 1902
Tracy Foundation, Inc., Emmet E. Tracy, Jr. and Marilyn H., MI, 1903
Trapp Family Foundation, Inc., MI, 1904
Travelers Aid Society of Metropolitan Detroit, MI, 2636
Tremble Foundation, Inc., MI, see 1784
Trico Foundation, The, MI, 1905
Triford Foundation, MI, 1906
Trillium Foundation, The, MI, 1907
Trinity Community Services & Educational Foundation, MI, 2637
Trinklein Educational Trust, Otto, MI, 1908
Trixie Puff Foundation, MI, 1909
Trone Scholarship Trust, Blanche Barr, MI, 1910
Troy Community Foundation, MI, see 2342
Troy Internal Medicine Foundation, MI, 2862
Trudell Scholarship Trust, MI, 1911
Trumbull Family Foundation, MI, 1912
Tubergen Foundation, Jerry L. & Marcia D., MI, 1913
Tucker Scholarship Fund, Reginald L., IL, 1914
Tuinstra Foundation, Doris, The, MI, 1915
Tuktawa Foundation, MI, 1916
Tumey & Grand Lodge, Jeremiah, MI, see 1917
Tumey Fund, Jeremiah, MI, 1917
Tuohy-University of Michigan Student Loan Fund, Berndine MacMullen, MI, 1918
Turfah Foundation, The, MI, 1919
Turn 2 Foundation, Inc., NY, 1920
Turner Foundation, Amherst and Janeth, MI, 1921
Turner Foundation, Inc., Jane Smith, MI, 1922
Turner Memorial Trust, Alice E., MI, 1923
Turner, Jr. Memorial Scholarship Foundation, Dr. William A., OH, 1924
Turtle Lake Wildlife Foundation, The, MI, 1925
Tuscola County Community Foundation, MI, 2400
Tyco Electronics Foundation, PA, 2288
Tzedukah Family Foundation, Alice & Ed Brickman, MI, 1926

U of M Scholarship Fund of Bay City, MI, see 1930
U.S. Asia Medical Foundation, MI, 1927
U.S. India Medical Foundation, MI, see 1927
U.S.-China Cultural Foundation, MI, 1928
Ufer Foundation, Bob, The, MI, 2289
United American Healthcare Foundation, MI, see 1359
United Jewish Foundation, MI, 2638
United Way for Southeastern Michigan, MI, 2639

United Way of Bay County, MI, 2640
United Way of Chippewa County, MI, 2641
United Way of Clare County, MI, 2642
United Way of Delta County, MI, 2643
United Way of Dickinson County, Inc., MI, 2644
United Way of Genesee County, MI, 2645
United Way of Gladwin County, MI, 2646
United Way of Gratiot County, MI, 2647
United Way of Greater Battle Creek, MI, 2648
United Way of Greater Niles, Inc., MI, 2649
United Way of Ionia County, MI, 2650
United Way of Isabella County, MI, 2651
United Way of Jackson County, MI, 2652
United Way of Lapeer County, MI, 2653
United Way of Manistee County, MI, 2654
United Way of Marquette County, MI, 2655
United Way of Mason County, MI, 2656
United Way of Midland County, MI, 2657
United Way of Monroe County, Inc., MI, 2658
United Way of Montcalm County, MI, 2659
United Way of Muskegon County, MI, 2660
United Way of Northeast Michigan, MI, 2661
United Way of Northwest Michigan, MI, 2662
United Way of Saginaw County, MI, 2663
United Way of Sanilac County, Inc., MI, 2664
United Way of Southwest Michigan, MI, 2665
United Way of St. Clair County, MI, 2666
United Way of Tuscola County, MI, 2667
United Way of Wexford County, MI, 2668
Universal Companies, Inc. Education Foundation, MI, see 2290
Universal Forest Products Education Foundation, MI, 2290
University of Michigan Club of Grand Rapids Scholarship Fund, The, MI, 1929
University of Michigan Scholarship Fund of Bay City, MI, 1930
University of Strathclyde USA Foundation, DC, 1931
University Renal Research and Education Association, MI, 2863
UNOVA Foundation, The, WA, 1932
Upjohn & Mary S. Kirby Memorial Trust, Millie K., MI, 2669
Upjohn Charitable Trust, Burton & Elizabeth, MI, 1933
Upjohn Foundation, Harold and Grace, MI, 1934
Upjohn Unemployment Trustee Corporation, W. E., MI, 2670
Upper Peninsula Community Foundation Alliance, MI, see 2341
Upton Foundation, Frederick S., MI, 1935
Uyham Memorial Foundation, Hui-Keng Pua, MI, 1936

V Care Jainism & Jivdaya Foundation, MI, 1937
Valassis Communications, Inc. Corporate Giving Program, MI, 2291
Valenti Foundation, The, MI, 1938
Van Andel Foundation, Jay and Betty, MI, 1939
Van Buren County United Way, MI, 2671
Van Camp Family Foundation, James and Alma, MI, 1940
Van Curler Foundation, MI, 1941
Van Dalson Foundation, W. S. & Lois, The, MI, 1942
Van Dam Charitable Foundation, MI, 1943
Van Den Bosch Gospel Foundation, William and Anna, MI, 1944
Van Dyke Family Charitable Foundation, IL, 1945
Van Elslander Family Foundation, MI, 1946
Van Gessel Scholarship Foundation, MI, 1947
Van Haften Charitable Trust, Peter, MI, 2672
Van Haften Trust, Peter, MI, 2673
Van Hollenbeck Foundation, Homer J., MI, 1948
Van Wormer Family Foundation, MI, 1949
Van Wyk Risk & Financial Management Corporate Giving Program, MI, 2292
VanAntwerp Family Foundation, MI, 1950
VandenBelt Trust No. II, Glen D., WI, 1951
Vander Kooy Foundation, Simon and Mary, MI, 1952
Vander Laan Family Foundation, MI, 1953
VanderArk Foundation, CO, 1954
Vanderwaals Foundation, James and Almeda, MI, 1955
Vanderweide Foundation, Robert & Cheri, MI, 1956
Vandomelen Foundation, William and Katherine, The, MI, 1957
VanKley Educational Foundation, Dr. Lavern and Betty, MI, 1958
Vanwingen Memorial Fund, Peter J. and Anne, MI, 1959

GEOGRAPHIC INDEX

Grantmakers in boldface type make grants on a national, regional, or international basis; the others generally limit giving to the city or state in which they are located.

ARIZONA
Paradise Valley: Estes 532, Reese 1542
Scottsdale: Dawson 410, Loichle 1119
Tucson: Jasam 922

ARKANSAS
North Little Rock: Sulieman 1832

CALIFORNIA
Carmel: Bunker 261
Gardena: Nissan 2263, Nissan 2264
La Jolla: Wilcox 2054
Laguna Hills: Moh 1300
Los Angeles: Enberg 524, J.C. 914
Morgan Hill: Marsh 1180
Pasadena: Pasant 1438
Rancho Santa Fe: Wierenga 2051
San Francisco: Hannan 780, Kanitz 965, Shook 1713
San Jose: House 869
Santa Monica: Landsberg 1071
Solana Beach: Eagle 504
Woodland Hills: Brooke 238
Woodside: Rothschild 1598

COLORADO
Colorado Springs: Dunagan 494
Denver: Skillin 1737
Englewood: VanderArk 1954
Highlands Ranch: Mol 1304
Steamboat Springs: Fox 608, Munn 1346

CONNECTICUT
Greenwich: PJM 1486

DELAWARE
Newark: Bartsch 111, Warner 1987
Wilmington: Esperance 530

DISTRICT OF COLUMBIA
Washington: University 1931

FLORIDA
Boca Raton: KMD 1020
Bradenton: Weigel 2003
Clearwater: Powell 1501, Robey 2840
Fort Lauderdale: Church 326, Friedman 623, **Hagen 758**, Kegel 984
Fort Myers: Kent 998
Highland Beach: Mondry 1310
Jacksonville: Fisher 578, Frank 610, Garrison 643, Lounsberry 1123, Watson 1993
Lauderdale By The Sea: Hasey 805
Marco Island: Cook 359
Miami: Ryder 2277
Naples: Crawford 377, Dexter 449, Hibbert 834, Ludy 1130, Moore 1317, Slocum 1748
Ocala: Corr 364
Port St. Lucie: Baese 84
Venice: Skandalaris 1734
Winter Park: Bush 274

GEORGIA
Atlanta: Blackney 177, Shaheen 1693

ILLINOIS
Chicago: Barron 107, Barth 2422, Borwell 203, Bosch 205, Brewer 229, Bruce 251, Burnett 264, Crane 376, Daverman 405, Gavin 650, Harris 797, Jentes 931, Keith 985, Loutit 1124, Loutit 1125, Lurie 1136, Northern 2265, Offield 1394, Pajeau 1421, Peters 1464, Regal 1544, Seabury 1673, Sidlik 1722, Souder 1768, Stulberg 1826, Tucker 1914, Vineyard 1971, Whitwam 2046, Young 2114
Evanston: Sagan 1620
Glenview: Delta 424
Hillside: Van Dyke 1945
Lisle: Meeks 1246
Northbrook: Hill 839, Wesselink 2024
Northfield: Ceres 304
Oak Brook: Huizenga 878
Rockford: Hutchcroft 889
Springfield: Hoogland 862
Winnetka: Denniston 428, Shelby 1698

INDIANA
Indianapolis: Neff 2822, Walther 2677
Muncie: Ball 92
Richmond: Elder 2190

IOWA
Des Moines: Cole 346

KANSAS
Leawood: Ross 2841

LOUISIANA
Metairie: Orten 1407
New Orleans: Behl 134, Behl 135

MARYLAND
Kensington: Broomfield 241

MASSACHUSETTS
Boston: Taylor 2859
Newton: Cowan 369
Worcester: Hanover 2218

MICHIGAN
Ada: Adopt 13, **Alticor 2138**, **Anthony 63**, Bos 204, Cole 343, Hansen 782, **Jonathan 941**, KINSHIP 1012, Shurlow 1719, Tassell 1860, Trillium 1907, Vos 2299
Addison: Knight 1025
Adrian: Adrian 2403, Baughey 2709, **Gleaner 2760**, Hickman 835, Lenawee 2536, Lenawee 2537, Merillat 1255, Price 1512, Robideau 1567, Roto 2276, Stubberfield 2858, Stubnitz 1824, Thompson 1887, Westfall 2028
Albion: Albion 2307, Albion-Homer 2404
Allegan: Allegan 2309, Allegan 2405, Perrigo 2266, Smith 1756
Allen Park: Detroit 2460, Detroit 2179
Allendale: Allendale 2310, Roon 1586, Thy 1892
Alma: Craig 374, Gratiot 2762, Leppien 1098, Luneack 1135, Pardee 2833, Smith 1755, United 2647
Almont: Four 2348
Alpena: Besser 155, Besser 2714, Community 2333, First 2201, Iosco 2359, North 2380, Straits 2397, United 2661
Alto: DeVries 444
Ann Arbor: A.I.R. 2691, Accelerated 2692, Alliance 40, Andrah 56, April 68, Arjuna 2699, Ave 83, Berry 152, BFK 162, Bonisteel 193, **Borders 2430**, **Borders 2153**, Brandon 217, Brauer 219, Brinkerhoff-Sample 232, Buhr 259, Burt 270, Cairn 281, Campbell 288, Carlson 291, Cascade 2721, **Chang 308**, Chisbetts 2730, **Cresswell 378**, D.U. 395, DHL 450, Domino's 2463, Domino's 2184, Duffy 490, **Earhart 506**, Ervin 528, Esser 531, Friedman 622, Futureation 2204, Gelman 657, Ghitalla 671, Good 702, **Griffin 737**, Guppy 2765, Haab 752, Halcyon 766, Harbaugh 2500, Haven 2503, Henley 820, **International 905**, Issa 2224, Jensen 930, Kay 978, Kelly 992, Key 1005, Knight 1026, Korybalski 1039, Kymal 1056, Light 2797, Maas 1145, Markel 1179, Martin 1186, Mason 1194, McGrae 1225, McKinley 2553, Mehra 1251, Mirafzali 1293, Moholy-Nagy 2818, Montague 1314, Mosaic 1329, **Ms. 2570**, National 2571, **Paideia 1419**, **Palestine 2590**, Parker 1435, Pietrasiuk 1478, Pollack 1493, Porter 1495, **ProQuest 2270**, Ranger 1529, Rapinchuk 1531, **Rislov 1559**, RNR 1562, Saddle 1619, Schriber 1662, Simmons 1729, Smith 1761, Speckhard 1776, Stern 1797, Temple 1871, **Turner 1921**, Ufer 2289, University 2863, **Van Curler 1941**, Vaughan 1962, Washtenaw 2678, Winkler 2073, Wise 2081, **Wolfe 2085**, Ypsilanti 2402, **Zazove 2122**, Zerbe 2127, Zimmer 2878
Arcadia: Gerberding 662
Auburn Hills: Champion 2158, DaimlerChrysler 2171, **DaimlerChrysler 2172**, Davidson 406, Deradoorian 429, Detroit 2180, Detroit 2182, Guardian 2215,

MEEMIC 2250, Pistons 2267, Reid 2839, Victor 1969, Volkswagen 2297, Volkswagen 2298

Augusta: Historic 2774

Bad Axe: Huron 2357

Baldwin: Lake 2364

Bath: Centennial 2723

Battle Creek: Battle Creek 2315, Binda 167, Brackett 214, Farley 545, Howard 872, **Kellogg 2233**, **Kellogg 2234**, **Kellogg 988**, Kellogg's 2235, LaMothe 1070, McCurdy 1218, Miller 1284, Navigations 2821, Peace 1443, Scofield 1670, Southwest 1772, Trone 1910, United 2648, Willard 2687, Winship 2076, Yankama 2108, Zanetti 2121

Bay City: Bay 2316, Kantzler 966, Law 1089, Pardee 2832, Rogers 1577, Sequin 1689, Smith 1752, United 2640, University 1930, Van Wormer 1949, Weidner 2684, Weinlander 2866, Wirt 2078

Bay Harbor: Bay Harbor 2317

Belleville: Abbatt 3, Lasko 1084, **Visteon 2296**

Bellevue: Blaske 180

Belmont: Aletheia 29, Brown 248, Conway 356, Koetje 1033, Verduin 1964, Wheeler 2036

Benton Harbor: Berrien 151, Giddey 675, United 2665, Whirlpool 2300, Whirlpool 2301

Benzonia: Johnson 938

Berkley: **McCarty 2552**, Molinello 1305, World 2100

Beverly Hills: Fieldman 567, Great 2491, Jones 946, Kensington 2530, Langbo 1073, Malloure 1160, Pellerito 1451, Rowan 1602

Big Rapids: Mecosta 2374, Mecosta-Osceola 2554

Bingham Farms: Blumenstein 188, Boschan 206, Gau 649, Ginsberg 685, Goodale 705, Katzman 973, Kleiman 1016, Meyer 1263, Michigan 2565, Milan 1273, Page 1418, Phelps 1471, Polakovic 1489, Rogers 1579, Rotter 1599, Schmier 1654, Stricof 1818, Vollbrecht 1976

Birmingham: Amber 2695, Andrews 57, Aries 72, Armstrong 2701, Baskin 2708, Berlin 148, Bernstein 150, Birmingham 2428, Blue 2717, Borman 198, Cameron 284, Cassel 295, **Cherri 318**, Dorrell 472, Doulos 476, Erb 526, Federov 555, Fenkell 558, Ferries 563, **Fitzgibbon 581**, Foundation 603, Goad 694, **Hagopian 762**, Harmon 793, Hodgkins 850, International 2781, **Johnson 939**, Kelter 993, Living 2798, Lyon 1139, Mahmud 1153, **May 1205**, **McDonald 1221**, Munder 2259, Nelson 1365, Parks 1437, Peslar 1463, **Pilgrim 1479**, Rattner 1533, Rosso 1596, Stonisch 1815, Stratton 1817, Taunt 1865, Toth 1900, **U.S. 1928**, Wasserman 1988, Wasserman 1990, Weisberg 2010, Wetsman 2031, Whitman 2044, Williams 2061, Workers 2098

Blissfield: Farver 547

Bloomfield: Bell 138, Lahser 2795, McBrearty 1208, Rogers 1580, Shin 1708

Bloomfield Hills: Allesee 39, Alpern 43, Alpern 44, Applebaum 67, Applebaum 2414, Aronoff 2702, Bargman 98, Barron 108, Bates 116, **Bath 118**, Becker 2711, **Berman 2425**, Beyer 160, Bittker 173, Bizer 175, Bloom 185, Blumberg 186, Brooks 240, Brown 243, Brown 249, Caldwell 282, **Cassel 296**, Castaing 298, Celani 303, Chandler 307, Cherney 317, Clannad 329, **Cohen 341**, Cooper 361, Coville-Triest 2455, Coyne 370, Cutting 393, Davis 408, **Day 411**, Deffenbaugh 417, Delta 425, Devereaux 436, Dickinson 2183, DiClemente 452, Diem 2741, **Dorfman 471**, Duffy 491, Dykstra 501, Emergency 521, Evereg 535, Fisher 2467, Fishman 580, Flint 586, Frankel 613, Frankel 2475, **Gagliardi 634**, Garber 2757, Googasian 709, Gornick 715, Green 2494, Gurwin 747, Haddow 2498, Hampson 774, Hamzavi 776, Harris 798, Hermelin 2508, Holley 856, Humphrey 882, Iacobelli 892, Imerman 898, Isakow 911, Jampel 919, Janes 920, **Jewish 2521**, Jewish 2522, Jewish 2523, Kahn 959, Katzman 971, Katzman 972, Khilanani 1006, Kogan 1034, Laker 1067, Larson 1079, Larson 1080, **Legion 1093**, Liebler 1106, Litvak 1115, Loomis 2243, Lowenstein 1127, Lubin 1128, Lyon 1140, M & M 1142, Manix 1168, Mathers 1196, May 1203, McElroy 1222,

Michell 1265, Minkin 1292, Miro 1294, Molnar 1308, Morgan 2258, Moscone 1330, MPS 1337, Nakadar 2820, Ogne 1395, Orley 1403, Ortiz 1408, Pappas 2592, Parker 1434, Peterson 1467, Physician 1474, Potiker 2601, Prentis 2602, Pulte 2271, Ran 1528, Rankauf 1530, Robbins 1564, **Robinson 1569**, Roney 1584, Rose 1589, Rosenthal 1591, Rost 1597, **Rukibai 1610**, Sandy 1634, Sankrithi 1635, Schlafer 1651, Sehn 1682, Seizert 1685, Shaevsky 2616, Shapiro 2617, Silverman 2850, Smith 1754, Smith 1758, Snider 1763, St. Clair 1782, Sternberg 1798, Stulberg 1827, Suter 1846, Tauber 2633, Taubman 2284, Taubman 1862, Taubman 1863, Taubman 1864, Thavarajah 1873, Thomas 1880, Timmis 1893, **Tracy 1902**, United 2638, **Vattikuti 1961**, Victor 2864, Village 2674, Vlasic 1974, Walsh 1981, Wanczyk 1985, Weinberg 2006, Weiner 2008, Weisberg 2011, Weisberg 2012, **Weisberg 2013**, Welch 2016, Westerman 2027, White 2038, Woodall 2094, Wyatt 2105, Yaffe 2107, Young 2116, Zionist 2131

Bloomfield Township: Ross 1594

Boyne City: Great 2492

Bradley: Robinson 1568

Bridgeport: Andersen 50

Bridgman: Kohn 1035

Brighton: Community 2330, Home 2513, **Johnson 936**, Livingston 2542, Ropp 1587, Rowan 1601, **Sage 1621**, Schulz 1665, Silver 1726

Buchanan: Michigan 2375

Byron Center: Aparche 66, Bott 207, Bouma 208, Buist 2719, Byron 2435, DJD 458, **Koster 1042**, Mast 1195, Northern 1383, Windemuller 2069

Cadillac: Cadillac 2321, Huckle 2515, United 2668

Caledonia: Cheff 315, Daystar 412, Elzinga 520, Fish 576, Miller 1283, Resnal 1549

Canton: Attwood 80, Canton 2322, Crowther 383, Michigan 1267, Richter 1554, Veri 1965

Caro: Rolka 1582, Scears 1644, Tuscola 2400, United 2667

Cass City: Rawson 1536

Cassopolis: **Lowe 2800**, McLoughlin 1237, Walters 1983

Cedar Springs: Cedar Springs 2442, Martin 1187

Centreville: St. Joseph 2628

Charlevoix: Char-Em 2443, Dauch 2735, Thom 1877, **Winn 2074**, Winn 2075

Charlotte: Eaton 2346, Eaton 2465, Spartan 1775, Wicker's 2047

Chassell: Heinrich 2771

Cheboygan: Cheboygan 2445, Harding 791

Chelsea: Burt 271, Chelsea 2446, Chelsea 316, Chelsea 2447

Chesterfield: LMC 1117, TLC 1899

Clare: United 2642

Clarklake: **Riley 1557**

Clarkston: Hartke 2769, Hehl 815, Kid 1007, Optimist 2585, SYTA 1852

Clarksville: Behrenwald 136

Clinton: Clinton 2731, Clinton 337, Weikart 2004

Clinton Township: Clinton 338, Daoud 401, Italian 2518, Petitpren 1469, Strunk 1822, Tamer 1855, Thormann 1890, Warchol 1986, Webber 1997

Clio: Kindred 1010

Clyde: Schneider 1657

Coldwater: Barnett 101, Barnett 102, Barnett 103, Barnett 104, Barnett 105, Branch 2320, Branch 2431, **Calling 283**, Fedewa 556, Juhl 952, Mayim 2805, Salisbury 1627, Skeen 1735, Taylor 1867, Taylor 1868

Coloma: **Degroot 419**

Commerce Township: Alon 42, Ferber 559, **Ferber 560**

Comstock Park: Buist 260

Concord: Hubbard 2778, Thorrez 1891

Constantine: Fibre 2200

Coopersville: Coopersville 2343, Lemmen 1096

Crystal Falls: Crystal 2344, Laing 1066

Dearborn: Buer 257, Doran 470, **Ford 2202**, Ford 2203, Helppie 817, Kasle 2232, Kosch 1040, Levy 1102, Levy 1103, Levy 1104, **Mousigian 1334**, Muirhead 1343, Noster 1384, SEMP 2845, Smoke 2619, **Society 2620**, Superior 1844

Dearborn Heights: Burns 266, Dearborn 2173, Imoberstag 899

Detroit: **Ackermans 11**, Agley 17, American 2139, Anderson 2411, Arden 71, Assistance 2418, AT&T 2142, Atanas 2420, Attanasio 78, Atterberry 79, AtWater 81, Auto 82, Bates 117, Battle 119, Berkery 145, Bettis 2427, Biedermann 164, Blissfield 183, Blissfield 2429, Blue 2150, Blue 2151, Bodman 2152, Bornman 200, Bornman 201, Braude 218, Bregi 222, Brems 223, Busby 272, Butzel 2156, Cable 2436, Caesar 280, Caring 2439, Carls 290, Charfoos 310, Cherlayne 2726, Clark 2450, Cole 345, Combs 349, Comerica 2167, Comerica 2168, Community 2335, Courtney 368, Crain 375, Cromarty 380, **Davis 2457**, Dennard 427, Detroit 2178, Detroit 2739, Detroit 2181, Detroit 435, Detroit 2740, Detroit 2461, DeVlieg 437, Donahey 466, Drew 481, DTE 2187, DTE 2188, Duchene 488, Edrington 511, Edwards 512, Farmer 2196, Flinn 585, Foley 2469, Foley 2470, Ford 591, Ford 592, Ford 593, Ford 594, Ford 595, Ford 596, Ford 597, **Free 2477**, Fund 632, Gabooney 633, Gallo 637, Gegax 655, **General 2205**, General 2206, Generation 659, Gershenson 667, Gilmour 2481, GM 2209, Gordy 714, Graham 718, Greater 726, Green 727, Green 729, Grosfeld 742, Hagelshaw 2499, Hamilton 771, Hannan 2768, Harden 787, Harder 2502, Harper 795, Harris 799, Hart 800, Hartmann 801, Henry 2506, Herdegen 824, Herrick 829, Hicks 836, Hope 866, Hospitalers 867, Hudson 876, Ilitch 2516, Inman 903, Investment 2782, Jackson 916, Jacurit 923, Jerome 2519, JPMorgan 2227, Kahn 2230, Kanzler 967, Kelly 989, Kling 1017, Knooihuizen 1027, Kocurek 1030, Kolene 2237, Kulma 1053, Kutz 1055, Laboratory 1060, Lahti 1063, Larson 1081, Latzer 1086, Lindsay 2540, Lovelight 2543, MacCrone 1146, Marcks 1176, Mardigian 1177, Martin 1190, Matson 1198, McCormick 1216, McGregor 1226, McKeen 1230, McKibben 1232, McLauchlin 1233, Mentlikowski 1254, Metro 1261, Mette 1262, Michigan 2564, Midgett 1270, Midgett 1271, Miller 1280, Miller 1286, Miller 2255, Mims 1290, Moore 1320, Morman 1326, Mozer 1335, Murff 2819, Mutter 1351, **National 1359**, Nevas 2573, Nicolay 1373, North 2826, Oakland 2580, Orris 1406, Overlook 1412, Parker 1436, Paul 1439, **Perry 1460**, Petersen 1466, Peterson 1468, **Pewabic 2594**, Phelps 1472, Ponting 1494, Project 2836, Ramser 1527, Reuter 1550, Reuther 2605, Richardson 1553, Riley 1558, Riley 2607, Robison 1570, Roche 1571, Rogers 1576, Royal 1603, Ruffner 1609, Russell 1612, Russell 1613, Samuels 1631, **San 1632**, Schreiber 1661, Schultz 1664, Schwartz 1667, Scully 1671, Sheldon 2615, Shapero 1695, **Share 2847**, Sharp 1697, Shiffman 1707, Sisson 1732, Skillman 1739, Small 1750, Smith 1753, Sojourner 2621, Speck 2624, **Sphinx 2626**, Stevenson 1799, Stieg 1803, Stokes 1811, Stone 1814, Strong 1820, Sturdevant 1828, Sundquist 1841, Swanson 1847, Tannahill 2632, **Teitel 1870**, Thompson 1883, Thompson 1888, Tigers 2286, Timmis 1894, Torgow 2861, Travelers 2636, Trinity 2637, Trixie 1909, Tumey 1917, Turner 1922, Tzedukah 1926, United 2639, Vincent 1970, VSA 2676, Watson 1992, Wayne 2681, **Wetmore 2030**, Whitney 2686, Wilde 2055, Williams 2062, Wilson 2065, Wilson 2067, Winkler 2072, WMY 2083, Wolff 2087, World 2873, Young 2690

Dewitt: **Ambrosiani 46**, Stepping 2856

Dexter: Brust 254, Lyons 1141, Martin 1185

Dollar Bay: Hamar 770

Douglas: Lugers 1131

Dowagiac: Cass 2441, Fitch 2752, St. Deny's 1784

Dundee: **Gygi 2216**, Holcim 2222

East China: Brown 244

Huntington Woods: Abu-Akeel 9, Brodsky 235, Burrier 268, Pitt 1484, Prentis 1506, Weinberg 2005, Zoller 2133

Indian River: Bauervic 122, Redman 2838

Interlochen: Penner 1454

Ionia: United 2650

Iron Mountain: Dickinson 2345, Dickinson 451, Flemington 583, Nelson 1366, Trudell 1911, United 2644

Iron River: Brennan 224

Ironwood: Banfield 95, Gogebic 2483, Ironwood 2517

Ishpeming: Ishpeming 2360

Ithaca: Gratiot 2354

Jackson: Alro 2137, Blakely 179, Bugas 258, Camp 285, **CMS 2165**, Consumers 2169, Consumers 2170, Copley 362, Curtis 389, Dorris 473, Ehmer 516, Gallant 636, Glick 691, Glick 692, Glick 693, Hancock 778, Hill 841, Hurst 886, Jackson 915, Jackson 2361, Jackson 2783, Manufacturing 2247, Michner 1269, Phantom 1470, Plumbers 2596, Raval 1534, Sadaqa 1618, Schmid 1653, Sigmund 1724, Small 1749, Stanton 1789, United 2652, Weatherwax 1996, Wright 2102

Jenison: Kerkstra 1004, **Redeemer 2837**

Kalamazoo: Antique 64, Arctica 69, **Arcus 70**, Arts 2415, Baker 88, Briarwood 230, Bronson 2433, Brown 245, Brown 2434, Burdick 263, Cascadia 294, Chase 313, Clapp 330, Connable 353, Dalton 398, Delano 423, Doctor 461, Eliason 2191, Fabri 2194, **Fetzer 2749**, Fletcher 584, Gary 645, Gilmore 2479, Gilmore 682, Gilmore 683, Gilmore 2480, Gilmore 684, Hammond 2217, Havirmill 809, Hinson 845, IDM 895, **International 2780**, Kalamazoo 2362, Kalamazoo 2526, Kalamazoo 2527, Kalamazoo 2528, Kalamazoo 2529, Kalleward 2231, Kinney 1011, **Krishnamurti 1050**, Lee 1091, Light 2539, Little 1113, Miller 1275, Miller 2257, Monroe 1312, Okun 1397, Olson 1400, Parfet 1430, Parish 1431, Parish 1432, Parish 1433, Pitkin 2595, Power 1502, Seelye 1679, Shubeck 1715, Stryker 1823, Stucki 1825, Ten 1872, Upjohn 2669, Upjohn 1933, Upjohn 1934, **Upjohn 2670**, Van Dalson 1942, Van Haften 2672, Van Haften 2673, Vandomelen 1957, Wattles 1994, Weisblat 2014, Woodworth 2095

Keego Harbor: **Africa 16**

Kentwood: Autocam 2143, Barber 97, Fox 607, Kennedy 996, Vander Laan 1953

Kewadin: Siebenthaler 1723

Kingsford: Norway 2382

L'Anse: Baraga 2313

Lake City: Missaukee 2377, Winkle 2871

Lake Leelanau: Lange 1074

Lake Odessa: Mackenzie's 2803

Lake Orion: Keep 2788, Kolo 2532, Stanton 1790

Lambertville: Bedford 2318

Lansing: Abrams 8, **Amy 48**, Capital 2323, Caravan 2438, Christian 323, Coon 360, Czado 394, Dunnings 497, Granger 722, Granger 723, Great 2763, Great 2493, Henry 2220, Jackson 2225, Kierstead 1009, Lansing 2534, Lansing 1075, Library 2538, Lions 2541, Memorial 2811, Meridian 2812, Michigan 2560, Michigan 2563, Michigan 2566, Mid-Michigan 2817, Reid 1547, Scholarship 1658, Thoman 1878, Voelker 2675, Waverly 2680, Whiteley 2039

Lapeer: Lapeer 2365, United 2653, Webster 1999

Lathrup Village: Dixie 457

Leland: Feather 553, Trumbull 1912

Leslie: Society 2853

Lexington: United 2664

Livonia: Del Signore 2458, Detroit 2738, Dinan 2742, DiPonio 455, **Foundation 2474**, H.O.N.O.R. 750, Keough 1003, Livonia 2368, Luhtanen 2244, Mauser 1201, Michigan 2567, Nagy 1355, Providence 1515, Rabahy 1521, Recreational 1540, Rosen 1590, Valassis 2291

Lowell: Boyd 213, Lowell 2801, Maas 1144, Rotary 2610, Ykema 2112

Ludington: Birtwistle 170, Community 2331, Great 2213, Ludington 2545, United 2656

Macatawa: Eldean 517

Mackinac Island: Mackinac 2370

Madison Heights: Fill 569, Gordon 711, O'Neill 2829

Mancelona: Snyder 1764

Manistee: Filer 2751, Foster 600, Grassland 724, Manistee 1167, Manistee 2371, Tuohy 1918, United 2654

Manistique: Schoolcraft 2389

Manitou Beach: Murdock 1348

Marcellus: Harmony 794, Hovarter 870, Lee 1092

Marne: Grand Rapids 2487

Marquette: Clark 331, Frazier 616, Great 2490, Hammel 772, Hirvonen 847, Kaufman 974, Lilja 1108, MacDonald 1147, Marquette 2548, Marquette 2372, Reynolds 1551, Rupp 2842, United 2655

Marshall: Cortright 365, Cronin 381, Homer 858, Marshall 2373, Marshall 2549

Mason: Dart 403, Mason 2550

Mattawan: Detwiler 2462, **Molitor 1306**

Mayville: Holcomb 852

Memphis: VanAntwerp 1950

Mendon: Haas 753

Menominee: M & M 2369

Metamora: **Animal 60**

Middleville: Thornapple 2635

Midland: **Allen 37**, Barstow 109, Bierlein 2148, Blake 178, Chemical 2160, Clare 2327, Dean 414, Doan 459, Doan 460, Dow 2185, **Dow 2186**, Dow 2743, Dow 478, Dow 479, Gerstacker 668, Hoffmeyer 2775, Hollenbeck 855, Ludington 1129, Midland 2376, Midland 2568, Miller 1279, **Oreffice 1402**, **Pardee 1428**, Pinney 1482, Rockwell 1573, Rogers 1578, Strosacker 1821, Sullivan 1834, Towsley 1901, United 2657

Milford: **Bretzlaff 228**, Iverson 912, **Maranatha 1175**, Miller 1278, Sarin 1639

Monroe: Community 2338, Duffey 489, **Fahd 2748**, Gertz 669, Knabusch 1021, Knabusch 1022, Knabusch 1023, La-Z-Boy 2239, Little 1114, Mercy 2555, Rhee 1552, Shoemaker 1710, Shoemaker 1711, Stoddard 1809, United 2658, Wells 2020, Whiting 2043

Morenci: Fay 552, Morenci 2569, Wirick 2077

Mount Clemens: Anton 65, Kaczperski 957, Macomb 1151, Stanton 1788, Wieczorek 2050

Mount Pleasant: Fabiano 2193, Halpin 769, Isabella 2223, Mount Pleasant 2378, United 2651

Munising: Alger 2308

Muskegon: Community 2332, Debower 415, Johnson 2524, Kaufman 975, Kee 981, Nordman 1382, Nugent 1387, United 2660

Negaunee: Negaunee 2379

New Baltimore: Anchor 2311, Zip 2132

Newaygo: Newaygo 1369

Newberry: Tahquamenon 2631

Niles: Davis 407, Hunter 884, **Kiamba 2790**, Niles 2825, Peach 1444, Plym 1488, United 2649, Wood 2093

North Muskegon: Cutler 392, Hilt 843, Walker 1979

Northport: Leelanau 2366

Northville: Beson 154, Conrad 2453, Dabney 396, Kebok 980, Lapham 1077, **Latvian 2535, Niemiec 1375**, Northville 2381, Northville 2577, Perrone 1459, Wolford 2088

Norton Shores: Bandstra 94

Novi: Americana 47, Finkel 571, Fisher 579, Foundation 606, Lehman 1094, Luyckx 2546, Michigan 2559, Novi 2578, Novi 2579, **Rotary 2611**, Wisne 2082

Oak Park: Latimer 1085, Mandelbaum 1165, Meer 1247, Nusbaum 1389, Shayevitz 2848, Shir 1709

Oakland: Oakland 2581, **York 2113**

Oakland Township: Preede 1504, Shereda 1703

Okemos: Akers 21, Delta 2459, Glassen 688, Greater 725, Maldonado 1159, Nickless 1371, **Quiachon 1520**

Olivet: Vomberg 1977

Ontonagon: Ontonagon 2584

Orchard Lake: Cejka 302, Farago 541, Kahn 961, Kondur 1036, NSF 1386, Stockbridge 1804, Trapp 1904, Tuktawa 1916

Oscoda: Oscoda 2586

Owosso: Bentley 143, Cook 358, Michigan 2815, Mitchell 1299, Schleider 1652, Shiawassee 2391, Shiawassee 2618

Oxford: Clark 332, Kent 1000

Parma: Michigan 2253

Paw Paw: Van Buren 2671

Perry: Perry 1461

Petoskey: Bryan 255, Burns 267, Catt 299, Kiwanis 1015, **Manthei 1174**, Murray 1350, Petoskey 2385, Youth 2118, Zelt 2125

Pigeon: LaVictoire 1087, Maust 1202, Wurst 2104

Pinconning: Magline 2246

Plainwell: Rotary 2612

Plymouth: Aho 18, Charis 311, Community 352, Diebolt 454, Dul 492, Dunning 496, Fieler 2750, Fike 568, Good 703, Guilliom 745, Irish 906, Loiselle 2799, Plymouth 2598, Plymouth 2599, Swiss 1851, TDR 1869, Thompson 1882, Thompson 1884, Young 2115

Pontiac: Hahn 763, Mally 1161

Port Huron: Acheson 10, Citizens 2163, Community 2339, Knowlton 2791, Michigan 2814, SEMCO 2278, United 2666, Wirtz 2079, Wirtz 2080, Women's 2688

Portage: Allen 35, Greene 733, Kalamazoo 2787, Kanaan 964, Monroe 1313, Swiat 1849

Portland: Portland 2600

Potterville: Labaro 1059

Rapid City: Let 2796

Reading: Alexandrowski 30

Redford: Nieman 2824, Peck 1450

Reed City: Osceola 2383

Remus: Laflin 1062

Richland: Ryan 1615

Riverview: Egger 515, Ott 1409

Rochester: Bryan 2718, Community 2337, Foundation 2472, General 658, McCardell 1211, Mueller 1341, Ram 1526, Seifert 1684, Sibert 1720, Skrzypczak 1740, **St. Joseph 1786**

Rochester Hills: Cash 2440, Cassie 297, Chortkiv 320, Cipa 328, Davis 409, Dura 2189, **Gofrank 696**, Johnson 935, Kirt 1013, Nock 1379, Obloy 1393, Stolaruk 1812, Wheeler 2035

Rockford: Byrne 278, Disselkoen 456, Hurst 887, **JCT 926**, Krause 1044, River 1560, Wolverine 2303, Wolverine 2304, **Wynalda 2106**

Romeo: L & L 2794

Romulus: McManus 1238

Roscommon: Krauss 1046, Roscommon 2386, Roscommon 2608, Schroeder 1663

Roseville: **Children's 2448**, **Ford 589**, Kiwanis 1014, Main 1157, Morawski 1322, Theuerkorn 1875

Royal Oak: Imerman 897, KidRelief 1008, McNish 1242, Misuraca 1297, Royal 1604

Saginaw: **Akbar 2694**, Altrusa 2406, Anderson 54, Anderson 55, **Balaji 89**, Barth 110, Beal 125, Bleasdale 182, Brown 242, Brunkow 253, Burch 262, Burt 2720, Camp 286, Danieleski 400, Doll 465, Edwards 513, Field 566, Harvey 804, Jury 955, Kahan 958, Katz 969, Kosins 1041, Loeb 1118, MacRae 1152, McDonald's 2807, McNally 1240, Morley 1325, Nickless 1372, Polasky 1491, Rebuilding 2604, Roethke 1575, Saginaw 2387, Saginaw 1622, Saginaw 1623, Sallness 1628, Sanders 1633, Summerland 1838, Turner 1923, United 2663, Wallace 1980, Wickes 2048, Wickson 2049, Yeo 2111, Zacharias 2119, Zehnder 2123, Zuehlke 2135

Saline: Arnold 75, Busch 273, de Irala 413, Foundation 2473, Redies 2273

Sandusky: Abdole 5, Coller 348, Sanilac 2388

Saranac: Saranac 1637

Winston Salem: Comloquoy 350

OHIO

Akron: Gorski 716
Beavercreek: Nowak 1385
Bowling Green: Sky 2279
Chagrin Falls: Turner 1924
Cincinnati: DSLT 486, Dubois 487, Heartland 811, Mariel 1178, Milacron 2254, Moore 1319, Myers 1352, Peters 1465, St. Clair 1783, Whiting 2042
Cleveland: Beach 124, Brier 231, Cleveland 2164, CRN 379, Diebel 453, Dumesnil 493, Gilbert 679, Hafer 757, Jubilee 2229, Lahti 1064, Leki 1095, Mackey 1149, McCalla 1210, McDermott 1219, Miller 1285, Monroe 1311, National 2260, NCC 2262, O'Brien 1390, Potts 1500, Refke 1543, Schiefer 1650, Thompson 1885, Williams 2060
Columbus: Grange 2212, Hildreth 838
Dayton: PAV 1442
Lexington: Hire 846
Maumee: Anderson 52
New Carlisle: Steele 1792
Oregon: Guiding 744
Sylvania: Mitchell 1298
Toledo: Andersons 2412, Bates 2145, Jobst 933, Oswald 2587
Worthington: Worthington 2101

OKLAHOMA

Tulsa: Sneed 1762

PENNSYLVANIA

Greencastle: Sunal 1840
Harrisburg: Tyco 2288
Philadelphia: Higginson 837
Pittsburgh: Shander 1694, Williams 2059
Swarthmore: Pryor 1516

RHODE ISLAND

Providence: Buster 275, Charter 2159, Cossin 366, Robbins 1565

TEXAS

Addison: Posey 1497
Austin: Tapestry 1857
Fort Worth: Quicksilver 2272
Houston: Guy 748, Lone 1120, Walzel 1984
Mountain Home: Brucker 252

VERMONT

Williston: Center 2724

VIRGINIA

McLean: Freiheit 620, JCM 925
Richmond: Bell 137

WASHINGTON

Everett: UNOVA 1932
Seattle: Fehsenfeld 557

WEST VIRGINIA

Williamstown: Farr 2197

WISCONSIN

Fond du Lac: Giddings 2208
Fox Point: Schregardus 1660
Green Bay: Green Bay 2214, WPS 2305
La Crosse: Talen 1854
Madison: Bradshaw 215
Marinette: Fernstrum 561
Milwaukee: Beauchamp 129, Bishop 172, Bray 2432, Bray 220, Brege 221, Carpenter 293, Curtis 390, Firestone 573, Firestone 574, Frank 609, Giddey 674, Gless 690, Green 728, Hess 831, Hess 832, Keeney 983, Kowalski 2238, Kronlund 1051, Lamberson 1069, Leslie 1099, McIntyre 1227, McIntyre 1228, McIntyre 1229, Miner 1291, Neal 1360, Nichols 2575, Pierson 1477, Ross 1595, Stockton 1805, Summerfield 1836, Summerfield 1837, Tantlinger 1856, VandenBelt 1951, Vellmure 1963, Vogt 1975, Wisconsin 2302
Minocqua: JKO 932
Pewaukee: Venturedyne 2295